# Dear Reader

*This 26th edition of the Michelin Guide Great Britain & Ireland offers the latest selection of hotels and restaurants.*
*Independently compiled by our inspectors, the Guide offers travellers a wide choice of establishments at all levels of comfort and price.*

*And on your travels look out for the many restaurants awarded the* **"Bib Gourmand"** *symbol, which indicates moderately priced menus and good value for money.*

*We are committed to providing readers with the most up to date information, and this edition has been revised with the greatest care.*

*That is why only this year's guide is worthy of your complete trust.*

*Thank you for your comments, which are always appreciated.*

*Bon voyage!*

# Contents

# Choosing a hotel or restaurant

*This guide offers a selection of hotels and restaurants to help the motorist on his travels. In each category establishments are listed in order of preference according to the degree of comfort they offer.*

## Categories

| | | |
|---|---|---|
| 🏨 | XXXXX | *Luxury in the traditional style* |
| 🏨 | XXXX | *Top class comfort* |
| 🏨 | XXX | *Very comfortable* |
| 🏨 | XX | *Comfortable* |
| 🏨 | X | *Quite comfortable* |
| | 🍴 | *Traditional pubs serving food* |
| ⌂ | | *Other recommended accommodation (Guesthouses, farmhouses and private homes)* |
| without rest. | | *The hotel has no restaurant* |
| | with rm | *The restaurant also offers accommodation* |

## Peaceful atmosphere and setting

*Certain establishments are distinguished in the guide by the red symbols shown below.*

*Your stay in such hotels will be particularly pleasant or restful, owing to the character of the building, its decor, the setting, the welcome and services offered, or simply the peace and quiet to be enjoyed there.*

| | | |
|---|---|---|
| 🏨 to 🏠, ⌂ | | *Pleasant hotels* |
| XXXXX to X, 🍴 | | *Pleasant restaurants* |
| « Park » | | *Particularly attractive feature* |
| | 🖐 | *Very quiet or quiet, secluded hotel* |
| | 🖐 | *Quiet hotel* |
| ≤ sea | | *Exceptional view* |
| ≤ | | *Interesting or extensive view* |

*The maps located at the beginning of each regional section in the guide indicate places with such peaceful, pleasant hotels and restaurants.*

*By consulting them before setting out and sending us your comments on your return you can help us with our enquiries.*

# *Hotel facilities*

*In general the hotels we recommend have full bathroom and toilet facilities in each room. This may not be the case, however, for certain rooms in categories 🏠, 🏠 and ⌂.*

| | |
|---|---|
| 30 rm | *Number of rooms* |
| ‖ | *Lift (elevator)* |
| ▤ | *Air conditioning* |
| TV | *Television in room* |
| ⇥ | *Establishment either partly or wholly reserved for non-smokers* |
| ☎ | *Telephone in room: direct-dialling for outside calls* |
| 📞 | *Modem point in the bedrooms* |
| ♿ | *Rooms accessible to disabled people* |
| 🏝 | *Meals served in garden or on terrace* |
| ⊼ ⊡ | *Outdoor or indoor swimming pool* |
| ᴶ6 ⌂s | *Exercise room – Sauna* |
| 🐎 | *Garden* |
| ✗ ▶18 | *Hotel tennis court – Golf course and number of holes* |
| ⊞ | *Landing stage* |
| ➷ | *Fishing available to hotel guests. A charge may be made* |
| 🛐 150 | *Equipped conference hall: maximum capacity* |
| 🚗 | *Hotel garage (additional charge in most cases)* |
| ℗ | *Car park for customers only* |
| 🐕̸ | *Dogs are excluded from all or part of the hotel* |
| Fax | *Telephone document transmission* |
| May-October | *Dates when open, as indicated by the hotelier* |
| season | *Probably open for the season – precise dates not available.* |
| | *Where no date or season is shown, establishments are open all year round.* |
| LL35 OSB | *Postal code* |

## Animals
*It is illegal to bring domestic animals (dogs, cats...) into Great Britain and Ireland.*

# Cuisine

## Stars

*Certain establishments deserve to be brought
to your attention for the particularly fine quality
of their cooking.* **Michelin stars** *are awarded
for the standard of meals served. For such
restaurants we list three culinary specialities
typical of their style of cooking to assist
you in your choice.*

සි සි සි **Exceptional cuisine, worth a special journey**

*One always eats here extremely well, sometimes
superbly. Fine wines, faultless service, elegant
surroundings. One will pay accordingly!*

සි සි **Excellent cooking, worth a detour**

*Specialities and wines of first class quality.
This will be reflected in the price.*

සි **A very good restaurant in its category**

*The star indicates a good place to stop on your journey.
But beware of comparing the star given
to an expensive « de luxe » establishment
to that of a simple restaurant where you can appreciate
fine cooking at a reasonable price.*

## The "Bib Gourmand"

Good food at moderate prices

*You may also like to know of other restaurants
with less elaborate, moderately priced menus
that offer good value for money
and serve carefully prepared meals.*
We bring them to your attention by marking them
with the **"Bib Gourmand"** and Meals *in the text of the
Guide, e.g.* Meals 19.00/25.00.

*Please refer to the map of star-rated restaurants
සිසිසි, සිසි, සි and the* **"Bib Gourmand"**,
*located at the beginning of each regional section
in the guide.*

# Prices

*Prices quoted are valid for autumn 1998. Changes may arise if goods and service costs are revised.*

*Hotels and restaurants in bold type have supplied details of all their rates and have assumed responsibility for maintaining them for all travellers in possession of this guide.*

*In some towns, when commercial or tourist events are taking place, the hotel rates are likely to be considerably higher.*

*Prices are given in £ sterling, except for the Republic of Ireland where Irish pounds (punt) are quoted. Where no mention s., t., or st. is shown, prices may be subject to the addition of service charge, V.A.T., or both (V.A.T. does not apply in the Channel Islands).*

*Your recommendation is self-evident if you always walk into a hotel guide in hand.*

## Meals

| | |
|---|---|
| Meals 13.00/28.00 | **Set meals** |
| | *Lunch 13.00, dinner 28.00 – including cover charge, where applicable* |
| Meals 19.00/25.00 | *See page 7* |
| s. | *Service only included* |
| t. | *V.A.T. only included* |
| st. | *Service and V.A.T. included* |
| 🍾 6.00 | *Price of 1/2 bottle or carafe of house wine* |

| | |
|---|---|
| Meals a la carte | **A la carte meals** |
| 20.00/35.00 | *The prices represent the range of charges from a simple to an elaborate 3 course meal and include a cover charge where applicable* |
| 🍵 9.50 | *Charge for full cooked breakfast (i.e. not included in the room rate)* |
| | *Continental breakfast may be available at a lower rate* |

*↑: Dinner in this category of establishment will generally be offered from a fixed price menu of limited choice, served at a set time to residents only. Lunch is rarely offered. Many will not be licensed to sell alcohol.*

## Rooms

rm 50.00/90.00   *Lowest price* 50.00, *per room for a comfortable*
*single and highest price* 90.00 *per room*
*for the best double or twin*

suites   *Check with the hotelier for prices*

rm ⌣ 55.00/85.00   *Full cooked breakfast (whether taken or not)*
*is included in the price of the room*

## Short breaks (SB)

*Many hotels offer a special rate for a stay*
*of two or more nights which comprises dinner,*
*room and breakfast usually for a minimum*
*of two people. Please enquire at hotel for rates.*

## Alcoholic beverages-conditions of sale

*The sale of alcoholic drinks is governed*
*in Great Britain and Ireland by licensing laws*
*which vary greatly from country to country.*

*Allowing for local variations, restaurants may stay*
*open and serve alcohol with a bona fide meal*
*during the afternoon. Hotel bars and public houses*
*are generally open between 11am and 11pm*
*at the discretion of the licensee. Hotel residents,*
*however, may buy drinks outside the permitted*
*hours at the discretion of the hotelier.*

*Children under the age of 14 are not allowed*
*in bars.*

## Deposits

*Some hotels will require a deposit, which confirms*
*the commitment of customer and hotelier alike.*
*Make sure the terms of the agreement are clear.*

## Credit cards

MC AE DC VISA JCB   *Credits cards accepted by the establishment:*
*MasterCard (Eurocard) – American Express – Diners*
*Club – Visa – Japan Credit Bureau*

## *Towns*

| | |
|---|---|
| ✉ York | *Postal adress* |
| **401** M 27, ⑩ | *Michelin map and co-ordinates or fold* |
| West Country G. | *See the Michelin Green Guide*<br>*The West Country of England* |
| pop. 1057 | *Population. (Crown copyright 1991. Published*<br>*by permission of the Controller of Her Majesty's*<br>*Sationery Office.)* |
| BX **A** | *Letters giving the location of a place*<br>*on the town plan* |
| ᛏ₁₈ | *Golf course and number of holes (handicap usually)*<br>*required, telephone reservation strongly advised)* |
| ⁂ ≤ | *Panoramic view, viewpoint* |
| ✈ | *Airport* |
| ⚓ | *Shipping line* |
| ⚓ | *Passenger transport only* |
| 🛈 | *Tourist Information Centre* |

### Standard Time

*In winter standard time throughout the British Isles*
*is Greenwich Mean Time (G.M.T.). In summer*
*British clocks are advanced by one hour to give*
*British Summer Time (B.S.T.). The actual dates*
*are announced annually but always occur over*
*weekends in March and October.*

# Sights

## Star-rating

| | |
|---|---|
| ★★★ | *Worth a journey* |
| ★★ | *Worth a detour* |
| ★ | *Interesting* |
| AC | *Admission charge* |

## Location

| | |
|---|---|
| See | *Sights in town* |
| Envir. | *On the outskirts* |
| Exc. | *In the surrounding area* |
| N, S, E, W | *The sight lies north, south, east or west of the town* |
| A 22 | *Take road A 22, indicated by the same symbol on the Guide map* |
| 2 m. | *Mileage* |

## Car, tyres

*The wearing of seat belts in Great Britain*
*is obligatory for drivers, front seat passengers*
*and rear seat passengers where seat belts are fitted.*
*It is illegal for front seat passengers*
*to carry children on their lap.*

*In the Republic of Ireland seat belts are*
*compulsory, if fitted, for drivers and front seat*
*passengers. Children under 12 are not allowed in*
*front seats unless in a suitable safety restraint.*

## Michelin tyre suppliers
## ATS tyre dealers

*The location of the nearest ATS tyre dealer can*
*be obtained by contacting the address below*
*between 9am and 5pm.*

> ATS HOUSE
> 180-188 Northolt Rd.
> Harrow
> Middlesex HA2 OED
> ☎ (0181) 966 6600

## Motoring organisations

*The major motoring organisations in Great Britain*
*and Ireland are the Automobile Association and the*
*Royal Automobile Club. Each provides services*
*in varying degrees for non-resident members*
*of affiliated clubs.*

AUTOMOBILE ASSOCIATION
Fanum House
BASINGSTOKE, Hants
RG21 2EA
☎ (0990) 448866

ROYAL AUTOMOBILE CLUB
RAC House, Lansdowne Rd.
CROYDON, Surrey CR9 2JA
☎ (0181) 917 2500

AUTOMOBILE ASSOCIATION
23 Rock Hill
BLACKROCK
Co-Dublin
☎ (01) 283 3555

ROYAL AUTOMOBILE CLUB
RAC IRELAND
New Mount House
22-24 Lower Mount St.
DUBLIN 2
☎ (01) 676 0113

# *Town plans*

ⓐ ● a    *Hotels – Restaurants*

## Sights

*Place of interest and its main entrance*
*Interesting place of worship*

## Roads

*Motorway*
*Junctions: complete, limited*
*Dual carriageway with motorway characteristics*
*Main traffic artery*
*Primary route*
*- (network currently being reclassified)*
*One-way street – Unsuitable for traffic, street subject to restrictions*
*Pedestrian street*
Piccadilly   *Shopping street – Car park*
*Gateway – Street passing under arch – Tunnel*
*Low headroom (16'6" max.) on major through routes*
*Station and railway*
*Funicular – Cable-car*
*Lever bridge – Car ferry*

## Various signs

*Tourist Information Centre*
*Mosque – Synagogue*
*Communications tower or mast – Ruins*
*Garden, park, wood – Cemetery*
*Stadium – Racecourse – Golf course*
*Golf course (with restrictions for visitors)*
*View – Panorama*
*Monument – Fountain – Hospital*
*Pleasure boat harbour – Lighthouse*
*Airport – Underground station*
*Ferry services:*
*- passengers and cars*
*Main post office with poste restante, telephone*
*Public buildings located by letter:*
C H   *County Council Offices – Town Hall*
M T U   *Museum – Theatre – University, College*
POL.   *Police (in large towns police headquarters)*

## London

**BRENT** WEMBLEY   *Borough – Area*
*Borough boundary – Area boundary*

13

# Ami lecteur

Cette 26ᵉ édition du Guide Michelin Great Britain & Ireland
propose une sélection actualisée d'hôtels
et de restaurants.
Réalisée en toute indépendance,
par nos inspecteurs, elle offre au voyageur
de passage un large choix d'adresses
à tous les niveaux de confort et de prix.

Sur votre route, pour trouver de bonnes
adresses à petits prix, suivez donc les
nombreux restaurants que vous signale le
**"Bib Gourmand"**.

Toujours soucieux d'apporter à nos lecteurs
l'information la plus récente,
nous avons mis à jour cette édition
avec le plus grand soin.
C'est pourquoi, seul le Guide de l'année
en cours mérite votre confiance.

Merci de vos commentaires toujours
appréciés.

Michelin vous souhaite «Bon voyage !»———

# *Sommaire*

# Le choix d'un hôtel, d'un restaurant

*Ce guide vous propose une sélection d'hôtels et restaurants établie à l'usage de l'automobiliste de passage. Les établissements, classés selon leur confort, sont cités par ordre de préférence dans chaque catégorie.*

## Catégories

| | | |
|---|---|---|
| 🏨 | XXXXX | *Grand luxe et tradition* |
| 🏨 | XXXX | *Grand confort* |
| 🏨 | XXX | *Très confortable* |
| 🏠 | XX | *De bon confort* |
| 🏠 | X | *Assez confortable* |
| | 🍺 | *Traditionnel "pub" anglais servant des repas* |
| ⌂ | | *Autre ressource hôtelière conseillée (Logis à la ferme, maison d'hôtes et cottages)* |
| without rest. | | *L'hôtel n'a pas de restaurant* |
| with rm | | *Le restaurant possède des chambres* |

## Agrément et tranquillité

*Certains établissements se distinguent dans le guide par les symboles rouges indiqués ci-après.*
*Le séjour dans ces hôtels se révèle particulièrement agréable ou reposant.*
*Cela peut tenir d'une part au caractère de l'édifice, au décor original, au site, à l'accueil et aux services qui sont proposés, d'autre part à la tranquillité des lieux.*

| | |
|---|---|
| 🏨 à 🏠, ⌂ | *Hôtels agréables* |
| XXXXX à X, 🍺 | *Restaurants agréables* |
| « Park » | *Élément particulièrement agréable* |
| 🕊 | *Hôtel très tranquille ou isolé et tranquille* |
| 🕊 | *Hôtel tranquille* |
| ← sea | *Vue exceptionnelle* |
| ← | *Vue intéressante ou étendue* |

*Les localités possédant des établissements agréables ou tranquilles sont repérées sur les cartes au début de chacune des régions traitées dans ce guide.*

*Consultez-les pour la préparation de vos voyages et donnez-nous vos appréciations à votre retour, vous faciliterez ainsi nos enquêtes.*

## *L'intallation*

*Les chambres des hôtels que nous recommandons possèdent, en général, des installations sanitaires complètes. Il est toutefois possible que dans les catégories 🏠, 🏠 et ⌂, certaines chambres en soient dépourvues.*

| | |
|---|---|
| 30 rm | *Nombre de chambres* |
| 🛗 | *Ascenseur* |
| ▤ | *Air conditionné* |
| 📺 | *Télévision dans la chambre* |
| ⊁ | *Établissement entièrement ou en partie réservé aux non-fumeurs* |
| ☎ | *Téléphone dans la chambre, direct avec l'extérieur* |
| ☏ | *Prise modem dans la chambre* |
| ♿ | *Chambres accessibles aux handicapés physiques* |
| 🍽 | *Repas servis au jardin ou en terrasse* |
| ⌦ ▣ | *Piscine : de plein air ou couverte* |
| ⛲ ≋s | *Salle de remise en forme – Sauna* |
| 🌲 | *Jardin de repos* |
| ⚼ ⌷₁₈ | *Tennis à l'hôtel – Golf et nombre de trous* |
| ⚓ | *Ponton d'amarrage* |
| ⤳ | *Pêche ouverte aux clients de l'hôtel (éventuellement payant)* |
| 🎓 150 | *Salles de conférences : capacité maximum* |
| ⬌ | *Garage dans l'hôtel (généralement payant)* |
| 🅿 | *Parking réservé à la clientèle* |
| 🐕 | *Accès interdit aux chiens (dans tout ou partie de l'établissement)* |
| Fax | *Transmission de documents par télécopie* |
| May-October | *Période d'ouverture, communiquée par l'hôtelier* |
| season | *Ouverture probable en saison mais dates non précisées. En l'absence de mention, l'établissement est ouvert toute l'année* |
| LL35 0SB | *Code postal de l'établissement* |

### Animaux

*L'introduction d'animaux domestiques (chiens, chats...) est interdite en Grande-Bretagne et en Irlande.*

# *La table*

## Les étoiles

*Certains établissements méritent d'être signalés
à votre attention pour la qualité de leur cuisine.
Nous les distinguons par les étoiles de bonne table.
Nous indiquons, pour ces établissements,
trois spécialités culinaires qui pourront orienter
votre choix.*

### ✿✿✿ Une des meilleures tables, vaut le voyage

*On y mange toujours très bien, parfois
merveilleusement. Grands vins, service impeccable,
cadre élégant... Prix en conséquence.*

### ✿✿ Table excellente, mérite un détour

*Spécialités et vins de choix...
Attendez-vous à une dépense en rapport.*

### ✿ Une très bonne table dans sa catégorie

*L'étoile marque une bonne étape
sur votre itinéraire.
Mais ne comparez pas l'étoile d'un établissement
de luxe à prix élevés avec celle d'une petite maison
où, à prix raisonnables, on sert également
une cuisine de qualité.*

## 🍴 Le "Bib Gourmand"

Repas soignés à prix modérés

*Vous souhaitez parfois trouver des tables
plus simples, à prix modérés ; c'est pourquoi nous avons
sélectionné des restaurants proposant, pour un
rapport qualité-prix particulièrement favorable,
un repas soigné.
Ces restaurants sont signalés par le* "Bib Gourmand" 🍴
*et* Meals
*Ex* Meals 19.00/25.00.

*Consultez les cartes des étoiles de bonne table
✿✿✿, ✿✿, ✿ et des* "Bib Gourmand" 🍴*,
placées au début de chacune des régions traitées
dans ce guide.*

# Les prix

*Les prix que nous indiquons dans ce guide ont été établis en automne 1998. Ils sont susceptibles de modifications, notamment en cas de variations des prix des biens et services.*

*Dans certaines villes, à l'occasion de manisfestations commerciales ou touristiques, les prix demandés par les hôteliers risquent d'être considérablement majorés. Les prix sont indiqués en livres sterling (1 £ = 100 pence), sauf en République d'Irlande où ils sont donnés en « Punts ». Lorsque les mentions* s., t., *ou* st. *ne figurent pas, les prix indiqués peuvent être majorés d'un pourcentage pour le service, la T.V.A., ou les deux (la T.V.A. n'est pas appliquée dans les Channel Islands). Les hôtels et restaurants figurent en gros caractères lorsque les hôteliers nous ont donné tous leurs prix et se sont engagés, sous leur propre responsabilité, à les appliquer aux touristes de passage porteurs de notre guide.*

*Entrez à l'hôtel le guide à la main, vous montrerez ainsi qu'il vous conduit là en confiance.*

## Repas

| | |
|---|---|
| Meals 13.00/28.00 | **Repas à prix fixe** |
| | *Déjeuner* 13.00, *dîner* 28.00. *Ces prix s'entendent couvert compris* |
| Meals 19.00/25.00 | *Voir page 19* |
| s. | *Service compris* |
| t. | *T.V.A. comprise* |
| st. | *Service et T.V.A. compris (prix nets)* |
| 🍾 6.00 | *Prix de la 1/2 bouteille ou carafe de vin ordinaire* |
| Meals à la carte | **Repas à la carte** |
| 20.00/35.00 | *Le 1$^{er}$ prix correspond à un repas simple mais soigné, comprenant : petite entrée, plat du jour garni, dessert. Le 2$^e$ prix concerne un repas plus complet, comprenant : entrée, plat principal, fromage ou dessert. Ces prix s'entendent couvert compris.* |
| ☕ 9.50 | *Prix du petit déjeuner à l'anglaise, s'il n'est pas compris dans celui de la chambre. Un petit déjeuner continental peut être obtenu à moindre prix.* |

*⌂: Dans les établissements de cette catégorie, le dîner est servi à heure fixe exclusivement aux personnes ayant une chambre. Le menu, à prix unique, offre un choix limité de plats. Le déjeuner est rarement proposé. Beaucoup de ces établissements ne sont pas autorisés à vendre des boissons alcoolisées.*

## Chambres

rm 50.00/90.00

*Prix minimum 50.00 d'une chambre pour une
personne et prix maximum 90.00 de la plus belle
chambre occupée par deux personnes*

suites

*Se renseigner auprès de l'hôtelier*

rm 🛏 55.00/85.00

*Le prix du petit déjeuner à l'anglaise est inclus
dans le prix de la chambre,
même s'il n'est pas consommé*

## Short breaks (SB)

*Certains hôtels proposent des conditions
avantageuses ou «Short Break» pour un séjour
minimum de 2 nuits. Ce forfait, calculé
par personne, pour 2 personnes au minimum,
comprend la chambre, le dîner et le petit déjeuner.
Se renseigner auprès de l'hôtelier.*

## La vente de boissons alcoolisées

*En Grande-Bretagne et en Irlande, la vente
de boissons alcoolisées est soumise à des lois
pouvant varier d'une région à l'autre.
D'une façon générale, les restaurants peuvent
demeurer ouverts l'après-midi et servir des boissons
alcoolisées dans la mesure où elles accompagnent
un repas suffisamment consistant. Les bars d'hôtel
et les pubs sont habituellement ouverts de 11 heures
à 23 heures. Néanmoins, l'hôtelier a toujours
la possibilité de servir, à sa clientèle,
des boissons alcoolisées en dehors des heures légales.
Les enfants au-dessous de 14 ans n'ont pas accès
aux bars.*

## Les arrhes

*Certains hôteliers demandent le versement d'arrhes.
Il s'agit d'un dépôt-garantie qui engage l'hôtelier
comme le client. Bien faire préciser les dispositions
de cette garantie.*

## Cartes de crédit

MC  AE  DC  VISA  JCB

*Cartes de crédit acceptées par l'établissement :
MasterCard (Eurocard) – American Express –
Diners Club – Visa – Japan Credit Bureau*

21

# Les villes

| | |
|---|---|
| ✉ York | Bureau de poste desservant la localité |
| **401** M 27, ⑩ | Numéro des cartes Michelin et carroyage ou numéro du pli |
| West Country G. | Voir le guide vert Michelin The West Country of England |
| pop. 1057 | Population |
| BX A | Lettres repérant un emplacement sur le plan |
| ⚐18 | Golf et nombre de trous (Handicap généralement demandé, réservation par téléphone vivement recommandée) |
| ❋ ≤ | Panorama, point de vue |
| ✈ | Aéroport |
| 🚢 | Transports maritimes |
| 🚢 | Transports maritimes (pour passagers seulement) |
| 🛈 | Information touristique |

## Heure légale

*Les visiteurs devront tenir compte de l'heure officielle.*
*En Grande-Bretagne : une heure de retard sur l'heure française.*

# Les curiosités

## Intérêt

| | |
|---|---|
| ★★★ | *Vaut le voyage* |
| ★★ | *Mérite un détour* |
| ★ | *Intéressant* |
| AC | *Entrée payante* |

## Situation

| | |
|---|---|
| See | *Dans la ville* |
| Envir. | *Aux environs de la ville* |
| Exc. | *Excursions dans la région* |
| N, S, E, W | *La curiosité est située :*<br>*au Nord, au Sud, à l'Est, à l'Ouest* |
| A 22 | *On s'y rend par la route A 22, repérée*<br>*par le même signe sur le plan du Guide* |
| 2 m. | *Distance en miles* |

## La voiture, les pneus

*En Grande-Bretagne, le port de la ceinture
de sécurité est obligatoire pour le conducteur
et le passager avant ainsi qu'à l'arrière, si le
véhicule en est équipé. La loi interdit au passager
avant de prendre un enfant sur ses genoux.*

*En République d'Irlande, le port de la ceinture
de sécurité est obligatoire pour le conducteur
et le passager avant si le véhicule en est équipé.
Les enfants de moins de 12 ans ne sont pas
autorisés à s'asseoir à l'avant, sauf si le véhicule
est muni d'un système d'attache approprié.*

### Fournisseurs de pneus michelin
### ATS Spécialistes du pneu

*Des renseignements sur le plus proche point
de vente de pneus ATS pourront être obtenus
en s'informant entre 9 h et 17 h à l'adresse
indiquée ci-dessous.*

> *ATS HOUSE*
> *180-188 Northolt Rd.*
> *Harrow*
> *Middlesex HA2 OED*
> *☎ (0181) 966 6600*

### Automobile clubs

*Les principales organisations de secours automobile
dans le pays sont l'Automobile Association et le
Royal Automobile Club, toutes deux offrant certains
de leurs services aux membres de clubs affiliés.*

*AUTOMOBILE ASSOCIATION*
*Fanum House*
*BASINGSTOKE, Hants*
*RG21 2EA*
*☎ (0990) 448866*

*AUTOMOBILE ASSOCIATION*
*23 Rock Hill*
*BLACKROCK*
*Co-Dublin*
*☎ (01) 283 3555*

*ROYAL AUTOMOBILE CLUB*
*RAC House, Lansdowne Rd.*
*CROYDON, Surrey CR9 2JA*
*☎ (0181) 917 2500*

*ROYAL AUTOMOBILE CLUB*
*RAC IRELAND New Mount*
*House*
*22-24 Lower Mount St.*
*DUBLIN 2*
*☎ (01) 676 0113*

# Les plans

e ● a   *Hôtels – Restaurants*

## Curiosités

*Bâtiment intéressant et entrée principale*
*Édifice religieux intéressant*

## Voirie

*Autoroute*
*- échangeurs : complet, partiel*
*Route à chaussées séparées de type autoroutier*
*Grand axe de circulation*
*Itinéraire principal (Primary route)*
*- réseau en cours de révision*
*Sens unique – Rue impraticable, réglementée*
*Rue piétonne*
Piccadilly  *Rue commerçante – Parc de stationnement*
*Porte – Passage sous voûte – Tunnel*
*Passage bas (inférieur à 16'6") sur les grandes voies de circulation*
*Gare et voie ferrée*
*Funiculaire – Téléphérique, télécabine*
*Pont mobile – Bac pour autos*

## Signes divers

*Information touristique*
*Mosquée – Synagogue*
*Tour ou pylône de télécommunication – Ruines*
*Jardin, parc, bois – Cimetière*
*Stade – Hippodrome – Golf*
*Golf (réservé)*
*Vue – Panorama*
*Monument – Fontaine – Hôpital*
*Port de plaisance – Phare*
*Aéroport – Station de métro*
*Transport par bateau :*
*- passagers et voitures*
*Bureau principal de poste restante, téléphone*
*Bâtiment public repéré par une lettre :*
C H   *- Bureau de l'Administration du Comté – Hôtel de ville*
M T U   *- Musée – Théâtre – Université, grande école*
POL   *- Police (commissariat central)*

## Londres

**BRENT** WEMBLEY   *Nom d'arrondissement (borough) – de quartier (area)*
*Limite de « borough » – d'« area »*

25

# Amico lettore

Questa 26*esima* edizione della Guida
Michelin Great Britain & Ireland
propone una selezione aggiornata
di alberghi e ristoranti.
Realizzata dai nostri ispettori in piena
autonomia, offre al viaggiatore di
passaggio un'ampia scelta a tutti i livelli
di confort e prezzo.

Sulla vostra strada per trovare buoni
indirizzi a prezzi interessanti, seguite
i numerosi ristoranti che vi segnala il
**"Bib Gourmand"**.

Con l'intento di fornire ai nostri lettori
l'informazione più recente, abbiamo
aggiornato questa edizione con la
massima cura.
Per questo solo la Guida dell'anno in
in corso merita pienamente la vostra
fiducia.

Grazie delle vostre segnalazioni
sempre gradite.

Michelin vi augura "Buon Viaggio!"_____

# Sommario

# La scelta di un albergo, di un ristorante

*Questa guida propone una selezione di alberghi e ristoranti per orientare la scelta dell'automobilista. Gli esercizi, classificati in base al confort che offrono, vengono citati in ordine di preferenza per ogni categoria.*

## Categorie

| | | |
|---|---|---|
| 🏨 | XXXXX | *Gran lusso e tradizione* |
| 🏨 | XXXX | *Gran confort* |
| 🏨 | XXX | *Molto confortevole* |
| 🏨 | XX | *Di buon confort* |
| 🏨 | X | *Abbastanza confortevole* |
| | 🍴 | *Pub tradizionali con cucina* |
| 🏠 | | *Altra forme di alloggio consigliate (Pensioni, Fattorie e Case private)* |
| without rest. | | *L'albergo non ha ristorante* |
| | with rm | *Il ristorante dispone di camere* |

## Amenità e tranquillità

*Alcuni esercizi sono evidenziati nella guida dai simboli rossi indicati qui di seguito. Il soggiorno in questi alberghi si rivela particolarmente ameno o riposante.*

*Ciò può dipendere sia dalle caratteristiche dell'edifico, dalle decorazioni non comuni, dalla sua posizione e dal servizio offerto, sia dalla tranquillità dei luoghi.*

| | |
|---|---|
| 🏨 a 🏠, 🏠 | *Alberghi ameni* |
| XXXXX a X, 🍴 | *Ristoranti ameni* |
| « Park » | *Un particolare piacevole* |
| 🌲 | *Albergo molto tranquillo o isolato e tranquillo* |
| 🌲 | *Albergo tranquillo* |
| ← sea | *Vista eccezionale* |
| ← | *Vista interessante o estesa* |

*Le località che possiedono degli esercizi ameni o tranquilli sono riportate sulle carte che precedono ciascuna delle regioni trattate nella guida.*

*Consultatele per la preparazione dei vostri viaggi e, al ritorno, inviateci i vostri pareri; in tal modo agevolerete le nostre inchieste.*

# Installazioni

Le camere degli alberghi che raccomandiamo
possiedono, generalmente, delle installazioni sanitarie
complete. È possibile tuttavia che nelle categorie
🏨, 🏨 e 🏠 alcune camere ne siano sprovviste.

| | |
|---|---|
| 30 rm | Numero di camere |
| 🛗 | Ascensore |
| ▤ | Aria condizionata |
| TV | Televisione in camera |
| ⊱✕ | Esercizio riservato completamente o in parte ai non fumatori |
| ☎ | Telefono in camera comunicante direttamente con l'esterno |
| 📞 | Presa modem in camera |
| ♿ | Camere di agevole accesso per portatori di handicap |
| 🏛 | Pasti serviti in giardino o in terrazza |
| ⌿ ▨ | Piscina: all'aperto, coperta |
| ⚡ 🆂 | Palestra – Sauna |
| 🎋 | Giardino |
| ✕ ⛳ | Tennis appatenente all'albergo – Golf e numero di buche |
| ⚓ | Pontile d'ormeggio |
| ⤳ | Pesca aperta ai clienti dell'albergo (eventualmente a pagamento) |
| 🏛 150 | Sale per conferenze: capienza massima |
| 🚗 | Garage nell'albergo (generalmente a pagamento) |
| ℗ | Parcheggio riservato alla clientela |
| 🐕🚫 | Accesso vietato ai cani (in tutto o in parte dell'esercizio |
| Fax | Trasmissione telefonica di documenti |
| May-October | Periodo di apertura, comunicato dall'albergatore |
| season | Probabile apertura in stagione, ma periodo non precisato. Gli esercizi senza tali menzioni sono aperti tutto l'anno. |
| LL35 OSB | Codice postale dell'esercizio |

## Animali

L'introduzione di animali domestici (cani, gatti...),
in Gran Bretagna e in Irlanda, è vietata.

# La tavola

## Le stelle

*Alcuni esercizi meritano di essere segnalati alla
vostra attenzione per la qualità particolare della
loro cucina; li abbiamo evidenziati
con le «stelle di ottima tavola».
Per ognuno di questi ristoranti indichiamo
tre specialità culinarie e alcuni vini locali
che potranno aiutarvi nella scelta.*

❀❀❀   **Una delle migliori tavole, vale il viaggio**

*Vi si mangia sempre molto bene, a volte
meravigliosamente. Grandi vini, servizio impeccabile,
ambientazione accurata... Prezzi conformi.*

❀❀   **Tavola eccellente, merita una deviazione**

*Specialità e vini scelti...
Aspettatevi una spesa in proporzione.*

❀   **Un'ottima tavola nella sua categoria**

*La stella indica una tappa gastronomica
sul Vostro itinerario.
Non mettete però a confronto la stella di un esercizio
di lusso, dai prezzi elevati, con quella di un piccolo
esercizio dove, a prezzi ragionevoli, viene offerta
una cucina di qualità.*

## 🎖 Il "Bib Gourmand"

Pasti accurati a prezzi contenuti

*Per quando desiderate trovare delle tavole più
semplici a prezzi contenuti abbiamo selezionato
dei ristoranti che, per un rapporto qualità-prezzo
particolarmente favorevole, offrono un pasto
accurato.
Questi ristoranti sono evidenziali nel testo con
il "Bib Gourmand" 🎖 e* Meals, *evidenziata in rosso,
davanti ai prezzi.
Ex.* 🎖 Meals 19.00/25.00.

*Consultate le carte delle stelle* ❀❀❀, ❀❀, ❀
*e con il "Bib Gourmand"* 🎖, *che precedono
ciascuna delle regioni trattate nella guida.*

# I prezzi

*I prezzi che indichiamo in questa guida sono stati stabiliti nel l'autunno 1998 e potranno pertanto subire delle variazioni in relazione ai cambiamenti dei prezzi di beni e servizi.*

*Gli alberghi e i ristoranti vengono menzionati in carattere grassetto quando gli albergatori ci hanno comunicato tutti i loro prezzi e si sono impegnati, sotto la propria responsabilità, ad applicarli ai turisti di passaggio, in possesso della nostra guida.*

*In alcune città, in occasione di manifestazioni turistiche o commerciali, i prezzi richiesti dagli albergatori potrebbero risultare considerevolmente più alti. I prezzi sono indicati in lire sterline (1 £ = 100 pence) ad eccezione per la Repubblica d'Irlanda dove sono indicati in « punts ». Quando non figurano le lettere s., t., o st. i prezzi indicati possono essere maggiorati per il servizio o per l'I.V.A. o per entrambi. (L'I.V.A. non viene applicata nelle Channel Islands).*

*Entrate nell'albergo o nel ristorante con la guida in mano, dimostrando in tal modo la fiducia in chi vi ha indirizzato.*

## Pasti

| | |
|---|---|
| Meals 13.00/28.00 | **Prezzo fisso** |
| | *Pranzo 13.00, cena 28.00. Questi prezzi comprendono il coperto* |
| Meals 19.00/25.00 | *Vedere p. 31* |
| s. | *Servizio compreso* |
| t. | *I.V.A. compresa* |
| st. | *Servizio ed I.V.A. compresi (prezzi netti)* |
| 🍶 6.00 | *Prezzo della mezza bottiglia o di una caraffa di vino* |

| | |
|---|---|
| Meals a la carte | **Alla carta** |
| 20.00/35.00 | *Il 1° prezzo corrisponde ad un pasto semplice comprendente: primo piatto, piatto del giorno con contorno, dessert. Il 2° prezzo corrisponde ad un pasto più completo comprendente: antipasto, piatto principale, formaggio e dessert* |
| | *Questi prezzi comprendono il coperto* |
| ☕ 9.50 | *Prezzo della prima colazione inglese se non è compreso nel prezzo della camera. Una prima colazione continentale può essere ottenuta a minor prezzo* |
| | *↑: Negli alberghi di questa categoria, la cena viene servita, ad un'ora stabilita, esclusivamente a chi vi alloggia. Il menu, a prezzo fisso, offre una scelta limitata di piatti. Raramente viene servito anche il pranzo. Molti di questi esercizi non hanno l'autorizzazione a vendere alcolici.* |

## Camere

**rm** 50.00/90.00

*Prezzo minimo 50.00, per una camera singola e prezzo massimo 90.00 per la camera più bella per due persone*

**suites** *Informarsi presso l'albergatore*

**rm** ☕ 55.00/85.00 *Il prezzo della prima colazione inglese è compreso nel prezzo della camera anche se non viene consumata*

## «Short Breaks» (SB.)

*Alcuni alberghi propongono delle condizioni particolarmente vantaggiose o short break per un soggiorno minimo di due notti.*
*Questo prezzo, calcolato per persona e per un minimo di due persone, comprende: camera, cena e prima colazione. Informarsi presso l'albergatore.*

## La vendita di bevande alcoliche

*La vendita di bevande alcoliche in Gran Bretagna è regolata da leggi che variano considerevolmente da regione a regione.*

*Eccezion fatta per varianti locali, i ristoranti possono rimanere aperti o servire bevande alcoliche con i pasti il pomeriggio. I bar degli hotel e i pub sono generalmente aperti dalle 11 alle 23, a discrezione del gestore. I clienti dell'hotel, comunque, possono acquistare bevande al di fuori delle ore stabilite se il direttore lo permette.*

*Il bambini al di sotto del 14 anni non possono entrare nei bar.*

## La caparra

*Alcuni albergatori chiedono il versamento di una caparra. Si tratta di un deposito-garanzia che impegna tanto l'albergatore che il cliente.*
*Vi consigliamo di farvi precisare le norme riguardanti la reciproca garanzia di tale caparra.*

## Carte di credito

*Carte di credito accettate dall'esercizio*
*MasterCard (Eurocard) – American Express – Diners Club – Visa – Japan Credit Bureau*

# Le città

| | |
|---|---|
| ✉ York | Sede dell'ufficio postale |
| **401** M 27, ⑩ | Numero della carta Michelin e del riquadro o numero della piega |
| West Country G. | Vedere la Guida Verde Michelin The West Country of England |
| pop. 1057 | Popolazione |
| BX **A** | Lettere indicanti l'ubicazione sulla pianta |
| 🏌18 | Golf e numero di buche (handicap generalmente richiesto, prenotazione telefonica vivamente consigliata) |
| ☀ ≼ | Panorama, vista |
| ✈ | Aeroporto |
| ⛴ | Trasporti marittimi |
| ⛵ | Trasporti marittimi (solo passeggeri) |
| 🛈 | Ufficio informazioni turistiche |

## Ora legale

I visitatori dovranno tenere in considerazione l'ora ufficiale in Gran Bretagna: un'ora di ritardo sull'ora italiana.

# Luoghi d'interesse

## Grado di interesse

| | |
|---|---|
| ★★★ | *Vale il viaggio* |
| ★★ | *Merita una deviazione* |
| ★ | *Interessante* |
| AC | *Entrata a pagamento* |

## Ubicazione

| | |
|---|---|
| See | *Nella città* |
| Envir. | *Nei dintorni della città* |
| Exc. | *Nella regione* |
| N, S, E, W | *Il luogo si trova : a Nord, a Sud, a Est a Ovest* |
| A 22 | *Ci si va per la strada A 22 indicata con lo stesso segno sulla pianta* |
| 2 m. | *Distanza in miglia* |

# L'automobile, I pneumatici

*In Gran Bretagna, l'uso delle cinture di sicurezza
è obbligatorio per il conducente ed il passeggero del
sedile anteriore, nonchè per i sedili posteriori, se ne sono
equipaggiati. La legge non consente al passaggero
davanti di tenere un bambino sulle ginocchia.*

*Nella Repubblica d'Irlanda, l'uso delle cinture di
sicurezza è obbligatorio per il conducente e il
passeggero davanti, se il veicolo ne è equipaggiato.
I bambini di meno di 12 anni non sono
autorizzati a viaggiare sul sedile anteriore, a meno
che questo non sia dotato di un sistema
di sicurezza esprassamente concepito.*

## Rivenditori di pneumatici Michelin
## ATS Specialista in pneumatici

*Potrete avere delle informazioni sul piú vicino
punto vendita di pneumatici ATS, rivolgendovi, tra
le 9 e le 17, all'indirizzo indicato qui di seguito:*

> ATS HOUSE
> 180-188 Northolt Rd.
> Harrow
> Middlesex HA2 OED
> ℰ (0181) 966 6600

## Automobile clubs

*Le principali organizzazioni di soccorso
automobilistico sono l'Automobile Association ed il
Royal Automobile Club: entrambe offrono alcuni
servizi ai membri affiliati.*

AUTOMOBILE ASSOCIATION
Fanum House
BASINGSTOKE, Hants
RG21 2EA
ℰ (0990) 448866

ROYAL AUTOMOBILE CLUB
RAC House, Lansdowne Rd.
CROYDON, Surrey CR9 2JA
ℰ (0181) 917 2500

AUTOMOBILE ASSOCIATION
23 Rock Hill
BLACKROCK
Co-Dublin
ℰ (01) 283 3555

ROYAL AUTOMOBILE CLUB
RAC IRELAND
New Mount House
22-24 Lower Mount St.
DUBLIN 2
ℰ (01) 676 0113

# Le piante

e ● a  *Alberghi – Ristoranti*

## Curiosità

*Edificio interessante ed entrata principale*

*Costruzione religiosa interessante*

## Viabilità

M 1  *Autostrada*

4  4  *- svincoli: completo, parziale*

*Strada a carreggiate separate di tipo autostradale*

*Asse principale di circolazione*

*Itinerario principale*

A 2  *- («Primary route», rete stradale in corso di revisione)*

*Senso unico – Via impraticabile, a circolazione regolamentata*

*Via pedonale*

.Piccadilly P  *Via commerciale – Parcheggio*

*Porta – Sottopassaggio – Galleria*

*Sottopassaggio (altezza inferiore a 16'6") sulle grandi vie di circolazione*

*Stazione e ferrovia*

*Funicolare – Funivia, Cabinovia*

B  *Ponte mobile – Traghetto per auto*

## Simboli vari

*Ufficio informazioni turistiche*

*Moschea – Sinagoga*

*Torre o pilone per telecomunicazioni – Ruderi*

*Giardino, parco, bosco – Cimitero*

*Stadio – Ippodromo – Golf*

*Golf riservato*

*Vista – Panorama*

*Monumento – Fontana – Ospedale*

*Porto per imbarcazioni da diporto – Faro*

*Aeroporto – Stazione della Metropolitana*

*Trasporto con traghetto:*
*- passeggeri ed autovetture*

*Ufficio centrale di fermo posta, telefono*

*Edificio pubblico indicato con lettera:*

C H  *- Sede dell'Amministrazione di Contea – Municipio*

M T U  *- Museo – Teatro – Università, grande scuola*

POL.  *- Polizia (Questura, nelle grandi città)*

## Londra

**BRENT** WEMBLEY  *Nome del distretto amministrativo (borough) – del quartiere (area)*

*Limite del «borough» – di «area»*

# *Lieber Leser*

*Die vorliegende 26. Ausgabe des Roten
Michelin-Führers
Great Britain & Ireland bringt eine aktuelle
Auswahl an Hotels
und Restaurants.
Sie wurde von unseren Inspektoren
in völliger Unabhängigkeit erstellt und bietet
dem
Reisenden eine breit gefächerte Auswahl von
Adressen
in allen Komfort- und Preisklassen.*

*Wenn Sie unterwegs gut und preiswert essen
möchten, folgen Sie dem* **"Bib Gourmand"**,
*der Ihnen den Weg zu zahlreichen
Restaurants mit besonders günstigem
Preis-/Leistungsverhältnis weist.*

*Im ständigen Bemühen, unsere Leser
mit aktuellen Informationen zu versorgen,
sind wir bei der Überarbeitung dieser
Ausgabe mit größter Sorgfalt vorgegangen.
Deshalb ist nur die Ausgabe des laufenden
Jahres
wirklich zuverlässig.*

*Vielen Dank für Ihre Anregungen und
Hinweise,
die uns stets willkommen sind.
Michelin wünscht Ihnen "Gute Reise!"*

# Inhaltsverzeichnis

# Wahl eines Hotels, eines Restaurants

Die Auswahl der in diesem Führer aufgeführten Hotels und Restaurants ist für Durchreisende gedacht. In jeder Kategorie drückt die Reihenfolge der Betriebe (sie sind nach ihrem Komfort klassifiziert) eine weitere Rangordnung aus.

## Kategorien

| | | |
|---|---|---|
| 🏨 | 🏨🏨🏨🏨🏨 | Großer Luxus und Tradition |
| 🏨 | 🏨🏨🏨🏨 | Großer Komfort |
| 🏨 | 🏨🏨🏨 | Sehr komfortabel |
| 🏨 | 🏨🏨 | Mit gutem Komfort |
| 🏨 | 🏨 | Mit standard Komfort |
| | 🍽 | Traditionelle Pubs die Speisen anbieten |
| 🏠 | | Andere empfohlene Übernachtungsmöglichkeiten (Gästehäuser, Bauernhäuser und Private Übernachtungsmöglichkeiten) und Pensionen |
| without rest. | | Hotel ohne restaurant |
| | with rm | Restaurant vermietet auch Zimmer |

## Annehmlichkeiten

Manche Häuser sind im Führer durch rote Symbole gekennzeichnet (s. unten). Der Aufenthalt in diesen ist wegen der schönen, ruhigen Lage, der nicht alltäglichen Einrichtung und Atmosphäre sowie dem gebotenen Service besonders angenehm und erholsam.

| | |
|---|---|
| 🏨🏨🏨 bis 🏨, 🏠 | Angenehme Hotels |
| 🏨🏨🏨🏨🏨 bis 🍽, 🍽 | Angenehme Restaurants |
| « Park » | Besondere Annehmlichkeit |
| 🖐 | Sehr ruhiges, oder abgelegenes und ruhiges Hotel |
| 🖐 | Ruhiges Hotel |
| ≤ sea | Reizvolle Aussicht |
| ≤ | Interessante oder weite Sicht |

Die den einzelnen Regionen vorangestellten Übersichtskarten, auf denen die Orte mit besonders angenehmen oder ruhigen Häusern eingezeichnet sind, helfen Ihnen bei der Reisevorbereitung. Teilen Sie uns bitte nach der Reise Ihre Erfahrungen und Meinungen mit. Sie helfen uns damit, den Führer weiter zu verbessern.

# Einrichtung

*Die meisten der empfohlenen Hotels verfügen über Zimmer, die alle oder doch zum größten Teil mit einer Naßzelle ausgestattet sind. In den Häusern der Kategorien 🏨, 🏠 und ⌂ kann diese jedoch in einigen Zimmern fehlen.*

| | |
|---|---|
| 30 rm | *Anzahl der Zimmer* |
| 🛗 | *Fahrstuhl* |
| ▤ | *Klimaanlage* |
| TV | *Fernsehen im Zimmer* |
| ⤬ | *Hotel ganz oder teilweise reserviert für Nichtraucher* |
| ☎ | *Zimmertelefon mit direkter Außenverbindung* |
| ✆ | *Modemanschluß im Zimmer* |
| ♿ | *Für Körperbehinderte leicht zugängliche Zimmer* |
| 🍽 | *Garten-, Terrassenrestaurant* |
| ⊼ ⊼ | *Freibad, Hallenbad* |
| 🏋 ⌾ | *Fitneßraum – Sauna* |
| ⛱ | *Liegewiese, Garten* |
| ✂ ⌗18 | *Hoteleigener Tennisplatz – Golfplatz und Lochzahl* |
| ⚓ | *Bootssteg* |
| ⤚ | *Angelmöglichkeit für Hotelgäste, evtl. gegen Gebühr* |
| 🖄 150 | *Konferenzräume: Höchstkapazität* |
| 🚗 | *Hotelgarage (wird gewöhnlich berechnet)* |
| 🅿 | *Parkplatz reserviert für Gäste* |
| 🐕̸ | *Hunde sind unerwünscht (im ganzen Haus bzw. in den Zimmern oder im Restaurant)* |
| Fax | *Telefonische Dokumentenübermittlung* |
| May-October | *Öffnungszeit, vom Hotelier mitgeteilt* |
| season | *Unbestimmte Öffnungszeit eines Saisonhotels. Die Häuser, für die wir keine Schließungszeiten angeben, sind im allgemeinen ganzjährig geöffnet* |
| LL35 OSB | *Angabe des Postbezirks (hinter der Hoteladresse)* |

## Tiere

*Das Mitführen von Haustieren (Hunde, Katzen u. dgl.) bei der Einreise in Großbritannien und Irland ist untersagt.*

42

# *Küche*

## Die Sterne

*Einige Häuser verdienen wegen ihrer überdurchschnittlich guten Küche Ihre besondere Beachtung. Auf diese Häuser weisen die Sterne hin. Bei den mit «Stern» ausgezeichneten Betrieben nennen wir drei kulinarische Spezialitäten, die Sie probieren sollten.*

❀❀❀ **Eine der besten Küchen: eine Reise wert**
*Mar ißt hier immer sehr gut, öfters auch exzellent, edle Weine, tadelloser Service, gepflegte Atmosphäre ... entsprechende Preise.*

❀❀ **Eine hervorragende Küche: verdient einen Umweg**
*Ausgesuchte Menus und Weine ... angemessene Preise.*

❀ **Eine sehr gute Küche: verdient Ihre besondere Beachtung**
*Der Stern bedeutet eine angenehme Unterbrechung Ihrer Reise.*

*Vergleichen Sie aber bitte nicht den Stern eines sehr teuren Luxusrestaurants mit dem Stern eines kleineren oder mittleren Hauses, wo man Ihnen zu einem annehmbaren Preis eine ebenfalls vorzügliche Mahlzeit reicht.*

## Der "Bib Gourmand"
Sorgfältig zubereitete, preiswerte Mahlzeiten

*Für Sie wird es interessant sein, auch solche Häuser kennenzulernen, die eine etwas einfachere, Küche zu einem besonders günstigen Preis/Leistungs-Verhältnis bieten.*
*Im Text sind die betreffenden Restaurants durch die Angabe "Bib Gourmand"  und* Meals *kenntlich gemacht, z. B.* Meals 19.00/25.00.

*Siehe Karten mit «Stern» ❀❀❀, ❀❀, ❀ und "Bib Gourmand" , die den einzelnen im Führer behandelten Regionen vorangestellt sind.*

43

# Preise

*Die in diesem Führer genannten Preise wurden uns
im Herbst 1998 angegeben. Sie können sich mit
den Preisen von Waren und Dienstleistungen ändern.*

*In einigen Städten werden bei kommerziellen oder
touristischen Veranstaltungen von den Hotels beträchtlich
erhöhte Preise verlangt.*

*Die Preise sind in Pfund Sterling angegeben
(1 £ = 100 pence) mit Ausnahme der
Republik Irland wo sie in Punts angegeben sind.*

*Wenn die Buchstaben* **s.**, **t.**, *oder* **st.** *nicht hinter
den angegebenen Preisen aufgeführt sind, können
sich diese um den Zuschlag für Bedienung und/oder
MWSt erhöhen (keine MWSt auf den Channel Islands).*

*Die Namen der Hotels und Restaurants, die ihre
Preise genannt haben, sind fett gedruckt.
Gleichzeitig haben sich diese Häuser verpflichtet,
die von den Hoteliers selbst angegebenen Preise den
Benutzern des Michelin-Führers zu berechnen.*

*Halten Sie beim Betreten des Hotels den Führer in
der Hand. Sie zeigen damit, daß Sie aufgrund
dieser Empfehlung gekommen sind.*

## Mahlzeiten

| | |
|---|---|
| Meals 13.00/28.00 | **Feste Menupreise** |
| | *Mittagessen* 13.00, *Abendessen* 28.00 *(inkl. Couvert)* |
| Meals 19.00/25.00 | *Siehe Seite 43* |
| s. | *Bedienung inkl.* |
| t. | *MWSt inkl.* |
| st. | *Bedienung und MWSt inkl.* |
| 🍷 6.00 | *Preis für 1/2 Flasche oder eine Karaffe Tafelwein* |

### Mahlzeiten «à la carte»

| | |
|---|---|
| Meals a la carte | |
| 20.00/35.00 | *Der erste Preis entspricht einer einfachen aber sorgfältig zubereiteten Mahlzeit, bestehend aus kleiner Vorspeise, Tagesgericht mit Beilage und Nachtisch. Der zweite Preis entspricht einer reichlicheren Mahlzeit mit Vorspeise, Hauptgericht, Käse oder Nachtisch (inkl. Couvert)* |
| ☕ 9.50 | *Preis des englischen Frühstücks, wenn dieser nicht im Übernachtungspreis enthalten ist. Einfaches, billigeres Frühstück (Continental breakfast) erhältlich* |

*🏠: In dieser Hotelkategorie wird ein Abendessen
normalerweise nur zu bestimmten Zeiten für
Hotelgäste angeboten. Es besteht aus einem Menu
mit begrenzter Auswahl zu festgesetztem Preis.
Mittagessen wird selten angeboten. Viele dieser Hotels
sind nicht berechtigt, alkoholische Getränke
auszuschenken.*

## Zimmer

**rm** 50.00/90.00

*Mindestpreis 50.00, für ein Einzelzimmer und Höchstpreis 90.00 für das schönste Doppelzimmer*

suites

*Preise auf Anfrage*

**rm** ⌣ 55.00/85.00

*Übernachtung mit englischem Frühstück, selbst wenn dieses nicht eingenommen wird*

## « Short breaks » (SB.)

*Einige Hotels bieten Vorzugskonditionen für einen Mindestaufenthalt von zwei Nächten oder mehr (Short Break). Der Preis ist pro Person kalkuliert, bei einer Mindestbeteiligung von zwei Personen und schließt das Zimmer, das Abendessen und das Frühstück ein.*

## Ausschank alkoholischer Getränke

*In Großbritanien und Irland unterliegt der Ausschank alkoholischer Getränke gesetzlichen Bestimmungen die von Land zu Land sehr verschieden sind.*

*Restaurants können nachmittags geöffnet sein und alkoholische Getränke ausschenken, wenn diese zu einer entsprechenden Mahlzeit genossen werden. Hotelbars und Pubs sind generell von 11 Uhr vormittags bis 23 Uhr abends geöffnet; Hotelgäste können alkoholische Getränke jedoch auch außerhalb der Öffnungszeiten serviert werden.*

*Kindern unter 14 Jahren ist der Aufenthalt in Bars untersagt.*

## Anzahlung

*Einige Hoteliers verlangen eine Anzahlung. Diese ist als Garantie sowohl für den Hotelier als auch für den Gast anzusehen.*

## Kreditkarten

*Vom Haus akzeptierte Kreditkarten: MasterCard (Eurocard) – American Express – Diners Club – Visa – Japan Credit Bureau*

# Städte

| | |
|---|---|
| ✉ York | Zuständiges Postamt |
| **401** M 27, ⑩ | Nummer der Michelin-Karte und Koordinaten des Planfeldes oder Faltseite |
| West Country G. | Siehe auch den grünen Michelinführer The West Country of England |
| pop. 1057 | Einwohnerzahl |
| BX A | Markierung auf dem Stadtplan |
| ⚑₁₈ | Öffentlicher Golfplatz und Lochzahl (Handicap erforderlich, telefonische Reservierung empfehlenswert) |
| ☀ ≼ | Rundblick, Aussichtspunkt |
| ✈ | Flughafen |
| ⛴ | Autofähre |
| ⛴ | Personenfähre |
| ❱ | Informationsstelle |

## Uhrzeit

*In Großbritannien ist eine Zeitverschiebung zu beachten und die Uhr gegenüber der deutschen Zeit um 1 Stunde zurückzustellen.*

## *Sehenswürdigkeiten*

## Bewertung

| | |
|---|---|
| ★★★ | *Eine Reise wert* |
| ★★ | *Verdient einen Umweg* |
| ★ | *Sehenswert* |
| AC | *Eintritt (gegen Gebühr)* |

## Lage

| | |
|---|---|
| See | *In der Stadt* |
| Envir. | *In der Umgebung der Stadt* |
| Exc. | *Ausflugsziele* |
| N, S, E, W | *Im Norden (N), Süden (S), Osten (E), Westen (W) der Stadt* |
| A 22 | *Zu erreichen über die Straße A 22* |
| 2 m. | *Entfernung in Meilen* |

# Das Auto, die Reifen

*In Großbritannien herrscht Anschnallpflicht für Fahrer, Beifahrer und auf dem Rücksitz, wenn Gurte vorhanden sind. Es ist verboten, Kinder auf den Vordersitzen auf dem Schoß zu befördern. In Irland besteht für den Fahrer und den Beifahrer Anschnallpflicht, wenn Gurte vorhanden sind, Kinder unter 12 Jahren dürfen allerdings nicht auf den Vordersitzen befördert werden, es sei denn es existiert ein entsprechender Kindersitz.*

## Lieferanten von Michelin-Reifen
## ATS Reifenhändler

*Die Anschrift der nächstgelegenen ATS-Verkaufsstelle erhalten Sie auf Anfrage (9-17 Uhr) bei*

> *ATS HOUSE*
> *180-188 Northolt Rd.*
> *Harrow*
> *Middlesex HA2 OED*
> *℘ (0181) 966 6600*

## Automobilclubs

*Die wichtigsten Automobilsclubs des Landes sind die Automobile Association und der Royal Automobile Club, die den Mitgliedern der der FIA angeschlossenen Automobilclubs Pannenhilfe leisten und einige ihrer Dienstleistungen anbieten.*

*AUTOMOBILE ASSOCIATION*
*Fanum House*
*BASINGSTOKE, Hants*
*RG21 2EA*
*℘ (0990) 448866*

*AUTOMOBILE ASSOCIATION*
*23 Rock Hill*
*BLACKROCK*
*Co-Dublin*
*℘ (01) 283 3555*

*ROYAL AUTOMOBILE CLUB*
*RAC House, Lansdowne Rd.*
*CROYDON, Surrey CR9 2JA*
*℘ (0181) 917 2500*

*ROYAL AUTOMOBILE CLUB*
*RAC IRELAND*
*New Mount House*
*22-24 Lower Mount St.*
*DUBLIN 2*
*℘ (01) 676 0113*

# Stadtpläne

@ ● a    *Hotels – Restaurants*

## Sehenswürdigkeiten

*Sehenswertes Gebäude mit Haupteingang*
*Sehenswerter Sakralbau*

## Straßen

*Autobahn*
*- Anschlußstellen: Autobahneinfahrt und/oder-ausfahrt,*
*Schnellstraße mit getrennten Fahrbahnen*
*Hauptverkehrsstraße*
*Fernverkehrsstraße (Primary route)*
*- Netz wird z.z. neu eingestuft*
*Einbahnstraße – Gesperrte Straße, mit*
*Verkehrsbeschränkungen*
*Fußgängerzone*
Piccadilly   *Einkaufsstraße – Parkplatz, Parkhaus*
*Tor – Passage – Tunnel*
*Unterführung (Höhe angegeben bis 16'6")*
*auf Hauptverkehrsstraßen*
*Bahnhof und Bahnlinie*
*Standseilbahn – Seilschwebebahn*
*Bewegliche Brücke – Autofähre*

## Sonstige Zeichen

*Informationsstelle*
*Moschee – Synagoge*
*Funk-, Fernsehturm – Ruine*
*Garten, Park, Wäldchen – Friedhof*
*Stadion – Pferderennbahn – Golfplatz*
*Golfplatz (Zutritt bedingt erlaubt)*
*Aussicht – Rundblick*
*Denkmal – Brunnen – Krankenhaus*
*Jachthafen – Leuchtturm*
*Flughafen – U-Bahnstation*
*Schiffsverbindungen: Autofähre*
*Hauptpostamt (postlagernde Sendungen), Telefon*
*Öffentliches Gebäude, durch einen Buchstaben gekennzeichnet:*
C H   *- Sitz der Grafschaftsverwaltung – Rathaus*
M T U   *- Museum – Theater – Universität, Hochschule*
POL.   *- Polizei (in größeren Städten Polizeipräsidium)*

## London

**BRENT** WEMBLEY   *Name des Verwaltungsbezirks (borough) –*
*des Stadtteils (area)*
*Grenze des « borough » – des « area »*

# Beer

*Beer is one of the oldest and most popular alcoholic drinks in the world. Traditional draught beer is made by grinding malted barley, heating it with water and adding hops which add the familiar aroma and bitterness.*

*Beers in Britain can be divided into 2 principal types: Ales and Lagers which differ principally in their respective warm and cool fermentations. In terms of sales the split between the two is approximately equal. Beer can also be divided into keg or cask.*

Keg beer – *is filtered, pasteurised and chilled and then packed into pressurised containers from which it gets its name.*

Cask beer – *or 'Real Ale' as it is often referred to, is not filtered, pasteurised or chilled and is served from casks using simple pumps. It is considered by some to be a more characterful, flavoursome and natural beer.*

*There are several different beer styles in Britain and Ireland:*

Bitter – *whilst it is the most popular traditional beer in England and Wales it is now outsold by lager. Although no precise definition exists it is usually paler and dryer than Mild with a high hop content and slightly bitter taste.*

Mild – *is largely found in Wales, the West Midlands and the North West of England. The name refers to the hop character as it is gentle, sweetish and full flavoured beer. It is generally lower in alcohol and sometimes darker in colour, caused by the addition of caramel or by using dark malt.*

Stout – *the great dry stouts are brewed in Ireland and are instantly recognisable by their black colour and creamy head. They have a pronounced roast flavour with plenty of hop bitterness.*

*In Scotland the beers produced are full bodied and malty and are often known simply as Light, Heavy, or Export which refers to the body and strength of the beer.*

*Although Ireland is most famous for its stouts, it also makes a range of beers which have variously been described as malty, buttery, rounded and fruity with a reddish tinge.*

# *Whisky*

The term whisky is derived from th Scottish Gealic *uisage beatha* and the Irish Gaelic *uisce beathadh, both meaning "water of life".* When spelt without an e it usually refers to Scotch Whisky which can only be produced in Scotland by the distillation of malted and unmalted barley, maize, rye, and mixtures of two or more of these. Often simply referred to as Scotch it can be divided into 2 basic types: malt whisky and grain whisky.

Malt whisky – *is made only from malted barley which is traditionally dried over peat fires. The malt is then milled and mixed with hot water before mashing turns the starches into sugars and the resulting liquid, called wort, is filtered out. Yeast is added and fermentation takes place followed by two distilling processes using a pot still. The whisky is matured in oak, ideally sherry casks, for at least three years which affects both its colour and flavour. All malts have a more distinctive smell and intense flavour than grain whiskies and each distillery will produce a completely individual whisky of great complexity. A single malt is the product of an individual distillery. There are approximately 100 malt whisky distilleries in Scotland.*

Grain whisky – *is made from a mixture of any malted or unmalted cereal such as maize or wheat and is distilled in the Coffey, or patent still, by a continuous process. Very little grain whisky is ever drunk unblended.*

Blended whisky – *is a mix of more than one malt whisky or a mix of malt and grain whiskies to produce a soft, smooth and consistent drink. There are over 2,000 such blends which form the vast majority of Scottish whisky production.*

Irish Whiskey – *differs from Scotch whisky both in its spelling and method of production. It is traditionally made from cereals, distilled three times and matured for at least 7 years. The different brands are as individual as straight malt and considered by some to be gentler in character.*

# La bière

La bière est l'une des plus anciennes et populaires boissons alcoolisées dans le monde. Pour produire la bière pression traditionnelle, on écrase l'orge maltée que l'on chauffe ensuite avec de l'eau à laquelle on ajoute le houblon. C'est ce qui lui donne son arôme et son goût amer bien connus.

Deux types de bières sont principalement vendues en Grande-Bretagne : les Ales fermentées à chaud et les Lagers fermentées à froid. Elles se divisent en « keg beer » et en « cask beer ».

Bière en keg : elle est filtrée, pasteurisée et refroidie, puis versée dans des tonnelets pressurisés appelés kegs.

Bière en cask ou « Real Ale » : elle n'est ni filtrée, ni pasteurisée, ni refroidie mais tirée directement du tonneau à l'aide d'une simple pompe. Selon certains, cette bière, de qualité bien distincte, a plus de saveur et est plus naturelle.

Types de bières vendues au Royaume-Uni et en Irlande :

Bitter – C'est la bière traditionnelle la plus populaire en Angleterre et au pays de Galles mais ses ventes diminuent au profit des lagers. La Bitter est généralement plus pâle et son goût plus sec que la Mild. Son contenu en houblon est élevé et elle a un goût légèrement amer.

La Mild se consomme surtout au pays de Galles, dans le Midlands de l'Ouest et dans le Nord-Ouest de l'Angleterre. On l'appelle ainsi en raison de son goût moelleux légèrement douceâtre conféré par le houblon. Cette bière, généralement moins alcoolisée, est plus foncée par le caramel qui lui est ajouté ou par l'utilisation de malt plus brun.

Stout – les grandes marques de bières brunes sont brassées en Irlande et sont reconnaissables par leur couleur noire rehaussée de mousse crémeuse. Elles ont un goût prononcé de houblon grillé et une saveur amère.

Celles produites en Écosse sont maltées; elles ont du corps et se dénomment le plus souvent Light, Heavy ou Export en référence au corps et à leur teneur en alcool.

# *Whisky*

*Le mot whisky est un dérivé du gaélique écossais* uisage beatha
*et du gaélique irlandais* uisce beathadh *signifiant tous deux « eau
de vie ». Quand il est écrit sans e, il se réfère au whisky écossais
qui ne peut être produit qu'en Écosse par la distillation
de céréales maltées ou non comme l'orge, le maïs, le seigle
ou d'un mélange de deux ou plus de ces céréales. Souvent appelé
tout simplement Scotch il se réfère à deux types de whiskies :
whisky pur malt ou whisky de grain.*

*Le whisky pur malt est fait seulement à partir d'orge maltée
qui est traditionnellement séchée au-dessus de feux de tourbe.
Le malt est moulu et mélangé avec de l'eau chaude, puis
le brassage transforme l'amidon en sucre; le moût est ensuite
filtré. On y ajoute de la levure et après la fermentation on fait
distiller deux fois dans un alambic. Le whisky est alors vieilli
pendant au moins trois ans dans des fûts de chêne, ayant
contenu de préférence du sherry, ce qui transforme son goût et
sa couleur. Tous les whiskies pur malt ont un arôme particulier
et une saveur plus intense que les whiskies de grain et chaque
distillerie produit son propre whisky avec des qualités bien
distinctes. Il y a environ une centaine de distilleries de whiskies
pur malt en Écosse.*

*Le whisky de grain est fait d'un mélange de céréales, maltées
ou non, comme le maïs ou le froment et est distillé
dans un alambic de type Coffey suivant un procédé continu.
Très peu de whiskies de grain sont consommés à l'état pur.
On procède à des mélanges pour la consommation.*

*Blended whisky est le mélange d'un ou de plusieurs whiskies pur
malt et de whiskies de grain afin de produire un alcool léger,
moelleux et de qualité. Il existe plus de 2 000 marques de blended
whiskies qui forment la majeure partie de la production écossaise.*

*Le whisky irlandais, différent du whisky écossais
par sa fabrication, est traditionnellement produit
à partir de céréales; il est ensuite distillé trois fois et vieilli
pendant au moins sept ans. Certains le trouvent plus moelleux.*

# Birra

*La birra è una delle bevande alcoliche più antiche e popolari. La tradizionale birra alla spina si ottiene macinando l'orzo, riscaldandolo con l'acqua e aggiungendo il luppolo, che le conferiscono l'aroma e il tipico sapore amaro.*

*Le birre britanniche si dividono in due tipi principali:* Ales e Lagers, *che differiscono essenzialmente per la fermentazione, rispettivamente calda e fredda. In termini di vendita, i due tipi approssimativamente si equivalgono. La birra può anche dividersi in* keg *(lett,* barilotto*), e* cask *(lett* botte*).*

*La* keg beer *è filtrata, pastorizzata e raffreddata, e poi messa in contenitori pressurizzati, da cui deriva il nome.*

*La* cask beer, *o* Real Ale, *come viene comunemente indicata, non è filtrata, pastorizzata o raffeddata, ed è servita dalle botti, usando semplici pompe. Alcuni la considerano una birra più ricca di carattere e di gusto e più naturale.*

*In Gran Bretagna e Irlanda, le birre si caratterizzano anche in base a « stili » diversi.*

*Le* bitter *costituisce la birra tradizionalmente più popolare in Inghilterra e nel Galles, ma è ora « superata » dalla* lager. *Non esiste definizione specifica per la birra* bitter, *ma si può dire che si tratta in genere di una birra più pallida e secca della* mild, *dall'alto contenuto di luppolo e dal gusto leggermente amaro.*

*La* mild *è diffusa in Galles, West Midlands e Inghilterra nord-occidentale. Il nome richiama il carattere del luppolo, essendo delicata, dolce e dal gusto pieno. Contiene solitamente una limitata quantità di alcol ed è talvolta scura per l'aggiunta di caramello e per l'impiego di malto scuro.*

*La secche* stouts *vengono prodotte in Irlanda e sono immediatamente riconoscibili dal colore nero e dalla schiuma cremosa. Hanno una decisa fragranza di tostatura e un gusto amaro di luppolo.*

54

# Whisky

*Il termine whisky deriva dal gealico scozzese* uisage beatha *e dal gaelico irlandese* uisce beathadh, *che significano «acqua di vita». Se scritto senza la e, indica di solito lo* Scotch Whisky, *che può essere unicamente prodotto in Scozia dalla distillazione di malto e orzo, granturco e segale, e dall'unione di due o più di questi ingredienti. Spesso chiamato semplicemente Scoveri, si divide in due tipi:* malt whisky *e* grain whisky.

*Il* malt whisky *viene prodotto unicamente con malto, tradizionalmente seccato su fuochi alimentati con torba. Il malto viene poi macinato e gli viene aggiunta acqua bollente prima che l'impasto muti gli amidi in zuccheri e il liquido che ne deriva, chiamato* wort *(mosto di malto), venga filtrato. Si amalgama poi il lievito e avviene la fermentazione, seguita da due processi di distillazione nell'alambicco. Il whisky è lasciato invecchiare in legno di quercia, idealmente in botti di sherry, per almeno tre anni, perchè acquisti colore e sapore. Ogni tipo di* malt whisky *ha un profumo più distintivo e un gusto più intenso del* grain whisky. *Ogni distilleria produce un whisky dal carattere individuale, che richiede un processo di grande complessità. Un solo* malt whisky *è il prodotto di una specifica distilleria. In Scozia, esistono circa 100 distillerie di* malt whisky.

*Il* grain whisky *è il risultato della fusione di qualsiasi cereale con o senza malto, come il granturco o il frumento, en viene distillato nel* Coffey, *o alambicco brevettato, grazie ad un processo continuo. È molto scarsa la quantità di* grain whisky *che si beve puro.*

*Il* blended whisky *nasce dalla fusione di più di un* malt whisky, *o da quella di* malt *e* grain whiskies. *Il risultato è una bevanda dal gusto delicato, dolce e pieno. Esistono più di 2000 whisky di questo tipo, che costituiscono la parte più consistente della produzione scozzese.*

# *Bier*

*Bier ist eines der ältesten und beliebtesten alkoholischen Getränke der Welt. Das traditionelle Faßbier wird aus gemahlener und gemalzter Gerste hergestellt, die in Wasser erhitzt wird. Durch Beigabe von Hopfen werden das bekannte Aroma und der typische bittere Geschmack erzeugt.*

*Die Biersorten in Großbritannien unterteilen sich in zwei Hauptgruppen:* Ales *und* Lagers, *wobei die Art der Gärung – im einen Fall warm, im anderen kalt – ausschlaggebend für das Endresultat ist. Beide Sorten haben hierzulande einen ungefähr gleichen Marktanteil. Da sich die meisten Brauvorgänge anfangs gleichen, entscheiden erst die Endphasen des Brauens, welche der verschiedenen Biersorten entsteht.*

*Darüber hinaus kann das englische Bier auch nach der Art seiner Abfüllung in Keg- bzw. Cask-Bier unterschieden werden:*

Keg beer *wird gefiltert, pasteurisiert, abgekühlt und anschließend in luftdichte, unter Druck gesetzte Metallbehälter gefüllt, von denen das Bier auch seinen Namen erhält.*

Cask beer, *gewöhnlich* Real Ale *genannt, wird weder gefiltert, noch pasteurisiert oder gekühlt, sondern mit einfachen (zumeist Hand-) Pumpen vom Faß gezapft.*

*Es gibt folgende Biersorten in Großbritannien und Irland:*
Bitter *ist das meistbekannte traditionelle Bier in England und Wales. Eine genaue Definition, was ein Bitter ausmacht, sucht man vergeblich; es ist gewöhnlich heller und trockener als das* Mild, *hat einen hohen Hopfenanteil und einen leicht bitteren Geschmack. In den letzten Jahren hat das – meist importierte oder in Lizenz gebraute –* Lager *ihm jedoch den Rang abgelaufen.*

Mild *ist übergiegend in Wales, in den westlichen Midlands und Nordwestengland zu finden. Der Name bezieht sich auf den Hopfenanteil, der es zu einem milden, etwas süßlichen und vollmundigen Bier macht. Es hat einen geringeren Alkoholgehalt und besitz wegen der Zugabe von Karamel oder dunklem Malz bisweilen eine dunklere Farbe.*

Stouts *von hervorragendem trockenem Geschmack werden in Irland gebraut und sind unmittelbar an ihrer schwarzen Farbe und der cremigen Blume erkennbar. Sie haben einen ausgesprochen starken Geschmack nach bitterem Hopfen.*

*In Schottland hergestellte Biere sind alkoholstark und malzig; sie sind oft einfach bekannt als:* Light, Heavy *oder* Export *– Bezeichnungen, die auf Körper und Stärke des Bieres hinweisen.*

# Whisky

Die Bezeichnung Whisky entstammt dem Gälischen, wo im Schottischen der Ausdruck uisage beatha, im Irischen des Ausdruck uisce beathadh jeweils « Wasser des Lebens » bedeuten. Wird Whisky ohne ein e am Ende geschrieben, ist Scotch Whisky gemeint, der nur in Schottland aus gemalzter und ungemalzter Gerste, Mais, Roggen oder aus Mischungen zweier oder mehrerer dieser Zutaten gebrannt werden darf. Oft auch nur als Scotch bezeichnet, kann dieser in zwei Grundarten unterschieden werden: malt whisky und grain whisky.

Malt (Malz) whisky wird nur aus gemalzter Gerste hergestellt, die traditionell über Torffeuern getrocknet wird. Danach wird das Malz gemahlen und mit heißem Wasser vermischt, wonach in der Maische die Stärke in Zucker umgewandelt wird. Die dadurch entstandene Flüssigkeit, « wort » genannt, wird gefiltert und mit Hefe versetzt, was den Gärungsprozess einleitet. Anschließend folgen zwei Destillierungen im herkömmlichen Topf über offenem Feuer. Der Whisky reift danach mindestens drei Jahre lang in Eichenholz, idealerweise in Sherry-Fässern, was sich sowohl auf Farbe wie auf Geschmack des Whiskys auswirkt. Alle malts haben einen ausgeprägteren Geruch und intensiveren Geschmack als die grain-Whiskies; und jede Destillerie erzeugt einen völlig eigenen Whisky mit individueller Geschmacksnote und großer Komplexität. Ein sogenannter single malt enstammt aus einer einzigen Destillerie. Es gibt ungefähr 100 Malt Whisky-Destillerien in Schottland.

Grain (Korn) whisky wird aus Mischungen von gemalzten und ungemalzten Getreidesorten, wie Mais oder Weizen, hergestellt und wird in einem kontinuierlichen Prozeß in dem sogenannten « Coffey » destilliert. Nur sehr wenige Kornwhisky-Sorten sind nicht das Ergebnis von blending, dem Abstimmen des Geschmacks durch Mischung.

Blended whisky wird aus mehr als einer Sorte Malt Whisky oder aus Malt und Grain Whiskies gemischt, um ein weiches, geschamcklich harmonisches Getränk von beständiger Güte zu garantieren. Die über 2000 im Handel zu findenden blends stellen den Großteil der schottischen Whiskyerzeugung dar.

Irish Whiskey unterscheidet sich vom Scotch Whisky sowohl in der Schreibweise wie auch dem Herstellungsverfahren. Er wird traditionell aus Getreide hergestellt, wird dreifach destilliert und reift mindestens sieben Jahre lang. Die verschiedenen Sorten sind so individuell ausgeprägt wie reine Malt Whiskies und werden oft als weicher und gefälliger empfunden.

# Starred establishments
# Les établissements à étoiles
# Gli esercizi con stelle
# Die Stern-Restaurants

## England

| | | | |
|---|---|---|---|
| **Bray-on-Thames** | *Waterside Inn* | **London** | *The Oak Room Marco Pierre White* |
| **London** | *Chez Nico at Ninety Park Lane (at Grosvenor House H.)* | | *(at Le Meridien Piccadilly H.)* |

## England

| | |
|---|---|
| **Bath** | *Lettonie* |
| **Chagford** | *Gidleigh Park* |
| **London** | *Le Gavroche* |
| - | *Gordon Ramsay* |
| - | *Pied à Terre* |
| - | *The Square* |
| - | *La Tante Claire (at the Berkeley H.)* |
| **Oxford** | *Le Manoir aux Quat' Saisons* |
| **Reading** | *L'Ortolan* |
| **Winteringham** | *Winteringham Fields* |

## Scotland

| | |
|---|---|
| **Ullapool** | *Altnabarrie Inn* |

## Ireland

**Republic of Ireland**

| | |
|---|---|
| **Dublin** | *Patrick Guilbaud* |

## England

| | | | |
|---|---|---|---|
| **Altrincham** | *Juniper* | **Faversham** | *Read's* |
| **Baslow** | *Fischer's at Baslow Hall* | **Folkestone** | *La Terrasse (at Sandgate H.)* |
| **Bath** | *Bath Priory* | | |
| - | *Homewood Park* | **Grantham** | *Harry's Place* |
| **Blackburn** | *Northcote Manor* | **Grasmere** | *Michaels Nook Country House* |
| **Blakeney** | *Morston Hall* | **Great Malvern** | *Croque-en-Bouche* |
| **Bourton-on-the-Water** | *Lords of the Manor* | **Ilkley** | *Box Tree* |
| **Bradford** | *Restaurant Nineteen* | **Leeds** | *Pool Court at 42* |
| **Bray-on-Thames** | *Fat Duck* | - | *Rascasse* |
| **Bristol** | *Harveys* | **London** | *Aubergine* |
| - | *Hunstrete House* | - | *The Café Royal Grill Room* |
| **Brockenhurst** | *Le Poussin* | - | *The Canteen* |
| **Channels Islands** | | - | *Capital* |
| **Gorey (Jersey)** | *Village Bistro* | - | *Chavot* |
| **St Saviour (Jersey)** | *Longueville Manor* | - | *Chez Bruce* |
| **Cheltenham** | *Le Champignon Sauvage* | - | *City Rhodes* |
| **Chester** | *Arkle (at Chester Grosvenor H.)* | - | *Connaught* |
| **Chipping Norton** | *Chavignol* | - | *L'Escargot* |
| **East Grinstead** | *Gravetye Manor* | - | *The Halkin* |
| **Emsworth** | *36 on the Quay* | - | *Interlude* |
| **Falmouth** | *Pennypots* | - | *Leith's* |

| | | |
|---|---|---|
| **London** | | *Monsieur Max* |
| - | *Nobu (at The Metropolitan* H.) | |
| - | | *L'Oranger* |
| - | *Oriental (at Dorchester* H.) | |
| - | *Richard Corrigan at Lindsay House* | |
| - | | *River Café* |
| - | *Les Saveurs de Jean-Christophe Novelli* | |
| - | | *Zafferano* |
| **Longridge** | | *Paul Heathcote's* |
| **Ludlow** | | *Merchant House* |
| - | *Mr Underbill's at Dinham Weir* | |
| - | | *Overton Grange* |
| **Lymington** | | *Gordleton Mill* |
| **Newcastle upon Tyne** | *21 Queen Street* | |
| **New Milton** | | *Chewton Glen* |
| **Norwich** | | *Adlard's* |
| **Oakham** | | *Hambleton Hall* |
| **Plymouth** | | *Chez Nous* |
| **Sheffield** | | *Old Vicarage* |
| **Shepton Mallet** | *Charlton House* | |
| **Taplow** | *Waldo's (at Cliveden* H.) | |
| **Tavistock** | | *Horn of Plenty* |
| **Ullswater** | *Sharrow Bay Country House* | |
| **Waterhouses** | | *Old Beams* |
| *Wight (Isle of)* | | |
| **Yarmouth** | | *The George* |

## Scotland

| | |
|---|---|
| **Aberfoyle** | *Braeva* |
| **Achiltibuie** | *Summer Isle.* |
| **Balloch** | *Georgian Room* |
| | *(at Cameron House* H. |
| **Fort William** | *Inverlochy Castl* |
| **Glasgow** | *One Devonshire Garden.* |
| **Gullane** | *La Potinièr* |
| **Port Appin** | *Aird* |
| **Portpatrick** | *Knockinaam Lodg* |

## Wales

| | |
|---|---|
| **Llyswen** | *Llangoed Ha* |

## Ireland

**Northern Ireland**

| | |
|---|---|
| **Bangor** | *Shank.* |
| **Belfast** | *Deane* |

**Republic of Ireland**

| | |
|---|---|
| **Ahakista** | *Shir* |
| **Dublin** | *Peacock Alle* |
| | *(at Fitzwilliam* H. |
| - | *Thornton* |
| **Kenmare** | *Par* |

60

# "Bib Gourmand"

*Good food at moderate prices* _____

*Repas soignés à prix modérés* _____

*Pasti accurati a prezzi contenuti* _____

*Sorgfältig zubereitete,*
*preiswerte Mahzeiten* _____

## 🙂 Meals

## England _____

| | | | |
|---|---|---|---|
| Barnsley | Armstrongs | London | Cafe Spice Namaste |
| Baslow | Café-Max | - | Chapter One |
| Bath | Moody Goose | - | Chapter Two |
| Biddenden | West House | - | Malabar |
| Blackpool | September Brasserie | - | Monsieur Max |
| Bridgnorth | Old Vicarage | - | Redmonds |
| Brighton and Hove | Black Chapati | - | Sabras |
| - | Terre à Terre | - | Woz |
| Bristol | Markwicks | Ludlow | Mr Underhill's |
| Cambridge | 22 Chesterton Road | | at Dinham Weir |
| *Channel Islands* | | - | Oaks |
| Gorey (Jersey) | Jersey Pottery | Maiden Newton | Le Petit Canard |
| | (Garden Rest.) | Maldon | Chigborough Lodge |
| - | Village Bistro | Manchester | Simply Heathcotes |
| Cheltenham | Le Petit Blanc | Milford-on-Sea | Rocher's |
| Chipping Campden | Churchill Arms | Nayland | White Hart |
| Devizes | George and Dragon | Newcastle upon Tyne | Café 21 |
| Drewsteignton | Hunts Tor | - | Forsters |
| Durham | Bistro 21 | Nottingham | Hart's |
| Eastbourne | Hungry Monk | - | Merchants |
| Eynsham | Baker's | Old Burghclere | Dew Pond |
| Faversham | Dove Inn | Oldham | Brasserie (at White Hart Inn) |
| Fordingbridge | Three Lions | Ombersley | The Venture In |
| Fowey | Food for Thought | Oxford | Le Petit Blanc |
| Halifax | Design House | Padstow | Brocks |
| Harrogate | The Bistro | Painswick | Country Elephant |
| Haworth | Weaver's | Pateley Bridge | Dusty Miller |
| Helmsley | Star Inn | Preston | Heathcotes Brasserie |
| Kendal | Punch Bowl Inn | Redruth | The Basset Count House |
| Kenilworth | Simpson's | Rushlake Green | Stone House |
| Keswick | Swinside Lodge | St Albans | Sukiyaki |
| Knaresborough | The General | St Ives | Pig "n" Fish |
| | Tarleton Inn | Salisbury | Howard's House |
| | (Bar/Brasserie) | Sheffield | Rafters |
| Leeds | Leodis | | Smith's of Sheffield |
| - | Paris | Shepton Mallet | Bowlish House |
| London | L'Accento | Skipton | Bar Brasserie |
| - | Cafe Spice Namaste | | (at Angel Inn) |

# Particularly pleasant Hotels
# Hôtels agréables
# Alberghi ameni
# Angenehme Hotels

## England

| London | Claridge's | New Milton | Chewton Glen |
|---|---|---|---|
| - | Dorchester | Taplow | Cliveden |
| - | The Savoy | | |

## Ireland *Republic of Ireland*

| Straffan | Kildare H. & Country Club |
|---|---|

## England

| Aylesbury | Hartwell House |
|---|---|
| Bath | Lucknam Park |
| - | The Royal Crescent |
| Daventry | Fawsley Hall |
| Ipswich | Hintlesham Hall |
| London | Connaught |
| Melton Mowbray | Stapleford Park |
| Oxford | Le Manoir aux Quat' Saisons |

## Scotland

| Dunkeld | Kinnaird |
|---|---|
| Fort William | Inverlochy Castle |
| Glasgow | One Devonshire Gardens |

## Wales

| Llyswen | Llangoed Hall |
|---|---|

## Ireland *Republic of Ireland*

| Dublin | The Merrion |
|---|---|
| Kenmare | Park |
| - | Sheen Falls Lodge |

## England

| Abberley | The Elms |
|---|---|
| Amberley | Amberley Castle |
| Bath | Bath Priory |
| - | Homewood Park |
| Bolton Abbey | Devonshire Arms Country House |
| Bourton-on-the-Water | Lords of the Manor |
| - | Lower Slaughter Manor |
| Bristol | Hunstrete House |
| Broadway | Buckland Manor |
| Castle Combe | Manor House |
| Chagford | Gidleigh Park |

| Channel Islands | |
|---|---|
| La Pulente (Jersey) | Atlantic |
| St Saviour (Jersey) | Longueville Manor |
| East Grinstead | Gravetye Manor |
| Evershot | Summer Lodge |
| Gillingham | Stock Hill Country House |
| Grasmere | Michaels Nook Country House |
| Leeds | 42 The Calls |
| London | Blakes |
| - | Capital |
| - | Cliveden Town House |

## England

| | |
|---|---|
| Ashwater | *Blagdon Manor Country H.* |
| Blakeney | *Morston Hall* |
| Bury St Edmunds | *Twelve Angel Hill (without rest)* |
| Calstock | *Danescombe Valley* |
| Chipping Campden | *Malt House* |
| Cranbrook | *Kennel Holt* |
| Dartmouth | *Nonsuch House* |
| Dulverton | *Ashwick House* |
| Horley | *Langshott Manor* |
| Keswick | *Swinside Lodge* |
| Leominster | *The Marsh* |
| Porlock | *Oaks* |
| Rushlake Green | *Stone House* |
| Salisbury | *Howard's House* |
| Staverton | *Kingston House* |
| Teignmouth | *Thomas Luny House (without rest)* |
| Tintagel | *Trebrea Lodge* |
| Wiveliscombe | *Langley House* |

## Scotland

| | |
|---|---|
| Kentallen | *Ardsheal House* |
| Lochinver | *The Albannach* |
| Maybole | *Ladyburn* |
| Muir of Ord | *Dower House* |
| Mull *(Isle of)* | *Ardfenaig House* |
| Perth | *Dupplin Castle* |

## Wales

| | |
|---|---|
| Betws-y-Coed | *Tan-y-Foel Country House* |
| Llansanffraid Glan Conwy | *Old Rectory* |

## Ireland

**Northern Ireland**

| | |
|---|---|
| Holywood | *Rayanne House* |

**Republic of Ireland**

| | |
|---|---|
| Bagenalstown | *Kilgraney Country House* |
| Dublin | *Butlers Town House* |
| Leenane | *Delphi Lodge* |
| Riverstown | *Coopershill* |
| Wicklow | *Old Rectory* |

## England

| | |
|---|---|
| Alnmouth | *High Buston Hall* |
| Andover | *Fishing Cottage* |
| Askrigg | *Helm Country House* |
| Bethersden | *Little Hodgeham (without rest)* |
| Billingshurst | *Old Wharf (without rest)* |
| Boroughbridge | *Brafferton Hall* |
| Broadway | *Old Rectory (without rest)* |
| Calne | *Chilvester Hill House* |
| Canterbury | *Thruxted Oast (without rest)* |
| Carlisle | *Number Thirty One* |
| Caxton | *Church Farm* |
| Cockermouth | *Low Hall (without rest)* |
| - | *New House Farm* |
| Coniston | *Appletree Holme* |
| Crackington Haven | *Manor Farm* |
| Cranbrook | *Old Cloth Hall* |
| East Hoathly | *Old Whyly* |
| East Retford | *Old Plough* |
| Faversham | *Frith Farm House* |
| Grindon | *Porch Farmhouse* |
| Hayling Island | *Cockle Warren Cottage* |
| Honiton | *Cokesputt House* |
| Iron Bridge | *Severn Lodge (without rest)* |
| Lewes | *Millers (without rest)* |
| Lizard | *Landewednack House* |
| Melksham | *Sandridge Park* |
| North Bovey | *Gate House* |
| Norton St. Philip | *Monmouth Lodge (without rest)* |
| Otley | *Bowerfield House* |
| Plymouth | *The Barn* |
| Ripley | *High Winsley Cottage* |
| St Blazey | *Nanscawen House (without rest)* |
| Seaford | *Old Parsonage (without rest)* |
| Stow-on-the-Wold | *College House* |
| Tavistock | *Quither Mill* |
| Tetbury | *Tavern House (without rest)* |
| Thame | *Upper Green Farm (without rest)* |
| Thoralby | *Littleburn* |
| Veryan | *Crugsillick Manor* |
| Worcester | *Upton House* |

## Scotland

| | |
|---|---|
| **Arran *(Isle of)*** | *Apple Lodge* |
| **Banff** | *Eden House* |
| **Earlston** | *Birkhill* |
| **Edinburgh** | *Drummond House (without rest)* |
| - | *17 Abercromby Place (without rest)* |
| - | *Sibbet House (without rest)* |
| - | *27 Heriot Row (without rest)* |
| **Fort William** | *The Grange (without rest)* |
| **Gairloch** | *Little Lodge* |
| **Glenborrodale** | *Feorag House* |
| **Innerleithen** | *The Ley* |
| **Islay *(Isle of)*** | *Kilmeny Farmhouse* |
| **Marnoch** | *Old Manse of Marnoch* |
| **Skye *(Isle of)*** | *Kinlochfollart* |

## Wales

| | |
|---|---|
| **Bala** | *Fron Feuno He* |
| **Betws-y-Coed** | *Penmachno H* |
| **Dollgellau** | *Abergwynant He* |

## Ireland

### Northern Ireland

| | |
|---|---|
| **Belfast** | *Cottage (without re.* |
| **Coleraine** | *Greenhill Hou* |
| **Dungannon** | *Grange Lod* |

### Republic of Ireland

| | |
|---|---|
| **Castlelyons** | *Ballyvolane Hou* |
| **Castlerea** | *Clonalis Hou* |
| **Inistioge** | *Berryh* |
| **Kanturk** | *Glenloha* |
| **Kenmare** | *Sallyport House (without res* |
| **Kilkenny** | *Blanchville Hou* |

# Particularly pleasant Restaurants
# Restaurants agréables
# Ristoranti ameni
# Angenehme Restaurants

### XXXXX

**England**

| | |
|---|---|
| London | *The Oak Room Marco Pierre White (at Le Meridien Piccadilly H.)* |

### XXXX

**England**

| | | | |
|---|---|---|---|
| Bray-on-Thames | *Waterside Inn (with rm)* | Taplow | *Waldo's (at Cliveden H.)* |
| London | *Grill Room (at Dorchester H.)* | Winteringham | *Winteringham Fields (with rm)* |

### XXX

**England**

| | | | |
|---|---|---|---|
| Baslow | *Fischer's at Baslow Hall (with rm)* | Moulsford | *Beetle & Wedge (with rm)* |
| | | Newcastle upon Tyne | *Horton Grange (with rm)* |
| Bath | *Lettonie (with rm)* | | |
| Dedham | *Le Talbooth* | Reading | *L'Ortolan* |
| Emsworth | *36 on the Quay* | Romsey | *Old Manor House* |
| London | *Goodes at Thomas Goode* | | |
| - | *Orrery* | **Scotland** | |
| - | *Oxo Tower* | Kingussie | *The Cross (with rm)* |
| - | *Le Pont de la Tour* | Peat Inn | *The Peat Inn (with rm)* |
| Lymington | *Gordleton Mill (with rm)* | | |

### XX

**England**

**Channel Islands**

| | | | |
|---|---|---|---|
| Gorey (Jersey) | *Jersey Pottery (Garden Rest)* | Painswick | *Country Elephant* |
| | | Waterhouses | *Old Beams (with rm)* |
| Eastbourne | *Hungry Monk* | | |
| Goring | *Leatherne Bottel* | **Scotland** | |
| Grantham | *Harry's Place* | Aberfoyle | *Braeval* |
| Great Driffield | *Rockingham (with rm)* | Darvel | *Scoretulloch House (with rm)* |
| London | *Quaglino's* | | |
| Moreton-in-Marsh | *Marsh Goose* | **Ireland** | |
| Padstow | *The Seafood (with rm)* | **Republic of Ireland** | |
| | | Ahakista | *Shiro* |

### X

**England**

**Channel Islands**

| | | | |
|---|---|---|---|
| Gorey (Jersey) | *Suma's* | **Ireland** | |
| Fordingbridge | *Three Lions (with rm)* | **Republic of Ireland** | |
| | | Kenmare | *Lime Tree* |

**Scotland**

| | |
|---|---|
| Gullane | *La Potinière* |

## England

| | | | |
|---|---|---|---|
| Aylesbury | *Bottle & Glass* | Nayland | *White Ha* |
| Broadhembury | *Drewe Arms* | Oundle | *The Falcon In* |
| Exeter | *Nobody Inn (with rm)* | Stadhampton | *Crazy Bear (with rm* |
| Great Yeldham | *White Hart* | Winchester | *Wykeham Arms (with rm* |
| Helmsley | *The Star Inn* | Witney | *The Boot In* |
| Keyston | *Pheasant Inn* | Yattendon | *Royal O* |
| Middleham | *Foresters Arms (with rm)* | | |

# England

## Channel Islands,

## Isle of Man

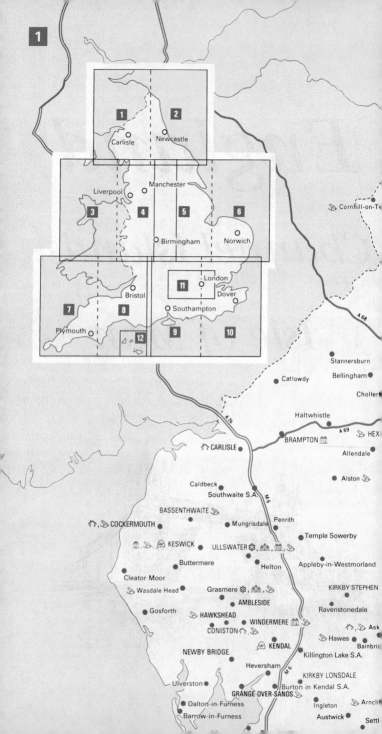

## *Place with at least*

*a hotel or restaurant* ● Ripon
*a pleasant hotel or restaurant* 🏨, ⌂, 🍴, 🍺
*a quiet, secluded hotel* 🪑
*a restaurant with* ✿, ✿✿, ✿✿✿, ☺ Meals
*See this town for establishments located in its vicinity* **LEICESTER**

## *Localité offrant au moins*

*une ressource hôtelière* ● Ripon
*un hôtel ou restaurant agréable* 🏨, ⌂, 🍴, 🍺
*un hôtel très tranquille, isolé* 🪑
*une bonne table à* ✿, ✿✿, ✿✿✿, ☺ Meals
*Localité groupant dans le texte les ressources de ses environs* **LEICESTER**

## *La località possiede come minimo*

*una risorsa alberghiera* ● Ripon
*Albergo o ristorante ameno* 🏨, ⌂, 🍴, 🍺
*un albergo molto tranquillo, isolato* 🪑
*un'ottima tavola con* ✿, ✿✿, ✿✿✿, ☺ Meals
*La località raggruppa nel suo testo le risorse dei dintorni* **LEICESTER**

## *Ort mit mindestens*

*einem Hotel oder Restaurant* ● Ripon
*ein angenehmes Hotel oder Restaurant* 🏨, ⌂, 🍴, 🍺
*einem sehr ruhigen und abgelegenen Hotel* 🪑
*einem Restaurant mit* ✿, ✿✿, ✿✿✿, ☺ Meals
*Ort mit Angaben über Hotels und Restaurants in der Umgebung* **LEICESTER**

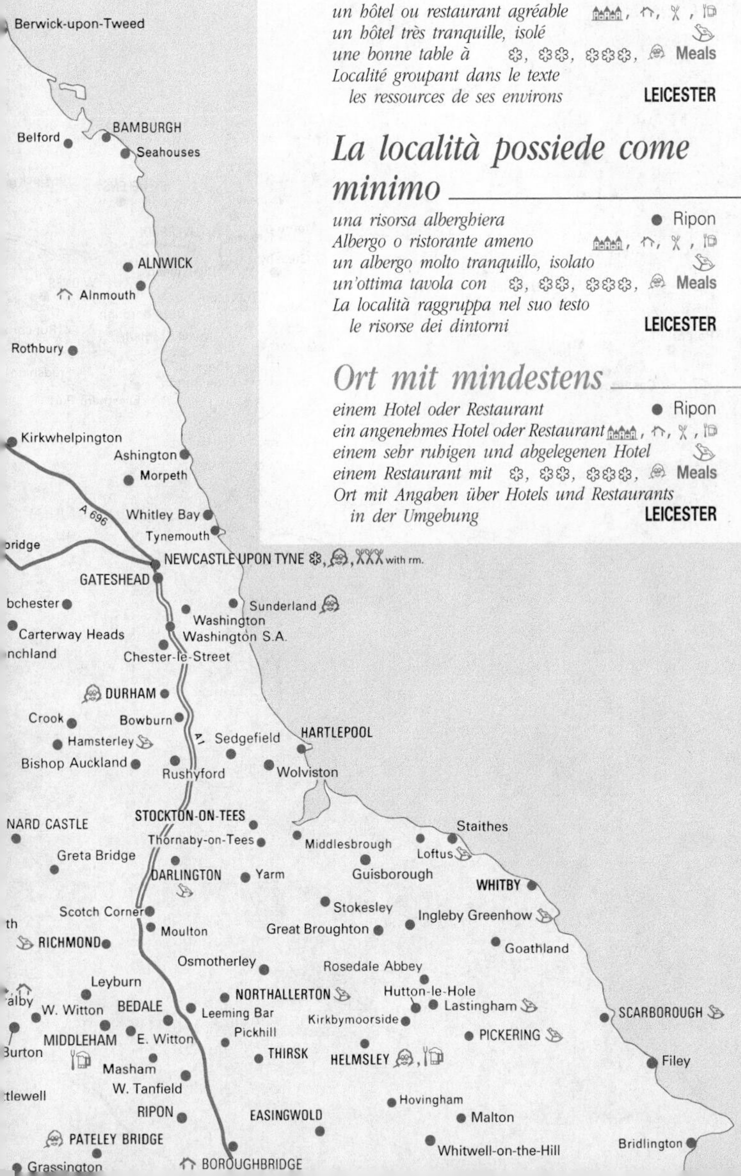

Berwick-upon-Tweed
BAMBURGH
Belford
Seahouses
ALNWICK
⌂ Alnmouth
Rothbury
Kirkwhelpington
Ashington
Morpeth
A 696
Whitley Bay
Tynemouth
ridge
NEWCASTLE UPON TYNE ✿, ☺, 🍴🍴🍴 with rm.
GATESHEAD
bchester
Sunderland ☺
Washington
Washington S.A.
Carterway Heads
nchland
Chester-le-Street
☺ DURHAM
Crook
Bowburn
A1
Hamsterley 🪑
Sedgefield
HARTLEPOOL
Bishop Auckland
Rushyford
Wolviston
STOCKTON-ON-TEES
NARD CASTLE
Thornaby-on-Tees
Staithes
Middlesbrough
Greta Bridge
Loftus 🪑
DARLINGTON 🪑
Yarm
Guisborough
WHITBY
Scotch Corner
Stokesley
Ingleby Greenhow 🪑
th
🪑 RICHMOND
Moulton
Great Broughton
Goathland
Osmotherley
Rosedale Abbey
Leyburn
⌂
alby
NORTHALLERTON 🪑
Hutton-le-Hole
W. Witton
BEDALE
Leeming Bar
Lastingham 🪑
SCARBOROUGH 🪑
Kirkbymoorside
MIDDLEHAM
E. Witton
Pickhill
PICKERING 🪑
Burton
🍺
THIRSK
HELMSLEY ☺, 🍺
Filey
Masham
W. Tanfield
tlewell
RIPON
Hovingham
EASINGWOLD
Malton
☺ PATELEY BRIDGE
Bridlington
Whitwell-on-the-Hill
Grassington
⌂ BOROUGHBRIDGE

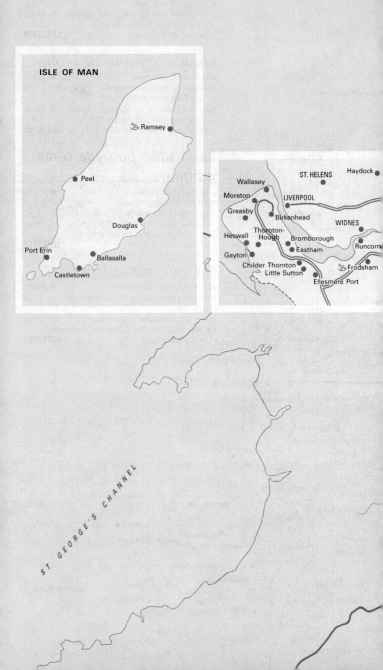

**3**

ISLE OF MAN

Ramsey

Peel

Douglas

Port Erin

Ballasalla

Castletown

Wallasey
Moreton
Greasby
Heswall
Gayton
Thornton-Hough
Childer Thornton
Little Sutton

ST. HELENS
LIVERPOOL
Birkenhead
Bromborough
Eastham
Ellesmere Port

Haydock
WIDNES
Runcorn
Frodsham

ST GEORGE'S CHANNEL

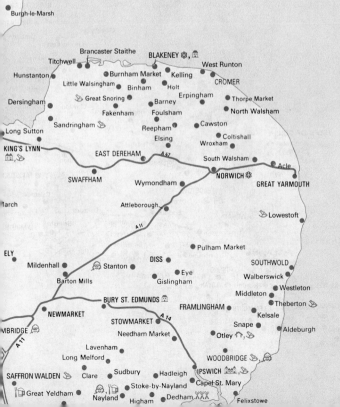

## 6

NORTH

SEA

Burgh-le-Marsh

Brancaster Staithe
Titchwell          BLAKENEY ✿, 🏛
                   West Runton
Hunstanton    Burnham Market    Kelling    CROMER
         Little Walsingham    Binham    Holt
Dersingham    🍀 Great Snoring    Barney    Erpingham    ✿ Thorpe Market
              Fakenham    Foulsham    North Walsham
Long Sutton   Sandringham 🦕    Reepham    Cawston
                              Elsing    Wroxham    Coltishall
KING'S LYNN
🏛,🦕          EAST DEREHAM    A47    South Walsham    Acle
         SWAFFHAM                    NORWICH ✿    GREAT YARMOUTH
                        Wymondham
March                                              🦕 Lowestoft
                   Attleborough
                        A11
ELY                              Pulham Market
    Mildenhall         🦕 Stanton    DISS              SOUTHWOLD
    Barton Mills              Eye        Walberswick
                        Gislingham    Middleton    Westleton
                                              Theberton 🦕
            BURY ST. EDMUNDS 🏛    FRAMLINGHAM    Kelsale
NEWMARKET              STOWMARKET    A14    Snape    Aldeburgh
MBRIDGE 🍺         Needham Market    Otley 🏹,🦕
    A11      Lavenham
         Long Melford              WOODBRIDGE 🦕
SAFFRON WALDEN 🦕   Clare   Sudbury   Hadleigh   IPSWICH 🏛,🦕
   🏠 Great Yeldham        🏠   Stoke-by-Nayland   Capel St. Mary
                   Nayland   Higham   Dedham ✕✕✕
                                              Felixstowe

7

BRISTOL CHANNEL

ISLE
OF LUNDY

WOOLACOMBE • West Do
Croyde •
Saunton
BARNSTAPLE
Appledore • BIDEFORD
Clovelly •
Umberleigh
Horns Cross
Parkham
Milton Damerel
Bude • Winkleigh
HATHERLEIGH
Clawton • Okehampton
Crackington Haven
Boscastle Virginstow • Ashwater
Tintagel Lewdown
Port Isaac Lifton Lydford
New Polzeath Altarnun TAVISTOCK
Rock Calstock
PADSTOW Yelverto
with rm. Liskeard
Bodmin Saltash PLYMOUTH
NEWQUAY A 30 Lostwithiel
Fraddon St. Blazey LOOE
St. Agnes ST. AUSTELL Lansallos Polperro
Portreath Grampound FOWEY
Illogan TRURO Tregony Mevagissey
Redruth VERYAN Portloe
Camborne Portscatho
ST. IVES MARAZION ST. MAWES
PENZANCE FALMOUTH
St. Just Constantine
Mousehole Gillan
Lamorna HELSTON
Mullion
Lizard

ISLES OF SCILLY

Bryher St. Martin's
Tresco
St. Mary's

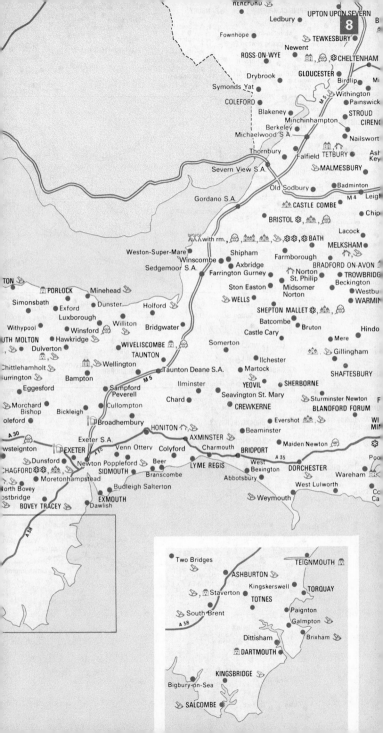

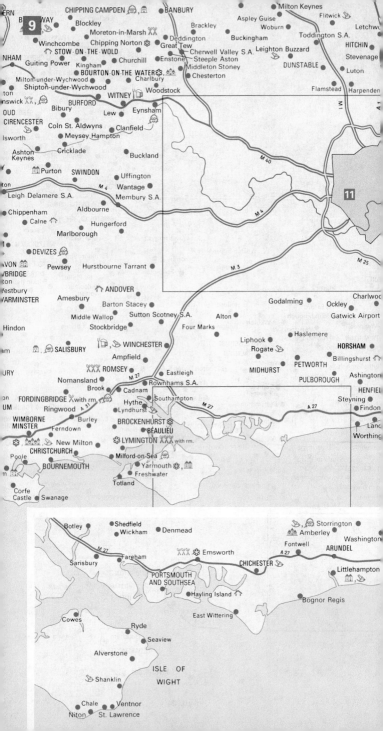

Melbourn

SAFFRON WALDEN

Clare

Sudbury

Hadleigh

IPSWICH

Capel St. Mary

Great Yeldham

Nayland

Stoke-by-Nayland

Higham

Dedham

Felixstowe

Baldock

Clavering

Thaxted

STANSTED AIRPORT

Wethersfield

Earls Colne

Coggeshall

Manningtree

Wix

Harwich and
Dovercourt

BISHOP'S STORTFORD

Braintree

Great
Dunmow

Felsted

COLCHESTER

Ware

Hertford

CHELMSFORD

Clacton-on-Sea

M 25

MALDON

Burnham-on-Crouch

LONDON

BASILDON

Rochford

Horndon-
on-the-Hill

Southend-on-Sea

Canvey Island

North Stifford

Gravesend

M 20

Rochester

Medway S.A.

WHITSTABLE

Birchington

Broadstairs

Cobham

Sittingbourne

Newington

FAVERSHAM

RAMSGATE

West Malling

Maidstone S.A.

CANTERBURY

Sandwich

M 23

MAIDSTONE

Lenham

Deal

M 25

Pluckley

Wye

Edenbridge

Penshurst

M 20

ASHFORD

Bethersden

DOVER

Horley

Turners Hill

ROYAL TUNBRIDGE WELLS

Biddenden

FOLKESTONE

EAST GRINSTEAD

Hartfield

CRANBROOK

A 259

Hythe

CRAWLEY

FOREST ROW

Wadhurst

Tenterden

New Romney

Channel Tunnel

Crowborough

Ticehurst

Wittersham

Uckfield

Fletchling

Uckfield

Sedlescombe

RYE

Haywards
Heath

Newick

Rushlake Green

Battle

Brede

Winchelsea

Hickstead

East Hoathly

Lewes

A 21

HERSTMONCEUX

BRIGHTON AND HOVE

HAILSHAM

Bexhill

Hastings and St. Leonards

Alfriston

Newhaven

EASTBOURNE

SEAFORD

ENGLISH CHANNEL

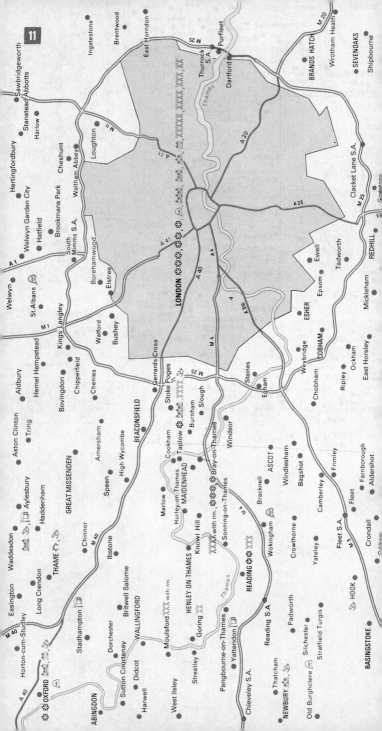

# Channel Islands

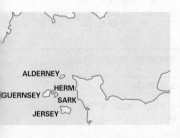

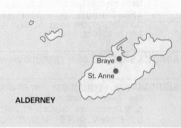

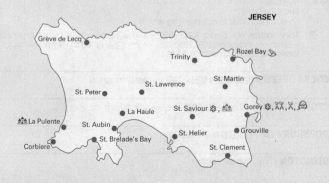

**ABBERLEY** *Worcestershire* 🔢 🔢 M 27 – *pop. 654* – ⊠ *Worcester.*
*London 137 – Birmingham 27 – Worcester 13.*

🏚 **The Elms** ⤵, WR6 6AT, West : 2 m. on A 443 ℘ (01299) 896666, Fax (01299) 896804, ≤,
🌣, « Queen Anne mansion », 🐎, park – ⇔ rest, 🆅 ☎ 🅿 – 🕍 30. 🥇 🆎 ⓓ 𝘝𝘐𝘚𝘈
**Meals** 15.00/29.00 **st.** – **16 rm** ⊑ 75.00/135.00 **st.**

---

**ABBOTSBURY** *Dorset* 🔢 🔢 M 32 *The West Country G. – pop. 422.*
See : *Town*★★ - *Chesil Beach*★★ - *Swannery*★ *AC* – *Sub-Tropical Gardens*★ *AC.*
Env. : *St. Catherine's Chapel*★,½m. *uphill (30 mn rtn on foot).*
Exc. : *Maiden Castle*★★ (≤★) *NE : 7½m.*
*London 146 – Exeter 50 – Bournemouth 44 – Weymouth 10.*

🏠 **Ilchester Arms,** 9 Market St., DT3 4JR, ℘ (01305) 871243, Fax (01305) 871225, Reservations (Freephone) 0800 118833 – ⇔ rest, 🆅 ☎ 🅿. 🥇 🆎 ⓓ 𝘝𝘐𝘚𝘈. 🌣
**Meals** a la carte approx. 10.90 **t.** – ⊑ 4.95 – **10 rm** 35.00/42.95 **t.** – SB.

⌂ **Abbey House** ⤵ without rest., Church St., DT3 4JJ, ℘ (01305) 871330,
Fax (01305) 871088, « Part 15C abbey infirmary », 🐎 – ⇔ 🆅 🅿. 🌣
**4 rm** ⊑ 60.00 **st.**, 1 suite.

---

**ABBOT'S SALFORD** *Warks.* 🔢 🔢 O 27 – *see Evesham (Worcestershire).*

---

**ABINGDON** *Oxon.* 🔢 🔢 Q 28 *Great Britain G. – pop. 35 234.*
See : *Town*★ – *County Hall*★.
🏌, 🏌 *Drayton Park, Steventon Rd, Drayton* ℘ (01235) 550607/528989.
🅱 *25 Bridge St., OX14 3HN* ℘ (01235) 522711.
*London 64 – Oxford 6 – Reading 25.*

🏚 **Upper Reaches,** Thames St., OX14 3JA, ℘ (01235) 522311, Fax (01235) 555182 – ⇔ 🆅
☎ 📞 🅿. 🥇 🆎 ⓓ 𝘝𝘐𝘚𝘈
**Meals** 9.95 **t.** (lunch) and a la carte 16.25/26.20 **t.** ∦ 9.00 – ⊑ 11.95 – **31 rm** 105.00/
180.00 **st.** – SB.

🏚 **Abingdon Four Pillars,** Marcham Rd, OX14 1TZ, West : 1 m. on A 415
℘ (01235) 553456, Fax (01235) 554117 – ⇔ 🆅 ☎ 📞 & 🅿 – 🕍 140. 🥇 🆎 ⓓ 𝘝𝘐𝘚𝘈
**Meals** (carving lunch) 12.95/15.95 **st.** and a la carte – ⊑ 7.95 – **63 rm** 85.00/90.00 **st.** – SB.

*at Frilford West : 3¾ m. on A 415 –* ⊠ *Abingdon.*

🏠 **Dog House,** Frilford Heath, OX13 6QJ, Northeast : 1 ¼ m. by A 338 on Cothill rd
℘ (01865) 390830, Fax (01865) 390860, 🐎 – ⇔ rm, 🆅 ☎ 📞 🅿. 🥇 🆎 ⓓ 𝘝𝘐𝘚𝘈
*closed 25 December* – **Meals** a la carte 13.50/19.70 ∦ 6.00 – ⊑ 7.50 – **19 rm** 71.00/82.00 **st.**

*at Kingston Bagpuize West : 7 m. by A 415 –* ⊠ *Abingdon.*

🏠 **Fallowfields** ⤵, Faringdon Rd, OX13 5BH, ℘ (01865) 820416, Fax (01865) 821275, ⟍,
🐎 – ⇔ 🆅 ☎ 📞 🅿. 🥇 🆎 𝘝𝘐𝘚𝘈
**Meals** (closed lunch Sunday and Monday) 25.50/27.50 **t.** and dinner a la carte ∦ 8.00 –
**10 rm** ⊑ 95.00/155.00 **st.** – SB.

---

**ACASTER MALBIS** *N. Yorks.* 🔢 Q 22 – *see York.*

---

**ACLE** *Norfolk* 🔢 Y 26 *Great Britain G. – pop. 2 208.*
Env. : *The Broads*★.
*London 118 – Great Yarmouth 8 – Norwich 11.*

🏠 **Travelodge,** Acle bypass, NR13 3BE, on A 47 at junction with B 1140 ℘ (01493) 751970,
Reservations (Freephone) 0800 850950 – ⇔ rm, 🆅 & 🅿. 🥇 🆎 ⓓ 𝘝𝘐𝘚𝘈 𝖩𝖢𝖡. 🌣
**Meals** (grill rest.) – **40 rm** 39.95/59.95 **t.**

---

**ACOCKS GREEN** *W. Mids* 🔢 ⑩ 🔢 ㉒ 🔢 ⑳ – *see Birmingham.*

---

**ACTON GREEN** *Herefordshire* 🔢 🔢 M 27 – *see Bromyard.*

---

**ADDERBURY** *Oxon.* 🔢 🔢 Q 27 – *see Banbury.*

---

**ADLINGTON** *Ches.* – *see Macclesfield.*

**ADLINGTON** *Lancs.* 402 404 M 23 – *pop. 8 556.*
*London 217 – Liverpool 35 – Manchester 21 – Preston 16.*

🏠 **Gladmar Country,** Railway Rd, PR6 9RG, ℘ *(01257) 480398, Fax (01257) 482681,* 🐾 –
📺 ☎ ⚓ 🅿. 🆏 🕮 ① *VISA* 🄹🄲🄱. 🕸
**Meals** *(closed Friday to Sunday)* (residents only) (dinner only) 13.50 **st.** ░ 5.00 – **20 rm**
⊂ 39.00/60.00 **st.**

---

**ALBRIGHTON** *Shrops.* 402 403 L 25 – *see Shrewsbury.*

---

**ALCESTER** *Warks.* 403 404 O 27 – *pop. 6 282.*
*London 104 – Birmingham 20 – Cheltenham 27 – Stratford-upon-Avon 8.*

🏠🏠 **Kings Court,** Kings Coughton, B49 5QQ, North : 1 ½ m. on A 435 ℘ *(01789) 763111,*
*Fax (01789) 400242,* 🐾 – 📺 ☎ & 🅿 – ⚕ 130. 🆏 🕮 *VISA*
*closed 24 December to 31 January* – **Meals** a la carte 14.95/19.95 **t.** ░ 3.95 – **42 rm**
⊂ 55.00/78.00 **st.** – SB.

🏠 **Throckmorton Arms,** Coughton, B49 5HX, North : 2 ¼ m. on A 435 ℘ *(01789) 762879,*
*Fax (01789) 762654* – 🕸 rest, 📺 ☎ 🅿. 🆏 🕮 ① *VISA* 🄹🄲🄱. 🕸
*closed 25 and 26 December* – **Meals** (in bar Sunday and Monday dinner) **t.** a la carte
9.60/17.50 ░ 5.45 – **10 rm** ⊂ 48.00/65.00 **t.**

🏠 **Travelodge,** Birmingham Rd, Oversley Hill Roundabout, B49 6AA, South : 1 m. by A 435 at
junction with A 46 ℘ *(01789) 766987, Fax (01789) 766987,* Reservations (Freephone) 0800
850950 – 🕸 rm, 📺 & 🅿. 🆏 🕮 ① *VISA* 🄹🄲🄱. 🕸
**Meals** (grill rest.) – **40 rm** 39.95/59.95 **t.**

---

**ALDBOURNE** *Wilts.* 403 404 P 29 – *pop. 1 682.*
*London 77 – Oxford 36 – Southampton 53 – Swindon 9.*

XX **Raffles,** 1 The Green, SN8 2BW, ℘ *(01672) 540700, Fax (01672) 540038* – 🆏 🕮 ① *VISA*
*closed Saturday lunch, Sunday dinner, Monday, 2 weeks late September, 25 to 31 January*
*and Bank Holidays* – **Meals** a la carte 15.10/24.90 **t.** ░ 5.50.

---

**ALDBURY** *Herts.* 404 S 28 – *pop. 891.*
*London 39 – Aylesbury 12 – Luton 20 – Oxford 36.*

🍴 **Valiant Trooper,** Trooper Rd, HP23 5RW, ℘ *(01442) 851203,* 🐾 – 🅿. 🆏 🕮 *VISA*
*closed Sunday dinner* – **Meals** 15.95 **t.** and a la carte.

---

**ALDEBURGH** *Suffolk* 404 Y 27 – *pop. 2 654.*
🐾 *Thorpeness Golf Hotel, Thorpeness* ℘ *(01728) 452176.*
🅱 *The Cinema, High St., IP15 5AU* ℘ *(01728) 453637 (summer only).*
*London 97 – Ipswich 24 – Norwich 41.*

🏠🏠 **Wentworth,** Wentworth Rd, IP15 5BD, ℘ *(01728) 452312, Fax (01728) 454343,* ≤ –
🕸 rm, 📺 ☎ ⚓ 🅿. 🆏 🕮 ① *VISA*
*closed 28 December* – **Meals** 12.50/12.95 **t.** – **38 rm** ⊂ (dinner included) 73.00/144.00 **t.** –
SB.

🏠🏠 **Brudenell,** The Parade, IP15 5BU, ℘ *(01728) 452071, Fax (01728) 454082,* ≤ – 🛗 🕸 📺 ☎
🅿. 🆏 🕮 ① *VISA* 🄹🄲🄱
**Meals** (light lunch Monday to Friday in summer, carving lunch Saturday and bar lunch in
winter)/dinner 19.95 **st.** and a la carte ░ 5.95 – ⊂ 9.50 – **47 rm** 65.00/85.00 **st.** – SB.

X **Lighthouse,** 77 High St., IP15 5AU, ℘ *(01728) 453377, Fax (01728) 453377* – 🕸. 🆏 *VISA*
🄹🄲🄱
*closed Sunday dinner-Monday lunch Christmas-Easter and 2 weeks January* – **Meals** 15.75 **t.**
(dinner) and lunch a la carte 15.40/19.95 **t.** ░ 5.95.

X **Regatta,** 171-173 High St., IP15 5AN, ℘ *(01728) 452011, Fax (01728) 452011* – 🆏 🕮 *VISA*
🄹🄲🄱
**Meals** *(closed Wednesday November-February)* a la carte 14.50/20.50 **t.** ░ 5.00.

---

**ALDERLEY EDGE** *Ches.* 402 403 404 N 24 – *pop. 5 280.*
🐾 *Wilmslow, Great Warford, Mobberley* ℘ *(01565) 872148* – 🐾 *Brook Lane* ℘ *(01625)*
*585583.*
*London 187 – Chester 34 – Manchester 14 – Stoke-on-Trent 25.*

🏠🏠 **Alderley Edge,** Macclesfield Rd, SK9 7BJ, ℘ *(01625) 583033, Fax (01625) 586343,* 🐾 –
📺 ☎ ⚓ 🅿 – ⚕ 120. 🆏 🕮 ① *VISA*. 🕸
**Meals** – (see *The Alderley* below) – ⊂ 8.50 – **46 rm** 99.50/175.00 **t.**

XXX **The Alderley** (at Alderley Edge H.), Macclesfield Rd, SK9 7BJ, ℰ (01625) 583033, *Fax (01625) 586343*, 🐎 – 🗏 ℗. **MO** AE ⓪ *VISA*
**Meals** 16.50/23.95 **t.** and a la carte ⓘ 8.50.

X **Est, Est, Est**, 75 London Rd, SK9 7YD, ℰ (01625) 583993, *Fax (01625) 583814* – 🗏. **MO** AE ⓪ *VISA*
*closed 25 and 26 December* – **Meals** - Italian - a la carte 13.15/20.45 **st.** ⓘ 5.75.

---

**ALDERNEY** 403 Q 33 and 230 ⑨ – *see Channel Islands.*

---

**ALDERSHOT** *Hants.* 404 R 30.
London 45 – Portsmouth 38 – Reading 22 – Winchester 32.

🏰 **Potters International**, 1 Fleet Rd, GU11 2ET, ℰ (01252) 344000, *Fax (01252) 311611*, ᒻᕲ, ᕵᕽ, ⬛, 🐎 – 🛗 🔟 & ℗ – 🔏 450. **MO** AE ⓪ *VISA*. 🕸
**Meals** *(closed Saturday lunch and Sunday dinner)* 12.50/17.50 **st.** – **94 rm** ⫴ 100.00/120.00 **st.**, 3 suites.

🏠 **Travel Inn**, Wellington Av., GU11 1SQ, East: on A 323 ℰ (01252) 344063, *Fax (01252) 344073* – 🌤 rm, 🔟 & ℗. **MO** AE ⓪ *VISA*. 🕸
**Meals** (grill rest.) – **40 rm** 38.00 **t.**

@ ATS Backwater Way, Ash Rd ℰ (01252) 20246

*The Guide is updated annually so renew your Guide every year.*

---

**ALDFIELD** *N. Yorks.* – *see Ripon.*

---

**ALDRIDGE** *W. Mids.* 402 403 404 O 26 – *pop. 16 862* – ⊠ *Walsall.*
London 130 – Birmingham 12 – Derby 32 – Leicester 40 – Stoke-on-Trent 38.

Plan : see Birmingham p. 3

🏰 **Fairlawns**, 178 Little Aston Rd, WS9 0NU, East: 1 m. on A 454 ℰ (01922) 455122, *Fax (01922) 743210*, ᒻᕲ, ᕵᕽ, ⬛, 🐎 – 🗏 rest, 🔟 ☎ ℗ – 🔏 80. **MO** AE ⓪ *VISA*
**Meals** *(closed Saturday lunch)* 16.95/25.95 **st.** and a la carte ⓘ 6.00 – **46 rm** ⫴ 67.50/89.50 **st.**, 6 suites – SB.                                                                    CT n

@ ATS 106 Leighswood Rd ℰ (01922) 451968

---

**ALDWINCLE** *Northants.* 402 404 S 26 – *pop. 310* – ⊠ *Oundle.*
London 84 – Cambridge 40 – Leicester 40 – Northampton 26 – Peterborough 18.

⌂ **The Maltings** 🌤 without rest., Main St., NN14 3EP, ℰ (01832) 720233, *Fax (01832) 720326*, 🐎 – 🌤 ℗. **MO** *VISA*. 🕸
*closed 1 week Christmas* – **3 rm** ⫴ 37.00/51.00.

---

**ALFRETON** *Derbs* 402 403 404 P 24 – *pop. 22 822.*
🏌 Shirland, Lower Delves ℰ (01773) 834935 – 🏌 Ormonde Fields, Nottingham Rd, Codnor, Ripley ℰ (01773) 742987.
London 134 – Derby 13 – Nottingham 19 – Sheffield 27.

🏠 **Travelodge**, Old Swanwick Colliery Rd, DE55 1HJ, South : ¾ m. by A 61 at junction with A 38 ℰ (01773) 520040, *Fax (01773) 520040*, Reservations (Freephone) 0800 850950 – 🌤 rm, 🔟 & ℗ – 🔏 50. **MO** AE ⓪ *VISA* JCB. 🕸
**Meals** (grill rest.) – **60 rm** 39.95/59.95 **t.**

🏠 **Travel Inn**, Carter Lane East, South Normanton, DE55 2EH, ℰ (01773) 862899, *Fax (01773) 861155* – 🛗 🌤 🔟 & ℗. **MO** AE ⓪ *VISA*. 🕸
**Meals** (grill rest.) – **42 rm** 38.00 **t.**

---

**ALFRISTON** *E. Sussex* 404 U 31 – *pop. 1 721* – ⊠ *Polegate.*
London 66 – Eastbourne 9 – Lewes 10 – Newhaven 8.

🏰 **Star Inn**, High St., BN26 5TA, ℰ (01323) 870495, *Fax (01323) 870922*, « Part 13C coaching inn » – 🌤 ☎ ℗ – 🔏 30. **MO** AE ⓪ *VISA*. 🕸
**Meals** (bar lunch Monday to Saturday)/dinner 18.00 **t.** ⓘ 7.75 – ⫴ 9.25 – **34 rm** 80.00/100.00 **st.** – SB.

XX **Moonrakers**, High St., BN26 5TD, ℰ (01323) 870472 – 🌤. **MO** AE *VISA* JCB. 🕸
*closed Sunday dinner and first 2 weeks January* – **Meals** (dinner only and Sunday lunch)/dinner 15.95 **t.** and a la carte ⓘ 4.75.

**ALLENDALE** Northd. **401 402** N 19 – *pop. 2 123* – ⌂ *Hexham*.
  ⛳ High Studdon, Allenheads Rd ℰ *(01434) 345005*.
  *London 314 – Carlisle 39 – Newcastle upon Tyne 33.*

  ⌂ **Thornley House,** NE47 9NH, West : ¾ m. on Whitfield rd ℰ *(01434) 683255*, 🍴 – ⇌ **P**
  **Meals** (by arrangement) (communal dining) 13.00 **st.** – **3 rm** ⌷ 30.00/37.00.

---

**ALLESLEY** W. Mids. **403 404** P 26 – *see Coventry*.

---

**ALMONDBURY** W. Yorks. **402** ⑲ – *see Huddersfield*.

---

**ALNMOUTH** Northd. **401 402** P 17 Great Britain G. – *pop. 586*.
  **Env. :** Warkworth Castle★ *AC, S : 4 m. by B 1338 and A 1068*.
  ⛳ Alnmouth Village, Marine Rd. ℰ *(01665) 830576*.
  *London 314 – Edinburgh 90 – Newcastle upon Tyne 37.*

  🏠 **Marine House,** 1 Marine Rd, NE66 2RW, ℰ *(01665) 830349*, ≤, 🍴 – ⇌ **TV P**. **AE VISA**
  *closed Christmas-New Year* – **Meals** (by arrangement) 15.95 **st.** ⓘ 6.50 – **10 rm** ⌷ (dinner included) 84.00 **st.** – SB.

  ⌂ **High Buston Hall** ⚘, High Buston, NE66 3QH, Southwest : 2 ¼ m. by B 1338 off A 1068
  ℰ *(01665) 830341, Fax (01665) 830341*, ≤, « Georgian house », 🍴 – ⇌ **TV P**. ⚖
  *closed 2 weeks Christmas-New Year* – **Meals** (by arrangement) (communal dining) 25.00 **st.**
  ⓘ 4.50 – **3 rm** ⌷ 35.00/65.00 **st.**

  ⌂ **The Grange** without rest., 20 Northumberland St., NE66 2RJ, ℰ *(01665) 830401*,
  *Fax (01665) 830401*, ≤, 🍴 – ⇌ **TV P**. ⚖
  *closed December and January* – **5 rm** ⌷ 25.00/55.00 **st.**

---

**ALNWICK** Northd. **401 402** O 17 Great Britain G. – *pop. 7 419*.
  **See :** Town ★ – Castle★★ *AC*.
  **Exc. :** Dunstanburgh Castle★ *AC, NE : 8 m. by B 1340 and Dunstan rd (last 2½m. on foot)*.
  ⛳ Swansfield Park ℰ *(01665) 602632*.
  🛈 The Shambles, NE66 1TN ℰ *(01665) 510665*.
  *London 320 – Edinburgh 86 – Newcastle upon Tyne 34.*

  🏠🏠 **White Swan,** Bondgate Within, NE66 1TD, ℰ *(01665) 602109, Fax (01665) 510400*,
  « Furnishings from SS Olympic » – ⇌ **TV** ☎ ✆ **P** – 🔬 150. **AE VISA**
  **Meals** (bar lunch Monday to Saturday)/dinner 18.95 **st.** ⓘ 6.45 – **58 rm** ⌷ 69.50/99.50 – SB.

  🏠 **Oaks,** South Rd, NE66 2PN, Southeast : ½ m. ℰ *(01665) 510014, Fax (01665) 603219* – **TV**
  ☎ **P**. **AE VISA**. ⚖
  **Meals** a la carte 10.15/20.75 **st.** – **12 rm** ⌷ 39.50/50.00 **st.**

  ⌂ **Charlton House,** 2 Aydon Gdns., South Rd, NE66 2NT, Southeast : ½ m.
  ℰ *(01665) 605185* – ⇌ **TV** ✆ **P**. ⚖
  *closed Christmas and New Year* – **Meals** (by arrangement) – **5 rm** ⌷ 19.00/38.00 **st.**

  ⌂ **Bondgate House,** 20 Bondgate Without, NE66 1PN, ℰ *(01665) 602025*,
  *Fax (01665) 602025* – ⇌ rest, **TV P**. **AE VISA JCB**. ⚖
  **Meals** (by arrangement) 12.00 **st.** ⓘ 3.50 – **8 rm** ⌷ 23.00/44.00 **st.** – SB.

**at Newton on the Moor** South : 5½ m. on A 1 – ⌂ Alnwick.

  🍴 **Cook and Barker Inn** with rm, NE65 9JY, ℰ *(01665) 575234, Fax (01665) 575234* – **TV**
  **P**. **AE VISA JCB**. ⚖
  **Meals** a la carte 17.20/26.20 **st.** ⓘ 4.95 – **4 rm** ⌷ 37.50/70.00 **st.** – SB.

---

**ALPORT** Derbs. – *see Bakewell*.

---

**ALSAGER** Ches. **402 403 404** N 24 Great Britain G. – *pop. 13 435* – ⌂ *Stoke-on-Trent (Staffs.)*.
  **Env. :** Little Moreton Hall★★ *AC, NE : 4 m. by A 50 and A 34*.
  *London 180 – Chester 36 – Liverpool 49 – Manchester 32 – Stoke-on-Trent 11.*

  🏠🏠 **Manor House,** Audley Rd, ST7 2QQ, Southeast : ¾ m. ℰ *(01270) 884000*,
  *Fax (01270) 882483*, 🏊, ⇌ rm, **TV** ☎ & **P** – 🔬 200. **AE VISA**. ⚖
  **Meals** 13.50/21.00 **st.** and a la carte ⓘ 5.95 – **57 rm** ⌷ 80.00/100.00 **st.** – SB.

  ⌂ **Sappho Cottage,** 118 Crewe Rd, ST7 2JA, ℰ *(01270) 882033, Fax (01270) 883556*, 🍴 –
  ⇌ **TV P**. ⚖
  **Meals** (by arrangement) (communal dining) 13.50 **s.** – **3 rm** ⌷ 27.50/45.00 **s.**

**ALSTON** *Cumbria* 401 402 M 19 – *pop. 2 065.*

🛆 *Alston Moor, The Hermitage ℰ (01434) 381675.*

🚩 *The Railway Station, CA9 3JB ℰ (01434) 381696 (summer only).*

*London 309 – Carlisle 28 – Newcastle upon Tyne 45.*

🏠 **Lovelady Shield Country House** ⌂, Nenthead Rd, CA9 3LF, East : 2 ½ m. on A 689 ℰ (01434) 381203, Fax (01434) 381515, ≤, ☞ – ⇔ rest, 📺 ☎ 🅿. ◍ 亜 *VISA* JCB
*closed January* – **Meals** (bar lunch)/dinner 29.50 **t.** ⓖ 6.75 – **12 rm** � (dinner included) 96.50/184.00 **t.** – SB.

🏠 **Nent Hall Country House,** CA9 3LQ, East : 2 ½ m. on A 689 ℰ (01434) 381584, Fax (01434) 382668, ☞ – ⇔ rest, 📺 ☎ ℰ ₺ 🅿. ◍ *VISA*
*restricted opening in winter* – **Meals** (dinner only) 12.50 **t.** and a la carte ⓖ 7.00 – **17 rm** ⊃ (dinner included) 59.50/95.00 **t.** – SB.

⌂ **High Windy Hall** ⌂, Middleton in Teesdale Rd, CA9 3EZ, ℰ (01434) 381547, Fax (01434) 382477, ≤ – ⇔ 📺 *VISA* JCB, ⌘
*April-November* – **Meals** (by arrangement) 21.00 **t.** ⓖ 5.50 – **5 rm** ⊃ 35.00/70.00 **t.** – SB.

---

**ALTARNUN** *Cornwall* 403 G 32 *The West Country G.* – *pop. 2 405* – ✉ *Launceston.*

See : *Church★*.

Env. : *Bodmin Moor★★*, *Laneast (St. Sidwell's★)*, *N : 2½m. by minor roads.*

*London 279 – Exeter 56 – Plymouth 36 – Truro 39.*

🏠 **Penhallow Manor Country House** ⌂, PL15 7SJ, ℰ (01566) 86206, Fax (01566) 86179, ⌇, ☞ – ⇔ rest, 📺 ☎ 🅿. ◍ 亜 *VISA*
*closed 3 January-14 February* – **Meals** (bar lunch)/dinner 21.50 **t.** ⓖ 6.50 – **7 rm** ⊃ 55.00/90.00 **st.** – SB.

---

**ALTON** *Hants.* 404 R 30 – *pop. 16 005.*

🛆 *Old Odiham Rd ℰ (01420) 82042.*

🚩 *7 Cross and Pillory Lane, GU34 1HL ℰ (01420) 88448.*

*London 53 – Reading 24 – Southampton 29 – Winchester 18.*

🏠 **Alton Grange,** London Rd, GU34 4EG, Northeast : 1 m. on A 339 ℰ (01420) 86565, Fax (01420) 541346, ☞ – ⇔ 📺 ☎ 🅿 – 🛆 80. ◍ 亜 ① *VISA* JCB, ⌘
*closed 24 December-2 January* – **Truffles : Meals** (closed Saturday lunch) a la carte 18.45/24.70 **t.** ⓖ 5.95 – **29 rm** ⊃ 67.00/95.00 **t.**

🏠 **Alton House,** Normandy St., GU34 1DW, ℰ (01420) 80033, Fax (01420) 89222, ⌇, ☞, ⌘ – ⇔ rm, 📺 ☎ 🅿 – 🛆 120. ◍ 亜 ① *VISA*, ⌘
*closed 26 December* – **Meals** 10.95/13.95 **t.** and a la carte ⓖ 4.50 – ⊃ 6.75 – **39 rm** 58.00/68.00 **t.** – SB.

🏠 **Swan,** High St., GU34 1AT, ℰ (01420) 83777, Fax (01420) 87975 – ⇔ 📺 ☎ 🅿 – 🛆 50. ◍ 亜 ① *VISA* JCB
**Meals** (bar lunch Monday to Saturday)/dinner a la carte approx. 17.10 **t.** – ⊃ 9.25 – **36 rm** 75.00/90.00 **t.** – SB.

---

**ALTON TOWERS** *Staffs.* 402 403 404 O 25.

*London 158 – Birmingham 48 – Derby 23 – Stafford 24 – Stoke-on-Trent 13.*

🏛 **Alton Towers,** ST10 4DB, ℰ (01538) 704600, Fax (01538) 704657, ≤, « Fantasy themed », ≘s, ⊠, ☞, park – 🛗 ⇔, 🍽 rest, 📺 ☎ ₺ 🅿 – 🛆 200. ◍ 亜 *VISA*, ⌘
*closed 24 to 30 December* – **Secret Garden : Meals** (light lunch)/dinner a la carte approx. 15.85 **st.** ⓖ 7.95 – ⊃ 4.95 – **175 rm** 99.00 **st.**

---

**ALTRINCHAM** *Gtr. Manchester* 402 403 404 N 23 – *pop. 40 042.*

🛆 *Altrincham Municipal, Stockport Rd, Timperley ℰ (0161) 928 0761 – Dunham Forest, Oldfield Lane ℰ (0161) 928 2605 – 🛆 Ringway, Hale Mount, Hale Barns ℰ (0161) 904 9609.*

🚩 *20 Stamford New Rd, WA14 1EJ ℰ (0161) 912 5931.*

*London 191 – Chester 30 – Liverpool 30 – Manchester 8.*

🏛 **Cresta Court,** Church St., WA14 4DP, on A 56 ℰ (0161) 927 7272, Fax (0161) 926 9194, ₣₅ – 🛗, ⇔ rest, 🍽 rest, 📺 ☎ 🅿 – 🛆 250. ◍ 亜 ① *VISA*
**Meals** (closed Saturday lunch) 13.95/16.95 **st.** and a la carte ⓖ 5.95 – ⊃ 7.95 – **138 rm** 78.50/130.00 **st.** – SB.

🏠 **Woodland Park,** Wellington Rd, WA15 7RG, off A 560 ℰ (0161) 928 8631, Fax (0161) 941 2821 – 🍽 rest, 📺 ☎ 🅿 – 🛆 200. ◍ 亜 ① *VISA* JCB, ⌘
**The Terrace : Meals** (closed Saturday and Sunday lunch) 12.95/14.95 **st.** and dinner a la carte ⓖ 7.10 – **46 rm** ⊃ 75.00/135.00 **t.** – SB.

🏠 **Bowdon,** Langham Rd, WA14 2HT, Southwest : 1 m. ℘ (0161) 928 7121, *Fax (0161) 927 7560* – ⇆ 🔟 ☎ 🅿 – 🏄 150. 🐠 🖭 ⓞ 𝘝𝘐𝘚𝘈. ⌘
**Meals** (buffet lunch Monday to Friday and bar lunch Saturday)/dinner 17.95 **t.** and a la carte ↥ 7.00 – ⌐ 9.50 – **89 rm** 76.00/120.00 **st.** – SB.

🏠 **George and Dragon - Premier Lodge,** Manchester Rd, WA14 4PH, on A 56 ℘ (0161) 928 9933, *Fax (0161) 929 8060,* Reservationa (Freephone) 0800 118833 – 📳, ⇆ rm, 🔟 ☎ 🅿 – 🏄 40. 🐠 🖭 ⓞ 𝘝𝘐𝘚𝘈. ⌘
**Meals** *(closed Saturday lunch)* (grill rest.) a la carte 12.65/21.35 **st.** – ⌐ 5.95 – **46 rm** 44.95 **t.**

🏠 **Pelican Inn - Premier Lodge,** Manchester Rd, West Timperley, WA14 5NH, North : 2 m. on A 56 ℘ (0161) 962 7414, *Fax (0161) 962 3456,* Reservations (Freephone) 0800 118833 – ⇆ rm, 🔟 ☎ 🅿 – 🏄 50. 🐠 🖭 ⓞ 𝘝𝘐𝘚𝘈. ⌘
**Meals** (grill rest.) a la carte 13.35/18.40 **st.** ↥ 4.50 – ⌐ 5.95 – **48 rm** 43.95 **st.**

XX **Juniper,** 21 The Downs, WA14 2QD, ℘ (0161) 929 4008, *Fax (0161) 929 4009* – 🍽. 🐠 🖭
❀ 𝘝𝘐𝘚𝘈. ⌘
*closed Monday lunch, Sunday, 1 week January, 1 week July and Bank Holidays* – **Meals** a la carte 29.00/35.50 **t.** ↥ 12.00
**Spec.** Cornish lobster bisque. Grilled sea bass with wild rice, broad beans and a red wine sauce. Rice pudding soufflé with honey ice cream.

**at Hale** *Southeast : 1 m. on B 5163* – ⊠ *Altrincham.*

X **Est, Est, Est,** 183 Ashley Rd, WA15 9SD, ℘ (0161) 928 1811 – 🍽. 🐠 🖭 𝘝𝘐𝘚𝘈
*closed Sunday and 25-26 December* – **Meals** - Italian - a la carte 18.85/21.40 **t.**

**at Halebarns** *Southeast : 3 m. on A 538* – ⊠ *Altrincham.*

🏠🏠 **Four Seasons,** Manchester Airport, Hale Rd, WA15 8XW, ℘ (0161) 904 0301, *Fax (0161) 980 1787,* ☞ – 📳, ⇆ rm, 🍽 rest, 🔟 ☎ 🅿 – 🏄 120. 🐠 🖭 𝘝𝘐𝘚𝘈. ⌘
**The Four Seasons :** Meals *(closed Saturday lunch)* 15.95/18.95 **st.** and a la carte ↥ 6.50 – ⌐ 10.50 – **146 rm** 99.50/109.50 **st.,** 4 suites.

🔧 ATS 74 Oakfield Rd ℘ (0161) 928 7024

---

**ALVECHURCH** *Worcs.* **403 404** O 26 – *pop. 5 829.*
London 113 – Birmingham 11 – Bromsgrove 6.

↑ **Alcott Farm** without rest., Weatheroak, B48 7EH, Northeast : 2 ¾ m. by Radford Rd on Beoley rd (Icknield St.) ℘ (01564) 824051, *Fax (01564) 824051,* ☞, park – ⇆ 🔟 🅿. ⌘
**4 rm** ⌐ 30.00/50.00 **s.**

---

**ALVELEY** *Shrops.* – *see Bridgnorth.*

---

**ALVERSTONE** *I.o.W.* **403 404** Q 32 – *see Wight (Isle of).*

---

**ALWALTON** *Cambs.* **402 404** T 26 – *see Peterborough.*

---

**AMBERLEY** *Glos.* **403 404** N 28 – *see Stroud.*

---

**AMBERLEY** *W. Sussex* **404** S 31 *Great Britain G.* – *pop. 525* – ⊠ *Arundel.*
Env. : *Bignor Roman Villa (mosaics★) AC, NW : 3½ m. by B 2139 via Bury.*
London 56 – Brighton 24 – Portsmouth 31.

🏠🏠 **Amberley Castle** ⟨, BN18 9ND, Southwest : ½ m. on B 2139 ℘ (01798) 831992, *Fax (01798) 831998,* « *14C castle, 12C origins* », ☞, park – ⇆ 🔟 ☎ 🅿 – 🏄 40. 🐠 🖭 ⓞ 𝘝𝘐𝘚𝘈. ⌘
**Queen's Room :** Meals (booking essential) 17.50/35.00 **t.** ↥ 8.95 – **15 rm** ⌐ 145.00/300.00 **t.** – SB.

---

**AMBLESIDE** *Cumbria* **402** L 20 *Great Britain G.* – *pop. 2 905.*
Env. : *Lake Windermere★★ – Dove Cottage, Grasmere★ AC AY* A – *Brockhole National Park Centre★ AC, SE : 3 m. by A 591 AZ.*
Exc. : *Wrynose Pass★★, W : 7½ m. by A 593 AY – Hard Knott Pass★★, W : 10 m. by A 593 AY.*
🛈 *Old Courthouse, Church St., LA22 0BT ℘ (015394) 32582 (closed Sunday and Monday in winter) AZ – Main Car Park, Waterhead, LA22 0EN ℘ (015394) 32729 (summer only) BY.*
London 278 – Carlisle 47 – Kendal 14.

# AMBLESIDE
# GRASMERE

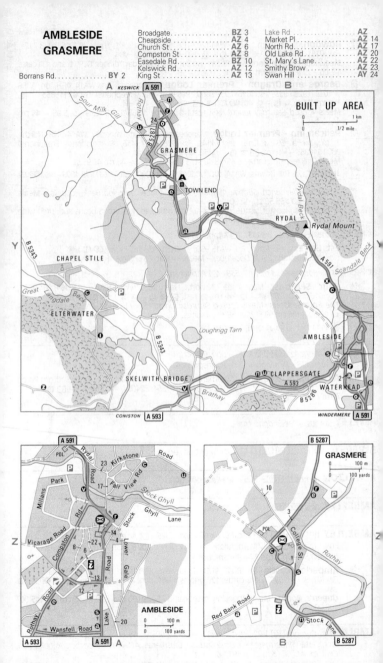

*Town plans:* roads most used by traffic and those on which guide listed hotels
and restaurants stand are fully drawn; the beginning only of
lesser roads is indicated.

88

**Rothay Manor**, Rothay Bridge, LA22 0EH, South : ½ m. on A 593 &#x1f4de; (015394) 33605, *Fax (015394) 33607*, ≤, ≈ – ✦✦ rest, ⊡ ☎ ⅙ ☐. ◷◷ ㊉ ⊙ *VISA*. ⅍  BY  r
*closed 3 January-5 February* – **Meals** (buffet lunch Monday to Saturday)/dinner 27.00 **t.** ⫳ 6.50 – **15 rm** ⊒ 75.00/135.00 **t.**, 3 suites – SB.

**Ambleside Salutation**, Lake Rd, LA22 9BX, &#x1f4de; (015394) 32244, *Fax (015394) 34157* – ✦✦ rest, ⊡ ☎ ☐ – ⚖ 30. ◷◷ ㊉ *VISA* ⊙  AZ  r
**Meals** (bar lunch)/dinner 16.00 **st.** and a la carte ⫳ 5.95 – **36 rm** ⊒ 48.50/97.00 **st.** – SB.

**Kirkstone Foot Country House**, Kirkstone Pass Rd, LA22 9EH, Northeast : ¼ m. &#x1f4de; (015394) 32232, *Fax (015394) 32805*, ≈ – ✦✦ rest, ⊡ ☎ ☐. ◷◷ ㊉ ⊙ *VISA* ⊙. ⅍
*closed 3 January-4 February* – **Meals** (dinner only) 21.95 **t.** and a la carte ⫳ 6.50 – **13 rm** ⊒ 50.00/98.00 **t.** – SB.  AZ  c

**Borrans Park**, Borrans Rd, LA22 0EN, &#x1f4de; (015394) 33454, *Fax (015394) 33003*, ≈ – ✦✦ ⊡ ☎ ⅙ ☐. ◷◷ *VISA* ⊙. ⅍  BY  a
*closed 1 week Christmas* – **Meals** (dinner only) 18.50 **st.** ⫳ 5.95 – **12 rm** ⊒ 52.50/85.00 **st.** – SB.

**Elder Grove**, Lake Rd, LA22 0DB, &#x1f4de; (015394) 32504, *Fax (015394) 32504* – ✦✦ rest, ⊡ ☎ ☐. ◷◷ ㊉ *VISA* ⊙  AZ  a
*mid February-mid November* – **Meals** (dinner only) 18.00 **t.** and a la carte ⫳ 5.00 – **12 rm** ⊒ (dinner included) 47.00/94.00 **t.** – SB.

**Rothay Garth**, Rothay Rd, LA22 0EE, &#x1f4de; (015394) 32217, *Fax (015394) 34400*, ≈ – ✦✦ ⊡ ☎ ☐. ◷◷ *VISA* ⊙. ⅍  AZ  e
**Meals** 9.50/15.00 **st.** and lunch a la carte ⫳ 5.50 – **15 rm** ⊒ (dinner included) 56.00/122.00 **st.**, 1 suite – SB.

**Laurel Villa**, Lake Rd, LA22 0DB, &#x1f4de; (015394) 33240 – ✦✦ ⊡ ☎ ☏ ☐. ◷◷ ㊉ *VISA*. ⅍
**Meals** (booking essential) (residents only) (dinner only) 25.00 **t.** ⫳ 20.00 – **8 rm** ⊒ 50.00/80.00 **t.**  AZ  s

**Riverside** ⅌ without rest., Under Loughrigg, LA22 9LJ, &#x1f4de; (015394) 32395, *Fax (015394) 32395*, ≈ – ⊡ ☎ ☏ ☐. ◷◷ *VISA*  BY  s
*10 February-14 November* – **4 rm** ⊒ 40.00/66.00 **st.**

**Crow How** ⅌, Rydal Rd, LA22 9PN, Northwest : ½ m. on A 591 &#x1f4de; (015394) 32193, *Fax (015394) 31770*, ≤, ≈ – ✦✦ rest, ⊡ ☐. ◷◷ *VISA*  BY  x
*closed 7 to 21 November* – **Meals** (dinner only) 15.95 **st.** ⫳ 6.25 – **9 rm** ⊒ 32.00/84.00 **st.** – SB.

**Rowanfield Country House** ⅌, Kirkstone Rd, LA22 9ET, Northeast : ¾ m. &#x1f4de; (015394) 33686, *Fax (015394) 31569*, ≤ Lake Windermere and Coniston Old Man, ≈ – ✦✦ ⊡ ☎ ◷◷ ㊉ *VISA* ⊙. ⅍  AZ  u
*March-mid November and Christmas-New Year* – **Meals** (by arrangement) 20.00 **st.** – **7 rm** ⊒ 51.00/68.00 **st.** – SB.

**Scandale Brow** without rest., Rydal Rd, LA22 9PL, Northwest : ½ m. on A 591 &#x1f4de; (015394) 34528, *Fax (015394) 34528*, ≈ – ✦✦ ⊡ ☐  BY  c
**3 rm** ⊒ 39.00/52.00 **s.**

**Glass House**, Rydal Rd, LA22 9AN, &#x1f4de; (015394) 32137, *Fax (015394) 31139*, « Converted mill » – ✦✦ ◷◷ *VISA*  AZ  v
*closed Monday November-Easter* – **Meals** a la carte 15.45/24.50 **st.**

**Drunken Duck Inn** with rm, Barngates, LA22 0NG, Southwest : 3 m. by A 593 and B 5286 on Tarn Hows rd &#x1f4de; (015394) 36347, *Fax (015394) 36781*, ≤, « Part 16C » – ✦✦ rest, ⊡ ☎ ☐. ◷◷ ㊉ *VISA* ⊙. ⅍
*closed 25 December* – **Meals** a la carte 14.85/24.50 **st.** – **9 rm** ⊒ 55.00/90.00 **t.**

**at Waterhead** *South : 1 m. on A 591* – BY – ✉ *Ambleside*.

**Wateredge**, Borrans Rd, LA22 0EP, &#x1f4de; (015394) 32332, *Fax (015394) 31878*, ≤, « Part 17C fishermen's cottages, lakeside setting », ≈ – ✦✦ rest, ⊡ ☎ ☐. ◷◷ ㊉ *VISA* ⊙. ⅍
*closed mid December-mid January* – **Meals** (light lunch)/dinner 30.00 **t.** – **22 rm** ⊒ (dinner included) 84.00/188.00 **t.** – SB.  BY  o

**Regent**, LA22 0ES, &#x1f4de; (015394) 32254, *Fax (015394) 31474*, ⬛ – ✦✦ rest, ⊡ ☎ ☐. ◷◷ *VISA* ⊙  BY  e
**Meals** (light lunch)/dinner 19.50 **t.** ⫳ 7.95 – **30 rm** ⊒ 59.00/93.00 **st.** – SB.

**at Clappersgate** *West : 1 m. on A 593* – BY – ✉ *Ambleside*.

**Nanny Brow Country House** ⅌, LA22 9NF, &#x1f4de; (015394) 32036, *Fax (015394) 32450*, ≤, « Landscaped gardens », ⬦ – ✦✦ ⊡ ☎ ☐. ◷◷ ㊉ ⊙ *VISA* ⊙  BY  u
**Meals** (dinner only) 27.50 **t.** ⫳ 7.00 – **17 rm** ⊒ (dinner included) 90.00/180.00 **t.**, 3 suites – SB.

**Grey Friar Lodge**, LA22 9NE, &#x1f4de; (015394) 33158, *Fax (015394) 33158*, ≤, ≈ – ✦✦ ⊡ ☐. ⅍  BY  n
*April-October and weekends only in March* – **Meals** (residents only) (dinner only) 18.50 **st.** ⫳ 4.25 – **8 rm** ⊒ (dinner included) 54.00/102.00 **st.** – SB.

**at Skelwith Bridge** West : 2½ m. on A 593 – AY – ⊠ Ambleside.

🏠 **Skelwith Bridge**, LA22 9NJ, ℘ (015394) 32115, Fax (015394) 34254 – ⇔ rest, 📺 ☎ 🅿
🐾 VISA JCB
AY v
closed 19 December-2 January – Meals (bar lunch Monday to Saturday)/dinner 19.45 st.
⌂ 8.50 – 29 rm ⊒ 48.00/86.00 st. – SB.

⌂ **Greenbank** without rest., LA22 9NW, on A 593 ℘ (015394) 33236, ≤, 🐾 – ⇔ 📺 🅿
closed 25-26 and 31 December – 3 rm ⊒ 26.00/42.00.

**at Elterwater** West : 4½ m. by A 593 off B 5343 – AY – ⊠ Ambleside.

🏨 **Langdale H. & Country Club**, Great Langdale, LA22 9JD, Northwest : 1 ¼ m. on B 5343
℘ (015394) 37302, Fax (015394) 37694, 🗗, ☎, 🏊, 🐾, park, 🎾, squash – ⇔ rest, 📺 ☎
🅿 – ⚿ 100. 🐾 VISA JCB 🎾
AY c
Meals (light lunch)/dinner 18.50 t. and a la carte ⌂ 7.50 – 65 rm ⊒ 125.00/200.00 t. – SB.

🏠 **Eltermere Country House** 🌟, LA22 9HY, ℘ (015394) 37207, Fax (015394) 37638, ≤,
🐾 – ⇔ rest, 📺 🅿. 🎾
AY i
restricted opening December and January – Meals (dinner only) 17.50 t. ⌂ 5.85 – 18 rm
⊒ 38.00/83.00 st. – SB.

**at Little Langdale** West : 4½ m. by A 593 – AY – ⊠ Langdale.

🏠 **Three Shires Inn** 🌟, LA22 9NZ, ℘ (015394) 37215, ≤, 🐾 – ⇔ rest, 🅿. 🐾 VISA. 🎾
restricted opening January and December – Meals (bar lunch)/dinner 18.50 t. and a la carte
⌂ 4.95 – 10 rm ⊒ 45.00/76.00 t. – SB.

---

**AMERSHAM (Old Town)** Bucks. 404 S 28 – pop. 21 711.
London 29 – Aylesbury 16 – Oxford 33.

🏠 **Crown**, 16 High St., HP7 0DH, ℘ (01494) 721541, Fax (01494) 431283, « Part 16C former
coaching inn », 🐾 – ⇔ rest 📺 ☎ 🅿 – ⚿ 30. 🐾 🖭 🅞 VISA. 🎾
Meals 14.95 st. (lunch) and dinner a la carte 19.40/35.85 st. ⌂ 9.00 – ⊒ 9.95 – 23 rm
115.00/150.00 st. – SB.

XX **King's Arms**, High St., HP7 0DJ, ℘ (01494) 726333, Fax (01494) 433480, « Part 15C inn »
– 🅿. 🐾 🖭 🅞 VISA JCB
closed Sunday dinner, Monday and 26-30 December – Meals 13.50/17.00 t. and a la carte
⌂ 5.00.

X **Gilbey's**, 1 Market Sq., HP7 0DF, ℘ (01494) 727242, Fax (01494) 531243, 🏤 – 🐾 🖭 🅞
VISA
closed 24 to 28 December – Meals a la carte 15.85/23.15 t.

---

**AMESBURY** Wilts. 403 404 O 30 The West Country G. – pop. 6 333.
Env. : Stonehenge★★★ AC, W : 2 m. by A 303.
Exc. : Wilton Village★ (Wilton House★★ AC, Wilton Carpet Factory★ AC), SW : 13 m. by
A 303, B 3083 and A 36.
🅱 Redworth House, Flower Lane, SP4 7HG ℘ (01980) 622833.
London 87 – Bristol 52 – Taunton 66.

🏠 **Travelodge**, SP4 7AS, North : ¼ m. at junction of A 303 with A 345 ℘ (01980) 624966,
Reservations (Freephone) 0800 850950 – ⇔ rm, 📺 ⅙ 🅿. 🐾 🖭 🅞 VISA JCB. 🎾
Meals (grill rest.) – 32 rm 39.95/59.95 t.

⌂ **Mandalay** without rest., 15 Stonehenge Rd, SP4 7BA, ℘ (01980) 623733,
Fax (01980) 626642, 🐾 – ⇔ 📺 ☎ 🅿. 🐾 🖭 🅞 VISA JCB. 🎾
5 rm ⊒ 28.00/32.00 s.

⌂ **Epworth House** without rest., 21 Edwards Rd, SP4 7LT, ℘ (01980) 624242,
Fax (01980) 590419, 🐾 – ⇔ 📺 🅿
closed 20 December-4 January – 4 rm ⊒ 42.00.

---

**AMPFIELD** Hants. 403 404 P 30 – pop. 1 523 – ⊠ Romsey.
🛝 Ampfield (Par Three), Winchester Rd ℘ (01794) 368480.
London 79 – Bournemouth 31 – Salisbury 19 – Southampton 11 – Winchester 7.

🏠 **Potters Heron**, Winchester Rd, SO51 9ZF, on A 3090 ℘ (01703) 266611,
Fax (01703) 251359, ☎ – ⅙ ⇔ 📺 ☎ 🅿 – ⚿ 150. 🐾 🖭 🅞 VISA. 🎾
Meals (bar lunch Monday to Saturday)/dinner 18.75 st. and a la carte ⌂ 7.25 – ⊒ 8.95 –
54 rm 85.00 st. – SB.

XX **Keats**, Winchester Rd, SO51 9BQ, on A 3090 ℘ (01794) 368252 – 🅿. 🐾 🖭 🅞 VISA JCB. 🎾
closed Sunday, Monday and 25-26 December – Meals - Italian - 10.00 t.
(lunch) and a la carte 17.70/23.70 t. ⌂ 5.40.

**AMPNEY CRUCIS** *Glos.* **403 404** O 28 – *see Cirencester.*

---

**L'ANCRESSE** *Guernsey (Channel Islands)* **403** P 33 and **230** ⑩ – *see Channel Islands.*

---

**ANDOVER** *Hants.* **403 404** P 30 – *pop. 34 647.*
　　🏌 *51 Winchester Rd* ℰ *(01264) 323980.*
　　🛈 *Town Mill House, Bridge St., SP10 1BL* ℰ *(01264) 324320.*
　　*London 74 – Bath 53 – Salisbury 17 – Winchester 11.*

🏨　**White Hart,** Bridge St., SP10 1BH, ℰ *(01264) 352266, Fax (01264) 323767,* ⅃₅, 全s – ⃗⃗⃗ rm, 🆃🆅 ☎ 🅿 – 🔬 65. 🆆🅾 🅰🅴 🅾 🆅🅸🆂🅰
　　*closed 24 to 28 December –* **Meals** *15.95* **t.** *and a la carte* ᵔ *6.00 –* 🖃 *7.95 –* **27 rm** *70.00/80.00* **t.** *– SB.*

**at Upper Clatford** *South : 1¾ m. by A 3057 –* ⊠ *Andover.*

🏠　**Fishing Cottage,** SP11 7HB, ℰ *(01264) 364214, Fax (01264) 364214,* ≤, « *Riverside setting* », 🐾, 🥀 – ⃗⃗⃗ 🆃🆅 🅿. ⠧
　　*accommodation booking essential –* **Meals** *(by arrangement) (communal dining) 25.00* **s.** *–* **3 rm** 🖃 *40.00/60.00* **st.**

🅖 *ATS 51a New St.* ℰ *(01264) 323606/7*

---

**ANDOVERSFORD** *Glos.* **403 404** O 28 – *see Cheltenham.*

---

**ANNITSFORD** *Northd.* **401** P 18 – *see Newcastle upon Tyne (Tyne and Wear).*

---

**ANSTY** *Warks.* – *see Coventry (W. Mids.).*

---

**APPLEBY-IN-WESTMORLAND** *Cumbria* **402** M 20 – *pop. 2 570 (inc. Bongate).*
　　🏌 *Appleby, Brackenber Moor* ℰ *(017683) 51432.*
　　🛈 *Moot Hall, Boroughgate, CA16 6XD* ℰ *(017683) 51177.*
　　*London 285 – Carlisle 33 – Kendal 24 – Middlesbrough 58.*

🏨　**Appleby Manor Country House** ⑤, Roman Rd, CA16 6JB, East : 1 m. by B 6542 and Station Rd ℰ *(017683) 51571, Fax (017683) 52888,* ≤, 全s, 🥀 – ⃗⃗⃗ rest, 🆃🆅 ☎ ℰ 🅿 – 🔬 40. 🆆🅾 🅰🅴 🅾 🆅🅸🆂🅰 🅹🅲🅱. ⠧
　　**Meals** *a la carte 16.85/26.35* **st.** ᵔ *5.95 –* **30 rm** 🖃 *78.00/116.00* **st.** *– SB.*

🏨　**Tufton Arms,** Market Sq., CA16 6XA, ℰ *(017683) 51593, Fax (017683) 52761,* 🐾 – 🆃🆅 ☎ 🅿 – 🔬 100. 🆆🅾 🅰🅴 🅾 🆅🅸🆂🅰 🅹🅲🅱
　　**Meals** *22.00* **t.** *(dinner) and a la carte 13.25/22.65* **t.** ᵔ *4.75 –* **19 rm** 🖃 *50.00/90.00* **t.,** *2 suites – SB.*

🏠　**Royal Oak Inn,** Bongate, CA16 6UN, Southeast : ½ m. on B 6542 ℰ *(017683) 51463, Fax (017683) 52300,* « *Part 16C and 17C* » – ⃗⃗⃗ rest, 🆃🆅 🅿. 🆆🅾 🅰🅴 🅾 🆅🅸🆂🅰 🅹🅲🅱
　　*closed 25 December –* **Meals** *and a la carte 12.00/23.00* **t.** ᵔ *5.00 –* **9 rm** 🖃 *35.00/85.00* **t.** *– SB.*

---

**APPLEDORE** *Devon* **403** H 30 *The West Country G. – pop. 2 187.*
　　*See : Town★.*
　　*London 228 – Barnstaple 12 – Exeter 46 – Plymouth 61 – Taunton 63.*

🏠　**West Farm,** Irsha St., EX39 1RY, West : ¼ m. ℰ *(01237) 425269,* « *17C house* », 🥀 – ⃗⃗⃗ rm, 🆃🆅. ⠧
　　**Meals** *(by arrangement) (communal dining) 22.50* **s.** *–* **3 rm** 🖃 *50.00/70.00* **s.**

---

**ARKESDEN** *Essex* – *see Saffron Walden.*

---

**ARNCLIFFE** *N. Yorks.* **402** N 21 – *pop. 79 –* ⊠ *Skipton.*
　　*London 232 – Kendal 41 – Leeds 41 – Preston 50 – York 52.*

🏨　**Amerdale House** ⑤, BD23 5QE, ℰ *(01756) 770250, Fax (01756) 770250,* ≤, 🥀 – ⃗⃗⃗ rest, 🆃🆅 🅿. 🆆🅾 🆅🅸🆂🅰. ⠧
　　*mid March-mid November –* **Meals** *(dinner only) 28.00* **t.** ᵔ *6.50 –* **11 rm** 🖃 *(dinner included) 75.50/131.00* **t.** *– SB.*

**ARUNDEL** W. Sussex **404** S 31 Great Britain G. – pop. 3 033.

See : Castle★★ AC.

🏛 61 High St., BN18 9AJ ℰ (01903) 882268.

London 58 – Brighton 21 – Southampton 41 – Worthing 9.

🏨 **Norfolk Arms,** 22 High St., BN18 9AD, ℰ (01903) 882101, Fax (01903) 884275 – ⚡ rest, 📺 ☎ ❷ – 🔬 100. ◍ 🆎 ◍ *VISA*
Meals 9.95/17.85 t. ⓐ 5.65 – **34 rm** ⚏ 70.00/110.00 t. – SB.

🏨 **Swan,** 27-29 High St., BN18 9AG, ℰ (01903) 882314, Fax (01903) 883759 – ⚡, ▤ rest, 📺 ☎ ❷, ◍ 🆎 ◍ *VISA*, ※
Meals 14.95 st. and a la carte ⓐ 5.50 – **15 rm** ⚏ 50.00/75.00 st. – SB.

🏨 **Comfort Inn,** Crossbush, BN17 7QQ, Southeast : 1 ¼ m. by A 27 on A 284 ℰ (01903) 840840, Fax (01903) 849849 – ⚡ rm, ▤ rest, 📺 ☎ ❷ – 🔬 30. ◍ 🆎 ◍ *VISA* ※
Meals 6.75 st. (lunch) and dinner a la carte 13.15/24.25 t. ⓐ 4.50 – ⚏ 6.75 – **53 rm** 49.50 st.

🏨 **Travel Inn,** Crossbush, BN18 9PQ, East : 1 m. on A 27 ℰ (01903) 882655, Fax (01903) 884381 – ⚡ 📺 ♿ ❷, ◍ 🆎 ◍ *VISA*. ※
Meals (grill rest.) – **30 rm** 38.00 t.

↥ **Portreeves Acre** without rest., The Causeway, BN18 9JL, ℰ (01903) 883277, 🌳 – 📺 ❷
closed 24 December-2 January – **3 rm** ⚏ 30.00/44.00 s.

**at Burpham** Northeast : 3 m. by A 27 – ✉ Arundel.

🏨 **Burpham Country** 🍃, BN18 9RJ, ℰ (01903) 882160, Fax (01903) 884627, ≤, 🌳 – ⚡ 📺 ☎ ❷, ◍ 🆎 *VISA*. ※
closed 25 December, 25 January-February and 23 to 30 September – **Meals** (closed Sunday and Monday) (dinner only) 23.00 t. ⓐ 6.75 – **10 rm** ⚏ 40.00/98.00 t. – SB.

✕✕ **George and Dragon,** BN18 9RR, ℰ (01903) 883131, Fax (01903) 883341 – ◍ 🆎 ◍ *VISA* *JCB*
closed Sunday dinner and 25 December – **Meals** (bar lunch Monday to Saturday)/dinner 19.75 t. ⓐ 5.75.

**at Walberton** West : 3 m. by A 27 off B 2132 – ✉ Arundel.

🏨 **Stakis Avisford Park,** Yapton Lane, BN18 0LS, on B 2132 ℰ (01243) 551215, Fax (01243) 552481, ≤, ☲, ⚏s, ⌤, 🏳, ⓟs, 🌳, park, ※, squash – ⚡ 📺 ☎ ❷ – 🔬 300. ◍ 🆎 *VISA*
Meals (closed Saturday lunch) (buffet lunch) 16.50/19.75 t. – ⚏ 10.50 – **134 rm** 100.00/160.00 st., 5 suites – SB.

🍴 **Royal Oak,** Yapton Lane, BN18 0LS, on B 2132 ℰ (01243) 552865 – ❷. ◍ 🆎 *VISA* *JCB*
closed Sunday dinner – **Meals** a la carte 14.25/22.70 t. ⓐ 6.50.

---

**ASCOT** Windsor & Maidenhead **404** R 29 – pop. 15 761 (inc. Sunningdale).

🏳 Mill Ride, North Ascot ℰ (01344) 886777.

London 36 – Reading 15.

🏨 **Royal Berkshire** 🍃, London Rd, Sunninghill, SL5 0PP, East : 2 m. on A 329 ℰ (01344) 623322, Fax (01344) 627100, « Queen Anne mansion », ⚏s, 🏳, 🌳, park, ※, squash – ⚡ 📺 ☎ ❷ – 🔬 70. ◍ 🆎
Meals – (see *Stateroom* below) – ⚏ 16.50 – **60 rm** 160.00/185.00 st., 3 suites – SB.

🏨 **Berystede,** Bagshot Rd, Sunninghill, SL5 9JH, South : 1½ m. on A 330 ℰ (01344) 623311, Fax (01344) 872301, ⌤, 🌳 – ▤, ⚡ rm, 📺 ☎ ❷ – 🔬 120. ◍ 🆎 ◍ *VISA*
(bar lunch Saturday) 22.50 t. (dinner) and a la carte 27.50/45.50 t. ⓐ 8.50 – ⚏ 14.00 – **90 rm** 135.00/155.00 st. – SB.

✕✕✕ **Stateroom** (at Royal Berkshire H.), London Rd, Sunninghill, SL5 0PP, East : 2 m. on A 329 ℰ (01344) 23322, Fax (01344) 27100, 🌳 – ⚡ ❷. ◍ 🆎 ◍ *VISA* *JCB*
Meals (closed Saturday lunch) (booking essential) 24.75/35.00 st. and a la carte ⓐ 18.00.

✕✕ **Ciao Ninety,** 6 Hermitage Par., High St., SL5 7TE, ℰ (01344) 622285 – ▤. ◍ 🆎 ◍ *VISA*. ※
closed Sunday – **Meals** - Italian - a la carte 24.00/25.50 t. ⓐ 5.00.

**at Sunninghill** South : 1½ m. by A 329 on B 3020 – ✉ Ascot.

🏨 **Highclere,** Kings Rd, SL5 9AD, ℰ (01344) 625220, Fax (01344) 872528 – 📺 ☎ ♿ ❷. ◍ 🆎 *VISA* *JCB*
Meals (closed Sunday dinner) a la carte 15.30/21.00 t. – **11 rm** ⚏ 75.00/105.00 t.

✕✕ **Jade Fountain,** 38 High St., SL5 9NE, ℰ (01344) 627070 – ▤. ◍ 🆎 ◍ *VISA* *JCB*
closed 24 to 27 December – **Meals** - Chinese (Canton, Peking) - a la carte 24.50 t. and a la carte ⓐ 6.50.

---

**ASENBY** N. Yorks. – see Thirsk.

**ASHBOURNE** *Derbs.* [402] [403] [404] O 24 *Great Britain G. – pop. 6 300.*
Env. : *Dovedale★★ (Ilam Rock★) NW : 6 m. by A 515.*
[i] *13 Market Pl., DE6 1EU ℘ (01335) 343666.*
*London 146 – Derby 14 – Manchester 48 – Nottingham 33 – Sheffield 44.*

🏨 **Callow Hall** 🐎, Mappleton Rd, DE6 2AA, West : ¾ m. by Union St. (off Market Pl.) ℘ (01335) 343403, *Fax (01335) 343624*, <, « Victorian country house », 🎣, 🌳, park – 🚭 rest, 📺 ☎ ♿ 🅿. [MC] [AE] [①] [VISA]
*closed 25-26 December and 1 January* – **Meals** *(closed Sunday dinner to non-residents)* (dinner only and Sunday lunch)/dinner 37.50 **t.** and a la carte 🍷 10.25 – **15 rm** ☕ 75.00/145.00 **t.**, 1 suite – SB.

🏨 **Hanover International,** Derby Rd, DE6 1XH, Southeast : 1 m. following signs for the A 52 (Derby) ℘ (01335) 346666, *Fax (01335) 346549*, 🏋, ♨, 🏊 – 🛗, 🚭 rm, 📺 ☎ ♿ 🅿 – 👥 200. [MC] [AE] [①] [VISA]. 🚫
*closed 25 to 29 December* – **Meals** (bar lunch)/dinner a la carte 8.85/30.70 **t.** 🍷 6.50 – **48 rm** ☕ 75.00/90.00 **st.**, 2 suites – SB.

🍴 **Ashbourne Gallery,** 50 St. John St., DE6 1GH, ℘ (01335) 347101, *Fax (01335) 347101* – [MC] [AE] [VISA] [JCB]
*closed Tuesday dinner, Sunday, Monday and 25 December* – **Meals** a la carte 16.00/47.70 **t.**

ATS Airfield Ind. Est., Blenheim Rd ℘ (01335) 344644

**ASHBURTON** *Devon* [403] I 32 *The West Country G. – pop. 3 660.*
Env. : *Dartmoor National Park★★.*
*London 220 – Exeter 20 – Plymouth 23.*

🏨 **Holne Chase** 🐎, TQ13 7NS, West : 3 m. on Two Bridges rd ℘ (01364) 631471, *Fax (01364) 631453*, <, 🎣, 🌳, park – 📺 ☎ 📞 🅿. [MC] [AE] [①] [VISA]
**Meals** – (see ***The Restaurant*** below) – **10 rm** ☕ 80.00/140.00 **st.**, 7 suites – SB.

🏨 **Dartmoor Lodge,** Peartree Cross, TQ13 7JW, ℘ (01364) 652232, *Fax (01364) 653990* – 🛗, 🚭 rm, 📺 ☎ ♿ 🅿 – 👥 100. [MC] [AE] [VISA]
**Meals** (bar lunch)/dinner 10.95 **t.** 🍷 5.25 – **30 rm** ☕ 40.00/60.00 **t.**

🏠 **Gages Mill,** Buckfastleigh Rd, TQ13 7JW, Southwest : 1 m. ℘ (01364) 652391, *Fax (01364) 652391*, 🌳 – 🚭 rest, 🅿. 🚫
*March-mid November* – **Meals** (by arrangement) 12.50 **st.** 🍷 4.00 – **8 rm** ☕ 24.50/49.00 **st.**

🍴🍴 **The Restaurant** (at Holne Chase H.), TQ13 7NS, West : 3 m. on Two Bridges rd ℘ (01364) 631471, *Fax (01364) 631453*, 🌳 – 🚭 🅿. [MC] [AE] [①] [VISA]
**Meals** (booking essential) 20.00/25.00 **t.** and a la carte 🍷 12.00.

**at Holne** *West : 4½ m. by Two Bridges rd – ✉ Ashburton.*

🏠 **Wellpritton Farm** 🐎, TQ13 7RX, East : 1 m. ℘ (01364) 631273, park – 🚭 rest, 🅿
**Meals** *(by arrangement)* 9.00 **st.** – **4 rm** ☕ 19.00/38.00 **st.**

**ASHBY DE LA ZOUCH** *Leics.* [402] [403] [404] P 25 – *pop. 10 595.*
⛳18 *Willesley Park, Measham Rd ℘ (01530) 411532.*
[i] *North St., LE65 1HU ℘ (01530) 411767.*
*London 119 – Birmingham 29 – Leicester 18 – Nottingham 22.*

🏨 **Fallen Knight,** Kilwardby St., LE65 2FQ, ℘ (01530) 412230, *Fax (01530) 417596* – 🛗 📺 ☎ 🅿 – 👥 70. [MC] [AE] [①] [VISA]
**Meals** 16.00/20.00 **t.** and a la carte 🍷 6.95 – **24 rm** ☕ 65.00/112.00 **t.**

🍴🍴 **Rajni,** 48 Tamworth Rd, LE65 2PR, South : ½ m. on B 5006 ℘ (01530) 560349, *Fax (01530) 560347* – ❄ 🅿. [MC] [AE] [①] [VISA]
*closed 25 December* – **Meals** - Indian - (lunch by arrangement)/dinner a la carte 7.85/18.00 **st.**

ATS Kilwardby St. ℘ (01530) 412791

**ASHFORD** *Kent* [404] W 30 – *pop. 52 002.*
*Channel Tunnel : Eurostar information and reservations ℘ (0990) 186186.*
[i] *18 The Churchyard, TN23 1QG ℘ (01233) 629165.*
*London 56 – Canterbury 14 – Dover 24 – Hastings 30 – Maidstone 19.*

🏨 **Eastwell Manor** 🐎, Eastwell Park, Boughton Lees, TN25 4HR, North : 3 m. by A 28 on A 251 ℘ (01233) 219955, *Fax (01233) 635530*, <, « Reconstructed period mansion in formal gardens », park, 🎾 – 🛗, 🚭 rest, 📺 ☎ 🅿 – 👥 80. [MC] [AE] [①] [VISA] [JCB]
**Meals** 15.00 **t.** (lunch) and a la carte 31.50/50.00 **t.** 🍷 7.75 – **20 rm** ☕ 190.00/220.00 **st.**, 3 suites – SB.

🏛️ **Ashford International,** Simone Weil Av., TN24 8UX, North : 1 ½ m. by A 20 ℰ (01233) 219988, Fax (01233) 647743, ₤₅, ☎, 🔲 – ⧉, ⅙ rm, 🍽️ rest, 📺 ☎ ₺ ❷ – 🏛️ 400. 🆎 🆊 🛈 _VISA_
**Brasserie Mistral :** Meals 12.50/16.50 **st.** ₰ 7.00 – **Alhambra :** Meals _(closed Sunday and Bank Holidays)_ (dinner only) a la carte 22.00/32.50 **st.** ₰ 7.00 – ⚏ 9.95 – **201 rm** 105.00/120.00 **st.**, 2 suites – SB.

🏛️ **Forte Posthouse Ashford,** Canterbury Rd, TN24 8QQ, North : ¾ m. on A 28 ℰ (01233) 625790, Fax (01233) 643176, ⟵ – ⅙ rm, 📺 ☎ ₺ ❷ – 🏛️ 100. 🆊 🆎 🛈 _VISA_ _JCB_, ❀
Meals a la carte 15.35/23.85 **st.** ₰ 6.95 – ⚏ 8.95 – **103 rm** 75.00 **st.** – SB.

🏛️ **Master Spearpoint,** Canterbury Rd, Kennington, TN24 9QR, Northeast : 2 m. on A 28 ℰ (01233) 636863, Fax (01233) 610119, ⟵ – 📺 ☎ ❷ – 🏛️ 70. 🆊 🆎 🛈 _VISA_
Meals _(closed Saturday lunch)_ (carving lunch)/dinner 15.00 **t.** and a la carte ₰ 4.95 – ⚏ 7.25 – **34 rm** 65.00/75.00 **t.** – SB.

**at Hothfield** _Northwest : 3½ m. by A 20 –_ ✉ _Ashford._

🏛️ **Holiday Inn Garden Court,** Maidstone Rd, TN26 1AR, North : 1 m. on A 20 ℰ (01233) 713333, Fax (01233) 712082, ⟵ – ⧉, ⅙ rm, 📺 ☎ ₺ ❷ – 🏛️ 70. 🆊 🆎 🛈 _VISA_ _JCB_
Meals _(closed Saturday lunch)_ 15.95 **st.** and a la carte ₰ 4.95 – ⚏ 8.95 – **104 rm** 69.50/95.00 **st.** – SB.

🏠 **Travel Inn,** Maidstone Rd, Hothfield Common, TN26 1AP, on A 20 ℰ (01233) 712571, Fax (01233) 713945 – ⅙ rm, 📺 ☎ ₺ ❷. 🆊 🆎 🛈 _VISA_. ❀
Meals (grill rest.) – **60 rm** 38.00 **t.**

🔧 ATS Henwood Ind. Est., Hythe Rd, Henwood ℰ (01233) 622450/624891

_Le Grand Londres (GREATER LONDON) est composé de la City
et de 32 arrondissements administratifs (Borough)
eux-mêmes divisés en quartiers ou en villages
ayant conservé leur caractère propre (Area)._

**ASHFORD-IN-THE-WATER** _Derbs._ 402 403 404 O 24 – _see Bakewell._

**ASHINGTON** _Northd._ 401 402 P 18.
_London 303 – Edinburgh 102 – Newcastle upon Tyne 17._

🏠 **Woodhorn Grange,** Queen Elizabeth 11 Country Park, Woodhorn, NE63 9AT, North : ½ m. by A 197 on A 189 ℰ (01670) 862332, Fax (01670) 860986 – 📺 ❷. 🆊 _VISA_. ❀
Meals (grill rest.) a la carte 7.50/13.50 **st.** ₰ 3.95 – ⚏ 5.45 – **14 rm** 38.00 **st.**

🔧 ATS Lintonville Terr. ℰ (01670) 817013

**ASHINGTON** _W. Sussex_ 404 S 31 – _pop. 2 852 –_ ✉ _Pulborough._
_London 50 – Brighton 20 – Worthing 9._

🏠 **Mill House** ⌖, Mill Lane, RH20 3BZ, ℰ (01903) 892426, Fax (01903) 892855, ⟵ – 📺 ☎ ❷ – 🏛️ 40. 🆊 🆎 _VISA_. ❀
Meals 16.00/19.50 **st.** and dinner a la carte ₰ 4.50 – **10 rm** ⚏ 49.00/87.00 **st.** – SB.

**ASHPRINGTON** _Devon_ 403 I 32 – _see Totnes._

**ASHTON-IN-MAKERFIELD** _Gtr. Manchester_ 402 M 23 – _pop. 28 105 –_ ✉ _Wigan._
_London 199 – Liverpool 21 – Manchester 20._

🏠 **Bay Horse - Premier Lodge,** 53 Warrington Rd, WN4 9PJ, South : ½ m. on A 49 ℰ (01942) 725032, Fax (01942) 719302, Reservations (Freephone) 0800 118833 – ⅙ rm, 📺 ☎ ₺ ₺ ❷. 🆊 🆎 🛈 _VISA_. ❀
Meals (grill rest.) a la carte 8.05/13.90 **st.** ₰ 4.25 – ⚏ 5.95 – **28 rm** 44.95 **t.** – SB.

**ASHTON KEYNES** _Wilts._ 403 404 O 29 – _pop. 1 682._
_London 98 – Bristol 40 – Gloucester 27 – Oxford 42 – Swindon 14._

🏡 **Two Cove House,** SN6 6NS, off Park Place ℰ (01285) 861221, ⟵ – ⅙ rest, ❷. ❀
closed 25 December – Meals (by arrangement) (communal dining) 17.50 **st.** – **3 rm** ⚏ 34.00/54.00 **st.**

**ASHTON-UNDER-LYNE** *Gtr. Manchester* **402 403 404** N 23 – *pop. 43 906.*
*London 209 – Leeds 40 – Manchester 7 – Sheffield 34.*

🏛 **York House,** York Pl., off Richmond St., OL6 7TT, ℘ *(0161) 330 9000, Fax (0161) 343 1613,*
🍴 – 🖵 ☎ 🅿 – 🔏 40. 🆀🅴 🆄🅴 ⓪ 𝑉𝐼𝑆𝐴 𝐽𝐶𝐵
*Meals (closed Saturday lunch and Sunday)* 8.75 **st.** (lunch) and a la carte 15.40/22.40 **st.**
🍴 5.00 – **34 rm** ⊒ 54.00/84.00 **st.**

⌂ **Woodlands** without rest., 33 Shepley Rd, Audenshaw, M34 5DL, Southwest : 2 m. by
A 635 and A 6017 on B 6169 ℘ *(0161) 336 4241* – 🖵 ☎ 🅿. 🆀🅾 𝑉𝐼𝑆𝐴. 🕸
**3 rm** 40.00/60.00 **s.**

**ASHWATER** *Devon* **403** H 31 – *pop. 623.*
*London 238 – Bideford 26 – Exeter 43 – Launceston 7 – Plymouth 34.*

🏛 **Blagdon Manor Country H.** 🌥, EX21 5DF, Northwest : 2 m. by Holsworthy rd on
Blagdon rd ℘ *(01409) 211224, Fax (01409) 211634,* ≼, « Part 17C », 🌳, park – 🕸 🖵 ☎ 📞
🅿. 🆀🅾 🆄🅴 𝑉𝐼𝑆𝐴 𝐽𝐶𝐵. 🕸
*closed 25 and 26 December* – **Meals** *(residents only) (communal dining) (dinner only)*
19.50 **st.** 🍴 5.00 – **7 rm** ⊒ 70.00/110.00 **t.**

**ASKRIGG** *N. Yorks.* **402** N 21 – *pop. 1 002* – ✉ *Leyburn.*
*London 251 – Kendal 32 – Leeds 70 – York 63.*

🏛 **King's Arms,** Market Pl., DL8 3HQ, ℘ *(01969) 650258, Fax (01969) 650635,* « Part 18C,
part 19C coaching inn » – 🕸 rest, 🖵 ☎ 🅿. 🆀🅾 𝑉𝐼𝑆𝐴 𝐽𝐶𝐵. 🕸
*Clubroom :* **Meals** *(dinner only and Sunday lunch)* a la carte 21.45/29.15 **t.** – *Silks Grill :*
**Meals** a la carte 14.50/28.85 **t.** – **11 rm** ⊒ 50.00/124.00 **t.** – SB.

⌂ **Helm Country House** 🌥, Helm, DL8 3JF, West : 1 ½ m., turning right at No Through
Rd sign after 1 m. ℘ *(01969) 650443, Fax (01969) 650443,* ≼ Wensleydale, « Part 17C stone
cottage » – 🕸 🖵 🅿. 🆀🅾 𝑉𝐼𝑆𝐴. 🕸
*closed November and December* – **Meals** 16.50 🍴 7.55 – **3 rm** ⊒ 48.00/72.00 – SB.

**ASPLEY GUISE** *Beds.* **404** S 27 – *pop. 2 236.*
🏌 *Woburn Sands, West Hill* ℘ *(01908) 582264* – 🏌 *Millbrook, Ampthill* ℘ *(01525) 840252.*
*London 52 – Bedford 13 – Luton 16 – Northampton 22.*

🏛 **Moore Place,** The Square, MK17 8DW, ℘ *(01908) 282000, Fax (01908) 281888,*
« Georgian mansion », 🌳 – 🖵 ☎ 🅿 – 🔏 50. 🆀🅾 🆄🅴 ⓪ 𝑉𝐼𝑆𝐴 𝐽𝐶𝐵
**Meals** *(bar lunch Saturday)* 14.50/22.95 **st.** and a la carte 🍴 7.95 – **53 rm** ⊒ 75.00/
100.00 **st.**, 1 suite – SB.

**ASTON CLINTON** *Bucks.* **404** R 28 – *pop. 3 467* – ✉ *Aylesbury.*
*London 42 – Aylesbury 4 – Oxford 26.*

🏛 **Bell Inn,** London Rd, HP22 5HP, ℘ *(01296) 630252, Fax (01296) 631250,* « Part 17C former
coaching inn » – 🕸 rest, 🖵 ☎ 📞 🅿 – 🔏 30. 🆀🅾 🆄🅴 𝑉𝐼𝑆𝐴 𝐽𝐶𝐵. 🕸
**Meals** 14.50 **t.** (lunch) and a la carte 25.50/39.00 **t.** 🍴 13.00 – ⊒ 9.50 – **15 rm** 60.00/
80.00 **st.**, 5 suites – SB.

🏛 **West Lodge,** London Rd, HP22 5HL, ℘ *(01296) 630362, Fax (01296) 630151,* 🛏, 🖵 –
🕸 rest, 🖵 ☎ 🅿. 🆀🅾 🆄🅴 ⓪ 𝑉𝐼𝑆𝐴 𝐽𝐶𝐵. 🕸
*Montgolfier :* **Meals** *(residents only Sunday to Thursday) (dinner only)* 25.00/30.00 **t.**
🍴 11.00 – **6 rm** ⊒ 44.00/65.00 **t.**

**ATHERSTONE** *Warks.* **403 404** P 26 – *pop. 10 677.*
*London 120 – Birmingham 22 – Coventry 15 – Leicester 30.*

XX **Chapel House** with rm, Friar's Gate, CV9 1EY, ℘ *(01827) 718949, Fax (01827) 717702,*
« Part Georgian former dower house », 🌳 – 🖵 ☎. 🆀🅾 🆄🅴 ⓪ 𝑉𝐼𝑆𝐴 𝐽𝐶𝐵. 🕸
*closed 24 to 26 December* – **Meals** *(closed Sunday dinner and Bank Holiday Mondays)* (lunch
by arrangement) 12.00 **t.** (lunch) and a la carte 18.20/28.95 **t.** 🍴 7.95 – **13 rm** ⊒ 57.50/
80.00 **t.**

**ATTLEBOROUGH** *Norfolk* **404** X 26 – *pop. 6 530.*
*London 94 – Cambridge 47 – Norwich 15.*

🏛 **Sherbourne Country House,** Norwich Rd, NR17 2JX, Northeast : ½ m.
℘ *(01953) 454363, Fax (01953) 453509,* 🌳 – 🕸 rest, 🖵 ☎ 🅿. 🆀🅾 𝑉𝐼𝑆𝐴. 🕸
*closed 25 and 26 December* – **Meals** 15.00/17.50 **t.** and a la carte 🍴 7.25 – **8 rm** ⊒ 30.00/
70.00 **t.** – SB.

🅐 ATS London Rd ℘ *(01953) 453883*

**AUSTWICK** N. Yorks. ⚄⚁⚁ M 21 – pop. 467 – ✉ Lancaster (Lancs.).
London 259 – Kendal 28 – Lancaster 20 – Leeds 46.

🏛 **The Traddock** ⌂, LA2 8BY, ℘ (015242) 51224, Fax (015242) 51224, 🛋 – 🏕 📺 ☎ 🅿 – 🔬 70. ⬤⑧ 𝘝𝘐𝘚𝘈. ⌖
Meals (dinner only) 20.00 st. 🍷 4.00 – **10 rm** ⛬ 39.00/70.00 st. – SB.

⌂ **Wood View,** The Green, LA2 8BB, ℘ (015242) 51268, 🛋 – 🏕 📺 🅿. ⬤⑧ 𝘝𝘐𝘚𝘈. ⌖
Meals (by arrangement) 15.00 st. – **6 rm** ⛬ 35.00/50.00 st. – SB.

**AVON DASSETT** Warks. – pop. 191 – ✉ Leamington Spa.
London 82 – Birmingham 37 – Coventry 22 – Oxford 34.

⌂ **Crandon House** ⌂ without rest., CV33 0AA, Northeast : 1 ¼ m. by Fenny Compton rd on Farnborough rd ℘ (01295) 770652, Fax (01295) 770652, ≤, 🛋, park – 🏕 📺 🅿. ⬤⑧ 𝘝𝘐𝘚𝘈. 𝘑𝘊𝘉. ⌖
closed 1 week Christmas – **5 rm** ⛬ 28.00/48.00 – SB.

**AXBRIDGE** Somerset ⚄⚂⚃ L 30 – pop. 1 773.
London 142 – Bristol 17 – Taunton 27 – Weston-Super-Mare 11.

🏛 **Oak House,** The Square, BS26 2AP, ℘ (01934) 732444, Fax (01934) 733112 – 🏕 rm, 📺 ☎. ⬤⑧ 𝘈𝘌 𝘝𝘐𝘚𝘈
Meals a la carte 13.50/22.80 t. 🍷 5.25 – **11 rm** ⛬ 48.00/68.00 t. – SB.

⌂ **The Parsonage** without rest., Parsonage Lane, Cheddar Rd, BS26 2DN, East : ¾ m. on B 371 ℘ (01934) 733078, 🛋 – 🏕 📺 🅿
closed 24 to 26 December – **3 rm** ⛬ 35.00/45.00 st.

---

| Les prix | Pour toutes précisions sur les prix indiqués dans ce guide, reportez-vous aux pages de l'introduction. |

---

**AXMINSTER** Devon ⚄⚂⚃ L 31 The West Country G. – pop. 3 472.
Env. : Lyme Regis★ - The Cobb★, SE : 5½ m. by A 35 and A 3070.
🖪 The Old Courthouse, Church St., EX13 5AQ ℘ (01297) 34386 (summer only).
London 156 – Exeter 27 – Lyme Regis 5.5 – Taunton 22 – Yeovil 24.

🏨 **Fairwater Head Country House** ⌂, Hawkchurch, EX13 5TX, Northeast : 5 ¼ m. by B 3261 and A 35 off B 3165 ℘ (01297) 678349, Fax (01297) 678459, ≤ Axe Vale, 🛋 – 🏕 rest, 📺 ☎ 🅿 𝘈𝘌 ⓞ 𝘝𝘐𝘚𝘈
closed January and February – Meals 11.50/20.50 t. and a la carte 🍷 6.50 – **20 rm** ⛬ 69.00/138.00 t. – SB.

**at Membury** North : 4½ m. by A 35 and Stockland rd – ✉ Axminster.

🏛 **Lea Hill** ⌂, EX13 7AQ, South : ½ m. ℘ (01404) 881881, Fax (01404) 881890, ≤, « Part 14C Devon longhouse », 🛋 – 🏕 rm, 📺 ☎ 🅿 𝘈𝘌 ⓞ 𝘝𝘐𝘚𝘈
closed January and February – Meals (bar lunch)/dinner 19.95 t. 🍷 7.20 – **9 rm** ⛬ (dinner included) 78.00/136.00 t., 2 suites – SB.

**AYCLIFFE** Darlington – see Darlington.

**AYLESBURY** Bucks. ⚄⚂⚃ R 28 Great Britain G. – pop. 58 058.
Env. : Waddesdon Manor★★, NW : 5½ m. by A 41 – Chiltern Hills★.
🖥 Weston Turville, New Rd ℘ (01296) 424084 – 🖥 Hulcott Lane, Bierton ℘ (01296) 393644.
🖪 8 Bourbon St., HP20 2RR ℘ (01296) 330559.
London 46 – Birmingham 72 – Northampton 37 – Oxford 22.

🏩 **Hartwell House** ⌂, Oxford Rd, HP17 8NL, Southwest : 2 m. on A 418 ℘ (01296) 747444, Fax (01296) 747450, ≤, « Part Jacobean, part Georgian house, former residence of Louis XVIII », 🍷, ☎, ◻, ◿, 🛋, park, ⋇ – 🛗 🏕 📺 ☎ 📞 🅿 – 🔬 80. ⬤⑧ 𝘝𝘐𝘚𝘈. ⌖
Meals 27.50/42.00 st. 🍷 6.45 – ⛬ 14.95 – **34 rm** 125.00/195.00 st., 13 suites 280.00/550.00 st. – SB.

🏨 **Forte Posthouse Aylesbury,** Aston Clinton Rd, HP22 5AA, Southeast : 2 m. on A 41 ℘ (01296) 393388, Fax (01296) 392211, 🍷, ☎, ◻, 🛋 – 🏕 rm, 📺 ☎ & 🅿 – 🔬 100. ⬤⑧ 𝘈𝘌 ⓞ 𝘝𝘐𝘚𝘈 𝘑𝘊𝘉
closed 31 December – Meals a la carte 17.45/27.35 st. 🍷 7.50 – ⛬ 9.95 – **92 rm** 85.00 t., 2 suites – SB.

🏠 **Holiday Inn Garden Court,** Buckingham Rd, HP19 3FY, North : 1 m. on A 413 ℰ (01296) 398839, Fax (01296) 394108, *f₆* – ❄️ rm, 📺 ☎ & 🅿 – 🔏 30. 🐵 🟊 AE ① *VISA*. ❄️
**Meals** (dinner only) (residents only) a la carte 9.85/14.70 st. – � 8.50 – **39 rm** 69.00 st.

🍴 **Bottle & Glass,** Gibraltar, HP17 8TY, Southwest : 5 m. on A 418 ℰ (01296) 748488, Fax (01296) 747673, « 17C thatched inn » – 🅿. 🐵 AE ① *VISA*
closed Sunday dinner and 25-26 December – **Meals** - Seafood specialities - a la carte 17.00/27.95 st.

🔧 ATS Gatehouse Way ℰ (01296) 433177

---

**AYMESTREY** *Herefordshire* 403 L 27 – pop. 301.
*London 156 – Birmingham 54 – Hereford 17 – Shrewsbury 35 – Worcester 31.*

🍴 **Riverside Inn,** HR6 9ST, ℰ (01568) 708440, Fax (01568) 709058, « 16C », ⤸, 🎋 – 🅿. 🐵 *VISA* JCB
closed 25 December – **Meals** 15.00 t. (dinner) and a la carte ᵢ 6.95.

---

**BABBACOMBE** *Torbay* 403 J 32 – see Torquay.

---

**BADBY** *Northants.* 403 404 Q 27 – see Daventry.

---

**BADINGHAM** *Suffolk* 404 Y 27 – see Framlingham.

---

**BADMINTON** *South Gloucestershire* 403 404 N 29 – pop. 2 167.
*London 114 – Bristol 19 – Gloucester 26 – Swindon 33.*

🏠 **Petty France,** Dunkirk, GL9 1AF, Northwest : 3 m. on A 46 ℰ (01454) 238361, Fax (01454) 238768, 🎋 – ❄️ rest, 📺 ☎ 🅿 – 🔏 25. 🐵 AE ① *VISA*
**Meals** 21.00 t. ᵢ 9.95 – � 3.50 – **20 rm** 69.00/119.00 t. – SB.

🏠 **Bodkin House,** Dunkirk, GL9 1AF, Northwest : 3 m. on A 46 ℰ (01454) 238310, Fax (01454) 238422 – ❄️ rest, 📺 ☎ 🅿. 🐵 AE ① *VISA* JCB. ❄️
**Meals** 15.95 t. and a la carte – **9 rm** � 52.00/87.00 t. – SB.

---

**BAGINTON** *Warks.* 403 404 P 26 – see Coventry.

---

**BAGSHOT** *Surrey* 404 R 29 – pop. 5 190.
*London 37 – Reading 17 – Southampton 49.*

🏨 **Pennyhill Park** ⤸, London Rd, GU19 5EU, Southwest : 1 m. on A 30 ℰ (01276) 471774, Fax (01276) 473217, ≤, « Gardens and parklands », *f₆*, ⤓, 🏊, ⤸, ❄️ – ❄️ rest, 📺 ☎ 🅿 – 🔏 150. 🐵 AE ① *VISA*
**St. James :** **Meals** (closed Saturday lunch) 17.50 st. (lunch) and a la carte 19.00/33.00 st. ᵢ 8.50 – (see also **The Latymer** below) – � 14.50 – **104 rm** 145.00/170.00 st., 10 suites – SB.

🏠 **Travel Inn,** London Rd, GU19 5HR, North : ½ m. on A 30 ℰ (01276) 473196, Fax (01276) 451357, 🎋 – ❄️ rm, 📺 ☎ 🅿. 🐵 AE ① *VISA*. ❄️
**Meals** (grill rest.) – **39 rm** 38.00 t.

XXX **The Latymer** (at Pennyhill Park H.), London Rd, GU19 5EU, Southwest : 1 m. on A 30 ℰ (01276) 471774, Fax (01276) 473217, 🏮, 🎋 – ❄️ ▤ 🅿. 🐵 AE ① *VISA* JCB
closed Saturday lunch – **Meals** (booking essential) 26.00/35.00 st. and a la carte ᵢ 16.00.

---

**BAINBRIDGE** *N. Yorks.* 402 N 21 – pop. 474 – ✉ Wensleydale.
*London 249 – Kendal 31 – Leeds 68 – York 61.*

🏠 **Rose and Crown,** DL8 3EE, ℰ (01969) 650225, Fax (01969) 650735 – 📺 🅿. 🐵 *VISA*
closed 25 December and 1 January – **Meals** (bar lunch Monday to Saturday)/dinner a la carte 14.95/23.75 st. ᵢ 6.00 – **12 rm** � 33.00/62.00 st.

---

**BAKEWELL** *Derbs.* 402 403 404 O 24 *Great Britain G.* – pop. 3 818.
Env. : Chatsworth★★★ (Park and Garden★★★) *AC*, NE : 2½ m. by A 619 – Haddon Hall★★ *AC*, SE : 2 m. by A 6.
🖪 Old Market Hall, Bridge St., DE45 1DS ℰ (01629) 813227.
*London 160 – Derby 26 – Manchester 37 – Nottingham 33 – Sheffield 17.*

🏨 **Rutland Arms,** The Square, DE45 1BT, ✆ (01629) 812812, *Fax (01629) 812309* – ❄ rest, 🖵 ☎ 🅿 – ▲ 100. 🆕 🆎 ⓪ 𝗩𝗜𝗦𝗔
Meals 17.95 t. (dinner) and lunch a la carte 17.50/30.00 t. ₰ 6.95 – **35 rm** � 54.00/105.00 t.
– SB.

🏨 **Milford House,** Mill St., DE45 1DA, ✆ (01629) 812130, 🌳 – 🖵 ☎ 🅿. 𝗩𝗜𝗦𝗔. ❄
*Easter-October* – **Meals** *(closed Sunday dinner to non-residents)* (dinner only) a la carte
11.90/16.90 t. ₰ 4.70 – **12 rm** ⊆ 37.60/75.00 t.

XX **Renaissance,** Bath St., DE45 1BX, ✆ (01629) 812687 – ❄. 🆕 𝗩𝗜𝗦𝗔
*closed Sunday dinner, Monday, first 2 weeks January and first 2 weeks August* – **Meals** -
French - (lunch booking essential) 19.95 t. and a la carte ₰ 5.00.

**at Great Longstone** *North : 4 m. by A 619 off B 6001* – ⊠ *Bakewell.*

🏨 **Croft Country House** ⌂, DE45 1TF, ✆ (01629) 640278, 🌳 – ▮🖥▮, ❄ rest, 🖵 🅿. 🆕
𝗩𝗜𝗦𝗔 𝗝𝗖𝗕. ❄
*closed 2 January-11 February* – **Meals** (dinner only) 24.50 t. ₰ 5.00 – **9 rm** ⊆ 60.00/
115.00 t. – SB.

**at Alport** *South : 4 m. by A 6 off B 5056* – ⊠ *Bakewell.*

⌂ **Rock House** without rest., DE45 1LG, ✆ (01629) 636736, 🌳 – ❄ ✆ 🅿. ❄
**3 rm** ⊆ 25.00/45.00 s.

**at Ashford-in-the-Water** *Northwest : 1¾ m. by A 6 and A 6020 on B 6465* – ⊠ *Bakewell.*

🏨 **Riverside House,** Fennel St., DE45 1QF, ✆ (01629) 814275, *Fax (01629) 812873,* 🌳 –
❄ 🖵 ☎ 🅿. 🆕 🆎 ⓪ 𝗩𝗜𝗦𝗔
**Meals** 18.95/33.00 t. – **15 rm** 95.00/150.00 t. – SB.

*Le Guide change, changez de* **guide Michelin** *tous les ans.*

---

**BALDERSTONE** *Lancs. – see Blackburn.*

---

**BALDOCK** *Herts.* 𝟰𝟬𝟰 T 28 *– pop. 9 232.*
*London 42 – Bedford 20 – Cambridge 21 – Luton 15.*

🏨 **Travelodge,** A 1 Great North Road, Hinxworth (southbound carriageway), SG7 5EX,
Northwest : 3 m. by A 507 on A 1 ✆ (01462) 835329, *Fax (01462) 835329,* Reservations
(Freephone) 0800 850950 – ❄ rm, 🖵 & 🅿. 🆕 🆎 ⓪ 𝗩𝗜𝗦𝗔 𝗝𝗖𝗕. ❄
**Meals** (grill rest.) – **40 rm** 39.95/59.95 t.

---

**BALLASALLA** *Isle of Man* 𝟰𝟬𝟮 G 21 *– see Man (Isle of).*

---

**BALSALL COMMON** *W. Mids. – see Coventry.*

---

**BAMBER BRIDGE** *Lancs.* 𝟰𝟬𝟮 M 22 *– see Preston.*

---

**BAMBURGH** *Northd.* 𝟰𝟬𝟭 𝟰𝟬𝟮 O 17 *Great Britain G. – pop. 582.*
See : *Castle★ AC.*
*London 337 – Edinburgh 77 – Newcastle upon Tyne 51.*

🏨 **Lord Crewe Arms,** Front St., NE69 7BL, ✆ (01668) 214243, *Fax (01668) 214273* –
❄ rest, 🖵 🅿. 🆕 𝗩𝗜𝗦𝗔 𝗝𝗖𝗕
*April-October* – **Meals** (bar lunch)/dinner 17.95 t. ₰ 4.95 – **22 rm** ⊆ 49.00/96.00 t. – SB.

**at Waren Mill** *West : 2¾ m. on B 1342* – ⊠ *Belford.*

🏨 **Waren House** ⌂, NE70 7EE, ✆ (01668) 214581, *Fax (01668) 214484,* ≤, 🌳 – ❄ 🖵 ☎
✆ 🅿 – ▲ 30. 🆕 🆎 ⓪ 𝗩𝗜𝗦𝗔 𝗝𝗖𝗕
**Meals** (dinner only) 22.45 st. ₰ 7.00 – **8 rm** ⊆ 85.00/135.00 st., 2 suites – SB.

---

**BAMPTON** *Devon* 𝟰𝟬𝟯 J 31 *– pop. 1 617.*
*London 189 – Exeter 18 – Minehead 21 – Taunton 15.*

🏨 **Bark House,** Oakfordbridge, EX16 9HZ, West : 3 m. by B 3227 on A 396
✆ (01398) 351236, 🌳 – ❄ rest, 🖵 ☎ 🅿
*restricted opening in winter* – **Meals** (booking essential) 13.50/19.75 st. ₰ 4.95 – **5 rm**
⊆ 29.50/78.00 st. – SB.

**BANBURY** Oxon. 403 404 P 27 Great Britain G. – pop. 39 906.

Exc.: Upton House★ AC, NW : 7 m. by A 422.

ᴨ₈ Cherwell Edge, Chacombe ℘ (01295) 711591.

🛈 Banbury Museum, 8 Horsefair, OX16 0AA ℘ (01295) 259855.

London 76 – Birmingham 40 – Coventry 25 – Oxford 23.

🏛 **Whately Hall**, Horsefair, by Banbury Cross, OX16 0AN, ℘ (01295) 263451, Fax (01295) 271736, « Part 17C », 🌿 – ⁜ 🆃🆅 ☎ 🅿 – 🕍 80. 🆀🆂 🅰🅴 ⑩ 𝘝𝘐𝘚𝘈. ⅏
closed 31 December and 1 January – Meals a la carte 14.50/31.25 t. ⅙ 6.90 – ⊡ 9.75 – 68 rm 80.00/85.00 st., 4 suites – SB.

🏛 **Banbury House**, 27-29 Oxford Rd, OX16 9AH, ℘ (01295) 259361, Fax (01295) 270954 – ⁜ rm, 🆃🆅 ☎ 🅿 – 🕍 70. 🆀🆂 🅰🅴 ⑩ 𝘝𝘐𝘚𝘈. ⅏
closed 24 to 30 December – Meals (bar lunch)/dinner 17.00 t. and a la carte ⅙ 7.50 – ⊡ 8.95 – 63 rm 73.00/110.00 t. – SB.

**at Adderbury** South : 3 m. on A 4260 – ⊠ Banbury.

🏛 **Red Lion**, The Green, OX17 3LU, ℘ (01295) 810269, Fax (01295) 811906, « Part 16C inn » – 🆃🆅 ☎ 🅿. 🆀🆂 🅰🅴 𝘝𝘐𝘚𝘈
Meals a la carte 15.15/23.15 t. – 12 rm ⊡ 55.00/65.00 st.

**at North Newington** West : 2¼ m. by B 4035 – ⊠ Banbury.

↑ **La Madonette Country Guest House** 🕉 without rest., OX15 6AA, ℘ (01295) 730212, Fax (01295) 730363, 🌿 – 🆃🆅 ☎ 🆅 🅿. 🆀🆂 🅰🅴 ⑩ 𝘝𝘐𝘚𝘈 𝙅𝘾𝘽. ⅏
5 rm ⊡ 40.00/58.00 t.

**at Wroxton** Northwest : 3 m. by B 4100 on A 422 – ⊠ Banbury.

🏛 **Wroxton House**, Silver St., OX15 6QB, ℘ (01295) 730777, Fax (01295) 730800 – ⁜ 🆃🆅 ☎ 🅿 – 🕍 40. 🆀🆂 🅰🅴 ⑩ 𝘝𝘐𝘚𝘈 𝙅𝘾𝘽. ⅏
Meals (closed Saturday lunch) 15.50/24.50 st. and a la carte ⅙ 6.95 – ⊡ 7.95 – 32 rm 89.00/125.00 st. – SB.

**at Shenington** Northwest : 6 m. by B 4100 off A 422 – ⊠ Banbury.

↑ **Sugarswell Farm** 🕉, OX15 6HW, Northwest : 2¼ m. on Edge Hill rd ℘ (01295) 680512, Fax (01295) 688149, ≤, 🌿, park – ⁜ 🅿. ⅏
Meals (by arrangement) (communal dining) 19.00 st. – 3 rm ⊡ 37.00/60.00.

🅖 ATS Beaumont Ind. Est., Beaumont Close ℘ (01295) 253525

---

**BANTHAM** Devon – see Kingsbridge.

---

**BARDWELL** Suffolk 404 W 27 – see Bury St. Edmunds.

---

**BARFORD** Warks. 403 404 P 27 – see Warwick.

---

**BAR HILL** Cambs. 404 U 27 – see Cambridge.

---

**BARNARD CASTLE** Durham 402 O 20 Great Britain G. – pop. 6 084.

See : Bowes Museum★ AC.

Exc.: Raby Castle★ AC, NE : 6½ m. by A 688.

ᴨ₈ Harmire Rd ℘ (01833) 638355.

🛈 Woodleigh, Flatts Rd, DL12 8AA ℘ (01833) 690909.

London 258 – Carlisle 63 – Leeds 68 – Middlesbrough 31 – Newcastle upon Tyne 39.

🏛 **Jersey Farm** 🕉, Darlington Rd, DL12 8TA, East : 1½ m. on A 67 ℘ (01833) 638223, Fax (01833) 631988, park – ⁜ rest, 🆃🆅 ☎ 🅿 – 🕍 100. 🆀🆂 𝘝𝘐𝘚𝘈
Meals (closed lunch Monday and Saturday) 16.50 t. and a la carte ⅙ 5.80 – 16 rm ⊡ 55.00/70.00 t., 4 suites – SB.

↑ **Homelands**, 85 Galgate, DL12 8ES, ℘ (01833) 638757, 🌿 – ⁜ rm, 🆃🆅 ☎. ⅏
Meals (by arrangement) 12.95 st. ⅙ 4.50 – 4 rm ⊡ 25.00/45.00 st.

↑ **Marwood House**, 98 Galgate, DL12 8BJ, ℘ (01833) 637493, ☎s – ⁜ 🆃🆅. ⅏
Meals (by arrangement) 12.00 st. – 4 rm ⊡ 19.00/40.00 st.

**at Romaldkirk** Northwest : 6 m. by A 67 on B 6277 – ⊠ Barnard Castle.

🏛 **Rose and Crown**, DL12 9EB, ℘ (01833) 650213, Fax (01833) 650828, « Part 18C coaching inn » – ⁜ rest, 🆃🆅 ☎ 🅿. 🆀🆂 𝘝𝘐𝘚𝘈
closed 25-26 December and 1 January – Meals (closed Sunday dinner to non-residents) (bar lunch)/dinner 12.95/24.00 st. ⅙ 6.25 – 10 rm ⊡ 62.00/82.00 st., 2 suites – SB.

**BARNARD GATE** *Oxon.* 🔟🔟 P 28 – *see Witney.*

---

**BARNEY** *Norfolk* 🔟🔟 W 25 – ⊠ *Fakenham.*
*London 187 – Cambridge 71 – King's Lynn 21 – Norwich 29.*

↑ **Old Brick Kilns,** Little Barney Lane, NR21 0NL, East : ¾ m. ℰ (01328) 878305, *Fax* (01328) 878948, ☞ – ⸹⸻ 🔟 ☎ ✆ ℗. ⬤🔟 𝗩𝗜𝗦𝗔 𝗝𝗖𝗕. ⠀
**Meals** (by arrangement) (communal dining) 15.00 **st.** – **3 rm** ⇆ 24.00/48.00 **st.** – SB.

---

**BARNSDALE BAR** *W. Yorks.* 🔟🔟 Q 23 – ⊠ *Pontefract.*
*London 181 – Leeds 22 – Nottingham 53 – Sheffield 26.*

🔟 **Travelodge,** WF8 3JB, on a A 1 (southbound carriageway) ℰ (01977) 620711, *Fax* (01977) 620711, Reservations (Freephone) 0800 850950 – ⸹⸻ rm, ▤ rest, 🔟 ☎ ℗. ⬤🔟 𝗔𝗘 ⓪ 𝗩𝗜𝗦𝗔 𝗝𝗖𝗕. ⠀
**Meals** (grill rest.) – **56 rm** 39.95/59.95 **t.**

---

**BARNSLEY** *Glos.* 🔟🔟 O28 – *see Cirencester.*

---

**BARNSLEY** *S. Yorks.* 🔟🔟 P 23 – pop. 75 120.
🔟 *Wakefield Rd, Staincross* ℰ (01226) 382856 – 🔟 *Silkstone, Field Head, Elmhirst Lane* ℰ (01226) 790328 – 🔟 *Wombwell Hillies, Wentworth View, Wombwell* ℰ (01226) 754433.
🔟 *56 Eldon St., S70 2JL* ℰ (01226) 206757.
*London 177 – Leeds 21 – Manchester 36 – Sheffield 15.*

🔟🔟🔟 **Ardsley House H. and Health Club,** Doncaster Rd, Ardsley, S71 5EH, East : 2 ¾ m. on A 635 ℰ (01226) 309955, *Fax* (01226) 205374, 🔟, ⸹, 🔟, ☞ – ⸹⸻ rm, ▤ rest, 🔟 ☎ ℗ – 🔟 350. ⬤🔟 𝗔𝗘 ⓪ 𝗩𝗜𝗦𝗔
**Meals** (closed Sunday dinner to non-residents) (bar lunch Saturday) 11.50/17.50 **t.** ⓵ 4.95 – ⇆ 9.00 – **73 rm** 67.00/95.00 **st.** – SB.

🔟🔟 **Tankersley Manor,** Church Lane, S75 3DQ, South : 6 ¼ m. by A 61 ℰ (01226) 744700, *Fax* (01226) 745405, ☞ – ⸹⸻ 🔟 ☎ ✆ ℗ – 🔟 340. ⬤🔟 𝗔𝗘 ⓪ 𝗩𝗜𝗦𝗔. ⠀
**Meals** (bar lunch Saturday and Sunday dinner) 10.95/19.95 **st.** and a la carte ⓵ 6.75 – **70 rm** ⇆ 65.00/85.00 **st.**

🔟 **Travel Inn,** Maple Rd, Tankersley, S74 3DL, South : 6 ½ m. by A 61 at junction with A 616 ℰ (01226) 350035, *Fax* (01226) 741524 – ⸹⸻ rm, ▤ rest, 🔟 ⅙ ℗. ⬤🔟 𝗔𝗘 ⓪ 𝗩𝗜𝗦𝗔. ⠀
**Meals** (grill rest.) – **42 rm** 38.00 **t.**

🔟 **Travelodge,** Doncaster Rd, S70 3PE, East : 2 m. on A 635 ℰ (01226) 298799, *Fax* (01226) 298799, Reservations (Freephone) 0800 850950 – ⸹⸻ rm, 🔟 ⅙ ℗. ⬤🔟 𝗔𝗘 ⓪ 𝗩𝗜𝗦𝗔 𝗝𝗖𝗕. ⠀
**Meals** (grill rest.) – **32 rm** 39.95/59.95 **t.**

🔟🔟 **Armstrongs,** 102 Dodworth Rd, S70 6HL, West : ½ m. on A 628 ℰ (01226) 240113 – ℗. ⬤🔟 𝗔𝗘 𝗩𝗜𝗦𝗔
*closed Saturday lunch, Sunday, Monday, 1 week January and 2 weeks in summer* – **Meals** 14.50/16.95 **t.** and dinner a la carte 18.95/27.15 **t.** ⓵ 5.95.

🔟 ATS Huddersfield Rd ℰ (01226) 281888/287406       ATS Wombwell Lane, Aldham Bridge, Wombwell
ℰ (01226) 753511

---

**BARNSTAPLE** *Devon* 🔟🔟 H 30 *The West Country G.* – pop. 20 740.
**See** : *Town⋆ - Long Bridge⋆.*
**Env.** : *Arlington Court⋆⋆ (Carriage Collection⋆) AC, NE : 6 m. by A 39.*
🔟 *Chulmleigh, Leigh Rd* ℰ (01769) 580519.
🔟 *North Devon Library, Tuly St., EX31 1EL* ℰ (01271) 388583.
*London 222 – Exeter 40 – Taunton 51.*

🔟🔟 **Barnstaple,** Braunton Rd, EX31 1LE, West : 1 ½ m. on A 361 ℰ (01271) 376221, *Fax* (01271) 324101, 🔟, ⸹, 🔟, 🔟 – ▤ rest, 🔟 ☎ ℗ – 🔟 350. ⬤🔟 𝗔𝗘 ⓪ 𝗩𝗜𝗦𝗔. ⠀
**Meals** (bar lunch Monday to Saturday)/dinner 15.00 **st.** and a la carte ⓵ 5.75 – ⇆ 5.00 – **60 rm** 54.00/84.00 **t.** – SB.

🔟🔟 **Lynwood House** with rm, Bishops Tawton Rd, EX32 9EF, South : 1 ½ m. by A 361 and Newport rd ℰ (01271) 343695, *Fax* (01271) 379340 – ⸹⸻ rest, 🔟 ☎ ℗. ⬤🔟 𝗔𝗘 ⓪ 𝗩𝗜𝗦𝗔. ⠀
*closed 26 December and 1 January* – **Meals** (closed Saturday lunch and Sunday) a la carte 20.75/43.00 **t.** ⓵ 5.50 – **5 rm** ⇆ 47.50/67.50 **t.** – SB.

at Bishop's Tawton *South : 2¾ m. by A 39 on A 377* – ✉ *Barnstaple*.

🏠 **Downrew House** ⤷, EX32 0DY, Southeast : 1 ½ m. on Chittlehampton rd
℘ (01271) 342497, *Fax (01271) 323947*, ≤, ⤳, ☞, park – 📺 ☎ 🅿 – 🔏 40. 🐼 🖭 *VISA*. 🛠
**Meals** 17.50/19.50 **t.** ≬ 6.00 – **12 rm** ⊠ 43.00/94.00 **t.** – SB.

🏠 **Halmpstone Manor** ⤷, EX32 0EA, Southeast : 3 m. by Chittlehampton rd
℘ (01271) 830321, *Fax (01271) 830826*, ≤, ☞ – ✲ rest, 📺 ☎ 🅿. 🐼 🖭 ⑩ *VISA* 𝗝𝗖𝗕
*closed Christmas and New Year* – **Meals** (lunch by arrangement)/dinner 32.50 **t.** ≬ 7.75 –
**5 rm** ⊠ 70.00/140.00 **t.**

🔘 ATS Pottington Ind. Est., Braunton Rd ℘ (01271) 342294/5

---

**BARROW-IN-FURNESS** *Cumbria* 📖 K 21 – *pop.* 48 947.

🏌 *Rakesmoore Lane, Hawcoat* ℘ (01229) 825444 – 🏌 *Furness, Walney Island* ℘ (01229) 471232.

🛈 *Forum 28, Duke St., LA14 1HU* ℘ (01229) 870156.
*London 295 – Kendal 34 – Lancaster 47.*

🏠 **Arlington House,** 200/202 Abbey Rd, LA14 5LD, North : 1 m. ℘ (01229) 831976,
*Fax (01229) 870990*, ⤳ – 📺 ☎ 🅿. 🐼 🖭 *VISA*. 🛠
*closed 25 and 26 December* – **Meals** *(closed Sunday)* (dinner only) a la carte 15.75/22.75 **t.**
≬ 5.25 – **8 rm** ⊠ 57.00/80.00 **t.**

🔘 ATS 149-151 Ainslie St. ℘ (01229) 828513

---

*Si vous cherchez un hôtel tranquille,*
*consultez d'abord les cartes de l'introduction*
*ou repérez dans le texte les établissements indiqués avec le signe* ⤷ *ou* ⤷.

---

**BARTON MILLS** *Suffolk.* 📖 V 26 – *pop.* 832.
*London 72 – Cambridge 21 – Ipswich 37 – Norwich 40.*

🏠 **Travelodge,** Fiveways Roundabout, IP28 6AE, on A 11 ℘ (01638) 717675, Reservations
(Freephone) 0800 850950 – 📺 ৬ 🅿. 🐼 🖭 ⑩ *VISA* 𝗝𝗖𝗕. 🛠
**Meals** (grill rest.) – **32 rm** 39.95/59.95 **t.**

---

**BARTON STACEY** *Hants.* 📖 📖 P 30 – *pop.* 741.
*London 76 – Andover 10 – Bath 60 – Salisbury 22 – Winchester 8.*

🏠 **Travelodge,** SO21 3NP, North : 1 ¼ m. on A 303 (westbound carriageway)
℘ (01264) 720260, Reservations (Freephone) 0800 850950 – 📺 ৬ 🅿. 🐼 🖭 ⑩ *VISA* 𝗝𝗖𝗕.
🛠
**Meals** (grill rest.) – **20 rm** 39.95/59.95 **t.**

---

**BARTON UNDER NEEDWOOD** *Staffs.* – *see Burton-upon-Trent.*

---

**BARWICK** *Somerset* 📖 📖 M 31 – *see Yeovil.*

---

**BASFORD** *Staffs.* – *see Stoke-on-Trent.*

---

**BASILDON** *Essex* 📖 V 29 – *pop.* 100 924.

🏌 *Clayhill Lane, Sparrow's Hearne* ℘ (01268) 533297 – 🏌, 🏌 *Langdon Hills, Lower Dunton Rd, Bulphan* ℘ (01268) 548444/544300.
*London 30 – Chelmsford 17 – Southend-on-Sea 13.*

🏠 **Campanile,** A 127 Southend Arterial Rd, Pipp's Hill, SS14 3AE, Northwest : 1 m. by A 176
at junction with A 127 ℘ (01268) 530810, *Fax (01268) 286710* – ✲ rm, 📺 ☎ 🅿 – 🔏 30.
🐼 🖭 *VISA*
**Meals** 10.85 **st.** and a la carte – ⊠ 4.50 – **97 rm** 38.00 **st.**

🏠 **Travel Inn,** High Rd, Fobbing, SS17 9NR, Southwest : 2 ¼ m. by A 176 at junction with
A 13 ℘ (01268) 554500, *Fax (01268) 581752* – ✲ rm, 📺 ৬ 🅿. 🐼 🖭 ⑩ *VISA*
**Meals** (grill rest.) – **60 rm** 38.00 **t.**

🏠 **Travel Inn,** Felmores, East Mayne, SS13 1BW, North : 1 ½ m. on A 132 ℘ (01268) 522227,
*Fax (01268) 530092* – ✲ rm, 📺 ৬ 🅿. 🐼 🖭 ⑩ *VISA*. 🛠
**Meals** (grill rest.) – **32 rm** 38.00 **t.**

**at Wickford** *North : 5¼ m. by A 132 –* ✉ *Basildon.*

🏨 **Chichester,** Old London Rd, Rawreth, SS11 8UE, East : 2¾ m. by A 129 ☎ (01268) 560555,
Fax (01268) 560580, ☞ – ✠ rest, ▤ rest, 📺 ☎ ℗ – 🔬 100. ◗▣ ▣ⓔ ⓞ *VISA* . ✿
*closed 24 to 31 December –* **Meals** *(closed Saturday lunch)* 12.50/15.75 **t.** – 🖵 8.95 – **34 rm**
63.50/65.50 **t.**

⬤ ATS Archers Field ☎ (01268) 525177

---

**BASINGSTOKE** *Hants.* 🄓🄓🄓 🄔🄓🄓 Q 30 – *pop. 77 837.*

🛆 *Test Valley, Micheldever Rd, Overton* ☎ *(01256) 771737 –* 🛆 *Weybrook Park, Aldermaston
Rd, Sherborne St John* ☎ *(01256) 320347.*

🄱 *Willis Museum, Old Town Hall, Market Pl., RG21 1QD* ☎ *(01256) 817618.*

*London 55 – Reading 17 – Southampton 31 – Winchester 18.*

## BASINGSTOKE

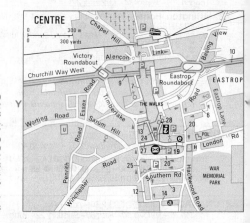

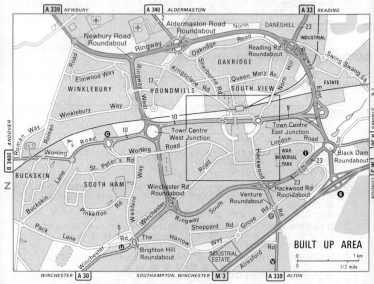

**Thistle Audleys Wood** ⟨S⟩, Alton Rd, RG25 2JT, South : 1 ½ m. on A 339 ℰ (01256) 817555, Fax (01256) 817500, « Gothic Renaissance mansion », park – ✻ rm, 🔟 ☎ ✆ & ₱ – 🔬 50. 🆀 🗚 ① 💵 ᴅᴄʙ
Z v
Meals (closed lunch Saturday and Bank Holidays) 20.00/26.00 st. and a la carte ⏍ 9.25 – ☑ 11.50 – **69 rm** 120.00/140.00 st., 2 suites – SB.

**Hilton National,** Old Common Rd, Black Dam, RG21 3PR, ℰ (01256) 460460, Fax (01256) 840441, ₤₅, ≘ – ✻ rm, ▤ rest, 🔟 ☎ ₱ – 🔬 150. 🆀 🗚 ①
Z i
Meals (closed lunch Saturday and Bank Holidays) (carving rest.) 15.50/18.50 st. and a la carte ⏍ 7.50 – ☑ 10.25 – **141 rm** 105.00 st.

**Red Lion,** London Rd, RG21 7NY, ℰ (01256) 328525, Fax (01256) 844056 – ✻ rm, 🔟 ☎ ₱ – 🔬 40. 🆀 🗚 ① 💵
Y e
Meals (bar lunch)/dinner a la carte 15.50/18.50 st. ⏍ 6.00 – **59 rm** ☑ 93.50/110.00 st.

**Forte Posthouse Basingstoke,** Grove Rd, RG21 3EE, South : 1 m. on A 339 ℰ (01256) 468181, Fax (01256) 840081 – ✻ rm, 🔟 ☎ ₱ – 🔬 150. 🆀 🗚 ① 💵 ᴅᴄʙ
Z e
Meals a la carte 13.50/29.00 st. ⏍ 4.95 – ☑ 9.95 – **84 rm** 85.00 t. – SB.

**Travel Inn,** Worting Rd, RG22 6PG, ℰ (01256) 811477, Fax (01256) 819329 – ✻ rm, 🔟 & ₱ 🆀 💵. ⌘
Z c
Meals (grill rest.) – **49 rm** 38.00 t.

**Travelodge,** Winchester Rd, RG22 5HN, Southwest : 2 ¼ m. by A 30 ℰ (01256) 843566, Reservations (Freephone) 0800 850950 – ✻ rm, 🔟 & ₱. 🆀 🗚 ① 💵 ᴅᴄʙ. ⌘
Z u
Meals (grill rest.) – **32 rm** 39.95/59.95 t.

**Fernbank** without rest., 4 Fairfields Rd, RG21 3DR, ℰ (01256) 321191, Fax (01256) 321191 – ✻ 🔟 ☎ ₱. 🆀 🗚 ① 💵. ⌘
Y a
closed 2 to 3 weeks Christmas – **16 rm** ☑ 47.00/65.00 st.

**at Oakley** West : 4 ¾ m. on B 3400 – Z.

**Beach Arms,** RG23 7EP, on B 3400 ℰ (01256) 780210, Fax (01256) 780557, 🎋 – 🔟 ☎ ✆ & ₱ – 🔬 25. 🆀 🗚 ① 💵. ⌘
Meals 10.00 st. (dinner) and a la carte 11.75/21.75 st. – ☑ 6.00 – **32 rm** 54.00 st.

ⓐ ATS Moniton Trading Est., West Ham Lane ℰ (01256) 351431　　ATS Armstrong Rd, Daneshill East ℰ (01256) 462448

---

# BASLOW Derbs. 402 403 404 P 24 Great Britain G. – pop. 1 184 – ⌧ Bakewell.

See : Chatsworth★★★ (Park and Garden★★★) AC.
London 161 – Derby 27 – Manchester 35 – Sheffield 13.

**Cavendish,** DE45 1SP, on A 619 ℰ (01246) 582311, Fax (01246) 582312, ≼ Chatsworth Park, « Collection of paintings and fine art », ◿, 🎋 – ✻ rest, 🔟 ☎ ₱ – 🔬 25. 🆀 🗚 ① 💵. ⌘
Meals 37.75 t. and a la carte 17.00/36.25 t. ⏍ 7.50 – ☑ 10.10 – **23 rm** 89.00/134.00 t., 1 suite – SB.

XXX **Fischer's at Baslow Hall** with rm, Calver Rd, DE45 1RR, on A 623 ℰ (01246) 583259, Fax (01246) 583818, « Edwardian manor house », 🎋 – ✻ rest, 🔟 ☎ ₱. 🆀 🗚 ① 💵. ⌘
❀ closed 25 and 26 December – Meals (closed Saturday lunch and Sunday dinner) 24.00/ 45.00 t. ⏍ 11.00 – (see also **Café-Max** below) – ☑ 8.50 – **5 rm** 80.00/130.00 t., 1 suite – SB
Spec. Pan-fried foie gras with a citrus sauce. Turbot with potato mousseline, courgette flowers stuffed with scallop mousse. Roast baby pineapple with coconut ice cream.

XX **Café-Max** (at Fischer's at Baslow Hall), Calver Rd, DE45 1RR, on A 623 ℰ (01246) 583259, Fax (01246) 583818, 🎋 – ✻ ₱. 🆀 🗚 ① 💵
closed Saturday dinner and Sunday – Meals and a la carte 20.75/27.50 t. ⏍ 11.00.

---

# BASSENTHWAITE Cumbria 401 402 K 19 – pop. 433.

London 300 – Carlisle 24 – Keswick 7.

**Armathwaite Hall** ⟨S⟩, CA12 4RE, West : 1 ½ m. on B 5291, ⌧ Keswick ℰ (017687) 76551, Fax (017687) 76220, ≼ Bassenthwaite Lake, « Part 18C mansion in extensive grounds », ₤₅, ≘, ◿, 🎋, 🎋, park, ❨ – ¦⭑, ✻ rest, 🔟 ☎ ₱ – 🔬 100. 🆀 🗚 ① 💵. ⌘
Meals 15.50/34.95 t. and dinner a la carte ⏍ 6.95 – **42 rm** ☑ 105.00/210.00 t. – SB.

**Castle Inn,** CA12 4RG, West : 1 m. on A 591 at junction with B 5291, ⌧ Keswick ℰ (017687) 76401, Fax (017687) 76604, ₤₅, ≘, ◿, 🎋, ❨ – ✻ rest, 🔟 ☎ ₱ – 🔬 120. 🆀 🗚 ① 💵
Meals (bar lunch)/dinner 18.95 st. ⏍ 4.95 – **48 rm** ☑ 82.00/115.00 st. – SB.

**Overwater Hall** ⟨S⟩, CA5 1HH, Northeast : 2 ¾ m. by A 591 off Uldale rd, ⌧ Carlisle ℰ (017687) 76566, Fax (017687) 76566, ≼, « 19C mansion », 🎋, park – ✻ rest, 🔟 ☎ ₱. 🆀 💵
closed 3 to 14 January – Meals (dinner only and Sunday lunch)/dinner 18.50 t. ⏍ 5.25 – **12 rm** ☑ (dinner included) 66.50/113.00 t. – SB.

🏠 **The Pheasant,** CA13 9YE, Southwest : 3 ¼ m. by B 5291 and A 66 on Wythop Mill rd, ⊠ Cockermouth ℰ (017687) 76234, Fax (017687) 76002, « 16C », � – ⅍⊱ rest, **ℙ**. **⓪❾** **VISA**. ⅍
*closed 25 December* – **Meals** 13.00/22.00 t. ⓵ 5.50 – **20 rm** ⊒ 66.00/110.00 t. – SB.

🏠 **Ravenstone Lodge,** CA12 4QG, South : 1 ½ m. on A 591 ℰ (017687) 76629, Fax (017687) 76629, ⩽, � – 📺 **ℙ**. **⓪❾** **VISA** **JCB**
**Meals** (residents only) (dinner only) 15.00 st. ⓵ 6.00 – **10 rm** ⊒ 30.50/61.00 st.

**at Ireby** North : 5 m. by A 591 on Ireby rd – ⊠ Carlisle.

↑ **Woodlands** ⅖, CA5 1EX, Northwest : ¼ m. on Mealsgate rd ℰ (016973) 71791, Fax (016973) 71482, � – ⅍⊱ 📺 **ℙ**. **⓪❾** **VISA**
*closed 3 to 31 January and December except Christmas and New Year* – **Meals** (by arrangement) 15.00 st. – **7 rm** ⊒ 44.00/65.00 st.

**at Boltongate** North : 6½ m. by A 591 and Ireby rd on Mealsgate rd – ⊠ Carlisle.

↑ **Boltongate Old Rectory** ⅖, CA5 1DA, ℰ (016973) 71647, Fax (016973) 71798, ⩽, « Part 15C », 🌫 – ⅍⊱ **ℙ**. **⓪❾** **VISA**. ⅍
*March-October* – **Meals** (by arrangement) (communal dining) 23.00 st. ⓵ 7.00 – **3 rm** ⊒ 55.00/76.00 t.

*Benachrichtigen Sie sofort das Hotel,*
*wenn Sie ein bestelltes Zimmer nicht belegen können.*

---

**BATCOMBE** Somerset **⓸⓪⓷** **⓸⓪⓸** M 30 – pop. 391 – ⊠ Shepton Mallet.
London 130 – Bristol 24 – Bournemouth 50 – Salisbury 40 – Taunton 40.

🍴 **Three Horseshoes Inn,** BA4 6HE, ℰ (01749) 850359, Fax (01749) 850615, 🌫 – **ℙ**. **⓪❾** **VISA** **JCB**
**Meals** a la carte 14.50/22.50 t. ⓵ 8.50.

---

**BATH** Bath & North East Somerset **⓸⓪⓷** **⓸⓪⓸** M 29 The West Country G. – pop. 85 202.

See : *City*★★★ – *Royal Crescent*★★★ AV (No 1 Royal Crescent★★ AC AV D) – *The Circus*★★★ AV – *Museum of Costume*★★★ AC AV M2 – *Royal Photographic Society National Centre of Photography*★★ AC BV M4 – *Roman Baths*★★ AC BX B – *Holburne Museum and Crafts Study Centre*★★ AC Y M1 – *Pump Room*★ BX A - *Assembly Rooms*★ AV – *Bath Abbey*★ BX – *Bath Industrial Heritage Centre*★ AC AV M3 – *Lansdown Crescent*★★ (Somerset Place★) Y – *Camden Crescent*★ Y – *Beckford Tower and Museum AC (prospect*★) Y M6 – *Museum of East Asian Art*★ AV M9 – *Orange Grove*★ BX.

Env. : – *Claverton (American Museum*★★ AC, Claverton Pumping Station★ AC) E : 3 m. by A 36 Y.

Exc. : *Corsham Court*★★ AC, NE : 8½ m. by A 4 – *Dyrham Park*★ AC, N : 6½ m. by A 4 and A 46.

🖥, 🖥, 🖥, Tracy Park, Bath Rd, Wick ℰ (0117) 937 2251 – 🖥 Lansdown ℰ (01225) 422138 – 🖥 Entry Hill ℰ (01225) 834248.

🅱 Abbey Chambers, Abbey Churchyard, BA1 1LY ℰ (01225) 462831.
London 119 – Bristol 13 – Southampton 63 – Taunton 49.

Plans on following pages

🏨 **Bath Spa** ⅖, Sydney Rd, BA2 6JF, ℰ (01225) 444424, Fax (01225) 444006, « Part 19C mansion in landscaped gardens », ⓕ₆, ⩗s, ⬜, ⅍ – 🍴 ⅍⊱ 📺 ☎ 🕭 **ℙ** – 🔏 120. **⓪❾** **⓪⓪** **VISA** **JCB**
Y  Z
**Alfresco :** **Meals** a la carte 20.00/35.75 t. ⓵ 9.50 – **Vellore :** **Meals** (dinner only and Sunday lunch)/dinner a la carte 24.25/40.75 t. ⓵ 9.50 – ⊒ 14.75 – **90 rm** 144.00/204.00 t., 8 suites – SB.

🏨 **The Royal Crescent,** 16 Royal Cres., BA1 2LS, ℰ (01225) 823333, Fax (01225) 339401, ⩽, « Restored 18C town houses in magnificent Georgian crescent », ⩗s, 🌫 – 🍴 ⅍⊱ 🏊 📺 ☎
🕭 🖫 – 🔏 60. **⓪❾** **⓪⓪** **VISA**
AV  a
**Pimpernel's :** **Meals** *(closed Sunday and Monday)* (dinner only) 42.00 st. ⓵ 10.00 – **The Brasserie :** **Meals** 19.50/31.00 st. and a la carte 23.50/34.00 st. ⓵ 10.00 – ⊒ 14.50 – **34 rm** 170.00/675.00 st., 11 suites 370.00/675.00 st..

🏨 **Homewood Park,** BA3 6BB, Southeast : 6 ½ m. on A 36 ℰ (01225) 723731, Fax (01225) 723820, ⩽, « Part Georgian country house », ⬜, 🌫, park, ⅍ – ⅍⊱ rest, 📺 ☎
⅍ ⊱ ☸ **ℙ**. **⓪❾** **⓪⓪** **VISA** **JCB**. ⅍
**Meals** 22.50 st. (lunch) and a la carte approx. 45.00 st. ⓵ 10.00 – **17 rm** ⊒ 105.00/200.00 st., 2 suites – SB
**Spec.** Confit of duck leg and foie gras with Sauternes jelly. Roast monkfish tail with girolles, clam and cockle sabayon. Almond parfait with white peach coulis.

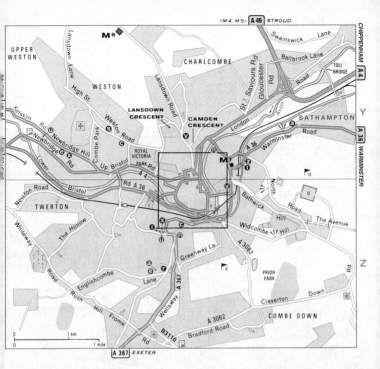

Swainswick Lane

**M** 6

UPPER WESTON

Lansdown Lane

CHARLCOMBE

Swainswick Lane

Bailbrook Lane

TOLL BRIDGE

WESTON

High St.

St Saviours Rd

Gloucester Rd

Road

Weston Road

LANSDOWN CRESCENT

Lansdown Road

CAMDEN CRESCENT

London Rd

BATHAMPTON

Warminster Road

Y

Combe Park

Newbridge Rd

Up. Bristol

ROYAL VICTORIA PARK

Rd

London

A 36

Avon

18

Newbridge Rd

Lower Bristol

Rd A 36

Bathwick

North Road

The Avenue

TWERTON

Newton Road

Bristol Road

The Hollow

Hill

Widcombe Hill

A 3062

Z

Whiteway

Englishcombe

Lane

Greenway La.

9

PRIOR PARK

Claverton Down

Rd

Rush Hill

Frome

Wellsway A 367

B3110

Bradford Road

COMBE DOWN

0          1 km
0                    1 mile

**A 367** EXETER

**Bath Priory,** Weston Rd, BA1 2XT, ℰ (01225) 331922, Fax (01225) 448276, ≤, 佘, ℔, ≋s, ⨯, ⬚, 雨 – ⇔ rest, ⊡ ☎ ✆ ⬢ ⬢. ⬚ ⅏ Ⓐ ⓪ *VISA* ⑂. Y c
Meals 18.50/37.50 t. ⅋ 9.00 – **28 rm** ⬚ (dinner included) 185.00/340.00 **st.** – SB
**Spec.** Pan-fried scallops with tagliolini, asparagus and lobster sauce. Roast best end of lamb, tomato couscous and thyme sauce. Warm chocolate tart, lime sauce and vanilla ice cream.

**Queensberry,** Russel St., BA1 2QF, ℰ (01225) 447928, Fax (01225) 446065, 雨 – ⅃ ⊡ ☎. ⅏ *VISA*. ⑂ AV x
closed 24 to 30 December – **Meals** – (see **Olive Tree** below) – ⬚ 8.50 – **29 rm** 100.00/220.00 **t.**

**Francis on the Square,** Queen Sq., BA1 2HH, ℰ (01225) 424257, Fax (01225) 319715 – ⅃ ⇔ ⊡ ⬢ – ⬚ 80. ⅏ Ⓐ ⓪ *VISA* AV i
Meals (bar lunch Monday to Saturday)/dinner 22.95 **t.** and a la carte ⅋ 9.00 – ⬚ 10.25 – **93 rm** 119.00/139.00 **t.**, 1 suite – SB.

**Hilton National,** Walcot St., BA1 5BJ, ℰ (01225) 463411, Fax (01225) 464393, ℔, ≋s, ⬚ – ⅃ ⇔ ⊡ ☎ ⬅ ⬢ – ⬚ 240. ⅏ Ⓐ ⓪ *VISA*. ⑂ BV i
Meals (closed 31 December) 15.50/18.50 **t.** and dinner a la carte ⅋ 6.50 – ⬚ 11.25 – **149 rm** 123.00/153.00 **st.**

**Fountain House** without rest., 9-11 Fountain Buildings, Lansdown Rd, BA1 5DV, ℰ (01225) 338622, Fax (01225) 445855 – ⅃ ⊡ ☎ ✆. ⅏ Ⓐ ⓪ *VISA* BV e
⬚ 7.50, **13 suites** 127.00/260.00 **st.**

**Stakis Bath,** Widcombe Basin, BA2 4JP, ℰ (01225) 338855, Fax (01225) 428941 – ⅃, ⇔ rm, ⊡ ☎ ⬢ – ⬚ 130. ⅏ Ⓐ ⓪ *VISA* BX r
Meals (bar lunch)/dinner 16.50 **t.** and a la carte – ⬚ 9.95 – **106 rm** 105.00/135.00 **st.** – SB.

**Lansdown Grove,** Lansdown Rd, BA1 5EH, ℰ (01225) 483888, Fax (01225) 483838, 雨 – ⅃ ⇔ ⊡ ☎ ⬢ – ⬚ 80. ⅏ Ⓐ ⓪ *VISA* Y v
Meals (bar lunch Monday to Saturday)/dinner 19.50 **st.** and a la carte ⅋ 6.00 – **49 rm** ⬚ 75.00/99.00 **st.** – SB.

**Pratt's,** South Par., BA2 4AB, ℰ (01225) 460441, Fax (01225) 448807 – ⅃ ⇔ ⊡ ☎ ✆ – ⬚ 50. ⅏ Ⓐ ⓪ *VISA* BX c
Meals (bar lunch Monday to Saturday)/dinner 16.95 **st.** and a la carte ⅋ 5.95 – **46 rm** ⬚ 65.00/95.00 **st.** – SB.

# BATH

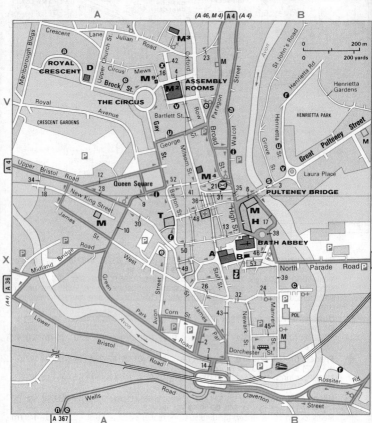

🏠 **Apsley House** without rest., 141 Newbridge Hill, BA1 3PT, ℘ (01225) 336966, Fax (01225) 425462, 🌲 – 📺 ☎ 📞 🄿. 🅼🅾 🆎 ⑩ 𝘝𝘐𝘚𝘈. ✻      Y x
closed 1 week Christmas – **9 rm** ⊇ 55.00/110.00 **st.**

🏠 **Villa Magdala** without rest., Henrietta Rd, BA2 6LX, ℘ (01225) 466329, Fax (01225) 483207, 🌲 – 🖇 📺 ☎ 🄿. 🅼🅾 🆎 𝘝𝘐𝘚𝘈 𝗝𝗖𝗕. ✻      BV r
**17 rm** ⊇ 60.00/95.00 **st.**

🏡 **Bath Tasburgh,** Warminster Rd, Bathampton, BA2 6SH, East : 1 m. on A 36 ℘ (01225) 425096, Fax (01225) 463842, ≤, 🌲, 🌲 – 🖇 📺 ☎ 🄿. 🅼🅾 🆎 𝘝𝘐𝘚𝘈. ✻      Y a
**Meals** (by arrangement) (dinner only) 18.50 **t.** ⋀ 6.50 – **12 rm** ⊇ 48.00/85.00 **st.**

🏡 **Brompton House** without rest., St. John's Rd, Bathwick, BA2 6PT, ℘ (01225) 420972, Fax (01225) 420505, 🌲 – 🖇 📺 ☎ 🄿. 🅼🅾 🆎 𝘝𝘐𝘚𝘈 𝗝𝗖𝗕. ✻      Y n
closed Christmas and New Year – **18 rm** ⊇ 45.00/95.00 **st.**

🏠 **Sydney Gardens** without rest., Sydney Rd, BA2 6NT, ℰ (01225) 464818,
*Fax (01225) 484347*, ≤, ᾰ – ⚒ 📺 ☎ 🄿. 🕿 AE 🎫 ᾧ.  Y  i
*closed 24 December-1 February* – **6 rm** ☑ 59.00/75.00 **t.**

🏠 **Siena** without rest., 25 Pulteney Rd, BA2 4EZ, ℰ (01225) 425495, *Fax (01225) 469029*, ᾰ –
⚒ 📺 ☎ 🄿 – 🔏 25. 🕿 AE ⓪ 🕿 🎫  Z  v
*closed 3 days Christmas* – **14 rm** ☑ 52.50/97.50 **st.**, 1 suite.

🏠 **Paradise House** without rest., 86-88 Holloway, BA2 4PX, ℰ (01225) 317723,
*Fax (01225) 482005*, ≤, ᾰ – 📺 ☎ ᾧ. 🕿 AE ⓪ 🕿.  Z  c
*closed 4 days Christmas* – **8 rm** ☑ 50.00/65.00 **st.**

🏠 **Holly Lodge** without rest., 8 Upper Oldfield Park, BA2 3JZ, ℰ (01225) 424042,
*Fax (01225) 481138*, ≤, ᾰ – ⚒ 📺 ☎ 🄿. 🕿 AE ⓪ 🕿 🎫.  Z  i
**7 rm** ☑ 48.00/89.00 **st.**

🏠 **Bloomfield House** without rest., 146 Bloomfield Rd, BA2 2AS, ℰ (01225) 420105,
*Fax (01225) 481958*, ≤, ᾰ – ⚒ 📺 ☎ ☏ 🄿. 🕿 🕿.  Z  r
**8 rm** ☑ 50.00/105.00 **st.**

🏠 **Cranleigh** without rest., 159 Newbridge Hill, BA1 3PX, ℰ (01225) 310197,
*Fax (01225) 423143*, ᾰ – ⚒ 📺 🄿. 🕿 🕿.  Y  e
*closed 24 to 26 December* – **5 rm** ☑ 48.00/75.00 **t.**

🏠 **Leighton House** without rest., 139 Wells Rd, BA2 3AL, ℰ (01225) 314769,
*Fax (01225) 443079*, ᾰ – ⚒ 📺 ☎ 🄿. 🕿 🕿 🎫.  AX  e
**7 rm** ☑ 60.00/75.00 **st.**

🏠 **Haydon House** without rest., 9 Bloomfield Park, off Bloomfield Rd, BA2 2BY,
ℰ (01225) 444919, *Fax (01225) 427351*, ᾰ – ⚒ 📺 ☎ ☏. 🕿 AE 🕿 🎫.  Z  a
**5 rm** ☑ 65.00/90.00 **st.**

🏠 **Laura Place** without rest., 3 Laura Pl., Great Pulteney St., BA2 4BH, ℰ (01225) 463815,
*Fax (01225) 310222* – 📺 ☎ 🄿. 🕿 AE 🕿.  BV  v
*closed Christmas* – **8 rm** ☑ 60.00/92.00 **st.**

🏠 **Dorian House** without rest., 1 Upper Oldfield Park, BA2 3JX, ℰ (01225) 426336,
*Fax (01225) 444699*, ≤, ᾰ – 📺 ☎ 🄿. 🕿 AE ⓪ 🕿.  Z  u
**8 rm** ☑ 45.00/75.00 **st.**

🏠 **Kennard** without rest., 11 Henrietta St., BA2 6LL, ℰ (01225) 310472, *Fax (01225) 460054* –
⚒ 📺 ☎ ☏ 🕿 AE ⓪ 🕿 🎫.  BV  u
**13 rm** ☑ 55.00/95.00 **st.**

🏠 **Gainsborough** without rest., Weston Lane, BA1 4AB, ℰ (01225) 311380,
*Fax (01225) 447411*, ᾰ – 📺 ☎ 🄿. 🕿 AE 🕿.  Y  s
*closed 23 December-7 January* – **17 rm** ☑ 45.00/84.00 **st.**

🏠 **Oldfields** without rest., 102 Wells Rd, BA2 3AL, ℰ (01225) 317984, *Fax (01225) 444471*, ᾰ
– ⚒ 📺 ☎ 🄿. 🕿 AE 🕿 🎫.  AX  n
*closed Christmas and January* – **14 rm** ☑ 60.00/80.00 **st.**

🏠 **Cheriton House** without rest., 9 Upper Oldfield Park, BA2 3JX, ℰ (01225) 429862,
*Fax (01225) 428403*, ᾰ – ⚒ 📺 ☎ ☏ 🄿. 🕿 AE ⓪ 🕿 🎫.  Z  u
**9 rm** ☑ 42.00/74.00 **st.**

🏠 **Meadowland** without rest., 36 Bloomfield Park, off Bloomfield Rd, BA2 2BX,
ℰ (01225) 311079, *Fax (01225) 311079*, ᾰ – ⚒ 📺 🄿. 🕿 🕿.  Z  e
**3 rm** ☑ 50.00/75.00 **st.**

🏠 **Badminton Villa** without rest., 10 Upper Oldfield Park, BA2 3JZ, ℰ (01225) 426347,
*Fax (01225) 420593*, ≤, ᾰ – ⚒ 📺 🄿. 🕿 🕿 🎫.  Z  x
*closed 23 December-1 January* – **4 rm** ☑ 45.00/60.00 **st.**

🏠 **Blairgowrie House** without rest., 55 Wellsway, BA2 4RT, ℰ (01225) 332266,
*Fax (01225) 484535* – 📺 🖴.  Z  n
**3 rm** ☑ 34.00/52.00.

🏠 **Oakleigh** without rest., 19 Upper Oldfield Park, BA2 3JX, ℰ (01225) 315698,
*Fax (01225) 448223* – 📺 🄿. 🕿 AE 🕿.  Z  i
**4 rm** ☑ 40.00/68.00 **st.**

🏠 **Brocks** without rest., 32 Brock St., BA1 2LN, ℰ (01225) 338374, *Fax (01225) 334245* – ⚒
📺 ☏. 🕿 🕿.  AV  e
*closed Christmas and 2 weeks January* – **6 rm** ☑ 50.00/70.00 **t.**

XXX **Lettonie** (Blunos) with rm, 35 Kelston Rd, BA1 3QH, ℰ (01225) 446676,
🕸🕸 *Fax (01225) 447541*, ≤, ᾰ – ⚒ 📺 ☎ 🄿. 🕿 AE ⓪ 🕿.  Y  u
*closed Sunday, Monday, 2 weeks January and 2 weeks August-Spetember* – **Meals** 25.00/
44.50 **t.** ᾧ 9.20 – **5 rm** ☑ 95.00/165.00 **st.**
**Spec.** Breast of quail with foie gras and chicken mousse on onion marmalade. Pan-fried
fillet and honey glazed belly of pork with a sage sauce. Assiette of apple.

XX **Olive Tree** (at Queensberry H.), Russel St., BA1 2QF, ℰ (01225) 447928, Fax (01225) 446065 – ✦ ▥. **MO** *VISA*                    AV   x
*closed Sunday lunch and 1 week Christmas* – Meals 14.50/22.00 **t.** and a la carte ⒜ 10.00.

XX **Moody Goose**, 7A Kingsmead Sq., BA1 2AB, ℰ (01225) 466688, Fax (01225) 466688 – **MO** **AE** **O** *VISA*                    AX   e
*closed Sunday, Bank Holidays except 25 December and 2 weeks spring* – Meals 14.00/ 20.00 **t.** and a la carte 22.00/29.50 **t.** ⒜ 9.00.

XX **Hole in the Wall**, 16 George St., BA1 2EH, ℰ (01225) 425242, Fax (01225) 425242 – ✦. **MO** **AE** *VISA*                    AV   u
*closed Sunday* – Meals 12.50/19.50 **t.** and a la carte ⒜ 7.00.

XX **Clos du Roy**, 1 Seven Dials, Saw Close, BA1 1EN, ℰ (01225) 444450, Fax (01225) 404044 – **MO** **AE** **O** *VISA* **JCB**                    AX   r
Meals 13.95/19.50 **t.** and a la carte ⒜ 7.50.

XX **Rajpoot**, Rajpoot House, Argyle St., BA2 4BA, ℰ (01225) 464758, Fax (01225) 444527 – ▥. **MO** **AE** **O** *VISA*                    BV   s
*closed 25 and 26 December* – Meals - Indian - 6.95/18.95 **t.** and a la carte ⒜ 5.50.

XX **Sukhothai**, 90a Walcot St., BA1 5BG, ℰ (01225) 462463, Fax (01225) 462463 – ▥. **MO** **AE** **O** *VISA* **JCB**                    BV   a
*closed Sunday and 25-26 December* – Meals - Thai - 6.95/16.00 **t.** and a la carte.

X **Woods**, 9-13 Alfred St., BA1 2QX, ℰ (01225) 314812, Fax (01225) 443146 – **MO** **AE** *VISA*                    AV   v
*closed Sunday dinner* – Meals a la carte 11.50/27.25 **t.** ⒜ 5.00.

X **No. 5 Bistro**, 5 Argyle St., BA2 4BA, ℰ (01225) 444499, Fax (01225) 318668 – ✦. **MO** **AE** **O** *VISA*                    BV   s
*closed Monday lunch, Sunday, 25-29 December and Bank Holidays* – Meals a la carte 16.10/ 27.65 **t.** ⒜ 7.50.

**at Box** (Wilts.) Northeast : 5½ m. on A 4 – Y – ✉ Corsham.

↑ **Manor Farm** without rest., Wadswick, SN13 8JB, Southeast : 2 m. by A 365 off B 3109 ℰ (01225) 810700, Fax (01225) 810307, « Working farm », 🐎, park – ✦ 📺 🅿. **MO** *VISA* **JCB**. ✵
*April-October* – 3 rm ⌑ 30.00/50.00 **s.**

**at Colerne** (Wilts.) Northeast : 6 ½ m. by A 4 – Y – , Batheaston rd and Bannerdown Rd – ✉ Chippenham.

🏛 **Lucknam Park** ⟩, SN14 8AZ, North : ½ m. on Marshfield rd ℰ (01225) 742777, Fax (01225) 743536, ≤, « Early 18C country house in park », ℐ♭, ≘s, ▨, 🐎, ❨ – ✦ rest, 📺 ☎ 🅿 – ⚒ 25. **MO** **AE** **O** *VISA* **JCB**. ✵
Meals (dinner only and Sunday lunch)/dinner 40.00 **t.** and a la carte 53.00/61.00 **t.** ⒜ 9.50 – ⌑ 18.00 – 37 rm 160.00/265.00 **t.**, 4 suites – SB.

**at Bathford** East : 3½ m. by A 4 – Y – off A 363 – ✉ Bath.

🏠 **The Lodge** without rest., Bathford Hill, BA1 7SL, ℰ (01225) 858467, Fax (01225) 858172, ℐ, 🐎 – 📺 ☎ 🅿. **MO** *VISA*. ✵
5 rm ⌑ 64.00/99.00 **st.**, 1 suite.

**at Monkton Combe** Southeast : 4½ m. by A 36 – Y – ✉ Bath.

↑ **Monkshill** ⟩ without rest., Shaft Rd, BA2 7HL, ℰ (01225) 833028, Fax (01225) 833028, ≤ Limpley Stoke Valley, « Antiques », 🐎 – ✦ 📺 🅿. **MO** *VISA*
*closed 1 week Christmas and New Year* – 3 rm ⌑ 60.00/75.00 **st.**

**at Limpley Stoke (Lower)** Southeast : 5½ m. by A 36 – Y – off B 3108 – ✉ Bath.

🏛 **Cliffe**, Cliffe Drive, Crowe Hill, BA3 6HY, ℰ (01225) 723226, Fax (01225) 723871, ≤, 🌳, ℐ, 🐎 – ✦ rest, 📺 ☎ 🅿. **MO** **AE** *VISA* **JCB**
Meals 12.75 **st.** (lunch) and a la carte 20.00/27.50 **st.** ⒜ 8.25 – 11 rm ⌑ 68.00/110.00 **st.** – SB.

**at Hinton Charterhouse** South : 5¾ m. by A 367 – Z – on B 3110 – ✉ Bath.

↑ **Green Lane House** without rest., Green Lane, BA3 6BL, ℰ (01225) 723631, Fax (01225) 723773, « 18C cottage » – ✦. **MO** **AE** *VISA*. ✵
4 rm ⌑ 42.00/54.00.

🔧 ATS London Rd ℰ (01225) 338899

**BATHFORD** Bath & North East Somerset **403 404** M 29 – see Bath.

108

**BATLEY** W. Yorks. 402 O 22 – pop. 48 030.
London 205 – Leeds 9 – Manchester 40 – Middlesbrough 76 – Sheffield 31.

🏨 **Alder House,** Towngate Rd, WF17 7HR, Southwest : 1 m. by B 6123 off Healey Lane
    *&* (01924) 444777, *Fax (01924) 442644*, ☞ – ⇆ 🖵 ☎ 🅿 – 🔬 80. ◑◉ 🅰🅴 ① 𝘝𝘐𝘚𝘈. ✵
    **Meals** (bar lunch Monday to Saturday and Sunday dinner)/dinner 16.95 **t.** 🛓 5.95 – **20 rm**
    ⇄ 48.00/75.00 **t.** – SB.

---

**BATTLE** E. Sussex 404 V 31 Great Britain G. – pop. 5 235.
See : Town★ – Abbey and Site of the Battle of Hastings★ AC.
🚩 88 High St., TN33 0AQ &* (01424) 773721.
London 55 – Brighton 34 – Folkestone 43 – Maidstone 30.

🏨 **Netherfield Place** ⌂, TN33 9PP, Northwest : 2 m. by A 2100 on Netherfield rd
    *&* (01424) 774455, *Fax (01424) 774024*, ≼, « Georgian style country house, gardens »,
    park, ✵ – 🖵 ☎ 🅿 – 🔬 50. ◑◉ 🅰🅴 ① 𝘝𝘐𝘚𝘈. ✵
    *closed 2 weeks Christmas-New Year* – **Meals** 17.50 **t.** (lunch) and a la carte 20.50/30.95 **t.**
    🛓 6.50 – **14 rm** ⇄ 67.50/160.00 **t.** – SB.

🏨 **PowderMills** ⌂, Powdermill Lane, TN33 0SP, South : 1 ½ m. by A 2100 on Catsfield rd
    *&* (01424) 775511, *Fax (01424) 774540*, ≼, « Part Georgian gunpowdermill, antiques », ⟋,
    ☞, park – 🔬 250. ◑◉ 🅰🅴 ① 𝘝𝘐𝘚𝘈
    **Meals** – (see *Orangery* below) – **35 rm** ⇄ 70.00/150.00 **t.** – SB.

🏨 **Burnt Wood House** ⌂, Powdermill Lane, TN33 0SU, South : 2 m. on A 2100 on
    Catsfield rd *&* (01424) 775151, *Fax (01424) 775151*, ≼, ⟋, ☞, park, ✵ – ⇆ rest, 🖵 ☎ 🅿.
    ◑◉ 🅰🅴 ① 𝘝𝘐𝘚𝘈
    **Meals** 10.65/19.50 **t.** 🛓 5.50 – **10 rm** ⇄ 50.00/70.00 **t.** – SB.

XX **Orangery** (at PowderMills H.), Powdermill Lane, TN33 0SP, South : 1 ½ m. by A 2100 on
    Catsfield rd *&* (01424) 775511, *Fax (01424) 774540*, ☞ – 🅿. ◑◉ 🅰🅴 ① 𝘝𝘐𝘚𝘈
    **Meals** *(closed Sunday dinner January-February to non-residents)* 14.95/25.50 **t.** 🛓 8.50.

---

**BEACONSFIELD** Bucks. 404 S 29 – pop. 12 292.
London 26 – Aylesbury 19 – Oxford 32.

🏨 **De Vere Bellhouse,** Oxford Rd, HP9 2XE, East : 1 ¾ m. on A 40 &* (01753) 887211,
    *Fax (01753) 888231*, 🇮⑥, ≘s, 🔲, ☞, squash – 🔟 ⇆ 🖵 ☎ 🅿 – 🔬 450. ◑◉ 🅰🅴 ① 𝘝𝘐𝘚𝘈
    **Archways :** Meals *(closed Saturday lunch)* 21.50 **st.** and a la carte 🛓 6.50 – **Brasserie :**
    Meals a la carte 15.45/23.60 **st.** 🛓 6.50 – **133 rm** ⇄ 135.00/155.00 **st.**, 3 suites – SB.

XX **Leigh House,** 53 Wycombe End, HP9 1LX, &* (01494) 676348, *Fax (01494) 676348* – ▤.
    ◑◉ 🅰🅴 ① 𝘝𝘐𝘚𝘈 𝗝𝗖𝗕. ✵
    **Meals** - Chinese (Peking) - 12.00/19.90 **t.** and a la carte.

**at Woouburn Common** Southwest : 3½ m. by A 40 – ✉ Beaconsfield.

🏨 **Chequers Inn** ⌂, Kiln Lane, HP10 0JQ, Southwest : 1 m. on Bourne End rd
    *&* (01628) 529575, *Fax (01628) 850124* – 🖵 ☎ 🅿 – 🔬 45. ◑◉ 🅰🅴 𝘝𝘐𝘚𝘈. ✵
    **Meals** 16.95/21.95 and a la carte 🛓 6.95 – **17 rm** ⇄ 87.50/92.50 **t.** – SB.

    🅰 ATS Warwick Rd &* (01494) 671338

---

**BEAMINSTER** Dorset 403 L 31 – pop. 2 769.
London 154 – Exeter 45 – Taunton 30 – Weymouth 29.

🏨 **Bridge House,** 3 Prout Bridge, DT8 3AY, &* (01308) 862200, *Fax (01308) 863700*, ☞ –
    ⇆ rest, 🖵 ☎ 🅿. ◑◉ 🅰🅴 ① 𝘝𝘐𝘚𝘈
    **Meals** 12.00/21.50 **t.** 🛓 5.00 – **14 rm** ⇄ 64.00/112.00 **t.** – SB.

⌂ **The Lodge** without rest., 9 Tunnel Rd, DT8 3BL, on A 3066 &* (01308) 863468, « Georgian
    country house », ☞, ✵ – ⇆ 🖵 🅿. ◑◉ 𝘝𝘐𝘚𝘈
    *Easter-October* – **3 rm** ⇄ 40.00/80.00 **s.**

*For the quickest route use the **Michelin Main Road Maps:***

**970** Europe, **974** Poland, **976** Czech Republic-Slovak Republic, **980** Greece,
**984** Germany, **985** Scandinavia-Finland, **986** Great Britain and Ireland,
**987** Germany-Austria-Benelux, **988** Italy, **989** France,
**990** Spain-Portugal.

**BEARSTED** Kent **404** V 30 – *see Maidstone*.

---

**BEAULIEU** Hants. **403 404** P 31 *Great Britain G.* – *pop. 726* – ⊠ Brockenhurst.
See : *Town*★★ - *National Motor Museum*★★ AC.
Env. : *Buckler's Hard*★ (*Maritime Museum*★ AC) SE : 2 m.
London 102 – Bournemouth 24 – Southampton 13 – Winchester 23.

🏠 **Montagu Arms**, Palace Lane, SO42 7ZL, ℰ (01590) 612324, Fax (01590) 612188, « Part 18C inn, gardens » – 📺 ☎ 🅿 – 🔬 40. 🕮 🎿 ⓪ 𝘝𝘐𝘚𝘈. ⪼
Meals (light lunch)/dinner 25.90 and a la carte ⋔ 11.50 – **22 rm** ⊇ 72.00/162.00 **st.**, 2 suites – SB.

**at Bucklers Hard** *South : 2½ m.* – ⊠ Brockenhurst.

🏠 **Master Builder's House**, SO42 7XB, ℰ (01590) 616253, Fax (01590) 616297, ≼, 🌫,
« Located in 18C maritime village », 🌿 – ⁂ 📺 ☎ 🅿 – 🔬 40. 🕮 🎿 𝘝𝘐𝘚𝘈. ⪼
Meals (*closed Sunday dinner*) 16.95 **t.** (lunch) and a la carte approx. 22.00 ⋔ 8.00 – **26 rm** ⊇ 90.00/185.00 **t.** – SB.

---

**BECKINGTON** Somerset **403 404** N 30 – *pop. 903* – ⊠ Bath (Bath & North East Somerset).
London 110 – Bristol 27 – Southampton 54 – Swindon 37.

🏠 **Travelodge**, BA3 6SF, on A 36 ℰ (01373) 830251, Fax (01373) 830251, Reservations (Freephone) 0800 850950 – ⁂ rm, 📺 ৬ 🅿. 🕮 🎿 ⓪ 𝘝𝘐𝘚𝘈 ᴊᴄʙ. ⪼
Meals (grill rest.) – **40 rm** 39.95/59.95 **t.**

🏠 **Woolpack Inn** with rm, Warminster Rd, BA3 6SP, ℰ (01373) 831244, Fax (01373) 831223, « Part 16C », 🌿 – ⁂ rest, 📺 ☎ 🅿. ⪼
Meals a la carte 15.30/21.85 **t.** ⋔ 7.95 – **11 rm** ⊇ 55.00/65.00 **t.** – SB.

*La guida cambia, cambiate la guida ogni anno.*

---

**BEDALE** N. Yorks. **402** P 21 – *pop. 2 828* – ⊠ Darlington.
🐂 Leyburn Rd ℰ (01677) 422568.
🅱 Bedale Hall, DL8 1AA ℰ (01677) 424604 (summer only).
London 225 – Leeds 45 – Newcastle Upon Tyne 30 – York 38.

↑ **Hyperion House** without rest., 88 South End, DL8 2DS, ℰ (01677) 422334, Fax (01677) 422334, 🌿 – ⁂ 📺 🅿. ⪼
closed 28 December-3 January and February – **3 rm** ⊇ 35.00/46.00 **st.**

**at Patrick Brompton** *Northwest : 3½ m. on A 684* – ⊠ Bedale.

🏠 **Elmfield House** ⪧, Arrathorne, DL8 1NE, Northwest : 2¼ m. by A 684 on Richmond rd ℰ (01677) 450558, Fax (01677) 450557, ⪦, 🌿, park – ⁂ rest, 📺 ☎ ৬ 🅿. 🕮 𝘝𝘐𝘚𝘈. ⪼
Meals (residents only) (dinner only) 12.00 **st.** ⋔ 3.50 – **9 rm** ⊇ 31.00/50.00 **st.**

---

**BEDFORD** Beds. **404** S 27 – *pop. 73 917*.
🐂 Bedfordshire, Bromham Rd, Biddenham ℰ (01234) 261669 Y – 🐂 Mowsbury, Kimbolton Rd ℰ (01234) 216374/771041.
🅱 10 St. Paul's Sq., MK40 1SL ℰ (01234) 215226.
London 59 – Cambridge 31 – Colchester 70 – Leicester 51 – Lincoln 95 – Luton 20 – Oxford 52 – Southend-on-Sea 85.

Plan opposite

🏠 **Barns**, Cardington Rd, MK44 3SA, East : 2 m. on A 603 ℰ (01234) 270044, Fax (01234) 273102, 🌿 – ⁂ 📺 ☎ ৬ ৬ 🅿 – 🔬 120. 🕮 🎿 ⓪ 𝘝𝘐𝘚𝘈. ⪼                          Y n
Meals a la carte 17.75/25.85 **st.** – ⊇ 9.75 – **48 rm** 80.00/145.00 **st.** – SB.

🏠 **Bedford Swan**, The Embankment, MK40 1RW, ℰ (01234) 346565, Fax (01234) 212009, 🏊 – ⁙, ▤ rest, 📺 ☎ 🅿 – 🔬 300. 🕮 🎿 ⓪ 𝘝𝘐𝘚𝘈. ⪼                          X a
Meals 16.50 **st.** and a la carte ⋔ 9.50 – ⊇ 7.25 – **114 rm** 75.00/84.00 **st.**, 1 suite – SB.

🏠 **Wayfarer**, 403 Goldington Rd, Goldington, MK41 0DS, East : 2 m. on A 428 ℰ (01234) 272707, Fax (01234) 272707 – 📺 ☎ ৬ 🅿. 🕮 🎿 ⓪ 𝘝𝘐𝘚𝘈. ⪼                          Y v
Meals (grill rest.) a la carte approx. 12.00 **t.** – **29 rm** ⊇ 55.00/65.00 **t.**

**at Elstow** *South : 2 m. by A 6 off A 5134* – ⊠ Bedford.

XX **St. Helena**, High St., MK42 9XP, ℰ (01234) 344848, « Part 16C house », 🌿 – 🅿. 🕮 🎿 ⓪ 𝘝𝘐𝘚𝘈                          Y r
closed Saturday lunch, Sunday, Monday and 25 to 31 December – Meals 17.75/30.00 **t.** ⋔ 8.50.

# BEDFORD

*Great Britain and Ireland* is now covered by an *Atlas* at a scale of 1 inch to 4.75 miles.

*Three easy to use versions: Paperback, Spiralbound and Hardback.*

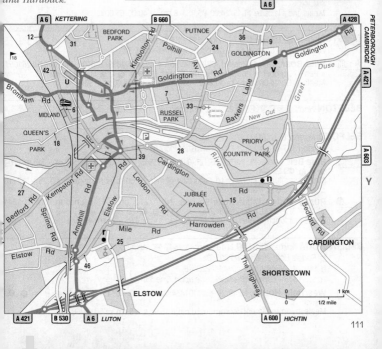

111

**at Houghton Conquest** South : 6½ m. by A 6 – Y – ⊠ Bedford.

XX **Knife and Cleaver** with rm, The Grove, MK45 3LA, ℰ (01234) 740387, Fax (01234) 740900, ㍿, ✿ – ⅏ ☎ ℗. ⬢⬢ ⒶⒺ ⓪ ⅦⅠⓈⒶ ⒿⒸⒷ, ⅍
closed 27 to 30 December – **Meals** (closed dinner Sunday and Bank Holidays except Good Friday) (bar lunch Saturday) 13.95/20.00 **t.** and a la carte ⑄ 7.00 – **9 rm** ⊇ 49.00/74.00 **t.**

**at Marston Moretaine** Southwest : 6¼ m. by A 6 – Y – off A 421 – ⊠ Bedford.

🏠 **Travelodge,** Beancroft Rd junction, MK43 0PZ, on A 421 ℰ (01234) 766755, Fax (01234) 766755, Reservations (Freephone) 0800 850950 – ⅏✱ rm, ⅏ & ℗. ⬢⬢ ⒶⒺ ⓪ ⅦⅠⓈⒶ ⒿⒸⒷ, ⅍
**Meals** (grill rest.) – **32 rm** 39.95/59.95 **t.**

XX **Moreteyne Manor,** Woburn Rd, MK43 0NG, ℰ (01234) 767003, ㍿, « 16C moated manor house », ✿ – ⅏✱ ℗. ⬢⬢ ⒶⒺ ⅦⅠⓈⒶ
closed Sunday dinner, 1 week spring and 1 week autumn – **Meals** (by arrangement Monday) 15.95/26.50 **t.** ⑄ 5.00.

**at Turvey** West : 8 m. on A 428 – Y – ⊠ Bedford.

🍴 **Three Cranes** with rm, MK43 8EP, ℰ (01234) 881305, Fax (01234) 881305 – ⅏✱ rm, ⅏ ℗. ⬢⬢ ⒶⒺ ⅦⅠⓈⒶ, ⅍
**Meals** a la carte 15.25/19.00 **t.** ⑄ 5.75 – **4 rm** ⊇ 40.00/55.00 **st.**

⬡ ATS 3 London Rd ℰ (01234) 358838

*Groß-London (GREATER LONDON) besteht aus der City und 32 Verwaltungsbezirken (Borough). Diese sind wiederum in kleinere Bezirke (Area) unterteilt, deren Mittelpunkt ehemalige Dörfer oder Stadtviertel sind, die oft ihren eigenen Charakter bewahrt haben.*

---

**BEER** Devon ⬛⬛⬛ K 31 The West Country G. – pop. 1 415 – ⊠ Seaton.
Env. : Seaton (≤★★) N ¾m.
🏌 Axe Cliff, Squires Lane, Axmouth, Seaton ℰ (01297) 24371.
London 170 – Exeter 22 – Taunton 28.

🍴 **Anchor Inn** with rm, Fore St., EX12 3ET, ℰ (01297) 20386, Fax (01297) 24474, ≤ – ⅏. ⬢⬢ ⅦⅠⓈⒶ, ⅍
**Meals** and a la carte 11.15/24.00 ⑄ 5.25 – **8 rm** ⊇ 40.00/65.00 **t.**

---

**BEESTON** Ches. ⬛⬛⬛ ⬛⬛⬛ ⬛⬛⬛ L 24 – pop. 196 – ⊠ Tarporley.
London 186 – Chester 15 – Liverpool 40 – Shrewsbury 32.

🏨 **Wild Boar,** Whitchurch Rd, CW6 9NW, on A 49 ℰ (01829) 260309, Fax (01829) 261081, « Part 17C timbered house » – ⅏✱ rm, ▤ rest, ⅏ ☎ & ℗ – ⬢ 50. ⬢⬢ ⒶⒺ ⅦⅠⓈⒶ
**Meals** 14.50/24.00 **st.** and a la carte – **37 rm** ⊇ 70.00/80.00 **st.** – SB.

---

**BEESTON** Notts. ⬛⬛⬛ ⬛⬛⬛ ⬛⬛⬛ Q 25 – see Nottingham.

---

**BELFORD** Northd. ⬛⬛⬛ ⬛⬛⬛ O 17 – pop. 1 177.
London 335 – Edinburgh 71 – Newcastle upon Tyne 49.

🏨 **Blue Bell,** Market Pl., NE70 7NE, ℰ (01668) 213543, Fax (01668) 213787, ✿ – ⅏✱ rest, ⅏ ☎ & ℗. ⬢⬢ ⒶⒺ ⅦⅠⓈⒶ
**Meals** (bar lunch Monday to Saturday)/dinner 21.00 **t.** and a la carte ⑄ 5.25 – **17 rm** ⊇ 64.00/88.00 **t.** – SB.

🏠 **Purdy Lodge,** Adderstone Services, NE70 7JU, on A 1 at junction with B 1341 ℰ (01668) 213000, Fax (01668) 213111 – ⅏ & ℗. ⬢⬢ ⒶⒺ ⓪ ⅦⅠⓈⒶ ⒿⒸⒷ
**Meals** (bar lunch)/dinner 17.95 **t.** and a la carte – ⊇ 4.95 – **20 rm** 42.50 **t.**

---

**BELLINGHAM** Northd. ⬛⬛⬛ ⬛⬛⬛ N 18 – pop. 1 164 – ⊠ Hexham.
🏌 Boggle Hole ℰ (01434) 220530.
🛈 Main St., NE48 2BQ ℰ (01434) 220616.
London 315 – Carlisle 48 – Newcastle upon Tyne 33.

⌂ **Westfield House,** NE48 2DP, ℰ (01434) 220340, Fax (01434) 220340, ✿ – ⅏✱ ℗. ⬢⬢ ⅦⅠⓈⒶ, ⅍
**Meals** (by arrangement) (communal dining) 15.50 **s.** – **5 rm** ⊇ 50.00/58.00 **s.** – SB.

**BELPER** *Derbs.* [402] [403] [404] P 24 – *pop. 18 213.*
*London 141 – Derby 8 – Manchester 55 – Nottingham 17.*

**Makeney Hall Country House** 🌿, Makeney, Milford, DE56 0RS, South : 2 m. by A 6 on Makeney rd ☎ (01332) 842999, *Fax (01332) 842777*, 🌳 – |\$|, ⊬ rm, [TV] ☎ ♿ [P] – 🏛 180. [MC] [AE] ⓓ [VISA] [JCB]
**Meals** *(closed Saturday lunch)* 13.50/19.50 **st.** and a la carte 🍷 7.95 – ☕ 9.75 – **45 rm** 82.00/99.00 **st.** – SB.

**BEPTON** *W. Sussex – see Midhurst.*

**BERKELEY** *Glos.* [403] [404] M 28 *Great Britain G. – pop. 1 550.*
**See** : *Berkeley Castle★★ AC.*
**Exc.** : *Wildfowl and Wetlands Trust, Slimbridge★ AC, NE : 6½ m. by B 4066 and A 38.*
*London 129 – Bristol 20 – Cardiff 50 – Gloucester 18.*

**Prince of Wales,** Berkeley Rd, GL13 9HD, Northeast : 2 ½ m. by B 4066 on A 38 ☎ (01453) 810474, *Fax (01453) 511370*, 🌳 – ⊬ rm, [TV] ☎ [P] – 🏛 200. [MC] [AE] ⓓ [VISA]
**Meals** (bar lunch)/dinner 13.50 **st.** and a la carte 🍷 6.20 – ☕ 6.00 – **43 rm** 50.00/60.00 **st.** – SB.

**The Old School House,** 34 Canonbury St., GL13 9BG, ☎ (01453) 811711, *Fax (01453) 511761* – ⊬ rest, [TV] ☎ 📞 [P]. [MC] [VISA] [JCB]
**Meals** *(closed Sunday to non-residents)* (dinner only) a la carte 16.95/22.85 **st.** 🍷 5.95 – **7 rm** ☕ 47.50/70.00 **st.** – SB.

**BERKSWELL** *W. Mids.* [403] [404] P 26 – *see Coventry.*

**BERWICK-UPON-TWEED** *Northd.* [401] [402] O 16 *Great Britain and Scotland G. – pop. 13 544.*
**See** : *Town★ - Walls★.*
**Env.** : *Foulden★, NW : 5 m. – Paxton House (Chippendale furniture★) AC, W : 5 m. by A 6105, A 1 and B 6461.*
**Exc.** : *St. Abb's Head★★ (≤★), NW : 12 m. by A 1, A 1107 and B 6438 – SW : Tweed Valley★★ – Eyemouth Museum★ AC, N : 7½ m. by A 1 and A 1107 – Holy Island★ (Priory ruins★ AC, Lindisfarne Castle★ AC), SE : 9 m. by A 1167 and A 1 – Manderston★ (stables★), W : 13 m. by A 6105 – Ladykirk (Kirk o'Steil★), SW : 8½ m. by A 698 and B 6470.*
⛳ *Goswick Beal ☎ (01289) 387256 –* ⛳ *Magdalene Fields ☎ (01289) 306384.*
[i] *Castlegate Car Park, TD15 1JS ☎ (01289) 330733.*
*London 349 – Edinburgh 57 – Newcastle upon Tyne 63.*

**Marshall Meadows Country House** 🌿, TD15 1UT, North : 2 ¾ m. by A 1 ☎ (01289) 331133, *Fax (01289) 331438*, 🌳, park – ⊬ rest, [TV] ☎ [P] – 🏛 180. [MC] [VISA] [JCB]
**Meals** 6.90/20.00 **st.** and a la carte 🍷 6.90 – **18 rm** ☕ 65.00/90.00 **st.**, 1 suite – SB.

**Harberton,** 181 Main St., Spittal, TD15 1RP, Southeast : 2 ¼ m. by A 1167 ☎ (01289) 308813, ≤, 🌳 – ⊬ [TV] [P]. ✗
*closed Christmas and New Year* – **Meals** 12.00 **s.** – **5 rm** ☕ 18.50/48.00 **s.** – SB.

Ⓜ ATS 78-80 Church St. ☎ (01289) 308222

**BETHERSDEN** *Kent* [404] W 30 – *pop. 1 341* – ✉ *Ashford.*
*London 63 – Folkestone 20 – Maidstone 27.*

**Little Hodgeham** 🌿, Smarden Rd, TN26 3HE, West : 2 m. ☎ (01233) 850323, « 15C cottage, antique furniture, gardens » – [P]. ✗
*mid March-August* – **Meals** (by arrangement) 15.50 **s.** – **3 rm** ☕ 46.50/73.00 **s.** – SB.

**BEVERLEY** *East Riding* [402] S 22 *Great Britain G. – pop. 23 632* – ✉ *Kingston-upon-Hull.*
**See** : *Town★ - Minster★★ – St. Mary's Church★.*
⛳ *The Westwood ☎ (01482) 867190.*
[i] *The Guildhall, Register Sq., HU17 9AU ☎ (01482) 867430.*
*London 188 – Kingston-upon-Hull 8 – Leeds 52 – York 29.*

**Lairgate,** 30 Lairgate, HU17 8EP, ☎ (01482) 882141, *Fax (01482) 861067* – [TV] ☎ 📞 [P]. [MC] [VISA]. ✗
**Meals** 14.95/15.95 **t.** and dinner a la carte – **22 rm** ☕ 50.00/85.00 **t.**

🍴🍴 **Cerutti 2,** Beverley Station, Station Sq., HU17 0AS, ☎ (01482) 866700 – [P]. [MC] [VISA] [JCB]
*closed Sunday and Bank Holidays* – **Meals** a la carte 16.90/23.75 **t.** 🍷 5.50.

**at Tickton** *Northeast : 3½ m. by A 1035 –* ⊠ *Kingston-upon-Hull.*

🏨 **Tickton Grange,** HU17 9SH, on A 1035 ℰ (01964) 543666, *Fax* (01964) 542556, 🌲 – 📺
☎ 🅿 – 🔬 80. 🆗 🆎 ① 𝘝𝘐𝘚𝘈. ✣
*closed 26 to 30 December* – **Meals** – (see **Squires Dining Room** below) – ⌂ 8.50 – **16 rm**
60.00/80.00 **t.** – SB.

✗✗ **Squires Dining Room** (at Tickton Grange), HU17 9SH, on A 1035 ℰ (01964) 543666,
*Fax* (01964) 542556 – 🅿. 🆗 🆎 ① 𝘝𝘐𝘚𝘈
*closed 26 to 30 December* – **Meals** 15.00/25.00 **t.** ⓘ 6.95.

**at Walkington** *Southwest : 3½ m. by A 164 on B 1230 –* ⊠ *Beverley.*

✗✗✗ **Manor House** ♨ with rm, Northlands, Newbald Rd, HU17 8RT, Northeast : 1 m. by
Northgate on Beverley rd ℰ (01482) 881645, *Fax* (01482) 866501, « Late 19C house, conservatory », 🌲 – 📺 ☎ 🅿. 🆗
*closed 25 December* – **Meals** *(closed Sunday)* (dinner only) 18.50 **t.** and a la carte ⓘ 5.00 – ⌂
8.50 – **7 rm** 70.00/100.00 **t.** – SB.

🔧 ATS 379 Grovehill Rd ℰ (01482) 868655

---

**BEXHILL** *E. Sussex* 𝟜𝟘𝟜 V 31 – *pop. 38 905.*

🏌 *Cooden Beach* ℰ (01424) 842040 – 🏌 *Highwoods, Ellerslie Lane* ℰ (01424) 212625.
🛈 *De la War Marina, TN40 1BQ* ℰ (01424) 212023.
*London 66 – Brighton 32 – Folkestone 42.*

🏨 **Jarvis Cooden Beach,** Cooden Sea Rd, Cooden Beach, TN39 4TT, West : 2 m. on B 2182
ℰ (01424) 842281, *Fax* (01424) 846142, ≤, ≘s, ⬚, ▣, 🌲 – ⅍ rm, 📺 ☎ 🅿 – 🔬 140. 🆗
🆎 ① 𝘝𝘐𝘚𝘈
**Meals** 13.50/15.95 **st.** and a la carte ⓘ 7.50 – **41 rm** ⌂ 79.00/104.00 – SB.

✗ **Leet Lychgates,** 5a Church St., Old Town, TN40 2HE, ℰ (01424) 212193,
*Fax* (01424) 212193 – ⅍. 🆗 𝘝𝘐𝘚𝘈
*closed Sunday dinner, Monday and Tuesday* – **Meals** (dniner only and Sunday lunch)
a la carte approx. 20.70 **st.** ⓘ 7.95.

---

**BIBURY** *Glos.* 𝟜𝟘𝟛 𝟜𝟘𝟜 O 28 *Great Britain G. – pop. 570 –* ⊠ *Cirencester.*

See : *Village★.*
*London 86 – Gloucester 26 – Oxford 30.*

🏨 **Swan,** GL7 5NW, ℰ (01285) 740695, *Fax* (01285) 740473, « Attractively furnished inn with
gardens and trout stream », ⍉ – ▯ ⅍ 📺 ☎. 🆗 🆎 ① 𝘝𝘐𝘚𝘈 𝘑𝘤𝘣. ✣
**Meals** (dinner only and Sunday lunch)/dinner 28.50 **st.** ⓘ 14.00 – **Jankowski's Brasserie :**
**Meals** a la carte 11.90/17.85 **st.** – **18 rm** ⌂ 99.00/235.00 **st.** – SB.

↑ **Cotteswold House** without rest., Arlington, GL7 5ND, on B 4425 ℰ (01285) 740609,
*Fax* (01285) 740609 – ⅍ 📺 🅿. ✣
**3 rm** ⌂ 30.00/45.00.

---

**BICKLEIGH** *Devon* 𝟜𝟘𝟛 J 31 *The West Country G. – pop. 3 595 –* ⊠ *Tiverton.*

See : *Village★★ - Devonshire's Centre, Bickleigh Mill★★ AC – Bickleigh Castle★ AC.*
Env. : *– Knightshayes Court★ AC, N : 4 m. by A 396.*
Exc. : *Uffculme (Coldharbour Mill★★ AC) NE : 7½ m.*
🏌 *Post Hill, Tiverton* ℰ (01884) 252114.
*London 195 – Exeter 9 – Taunton 31.*

🏠 **Fisherman's Cot,** EX16 8RW, on A 396 ℰ (01884) 855289, *Fax* (01884) 855241, « Riverside setting », ⍉, 🌲 – ⅍ rm, 📺 ☎ 🅿. 🆗 𝘝𝘐𝘚𝘈
**Meals** (carving lunch)/dinner a la carte 9.85/18.85 **st.** – **21 rm** ⌂ 46.00/66.00 **st.** – SB.

🏠 **Bickleigh Cottage,** Bickleigh Bridge, EX16 8RJ, on A 396 ℰ (01884) 855230, « Part 17C
thatched cottage, riverside setting », 🌲 – ⅍ rest, 🅿. 🆗 𝘝𝘐𝘚𝘈. ✣
*April-October* – **Meals** (residents only) (dinner only) 11.50 **t.** ⓘ 3.50 – **8 rm** ⌂ 28.50/48.00 **t.**

---

**BICKLEY MOSS** *Ches.* 𝟜𝟘𝟚 𝟜𝟘𝟜 L 24 – ⊠ *Malpas.*

*London 180 – Birmingham 63 – Chester 16 – Shrewsbury 27 – Stoke-on-Trent 25.*

✗ **Cholmondeley Arms** with rm, Cholmondeley, SY14 8BT, North : 1 ½ m. on A 49
ℰ (01829) 720300, *Fax* (01829) 720123, « Converted schoolhouse », 🌲 – 📺 ☎ 🅿. 🆗 𝘝𝘐𝘚𝘈
**Meals** a la carte 12.40/21.40 **t.** – **6 rm** ⌂ 45.00/60.00 – SB.

**BIDDENDEN** *Kent* 404 V 30 *Great Britain G.* – pop. 2 205 – ⊠ *Ashford.*
Env. : *Sissinghurst Castle Garden★ AC, W : 3 m. by A 262.*
🇫 *Chart Hills, Week Lane* ℰ *(01580) 292222.*
*London 50 – Folkestone 28 – Hastings 25 – Maidstone 14.*

XX **West House,** 28 High St., TN27 8AH, ℰ *(01580) 291341,* « *Part 16C* » – 🅿. 🝔 VISA JCB
🏖 *closed Sunday dinner, Monday, Tuesday, 25 December, 1 January, 2 weeks spring and 2 weeks autumn* – Meals *(dinner only and Sunday lunch)/dinner 17.50/22.50* t. 👗 *7.50.*

---

**BIDEFORD** *Devon* 403 H 30 *The West Country G.* – pop. 13 066.
See : *Bridge★★ – Burton Art Gallery★ AC.*
Env. : *Appledore★, N : 2 m.*
Exc. : *Clovelly★★, W : 11 m. by A 39 and B 3237 – Lundy Island★★, NW : by ferry – Rosemoor★ – Great Torrington (Dartington Crystal★ AC) SE : 7½ m. by A 386.*
🇫 *Royal North Devon, Golf Links Rd, Westward Ho* ℰ *(01237) 473824 –* 🇫 *Torrington, Weare Trees* ℰ *(01805) 622229.*
⛴ *to Lundy Island (Lundy Co. Ltd) (2 h 15 mn).*
🄱 *Victoria Park, The Quay, EX39 2QQ* ℰ *(01237) 477676.*
*London 231 – Exeter 43 – Plymouth 58 – Taunton 60.*

🏠 **Yeoldon House** 🐦, *Durrant Lane, EX39 2RL, North : 1½ m. by B 3235 off A 386*
ℰ *(01237) 474400, Fax (01237) 476618,* ≼, 🌳, park – ⅍ rest, 🆃 ☎ 🅿. 🝔 VISA JCB
*closed 24 to 26 December* – Meals *(dinner only and Sunday lunch)/dinner 21.50* st. *and a la carte* 👗 *7.50* – **10 rm** ⊊ *50.00/90.00* st.

🏠 **Newbridge,** *Heywood Rd, Northam, EX39 3QA, North : 1¼ m. by B 3235 on A 386*
ℰ *(01237) 474989, Fax (01237) 474989 –* ⅍ rest, 🆃 ☎ 🅿. 🝔 VISA. ⌗
Meals *(dinner only and Sunday lunch)/dinner 14.50* st. 👗 *6.00* – **10 rm** ⊊ *35.00/70.00* st. – SB.

**at Instow** *North : 3 m. by A 386 on B 3233 –* ⊠ *Bideford.*

🏨 **Commodore,** *Marine Par., EX39 4JN,* ℰ *(01271) 860347, Fax (01271) 861233,* ≼ Taw and Torridge estuaries, 🌳 – 🆃 ☎ 🅿 – 🔏 *200.* 🝔 VISA.
*closed 23 to 27 and 31 December* – Meals *(dinner only and Sunday lunch)/dinner 22.00* t. *and a la carte* 👗 *5.00* – **20 rm** ⊊ *(dinner included) 62.50/130.00* t. – SB.

**at Eastleigh** *Northeast : 2½ m. by A 386 (via Old Barnstaple Rd) –* ⊠ *Bideford.*

⌂ **The Pines at Eastleigh,** *Old Barnstaple Rd, EX39 4PA,* ℰ *(01271) 860561, Fax (01271) 861248,* ≼, 🌳 – ⅍ 🆃 ☎ 🅿. 🝔 VISA
*closed January and November* – Meals *(by arrangement) 15.50* st. 👗 *4.00* – **6 rm** ⊊ *30.00/ 60.00* st. – SB.

🔧 ATS New Rd ℰ *(01237) 472451*

---

**BIGBURY-ON-SEA** *Devon* 403 I 33 – pop. 600 – ⊠ *Kingsbridge.*
*London 196 – Exeter 42 – Plymouth 17.*

🏠 **Henley** 🐦, *Folly Hill, TQ7 4AR,* ℰ *(01548) 810240, Fax (01548) 810020,* ≼ Bigbury Bay and Bolt Tail, 🌳 – ⅍ 🆃 ☎ 🅿. 🝔 AE VISA
*April-late November* – Meals *(residents only) (dinner only) 17.00* t. 👗 *5.50* – **6 rm** ⊊ *40.00/ 68.00* t. – SB.

---

**BIGGLESWADE** *Beds.* 404 T 27 – pop. 12 350.
*London 44 – Bedford 11 – Cambridge 23 – Peterborough 37.*

🏠 **Stratton House,** *London Rd, SG18 8ED,* ℰ *(01767) 312442, Fax (01767) 600416 –* ▦ rest,
🆃 ☎ ✆ 🅿 – 🔏 *40.* 🝔 AE VISA. ⌗
Meals *(bar lunch)/dinner 12.75* t. *and a la carte* 👗 *4.75* – **31 rm** ⊊ *50.50/82.00* t. – SB.

---

**BILBROUGH** *N. Yorks.* 402 Q 22 – see York.

---

**BILLESLEY** *Warks.* – see Stratford-upon-Avon.

---

**BILLINGSHURST** *W. Sussex* 404 S 30 – pop. 4 980.
*London 44 – Brighton 24 – Guildford 25 – Portsmouth 40.*

🏠 **Travelodge,** *Five Oaks, Staines Rd., RH14 9AE, North : 1 m. on A 29* ℰ *(01403) 782711,*
*Reservations (Freephone) 0800 850950 –* ⅍ rm, 🆃 ⅗ 🅿. 🝔 AE ⓪ VISA JCB. ⌗
Meals *(grill rest.)* – **26 rm** *39.95/59.95* t.

↑ **Old Wharf** ⌂ without rest., Wharf Farm, Newbridge, RH14 0JG, West : 1 ¾ m. on A 272 ℘ (01403) 784096, Fax (01403) 784096, ≤, « Restored canalside warehouse », ⌇, 🐎, park 🍴 – ⇘ 📺 📞 🅿. ⫫❾ 🅰🅴 𝘝𝘐𝘚𝘈. 🛇
closed 2 weeks Christmas-New Year and restricted opening January-Easter – **3 rm** ☞ 40.00/75.00 **st.**

✗ **Badgers Bistro**, 87 High St., RH14 9QX, ℘ (01403) 783547, Fax (01403) 783547 – 🅿. ⫫❾ 🅰🅴 𝘝𝘐𝘚𝘈 𝐉𝐂𝐁
closed Sunday and Monday, 1 week January and 2 weeks autumn – **Meals** - French - a la carte 22.95/25.95 **t.**

---

**BILSBORROW** Lancs. – see Garstang.

---

**BINBROOK** Lincs. ⓸⓿⓶ ⓸⓿⓸ T 23 – pop. 1 605.
London 162 – Great Grimsby 10 – Lincoln 26 – Scunthorpe 32.

↑ **Hoe Hill**, Swinhope, LN8 6HX, Northeast : 1 m. on B 1203 ℘ (01472) 398206, 🐎 – ⇘ 🅿 🛇
closed January – **Meals** (by arrangement) 14.00 – **3 rm** ☞ 18.00/50.00.

---

**BINGHAM** Notts. ⓸⓿⓶ ⓸⓿⓸ R 25 – pop. 7 057.
London 125 – Lincoln 28 – Nottingham 11 – Sheffield 35.

🏨 **Yeung Sing**, Market St., NG13 8AB, ℘ (01949) 831831, Fax (01949) 838833 – 🛏 📺 ☎ 🅿. ⫫❾ 🅰🅴 𝘝𝘐𝘚𝘈. 🛇
closed 25 and 26 December – **Meals** – (see below) – **15 rm** ☞ 43.00/56.00 **t.**

✗✗ **Yeung Sing** (at Yeung Sing H.), Market St., NG13 8AB, ℘ (01949) 831222, Fax (01949) 838833 – 🍴 🅿. ⫫❾ 🅰🅴 𝘝𝘐𝘚𝘈
closed 25 and 26 December – **Meals** - Chinese (Canton) - (dinner only and Sunday lunch)/ dinner 15.00 **t.** and a la carte ⑃ 6.80.

🅰 ATS 1 Moorbridge Rd ℘ (01949) 837717

---

**BINGLEY** W. Yorks. ⓸⓿⓶ O 22 – pop. 19 585 – ⊠ Bradford.
🛐 St. Ives Est. ℘ (01274) 562436.
London 204 – Bradford 6 – Skipton 13.

🏨🏨 **Jarvis Bankfield**, Bradford Rd, BD16 1TU, Southeast : 1 ½ m. on A 650 ℘ (01274) 567123, Fax (01274) 551331, 🐎 – 🛏, ⇘ rm, ▤ rest, 📺 ☎ ⑃ 🅿 – 🔬 250. ⫫❾ 🅰🅴 ⓞ 𝘝𝘐𝘚𝘈 𝐉𝐂𝐁
Meals 8.95/16.95 **t.** and dinner a la carte ⑃ 6.50 – ☞ 8.50 – **103 rm** 75.00/95.00 **st.** – SB.

🏨 **Five Rise Locks**, Beck Lane, BD16 4DD, via Park Rd ℘ (01274) 565296, Fax (01274) 568828, 🐎 – ⇘ 📺 ☎ 📞 🅿. ⫫❾ 𝘝𝘐𝘚𝘈 𝐉𝐂𝐁
**Meals** (residents only) (dinner only) 15.00 **t.** and a la carte ⑃ 5.00 – **9 rm** ☞ 47.00/59.00 **t.** – SB.

---

**BINHAM** Norfolk ⓸⓿⓸ W 25 – pop. 281 – ⊠ Fakenham.
London 123 – Cambridge 75 – King's Lynn 31 – Norwich 29.

↑ **Field House** ⌂, Walsingham Rd, NR21 0BU, Southwest : 1 ½ m. on Walsingham rd ℘ (01328) 830639, « Georgian farmhouse », 🐎 – ⇘ 📺 🅿. 🛇
closed 24 to 26 December and November – **Meals** (by arrangement) 15.00 **s.** – **3 rm** ☞ 34.00/52.00 **s.**

---

**BINLEY** W. Mids. – see Coventry.

---

**BINTON** Warks. – see Stratford-upon-Avon.

---

**BIRCHINGTON** Kent ⓸⓿⓸ X 29 – pop. 9 859.
London 71 – Dover 20 – Maidstone 40 – Margate 5.

🏨 **Crown Inn (Cherry Brandy House)**, Ramsgate Rd, Sarre, CT7 0LF, Southwest : 4 m. on A 28 ℘ (01843) 847808, Fax (01843) 847914, 🐎 – 📺 ☎ ⑃ 🅿. ⫫❾ 🅰🅴 ⓞ 𝘝𝘐𝘚𝘈. 🛇
**Meals** (bar lunch Monday to Saturday)/dinner a la carte 17.40/20.50 **t.** ⑃ 6.25 – **12 rm** ☞ 42.50/52.50 – SB.

**BIRCH SERVICE AREA** *Gtr. Manchester* **402** ㉒ **403** ③ **404** ⑩ – ⊠ *Heywood (Lancs.).*

🏠 **Travelodge,** OL10 2HQ, on M 62 between junctions 18 and 19 *ℰ* (0161) 655 3403, *Fax* (0161) 655 3358, Reservations (Freephone) 0800 850950 – ⤢ 🔟 ☎ ᕪ ᕤ. ⓪Ⓞ ᴀᴇ ⓪ 𝘝𝘐𝘚𝘈 ᴊᴄʙ. ⅋
**Meals** (grill rest.) – **55 rm** 39.95/59.95 **t.**

🏠 **Travelodge** without rest., OL10 2HQ, M 62 (westbound) between junctions 18 and 19 *ℰ* (0161) 643 9419, Reservations (Freephone) 0800 850950 – ⤢ 🔟 ☎ ᕪ ᕤ. ⓪Ⓞ ᴀᴇ ⓪ 𝘝𝘐𝘚𝘈 ᴊᴄʙ. ⅋
**35 rm** 39.95/59.95 **t.**

**BIRDLIP** *Glos.* **403** **404** N 28 *Great Britain G.* – ⊠ *Gloucester.*
**Env.** : Crickley Hill Country Park (≤★) *N* : 1½ m. by B 4070 and A 417.
*London 107 – Bristol 51 – Gloucester 9 – Oxford 44 – Swindon 24.*

🏛 **Royal George,** GL4 8JH, *ℰ* (01452) 862506, *Fax* (01452) 862277, ⌨ – ⤢ rm, 🔟 ☎ ᕤ – ᴀ̂ 100. ⓪Ⓞ ᴀᴇ 𝘝𝘐𝘚𝘈. ⅋
**Meals** (bar lunch Monday to Saturday)/dinner 16.95 **t.** and a la carte ᐧ 5.95 – **34 rm** ⊇ 65.00/80.00 **st.** – SB.

✗ **Kingshead House,** GL4 8JH, *ℰ* (01452) 862299 – ᕤ. ⓪Ⓞ ᴀᴇ 𝘝𝘐𝘚𝘈
*closed Saturday lunch, Sunday dinner, Monday, 25-26 December and 1-5 January* – **Meals** 28.50 **t.** (dinner) and lunch a la carte 18.50/22.50 **t.** ᐧ 6.50.

**BIRKENHEAD** *Mersey.* **402** **403** K 23 – pop. 93 087.
ᵣ₈ *Arrowe Park, Woodchurch* *ℰ* (0151) 677 1527 – ᵣ₈ *Prenton, Golf Links Rd, Prenton* *ℰ* (0151) 608 1461.
*Mersey Tunnels (toll).*
⇐ to Liverpool and Wallasey (Mersey Ferries) frequent services (10 mn).
🛈 *Woodside Visitors Centre, Woodside Ferry Terminal, L41 6DU* *ℰ* (0151) 647 6780.
*London 222 – Liverpool 2.*

Plan : see Liverpool p. 3

🏛 **Bowler Hat,** 2 Talbot Rd, Oxton, L43 2HH, *ℰ* (0151) 652 4931, *Fax* (0151) 653 8127, ⌨ – 🔟 ☎ ᕤ – ᴀ̂ 200. ⓪Ⓞ ᴀᴇ ⓪ 𝘝𝘐𝘚𝘈
**Meals** (bar lunch Saturday) 17.50 **t.** and a la carte ᐧ 5.95 – ⊇ 8.50 – **32 rm** 80.00/102.00 **t.** – SB.

⑩ ATS 40 Mill Lane, Wallasey, Wirral *ℰ* (0151) 638 1949/8606

# BIRMINGHAM

W. Mids. **403** **404** O 26 *Great Britain G. – pop. 965 928.*

*London 122 – Bristol 91 – Liverpool 103 – Manchester 86 – Nottingham 50.*

## TOURIST INFORMATION

🚹 *Convention & Visitor Bureau, 2 City Arcade, B2 4TX* ℘ *(0121) 643 2514, Fax (0121) 616 1038*
🚹 *Convention & Visitor Bureau, National Exhibition Centre, B40 1NT* ℘ *(0121) 780 4321*
🚹 *Birmingham Airport, Information Desk, B26 3QJ* ℘ *(0121) 767 7145/7146.*

## PRACTICAL INFORMATION

🏌 *Edgbaston, Church Road* ℘ *(0121) 454 1736, FX.*
🏌 *Hilltop, Park Lane, Handsworth* ℘ *(0121) 554 4463, CU.*
🏌 *Hatchford Brook, Coventry Road, Sheldon* ℘ *(0121) 743 9821.*
🏌 *Brand Hall, Heron Road, Oldbury, Warley* ℘ *(0121) 552 2195, BU.*
🏌 *Harborne Church Farm, Vicarage Road, Harborne* ℘ *(0121) 427 1204, EX.*
✈ *Birmingham International Airport :* ℘ *(0121) 767 5511, E : 6½ m. by A 45 DU.*

## SIGHTS

**See :** *City★ – Museum and Art Gallery★★* JZ **M2** *– Barber Institute of Fine Arts★★*
*(at Birmingham University)* EX *– Cathedral of St. Philip (stained glass portrayals★ )* KYZ.
**Env. :** *Aston Hall★★* FV **M.**
**Exc. :** *Black Country Museum★, Dudley, NW : 10 m. by A 456 and A 4123* AU.

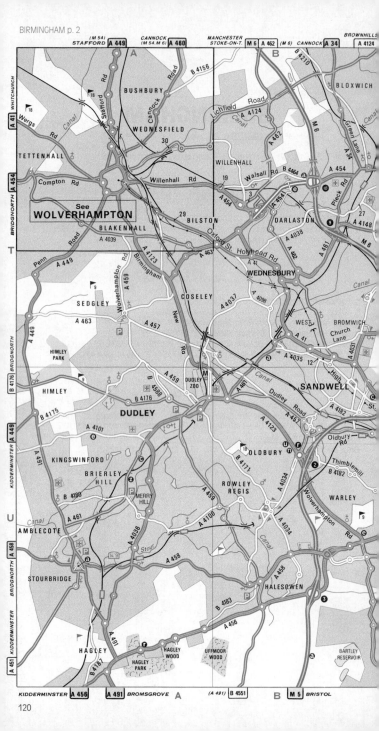

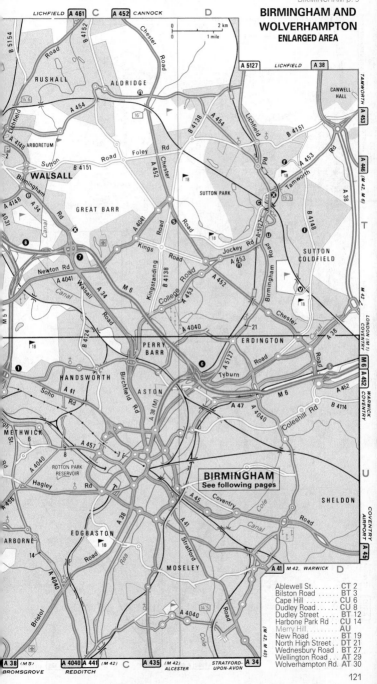

121

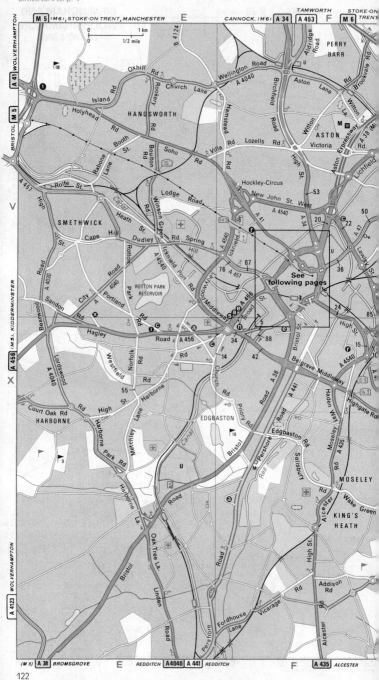

## BUILT UP AREA

Bath Row . . . . . . . . . . **FX** 5
Bordesley
Middleway . . . . . . . **FX** 10
Calthorpe Rd . . . . . . **FX** 14
Camp Hill . . . . . . . . . **FX** 15
Darmouth
Middleway . . . . . . . **FV** 22
Digbeth . . . . . . . . . . . **FV** 24
Dudley Park Rd . . . . **GX** 25
High St . . . . . . . . . . . **GV** 31
Islington Row
Middleway . . . . . . . **FX** 34
Jennen's Rd . . . . . . . **FV** 36
Lee Bank Middleway **FX** 42

Nechell's
Parkway . . . . . . . . . **FV** 50
New Town
Row . . . . . . . . . . . **FV** 53
Nursery Rd . . . . . . . . **EX** 55
Saltley Rd . . . . . . . . . **GV** 66
Sand Pits
Parade . . . . . . . . . . **FV** 67
Solihull Lane . . . . . . **GX** 74
Summer Hill Rd . . . . **FV** 76
Watery Lane . . . . . . . **FV** 85
Westley Rd . . . . . . . . **GX** 87
Wheeley's Lane . . . . **FX** 88

For Street Index
see Birmingham p. 7

123

## CENTRE

---

**«Short Breaks»**

Many hotels now offer a special rate for a stay of 2 nights
which includes dinner, bed and breakfast.

## STREET INDEX TO BIRMINGHAM TOWN PLANS

---

« **Short Breaks** » (SB)
De nombreux hôtels proposent des conditions avantageuses
pour un séjour de deux nuits comprenant la chambre, le dîner et le petit déjeuner.

**Town plans** : Birmingham pp. 2-7
Except where otherwise stated see pp. 6 and 7

🏨🏨🏨 **Hyatt Regency,** 2 Bridge St., B1 2JZ, ℰ (0121) 643 1234, *Fax (0121) 616 2323*, ≤, ᵢᵟ, ⇆
☒ – ⧉, ⥰ rm, ☰ ⊡ ☎ ᵭ ⇦ – ᵴ 250. ◍❾ ⚎ ⓪ 𝘝𝘐𝘚𝘈. ⅍ JZ
Meals – **Number 282 :** Meals *(closed Sunday and Bank Holidays)* 16.00 t
(lunch) and a la carte 23.25/28.25 t. ⅃ 7.50 – ☐ 12.00 – **308 rm** 155.00/180.00 st., 11 suites

🏨🏨🏨 **Swallow,** 12 Hagley Rd, B16 8SJ, ℰ (0121) 452 1144, *Fax (0121) 456 3442*, ᵢᵟ, ☒ – ⧉
⥰ rm, ☰ ⊡ ☎ ᵭ ⴵ – ᵴ 25. ◍❾ ⚎ ⓪ 𝘝𝘐𝘚𝘈 p. 4 FX
**Langtrys :** Meals a la carte 20.90/32.45 t. ⅃ 9.00 – (see also **Sir Edward Elgar's** below) –
**94 rm** ☐ 160.00/200.00 st., 4 suites – SB.

🏨🏨 **Crowne Plaza Birmingham,** Central Sq., Holliday St., B1 1HH, ℰ (0121) 631 2000
*Fax (0121) 643 9018*, ᵢᵟ, ⇆, ☒ – ⧉, ⥰ rm, ☰ ⊡ ☎ ᵭ ᵭ ⴵ – ᵴ 150. ◍❾ ⚎ ⓪ 𝘝𝘐𝘚𝘈
ᴊᴄʙ JZ
Meals *(closed Saturday lunch)* (carving rest.) 14.95/18.95 st. and dinner a la carte – ☐ 12.50
– **281 rm** 125.00/135.00 st., 3 suites – SB.

🏨🏨 **Copthorne,** Paradise Circus, B3 3HJ, ℰ (0121) 200 2727, *Fax (0121) 200 1197*, ᵢᵟ, ⇆, ☒
– ⧉, ⥰ rm, ☰ rest, ⊡ ☎ ᵭ ⴵ – ᵴ 180. ◍❾ ⚎ ⓪ 𝘝𝘐𝘚𝘈. ⅍ JZ
**Goldsmiths :** Meals (dinner only except Sunday) a la carte approx. 26.95 st. ⅃ 7.50 – **Gol-**
**dies :** Meals a la carte 17.50/25.95 st. ⅃ 7.50 – ☐ 12.75 – **209 rm** 130.00/170.00 st.
3 suites – SB.

🏨🏨 **The Burlington,** Burlington Arcade, 126 New St., B2 4JQ, ℰ (0121) 643 9191
*Fax (0121) 643 5075*, ᵢᵟ, ⇆ – ⧉, ⥰ rm, ☰ rest, ⊡ ☎ ᵲ – ᵴ 400. ◍❾ ⚎ ⓪ 𝘝𝘐𝘚𝘈. ⅍
*closed 25 December* – **Berlioz :** Meals *(closed lunch Saturday and Sunday)* 13.95/21.95 t
and a la carte – ☐ 12.50 – **107 rm** 110.00/120.00 st., 5 suites. KY

🏨🏨 **Jonathan's,** 16-24 Wolverhampton Rd, Oldbury, B68 0LH, West : 4 m. by A 456
ℰ (0121) 429 3757, *Fax (0121) 434 3107*, « Authentic Victorian furnishings and memor-
abilia » – ⥰, ☰ rest, ⊡ ☎ ☎ – ᵴ 100. ◍❾ ⚎ ⓪ 𝘝𝘐𝘚𝘈 p. 2 BU
**Boulton Watt Bistro :** Meals 8.95 t. and a la carte – **Victorian Restaurant :** Meals
English - *(closed Saturday lunch and Sunday dinner)* (booking essential) 15.90 t
(lunch) and a la carte 22.30/47.30 t. ⅃ 6.80 – **44 rm** ☐ 88.00/150.00 st. – SB.

🏨🏨 **Birmingham Grand Moathouse,** Colmore Row, B3 2DA, ℰ (0121) 607 9988
*Fax (0121) 233 1465* – ⧉, ⥰ rm, ☰ rest, ⊡ ☎ – ᵴ 500. ◍❾ ⚎ ⓪ 𝘝𝘐𝘚𝘈 JKY
**Chamberlains :** Meals *(closed Saturday lunch and Sunday)* 16.50 st. and a la carte ⅃ 5.75 –
**Hugo's :** Meals a la carte 9.20/20.10 st. ⅃ 5.75 – ☐ 10.50 – **170 rm** 115.00/135.00 st
3 suites – SB.

🏨🏨 **Forte Posthouse Birmingham City,** Smallbrook, Queensway, B5 4EW
ℰ (0121) 643 8171, *Fax (0121) 631 2528*, ᵢᵟ, ⇆, ☒, squash – ⧉, ⥰ rm, ☰ ⊡ ☎ ☎ –
ᵴ 630. ◍❾ ⚎ ⓪ 𝘝𝘐𝘚𝘈 ᴊᴄʙ KZ
Meals (carving rest.) 12.95/17.75 t. ⅃ 5.75 – ☐ 9.95 – **250 rm** 95.00 st., 1 suite – SB.

🏨🏨 **Plough and Harrow,** 135 Hagley Rd, Edgbaston, B16 8LS, ℰ (0121) 454 4111
*Fax 1454 1868*, ⛲ – ⧉ ⥰ rm, ⊡ ☎ ☎ – ᵴ 70. ◍❾ ⚎ ⓪ 𝘝𝘐𝘚𝘈 ᴊᴄʙ p.4 EX
Meals *(closed Saturday lunch and dinner Bank Holiday Monday)* 15.95 st
(lunch) and a la carte 20.20/31.15 st. ⅃ 6.95 – ☐ 10.75 – **42 rm** 95.00/115.00 st., 2 suites –
SB.

🏨 **Thistle Strathallan,** 225 Hagley Rd, Edgbaston, B16 9RY, ℰ (0121) 455 9777
*Fax (0121) 454 9432* – ⧉, ⥰ rm, ☰ rest, ⊡ ☎ ☎ – ᵴ 170. ◍❾ ⚎ ⓪ 𝘝𝘐𝘚𝘈 p. 4 EX
Meals (bar lunch Saturday) a la carte 15.25/25.05 st. ⅃ 7.25 – ☐ 11.00 – **148 rm** 108.00
131.00 st., 3 suites – SB.

🏨 **Novotel,** 70 Broad St., B1 2HT, ℰ (0121) 643 2000, *Fax (0121) 643 9796*, ᵢᵟ, ⇆ – ⧉
⥰ rm, ☰ rest, ⊡ ☎ ᵲ ⇦ – ᵴ 300. ◍❾ ⚎ ⓪ 𝘝𝘐𝘚𝘈 p. 4 FV
Meals 15.00 t. (dinner) and a la carte 15.40/23.35 t. – ☐ 9.95 – **148 rm** 95.00 st.

🏨 **Chamberlain,** Alcester St., B12 0PJ, ℰ (0121) 606 9000, *Fax (0121) 606 9001* – ⧉ ⥰
☰ rest, ⊡ ☎ ⇦ – ᵴ 400. ◍❾ ⚎ ⓪ 𝘝𝘐𝘚𝘈. ⅍ p. 4 FX
Meals *(closed Saturday lunch)* (carving rest.) 6.00/10.00 st. – **250 rm** ☐ 35.00/80.00 st.

🏨 **Asquith House,** 19 Portland Rd, off Hagley Rd, Edgbaston, B16 9HN, ℰ (0121) 454 5282
*Fax (0121) 456 4668*, « Victorian house », ⛲ – ⊡ ☎. ◍❾ ⚎ 𝘝𝘐𝘚𝘈. ⅍ p. 4 EX
*closed 25-26 December and 1 January* – Meals (by arrangement Saturday and Sunday)
16.95/27.95 t. and a la carte ⅃ 4.50 – **10 rm** ☐ 65.00/87.00 t.

🏨 **Westbourne Lodge,** 27-29 Fountain Rd, Edgbaston, B17 8NJ, ℰ (0121) 429 1003
*Fax (0121) 429 7436*, ⛲, ⛲ – ⥰ rm, ⊡ ☎ ☎. ◍❾ ⚎ 𝘝𝘐𝘚𝘈 ᴊᴄʙ p.4 EV
Meals (booking essential to non-residents) 14.95 t. – **21 rm** ☐ 49.50/69.50 t. – SB.

🏠 **Copperfield House**, 60 Upland Rd, Selly Park, B29 7JS, ℰ (0121) 472 8344, *Fax (0121) 415 5655*, 🌲 – 🍴 rest, 📺 ☎ 🅿. 🐝 🆑 *VISA*. ⚘ p. 4 FX a
**Meals** *(closed Sunday dinner)* (bar lunch)/dinner 17.00 t. ⓖ 6.00 – **17 rm** � 57.50/67.50 st. – SB.

🏠 **Lodge Inn**, 80 Broad St., BI5 1LY, ℰ (0121) 633 0144, *Fax (0121) 633 9203* – |𝄐|, 🍴 rm, ▤ rest, 📺 ⚙ 🅿. 🐝 🆑 ⓞ *VISA*. ⚘ FVX s
**Meals** (grill rest.) 7.00 **st.** (lunch) and a la carte 14.55/20.75 st. – ⊇ 5.50 – **60 rm** 39.00 t.

🏠 **Travel Inn**, Richard St., Waterlinks, B7 4AA, ℰ (0121) 333 6484, *Fax (0121) 333 6490* – |𝄐|, 🍴 rm, ▤ rest, 📺 ⚙ 🅿. 🐝 🆑 ⓞ *VISA*. ⚘ p. 4 FV c
**Meals** (grill rest.) (dinner only) – **60 rm** 38.00 t.

🏠 **Travelodge**, 1741 Coventry Rd, Yardley, B26 1DS, Southeast : 5 m. by A 41 on A 45 ℰ (0121) 764 5882, *Fax (0121) 764 5882*, Reservations (Freephone) 0800 850950 – 🍴 rm, 📺 ⚙ 🅿. 🐝 🆑 ⓞ *VISA*. ⚘ HX e
**Meals** (grill rest.) – **40 rm** 39.95/59.95 t.

🏠 **Travelodge**, 230 Broad St., B15 1AY, ℰ (0121) 644 5266, *Fax (0121) 644 5251*, Reservations (Freephone) 0800 850950 – |𝄐| 🍴 📺 ⚙ &. 🐝 🆑 ⓞ *VISA* JCB. ⚘ p. 4 FV n
**Meals** (grill rest.) – **136 rm** 39.95/59.95 t.

🏠 **Travel Inn**, 20-22 Bridge St., B1 2JH, ℰ (0121) 633 4820, *Fax (0121) 633 4779* – |𝄐|, 🍴 rm, 📺 ⚙ 🅿 – ⚿ 40. 🐝 🆑. ⚘ JZ c
**Meals** (grill rest.) – **53 rm** 38.00 t.

🏠 **Campanile**, 55 Irving St., B1 1DH, ℰ (0121) 622 4925, *Fax (0121) 622 4195* – 🍴 rm, 📺 ☎ & 🅿 – ⚿ 35. 🐝 🆑 ⓞ *VISA* p. 4 FX e
**Meals** (grill rest.) 10.85 **st.** and a la carte – ⊇ 4.50 – **46 rm** 36.50 st.

XXXX **Sir Edward Elgar's** (at Swallow H.), 12 Hagley Rd, B16 8SJ, ℰ (0121) 452 1144, *Fax (0121) 456 3442* – ▤ 🅿. 🐝 🆑 ⓞ *VISA* p. 4 FX c
**Meals** 21.50/27.00 t. and a la carte ⓖ 9.00.

XX **Gilmore**, 27 Warstone Lane, Hockley, ℰ (0121) 233 3655, « Former rolling mill » – 🐝 🆑 ⓞ *VISA* JCB FV r
*closed Saturday lunch, Sunday, Monday, 1 week Easter, 2 weeks August and 1 week January* – **Meals** 14.50/19.50 t. ⓖ 5.00.

XX **Henry's**, 27 St. Paul's Sq., B3 1RB, ℰ (0121) 200 1136, *Fax (0121) 200 1190* – ▤. 🐝 🆑 ⓞ *VISA* JY a
*closed Sunday, 25-26 December and Bank Holidays* – **Meals** - Chinese (Canton) - 15.00 t. and a la carte ⓖ 5.00.

XX **Leftbank**, 79 Broad St., B15 1AH, ℰ (0121) 643 4464, *Fax (0121) 643 5793* – 🐝 🆑 ⓞ *VISA*
*closed Saturday lunch, Sunday, 25 December-2 January and Bank Holidays* – **Meals** 14.50 t. (lunch) and a la carte 24.40/34.50 t. ⓖ 8.90. p. 4 FV a

XX **Shimla Pinks**, 214 Broad St., B15 1AY, ℰ (0121) 685 0366, *Fax (0121) 643 6383* – ▤. 🐝 🆑 ⓞ *VISA* p. 4 FX n
*closed lunch Saturday and Sunday, 25 and 26 December and 1 January* – **Meals** - Indian - 6.95/12.95 t. and a la carte.

X **Oceanic**, 89 Livery St., B3 1RJ, ℰ (0121) 236 7500, *Fax (0121) 236 7550* – 🐝 🆑 ⓞ *VISA* JCB JY e
*closed Saturday lunch, Monday dinner, Sunday and 25 December* – **Meals** a la carte 19.85/34.85 t.

**at Hall Green** Southeast : 5 ¾ m. by A 41 on A 34 – ✉ Birmingham.

XX **Mizan**, 1347 Stratford Rd, B28 9HW, ℰ (0121) 777 3185 – ▤. 🐝 🆑 *VISA* GX a
*closed lunch Friday to Tuesday* – **Meals** - Indian - 4.75/13.50 t. and a la carte.

**at Birmingham Airport** Southeast : 9 m. by A 45 – DU – ✉ Birmingham.

🏠🏠 **Novotel**, Passenger Terminal, B26 3QL, ℰ (0121) 782 7000, *Fax (0121) 782 0445* – |𝄐|, 🍴 rm, 📺 ☎ ⚙ & – ⚿ 35. 🐝 🆑 ⓞ *VISA*
*closed 24 and 25 December* – **Meals** *(closed lunch Saturday and Sunday)* 12.00/18.75 st. and a la carte – ⊇ 9.95 – **195 rm** 92.50 st.

🏠🏠 **Forte Posthouse Birmingham Airport**, Coventry Rd, B26 3QW, on A 45 ℰ (0121) 782 8141, *Fax (0121) 782 2476* – 🍴 rm, 📺 ☎ ⚙ 🅿 – ⚿ 130. 🐝 🆑 ⓞ *VISA*
**Meals** *(closed Sunday)* a la carte 14.35/23.35 st. ⓖ 7.50 – ⊇ 9.95 – **141 rm** 115.00/135.00 st. – SB.

**at National Exhibition Centre** Southeast : 9½ m. on A 45 – DU – ✉ Birmingham.

🏠🏠🏠 **Stakis Birmingham Metropole**, Bickenhill, B40 1PP, ℰ (0121) 780 4242, *Fax (0121) 780 3923*, ⅙6, 🏊, ▨ – |𝄐|, 🍴 rm, ▤ 📺 ⚙ & 🅿 – ⚿ 2000. 🐝 🆑 ⓞ *VISA*
*closed 24 to 30 December* – **Meals** (carving rest.) 27.25 **st.** – **Primavera :** **Meals** - Italian - *(closed Sunday and Bank Holidays)* a la carte 30.00/42.00 st. – **779 rm** ⊇ 187.00/235.00 t., 15 suites – SB.

**at Acocks Green** Southwest : 5 m. by A 41 – ⊠ Birmingham.

🏨 **Westley,** Westley Rd, B27 7UJ, ℰ (0121) 706 4312, Fax (0121) 706 2824 – 📺 ☎ 🅿 -
🔩 80. 🐠 🖭 ⓞ 🚾. ⁂                                                                 GX
closed 25 December – **Meals** (bar lunch Monday to Saturday)/dinner 13.95 t. and a la carte
⪙ 6.50 – ⊇ 7.95 – **36 rm** 68.95/94.00 st.

**at Northfield** Southwest : 6 m. by A 38 – CU – ⊠ Birmingham.

🏨 **Norwood,** 87-89 Bunbury Rd, B31 2ET, via Church Rd ℰ (0121) 411 2202
Fax (0121) 411 2202, 🚗 – 📺 ☎ 🅿. 🐠 🖭 ⓞ 🚾 🆑🅱. ⁂
**Meals** (barmeals only Friday to Sunday) (dinner only) 17.50 s. – **18 rm** ⊇ 62.50/72.50 st. -
SB.

**at Kings Norton** Southwest : 7 m. on A 441 – EX – ⊠ Birmingham.

🏨 **Mill House,** 180 Lifford Lane, B30 3NT, ℰ (0121) 459 5800, Fax (0121) 459 8553, 🚗 – ⁂✲
📺 ☎ 🅿. 🐠 🖭 ⓞ 🚾. ⁂
closed 1 to 16 January – **Meals** – (see **Lombard Room** below) – **8 rm** ⊇ 98.00/120.00 st.
1 suite – SB.

𝕏𝕏𝕏 **Lombard Room,** 180 Lifford Lane, B30 3NT, ℰ (0121) 459 5800, Fax (0121) 459 8553
🏠, 🚗 – ⁂✲ 🍽 🐠 🖭 ⓞ 🚾
closed lunch Monday and Saturday, Sunday dinner and 1-16 January – **Meals** 17.85/26.50 st
⪙ 7.00.

**at Oldbury** West : 7 ¾ m. by A 456 on A 4123 – ⊠ Birmingham.

🏨 **Holiday Inn Express** without rest., Birchley Park, B69 2BD, ℰ (0121) 511 0000
Fax (0121) 511 0051 – 🛗, ⁂✲ rm, 🍽 rest, 📺 ☎ 📞 🔥 🅿 – 🔩 30. 🐠 🖭 ⓞ 🚾 🆑🅱
**109 rm** 52.50 st.                                                                BU

🏨 **Travel Inn,** Wolverhampton Rd, B69 2BH, on A 4123 ℰ (0121) 552 3031
Fax (0121) 552 1012 – ⁂✲ rm, 🍽 rest, 📺 🔥 🅿. 🐠 🖭 ⓞ 🚾. ⁂                      BU
**Meals** (grill rest.) – **40 rm** 38.00 t.

🏨 **Travelodge,** Wolverhampton Rd, B69 2BH, on A 4123 ℰ (0121) 552 2967, Reservation
(Freephone) 0800 850950 – ⁂✲ rm, 📺 🔥 🅿. 🐠 🖭 ⓞ 🚾 🆑🅱. ⁂                       BU
**Meals** (grill rest.) – **33 rm** 39.95/59.95 t.

**at Great Barr** Northwest : 6 m. on A 34 – ⊠ Birmingham.

🏨 **Forte Posthouse Birmingham,** Chapel Lane, B43 7BG, ℰ (0121) 357 7444
Fax (0121) 357 7503, 🏋, �, 🔲 – ⁂✲ rm, 📺 ☎ 🅿 – 🔩 120. 🐠 🖭 ⓞ 🚾            CT
**Meals** a la carte 12.05/26.90 st. ⪙ 7.50 – ⊇ 9.95 – **192 rm** 85.00 st.

**at West Bromwich** Northwest : 6 m. on A 41 – ⊠ Birmingham.

🏨 **Moat House Birmingham,** Birmingham Rd, B70 6RS, ℰ (0121) 609 9988
Fax (0121) 525 7403, 🏋, 🛗, ⁂✲ rm, 🍽 rest, 📺 ☎ 🅿 – 🔩 180. 🐠 🖭 ⓞ 🚾          BU
**Meals** a la carte 16.15/26.60 st. ⪙ 5.75 – ⊇ 8.95 – **168 rm** 105.00/120.00 st. – SB.

◉ ATS 1558 Pershore Rd., Stirchley                     ATS 43 Whitmore Rd, Small Heath
ℰ (0121) 458 2951                                       ℰ (0121) 772 2571
ATS 158 Slade Rd, Erdington ℰ (0121) 327 2783          ATS Dudley Rd, Halesowen ℰ (0121) 550 2464
ATS 94 Aldridge Rd, Perry Barr ℰ (0121) 356 5925       ATS 947 Bristol Rd South, Northfield
ATS 314 Bearwood Rd, Bearwood                           ℰ (0121) 475 1244
ℰ (0121) 420 2000                                       ATS 87 Old Meeting St., West Bromwich
ATS 427 Bordesley Green, Bordesley Green                ℰ (0121) 553 3495
ℰ (0121) 772 6514

---

**BIRMINGHAM AIRPORT** W. Mids. 🗺️🗺️ O 26 – see Birmingham.

---

**BIRTLE** Gtr. Manchester 🗺️ ③ – see Bury.

---

**BISHOP AUCKLAND** Durham 🗺️🗺️ P 20 – pop. 23 154.

🏌 High Plains, Durham Rd ℰ (01388) 602198 – 🏌 Oakleaf, School Aycliffe Lane, Newton
Aycliffe ℰ (01325) 310820 – 🏌 Woodham G. & C.C., Burnhill Way, Newton Aycliffe ℰ (01325)
320574.
London 253 – Carlisle 73 – Middlesbrough 24 – Newcastle upon Tyne 28 – Sunderland 25.

🏨 **Park Head,** Park View Terr., New Coundon, DL14 8QB, Northeast : 1 ¾ m. by A 689 or
A 688 ℰ (01388) 661727, Fax (01388) 661727 – ⁂✲ rm, 📺 ☎ 🅿. 🐠 🖭 🚾. ⁂
**Meals** (bar lunch Monday to Saturday)/dinner a la carte 8.95/22.95 st. ⪙ 4.75 – **31 rm**
⊇ 48.00/68.00 st. – SB.

◉ ATS Cockton Hill ℰ (01388) 603681

**BISHOP'S HULL** *Somerset – see Taunton.*

---

**BISHOP'S STORTFORD** *Herts.* 404 U 28 – *pop. 28 403.*

✈ *Stansted Airport :* ℰ *(01279) 680500, NE : 3½ m.*

🛈 *The Old Monastery, Windhill, CM23 2ND* ℰ *(01279) 655831.*

*London 34 – Cambridge 27 – Chelmsford 19 – Colchester 33.*

🏠 **The Cottage** ♨ without rest., 71 Birchanger Lane, CM23 5QA, Northeast : 2 ¼ m. by B 1383 on Birchanger rd ℰ (01279) 812349, Fax (01279) 815045, « Part 17C and 18C cottages », ☞ – ✆ 📺 🅿 ♨ VISA JCB ✖
closed 2 weeks Christmas and New Year – **15 rm** ⊑ 35.00/55.00 t.

✕ **The Lemon Tree,** 14-16 Water Lane, CM23 2LB, ℰ (01279) 757788, Fax (01279) 757766 – ♨ VISA JCB
closed Sunday dinner, Monday, 25-26 December and 1 to 8 January – **Meals** a la carte 20.50/28.00 t. ⌗ 5.50.

**at Hatfield Heath** *(Essex) Southeast : 6 m. on a 1060 –* ✉ *Bishop's Stortford.*

🏨 **Down Hall Country House** ♨, CM22 7AS, South : 1 ½ m. by Matching Lane ℰ (01279) 731441, Fax (01279) 730416, ≼, « 19C Italianate mansion », ℔, ☎, 🔲, ☞, park, ✖ – ⫴ 📺 ☎ 🅿 – 🔏 250. ♨ AE ⓪ VISA
**Meals** (carving lunch) 18.50/25.00 st. and a la carte – **Downham :** **Meals** (closed lunch Monday to Friday) a la carte 28.50/37.00 st. ⌗ 7.00 – ⊑ 10.25 – **103 rm** 115.00/163.00 st. – SB.

🔧 ATS Unit 7, Twyford Business Park, London Rd ℰ (01279) 507915

---

**BISHOP'S TAWTON** *Devon* 403 H 30 – *see Barnstaple.*

---

**BLABY** *Leics.* 402 403 404 Q 26 – *pop. 6 538.*

*London 100 – Coventry 10 – Leicester 4 – Northampton 38.*

🏨 **Time Out,** 15 Enderby Rd, LE8 4GD, ℰ (01162) 787898, Fax (01162) 781974, ℔, ☎, 🔲 – ▤ rest, 📺 ☎ ✆ & 🅿 – 🔏 40. ♨ AE ⓪ VISA JCB
**Meals** 17.95 st. (dinner) and a la carte 20.00/24.00 st. ⌗ 6.75 – ⊑ 9.95 – **25 rm** 79.00/90.00 st. – SB.

---

**BLACKBURN** 402 M 22 – *pop. 105 994.*

🏌 *Pleasington* ℰ *(01254) 202177 –* 🏌 *Wilpshire, 72 Whalley Rd* ℰ *(01254) 248260 –* 🏌 *Great Harwood, Harwood Bar* ℰ *(01254) 884391.*

🛈 *King George's Hall, Northgate, BB2 1AA* ℰ *(01254) 53277.*

*London 228 – Leeds 47 – Liverpool 39 – Manchester 24 – Preston 11.*

**at Langho** *North : 4½ m. on A 666 –* ✉ *Whalley.*

🏨 **Mytton Fold Farm H. and Golf Club,** Whalley Rd, BB6 8AB, Northeast : 1 m. by A 66 on Whalley rd ℰ (01254) 240662, Fax (01254) 248119, 🏌, ☞ – ✆ rest, 📺 ☎ 🅿 – 🔏 250. ♨ AE VISA ✖
closed 24 December-2 January – **Meals** (bar lunch Monday to Saturday)/dinner 16.00 st. ⌗ 5.45 – **27 rm** ⊑ 49.00/88.00 st. – SB.

🏠 **Petre Lodge,** Northcote Rd, BB6 8BG, Northeast : ½ m. ℰ (01254) 245506, Fax (01254) 245506 – ✆ 📺 ☎ 🅿 ♨ AE VISA JCB ✖
**Meals** (residents only) (dinner only) a la carte 9.95/15.90 st. – **9 rm** ⊑ 49.00/59.00 st.

✕✕✕ **Northcote Manor** (Haworth) with rm, Northcote Rd, BB6 8BE, North : ½ m. on A 59 at
⇱  junction with A 666 ℰ (01254) 240555, Fax (01254) 246568, ☞ – ✆ rest, 📺 ☎ ✆ 🅿. ♨
AE ⓪ VISA ✖
closed 25 December and 1 January – **Meals** 16.00 t. (lunch) and a la carte 29.35/52.45 t. ⌗ 11.50 – **14 rm** ⊑ 90.00/130.00 t. – SB
**Spec.** Smoked salmon with a tian of mussels and tomatoes. Shoulder of pork with black pudding mash and wilted greens. Apple crumble soufflé with Lancashire cheese ice cream.

**at Clayton-le-Dale** *North : 4 ¾ m. by A 666 on B 6245 –* ✉ *Blackburn.*

✕✕ **Shajan,** Longsight Rd, BB1 9EX, Southwest : ½ m. on A 59 ℰ (01254) 813234 – ▤ 🅿. ♨ ⓪ VISA
**Meals** - Indian - (buffet lunch Sunday) a la carte 9.60/18.15 t. ⌗ 4.50.

**at Mellor** *Northwest : 4 m. by A 677 –* ✉ *Blackburn.*

🏨 **Millstone,** Church Lane, BB2 7JR, ℰ (01254) 813333, Fax (01254) 812628 – ✆ 📺 ☎ 🅿 – 🔏 25. ♨ AE ⓪ VISA
*Millers :* **Meals** (bar lunch Saturday) 20.00 t. (dinner) and a la carte 20.00/30.00 t. ⌗ 9.00 – **22 rm** ⊑ 84.00/114.00 st., 2 suites.

**at Balderstone** Northwest : 6½ m. by A 677 off A 59 – ⊠ Blackburn.

🏠 **Boddington Arms - Premier Lodge,** Myerscough Rd, BB2 7LE, on A 59
ℰ (01254) 813900, Fax (01254) 814079, Reservations (Freephone) 0800 118833 – ⊁ rm
🗏 rest, 📺 ☎ & 🅟. 🐵 ⅍ ⑩ 𝒱𝐼𝒮𝒜. ⋘
**Meals** (grill rest.) (in bar) a la carte 7.65/15.05 **st.** ⅄ 4.25 – ⇌ 5.95 – **20 rm** 44.95 **st.** – SB.

🕔 ATS Pendle St., Copy Nook ℰ (01254) 55963/59272/665115

---

**BLACKPOOL** 🄰🄾🄸 K 22 Great Britain G. – pop. 146 262.

**See :** Tower★ AC AY A.

🏌 Blackpool Park, North Park Drive, no telephone booking BY – 🏌 Poulton-le-Fylde, Myrtle Farm, Breck Rd ℰ (01253) 892444.

✈ Blackpool Airport : ℰ (01253) 343434, S : 3 m. by A 584.

🛈 1 Clifton St., FY1 1LY ℰ (01253) 21623 – Pleasure Beach, 11 Ocean Boulevard, South Promenade, FY4 1PL ℰ (01253) 403223 (summer only).

London 246 – Leeds 88 – Liverpool 56 – Manchester 51 – Middlesbrough 123.

Plan opposite

🏨 **Stakis Blackpool,** North Promenade, FY1 2JQ, ℰ (01253) 623434, Fax (01253) 627864
≤, 🔲 – 🛊, ⊁ rm, 🗏 rest, 🐵 ⅍ ⑩ 𝒱𝐼𝒮𝒜 𝒥𝒞𝐵.                                      AY ×
**The Promenade :** **Meals** (carving rest.) (bar lunch)/dinner 19.25 **t.** – ⇌ 9.50 – **268 rm** 130.00/150.00 **st.,** 6 suites – SB.

🏨 **Imperial,** North Promenade, FY1 2HB, ℰ (01253) 623971, Fax (01253) 751784, ≤, 𝐅𝟨, ⇋𝐬, 🔲 – 🛊, ⊁ rm, 📺 ☎ 🅟 – 🛆 400. 🐵 ⅍ ⑩ 𝒱𝐼𝒮𝒜 𝒥𝒞𝐵.                      AY c
**Palm Court :** **Meals** 8.45/22.50 **st.** and a la carte ⅄ 8.75 – ⇌ 10.95 – **173 rm** 134.00/ 149.00 **st.,** 10 suites – SB.

🏨 **De Vere,** East Park Drive, FY3 8LL, ℰ (01253) 838866, Fax (01253) 798800, 𝐅𝟨, ⇋𝐬, 🔲, 🗏 ⋘, squash – 🛊, ⊁ rm, 🗏 rest, 📺 ☎ ⅍ & 🅟 – 🛆 500. 🐵 ⅍ ⑩ 𝒱𝐼𝒮𝒜. ⋘          BZ a
**Meals** 13.50/17.95 **t.** and a la carte – **162 rm** ⇌ 140.00/150.00 **st.,** 2 suites – SB.

🏨 **Savoy,** Queens Promenade, FY2 9SJ, ℰ (01253) 352561, Fax (01253) 500735 – 🛊 📺 ☎ 🅟 – 🛆 300. 🐵 ⅍ ⑩ 𝒱𝐼𝒮𝒜. ⋘                                              AY z
**Meals** (bar lunch Monday to Saturday)/dinner 14.50 **t.** and a la carte ⅄ 6.50 – **128 rm** ⇌ 80.00/120.00 **t.,** 3 suites – SB.

🏨 **Libertys on the Square** without rest., Cocker Sq., North Promenade, FY1 1RX ℰ (01253) 291155, Fax (01253) 752271, ≤ – 🛊 📺 ☎ 🅟. 🐵 ⅍ 𝒱𝐼𝒮𝒜. ⋘              AY r
**Meals** (dinner only) 10.95 **st.** ⅄ 4.95 – **38 rm** ⇌ 49.00/75.00 **st.** – SB.

🏠 **Berwyn,** 1-2 Finchley Rd, Gynn Sq., FY1 2LP, ℰ (01253) 352896, Fax (01253) 594391 – 📺 ☎. 🐵 𝒱𝐼𝒮𝒜 𝒥𝒞𝐵. ⋘                                                  AY e
**Meals** (residents only) (dinner only) 9.00 **t.** and a la carte ⅄ 5.00 – **20 rm** ⇌ 34.00/80.00 **t.** – SB.

🏠 **Travel Inn,** Devonshire Rd, Bispham, FY2 0AR, ℰ (01253) 354942, Fax (01253) 590498 – ⊁ rm, 🗏 rest, 📺 ⅍ 🅟 – 🛆 40. 🐵 ⅍ ⑩ 𝒱𝐼𝒮𝒜                              BY •
**Meals** (grill rest.) – **40 rm** 38.00 **t.**

🏠 **Travel Inn,** Yeadon Way, South Shore, FY1 6BF, ℰ (01253) 341415, Fax (01253) 343805 – ⊁ rm, 🗏 rest, 📺 ⅍ 🅟 – 🛆 40. 🐵 ⅍ ⑩ 𝒱𝐼𝒮𝒜. ⋘                          AZ e
**Meals** (grill rest.) – **40 rm** 38.00 **t.**

⬝ **Sunray,** 42 Knowle Av., off Queens Promenade, FY2 9TQ, ℰ (01253) 351937, Fax (01253) 593307 – ⊁ rest, 📺 ☎ 🅟. 🐵 ⅍ 𝒱𝐼𝒮𝒜                                BY c
closed mid December-mid January – **Meals** (by arrangement) 13.00 **s.** – **9 rm** ⇌ 29.00/ 58.00 **s.** – SB.

⬝ **Burlees,** 40 Knowle Av., off Queen's Promenade, FY2 9TQ, ℰ (01253) 354535, Fax (01253) 354535 – ⊁ 📺 🅟. 🐵 𝒱𝐼𝒮𝒜. ⋘                                      BY e
March-mid November – **Meals** (by arrangement) 9.00 **st.** ⅄ 4.00 – **9 rm** ⇌ 25.50/51.00 **st.** – SB.

⬝ **Grosvenor View,** 7-9 King Edward Av., FY2 9TD, ℰ (01253) 352851, Fax (01253) 352109 – ⊁ 🅟. 🐵 ⅍ 𝒱𝐼𝒮𝒜. ⋘                                                AY v
restricted opening January and February – **Meals** (by arrangement) 6.50 **st.** – **17 rm** ⇌ 20.00/40.00 **st.**

⬝ **Bambi** without rest., 27 Bright St., South Shore, FY4 1BS, ℰ (01253) 343756, Fax (01253) 343756 – 📺. 🐵 ⅍ ⑩ 𝒱𝐼𝒮𝒜. ⋘                                    AZ e
March-November – **5 rm** ⇌ 18.00/36.00 **s.**

✗ **September Brasserie,** 15-17 Queen St., FY1 1PU, ℰ (01253) 623282, Fax (01253) 299455 – 🐵 ⅍ ⑩ 𝒱𝐼𝒮𝒜 𝒥𝒞𝐵.                                            AY
closed Sunday, Monday, 2 weeks summer and 1 week winter – **Meals** 13.40/18.00 **t.** and a la carte 18.50/24.75 **t.** ⅄ 7.50.

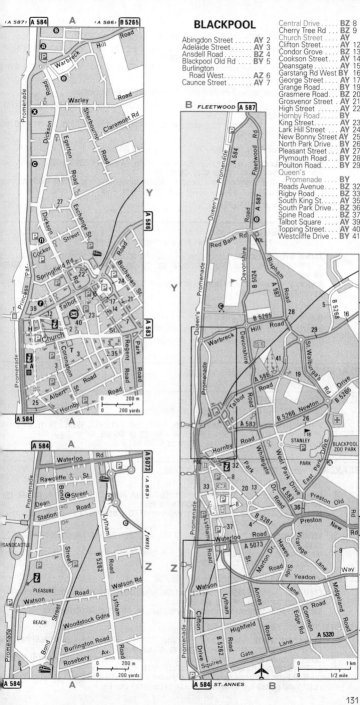

# BLACKPOOL

**at Little Thornton** *Northeast : 5 m. by A 586 – BY – off A 588 –* ⊠ *Blackpool.*

XX **River House** ॐ with rm, Skippool Creek, Wyre Rd, FY5 5LF, ℘ (01253) 883497, Fax (01253) 892083, ≤, ㈜ – ☒ ☎ ❤ ℗. ◍◎ *VISA*
Meals *(closed Sunday dinner)* (booking essential) 25.00 **t.** and a la carte ⌖ 7.50 – **4 rm** ☷ 65.00/80.00 **t.** – SB.

**at Little Singleton** *Northeast : 6 m. by A 586 – BY – on A 585 –* ⊠ *Blackpool.*

⌂ **Mains Hall,** 86 Mains Lane, FY6 7LE, ℘ (01253) 885130, Fax (01253) 894132, ㈜ – ⅏ rm, ☒ ☎ ℗. ◍◎ ፙ ⒪ *VISA*
Meals (light lunch Monday to Friday)/dinner a la carte approx. 18.00 **st.** ⌖ 5.00 – **10 rm** ☷ 55.00/100.00 **st.** – SB.

**at Singleton** *Northeast : 7 m. by A 586 – BY – on B 5260 –* ⊠ *Blackpool.*

⌂ **Singleton Lodge** ॐ, Lodge Lane, FY6 8LT, North : ¼ m. on B 5260 ℘ (01253) 883854, Fax (01253) 894432, ㈜ – ☒ ☎ ❤ ℗. ◍◎ ፙ *VISA*
closed 25 to 26 December and 1 January – **Meals** (dinner only and Sunday lunch)/dinner a la carte 13.75/21.50 **t.** ⌖ 5.00 – **12 rm** ☷ 55.00/80.00 **st.** – SB.

⓪ ATS Clifton Rd ℘ (01253) 695033

**BLACKROD** *Lancs.* 402 404 M 23 – *pop. 5 681.*
*London 220 – Burnley 25 – Liverpool 31 – Manchester 16 – Preston 18.*

🏛 **Jarvis International,** Manchester Rd, BL6 5RU, Southeast : 1 ½ m. by B 5408 on A 6 ℘ (01942) 814598, Fax (01942) 813427, ₤₅, ⌨, ◪ – ⚑, ⅏ rm, ☒ ☎ ℗ – ⚖ 250. ◍◎ ፙ ⒪ *VISA*. ⨯
*Regency :* Meals (bar lunch Monday to Saturday) 17.50 **st.** and a la carte ⌖ 11.50 – ☷ 8.95 – **91 rm** 89.00/119.00 **st.** – SB.

*When looking for a quiet hotel*
*use the maps found in the introduction*
*or look for establishments with the sign* ॐ *or* ॐ.

**BLACKWATER** *Cornwall* 403 E 33 – *see Truro.*

**BLAKENEY** *Glos.* 403 404 M 28.
*London 134 – Bristol 31 – Gloucester 16 – Newport 31.*

⌂ **Viney Hill Country Guesthouse,** Viney Hill, GL15 4LT, West : ¾ m. by A 48 ℘ (01594) 516000, Fax (01594) 516018, ㈜ – ⅏ ☒ ℗. ◍◎ *VISA*. ⨯
Meals (by arrangement) 17.00 **st.** – **6 rm** ☷ 32.00/48.00 **st.** – SB.

**BLAKENEY** *Norfolk* 404 X 25 – *pop. 1 628 –* ⊠ *Holt.*
*London 127 – King's Lynn 37 – Norwich 28.*

🏛 **Blakeney,** The Quay, NR25 7NE, ℘ (01263) 740797, Fax (01263) 740795, ≤, ₤₅, ⌨, ◪ ㈜ – ⚑, ⅏ rest, ☒ ☎ ℗ – ⚖ 200. ◍◎ ፙ ⒪ *VISA*
Meals (light lunch Monday to Saturday)/dinner 17.50 **t.** and a la carte ⌖ 4.95 – **59 rm** ☷ (dinner included) 87.00/218.00 **t.** – SB.

🍴 **White Horse** with rm, 4 High St., NR25 7AL, ℘ (01263) 740574, Fax (01263) 741303 – ☒ ☎ ℗. ◍◎ ፙ *VISA*. ⨯
Meals *(closed Sunday and Monday except Bank Holidays)* (bar lunch)/dinner a la carte 15.95/22.95 **t.** – **10 rm** ☷ 35.00/80.00 **t.**

**at Cley next the Sea** *East : 1½ m. on A 149 –* ⊠ *Holt.*

⌂ **Cley Mill** ॐ, NR25 7RP, ℘ (01263) 740209, Fax (01263) 740209, ≤, « 18C redbrick windmill on saltmarshes », ㈜ – ℗. ◍◎ *VISA*
Meals (by arrangement) (communal dining) 15.00 **st.** – **6 rm** ☷ 30.00/69.00 **st.**

**at Morston** *West : 1½ m. on A 149 –* ⊠ *Holt.*

⌂ **Morston Hall** (Blackiston) ॐ, The Street, NR25 7AA, ℘ (01263) 741041, Fax (01263) 740419, ㈜ – ⅏ rest, ☒ ☎ ℗. ◍◎ ፙ ⒪ *VISA*
closed 4 to 24 January – **Meals** (set menu only) (dinner only and Sunday lunch) 30.00 **t** ⌖ 9.75 – **6 rm** ☷ (dinner included) 100.00/190.00 **t.** – SB
**Spec.** Lobster and asparagus fricasée with chervil fumé. Roast best end of lamb, fondant potato and niçoise jus. Vanilla soufflé, compote of raspberries.

**LANCHLAND** *Northd.* [401] [402] N 19 – *pop. 135* – ✉ *Consett (Durham).*
*London 298 – Carlisle 47 – Newcastle upon Tyne 24.*

🏨 **Lord Crewe Arms** 🕊, DH8 9SP, ☏ (01434) 675251, *Fax (01434) 675337,* « Part 13C abbey », 🌳 – [TV] ☎ 📞. ⊕ AE ◐ VISA
**Meals** (bar lunch Monday to Saturday)/dinner 28.00 **t.** 🍷 7.00 – **20 rm** ☕ 80.00/110.00 **t.** – SB.

**LANDFORD FORUM** *Dorset* [403] [404] N 31 *The West Country G. – pop. 8 880.*
See : *Town*★.
Env. : *Kingston Lacy*★★ *AC, SE : 5½ m. by B 3082 – Royal Signals Museum*★, *NE : 2 m. by B 3082.*
Exc. : *Milton Abbas*★, *SW : 8 m. by A 354 – Sturminster Newton*★, *NW : 8 m. by A 357.*
⛳18 *Ashley Wood, Tarrant Rawston* ☏ *(01258) 452253.*
ℹ *Marsh & Ham Car Park, West St., DT11 7AW* ☏ *(01258) 454770.*
*London 124 – Bournemouth 17 – Dorchester 17 – Salisbury 24.*

🏨 **Crown,** West St., DT11 7AJ, ☏ (01258) 456626, *Fax (01258) 451084,* 🎣, 🌳 – ⇕, 🚭 rm, [TV] ☎ [P] – 👥 200. ⊕ AE ◐ VISA
*closed 25 to 28 December* – **Meals** *(closed Saturday lunch)* 13.95 **t.** and a la carte 🍷 5.50 – **32 rm** ☕ 65.00/90.00 **t.** – SB.

**t Pimperne** *Northeast : 2½ m. on A 354 –* ✉ *Blandford Forum.*

🏨 **Anvil,** Salisbury Rd, DT11 8UQ, ☏ (01258) 453431, *Fax (01258) 480182* – [TV] ☎ 📞 [P]. ⊕ AE ◐ VISA
**Meals** 7.50/9.95 **st.** and a la carte 🍷 5.50 – **11 rm** ☕ 47.50/75.00 **st.**

**t Chettle** *Northeast : 7¼ m. by A 354 –* ✉ *Blandford Forum.*

🍴🍴 **Castleman** 🕊 with rm, DT11 8DB, ☏ (01258) 830096, *Fax (01258) 830051,* <, « Part 16C dower house with Victorian additions », 🌳 – 🚭 rest, [TV] ☎ [P]. ⊕ VISA JCB. 🚫🐕
*closed 26 December and February* – **Meals** (dinner only and Sunday lunch)/dinner a la carte 14.00/21.50 **t.** 🍷 4.50 – **8 rm** ☕ 40.00/70.00 **t.**

⊙ ATS 8 Dmory Court St. ☏ (01258) 454101

**LAWITH** *Cumbria* [402] K 21 – *see Coniston.*

**LEDINGTON** *Glos.* [403] [404] P 28 – *see Stow-on-the-Wold.*

**LOCKLEY** *Glos.* [403] [404] O 27 – *pop. 1 668* – ✉ *Moreton-in-Marsh.*
*London 89 – Birmingham 40 – Gloucester 29 – Oxford 33.*

🏨 **Crown Inn,** High St., GL56 9EX, ☏ (01386) 700245, *Fax (01386) 700247,* « Converted 15C coach house and cottages », 🌳 – [TV] ☎ 📞 [P]. ⊕ AE ◐ VISA
**Meals** a la carte 16.35/30.35 **t.** 🍷 6.95 – **21 rm** ☕ 64.00/126.00 **t.** – SB.

**LUNSDON** *Wilts.* [403] [404] O 29 – *see Swindon.*

**LYTH** *Notts.* [402] [403] [404] Q 23 – *pop. 1 867* – ✉ *Worksop.*
*London 166 – Doncaster 13 – Lincoln 30 – Nottingham 32 – Sheffield 20.*

🏨 **Charnwood,** Sheffield Rd, S81 8HF, West : ¾ m. on A 634 ☏ (01909) 591610, *Fax (01909) 591429,* 🏋, 🌳 – 🚭 rm, [TV] ☎ [P] – 👥 120. ⊕ AE ◐ VISA JCB. 🚫🐕
**Meals** 11.95/17.95 **t.** and a la carte 🍷 5.45 – **33 rm** ☕ 65.00/90.00 **t.** – SB.

🏨 **Travelodge,** Hilltop roundabout, S81 8HG, North : ¾ m. by B 6045 at junction of A 1 (M) with A 614 ☏ (01909) 591841, *Fax (01909) 591831,* Reservations (Freephone) 0800 850950 – 🚭 [TV] ♿ [P]. ⊕ AE ◐ VISA JCB. 🚫🐕
**Meals** (grill rest.) – **39 rm** 39.95/59.95 **t.**

**ODMIN** *Cornwall* [403] F 32 *The West Country G. – pop. 12 553.*
See : *St. Petroc Church*★.
Env. : *Bodmin Moor*★★ *– Lanhydrock*★★, *S : 3 m. by B 3269 – Blisland*★ *(Church*★*), N : 5½ m. by A 30 and minor roads – Pencarrow*★, *NW : 4 m. by A 389 and minor roads – Cardinham (Church*★*), NE : 4 m. by A 30 and minor rd – St. Mabyn (Church*★*), N : 5½ m. by A 389, B 3266 and minor rd.*
Exc. : *St. Tudy*★, *N : 7 m. by A 389, B 3266 and minor rd.*
ℹ *Shire House, Mount Folly Sq., PL31 2DQ* ☏ *(01208) 76616.*
*London 270 – Newquay 18 – Plymouth 32 – Truro 23.*

⬆ **Mount Pleasant Moorland** ⬩, Mount, PL30 4EX, East : 7 ¼ m. by A 30 on Warlegga rd ℘ (01208) 821342, ≤, 🛁, 🐾 – ✦ 🅿. 📟 🆅🅸🆂🅰 🅹🅲🅱. ❀
*Easter-September* – **Meals** 13.00 **s.** – **7 rm** ⊒ 27.50/55.00 **s.**

⑩ ATS Church Sq. ℘ (01208) 74353/73757

---

**BODYMOOR HEATH** *Staffs.* 🔢🔢🔢 O 26 – *see Tamworth.*

---

**BOGNOR REGIS** *W. Sussex* 🔢 R 31 – *pop. 19 836.*
🄱 *Belmont St., PO21 1BJ* ℘ (01243) 823140.
*London 65 – Brighton 29 – Portsmouth 24 – Southampton 36.*

🏨 **Robin Hood,** Shripney Rd, PO22 9PA, North : 3 m. on A 29 ℘ (01243) 82232▮
*Fax (01243) 841430* – 📺 ☎ 🅿 – 🛁 40. 📟 🆎 ⑩ 🆅🅸🆂🅰 🅹🅲🅱. ❀
**Meals** a la carte 13.75/19.95 **t.** – **24 rm** ⊒ 45.00/70.00 **st.**.

🏨 **Inglenook,** 255 Pagham Rd, Nyetimber, PO21 3QB, West : 2 ½ m. ℘ (01243) 26249▮
*Fax (01243) 262668, « Part 16C »,* 🐾 – 📺 ☎ ✆ 🅿 – 🛁 100. 📟 🆎 ⑩ 🆅🅸🆂🅰
**Meals** 11.50/15.95 **t.** and a la carte ⓐ 4.50 – **18 rm** ⊒ 60.00/90.00 **t.** – SB.

---

**BOLDON** *Tyne and Wear* 🔢🔢 O 19 – *see Newcastle upon Tyne.*

---

**BOLLINGTON** *Ches.* 🔢🔢🔢 N 24 – *see Macclesfield.*

---

*Si vous cherchez un hôtel tranquille,*
*consultez d'abord les cartes de l'introduction*
*ou repérez dans le texte les établissements indiqués avec le signe* ⬩ *ou* ⬩

---

**BOLTON** *Gtr. Manchester* 🔢🔢 M 23 – *pop. 139 020.*
🛅 *Regent Park, Links Rd, Chorley New Road* ℘ (01204) 844170 – 🛅 *Lostock Park* ℘ (0120▮ 843278 –* 🛅 *Bolton Old Links, Chorley Old Rd, Montserrat* ℘ (01204) 840050.
🄱 *Town Hall, Victoria Sq, BL1 1RU* ℘ (01204) 364333.
*London 214 – Burnley 19 – Liverpool 32 – Manchester 11 – Preston 23.*

🏨 **Bolton Moat House,** 1 Higher Bridge St., BL1 2EW, ℘ (01204) 87998▮
*Fax (01204) 380777, « Cloisters restaurant in 19C church »,* 🏋, ☎, 🖥 – ▮, ✦ rm, 🖳 res 📺 ☎ ♿ 🅿 – 🛁 300. 📟 🆎 ⑩ 🆅🅸🆂🅰. ❀
**Meals** *(closed Saturday lunch)* 15.50 **st.** (dinner) and a la carte 17.40/22.85 **st.** ⓐ 5.95 – ▮ 9.95 – **126 rm** 110.00/125.00 **st.**, 2 suites – SB.

🏨 **Pack Horse,** Nelson Sq., Bradshawgate, BL1 1DP, ℘ (01204) 527261, *Fax (01204) 3643▮* – ▮, ✦ rm, 📺 ☎ – 🛁 250. 📟 🆎 ⑩ 🆅🅸🆂🅰. ❀
**Meals** *(closed Sunday)* a la carte 13.00/25.00 ⓐ 6.00 – **74 rm** ⊒ 79.00/99.00 **st.**

🏨 **Beaumont,** Beaumont Rd, BL3 4TA, Southwest : 2 ½ m. by A 676 on A 5▮
℘ (01204) 651511, *Fax (01204) 61064* – ✦ rm, 📺 ☎ 🅿 – 🛁 120. 📟 🆎 ⑩ 🆅🅸🆂🅰
**Meals** a la carte 18.85/27.40 **st.** ⓐ 8.95 – ⊒ 8.95 – **96 rm** 69.00/85.00 **t.** – SB.

**at Egerton** North : 3½ m. on A 666 – ✉ Bolton.

🏨 **Egerton House,** Blackburn Rd, BL7 9PL, ℘ (01204) 307171, *Fax (01204) 593030,* 🐾 ✦ 📺 ☎ 🅿 – 🛁 150. 📟 🆎 ⑩ 🆅🅸🆂🅰. ❀
**Meals** *(closed Saturday lunch)* 16.00/27.50 **t.** and a la carte ⓐ 6.50 – ⊒ 9.00 – **32 rm** 105.0▮ 130.00 **t.** – SB.

**at Bromley Cross** North : 3¼ m. by A 676 on B 6472 – ✉ Bolton.

🏨 **Last Drop Village,** Hospital Rd, BL7 9PZ, Northwest : 1 m. by B 6472 on Hospital R▮ ℘ (01204) 591131, *Fax (01204) 304122, « Village created from restored farm buildings* 🏋, ☎, 🖥, 🐾, squash – ✦ rm, 📺 ☎ 🅿 – 🛁 200. 📟 🆎 ⑩ 🆅🅸🆂🅰. ❀
**Meals** *(closed Saturday lunch)* 12.95/22.95 **t.** and dinner a la carte ⓐ 7.95 – ⊒ 9.95 – **125 r▮** 99.50/123.00 **st.**, 3 suites – SB.

🏨 **Quarlton Manor Farm** ⬩, Plantation Rd, Edgworth, BL7 0DD, Northeast : 4 ¾ m. ▮ B 6472 and B 6391 following signs for Edgeworth and Blackburn ℘ (01204) 85227▮ *Fax (01204) 852286,* ≤, *« Part 17C farmhouse »,* 🐾, park – ✦ 📺 🅿. 📟 🆅🅸🆂🅰 🅹🅲🅱
**Meals** 19.00/23.50 **t.** and a la carte ⓐ 5.00 – **5 rm** ⊒ 44.00/88.00 **st.** – SB.

⑩ ATS Foundry St. ℘ (01204) 522144/527841/     ATS 101 Chorley New Rd, Horwich 388681
ATS Chorley Rd, Fourgates, Westhoughton ℘ (01942) 813024

**OLTON ABBEY** N. Yorks. 402 O 22 Great Britain G. – pop. 117 – ⊠ Skipton.

    See : Bolton Priory★ AC.

    London 216 – Harrogate 18 – Leeds 23 – Skipton 6.

🏨 **Devonshire Arms Country House** ⅏, BD23 6AJ, ℰ (01756) 710441, Fax (01756) 710564, ≼, « Part 17C restored coaching inn, collection of fine art and antiques », ₤ᴙ, ⇋s, ◘, ⅏, park, ⅍ – ⅍ rm, 🆃🆅 ☎ 🄿 – 🔏 90. 🐵 🆎 ⓞ 🆅🅸🆂🄰
    **The Burlington :** Meals (dinner only and Sunday lunch)/dinner 18.95/37.00 st. - (see also **Devonshire Brasserie and Bar** below) – 38 rm ⇆ 110.00/155.00 st., 3 suites – SB.

✗ **Devonshire Brasserie and Bar** (at Devonshire Arms Country House), BD23 6AJ, ℰ (01756) 710710, Fax (01756) 710564, « Contemporary decor » – ⅍ ▤ 🄿. 🐵 🆎 ⓞ 🆅🅸🆂🄰
    Meals a la carte 20.00/23.75 st.

---

**OLTONGATE** Cumbria – see Bassenthwaite.

---

**OREHAMWOOD** Herts. 404 T 29 – pop. 29 837.

    London 10 – Luton 20.

        Plan : see Greater London (North West) p. 5

🏨 **Elstree Moat House**, Barnet bypass, WD6 5PU, at junction of A 5135 with A 1 ℰ (0181) 214 9988, Fax (0181) 207 3194, ₤ᴙ, ⇋s, ◘ – ⧫, ⅍ rm, ▤ rest, 🆃🆅 ☎ ⅋ 🄿 – 🔏 400. 🐵 🆎 ⓞ 🆅🅸🆂🄰. ⅍
                                                            CT s
    Meals (bar lunch Saturday) 19.50/15.95 t. and a la carte ᐟ 6.30 – ⇆ 10.25 – 131 rm 130.00/195.00 st. – SB.

---

**OROUGHBRIDGE** N.Yorks 402 P 21 – pop. 1 903.

    London 215 – Leeds 19 – Middlesbrough 36 – York 16.

🏨 **Rose Manor**, Horsefair, YO51 9LL, ℰ (01423) 322245, Fax (01423) 324920, ⅏ – ⅍ rm, 🆃🆅 ☎ 🄿 – 🔏 250. 🐵 🆎 ⓞ 🆅🅸🆂🄰. ⅍
    closed 26 to 30 December – Meals 17.50 st. (dinner) and a la carte 18.35/22.65 st. ᐟ 4.50 – 17 rm ⇆ 74.75/103.50 t., 1 suite – SB.

🏨 **Crown**, Horsefair, YO51 9LB, ℰ (01423) 322328, Fax (01423) 324512 – ⧫, ⅍ rm, 🆃🆅 ☎ 🄿 – 🔏 180. 🐵 🆎 ⓞ 🆅🅸🆂🄰
    Meals (bar lunch Monday to Saturday)/dinner 18.95 t. and a la carte – 40 rm ⇆ 50.00/90.00 t. – SB.

**: Brafferton Helperby** Northeast : 5 m. by B 6265 and Easingwold rd on Helperby rd – ⊠ York.

⌂ **Brafferton Hall** ⅏, YO61 2NZ, by Hall Lane ℰ (01423) 360352, Fax (01423) 360352, ⅏ – ⅍ 🆃🆅 🄿. 🐵 🆎 🆅🅸🆂🄰
    Meals (by arrangement) (communal dining) 19.50 s. – 4 rm ⇆ 38.00/70.00 s.

⌂ **Laurel Manor Farm** ⅏, YO61 2NZ, by Hall Lane ℰ (01423) 360436, Fax (01423) 360437, « 18C farmhouse », ⅏, ⅏, park, ⅍ – 🆃🆅 🄿
    Meals (by arrangement) (communal dining) 20.00 st. – 3 rm ⇆ 25.00/50.00 st.

---

**ORROWDALE** Cumbria 402 K 20 – see Keswick.

---

**OSCASTLE** Cornwall 403 F 31 The West Country G..

    See : Village★.

    Env. : Church★ – Old Post Office★.

    London 260 – Bude 14 – Exeter 59 – Plymouth 43.

🏠 **Bottreaux House**, PL35 0BG, South : ¾ m. by B 3263 on B 3266 ℰ (01840) 250231, Fax (01840) 250170 – ⅍ 🆃🆅 ☎ 🄿. 🐵 🆎 🆅🅸🆂🄰 🄹🄲🄱
    restricted opening in winter – Meals (closed Sunday) (dinner only) a la carte approx. 20.00 t. ᐟ 6.00 – 7 rm ⇆ 30.00/56.00 st. – SB.

⌂ **Trerosewill Farm** ⅏, Paradise, PL35 0DL, South : 1 m. off B 263 ℰ (01840) 250545, Fax (01840) 250545, ≼, « Working farm », ⅏, park – ⅍ 🆃🆅 🄿. 🐵 🆅🅸🆂🄰 🄹🄲🄱. ⅍
    closed Christmas and New Year – Meals 19.00 t. ᐟ 4.00 – 6 rm ⇆ 30.00/58.00 st. – SB.

⌂ **St. Christopher's**, High St., PL35 0BD, South : ¾ m. by B 3263 off B 3266 ℰ (01840) 250412 – ⅍ 🆃🆅 🄿. 🐵 🆅🅸🆂🄰
    Meals 11.50 t. ᐟ 4.00 – 9 rm ⇆ 21.00/42.00 t.

---

**OSHAM** W. Sussex 404 R 31 – see Chichester.

**BOSTON** Lincs. 402 404 T 25 Great Britain G. – pop. 34 606.

See : St. Botolph's Church★.

Exc. : Tattershal Castle★, NW : 15 m. by A 1121, B 1192 and A 153 – Battle of Brita Memorial Flight, RAF Coningsby★, NW : 14 m. on A 1121, B 1192 and A 153.

🏌 Cowbridge, Horncastle Rd ℰ (01205) 362306.

🛈 Blackfriars Arts Centre, Spain Lane, PE21 6HP ℰ (1205) 356656.

London 122 – Lincoln 35 – Nottingham 55.

🏨 **Comfort Inn,** Donnington Rd, Bicker Bar Roundabout, PE20 3AN, Southwest : 8 m. junction of A 17 with A 52 ℰ (01205) 820118, Fax (01205) 820228 – ⇄ rm, 🍽 rest, 📺 ☎ 🅿 – 🔬 90. 🐵 🆎 ⓪ 𝘝𝘐𝘚𝘈

Meals (bar lunch)/dinner 9.75 st. and a la carte ↑ 4.50 – � 6.75 – **55 rm** 39.75 st.

🔧 ATS London Rd ℰ (01205) 362854

---

**BOSTON SPA** W. Yorks. 402 P 22 – pop. 4 135.

London 127 – Harrogate 12 – Leeds 12 – York 16.

⌂ **Four Gables** without rest., Oaks Lane, LS23 6DS, West : ¼ m. off A 659 turning left aft Westwood Way ℰ (01937) 849031, Fax (01937) 849031, 🌳 – ⇄ 📺 🅿. ⋙

closed Christmas and New Year – **3 rm** ⊆ 31.00/57.00 st.

---

**BOTLEY** Hants. 403 404 Q 31 – pop. 2 297 – ⊠ Southampton.

🏌 Botley Park H. & C.C., Winchester Rd, Boorley Green ℰ (01489) 780888 ext : 444.

London 83 – Portsmouth 17 – Southampton 6 – Winchester 11.

🏨 **Botley Park,** Winchester Rd, Boorley Green, SO32 2UA, Northwest : 1 ½ m. on B 335 ℰ (01489) 780888, Fax (01489) 789242, 👌, ☎s, ▣, 🏌, park, ⚒, squash – ⇄, 🍽 rest, ▯ ☎ ⌚ ♿ 🅿 – 🔬 250. 🐵 🆎 ⓪ 𝘝𝘐𝘚𝘈 𝘑𝘊𝘉

Meals (closed Saturday lunch) (dancing Saturday evening in winter) 14.50/23.50 s and a la carte ↑ 6.00 – ⊆ 10.25 – **100 rm** 109.00/190.00 st. – SB.

---

| Les prix | Pour toutes précisions sur les prix indiqués dans ce guide, reportez-vous aux pages de l'introduction. |
|---|---|

---

**BOUGHTON** Kent – see Faversham.

---

**BOUGHTON MONCHELSEA** Kent – see Maidstone.

---

**BOURNE** Lincs. 402 404 S 25 – pop. 8 777.

London 101 – Leicester 42 – Lincoln 35 – Nottingham 42.

🏨 **Bourne Eau House** without rest., 30 South St., PE10 9LY, on A 15 ℰ (01778) 42362 « Part Elizabethan and Georgian house », 🌳 – ⇄ 📺 ⌚ 🅿. ⋙

**3 rm** ⊆ 35.00/70.00 st.

**at Toft** Southwest : 3 m. by A 151 on A 6121 – ⊠ Bourne.

🏨 **Toft House,** Main Rd, Toft, PE10 0JT, ℰ (01778) 590614, Fax (01778) 590264, 🏌, 🌳 – ▯ ☎ 🅿 – 🔬 70. 🐵 𝘝𝘐𝘚𝘈. ⋙

closed 25 and 26 December – **Meals** (closed Sunday dinner) 14.95 t. ↑ 4.00 – **22 r** ⊆ 45.00/68.00 t.

🔧 ATS 18 Abbey Rd ℰ (01778) 422811

---

**BOURNEMOUTH** 403 404 O 31 The West Country G. – pop. 155 488.

See : Compton Acres★★ (English Garden ⩽★★★) AC AX – Russell-Cotes Art Gallery an Museum★★ AC DZ - Shelley Rooms AC EX.

Env. : – Poole★, W : 4 m. by A 338 – Brownsea Island★ (Baden-Powell Stone ⩽★★) AC, boat from Sandbanks BX or Poole Quay – Christchurch★ (priory★) E : 4½ m. on A 35.

Exc. : Corfe Castle★, SW : 18 m. by A 35 and A 351 – Lulworth Cove★ (Blue Pool★) W : 8 of Corfe Castle by B 3070 – Swanage★, E : 5 m. of Corfe Castle by A 351.

🏌 Queens Park, Queens Park West Drive ℰ (01202) 396198/302611, DV – 🏌 Meyrick Par Central Drive ℰ (01202) 290307, CY.

✈ Bournemouth (Hurn) Airport : ℰ (01202) 593939, N : 5 m. by Hurn - DV.

🛈 Westover Rd, BH1 2BU ℰ (01202) 451700.

London 114 – Bristol 76 – Southampton 34.

**Swallow Highcliff,** St. Michael's Rd, West Cliff, BH2 5DU, ✆ (01202) 557702, *Fax (01202) 292734*, ←, ⅟₆, ⌂, ⛱, ⛱, ⛳, ✗ – |‡|, ⇔ rm, TV ☎ P – 🔨 450. ⓂⓒAE ⓓ VISA. ✗ CZ z
Meals 13.00/22.00 **st.** and dinner a la carte – **154 rm** ⊐ 90.00/165.00 **st.**, 3 suites – SB.

**Royal Bath,** Bath Rd, BH1 2EW, ✆ (01202) 555555, *Fax (01202) 554158*, ←, ⅟₆, ⌂, ⛱, ⛳ – |‡| TV ☎ 🚗 – 🔨 400. ⓂⓒAE ⓓ VISA. ✗ DZ a
Meals (dinner only) a la carte 23.00/42.00 **st.** – (see also ***Oscars*** below) – **124 rm** ⊐ 125.00/175.00 **st.**, 7 suites – SB.

**Carlton,** East Overcliff, BH1 3DN, ✆ (01202) 552011, *Fax (01202) 299573*, ←, ⌂, ⅟₆, ⌂, ⛱, ⛱, ⛳ – |‡|, ⇔ rest, ≡ rest, TV ☎ P – 🔨 160. ⓂⓒAE ⓓ VISA JCB. ✗ EZ a
Meals 16.50/25.00 **st.** and a la carte ⅰ 8.50 – **69 rm** ⊐ 135.00/220.00 **st.**, 5 suites.

**Norfolk Royale,** Richmond Hill, BH2 6EN, ✆ (01202) 551521, *Fax (01202) 299729*, ⌂, ⛱ – |‡|, ⇔ rm, ≡ rest, TV ☎ 🚗 – 🔨 90. ⓂⓒAE ⓓ VISA. ✗ CY u
*closed 30 December-2 January* – ***The Orangery*:** **Meals** 10.50/22.50 **st.** and a la carte ⅰ 7.50 – **90 rm** ⊐ 105.00/175.00 **st.**, 5 suites – SB.

**Stakis Bournemouth,** Westover Rd, BH1 2BZ, ✆ (01202) 557681, *Fax (01202) 554918*, ←, ⅟₆, ⌂, ⛱ – |‡| TV ☎ 🚗 – 🔨 300. ⓂⓒAE ⓓ VISA DZ n
Meals 13.75/20.35 **t.** – ⊐ 9.50 – **114 rm** 105.00/140.00 **st.**, 6 suites – SB.

**Chine,** Boscombe Spa Rd, BH5 1AX, ✆ (01202) 396234, *Fax (01202) 391737*, ←, ⌂, ⛱, ⛱, ⛳ – |‡|, ⇔ rm, TV ☎ P – 🔨 120. ⓂⓒAE ⓓ VISA. ✗ DX e
*closed 28 December-2 January* – **Meals** (bar lunch Saturday) 13.50/18.50 **st.** and a la carte ⅰ 6.50 – **92 rm** ⊐ (dinner included) 100.00/180.00 **t.** – SB.

**Miramar,** 19 Grove Rd, East Overcliff, BH1 3AL, ✆ (01202) 556581, *Fax (01202) 291242*, ←, ⛳ – |‡|, ⇔ rest, TV ☎ P – 🔨 80. ⓂⓒAE VISA JCB DZ u
Meals *(closed Saturday lunch)* 8.25/19.95 **t.** ⅰ 7.95 – **38 rm** ⊐ 65.00/170.00 **t.** – SB.

**Connaught,** West Hill Rd, West Cliff, BH2 5PH, ✆ (01202) 298020, *Fax (01202) 298028*, ⅟₆, ⌂, ⛱, ⛱ – |‡|, ⇔ rm, TV ☎ ♿ P – 🔨 250. ⓂⓒAE ⓓ VISA CZ s
Meals (bar lunch Monday to Saturday)/dinner 15.00 **st.** and a la carte ⅰ 4.95 – **55 rm** ⊐ 65.00/110.00 **st.**, 1 suite – SB.

**Marsham Court,** Russell-Cotes Rd, East Cliff, BH1 3AB, ✆ (01202) 552111, *Fax (01202) 294744*, ←, ⛱ – |‡| TV ☎ ✆ P – 🔨 200. ⓂⓒAE VISA. ✗ DZ e
Meals (bar lunch)/dinner 17.00 **st.** ⅰ 5.00 – **85 rm** ⊐ 56.00/92.00 **t.**, 1 suite – SB.

**Anglo-Swiss,** 16 Gervis Rd, East Cliff, BH1 3EQ, ✆ (01202) 554794, *Fax (01202) 299615*, ⌂, ⛱ – |‡| TV ☎ P – 🔨 80. ⓂⓒAE ⓓ VISA EY e
Meals (bar lunch Monday to Saturday)/dinner 17.95 **st.** and a la carte ⅰ 5.75 – ⊐ 9.25 – **65 rm** 70.00/135.00 **st.** – SB.

**East Cliff Court,** East Overcliff Drive, BH1 3AN, ✆ (01202) 554545, *Fax (01202) 557456*, ←, ⌂, ⛱ – |‡|, ⇔ rest, TV ☎ P – 🔨 100. ⓂⓒAE ⓓ VISA. ✗ EZ v
Meals 14.95/23.95 **st.** and a la carte ⅰ 8.95 – **70 rm** ⊐ 90.00/190.00 **st.** – SB.

**Durley Hall,** Durley Chine Rd, BH2 5JS, ✆ (01202) 751000, *Fax (01202) 757585*, ⅟₆, ⌂, ⛱, ⛱ – |‡| TV ☎ P – 🔨 160. ⓂⓒAE ⓓ VISA. ✗ CZ e
*closed 31 December* – **Meals** (buffet lunch Monday to Saturday)/dinner 16.50 **st.** and a la carte ⅰ 3.95 – **81 rm** ⊐ 55.00/130.00 **st.** – SB.

**Collingwood,** 11 Priory Rd, BH2 5DF, ✆ (01202) 557575, ⌂, ⛱ – |‡|, ⇔ rest, TV ☎ P. Ⓜⓒ ⓓ VISA CZ n
Meals (bar lunch Monday to Saturday)/dinner 16.95 **st.** ⅰ 4.95 – **53 rm** ⊐ (dinner included) 50.00/104.00 **st.** – SB.

**Belvedere,** 14 Bath Rd, BH1 2EU, ✆ (01202) 297556, *Fax (01202) 294699* – |‡| TV ☎ P – 🔨 80. ⓂⓒAE ⓓ VISA JCB. ✗ DYZ c
Meals (bar lunch Monday to Saturday)/dinner 15.50 **t.** and a la carte ⅰ 4.95 – **61 rm** ⊐ 49.00/91.00 **t.** – SB.

**Tudor Grange,** 31 Gervis Rd, East Cliff, BH1 3EE, ✆ (01202) 291472, *Fax (01202) 311503*, ⛳ – TV ☎ ✆ P. ⓂⓒAE VISA. ✗ EY o
Meals (residents only) (dinner only) 15.00 **st.** ⅰ 6.00 – **11 rm** ⊐ 32.50/65.00 **t.**

**Boltons,** 9 Durley Chine Road South, West Cliff, BH2 5JT, ✆ (01202) 751517, *Fax (01202) 751629*, ⛱, ⛳ – TV ☎ P. Ⓜⓒ VISA CZ a
*restricted opening in winter* – **Meals** (dinner only) 12.50 **st.** – **11 rm** ⊐ 28.50/60.00 **st.**

**Silver Trees** without rest., 57 Wimborne Rd, BH3 7AL, ✆ (01202) 556040, *Fax (01202) 556040*, ⛳ – TV P. ⓂⓒAE VISA. ✗ CV e
*closed Christmas and New Year* – **5 rm** ⊐ 27.00/45.00 **s.**

**Valberg,** 1A Wollstonecraft Rd, Boscombe, BH5 1JQ, ✆ (01202) 394644, ⛳ – ⇔ rest, TV P. ✗ EX v
*restricted opening in winter* – **Meals** (by arrangement) 8.50 – **10 rm** ⊐ 27.00/44.00.

✗✗✗ **Oscars** (at Royal Bath H.), Bath Rd, BH1 2EW, ✆ (01202) 555555, *Fax (01202) 554158* – 🚗. ⓂⓒAE ⓓ VISA DZ a
*closed Sunday dinner* – **Meals** 17.50/30.00 **st.** and a la carte.

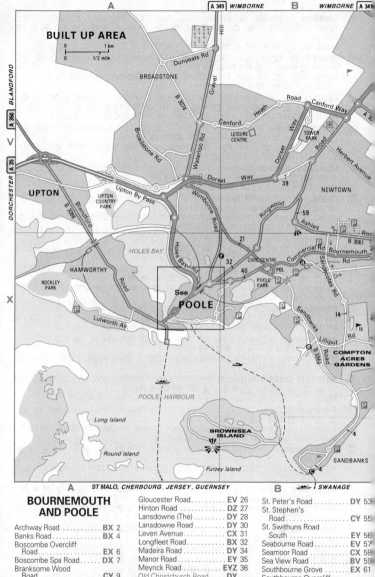

A    ST MALO, CHERBOURG, JERSEY, GUERNSEY    B    SWANAGE

# BOURNEMOUTH AND POOLE

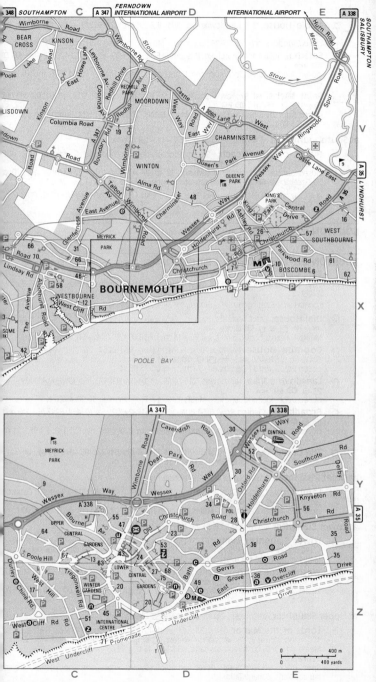

XX **Noble House,** 3-5 Lansdowne Rd, BH1 1RZ, ✆ (01202) 291277 – ▤. MC AE ① VISA JCB DEY
*closed Sunday lunch and 25-26 December* – **Meals** - Chinese - a la carte 9.00/15.90 **t.**

XX **Salathai,** 1066 Christchurch Rd, Boscombe East, BH7 6DS, ✆ (01202) 420772 – ▤. MC AE VISA JCB EV z
*closed Sunday, 25-26 December and 1 January* – **Meals** - Thai - 7.95/14.25 **t.** and a la carte ⅰ 7.50.

X **Saint Michel** (at Swallow Highcliff H.), St. Michaels Rd, BH2 5DU, ✆ (01202) 315716 *Fax (01202) 315716* – MC VISA CZ z
*closed Saturday lunch and Sunday dinner* – **Meals** - Brasserie 12.50 **t.** (lunch) and a la carte 17.90/26.80 **t.** ⅰ 4.50.

**at Southbourne** *East : 3 ¾ m. by A 35 on B 3059* – **EV** – ✉ *Bournemouth.*

X **Bistro on the Beach,** Solent Promenade, Southbourne Coast Rd, B46 4BE ✆ (01202) 431473, ≤ – MC VISA
*closed Sunday to Tuesday, 1 January, 12 to 27 April, 1 to 24 November and 20 to 26 December* – **Meals** (booking essential) (dinner only) 13.95 **t.** and a la carte ⅰ 6.00.

ATS 892 Christchurch Rd, Boscombe ✆ (01202) 424457

ATS 1 Fernside Rd, Poole ✆ (01202) 733301/733326

**BOURTON** *Shrops.* 402 403 M 26 – *see Much Wenlock.*

**BOURTON-ON-THE-WATER** *Glos.* 403 404 O 28 *Great Britain G.* – *pop. 2 239.*

See : *Town*★.

**Env.** : *Northleach (Church of SS. Peter and Paul*★, *Wool Merchants' Brasses*★*), SW : 5 m. by A 429.*

*London 91 – Birmingham 47 – Gloucester 24 – Oxford 36.*

**Dial House,** The Chestnuts, High St., GL54 2AN, ✆ (01451) 822244, *Fax (01451) 810126*, – ⅹ TV ☎ P. MC AE VISA.
**Meals** a la carte 17.10/25.40 **t.** ⅰ 6.95 – **13 rm** ▭ 58.00/120.00 **t.** – SB.

**Coombe House** without rest., Rissington Rd, GL54 2DT, ✆ (01451) 821966 *Fax (01451) 810477*, – ⅹ TV P. MC AE VISA.
*closed 24, 25 and 31 December* – **7 rm** ▭ 48.00/75.00 **st.**

**Lansdowne Villa,** Lansdowne, GL54 2AT, ✆ (01451) 820673, *Fax (01451) 822099* – ⅹ TV P. MC VISA JCB.
*closed December and January* – **Meals** 12.95 ⅰ 3.75 – **12 rm** ▭ 30.00/45.00 **t.**

**Broadlands,** Clapton Row, GL54 2DN, ✆ (01451) 822002, *Fax (01451) 821776* – ⅹ rest TV P. MC VISA JCB.
*closed 25 December and 2 to 15 January* – **Meals** (by arrangement) 12.50 **st.** ⅰ 4.95 – **11 rm** ▭ 40.00/58.00 **st.**

**The Lawns** without rest., Station Rd, GL54 2ER, ✆ (01451) 821195 – ⅹ TV P.
*closed 24 December-3 January* – **5 rm** ▭ 50.00 **s.**

**at Great Rissington** *Southeast : 3 ¼ m.* – ✉ *Cheltenham.*

**Lamb Inn** with rm, GL54 2LP, ✆ (01451) 820388, *Fax (01451) 820724*, « Part 17C Cotswold stone inn », – P. MC AE VISA
*closed 25 and 26 December* – **Meals** a la carte 14.45/17.70 **t.** – **14 rm** ▭ 35.00/85.00 **t.**

**at Lower Slaughter** *Northwest : 1 ¾ m. by A 429* – ✉ *Cheltenham.*

**Lower Slaughter Manor** ⛰, GL54 2HP, ✆ (01451) 820456, *Fax (01451) 822150*, ≤, « 17C manor house, gardens », ▢, ✂ – ⅹ rest, TV ☎ P – 🏛 25. MC AE ① VISA.
**Meals** 20.00/45.00 **t.** ⅰ 6.50 – **12 rm** ▭ 135.00/300.00 **t.**, 3 suites – SB.

**Washbourne Court,** GL54 2HS, ✆ (01451) 822143, *Fax (01451) 821045*, « Part 17C house », ✂ – ⅹ rest, TV ☎ P. MC AE ① VISA.
**Meals** 23.00 **t.** (lunch) and a la carte 31.00/40.50 **t.** ⅰ 11.00 – ▭ 12.00 – **19 rm** 100.00/180.00 **t.**, 9 suites.

**at Upper Slaughter** *Northwest : 2 ¾ m. by A 429* – ✉ *Cheltenham.*

✿ **Lords of the Manor** ⛰, GL54 2JD, ✆ (01451) 820243, *Fax (01451) 820696*, ≤, « Part 17C manor house », park – ⅹ rest, TV ☎ P – 🏛 30. MC AE ① VISA JCB.
**Meals** 21.50/35.00 **t.** and a la carte 45.00/58.45 **t.** ⅰ 15.00 – **26 rm** ▭ 95.00/295.00 **t.** 1 suite – SB
**Spec.** Black pudding, potato purée and onion soubise. Roast John Dory, rösti potato and haricot blanc. Banana Tatin.

**DVEY TRACEY** Devon **403** I 32 The West Country G. – pop. 3 492 – ⊠ Newton Abbot.
See : St. Peter, St. Paul and St. Thomas of Canterbury Church★.
Env. : Dartmoor National Park★★.
☗ Newton Abbot ℰ (01626) 52460.
London 214 – Exeter 14 – Plymouth 32.

🏨 **Edgemoor**, Haytor Rd, TQ13 9LE, West : 1 m. on B 3387 ℰ (01626) 832466,
Fax (01626) 834760, 舟 – ⵚ rest, ⊡ ☎ ℗ – 益 60. ⓪ ⒜ ⓪ 𝘝𝘐𝘚𝘈
Meals (booking essential) 15.95/22.50 st. ⓵ 4.75 – 17 rm ⊡ 55.00/100.00 t. – SB.

🏠 **Coombe Cross**, Coombe Cross, TQ13 9EY, East : ½ m. on B 3344 ℰ (01626) 832476,
Fax (01626) 835298, ≤, ⌂₆, ⇌, ☒, 舟 – ⵚ rest, ⊡ ☎ ℗. ⓪ ⒜ ⓪ 𝘝𝘐𝘚𝘈
closed 27 November-26 December – Meals (bar lunch)/dinner 19.95 st. ⓵ 5.95 – 20 rm
⊡ 40.00/68.00 t. – SB.

⌂ **Front House Lodge**, East St., TQ13 9EL, ℰ (01626) 832202, Fax (01626) 832202, 舟 –
ⵚ ⊡ ℗. ⓪ 𝘝𝘐𝘚𝘈 𝘑𝘊𝘉. ⌘
Meals (by arrangement) 15.00 st. – 6 rm ⊡ 30.00/48.00 s.

**Haytor** West : 2½ m. on B 3387 – ⊠ Bovey Tracey.

🏨 **Bel Alp House** ⌂, TQ13 9XX, on B 3387 ℰ (01364) 661217, Fax (01364) 661292, ≤
countryside, « Country house atmosphere », 舟 – ⵚ rest, ⊡ ☎ ℗. ⓪ ⒜ ⓪ 𝘝𝘐𝘚𝘈 𝘑𝘊𝘉.
⌘
restricted opening in winter – Meals (booking essential to non-residents) (light lunch)/
dinner 22.50 st. ⓵ 6.40 – 8 rm ⊡ 75.00/150.00 st.

**Haytor Vale** West : 3½ m. by B 3387 – ⊠ Newton Abbot.

🏠 **Rock Inn**, TQ13 9XP, ℰ (01364) 661305, Fax (01364) 661242, « 18C », 舟 – ⵚ ⊡ ☎ ℰ
℗. ⓪ ⒜ 𝘝𝘐𝘚𝘈 𝘑𝘊𝘉
Four Seasons : Meals 25.95 t. (dinner) and a la carte 17.95/25.75 t. ⓵ 6.95 – 9 rm
⊡ 49.95/105.00 t. – SB.

**VINGDON** Herts. **404** S 28 – pop. 4 491.
London 35 – Aylesbury 29 – Maidenhead 21 – Oxford 31.

🏨 **Bobsleigh Inn**, Hempstead Rd, HP3 0DS, on B 4505 ℰ (01442) 833276,
Fax (01442) 832471, ☒, 舟 – ⊡ ☎ ☾ ℗ – 益 60. ⓪ ⒜ 𝘝𝘐𝘚𝘈
closed 1 week Christmas – Meals (closed Monday lunch and Sunday) 15.95/20.95 st.
and a la carte ⓵ 6.50 – 44 rm ⊡ 67.00/97.00 st. – SB.

**WBURN** Durham **401** **402** P 19 – pop. 3 296.
London 265 – Durham 3 – Middlesbrough 20.

**RoadChef Lodge** without rest., Tursdale Rd, DH6 5NP, at junction 61 of A 1(M)
ℰ (0191) 377 3666, Fax (0191) 377 1448, Reservations (Freephone) 0800 834719 – ⵚ ⊡ ☎
☾ ℗. ⓪ ⒜ ⓪ 𝘝𝘐𝘚𝘈. ⌘
closed 24 December – 38 rm 45.95 t.

**WNESS-ON-WINDERMERE** Cumbria **402** L20 – see Windermere.

**X** Wilts. **403** **404** M 29 – see Bath (Bath & North East Somerset).

**ACKLEY** Northants. **403** **404** Q 27 – pop. 9 113.
🛈 2 Bridge St., NN13 5EP ℰ (01280) 700111.
London 67 – Birmingham 53 – Northampton 21 – Oxford 21.

🏠 **Crown**, 20 Market Pl., NN13 7DP, ℰ (01280) 702210, Fax (01280) 701840 – ⊡ ☎ – 益 60.
⓪ ⒜ ⓪ 𝘝𝘐𝘚𝘈. ⌘
Meals (bar lunch)/dinner 10.50 st. and a la carte – ⊡ 7.25 – 19 rm 65.00/75.00 t. – SB.

⓪ ATS Station Building, Northampton Rd ℰ (01280) 702000/703188

**ACKNELL** Bracknell Forest **404** R 29 – pop. 60 895.
☗ Downshire, Easthampstead Park, Wokingham ℰ (01344) 302030.
🛈 The Look Out, Nine Mile Ride, RG12 7QW ℰ (01344) 868196.
London 35 – Reading 11.

🏨 **Coppid Beech,** John Nike Way, RG12 8TF, Northwest : 3 m. by A 329 on B 34
ℰ (01344) 303333, *Fax (01344) 301200*, Ⅰ♣, ≘ˢ, ⬜ – ⅼ▮, ⅀ rm, ▤ rest, ▦ ☎ ₺ ℗
⅍ 350. ⑩ ◭ ⑪ 🆅🆂🅰 JCB. ⅍
*Rowans :* Meals *(closed Saturday lunch)* 23.95 t. and a la carte ⅼ 8.75 – **195 rm** ⋍ 175.0
205.00 t., 10 suites – SB.

🏨 **Hilton National Bracknell,** Bagshot Rd, RG12 0QJ, South : 2 m. on A 3
ℰ (01344) 424801, *Fax (01344) 487454*, ≘ˢ – ⅼ▮, ⅀ rm, ▤ rest, ▦ ☎ ℗ – ⅍ 450. ⑩
⑪ 🆅🆂🅰 JCB
Meals *(closed Saturday lunch)* 15.95/18.50 t. and a la carte ⅼ 6.50 – ⋍ 11.95 – **167 r**
137.00/177.00 st. – SB.

🏨 **Travel Inn,** Arlington Sq., Wokingham Rd, RG12 1WA, West : ½ m. on A 329 at "3.
roundabout ℰ (01344) 486320, *Fax (01344) 486172* – ⅀ rm, ▦ ₺ ℗. ⑩ ◭ ⑪ 🆅🆂🅰
Meals (grill rest.) – **40 rm** 38.00 t.

---

**BRADFORD** W. Yorks. ꛴⓪꛴ O 22 *Great Britain G.* – pop. 289 376.

See : *City★*.

🏌 *West Bowling, Newall Hall, Rooley Lane* ℰ *(01274) 724449* BY – 🏌 *Woodhall H*
*Woodhall Rd, Calverley, Pudsley* ℰ *(0113) 256 4771* – 🏌 *Bradford Moor, Scarr Hall, Poll*
*Lane* ℰ *(01274) 771716* BX – 🏌 *East Bierley, South View Rd* ℰ *(01274) 681023* BX
🏌 *Queensbury, Brighouse Rd* ℰ *(01274) 882155*, AY.

✈ *Leeds and Bradford Airport :* ℰ *(0113) 250 9696, NE : 6 m. by A 658* BX.

🛈 *National Museum of Photography, Film & TV, Pictureville, BD1 1NQ* ℰ *(01274) 753678.*
*London 212 – Leeds 9 – Manchester 39 – Middlesbrough 75 – Sheffield 45.*

Plan of Enlarged Area : see Leeds

🏨 **Cedar Court,** Mayo Av., off Rooley Lane, BD5 8HZ, ℰ *(01274) 406606, Fax (01274) 4066*
Ⅰ♣, ≘ˢ, ⬜ – ⅼ▮, ⅀ rm, ▤ rest, ▦ ☎ ₺ ℗ – ⅍ 600. ⑩ ◭ ⑪ 🆅🆂🅰 JCB          BY
*Four Seasons :* Meals *(closed Saturday lunch)* 13.25/19.50 t. and a la carte ⅼ 10.95 –
9.50 – **130 rm** 99.00 st., 1 suite – SB.

🏨 **Quality Victoria,** Bridge St., BD1 1JX, ℰ *(01274) 728706, Fax (01274) 736358*, Ⅰ♣, ≘
ⅼ▮, ⅀ rm, ▦ ☎ ℗ – ⅍ 150. ⑩ ◭ 🆅🆂🅰                                            BZ
*Vic and Bert's :* Meals 14.50 st. and a la carte ⅼ 4.50 – ⋍ 9.50 – **57 rm** 66.50/80.25
3 suites.

🏨 **Stakis Bradford,** Hall Ings, BD1 5SH, ℰ *(01274) 734734, Fax (01274) 306146* – ⅼ▮, ⅀
▤ rest, ▦ ☎ ₺ – ⅍ 700. ⑩ ◭ ⑪ 🆅🆂🅰                                            BZ
Meals *(closed Sunday lunch)* (grill rest.) a la carte 11.45/18.00 t. – ⋍ 8.95 – **116 rm** 99.0
119.00 st., 4 suites – SB.

🏨 **Courtyard by Marriott Leeds/Bradford,** The Pastures, Tong Lane, BD4 0
Southeast : 4 ¾ m. by A 650 and B 6135 on Tong Lane ℰ *(0113) 28546*
*Fax (0113) 2853661*, Ⅰ♣, ⅍ – ⅼ▮, ⅀ rm, ▦ ☎ ℗ – ⅍ 250. ⑩ ◭ ⑪ 🆅🆂🅰. ⅍
Meals a la carte 14.70/22.75 st. ⅼ 7.25 – ⋍ 9.50 – **53 rm** 76.00 st. – SB.
on Leeds town plan BX

🏨 **Guide Post,** Common Rd, Low Moor, BD12 0ST, South : 3 m. by A 641 off A
ℰ *(01274) 607866, Fax (01274) 671085* – ⅀ rm, ▦ ☎ ℗ – ⅍ 100. ⑩ ◭ ⑪ 🆅🆂🅰 JCB.
Meals *(closed Saturday lunch and Sunday dinner)* 9.95/14.95 t. and dinner a la carte ⅼ 3
– **43 rm** ⋍ 60.00/90.00 t.                                          on Leeds town plan AX

🏨 **Novotel Bradford,** Euroway Trading Estate, Merrydale Rd, BD4 6SA, South : 3 ½ m. b
641 and A 6117 off M 606 ℰ *(01274) 683683, Fax (01274) 651342*, ⬜ – ⅼ▮, ⅀ rm, ▦
℗ – ⅍ 300. ⑩ ◭ ⑪ 🆅🆂🅰                                          on Leeds town plan AX
Meals 13.50 st. and a la carte – ⋍ 8.50 – **127 rm** 59.00 st. – SB.

🏨 **Travel Inn,** Whitehall Rd, Cleckheaton, BD19 6HG, South : 5 ½ m. by A 650, A 6177, M 6
off A 58 ℰ *(01274) 862828, Fax (01274) 852973* – ⅀ rm, ▤ rest, ▦ ₺ ℗. ⑩ ◭ ⑪
⅍                                                                 on Leeds town plan BX
Meals (grill rest.) – **40 rm** 38.00 t.

XXX **Restaurant Nineteen** (Smith) with rm, 19 North Park Rd, Heaton, BD9 4
❀ ℰ *(01274) 492559, Fax (01274) 483827* – ▦ ☎ ℗. ⑩ ◭ 🆅🆂🅰. ⅍          AX
closed Sunday, Monday, 1 week June, 1 week August and 2 weeks December-Januar
Meals *(dinner only)* 28.00 t. ⅼ 8.75 – ⋍ 7.50 – **4 rm** 70.00/85.00 st.
Spec. Gorgonzola tart with rocket salad and chutney. Rack of lamb with rosemary, thy
and lamb charlotte. Poached pears with Bakewell tart ice cream and raspberry sauce.

**at Gomersal** *Southeast : 7 m. by A 650 on A 651* – BY – ✉ *Bradford.*

🏨 **Gomersal Park,** Moor Lane, BD19 4LJ, Northeast : 1 ½ m. by A 651 off A
ℰ *(01274) 869386, Fax (01274) 861042*, Ⅰ♣, ≘ˢ, ⬜, ⅍ – ▦ ☎ ℗ – ⅍ 200. ⑩ ◭
🆅🆂🅰 JCB                                                                     BU
Meals *(closed Saturday lunch)* 11.95/16.95 t. ⅼ 6.95 – ⋍ 8.25 – **52 rm** 83.00/99.00 t. – S

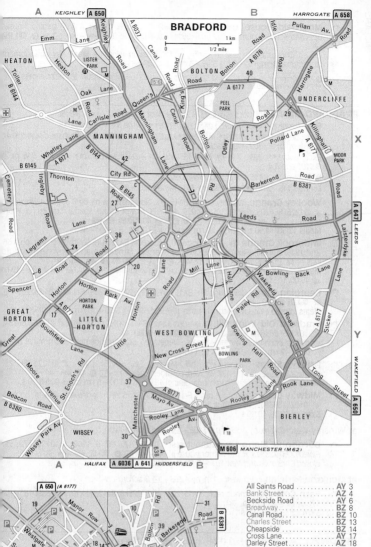

BRADFORD

↑ **Moorfield House**, Oxford Rd, BD19 4HD, South : ¼ m. off A 651, behind houses opposite Kebble Court  🅿 (01274) 870611, Fax (01274) 851887, �₩ – ✝ 📺 ☎ 🅿. 🕲 𝓥𝓘𝓢𝓐 🕉
closed Christmas, 1 week in spring and 1 week in winter – **Meals** (by arrangement) (communal dining) 12.00 t. ⅜ 5.95 – **3 rm** ⊑ 42.00/58.00 t.

🅰 ATS 8 Cranmer Rd 🅿 (01274) 632233/632106     ATS Tong Street (ASDA) 🅿 (01274) 680155
ATS 177 Thornton Rd 🅿 (01274) 731141/723015

---

**BRADFORD-ON-AVON** Wilts. 🔢🔢 N 29 The West Country G. – pop. 8 815.
See : Town★★ - Saxon Church of St. Lawrence★★ - Tithe Barn★ - Bridge★.
Env. : Great Chalfield Manor★ (All Saints★) AC, NE : 3 m. by B 3109 – Westwood Manor★ AC
S : 1½ m. by B 3109 – Top Rank Tory (≤★).
Exc. : Bath★★★, NW : 7½ m. by A 363 and A 4 – Corsham Court★★ AC, NE : 6½ m. by B 3109 and A 4.
🎫 34 Silver St., BA15 1JX 🅿 (01225) 865797.
London 118 – Bristol 24 – Salisbury 35 – Swindon 33.

🏨 **Woolley Grange**, Woolley Green, BA15 1TX, Northeast : ¾ m. by B 3107 on Woolley St
🅿 (01225) 864705, Fax (01225) 864059, ≤, « 17C manor house, special facilities for young children », 🏊, 🌳, 🎾 – ✝ rest, 📺 ☎ 🅿 – 🛎 40. 🕲 🄰🄴 🄾 𝓥𝓘𝓢𝓐
**Meals** 15.50/34.50 t. ⅜ 5.95 – **20 rm** ⊑ 95.00/99.00 st., 3 suites – SB.

🏨 **Widbrook Grange** 🦢, Trowbridge Rd, Widbrook, BA15 1UH, Southeast : 1 m. on A 363
🅿 (01225) 864750, Fax (01225) 862890, « Georgian farmhouse and converted outbuildings », ⅙₄, �ᵗᵛ, 🌳, park – ✝ 📺 ☎ ❖ 🅿 – 🛎 25. 🕲 🄰🄴 🄾 𝓥𝓘𝓢𝓐 𝓙𝓒𝓑 🕉
**Meals** (closed Friday to Sunday) (residents only) (dinner only) 24.50 t. ⅜ 7.50 – **19 rm** ⊑ 45.00/105.00 t.

🏠 **Georgian Lodge**, 25 Bridge St., BA15 1BY, 🅿 (01225) 862268, Fax (01225) 862218 – 📺 ☎. 🕲 🄰🄴 🄾 𝓥𝓘𝓢𝓐. 🕉
**Meals** (closed Monday lunch) a la carte 16.75/21.50 st. ⅜ 5.00 – **10 rm** ⊑ 30.00/58.00 st.

↑ **Bradford Old Windmill**, 4 Masons Lane, BA15 1QN, on A 363 🅿 (01225) 866842, Fax (01225) 866648, ≤, 🌳 – ✝ 📺 🅿. 🕲 🄰🄴 🄾 𝓥𝓘𝓢𝓐. 🕉
restricted opening in winter – **Meals** - Vegetarian - (by arrangement) (communal dining) 20.00 s. – **2 rm** ⊑ 65.00/99.00 s., 1 suite.

↑ **Priory Steps**, Newtown, off Market St., BA15 1NQ, 🅿 (01225) 862230, Fax (01225) 866248, ≤, « 17C weavers cottages », 🌳 – ✝ 📺 🅿. 🕲 𝓥𝓘𝓢𝓐. 🕉
**Meals** (by arrangement) (communal dining) 19.00 st. ⅜ 4.00 – **5 rm** ⊑ 53.00/68.00 s.

↑ **Midway Cottage** without rest., Farleigh Wick, BA15 2PU, Northwest : 2¾ m. on A 363
🅿 (01225) 863932, 🌳 – 📺 ☎ ❖ 🅿. 🕉
**3 rm** ⊑ 38.00/40.00 s.

**at Winsley** West : 2½ m. by A 363 on B 3108 – ✉ Bradford-on-Avon.

↑ **Burghope Manor** 🦢 without rest., BA15 2LA, off B 3108 🅿 (01225) 723557, Fax (01225) 723113, « 13C manor house », 🌳 – ✝ 📺 🅿. 🕲 🄰🄴 𝓥𝓘𝓢𝓐 𝓙𝓒𝓑. 🕉
closed Christmas and New Year – **5 rm** ⊑ 60.00/80.00 st.

**at Monkton Farleigh** Northwest : 4 m. by A 363 – ✉ Bradford-on-Avon.

↑ **Fern Cottage** without rest., BA15 2QJ, 🅿 (01225) 859412, Fax (01225) 859018, « Part 17C », 🌳 – ✝ 📺 🅿. 🕉
**3 rm** ⊑ 35.00/60.00 st.

---

**BRADWELL** Derbs. 🔢🔢🔢 O 24 – pop. 1 728 – ✉ Sheffield.
London 181 – Derby 51 – Manchester 32 – Sheffield 16 – Stoke-on-Trent 41.

↑ **Stoney Ridge** 🦢 without rest., Granby Rd, S33 9HU, West : ¾ m. via Town Lane
🅿 (01433) 620538, 🖾, 🌳 – 📺 🅿. 🕲 𝓥𝓘𝓢𝓐 𝓙𝓒𝓑
**4 rm** ⊑ 30.00/56.00.

---

**BRAFFERTON HELPERBY** N. Yorks 🔢 P 21 – see Boroughbridge.

---

**BRAINTREE** Essex 🔢 V 28 – pop. 33 229.
🏌 Kings Lane, Stisted 🅿 (01376) 346079 – 🏌 Towerlands, Panfield Rd 🅿 (01376) 326802.
🎫 Town Hall Centre, Market Sq., CM7 6YG 🅿 (01376) 550066.
London 45 – Cambridge 38 – Chelmsford 12 – Colchester 15.

🏨 **White Hart,** Bocking End, CM7 9AB, ☎ (01376) 321401, *Fax (01376) 552628,* 🛗 – 🚭 rm, [TV] ☎ [P] – 🏫 40. [MO] [AE] [VISA] [JCB]. 🐕
**Meals** (grill rest.) a la carte 16.45/24.95 **t.** 🍷 5.25 – ☕ 5.95 – **31 rm** 53.00/60.00 **t.** – SB.

🏨 **Travel Inn,** Galley's Corner, CM7 8GG, Southeast : 2 m. by B 1018 on A 120 ☎ (01376) 340914, *Fax (01376) 370437* – 🚭 rm, [TV] ♿ [P]. [MO] [AE] [DC] [VISA]
**Meals** (grill rest.) – **40 rm** 38.00 **t.**

🔧 ATS 271-275 Rayne Rd ☎ (01376) 323306

---

**BRAITHWAITE** *Cumbria* [401] [402] K 20 – *see Keswick.*

---

**BRAMHALL** *Gtr. Manchester* [402] [403] [404] N 23 – *pop. 39 730 (inc. Hazel Grove)* – ✉ *Stockport.*
*London 190 – Chesterfield 35 – Manchester 11.*

🏨 **County H. Bramhall,** Bramhall Lane South, SK7 2EB, on A 5102 ☎ (0161) 455 9988, *Fax (0161) 440 8071* – [TV] ☎ ♿ [P] – 🏫 200. [MO] [AE] [DC] [VISA]. 🐕
**Meals** (bar lunch Saturday) a la carte 12.95/22.25 **st.** 🍷 4.50 – ☕ 9.50 – **65 rm** 97.50/137.50 **st.** – SB.

---

**BRAMHOPE** *W. Yorks.* [402] P 22 – *see Leeds.*

---

**BRAMLEY** *S. Yorks.* [402] [403] [404] Q 23 – *see Rotherham.*

---

**BRAMPTON** *Cumbria* [401] [402] L 19 *Great Britain G.* – *pop. 3 957.*
**Env.** : *Hadrian's Wall★★, NW : by A 6077.*
⛳18 *Talkin Tarn ☎ (016977) 2255.*
ℹ *Moot Hall, Market Pl., CA8 1RA ☎ (016977) 3433 (summer only).*
*London 317 – Carlisle 9 – Newcastle upon Tyne 49.*

🏨 **Farlam Hall** 🐦, CA8 2NG, Southeast : 2 ¾ m. on A 689 ☎ (016977) 46234, *Fax (016977) 46683,* ≤, « Gardens » – [TV] ☎ [P]. [MO] [VISA]
*closed 24 to 31 December* – **Meals** (dinner only) 31.00 **t.** 🍷 6.75 – **12 rm** ☕ (dinner included) 115.00/240.00 **t.** – SB.

🏨 **Kirby Moor Country House,** Longtown Rd, CA8 2AB, North : ½ m. on A 6071 ☎ (016977) 3893, *Fax (016977) 41847,* 🌳 – 🚭 rest, [TV] ☎ [P]. [MO] [VISA]. 🐕
**Meals** *(closed Monday)* 12.95 **st.** and a la carte 🍷 5.50 – **6 rm** ☕ 38.00/64.00 **st.** – SB.

**at Kirkcambeck** *North : 7 ¾ m. by A 6071 and Walton rd* – ✉ *Brampton.*

🏠 **Cracrop Farm** 🐦 without rest., CA8 2BW, West : 1 m. by B 6318 on Stapleton rd ☎ (016977) 48245, *Fax (016977) 48333,* ≤, « Working farm », 🛗, 🌳, park – 🚭 [TV] [P]. [MO] [AE] [VISA]. 🐕
*closed 1 week Christmas* – **3 rm** ☕ 25.00/50.00 **st.**

---

**BRANCASTER STAITHE** *Norfolk* [404] V 25.
*London 131 – Cambridge 74 – Norwich 39.*

🍺 **The White Horse,** Main Rd, PE31 8BW, ☎ (01485) 210262, *Fax (01485) 210262,* ≤, 🌳 – [P]. [MO] [AE] [VISA]
**Meals** a la carte 12.95/24.15 **t.** 🍷 4.00.

---

**BRANDESBURTON** *East Riding* [402] T 22 – *pop. 1 835* – ✉ *Great Driffield.*
*London 197 – Kingston-upon-Hull 16 – York 37.*

🏨 **Burton Lodge,** YO25 8RU, Southwest : ½ m. on Leven rd ☎ (01964) 542847, *Fax (01964) 542847,* ⛳18, 🌳, 🎾 – 🚭 rest, [TV] ☎ [P]. [MO] [AE] [VISA] [JCB]
*closed 25 and 26 December* – **Meals** (residents only) (dinner only) 13.50 **st.** – **9 rm** ☕ 36.00/52.00 **st.** – SB.

---

**BRANDON** *Warks.* [403] [404] P 26 – *see Coventry (W. Mids.).*

---

**BRANDS HATCH** *Kent* [404] ㊹ – ✉ *Dartford.*
⛳9 *Corinthian, Gay Dawn Farm, Fawkham, Dartford ☎ (01474) 707559.*
*London 22 – Maidstone 18.*

🏨 **Thistle Brands Hatch,** DA3 8PE, on A 20 ☎ (01474) 854900, *Fax (01474) 853220* – 🚭 rm, ▤ rest, [TV] ☎ ♿ [P] – 🏫 270. [MO] [AE] [DC] [VISA] [JCB]
***Genevieves :*** **Meals** 15.95/22.50 **st.** and a la carte 🍷 7.00 – ***Bugatti Brasserie :*** **Meals** a la carte 13.70/25.55 **st.** 🍷 7.00 – ☕ 11.00 – **121 rm** 99.00/150.00 **st.** – SB.

**at Fawkham Green** *East : 1½ m. by A 20 – ✉ Ash Green.*

🏨 **Brands Hatch Place,** DA3 8NQ, ✆ (01474) 872239, *Fax (01474) 879652,* Fø, ≘s, 🏊, park, 🎾, squash – ⇔ rm, 📺 ☎ 🅿 – 🏛 120. 🅼🅲 AE ① VISA. ✂
Meals 14.95/21.95 **t.** and a la carte 🍷 7.00 – ☕ 9.50 – **41 rm** 85.00/99.00 **st.** – SB.

---

**BRANSCOMBE** *Devon* 403 K 31 *The West Country G. – pop. 501 – ✉ Seaton.*
See : *Village*★.
Env. : *Seaton (<★★), NW : 3 m – Colyton*★.
*London 167 – Exeter 20 – Lyme Regis 11.*

🏠 **Masons Arms,** EX12 3DJ, ✆ (01297) 680300, *Fax (01297) 680500,* « 14C inn » – ⇔ rest 📺 ☎ 🅿 – 🏛 100. 🅼🅲 VISA
Meals (bar lunch Monday to Saturday)/dinner 22.00 **st.** 🍷 6.00 – **21 rm** ☕ 22.00/96.00 **st.** – SB.

---

**BRANSTON** *Lincs.* 402 404 S 24 – *see Lincoln.*

---

**BRANSTON** *Staffs. – see Burton-upon-Trent.*

---

**BRAYE** *Alderney (Channel Islands)* 403 Q 33 and 230 ⑨ – *see Channel Islands.*

*Le Guide change, changez de* ***guide Michelin*** *tous les ans.*

---

**BRAY-ON-THAMES** *Windsor & Maidenhead* 404 R 29 – *pop. 8 121 – ✉ Maidenhead.*
*London 34 – Reading 13.*

Plan : see Maidenhead

🏨 **Monkey Island,** SL6 2EE, Southeast : ¾ m. by Upper Bray Rd and Old Mill Lan… ✆ (01628) 23400, *Fax (01628) 784732,* <, 🏖, « Island on River Thames », Fø, 🎣, 🌳 – 📺 ☎ 🅿 – 🏛 150. 🅼🅲 AE ① VISA. ✂
*closed 26 December-15 January* – **Meals** *(closed Saturday lunch)* 21.50/29.50 t… and a la carte – ☕ 12.00 – **23 rm** 100.00/145.00 **t.**, 2 suites – SB.

🏨 **Chauntry House,** 1 High St., SL6 2AB, ✆ (01628) 673991, *Fax (01628) 773089,* 🌳 … ⇔ rest, 📺 ☎ 🅿. 🅼🅲 AE ① VISA JCB. ✂ X
*closed 24 December-2 January* – **Meals** *(closed Sunday and Bank Holidays)* 30.00 **st**… (dinner) and a la carte 27.00/35.00 **st.** 🍷 6.00 – **15 rm** ☕ 100.00/145.00 **st.**

XXXX ❀❀❀ **Waterside Inn** (Roux) with rm, Ferry Rd, SL6 2AT, ✆ (01628) 620691, *Fax (01628) 78471…* « < Thames-side setting » – ⚓, ▤ rest, 📺 ☎ 🅿. 🅼🅲 AE ① VISA JCB. ✂ X
*closed 5 to 8 April and 26 December-28 January* – **Meals** - French - *(closed Tuesday lunch… Sunday dinner from October-April and Monday)* 29.50-44.50/67.50 **t.** and a la carte 59.30… 88.50 **t.** 🍷 11.00 – **8 rm** 140.00/170.00 **st.**, 1 suite
**Spec.** Tronçonnettes de homard poêlées minute au Porto blanc. Filets de lapereau grillé… aux marrons glacés. Soufflé chaud aux framboises.

XX ❀ **Fat Duck** (Blumenthal), High St., SL6 2AQ, ✆ (01628) 580333, *Fax (01628) 776188,* 🌳 🅼🅲 AE VISA X
*closed Sunday dinner, Monday and 2 weeks Christmas* – **Meals** 22.50 **t.** (lunch) and a la cart… 31.50/51.00 **t.**
**Spec.** Crab feuillantine with marinated salmon, roast foie gras, oyster vinaigrette. Jambon… neau of Trelough duck 'petit salé', pommes purées. Chocolate tart with milk ice crean… pistachio sauce.

🍺 **The Fish,** Old Mill Lane, SL6 2BG, ✆ (01628) 781111, *Fax (01628) 623571* – 🅿. 🅼🅲 VISA
*closed Sunday dinner, Monday and 1 week Christmas* – **Meals** - Seafood - a la carte 18.70… 33.20 **t.**

---

**BREADSALL** *Derby – see Derby.*

---

**BREDE** *E. Sussex* 404 V 31 – *pop. 1 764.*
*London 62 – Brighton 43 – Canterbury 41 – Hastings 7 – Maidstone 25.*

⌂ **Arndale Cottage** without rest., Northiam Rd, Broad Oak, TN31 6EP, North : 1 ½ m. on … 28 ✆ (01424) 882813, *Fax (01424) 882813,* 🌳 – ⇔ 📺 🅿. ✂
*closed 23 to 31 December* – **3 rm** ☕ 30.00/45.00 **s.**

**BREDWARDINE** Herefordshire 403 L 27 – ⊠ Hereford.
London 150 – Hereford 12 – Newport 51.

↑ **Brobury House** ⊗ without rest., Brobury, HR3 6BS, ℘ (01981) 500595, Fax (01981) 500229, « Victorian country house, gardens », ⌐, park – ⇆ ℗. ⚫ 𝒱𝒮𝒜. ⊛
4 rm ⊆ 40.00/90.00.

↑ **Bredwardine Hall** ⊗, HR3 6DB, ℘ (01981) 500596, Fax (01981) 500596, ⌨ – ⇆ 📺
℗. ⊛
closed December – **Meals** (by arrangement) 12.00 st. ‖ 5.50 – **5 rm** ⊆ 30.00/52.00 st. – SB.

**BRENTWOOD** Essex 404 V 29 – pop. 49 463.
⌐₁₈ Bentley G. & C.C., Ongar Road ℘ (01277) 373179 – ⌐₉, ⌐₁₈, Warley Park, Magpie Lane, Little Warley ℘ (01277) 224891.
🅱 14 Ongar Rd, CM15 9AX ℘ (01277) 200300.
London 22 – Chelmsford 11 – Southend-on-Sea 21.

🏢 **Marygreen Manor,** London Rd, CM14 4NR, Southwest : 1 ¼ m. on A 1023
℘ (01277) 225252, Fax (01277) 262809, ⌨ – ⇆ rm, 📺 ☎ ✆ ⅗ ℗ – ⚖ 50. ⚫ ᴁ ⓪ 𝒱𝒮𝒜.
⊛
**Meals** 17.00/27.00 t. and a la carte ‖ 6.50 – ⊆ 10.50 – **53 rm** 111.50/129.50 st., 1 suite.

🏢 **Forte Posthouse Brentwood,** Brook St., CM14 5NF, Southwest : 1 ½ m. on A 1023
℘ (01277) 260260, Fax (01277) 264264, ⌐₆, ≋, ◰ – ⌸, ⇆ rm, 📺 ☎ ℗ – ⚖ 100. ⚫ ᴁ
⓪ 𝒱𝒮𝒜 ᴊᴄʙ. ⊛
**Meals** a la carte 15.00/23.00 st. ‖ 6.00 – ⊆ 9.75 – **145 rm** 109.00 st.

Ⓐ ATS Fairfield Rd ℘ (01277) 211079　　　　　Unit 30, Wash Rd, Hutton Ind. Est., Hutton
　　　　　　　　　　　　　　　　　　　　　　℘ (01277) 262877

**BRETFORTON** Glos. 403 404 O 27 – see Chipping Campden.

**BRIDGNORTH** Shrops. 402 403 404 M 26 Great Britain G. – pop. 11 229.
Exc. : Ironbridge Gorge Museum★★ AC (The Iron Bridge★★ - Coalport China Museum★★ - Blists Hill Open Air Museum★★ - Museum of the River and Visitor Centre★) NW : 8 m. by B 4373.
⌐₁₈ Stanley Lane ℘ (01746) 763315.
🅱 The Library, Listley St., WV16 4AW ℘ (01746) 763257.
London 146 – Birmingham 26 – Shrewsbury 20 – Worcester 29.

🏠 **Cross Lane House,** Cross Lane Head, WV16 4SJ, North : 1 ½ m. on B 4373
℘ (01746) 764887, Fax (01746) 768667, ≤, ⌨ – ⇆ 📺 ℗. ⚫ ᴁ 𝒱𝒮𝒜 ᴊᴄʙ
**Meals** (residents only) (lunch by arrangement)/dinner 17.50 st. ‖ 6.25 – **9 rm** ⊆ 42.50/65.00 st. – SB.

**at Worfield** Northeast : 4 m. by A 454 – ⊠ Bridgnorth.

🏨 **Old Vicarage** ⊗, WV15 5JZ, ℘ (01746) 716497, Fax (01746) 716552, « Edwardian parsonage », ⌨ – ⇆ 📺 ☎ ✆ ℗. ⚫ 𝒱𝒮𝒜
closed 25 to 31 December – **Meals** (booking essential) (lunch by arrangement Monday to Saturday)/dinner 25.00 st. and a la carte ‖ 7.70 – **13 rm** ⊆ 70.00/160.00 st., 1 suite – SB.

**at Alveley** Southeast : 7 m. by A 442 – ⊠ Bridgnorth.

🏢 **Mill,** Birdsgreen, WV15 6HL, Northeast : ¾ m. ℘ (01746) 780437, Fax (01746) 780850, ⌨ –
⌸, ⇆ rest, 📺 ☎ ℗ – ⚖ 200. ⚫ ᴁ ⓪ 𝒱𝒮𝒜. ⊛
**Meals** 10.50/19.50 t. and a la carte ‖ 6.20 – ⊆ 6.00 – **21 rm** 69.50/100.00 t. – SB.

**BRIDGWATER** Somerset 403 L 30 The West Country G. – pop. 34 610.
See : Town★ – Castle Street★ – St. Mary's★ – Admiral Blake Museum★ AC.
Env. : Westonzoyland (St. Mary's Church★★) SE : 4 m. by A 372 – North Petherton (Church Tower★★) S : 3½ m. by A 38.
Exc. : Stogursey Priory Church★★, NW : 14 m. by A 39.
⌐₁₈ Enmore Park,Enmore ℘ (01278) 671244.
🅱 50 High St., TA6 3BL ℘ (01278) 427652 (summer only).
London 160 – Bristol 39 – Taunton 11.

🏨 **Walnut Tree,** North Petherton, TA6 6QA, South : 3 m. on A 38 ℘ (01278) 662255,
Fax (01278) 663946 – ⇆ rm, ▤ rest, 📺 ☎ ✆ ℗ – ⚖ 120. ⚫ ᴁ ⓪ 𝒱𝒮𝒜 ᴊᴄʙ. ⊛
**Meals** 8.70/15.50 t. and a la carte ‖ 6.90 – ⊆ 6.50 – **31 rm** 63.00/76.00 t., 1 suite.

Ⓐ ATS Friarn St. ℘ (01278) 455891/455795

**BRIDLINGTON** East Riding 402 T 21 Great Britain G. – pop. 31 334.

Env. : Flamborough Head★, NE : 5 ½ m. by B 1255 and B 1259 – Burton Agnes Hall★ AC SW : 6 m. by A 166.

🛅 Belvedere Rd ℰ (01262) 672092/606367 – 🛅 Flamborough Head, Lighthouse Rd, Flamborough ℰ (01262) 850333/850417.

🖪 25 Prince St., YO15 2NP ℰ (01262) 673474.

London 236 – Kingston-upon-Hull 29 – York 41.

🏨 **Expanse,** North Marine Drive, YO15 2LS, ℰ (01262) 675347, Fax (01262) 604928, ≼ – 📳 📺 ☎ 🅿. 🐗 🖭 ⓪ 🝙 JCB. ⁕
Meals 9.25/15.00 st. and dinner a la carte 🖟 4.35 – **48 rm** ☲ 29.50/80.00 st. – SB.

Ⓐ ATS Springfield Av. ℰ (01262) 675571

---

**BRIDPORT** Dorset 403 L 31 The West Country G. – pop. 7 278.

Env. : Parnham House★★ AC, N : 6 m. by A 3066 – Mapperton Gardens★, N : 4 m. by A 3066 and minor rd.

Exc. : – Lyme Regis★ – The Cobb★, W : 11 m. by A 35 and A 3052.

🛅 Bridport and West Dorset, East Cliff, West Bay ℰ (01308) 422597.

🖪 32 South St., DT6 3NQ ℰ (01308) 424901.

London 150 – Exeter 38 – Taunton 33 – Weymouth 19.

🏨 **Roundham House,** Roundham Gdns, West Bay Rd, DT6 4BD, South : 1 m. by B 3157 ℰ (01308) 422753, Fax (01308) 421500, ≼, 🏂 – ⁕ rest, 📺 ☎ 🅿. 🐗 🝙 JCB
closed January and February – **Meals** (dinner only) 17.50 t. and a la carte 🖟 6.25 – **8 rm** ☲ 40.00/75.00 t. – SB.

🏠 **Britmead House,** West Bay Rd, DT6 4EG, South : 1 m. on B 3157 ℰ (01308) 422941, Fax (01308) 422516, 🏂 – ⁕ rest, 📺 🅿. 🐗 🖭 ⓪ 🝙. ⁕
Meals 14.00 st. 4.50 – **7 rm** ☲ 37.00/60.00 st. – SB.

✗ **Riverside,** West Bay, DT6 4EZ, South : 1 ¾ m. by B 3157 ℰ (01308) 422011 – 🐗 🝙 JCB
closed Sunday dinner, Monday except Bank Holidays and 6 December-28 February – **Meals** - Seafood - (booking essential) a la carte 17.50/29.50 t. 🖟 6.50.

**at Shipton Gorge** Southeast : 3 m. by A 35 – ✉ Bridport.

🏠 **Innsacre Farmhouse** ♨, Shipton Lane, DT6 4LJ, North : 1 m. ℰ (01308) 456137, Fax (01308) 456137, 🏂 – ⁕ 📺 🝙
closed 24 December-1 January – **Meals** (by arrangement) 14.50 – **4 rm** ☲ 45.00/65.00.

Ⓐ ATS Victoria Grove ℰ (01308) 423661

---

**BRIGHOUSE** W. Yorks. 402 O 22 – pop. 32 198.

London 213 – Bradford 12 – Burnley 28 – Manchester 35 – Sheffield 39.

🏨 **Forte Posthouse Brighouse,** Clifton Village, HD6 4HW, Southeast : 1 m. on A 644 ℰ (01484) 400400, Fax (01484) 400068, 🖪, 🛋, ⃞ – ⁕ rm, 📺 ☎ 🅿 – 🕍 150. 🐗 🖭 ⓪ 🝙
Meals 12.95/17.95 st. and a la carte 🖟 7.95 – ☲ 10.95 – **92 rm** 95.00 st., 2 suites – SB.

✗ **Brook's,** 6 Bradford Rd, HD6 1RW, ℰ (01484) 715284, Fax (01484) 712641 – ⁕. 🐗 🝙
closed Sunday except 21 March, 1 week August and 2 weeks January – **Meals** (dinner only and lunch in December)/dinner 21.95 t. 🖟 6.95.

---

**BRIGHTON AND HOVE** 404 T 31 Great Britain G. – pop. 192 453.

See : Town★★ - Royal Pavilion★★★ AC CZ – Seafront★★ – The Lanes★ BCZ – St. Bartholomew's★ AC CX B – Art Gallery and Museum (20C decorative arts★) CY M.

Env. : Devil's Dyke (≼★) NW : 5 m. by Dyke Rd (B 2121) BY.

🛅 East Brighton, Roedean Rd ℰ (01273) 604838 CV – 🛅 The Dyke, Devil's Dyke, Dyke Rd ℰ (01273) 857296, BV – 🛅 Hollingbury Park, Ditchling Rd ℰ (01273) 552010, CV – 🛅 Waterhall, Devils Dyke Rd ℰ (01273) 508658, AV.

✈ Shoreham Airport : ℰ (01273) 296900, W : 8 m. by A 27 AV.

🖪 10 Bartholomew Sq., BN1 1JS ℰ (01273) 323755.

London 53 – Portsmouth 48 – Southampton 61.

Plans on following pages

🏨 **Grand,** Kings Rd, BN1 2FW, ℰ (01273) 321188, Fax (01273) 202694, ≼, 🖪, 🛋, ⃞ – 📳 📺 ☎ 🅿 ⇔ – 🕍 800. 🐗 🖭 ⓪ 🝙
BZ v
Meals 19.50/30.00 and a la carte 🖟 8.00 – **195 rm** ☲ 145.00/270.00 st., 5 suites – SB.

🏨 **Thistle Brighton,** Kings Rd, BN1 2GS, ℰ (01273) 206700, Fax (01273) 820692, ≼, 🖪, 🛋, ⃞ – 📳 ⁕ rm, 📺 ☎ 🅺 ⇔ – 🕍 300. 🐗 🖭 ⓪ 🝙
CZ n
**Promenade :** Meals 16.50/18.50 st. and a la carte 🖟 7.95 – (see also **La Noblesse** below) – ☲ 12.00 – **200 rm** ☲ 150.00/170.00 st., 4 suites – SB.

**Stakis Brighton Metropole**, Kings Rd, BN1 2FU, ℰ (01273) 775432, *Fax (01273) 207764*, ≤, *f₆*, ≘s, ▨ – ⫴, ½≈ rm, ▤ ▥ ☎ ⇔ – ⥄ 1200. **⑩** Æ **①** *VISA* JCB
BZ s
**Meals** 31.35 t. and a la carte – ☲ 8.95 – **316 rm** 160.00/226.00 st., 10 suites – SB.

**Stakis Bedford**, Kings Rd, BN1 2JF, ℰ (01273) 329744, *Fax (01273) 775877*, ≤, ≘s, ▨ – ⫴, ▤ rest, ▥ ☎ ⇔ – ⥄ 450. **⑩** Æ **①** *VISA* JCB
BZ c
**Meals** (carving rest.) 16.45/19.80 and dinner a la carte – ☲ 7.50 – **129 rm** 145.00/225.00 st., 2 suites.

**Brighton Oak**, West St., BN1 2RQ, ℰ (01273) 220033, *Fax (01273) 778000* – ⫴, ½≈ rm, ▤ rest, ▥ ☎ ♿ – ⥄ 200. **⑩** Æ **①** *VISA*
BZ i
**Meals** (bar lunch Monday to Saturday)/dinner 14.75 t. and a la carte ⌀ 7.50 – ☲ 7.95 – **136 rm** 56.00/132.00 st., 2 suites.

**Jarvis Norfolk**, 149 Kings Rd, BN1 2PP, ℰ (01273) 738201, *Fax (01273) 821752*, ≘s, ▨ – ⫴ ½≈ ▥ ☎ ♿ ⇔ – ⥄ 60. **⑩** Æ **①** *VISA*
BZ r
**Meals** (bar lunch Monday to Saturday)/dinner 16.95 st. and a la carte ⌀ 7.00 – ☲ 8.95 – **122 rm** 92.00/108.00 st. – SB.

**Jarvis Preston Park**, 216 Preston Rd, BN1 6UU, North : 1 ½ m. on A 23 ℰ (01273) 507853, *Fax (01273) 540039*, ≘s, ▨ – ½≈ ▥ ☎ ♿ – ⥄ 60. **⑩** Æ **①** *VISA*
**Meals** (bar lunch Monday to Saturday)/dinner 15.95 t. and a la carte ⌀ 6.95 – ☲ 8.50 – **33 rm** 79.00/95.00 t. – SB.
BV a

**Topps** without rest., 17 Regency Sq., BN1 2FG, ℰ (01273) 729334, *Fax (01273) 203679* – ⫴ ▥ ☎ **⑩** Æ **①** *VISA* JCB ⚘
BZ a
**15 rm** ☲ 49.00/129.00 st.

**Adelaide** without rest., 51 Regency Sq., BN1 2FF, ℰ (01273) 205286, *Fax (01273) 220904* – ▥ ☎ **⑩** Æ *VISA* ⚘
BZ z
**12 rm** ☲ 41.00/82.00 st.

**Allendale**, 3 New Steine, BN2 1PB, ℰ (01273) 675436, *Fax (01273) 602603* – ½≈ rest, ▥ ☎ **⑩** Æ **①** *VISA* JCB ⚘
CZ u
**Meals** (by arrangement) (dinner only) 7.50 st. ⌀ 3.50 – **12 rm** ☲ 35.00/70.00 st.

**Prince Regent** without rest., 29 Regency Sq., BN1 2FH, ℰ (01273) 329962, *Fax (01273) 748162* – ▥ ☎ **⑩** Æ *VISA* JCB ⚘
BZ u
closed 25 and 26 December – **20 rm** ☲ 36.00/90.00 t.

**Amblecliff** without rest., 35 Upper Rock Gdns., BN2 1QF, ℰ (01273) 681161, *Fax (01273) 676945* – ½≈ ▥ ☎ **⑩** Æ *VISA* ⚘
CZ s
closed mid December–mid January – **8 rm** ☲ 45.00/65.00 t.

**Ainsley House**, 28 New Steine, BN2 1PD, ℰ (01273) 605310, *Fax (01273) 688604* – ½≈ rest, ▥ ☎ ♿ **⑩** Æ **①** *VISA* JCB ⚘
CZ r
closed 1 week Christmas – **Meals** (by arrangement) (dinner only) 19.00 st. – **11 rm** ☲ 30.00/68.00 st.

**New Steine** without rest., 12a New Steine, BN2 1PB, ℰ (01273) 681546, *Fax (01273) 681546* – ▥ **⑩** *VISA* ⚘
CZ v
closed 18 December–31 January – **10 rm** ☲ 25.00/59.00 st.

**Kempton House** without rest., 33-34 Marine Par., BN2 1TR, ℰ (01273) 570248, *Fax (01273) 570248*, ≤ – ▥ ☎ ♿ **⑩** Æ *VISA*
CZ a
**12 rm** ☲ 35.00/68.00 st.

XXX **La Noblesse** (at Thistle Brighton H.), Kings Rd, BN1 2GS, ℰ (01273) 206700, *Fax (01273) 820692* – ▤ ⇔ **⑩** Æ **①** *VISA*
CZ n
**Meals** (closed Monday) (dinner only) 28.50 st. ⌀ 7.95.

XX **One Paston Place**, 1 Paston Pl., Kemp Town, BN2 1HA, ℰ (01273) 606933, *Fax (01273) 675686* – ▤ **⑩** Æ **①** *VISA* JCB
CV a
closed Sunday, Monday, first 2 weeks January and first 2 weeks August – **Meals** 18.50 t. (lunch) and a la carte 26.50/32.00 t. ⌀ 5.50.

XX **Victor's**, 11 Little East St., BN1 1HT, ℰ (01273) 774545, *Fax (01273) 736487* – **⑩** Æ *VISA*
CZ s
closed 17 January and 2 weeks March – **Meals** - French - 9.95/14.95 t. and a la carte ⌀ 6.25.

XX **La Marinade**, 77 St. Georges Rd, Kemp Town, BN2 1EF, ℰ (01273) 600992, *Fax (01273) 600992* – ▤ **⑩** Æ **①** *VISA*
CV c
closed Sunday dinner, Monday, 1 week spring and 1 week winter – **Meals** - French - 13.50/18.50 t. ⌀ 7.00.

X **Terre à Terre**, 71 East St., BN1 1NQ, ℰ (01273) 729051, *Fax (01273) 327561* – **⑩** **①** *VISA* ⚘
closed Monday lunch and 24-26 December – **Meals** - Vegetarian - (light lunch)/dinner a la carte 14.65/17.00 t. ⌀ 6.25.
CZ e

X **Whytes**, 33 Western St., BN1 2PG, ℰ (01273) 776618 – **⑩** Æ *VISA*
BZ o
closed Sunday, Monday and 26 to 31 December – **Meals** (booking essential) (dinner only) 20.50 t. ⌀ 7.75.

# BRIGHTON AND HOVE

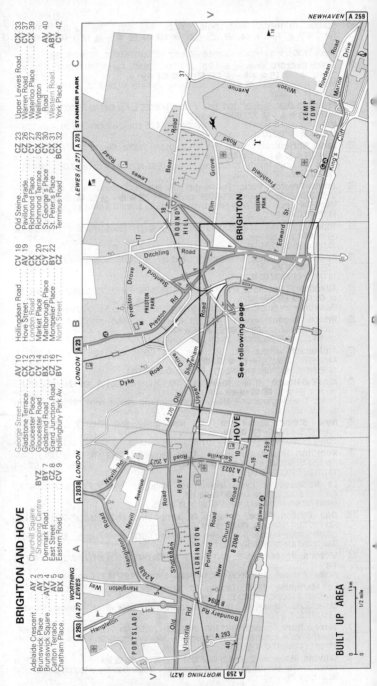

BUILT UP AREA

NEWHAVEN A 259

CENTRE

A 2073
A 259
A 2066
B 2066
A 259

BRIGHTON

HOVE

ROYAL PAVILION

THE LANES

THE BRIGHTON CENTRE

CHURCHILL SQ. SHOPPING CENTRE

ST. ANN'S WELL GARDENS

300 m
300 yards

151

✗ **Havana,** 32 Duke St., BN1 1AG, ℰ (01273) 773388, Fax (01273) 748923 – 🝏 🖭 🛈 𝖵𝖨𝖲𝖠
Meals 19.95 t. and a la carte ⅃ 5.95.  CZ

✗ **Black Chapati,** 12 Circus Par., off New England Rd, BN1 4GW, ℰ (01273) 699011 – 🝏 🅐
𝖵𝖨𝖲𝖠  CX
closed Sunday, Monday, 2 weeks July and 2 weeks Christmas – Meals - Asian specialities
(dinner only) 10.00 t. and a la carte 17.85/21.95 t.

at Hove.

🔒 **Claremont House,** Second Av., BN3 2LL, ℰ (01273) 735161, Fax (01273) 735161, 🚗
🖭 ☎ 🅰🅴 🛈 𝖵𝖨𝖲𝖠 𝖩𝖢𝖡  AY
Meals (bar lunch)/dinner 9.50 st. and a la carte 4.00 – **12 rm** 🖃 45.00/78.00 st. – SB.

✗ **Le Classique,** 37 Waterloo St., BN3 1AY, ℰ (01273) 734140 – ✦, 🝏 🅰🅴 🛈 𝖵𝖨𝖲𝖠  BY
closed Sunday, Monday and 25 December – Meals - French - (dinner only) 15.25 t
and a la carte ⅃ 4.95.

✗ **Quentin's,** 42 Western Rd, BN3 1JD, ℰ (01273) 822734 – 🝏 🅰🅴 🛈 𝖵𝖨𝖲𝖠  AZ
closed Saturday lunch, Sunday, Monday, last week August and first week September -
Meals 18.95 t. and a la carte.

🔘 ATS 40 Bristol Gdns ℰ (01273) 680150/686344      ATS Franklin Rd, Portslade ℰ (01273) 415327/
414488

---

**BRIMFIELD** Herefordshire 403 404 L 27 Great Britain G. – pop. 626 – ⊠ Ludlow (Shrops.).
Env. : Berrington Hall★ AC, S : 3 m. by A 49.
London 149 – Birmingham 41 – Hereford 21 – Shrewsbury 32 – Worcester 33.

🔒 **Travelodge,** Woofferton, SY8 4AL, North : ½ m. on A 49 ℰ (01584) 711695
Fax (01584) 711695, Reservations (Freephone) 0800 850950 – ✦ rm, 🖭 ₺ 🅿. 🝏 🅰🅴 🔘
𝖵𝖨𝖲𝖠 𝖩𝖢𝖡. ⌖
Meals (grill rest.) – **32 rm** 39.95/59.95 t.

↟ **The Marcle,** SY8 4NE, ℰ (01584) 711459, Fax (01584) 711459, « 16C cottage », 🚗 – ✦
🖭 🅿. ⌖
closed mid December-mid January – Meals (by arrangement) 19.50 s. – **3 rm** 🖃 40.00
58.00 s. – SB.

🝙 **Roebuck Inn** with rm, SY8 4NE, ℰ (01584) 711230, Fax (01584) 711654, 🏡 – 🖭 ☎ 🅿
🝏 𝖵𝖨𝖲𝖠
closed 25 December – Meals a la carte 13.70/29.40 t. ⅃ 6.50 – **3 rm** 🖃 45.00/60.00 t.

---

**BRIMSCOMBE** Glos. 403 404 N 28 – see Stroud.

---

**BRISTOL** Bristol 403 404 M 29 The West Country G. – pop. 407 992.
See : City★★ – St. Mary Redcliffe★★ DZ – Brandon Hill★★ AX – Georgian House★★ AX A
Harbourside Industrial Museum★★ CZ M2 – SS Great Britain★★ AC AX B – The Old City★
CYZ : Theatre Royal★★ CZ T – Merchant Seamen's Almshouses★ K – St. Stephen's City★ C
D – St. John the Baptist★ CY – College Green★ CYZ (Bristol Cathedral★, Lord Mayor'
Chapel★) – The Exploratory Hands-on Science Centre★ DZ – City Museum and Art Gallery★
AX M.
Env. : Clifton★★ AX (Suspension Bridge★★ (toll), R.C. Cathedral of St. Peter and St. Paul★★
F, Bristol Zoological Gardens★★ AC, Village★) – Blaise Hamlet★★ – Blaise Castle House
Museum★, NW : 5 m. by A 4018 and B 4057 AV.
Exc. : Bath★★★, SE : 13 m. by A 4 BX – Chew Magna★ (Stanton Drew Stone Circles★ AC) S
8 m. by A 37 – BX – and B 3130 – Clevedon★ (Clevedon Court★ AC, ⩽★) W : 11½ m. b
A 370, B 3128 – AX – and B 3130.
🛇 Mangotsfield, Carsons Rd ℰ (0117) 956 5501, BV – 🛇 Beggar Bush Lane, Failand, Clifto
ℰ (01275) 393117/393474, AX – 🛇 Knowle, Fairway, West Town Lane, Brislington ℰ (0117
977 6341, BX – 🛇 Long Ashton, Clarken Coombe ℰ (01275) 392229, AX – 🛇 Stockwoo
Vale, Stockwood Lane, Keynsham ℰ (0117) 986 6505, BX.
Severn Bridge (toll).
✈ Bristol Airport : ℰ (01275) 474444, SW : 7 m. by A 38 AX.
🛈 St. Nicholas Church, St. Nicholas St., BS1 1UE ℰ (0117) 926 0767 – Bristol Airport, BS1.
3DY ℰ (01275) 474444.
London 121 – Birmingham 91.

Plans on following pages

🏨 **Swallow Royal,** College Green, BS1 5TA, ℰ (0117) 925 5100, Fax (0117) 925 1515, 🝙
🛥, 🔲 – 🛗, ✦ rm, ▥ 🖭 ☎ ₺ 🖎 – 🔏 300. 🝏 🅰🅴 🛈 𝖵𝖨𝖲𝖠  CZ
**Terrace :** Meals 18.00/22.00 st. and a la carte ⅃ 8.00 – **Palm Court :** Meals (closed Sunda
and Bank Holidays) (dinner only) 26.50 st. and a la carte ⅃ 8.00 – **230 rm** 🖃 140.00
160.00 st., 12 suites – SB.

🏨🏨🏨🏨 **Bristol Marriott**, 2 Lower Castle St., Old Market, BS1 3AD, ✆ (0117) 929 4281, Fax (0117) 922 5838, ≼, ℩₆, ⇔, ⬛ – ▯$, ↦ rm, ▤ ▥ ☎ ✆ & ➋ – ♨ 600. 🆎 🆎 ① 🆅🆂🅰
🅹🅲🅱. ⌘
DY s
*Le Chateau :* Meals (dinner only) 17.50 **st.** ▯ 7.25 – **The Brasserie :** Meals *(closed lunch Saturday and Sunday)* 15.95 **st.** (dinner) and a la carte 15.75/28.45 **st.** ▯ 7.45 – ⌷ 11.95 –
**281 rm** 110.00 **st.**, 8 suites – SB.

🏨🏨🏨 **Thiste Grand**, Broad St., BS1 2EL, ✆ (0117) 929 1645, Fax (0117) 922 7619 – ▯$, ↦ rm,
▥ ▥ ☎ ➋ – ♨ 600. 🆎 🆎 ① 🆅🆂🅰
CY a
Meals *(closed lunch Saturday and Sunday except 21 March)* 14.00/17.50 **st.** and a la carte
▯ 4.75 – ⌷ 11.25 – **178 rm** 110.00/120.00 **st.**, 4 suites – SB.

🏨🏨🏨 **Holiday Inn Crowne Plaza Bristol**, Victoria St., BS1 6HY, ✆ (0117) 976 9988,
Fax (0117) 925 5040, ℩₆ – ▯$, ↦ rm, ▤ rest, ▥ ☎ ✆ ➋ – ♨ 180. 🆎 🆎 ① 🆅🆂🅰 🅹🅲🅱
Meals 17.95 **st.** (dinner) and a la carte 12.15/29.15 **st.** ▯ 6.00 – ⌷ 10.50 – **128 rm** 130.00/
140.00 **st.** – SB.
DZ a

🏨🏨🏨 **Jurys Bristol**, Prince St., BS1 4QF, ✆ (0117) 923 0333, Fax (0117) 923 0300, ≼ – ▯$,
↦ rm, ▤ rest, ▥ ☎ & ➋ – ♨ 300. 🆎 🆎 ① 🆅🆂🅰
CZ e
*Unicorn :* Meals (dinner only) 18.50 **st.** ▯ 5.75 – *Quayside :* Meals 9.95/15.95 **st.** and dinner a la carte ▯ 5.75 – ⌷ 7.50 – **187 rm** 115.00 **st.** – SB.

🏨🏨🏨 **Hilton National Bristol**, Redcliffe Way, BS1 6NJ, ✆ (0117) 926 0041,
Fax (0117) 923 0089, ℩₆, ⇔, ⬛ – ▯$, ↦ rm, ▤ rest, ▥ ☎ & ➋ – ♨ 300. 🆎 🆎 ① 🆅🆂🅰
🅹🅲🅱. ⌘
DZ n
Meals *(closed Saturday lunch)* 13.50/17.50 **st.** and a la carte ▯ 6.25 – ⌷ 12.50 – **201 rm**
110.00/150.00 **st.**

🏨 **Westbury Park** without rest., 37 Westbury Rd, BS9 3AU, ✆ (0117) 962 0465,
Fax (0117) 962 8607 – ▥ ☎ ✆. 🆎 🆎 ① 🆅🆂🅰
AV u
8 rm ⌷ 42.00/52.00 **st.**

🏨 **Courtlands**, 1 Redland Court Rd, Redland, BS6 7EE, ✆ (0117) 942 4432,
Fax (0117) 923 2432, ≢ – ↦ rest, ▥ ☎ ➋. 🆎 🆎 🆅🆂🅰
AX v
closed 2 weeks Christmas-New Year – Meals *(closed Saturday, Sunday and Bank Holidays)*
(dinner only) a la carte 9.25/17.15 **st.** ▯ 4.00 – **25 rm** ⌷ 48.00/58.00 **st.**

🍴🍴🍴 **Harveys**, 12 Denmark St., BS1 5DQ, ✆ (0117) 927 5034, Fax (0117) 927 5003, « Medieval
❀ cellars and wine museum » – ▤. 🆎 🆎 ① 🆅🆂🅰
CY c
closed Saturday lunch, Sunday, third week February, Easter, 2 weeks August and Christmas
– Meals 17.95/39.95 **st.** ▯ 14.00
**Spec.** Grilled scallops with caviar and a light mussel and lobster jus. Roast farm pigeon with
sauté potatoes, sherry vinegar jus. Warm bitter chocolate tart with citrus fruits.

🍴🍴 **Markwicks**, 43 Corn St., BS1 1HT, ✆ (0117) 926 2658, Fax (0117) 926 2658 – 🆎 🆎 🆅🆂🅰
⊛ 🅹🅲🅱
CY i
closed Saturday lunch, Sunday, Monday, 1 week Easter, 2 weeks late August and Christmas-
New Year – Meals 16.00/23.50 **t.** and a la carte 23.70/29.70 **t.**

🍴🍴 **Hunt's**, 26 Broad St., BS1 2HG, ✆ (0117) 926 5580, Fax (0117) 926 5580 – 🆎 🆎 🆅🆂🅰
🅹🅲🅱
CY r
closed Saturday lunch, Sunday, Monday, 1 week Easter, 2 weeks August and 10 days
Christmas – Meals a la carte 22.15/28.40 **t.** ▯ 9.50.

🍴🍴 **Redcliffs**, Redcliff Quay, 125 Redcliff St., BS1 6HQ, ✆ (0117) 987 2270,
Fax (0117) 930 4255, ≼, ㊟ – 🆎 🆎 ① 🆅🆂🅰
DZ e
closed Saturday lunch, Sunday dinner and 1 week Christmas – Meals 12.95/17.95 **t.** ▯ 5.75 –
(see also *River Cafe* below).

🍴🍴 **Michaels**, 129 Hotwell Rd, BS8 4RU, ✆ (0117) 929 0554, Fax (0117) 925 3629 – ↦. 🆎 🆎
① 🆅🆂🅰
AX z
closed Sunday dinner and 26 December – Meals (dinner only and Sunday lunch)/dinner
12.95/17.95 **t.** and a la carte ▯ 5.95.

🍴🍴 **Jameson's**, 30-32 Upper Maudlin St., BS2 8DJ, ✆ (0117) 927 6565, Fax (0117) 929 1790 –
🆎 🆎 ① 🆅🆂🅰
CY e
closed Saturday lunch, Sunday dinner and Bank Holidays – Meals 10.50/21.50 **t.**
and a la carte ▯ 5.00.

🍴🍴 **China Palace**, 18a Baldwin St., BS1 1SE, ✆ (0117) 926 2719, Fax (0117) 925 6168 – ▤. 🆎
🆎 🆅🆂🅰 🅹🅲🅱
CY x
closed 25 and 26 December – Meals - Chinese - a la carte 19.15/30.50 **t.** ▯ 6.00.

🍴 **Riverstation**, The Grove, BS6 4RD, ✆ (0117) 914 4434, Fax (0117) 934 9990, ㊟, « Riverside setting » – ▤. 🆎 🆎 ① 🆅🆂🅰
CZ c
closed lunch Saturday and Christmas – Meals a la carte 19.45/27.50 **t.** ▯ 7.80.

🍴 **Red Snapper**, 1 Chandos Rd, Redland, BS6 6PG, ✆ (0117) 973 7999 – 🆎 🆎 🆅🆂🅰 AX c
closed Monday lunch, Sunday dinner and 25 December-1 January – Meals 12.00 **t.**
(lunch) and dinner a la carte 17.50/24.50 **t.**

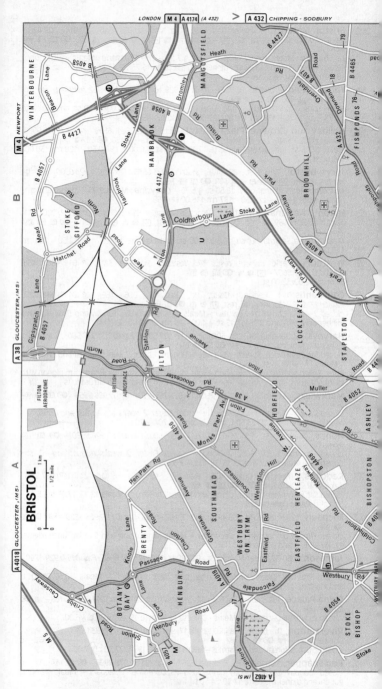

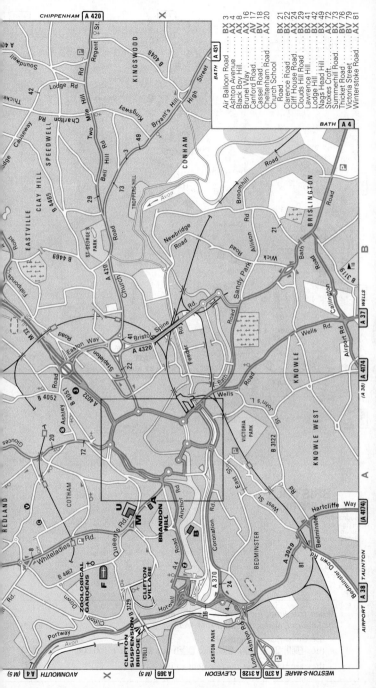

155

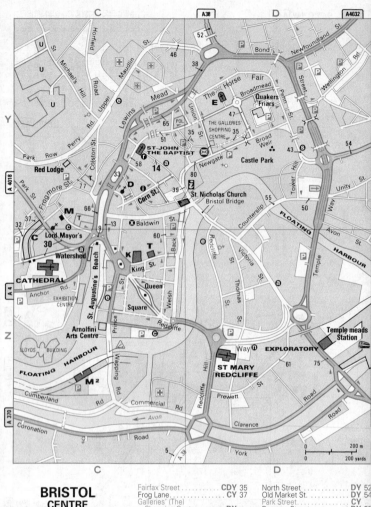

# BRISTOL
## CENTRE

*When travelling for business or pleasure*
*in England, Wales, Scotland and Ireland:*

- use the series of five maps
　(nos **401**, **402**, **403**, **404** and **923**) at a scale of 1:400 000

- they are the perfect complement to this Guide

🍴 **River Cafe** (at Redcliffs), Redcliff Quay, 125 Redcliff St., BS1 6HQ, ✆ (0117) 987 2270, *Fax (0117) 930 4255*, ⛱, « Riverside setting » – [MC] [AE] [DC] [VISA] **DZ e**
*closed Sunday dinner* – **Meals** 16.95 **t.**.

🍴 **Bell's Diner,** 1 York Rd, Montpelier, BS6 5QB, ✆ (0117) 924 0357, *Fax (0117) 924 4280* – 🚭. [MC] [VISA] **AX s**
*closed lunch Monday, Sunday dinner, 23 August-1 September and 24 to 30 December* – **Meals** 15.95 **t.** 🍷 8.75.

**at Patchway** *(South Gloucestershire) North : 6½ m. on A 38* – **BV** – ✉ *Bristol.*

🏨 **Aztec,** Aztec West Business Park, BS12 4TS, North : 1 m. by A 38 ✆ (01454) 201090, *Fax (01454) 201593*, 🏋, ♨, 🏊, 🌳, squash – ⇅ 🚭 [TV] ☎ ♿ 🅿 – 👥 200. [MC] [AE] [DC] [VISA]
**Meals** *(closed lunch Saturday)* 10.00/20.00 **t.** and dinner a la carte 🍷 9.00 – **126 rm** ☕ 129.00/174.00 **st.**, 3 suites.

🏨 **Stakis Bristol,** Woodlands Lane, Bradley Stoke, BS12 4JF, North : 1 m. by A 38 ✆ (01454) 201144, *Fax (01454) 612022*, 🏋, ♨, 🏊 – 🚭 rm, ❄ rest, [TV] ☎ ♿ 🅿 – 👥 200. [MC] [AE] [DC] [VISA]. 🚫
**Meals** *(closed Saturday lunch and New Year)* (carving rest.) 12.95/17.95 **t.** – ☕ 9.95 – **142 rm** 126.00/161.00 **st.** – SB.

**at Cribbs Causeway** *North : 6¾ m. on A 4018* – ✉ *Bristol.*

🏨 **Travelodge,** BS10 7TL, ✆ (0117) 501530, Reservations (Freephone) 0800 850950 – 🚭 rm, [TV] ♿ 🅿. [MC] [AE] [DC] [VISA] [JCB]. 🚫 **AV e**
**Meals** (grill rest.) – **40 rm** 39.95/59.95 **t.**

**at Hambrook** *(South Gloucestershire) Northeast : 5½ m. by M 32 on A 4174* – ✉ *Bristol.*

🏨 **Forte Posthouse Bristol,** Filton Rd, BS16 1QX, ✆ (0117) 956 4242, *Fax (0117) 956 9735*, 🏋, ♨, 🏊, park – ⇅, 🚭 rm, ❄ rest, [TV] ☎ 🅿 – 👥 120. [MC] [AE] [DC] [VISA] **BV o**
**Meals** a la carte 13.95/18.95 **st.** 🍷 7.00 – ☕ 10.95 – **196 rm** 99.00/119.00 **st.**, 2 suites – SB.

**at Mangotsfield** *Northeast : 5¾ m. by M 32 on A 4174 -* **BV** – ✉ *Bristol.*

🏨 **Travel Inn,** 200-202 Westerleigh Rd, BS16 7AN, East : ¾ m. off A 4174 ✆ (0117) 956 4755, *Fax (0117) 956 4644* – 🚭 rm, [TV] ♿ 🅿. [MC] [AE] [DC] [VISA]
**Meals** (grill rest.) – **40 rm** 38.00 **t.**

**at Winterbourne** *(South Gloucestershire) Northeast : 7½ m. by M 32 and A 4174 on B 4058* – **BV** – ✉ *Bristol.*

🏨 **Jarvis Grange H. & Country Club,** Northwoods, BS36 1RP, Northwest : 2 m. by B 4057 on B 4427 ✆ (01454) 777333, *Fax (01454) 777447*, ♨, 🏊, park – 🚭 [TV] ☎ 🅿 – 👥 150. [MC] [AE] [DC] [VISA]
**Meals** *(closed Saturday lunch)* 15.95/19.50 **st.** and a la carte 🍷 7.00 – ☕ 9.50 – **68 rm** 115.00/125.00 **st.** – SB.

**at Keynsham** *Southeast : 5½ m. by A 4 and B 4175* – **BX** – ✉ *Bristol.*

🏨 **The Grange,** 42 Bath Rd, BS31 1SN, ✆ (0117) 986 9181, *Fax (0117) 986 6373*, 🌳 – 🚭 rm, [TV] ☎ ♿ 🅿. [MC] [AE] [VISA]. 🚫
**Meals** (bar lunch)/dinner 15.50 **st.** 🍷 5.50 – **29 rm** ☕ 48.00/85.00 **st.** – SB.

**at Saltford** *(Bath & North East Somerset) Southeast : 7½ m. on A 4* – **BX** – ✉ *Bristol.*

🏨 **Brunel's Tunnel House,** High St., BS18 3BQ, off Beech Rd ✆ (01225) 873873, *Fax (01225) 874875*, 🌳 – [TV] ☎ 🅿. [MC] [AE] [VISA] [JCB]
*closed 24 December-1 January* – **Meals** *(closed Friday to Sunday)* (by arrangement) (dinner only) 17.00 **st.** 🍷 4.50 – **8 rm** ☕ 52.00/62.00 **st.**

**at Chelwood** *(Bath & North East Somerset) Southeast : 8½ m. by A 37* – **BX** – *on A 368* – ✉ *Bristol.*

🏨 **Chelwood House,** BS39 4NH, Southwest : ¾ m. on A 37 ✆ (01761) 490730, *Fax (01761) 490072*, <, 🌳 – 🚭 rest, [TV] ☎ 🅿. [MC] [AE] [VISA] [JCB]
**Meals** *(closed Sunday)* (dinner only) a la carte 16.45/23.50 **t.** 🍷 3.95 – **11 rm** ☕ 49.50/88.00 **st.**

**at Hunstrete** *(Bath & North East Somerset) Southeast : 10 m. by A 4 and A 37* – **BX** – *off A 368* – ✉ *Bristol.*

🏨 ✿ **Hunstrete House** 🐦, BS18 4NS, ✆ (01761) 490490, *Fax (01761) 490732*, <, ⛱, « Late 17C country house, gardens and deer park », 🏊, 🎾 – 🚭 rest, [TV] ☎ 📞 🅿 – 👥 40. [MC] [AE] [DC] [VISA] [JCB]. 🚫
**Meals** 19.95 **st.** (lunch) and a la carte 37.00/47.00 **st.** 🍷 7.50 – **22 rm** ☕ 120.00/180.00 **st.**, 1 suite – SB
**Spec.** Potage of oysters, mussels and cockles with herbs and caviar. Roast squab pigeon with boudin blanc ravioli, foie gras and Sauternes sauce. Hazelnut and apricot parfait with nougatine and chocolate sauce.

**at Stanton Wick** *(Bath & North East Somerset) South : 9 m. by A 37 and A 368 on Stanton Wick rd – BX – ✉ Bristol.*

**Carpenters Arms** with rm, BS18 4BX, ✆ (01761) 490202, *Fax (01761) 490763* – ⇔ rm, TV ☎ P. MC AE ⊙ VISA. ✻
**Meals** a la carte 14.00/22.00 **t.** 5.75 – **12 rm** ☐ 52.50/69.50 **t.** – SB.

ATS 68-72 Avon St. ✆ (0117) 971 8140
ATS 551 Gloucester Rd, Horfield ✆ (0117) 951 4525
ATS 58-60 Broad St., Staple Hill ✆ (0117) 956 4741/956 5396/956 4594/957 1483 957 1483
ATS 34-38 St. Johns Lane, Bedminster ✆ (0117) 977 6418/977 0674

**BRITWELL SALOME** *Oxon. – pop. 187.*
*London 75 – Oxford 21 – Reading 19.*

**The Goose,** OX9 5LG, ✆ (01491) 612304, *Fax (01491) 614822* – ⇔ P. MC VISA
*closed Sunday dinner, Monday and 1 to 11 January* – **Meals** 25.00 **t.** (dinner) and lunch a la carte 22.00/27.50 **t.**

**BRIXHAM** *Devon* 403 J 32 *The West Country G. – pop. 15 865.*
**Env.** : *Berry Head★ (≤★★★) NE : 1½ m.*
*The Old Market House, The Quay, TQ5 8TB ✆ (01803) 852861.*
*London 230 – Exeter 30 – Plymouth 32 – Torquay 8.*

**Berry Head** ⛰, Berry Head Rd, TQ5 9AJ, ✆ (01803) 853225, *Fax (01803) 882084*, ≤ Torbay, ⛱ – TV ☎ P – 300. MC AE VISA
**Meals** a la carte 11.00/19.00 **st.** 4.50 – **32 rm** ☐ (dinner included) 55.00/144.00 – SB.

**Quayside,** 41 King St., TQ5 9TJ, ✆ (01803) 855751, *Fax (01803) 882733*, ≤ – ⇔ rest, TV ☎ P. MC AE ⊙ VISA JCB
**Meals** (bar lunch)/dinner a la carte 21.40/28.45 **st.** 4.75 – **29 rm** ☐ 52.00/82.00 **st.** – SB.

**BROAD CAMPDEN** *Glos. – see Chipping Campden.*

**BROADHEMBURY** *Devon* 403 K 31 *– pop. 617 – ✉ Honiton.*
*London 191 – Exeter 17 – Honiton 5 – Taunton 23.*

**Drewe Arms,** EX14 0NF, ✆ (01404) 841267, *Fax (01404) 841267*, « Part 13C thatched inn », ⛱ – P
*closed Sunday dinner* – **Meals** - Seafood - 22.00 **t.** and a la carte 18.00/23.00 **t.** 7.50.

**BROADSTAIRS** *Kent* 404 Y 29 *– pop. 22 116.*
*North Foreland, Convent Rd, Broadstairs ✆ (01843) 862140.*
*6b High St., CT10 1LH ✆ (01843) 862242.*
*London 78 – Dover 21 – Maidstone 47.*

**Castlemere,** 15 Western Esplanade, CT10 1TD, South : 1 m. by Queens Rd (A 255) and West Cliffe Rd ✆ (01843) 861566, *Fax (01843) 866379*, ≤, ⛱ – TV ☎ ✆ P. MC VISA
**Meals** 9.50/12.00 **t.** – ☐ 5.75 – **34 rm** 40.00/78.00 **t.** – SB.

**Marchesi,** 18 Albion St., CT10 1LU, ✆ (01843) 862481, *Fax (01843) 861509*, ≤, ⛱ – ⇔ P. MC AE ⊙ VISA
*closed Sunday dinner and 27 to 30 December* – **Meals** 11.00/15.00 **st.** and a la carte 5.50.

**BROADWAY** *Worcestershire* 403 404 O 27 *Great Britain G. – pop. 2 328.*
**See** : *Town★.*
**Env.** : *Country Park (Broadway Tower ✻★★), SE : 2 m. by A 44 – Snowshill Manor★ (Terrace Garden★) AC, S : 2½ m.*
*1 Cotswold Court, WR12 7AA ✆ (01386) 852937 (summer only).*
*London 93 – Birmingham 36 – Cheltenham 15 – Worcester 22.*

**Lygon Arms,** High St., WR12 7DU, ✆ (01386) 852255, *Fax (01386) 858611*, « Part 16C inn », Fø, ⛆, ◻, ⛱, ✻ – TV ☎ ✆ P – 80. MC AE ⊙ VISA JCB
**Meals** 25.50/39.50 **t.** and a la carte 7.00 – ☐ 9.20 – **61 rm** 143.00/195.00, 4 suites – SB.

**Broadway,** The Green, WR12 7AA, ✆ (01386) 852401, *Fax (01386) 853879*, ⛱ – ⇔ TV ☎ P. MC AE ⊙ VISA JCB
**Meals** 10.95/19.95 **t.** 9.95 – **20 rm** ☐ 52.50/105.00 **t.** – SB.

🏠 **Collin House** ⬧, Collin Lane, WR12 7PB, Northwest : 1 ¼ m. by A 44 ℘ (01386) 858354, Fax (01386) 858697, « 17C », 🛒 – 📺 📶 🐾 💳 ⚞ ⚟. ⚗
closed 24 to 28 December – **Meals** 17.00 **t.** (lunch) and dinner a la carte 17.00/26.00 **t.** ¶ 8.50 – **7 rm** 🖵 48.00/102.00 **t.** – SB.

🏠 **Barn House** without rest., 152 High St., WR12 7AJ, ℘ (01386) 858633, Fax (01386) 858633, « 17C », ⬛, 🛒, park – ⚟ 📺 📶
**3 rm** 🖵 35.00/75.00 **st.**, 1 suite.

🏠 **Windrush House** without rest., Station Rd, WR12 7DE, ℘ (01386) 853577, 🛒 – ⚞ 📺 📶
closed 25 and 26 December – **4 rm** 🖵 25.00/50.00 **st.**

🏠 **Olive Branch** without rest., 78 High St., WR12 7AJ, ℘ (01386) 853440, Fax (01386) 853440, 🛒 – 📺 📶. ⚟. ⚗
**7 rm** 🖵 22.00/56.00 **st.**

🏠 **Small Talk Lodge,** Keil Close, 32 High St., WR12 7DP, ℘ (01386) 858953 – ⚞ rest, 📺 📶. 📶 💳 ⚞⚟
**Meals** (by arrangement) 15.00 **st.** ¶ 4.50 – **8 rm** 🖵 37.50/56.00 **st.** – SB.

🏠 **Whiteacres** without rest., Station Rd, WR12 7DE, ℘ (01386) 852320, 🛒 – ⚞ 📺 📶. ⚗
March-October – **6 rm** 🖵 30.00/42.00 **st.**

**t Willersey** (Glos.) North : 2 m. on B 4632 – ⬤ Broadway.

🏠 **Old Rectory** ⬧ without rest., Church St., WR12 7PN, ℘ (01386) 853729, Fax (01386) 858061, « Part 17C », 🛒 – ⚞ 📺 ☎ 📶. 📶 ⚞ 💳 ⚞⚟. ⚗
closed 22 to 27 December – **8 rm** 🖵 55.00/98.00 **st.**

**t Willersey Hill** (Glos.) East : 2 m. by A 44 – ⬤ Broadway.

🏛️ **Dormy House,** WR12 7LF, ℘ (01386) 852711, Fax (01386) 858636, ⌘, ⚞, 🛒 – 📺 ☎ ⚘ 📶 – 🔔 170. 📶 ⚞ ⚪ 💳
closed 24 and 28 December – **Meals** (bar lunch Saturday) 30.50 **t.** (dinner) and a la carte 34.00/39.45 **t.** ¶ 8.75 – **46 rm** 🖵 71.00/142.00 **t.**, 3 suites – SB.

**t Buckland** (Glos.) Southwest : 2 ¼ m. by B 4632 – ⬤ Broadway.

🏛️ **Buckland Manor** ⬧, WR12 7LY, ℘ (01386) 852626, Fax (01386) 853557, ≤, « Part 13C manor house in extensive gardens », ⚕, ⚙ – ⚞ rest, 📺 ☎ 📶. 📶 ⚞ 💳 ⚞⚟. ⚗
**Meals** 28.50 **t.** (lunch) and dinner a la carte 20.25/43.00 **t.** ¶ 8.50 – **13 rm** 🖵 185.00/335.00 **t.** – SB.

**t Wormington** (Glos.) Southwest : 4 ¼ m. by B 4632 on Wormington rd – ⬤ Broadway.

🏠 **Leasow House** ⬧ without rest., Laverton Meadow, WR12 7NA, East : 1 ¼ m. ℘ (01386) 584526, Fax (01386) 584596, ≤, 🛒 – 📺 ☎ ⚘ 📶. 📶 ⚞ 💳
**7 rm** 🖵 43.00/65.00 **s.**

---

**ROADWELL** Glos. 🔢🔢 O 28 – see Stow-on-the-Wold.

---

**ROCKDISH** Norfolk 🔢 X 26 – see Diss.

---

**ROCKENHURST** Hants. 🔢🔢 P 31 Great Britain G. – pop. 3 048.
Env. : New Forest★★ (Rhinefield Ornamental Drive★★, Bolderwood Ornamental Drive★★).
London 99 – Bournemouth 17 – Southampton 14 – Winchester 27.

🏛️ **Rhinefield House** ⬧, Rhinefield Rd, SO42 7QB, Northwest : 3 m. ℘ (01590) 622922, Fax (01590) 622800, « Victorian country mansion, formal gardens », ⌘, ⚞, ⚕, park, ⚙ – ⚞ 📺 ☎ 📶 – 🔔 120. 📶 ⚞ ⚪ 💳. ⚗
**Armada :** **Meals** 25.50 **st.** (dinner) and a la carte 31.95/36.25 **st.** – **34 rm** 🖵 110.00/145.00 **st.** – SB.

🏨 **New Park Manor** ⬧, Lyndhurst Rd, SO42 7QH, North : 1 ½ m. on A 337 ℘ (01590) 623467, Fax (01590) 622268, ≤, ⚕, 🛒, ⚙ – ⚞ 📺 ☎ 📶 – 🔔 75. 📶 ⚞ ⚪ 💳 ⚞⚟.
**Stag :** **Meals** 14.95/27.00 **t.** and dinner a la carte ¶ 8.00 – **24 rm** 🖵 85.00/185.00 **t.** – SB.

🏨 **Careys Manor,** Lyndhurst Rd, SO42 7RH, on A 337 ℘ (01590) 623551, Fax (01590) 622799, ⌘, ⚞, ⬛ – ⚞ 📺 ☎ 📶 – 🔔 100. 📶 ⚞ ⚪ 💳
**Meals** 24.45 **t.** and a la carte – **Blaireau's** (℘ (01590) 623032) **: Meals** - French - a la carte 15.85/23.65 **t.** ¶ 5.85 – **78 rm** 🖵 83.00/179.00 **t.**, 1 suite – SB.

🏨 **Whitley Ridge** ⬧, Beaulieu Rd, SO42 7QL, East : 1 m. on B 3055 ℘ (01590) 622354, Fax (01590) 622856, ≤, « Part Georgian », 🛒, ⚙ – ⚞ rest, 📺 ☎ ⚘ 📶. 📶 ⚞ ⚪ 💳 ⚞⚟
**Meals** (bar lunch Monday to Saturday)/dinner 19.50 **t.** and a la carte ¶ 7.40 – **14 rm** 🖵 56.00/120.00 **t.** – SB.

🏥 **Cloud,** Meerut Rd, SO42 7TD, ℘ (01590) 622165, Fax (01590) 622818 – ᐸᐁ rest, 📺 ☎ ☻
**⬛ VISA**
closed first 3 weeks January – Meals 9.95/17.00 st. ⋮ 7.95 – **16 rm** ⌧ 52.00/84.00 t. – SB.

🏥 **Cottage** without rest., Sway Rd, SO42 7SH, ℘ (01590) 622296, Fax (01590) 623014, ⌘
ᐸᐁ 📺 ☻. ⬛ VISA
March-November – **6 rm** ⌧ 55.00/85.00 st.

XXX **Le Poussin** (Aitken), The Courtyard, rear of 49-51 Brookley Rd, SO42 7R
㊉ ℘ (01590) 623063, Fax (01590) 623144, ☞ – ᐸᐁ. ⬛ VISA
closed Monday and Tuesday – Meals (booking essential) 15.00/30.00 t. ⋮ 7.00
**Spec.** Fillet of brill with oyster fungi, leek purée, white truffle butter sauce. Slow braise
haunch of venison with cep dumpling, red wine sauce. Passion fruit soufflé with exotic fru
sorbet.

XX **Thatched Cottage** with rm, 16 Brookley Rd, SO42 7RR, ℘ (01590) 62309
Fax (01590) 623479, « 17C farmhouse » – ᐸᐁ rest, 📺 ☎ ☻. ⬛ VISA JCB. ⌖
restricted opening in winter – Meals (closed Sunday dinner and Monday) (booking essen
tial) (light lunch)/dinner 30.00 t. ⋮ 10.00 – **5 rm** ⌧ 70.00/155.00 st. – SB.

**at Sway** Southwest : 3 m. by B 3055 – ⌧ Lymington.

⌂ **Nurse's Cottage,** Station Rd, SO41 6BA, ℘ (01590) 683402, Fax (01590) 683402, ⌘
ᐸᐁ 📺 ☎ ☻ ☻. ⬛ VISA ⌖
closed 17 to 21 January, 21 February-11 March, 9 November-16 December – Meals (k
arrangement) 19.75 ⋮ 6.25 – **3 rm** ⌧ 50.00/85.00 – SB.

*Wenn Sie ein ruhiges Hotel suchen,*
*benutzen Sie zuerst die Karte in der Einleitung*
*oder wählen Sie im Text ein Hotel mit dem Zeichen ⌖ oder ⌖.*

---

**BROMBOROUGH** Mersey. 402 403 L 24 – pop. 14 518 – ⌧ Wirral.
🖈 Raby Hall Rd ℘ (0151) 334 2155.
London 210 – Chester 14 – Liverpool 6.5 – Manchester 46.

🏨 **The Village H. & Leisure Club,** Pool Lane, L62 4UE, on A 41 ℘ (0151) 643 161
Fax (0151) 643 1420, ⌦, ⌘, ⌧, ⌖, squash – ⌸ ᐸᐁ, 🍽 rest, 📺 ☎ ☻ ☻ ☻ – ⌴ 200. ⬛ ☻
① VISA
Meals a la carte 11.50/24.50 st. – **91 rm** ⌧ 87.00/99.00 st. – SB.

🏥 **Travel Inn,** High St., L62 7HZ, ℘ (0151) 334 2917, Fax (0151) 334 0443 – ᐸᐁ rm, 📺 ☻
⌴ 80. ⬛ ⬛ ① VISA ⌖
Meals (grill rest.) – **32 rm** 38.00 t.

---

**BROME** Suffolk 404 X 26 – see Diss (Norfolk).

---

**BROMLEY CROSS** Gtr. Manchester 402 404 M 23 – see Bolton.

---

**BROMSGROVE** Worcestershire 403 404 N 26 – pop. 26 366.
🖸 Bromsgrove Museum, 26 Birmingham Rd, B61 0DD ℘ (01527) 831809.
London 117 – Birmingham 14 – Bristol 71 – Worcester 13.

🏨 **Stakis Bromsgrove,** Birmingham Rd, B61 0JB, North : 2 ½ m. on A 3
℘ (0121) 447 7888, Fax (0121) 447 7273, ⌦, ⌘, ⌧, ☞ – ᐸᐁ rm, 🍽 rest, 📺 ☎ ☻ ☻ ☻
⌴ 250. ⬛ ⬛ ① VISA
Meals (closed Saturday lunch) (carving lunch) 16.95/18.95 t. and dinner a la carte – ⌧ 9.7
– **146 rm** 130.00/180.00 st., 2 suites – SB.

🏨 **Pine Lodge,** 85 Kidderminster Rd, B61 9AB, West : 1 m. on A 448 ℘ (01527) 57660
Fax (01527) 878981, ⌦, ⌘, ⌧ – ⌸ ᐸᐁ, 🍽 rest, 📺 ☎ ☻ ☻ – ⌴ 200. ⬛ ⬛ ① VISA
Meals (closed Saturday lunch) 16.50/18.75 st. and a la carte ⋮ 7.95 – **113 rm** ⌧ 105.00
120.00 st., 1 suite – SB.

🏥 **Grafton Manor,** Grafton Lane, B61 7HA, Southwest : 1 ¾ m. by Worcester R
℘ (01527) 579007, Fax (01527) 575221, « 16C and 18C manor », ⌘, park – ᐸᐁ rest, 📺 ☎
☻ ☻. ⬛ ⬛ ① VISA ⌖
Meals (closed Saturday lunch) 20.50/27.85 st. ⋮ 6.80 – **7 rm** ⌧ 85.00/125.00 st., 2 suites
SB.

🏥 **Bromsgrove Country,** 249 Worcester Rd, Stoke Heath, B61 7JA, Southwest : 2 n
℘ (01527) 835522, Fax (01527) 871257, ☞ – ᐸᐁ 📺 ☻. ⬛ ⬛ VISA ⌖
closed Christmas-New Year – Meals (residents only) (dinner only) a la carte approx. 12.00 s
⋮ 4.50 – ⌧ 5.50 – **8 rm** 45.00/49.00 st.

**BROMYARD** Herefordshire 🔢🔢 M 27 – pop. 3 117.
    🛈 T.I.C. & Heritage Centre, 1 Rowberry St., HR7 4DU ℘ (01885) 482038.
    London 138 – Hereford 15 – Leominster 13 – Worcester 14.

↑ **Granary** ⌂, Church House Farm, Collington, HR7 4NA, North : 4 1/4 m. by B 4214, Edvin
Loach rd and Ripplewood rd ℘ (01885) 410345, « Working farm », park – ⬦ rest, 📺 🅿.
⌘
**Meals** (by arrangement) 15.00 **t.** – **5 rm** ⌤ 22.00/44.00.

**at Acton Green** Southeast : 4 3/4 m. by A 44 on B 4220 – ✉ Bromyard.

↑ **Hidelow House** ⌂, Acton Beauchamp, WR6 5AH, South : 1/4 m. ℘ (01886) 884547,
Fax (01886) 884060, ⌗ – ⬦ 📺 🅿. ⌘
closed 25 December – **Meals** (by arrangement) (communal dining) 11.50 **s.** – **3 rm**
⌤ 22.00/50.00 **s.**

**BROOK** Hants. 🔢🔢 P 31 – ✉ Lyndhurst.
    London 92 – Bournemouth 24 – Southampton 14.

🏛 **Bell Inn**, SO43 7HE, ℘ (01703) 812214, Fax (01703) 813958, ⬛ – ⬦ 📺 ☎ 🅿 – ⚒ 40. 🆎
🆎 ⓞ 𝘝𝘐𝘚𝘈
**Meals** (bar lunch Monday to Saturday)/dinner 26.50 **st.** ⓖ 7.00 – **26 rm** ⌤ 54.00/85.00 **st.** –
SB.

**BROOKMANS PARK** Herts. 🔢 T 28 – pop. 3 315.
    London 21 – Luton 21.

✕✕ **Villa Rosa**, 3 Great North Rd, AL9 6LB, Southeast : 1 3/4 m. on A 1000 ℘ (01707) 651444,
Fax (01707) 654970 – 🅿. 🆎 🆎 ⓞ 𝘝𝘐𝘚𝘈 𝘑𝘊𝘉
closed Saturday lunch, Sunday and Bank Holidays – **Meals** - Italian - a la carte 18.45/23.00 **t.**
ⓖ 5.00.

**BROUGHTON** Lancs. 🔢 L 22 – see Preston.

**BROUGHTON ASTLEY** Leics. 🔢 Q 26 – pop. 6 487.
    London 100 – Coventry 22 – Leicester 11 – Northampton 30.

🏛 **Mill on the Soar**, Coventry Rd, Sutton in the Elms, LE9 6JU, Northwest : 1 1/2 m. by B 581
on B 4114 ℘ (01455) 282419, Fax (01455) 285937, ⌇ – ⬦ rm, 📺 ☎ 🅿 – ⚒ 40. 🆎 🆎 ⓞ
𝘝𝘐𝘚𝘈. ⌘
**Meals** (in bar) (buffet lunch) a la carte 12.10/18.00 – ⌤ 4.95 – **20 rm** 39.50 **t.**

**BROXTED** Essex 🔢 U 28 – see Stansted Airport.

**BROXTON** Ches. 🔢🔢 L 24 – pop. 417.
    London 197 – Birmingham 68 – Chester 12 – Manchester 44 – Stoke-on-Trent 29.

🏛🏛 **Carden Park** ⌂, CH3 9DQ, West : 1 1/2 m. on A 534 ℘ (01829) 731000,
Fax (01829) 731032, ⌗, 𝘐𝘴, ☎, 🏊, ⬛, ⌗, park, ✕ – 🍴 ⬦, ▤ rest, 📺 ☎ & 🅿 – ⚒ 400.
🆎 🆎 ⓞ 𝘝𝘐𝘚𝘈. ⌘
**Garden Restaurant** : Meals (dinner only and Sunday lunch)/dinner 21.95 **st.** – **Brasserie :**
Meals 14.95 **st.** ⓖ 9.00 – ⌤ 10.95 – **192 rm** 110.00/250.00 **st.** – SB.

🏛 **Broxton Hall Country House**, Whitchurch Rd, CH3 9JS, on A 41 at junction with A 534
℘ (01829) 782321, Fax (01829) 782330, « Part 17C timbered house », ⌗ – 📺 ☎ 🅿. 🆎 🆎
ⓞ 𝘝𝘐𝘚𝘈 𝘑𝘊𝘉
closed 25-26 December and 1 January – **Meals** 15.50/22.50 **t.** and lunch a la carte ⓖ 6.00 –
**10 rm** ⌤ 60.00/80.00 **st.** – SB.

**BRUTON** Somerset 🔢🔢 M 30 The West Country G. – pop. 2 111.
    Exc. : Stourhead★★★ AC, W : 8 m. by B 3081.
    London 118 – Bristol 27 – Bournemouth 44 – Salisbury 35 – Taunton 36.

✕✕ **Truffles**, 95 High St., BA10 0AR, ℘ (01749) 812255, Fax (01749) 812255 – 🆎 𝘝𝘐𝘚𝘈. ⌘
closed lunch Tuesday to Friday, Monday, 2 weeks February and 1 week September – **Meals**
13.95/23.50 **t.** ⓖ 6.95.

**BRYHER** Cornwall 🔢 ⑩ – see Scilly (Isles of).

**BUCKDEN** *Cambs.* 🔟🔟 T 27 – *pop. 2 534* – ✉ *Huntingdon.*
*London 65 – Bedford 15 – Cambridge 20 – Northampton 31.*

🏠 **George Coaching Inn,** Olde Great North Rd, PE18 9XA, ℰ (01480) 810307, *Fax (01480) 811274* – 📺 ☎ 📶, 🆗 🆎 𝖵𝖨𝖲𝖠
**Meals** a la carte 15.00/23.00 t. ⬧ 4.70 – **16 rm** ☯ 63.00/88.00 st. – SB.

🏠 **Lion,** High St., PE18 9XA, ℰ (01480) 810313, *Fax (01480) 811070*, « Part 15C inn » – 📺 ☎ 📶 🅿, 🆗 🆎 ⓞ 𝖵𝖨𝖲𝖠 𝖩𝖢𝖡
**Meals** 10.50/17.00 t. and a la carte ⬧ 4.25 – **15 rm** ☯ 62.50/90.00 t. – SB.

---

**BUCKINGHAM** *Bucks.* 🔟🔟 🔟🔟 Q 27 *Great Britain G.* – *pop. 10 168.*
Env. : *Stowe Gardens*★★, *NW : 3 m. by minor rd.*
Exc. : *Claydon House*★ *AC, S : 8 m. by A 413.*
🔟 *Silverstone, Silverstone Rd, Stowe* ℰ (01280) 850005 – 🔟 *Tingewick Rd* ℰ (0128C 813282.*
*London 64 – Birmingham 61 – Northampton 20 – Oxford 25.*

🏛 **Villiers,** 3 Castle St., MK18 1BS, ℰ (01280) 822444, *Fax (01280) 822113* – ▯, ▤ rest, 📺 ☎ 🅿 – 🔬 250. 🆗 🆎 ⓞ 𝖵𝖨𝖲𝖠, 🛇
*Henry's :* **Meals** (dinner only and Sunday lunch)/dinner 15.75/18.75 st. and a la carte ⬧ 8.7( – *Café Porcini :* **Meals** - italian - a la carte 8.00/15.00 st. ⬧ 5.50 – **34 rm** ☯ 85.00/99.00 st. 4 suites.

🏠 **Buckingham Four Pillars,** Buckingham Ring Rd, MK18 1RY, South : 1 ¼ m. by Bridge St. on A 421 ℰ (01280) 822622, *Fax (01280) 823074*, 🖥, 🗭, 🔲 - 🛏 rm, ▤ rest, 📺 ☎ ⬧ 🅿 – 🔬 160. 🆗 🆎 ⓞ 𝖵𝖨𝖲𝖠, 🛇
**Meals** (carving lunch Sunday and carving dinner Tuesday and Saturday) 12.95/15.95 st and a la carte – **70 rm** 76.00/86.00 st. – SB.

---

**BUCKLAND** *Glos.* 🔟🔟 🔟🔟 O 27 – *see Broadway (Worcestershire).*

---

**BUCKLAND** *Oxon.* 🔟🔟 🔟🔟 P 28 – ✉ *Faringdon.*
*London 78 – Oxford 16 – Swindon 15.*

🍴 **Lamb Inn** with rm, Lamb Lane, SN7 8QN, ℰ (01367) 870484, *Fax (01367) 870675* – 📺 ☎ 🅿, 🆗 🆎 𝖵𝖨𝖲𝖠 𝖩𝖢𝖡, 🛇
*closed 24 to 26 December* – **Meals** (restricted menu Monday) (bar lunch Monday t( Saturday)/dinner a la carte 12.85/32.95 t. ⬧ 7.95 – **4 rm** ☯ 35.00/55.00 st.

---

**BUCKLERS HARD** *Hants.* 🔟🔟 🔟🔟 P 31 – *see Beaulieu.*

---

**BUDE** *Cornwall* 🔟🔟 G 31 *The West Country G.* – *pop. 3 681.*
See : *The Breakwater*★★ – *Compass Point* (≤★).
Env. : *Poughill*★ *(church*★★*), N : 2 ½ m. - E : Tamar River*★★ *– Kilkhampton (Church*★ NE : 5 ½ m. by A 39 – Stratton (Church*★*), E : 1 ½ m. – Launcells (Church*★*), E : 3 m. b A 3072 – Marhamchurch (St. Morwenne's Church*★*), SE : 2 ½ m. by A 39 – Pound stock*★ *(≤★★, church*★*, guildhouse*★*), S : 4½ m. by A 39.*
Exc. : *Morwenstow (cliffs*★★*, church*★*), N : 8½ m. by A 39 and minor roads – Jacobstov (Church*★*), S : 7 m. by A 39.*
🔟 *Burn View* ℰ (01288) 352006.
🅱 *Bude Vistor Centre, The Crescent, EX23 8LE* ℰ (01288) 354240.
*London 252 – Exeter 51 – Plymouth 44 – Truro 53.*

🏠 **Falcon,** Breakwater Rd, EX23 8SD, ℰ (01288) 352005, *Fax (01288) 356359*, ≤, 🗭 – 📺 ☎ 🅿, 🆗 🆎 ⓞ 𝖵𝖨𝖲𝖠
**Meals** (bar lunch Monday to Saturday)/dinner 16.00 st. and a la carte ⬧ 5.50 – **22 rm** ☯ 38.00/76.00 st. – SB.

🏠 **Hartland,** Hartland Terr., EX23 8JY, ℰ (01288) 355661, *Fax (01288) 355664*, ≤, 🔲 – ▯ 🛏 rm, 📺 ☎ 🅿
*March-November and Christmas* – **Meals** (bar lunch)/dinner 19.00 t. ⬧ 5.10 – **28 rm** ☯ 43.00/72.00 t. – SB.

🏠 **Cliff,** Crooklets Beach, EX23 8NG, ℰ (01288) 353110, *Fax (01288) 353110*, 🔲, 🗭, 🎾 – 🛏 rest, 📺 ☎ 🅿, 🆗 𝖵𝖨𝖲𝖠 𝖩𝖢𝖡
*April-September* – **Meals** (bar lunch)/dinner 12.50 st. ⬧ 4.00 – **15 rm** ☯ 32.00/60.00 st. - SB.

🏠 **Camelot,** Downs View, EX23 8RE, ℰ (01288) 352361, *Fax (01288) 355470*, 🗭 – 🛏 rest 📺 ☎ 🅿, 🆗 𝖵𝖨𝖲𝖠, 🛇
**Meals** (bar lunch)/dinner 14.95 st. ⬧ 5.50 – **21 rm** ☯ 28.00/56.00 st. – SB.

🏠 **Bude Haven,** Flexbury Av., EX23 8NS, ℰ (01288) 352305, *Fax (01258) 352305* – ☆※ 🖵 🅿.
🖸 🖭 𝑽𝑰𝑺𝑨. ※
*closed 1 week New Year* – **Meals** (bar lunch)/dinner 10.00 **st.** ▮ 3.75 – **12 rm** ⌷ 27.50/
50.00 **st.** – SB.

---

**BUDLEIGH SALTERTON** *Devon* 🕮🔢 K 32 *The West Country G.* – *pop. 3 759.*
**Env. :** *East Budleigh (Church★), N : 2½ m. by A 376 – Bicton★ (Gardens★) AC, N : 3 m. by
A 376.*
🖪 *East Devon, North View Rd* ℰ (01395) 442018.
🖪 *Fore St., EX9 6NG* ℰ (01395) 445275.
*London 182 – Exeter 16 – Plymouth 55.*

↑ **Long Range,** 5 Vales Rd, EX9 6HS, by Raleigh Rd ℰ (01395) 443321, *Fax (01395) 445220,*
� – ☆※ 🖵 🅿. ※
**Meals** 17.50 **st.** ▮ 4.75 – **6 rm** ⌷ 37.50/55.00 **st.**

---

**BUDOCK WATER** *Cornwall – see Falmouth.*

---

**BUNBURY** *Ches.* 🔢🔢🔢 M 24 – *see Tarporley.*

---

**BURFORD** *Oxon.* 🔢🔢 P 28 – *pop. 1 171.*
🖪 ℰ (01993) 822149.
🖪 *The Brewery, Sheep St., OX18 4LP* ℰ (01993) 823558.
*London 76 – Birmingham 55 – Gloucester 32 – Oxford 20.*

🏨 **Bay Tree,** 12-14 Sheep St., OX18 4LW, ℰ (01993) 822791, *Fax (01993) 823008,* « 16C
house, antique furnishings », � – ☆※ rest, 🖵 ☎ 🅿 – 🔏 30. 🖸 🖭 ⓞ 𝑽𝑰𝑺𝑨 𝑱𝑪𝑩. ※
**Meals** 16.95/24.95 **t.** – **19 rm** ⌷ 80.00/125.00 **t.,** 2 suites – SB.

🏠 **Lamb Inn,** Sheep St., OX18 4LR, ℰ (01993) 823155, *Fax (01993) 822228,* « Part 14C,
antique furnishings », � – ☆※ rest, 🖵 ☎. 🖸 𝑽𝑰𝑺𝑨 𝑱𝑪𝑩
*closed 25 and 26 December* – **Meals** 24.00 **t.** ▮ 5.00 – **15 rm** ⌷ 57.50/100.00 **t.** – SB.

🏠 **Golden Pheasant,** 91 High St., OX18 4QA, ℰ (01993) 823223, *Fax (01993) 822621* –
☆※ rest, 🖵 ☎ 🅿. 🖸 🖭 𝑽𝑰𝑺𝑨.
**Meals** (bar lunch Monday to Saturday)/dinner a la carte 16.40/26.20 **t.** ▮ 6.95 – **12 rm**
⌷ 50.00/105.00 **t.** – SB.

🏠 **Burford House** without rest., 99 High St., OX18 4QA, ℰ (01993) 823151,
*Fax (01993) 823240,* � – ☆※ 🖵. 🖸 🖭 𝑽𝑰𝑺𝑨. ※
**7 rm** ⌷ 75.00/120.00 **t.**

🏠 **Inn For All Seasons,** The Barringtons, OX18 4TN, West : 3 ¼ m. on A 40
ℰ (01451) 844324, *Fax (01451) 844375,* � – 🖵 ☎ 🅿 – 🔏 35. 🖸 🖭 𝑽𝑰𝑺𝑨
*closed 25 and 26 December* – **Meals** 16.50 **t.** (dinner) and a la carte 15.00/23.70 **t.** ▮ 4.95 –
**10 rm** ⌷ 45.00/79.00 **st.** – SB.

🏠 **Travelodge,** Bury Barn, OX7 5TB, on A 40 (Burford roundabout) ℰ (01993) 822699,
Reservations (Freephone) 0800 850950 – 🖵 ⅙ 🅿. 🖸 🖭 ⓞ 𝑽𝑰𝑺𝑨 𝑱𝑪𝑩. ※
**Meals** (grill rest.) – **40 rm** 39.95/59.95 **t.**

**at Fulbrook** *Northeast : ¾ m. on A 361 –* ✉ *Burford.*

🏠 **Elm House** ⏁, Meadow Lane, OX18 4BW, ℰ (01993) 823611, *Fax (01993) 823937,* � –
☆※ 🖵 🅿. 🖸 𝑽𝑰𝑺𝑨 𝑱𝑪𝑩
*closed 2 January-1 February* – **Meals** (residents only) (dinner only) 20.00 ▮ 4.95 – **7 rm**
⌷ 45.00/75.00 **t.** – SB.

---

**BURGH-LE-MARSH** *Lincs.* 🔢🔢 U 24 – *pop. 2 718.*
*London 110 – Boston 29 – Great Grimsby 38 – Lincoln 25.*

🍴 **Windmill,** 46 High St., PE24 5JT, ℰ (01754) 810281, *Fax (01754) 811011* – 🅿. 🖸 🖭 𝑽𝑰𝑺𝑨
*closed Sunday dinner, Monday and 1 week spring* – **Meals** (dinner only and Sunday lunch)/
dinner a la carte 11.75/19.50 **st.** ▮ 5.75.

---

**BURLAND** *Ches. – see Nantwich.*

*Se cercate un albergo tranquillo,*
*oltre a consultare le carte dell'introduzione,*
*rintracciate nell'elenco degli esercizi quelli con il simbolo ⏁ o ⏁.*

**BURLEY** Hants. 403 404 O 31 Great Britain G. – pop. 1 438 – ⊠ Ringwood.
Env. : New Forest★★ (Rhinefield Ornamental Drive★★, Bolderwood Ornamental Drive★★).
London 102 – Bournemouth 17 – Southampton 17 – Winchester 30.

🏠 **Tree House,** The Cross, BH24 4AB, ℰ (01425) 403448, Fax (01425) 402058 – 📺 ☎ 🅿. 🆀 𝐖𝐒𝐀. ⋘
closed January – **Meals** a la carte 11.65/22.95 **t.** – **8 rm** � 40.00/90.00 **st.** – SB.

**BURLEY IN WHARFEDALE** W. Yorks. 402 O 22 – pop. 5 528.
London 218 – Bradford 14 – Harrogate 15 – Leeds 14 – Preston 52.

XX **David Woolley's,** 78 Main St., LS29 7BT, ℰ (01943) 864602 – 🅿. 🆀 𝐖𝐒𝐀
closed Sunday, 25-26 December and 1 January – **Meals** (dinner only) 14.95 **t.** and a la carte
⸹ 4.50.

**BURNHAM** Bucks. 404 S 29 – pop. 11 169.
London 33 – Oxford 37 – Reading 17.

🏰 **County H. Burnham Beeches** 🔈, Grove Rd, SL1 8DP, Northwest : 1 m. by Britwell R
ℰ (01628) 429955, Fax (01628) 603994, 𝕃∮, 🛱, 𝕏, ⋐, park, ⋘ – 🛏, ⋘ rm, 📺 ☎ 🕭 🅿 –
🔏 180. 🆀🛇 🆎 ⓞ 𝐖𝐒𝐀. ⋘
**Grays :** **Meals** 15.00/22.50 **st.** and a la carte ⸹ 6.50 – ⊆ 10.00 – **82 rm** 150.00/160.00 **t**
2 suites – SB.

*Keine Aufnahme in den **Michelin-Führer** durch*
*- falsche Information oder*
*- Bezahlung!*

**BURNHAM MARKET** Norfolk 404 W 25 Great Britain G. – pop. 898.
Env. : Holkham Hall★★ AC, E : 3 m. by B 1155.
London 128 – Cambridge 71 – Norwich 36.

🏠 **Hoste Arms,** The Green, PE31 8HD, ℰ (01328) 738777, Fax (01328) 730103, « 17C inn »
⋐ – 📺 🅿. 🆀🛇 𝐖𝐒𝐀
**Meals** – (see **The Restaurant** below) – **20 rm** ⊆ 60.00/88.00 **t.** – SB.

🏠 **Railway Inn** without rest., Creake Rd, PE31 8EN, ℰ (01328) 730505, Fax (01328) 73010
– 📺 🅿. 🆀🛇 𝐖𝐒𝐀
**Meals** – (see **The Restaurant** below) – **6 rm** ⊆ 42.00/58.00 **t.**

X **The Restaurant** (at Hoste Arms H.), The Green, PE31 8HD, ℰ (01328) 738777
Fax (01328) 730103 – ⋘ 🅿. 🆀🛇 𝐖𝐒𝐀
**Meals** (booking essential) a la carte 14.40/24.25 **t.** ⸹ 7.95.

**BURNHAM-ON-CROUCH** Essex 404 W 29 – pop. 7 067.
London 52 – Chelmsford 19 – Colchester 32 – Southend-on-Sea 25.

XXX **Contented Sole,** 80 High St., CM0 8AA, ℰ (01621) 782139 – 🆀🛇 𝐖𝐒𝐀
closed Sunday dinner, Monday, 2 weeks July and 2 weeks Christmas – **Meals** (dinner only
and Sunday lunch)/dinner 13.95 **st.** and a la carte ⸹ 6.95.

**BURNLEY** Lancs. 402 N 22 – pop. 74 661.
🛆, 🛆 Towneley, Towneley Park, Todmorden Rd ℰ (01282) 451636 – 🛆 Glen View ℰ (01282
421045.
🖪 Burnley Mechanics, Manchester Rd, BB11 1JA ℰ (01282) 455485.
London 236 – Bradford 32 – Leeds 37 – Liverpool 55 – Manchester 25 – Middlesbrough 10
– Preston 22 – Sheffield 68.

🏰 **Oaks,** Colne Rd, Reedley, BB10 2LF, Northeast : 2 ½ m. on A 56 ℰ (01282) 414141
Fax (01282) 433401, 𝕃∮, 🛱, 𝕏, ⋐ – ⋘ rm, 📺 ☎ 🅿 – 🔏 120. 🆀🛇 🆎 ⓞ 𝐖𝐒𝐀
**Meals** (closed Saturday and Sunday) (lunch only) 20.00/30.00 **t.** ⸹ 9.00 – **Quills :** **Meals**
(dinner only) 18.00 **t.** and a la carte ⸹ 9.00 – **53 rm** ⊆ 97.00/142.00 **st.**

🏠 **Rosehill House,** Rosehill Av., Manchester Rd, BB11 2PW, South : 1 ¼ m. by A 56
ℰ (01282) 453931, Fax (01282) 455628, ⋐ – ⋘ 📺 ☎ 🕭 🅿. 🆀🛇 🆎 ⓞ 𝐖𝐒𝐀 𝐉𝐂𝐁
closed 26 December – **Meals** a la carte 14.45/26.95 **t.** ⸹ 6.95 – **25 rm** ⊆ 40.00/85.00 **t.**

🏠 **The Alexander,** 2 Tarleton Av., off Todmorden Rd, BB11 3ET, South : ¾ m. by A 67
ℰ (01282) 422684, Fax (01282) 424094, ⋐ – 📺 ☎ 🅿. 🆀🛇 🆎 ⓞ 𝐖𝐒𝐀. ⋘
**Meals** (closed Saturday lunch and Sunday dinner) 7.95/14.00 **st.** and a la carte ⸹ 4.95 –
**16 rm** ⊆ 39.50/49.00 **st.**

🏠 **Travel Inn,** Queen Victoria, Queen Victoria Rd, BB10 3EF, East : ¾ m. by A 671 on A 6114 ℰ (01282) 450250, *Fax (01282) 452811* – ↤ rm, ▤ rest, 📺 ㄟ ℗ – 🛦 40. 🆎 ㎒ ⓞ 𝘝𝘐𝘚𝘈. ⛝
Meals (grill rest.) – **40 rm** 38.00 **t.**

🏠 **Travelodge,** Cavalry Barracks, Barracks Rd, BB11 4AS, West : ½ m. at junction of A 671 with A 679 ℰ (01282) 416039, *Fax (01282) 416039,* Reservations (Freephone) 0800 850950 – ↤ rm, 📺 ㄟ ℗. 🆎 ㎒ ⓞ 𝘝𝘐𝘚𝘈 𝘑𝘊𝘉. ⛝
Meals (grill rest.) – **32 rm** 39.95/59.95 **t.**

⓪ ATS Healey Wood Rd ℰ (01282) 422409/38423/451624

---

**BURNSALL** N. Yorks. 402 O 21 – pop. 108 – ✉ Skipton.
London 223 – Bradford 26 – Leeds 29.

🏠 **Red Lion,** BD23 6BU, ℰ (01756) 720204, *Fax (01756) 720292*, ≤, « Part 16C inn », ≒ – ↤ 📺 ☎ ℗. 🆎 ㎒ 𝘝𝘐𝘚𝘈 𝘑𝘊𝘉. ⛝
Meals – (see *The Restaurant* below) – **11 rm** ⊇ 47.00/95.00 **st.** – SB.

✕✕ **The Restaurant** (at Red Lion H.), BD23 6BU, ℰ (01756) 720204, *Fax (01756) 720292,* « Part 16C inn » – ↤ ℗. 🆎 ㎒ 𝘝𝘐𝘚𝘈 𝘑𝘊𝘉
Meals (bar lunch Monday to Saturday)/dinner 23.95 **st.** ⓖ 6.95.

---

**BURNT YATES** N. Yorks. – see Ripley.

---

**BURPHAM** W. Sussex 404 S 30 – see Arundel.

---

**BURRINGTON** Devon 403 I 31 – pop. 533.
London 260 – Barnstaple 14 – Exeter 28 – Taunton 50.

🏠🏠 **Northcote Manor** ⅏, EX37 9LZ, Northwest : 1 ½ m. by Barnstaple rd ℰ (01769) 560501, *Fax (01769) 560770,* ≤, « 17C manor house », ☞, park, ✕ – ↤ rest, 📺 ☎ ℗. 🆎 ㎒ ⓞ 𝘝𝘐𝘚𝘈 𝘑𝘊𝘉
Meals (booking essential) (dinner only) 24.50 **st.** ⓖ 12.00 – **12 rm** ⊇ (dinner included) 91.00/140.00 **st.**, 1 suite – SB.

---

**BURSLEM** Stoke-on-Trent 402 403 404 N 24 – see Stoke-on-Trent.

---

**BURSTALL** Suffolk – see Ipswich.

---

**BURTON-IN-KENDAL SERVICE AREA** Cumbria 402 L 21 – ✉ Carnforth.

🏠 **Travelodge,** LA6 1JF, on M 6 northbound carriageway between junctions 35 and 36 ℰ (01524) 784012, *Fax (01524) 784014,* Reservations (Freephone) 0800 850950 – ↤ 📺 ☎ ㄟ ℗. 🆎 ㎒ ⓞ 𝘝𝘐𝘚𝘈 𝘑𝘊𝘉. ⛝
Meals (grill rest.) – **47 rm** 39.95/59.95 **t.**

---

**BURTON-UPON-TRENT** Staffs. 402 403 404 O 25 – pop. 60 525.
🏌 Branston G. & C.C., Burton Rd ℰ (01283) 512211 – 🏌 Craythorne, Craythorne Rd, Stretton ℰ (01283) 564329.
🛈 Unit 40, Octagon Centre, New St., DE14 3TN ℰ (01283) 516609.
London 128 – Birmingham 29 – Leicester 27 – Nottingham 27 – Stafford 27.

🏠🏠 **Stanhope Arms,** Ashby Road East, DE15 0PU, Southeast : 2 ½ m. on A 50 ℰ (01283) 217954, *Fax (01283) 226199* – 📺 ☎ ℗ – 🛦 150. 🆎 𝘝𝘐𝘚𝘈. ⛝
a la carte 9.00/19.90 **st.** ⓖ 2.95 – ⊇ 5.95 – **23 rm** 45.50 **st.**

**at Stretton** North : 3½ m. by A 50 off A 5121 – ✉ Burton-upon-Trent.

✕✕✕ **Dovecliff Hall** ⅏ with rm, Dovecliff Rd, DE13 0DJ, Northeast : 1 m. ℰ (01283) 531818, *Fax (01283) 516546,* ≤, ☞, « Restored Georgian house, gardens », ≒, park – 📺 ☎ ℗. 🆎 ㎒ 𝘝𝘐𝘚𝘈. ⛝
Meals (closed Monday lunch and Sunday dinner) 13.50/22.50 **t.** and dinner a la carte ⓖ 9.00 – **7 rm** ⊇ 55.00/105.00 **t.** – SB.

**at Rolleston-on-Dove** North : 3¾ m. by A 50 on Rolleston Rd – ✉ Burton-upon-Trent.

🏠🏠 **Brookhouse Inn,** Brookside, DE13 9AA, ℰ (01283) 814188, *Fax (01283) 813644,* « Part 17C house, antiques », ☞ – 📺 ☎ ℗. 🆎 ㎒ ⓞ 𝘝𝘐𝘚𝘈 𝘑𝘊𝘉. ⛝
Meals (closed Saturday lunch and Sunday dinner) 10.25 **t.** (lunch) and a la carte 18.70/ 27.70 **t.** ⓖ 4.95 – **21 rm** ⊇ 72.00/95.00 **st.** – SB.

**at Newton Solney** Northeast : 3 m. by A 50 on B 5008 – ⊠ Burton-upon-Trent.

🏨 **Newton Park,** Newton Rd, DE15 0SS, ℰ (01283) 703568, Fax (01283) 703214, 🐎 – |≒
      ⇔ rm, 🆃 ☎ & 🅿 – 🕍 100. ⓒⓄ 🅰🅴 ⓄⒹ 🆅🅸🆂🅰. ✼
      **Meals** (bar lunch Monday to Saturday)/dinner 14.95/17.95 **st.** – � 8.95 – **51 rm** 89.00
      115.00 – SB.

**at Branston** Southwest : 1½ m. on A 5121 – ⊠ Burton-upon-Trent.

🏨 **Riverside,** Riverside Drive, off Warren Lane, DE14 3EP, ℰ (01283) 511234
      Fax (01283) 511441, ⚓, 🐎 – 🆃 ☎ 🅿 – 🕍 150. ⓒⓄ 🅰🅴 🆅🅸🆂🅰
      **Meals** (closed Saturday lunch) 18.95 **t.** (dinner) and a la carte 16.15/27.45 **t.** ◊ 6.95 – **22 rm**
      ⊠ 62.50/67.50 **t.**

**at Barton-under-Needwood** Southwest : 5 m. by A 5121 on A 38 – ⊠ Burton-upon-Trent.

🏨 **Travelodge,** Lichfield Rd, DE13 8EG, on A 38 (northbound carriageway)
      ℰ (01283) 716343, Fax (01283) 716343, Reservations (Freephone) 0800 850950 – ⇔ rm
      🆃 & 🅿. ⓒⓄ 🅰🅴 ⓄⒹ 🆅🅸🆂🅰 🅹🅲🅱. ✼
      **Meals** (grill rest.) – **20 rm** 39.95/59.95 **t.**

🏨 **Travelodge,** DE13 8EH, on A 38 (southbound carriageway) ℰ (01283) 716784, Reserva-
      tions (Freephone) 0800 850950 – ⇔ rm, 🆃 & 🅿. ⓒⓄ 🅰🅴 ⓄⒹ 🆅🅸🆂🅰 🅹🅲🅱. ✼
      **Meals** (grill rest.) – **40 rm** 39.95/59.95 **t.**

      ⓐ ATS Nicholson Way, off Wellington Rd ℰ (01283) 565994/563170

---

**BURTONWOOD SERVICE AREA** Ches. 🟦🟦🟦 M 23 – ⊠ Warrington.

🏨 **Welcome Lodge,** WA5 3AX, M 62 (westbound carriageway) ℰ (01925) 710376
      Fax (01925) 710378, Reservations (Freephone) 0800 7314466 – ⇔ rm, 🆃 & 🅿. ⓒⓄ 🅰🅴 ⓄⒹ
      🆅🅸🆂🅰
      **Meals** (grill rest.) – ⊠ 7.50 – **40 rm** 50.00 **t.**

---

**BURY** Gtr. Manchester 🟦🟦🟦 N 23 🟦🟦🟦 ③ 🟦🟦🟦 N 23 – pop. 62 633.
      🏌 Greenmount ℰ (01204) 883712.
      🄱 The Mets Art Centre, Market St., BL9 0BW ℰ (0161) 705 5111.
      London 211 – Leeds 45 – Liverpool 35 – Manchester 9.

✗ **Est, Est, Est,** 703 Manchester Rd, BL9 0ED, South : 2 m. on A 56 ℰ (0161) 766 4869
      Fax (0161) 766 4869 – 🖿 🅿. ⓒⓄ 🅰🅴 ⓄⒹ 🆅🅸🆂🅰
      closed Saturday lunch and 25-26 December – **Meals** - Italian - a la carte 12.65/24.70 **t.**
      ◊ 5.05.

**at Walmersley** North : 1¾ m. on A 56 – ⊠ Bury.

🏨 **Red Hall,** Manchester Rd, BL9 5NA, North : 1 ¼ m. on A 56 ℰ (01706) 822476
      Fax (01706) 828086 – ⇔ rest, 🆃 ☎ 🅿 – 🕍 45. ⓒⓄ 🅰🅴 ⓄⒹ 🆅🅸🆂🅰 🅹🅲🅱. ✼
      closed 24 December-3 January – **Meals** (closed lunch Monday and Saturday) a la carte
      19.80/20.85 **t.** ◊ 5.60 – **20 rm** ⊠ 50.00/62.00 **t.**

**at Birtle** Northeast : 3 m. by B 6222 – ⊠ Bury.

🏨 **Normandie** ⚑, Elbut Lane, BL9 6UT, ℰ (0161) 764 1170, Fax (0161) 764 4866, ← – |≒ 🆃
      ☎ 🅿. ⓒⓄ 🅰🅴 ⓄⒹ 🆅🅸🆂🅰 🅹🅲🅱. ✼
      closed 26 December-4 January and 1 week Easter – **Meals** – (see **The Restaurant** below) –
      ⊠ 6.95 – **23 rm** 49.00/79.00 **t.**

✗✗✗ **The Restaurant** (at Normandie H.), Elbut Lane, BL9 6UT, ℰ (0161) 764 1170
      Fax (0161) 764 4866, ← – 🅿. ⓒⓄ 🅰🅴 ⓄⒹ 🆅🅸🆂🅰 🅹🅲🅱
      closed Saturday lunch, Sunday, 26 December-4 January and 1 week Easter – **Meals** (booking
      essential) 12.50/15.00 **t.** and a la carte ◊ 5.00.

      ⓐ ATS John St. ℰ (0161) 764 2830/6860

---

**BURY ST. EDMUNDS** Suffolk 🟦🟦🟦 W 27 Great Britain G. – pop. 31 237.
      See : Town★ – Abbey and Cathedral★.
      Env. : Ickworth House★ AC, SW : 3 m. by A 143.
      🏌 Suffolk G. & C.C., St. John's Hill Plantation, The Street ℰ (01284) 706777.
      🄱 6 Angel Hill, IP33 1UZ ℰ (01284) 764667.
      London 79 – Cambridge 27 – Ipswich 26 – Norwich 41.

🏨 **Angel,** 3 Angel Hill, IP33 1LT, ℰ (01284) 753926, Fax (01284) 750092 – ⇔ rm, 🆃 ☎ 🅿 –
      🕍 140. ⓒⓄ 🅰🅴 ⓄⒹ 🆅🅸🆂🅰
      **Meals** (closed Sunday dinner) 15.00 **st.** (lunch) and a la carte 17.65/34.35 **t.** ◊ 8.35 – ⊠
      11.00 – **42 rm** 67.00/78.00 **st.**, 1 suite.

🏛 **Priory,** Tollgate, IP32 6EH, North : 1 ¾ m. by A 1101 on B 1106 ℰ (01284) 766181,
*Fax (01284) 767604,* 🛲 – ⛐ 📺 ☎ 🅿 – ♨ 60. 🚳 🝰 ⓪ 𝑽𝑰𝑺𝑨 𝑱𝑪𝑩
*closed 25 and 26 December* – **Meals** *(closed Sunday lunch)* 21.00 t. and a la carte ⅄ 7.25 –
**25 rm** ⌑ 65.00/105.00 t. – SB.

🏛🏛 **Butterfly,** Symonds Rd, IP32 7BW, Southeast : 1 ½ m. by A 1302 and A 134 at junction
with A 14 ℰ (01284) 760884, *Fax (01284) 755476* – ⛐ rm, 📺 ☎ 🅿 – ♨ 60. 🚳 🝰 ⓪ 𝑽𝑰𝑺𝑨
𝑱𝑪𝑩 %
**Meals** 15.00/17.50 t. and a la carte – ⌑ 7.50 – **65 rm** 62.50 t. – SB.

🏛 **Twelve Angel Hill** without rest., 12 Angel Hill, IP33 1UZ, ℰ (01284) 704088,
*Fax (01284) 725549,* 🛲 – ⛐ 📺 ☎ 🅿. 🚳 🝰 ⓪ 𝑽𝑰𝑺𝑨. %
*closed January* – **6 rm** ⌑ 50.00/85.00 st.

🏛 **Ounce House** without rest., Northgate St., IP33 1HP, ℰ (01284) 761779,
*Fax (01284) 768315,* 🛲 – ⛐ 📺 ☎ 🅿. 🚳 🝰 𝑽𝑰𝑺𝑨. %
**3 rm** ⌑ 55.00/85.00 st.

🏛 **The Abbey** without rest., 35 Southgate St., IP33 2AZ, ℰ (01284) 762020,
*Fax (01284) 724770* – ⛐ 📺 ☎ ✆ 🅿. 🚳 🝰 ⓪ 𝑽𝑰𝑺𝑨. %
**10 rm** ⌑ 54.50/68.00 t., 2 suites.

**at Ixworth** *Northeast : 7 m. by A 143* – ✉ *Bury St. Edmunds.*

XX **Theobalds,** 68 High St., IP31 2HJ, ℰ (01359) 231707, *Fax (01359) 231707,* � – 🚳 𝑽𝑰𝑺𝑨
*closed Saturday lunch, Sunday dinner, Monday, 2 weeks August and Bank Holidays* – **Meals**
17.50 t. (lunch) and a la carte 24.20/30.25 t. ⅄ 7.75.

**at Bardwell** *Northeast : 9 ¾ m. by A 143 and A 1088 on Bardwell rd* – ✉ *Bury St. Edmunds.*

🍴 **Six Bells Country Inn** with rm, The Green, IP31 1AW, ℰ (01359) 250820,
*Fax (01359) 250820,* 🛲 – 📺 ☎ 🅿. 🚳 🝰 𝑽𝑰𝑺𝑨. %
*closed 25 and 26 December* – **Meals** *(light lunch Monday)* 12.50 st. (dinner) and a la carte
11.50/21.40 st. ⅄ 5.00 – **9 rm** ⌑ 45.00/60.00 st. – SB.

**at Rougham Green** *Southeast : 4 m. by A 1302 and A 134 off A 14* – ✉ *Bury St. Edmunds.*

🏛🏛 **Ravenwood Hall,** IP30 9JA, ℰ (01359) 270345, *Fax (01359) 270788,* ⥾, 🛲, park, % –
⛐ 📺 ☎ 🅿 – ♨ 150. 🚳 🝰 ⓪ 𝑽𝑰𝑺𝑨 𝑱𝑪𝑩
**Meals** 18.95 t. and a la carte ⅄ 4.75 – **14 rm** ⌑ 63.00/115.00 t. – SB.

**at Horringer** *Southwest : 3 m. on A 143* – ✉ *Bury St. Edmunds.*

🍴 **Beehive,** IP29 5SN, ℰ (01284) 735260, *Fax (01284) 830321,* � – 🅿. 🚳 𝑽𝑰𝑺𝑨
*closed Sunday dinner and 25-26 December* – **Meals** a la carte 14.45/22.35 t. ⅄ 5.85.

**at Fornham All Saints** *Northwest : 3 ¼ m. by A 1101 on B 1106* – ✉ *Bury St. Edmunds.*

🏠 **Fornham Hall** without rest., IP28 6JJ, ℰ (01284) 725266, « Part Georgian house, Tudor
origins », 🛲 – ⛐ 🅿. 🚳 𝑽𝑰𝑺𝑨. %
**3 rm** ⌑ 40.00/85.00 st., 1 suite.

⊙ ATS Units 1 and 3, Ailwin Rd, Moreton Hall Ind. Est. ℰ (01284) 705610

---

**BUSHEY** *Herts.* 🔢 S 29.
🏌 *Bushey Hall, Bushey Hall Drive* ℰ *(01923) 222253,* BT – 🏌 *Bushey G. & C.C., High St.*
ℰ *(0181) 950 2283,* BT.
*London 18 – Luton 21 – Watford 3.*

Plan : see Greater London (North-West) p. 4

XX **st James,** 30 High St., WD2 3DN, ℰ (0181) 950 2480, *Fax (0181) 950 4107* – ▤. 🚳 🝰
𝑽𝑰𝑺𝑨                                                                                           BT  c
*closed Sunday, 25-26 December and Bank Holidays* – **Meals** a la carte 20.10/24.30 t. ⅄ 8.75.

---

**BUTTERMERE** *Cumbria* 🔢 K 20 – *pop. 139* – ✉ *Cockermouth.*
*London 306 – Carlisle 35 – Kendal 43.*

🏛 **Bridge,** CA13 9UZ, ℰ (017687) 70252, *Fax (017687) 70215,* ≤ – ⛐ rest, ☎ 🅿. 🚳 𝑽𝑰𝑺𝑨
**Meals** *(booking essential)* (bar lunch)/dinner 21.00 t. and a la carte ⅄ 5.95 – **22 rm** ⌑
*(dinner included)* 60.00/142.00 t. – SB.

---

**BUTTERTON** *Staffs.* – *see Leek.*

*Si vous cherchez un hôtel tranquille,*
*consultez d'abord les cartes de l'introduction*
*ou repérez dans le texte les établissements indiqués avec le signe 🟲 ou 🟲.*

**BUXTON** Derbs. 402 403 404 O 24 – pop. 19 854.

🏌 Buxton and High Peak, Townend ℰ (01298) 23453.

🛈 The Crescent, SK17 6BQ ℰ (01298) 25106.

London 172 – Derby 38 – Manchester 25 – Stoke-on-Trent 24.

🏨 **Lee Wood,** The Park, SK17 6TQ, on A 5004 ℰ (01298) 23002, Fax (01298) 23228, 🌲 – 📶
🍴 rm, 📺 ☎ 🌿 🅿 – 🔬 100. 🐵 🆎 ① 𝘝𝘐𝘚𝘈 𝗝𝗖𝗕. 🎇
Meals 13.75/23.95 **st.** and a la carte ♦ 6.25 – ☑ 9.00 – **37 rm** 66.00/92.00 **st.** – SB.

⌂ **Coningsby,** 6 Macclesfield Rd, SK17 9AH, ℰ (01298) 26735, Fax (01298) 26735, 🌲 – ⊱
📺 🅿. 🎇
February-October – Meals (by arrangement) 15.50 **st.** – **3 rm** ☑ 40.00/55.00 **st.**

⌂ **Lakenham** without rest., 11 Burlington Rd, SK17 9AL, ℰ (01298) 79209 – 📺 🅿
**6 rm** ☑ 50.00/55.00 **st.**

🔧 ATS Staden Lane Ind. Park ℰ (01298) 25608/25655

---

**BYFORD** Herefordshire 403 L 27 – see Hereford.

---

**CADNAM** Hants. 403 404 P 31 – pop. 1 866.

London 91 – Salisbury 16 – Southampton 8 – Winchester 19.

⌂ **Walnut Cottage** without rest., Old Romsey Rd, SO40 2NP, off A 31 ℰ (01703) 812275
Fax (01703) 812275, 🌲 – 📺 🅿. 🎇
closed 24 to 27 December – **3 rm** ☑ 30.00/44.00.

---

**CAISTOR ST. EDMUND** Norfolk 404 X 26 – see Norwich.

---

**CALCOT** Glos. – see Tetbury.

---

**CALDBECK** Cumbria 401 402 K 19 – pop. 688 – ✉ Wigton.

London 308 – Carlisle 13 – Keswick 16 – Workington 23.

⌂ **Parkend** ⅊, Park End, CA7 8HH, Southwest : 1 ½ m. on B 5299 ℰ (016974) 78494
Fax (016974) 78580, « Converted 17C farmhouse », 🌲 – ⊱ rest, 📺 🅿. 🐵 🆎 ① 𝘝𝘐𝘚𝘈
Meals (by arrangement) 13.00 **st.** ♦ 3.50 – **6 rm** ☑ 28.00/48.00 **st.**

---

**CALNE** Wilts. 403 404 O 29 The West Country G. – pop. 11 516.

Env. : Bowood House★ AC, (Library ≤★) SW : 2 m. by A 4 – Avebury★★ (The Stones★ Church★) E : 6 m. by A 4.

London 91 – Bristol 33 – Swindon 17.

⌂ **Chilvester Hill House,** SN11 0LP, West : ¾ m. by A 4 on Bremhill rd ℰ (01249) 813981,
Fax (01249) 814217, 🌲 – ⊱ rest, 📺 🅿. 🐵 🆎 ① 𝘝𝘐𝘚𝘈. 🎇
Meals (by arrangement) (communal dining) 18.00/25.00 **st.** ♦ 6.25 – **3 rm** ☑ 45.00/
85.00 **st.**

🔧 ATS Unit 4, Maundrell Rd., Portemarsh Ind. Est. ℰ (01249) 821622

---

**CALSTOCK** Cornwall 403 H 32 The West Country G. – pop. 5 964 – ✉ Tavistock.

Env. : Tamar River★★ – Cotehele★ AC, SW : 1 m. - Morwellham★ AC, NE : 1½ m.

London 246 – Exeter 48 – Plymouth 22.

🏠 **Danescombe Valley** ⅊, Lower Kelly, PL18 9RY, West : ½ m. ℰ (01822) 832414,
Fax (01822) 832446, « Victorian villa, ≤ River Tamar and Calstock Viaduct » – 🔽, ⊱ rest, 🅿
🐵 🆎 ① 𝘝𝘐𝘚𝘈. 🎇
March-October – Meals (booking essential to non-residents) (dinner only Friday and
Saturday) 30.00 **st.** ♦ 4.50 – **5 rm** ☑ 60.00/100.00 **st.**

---

**CAMBERLEY** Surrey 404 R 29 – pop. 46 120 (inc. Frimley).

London 40 – Reading 13 – Southampton 48.

🏨 **Frimley Hall** ⅊, Lime Av. via Conifer Drive, GU15 2BG, East : ¾ m. off Portsmouth Rd
(A 325) ℰ (01276) 28321, Fax (01276) 691253, 🌲 – ⊱ 📺 ☎ 🅿 – 🔬 60. 🐵 🆎 ① 𝘝𝘐𝘚𝘈 𝗝𝗖𝗕
Meals 10.00/15.00 **st.** and a la carte ♦ 6.50 – ☑ 12.50 – **86 rm** 145.00/185.00 **st.** – SB.

🏠 **Travel Inn,** 221 Yorktown Rd, GU47 0RT, West : 2 m. by A 30 and A 321 on A 3095
ℰ (01276) 878181, Fax (01276) 890648 – ⊱ rm, 📺 ♿ 🅿. 🐵 🆎 ① 𝘝𝘐𝘚𝘈. 🎇
Meals (grill rest.) – **40 rm** 38.00 **t.**

**CAMBORNE** Cornwall **403** E 33 *The West Country G. – pop. 35 915 (inc. Redruth).*
Env. : Carn Brea (≤★★), NE : 3 m. by A 3047 and minor rd.
London 299 – Falmouth 14 – Penzance 16 – Truro 14.

🏠 **Tyack's,** 27 Commercial St., TR14 8LD, ℘ (01209) 612424, *Fax (01209) 612435* – ¥ rm, 📺
🕿 **P**. ⁐ ☒ ⓪ *VISA* JCB, ⅍
**Meals** a la carte 15.70/25.50 t. ⅃ 4.50 – **13 rm** ⇌ 45.00/75.00 t., 2 suites.

---

**CAMBRIDGE** Cambs. **404** U 27 *Great Britain G. – pop. 95 682.*
See : Town★★★ – St. John's College★★★ AC Y – King's College★★ (King's College
Chapel★★★) Z The Backs★★ YZ – Fitzwilliam Museum★★ Z M1 – Trinity College★★ Y –
Clare College★ Z B – Kettle's Yard★ Y M2 – Queen's College★ AC Z.
Exc. : Audley End★★, S : 13 m. on Trumpington Rd, A 1309, A 1301 and B 1383 – Imperial
War Museum★, Duxford, S : 9 m. on M 11.
🏌 Cambridgeshire Moat House Hotel, Bar Hill ℘ (01954) 780555 X.
✈ Cambridge Airport : ℘ (01223) 373737, E : 2 m. on A 1303 X.
🛈 Wheeler St., CB2 3QB ℘ (01223) 322640.
London 55 – Coventry 88 – Kingston-upon-Hull 137 – Ipswich 54 – Leicester 74 – Norwich 61
– Nottingham 88 – Oxford 100.

Plan on next page

🏨 **Cambridge Garden House Moat House,** Granta Pl., off Mill Lane, CB2 1RT,
℘ (01223) 259988, *Fax (01223) 316605,* ≤, ⅃₆, ≋, ☒, ☞ – ⅃, ¥ rm, 📺 🕿 ⎙ **P** –
⅍ 250. ⁐ ☒ ⓪ *VISA*                                                                                  Z n
**Meals** 12.95/17.95 st. and a la carte ⅃ 6.95 – ⇌ 12.95 – **117 rm** 120.00/195.00 st. – SB.

🏨 **Holiday Inn,** Downing St., CB2 3DT, ℘ (01223) 464466, *Fax (01223) 464440* – ⅃, ¥ rm,
▤ 📺 🕿 ⅄ **P** – ⅍ 150. ⁐ ☒ ⓪ *VISA* JCB, ⅍                                                Z a
**Meals** (bar lunch)/dinner a la carte 15.65/26.40 t. – ⇌ 11.95 – **194 rm** 118.00/145.00 st.,
2 suites – SB.

🏨 **University Arms,** Regent St., CB2 1AD, ℘ (01223) 351241, *Fax (01223) 315256* – ⅃,
¥ rm, 📺 🕿 ⎙ ⅄ **P** – ⅍ 300. ⁐ ☒ ⓪ *VISA*, ⅍                                            Z e
**Meals** *(closed Saturday lunch)* 12.95/20.00 st. and dinner a la carte ⅃ 7.00 – **114 rm**
⇌ 105.00/140.00 st., 1 suite – SB.

🏠 **Gonville,** Gonville Pl., CB1 1LY, ℘ (01223) 366611, *Fax (01223) 315470* – ⅃ ¥, ▤ rest, 📺
🕿 ⎙ **P** – ⅍ 200. ⁐ ☒ ⓪ *VISA*, ⅍                                                          Z r
**Meals** 13.50/17.95 st. and a la carte ⅃ 7.00 – **64 rm** ⇌ 87.00/107.50 st. – SB.

🏠 **Arundel House,** Chesterton Rd, CB4 3AN, ℘ (01223) 367701, *Fax (01223) 367721* – ¥,
▤ rest, 📺 🕿 ⎙ **P** – ⅍ 50. ⁐ ☒ ⓪ *VISA*, ⅍                                               Y u
closed 25 and 26 December – **Meals** 11.95/15.95 t. and a la carte ⅃ 4.95 – ⇌ 3.95 – **105 rm**
69.00/92.50 t. – SB.

🏠 **Centennial,** 63-71 Hills Rd, CB2 1PG, ℘ (01223) 314652, *Fax (01223) 315443* – ¥ rm, 📺
🕿 ⎙ **P**. ⁐ ☒ ⓪ *VISA*, ⅍                                                                    X x
closed 23 December-1 January – **Meals** (dinner only) 15.50 t. and a la carte ⅃ 3.75 – **39 rm**
⇌ 69.00/93.00 t. – SB.

🏠 **Cambridge Lodge,** 139 Huntingdon Rd, CB3 0DQ, ℘ (01223) 352833,
*Fax (01223) 355166,* ☞ – 📺 🕿 ⎙ **P** – ⅍ 25. ⁐ ☒ ⓪ *VISA*, ⅍                           X i
**Meals** *(closed Sunday dinner)* 15.90/20.50 t. and a la carte ⅃ 5.50 – **13 rm** ⇌ 58.00/90.00 t.

⌂ **Brooklands,** 95 Cherry Hinton Rd, CB1 4BS, ℘ (01223) 242035, *Fax (01223) 242035,* ≋ –
¥ 📺 **P**. ⁐ ☒ ⓪ *VISA* JCB, ⅍                                                               X e
**Meals** 9.00 st. – **5 rm** ⇌ 30.00/48.00 st.

XXX **Midsummer House,** Midsummer Common, CB4 1HA, ℘ (01223) 369299,
*Fax (01223) 302672,* « Attractively situated beside River Cam, overlooking Midsummer
Common », ☞ – ⁐ ☒ *VISA* JCB                                                                  Y a
closed Saturday lunch, Sunday dinner, Monday and 26 December-2 January – **Meals** 23.00/
39.50 t. and a la carte ⅃ 6.95.

XX **22 Chesterton Road,** 22 Chesterton Rd, CB4 3AX, ℘ (01223) 351880,
𝄐 *Fax (01223) 323814* – ▤. ⁐ ☒ *VISA* JCB                                                    Y c
closed Sunday, Monday and 1 week Christmas – **Meals** (booking essential) (dinner only)
23.50 t. ⅃ 7.45.

**at Impington** North : 2 m. on B 1049 at junction with A 14 – X – ⌑ Cambridge.

🏨 **Forte Posthouse Cambridge,** Lakeview, Bridge Rd, CB4 4PH, ℘ (01223) 237000,
*Fax (01223) 233426,* ⅃₆, ≋, ☒, ☞ – ¥ rm, 📺 🕿 ⅄ **P** – ⅍ 70. ⁐ ☒ ⓪ *VISA*
**Meals** a la carte 15.30/26.80 st. ⅃ 7.95 – ⇌ 9.95 – **118 rm** 99.00 st. – SB.

**at Histon** North : 3 m. on B 1049 – X – ⌑ Cambridge.

XX **Phoenix,** 20 The Green, CB4 4JA, ℘ (01223) 233766 – ▤ **P**. ⁐ ☒ *VISA*
closed 25 to 27 December – **Meals** - Chinese (Peking, Szechuan) - 15.50 t. and a la carte
⅃ 9.00.

# CAMBRIDGE

## COLLEGES

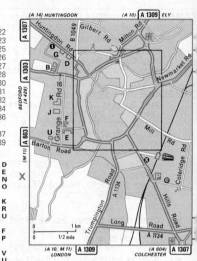

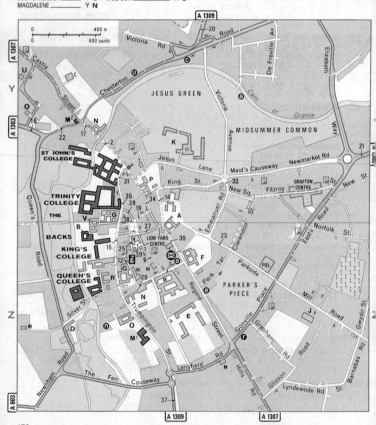

**at Little Shelford** *South : 5½ m. by A 1309 – X – off A 10 – ✉ Cambridge.*

XX **Sycamore House,** 1 Church St., CB2 5HG, ☏ (01223) 843396 – ⇔ P. MC VISA
*closed Sunday, Monday and Christmas-New Year* – **Meals** (dinner only) 22.50 **t.**.

**at Duxford** *South : 9½ m. by A 1309 – X – A 1301 and A 505 on B 1379 – ✉ Cambridge.*

**Duxford Lodge,** Ickleton Rd, CB2 4RU, ☏ (01223) 836444, *Fax (01223) 832271*, – TV ☎ P – 30. MC AE VISA JCB. ✻
*closed 25 to 30 December* – ***Le Paradis :*** **Meals** *(closed Saturday lunch)* 19.50 **st.** and a la carte 7.00 – **15 rm** 73.00/98.00 **st.**

**at Madingley** *West : 4½ m. by A 1303 – X.*

XX **Three Horseshoes,** High St., CB3 8AB, ☏ (01954) 210221, *Fax (01954) 212043*, – P. MC AE VISA
**Meals** *(closed Sunday dinner)* a la carte 15.00/27.00 **t.** 4.50.

**at Bar Hill** *Northwest : 5½ m. by A 1307 – X – off A 14.*

**Cambridgeshire Moat House,** CB3 8EU, ☏ (01954) 249988, *Fax (01954) 780010*, , , 18, , – ⇔ rm, TV ☎ P – 200. MC AE VISA
**Meals** *(closed Saturday lunch)* 17.50 **t.** (dinner) and a la carte 16.20/27.70 **t.** 6.75 – 9.95 – **99 rm** 105.00 **st.** – SB.

**at Lolworth Service Area** *Northwest : 6 m. by A 1307 – X – on A 14 – ✉ Cambridge.*

**Travelodge,** CB3 8DR, (northbound carriageway) ☏ (01954) 781335, Reservations (Freephone) 0800 850950 – ⇔ rm, TV & P. MC AE VISA JCB. ✻
**Meals** (grill rest.) – **20 rm** 39.95/59.95 **t.**

**at Swavesey Service Area** *Northwest : 8 m. by A 1307 on A 14 – X – ✉ Cambridge.*

**Travelodge,** CB4 5QA, (southbound carriageway) ☏ (01954) 789113, Reservations (Freephone) 0800 850950 – ⇔ rm, TV & P. MC AE VISA JCB. ✻
**Meals** (grill rest.) – **36 rm** 39.95/59.95 **t.**

ATS 143 Histon Rd ☏ (01223) 454631/454640

---

**CANNOCK** *Staffs.* 402 403 404 N 25 *Great Britain G. – pop. 60 106.*

Exc. : *Weston Park★★ AC, W : 11 m. by A 5.*

18 *Cannock Park, Stafford Rd ☏ (01543) 578850.*

*London 135 – Birmingham 20 – Derby 36 – Leicester 51 – Shrewsbury 32 – Stoke-on-Trent 28.*

**Roman Way,** Watling St., Hatherton, WS11 1SH, Southwest : 1 ¼ m. by A 4601 on A 5 ☏ (01543) 572121, *Fax (01543) 502742* – ⇔ rm, TV ☎ & P – 150. MC AE VISA
**Meals** dinner a la carte 13.70/18.90 **st.** 6.50 – 9.75 – **56 rm** 80.00/115.00 **st.** – SB.

**Travel Inn,** Watling St., WS11 1SJ, Southwest : 1 m. at junction of A 4601 with A 5 ☏ (01543) 572721, *Fax (01543) 466130* – ⇔ rm, TV & P – 100. MC AE VISA. ✻
**Meals** (grill rest.) – **60 rm** 38.00 **t.**

ATS Cannock Rd, Chadsmoor ☏ (01543) 574580/504985 ATS Cannock Rd, Heath Hayes ☏ (01543) 274200

---

**CANON PYON** *Herefordshire* 403 L 27 – *see Hereford.*

---

**CANTERBURY** *Kent* 404 X 30 *Great Britain G. – pop. 36 464.*

See : *City★★★ - Cathedral★★★* **Y** - *St. Augustine's Abbey★★ AC* **YZ K** – *King's School★* **Y B** – *Mercery Lane★* **Y 12** - *Christ Church Gate★* **Y A** – *Weavers★* **Y D** – *Hospital of St. Thomas the Martyr, Eastbridge★* **Y E** – *Poor Priests Hospital★ AC* **Y M1** – *St. Martin's Church★* **Y N** – *West Gate★ AC* **Y R.**

*34 St. Margaret's St., CT1 2TG ☏ (01227) 766567.*

*London 59 – Brighton 76 – Dover 15 – Maidstone 28 – Margate 17.*

Plan on next page

**County,** High St., CT1 2RX, ☏ (01227) 766266, *Fax (01227) 451512* – |‡|, ⇔ rm, TV ☎ – P – 140. MC AE VISA JCB. ✻ **Y n**
***Sullys :*** **Meals** 18.00/24.50 **t.** and a la carte 10.00 – 9.50 – **72 rm** 86.00/118.00 **st.**, 1 suite – SB.

**Falstaff,** 8-12 St. Dunstan's St., CT2 8AF, ☏ (01227) 462138, *Fax (01227) 463525*, « Part 15C coaching inn » – ⇔ TV ☎ P – 50. MC AE VISA JCB. ✻ **Y a**
***Othello's :*** **Meals** 14.95 **t.** and dinner a la carte 6.50 – 8.95 – **24 rm** 75.00/95.00 **st.** – SB.

## CANTERBURY



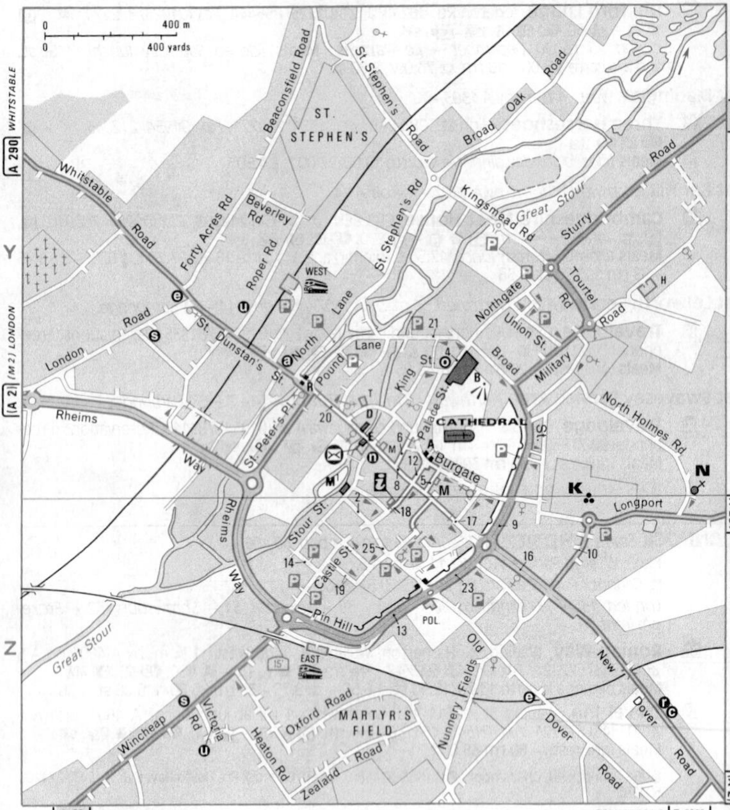


[H] **Thanington** without rest., 140 Wincheap, CT1 3RY, ☎ (01227) 453227, *Fax (01227) 453225*, ⛉, 🌳 – 🚭 [TV] ☎ [P]. [MC] [AE] [D] [VISA] [JCB] — Z
**15 rm** ☕ 52.00/85.00 **st.**

[H] **Ebury,** 65-67 New Dover Rd, CT1 3DX, ☎ (01227) 768433, *Fax (01227) 459187*, ⛉, 🌳 – [TV] ☎ [P]. [MC] [AE] [D] [VISA] [JCB] — Z
*closed 22 December-13 January* – **Meals** (light dinner Sunday) (dinner only) a la carte 14.15/19.50 **t.** 🍷 5.80 – **15 rm** ☕ 45.00/75.00 **st.** – SB.

[H] **Pointers,** 1 London Rd, CT2 8LR, ☎ (01227) 456846, *Fax (01227) 452786* – [TV] ☎ 📞 [P]. [MC] [AE] [D] [VISA] [JCB] — Y
*closed 20 December-mid January* – **Meals** (dinner only) 14.50 **t.** 🍷 4.60 – **12 rm** ☕ 45.00/65.00 **t.** – SB.

⌂ **Magnolia House,** 36 St. Dunstan's Terr., CT2 8AX, ☎ (01227) 765121, *Fax (01227) 765121*, 🌳 – 🚭 [TV] [P]. [MC] [AE] [D] [VISA]. 🚫 — Y
**Meals** (by arrangement) 18.00 **st.** – **7 rm** ☕ 36.00/95.00 **st.** – SB.

⌂ **Alexandra House** without rest., 1 Roper Rd, CT2 7EH, ☎ (01227) 767011, *Fax (01227) 786617*, 🌳 – [TV] [P]. 🚫 — Y
**7 rm** ☕ 26.00/52.00.

⭡ **Clare Ellen** without rest., 9 Victoria Rd, CT1 3SG, ℘ (01227) 760205, *Fax (01227) 784482,* 𝄞 – 🖵 ⇔ 🅿. 🆎 *VISA* JCB. ⛝         Z u
6 rm ⊇ 25.00/48.00.

⭡ **Zan Stel Lodge** without rest., 140 Old Dover Rd, CT1 3NX, ℘ (01227) 453654, 𝄞 – 🖵 🅿         Z e
*closed 25-26 and 31 December and 1 January* – 4 rm ⊇ 40.00/52.00.

ⵝⵝ **La Bonne Cuisine** (at Canterbury H.), 71 New Dover Rd, CT1 3DZ, ℘ (01227) 450551, *Fax (01227) 780145* – 🅿. 🆎 *VISA*         Z c
**Meals** - French - 17.00 **st.** and a la carte ₰ 6.00.

ⵝⵝ **Tuo e Mio**, 16 The Borough, CT1 2DR, ℘ (01227) 761471 – 🆎 🆎 ⓘ *VISA* JCB
*closed Tuesday lunch, Monday, last 2 weeks February and last 2 weeks August* – **Meals** - Italian - 13.00 **st.** (lunch) and a la carte 16.00/26.00 **t.** ₰ 4.50.         Y o

**at Littlebourne** *East : 3 ¾ m. on A 257* – Z – ✉ *Canterbury.*

🏠 **Bow Window Inn**, 50 High St., CT3 1ST, ℘ (01227) 721264, *Fax (01227) 721250* – ⅍ rest, 🖵 ☎ ✆ 🅿. 🆎 🆎 *VISA*. ⛝
**Meals** *(closed Sunday dinner)* a la carte 13.00/18.50 **t.** ₰ 5.00 – **8 rm** ⊇ 45.00/58.00 **t.** – SB.

**at Chartham** *Southwest : 3 ¼ m. by A 28* – Z – ✉ *Canterbury.*

⭡ **Thruxted Oast** ⚘ without rest., Mystole, CT4 7BX, Southwest : 1 ½ m. by Rattington St., turning right at T-junction after ½ m. on Mystole Lane ℘ (01227) 730080, *Fax (01227) 730056,* ≤, 𝄞 – ⅍ 🖵 ☎ 🅿. 🆎 🆎 *VISA*. ⛝
*closed 25 December* – 3 rm ⊇ 68.00/78.00 **st.**

⭡ **Old Rectory**, Ashford Rd, CT4 7HS, on A 28 ℘ (01227) 730075, *Fax (01227) 731929,* 𝄞 – ⅍ 🅿. 🆎 *VISA*. ⛝
*closed 17 December-17 January* – **Meals** (by arrangement) (communal dining) 18.00 **st.** – 3 rm ⊇ 40.00/60.00 **st.**

**at Chartham Hatch** *West : 3 ¼ m. by A 28* – Z – ✉ *Canterbury.*

🏛 **Howfield Manor**, Howfield Lane, CT4 7HQ, Southeast : 1 m. ℘ (01227) 738294, *Fax (01227) 731535,* 𝄞 – 🖵 ☎ 🅿 – 🕭 100. 🆎 🆎 *VISA* JCB. ⛝
*Old Well :* **Meals** 13.95/18.95 **st.** and a la carte ₰ 6.50 – **15 rm** ⊇ 70.00/92.50 **st.** – SB.

**at Gate Service Area** *West : 4 ½ m. on A 2* – Y – ✉ *Faversham.*

🏠 **Travelodge**, Dunkirk, ME13 9LN, (westbound carriageway) ℘ (01227) 752781, Reservations (Freephone) 0800 850950 – ⅍ rm, 🖵 ⅘ 🅿. 🆎 🆎 ⓘ *VISA* JCB. ⛝
**Meals** (grill rest.) – **40 rm** 39.95/59.95 **t.**

🅿 ATS 29 Sturry Rd ℘ (01227) 464867/765021

**CANVEY ISLAND** *Essex* 🟦🟦🟦 V 29 – *pop. 36 859.*
*London 35 – Chelmsford 19 – Maidstone 44 – Southend-on-Sea 13.*

🏠 **Oysterfleet**, Knightswick Rd, SS8 7UX, ℘ (01268) 510111, *Fax (01268) 511420,* 𝄞 – 🛗 🖵 ⅘ 🅿 – 🕭 150. 🆎 *VISA*. ⛝
**Meals** 10.00 **st.** and a la carte ₰ 4.25 – ⊇ 4.50 – **24 rm** 38.00/50.00 **st.**

**CAPEL ST. MARY** *Suffolk* 🟦🟦🟦 X 27 – *pop. 3 176* – ✉ *Ipswich.*
*London 78 – Cambridge 52 – Colchester 18 – Ipswich 3.*

🏠 **Travelodge**, Bentley Services, IP9 2JP, West : ½ m. on A 12 ℘ (01473) 312157, *Fax (01473) 312157,* Reservations (Freephone) 0800 850950 – ⅍ rm, 🖵 ⅘ 🅿. 🆎 🆎 ⓘ *VISA* JCB. ⛝
**Meals** (grill rest.) – **32 rm** 39.95/59.95 **t.**

**CARBIS BAY** *Cornwall* 🟦🟦🟦 D 33 – *see St. Ives.*

**CARCROFT** *S. Yorks.* 🟦🟦🟦 🟦🟦🟦 🟦🟦🟦 Q 23 – *see Doncaster.*

**CARLISLE** Cumbria **401** **402** L 19 Great Britain G. – pop. 72 439.

See : Town★ - Cathedral★ (Painted Ceiling★) AY E – Tithe Barn★ BY A.

Env. : Hadrian's Wall★★, N : by A 7 AY.

🏌 Aglionby 🐾 (01228) 513303 BY – 🏌 Stony Holme, St. Aidan's Rd 🐾 (01228) 34856, BY -
🏌 Dalston Hall, Dalston 🐾 (01228) 710165, AZ.

✈ Carlisle Airport 🐾 (01228) 573641, NW : 5½ m. by A 7 – BY – and B 6264 – **Terminal
Bus Station**, Lowther Street.

🛈 Carlisle Visitor Centre, Old Town Hall, Green Market, CA3 8JH 🐾 (01228) 512444.

London 317 – Blackpool 95 – Edinburgh 101 – Glasgow 100 – Leeds 124 – Liverpool 127 -
Manchester 122 – Newcastle upon Tyne 59.

### CARLISLE

| | | | | | |
|---|---|---|---|---|---|
| Annetwell Street | **AY** 2 | Charlotte Street | **AZ** 7 | Scotch Street | **BY** 1 |
| Botchergate | **BZ** | Chiswick Street | **BY** 8 | Spencer Street | **BY** 2 |
| Bridge Street | **AY** 3 | Church Street | **AY** 10 | Tait Street | **BZ** 2 |
| Brunswick Street | **BZ** 4 | Eden Bridge | **BY** 12 | The Lanes | |
| Castle Street | **BY** 5 | English Street | **BY** 13 | Shopping Centre | **BY** |
| Cecil Street | **BZ** 6 | Lonsdale Street | **BY** 14 | Victoria Viaduct | **ABZ** 2 |
| | | Lowther Street | **BY** 15 | West Tower Street | **BY** 2 |
| | | Port Road | **AY** 16 | West Walls | **ABY** 2 |
| | | St. Marys Gate | **BY** 17 | Wigton Road | **AZ** 2 |

🏛🏛 **Cumbrian,** Court Sq., CA1 1QY, 🐾 (01228) 531951, Fax (01228) 547799 – 🛗, ❊ rm, 📺 ☎
♿ 🚗 – 🔬 300. 🆎 🅰🅴 ⓞ 𝘝𝘐𝘚𝘈                                                                    BZ a
Meals (bar lunch)/dinner 16.95 st. and a la carte ⅟ 5.00 – **70 rm** ⊒ 71.50/98.00 st. – SB.

🏨 **Cumbria Park,** 32 Scotland Rd, CA3 9DG, North : 1 m. on A 7 🐾 (01228) 522887
Fax (01228) 514796 – 🛗, ❊ rm, 📺 ☎ 🅿 – 🔬 150. 🆎 🅰🅴 ⓞ 𝘝𝘐𝘚𝘈 𝗝𝗖𝗕,
closed 25 and 26 December – **Meals** (closed Sunday lunch) 12.95/16.95 – **47 rm** ⊒ 92.50/
122.50 t.

🏠 **Gosling Bridge - Premier Lodge,** Kingstown Rd, CA3 0AT, North : 1 ¾ m. on A 7
🐾 (01228) 515294, Fax (01228) 515220, Reservations (Freephone) 0800 118833 – ❊ rm
📺 🦽 ♿ 🅿. 🆎 🅰🅴 ⓞ 𝘝𝘐𝘚𝘈. ❄
Meals (grill rest.) a la carte 8.40/15.15 st. ⅟ 4.25 – ⊒ 5.95 – **30 rm** 44.95 st. – SB.

🏠 **Number Thirty One,** 31 Howard Pl., CA1 1HR, 🐾 (01228) 597080, Fax (01228) 597080
« Victorian town house » – ❊ 📺. 🆎 🅰🅴 𝘝𝘐𝘚𝘈. ❄                                        BY a
March-November – **Meals** (by arrangement) 20.00 – **3 rm** ⊒ 40.00/86.00 – SB.

↑ **Beeches** without rest., Wood St., CA1 2SF, East : 1 ½ m. by A 69 off Victoria Rd
   *℘ (01228) 511962, 🚗 – 📺 🅿*
   **3 rm** 🖵 25.00/40.00 **st.**

↑ **Courtfield House** without rest., 169 Warwick Rd, CA1 1LP, *℘ (01228) 522767* – 📺 ✇.
   %%                                        BY  c
   *closed 25 December* – **5 rm** 🖵 25.00/40.00.

↑ **Fern Lee**, 9 St. Aidan's Rd, CA1 1LT, *℘ (01228) 511930, Fax (01228) 511930* – ⇔ rm, 📺 ✇
   🅿. %%                                         BY  e
   **Meals** (by arrangement) 9.00 **st.** – **8 rm** 🖵 25.00/40.00 **st.** – SB.

↑ **Langleigh House** without rest., 6 Howard Pl., CA1 1HR, *℘ (01228) 530440,*
   *Fax (01228) 530440* – 📺 🅿. %%                               BY  s
   *closed 23 to 28 December* – **4 rm** 🖵 28.00/38.00 **s.**

%%%% **No. 10**, 10 Eden Mount, Stanwix, CA3 9LY, North : ¾ m. on A 7. *℘ (01228) 524183* – ◉◉ 𝔸𝔼
   *VISA*
   *closed Sunday, Monday and February* – **Meals** (dinner only) a la carte 15.10/21.45 **t.** ♨ 6.50.

**at Kingstown** *North : 3 m. by A 7 – BY – at junction 44 of M 6 – ✉ Carlisle.*

🏨 **Forte Posthouse Carlisle**, Park House Rd, Kingstown, CA3 0HR, on A 7
   *℘ (01228) 531201, Fax (01228) 543178*, 𝄜, �. 🖾 – ⇔ rm, 📺 ☎ & 🅿 – 🔬 140. ◉◉ 𝔸𝔼
   ◉ *VISA JCB*
   **Meals** a la carte 13.05/28.30 **t.** ♨ 5.95 – 🖵 9.95 – **127 rm** 75.00 **st.** – SB.

**at High Crosby** *Northeast : 5 m. by A 7 and B 6264 – BY – off A 689 – ✉ Carlisle.*

🏨 **Crosby Lodge Country House** ⤴, CA6 4QZ, *℘ (01228) 573618, Fax (01228) 573428,*
   ≤, « 18C country mansion », 🚗 – ⇔ rest, 📺 ☎ 🅿. ◉◉ 𝔸𝔼 *VISA JCB*. %%
   *closed 24 December-20 January* – **Meals** (Sunday dinner residents only) 16.50/28.50 **t.**
   and a la carte ♨ 8.40 – **11 rm** 🖵 85.00/130.00 **t.** – SB.

**at Wetheral** *East : 6¼ m. by A 69 – BZ – on B 6263 – ✉ Carlisle.*

🏨🏨 **Crown**, CA4 8ES, *℘ (01228) 561888, Fax (01228) 561637*, 𝄜, 🚗, 🖾, 🚗, squash – ⇔ rm,
   📺 ☎ & 🅿 – 🔬 175. ◉◉ 𝔸𝔼 ◉ *VISA*
   **Meals** (bar lunch Saturday) 10.00/20.00 **t.** and dinner a la carte ♨ 9.00 – **49 rm** 🖵 102.00/
   136.00 **st.**, 2 suites.

   ◍ ATS Rosehill Ind. Est., Montgomery Way *℘ (01228) 25277*

---

**CARLTON-IN-COVERDALE** N. Yorks. 𝟜𝟘𝟚 O 21 – *see Middleham.*

---

**CARLYON BAY** Cornwall 𝟜𝟘𝟛 F 33 – *see St. Austell.*

---

**CARNFORTH** Lancs. 𝟜𝟘𝟚 L 21 – *see Lancaster.*

---

**CARNON DOWNS** Cornwall 𝟜𝟘𝟛 E 33 – *see Truro.*

---

**CARTERWAY HEADS** Northd 𝟜𝟘𝟙 𝟜𝟘𝟚 O 19 – ✉ Shotley Bridge.
   London 272 – Carlisle 59 – Newcastle upon Tyne 21.

🍽 **Manor House Inn**, DH8 9LX, on A 68 *℘ (01207) 255268* – ⇔ 🅿. ◉◉ 𝔸𝔼 *VISA*
   *closed lunch 25 December* – **Meals** 14.50/15.50 **t.** and a la carte ♨ 5.20.

---

**CARTMEL** Cumbria 𝟜𝟘𝟚 L 21 – *see Grange-over-Sands.*

---

**CARTMELL FELL** Cumbria 𝟜𝟘𝟚 L 21 – *see Newby Bridge.*

---

**CASTLE ASHBY** Northants. 𝟜𝟘𝟜 R 27 – pop. 138 – ✉ Northampton.
   London 76 – Bedford 15 – Northampton 11.

🏨 **Falcon** ⤴, NN7 1LF, *℘ (01604) 696200, Fax (01604) 696673*, 🍴, « Part 16C inn », 🚗 –
   📺 ☎ & 🅿. ◉◉ 𝔸𝔼 *VISA JCB*
   **Meals** 22.00 **t.** and a la carte ♨ 5.95 – 🖵 7.50 – **16 rm** 70.00/77.50 **st.** – SB.

*La guida cambia, cambiate la guida ogni anno.*

**CASTLE CARY** Somerset 403 404 M 30 – pop. 2 904.

London 125 – Bristol 28 – Taunton 31 – Yeovil 13.

🏛 **George**, Market Pl., BA7 7AH, ℘ (01963) 350761, Fax (01963) 350035, « Part 15C inn » – ▥ ☎ 🅿 AE VISA JCB

Meals (bar meals Monday to Saturday lunch and Sunday dinner)/dinner a la carte 13.25/24.85 t. ▯ 5.25 – **14 rm** ⊡ 45.00/85.00 t. – SB.

XX **Bond's** with rm, Ansford Hill, Ansford, BA7 7JP, North : ¾ m. by Ansford Rd on A 371 ℘ (01963) 350464, Fax (01963) 350464, 屛 – ▥ ☎ ☏ 🅿 AE VISA. ℅

closed 1 week Christmas – Meals (light lunch)/dinner 14.50 st. and a la carte ▯ 5.00 – **7 rm** ⊡ (dinner included) 62.00/127.00 st. – SB.

**CASTLE COMBE** Wilts. 403 404 N 29 The West Country G. – pop. 347 – ⊠ Chippenham.

See : Village★★.

London 110 – Bristol 23 – Chippenham 6.

🏛🏛 **Manor House** ⍓, SN14 7HR, ℘ (01249) 782206, Fax (01249) 782159, « Part 14C manor house in park », ⌇, 🐟, ↻, 屛, ℁ – ⊱≈ rest, ▥ ☎ 🅿 – 🕰 50. AE ① VISA. ℅

Meals 16.95/35.00 t. and dinner a la carte 41.00/60.95 t. ▯ 13.50 – ⊡ 13.00 – **43 rm** 120.00/350.00 t. – SB.

🏛 **Castle Inn**, SN14 7HN, ℘ (01249) 783030, Fax (01249) 782315, « Part 12C » – ⊱≈ ▥ ☎ AE ① VISA JCB. ℅

Meals a la carte 14.70/21.65 t. ▯ 5.00 – **11 rm** ⊡ 65.00/110.00 t. – SB.

**at Ford** South : 1 ¾ m. on A 420 – ⊠ Chippenham.

🏛 **White Hart Inn**, SN14 8RP, ℘ (01249) 782213, Fax (01249) 783075 – ▥ ☎ 🅿 AE VISA

Meals a la carte 16.20/24.25 t. ▯ 7.50 – **11 rm** ⊡ 55.00/85.00 t.

**at Nettleton Shrub** West : 2 m. by B 4039 on Nettleton rd (Fosse Way) – ⊠ Chippenham.

↑ **Fosse Farmhouse**, SN14 7NJ, ℘ (01249) 782286, Fax (01249) 783066, 屛 – ⊱≈ rest, ▥ 🅿. AE VISA JCB. ℅

Meals 26.00 t. ▯ 6.50 – **5 rm** ⊡ 60.00/125.00 t.

**CASTLE DONINGTON** Leics. 402 403 404 P 25 – pop. 6 007 – ⊠ Derby.

✈ East Midlands Airport : ℘ (01332) 852852, S : by B 6540 and A 453.

London 123 – Birmingham 38 – Leicester 23 – Nottingham 13.

🏛🏛🏛 **Hilton National**, East Midlands Airport, Derby Rd, Lockington, DE74 2YW, East : 6 ½ m. by High St. and A 453 on A 6 at junction 24 of M 1 ℘ (01509) 674000, Fax (01509) 672412, ▮❺, ⊆s, ▨ – ⍰, ⊱≈ rm, ▤ ▥ ☎ & 🅿 – 🕰 350. AE ① VISA

Meals (closed Saturday lunch) 12.50/18.75 st. and a la carte – ⊡ 10.75 – **151 rm** 135.00/150.00 st., 1 suite – SB.

🏛🏛 **Thistle Donington**, East Midlands Airport, DE74 2SH, Southeast : 3 ¼ m. by High St. on A 453 ℘ (01332) 850700, Fax (01332) 850823, ▮❺, ⊆s, ▨ – ⊱≈ ▥ ☎ & 🅿 – 🕰 220. AE ① VISA JCB

Meals (closed dinner 25 December-2 January) (bar lunch Saturday and Bank Holidays) 15.00/21.00 st. and a la carte – ⊡ 11.00 – **110 rm** 116.00/180.00 st. – SB.

🏛 **Priest House on the River**, Kings Mills, DE74 2RR, West : 1 ¾ m. by Park Lane ℘ (01332) 810649, Fax (01332) 811141, ≤, « Riverside setting », ↻, park – ⊱≈ rest, ▥ ☎ 🅿 – 🕰 130. AE ① VISA

Meals (bar lunch Saturday) 16.50/23.50 t. and a la carte ▯ 9.50 – ⊡ 9.75 – **43 rm** 109.00/129.00 st., 2 suites – SB.

🏛 **Donington Manor**, High St., DE74 2PP, ℘ (01332) 810253, Fax (01332) 850330 – ▥ ☎ 🅿 – 🕰 80. AE ① VISA. ℅

closed 24 to 30 December – Meals (closed Saturday lunch) 7.90/15.00 st. and dinner a la carte ▯ 5.00 – **25 rm** ⊡ 63.00/88.00 st.

**CASTLETON** Derbs. 402 403 404 O 23 Great Britain G. – pop. 689 – ⊠ Sheffield (S. Yorks.).

Env. : Blue John Caverns★ AC, W : 1 m.

London 181 – Derby 49 – Manchester 30 – Sheffield 16 – Stoke-on-Trent 39.

🏛 **Ye Olde Nags Head**, Cross St., S33 8WH, ℘ (01433) 620248, Fax (01433) 621604 – ⊱≈ rest, ▥ ☎ 🅿. AE ① VISA

Meals 17.95 t. and a la carte – **9 rm** ⊡ 49.50/104.50 t. – SB.

**CASTLETOWN** Isle of Man 402 G 21 – see Man (Isle of).

**CATEL** Guernsey (Channel Islands) 403 P 33 and 230 ⑨ – see Channel Islands.

**CATLOWDY** Cumbria 401 402 L 18 – ✉ Carlisle.

London 333 – Carlisle 16 – Dumfries 36 – Hawick 31 – Newcastle upon Tyne 65.

↑ **Bessiestown Farm** ⓢ, CA6 5QP, ℰ (01228) 577219, Fax (01228) 577219, « Working farm », 🔄, ⌖, park – ⤡ 📺 🅿 ⓒⓞ 𝚅𝙸𝚂𝙰. 🛇
closed 25 December – **Meals** (by arrangement) 11.00 s. – **6 rm** ☲ 31.00/60.00.

---

**CAUNTON** Notts. 402 404 R 24 – see Newark-on-Trent.

---

**CAWSTON** Norfolk 404 X 25 Great Britain G. – pop. 2 265 – ✉ Norwich.

Env. : Blicking Hall★★ AC, NE : 5 m. by B 1145 and B 1354.
London 122 – Cromer 15 – King's Lynn 42 – Norwich 13.

🏛 **Grey Gables** ⓢ, Norwich Rd, NR10 4EY, South : 1 m. ℰ (01603) 871259, Fax (01603) 871259, ⌖, ⌖ – ⤡ 📺 🅿 ⓒⓞ 𝚅𝙸𝚂𝙰
closed 25 and 26 December – **Meals** (lunch by arrangement)/dinner 18.00 st. 🍷 5.95 – **8 rm** ☲ 21.00/64.00 st. – SB.

↑ **The Walnuts** without rest., 8-12 New St., NR10 4AL, ℰ (01603) 871357, Fax (01603) 871357, 🔄, ⌖ – ⤡ 🅿. 🛇
closed 25 and 26 December – **3 rm** ☲ 32.00/46.00 s.

---

**CAXTON** Cambs.

London 67 – Bedford 18 – Cambridge 12 – Huntingdon 7.

↑ **Church Farm** ⓢ, Gransden Rd, CB3 8PL, ℰ (01954) 719543, Fax (01954) 718999, « Part 17C farmhouse », ⌖, ⌖ – ⤡ 🅿. ⓒⓞ 𝚅𝙸𝚂𝙰. 🛇
closed 1 week February, 1 week November and 1 week Christmas – **Meals** (communal dining) 19.50 🍷 5.50 – **4 rm** ☲ 40.00/74.00.

---

**CHADDESLEY CORBETT** Worcestershire 403 404 N 26 – see Kidderminster.

---

**CHAGFORD** Devon 403 I 31 The West Country G. – pop. 1 417.

Env. : Dartmoor National Park★★.
London 218 – Exeter 17 – Plymouth 28.

🏛🏛 **Gidleigh Park** ⓢ, TQ13 8HH, Northwest : 2 m. by Gidleigh Rd ℰ (01647) 432367,
✿✿ Fax (01647) 432574, ≤ Teign Valley, woodland and Meldon Hill, « Timbered country house, water garden », 🔄, park, ✲ – ⤡ rest, 📺 ☎ 🅿. ⓒⓞ ⓞ 𝚅𝙸𝚂𝙰
**Meals** (booking essential) 22.00-60.00/60.00-65.00 st. 🍷 10.00 – **13 rm** (dinner included) 235.00/440.00 st., 2 suites
**Spec.** Roast langoustines with leek salad and langoustine butter sauce. Fillet of local beef with roast shallots and red wine sauce. Poached cherries with cherry and Kirsch ice cream.

🏛 **Glendarah House** without rest., Lower St., TQ13 8BZ, ℰ (01647) 433270, Fax (01647) 433483, ≤, ⌖ – ⤡ 📺 🅿. ⓒⓞ 𝚅𝙸𝚂𝙰. 🛇
closed 1 week Christmas – **6 rm** ☲ 30.00/54.00 st.

↑ **Thornworthy House** ⓢ, Thornworthy, TQ13 8EY, Southwest : 3 m. by Fernworthy rd on Thornworthy rd ℰ (01647) 433297, Fax (01647) 433297, ≤, « Country house atmosphere », ⌖, park, ✲ – ⤡ 📺 🅿
closed January – **Meals** (by arrangement) 18.00 st. 🍷 5.00 – ☲ 5.50 – **3 rm** 30.00/65.00 st.

✕✕ **22 Mill Street** with rm, 22 Mill St., TQ13 8AW, ℰ (01647) 432244 – ⤡ rest, 📺. ⓒⓞ 𝚅𝙸𝚂𝙰
closed Monday lunch, Sunday except Bank Holidays, 25-26 December and 2 weeks January – **Meals** 14.95/24.95 st. 🍷 8.10 – **2 rm** ☲ 30.00/42.00 st.

**at Sandypark** Northeast : 2¼ m. on A 382 – ✉ Chagford.

🏛🏛 **Mill End**, TQ13 8JN, on A 382 ℰ (01647) 432282, Fax (01647) 433106, « Country house with water mill », 🔄, ⌖ – ⤡ rest, 📺 ☎ 🅿. ⓒⓞ ⓐⓔ 𝚅𝙸𝚂𝙰 𝙹𝙲𝙱
**Meals** 15.00 t. (lunch) and dinner a la carte approx. 25.00 🍷 9.50 – **17 rm** ☲ (dinner included) 75.00/156.00 t. – SB.

🏛🏛 **Great Tree** ⓢ, TQ13 8JS, on A 382 ℰ (01647) 432491, Fax (01647) 432562, ≤, 🔄, ⌖, park – ⤡ rest, 📺 ☎ 📞 🅿. ⓒⓞ ⓐⓔ ⓞ 𝚅𝙸𝚂𝙰
**Meals** (bar lunch)/dinner 21.00 t. 🍷 5.95 – **10 rm** ☲ 58.00/128.00 t.

**at Easton** Northeast : 1½ m. on A 382 – ✉ Chagford.

🏛 **Easton Court**, TQ13 8JL, ℰ (01647) 433469, Fax (01647) 433654, « Part 15C thatched house », ⌖ – ⤡ rest, 📺 ☎. ⓒⓞ ⓐⓔ 𝚅𝙸𝚂𝙰
closed January – **Meals** (dinner only) 22.00 st. 🍷 6.95 – **8 rm** ☲ 45.00/90.00 – SB.

---

**CHALE** I.O.W. 403 404 Q 32 – see Wight (Isle of).

ENGLAND

CHANNEL ISLANDS 403 OPQ 33 and 230 ⑨ ⑩ ⑪ The West Country G. – pop. 145 920.

## ALDERNEY

403 Q 33 and 230 ⑨ The West Country G. – pop. 2 297.

See : Braye Bay★ – Mannez Garenne (≤★ from Quesnard Lighthouse) – Telegraph Bay★ – Vallee des Trois Vaux★ – Clonque Bay★.

✈ ℰ (01481) 822551 - Booking Office : Aurigny Air Services ℰ (01481) 822888.

⛴ to Weymouth, (Guernsey) St. Peter Port and France (St. Malo) (Condor Ferries Ltd. daily.

⛴ to France (St. Malo) (Condor Ferries Ltd) weekly.

🛈 States Office, Queen Elizabeth II St. GY9 3AA ℰ (01481) 822994/822811.

### Braye.

✕ **First and Last,** GY9 3TH, ℰ (01481) 823162, ≤ harbour – ⬤⬤ AE ⓞ VISA
April-December – **Meals** (closed Monday) (dinner only) 12.95 and a la carte ♦ 3.95.

### St. Anne.

🏠🏠 **Chez André,** Victoria St., GY9 3TA, ℰ (01481) 822777, Fax (01481) 822962 – ⇔ 🔟 ☎ ⬤⬤
AE VISA
**Meals** (closed dinner Wednesday and Sunday in winter) (buffet dinner Sunday) 15.00 (dinner) and a la carte 15.50/34.50 ♦ 7.00 – 🖃 6.80 – **11 rm** 45.00/90.00 – SB.

🏠🏠 **Belle Vue,** The Butes, GY9 3UN, ℰ (01481) 822844, Fax (01481) 823601 – ⇔ rest, 🔟 ☎.
⬤⬤ VISA JCB. ⅋
closed 24 to 26 December – **Meals** a la carte 13.75/26.45 s. ♦ 4.00 – **27 rm** 🖃 42.50/85.00 s. – SB.

🏠 **Inchalla** 🕭, Le Val, GY9 3UL, ℰ (01481) 823220, Fax (01481) 824045, 🕭, 🞐 – 🔟 ☎ ℗.
⬤⬤ AE VISA. ⅋
closed 23 December-2 January – **Meals** (closed Sunday dinner) a la carte 15.00/25.25 ♦ 4.50 – **9 rm** 🖃 68.00/88.00.

↥ **Chez Nous** without rest., Les Venelles, GY9 3TW, ℰ (01481) 823633, Fax (01481) 823732 – ⇔ 🔟 ☎. AE. ⅋
16 April-5 October – **3 rm** 🖃 33.00/56.00.

🏠 **Rose and Crown** without rest., Le Huret, GY9 3TR, ℰ (01481) 823414, Fax (01481) 823615, 🞐 – 🔟 ☎ ⅌. ⬤⬤ AE ⓞ VISA JCB. ⅋
mid March-October – **6 rm** 🖃 40.00/80.00.

## GUERNSEY

403 OP 33 and 230 ⑨ ⑩ The West Country G. – pop. 58 867.

See : Island★ – Pezeries Point★★ – Icart Point★★ – Côbo Bay★★ – St. Martin's Point★★ – St. Apolline's Chapel★ – Vale Castle★ – Fort Doyle★ – La Gran'mere du Chimquiere★ – Rocquaine Bay★ – Jerbourg Point★.

✈ Service Air ℰ (01481) 37682, Aurigny Air ℰ (01481) 37426.

⛴ from St. Peter Port to France (St. Malo) (Emeraude Lines) (summer only) (2 h 50 mn) – from St. Peter Port to Jersey (St. Helier) (Condor Ferries Ltd) 2 daily (1 h 15 mn) – from St. Peter Port to Jersey (St. Helier) and Poole (Condor Ferries Ltd).

⛴ from St. Peter Port to France (St. Malo, Granville and Carteret) (Emeraude Lines) (summer only) – from St. Peter Port to France (St. Malo) via Sark and Jersey (St. Helier) (Condor Ferries Ltd) 2 weekly – from St. Peter Port to Herm (Herm Seaway) (25 mn) – from St. Peter Port to Sark (Isle of Sark Shipping Co. Ltd) (summer only) (45 mn) – from St. Peter Port to Jersey (St. Helier) (Condor Ferries Ltd) (50 mn) – from St. Peter Port to Jersey (St. Helier) via Sark (Condor Ltd) weekly.

🛈 P.O. Box 23, North Esplanade, GY1 3AN ℰ (01481) 723552 – The Airport, La Villiaze, Forest ℰ (01481) 37267.

### L'Ancresse.

St. Peter Port 4.

🏠 **Symphony House** 🕭, Hacse Lane, GY3 5DS, ℰ (01481) 45418, Fax (01481) 43581, 🞐, 🞐 – 🔟 ☎ ℗. ⬤⬤ VISA JCB. ⅋
**Symphony's :** **Meals** (bar lunch Monday to Saturday)/dinner 14.50 and a la carte Tuesday to Saturday ♦ 7.95 – **15 rm** 🖃 35.00/70.00 – SB.

### Catel/Castel. ·

🏠🏠 **Hougue du Pommier** 🕭, Hougue du Pommier Rd, GY5 7FQ, ℰ (01481) 56531, Fax (01481) 56260, 🞐, 🞐 – ⇔ 🔟 ☎ ⟷ ℗. ⬤⬤ AE VISA
**Meals** (bar lunch Monday to Saturday)/dinner 16.50 and a la carte ♦ 6.80 – **43 rm** 🖃 45.00/90.00 – SB.

**Fermain Bay** – ⊠ *St. Peter Port.*

🏨 **La Favorita** ⊗, Fermain Lane, GY4 6SD, ℘ (01481) 35666, *Fax (01481) 35413*, ≤, 🐬, 🕿, 🔍, ☞ – 🛄 🕸 📺 ☎ 🅿. ⬢ 💳 💳 ⬤ 𝘝𝘐𝘚𝘈. 🎾
*closed January-mid February* – **Meals** 14.50 **s.** (dinner) and a la carte 14.00/18.25 **s.** – **37 rm** ⊇ 55.50/96.00 **s.** – SB.

**Forest** – *pop. 1 386.*

🏨 **Mallard**, GY8 0HG, ℘ (01481) 64164, *Fax (01481) 65732*, 𝟭₅, 🕿, 🔍, ☞, 🎾 – 📺 ☎ 🅿 – 🔏 40. 💳 𝘝𝘐𝘚𝘈
**Meals** a la carte 11.70/26.40 – *All Stars :* **Meals** a la carte 11.70/26.40 ⅙ 6.95 – ⊇ 5.25 – **47 rm** 69.50.

🏠 **Tudor Lodge Deer Farm** without rest., Forest Rd, GY8 0AG, ℘ (01481) 37849, *Fax (01481) 35662*, ☞, park – 📺 ☎ 🅿. 🎾
*closed December-mid January* – **5 rm** ⊇ 35.00/50.00.

🏠 **Mon Plaisir** without rest., Rue des Landes, GY8 0DY, ℘ (01481) 64498, *Fax (01481) 63493*, ☞ – 📺 🅿. 🎾
*restricted opening in winter* – **5 rm** ⊇ 29.00/48.00.

**Pembroke Bay** – ⊠ *Vale.*
*St. Peter Port 5.*

🏨 **Pembroke Bay** ⊗, GY3 5BY, ℘ (01481) 47573, *Fax (01481) 48838*, ≤, 🔍, ☞, 🎾 – 🛄 📺 ☎ 🅿. 💳 💳 𝘝𝘐𝘚𝘈
*April-October* – **Meals** – (see *Riva* below) – **12 rm** ⊇ 60.00/98.00 **s.**

🍴 **Riva** (at Pembroke Bay H.), GY3 5BY, ℘ (01481) 41175, *Fax (01481) 41175*, ☞ – 🅿. 💳 𝘝𝘐𝘚𝘈
*April-October* – **Meals** - Italian - 15.00 **s.** (dinner) and a la carte 13.50/22.50 **s.** ⅙ 5.00.

**St. Martin** – *pop. 6 082.*
*St. Peter Port 2.*

🏨 **Jerbourg** ⊗, Jerbourg Point, GY4 6BJ, ℘ (01481) 38826, *Fax (01481) 38238*, ≤ sea and neighbouring Channel Islands, ☞ – 🕸 rm, 🍴 rest, 📺 ☎ 🅿. 💳 𝘝𝘐𝘚𝘈. 🎾
**Meals** 16.95 (dinner) and a la carte 10.85/23.75 ⅙ 4.50 – **32 rm** ⊇ 45.00/130.00 – SB.

🏨 **Idlerocks** ⊗, Jerbourg Point, GY4 6BJ, ℘ (01481) 37711, *Fax (01481) 35592*, ≤ sea and neighbouring Channel Islands, 🕿, 🔍, ☞, park – 🕸 📺 ☎ 🅿. 💳 💳 ⬤ 𝘝𝘐𝘚𝘈
**Meals** (bar lunch Monday to Saturday)/dinner 14.50 and a la carte ⅙ 5.00 – **28 rm** ⊇ (dinner included) 51.00/184.00 – SB.

🏨 **Bon Port** ⊗, Moulin Huet Bay, GY4 6EW, ℘ (01481) 39249, *Fax (01481) 39596*, ≤ Moulin Huet Bay and Jerbourg Point, 🕿, ☞ – 🕸 rest, 📺 ☎ 🅿. 💳 💳 ⬤ 𝘝𝘐𝘚𝘈. 🎾
**Meals** (bar lunch Monday to Saturday)/dinner 17.50 and a la carte ⅙ 8.00 – **18 rm** ⊇ 70.20/108.00 – SB.

🏨 **Green Acres** ⊗, Les Hubits, GY4 6LS, ℘ (01481) 35711, *Fax (01481) 35978*, 🔍, ☞ – 🕸 rest, 🍴 rest, 📺 ☎ 🅿 – 🔏 40. 💳 💳 𝘝𝘐𝘚𝘈 𝘑𝘊𝘉. 🎾
*21 March-October* – **Meals** (bar lunch)/dinner 14.50 and a la carte ⅙ 6.80 – **48 rm** ⊇ 53.00/86.00.

🏨 **Saints Bay** ⊗, Icart, GY4 6JG, ℘ (01481) 38888, *Fax (01481) 35558*, 🔍, ☞ – 🕸 rest, 📺 ☎ 🕻 🅿. 💳 💳 ⬤ 𝘝𝘐𝘚𝘈. 🎾
*March-October* – **Meals** (bar lunch)/dinner 14.50 and a la carte – **36 rm** ⊇ (dinner included) 53.50/107.00 – SB.

🏨 **Bella Luce**, La Fosse, Moulin Huet, GY4 6EB, ℘ (01481) 38764, *Fax (01481) 39561*, 🕿, 🔍, ☞ – 🕸 rest, 🍴 rest, 📺 ☎ 🅿. 💳 💳 𝘝𝘐𝘚𝘈. 🎾
**Meals** (bar lunch Monday to Saturday)/dinner 16.00 and a la carte ⅙ 5.00 – **31 rm** ⊇ 62.00/100.00 – SB.

🏨 **St. Margarets Lodge**, Forest Rd, GY4 6UE, ℘ (01481) 35757, *Fax (01481) 37594*, 🕿, 🔍, ☞ – 🛄, 🕸 rest, 📺 ☎ 🅿 – 🔏 120. 💳 💳 ⬤ 𝘝𝘐𝘚𝘈. 🎾
**Meals** (bar lunch Monday to Saturday)/dinner 15.95 and a la carte ⅙ 5.25 – **47 rm** ⊇ 64.00/162.00 – SB.

🏨 **La Barbarie** ⊗, Saints Bay, GY4 6ES, ℘ (01481) 235217, *Fax (01481) 235208*, 🔍, ☞ – 📺 ☎ 🅿. 💳 𝘝𝘐𝘚𝘈. 🎾
**Meals** (bar lunch Monday to Saturday)/dinner 15.75 and a la carte ⅙ 5.00 – **22 rm** ⊇ 52.00/80.00, 1 suite.

🏨 **La Cloche** ⊗, Les Traudes, GY4 6LR, ℘ (01481) 35421, *Fax (01481) 38258*, 🔍, ☞ – 🕸 📺 ☎ 🅿. 💳 𝘝𝘐𝘚𝘈. 🎾
*mid April-mid October* – **Meals** (residents only) (dinner only) 14.00 ⅙ 3.75 – **10 rm** ⊇ (dinner included) 57.75/93.00.

🏠 **La Michele** 🔇, Les Hubits, GY4 6NB, ☎ (01481) 38065, *Fax (01481) 39492*, 🏊, 🌳 – 🚭 rest, 📺 ☎ 🅿. [MC] [AE] [VISA]. 🐕
*April-October* – **Meals** (residents only) (dinner only) 9.50 🍷 4.00 – **13 rm** ☕ (dinner included) 49.00/88.00 **s.** – SB.

🏠 **Farnborough** without rest., Les Damouettes Lane, GY1 1ZN, off Les Hubits ☎ (01481) 37756, *Fax (01481) 34082*, 🌳 – 📺 ☎ 🅿. [MC] [VISA]. 🐕
*April-September* – **11 rm** ☕ 35.00/60.00 **s.**

## St. Peter Port *The West Country G. – pop. 16 648.*

See : *Town*★★ – *St. Peter's Church*★ **Z** – *Hauteville House*★ **AC Z** – *Castle Cornet*★ (<★) **AC Z**.
Env. : *Saumarez Park*★ *(Guernsey Folk Museum*★*), W : 2 m. by road to Catel* **Z** – *Little Chapel*★, *SW : 2¼m. by Mount Durand road* **Z**.
⛳18 *Rohais, St. Pierre Park* ☎ *(01481) 727039*, **Z**.

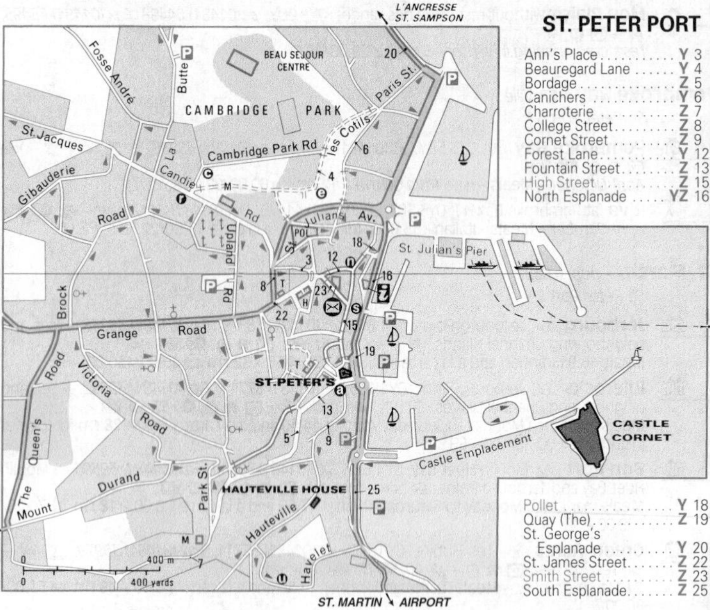


### ST. PETER PORT

| | | |
|---|---|---|
| Ann's Place | Y | 3 |
| Beauregard Lane | Y | 4 |
| Bordage | Z | 5 |
| Canichers | Y | 6 |
| Charroterie | Z | 7 |
| College Street | Z | 8 |
| Cornet Street | Z | 9 |
| Forest Lane | Y | 12 |
| Fountain Street | Z | 13 |
| High Street | Z | 15 |
| North Esplanade | YZ | 16 |
| Pollet | Y | 18 |
| Quay (The) | Z | 19 |
| St. George's Esplanade | Y | 20 |
| St. James Street | Z | 22 |
| Smith Street | Z | 23 |
| South Esplanade | Z | 25 |

🏨 **St. Pierre Park,** Rohais, GY1 1FD, West : 1 ½ m. by Grange Rd ☎ (01481) 728282, *Fax (01481) 712041*, <, 🏋, 🏊, 🏊, ⛳9, 🌳, park, 🎾 – 🛗, 🚭 rm, ▤ rest, 📺 ☎ 🅿 – 🎤 200. [MC] [AE] [DC] [VISA]. 🐕
***Café Renoir :*** **Meals** 17.00 **s.** (dinner) and a la carte 10.40/21.40 **s.** 🍷 5.95 – (see also ***Victor Hugo*** below) – **132 rm** ☕ 135.00/260.00 **s.**

🏨 **Duke of Richmond,** Cambridge Park, GY1 1UY, ☎ (01481) 726221, *Fax (01481) 728945*, <, 🏊 – 🛗, 🚭 rm, ▤ rest, 📺 ☎ – 🎤 100. [MC] [AE] [DC] [VISA] Y c
**Meals** 9.00/15.00 **s.** and a la carte 🍷 5.00 – **73 rm** ☕ 55.00/100.00 **s.**, 1 suite – SB.

🏨 **De Havelet,** Havelet, GY1 1BA, ☎ (01481) 722199, *Fax (01481) 714057*, 🏊, 🏊, 🌳 – 🚭 rest, 📺 ☎ 🅿. [MC] [AE] [DC] [VISA]. 🐕 Z u
***Wellington Boot :*** **Meals** (dinner only and Sunday lunch)/dinner 14.50 **s.** and a la carte 🍷 4.50 – ***Havelet Grill :*** **Meals** *(closed Sunday lunch and Monday dinner)* 9.95/15.00 **s.** and a la carte 🍷 4.50 – **34 rm** 85.00/124.00.

🏨 **Moore's Central,** Le Pollet, GY1 1WH, ☎ (01481) 724452, *Fax (01481) 714037*, 🏋, 🏊 – 🛗 📺 ☎. [MC] [AE] [DC] [VISA]. 🐕 Y n
***Library :*** **Meals** (carving rest.) a la carte 9.95/24.50 🍷 4.75 – ***Conservatory :*** **Meals** 10.00/15.50 and a la carte 🍷 4.75 – **49 rm** ☕ 75.00/102.00 – SB.

🏨 **La Frégate** 🔇, Les Cotils, GY1 1UT, ☎ (01481) 724624, *Fax (01481) 720443*, < town and harbour, 🌳 – 📺 ☎ 🅿. [MC] [AE] [DC] [VISA] [JCB]. 🐕 Y e
**Meals** 13.50/20.00 **s.** and a la carte 🍷 5.00 – **13 rm** ☕ 60.00/100.00.

↑ **Midhurst House,** Candie Rd, GY1 1UP, ℘ (01481) 724391, *Fax (01481) 729451*, ☞ –
※ rest, 🔟 ☎ ℃. ◎③ *VISA*. ※                                                                        Y  r
*April-mid October –* **Meals** (by arrangement) 12.00 ⅙ 5.00 – **6 rm** � 78.00 s.

XXXX **Victor Hugo** (at St. Pierre Park H.), Rohais, GY1 1FD, West : 1 ½ m. by Grange Rd
℘ (01481) 728282, *Fax (01481) 712041 –* 🖿 **ℙ**. ◎③ 🕮 ① *VISA*
*closed Saturday lunch and Sunday dinner –* **Meals** - Seafood - 14.50/19.95 s. and a la carte
⅙ 6.75.

XXX **Battens,** 1 Fountain St., GY1 1DA, ℘ (01481) 729939, *Fax (01481) 729938*, ≼ – ❙ 🖿. ◎③ 🕮
*VISA*                                                                                               Z  a
*closed Sunday and 25-26 December –* **Meals** (booking essential) 29.50 and a la carte ⅙ 6.20
– (see also *Zoe Room* below).

XX **Zoe Room** (at Battens), 1 Fountain St., GY1 1DA, ℘ (01481) 729939, *Fax (01481) 729938*,
≼ – ❙ 🖿. ◎③ 🕮 *VISA*                                                                               Z  a
*closed Sunday and 25-26 December –* **Meals** 10.50/23.50 and a la carte ⅙ 6.20.

XX **The Absolute End,** Longstore, GY1 2BG, North : ¾ m. by St. George's Esplanade
℘ (01481) 723822, *Fax (01481) 729129 –* ◎③ 🕮 *VISA*
*closed Sunday and January –* **Meals** - Seafood - 11.00 s. (lunch) and a la carte 14.50/29.75 s.
⅙ 4.00.

XX **Le Nautique,** Quay Steps, GY1 2LE, ℘ (01481) 721714, *Fax (01481) 721786*, ≼ – ◎③ 🕮 ①
*VISA* 🇯🇨🇧                                                                                          Z  s
*closed Sunday and 25 December-14 January –* **Meals** a la carte 17.50/27.00 ⅙ 5.50.

**St. Saviour** *– pop. 2 419.*

St. Peter Port 4.

🏨 **L'Atlantique,** Perelle Bay, GY7 9NA, ℘ (01481) 64056, *Fax (01481) 63800*, ≼, ☄, ☞ –
※ rm, 🔟 ☎ ℙ. ◎③ 🕮 *VISA*. ※
*March-October –* **Meals** (bar lunch Monday to Saturday) – (see also *Green Room* below) –
**23 rm** ⊏byzantine 44.50/89.00.

🏠 **Les Piques Country** ⌂, Rue des Piques, GY7 9FW, ℘ (01481) 64515,
*Fax (01481) 65857,* « Part 15C farmhouse », ⌂, ☄, ☞, ※ – 🔟 ☎ ℙ. ◎③ *VISA*. ※
*closed 20 December-10 January –* **Meals** 14.50 (dinner) and a la carte 12.40/28.30 ⅙ 4.25 –
**17 rm** ⊏byzantine 60.00/100.00, 3 suites.

XX **Green Room** (at L'Atlantique H.), Perelle Bay, GY7 9NA, ℘ (01481) 64056,
*Fax (01481) 63800,* ☞ – ℙ. ◎③ 🕮 *VISA*
*closed January and February –* **Meals** (dinner only and Sunday lunch)/dinner 16.00
and a la carte ⅙ 5.40.

🍴 **Auberge du Val** ⌂, Sous L'Eglise, GY7 9FX, ℘ (01481) 63862, *Fax (01481) 64835*, 😋,
« Converted 19C farmhouse, herb garden », ⌂ – 🔟 ☎ ℙ. ◎③ 🕮 *VISA* 🇯🇨🇧. ※
**Meals** *(closed Sunday dinner, Monday except lunch Bank Holidays and 25-26 December)*
a la carte approx. 18.50 – **8 rm** ⊏byzantine 30.00/66.00.

**Vazon Bay** *– ✉ Catel.*

🏨 **La Grande Mare,** Vazon Coast Rd, GY5 7LL, ℘ (01481) 56576, *Fax (01481) 56532*, ≼, 😋,
🛵, ⌂, ☄, 🪑, ☄, ☞ – ❙ 🔟 ☎ ℙ. ◎③ 🕮 ① *VISA*. ※
**Meals** 11.95/16.95 and dinner a la carte – **11 rm** ⊏byzantine 67.00/114.00, **13 suites** 180.00 – SB.

---

*Pour voyager en* **EUROPE** *utilisez :*

les cartes Michelin grandes routes.

les cartes Michelin détaillées.

les guides Rouges Michelin (hôtels et restaurants) :
   *Benelux - Deutschland - España Portugal - Europe - France - Great Britain
   and Ireland - Italia - Suisse.*

les guides Verts Michelin (paysages, monuments et routes touristiques) :
   *Allemagne - Autriche - Belgique Grand-Duché de Luxembourg - Canada -
   Ecosse - Espagne - France - Grande-Bretagne - Grèce - Hollande - Italie -
   Irlande - Londres - Portugal - Rome - Suisse*
   *... et la collection sur la France.*

## HERM

[403] P 33 and [230] [10] *The West Country G. – pop. 97.*

**See** : *Le Grand Monceau★.*

⛴ *to Guernsey (St. Peter Port) (Herm Seaway) (20 mn).*

[i] *Administration Office, GY1 3HR ℰ (01481) 700334.*

🏨 **White House** 🔇, GY1 3HR, ℰ (01481) 722159, *Fax (01481) 710066,* « Private island setting ⩽ Belle Greve Bay and Guernsey », 🏊, 🌳, park, 🎾 – 🚭 rest. [MC] [AE] [VISA]. 🚫🐕
*April-October* – ***Conservatory*** **:** Meals 12.50/17.50 🍷 7.25 – ***Ship Inn*** **:** Meals *(closed dinner Sunday and Monday)* (bar lunch)/dinner 19.50 – **38 rm** ☕ (dinner included) 54.50/152.00.

## JERSEY

[403] OP 33 and [230] [11] *The West Country G. – pop. 85 150.*

**See** : *Island★★ – Jersey Zoo★★ AC – Jersey Museum★ – Eric Young Orchid Foundation★ – St. Catherine's Bay★ (⩽★★) – Grosnez Point★ – Devil's Hole★ – St. Matthews Church, Millbrook (glasswork★) – La Hougue Bie★ (Neolithic tomb★ AC) – Waterworks Valley – Hamptonne Country Life Museum★ – St. Catherine's Bay★ (⩽★★) – Noirmont Point★.*

✈ *States of Jersey Airport : ℰ (01534) 492000.*

⛴ *from St. Helier to France (St. Malo) (Emeraude Lines) (summer only) (2 h 10 mn) – from St. Helier to France (St. Malo) and Poole (Condor Ferries Ltd) daily – from St. Helier to Sark (Condor Ferries Ltd) 1 daily (45 mn) – from St. Helier to Guernsey (St. Peter Port) and Poole (Condor Ferries Ltd).*

🚤 *from St. Helier to France (Granville and St. Malo) (Emeraude Lines and Condor Ferries Ltd) (summer only) – from St. Helier to France (St. Malo) (Condor Ferries Ltd) 3 weekly – from Gorey to France (Carteret) (Emeraude Lines) (summer only) (30-40 mn) – from St. Helier to Guernsey (St. Peter Port) (50 mn), to Sark (45 mn) (Condor Ferries Ltd) – from St. Helier to Guernsey (St. Peter Port) via Sark (Condor Ltd) daily except Sunday.*

[i] *Liberation Square, St. Helier, JE1 1BB ℰ (01534) 500777.*

### Corbiere – ✉ *St. Brelade.*

*St. Helier 8.*

XXX **Sea Crest** 🔇 with rm, Petit Port, JE3 8HH, ℰ (01534) 46353, *Fax (01534) 47316,* ⩽, ⛱, 🌳 – ❄ rest, [TV] ☎ [P]. [MC] [AE] [VISA]. 🚫🐕
*closed mid January-mid February* – **Meals** *(closed Sunday dinner October-March and Monday)* 13.50/21.50 and a la carte 🍷 6.50 – **7 rm** ☕ 75.00/120.00.

### Gorey *The West Country G.* – ✉ *St. Martin.*

**See** : *Mont Orgueil Castle★ (⩽★★) AC.*

*St. Helier 4.*

🏨 **Old Court House,** Gorey Village, JE3 9FS, ℰ (01534) 854444, *Fax (01534) 853587,* 🧖, 🏊, 🌳 – ⇅ [TV] ☎ [P]. [MC] [AE] [O] [VISA] [JCB]. 🚫🐕
*April-mid October* – **Meals** (bar lunch)/dinner 14.00 **s.** and a la carte 🍷 3.70 – **58 rm** ☕ (dinner included) 58.00/117.00 **s.**

🏨 **Moorings,** Gorey Pier, JE3 6EW, ℰ (01534) 853633, *Fax (01534) 857618* – ❄ rest, [TV] ☎. [MC] [AE] [VISA] [JCB]. 🚫🐕
Meals 11.50/14.50 and a la carte 🍷 7.50 – **16 rm** ☕ 36.00/72.00 – SB.

🏨 **Maison Gorey,** Gorey Village, JE3 9EP, ℰ (01534) 857775, *Fax (01534) 857779* – 🚭 rest, [TV] ☎. [MC] [AE] [O] [VISA]. 🚫🐕
*May-September* – **Meals** (dinner only) 9.50 4.90 – **30 rm** ☕ 45.00/90.00.

XX 🙂 **Jersey Pottery (Garden Restaurant),** Gorey Village, JE3 9EP, ℰ (01534) 851119, *Fax (01534) 856403,* « Working pottery », 🌳 – 🚭 [P]. [MC] [AE] [O] [VISA] [JCB]
*closed 10 days Christmas* – **Meals** - Seafood - (lunch only) a la carte 23.20/32.00 **s.** 🍷 7.00.

X **Suma's,** Gorey Hill, JE3 6ET, ℰ (01534) 853291, *Fax (01534) 851913,* ⩽, ⛱ – ❄. [MC] [AE] [O] [VISA]
*closed Sunday dinner and 22 December-15 January* – **Meals** (booking essential) 13.75 **s.** (lunch) and a la carte 17.00/27.25 **s.**

X ✿ 🙂 **Village Bistro** (Cameron), Gorey Village, JE3 9EP, ℰ (01534) 853429, *Fax (01534) 853429,* ⛱ – [MC] [VISA]
*closed Monday except Bank Holidays, 1 week February and 1 week October* – **Meals** (dinner booking essential) 12.50 (lunch) and a la carte 19.60/26.20 🍷 4.50
**Spec.** Risotto of king prawns and mushrooms. Calves liver with avocado, garlic, thyme butter and beetroot jus. Cointreau and orange crème brûlée, citrus compote.

**Grève De Lecq** – ✉ St. Ouen.

🏠 **Des Pierres**, JE3 2DT, on B 65 ℰ (01534) 481858, *Fax (01534) 485273* – 📺 🄿. 🕮 🄰🄴 *VISA*.
⠀ 彩
*April-October* – **Meals** (residents only) (dinner only) 9.85 **s.** – **16 rm** ⊇ (dinner included)
40.00/80.00 – SB.

**Grouville** – *pop. 4 658.*

🏠 **Lavender Villa**, Rue a Don, JE3 9DX, on A 3 ℰ (01534) 854937, *Fax (01534) 856147*, 🐎 –
⠀ ✸ rest, 📺 🄿. 🕮 🄰🄴 *VISA*. 彩
*mid March-October* – **Meals** (residents only) (dinner only) 8.00 🛦 3.90 – **21 rm** ⊇ (dinner
included) 35.00/70.00.

**La Haule** – ✉ St. Brelade.

🏨 **La Place** ⟋, Route du Coin, JE3 8BT, by B 25 on B 43 ℰ (01534) 44261,
⠀ *Fax (01534) 45164*, 🍴, �¬, 🗻, 🐎 – ✸ rm, 📺 🄾 🄿 – 🔏 100. 🕮 🄰🄴 *VISA*
⠀ **Knights:** Meals (dinner only and Sunday lunch)/dinner a la carte 22.75/31.00 🛦 5.50 –
⠀ **42 rm** ⊇ 96.00/132.00 **s.**

🏨 **La Haule Manor**, St. Aubin's Bay, JE3 8BS, ℰ (01534) 741426, *Fax (01534) 745501*,
⠀ ≤ St. Aubin's Fort and Bay, 🐎 – ✸ rest, 📺 🄿 🐎
⠀ **Meals** 13.95/17.95 **s.** and a la carte 🛦 6.80 – **14 rm** ⊇ 89.90/159.00 **s.**

🏠 **Au Caprice**, Route de la Haule, JE3 8BA, on A 1 ℰ (01534) 22083, *Fax (01534) 26199* –
⠀ ✸ rest, 📺. 🕮 🄰🄴 *VISA* 🄹🄲🄱. 彩
*April-October* – **Meals** (by arrangement) 6.00 – **12 rm** ⊇ 54.00.

**La Pulente** – ✉ St. Brelade.

⛳ *Les Mielles G. & C.C., St. Ouens Bay ℰ (01534) 482787.*
⠀ *St. Helier 7.*

🏨 **Atlantic** ⟋, JE3 8HE, ℰ (01534) 744101, *Fax (01534) 744102*, ≤, 🍴, 🛌, 🚬, 🗻, 🖭, 🐎,
⠀ 🎾 – ▯ 📺 🄾 🄿 – 🔏 60. 🕮 🄰🄴 🄾 *VISA* 🄹🄲🄱. 彩
*closed January and February* – **Meals** 16.00/24.50 **s.** and dinner a la carte 25.25/42.20 **s.**
🛦 9.00 – **49 rm** ⊇ 125.00/220.00 **s.**, 1 suite – SB.

**Rozel Bay** – ✉ St. Martin.
⠀ *St. Helier 6.*

🏨 **Chateau La Chaire** ⟋, Rozel Valley, JE3 6AJ, ℰ (01534) 863354, *Fax (01534) 865137*,
⠀ « Victorian country house », 🐎 – 📺 🄾 🄿. 🕮 🄰🄴 🄾 *VISA* 🄹🄲🄱. 彩
⠀ **Meals** – (see *The Restaurant* below) – **13 rm** ⊇ 95.00/150.00 **s.**, 1 suite – SB.

🏨 **Beau Couperon**, JE3 6AN, ℰ (01534) 865522, *Fax (01534) 865332*, ≤, 🗻 – ✸ rest, 📺
⠀ 🄾 🄿. 🕮 🄰🄴 🄾 *VISA* 🄹🄲🄱. 彩
*May-3 October* – **Meals** 15.00 **s.** (dinner) and a la carte 14.45/25.35 **s.** 🛦 4.95 – **36 rm**
⠀ ⊇ 82.50/120.00 **s.**

🍴🍴🍴 **The Restaurant** (at Chateau La Chaire H.), Rozel Valley, JE3 6AJ, ℰ (01534) 863354,
⠀ *Fax (01534) 865137*, 🍴 – ✸ 🄿. 🕮 🄰🄴 🄾 *VISA* 🄹🄲🄱.
⠀ **Meals** 18.95 (lunch) and dinner a la carte approx. 26.50 🛦 6.50.

**St. Aubin.**
⠀ *St. Helier 4.*

🏨 **La Tour**, High St., JE3 8BZ, ℰ (01534) 43770, *Fax (01534) 47143*, ≤ St. Aubin's Fort and
⠀ Bay, 🐎 – 📺 🄾 🄿. 🕮 *VISA*. 彩
⠀ **Rooks:** Meals (dinner only) 11.50 and a la carte 🛦 4.50 – **24 rm** ⊇ 44.00/98.00, 1 suite.

🏨 **Somerville**, Mont du Boulevard, JE3 8AD, South : ¾ m. via harbour ℰ (01534) 41226,
⠀ *Fax (01534) 46621*, ≤ St. Aubin's Bay, 🗻, 🐎 – ▯ 📺 🄾 🄿. 🕮 🄰🄴 *VISA*. 彩
*closed early January-early April* – **Meals** (live music and dancing Saturday) (bar lunch
Monday to Saturday)/dinner 15.00 – **59 rm** ⊇ 80.50/140.00 **s.** – SB.

🏨 **Mont de La Roque**, Mont de La Roque, JE3 8BQ, ℰ (01534) 42942, *Fax (01534) 47841*, ≤
⠀ St. Aubin's Fort and Bay, 🖭 – ▬ rest, 📺 🄾 🄿. 🕮 🄰🄴 *VISA*. 彩
*March-October* – **Le Mirage:** Meals (dinner only and Sunday lunch)/dinner 12.95/14.95
and a la carte 🛦 3.75 – **29 rm** ⊇ 33.75/135.00 **s.**, 2 suites.

🏠 **Panorama** without rest., High St., JE3 8BZ, ℰ (01534) 742429, *Fax (01534) 745940*, ≤ St.
⠀ Aubin's Fort and Bay, 🐎 – 📺. 🕮 🄾 *VISA*. 彩
*mid March-mid December* – **17 rm** ⊇ 44.00/78.00.

🏠 **St. Magloire**, High St., JE3 8BZ, ℰ (01534) 41302, *Fax (01534) 44148* – ✸ rest, 📺. 🕮
⠀ *VISA*. 彩
*18 March-18 October* – **Meals** (residents only) (dinner only) 7.00 🛦 2.75 – **12 rm** ⊇ 30.00/
51.00.

⌂ **Sabots d'or,** High St., JE3 8BZ, ℘ (01534) 43732, Fax (01534) 490142 – ⅍ rest, ⊡. 🕮 AE ⓪ VISA
*restricted opening in winter* – **Meals** 7.00 s. – **12 rm** ⊡ 21.00/50.00 s.

🏠 **Old Court House Inn** with rm, St. Aubin's Harbour, JE3 8AB, ℘ (01534) 746433, Fax (01534) 745103, ≼, 斎 – ⊡ ☎. 🕮 AE ⓪ VISA. ⅍
**Meals** *(closed 25 December)* 10.95/17.95 and a la carte ⅃ 4.95 – **8 rm** ⊡ 50.00/100.00
1 suite – SB.

## St. Brelade's Bay *The West Country G.* – pop. 9 560 – ⊠ *St. Brelade.*
See : *Fishermen's Chapel (frescoes★ ).*
*St. Helier 6.*

🏰 **L'Horizon,** JE3 8EF, ℘ (01534) 43101, Fax (01534) 46269, ≼ St. Brelade's Bay, 斎, Ⅰ₅, ⪚s ◫ – ⮑ ⊡ ☎ & ② – 🔬 150. 🕮 AE ⓪ VISA. ⅍
*Crystal Room :* **Meals** (dinner only and Sunday lunch)/dinner 25.00 **st.** and a la carte ⅃ 8.0⚫ – (see also **The Grill** below) – **104 rm** ⊡ 165.00/230.00 s., 3 suites – SB.

🏰 **St. Brelade's Bay,** Rue de la Baie, JE3 8EF, ℘ (01534) 46141, Fax (01534) 47278, ≼ St. Brelade's Bay, ⪚s, ⊠, 斎, ⅍ – ⮑ ⊡ ☎ ②. 🕮 VISA. ⅍
*May-September* – **Meals** 15.00/25.00 and a la carte ⅃ 7.00 – **80 rm** ⊡ 93.00/186.00 s. 1 suite.

🏨 **Golden Sands,** La Route de la Baie, JE3 8EF, ℘ (01534) 41241, Fax (01534) 499366, ≼ - ⮑, ⅍ rest, ⊡ ☎. 🕮 AE VISA. ⅍
*April-late October* – **Meals** (bar lunch)/dinner 16.00 ⅃ 6.00 – **62 rm** ⊡ 91.00/118.00 s.

🏨 **Chateau Valeuse,** Rue de la Valeuse, JE3 8EE, ℘ (01534) 746281, Fax (01534) 74711⚪, ⊠, 斎 – ⅍ rest, ⊡ ☎ ②. 🕮 VISA JCB. ⅍
*April-18 October* – **Meals** *(closed Sunday dinner)* 11.00/17.00 and a la carte ⅃ 5.00 – **34 rm** ⊡ 29.00/118.00 – SB.

XXX **The Grill** (at L'Horizon H.), JE3 8EF, ℘ (01534) 490082, Fax (01534) 46269 – ▤ ②. 🕮 AE ⓪ VISA
*closed Sunday and Monday lunch* – **Meals** a la carte 20.00/34.95 s. ⅃ 10.00.

## St. Clement – pop. 7 986.
⛳ *St. Clements* ℘ (01534) 821938.
*St. Helier 2.*

⌂ **Playa D'Or** without rest., Greve d'Azette, JE2 6SA, West : 2 m. on A 4 ℘ (01534) 722861, Fax (01534) 769668 – ⅍ ⊡ ②. 🕮 AE ⓪ VISA. ⅍
*closed December and January* – **15 rm** ⊡ 25.00/50.00 s.

## St. Helier *The West Country G.* – pop. 27 523.
See : *Jersey Museum★ AC* Z – *Elizabeth Castle (≼★) AC* Z – *Fort Regent (≼★ AC)* Z.
Env. : *St. Peter's Valley - German Underground Hospital★ AC, NW : 4 m. by A 1, A 11 St Peter's Valley rd and C 112.*

Plan opposite

🏰 **De Vere Grand,** Esplanade, JE4 8WD, ℘ (01534) 722301, Fax (01534) 737815, ≼, Ⅰ₅, ⪚s ◫ – ⮑, ▤ rest, ⊡ ☎ & – 🔬 180. 🕮 AE ⓪ VISA. ⅍                    Y u
**Meals** 15.50/23.50 ⅃ 7.00 – (see also **Victoria's** below) – **109 rm** ⊡ 105.00/175.00 s., 5 suites – SB.

🏰 **Hotel de France,** St. Saviours Rd, JE1 7XP, ℘ (01534) 614000, Fax (01534) 614999, Ⅰ₅, ⪚s, ⊠, ◫, 斎, squash – ⮑ ⊡ ☎ ② – 🔬 1000. 🕮 AE ⓪ VISA. ⅍                    Y o
*closed Christmas* – **Meals** 19.50 s. (dinner) and a la carte 18.00/26.00 s. ⅃ 4.00 – **320 rm** ⊡ 99.00/155.00 s. – SB.

🏰 **Pomme d'Or,** Liberation Sq., JE1 3UF, ℘ (01534) 880110, Fax (01534) 37781 – ⮑, ⅍ rm, ▤ rest, ⊡ ☎ – 🔬 180. 🕮 AE ⓪ VISA                    Z u
*Harbour Room :* **Meals** (carving rest.) 12.50/16.50 s. and a la carte ⅃ 4.25 – (see also *La Petite Pomme* below) – **145 rm** ⊡ 75.00/120.00 s., 2 suites – SB.

🏨 **De la Plage,** Havre des Pas, JE2 4UQ, ℘ (01534) 723474, Fax (01534) 768642, ≼, Ⅰ₅ – ⮑ ⊡ ☎ ②. 🕮 AE ⓪ VISA JCB. ⅍                    Z s
*24 April-October* – **Meals** (bar lunch)/dinner 16.50 and a la carte ⅃ 4.50 – **78 rm** ⊡ 46.00/120.00 – SB.

🏨 **Apollo,** 9 St. Saviour's Rd, JE2 4LA, ℘ (01534) 25441, Fax (01534) 22120, Ⅰ₅, ⪚s, ⊠, ◫ – ⮑ ⊡ ☎ ②. 🕮 AE ⓪ VISA. ⅍                    Z e
**Meals** a la carte 7.50/14.25 ⅃ 4.50 – **85 rm** ⊡ 41.50/83.00 – SB.

184

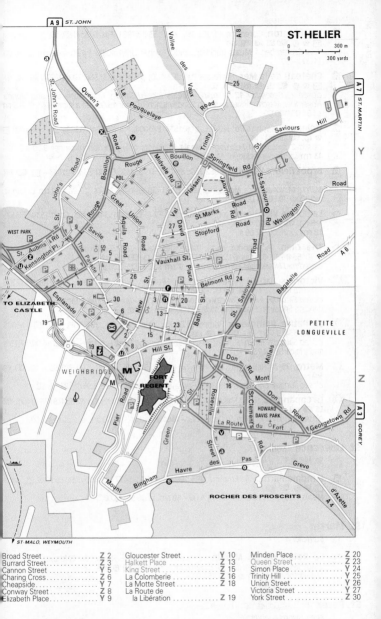

血血 **Queens,** Queens Rd, JE2 3GR, ℰ (01534) 22239, *Fax (01534) 21930* – 📶, ⭍⚛ rest, 📺 ☎ 🅿.
🔟⑧ 🆎 ⓪ *VISA* JCB. 🛇
**Meals** (residents only) (dinner only) 8.00 **s**. ⓐ 5.00 – **37 rm** ⊇ 30.00/90.00 **s**.    **Y X**

血血 **Laurels,** La route du Fort, JE2 4PA, ℰ (01534) 36444, *Fax (01534) 59904* – ⭍⚛ rest, 📺 ☎
🅿 🔟⑧ 🆎 ⓪ *VISA*    **Z V**
*mid March-October* – **Meals** (residents only) (dinner only) 9.50 **s**. ⓐ 4.90 – **37 rm** ⊇ 57.50/
105.00 – SB.

185

🏨 **Washington,** Clarendon Rd, JE2 3YS, 𝒫 (01534) 37981, Fax (01534) 89899, ⬛ – 🗝 rest 📺 ☎ 🅿. 🆗 🗚 ⓪ 𝓥𝓘𝓢𝓐. 🕸
Y e
April-September – **Meals** (residents only) (dinner only) 10.00 ᛚ 4.90 – **36 rm** ⫣ 50.00/ 116.00 – SB.

🏨 **Chateau de la Mer,** Havre des Pas, JE2 4UQ, 𝒫 (01534) 33366, Fax (01534) 36544, ≼ – 📺 ☎ 🅿. 🆗 🗚 ⓪ 𝓥𝓘𝓢𝓐 𝗝𝗖𝗕. 🕸
Z c
closed 23 December-12 February – **Meals** (closed Sunday November-June and Monday November-March) (dinner only and Sunday lunch)/dinner 15.50 and a la carte ᛚ 3.95 – **5 rm** ⫣ 54.00/100.00.

🏨 **Uplands,** St. John's Rd, JE2 3LE, 𝒫 (01534) 873006, Fax (01534) 639899, ⬛ – 🗝 rest. 📺 ☎ 🅿. 🆗 🗚 𝓥𝓘𝓢𝓐. 🕸
Y a
closed 2 January-14 February – **Meals** (residents only) (bar lunch)/dinner 9.00 ᛚ 5.70 – **43 rm** ⫣ (dinner included) 44.00/88.00.

🏨 **Brookfield,** 24 Raleigh Av., JE2 3ZG, 𝒫 (01534) 723168, Fax (01534) 721543 – 📺. 🆗 𝓥𝓘𝓢𝓐 🕸
Y v
March-14 November – **Meals** (residents only) (dinner only) 7.00 s. ᛚ 2.80 – **20 rm** ⫣ (dinner included) 29.50/65.00 s.

⌂ **La Bonne Vie** without rest., Roseville St., JE2 4PL, 𝒫 (01534) 35955, Fax (01534) 33357 – 🗝 📺. 🆗 ⓪ 𝓥𝓘𝓢𝓐. 🕸
Z a
**10 rm** ⫣ 26.00/57.00 s.

⌂ **The Glen** ⌕ without rest., Vallee des Vaux, JE2 3GB, North : 1 ¼ m. by A 8 𝒫 (01534) 732062, Fax (01534) 880738, ☞ – 📺 🅿. 🆗 𝓥𝓘𝓢𝓐. 🕸
closed mid November-early February – **7 rm** ⫣ 28.00/60.00 s.

𝖃𝖃𝖃 **Victoria's** (at De Vere Grand H.), Peirson Rd, JE4 8WD, 𝒫 (01534) 872255 Fax (01534) 737815 – ▤. 🆗 🗚 ⓪ 𝓥𝓘𝓢𝓐
Y z
closed Saturday lunch, Sunday dinner and Bank Holiday Mondays – **Meals** (live music and dancing Friday and Saturday) 15.50/23.50 and a la carte ᛚ 7.00.

𝖃𝖃𝖃 **La Petite Pomme** (at Pomme d'Or H.), Liberation Sq., JE1 3UF, 𝒫 (01534) 66608 Fax (01534) 37781 – ▤. 🆗 🗚 ⓪ 𝓥𝓘𝓢𝓐
Z u
closed Saturday lunch, Sunday, 25-26 December and Bank Holidays – **Meals** 14.00/17.25 s. and a la carte ᛚ 4.25.

𝖃𝖃 **Metro,** 75-77 Halkett Pl., JE2 4WH, 𝒫 (01534) 510096, Fax (01534) 510099 – ▤. 🆗 🄾 𝓥𝓘𝓢𝓐
YZ r
closed Sunday, Christmas and Bank Holidays – **Meals** a la carte 16.95/26.85 ᛚ 8.50.

𝖃𝖃 **La Capannina,** 65-67 Halkett Pl., JE2 4WG, 𝒫 (01534) 34602, Fax (01534) 877628 – ▤. 🆗 🗚 ⓪ 𝓥𝓘𝓢𝓐
Z n
closed Sunday and 25 to 30 December – **Meals** - Italian - 17.00 and a la carte ᛚ 6.00.

## St. Lawrence – pop. 4 773.
St. Helier 3.

🏨 **Elmdale Farm,** Ville Emphrie, JE3 1EF, 𝒫 (01534) 34779, Fax (01534) 601115, ⬛, ☞ – 📺 ☎ 🅿. 🆗 𝓥𝓘𝓢𝓐. 🕸
**Meals** 7.95/12.95 and a la carte ᛚ 4.00 – **19 rm** ⫣ 36.50/73.00.

## St. Martin – pop. 3 423.
St. Helier 4.

⌂ **Le Relais de St. Martin** without rest., Grande Route de Faldouet, JE3 6UG, 𝒫 (01534) 853271, Fax (01534) 855241, ☞ – 🗝 rest. 📺 🅿. 𝓥𝓘𝓢𝓐. 🕸
May-October – **11 rm** ⫣ 27.00/54.00.

## St. Peter The West Country G. – pop. 4 228.
See : Living Legend★.
St. Helier 5.

🏨 **Greenhill's Country H.** ⌕, Mont de l'Ecole, Coin Varin, JE3 7EL, on C 112 𝒫 (01534) 481042, Fax (01534) 485322, « Part 17C farmhouse », ⬛, ☞ – 🗝 rest, ▤ rest. 📺 ☎ 🅿. 🆗 🗚 ⓪ 𝓥𝓘𝓢𝓐. 🕸
March-November – **Meals** 12.50/19.50 and a la carte ᛚ 5.20 – **24 rm** ⫣ 48.00/116.00, 1 suite – SB.

**St. Saviour** – pop. 12 680.
*St. Helier 1.*

🏠 **Longueville Manor,** Longueville Rd, JE2 7WF, on A 3 *&* (01534) 725501,
✿ *Fax (01534) 731613,* « Former manor house with Jacobean panelling », 🛴, 🌳, park, 🎾 –
📶, 🔆 rest, 📺 ☎ 🅿. 🕿 🅰🅴 ⓞ 𝘝𝘐𝘚𝘈
**Meals** 20.00/38.00 **s.** and dinner a la carte 39.00/45.75 **s.** ⓛ 9.00 – **30 rm** ☷ 165.00/
255.00 **s.**, 2 suites – SB
**Spec.** Grilled Jersey scallops on basil scented roast vegetables. Millefeuille of monkfish with
roast tomatoes, shallots and Parma ham. Best end of lamb with butter beans and plum
tomatoes.

🏠 **Champ Colin** ⌂ without rest., Rue du Champ Colin, Houge Bie, JE2 7UN,
*&* (01534) 851877, *Fax (01534) 854902,* « Part 19C farmhouse, antiques », 🌳 – 🔆 📺 🅿.
🕿 🅰🅴 𝘝𝘐𝘚𝘈 𝗝𝗖𝗕. 🛠
*closed 20 December-5 January –* **3 rm** ☷ 50.00.

**Trinity** – pop. 2 639.

🏠 **The Highfield Country H.,** Route d'Ebenezer, JE3 5DT, Northwest : ½ m. on A 8
*&* (01534) 862194, *Fax (01534) 865342,* Ⅰ₅, ≋, 🌳 – 📶, 🔆 rest, 📺 ☎ 🅿. 🕿 🅰🅴 𝘝𝘐𝘚𝘈 𝗝𝗖𝗕.
🛠
*Easter-October –* **Meals** (dinner only) 13.00 **s.** and a la carte ⓛ 4.75 – **28 rm** ☷ 43.00/
86.00 **s.**, 10 suites.

## SARK

**403** P 33 and **230** ⑩ *The West Country G.* – pop. 550.

See : *Island*★★ – *La Coupée*★★★ – *Port du Moulin*★★ – *Creux Harbour*★ – *La Seigneurie*★ AC
– *Pilcher Monument*★ – *Hog's Back*★.

🚢 to St. Helier (Condor Ferries Ltd) 1 daily (45 mn).

🚢 to France (St. Malo) via Jersey (St. Helier) (Condor Ferries Ltd) 3 weekly – to Guernsey
(St. Peter Port) (Isle of Sark Shipping Co. Ltd and Condor Ferries Ltd) (summer only) (45 mn).
🖪 Harbour Hill, GY9 0SB *&* (01481) 832345.

🏠 **Dixcart** ⌂, GY9 0SD, *&* (01481) 832015, *Fax (01481) 832164,* 🏡, « Part 16C farmhouse », 🌳, park – ☎. 🕿 🅰🅴 𝘝𝘐𝘚𝘈 𝗝𝗖𝗕
**Meals** (booking essential in winter) 12.00 (dinner) and a la carte 15.00/25.75 ⓛ 4.00 – **15 rm**
☷ 45.00/90.00.

🏠 **Stocks Island** ⌂, GY9 0SD, *&* (01481) 832001, *Fax (01481) 832130,* 🏡, 🛴, 🌳 –
🔆 rest. 🕿 🅰🅴 ⓞ 𝘝𝘐𝘚𝘈 𝗝𝗖𝗕
*2 April-2 October –* **Meals** 10.00/16.00 **s.** and a la carte ⓛ 5.00 – **23 rm** ☷ (dinner included)
59.00/118.00 **s.** – SB.

🏠 **Petit Champ** ⌂, GY9 0SF, *&* (01481) 832046, *Fax (01481) 832469,* ≼ coast, Herm, Jetou
and Guernsey, 🛴, 🌳 – 🔆 rest. 🕿 🅰🅴 ⓞ 𝘝𝘐𝘚𝘈. 🛠
*2 April-1 October –* **Meals** 17.50 **s.** (dinner) and a la carte 9.50/25.05 **s.** ⓛ 4.50 – **16 rm** ☷
(dinner included) 53.00/112.00.

🍴🍴 **La Sablonnerie** ⌂ with rm, Little Sark, GY9 0SD, *&* (01481) 832061, *Fax (01481) 832408,*
🏡, « Part 16C farmhouse », 🌳 – 🅰🅴 𝘝𝘐𝘚𝘈. 🛠
*Easter-mid October –* **Meals** 22.80/25.80 and a la carte ⓛ 5.50 – **21 rm** ☷ (dinner included)
58.50/144.00, 2 suites.

🍴 **Founiais,** Harbour Hill, GY9 0SB, *&* (01481) 832626, *Fax (01481) 832642,* 🏡 – 🕿 𝘝𝘐𝘚𝘈 𝗝𝗖𝗕
*March-October –* **Meals** a la carte 13.20/21.90 ⓛ 4.00.

---

**CHANNEL TUNNEL** Kent **404** X 30 – *see Folkestone.*

---

**CHAPELTOWN** N. Yorks. **402 403 404** P 23 – *see Sheffield.*

---

**CHARD** Somerset **403** L 31 – pop. 10 770.
🖪 *The Guildhall, Fore St., TA20 1PP &* (01460) 67463.
*London 157 – Exeter 32 – Lyme Regis 12 – Taunton 18 – Yeovil 17.*

🏠 **Lordleaze,** Henderson Drive, TA20 2HW, Southeast : 1 ½ m. by A 358 off Forton rd
*&* (01460) 61066, *Fax (01460) 66468* – 🔆 📺 ☎ 🅿 – 🔬 120. 🕿 🅰🅴 𝘝𝘐𝘚𝘈
**Meals** a la carte 8.65/14.25 **s.** ⓛ 5.65 – **16 rm** ☷ 49.50/80.00 **st.** – SB.

🔧 ATS Crewkerne Rd *&* (01460) 63773

---

**CHARINGWORTH** Glos. – *see Chipping Campden.*

**CHARLBURY** *Oxon.* **403 404** P 28 – *pop. 2 694.*
*London 72 – Birmingham 50 – Oxford 15.*

🏠 **Bell,** Church St., OX7 3PP, ℘ (01608) 810278, *Fax (01608) 811447* – 📺 ☎ 🅿 – 🛋 50. 🕮 🄰
🆅🆂🄰 🅹🄲🄱
**Meals** a la carte 10.70/22.45 **t.** ⓙ 5.95 – **13 rm** ⊊ 55.00/85.00 **t.** – SB.

🍴 **Bull Inn** with rm, Sheep St., OX7 3RR, ℘ (01608) 810689 – 📺 🅿. 🕮 🆅🆂🄰 🅹🄲🄱. ⚘
*closed Sunday dinner, Monday except Bank Holidays, 25 December and 1 January* – **Meal**
a la carte 12.90/26.45 **t.** ⓙ 7.25 – **3 rm** ⊊ 50.00/60.00 **t.**

---

**CHARLECOTE** *Warks.* **403 404** P 27 – *see Stratford-upon-Avon.*

---

**CHARLESTOWN** *Cornwall* **403** F 32 – *see St. Austell.*

---

**CHARLTON** *W. Sussex* **404** R 31 – *see Chichester.*

---

**CHARLWOOD** *Surrey* **404** T 30 – *pop. 1 969* – ✉ *Horley.*
*London 30 – Brighton 29 – Royal Tunbridge Wells 28.*

🏨 **Stanhill Court** 🏡, Stan Hill, RH6 0EP, Northwest : 1 m. ℘ (01293) 862166
*Fax (01293) 862773*, ≤, « 19C Scottish baronial style interior », 🞨, 🞨, park – 🛬 📺 ☎ 🅿 –
🛋 170. 🕮 🄰🄴 🄾 🆅🆂🄰 🅹🄲🄱. ⚘
**Meals** (bar lunch Saturday) 16.95 **st.** (lunch) and a la carte 27.50/31.25 **st.** ⓙ 5.95 – ⊊ 10.2
– **13 rm** 95.00/150.00 **t.** – SB.

---

**CHARMOUTH** *Dorset* **403** L 31 – *pop. 1 497* – ✉ *Bridport.*
*London 157 – Dorchester 22 – Exeter 31 – Taunton 27.*

🏠 **Thatch Lodge,** The Street, DT6 6PQ, ℘ (01297) 560407, *Fax (01297) 560407*, « Part 14C
thatched cottage », 🞨 – 🛬 📺 🅿. ⚘
*closed mid January-mid March* – **Meals** (by arrangement) (dinner only) 24.50 **t.** ⓙ 6.50 –
**7 rm** ⊊ 41.50/96.00 **t.**

🏠 **White House,** 2 Hillside, The Street, DT6 6PJ, ℘ (01297) 560411, *Fax (01297) 560702* –
🛬 📺 ☎ 🕻 🅿. 🕮 🄰🄴 🄾 🆅🆂🄰 🅹🄲🄱
**Meals** (dinner only) 18.50 **t.** ⓙ 6.00 – **10 rm** ⊊ 48.50/77.00 **t.** – SB.

↑ **Hensleigh** without rest., Lower Sea Lane, DT6 6LW, ℘ (01297) 56083C
*Fax (01297) 560830* – 🛬 📺 🅿. 🕮 🄰🄴 🆅🆂🄰 🅹🄲🄱
*March-November* – **11 rm** ⊊ 27.00/54.00 **t.** – SB.

---

**CHARTHAM** *Kent* **404** X 30 – *see Canterbury.*

---

**CHARTHAM HATCH** *Kent* **404** X 30 – *see Canterbury.*

---

**CHATTERIS** *Cambs.* **402 404** U 26 – *pop. 7 261.*
*London 85 – Cambridge 26 – Norwich 71.*

🏠 **Cross Keys,** 12-16 Market Hill, PE16 6BA, ℘ (01354) 693036, *Fax (01354) 693036*, « Par
17C inn » – 📺 ☎. 🕮 🆅🆂🄰 🅹🄲🄱. ⚘
*closed 26 to 28 December* – **Meals** 8.95 **t.** (lunch) and a la carte 12.95/15.95 **t.** ⓙ 4.45 –
**12 rm** ⊊ 32.50/55.00 **st.** – SB.

---

**CHEADLE** *Ches.* **402 403** N 23.
*London 200 – Manchester 7 – Stoke-on-Trent 33.*

🏨 **Village H. & Leisure Club,** Cheadle Rd, SK8 1HW, South : ¾ m. by A 5149
℘ (0161) 428 0404, *Fax (0161) 428 1191*, 🝔, 🛬, 🞨, squash – 🞨, 🛬 rm, 🞨 rest, 📺 ☎ &
🅿 – 🛋 200. 🕮 🄰🄴 🄾 🆅🆂🄰 🅹🄲🄱
**Meals** (grill rest.) 13.95 **st.** and a la carte – **73 rm** ⊊ 88.00/103.00 **st.**

🏠 **Travel Inn,** Royal Crescent, Cheadle Royal Retail Park, SK8 3FE, Southwest : 2 m. by A 560
off A 34 ℘ (0161) 491 5884, *Fax (0161) 491 5886* – 🞨, 🛬 rm, 🞨 rest, 📺 & 🅿. 🕮 🄰🄴 🄾
🆅🆂🄰. ⚘
**Meals** (grill rest.) – **40 rm** 38.00 **t.**

↑ **Spring Cottage** without rest., 60 Hulme Hall Rd, Cheadle Hulme, SK8 6JZ, South : 2 ¼ m.
by A 5149 on B 5095 ℘ (0161) 485 1037 – 📺 🅿. 🕮 🆅🆂🄰
**6 rm** ⊊ 20.00/39.00.

**CHEDDLETON** Staffs. 402 403 404 N 24 – pop. 3 534 – ⊠ Leek.
London 125 – Birmingham 48 – Derby 33 – Manchester 42 – Stoke-on-Trent 11.

⌂ **Choir Cottage** without rest., Ostlers Lane, via Hollows Lane (opposite Red Lion on A 520), ST13 7HS, ℰ (01538) 360561 – 📺 ℗. ⁂
closed 25 and 26 December – **3 rm** � 35.00/59.00 st.

---

**CHELMSFORD** Essex 404 V 28 – pop. 97 451.
🛈 E Block, County Hall, Market Rd, CM1 1GG ℰ (01245) 283400.
London 33 – Cambridge 46 – Ipswich 40 – Southend-on-Sea 19.

🏨 **County,** 29 Rainsford Rd, CM1 2QA, ℰ (01245) 491911, Fax (01245) 492762 – 📺 ☎ ℗ –
🔥 200. ◑◒ 🄰🄴 ① 𝑉𝐼𝑆𝐴. ⁂
closed Christmas-New Year – Meals 18.95 st. and a la carte ₰ 7.75 – **34 rm** ⊐ 73.00/
83.00 st., 1 suite.

🏨 **Travel Inn,** Chelmsford Service Area, Colchester Rd, Springfield, CM2 5PY, Northeast : at
junction of A 12 with A 138 and A 130 ℰ (01245) 464008, Fax (01245) 464010 – 📳, ↪← rm,
📺 ᕘ ℗ – 🔥 35. ◑◒ 🄰🄴 ① 𝑉𝐼𝑆𝐴. ⁂
Meals (grill rest.) – **61 rm** 38.00 t.

**at Great Baddow** Southeast : 3 m. by A 414 – ⊠ Chelmsford.

🏰 **Pontlands Park** ⌂, West Hanningfield Rd, CM2 8HR, ℰ (01245) 476444,
Fax (01245) 478393, ≤, ⇔, ⊒, ◪, ☞ – 📺 ☎ ℗ – 🔥 40. ◑◒ 🄰🄴 ① 𝑉𝐼𝑆𝐴. ⁂
closed 24 to 31 December – **The Conservatory :** Meals (closed Monday and Saturday
lunch and Sunday dinner to non-residents) (dancing Friday evening) 21.00 st. and a la carte
₰ 7.50 – ⊐ 10.00 – **16 rm** 90.00/120.00 st., 1 suite.

🅰 ATS 375 Springfield Rd ℰ (01245) 257795

---

**CHELTENHAM** Glos. 403 404 N 28 Great Britain G. – pop. 91 301.
See : Town★ – Pittville Pump Room★ AC A A.
Exc. : Sudeley Castle★ (Paintings★) AC, NE : 7 m. by B 4632 A.
🆖 Cleeve Hill ℰ (01242) 672025 A – 🆖 Cotswold Hills, Ullenwood ℰ (01242) 522421, A.
🛈 77 Promenade, GL50 1PP ℰ (01242) 522878.
London 99 – Birmingham 48 – Bristol 40 – Gloucester 9 – Oxford 43.

Plan on next page

🏰 **Queen's,** Promenade, GL50 1NN, ℰ (01242) 514724, Fax (01242) 224145, ☞ – 📳 ↪← 📺
ᕘ ℗ – 🔥 80. ◑◒ 🄰🄴 ① 𝑉𝐼𝑆𝐴 𝐽𝐶𝐵                                                          B n
**Napier :** Meals 15.95/24.50 st. and a la carte ₰ 10.45 – ⊐ 10.95 – **74 rm** 95.00/175.00 st. –
SB.

🏰 **Thistle Golden Valley,** Gloucester Rd, GL51 0TS, West : 2 m. on A 40 ℰ (01242) 232691,
Fax (01242) 221846, 🖪, ⇔, ◪, ☞, ⁂ – 📳, ↪← rm, 🍽 rest, 📺 ☎ ℗ – 🔥 220. ◑◒ 🄰🄴 ①
𝑉𝐼𝑆𝐴 𝐽𝐶𝐵
**Burford Room :** Meals 15.50/23.50 t. and a la carte ₰ 5.75 – ⊐ 10.00 – **118 rm** 99.00/
109.00 t., 4 suites – SB.

🏰 **Cheltenham Park,** Cirencester Rd, Charlton Kings, GL53 8EA, ℰ (01242) 222021,
Fax (01242) 226935, 🖪, ⇔, ◪, ☞ – ↪←, 🍽 rest, 📺 ☎ ₺ ℗ – 🔥 350. ◑◒ 🄰🄴 ① 𝑉𝐼𝑆𝐴.
⁂                                                                                            A e
Meals (closed Saturday lunch) 14.00/20.00 st. ₰ 5.95 – **143 rm** ⊐ 99.00/130.00 st., 1 suite –
SB.

🏛 **On the Park,** 38 Evesham Rd, GL52 2AH, ℰ (01242) 518898, Fax (01242) 511526,
« Regency town house », ☞ – ↪← rest, 📺 ᕘ ℃. ◑◒ 🄰🄴 ① 𝑉𝐼𝑆𝐴. ⁂                            C r
Meals (booking essential) 22.50 t. (dinner) and a la carte 17.75/28.50 t. – ⊐ 8.50 – **12 rm**
78.50/115.50 t. – SB.

🏛 **Prestbury House,** The Burgage, GL52 3DN, Northeast : 1 ½ m. by Prestbury Rd (B 4632)
off Tatchley Lane ℰ (01242) 529533, Fax (01242) 227076, ☞ – ↪← rm, 📺 ☎ ℗ – 🔥 30. ◑◒
🄰🄴 ① 𝑉𝐼𝑆𝐴. ⁂                                                                              A r
Meals 22.50 t. and a la carte ₰ 4.50 – **16 rm** ⊐ 77.00/94.00 st. – SB.

🏠 **Charlton Kings,** London Rd, Charlton Kings, GL52 6UU, ℰ (01242) 231061,
Fax (01242) 241900, ☞ – ↪← 📺 ☎ ℗. ◑◒ 🄰🄴 𝑉𝐼𝑆𝐴 𝐽𝐶𝐵                                         A c
Meals (dinner only) 17.95 t. ₰ 6.20 – **14 rm** ⊐ 57.50/98.00 t.

🏠 **Lypiatt House** without rest., Lypiatt Rd, GL50 2QW, ℰ (01242) 224994,
Fax (01242) 224996 – 📺 ℃ ℗. ◑◒ 🄰🄴 𝑉𝐼𝑆𝐴. ⁂                                                 B c
**10 rm** ⊐ 50.00/75.00 st.

🏠 **Milton House,** 12 Royal Parade, Bayshill Rd, GL50 3AY, ℰ (01242) 582601,
Fax (01242) 222326 – ↪← 📺 ☎ ℗. ◑◒ 🄰🄴 ① 𝑉𝐼𝑆𝐴                                               B e
closed 24 December-2 January – Meals (by arrangement) (dinner only) 25.00 st. ₰ 3.50 –
**8 rm** ⊐ 40.00/68.00 st.

# CHELTENHAM

CENTRE

🛏 **Regency House**, 50 Clarence Sq., GL50 4JR, ℰ (01242) 582718, *Fax (01242) 262697*, �̃ – 🌤 📺 ☎ 💳 🆎 *VISA*. ⌘
C c
*closed 24 December-2 January* – **Meals** *(closed Sunday dinner)* 17.95 **t**. 🍴 4.50 – **8 rm** ⌑ 38.00/58.00 **st**.

🛏 **Wyastone**, Parabola Rd, GL50 3BG, ℰ (01242) 245549, *Fax (01242) 522659* – 🌤 rest, 📺 ☎ ⇦ 🅿. 💳 🆎 *VISA*. ⌘
B i
*closed 23 December-4 January* – **Meals** (dinner only) a la carte approx. 18.00 🍴 5.50 – **13 rm** ⌑ 53.00/74.00 **st**.

🛏 **Stretton Lodge**, Western Rd, GL50 3RN, ℰ (01242) 570771, *Fax (01242) 528724*, �̃ – 🌤 📺 ☎ 📞 🅿. 💳 🆎 *VISA* JCB
B v
**Meals** a la carte 17.70/22.50 **st**. 🍴 6.50 – **5 rm** ⌑ 50.00/80.00 **st**. – SB.

🛏 **Beaumont House**, Shurdington Rd, GL53 0JE, ℰ (01242) 245986, *Fax (01242) 520044*, �̃ – 🌤 rest, 📺 ☎ 📞 🅿. 💳 🆎 *VISA* JCB. ⌘
A u
*closed 25 and 26 December* – **Meals** (dinner only) 21.95 **t**. 🍴 4.50 – **15 rm** ⌑ 39.00/65.00 **t**. – SB.

🛏 **Travel Inn**, Tewkesbury Rd, Uckington, GL51 9SL, Northwest : 1 ¾ m. on A 4019 at junction with B 4634 ℰ (01242) 233847, *Fax (01242) 244887* – 🌤 rm, 📺 ⅓ 🅿. 💳 🆎 ⓪ *VISA*. ⌘
A a
**Meals** (grill rest.) – **40 rm** 38.00 **t**.

↑ **Hannaford's** without rest., 20 Evesham Rd, GL52 2AB, ℰ (01242) 515181, *Fax (01242) 257571* – 🌤 rest, 📺 ☎. 💳 🆎 *VISA*. ⌘
C u
*closed 20 December-7 January* – **8 rm** ⌑ 38.00/65.00 **t**.

↑ **Hunting Butts Farm**, Swindon Lane, GL50 4NZ, North : 1 ½ m. by A 435 ℰ (01242) 524982, *Fax (01242) 251507*, ≤, « Working farm », �̃ – 🌤 rest, 📺 🅿
A n
**Meals** (by arrangement) 12.50 **st**. – **7 rm** ⌑ 27.50/50.00 **st**.

↑ **Hollington House**, 115 Hales Rd, GL52 6ST, ℰ (01242) 256652, *Fax (01242) 570280*, �̃ – 🌤 rest, 📺 📞 🅿. 💳 🆎 *VISA*. ⌘
A s
**Meals** (by arrangement) 15.00 **st**. and a la carte 🍴 5.00 – **9 rm** ⌑ 40.00/65.00 **st**. – SB.

XX **Le Champignon Sauvage** (Everitt-Matthias), 24-26 Suffolk Rd, GL50 2AQ, ⌘ ℰ (01242) 573449, *Fax (01242) 573449* – 💳 🆎 ⓪ *VISA* JCB
B a
*closed Sunday, Monday, 2 weeks in summer, 1 week Christmas and Bank Holidays* – **Meals** 18.50/35.00 **t**. 🍴 5.25
**Spec.** Roasted foie gras, soured cabbage and Banyuls sauce. Fillet of pork, black pudding, pork dumplings and cider sauce. Feuillantine of mango, Thai spiced cream and red wine syrup.

XX **Mayflower**, 32-34 Clarence St., GL50 3NX, ℰ (01242) 522426, *Fax (01242) 251667* – 🍽. 💳 🆎 ⓪ *VISA* JCB
B r
*closed Sunday lunch and 24 to 26 December* – **Meals** - Chinese - 6.75/16.00 **t**. and a la carte 🍴 6.75.

X **Le Petit Blanc**, The Promenade, GL50 1NN, ℰ (01242) 266800, *Fax (01242) 266801* – 🌤 🍽. 💳 🆎 ⓪ *VISA*
B n
*closed 25 December* – **Meals** - Brasserie - 14.00 **t**. and a la carte 15.75/26.75 **t**.

X **Vanilla**, 9-10 Cambray Pl., GL50 1JS, ℰ (01242) 228228, *Fax (01242) 228228* – 💳 🆎 *VISA* JCB
C e
*closed Saturday lunch, Sunday, Monday, 25-26 December and 1 January* – **Meals** 10.95 **t**. (lunch) and a la carte 17.95/24.05 **t**. 🍴 5.80.

**at Woolstone** *North : 6 ¼ m. by A 435* – A – ✉ *Cheltenham*.

↑ **Old Rectory** 🦢 without rest., GL52 4RG, ℰ (01242) 673766, ≤, �̃ – 🌤 📺 🅿. ⌘
*March-November* – **3 rm** ⌑ 32.00/48.00 **t**.

**at Cleeve Hill** *Northeast : 4 m. on B 4632* – A – ✉ *Cheltenham*.

🏨 **Rising Sun**, GL52 3PX, ℰ (01242) 676281, *Fax (01242) 673069*, ≤, 😔, �̃ – 🌤 📺 ☎ 🅿. 💳 🆎 ⓪ *VISA*. ⌘
**Meals** (dinner only and Sunday lunch)/dinner 18.50 **t**. – **24 rm** ⌑ 79.50/95.00 **t**. – SB.

🛏 **Cleeve Hill** without rest., GL52 3PR, ℰ (01242) 672052, *Fax (01242) 679969*, ≤, �̃ – 🌤 📺 ☎ 🅿. 💳 *VISA*. ⌘
*closed Christmas and New Year* – **9 rm** ⌑ 50.00/80.00 **st**.

**at Andoversford** *Southeast : 6 m. on A 40* – A – ✉ *Cheltenham*.

🍴 **Kilkenny Inn**, GL54 4LN, Southwest : 1 ¼ m. on A 436 ℰ (01242) 820341, *Fax (01242) 820133*, �̃ – 🅿. 💳 *VISA*
*closed Sunday dinner January-March, 11-12 January and 25-26 December* – **Meals** a la carte 14.70/20.05 **t**. 🍴 5.70.

**at Shurdington** *Southwest : 3 ¾ m. on A 46* – A – ⊠ *Cheltenham.*

🏛 **Greenway** ⤢, GL51 5UG, ℰ (01242) 862352, *Fax (01242) 862780*, ≼, « Part 16C Cotswold country house, gardens » – ⇟⊷ rm, 🆅 ☎ 🄿 – 🄰 30. 🆆🅾 🅰🅴 ① 𝘝𝘐𝘚𝘈. ⪥
**Meals** *(closed Saturday lunch)* 19.45/32.00 **t.** and dinner a la carte ᛰ 16.00 – **19 rm** ⚏ 95.00/205.00 **t.** – SB.

🏛 **Cheltenham and Gloucester Moat House,** Shurdington Rd, GL3 4PB, Southwest 1 ¼ m. on A 46 ℰ (01452) 519988, *Fax (01452) 519977*, 🏖, 𝙄🅱, ⫩, 🔲 – 🖈, ⇟⊷ rm, 🔳 rest 🆅 ☎ ⚒ ᾧ 🄿 – 🄰 340. 🆆🅾 🅰🅴 ① 𝘝𝘐𝘚𝘈
**Meals** *(closed Saturday lunch)* 16.50/19.50 **st.** and a la carte ᛰ 7.00 – ⚏ 9.95 – **94 rm** 100.00/115.00 **st.**, 2 suites – SB.

**at Staverton** *West : 4 ¼ m. by A 40* – A – ⊠ *Cheltenham.*

🏨 **White House,** Gloucester Rd, GL51 0ST, on B 4063 ℰ (01452) 713226, *Fax (01452) 85759* – 🆅 ☎ 🄿 – 🄰 200. 🆆🅾 🅰🅴 ① 𝘝𝘐𝘚𝘈 𝙅𝘊𝘉
**Meals** 13.50 **st.** (lunch) and dinner a la carte 18.20/28.60 **st.** ᛰ 5.50 – **47 rm** ⚏ 75.00 95.00 **st.**, 2 suites – SB.

⊚ ATS Chosen View Rd ℰ (01242) 521288        ATS 99-101 London Rd ℰ (01242) 519814

---

**CHELWOOD** *Bath & North East Somerset – see Bristol.*

---

**CHENIES** *Bucks.* 🄸🄰🄸 S 28 – pop. 258 – ⊠ *Rickmansworth (Herts.).*
*London 30 – Aylesbury 18 – Watford 7.*

🏨 **Bedford Arms,** WD3 6EQ, ℰ (01923) 283301, *Fax (01923) 284825*, 🏖, 🌳 – ⇟⊷ rm, 🆅 ☎ 🄿 🆆🅾 🅰🅴 ① 𝘝𝘐𝘚𝘈 𝙅𝘊𝘉. ⪥
**Meals** *(bar lunch Saturday)* 18.50/23.00 **t.** and a la carte ᛰ 6.50 – ⚏ 11.50 – **10 rm** 145.00. 185.00 **t.** – SB.

---

**CHERWELL VALLEY SERVICE AREA** *Oxon.* 🄰🄾🄸 🄰🄾🄸 Q 28 – ⊠ *Bicester.*

🏠 **Travelodge,** Northampton Rd, Ardley, OX6 9RD, M 40, junction 10 ℰ (01869) 346060 *Fax (01869) 345030*, Reservations (Freephone) 0800 850950 – ⇟⊷ 🆅 ☎ ᾧ 🄿. 🆆🅾 🅰🅴 ① 𝘝𝘐𝘚 𝙅𝘊𝘉. ⪥
**Meals** (grill rest.) – **98 rms** 39.95/59.95 **t.**

---

**CHESHUNT** *Herts.* 🄰🄾🄸 T 28 – pop. 51 998 – ⊠ *Broxbourne.*
🅸🄱 *Cheshunt, Park Lane* ℰ (01992) 29777.
*London 22 – Cambridge 40 – Ipswich 70 – Luton 34 – Southend-on-Sea 39.*

🏛 **Cheshunt Marriott,** Halfhide Lane, Turnford, EN10 6NG, Northwest : 1 ¼ m. off B 176 ℰ (01992) 451245, *Fax (01992) 440120*, 𝙄🅱, 🔲, 🌳 – 🖈 ⇟⊷ 🔳 🆅 ☎ ⚒ ᾧ 🄿 – 🄰 120. 🆆🅾 🅰🅴 ① 𝘝𝘐𝘚𝘈 𝙅𝘊𝘉
**Meals** *(bar lunch Saturday)* (dinner only) a la carte 16.00/30.00 **t.** – ⚏ 10.50 – **130 rm** 140.00 **t.**, 12 suites – SB.

---

**CHESTER** *Ches.* 🄰🄾🄸 🄰🄾🄸 L 24 *Great Britain G.* – pop. 80 110.
See : *City*★★ – *The Rows*★★ – *Cathedral*★ – *City Walls*★.
Env. : *Chester Zoo*★ *AC*, N : 3 m. by A 5116.
🅸🄱 *Upton-by-Chester, Upton Lane* ℰ (01244) 381183 – 🅸🄱 *Curzon Park* ℰ (01244) 675130.
🄱 *Town Hall, Northgate St., CH1 2HJ* ℰ (01244) 317962 – Chester Visitor Centre, Vicars Lane CH1 1QX ℰ (01244) 351609/319019.
*London 207 – Birkenhead 7 – Birmingham 91 – Liverpool 19 – Manchester 40 – Preston 52 – Sheffield 76 – Stoke-on-Trent 38.*

Plan opposite

🏛 **Chester Grosvenor,** Eastgate, CH1 1LT, ℰ (01244) 324024, *Fax (01244) 313246*, 𝙄🅱, ⫩ – 🖈 🔳 🆅 ☎ ᾧ 🄿 – 🄰 250. 🆆🅾 🅰🅴 ① 𝘝𝘐𝘚𝘈 𝙅𝘊𝘉. ⪥
*closed 25 and 26 December* – **Meals** – (see **Arkle** and **La Brasserie** below) – ⚏ 12.50 – **82 rm** 130.00/225.00, 3 suites.

🏛 **Crabwall Manor** ⤢, Parkgate Rd, Mollington, CH1 6NE, Northwest : 2 ¼ m. on A 540 ℰ (01244) 851666, *Fax (01244) 851400*, « Part 16C manor », 🌳, park – 🔳 rest, 🆅 ☎ 🄿 – 🄰 100. 🆆🅾 🅰🅴 ① 𝘝𝘐𝘚𝘈 𝙅𝘊𝘉. ⪥
**Meals** – (see **The Restaurant** below) – ⚏ 10.00 – **42 rm** 110.00/150.00 **t.**, 6 suites – SB.

# CHESTER



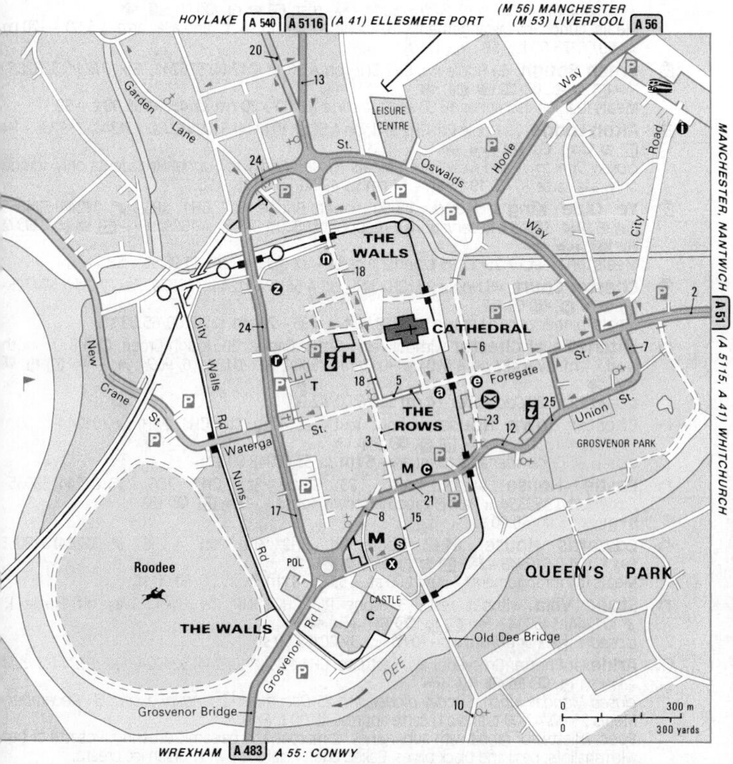


**Moat House Chester,** Trinity St., CH1 2BD, ☎ (01244) 899988, *Fax (01244) 316118*, Fƅ, ≘s – |♯|, ⇎ rm, ▤ rest, TV ☎ & P – 🎭 500. MC AE O VISA JCB. ✂ r
***The Paddocks :*** Meals (dinner only and Sunday lunch)/dinner 14.95 **t.** and a la carte 🍷 7.95 – ☕ 9.50 – **149 rm** 115.00/135.00 **st.**, 3 suites – SB.

**Mollington Banastre,** Parkgate Rd, Mollington, CH1 6NN, Northwest : 2 ¼ m. on A 540 ☎ (01244) 851471, *Fax (01244) 851165*, Fƅ, ≘s, 🏊, 🌳, squash – |♯| ⇎, ▤ rest, TV ☎ P – 🎭 250. MC AE O VISA
Meals *(closed Saturday lunch)* 19.00/22.00 **t.** and a la carte 🍷 8.00 – ☕ 10.50 – **63 rm** 88.00/110.00 **st.** – SB.

**Hoole Hall,** Warrington Rd, Hoole, CH2 3PD, Northeast : 2 m. on A 56 ☎ (01244) 350011, *Fax (01244) 320251*, 🌳 – |♯| ⇎ TV ☎ & P – 🎭 150. MC AE O VISA
***Dudleys :*** Meals *(closed Saturday lunch and Bank Holidays)* (buffet lunch Monday to Friday) 10.50/17.95 **st.** and a la carte 🍷 5.95 – ☕ 9.25 – **97 rm** 80.00/95.00 **st.** – SB.

**The Queen,** City Rd, CH1 3AH, ☎ (01244) 350100, *Fax (01244) 318483*, 🌳 – |♯| ⇎ TV ☎ & P – 🎭 220. MC AE O VISA i
***The Garden :*** Meals 13.50/16.95 **st.** and a la carte 🍷 5.50 – ☕ 7.95 – **127 rm** 99.00/125.00 **st.**, 1 suite – SB.

**Blossoms,** St. John St., CH1 1HL, ☎ (01244) 323186, *Fax (01244) 346433* – |♯| ⇎ TV ☎ – 🎭 100. MC AE O VISA JCB e
Meals a la carte 10.85/21.00 **st.** 🍷 7.95 – ☕ 9.25 – **63 rm** 80.00/100.00 **st.**, 1 suite – SB.

**Redland** without rest., 64 Hough Green, CH4 8JY, Southwest : 1 m. by A 483 on A 5104 ♦ (01244) 671024, *Fax (01244) 681309*, « Victorian town house », ≊ – ⇔ ⊡ ☎ ❷. ⊛⑨ 𝑽𝑰𝑺𝑨. ※
*closed 1 January and 25 December* – **12 rm** ⊃ 45.00/75.00 **t.**

**Cavendish,** 42-44 Hough Green, CH4 8JQ, Southwest : 1 m. by A 483 on A 5104 ♦ (01244) 675100, *Fax (01244) 678844* – ⇔ rest, ⊡ ☎ ❷. ⊛⑨ 𝑨𝑬 𝑽𝑰𝑺𝑨. ※
**Meals** *(lunch by arrangement) (residents only)* 15.95 **t.** and a la carte ⅄ 5.80 – **20 rm** ⊃ 50.00/75.00 **t.** – SB.

**Green Bough,** 60 Hoole Rd, CH2 3NL, on A 56 ♦ (01244) 326241, *Fax (01244) 326265* – ⇔ ⊡ ☎ ❷. ⊛⑨ 𝑨𝑬 ⑨ 𝑽𝑰𝑺𝑨. ※
**Meals** *(bar lunch)/dinner* 16.00 and a la carte ⅄ 6.00 – **20 rm** ⊃ 45.00/55.00 **t.** – SB.

**Alton Lodge,** 78 Hoole Rd, CH2 3NT, on A 56 ♦ (01244) 310213, *Fax (01244) 319206* – ⇔ ⊡ ☎ ❖ ❷. ⊛⑨ 𝑽𝑰𝑺𝑨 𝑱𝑪𝑩. ※
*closed Christmas and New Year* – **Meals** *(closed Friday to Sunday) (residents only) (dinner only)* a la carte 10.45/19.25 **st.** – **17 rm** ⊃ 42.50/59.50 **st.** – SB.

**Ye Olde King's Head,** 48-50 Lower Bridge St., CH1 1RS, ♦ (01244) 324855 *Fax (01244) 315693*, Reservations (Freephone) 0800 118833, « 16C inn » – ⊡ ☎ ⇦. ⊛⑨ 𝑨𝑬 ⑨ 𝑽𝑰𝑺𝑨 𝑱𝑪𝑩. ※
**Meals** *(grill rest.)* 7.25/12.95 **t.** and a la carte – ⅄ 5.95 – **8 rm** 44.95 **st.** – SB.

**Chester Court,** 48 Hoole Rd, CH2 3NL, on A 56 ♦ (01244) 320779, *Fax (01244) 344795* – ⊡ ☎ ❖ ❷. ⊛⑨ 𝑨𝑬 𝑽𝑰𝑺𝑨
**Meals** *(dinner only)* a la carte 9.15/19.90 **t.** ⅄ 4.95 – **20 rm** ⊃ 42.00/65.00 **st.**

**Mitchell's of Chester** without rest., Green Gables, 28 Hough Green, CH4 8JQ, South west : 1 m. by A 483 on A 5104 ♦ (01244) 679004, *Fax (01244) 679004*, ≈ – ⇔ ⊡ ❷. ⊛⑨ 𝑽𝑰𝑺𝑨. ※
*closed 22 to 29 December* – **4 rm** ⊃ 28.00/42.00.

**Chester Town House** without rest., 23 King St., CH1 2AH, ♦ (01244) 350021 *Fax (01244) 350021* – ⇔ ⊡ ❷. ⊛⑨ 𝑽𝑰𝑺𝑨
*closed 25 December and 1 January* – **5 rm** ⊃ 35.00/48.00 **st.**

**Castle House** without rest., 23 Castle St., CH1 2DS, ♦ (01244) 350354 *Fax (01244) 350354*, « Part Elizabethan town house » – ⇔ ⊡. ⊛⑨ 𝑽𝑰𝑺𝑨
**5 rm** ⊃ 23.00/46.00 **s.**

**Edwards House,** 61-63 Hoole Rd, CH2 3NJ, on A 56 ♦ (01244) 318055 *Fax (01244) 310948* – ⇔ ⊡ ☎ ❷. ⊛⑨ ⑨ 𝑽𝑰𝑺𝑨. ※
**Meals** *(by arrangement)* 7.50/11.00 **st.** ⅄ 5.00 – **8 rm** ⊃ 25.00/50.00 **st.**

**Stone Villa** without rest., 3 Stone Pl., CH2 3NR, by Hoole Way off Hoole Rd ♦ (01244) 345014 – ⇔ ⊡ ❷. ⊛⑨ 𝑽𝑰𝑺𝑨 𝑱𝑪𝑩. ※
*closed 1 week at Christmas* – **10 rm** ⊃ 32.00/52.00 **st.**

XXXX **Arkle** (at Chester Grosvenor H.), Eastgate, CH1 1LT, ♦ (01244) 324024, *Fax (01244) 31324* ✿ – ⇔ ⊟ ❷. ⊛⑨ 𝑨𝑬 ⑨ 𝑽𝑰𝑺𝑨 𝑱𝑪𝑩
*closed Monday lunch, Sunday dinner and 25 December-2 January except 31 December* – **Meals** 25.00/42.00 **t.** and a la carte approx. 48.00 **t.** ⅄ 10.75
**Spec.** Rillettes of rabbit with aubergines, tomatoes and balsamic dressing. Rosette of bee with shallots, basil and black olives. Baked cherry clafoutis with Kirsch ice cream.

XXX **The Restaurant** (at Crabwall Manor H.), Parkgate Rd, Mollington, CH1 6NE, Northwest 2¼ m. on A 540 ♦ (01244) 851666, *Fax (01244) 851400*, ≈ – ⊟ ❷. ⊛⑨ 𝑨𝑬 ⑨ 𝑽𝑰𝑺𝑨 𝑱𝑪𝑩
**Meals** a la carte 32.00/43.00 **t.**

XX **La Brasserie** (at Chester Grosvenor H.), Eastgate, CH1 1LT, ♦ (01244) 324024 *Fax (01244) 313246* – ⊟ ❷. ⊛⑨ 𝑨𝑬 ⑨ 𝑽𝑰𝑺𝑨 𝑱𝑪𝑩
*closed 25 and 26 December* – **Meals** a la carte 23.45/39.70 **t.** ⅄ 9.95.

X **Est, Est, Est,** Newgate House, Newgate St., CH1 1DE, ♦ (01244) 400507 *Fax (01244) 400507* – ⊟. ⊛⑨ 𝑨𝑬 ⑨ 𝑽𝑰𝑺𝑨 𝑱𝑪𝑩
*closed 25 and 26 December* – **Meals** - Italian - a la carte 11.75/19.00 **t.** ⅄ 5.05.

X **Blue Bell,** 65 Northgate St., CH1 2HQ, ♦ (01244) 317758, *Fax (01244) 317759*, ♨ « Converted 15C inn » – ⊟ 𝑽𝑰𝑺𝑨 𝑱𝑪𝑩
*closed 25-26 December and 1 January* – **Meals** 16.00 **t.** *(dinner)* and a la carte 13.30/28.45 **t.** ⅄ 6.95.

**at Mickle Trafford** Northeast : 2½ m. by A 56 – ⊠ Chester.

**Royal Oak,** Warrington Rd, CH2 4EX, on A 56 ♦ (01244) 301391, *Fax (01244) 302001*, ≈ ⇔ ⊡ ☎ ❖ ❷. ⊛⑨ 𝑨𝑬 ⑨ 𝑽𝑰𝑺𝑨. ※
**Meals** *(closed 24 to 26 December) (grill rest.)* a la carte 10.90/15.35 **st.** – **36 rm** ⊃ 62.00 72.00 **st.** – SB.

**at Rowton** Southeast : 3 m. by A 41 – ⊠ Chester.

**Rowton Hall,** Whitchurch Rd, CH3 6AD, ♦ (01244) 335262, *Fax (01244) 335464*, ♋, ≊ ▨, ≈, ※ – ⊡ ☎ ❖ ❷ – ⚏ 200. ⊛⑨ 𝑨𝑬 ⑨ 𝑽𝑰𝑺𝑨
**Meals** 12.50/20.50 **t.** and dinner a la carte – **42 rm** ⊃ 75.00/115.00 **t.** – SB.

t **Sealand** *(Clwyd) Northwest : 4 m. on A 548 –* ⊠ *Deeside.*

🏦 **Gateway to Wales,** Welsh Rd, CH5 2HX, Northwest : 1 ½ m. at junction of A 550 with A 548 ℘ (01244) 830332, *Fax* (01244) 836190, *Ⅰ₅*, ⇌, ◨ – ◧ ✸ 📺 ☎ ◞ & ㉠ – ᵅ 120. ◍⑨ ㏂ ⓪ 𝒱𝐼𝒮𝒜. ⅍
*The Regency :* Meals 14.00/17.95 **t.** and a la carte ⅃ 7.50 – **38 rm** ⊇ 65.00/90.00 **t.**, 1 suite – SB.

t **Two Mills** *Northwest : 5¾ m. on A 540 at junction with A 550 –* ⊠ *Ledsham.*

🏛 **Tudor Rose - Premier Lodge,** Parkgate Rd, L66 9PD, ℘ (0151) 339 2399, *Fax* (0151) 347 1725, *Reservations (Freephone)* 0800 118833 – ◧, ✸ rm, 📺 ☎ ◞ & ㉠. ◍⑨ ㏂ ⓪ 𝒱𝐼𝒮𝒜. ⅍
Meals (grill rest.) 7.25/13.00 **t.** and a la carte – ⊇ 5.95 – **31 rm** 44.95 **t.** – SB.

t **Puddington** *Northwest : 7¼ m. by A 540 –* ⊠ *South Wirral.*

✕✕✕ **Craxton Wood** ᔓ with rm, Parkgate Rd, L66 9PB, on A 540 ℘ (0151) 339 4717, *Fax* (0151) 339 1740, ≼, ≉, park – 📺 ☎ ㉠. ◍⑨ ㏂ ⓪ 𝒱𝐼𝒮𝒜
Meals 24.85 **t.** and a la carte ⅃ 10.20 – **13 rm** ⊇ 75.00/140.00 **st.**, 1 suite – SB.

🔘 ATS 7 Bumpers Lane, Sealand Trading Est. ℘ (01244) 375154

---

**CHESTERFIELD** *Derbs.* 𝟰𝟬𝟮 𝟰𝟬𝟯 𝟰𝟬𝟰 P 24 *Great Britain G. – pop. 71 945.*

Env. : *Bolsover Castle★ AC, E : 5 m. by A 632.*

⌗₈, ⌗₉ *Chesterfield Municipal, Murray House, Crow Lane* ℘ (01246) 273887 – ⌗₈ *Grassmoor, North Wingfield Rd* ℘ (01246) 856044.

🇯 *Peacock Information Centre, Low Pavement, S40 1PB* ℘ (01246) 67777/8.
*London 152 – Derby 24 – Nottingham 25 – Sheffield 12.*

🏛 **Travelodge,** Brimington Road North, Wittington Moor, S41 9BE, North : 2 m. on A 61 ℘ (01246) 455411, *Fax* (01246) 455411, *Reservations (Freephone)* 0800 850950 – ✸ rm, ▤ rest, 📺 & ㉠. ◍⑨ ㏂ ⓪ 𝒱𝐼𝒮𝒜 𝐽𝐶𝐵. ⅍
Meals (grill rest.) – **20 rm** 39.95/59.95 **t.**

🔘 ATS 512 Sheffield Rd ℘ (01246) 452281

---

**CHESTER-LE-STREET** *Durham* 𝟰𝟬𝟭 𝟰𝟬𝟮 P 19 *– pop. 35 123.*

⌗₈ *Lumley Park* ℘ (0191) 388 3218 – ⌗₈ *Roseberry Grange, Grange Villa* ℘ (0191) 370 0670.
*London 275 – Durham 7 – Newcastle upon Tyne 8.*

🏯 **Lumley Castle,** DH3 4NX, East : 1 m. on B 1284 ℘ (0191) 389 1111, *Fax* (0191) 387 1437, « 13C », ≉ – ✸ rm, 📺 ☎ ㉠ – ᵅ 150. ◍⑨ ㏂ ⓪ 𝒱𝐼𝒮𝒜 𝐽𝐶𝐵. ⅍
closed 25-26 December and 1 January – Meals (bar lunch)/dinner a la carte 27.00/40.50 **st.** ⅃ 6.50 – ⊇ 12.00 – **58 rm** 89.50/165.00 **st.**, 1 suite – SB.

---

**CHESTERTON** *Oxon.* 𝟰𝟬𝟰 Q 28 *– pop. 806 –* ⊠ *Bicester.*

⌗₈ *Chesterton , Bicester* ℘ (01869) 241204.
*London 69 – Birmingham 65 – Northampton 36 – Oxford 15.*

🏦 **Bignell Park,** OX6 8UE, on A 4095 ℘ (01869) 241444, *Fax* (01869) 241444, ≉ – 📺 ☎ ㉠. ◍⑨ ㏂ ⓪ 𝒱𝐼𝒮𝒜. ⅍
Meals (closed Sunday lunch) 18.00 **t.** (lunch) and dinner a la carte 24.50/34.50 **t.** ⅃ 6.95 – **14 rm** ⊇ 70.00/90.00 **t.**

---

**CHETTLE** *Dorset – see Blandford Forum.*

---

**CHICHESTER** *W. Sussex* 𝟰𝟬𝟰 R 31 *Great Britain G. – pop. 26 572.*

See : *City★ – Cathedral★ BZ A – St. Mary's Hospital★ BY D – Pallant House★ AC BZ M.*
Env. : *Fishbourne Roman Palace (mosaics★) AC AZ R.*
Exc. : *Weald and Downland Open Air Museum★ AC, N : 6 m. by A 286 AY.*
⌗₈ *Goodwood* ℘ (01243) 775987, AY – ⌗₈, ⌗₈, ⌗₉ *Chichester Golf Centre, Hunston Village* ℘ (01243) 533833, AZ.
🇯 *29a South St., PO19 1AH* ℘ (01243) 775888.
*London 69 – Brighton 31 – Portsmouth 18 – Southampton 30.*

## CHICHESTER

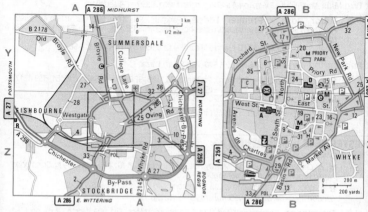

---

🏨 **Jarvis Chichester,** Westhampnett, PO19 4UL, ℰ (01243) 786351, Fax (01243) 782371
⇌, 🔲 – ⇎ 🔲 ☎ & 🅿 – 🔬 300. 🆚 🆎 ⓞ 𝘝𝘐𝘚𝘈　　　　　　　　　　　AY　e
**Meals** (bar lunch Monday to Saturday)/dinner 15.95 **t.** ░ 7.00 – ☲ 8.50 – **76 rm** 94.00,
164.00 **t.**, 1 suite – SB.

🏨 **Suffolk House,** 3 East Row, PO19 1PD, ℰ (01243) 778899, Fax (01243) 787282, 🍴 –
⇎ rest, 🔲 ☎ ℰ, 🆚 🆎 ⓞ 𝘝𝘐𝘚𝘈, ⌘　　　　　　　　　　　　　　　　　　BY　a
**Meals** (closed Sunday lunch) 10.50/14.75 **st.** and dinner a la carte ░ 4.00 – **11 rm** ☲ 59.00,
112.00 **st.**

🏨 **Crouchers Bottom,** Birdham Rd, Apuldram, PO20 7EH, Southwest : 2 ½ m. on A 286
ℰ (01243) 784995, Fax (01243) 539797, ≼, 🍴 – ⇎ 🔲 ☎ & 🅿. 🆚 🆎 𝘝𝘐𝘚𝘈. ⌘
**Meals** (dinner only) 19.50 **t.** and a la carte ░ 8.95 – **16 rm** ☲ 50.00/120.00 **t.** – SB.

✕✕ **Comme ça,** 67 Broyle Rd, PO19 4BD, on A 286 ℰ (01243) 788724, Fax (01243) 530052
🍴, 🍴 – ⇎ 🅿. 🆚 🆎 ⓞ 𝘝𝘐𝘚𝘈　　　　　　　　　　　　　　　　　　　　AY　c
closed Sunday dinner and Monday – **Meals** - French - 17.75 **t.** (lunch) and a la carte approx
23.45 **t.** ░ 11.00.

**at Charlton** North : 6 ¼ m. by A 286 – AY – ✉ Chichester.

🏨 **Woodstock House,** PO18 0HU, ℰ (01243) 811666, Fax (01243) 811666, 🍴 – ⇎ 🔲 ☎
🅿. 🆚 🆎 𝘝𝘐𝘚𝘈. ⌘
closed Sunday, Monday, 3 days Christmas, 1 week February and 1 week November – **Meals**
(dinner only) a la carte approx. 19.95 **st.** ░ 7.00 – **11 rm** ☲ 38.50/120.00 **t.** – SB.

**at Chilgrove** North : 6 ½ m. by A 286 – AY – on B 2141 – ✉ Chichester.

⌂ **Forge Cottage,** PO18 9HX, ℰ (01243) 535333, Fax (01243) 535363, « Converted 17C
forge », 🍴 – ⇎ 🔲 ☎ 🅿. 🆚 🆎 ⓞ 𝘝𝘐𝘚𝘈 𝗝𝗖𝗕. ⌘
closed 2 weeks February – **Meals** (by arrangement) 16.00/25.00 **st.** ░ 7.00 – **5 rm** ☲ 35.00/
79.00 **st.**

**at Halnaker** Northeast : 3 ¼ m. on A 285 – BY – ✉ Chichester.

⌂ **Old Store** without rest., Stane St., PO18 0QL, on A 285 ℰ (01243) 531977,
Fax (01243) 531977, 🍴 – 🔲 🅿. 🆚 𝘝𝘐𝘚𝘈. ⌘
closed Christmas and New Year – **7 rm** ☲ 28.00/55.00 **st.**

**at Goodwood** Northeast : 3 ½ m. by A 27 – AY – on East Dean Rd – ✉ Chichester.

🏨 **Marriott Goodwood Park H. & Country Club,** PO18 0QB, ℰ (01243) 775537,
Fax (01243) 520120, ♨, ⇌, 🔲, 🏌, 🍴, park, ✼ – ⇎ 🔲 ☎ ℰ 🅿 – 🔬 120. 🆚 🆎 ⓞ 𝘝𝘐𝘚𝘈
𝗝𝗖𝗕. ⌘
**Meals** 15.95/22.95 **st.** and a la carte ░ 7.75 – ☲ 11.95 – **93 rm** 70.00 **st.**, 1 suite.

**at Bosham** *West : 4 m. by A 259 – AZ – ✉ Chichester.*

**Millstream,** Bosham Lane, PO18 8HL, ✆ (01243) 573234, *Fax (01243) 573459*, – ⊁ TV ☎ P. MC AE D VISA
Meals 15.50/22.00 **t.** and lunch a la carte 5.75 – **33 rm** 69.00/145.00 **st.** – SB.

**Hatpins** without rest., Bosham Lane, PO18 8HG, ✆ (01243) 572644, *Fax (01243) 572644*, – ⊁ TV P. ✻
**3 rm** 35.00/80.00.

**at Chidham** *West : 6 m. by A 259 – AZ – ✉ Chichester.*

**Old Rectory** without rest., Cot Lane, PO18 8TA, ✆ (01243) 572088, *Fax (01243) 572088*, – ⊁ TV P
*restricted opening January and February* – **4 rm** 25.00/54.00 **t.**

**at Funtington** *Northwest : 4 ¾ m. by B 2178 on B 2146 – AY – ✉ Chichester.*

**Hallidays,** Watery Lane, PO18 9LF, ✆ (01243) 575331, « Part 13C thatched cottages » – P. MC VISA JCB
*closed Saturday lunch, Sunday dinner, Monday, 1 week late spring and 1 week late summer* – **Meals** 12.50 **t.** (lunch) and a la carte 19.50/26.25 **t.** 8.50.

ATS Terminus Rd Ind Est. ✆ (01243) 773100

---

**CHIDHAM** *W. Sussex – see Chichester.*

*Le Grand Londres (GREATER LONDON) est composé de la City et de 32 arrondissements administratifs (Borough) eux-mêmes divisés en quartiers ou en villages ayant conservé leur caractère propre (Area).*

---

**CHIEVELEY SERVICE AREA** *Newbury* 403 404 Q 29 – ✉ *Thatcham.*

**Travelodge,** Oxford Rd, Hermitage, RG18 9XX, at junction 13 of M 4 ✆ (01635) 248024, *Fax (01635) 247886*, Reservations (Freephone) 0800 850950 – ⊁ TV ♿ P. MC AE D VISA JCB. ✻
**Meals** (grill rest.) – **44 rm** 39.95/59.95 **t.**

---

**CHILDER THORNTON** *Ches. – ✉ Wirral.*
*London 200 – Birkenhead 7 – Chester 12.*

**Travel Inn,** New Chester Rd, L66 1QW, on A 41 ✆ (0151) 339 8101, *Fax (0151) 347 1401* – ⊁ rm, TV ♿ P. MC AE D VISA. ✻
**Meals** (grill rest.) – **31 rm** 38.00 **t.**

---

**CHILGROVE** *W. Sussex* 404 R 31 – *see Chichester.*

---

**CHILLINGTON** *Devon* 403 I 33 – *see Kingsbridge.*

---

**CHINLEY** *Derbs.* 402 403 404 O 23 – ✉ *Stockport (Ches.).*
*London 187 – Manchester 24 – Sheffield 25.*

**Ashen Clough** , SK23 6AH, North : 1 ½ m. by Maynestone Rd ✆ (01663) 750311, ←, , park – ⊁ rm, P. ✻
**Meals** (by arrangement) (communal dining) 20.00 5.00 – **3 rm** 45.00/70.00.

---

**CHINNOR** *Oxon.* 404 R 28 *The West Country G. – pop. 5 599.*
Exc. : *Ridgeway Path*★★.
*London 45 – Oxford 19.*

**Cross Lanes Cottage** without rest., West Lane, Bledlow, HP27 9PF, Northeast : 1 ½ m. on B 4009 ✆ (01844) 345339, « Part 16C », – ⊁ TV P. ✻
**3 rm** 40.00/50.00.

**Sir Charles Napier Inn,** Sprig's Alley, by Bledlow Ridge rd, OX9 4BX, Southeast : 2 ½ m. ✆ (01494) 483011, *Fax (01494) 485434*, , « Characterful inn », – P. MC AE VISA
*closed Sunday dinner and Monday* – **Meals** a la carte 22.75/31.00 **t.** 6.00.

## CHIPPENHAM Wilts. 403 404 N 29 *The West Country G.* – pop. 26 376.

See : *Yelde Hall★*.

Env. : *Corsham Court★★ AC*, SW : 4 m. by A 4 – *Sheldon Manor★ AC*, W : 1½ m. by A 420 – *Biddestone★*, W : 3½ m. – *Bowood House★ AC* (Library ≼★) SE : 5 m. by A 4 and A 342.

Exc. : *Castle Combe★★*, NW : 6 m. by A 420 and B 4039.

⌧ *Monkton Park (Par Three)* ☎ (01249) 653928.

🖪 *The Citadel, Bath Rd, SN15 2AA* ☎ (01249) 657733.

London 106 – Bristol 27 – Southampton 64 – Swindon 21.

🏨 **Stanton Manor,** Stanton St. Quintin, SN14 6DQ, North : 5 m. by A 42 ☎ (01666) 837552, Fax (01666) 837022, 爾 – 🔟 ☎ ℗. 🐠 ঊ 🝐 *VISA*. ※
*closed 2 weeks August and 26 December-5 January* – Meals (residents only) a la carte 16.25/20.25 t. ⬧ 5.75 – **10 rm** ⫴ 75.00/95.00 st.

◉ ATS Cocklebury Rd ☎ (01249) 653541

---

## CHIPPERFIELD Herts. 404 ⓐ – pop. 1 680 – ⌧ Kings Langley.

London 27 – Hemel Hempstead 5 – Watford 6.

🏨 **Two Brewers Inn,** The Common, WD4 9BS, ☎ (01923) 265266, Fax (01923) 261884 – ⅙✕ 🔟 ☎ ℗ – 🕍 25. 🐠 ঊ 🝐 *VISA* 🝣. ※
*closed 2 days Christmas* – Meals a la carte 10.00/20.00 t. – ⫴ 6.95 – **20 rm** 85.00 t.

---

## CHIPPING Lancs. 402 M 22 – pop. 1 392 – ⌧ Preston.

London 233 – Lancaster 30 – Leeds 54 – Manchester 40 – Preston 12.

🏨 **Gibbon Bridge** ﹩, PR3 2TQ, East : 1 m. on Clitheroe rd ☎ (01995) 61456 Fax (01995) 61277, ≼, ⌧, ⛺, 爾, park, ※ – ⧉ 🔟 ☎ ⬧ ℗ – 🕍 30. 🐠 ঊ 🝐 *VISA*. ※
Meals 14.00/20.00 t. and dinner a la carte ⬧ 5.95 – **12 rm** ⫴ 69.00/110.00 t., **18 suites** 160.00/300.00 st. – SB.

---

## CHIPPING CAMPDEN Glos. 403 404 O 27 *Great Britain G.* – pop. 1 741.

See : *Town★*.

Env. : *Hidcote Manor Garden★★ AC*, NE : 2½ m.

🖪 *The Guildhall, OX7 5NJ* ☎ (01608) 644379.

London 93 – Cheltenham 21 – Oxford 37 – Stratford-upon-Avon 12.

🏨 **Cotswold House,** The Square, GL55 6AN, ☎ (01386) 840330, Fax (01386) 840310, « Attractively converted Regency town house », 爾 – ⅙✕ rest, 🔟 ☎ ⬧ ℗ – 🕍 30. 🐠 ঊ 🝐 *VISA*. ※
*closed 3 days Christmas* – **Garden Room :** Meals (dinner only and Sunday lunch)/dinner 16.50/21.50 t. and dinner a la carte ⬧ 7.00 – **Forbes Brasserie :** Meals a la carte 13.00/18.00 t. – **15 rm** ⫴ 55.00/150.00 t. – SB.

🏨 **Seymour House,** High St., GL55 6AH, ☎ (01386) 840429, Fax (01386) 840369, « Mature grapevine in restaurant », 爾 – ⅙✕ rest, 🔟 ☎ ℗. 🐠 ঊ 🝐 *VISA*. ※
Meals 15.50/24.95 st. ⬧ 7.00 – **12 rm** ⫴ 65.00/90.00 st., 3 suites – SB.

🏨 **Noel Arms,** High St., GL55 6AT, ☎ (01386) 840317, Fax (01386) 841136 – ⅙✕ rest, 🔟 ☎ ⬧ ℗ – 🕍 40. 🐠 ঊ 🝐 *VISA* 🝣
Meals (bar lunch Monday to Saturday)/dinner 21.95 t. and a la carte ⬧ 7.25 – **26 rm** ⫴ 75.00/120.00 st. – SB.

🍴 **Eight Bells Inn,** Church St., GL55 6JG, ☎ (01386) 840371, Fax (01386) 841669, « 14C inn » – ⅙✕. 🐠 ঊ 🝐 *VISA*
*closed 25 December* – Meals a la carte 12.70/20.50 t.

**at Mickleton** North : 3 ¼ m. by B 4035 and B 4081 on B 4632 – ⌧ Chipping Campden.

🏨 **Three Ways House,** GL55 6SB, ☎ (01386) 438429, Fax (01386) 438118, 爾 – ⅙✕ rest, 🔟 ☎ ℗ – 🕍 80. 🐠 ঊ 🝐 *VISA* 🝣
Meals (bar lunch Monday to Saturday)/dinner 16.00/22.00 st. and dinner a la carte ⬧ 7.50 – **41 rm** ⫴ 65.00/93.00 st. – SB.

**at Charingworth** East : 3 m. by B 4035 – ⌧ Chipping Campden.

🏨 **Charingworth Manor** ﹩, GL55 6NS, on B 4035 ☎ (01386) 593555, Fax (01386) 593353, ≼, « Part early 14C manor house with Jacobean additions », ⛺, ⌧, 爾, park, ※ – ⅙✕ rest, 🔟 ☎ ℗ – 🕍 30. 🐠 ঊ 🝐 *VISA*. ※
Meals 17.50/37.50 st. ⬧ 9.50 – **26 rm** ⫴ 95.00/260.00 st. – SB.

**at Paxford** Southeast : 3 m. by B 4035 – ⌧ Chipping Campden.

🍴 **Churchill Arms** with rm, GL55 6XH, ☎ (01386) 594000, Fax (01386) 594005, 爺 – 🔟 ☎. 🐠 *VISA* 🝣
Meals (bookings not accepted) a la carte 14.95/25.50 t. – **4 rm** ⫴ 40.00/60.00 t.

t Broad Campden *South : 1¼ m. by B 4081* – ⊠ *Chipping Campden.*

🏠 **Malt House** ⟲, GL55 6UU, ℰ (01386) 840295, Fax (01386) 841334, « 17C », ℱ – 📺 📵.
🐾 🖭 ⑩ 𝘝𝘐𝘚𝘈 𝘑𝘊𝘉
*closed 24 to 26 December* – **Meals** *(closed Tuesday and Wednesday)* (dinner only) 26.50 **t.**
🍴 8.50 – **7 rm** ⇆ 69.50/97.50 **t.**, 1 suite – SB.

⌂ **Marnic House** without rest., GL55 6UR, ℰ (01386) 840014, Fax (01386) 840441, ℱ – ⁂
📺 📵. ⁒
*closed 25 December and 1 January* – **3 rm** ⇆ 36.00/44.00 **st.**

t Bretforton *Northwest : 5½ m. on B 4035* – ⊠ *Evesham.*

⌂ **The Pond House** ⟲ without rest., Lower Fields, Weston Rd, WR11 5QA, Southeast :
2 m. on B 4035 ℰ (01386) 831687, ≤, ℱ – ⁂ 📺 📵. ⁒
*minimum 2 night stay January, February and December* **4 rm** ⇆ 38.00/48.00 **s.**

**CHIPPING NORTON** *Oxon* 🆗🆗 P 28 *Great Britain G.* – *pop. 5 386.*
Env. : Chastleton House★★, *NW : 4 m. by A 44.*
⛳ Lyneham ℰ (01993) 831841 – ⛳ Southcombe ℰ (01608) 642383.
*London 77 – Birmingham 44 – Gloucester 36 – Oxford 21.*

XXX **Chavignol,** 7 Horsefair, OX7 5AL, ℰ (01608) 644490, Fax (01608) 644490 – ⁂. 🐾 🖭 𝘝𝘐𝘚𝘈
🏵 *closed Sunday, Monday, 3 weeks January and 1 week in autumn* – **Meals** (booking essential)
26.00/37.00 **t.** 🍴 9.00
**Spec.** Warm tartlet of braised onion and sage, foie gras, chicory jus. Beef fillet with bubble
and squeak and Madeira sauce. Honey ice cream in a fig and mulled wine soup.

XX **Morel's,** 2 Horsefair, OX7 5AQ, ℰ (01608) 641075, Fax (01608) 641075 – ⁂. 🐾 𝘝𝘐𝘚𝘈 𝘑𝘊𝘉
*closed Sunday dinner, Monday, first 3 weeks January and 1 week September* – **Meals** -
French - 14.50/24.00 **t.** 🍴 7.50.

**CHISELDON** *Wilts.* 🆗🆗 O 29 *– see Swindon.*

**CHITTLEHAMHOLT** *Devon* 🆗 I 31 *– pop. 194* – ⊠ *Umberleigh.*
*London 216 – Barnstaple 14 – Exeter 28 – Taunton 45.*

🏨 **Highbullen** ⟲, EX37 9HD, ℰ (01769) 540561, Fax (01769) 540492, ≤, ⛳, ⏃, 🏊, ⛳, 🎣,
ℱ, park, ℀indoor/outdoor, squash – ⁂ rest, 📺 📵 📶 – 🛅 25. 🐾 𝘝𝘐𝘚𝘈 ⁒
**Meals** (bar lunch)/dinner 20.00 **st.** and a la carte 🍴 4.75 – ⇆ 4.50 – **35 rm** (dinner included)
90.00/180.00 **st.** – SB.

**CHOBHAM** *Surrey* 🆗 S 29 *– pop. 3 411* – ⊠ *Woking.*
*London 35 – Reading 21 – Southampton 53.*

⌂ **Knaphill Manor** ⟲ without rest., Carthouse Lane, GU21 4XT, Southwest : 1 m. by Castle
Grove Rd and Guildford Rd ℰ (01276) 857962, Fax (01276) 855503, ≤, ℱ – 📺 📵. 🐾 𝘝𝘐𝘚𝘈.
⁒
*closed Easter and 1 week Christmas* – **3 rm** ⇆ 50.00/75.00 **s.**

XX **Quails,** 1 Bagshot Rd, GU24 8BP, ℰ (01276) 858491, Fax (01276) 858491 – 🔳. 🐾 🖭 ⑩
𝘝𝘐𝘚𝘈
*closed Saturday lunch, Sunday, Monday and 1 week Christmas* – **Meals** 14.95/18.95 **t.**
and a la carte 🍴 4.95.

**CHOLLERFORD** *Northd.* 🆗🆗 N 18 *Great Britain G.* – ⊠ *Hexham.*
Env. : Hadrian's Wall★★ – Chesters★ (Bath House★) AC, *W : ½ m. by B 6318.*
*London 303 – Carlisle 36 – Newcastle upon Tyne 21.*

🏩 **George,** NE46 4EW, ℰ (01434) 681611, Fax (01434) 681727, ≤, « Riverside gardens », 🏋,
🏊, ⏃, 🎣 – ⁂ rm, 📺 ☎ 🕭 📵 – 🛅 65. 🐾 🖭 ⑩ 𝘝𝘐𝘚𝘈
**Meals** 15.00/24.95 **st.** and a la carte 🍴 7.25 – **46 rm** ⇆ 100.00/150.00 **st.** – SB.

**CHORLEY** *Lancs.* 🆗🆗 M 23 *– pop. 33 536.*
⛳ Duxbury Park, Duxbury Hall Rd ℰ (01257) 265380 – ⛳ Shaw Hill Hotel G. & C.C., Preston
Rd, Whittle-le-Woods ℰ (01257) 269221.
*London 222 – Blackpool 30 – Liverpool 32 – Manchester 26.*

🏠 **Yarrow Bridge - Premier Lodge,** Bolton Rd, PR7 4AB, South : 1 m. on A 6
ℰ (01257) 265989, Fax (01257) 230821, Reservations (Freephone) 0800 118833 – ⁂ 📺 ☎
🕭 🕭 📵. 🐾 🖭 ⑩ 𝘝𝘐𝘚𝘈. ⁒
**Meals** (grill rest.) a la carte 7.20/15.05 **t.** 🍴 4.25 – ⇆ 5.95 – **29 rm** 45.50 **t.** – SB.

**at Whittle-le-Woods** *North : 2 m. on A 6 – ✉ Chorley.*

**Shaw Hill H. Golf & Country Club** ⛳, Preston Rd, PR6 7PP, ☎ (01257) 26922 *Fax (01257) 261223,* 18 – [TV] ☎ [P] – 200. [MC] [AE] [VISA]
***Vardon :*** Meals (bar lunch Saturday) 13.00/19.95 **st.** and a la carte 8.00 – **30 rm** 70.0 100.00 **st.** – SB.

**Parkville Country House,** 174 Preston Rd, PR6 7HE, ☎ (01257) 26188 *Fax (01257) 273171,* – [TV] ☎ [P]. [MC] [AE] [VISA] JCB.
*closed 1 week Christmas* – **Meals** *(closed Sunday)* (dinner only) a la carte 17.55/26.65 7.50 – **13 rm** 55.00/70.00 **t.**

ATS 18 Westminster Rd ☎ (01257) 262000/265472

**CHORLTON CUM HARDY** *Gtr. Manchester* [402] [403] [404] N 23 – *see Manchester.*

**CHRISTCHURCH** *Dorset* [403] [404] O 31 *The West Country G. – pop. 36 379.*

See : *Town★ – Priory★.*
Env. : *Hengistbury Head★ (≤★★) SW : 4½ m. by A 35 and B 3059.*
18 *Highcliffe Castle, 107 Lymington Rd, Highcliffe-on-Sea ☎ (01425) 272953 –* 9 *Barrack R Iford ☎ (01202) 473817.*
*23 High St., BH23 1AB ☎ (01202) 471780.*
*London 111 – Bournemouth 6 – Salisbury 26 – Southampton 24 – Winchester 39.*

**Travel Inn,** Barrack Rd, BH23 2BN, West : ¾ m. on A 35 ☎ (01202) 485215 – rm, [TV] [P]. [MC] [AE] [VISA].
Meals (grill rest.) – **40 rm** 38.00 **t.**

**Travel Inn,** Somerford Rd, BH23 3QG, East : 2 m. by A 35 on B 3059 ☎ (01202) 48537 *Fax (01202) 474939* – rm, [TV] [P]. [MC] [AE] [VISA].
Meals (grill rest.) – **70 rm** 38.00 **t.**

🍴 **Splinters,** 12 Church St., BH23 1BW, ☎ (01202) 483454, *Fax (01202) 483454* – [MC] [AE] [VISA] JCB
*closed Sunday dinner except Bank Holiday weekends, Monday and 26 December 10 January* – **Meals** a la carte 24.95/29.95 **t.** 6.00.

**at Mudeford** *Southeast : 2 m. – ✉ Christchurch.*

**Avonmouth,** 95 Mudeford, BH23 3NT, ☎ (01202) 483434, *Fax (01202) 479004,* ≤, – [TV] ☎ [P] – 60. [MC] [AE] [VISA].
Meals (bar lunch Monday to Saturday)/dinner 20.00 **st.** and a la carte 7.50 – 9.95 **40 rm** 80.00/115.00 **st.** – SB.

**Waterford Lodge,** 87 Bure Lane, Friars Cliff, BH23 4DN, ☎ (01425) 272948 *Fax (01425) 279130,* – [TV] ☎ [P] – 80. [MC] [AE] [VISA].
*closed 27 December-2 January* – **Meals** 14.50/24.95 **t.** 8.30 – 9.00 – **17 rm** 78.00 90.00 **t.** – SB.

**CHURCHILL** *Oxon.* [403] [404] P 28 – *pop. 502 – ✉ Chipping Norton.*
*London 79 – Birmingham 46 – Cheltenham 29 – Oxford 23 – Swindon 31.*

**The Forge** without rest., OX7 6NJ, ☎ (01608) 658173, *Fax (01608) 659262* – [TV] [P]. [MC] [VISA].
**5 rm** 35.00/60.00 **st.**

**CHURCH STRETTON** *Shrops.* [402] [403] L 26 *Great Britain G. – pop. 3 435.*

Env. : *Wenlock Edge★, E : by B 4371.*
18 *Trevor Hill ☎ (01694) 722281.*
*London 166 – Birmingham 46 – Hereford 39 – Shrewsbury 14.*

**Mynd House,** Ludlow Rd, Little Stretton, SY6 6RB, Southwest : 1 ¼ m. on B 437 ☎ (01694) 722212, *Fax (01694) 724180,* – [TV] ☎ [P]. [MC] [AE] [VISA]
*closed January* – **Meals** (booking essential) (bar lunch)/dinner a la carte approx. 27.00 **t.** 7.00 – **4 rm** 60.00/70.00 **t.**, 2 suites – SB.

**Jinlye** , Castle Hill, All Stretton, SY6 6JP, North : 2 ¼ m. by B 4370 turning left beside telephone box in All Stretton ☎ (01694) 723243, *Fax (01694) 723243,* ≤, « 16C », , park – [TV] [P]. [MC] [VISA].
Meals (by arrangement) (communal dining) 17.50 **t.** – **8 rm** 42.00/76.00 **t.** – SB.

⌂ **Inwood Farm** ⑁, All Stretton, SY6 6LA, North : 1 ½ m. by B 4370 ℰ (01694) 724046, ≤, ⚘, park – ⤬ ☏ ⓟ ⚘
*March-November* – **Meals** (communal dining) 17.50 **st.** – **3 rm** ⊒ 40.00/60.00 **st.**

✗ **The Studio**, 59 High St., SY6 6BY, ℰ (01694) 722672, ⚘ – ⤬ ⓶ ⥈⥈
*closed Tuesday lunch, Monday and 2 weeks Christmas-New Year* – **Meals** 10.95 **t.** (lunch) and a la carte 14.45/22.85 **t.** ⌑ 5.75.

**at Woolstaston** *Northwest : 5½ m. by A 49.*

⌂ **Rectory Farm** ⑁ without rest., SY6 6NN, ℰ (01694) 751306, ≤, « 17C timbered house », ⚘ – ⤬ ☏ ⓟ ⚘
*March-mid December* – **3 rm** ⊒ 26.00/44.00.

Ⓐ ATS Crossways ℰ (01694) 722526/722112

---

**CIRENCESTER** *Glos.* 🄳🄳🄳 🄳🄳🄳 O 28 *Great Britain G.* – *pop. 15 221.*
See : *Town★ – Church of St. John the Baptist★ – Corinium Museum★ (Mosaic pavements★)* AC.
Env. : *Fairford : Church of St. Mary★ (stained glass windows★★) E : 7 m. by A 417.*
🛆 *Cheltenham Rd* ℰ (01285) 653939.
🛈 *Corn Hall, Market Pl., GL7 2NW* ℰ (01285) 654180.
*London 97 – Bristol 37 – Gloucester 19 – Oxford 37.*

🏨 **Jarvis Fleece**, Market Pl., GL7 2NZ, ℰ (01285) 658507, *Fax (01285) 651017* – ⤬ rest, ☏ ⓟ – ⓶ 25. ⓶ ⓶ ⑩ ⥈⥈ ⥈⥈ ⚘
*closed 31 December* – **Meals** (bar lunch Monday to Saturday)/dinner 13.95 **t.** ⌑ 6.00 – ⊒ 8.50 – **30 rm** 79.00/89.00 **t.** – SB.

⌂ **Wimborne House** without rest., 91 Victoria Rd, GL7 1ES, ℰ (01285) 653890, *Fax (01285) 653890*, ⚘ – ⤬ ☏ ⓟ ⚘
*closed 22 December-1 January* – **Meals** – **5 rm** ⊒ 25.00/45.00 **s.**

⌂ **The Ivy House** without rest., 2 Victoria Rd, GL7 1EN, ℰ (01285) 656626 – ⤬ ☏ ⚘
**4 rm** ⊒ 30.00/45.00 **s.**

✗ **Harry Hare's**, 3 Gosditch St., GL7 2AG, ℰ (01285) 652375, *Fax (01285) 641691*, ⚘ – ⓶ ⥈⥈ ⥈⥈
*closed first 2 weeks January* – **Meals** a la carte 16.95/23.40 **t.**

**at Barnsley** *Northeast : 4 m. by A 429 on B 4425 – ⊠ Cirencester.*

🍺 **Village Pub** with rm, GL7 5EF, ℰ (01285) 740421 – ☏ ☎ ⓟ ⓶ ⥈⥈ ⥈⥈ ⥈⥈
*closed 25 December* – **Meals** a la carte 10.90/16.95 **t.** – **6 rm** ⊒ 32.50/47.50 **t.**

**at Ampney Crucis** *East : 2 ¾ m. by A 417 – ⊠ Cirencester.*

🏨 **Crown of Crucis**, GL7 5RS, on A 417 ℰ (01285) 851806, *Fax (01285) 851735*, ⚘ – ⤬ rm, ☏ ☎ ⓟ – ⓶ 80. ⓶ ⓶ ⑩ ⥈⥈ ⚘
*closed 24 to 30 December* – **Meals** (bar lunch)/dinner 15.50 **t.** and a la carte ⌑ 4.50 – **25 rm** ⊒ 58.00/85.00 **t.** – SB.

⌂ **Waterton Garden Cottage** ⑁ without rest., GL7 5RX, South : ½ m. by Driffield rd turning right into unmarked driveway ℰ (01285) 851303, « Converted Victorian stables, walled garden » – ⓟ ⚘
*closed last 2 weeks August, Christmas and New Year* – **3 rm** ⊒ 25.00/45.00 **s.**

**at Ewen** *Southwest : 3¼ m. by A 429 – ⊠ Cirencester.*

🍺 **Wild Duck Inn** with rm, Drake's Island, GL7 6BY, ℰ (01285) 770310, *Fax (01285) 770924*, « Part 16C former farm buildings », ⚘ – ☏ ☎ ⓟ ⓶ ⓶ ⥈⥈
**Meals** a la carte 11.90/17.90 **t.** – ⊒ 5.00 – **10 rm** 49.50/90.00 **t.**

**at Kemble** *Southwest : 4 m. by A 433 on A 429 – ⊠ Cirencester.*

⌂ **Smerrill Barns** without rest., GL7 6BW, North : 1 ¼ m. on A 429 ℰ (01285) 770907, *Fax (01285) 770706*, « Converted 18C barn » – ⤬ ☏ ⓟ ⓶ ⥈⥈ ⥈⥈ ⚘
**7 rm** ⊒ 38.00/60.00 **t.**

**at Stratton** *Northwest : 1¼ m. on A 417 – ⊠ Cirencester.*

🏨 **Stratton House**, Gloucester Rd, GL7 2LE, ℰ (01285) 651761, *Fax (01285) 640024*, ⚘ – ⤬ ☏ ☎ ⓟ – ⓶ 150. ⓶ ⓶ ⑩ ⥈⥈
**Meals** (bar lunch Monday to Saturday)/dinner 18.75 **st.** and a la carte ⌑ 5.95 – **41 rm** ⊒ 85.00/95.00 **st.** – SB.

Ⓐ ATS 1 Mercian Close, Watermoor End ℰ (01285) 657761

*The Guide is updated annually so renew your Guide every year.*

**CLACKET LANE SERVICE AREA** Surrey 404 U 30 – ⊠ Westerham.

🏠 **RoadChef Lodge** without rest., TN16 2ER, M 25 between junctions 5 and 6 (westbound carriageway) 🖉 (01959) 565789, Fax (01959) 561311, Reservations (Freephone) 08C 834719 – ⇔ 📺 ☎ ⚹ ⓟ. ⓮ 延 ⓞ 𝗩𝗜𝗦𝗔. ⚒
closed Christmas and New Year – **58 rm** 49.95 t.

---

**CLACTON-ON-SEA** Essex 404 X 28 – pop. 45 065.
🖳 West Rd 🖉 (01255) 424331.
🖪 23 Pier Av., CO15 1QD 🖉 (01255) 423400.
London 76 – Chelmsford 37 – Colchester 14 – Ipswich 28.

🏠 **Chudleigh**, 13 Agate Rd, Marine Parade West, CO15 1RA, 🖉 (01255) 425407 Fax (01255) 425407 – 📺 ⓟ. ⓮ 延 ⓞ 𝗩𝗜𝗦𝗔 𝗝𝗖𝗕
restricted opening January and October – **Meals** (closed November-Easter) (dinner only) 12.50 t. ⚐ 4.00 – **10 rm** ⊊ 32.50/50.00.

⒜ ATS 46 High St. 🖉 (01255) 420659

---

**CLANFIELD** Oxon. 403 404 P 28 – pop. 1 709 (inc. Shilton).
London 75 – Oxford 24 – Swindon 16.

XXX **Plough at Clanfield** with rm, Bourton Rd, OX18 2RB, on A 4095 🖉 (01367) 810222 Fax (01367) 810596, « Elizabethan manor house », 🌫 – ⇔ 📺 ☎ ⓟ. ⓮ 延 ⓞ 𝗩𝗜𝗦𝗔 𝗝𝗖𝗕 ⚒
closed 25 to 30 December – **Meals** 32.50 t. (dinner) and lunch a la carte 18.25/22.60 t ⚐ 8.50 – **6 rm** ⊊ 65.00/125.00 t. – SB.

*For the quickest route use the **Michelin Main Road Maps**:*

**970** Europe, **974** Poland, **976** Czech Republic-Slovak Republic, **980** Greece **984** Germany, **985** Scandinavia-Finland, **986** Great Britain and Ireland, **987** Germany-Austria-Benelux, **988** Italy, **989** France, **990** Spain-Portugal.

---

**CLAPPERSGATE** Cumbria – see Ambleside.

---

**CLARE** Suffolk 404 V 27 – pop. 1 976 – ⊠ Sudbury.
London 67 – Cambridge 27 – Colchester 24 – Ipswich 32 – Bury St.Edmunds 16.

⌂ **Ship Stores**, 22 Callis St., CO10 8PX, 🖉 (01787) 277834 – ⇔ rm, 📺. ⓮ 𝗩𝗜𝗦𝗔 𝗝𝗖𝗕. ⚒
**Meals** (by arrangement) 9.50 s. – **5 rm** ⊊ 34.00/44.00 s.

---

**CLAVERING** Essex 404 U 28 – pop. 1 663 – ⊠ Saffron Walden.
London 44 – Cambridge 25 – Colchester 44 – Luton 29.

🏠 **Cricketers** with rm, CB11 4QT, 🖉 (01799) 550442, Fax (01799) 550882, 🌫 – 📺 ☎ ⚹ ⚹, ⓟ. ⓮ 延 𝗩𝗜𝗦𝗔. ⚒
closed 25 and 26 December – **Meals** (lunch in bar)/dinner 23.00 t. and a la carte ⚐ 6.80 – **6 rm** ⊊ 60.00/80.00 t.

---

**CLAWTON** Devon 403 H 31 The West Country G. – pop. 292 – ⊠ Holsworthy.
Env. : W : Tamar River★★.
London 240 – Exeter 39 – Plymouth 36.

🏠 **Court Barn Country House** ⚘, EX22 6PS, West : ½ m. 🖉 (01409) 271219, Fax (01409) 271309, 🌫, ⚒ – ⇔ rm, 📺 ☎ ⓟ
**Meals** (booking essential) 12.95/21.00 t. ⚐ 5.00 – **8 rm** ⊊ (dinner included) 40.00/100.00 t. – SB.

---

**CLAYDON** Suffolk 404 X 27 – see Ipswich.

---

**CLAYGATE** Surrey 404 ㊷ – see Esher.

---

**CLAYTON-LE-DALE** Lancs. – see Blackburn.

**CLAYTON-LE-MOORS** *Lancs.* 402 M 22 – *pop. 6 961* – ⊠ *Accrington.*
*London 232 – Blackburn 3.5 – Lancaster 37 – Leeds 44 – Preston 14.*

🏛 **Dunkenhalgh,** Blackburn Rd, BB5 5JP, Southwest : 1 ½ m. on A 678 ℰ (01254) 398021, *Fax* (01254) 872230, ℔, ⌨, ◻, ∰, park – ✦ 📺 ☎ ❷ – 🔬 400. 🐼 ᴁ ① 𝘝𝘐𝘚𝘈
*Cameo :* Meals *(closed Saturday lunch)* 13.95/22.95 **t.** and a la carte ⌗ 7.50 – ⌑ 8.95 –
**120 rm** 118.00, 1 suite – SB.

🏠 **Sparth House,** Whalley Rd, BB5 5RP, ℰ (01254) 872263, *Fax* (01254) 872263, ∰ –
✦ rest, 📺 ☎ ❷ – 🔬 100. 🐼 𝘝𝘐𝘚𝘈. ✿
**Meals** 17.95 **t.** and a la carte ⌗ 6.45 – **16 rm** ⌑ 48.25/78.50 **t.** – SB.

---

**CLAYTON-LE-WOODS** *Lancs.* 402 M 24 – *pop. 14 173* – ⊠ *Chorley.*
*London 220 – Liverpool 31 – Manchester 26 – Preston 5.5.*

🏨 **The Pines,** Preston Rd, PR6 7ED, on A 6 at junction with B 5256 ℰ (01772) 338551,
*Fax* (01772) 629002, ∰ – ✦ rm, 📺 ☎ ❷ – 🔬 200. 🐼 ᴁ ① 𝘝𝘐𝘚𝘈. ✿
*closed 26 December* – **Meals** 12.00/18.50 **t.** and a la carte ⌗ 4.95 – **36 rm** ⌑ 75.00/85.00 **t.**,
2 suites – SB.

🏠 **Travelodge,** Preston Rd, PR6 7JB, on A 6 ℰ (01772) 311963, *Fax* (01772) 311963, Reservations (Freephone) 0800 850950 – ✦ rm, 📺 ⌖ ❷. 🐼 ᴁ ① 𝘝𝘐𝘚𝘈 𝗝𝗖𝗕. ✿
**Meals** (grill rest.) – **40 rm** 39.95/59.95 **t.**

---

**CLAYTON WEST** *W. Yorks* 402 404 P 23 – *pop. 7 988 (inc. Skelmanthorpe)* – ⊠ *Huddersfield.*
*London 190 – Leeds 19 – Manchester 35 – Sheffield 24.*

🏨 **Bagden Hall,** Wakefield Rd, Scissett, HD8 9LE, Southwest : 1 m. on A 636
ℰ (01484) 865330, *Fax* (01484) 861001, ℔, ∰ – ▦ rest, 📺 ☎ ⌖ ❷ – 🔬 70. 🐼 ᴁ ① 𝘝𝘐𝘚𝘈.
✿
**Meals** 10.75/17.95 **st.** and dinner a la carte ⌗ 4.95 – **17 rm** ⌑ 60.00/100.00 **st.**

---

**CLEARWELL** *Glos.* – *see Coleford.*

---

**CLEATOR MOOR** *Cumbria* 402 J 20 – *pop. 6 410.*
*London 317 – Carlisle 31 – Keswick 25 – Whitehaven 7.*

🏛 **Ennerdale Country House,** Cleator, CA23 3DT, South : 1 ½ m. by B 5295 on A 5086
ℰ (01946) 813907, *Fax* (01946) 815260, ∰ – ✦ rest, 📺 ☎ ❷ – 🔬 150. 🐼 ᴁ ① 𝘝𝘐𝘚𝘈 𝗝𝗖𝗕
**Meals** 10.95/18.50 **st.** ⌗ 5.95 – **28 rm** ⌑ 80.00/90.00 **st.**, 2 suites – SB.

---

**CLEETHORPES** *North East Lincolnshire* 402 404 U 23 – *pop. 32 719.*
✈ *Humberside Airport :* ℰ (01652) 688456, W : 16 m. by A 46 and A 18 Y.
🛈 *42-43 Alexandra Rd, DN35 8LE* ℰ (01472) 200220.
*London 171 – Boston 49 – Lincoln 38 – Sheffield 77.*

🏨 **Kingsway,** Kingsway, DN35 0AE, ℰ (01472) 601122, *Fax* (01472) 601381, ≼ – 📺 ☎ ⌖
❷. 🐼 ᴁ ① 𝘝𝘐𝘚𝘈. ✿
*closed 25 and 26 December* – **Meals** 14.75/17.95 **t.** and a la carte ⌗ 5.50 – **50 rm** ⌑ 68.00/
90.00 **t.** – SB.

---

**CLEEVE HILL** *Glos.* 403 404 N 28 – *see Cheltenham.*

---

**CLEY NEXT THE SEA** *Norfolk* 404 X 25 – *see Blakeney.*

---

**CLIMPING** *W. Sussex* 404 S 31 – *see Littlehampton.*

---

**CLITHEROE** *Lancs.* 402 M 22 – *pop. 13 548.*
🛈 *Whalley Rd* ℰ (01200) 422618.
🛈 *12-14 Market Pl., BB7 2DA* ℰ (01200) 425566.
*London 64 – Blackpool 35 – Manchester 31.*

🏠 **Brooklyn,** 32 Pimlico Rd, BB7 2AH, ℰ (01200) 428268 – ✦ rm, 📺. 🐼 𝘝𝘐𝘚𝘈 𝗝𝗖𝗕. ✿
*closed 24 to 26 December* – **Meals** (by arrangement) 10.00 **s.** – **4 rm** ⌑ 27.50/43.00 **s.**

✗ **Auctioneer,** New Market St., BB7 2JW, ℰ (01200) 427153, *Fax* (01200) 427153 – 🐼 ᴁ
𝘝𝘐𝘚𝘈
*closed Tuesday and Wednesday lunch and Monday* – **Meals** 8.75/19.75 **t.** and a la carte
⌗ 6.50.

**at Waddington** *North : 1 ¾ m. on B 6478 – ✉ Clitheroe.*

**Peter Barn** without rest., Rabbit Lane, via Cross Lane, BB7 3JH, Northwest : 1 ½ m. b B 6478 ☏ (01200) 428585, – P. 
*closed 25 December-1 January* – **3 rm** 25.00/44.00.

ATS Salthill Rd ☏ (01200) 23011

**CLOVELLY** *Devon* 403 G 31 *The West Country G. – pop. 439 – ✉ Bideford.*

See : *Village★★.*

Env. : *SW : Tamar River★★.*

Exc. : *Hartland : Hartland Church★ – Hartland Quay★ (viewpoint★★) – Hartland Point ≤★★★ W : 6 ½ m. by B 3237 and B 3248 – Morwenstow (Church★, cliffs★★), SW : 11 ½ m. by A 39 – to Isle of Lundy (Lundy Co. Ltd) (summer only) (1 h 30 mn).*

*London 241 – Barnstaple 18 – Exeter 52 – Penzance 92.*

**Red Lion**, The Quay, EX39 5TF, ☏ (01237) 431237, *Fax (01237) 431044*, ≤ – TV ☎ P. MC AE VISA.
Meals (bar lunch)/dinner 18.50 **st.** 6.45 – **11 rm** (dinner included) 77.00/124.00 **st.** – SB.

**New Inn,** High St., EX39 5TQ, ☏ (01237) 431303, *Fax (01237) 431636*, « 17C » – TV ☎. MC AE VISA.
Meals (bar lunch)/dinner 17.50 **st.** 6.45 – **8 rm** (dinner included) 70.00/110.00 **st.** – SB

**COATHAM MUNDEVILLE** *Durham* 402 P 20 – *see Darlington.*

**COBHAM** *Kent* 404 V 29 – *pop. 1 586 (inc. Luddesdown) – ✉ Gravesend.*

*London 27 – Maidstone 13 – Rochester 6.*

**Ye Olde Leather Bottle,** The Street, DA12 3BZ, ☏ (01474) 814327, *Fax (01474) 812086* « 17C inn », – TV ☎ P. MC AE VISA.
**Meals** a la carte 12.25/20.85 **st.** – 5.50 – **6 rm** 37.50/60.00 **st.** – SB.

**COBHAM** *Surrey* 404 S 30 – *pop. 15 254 (inc. Oxshott).*

*London 24 – Guildford 10.*

**Hilton National,** Seven Hills Road South, KT11 1EW, West : 1 ½ m. by A 245 ☏ (01932) 864471, *Fax (01932) 868017*, , , , , park, , squash – , rm, TV ☎ P – 300. MC AE VISA JCB
**Meals** (bar lunch Saturday) (dancing Saturday evening) 17.50/21.95 and a la carte – 11.95 – **149 rm** 164.00/199.00 **st.**, 1 suite – SB.

**The Fairmile - Premier Lodge,** Portsmouth Rd, Fairmile, KT11 1BW, Northeast : 1 m on A 307 ☏ (01932) 868141, *Fax (01932) 866478*, Reservations (Freephone) 0800 118833 – rm, TV ☎ P. MC AE VISA.
**Meals** (grill rest.) a la carte 9.95/14.95 **t.** 4.55 – 5.95 – **48 rm** 48.95 **t.**

**Cedar House,** Mill Rd, KT11 3AL, ☏ (01932) 863424, *Fax (01932) 862023*, – TV ☎ P MC AE VISA.
**Meals** 12.95/19.95 **t.** and a la carte 6.50 – **6 rm** 85.00/95.00 **st.**

**at Stoke D'Abernon** *Southeast : 1 ½ m. on A 245 – ✉ Cobham.*

**Woodlands Park,** Woodlands Lane, KT11 3QB, on A 245 ☏ (01372) 843933 *Fax (01372) 842704*, , park, – TV ☎ P – 280. MC AE VISA.
**Meals** *(closed Saturday lunch and Sunday dinner)* 16.95/24.00 **t.** and a la carte – 11.75 – **59 rm** 115.00/155.00 **t.** – SB.

**COCKERMOUTH** *Cumbria* 401 402 J 20 – *pop. 7 702.*

*Embleton ☏ (017687) 76223/76941.*

*Town Hall, Market St., CA13 9NP ☏ (01900) 822634.*

*London 306 – Carlisle 25 – Keswick 13.*

**Trout,** Crown St., CA13 0EJ, ☏ (01900) 823591, *Fax (01900) 827514*, , – TV ☎ P – 50. MC AE VISA
**Meals** 11.95/20.45 **t.** and a la carte 6.45 – **32 rm** 59.95/150.00 **t.** – SB.

**Low Hall** without rest., Brandlingill, CA13 0RE, South : 3 ¼ m. by A 5086 on Embleton rd ☏ (01900) 826654, ≤, « Part 17C farmhouse », – P. MC VISA.
*closed 19 December-4 January* – **3 rm** 25.00/60.00 **st.**

**t Lorton** *Southeast : 4¼ m. by B 5292 –* ⊠ *Cockermouth.*

⌂ **New House Farm** ⌛, CA13 9UU, South : 1 ¼ m. on B 5289 *℘* (01900) 85404, *Fax (01900) 85404*, ≼, « Part 17C and 19C farmhouse », ⩩, park – ⌖⌖ **@**
**Meals** 20.00 st. ⌂ 5.95 – **3 rm** ⌑ (dinner included) 70.00/110.00 st. – SB.

⌂ **Winder Hall** ⌛, Low Lorton, CA13 9UP, on B 5289 *℘* (01900) 85107, « Part 17C manor house », ⩩ – ⌖⌖ 🆅 **@**. **@** **VISA** **JCB**. ⌗
*closed January and Christmas* – **Meals** 16.00 st. ⌂ 5.00 – **6 rm** ⌑ 35.00/70.00 st. – SB.

---

**COGGESHALL** *Essex* **404** *W 28 – pop. 3 927 –* ⊠ *Colchester.*
*London 49 – Braintree 6 – Chelmsford 16 – Colchester 9.*

🏨 **White Hart,** Market End, CO6 1NH, *℘* (01376) 561654, *Fax (01376) 561789*, « Part 15C guildhall », ⩩ – 🆅 ☎ **@**. **@** **AE** **VISA** **JCB**. ⌗
**Meals** - Italian - (in bar Sunday dinner) 14.95 t. (dinner) and a la carte 19.65/35.85 t. ⌂ 7.50 – **18 rm** ⌑ 61.50/97.00 t. – SB.

%% **Baumann's Brasserie,** 4-6 Stoneham St., CO6 1TT, *℘* (01376) 561453, *Fax (01376) 563762* – **@** **AE** **VISA** **JCB**
*closed Sunday dinner, Monday and first 2 weeks January* – **Meals** 12.50 t. (lunch) and a la carte 17.85/27.00 t. ⌂ 9.25.

*Pour voyager rapidement, utilisez les **cartes Michelin "Grandes Routes"** :*

**970** Europe, **976** République Tchèque-République Slovaque, **980** Grèce, **984** Allemagne, **985** Scandinavie-Finlande, **986** Grande-Bretagne-Irlande, **987** Allemagne-Autriche-Benelux, **988** Italie, **989** France, **990** Espagne-Portugal.

---

**COLCHESTER** *Essex* **404** *W 28 Great Britain G. – pop. 96 063.*
See : *Castle and Museum★ AC.*
🅱 *Birch Grove, Layer Rd ℘ (01206) 734276.*
🅱 *1 Queen St., CO1 2PJ ℘ (01206) 282920.*
*London 52 – Cambridge 48 – Ipswich 18 – Luton 76 – Southend-on-Sea 41.*

Plans on following pages

🏨 **George,** 116 High St., CO1 1TD, *℘* (01206) 578494, *Fax (01206) 761732* – ⌖⌖ rm, ▤ rest, 🆅 ☎ **@** – ⌂ 70. **@** **AE** **@** **VISA** **JCB**. ⌗                                   BZ **b**
*closed 31 December* – **Meals** *(closed dinner 25 and 26 December)* 10.90/16.95 t. and a la carte ⌂ 7.95 – ⌑ 8.25 – **45 rm** 69.50/96.50 st.

🏨 **Rose and Crown,** East St., Eastgates, CO1 2TZ, *℘* (01206) 866677, *Fax (01206) 866616*, « Part 15C inn » – ⌖⌖ rm, 🆅 ☎ & **@** – ⌂ 100. **@** **AE** **@** **VISA** **JCB**. ⌗        CZ **d**
*closed 26 to 28 December* – **Meals** *(closed Sunday dinner)* a la carte 24.85/33.20 t. ⌂ 8.75 – ⌑ 6.95 – **29 rm** 65.00/99.00 t. – SB.

🏨 **Red Lion,** 43 High St., CO1 1DJ, *℘* (01206) 577986, *Fax (01206) 578207*, « Part 15C inn » – 🆅 ☎ – ⌂ 40. **@** **AE** **@** **VISA** **JCB**                                                      BZ **a**
*The Parliament :* **Meals** 13.95 t. (dinner) and a la carte 12.40/18.50 t. ⌂ 6.00 – **22 rm** ⌑ 57.50/75.00 st. – SB.

🏨 **Butterfly,** Old Ipswich Rd, CO7 7QY, Northeast : 4 ¼ m. by A 1232 at junction of A 12 with A 120 (via sliproad to A 120) *℘* (01206) 230900, *Fax (01206) 231095* – ⌖⌖ rm, 🆅 ☎ & **@** – ⌂ 80. **@** **AE** **@** **VISA**. ⌗                                                                        CY
**Meals** 15.00/17.50 t. and a la carte – ⌑ 7.50 – **50 rm** 65.00 t. – SB.

🏨 **Travel Inn,** Severalls Business Park, Ipswich Rd, CO4 4NP, North : 2 ¾ m. on A 1232 *℘* (01206) 855001, *Fax (01206) 211388* – ⌖⌖ rm, 🆅 & **@**. **@** **AE** **@** **VISA**     CY
**Meals** (grill rest.) – **40 rm** 38.00 t.

🏨 **D'Arcy House,** 3-5 Culver Street East, CO1 1LD, *℘* (01206) 768111, *Fax (01206) 763938* – 🆅. **@** **VISA**. ⌗                                                                            BZ **c**
**Meals** *(closed Sunday and Monday)* 8.90 (lunch) and a la carte 9.80/13.40 st. – **4 rm** ⌑ 32.00/52.00 t.

⌂ **Four Sevens,** 28 Inglis Rd, CO3 3HU, off Maldon Rd (B 1022) *℘* (01206) 546093, *Fax (01206) 546093*, ⩩ – ⌖⌖ rest, 🆅. ⌗                                                        AZ **f**
**Meals** (by arrangement) 15.00 s. – **6 rm** ⌑ 40.00/50.00 s.

%% **North Hill Exchange Brasserie,** 19-20 North Hill, CO1 1DZ, *℘* (01206) 769988, *Fax (01206) 766898* – **@** **AE** **@** **VISA**                                                  BY **n**
*closed Monday* – **Meals** 9.95 st. and a la carte.

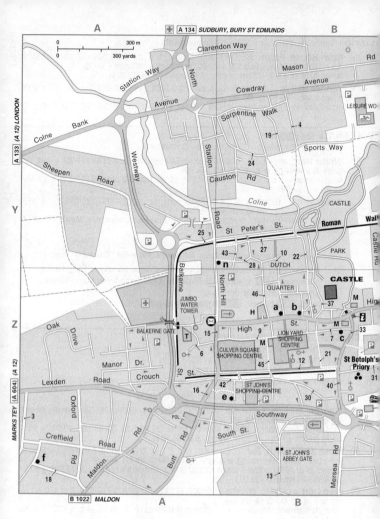

✕ **Warehouse Brasserie,** 12a Chapel St. North, CO2 7AT, ✆ (01206) 765656, Fax (01206) 765656 – 🔲. ⦿ 🆎 ⦿ *VISA* BZ e closed Sunday dinner, 25-26 December and Easter Monday – **Meals** 7.95/12.95 and a la carte 🕯 6.25.

**at Eight Ash Green** West : 4 m. by A 604 – AZ – ⊠ Colchester.

🏰 **Forte Posthouse Colchester,** Abbotts Lane, CO6 3QL, at junction of A 604 with A 12 ✆ (01206) 767740, Fax (01206) 766577, 🕭, 🛋, 🔲, ✕ – ⋟ rm, 🆃🆅 ☎ 🕭 🅟 – 🔬 150. ⦿ 🆎 ⦿ *VISA*
**Meals** a la carte 13.85/24.85 **st.** 🕯 6.45 – ⊆ 8.95 – **110 rm** 69.00 **st.** – SB.

**at Marks Tey** West : 5 m. by A 12 at junction with A 120 – AZ – ⊠ Colchester.

🏰 **Marks Tey,** London Rd, CO6 1DU, on B 1408 ✆ (01206) 210001, Fax (01206) 212167, 🕭, 🛋, 🔲, ✕ – ⋟ rm, 🔲 rest, 🆃🆅 ☎ 🅟 – 🔬 200. ⦿ 🆎 ⦿ *VISA*. ✕
**Meals** 15.50 **st.** and a la carte 🕯 9.95 – ⊆ 7.25 – **109 rm** 67.50/75.00 **st.,** 1 suite – SB.

ⓐ ATS East Hill ✆ (01206) 866484/867471
ATS 451 Ipswich Rd ✆ (01206) 841404

ATS Telford Way, Severalls Park Ind. Est.
✆ (01206) 845641

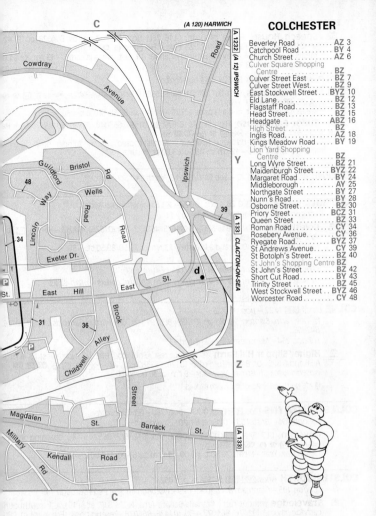

## COLCHESTER

| | |
|---|---|
| Beverley Road | AZ 3 |
| Catchpool Road | BY 4 |
| Church Street | AZ 6 |
| Culver Square Shopping Centre | BZ |
| Culver Street East | BZ 7 |
| Culver Street West | BZ 9 |
| East Stockwell Street | BYZ 10 |
| Eld Lane | BZ 12 |
| Flagstaff Road | BZ 13 |
| Head Street | BZ 15 |
| Headgate | ABZ 16 |
| High Street | BZ |
| Inglis Road | AZ 18 |
| Kings Meadow Road | BY 19 |
| Lion Yard Shopping Centre | BZ |
| Long Wyre Street | BZ 21 |
| Maidenburgh Street | BYZ 22 |
| Margaret Road | BY 24 |
| Middleborough | AY 25 |
| Northgate Street | BY 27 |
| Nunn's Road | BY 28 |
| Osborne Street | BZ 30 |
| Priory Street | BCZ 31 |
| Queen Street | BZ 33 |
| Roman Road | CY 34 |
| Rosebery Avenue | CY 36 |
| Ryegate Road | BYZ 37 |
| St Andrews Avenue | CY 39 |
| St Botolph's Street | BZ 40 |
| St John's Shopping Centre | BZ |
| St John's Street | BZ 42 |
| Short Cut Road | BY 43 |
| Trinity Street | BZ 45 |
| West Stockwell Street | BYZ 46 |
| Worcester Road | CY 48 |

*The Guide is updated annually so renew your Guide every year.*

---

**COLDRED** Kent – see Dover.

---

**COLEFORD** Devon 403 I 31 – ⊠ Crediton.
London 214 – Barnstaple 29 – Exeter 14 – Taunton 42.

**New Inn** with rm, EX17 5BZ, ℘ (01363) 84242, Fax (01363) 85044, « Part 13C thatched inn » – 📺 **Q**. 🆀🆂 🅰🅴 🅾 💳 💳. ℅
closed 25 and 26 December – **Meals** a la carte 12.85/22.85 **st.** ⧄ 7.50 – **5 rm** ⊇ 46.00/70.00 **st.** – SB.

---

**COLEFORD** Glos. 403 404 M 28 Great Britain G. – pop. 9 567.
Env. : W : Wye Valley★.
🔸 Forest of Dean, Lords Hills ℘ (01594) 832583 – 🔸 Forest Hills, Mile End Rd ℘ (01594) 810620 – 🛈 High St., GL16 8HG ℘ (01594) 836307.
London 143 – Bristol 28 – Gloucester 19 – Newport 29.

COLEFORD

🏠 **Speech House,** Forest of Dean, GL16 7EL, Northeast : 3 m. by B 4028 on B 42
⚓ (01594) 822607, *Fax (01594) 823658,* 🌳 – 🐾 📺 ☎ 🄿. 🐵 🄰🄴 🄾 *VISA*
**Meals** (bar lunch Monday to Saturday)/dinner 19.50 **t.** and a la carte – **13 rm** ⌑ 54.0
75.50 **t.,** 1 suite – SB.

**at Clearwell** *South : 2 m. by B 4228 –* ✉ *Coleford.*

🏠 **Wyndham Arms,** GL16 8JT, ⚓ (01594) 833666, *Fax (01594) 836450 –* 🐾 rest, 📺 ☎ 🄿
🄰 55. 🐵 🄰🄴 🄾 *VISA* 🄹🄲🄱
**Meals** 13.75/18.25 **t.** and a la carte ↓ 5.75 – **17 rm** ⌑ 56.50/80.00 **t.** – SB.

🏠 **Tudor Farmhouse,** High St., GL16 8JS, ⚓ (01594) 833046, *Fax (01594) 837093,* « Pa
13C and 16C », 🌳 – 🐾 📺 ☎ 🄿. 🐵 🄰🄴 *VISA*
*closed Christmas and Bank Holidays –* **Meals** *(closed Sunday)* (dinner only) 18.95 s
and a la carte ↓ 4.95 – **12 rm** ⌑ 48.50/68.00 **st.,** 1 suite – SB.

---

**COLERNE** *Wilts.* 🄼🄾🄸 🄼🄾🄾 M 29 – *see Bath (Bath & North East Somerset).*

---

**COLESHILL** *Warks.* 🄼🄾🄸 🄼🄾🄾 O 26 – *pop. 6 324 –* ✉ *Birmingham (W. Mids.).*
*London 113 – Birmingham 8 – Coventry 11.*

🏠 **Coleshill,** 152 High St., B46 3BG, ⚓ (01675) 465527, *Fax (01675) 464013 –* 🐾 rm, 📺 ☎
🄿 – 🄰 150. 🐵 🄾 *VISA*
**Meals** (grill rest.) 15.00 **t.** and a la carte – **23 rm** ⌑ 79.50/89.50 **st.** – SB.

*Great Britain* and *Ireland* are covered entirely
at a scale of 16 miles to 1 inch by our «**Main roads**» map 🄺🄴🄸.

---

**COLNE** *Lancs.* 🄼🄾🄸 N 22 – *pop. 18 776.*
🏌 *Law Farm, Skipton Old Rd* ⚓ (01282) 863391 – 🏌 *Ghyll Brow, Barnoldswick* ⚓ *(0128*
*842466.*
*London 234 – Manchester 29 – Preston 26.*

🏠 **Higher Slipper Hill Farm** 🔈 *without rest.,* Foulridge, BB8 7LY, Northwest : 3 ¾ m. b
A 56 and B 6251 on Barrowford rd ⚓ (01282) 863602, ≤, 🌳 – 🐾 rm, 📺 🄿. 🐵 🄰🄴 *VISA*. ≤
*closed 1 week Christmas-New Year –* **9 rm** ⌑ 36.00/50.00.

🅐 ATS North Valley Road ⚓ (01282) 870645

---

**COLN ST. ALDWYNS** *Glos.* 🄼🄾🄸 🄼🄾🄾 O 28 – *pop. 260 –* ✉ *Cirencester.*
*London 101 – Bristol 53 – Gloucester 20 – Swindon 15.*

🏠 **New Inn,** GL7 5AN, ⚓ (01285) 750651, *Fax (01285) 750657,* « 16C coaching inn »
🐾 rest, 📺 ☎ 🄿. 🐵 🄰🄴 *VISA*. ≤
*closed New Year –* **Meals** 26.50 **t.** ↓ 9.00 – **14 rm** ⌑ 65.00/110.00 **t.** – SB.

---

**COLSTERWORTH** *Lincs.* 🄼🄾🄸 🄼🄾🄾 S 25 – *pop. 1 452.*
*London 105 – Grantham 8 – Leicester 29 – Nottingham 32 – Peterborough 14.*

🏠 **Travelodge** *without rest.,* Granada Service Area, NG33 5JR, at A 151/A 1 (southboun
carriageway) ⚓ (01476) 861077, *Fax (01476) 861078,* Reservations (Freephone) 080
850950 – 🐾 📺 ☎ ⅙ 🄿 – 🄰 30. 🐵 🄰🄴 🄾 *VISA* 🄹🄲🄱. ≤
**31 rm** 39.95/59.95 **t.**

🏠 **Travelodge,** NG33 5JJ, East : ½ m. by B 6403 on A 1 (southbound carriageway
⚓ (01476) 861181, *Fax (01476) 861181,* Reservations (Freephone) 0800 850950 – 🐾 rm
📺 ⅙ 🄿. 🐵 🄰🄴 🄾 *VISA* 🄹🄲🄱. ≤
**Meals** (grill rest.) – **32 rm** 39.95/59.95 **t.**

🏠 **Travelodge,** New Fox, South Witham, NG33 5LN, South : 3 m. by B 6403 on A 1 (north
bound carriageway) ⚓ (01572) 767586, *Fax (01572) 767586,* Reservations (Freephone) 080
850950 – 🐾 rm, 📺 ⅙ 🄿. 🐵 🄰🄴 🄾 *VISA* 🄹🄲🄱. ≤
**Meals** (grill rest.) – **32 rm** 39.95/59.95 **t.**

---

**COLSTON BASSETT** *Notts.* 🄼🄾🄸 🄼🄾🄾 R 25 – *pop. 239 –* ✉ *Nottingham.*
*London 129 – Lincoln 40 – Nottingham 15 – Sheffield 51.*

🏠 **Martins Arms** *with rm,* School Lane, NG12 3FD, ⚓ (01949) 81361, *Fax (01949) 81309*
🍴 – 🐾 🄿. 🐵 🄾 *VISA*
*closed 25 December –* **Meals** *(closed Sunday dinner)* 16.95/23.95 **st.** and a la carte ↓ 8.95 -
**2 rm** ⌑ 35.00/65.00 **st.** – SB.

**COLTISHALL** Norfolk 404 Y 25 *Great Britain G. – pop. 1 992 – ⊠ Norwich.*

Env. : *The Broads★.*
London 133 – Norwich 8.

🏨 **Norfolk Mead** ⤸, Church Loke, NR12 7DN, ℘ (01603) 737531, Fax (01603) 737521, ⤸, ⤸, ⤸ – ⤸ 📺 ☎ 🅿, ⚈ 🆎 *VISA*
Meals 12.95/18.50 t. and a la carte ≬ 6.50 – **9 rm** ⊑ 65.00/99.00 t. – SB.

🏠 **King's Head** with rm, Wroxham Rd, NR12 7EA, ℘ (01603) 737426, Fax (01603) 736542 – 📺 🅿, ⚈ *VISA*. ⤸
Meals a la carte 15.50/25.50 t. ≬ 6.00 – **2 rm** ⊑ 22.50/50.00 t.

---

**COLWALL** Herefordshire – *see Great Malvern.*

---

**COLYFORD** Devon 403 K 31 *Great Britain G. – ⊠ Colyton.*

Env. : *Colyton★ (Church★), N : 1 m. on B 3161 – Axmouth (≤★), S : 1 m. by A 3052 and B 3172.*
London 168 – Exeter 21 – Taunton 30 – Torquay 46 – Yeovil 32.

🏠 **Swallows Eaves,** EX13 6QJ, ℘ (01297) 553184, Fax (01297) 553574, ⤸ – ⤸ 📺 🅿, ⚈ *VISA*. ⤸
Meals (dinner only) 22.00 **st.** – **8 rm** ⊑ 40.00/80.00 **st.** – SB.

---

**COMPTON ABBAS** Dorset – *see Shaftesbury.*

---

**CONGLETON** Ches. 402 403 404 N 24 *Great Britain G. – pop. 24 897.*

Env. : *Little Moreton Hall★★ AC, SW : 3 m. by A 34.*
🏌 Biddulph Rd ℘ (01260) 273540.
🏛 Town Hall, High St., CW12 1BN ℘ (01260) 271095.
London 183 – Liverpool 50 – Manchester 25 – Sheffield 46 – Stoke-on-Trent 13.

🏠 **Sandhole Farm** ⤸ without rest., Hulme Walfield, CW12 2JH, North : 2 ¼ m. on A 34 ℘ (01260) 224419, Fax (01260) 224766, ⤸, park – ⤸ 📺 ☎ ◆ 🅿, ⚈ 🆎 *VISA*. ⤸
**18 rm** ⊑ 39.00/49.00 t.

XXX **Old Barn** (at The Plough Inn), Macclesfield Rd, Eaton, CW12 2NH, Northeast : 2 m. on A 536 ℘ (01260) 280207, Fax (01260) 298377, « Re-assembled part 17C timber framed barn » – ⤸ rm, 🍽 rest, 📺 ☎ ◆ 🅿, ⚈ 🆎 *VISA* JCB. ⤸
Meals *(closed Sunday dinner and Monday)* (dinner only and Sunday lunch)/dinner 18.95/ 27.50 **st.** and a la carte ≬ 10.00 – **8 rm** ⊑ 55.00/70.00 t. – SB.

🚗 ATS Brookside ℘ (01260) 273720

---

**CONISTON** Cumbria 402 K 20 *Great Britain G. – pop. 1 304.*

Env. : *Coniston Water★ – Brantwood★ AC, SE : 2 m. on east side of Coniston Water.*
Exc. : *Hard Knott Pass★★, Wrynose Pass★★, NW : 10 m. by A 593 and minor road.*
🏛 Ruskin Av., LA21 8EH ℘ (015394) 41533 (summer only).
London 285 – Carlisle 55 – Kendal 22 – Lancaster 42.

🏨 **Coniston Lodge,** Station Rd, LA21 8HH, ℘ (015394) 41201, Fax (015394) 41201 – ⤸ 📺 ☎ 🅿, ⚈ 🆎 *VISA*. ⤸
closed 23 to 28 December and 3 weeks January-February – Meals *(closed Sunday and Monday)* (dinner only) 19.50 **t.** ≬ 7.50 – **6 rm** ⊑ 46.50/79.00 **t.**

**at Water Yeat** South : 6½ m. by A 593 on A 5084 – ⊠ Ulverston.

🏠 **Water Yeat,** LA12 8DJ, ℘ (01229) 885306, Fax (01229) 885306, ⤸ – ⤸ 🅿, ⤸
closed mid December-mid February and 1 week July – Meals (by arrangement) 21.00 **st.** ≬ 7.50 – **5 rm** ⊑ 38.50/63.00 **st.** – SB.

**at Blawith** South : 7¼ m. by A 593 on A 5084 – ⊠ Ulverston.

🏠 **Appletree Holme** ⤸, LA12 8EL, West : 1 m. taking unmarked road opposite church and then right hand fork ℘ (01229) 885618, ≤, ⤸ – ⤸ 📺 🅿, ⚈ *VISA*. ⤸
Meals 23.50 – **4 rm** ⊑ (dinner included) 78.50/137.00 **st.** – SB.

**at Torver** Southwest : 2¼ m. on A 593 – ⊠ Coniston.

🏨 **Wheelgate Country House** without rest., Little Arrow, LA21 8AU, Northeast : ¾ m. on A 593 ℘ (015394) 41418, Fax (015394) 41114, « Part 17C farmhouse », ⤸ – ⤸ 📺 🅿, ⚈ *VISA*. ⤸
March-November – **5 rm** ⊑ 35.00/62.00 **st.**

🏠 **Old Rectory** ♨, LA21 8AX, Northeast : ¼ m. by A 593 ℰ (015394) 4135
Fax (015394) 41156, ≤, 🌳 – ⇆ 📺 🅿. ⑳ 🆚 🆑
Meals (residents only) (dinner only) 18.00 st. ◊ 4.95 – 7 rm ⌑ 33.00/78.00 st., 1 suite – SE

⌂ **Arrowfield Country** without rest., Little Arrow, LA21 8AU, Northeast : ¾ m. on A 59
ℰ (015394) 41741, ≤, 🌳 – ⇆ 📺 🅿. ⌘
March-November – 5 rm ⌑ 24.00/48.00 st.

---

**CONSTANTINE** Cornwall 403 E 33 – ✉ Falmouth.
Env. : Mawgan-in-Meneage (Church★), S : 3 m. by minor roads.
London 303 – Falmouth 15 – Penzance 25 – Truro 24.

🍴 **Trengilly Wartha Inn** ♨ with rm, Nancenoy, TR11 5RP, South : 1½ m. by Fore St. or
Port Navas rd ℰ (01326) 340332, Fax (01326) 340332, 🌳 – ⇆ 📺 ☎ 🅿. 🆎 🆎 ① 🆚 Jc
Meals (closed 25 December) (bar lunch)/dinner 22.50 t. ◊ 5.20 – 8 rm ⌑ 44.00/66.80 st.
SB.

---

**CONSTANTINE BAY** Cornwall 403 E 32 – see Padstow.

---

**COOKHAM** Windsor & Maidenhead 404 R 29 Great Britain G. – pop. 6 096 – ✉ Maidenhead.
See : Stanley Spencer Gallery★ AC.
London 32 – High Wycombe 7 – Reading 16.

✕✕ **Alfonso's**, 19 Station Hill Par., SL6 9BR, ℰ (01628) 525775 – ⑳ 🆎 ① 🆚
closed Saturday lunch, Sunday, 2 weeks August, Christmas Day and Bank Holidays – Meal
10.00 (lunch) and a la carte 18.00/40.00 st. ◊ 4.50.

🍴 **Bel and the Dragon**, High St., SL6 9SQ, ℰ (01628) 521263, Fax (01628) 851008, 🍽 – ⑳
🆎 🆚
Meals a la carte 16.95/29.00 t.

---

**COPDOCK** Suffolk 404 X 27 – see Ipswich.

---

**COPTHORNE** W. Sussex 404 T 30 – see Crawley.

---

**CORBIERE** Jersey (Channel Islands) 403 P 33 and 230 ⑩ ⑪ – see Channel Islands.

---

**CORBRIDGE** Northd. 401 402 N 19 Great Britain G. – pop. 2 719.
Env. : Hadrian's Wall★★, N : 3 m. by A 68 – Corstopitum★ AC, NW : ½ m.
🖪 Hill St., NE45 5AA ℰ (01434) 632815 (summer only).
London 300 – Hexham 3 – Newcastle upon Tyne 18.

🏠 **Angel Inn**, Main St., NE45 5LA, ℰ (01434) 632119, Fax (01434) 632119, « 18C former
posting inn » – ⇆ rest, 📺 ☎ ✆ 🅿. ⑳ 🆎 ① 🆚 Jcb. ⌘
Meals 15.95 t. and a la carte ◊ 5.40 – 5 rm ⌑ 49.50/74.00 t.

🏠 **Riverside** without rest., Main St., NE45 5LE, ℰ (01434) 632942, Fax (01434) 633883 – 📺
☎ 🅿. ⑳ 🆎 🆚 Jcb
closed 2 weeks November and Christmas-New Year – 10 rm ⌑ 36.00/55.00 t.

🏠 **Lion of Corbridge**, Bridge End, NE45 5AX, ℰ (01434) 632504, Fax (01434) 632571 –
⇆ rest, 📺 ☎ 🅿. ⑳ 🆎 ① 🆚 Jcb. ⌘
closed 25-26 December and 1 January – Meals (closed Monday dinner and Sunday)
a la carte 12.15/16.15 t. ◊ 4.85 – 14 rm ⌑ 48.00/74.00 t. – SB.

✕✕✕ **Ramblers Country House**, Farnley, NE45 5RN, South : 1 m. on Riding Mill Rd
ℰ (01434) 632424, Fax (01434) 633656 – 🅿. ⑳ 🆎 ① 🆚 Jcb
closed Sunday dinner and Monday – Meals (dinner only and Sunday lunch)/dinner 14.95/
19.95 t. and a la carte ◊ 4.95.

✕✕ **Valley**, The Old Station House, Station Rd, NE45 5AY, South : ½ m. by Riding Mill rd
ℰ (01434) 633434, Fax (01434) 633923 – ⑳ 🆎 ① 🆚
closed Sunday – Meals - Indian - (dinner only) 20.25 st. and a la carte ◊ 7.95.

---

**CORBY** Northants. 404 R 26 Great Britain G. – pop. 49 053.
Env. : Boughton House★★ AC, S : 5½ m. by A 6116 and A 43.
🖪 Stamford Rd, Weldon ℰ (01536) 260756.
🖪 Civic Centre, George St., NN17 1QB ℰ (01536) 407507.
London 100 – Leicester 26 – Northampton 22 – Peterborough 24.

🏨 **Stakis Corby,** Geddington Rd, NN18 8ET, East : 2 ½ m. on A 6116 ☎ (01536) 401020, *Fax (01536) 400767*, 🏋, ♨, 🏊 – 🛗, 🚭 rm, ❄ rest, 📺 ☏ ♿ 🅿 – 👥 190. [MO] [AE] [D] [VISA]. 🚫🐕
**Meals** (carving lunch Monday to Friday) (bar lunch Saturday) (live music and dancing Saturday evening) 13.50/18.50 **st.** and dinner a la carte – ☕ 10.50 – **101 rm** 101.00/136.00 **st.**, 2 suites – SB.

🏨 **Rockingham Forest,** Rockingham Rd, NN17 1AE, North : 2 ½ m. on A 6116 ☎ (01536) 401348, *Fax (01536) 266383* – 🚭 rm, 📺 ☏ 🅿 – 👥 400. [MO] [AE] [D] [VISA]
**Meals** (bar lunch Monday to Saturday)/dinner 15.95 **st.** and a la carte 🍷 7.95 – ☕ 8.50 – **70 rm** 65.00/80.00 **st.** – SB.

🛞 ATS St. James Rd ☎ (01536) 269519

---

**CORFE CASTLE** *Dorset* [403] [404] N 32 *The West Country G.* – *pop. 1 335* – ✉ *Wareham.*
See : *Castle★ (≤★★) AC.*
*London 129 – Bournemouth 18 – Weymouth 23.*

🏨 **Mortons House,** 45 East St., BH20 5EE, ☎ (01929) 480988, *Fax (01929) 480820*, ≤, « Part Elizabethan manor », 🌳 – 🚭 rest, 📺 ☏ 🅿. [MO] [AE] [D] [VISA]
**Meals** 15.00/22.50 **t.** and dinner a la carte 🍷 6.50 – **16 rm** ☕ 65.00/90.00 **t.**, 1 suite – SB.

---

**CORNHILL-ON-TWEED** *Northd.* [401] [402] N 17 *Scotland G.* – *pop. 317.*
Env. : *Ladykirk (Kirk o'Steil★), NE : 6 m. by A 698 and B 6470.*
*London 345 – Edinburgh 49 – Newcastle upon Tyne 59.*

🏨 **Tillmouth Park** 🌙, TD12 4UU, Northeast : 2 ½ m. on A 698 ☎ (01890) 882255, *Fax (01890) 882540*, ≤, « 19C country house », 🎣, 🌳, park – 📺 ☏ 🅿. [MO] [AE] [D] [VISA]
*closed 26 December* – **Meals** 8.50/25.00 **t.** and a la carte 🍷 7.00 – **14 rm** ☕ 90.00/160.00 **t.** – SB.

🏨 **Coach House,** Crookham, TD12 4TD, East : 4 m. on A 697 ☎ (01890) 820293, *Fax (01890) 820284*, 🌳 – 🚭 rest, 📺 ☏ ♿ 🅿. [MO] [VISA]. 🚫🐕
*Easter-October* – **Meals** (dinner only) 16.50 **t.** 🍷 3.95 – **9 rm** ☕ 36.00/72.00 **t.**

---

**CORSE LAWN** *Worcestershire* – *see Tewkesbury (Glos.).*

---

**COSGROVE** *Northants.* [404] R 27 – *see Stony Stratford.*

---

**COSHAM** *Portsmouth* [403] [404] Q 31 – *see Portsmouth and Southsea.*

---

**COVENEY** *Cambs.* – *see Ely.*

---

**COVENTRY** *W. Mids.* [403] [404] P 26 *Great Britain G.* – *pop. 299 316.*
See : *City★ - Cathedral★★★ AC* **AV** – *Old Cathedral★* **AV A** – *Museum of British Road Transport★ AC* **AV M1**.
⛳18 *Windmill Village, Birmingham Rd, Allesley* ☎ *(01203) 404041* – ⛳9 *Sphinx, Sphinx Drive* ☎ *(01203) 451361.*
ℹ *Bayley Lane, CV1 5RN* ☎ *(01203) 832303/832304.*
*London 100 – Birmingham 18 – Bristol 96 – Nottingham 52.*

Plans on following pages

🏨 **Britannia,** Cathedral Sq., CV1 5RP, ☎ (01203) 633733, *Fax (01203) 225299* – 🛗, 🚭 rm, ❄ rest, 📺 ☏ 🅿 – 👥 400. [MO] [AE] [D] [VISA] AV n
**Meals** *(closed Saturday lunch)* 9.50/12.50 **st.** 🍷 5.60 – ☕ 8.95 – **180 rm** 110.00/120.00 **st.**, 10 suites – SB.

🏨 **Brooklands Grange,** Holyhead Rd, CV5 8HX, Northwest : 2 ½ m. on A 4114 ☎ (01203) 601601, *Fax (01203) 601277*, 🌳 – 📺 ☏ 🅿. [MO] [AE] [D] [VISA]. 🚫🐕 AY e
*closed 26 December and 1 January* – **Meals** *(restricted menu Sunday dinner)* a la carte 20.00/23.80 **t.** 🍷 5.00 – **30 rm** ☕ 90.00/115.00 **st.** – SB.

🏨 **Leofric,** Broadgate, CV1 1LZ, ☎ (01203) 221371, *Fax (01203) 551352* – 🛗, 🚭 rm, ❄ rest, 📺 ☏ 📞 🅿 – 👥 600. [MO] [AE] [VISA] [JCB] AV r
**Meals** (carving lunch)/dinner 15.50 **t.** and a la carte – ☕ 8.95 – **89 rm** 86.00/110.00 **st.**, 5 suites – SB.

🏨 **Travel Inn,** Rugby Rd, Binley Woods, CV3 2TA, at junction of A 46 with A 428 ☎ (01203) 636585, *Fax (01203) 431178* – 🚭 rm, 📺 ♿ 🅿. [MO] [AE] [D] [VISA]. 🚫🐕 BZ n
**Meals** (grill rest.) – **50 rm** 38.00 **t.**

# COVENTRY

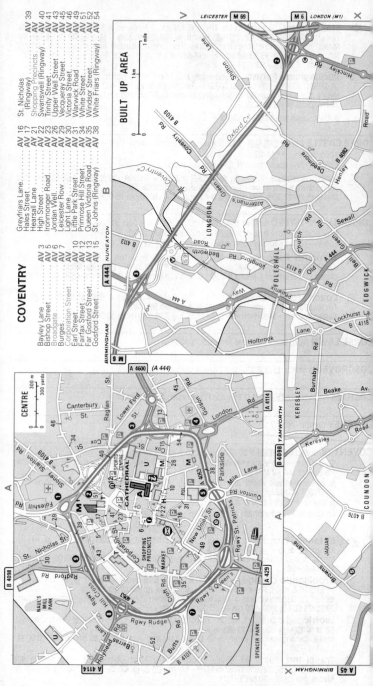

BUILT UP AREA

CENTRE

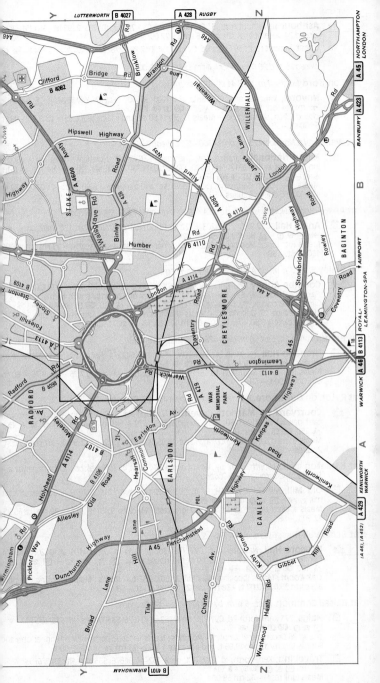

↑ **Ashbourne** without rest., 33 St. Patricks Rd, CV1 2LP, ℰ (01203) 229518 – ✦ 📺 ⅏
*closed 24 December-2 January* – **5 rm** ⚌ 22.00/38.00 **st.**
AV

↑ **Crest** without rest., 39 Friars Rd, CV1 2LJ, ℰ (01203) 227822, Fax (01203) 227244 – ✦ 📺
⅏
*closed 25 and 26 December* – **4 rm** ⚌ 25.00/48.00.
AV

**at Longford** *North : 4 m. on B 4113* – ⊠ *Coventry.*

🏨 **Novotel,** Wilsons Lane, CV6 6HL, ℰ (01203) 365000, Fax (01203) 362422, ⍭, ⌧ – ⎮⎮
✦ rm, ▤ rest, 📺 ☎ ὦ 🄿 – 🔬 200. OD AE ⓞ VISA ⅏
BV
*closed 23 to 27 December* – **Meals** 12.50/14.50 **st.** and a la carte ⒜ 6.95 – ⚌ 8.50 – **98 rm**
64.50 **st.** – SB.

**at Walsgrave** *Northeast : 3 m. on A 4600* – ⊠ *Coventry.*

🏨 **Hilton National,** Paradise Way, The Triangle, CV2 2ST, Northeast : 1 m. by A 4600 ⍺
junction 2 of M 6 ℰ (01203) 603000, Fax (01203) 603011, ⒡s, ⓐ, ⍂ – ⎮⎮, ✦ rm, ▤ 📺 ☎
ὦ 🄿 – 🔬 600. OD AE ⓞ VISA JCB
BX
**Meals** (bar lunch Saturday) 15.50/19.50 **st.** and a la carte ⒜ 6.50 – ⚌ 11.00 – **172 rm**
125.00/165.00 **st.,** 3 suites – SB.

**at Ansty** *(Warks.) Northeast : 5¾ m. by A 4600* – BY – *on B 4065* – ⊠ *Coventry.*

🏨 **Ansty Hall,** CV7 9HZ, ℰ (01203) 612222, Fax (01203) 602155, « Part 17C mansion », ⌧
✦ 📺 ☎ 🄿 – 🔬 80. OD AE ⓞ VISA ⅏
**Meals** (bar lunch Monday to Saturday)/dinner 22.95 **st.** and a la carte – **29 rm** ⚌ 105.00
130.00 **st.** – SB.

**at Binley** *East : 3½ m. on A 428* – BY – ⊠ *Coventry.*

🏨 **Coombe Abbey** ⍦, Brinklow Rd, CV3 2AB, East : 2 m. on B 4027 ℰ (01203) 450450
Fax (01203) 635101, ≤, « Former Cistercian abbey of 12C origins with formal gardens b⍺
Capability Brown », ⍭, park – ⎮⎮, ✦ rm, 📺 ☎ ὦ 🄿 – 🔬 120. OD AE ⓞ VISA JCB ⅏
*closed 24 to 27 December* – **Meals** (bar lunch Monday to Saturday)/dinner 24.50 **st.**
and a la carte ⒜ 9.50 – ⚌ 12.00 – **61 rm** 125.00/180.00 **st.,** 1 suite – SB.

**at Brandon** *(Warks.) East : 6 m. on A 428* – BZ – ⊠ *Coventry.*

🏨 **Brandon Hall** ⍦, Main St., CV8 3FW, ℰ (01203) 542571, Fax (01203) 544909, ⌧, park
squash – ✦ 📺 ☎ 🄿 – 🔬 100. OD AE ⓞ VISA
**Meals** (bar lunch Saturday) 10.95/19.95 **t.** and dinner a la carte ⒜ 7.75 – ⚌ 9.75 – **60 rm**
89.00/110.00 **t.** – SB.

**at Ryton on Dunsmore** *Southeast : 4¾ m. by A 45* – ⊠ *Coventry.*

🏨 **Courtyard by Marriott Coventry,** London Rd, CV8 3DY, on A 45 (northbound
carriageway) ℰ (01203) 301585, Fax (01203) 301610 – ✦ rm, ▤ rest, 📺 ☎ ❤ ὦ 🄿 –
🔬 250. OD AE ⓞ VISA JCB
BZ
**Meals** *(closed Saturday lunch)* a la carte 14.95/20.50 **st.** ⒜ 7.25 – ⚌ 9.50 – **47 rm** 95.00 **t.**
2 suites – SB.

**at Baginton** *(Warks.) South : 3 m. by A 4114 and A 444 off A 45 (off westbound carriageway and
Howes Lane turning)* – ⊠ *Coventry.*

🏨 **Old Mill,** Mill Hill, CV8 3AH, ℰ (01203) 302241, Fax (01203) 307070, « Converted corn
mill », ⌧ – 📺 ☎ 🄿. OD AE ⓞ VISA ⅏
BZ ⍺
**Meals** *(closed dinner 25 December)* (grill rest.) a la carte 9.45/19.20 **t.** – **20 rm** ⚌ 65.95/
72.90 **t.** – SB.

**at Berkswell** *West : 6½ m. by B 4101* – AY – ⊠ *Coventry.*

🏨 **Nailcote Hall,** Nailcote Lane, CV7 7DE, South : 1 ½ m. on B 4101 ℰ (01203) 466174
Fax (01203) 470720, « Part 17C timbered house », ⒡s, ⍂, ⒝, ⌧, ⅏ – 📺 ☎ ὦ 🄿 –
🔬 100. OD AE ⓞ VISA JCB
***Oak Room :*** **Meals** (booking essential) 21.50/29.50 **t.** – ***Rick's :*** **Meals** (booking essential
a la carte 25.00/40.00 **t.** – **38 rm** ⚌ 125.00/135.00 **st.** – SB.

**at Balsall Common** *West : 6¾ m. by B 4101* – AY – ⊠ *Coventry.*

🏨 **Haigs,** 273 Kenilworth Rd, CV7 7EL, on A 452 ℰ (01676) 533004, Fax (01676) 535132, ⌧ –
📺 ☎ 🄿. OD AE VISA ⅏
*closed 26 December-4 January* – ***Poppy's :*** **Meals** *(closed Sunday dinner)* (dinner only and
Sunday lunch)/dinner 19.95 **t.** and a la carte ⒜ 5.00 – **23 rm** ⚌ 58.00/79.50 **t.**

🏨 **Travel Inn,** Kenilworth Rd, CV7 7EX, on A 452 ℰ (01676) 533118, Fax (01676) 535926 –
✦ rm, ὦ 🄿. OD AE ⓞ VISA
**Meals** (grill rest.) – **42 rm** 38.00 **t.**

**at Allesley** *Northwest : 3 m. on A 4114 – ✉ Coventry.*

**Allesley,** Birmingham Rd, CV5 9GP, ✆ (01203) 403272, *Fax (01203) 405190* – |♯|, ▤ rest, TV ☎ ✆ P – 🏛 450. MC AE ① VISA. ✗ AY r
Meals 15.00/18.50 **st.** and a la carte – **90 rm** ⊆ 102.00/120.00 **st.**

**Brookfields** without rest., 134 Butt Lane, CV5 9FE, ✆ (01203) 404866, *Fax (01203) 402022*, ⊼ – P. ✗ AX s
**4 rm** ⊆ 28.00/48.00 **s.**

**at Meriden** *Northwest : 6 m. by A 45 on B 4104 – AX – ✉ Coventry.*

**Marriott Forest of Arden H. & Country Club,** Maxstoke Lane, CV7 7HR, Northwest : 2 ¾ m. by Maxstoke rd ✆ (01676) 522335, *Fax (01676) 523711*, Lб, ≘s, 🏊, 18, ⌒, park, ✗ – |♯| ⊁, ▤ rest, TV ☎ ♿ P – 🏛 400. MC AE ① VISA JCB. ✗
Meals *(closed Saturday lunch)* 16.50 **t.** (lunch) and dinner a la carte 18.00/23.75 **t.** 🍷 7.50 – ⊆ 11.95 – **152 rm** 107.00/167.00 **st.**, 2 suites – SB.

**Manor,** Main Rd, CV7 7NH, ✆ (01676) 522735, *Fax (01676) 522186*, ⊼ – ⊁ TV ☎ ♿ P – 🏛 275. MC AE ① VISA
Meals *(closed Saturday lunch)* 18.50/19.50 **st.** and a la carte 🍷 6.95 – **114 rm** ⊆ 110.00/120.00 **st.** – SB.

ATS Ashmore Lake Way, Willenhall ✆ (01902) 602555/605098

ATS Kingswood Close, off Holbrook Lane, Holbrooks ✆ (01203) 638554

---

**COWAN BRIDGE** *Cumbria* 402 M 21 – *see Kirkby Lonsdale.*

*Le Guide change, changez de* ***guide Michelin*** *tous les ans.*

---

**COWES** *I.O.W.* 403 404 PQ 31 – *see Wight (Isle of).*

---

**COWLEY** *Oxon. – see Oxford.*

---

**CRACKINGTON HAVEN** *Cornwall* 403 G 31 *The West Country G.* – ✉ *Bude.*

Env. : *Poundstock★ (≤★★, church★, guildhouse★), NE : 5 ½ m. by A 39 – Jacobstow (Church★), E : 3½ m.*

*London 262 – Bude 11 – Truro 42.*

**Manor Farm** ⛰, EX23 0JW, Southeast : 1 ¼ m. by Boscastle rd taking left turn onto Church Park Rd after 1.1 m. then taking first right onto unmarked lane ✆ (01840) 230304, ≤, « Part 11C manor », ⊼, park – ⊁ P. ✗
*closed 25 December* – **Meals** (by arrangement) (communal dining) 15.00 **s.** 🍷 6.00 – **4 rm** ⊆ 35.00/60.00 **s.**

**Trevigue** ⛰, EX23 0LQ, Southeast : 1 ¼ m. on High Cliff rd ✆ (01840) 230418, *Fax (01840) 230418*, « 16C farmhouse, working farm » – ⊁ P. ✗
*March-October* – **Meals** (by arrangement) (communal dining) 18.00 **t.** 🍷 6.00 – **4 rm** ⊆ 40.00/60.00.

---

**CRANBROOK** *Kent* 404 V 30 *Great Britain G. – pop. 3 522.*

Env. : *Sissinghurst Castle★ AC, NE : 2½ m. by A 229 and A 262.*

ℹ *Vestry Hall, Stone St., TN17 3HA ✆ (01580) 712538 (summer only).*

*London 53 – Hastings 19 – Maidstone 15.*

**Kennel Holt** ⛰, Goudhurst Rd, TN17 2PT, Northwest : 2 ¼ m. by A 229 on A 262 ✆ (01580) 712032, *Fax (01580) 715495*, « Gardens » – ⊁ rest, TV ☎ P. MC AE VISA JCB. ✗
*closed 2 weeks January* – **Meals** *(closed Sunday dinner to non-residents and Monday)* (lunch by arrangement)/dinner 27.50 **t.** 🍷 7.00 – **10 rm** ⊆ 90.00/185.00 **st.**

**Hartley Mount,** TN17 3QX, South : ½ m. on A 229 ✆ (01580) 712230, *Fax (01580) 715733*, ⊼ – ⊁ TV ☎ 🚗 P. MC AE VISA JCB. ✗
**Meals** (dinner only) 17.50 **s.** and a la carte 🍷 5.50 – **6 rm** ⊆ 60.00/90.00 **s.** – SB.

**Old Cloth Hall** ⛰, TN17 3NR, East : 1 m. by Tenterden Rd ✆ (01580) 712220, *Fax (01580) 712220*, ≤, « Tudor manor house, gardens », park – ⊁ rm, TV P. ✗
*closed Christmas* – **Meals** (by arrangement) (communal dining) 22.00 **st.** – **3 rm** ⊆ 50.00/100.00 **st.**

**Soho South,** 23 Stone St., TN17 3HF, ✆ (01580) 714666, *Fax (01580) 715653* – MC VISA
*closed Sunday to Tuesday, 25 December-1 January and 2 weeks in summer* – **Meals** a la carte 14.30/24.00 🍷 4.80.

ENGLAND

CRANBROOK

**at Sissinghurst** Northeast : 1 ¾ m. by B 2189 on A 262 – ⊠ Cranbrook.

※ **Rankins**, The Street, TN17 2JH, on A 262 ℰ (01580) 713964 – 🕮 𝖵𝖨𝖲𝖠
closed Sunday dinner, Monday, Tuesday and Bank Holidays except Good Friday, restricted
opening in winter – **Meals** (dinner only and Sunday lunch)/dinner 25.00 t. 🛆 6.50.

**CRANTOCK** Cornwall 403 E 32 – see Newquay.

**CRAVEN ARMS** Shrops. 402 403 L 26 Great Britain G. – pop. 1 892.
Env. : Wenlock Edge★, NE : by B 4368.
London 170 – Birmingham 47 – Hereford 32 – Shrewsbury 21.

↑ **Old Rectory** ⌂, Hopesay, SY7 8HD, West : 4 m. by B 4368 ℰ (01588) 660245,
Fax (01588) 660502, ≼, « Part 17C », 🐎 – ✦ 📺 🅿. 🛠
closed Christmas and New Year – **Meals** (by arrangement) (communal dining) 20.00 st.
🛆 6.50 – **3 rm** 🖙 70.00 st.

**CRAWLEY** Hants. 403 404 P 30 – see Winchester.

**CRAWLEY** W. Sussex 404 T 30 – pop. 88 203.
🗽, 🗽 Cottesmore, Buchan Hill, Pease Pottage ℰ (01293) 528256 – 🗽, 🗽 Tilgate Forest,
Titmus Drive, Tilgate ℰ (01293) 530103 – 🗽 Gatwick Manor, London Rd, Lowfield Heath
ℰ (01293) 538587 – 🗽 Pease Pottage, Horsham Rd ℰ (01293) 521706.
London 33 – Brighton 21 – Lewes 23 – Royal Tunbridge Wells 23.

Plan of enlarged Area : see Gatwick

🏨🏨 **Holiday Inn London Gatwick**, Langley Drive, Tushmore Roundabout, RH11 7SX,
ℰ (01293) 529991, Fax (01293) 515913, 🖪, ☎, 🔲 – ⧄, ✦ rm, 🗏 📺 ☎ ఉ 🅿 – 🛆 275. 🕮
🄰🄴 🕕 𝖵𝖨𝖲𝖠. 🛠                                                                                                  BY n
**Colonnade :** Meals (dinner only and Sunday lunch)/dinner a la carte 17.40/26.15 st. – **La
Brasserie :** Meals a la carte 15.00/22.15 st. – 🖙 12.50 – **218 rm** 150.00 st., 2 suites.

🏨🏨 **Europa Gatwick**, Balcombe Rd, Maidenbower, RH10 7ZR, East : 2 ½ m. by Haslett Av.
and Worth Rd on B 2036 ℰ (01293) 886666, Fax (01293) 886781, 🖪, ☎, 🔲, 🐎 – ⧄,
✦ rm, 📺 ☎ ఉ 🅿 – 🛆 300. 🕮 🄰🄴 🕕 𝖵𝖨𝖲𝖠. 🛠              on Gatwick town plan  Z a
**Mediterranee :** Meals (dinner only and Sunday lunch)/dinner 13.50 st. and a la carte – 🖙
9.95 – **207 rm** 100.00/125.00 st., 4 suites.

🏨🏨 **George**, High St., RH10 1BS, ℰ (01293) 524215, Fax (01293) 548565 – ✦ 📺 ☎ 🅿 –
🛆 160. 🕮 🄰🄴 🕕 𝖵𝖨𝖲𝖠                                                                                         BY o
**Meals** (bar lunch Monday to Saturday)/dinner a la carte 13.00/21.50 st. – 🖙 9.75 – **80 rm**
70.00/80.00 st. – SB.

🏨 **Goffs Park - Premier Lodge**, Goffs Park Rd, Southgate, RH11 8AX, ℰ (01293) 535447,
Fax (01293) 542050, Reservations (Freephone) 0800 118833, 🐎 – ✦ rm, 🗏 rest, 📺 ☎ 🖐
ఉ 🅿 – 🛆 150. 🕮 🄰🄴 🕕 𝖵𝖨𝖲𝖠. 🛠                                                                         AZ a
**Meals** (grill rest.) 7.25/12.95 st. and a la carte 🛆 5.00 – 🖙 7.00 – **57 rm** 48.95 st.

**at Copthorne** Northeast : 4½ m. on A 264 – BY.

🏨🏨 **Copthorne London Gatwick**, Copthorne Way, RH10 3PG, ℰ (01342) 714971,
Fax (01342) 717375, 🖪, ☎, 🔲, 🐎, park, ※, squash – ✦ rm, 📺 ☎ 🅿 – 🛆 120. 🕮 🄰🄴
🕕 𝖵𝖨𝖲𝖠 🄹🄲🄱
**Lion D'Or :** Meals (closed Saturday lunch, Sunday and Bank Holidays) 18.95/23.95 t.
and a la carte 🛆 11.25 – **Brasserie :** Meals (carving lunch) 16.95 t. and a la carte – 🖙 12.50 –
**227 rm** 120.00/130.00 st.

🏨🏨 **Copthorne Effingham Park**, West Park Rd, RH10 3EU, on B 2028 ℰ (01342) 714994,
Fax (01342) 716039, ≼, 🖪, ☎, 🔲, 🗽, 🐎, park, ※ – ⧄, ✦ rm, 📺 ☎ 🅿 – 🛆 600. 🕮 🄰🄴
🕕 𝖵𝖨𝖲𝖠. 🛠
**Terrace :** Meals (bar lunch)/dinner a la carte 20.45/31.75 t. 🛆 6.50 – 🖙 12.50 – **119 rm**
120.00/130.00 t., 3 suites.

**at Three Bridges** East : 1 m. on Haslett Avenue East – BY – ⊠ Crawley.

🏨🏨 **Jarvis International Gatwick**, Tinsley Lane South, RH10 2XH, North : ½ m. by Hazel-
wick Av. ℰ (01293) 561186, Fax (01293) 561169, 🖪, ☎, 🔲 – ⧄, ✦ rm, 🗏 📺 ☎ ఉ 🅿 –
🛆 210. 🕮 🄰🄴 🕕 𝖵𝖨𝖲𝖠 🄹🄲🄱. 🛠                                             on Gatwick town plan  Y n
**Meals** (closed Sunday lunch) 17.95 st. and a la carte 🛆 7.00 – 🖙 11.95 – **151 rm** 115.00/
135.00 st.

🅐 ATS Reynolds Rd, West Green ℰ (01293) 533151/2

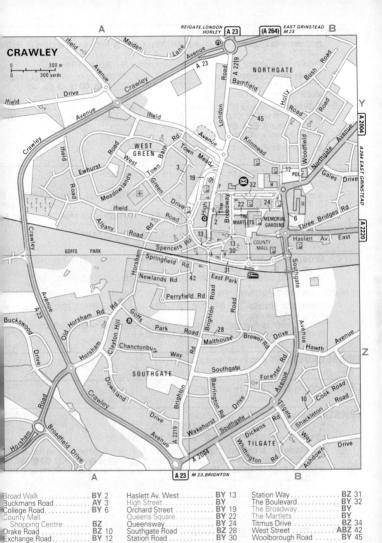

# CRAWLEY

REIGATE, LONDON HORLEY **A 23**　(A 264)　EAST GRINSTEAD M 23

0      300 m
0      300 yards

Bitte beachten Sie die Geschwindigkeitsbeschränkungen in Großbritannien

- 60 mph (= 96 km/h) außerhalb geschlossener Ortschaften
- 70 mph (= 112 km/h) auf Straßen mit getrennten Fahrbahnen und Autobahnen.

---

**CRESSAGE** Shrops. **402 403 404** M 26 – pop. 810 – ⊠ Shrewsbury.
London 163 – Birmingham 46 – Chester 48 – Manchester 73 – Shrewsbury 6 – Stoke-on-Trent 34.

**Cholmondeley Riverside Inn** with rm, SY5 6AF, Northwest : 1 ½ m. on A 458 ℰ (01952) 510900, Fax (01952) 510980, ≤, 佘, « Riverside setting », ≤, ☞ – ☑ ☎ ℗ ◑◎
**VISA**
closed 25 December – **Meals** a la carte 11.85/23.15 **t.** – 6 rm ☑ 50.00/90.00 **t.** – SB.

217

**CREWE** Ches. 402 403 404 M 24 – pop. 63 351.

   ⟨g⟩ Queen's Park, Queen's Park Drive ℘ (01270) 666724 – ⟨g⟩ Fields Rd, Haslington ℘ (01270) 584227.

   London 174 – Chester 24 – Liverpool 49 – Manchester 36 – Stoke-on-Trent 15.

   🏨 **Travel Inn,** Coppenhall Lane, Woolstanwood, CW2 8SD, West : 2 m. on A 532 at junction with A 530 ℘ (01270) 251126, Fax (01270) 256316 – ⇥ ⟲ TV & ℗. ⦿ AE ① VISA. ⊗
   **Meals** (grill rest.) – **41 rm** 38.00 **t.**

   🏨 **Travelodge,** Alsager Rd, Barthomley, CW2 5PT, Southeast : 5 ½ m. by A 5020 on A 500 at junction with M 6 ℘ (01270) 883157, Fax (01270) 883157, Reservations (Freephone) 0800 850950 – ⇥ rm, TV & ℗. ⦿ AE ① VISA JCB. ⊗
   **Meals** (grill rest.) – **42 rm** 39.95/59.95 **t.**

   ⓐ ATS Cresty Rd ℘ (01270) 256285

---

**CREWKERNE** Somerset 403 L 31 The West Country G. – pop. 7 142.

   See : Church★.
   Env. : Forde Abbey★ AC, SW : 8 m. by B 3165 and B 3162 – Clapton Court Gardens★ AC, S : 3 ½ m. by B 3165.
   Exc. : Montacute House★★ AC, NE : 7 m. by A 30 – Parnham House★★ AC, SE : 7 ½ m. by A 356 and A 3066.
   ⟨g⟩ Windwhistle G. & C.C., Cricket St. Thomas, Chard ℘ (01460) 30231.
   London 145 – Exeter 38 – Southampton 81 – Taunton 20.

   ⌂ **Broadview Gardens,** East Crewkerne, TA18 7AG, ℘ (01460) 73424, Fax (01460) 73424, ⩽, ☞ – ⇥ TV ℗. ⦿ VISA
   **Meals** (by arrangement) (communal dining) 14.00 – **3 rm** ⌷ 25.00/56.00 **st.** – SB.

**at Middle Chinnock** Northeast : 3 ¾ m. by A 30 off West Chinnock rd – ⊠ Crewkerne.

   ⌂ **Chinnock House** ⌀, TA18 7PN, ℘ (01935) 881229, Fax (01935) 881229, « Georgian house », ⌇, ☞ – ℗. ⊗
   closed Christmas, New Year, 2 weeks spring and 2 weeks winter – **Meals** (by arrangement) (communal dining) 22.00 **s.** – **3 rm** ⌷ 35.00/55.00 **s.**

---

**CRIBBS CAUSEWAY** Bristol – see Bristol.

---

**CRICK** Northants. 403 404 Q 26 – see Rugby.

---

**CRICKLADE** Wilts 403 404 O 29 – pop. 3 808.

   ⟨g⟩ Cricklade Hotel, Common Hill ℘ (01793) 750751.
   London 90 – Bristol 45 – Gloucester 27 – Oxford 34 – Swindon 6.

   🏨 **Cricklade H. & Country Club,** Common Hill, SN6 6HA, Southwest : 1 m. on B 4040 ℘ (01793) 750751, Fax (01793) 751767, ⩽, ₤₆, ⌷, ⟨g⟩, ⊗ – TV ☎ ℗ – 🔬 120. ⦿ AE VISA. ⊗
   closed 24 to 26 December – **Meals** 15.50/20.00 **t.** and a la carte ⅄ 6.50 – **46 rm** ⌷ 82.00/130.00 – SB.

---

**CROCKERTON** Wilts. – see Warminster.

---

**CROFT-ON-TEES** Durham 402 P 20 – see Darlington.

---

**CROMER** Norfolk 404 X 25 – pop. 7 267.

   ⟨g⟩ Royal Cromer, Overstrand Rd ℘ (01263) 512884.
   🛈 Bus Station, Prince of Wales Rd, NR27 9HS ℘ (01263) 512497.
   London 132 – Norwich 23.

   ⌂ **Morden House,** 20 Cliff Av., NR27 0AN, ℘ (01263) 513396, ☞ – ⇥ TV ℗. ①
   **Meals** 13.50 ⅄ 5.50 – **6 rm** ⌷ 25.00/50.00 – SB.

   ⌂ **Birch House,** 34 Cabbell Rd, NR27 9HX, ℘ (01263) 512521 – ⇥ TV. ⦿ AE VISA JCB. ⊗
   closed 23 to 30 December – **Meals** (by arrangement) 8.00 – **8 rm** ⌷ 18.00/42.00 **s.**

**at Northrepps** Southeast : 3 m. by A 140 and Northrepps rd – ⊠ Cromer.

   ⌂ **Shrublands Farm,** NR27 0AA, ℘ (01263) 579297, Fax (01263) 579297, « Working farm », ☞ – ⇥ ℗. ⊗
   closed last 2 weeks December – **Meals** (by arrangement) (communal dining) 14.00 **s.** – **3 rm** ⌷ 27.00/46.00.

**CRONDALL** Hants. 404 R 30 – pop. 6 113.
London 56 – Reading 21 – Winchester 30.

XX **The Chesa,** Bowling Alley, GU10 5RJ, North : 1 m. ℘ (01252) 850328, Fax (01252) 850328 – 📵. 🐠 📧 *VISA*
closed Saturday lunch, Sunday dinner, Monday, Tuesday and 2 weeks January – **Meals** (booking essential) (lunch by arrangement)/dinner a la carte 22.50/26.00 t. 🍷 6.00.

---

**CRONTON** Mersey. 402 403 404 L 23 – see Widnes.

---

**CROOK** Durham 401 402 O 19 – pop. 8 246 – ⊠ Bishop Auckland.
🏌 Low Job's Hill ℘ (01388) 762429.
London 261 – Carlisle 65 – Middlesbrough 34 – Newcastle upon Tyne 27.

🏠 **Duke of York Inn,** Fir Tree, DL15 8DG, Southwest : 3 ½ m. by A 689 off A 68 ℘ (01388) 762848 – 📺 🕿 📵. 🐠 ⓪ *VISA*. ⪦
**Meals** a la carte 15.00/24.15 t. 🍷 4.95 – **4 rm** ⌑ 52.00/69.00 t. – SB.

↟ **Greenhead Country House** without rest., Fir Tree, DL15 8BL, Southwest : 3 ½ m. by A 689 off A 68 ℘ (01388) 763143, Fax (01388) 763143, ✿ – 📺 📵. 🐠 *VISA*. ⪦
**7 rm** ⌑ 40.00/55.00 s.

---

**CROPTON** N. Yorks. 402 R 21 – see Pickering.

---

**CROSBY** Mersey. 402 403 K 23 – see Liverpool.

---

**CROSBY GARRETT** Cumbria – see Kirkby Stephen.

---

**CROSS HOUSES** Shrops. 402 403 L 25 – see Shrewsbury.

---

**CROSTHWAITE** Cumbria 402 L 21 – see Kendal.

---

**CROWBOROUGH** E. Sussex 404 U 30 – pop. 19 563.
London 45 – Brighton 25 – Maidstone 26.

🏨 **Winston Manor,** TN6 1AD, on A 26 ℘ (01892) 652772, Fax (01892) 665537, ₷, ♨, ⬛ – 📶 📺 🕿 📵 – 🔬 300. 🐠 📧 ⓪ *VISA*. ⪦
closed 25 to 30 December – **Meals** (bar lunch Monday to Saturday)/dinner 21.50 t. and a la carte 🍷 5.95 – **51 rm** ⌑ 95.00/115.00 t. – SB.

🅐 ATS Church Rd ℘ (01892) 662100

---

**CROWTHORNE** Bracknell Forest 404 R 29 – pop. 21 500.
London 42 – Reading 15.

XX **Beijing,** 103 Old Wokingham Rd, RG45 6LH, Northeast : ¾ m. by A 3095 ℘ (01344) 778802 – 🗏 📵. 🐠 📧 ⓪ *VISA* JCB
closed Sunday lunch and Bank Holidays – **Meals** - Chinese - 15.50/18.50 t. and a la carte.

---

**CROXDALE** Durham – see Durham.

---

**CROYDE** Devon 403 H 30 – ⊠ Braunton.
London 232 – Barnstaple 10 – Exeter 50 – Taunton 61.

🏨 **Croyde Bay House** ⪦, Moor Lane, Croyde Bay, EX33 1PA, Northwest : 1 m. by Baggy Point rd ℘ (01271) 890270, ≤ Croyde Bay, ✿ – ⪦ rm, 📺 🕿 📵. 🐠 *VISA* JCB
March-mid November – **Meals** (dinner only) 19.50 st. 🍷 4.50 – **7 rm** ⌑ (dinner included) 67.50/115.00 t. – SB.

🏨 **Kittiwell House,** St. Mary's Rd, EX33 1PG, ℘ (01271) 890247, Fax (01271) 890469, « 16C thatched Devon longhouse » – ⪦ rm, 📺 🕿 📵. 🐠 📧 *VISA* JCB
closed January – **Meals** (dinner only and Sunday lunch)/dinner 19.90 t. and a la carte 🍷 5.30 – **12 rm** ⌑ (dinner included) 67.00/122.00 t. – SB.

↟ **Whiteleaf** without rest., Hobbs Hill, EX33 1PN, ℘ (01271) 890266, ✿ – 📺 🕿 📵. 🐠 📧 *VISA* JCB
**4 rm** ⌑ 37.00/60.00 t.

**CRUDWELL** Wilts. 403 404 N 29 – see Malmesbury.

---

**CUCKFIELD** W. Sussex 404 T 30 – pop. 2 879.
London 40 – Brighton 15.

🏨 **Ockenden Manor** ⌖, Ockenden Lane, RH17 5LD, ℘ (01444) 416111, Fax (01444) 415549, « Part 16C manor house », 🌳 – ⇔ rest, 📺 ☎ 🅿 – 🛋 50. 🆑 🆎 ⓞ VISA. ⌖
Meals 19.50/32.50 t. and a la carte 30.50/49.00 t. ⌖ 7.50 – ⌐ 5.00 – **20 rm** 105.00/195.00, 2 suites – SB.

---

**CULLOMPTON** Devon 403 J 31 The West Country G. – pop. 5 676.
See : Town★ – St. Andrew's Church★.
Env. : Uffculme (Coldharbour Mill★★ AC) NE : 5½ m. by B 3181 and B 3391.
Exc. : Killerton★★, SW : 6½ m. by B 3181 and B 3185.
🏌 Padbrook Park ℘ (01884) 38286.
London 197 – Exeter 15 – Taunton 29.

🏨 **Manor**, 2-4 Fore St., EX15 1JL, ℘ (01884) 32281, Fax (01884) 38344 – 📺 ☎ 🅿. 🆑 VISA
Meals (closed Sunday dinner and Bank Holidays) (bar lunch)/dinner a la carte 14.10/21.20 t. – **10 rm** ⌐ 46.50/65.00.

---

**CUMNOR** Oxon. 403 404 P 28 – see Oxford.

---

**CURDWORTH** W. Mids. 402 ⑩ 403 ㉛ 404 ⑳ – see Sutton Coldfield.

---

**DALTON** N. Yorks. 402 O 20 – see Richmond.

---

**DALTON-IN-FURNESS** Cumbria 402 K 21 – pop. 7 550.
🏌 The Dunnerholme, Duddon Rd, Askham-in-Furness ℘ (01229) 262675.
London 283 – Barrow-in-Furness 3.5 – Kendal 30 – Lancaster 41.

🏨 **Clarence House Country**, Skelgate, LA15 8BQ, Northwest : ½ m. on Askam rd ℘ (01229) 462508, Fax (01229) 467177, 🌳 – 📺 ☎ 🅿 – 🛋 40. 🆑 🆎 VISA JCB
Meals 10.95/19.95 t. and a la carte ⌖ 6.80 – **19 rm** ⌐ 65.00/75.00 t. – SB.

---

**DARESBURY** Warrington 402 403 404 M 23 – pop. 1 579 – ✉ Warrington.
London 197 – Chester 16 – Liverpool 22 – Manchester 25.

🏨 **Daresbury Park**, Chester Rd, WA4 4BB, on A 56 ℘ (01925) 267331, Fax (01925) 265615, ⌖, ⌖, ☒, squash – 📳, ⇔ rm, ▤ rest, 📺 ☎ 🅿 – 🛋 300. 🆑 🆎 ⓞ VISA JCB
The Looking Glass : Meals (closed Saturday lunch) (carving rest.) 15.00/18.00 st. – The Terrace : Meals (dinner only) 30.00 t. and a la carte – **140 rm** ⌐ 140.00 st. – SB.

---

**DARGATE** Kent – see Faversham.

---

**DARLEY ABBEY** Derbs. 402 403 404 P 25 – see Derby.

---

**DARLINGTON** 402 P 20 – pop. 86 767.
🏌 Blackwell Grange, Briar Close ℘ (01325) 464464 – 🏌 Stressholme, Snipe Lane ℘ (01325) 461002.
✈ Teesside Airport : ℘ (01325) 332811, E : 6 m. by A 67.
🛈 4 West Row, DL1 5PL ℘ (01325) 382698.
London 251 – Leeds 61 – Middlesbrough 14 – Newcastle upon Tyne 35.

🏨 **Blackwell Grange**, Blackwell Grange, DL3 8QH, Southwest : 1 m. on A 167 ℘ (01325) 509955, Fax (01325) 380899, ⌖, ☎, ☒, 🏌, 🌳 – 📳 ⇔ 📺 ☎ 🅿 – 🛋 300. 🆑 🆎 ⓞ VISA. ⌖
Meals (closed Saturday lunch) 8.95/15.95 st. and a la carte ⌖ 4.95 – ⌐ 9.75 – **99 rm** 90.00/130.00 st. – SB.

🏨 **Grange**, Southend Av., DL3 7HZ, Northwest : ¾ m. by A 167 on B 6280 ℘ (01325) 365859, Fax (01325) 487111 – ▤ 📺 ☎ 🅿 – 🛋 100. 🆑 🆎 ⓞ VISA
Meals – (see **Maxines** below) – **14 rm** ⌐ 105.00 t. – SB.

⌂ **Balmoral** without rest., 63 Woodland Rd, DL3 7BQ, ℰ (01325) 461908, *Fax (01325) 461908* – ⬤ ☎ ⬤. ⬤
*closed 25 December* – **9 rm** ⬜ 28.00/45.00 **st.**

XX **Maxines** (at Grange H.), Southend Av., DL3 7HZ, Northwest : ¾ m. by A 167 on B 6280 ℰ (01325) 365858, *Fax (01325) 487111* – ▤ ⬤. ⬤ AE ⬤ *VISA*
*closed Tuesday and Saturday lunch, Sunday dinner and Monday* – **Meals** 16.00 **t.** (lunch) and a la carte 21.40/29.60 **t.**

at **Coatham Mundeville** *North : 4 m. on A 167* – ✉ *Darlington*.

▲▲▲ **Hall Garth Golf** & Country Club, DL1 3LU, East : ¼ m. on Brafferton rd ℰ (01325) 300400, *Fax (01325) 310083*, *f₆*, ☎s, ⬜, *f₅*, ⇆, ℀ – ⬤ ☎ ⬤ ⬤ – ⚖ 300. ⬤
AE ⬤ *VISA*. ℀
*Hugo's :* **Meals** (bar meals Monday to Saturday lunch and Sunday dinner)/dinner a la carte 23.00/30.00 **st.** ₦ 5.95 – ⬜ 11.95 – **40 rm** 95.00/120.00 **st.**, 1 suite – SB.

at **Aycliffe** *North : 5½ m. on A 167* – ✉ *Darlington*.

⎸🔲 **The County,** 13 The Green, DL5 6LX, ℰ (01325) 312273 – ⬤ ⬤. ⬤ ⬤ *VISA*
*closed dinner Sunday and Monday* – **Meals** (booking essential) a la carte 14.20/22.20 **t.**

at **Croft-on-Tees** *South : 3½ m. on A 167* – ✉ *Darlington*.

🏠 **Clow Beck House** ⬀, Monk End Farm, DL2 2SW, West : ½ m. by South Parade ℰ (01325) 721075, *Fax (01325) 720419*, ≼, « Working farm », ⬍, ⇆, park – ⬤ ☎ & ⬤. ⬤
AE *VISA*. ℀
**Meals** (residents only) (dinner only) a la carte 17.00/24.00 **st.** – **14 rm** ⬜ 40.00/60.00 **st.**

at **Headlam** *Northwest : 6 m. by A 67* – ✉ *Gainford*.

▥▥ **Headlam Hall** ⬀, DL2 3HA, ℰ (01325) 730238, *Fax (01325) 730790*, ≼, « Part Jacobean and part Georgian manor house, gardens », ☎s, ⬜, park, ℀ – ⬤ ☎ ☎ ⬤ – ⚖ 150. ⬤ AE ⬤ *VISA*. ℀
*closed 25 and 26 December* – **Meals** (lunch by arrangement) 13.50/19.00 **st.** and a la carte ₦ 4.50 – **34 rm** ⬜ 61.00/90.00 **st.**, 2 suites – SB.

at **Heighington** *Northwest : 6 m. by A 68 off A 6072* – ✉ *Darlington*.

⌂ **Eldon House** without rest., East Green, DL5 6PP, ℰ (01325) 312270, *Fax (01325) 315580*, « Part 17C », ⇆, ℀ – ⬤
**3 rm** ⬜ 30.00/50.00 **s.**

at **Redworth** *Northwest : 7 m. by A 68 on A 6072* – ✉ *Bishop Auckland*.

▦▦▦ **Redworth Hall H.** & Country Club ⬀, DL5 6NL, on A 6072 ℰ (01388) 772442, *Fax (01388) 775112*, « Part 18C and 19C manor house of Elizabethan origins », *f₆*, ☎s, ⬜, ⇆, park, ℀, squash – |✦|, ⬤ rm, ▤ rest, ⬤ ☎ ⬤ – ⚖ 300. ⬤ AE ⬤ *VISA* JCB
*Conservatory :* **Meals** 14.95/22.00 **st.** and a la carte ₦ 7.95 – (see also *The Blue Room* below) – ⬜ 12.50 – **96 rm** 112.00/122.00 **st.**, 4 suites – SB.

XXX **The Blue Room** (at Redworth Hall H. & Country Club), DL5 6NL, on A 6072 ℰ (01388) 772442, *Fax (01388) 775112*, « Part 18C and 19C manor house of Elizabethan origins », ⇆, park – ⬤ ⬤. ⬤ AE ⬤ *VISA* JCB
*closed Sunday and Bank Holiday Monday* – **Meals** (dinner only) 36.50 **st.** ₦ 7.90.

Ⓐ ATS Albert St., off Neasham Rd
ℰ (01325) 469271/469693

ATS Leaside, Aycliffe Ind. Est., Aycliffe
ℰ (01325) 313186/321622

---

**DARTFORD** *Kent* 🔲🔲🔲 U 29 – *pop. 59 411.*
*Dartford Tunnel and Bridge (toll).*
🛈 *The Clocktower, Suffolk Rd, DA1 1EJ* ℰ (01322) 343243.
*London 20 – Hastings 51 – Maidstone 22.*

▲▲▲ **Stakis Dartford Bridge,** Masthead Close, Crossways Business Park, DA2 6QF, Northeast : 2 ½ m. by A 226, Cotton Lane and Crossways Boulevard ℰ (01322) 284444, *Fax (01322) 288225*, *f₆*, ☎s, ⬜, ℀ – |✦|, ⬤ rm, ▤ ⬤ ☎ ☎ & ⬤ – ⚖ 240. ⬤ AE ⬤ *VISA*
**Meals** *(closed Saturday lunch)* 16.95/19.95 **t.** and a la carte – ⬜ 7.50 – **172 rm** 119.00/159.00 **st.**, 4 suites – SB.

🏠 **Campanile,** Dartford Bridge, Clipper Boulevard West, Edison's Park, Crossways, DA2 6QN, Northeast : 3 m. by A 226, Cotton Lane and Galleon Boulevard ℰ (01322) 278925, *Fax (01322) 278948* – ⬤ ⬤ ☎ & ⬤. ⬤ AE ⬤ *VISA*
**Meals** 10.85 **st.** and a la carte – ⬜ 4.50 – **125 rm** 38.00 **st.**

---

**DARTINGTON** *Devon* 🔲🔲🔲 I 32 – *see Totnes.*

**DARTMOUTH** Devon 🗺️ J 32 *The West Country G. – pop. 5 676.*

*See : Town★★ (≤★) – Old Town - Butterwalk★ - Dartmouth Castle (≤★★★) AC.*

*Exc. : Start Point (≤★) S : 13 m. (including 1 m. on foot).*

🖪 *The Engine House, Mayor's Av., TQ6 9YY ℰ (01803) 834224.*

*London 236 – Exeter 36 – Plymouth 35.*

🏨 **Royal Castle,** 11 The Quay, TQ6 9PS, ℰ (01803) 833033, Fax (01803) 835445, ≤ – ↔ rest
📺 ☎. 🆔 🅰🅴 🆅🅸🆂🅰
**Meals** (bar lunch Monday to Saturday)/dinner 18.50 **t.** and a la carte 🛈 7.00 – **25 rm**
😄 63.45/131.90 **t.** – SB.

🏨 **Dart Marina,** Sandquay, TQ6 9PH, ℰ (01803) 832580, Fax (01803) 835040, ≤ Dart Marina
– ↔, 🍽 rest, 📺 ☎ 🆔 🅰🅴 🅾 🆅🅸🆂🅰 🅹🅲🅱. ⁓
**Meals** (bar lunch Monday to Saturday)/dinner a la carte 17.45/24.15 **t.** 🛈 5.95 – 😄 9.95 -
**50 rm** 70.00/90.00 **st.** – SB.

🏠 **Ford House,** 44 Victoria Rd, TQ6 9DX, ℰ (01803) 834047, Fax (01803) 834047, 🌳 – 📺 ☎
🅿. 🆔 🆅🅸🆂🅰
*April-October –* **Meals** (residents only) (communal dining) (dinner only) (unlicensed)
25.00 **st.** – **4 rm** 😄 45.00/70.00 **st.** – SB.

🏠 **Boringdon House** without rest., 1 Church Rd, TQ6 9HQ, ℰ (01803) 832235, « Georgian
house », 🌳 – ↔ 📺 🅿. ⁓
**3 rm** 😄 39.00/50.00 **s.**

🏠 **Wadstray House** ⤴ without rest., Blackawton, TQ9 7DE, West : 4 ½ m. on A 3122
ℰ (01803) 712539, Fax (01803) 712539, 🌳 – ↔ 📺 🅿. ⁓
*closed 25 and 26 December –* **3 rm** 😄 45.00/60.00 **st.**

🏠 **Hedley House** without rest., Newcomen Rd, TQ6 9BN, ℰ (01803) 835849, ≤ Dart Estu
ary and Kingswear – ↔. ⁓
**3 rm** 😄 50.00/80.00 **s.**

🏠 **Woodside Cottage** ⤴ without rest., Blackawton, TQ9 7BL, West : 5 ½ m. by A 3122 on
Blackawton rd ℰ (01803) 712375, Fax (01803) 712605, ≤, 🌳 – ↔ 📺 🅿. ⁓
*February-October –* **3 rm** 😄 38.00/44.00 **t.**

🍴🍴 **Carved Angel,** 2 South Embankment, TQ6 9BH, ℰ (01803) 832465, Fax (01803) 835147
≤ Dart Estuary – ↔. 🆔 🆅🅸🆂🅰
*closed Sunday dinner, Monday, 1 January-14 February and 23 to 27 December –* **Meals**
30.00/48.00 **st.** and lunch a la carte 🛈 7.50.

🍴🍴 **Aragua,** St. Saviours Sq., TQ6 9DH, ℰ (01803) 832224, Fax (01803) 832224 – 🅿. 🆔 🅰
🆅🅸🆂🅰
*closed Sunday dinner, Monday, Tuesday, 3 weeks March, last week June and 3 weeks
December –* **Meals** (dinner only and Sunday lunch)/dinner a la carte 22.75/30.00 **st.**

**at Kingswear** *East : via lower ferry taking first right onto Church Hill before Steam Packet Inn -*
✉ *Dartmouth.*

🏠 **Nonsuch House,** Church Hill, TQ6 0BX, ℰ (01803) 752829, Fax (01803) 752829, ≤ Dart
mouth Castle and Warfleet – ↔ 📺. ⁓
**Meals** (residents only) (dinner only) (unlicensed) 17.50 **st.** – **5 rm** 😄 52.50/75.00 **st.**

**at Stoke Fleming** *Southwest : 3 m. on A 379 –* ✉ *Dartmouth.*

🏨 **Stoke Lodge,** Cinders Lane, TQ6 ORA, ℰ (01803) 770523, Fax (01803) 770851, ≤, 🛝, 🏊
🖦, 🌳, ⁓ – 📺 ☎ 🅿. 🆔 🅰🅴 🆅🅸🆂🅰
**Meals** 11.95/16.25 **t.** and a la carte 🛈 5.95 – **26 rm** 😄 52.00/95.00 **t.** – SB.

---

**DAVENTRY** Northants 🗺️ Q 27 – *pop. 18 099.*

🛝 *Norton Rd ℰ (01327) 702829 – 🛝, 🛝 Hellidon Lakes Hotel & C.C., Hellidon ℰ (01327)
62550 – 🛝 Staverton Park, Staverton ℰ (01327) 302000/302118.*

🖪 *Moot Hall, Market Sq., NN11 4BH ℰ (01327) 300277.*

*London 79 – Coventry 23 – Northampton 13 – Oxford 46.*

🏨 **Fawsley Hall** ⤴, Fawsley, NN11 3BA, South : 6 ½ m. by A 45 off A 361
ℰ (01327) 892000, Fax (01327) 892001, ≤, « Tudor manor house with Georgian and Victor
ian additions », 🐟, 🌳, park, ⁓ – 📺 ☎ 🅲 🅿 – 🔬 200. 🆔 🅰🅴 🅾 🆅🅸🆂🅰. ⁓
**Meals** 22.50/35.50 **st.** 🛈 10.00 – **28 rm** 😄 160.00/260.00 **st.**, 2 suites – SB.

🏨 **Hanover International H. and Club Daventry,** Sedgemoor Way, off Ashby Rd
NN11 5SG, North : 2 m. on A 361 ℰ (01327) 301777, Fax (01327) 706313, 🛝, �)s, 🏊 – 🛝
↔, 🍽 rest, 📺 ☎ 🅱 🅿 – 🔬 600. 🆔 🅰🅴 🅾 🆅🅸🆂🅰. ⁓
**Meals** 13.00/18.50 **st.** and dinner a la carte 🛈 9.50 – 😄 10.00 – **136 rm** 100.00 **st.**, 2 suites
SB.

**at Flore** *East : 6 m. on A 45 –* ⊠ *Northampton.*

🏨 **Courtyard by Marriott Daventry,** High St., NN7 4LP, East : ½ m. on A 45 𝒫 (01327) 349022, Fax (01327) 349017, *f₆* – ⁕⁕ rm, ▤ rest, ▥ ☎ & ♓ – ⚿ 80. ◍ ◭ ◍ VISA. ⁕⁕
Meals a la carte 16.00/21.00 **st.** ♦ 7.25 – ⊑ 9.50 – **53 rm** 75.00 **st.** – SB.

**at Everdon** *Southeast : 7 m. by A 45, A 361 and B 4037 on Everdon rd –* ⊠ *Daventry.*

⌂ **Threeways House,** NN11 6BL, 𝒫 (01327) 361631, Fax (01327) 361359, *☞* – ⁕⁕ rest, ▥ ♓ ⁕⁕
Meals (by arrangement) (communal dining) 15.00 **st.** – **3 rm** ⊑ 30.00/55.00 **st.**

**at Badby** *South : 3½ m. by A 45 on A 361 –* ⊠ *Daventry.*

🏨 **Windmill Inn,** Main St., NN11 3AN, 𝒫 (01327) 702363, Fax (01327) 311521 – ▥ ☎ ♓ – ⚿ 50. ◍ ◭ VISA
Meals a la carte 11.85/16.95 **t.** ♦ 5.00 – **8 rm** ⊑ 49.00/79.00 **st.** – SB.

**at Helidon** *Southwest : 6½ m. by A 45 and A 361 on Hellidon rd –* ⊠ *Daventry.*

🏨🏨 **Hellidon Lakes H. & Country Club** ⑁, NN11 6LN, Southwest : ¾ m. 𝒫 (01327) 262550, Fax (01327) 262559, ≼, *f₆*, ▨, ⓝ, ⓝ, ☜, park, ⁕ – ▥ ☎ & ♓ – ⚿ 200. ◍ ◭ ◍ VISA. ⁕⁕
closed 25 December – Meals (lunch by arrangement)/dinner 22.50 **t.** and a la carte ♦ 10.60 – **43 rm** ⊑ 94.50/125.00 **t.**, 2 suites – SB.

*Si vous cherchez un hôtel tranquille,*
*consultez d'abord les cartes de l'introduction*
*ou repérez dans le texte les établissements indiqués avec le signe* ⑁ *ou* ⑁.

---

**DAWLISH** *Devon* 🕮 J 32 – pop. 9 648.
🕮 Warren 𝒫 (01626) 862255.
🎫 The Lawn, EX7 9PW 𝒫 (01626) 863589.
London 215 – Exeter 13 – Plymouth 40 – Torquay 11.

🏨 **Langstone Cliff,** Dawlish Warren, EX7 0NA, North : 2 m. by A 379 𝒫 (01626) 868000, Fax (01626) 868006, ▨, ▨, *☞*, park, ⁕ – ▮ ▥ ☎ ♓ – ⚿ 400. ◍ ◭ ◍ VISA
Meals (lunch by arrangement Monday to Saturday) 11.50/15.50 **st.** ♦ 4.50 – **67 rm** ⊑ 51.00/102.00 **st.** – SB.

---

**DEAL** *Kent* 🕮 Y 30 – pop. 28 504.
🕮 Walmer & Kingsdown, The Leas, Kingsdown 𝒫 (01304) 373256.
🎫 Town Hall, High St., CT14 6BB 𝒫 (01304) 369576.
London 78 – Canterbury 19 – Dover 8.5 – Margate 16.

🏨 **Royal,** Beach St., CT14 6JD, 𝒫 (01304) 375555, Fax (01304) 372270, ≼, 🍴 – ⁕⁕ rm, ▥ ☎. ◍ ◭ VISA. ⁕⁕
*The Boathouse :* Meals - Seafood - (closed Monday lunch and Sunday dinner) 12.50 **t.** and a la carte ♦ 3.50 – **19 rm** ⊑ 40.00/85.00 **t.** – SB.

⌂ **Sutherland House,** 186 London Rd, CT14 9PT, 𝒫 (01304) 362853, Fax (01304) 381146, *☞* – ⁕⁕ rm, ▥ ☎ ℃ ♓. ◍ ◭ VISA JCB. ⁕⁕
Meals (by arrangement) 19.00 **st.** ♦ 4.75 – **4 rm** ⊑ 35.00/50.00 **st.** – SB.

🍽🍽 **Dunkerley's** *(Restaurant)* with rm, 19 Beach St., CT14 7AH, 𝒫 (01304) 375016, Fax (01304) 380187, ≼ – ⁕⁕ rest, ▥ ☎ ℃. ◍ ◭ ◍ VISA. ⁕⁕
Meals (closed Monday) 9.75 **t.** (lunch) and a la carte 16.95/34.85 **t.** ♦ 4.75 – **16 rm** ⊑ 45.00/100.00 **t.** – SB.

◍ ATS 40 Gilford Rd 𝒫 (01304) 361543

---

**DEDDINGTON** *Oxon.* 🕮🕮 Q 28 – pop. 2 319.
London 72 – Birmingham 46 – Coventry 33 – Oxford 18.

🏨 **Holcombe,** High St., OX15 0SL, 𝒫 (01869) 338274, Fax (01869) 337167, *☞* – ▥ ☎ ♓. ◍ ◭ VISA
closed 23 December-5 January – Meals 14.95/22.95 **st.** and a la carte ♦ 6.50 – **17 rm** ⊑ 65.00/95.00 **st.** – SB.

🍽 **Dexter's,** 37 Market Pl., OX15 0SE, 𝒫 (01869) 338813, Fax (01869) 338813 – ◍ ◭ VISA JCB
closed Sunday dinner, Monday and 25 December-1 January – Meals 13.50/19.95 **t.** and a la carte ♦ 11.50.

**DEDHAM** *Essex* [404] W 28 *Great Britain G. – pop. 1 847 – ✉ Colchester.*
Env. : *Stour Valley★ – Flatford Mill★, E : 6 m. by B 1029, A 12 and B 1070.*
*London 63 – Chelmsford 30 – Colchester 8 – Ipswich 12.*

🏨🏨🏨 **Maison Talbooth** 🕊, Stratford Rd, CO7 6HN, West : ½ m. ☎ (01206) 322367, *Fax (01206) 322752*, <, 🌳 – [TV] ☏ Ⓟ. [MC] [AE] [O] VISA JCB. 🐕
Meals – (see ***Le Talbooth*** below) – ☕ 7.50 – **9 rm** 95.00/150.00 **t.**, 1 suite – SB.

🍴🍴🍴 **Le Talbooth,** Gun Hill, CO7 6HP, West : 1 m. ☎ (01206) 323150, *Fax (01206) 322309*, « Part Tudor house in attractive riverside setting », 🌳 – Ⓟ. [MC] [AE] VISA. 🐕
*closed Sunday dinner September-April* – **Meals** 19.00/24.00 **t.** and a la carte 32.50/41.00 **t.** 🍷 6.50.

🍴🍴 **Fountain House & Dedham Hall** 🕊 with rm, Brook St., CO7 6AD, ☎ (01206) 323027, *Fax (01206) 323293*, 🌳 – 🚭 rest, [TV] Ⓟ. [MC] VISA. 🐕
*closed 25 and 26 December* – **Meals** *(closed Sunday dinner and Monday)* (dinner only and Sunday lunch)/dinner 19.95 **t.** 🍷 9.00 – **5 rm** ☕ 45.00/65.00 **st.**

**DENMEAD** *Hants.* [403] Q 31 – *pop. 5 626.*
*London 70 – Portsmouth 11 – Southampton 27.*

🍴🍴 **Barnard's,** Hambledon Rd, PO7 6NU, ☎ (01705) 257788, *Fax (01705) 257788*, 🌳 – 🚭. [MC] [AE] VISA JCB
*closed Saturday lunch, Sunday, Monday, 1 week Easter, 1 week August and 1 week Christmas* – **Meals** 11.00/18.00 **t.** and a la carte 🍷 7.50.

**DENTON** *Gtr. Manchester* [402] [404] N 23 – *pop. 37 785.*
⛳18 *Denton, Manchester Rd ☎ (0161) 336 3218.*
*London 196 – Chesterfield 41 – Manchester 6.*

🏨🏨 **Old Rectory,** Meadow Lane, Haughton Green, M34 1GD, South : 2 m. by A 6017, Two Trees Lane and Haughton Green Rd ☎ (0161) 336 7516, *Fax (0161) 320 3212*, 🌳 – 🚭, ▤ rest, [TV] ☏ Ⓟ – 👥 100. [MC] [AE] [O] VISA
**Meals** *(closed Saturday lunch)* 11.95/16.95 **st.** and a la carte 🍷 7.95 – **36 rm** ☕ 69.00/89.00 **st.** – SB.

🏨 **Travel Inn,** Manchester Rd, M34 3SJ, West : 1 m. by A 57 at junction of M 66 and M 67 ☎ (0161) 320 1116, *Fax (0161) 320 1098* – 🚭 rm, ▤ rest, [TV] ♿ Ⓟ. [MC] [AE] [O] VISA
**Meals** (grill rest.) – **40 rm** 38.00 **t.**

**DERBY** [402] [403] [404] P 25 *Great Britain G. – pop. 223 836.*
See : *City★ – Museum and Art Gallery★ (Collection of Derby Porcelain★)* **YZ M1** – *Royal Crown Derby Museum★ AC* **Z M2.**
Env. : *Kedleston Hall★★ AC, NW : 4½ m. by Kedleston Rd* **X.**
⛳18 *Wilmore Rd, Sinfin ☎ (01332) 766323* – ⛳18 *Mickleover, Uttoxeter Rd ☎ (01332) 513339* – ⛳18 *Kedleston Park ☎ (01332) 840035* – ⛳18, ⛳18 *Breadsall Priory Hotel G. & C.C., Moor Rd, Morley ☎ (01332) 832235* – ⛳18 *Allestree Park, Allestree Hall, Allestree ☎ (01332) 550616.*
✈ *East Midlands Airport, Castle Donington : ☎ (01332) 852852, SE : 12 m. by A 6* **X.**
[i] *Assembly Rooms, Market Pl., DE1 3AH ☎ (01332) 255802.*
*London 132 – Birmingham 40 – Coventry 49 – Leicester 29 – Manchester 62 – Nottingham 16 – Sheffield 47 – Stoke-on-Trent 35.*

Plan opposite

🏨🏨🏨 **Midland,** Midland Rd, DE1 2SQ, ☎ (01332) 345894, *Fax (01332) 293522*, 🌳 – 🛗, 🚭 rm, [TV] ☏ ♿ Ⓟ – 👥 150. [MC] [AE] [O] VISA JCB. 🐕 Z i
**Meals** *(closed Saturday lunch)* 14.00/19.50 **st.** 🍷 5.95 – ☕ 10.50 – **97 rm** 76.00/82.00 **st.**, 1 suite.

🏨🏨 **La Gondola,** 220 Osmaston Rd, DE23 8JX, ☎ (01332) 332895, *Fax (01332) 384512* – [TV] ☏ Ⓟ – 👥 70. [MC] [AE] [O] VISA. 🐕 X c
**Meals** - Italian - *(closed Sunday)* (dancing Saturday) 8.50/13.50 **t.** and a la carte 🍷 6.50 – **19 rm** ☕ 47.00/58.00 **t.**, 1 suite – SB.

🏨🏨 **Royal Stuart,** 119 London Rd, DE1 2QR, ☎ (01332) 340633, *Fax (01332) 293502* – 🚭 [TV] ☏ Ⓟ – 👥 150. [MC] [AE] VISA Z o
**Meals** *(closed Saturday lunch)* 9.95/16.95 **st.** and a la carte 🍷 6.35 – ☕ 7.50 – **101 rm** 52.00/62.00 **st.**

🏨 **Oast House - Premier Lodge,** Foresters Leisure Park, 220 Osmaston Park Rd, DE23 8AG, ☎ (01332) 270027, *Fax (01332) 270528*, Reservations (Freephone) 0800 118833 – 🚭 rm, [TV] ☏ ♿ Ⓟ – 👥 40. [MC] [AE] [O] VISA JCB. 🐕 X e
**Meals** (grill rest.) 10.95 **st.** and a la carte – ☕ 5.95 – **26 rm** 44.95 **st.** – SB.

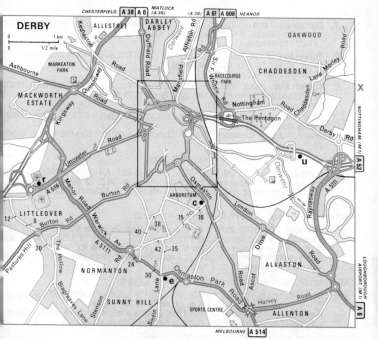

0 ____ 1 km
0 ____ 1/2 mile

ALLESTREE · DARLEY ABBEY · OAKWOOD

Kedleston Rd · Duffield Road · Derwent · Alfreton Rd · Sir F. Whittle Rd · Morley Lane

Ashbourne · MARKEATON PARK · Queensway · Mansfield Rd · RACECOURSE PARK · CHADDESDEN · Chaddesden Lane

MACKWORTH ESTATE · Kingsway · Road · Nottingham · The Pentagon · Derby Rd · X

Uttoxeter Rd · Manor Road · Osmaston · Derwent · u · NOTTINGHAM (M 1) A 52

12 · r · Burton Rd · Warwick · ARBORETUM · c · London · Raynesway · A 5111 · LOUGHBOROUGH AIRPORT. (M 1)

LITTLEOVER · 8 · Burton · A 5111 · 15 · 16 · Drive · A 6

Pastures Hill · 20 · Av. · 40 · 38 · Ascot · ALVASTON

The Hollow · Blagreaves Lane · Warwick Rd · 24 · 42 · 35 · Road

NORMANTON · 30 · e · Osmaston Park · Road · Harvey · Road

Stenson · Sinfin · SUNNY HILL · Lane · Road · ALLENTON

SPORTS CENTRE

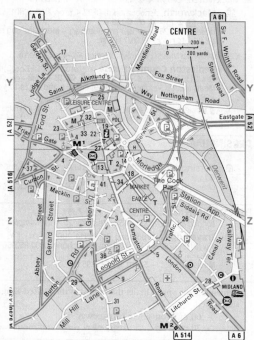

0 ____ 200 m
0 ____ 200 yards

Derwent · Garden St. · Mansfield Road · Sir F. Whittle Road · Stores Road

Lodge La. · 17 · Fox Street · Y

Saint · Alkmund's · Way · Nottingham · Road · Eastgate A 52

A 52 · Ford St. · 25 · Derwent St.

Friar · 23 · LEISURE CENTRE · M · POL

Gate · M · 32 · M · 33 · 22 · 19 · H · Morledge

A 516 · 37 · 4 · 13 · 27 · T · 2 · 4 · The Cock Pitt

Curzon · St. · 41 · 34 · 18 · Station App.

Macklin · Green La. · MARKET · Siddals Rd · 26

Street · EAGLE CENTRE · T · Traffic · Z

Gerrard · Street · 3 · Osmaston · Canal St. · Railway Ter.

Abbey · 36 · Leopold St. · London · 28 · MIDLAND

Burton · 29 · 9 · Road · Litchurch St.

Mill · Hill · Lane · 31 · 5 · M · A 514 · A 6

A 38 (A 38)

🏨 **European Inn** without rest., Midland Rd, DE1 2SL, ✆ (01332) 292000, *Fax (01332) 293940* – 🛗 🚭 [TV] ☎ ♿ [P] – 👥 120. [MC] [AE] [D] VISA Z c
☕ 6.00 – **86 rm** 42.50 **t.**

🏨 **Travel Inn,** Wyvern Business Park, DE21 6BF, ✆ (01332) 667826, *Fax (01332) 667827* – 🛗, 🚭 rm, ❄ rest, [TV] ♿ [P]. [MC] [AE] [D] VISA. 🐕 X u
**Meals** (grill rest.) – **82 rm** 38.00 **t.**

🏨 **Travel Inn,** Manor Park Way, Uttoxeter New Rd, DE22 3NA, ✆ (01332) 203003, *Fax (01332) 207506* – 🚭 rm, ❄ rest, [TV] ♿ [P]. [MC] [AE] [D] VISA. 🐕 X r
**Meals** (grill rest.) – **43 rm** 38.00 **t.**

XX **New Water Margin,** 72-74 Burton Rd, DE1 1TG, ✆ (01332) 364754, *Fax (01332) 290482* – ❄ [P]. [MC] [AE] [D] VISA Z e
*closed 25 and 26 December* – **Meals** - Chinese (Canton) - 11.00/14.80 **t.** and a la carte 🍷 3.75.

**at Darley Abbey** *North : 2½ m. off A 38 – **X** – ✉ Derby.*

XX **Darleys,** Darley Abbey Mill, DE22 1DZ, ✆ (01332) 364987, *Fax (01332) 364987,* « Converted cotton mill in attractive riverside setting » – 🚭 ❄ [P]. [MC] [AE] [D] VISA JCB
*closed Sunday dinner and Bank Holidays* – **Meals** 13.50 **t.** (lunch) and a la carte 22.30/36.00 **t.** 🍷 6.00.

**at Breadsall** *Northeast : 4 m. by A 52 off A 61 – **X** – ✉ Derby.*

🏨 **Marriott Breadsall Priory H. & Country Club** 🐦, Moor Rd, Morley, DE7 6DL, Northeast : 1 ¼ m. by Rectory Lane ✆ (01332) 832235, *Fax (01332) 833509,* ←, 🏊, 🏋, 🏊, 🏊, ⛳, 🌳, 🎾 – 🛗 🚭, ❄ rest, [TV] ☎ 📞 ♿ [P] – 👥 120. [MC] [AE] [D] VISA. 🐕
***Priory :*** **Meals** a la carte 18.65/22.75 **st.** – ***Long Weekend :*** **Meals** a la carte 11.20/19.45 **st.** – ☕ 11.95 – **107 rm** 87.00 **st.**, 5 suites – SB.

**at Mickleover** *Southwest : 3 m. by A 38 and A 516 – **X** – ✉ Derby.*

🏨 **Mickleover Court,** Etwall Rd, DE3 5XX, ✆ (01332) 521234, *Fax (01332) 521238,* 🏋, 🏊, 🏊 – 🛗, 🚭 rm, ❄ [TV] ☎ 📞 ♿ [P] – 👥 200. [MC] [AE] [D] VISA JCB. 🐕
***Avesbury :*** **Meals** a la carte 17.25/24.25 **st.** 🍷 7.00 – ***Stelline Trattoria :*** **Meals** - Italian - a la carte 13.40/24.40 **st.** 🍷 6.50 – **72 rm** ☕ 120.00/150.00 **st.**, 8 suites – SB.

**at Mackworth** *Northwest : 2 ¾ m. by A 52 – **X** – ✉ Derby.*

🏨 **Mackworth,** Ashbourne Rd, DE22 4LY, on A 52 ✆ (01332) 824324, *Fax (01332) 824692,* 🌳 – [TV] ☎ [P] – 👥 60. [MC] [AE] VISA
*closed 24 to 26 December and 1 January* – **Meals** (carving rest.) 6.95/7.95 **t.** and a la carte 🍷 5.95 – **14 rm** ☕ 49.00/79.00 **st.**

**at Kedleston** *Northwest : 4 m. by Kedleston Rd – **X** – ✉ Derby.*

🏨 **Kedleston Country House,** Kedleston Rd, DE22 5JD, East : 2 m. ✆ (01332) 559202, *Fax (01332) 558822,* ← – [TV] ☎ 📞 ♿ [P]. [MC] [AE] [D] VISA JCB. 🐕
**Meals** *(closed Sunday dinner)* 12.95/16.95 **t.** and a la carte 🍷 7.50 – **14 rm** ☕ 45.00/60.00 **t.** – SB.

[M] ATS Gosforth Rd, off Ascot Drive ✆ (01332) 340854

ATS 67 Bridge St. ✆ (01332) 347327
ATS 59 Kedleston Rd ✆ (01332) 297878

---

**DERSINGHAM** *Norfolk* [402] [404] V 25 – *pop. 3 961.*
*London 112 – King's Lynn 10 – Norwich 48.*

🏨 **Dersingham Hall,** Chapel Rd, PE31 6AY, on B 1440 ✆ (01485) 543514 – 🚭 rest, [TV] [P] [MC] VISA
*closed 25 and 26 December* – **Meals** 11.00 **t.** and a la carte 🍷 4.95 – **4 rm** ☕ 35.00/55.00 **t.**

---

**DESBOROUGH** *Northants.* [404] R 26 – *pop. 7 351.*
*London 83 – Birmingham 52 – Leicester 20 – Northampton 20.*

🏨 **Travelodge,** Harborough Rd, NN14 2UG, North : 1 ½ m. on A 6 ✆ (01536) 762034, *Fax (01536) 762034,* Reservations (Freephone) 0800 850950 – 🚭 rm, [TV] ♿ [P]. [MC] [AE] [D] VISA JCB. 🐕
**Meals** (grill rest.) – **32 rm** 39.95/59.95 **t.**

Remember the speed limits that apply in the United Kingdom, unless otherwise signposted.
- 60 mph on single carriageway roads
- 70 mph on dual carriageway roads and motorways

**DEVIZES** Wilts. 403 404 O 29 The West Country G. – pop. 13 205.

See : St. John's Church★★ – Market Place★ – Devizes Museum★ AC.

Env. : Potterne (Porch House★★ ) S : 2½ m. by A 360 – E : Vale of Pewsey★.

Exc. : Stonehenge★★★ AC, SE : 16 m. by A 360 and A 344 – Avebury★★ (The Stones★, Church★ ) NE : 7 m. by A 361.

᛬ Erlestoke Sands, Erlestoke ℘ (01380) 831069.

🖪 39 St. John's St., SN10 1BL ℘ (01380) 729408.

London 98 – Bristol 38 – Salisbury 25 – Swindon 19.

**at Erlestoke** Southwest : 8 m. by A 360 on B 3098 – ⊠ Devizes.

⌂ **Longwater** ⌖ without rest., Lower Rd, SN10 5UE, ℘ (01380) 830095, Fax (01380) 830095, ⌲, ☞, park – ⌱⌖ 🏧 🅿
restricted opening in winter – **5 rm** ⊆ 30.00/50.00 s.

**at Rowde** Northwest : 2 m. by A 361 on A 342 – ⊠ Devizes.

🍴 **George & Dragon**, High St., SN10 2PN, on A 342 ℘ (01380) 723053, Fax (01380) 724738, ☞ – ⌱⌖ 🅿, 🆎 VISA
closed Sunday, Monday, 25 December and 1 January – Meals (booking essential) 10.00 t. (lunch) and a la carte 16.50/27.00 t.

**DEWSBURY** W. Yorks. 402 P 22 – pop. 50 168.

London 205 – Leeds 9 – Manchester 40 – Middlesbrough 76 – Sheffield 31.

🏠 **Heath Cottage**, Wakefield Rd, WF12 8ET, East : ¾ m. on A 638 ℘ (01924) 465399, Fax (01924) 459405 – ⌱⌖, 🍽 rest, 🏧 ☎ 🅿 – 🔏 70. 🆎 VISA. ⌖
Meals (closed Saturday lunch) (booking essential Bank Holiday Monday) 10.00/13.95 st. and a la carte ⌊ 4.95 – **29 rm** ⊆ 52.00/70.00 st. – SB.

**at Whitley** Southwest : 4 m. by B 6409 and B 6117 on Whitley rd – ⊠ Dewsbury.

🏠 **Woolpack Country Inn**, Whitley Rd, WF12 0LZ, ℘ (01924) 499999, Fax (01924) 495289 – 🏧 ☎ 🅿, 🆎 AE ⓞ VISA. ⌖
Meals 7.50 st. (lunch) and a la carte 13.20/25.70 st. ⌊ 5.00 – **14 rm** ⊆ 42.50/57.50 st.

---

| Les prix | Pour toutes précisions sur les prix indiqués dans ce guide, reportez-vous aux pages de l'introduction. |
|---|---|

---

**DIDCOT** Oxon. 403 404 Q 29 – ⊠ Abingdon.

🖪 The Car Park, Station Rd, OX11 7NR ℘ (01235) 813243.

London 58 – Oxford 15 – Reading 20 – Swindon 31.

🏠 **Travel Inn**, Milton Heights, Milton, OX14 4DP, Northwest : 3 ¼ m. by B 4493 on A 4130 ℘ (01235) 835168, Fax (01235) 835187 – ⌱⌖ rm, 🍽 rest, 🏧 ⌖ 🅿, 🆎 AE ⓞ VISA. ⌖
Meals (grill rest.) – **40 rm** 38.00 t.

◉ ATS 1 Park Rd ℘ (01235) 812389/812815

**DIDDLEBURY** Shrops. 402 403 L 26 Great Britain G. – pop. 911 – ⊠ Craven Arms.

Env. : NW : Wenlock Edge★.

London 169 – Birmingham 46.

🏠 **Delbury Hall** ⌖, SY7 9DH, entrance on B 4368 beside lodge, opposite 40 mph sign ℘ (01584) 841267, Fax (01584) 841441, ⌲, « Georgian mansion », ⌲, ☞, park, ⌖ – ⌱⌖ 🏧 ☎ 🅿, 🆎 VISA JCB. ⌖
closed 25 December – Meals (booking essential) (residents only) (communal dining) (dinner only) 28.00 t. ⌊ 8.00 – **4 rm** ⊆ 50.00/95.00 t.

**DIDSBURY** Gtr. Manchester 402 403 404 N 23 – see Manchester.

**DISLEY** Ches. 402 403 404 N 23 – pop. 3 743 – ⊠ Stockport.

London 187 – Chesterfield 35 – Manchester 12.

🏛 **Stakis Moorside** ⌖, Mudhurst Lane, Higher Disley, SK12 2AP, Southeast : 2 m. by Buxton Old Rd ℘ (01663) 764151, Fax (01663) 762794, ⌲, ⌊₄, ⌲, ⌧, ⌖, squash – 🍽,
⌱⌖ rm, 🏧 ☎ 🅿 – 🔏 300. 🆎 AE ⓞ VISA. ⌖
Meals (bar lunch Saturday) 18.95 st. (dinner) and a la carte 21.20/40.50 st. – ⊆ 9.75 – **93 rm** 95.00/130.00 st., 1 suite – SB.

**DISS** Norfolk 404 X 26 – pop. 6 538.

🖪 Meres Mouth, Mere St., IP22 3AG 𝒫 (01379) 650523.
London 98 – Ipswich 25 – Norwich 21 – Thetford 17.

⌂ **Malt House** without rest., Palgrave, IP22 1AE, Southwest : 1 m. by Denmark St.
𝒫 (01379) 642107, Fax (01379) 640315, « Gardens » – 🔆 📺 🅿. 🕮 🅾 VISA JCB. 🦃
closed 15 December-15 January – **3 rm** ⊇ 38.00/65.00 **s.**

✗ **Weavers,** Market Hill, IP22 3JZ, 𝒫 (01379) 642411, « Part 15C weaver's cottage » – 🕮 🕮
🅾 VISA JCB
closed Saturday and Monday lunch, Sunday, last week August and 1 week Christmas –
**Meals** 10.75/13.50 **st.** 🍷 8.95.

**at Brockdish** East : 7 m. by A 1066, A 140 and A 143 – ✉ Diss.

⌂ **Grove Thorpe,** Grove Rd, IP21 4JE, North : ¾ m. 𝒫 (01379) 668305, Fax (01379) 668305,
« 17C bailiffs house », 🐾, 🌳 – 🅿. 🦃
**Meals** (by arrangement) (communal dining) 16.00 **s.** – **3 rm** ⊇ 38.00/60.00 **s.** – SB.

**at Brome** (Suffolk) Southeast : 2 ¾ m. by A 1066 on B 1077 – ✉ Eye.

🏨 **Cornwallis Arms** ⌂, IP23 8AJ, 𝒫 (01379) 870326, Fax (01379) 870051, « Part 16C
house, topiary gardens », park – 📺 ☎ 🅿. 🏊 30. 🕮 🕮 🅾 VISA JCB
*Oaksmere :* **Meals** a la carte 24.00/29.00 **t.** 🍷 8.10 – **16 rm** ⊇ 75.00/120.00 **t.** – SB.

**at Wingfield** Southeast : 7 m. by A 1066 and B 1118.

🍸 **De La Pole Arms,** Church Rd, IP21 5RA, 𝒫 (01379) 384545, Fax (01379) 384377, « Part
17C inn » – 🅿. 🕮 VISA
closed Monday January-March – **Meals** a la carte 14.35/22.00 **t.** 🍷 9.50.

**at Fersfield** Northwest : 7 m. by A 1066 – ✉ Diss.

⌂ **Strenneth** ⌂ without rest., Airfield Rd, IP22 2BP, 𝒫 (01379) 688182,
Fax (01379) 688260, « Part 17C farmhouse », 🌳 – 🔆 📺 🅿. 🕮 VISA
**7 rm** ⊇ 27.00/63.00 **s.**

🔧 ATS Shelfanger Rd 𝒫 (01379) 642861

---

**DITTISHAM** Devon 403 J 32 – pop. 463 – ✉ Dartmouth.
London 214 – Exeter 33 – Plymouth 34.

🍸 **Red Lion Inn** with rm, TQ6 0ES, 𝒫 (01803) 722235, ≼ – 📺 ☎ 🅿. 🕮 VISA
closed 25 and 26 December – **Meals** (in bar Monday dinner) a la carte 10.35/20.65 **t.** 🍷 4.90 –
**6 rm** ⊇ 27.50/70.00 **t.**

---

**DITTON PRIORS** Shrops. 403 404 M 26 – pop. 680 – ✉ Bridgnorth.
London 154 – Birmingham 34 – Ludlow 13 – Shrewsbury 21.

✗✗ **Howard Arms,** WV16 6SQ, 𝒫 (01746) 712200, 🌳 – 🔆 🅿. 🕮 VISA
closed Sunday dinner, Monday and 2 weeks September – **Meals** (dinner only and Sunday
lunch)/dinner 22.00 **t.** 🍷 5.00.

---

**DODDISCOMBSLEIGH** Devon 403 J 31 – see Exeter.

---

**DONCASTER** S. Yorks. 402 403 404 Q 23 – pop. 71 595.
🖈 Doncaster Town Moor, Bawtry Rd, Belle Vue 𝒫 (01302) 533778, B – 🖈 Crookhill Park,
Conisborough 𝒫 (01709) 862979 – 🖈 Wheatley, Amthorpe Rd 𝒫 (01302) 831655, B –
🖈 Owston Park, Owston Hall, Owston 𝒫 (01302) 330821.
🖪 Central Library, Waterdale, DN1 3JE 𝒫 (01302) 734309.
London 173 – Kingston-upon-Hull 46 – Leeds 30 – Nottingham 46 – Sheffield 19.

Plans on following pages

🏨🏨 **Doncaster Moat House,** Warmsworth, DN4 9UX, Southwest : 2 ¾ m. on A 630
𝒫 (01302) 799988, Fax (01302) 310197, 🏋, ≼, 🏊, – 🛗 🔆 rm, 🍽 rest, 📺 ☎ 🕭 🅿 –
🏊 400. 🕮 🕮 🅾 VISA
A  V
**Meals** (closed Saturday lunch) 16.00 **st.** (dinner) and a la carte 13.15/23.15 **st.** 🍷 5.75 – ⊇
8.50 – **98 rm** 95.00/120.00 **st.,** 2 suites – SB.

🏨 **Mount Pleasant,** Great North Rd, DN11 0HP, Southeast : 6 m. on A 638
𝒫 (01302) 868219, Fax (01302) 865130, 🌳 – 🔆 📺 ☎ 🕭 🅿 – 🏊 100. 🕮 🕮 🅾 VISA. 🦃
closed 25 December – **Meals** 12.95/18.50 **t.** and a la carte 🍷 8.95 – **33 rm** ⊇ 55.00/94.00 **t.**

🏨 **Grand St. Leger,** Racecourse Roundabout, Bennetthorpe, DN2 6AX, Southeast : 1 ½ m.
on A 638 𝒫 (01302) 364111, Fax (01302) 329865 – 🔆 rm, 📺 ☎ 🅿 – 🏊 80. 🕮 🕮 🅾 VISA
**Meals** 12.50/18.50 **t.** and a la carte 🍷 8.50 – **20 rm** ⊇ 66.00/80.00 **t.** – SB.
B  b

# DONCASTER

**Punch's,** Bawtry Rd, Bessacarr, DN4 7BS, Southeast : 3 m. on A 638 𝒫 (01302) 370037,
*Fax (01302) 379021* – ✲ ▥ ☎ & ₧ – ⌗ 40. ⓶ ﹅ ﹅ . ✄
**B n**
**Meals** (carving rest.) a la carte 11.00/15.50 **t.** – **24 rm** ⌐ 55.00/74.00 **st.** – SB.

**Travel Inn,** South Entry Drive, White Rose Way, DN4 5JH, South : 1 ½ m. by A 6182
𝒫 (01302) 361134, *Fax (01302) 364811* – |⋣|, ✲ rm, ▤ rest, ▥ & ₧. ⓶ ﹅ ◑ ﹅
**Meals** (grill rest.) – **42 rm** 38.00 **t.**

**Campanile,** Doncaster Leisure Park, Bawtry Rd, DN4 7PD, Southeast : 2 m. on A 638
𝒫 (01302) 370770, *Fax (01302) 370813,* ⌂ – ✲ rm, ▥ ☎ ₧ – ⌗ 35. ⓶ ﹅ ◑ ﹅
**Meals** (grill rest.) 10.85 **st.** and a la carte – ⌐ 4.50 – **50 rm** 36.50 **st.**
**B x**

**Aagrah,** Great North Rd, Woodlands, DN6 7RA, Northwest : 4 m. on A 638
𝒫 (01302) 728888 – ▤ ₧. ⓶ ﹅ ﹅ ﹅
**A r**
*closed 25 December* – **Meals** - Indian (Kashmiri) - (booking essential) (dinner only) a la carte
13.70/17.05 **t.**

229

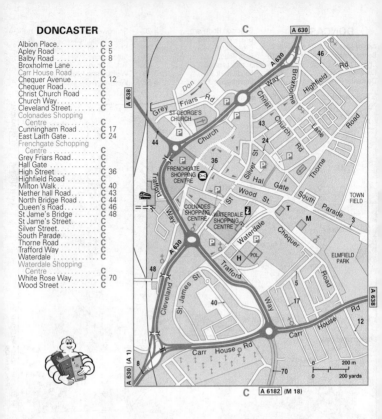

## DONCASTER



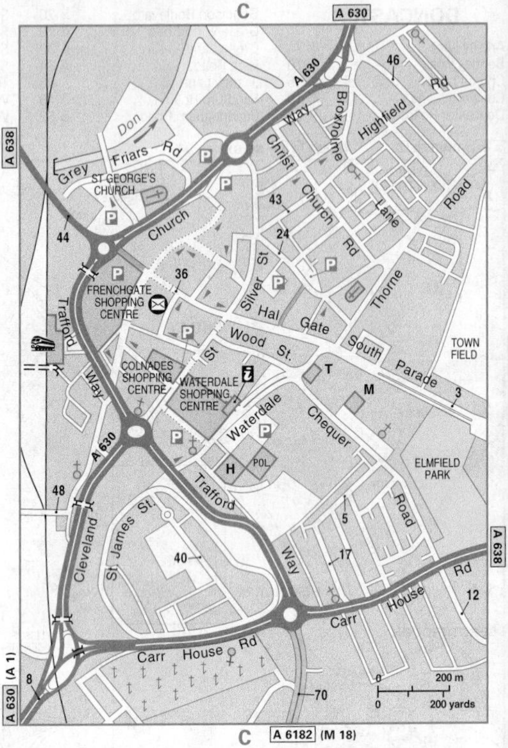

**at Carcroft** *Northwest : 6½ m. by A 638 on A 1 – A – ✉ Doncaster.*

**Travelodge,** Great North Rd, DN6 8LR, (northbound carriageway) ☏ (01302) 330841, *Fax (01302) 330841,* Reservations (Freephone) 0800 850950 – ⇔ rm, ▤ rest, TV ♿ P. MC AE D VISA JCB. ⛔
**Meals** (grill rest.) – **40 rm** 39.95/59.95 **t.**

ATS Heavens Walk ☏ (01302) 367337/360249/340797

---

**DORCHESTER** *Dorset* 403 404 M 31 *The West Country G. – pop. 15 037.*

**See :** *Town★ - Dorset County Museum★ AC.*

**Env. :** *Maiden Castle★★ (≤★) SW : 2½ m. – Puddletown Church★, NE : 5½ m. by A 35.*

**Exc. :** *Moreton Church★★, E : 7½ m. – Bere Regis★ (St. John the Baptist Church★ - Roof★★) NE : 11 m. by A 35 – Athelhampton House★ AC, NE : 6½ m. by A 35 - Cerne Abbas★, N : 7 m. by A 352 – Milton Abbas★, NE : 12 m. on A 354 and by-road.*

*18 Came Down ☏ (01305) 812531.*

*Unit 11, Antelope Walk, Dorchester, DT1 1BE ☏ (01305) 267992.*

*London 135 – Bournemouth 27 – Exeter 53 – Southampton 53.*

**Casterbridge** without rest., 49 High East St., DT1 1HU, ☏ (01305) 264043, *Fax (01305) 260884,* « Georgian town house » – TV ☎ ✆. MC AE D VISA JCB. ⛔
*closed 25 and 26 December* – **14 rm** ☐ 40.00/85.00 **st.**

**Yalbury Cottage** 🐕, Lower Bockhampton, DT2 8PZ, East : 2 ¼ m. by B 3150 and Bockhampton rd ☏ (01305) 262382, *Fax (01305) 266412,* « Part 17C cottage », 🚗 – ⇔ TV ☎ P. MC VISA JCB
*closed 28 December-29 January* – **Meals** (dinner only) 21.00 **t.** 🍷 5.50 – **8 rm** ☐ 49.00/74.00 **st.** – SB.

🏛 **Westwood House** without rest., 29 High West St., DT1 1UP, ℰ (01305) 268018, Fax (01305) 250282 – 📺 ☎. 🆗 🅰🅴 𝘝𝘐𝘚𝘈
6 rm ⌑ 47.50/85.00 st.

XX **Mock Turtle**, 34 High West St., DT1 1UP, ℰ (01305) 264011 – 🆗 𝘝𝘐𝘚𝘈
closed lunch Saturday and Monday, Sunday, 1 January and 25-26 December – **Meals** 14.95/21.75 t. ⓙ 6.00.

**at Winterbourne Steepleton** West : 4 ¾ m. by B 3150 and A 35 on B 3159 – ✉ Dorchester.

🏠 **Old Rectory** without rest., DT2 9LG, ℰ (01305) 889468, Fax (01305) 889737, 🌿 – ⇔ 🄿. ❀
closed 25 December-1 January – **3 rm** ⌑ 40.00/100.00 st.

**at Frampton** Northwest : 6 m. by B 3147 and A 37 on A 356 – ✉ Dorchester.

🏠 **Hyde Farm House** ⬦, DT2 9NG, Northwest : ½ m. on A 356 ℰ (01300) 320272, ≤, « Part 18C and 19C », 🌿 – ⇔ rm, 🄿. ❀
closed Christmas – **Meals** 15.00 – **3 rm** ⌑ 30.00/60.00 st.

⬤ ATS Unit 4, Great Western Ind. Centre ℰ (01305) 264756     ATS Units 1/2, Jonson Trading Est. ℰ (01305) 264308

---

**DORCHESTER** Oxon. 🔢🔢 Q 29 Great Britain G. – pop. 2 256.
See : Town★.
Exc. : Ridgeway Path★★.
London 51 – Abingdon 6 – Oxford 8 – Reading 17.

🏛 **George**, 23 High St., OX10 7HH, ℰ (01865) 340404, Fax (01865) 341620, « Part 14C coaching inn », 🌿 – 📺 ☎ 🄿 – 🔬 40. 🆗 🅰🅴 𝘝𝘐𝘚𝘈
**Meals** 17.00/20.00 t. and a la carte ⓙ 8.40 – **18 rm** ⌑ 69.00/87.50 t. – SB.

🏛 **White Hart**, 26 High St., OX10 7HN, ℰ (01865) 340074, Fax (01865) 341082, « 17C coaching inn » – 📺 ☎ 🄿 – 🔬 40. 🆗 🅰🅴 🅾 𝘝𝘐𝘚𝘈 🅹🅲🅱
**Meals** 16.50 t. and a la carte – **15 rm** ⌑ 65.00/85.00 t., 4 suites – SB.

**Les prix**     Pour toutes précisions sur les prix indiqués dans ce guide, reportez-vous aux pages de l'introduction.

---

**DORKING** Surrey 🔢 T 30 – pop. 15 658.
London 26 – Brighton 39 – Guildford 12 – Worthing 33.

🏛 **Burford Bridge**, Box Hill, RH5 6BX, North : 1 ½ m. on A 24 ℰ (01306) 884561, Fax (01306) 880386, ⤢, 🌿 – ⇔ 📺 ☎ ⓒ 🄿 – 🔬 300. 🆗 🅰🅴 🅾 𝘝𝘐𝘚𝘈 🅹🅲🅱
**Meals** 20.00/25.00 t. and a la carte ⓙ 8.00 – ⌑ 12.50 – **57 rm** 135.00 st. – SB.

🏛 **White Horse**, High St., RH4 1BE, ℰ (01306) 881138, Fax (01306) 887241 – ⇔ rm, 📺 ☎ 🄿 – 🔬 50. 🆗 🅰🅴 🅾 𝘝𝘐𝘚𝘈
**Meals** 10.50/14.75 st. and a la carte ⓙ 8.50 – ⌑ 8.50 – **68 rm** 90.00/125.00 st.

🏛 **Travelodge**, Reigate Rd, RH4 1QB, East : ½ m. on A 25 ℰ (01306) 740361, Reservations (Freephone) 0800 850950 – ⇔ 📺 🄿 🄿 🆗 🅰🅴 🅾 𝘝𝘐𝘚𝘈 🅹🅲🅱. ❀
**Meals** (grill rest.) – **54 rm** 39.95/59.95 t.

XX **Partner's and Sons**, 2-4 West St., RH4 1BL, ℰ (01306) 882826, Fax (01306) 885741 – ⇔ ▤. 🆗 🅰🅴 🅾 𝘝𝘐𝘚𝘈 🅹🅲🅱
closed Sunday and January – **Meals** 16.00/29.50 t. ⓙ 5.50.

---

**DORRINGTON** Shrops. 🔢🔢 L 26 – see Shrewsbury.

---

**DOUGLAS** Isle of Man 🔢 G 21 – see Man (Isle of).

---

**DOULTING** Somerset 🔢🔢 M 30 – see Shepton Mallet.

---

**DOVER** Kent 🔢 Y 30 Great Britain G. – pop. 34 179.
See : Castle★★ AC Y.
⛴ to France (Calais) (P & O/Stena Line) (1 h 30 mn) – to France (Calais) (SeaFrance Ltd) frequent services (1 h 30 mn) – to France (Calais) (Hoverspeed Ltd) frequent services daily (35 mn).
🅱 Townwall St., CT16 1JR ℰ (01304) 205108.
London 76 – Brighton 84.

# DOVER

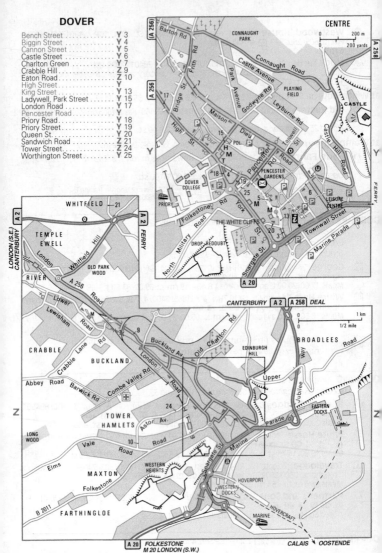

🏨 **Churchill,** Dover Waterfront, CT17 9BP, ☎ (01304) 203633, *Fax (01304) 216320,* ≼ − 🛗 ⁵⁄⁴ 🔟 ☎ 🅿 − 🔬 120. 🅼🅾 🅰🅴 🅾 *VISA*. 🛠
Meals 12.95/17.00 **t.** and dinner a la carte ♣ 6.25 − ⌂ 9.00 − **68 rm** 65.00/85.00 **st.**

🏨 **Forte Posthouse Dover,** Singledge Lane, Whitfield, CT16 3LF, Northwest : 3 ½ m. by A 256 on A 2 ☎ (01304) 821222, *Fax (01304) 825576* − ⁵⁄⁴ rm, 🔟 ☎ 🕭 🅿 − 🔬 40. 🅼🅾 🅰🅴 🅾 *VISA* 🅹🅲🅱
Meals a la carte 18.25/26.75 **t.** ♣ 7.50 − ⌂ 8.95 − **68 rm** 79.00 **st.** − SB.

🏠 **Travel Inn,** Folkestone Rd, CT15 7AB, Southwest : 2 ½ m. on B 2011 ☎ (01304) 213339 *Fax (01304) 214504* − ⁵⁄⁴ rm, 🕭 🅿. 🅼🅾 🅰🅴 🅾 *VISA*. 🛠
closed 24 and 25 December − Meals (grill rest.) − **62 rm** 38.00 **t.**

↑ **East Lee** without rest., 108 Maison Dieu Rd, CT16 1RT, ☎ (01304) 210176, *Fax (01304) 210176* − ⁵⁄⁴ 🔟 ☎. 🅼🅾 *VISA*. 🛠
**4 rm** ⌂ 40.00/48.00.

↥ **Number One** without rest., 1 Castle St., CT16 1QH, ℰ (01304) 202007, *Fax (01304) 214078*, 🍽 – 📺 🚗. ℅
Y u
*closed 24 to 28 December* – **5 rm** ☲ 30.00/46.00.

**at St. Margaret's at Cliffe** *Northeast : 4 m. by A 258 – Z – on B 2058 –* ⊠ *Dover.*

🏨 **Wallett's Court**, West Cliffe, CT15 6EW, Northwest : ¾ m. on B 2058 ℰ (01304) 852424, *Fax (01304) 853430*, « Part 17C manor house », ⌁, 🔲, 🍽, ℅ – 📺 ☎ 🕻 🅿. 🐵 🗚 ⓪ 𝘝𝘐𝘚𝘈 JCB. ℅
*closed 24 to 28 December* – **Meals** – (see *The Restaurant* below) – **16 rm** ☲ 65.00/120.00 t. – SB.

XX **The Restaurant** (at Wallett's Court H.), West Cliffe, CT15 6EW, Northwest : ¾ m. on B 2058 ℰ (01304) 852424, *Fax (01304) 853430*, 🍽 – ☒ 🅿. 🐵 🗚 ⓪ 𝘝𝘐𝘚𝘈 JCB
*closed 4 days Christmas* – **Meals** (dinner only) 25.00 t. and a la carte ₰ 7.50.

**at Coldred** *Northwest : 6 m. by A 256 off A 2 – Z –* ⊠ *Dover.*

↥ **Coldred Court** ⌕, Church Rd, CT15 5AQ, ℰ (01304) 830816, *Fax (01304) 830816*, « 17C farmhouse », 🍽 – ☒ rm, 📺 🅿. ℅
*closed Christmas* – **Meals** (by arrangement) (communal dining) 15.00 – **3 rm** ☲ 45.00/55.00.

🅐 ATS Unit 14, Holmeston Rd, Poulton Ind Est. ℰ (01304) 212898/212214

*La guida cambia, cambiate la guida ogni anno.*

---

**DOVERIDGE** *Derbs.* 402 403 404 O 25 – *see Uttoxeter.*

---

**DOWN HATHERLEY** *Glos.* – *see Gloucester.*

---

**DOWNTON** *Wilts.* 403 404 O 31 – *see Salisbury.*

---

**DREWSTEIGNTON** *Devon* 403 I 31 *The West Country G.* – *pop. 668.*
Env. : Dartmoor National Park★★.
London 216 – Exeter 15 – Plymouth 46.

↥ **Hunts Tor**, EX6 6QW, ℰ (01647) 281228, *Fax (01647) 281228* – ☒ rest, 📺
March-October – **Meals** (set menu only) (booking essential-minimum 24 hours notice required) 20.00-23.00 st. ₰ 8.80 – **3 rm** ☲ 32.00/65.00 st.

---

**DRIFFIELD** *East Riding* 402 S 21 – *see Great Driffield.*

---

**DRIFT** *Cornwall* – *see Penzance.*

---

**DRIGHLINGTON** *W. Yorks.* 402 P 22 – *see Leeds.*

---

**DROITWICH** *Worcestershire* 403 404 N 27 – *pop. 20 966.*
🏌 Ombersley, Bishopswood Rd ℰ (01905) 620747 – 🏌 Ford Lane ℰ (01905) 770129.
🄳 St. Richard's House, Victoria Sq., WR9 8DS ℰ (01905) 774312.
London 129 – Birmingham 20 – Bristol 66 – Worcester 6.

🏨 **Travelodge**, Rashwood Hill, WR9 8DA, Northeast : 1 ½ m. on A 38 ℰ (01527) 861545, Reservations (Freephone) 0800 850950 – ☒ rm, 📺 ᴅ 🅿. 🐵 🗚 ⓪ 𝘝𝘐𝘚𝘈 JCB. ℅
**Meals** (grill rest.) – **32 rm** 39.95/59.95 t.

XX **Rossini's**, 6 Worcester Rd, WR9 8AB, ℰ (01905) 794799 – ☰ 🅿. 🐵 🗚 𝘝𝘐𝘚𝘈
*closed Sunday and 25-26 December* – **Meals** - Italian - 11.90/15.90 t. and a la carte ₰ 5.50.

**at Oddingley** *Southeast : 3 m. by B 4090.*

↥ **Church Farm House**, WR9 7NE, Southeast : ¼ m. on Netherwood rd ℰ (01905) 772387, *Fax (01905) 772387*, 🍽, park – ☒ 📺 🅿. ℅
*closed 22 December-2 January* – **Meals** (by arrangement) (communal dining) 20.00 s. ₰ 5.00 – **3 rm** ☲ 40.00/59.00 s.

**at Smite** South : 3 ¾ m. by B 4090 and A 38 off A 4538 – ⊠ Worcester.

🏠 **Pear Tree**, WR3 8SY, ℰ (01905) 756565, Fax (01905) 756777 – ⇔ rm, 📺 ☎ ₺ ❷ –
🛗 280. 🐠 🖭 ⑩ 𝗩𝗜𝗦𝗔 🗯️. ✹
Meals (carving lunch Sunday) a la carte 12.40/24.00 st. ₷ 5.50 – **21 rm** ⊷ 75.00/95.00 st.,
3 suites – SB.

**at Hadley Heath** Southwest : 4 m. by Ombersley Way, A 4133 and Ladywood rd – ⊠ Droitwich.

🏠 **Hadley Bowling Green Inn**, WR9 0AR, ℰ (01905) 620294, Fax (01905) 620771 – 📺 ☎
📞 ❷. 🐠 🖭 𝗩𝗜𝗦𝗔
accommodation closed 25 December – **Meals** (in bar Monday to Saturday) a la carte 13.25/
20.25 st. ₷ 5.25 – **14 rm** ⊷ 58.00/69.00 st.

---

**DRONFIELD** Derbs. 🏷️🏷️🏷️ P 24 – pop. 22 985 – ⊠ Sheffield (S. Yorks.).
London 158 – Derby 30 – Nottingham 31 – Sheffield 6.

🏠 **Manor House**, 10-15 High St., S18 1PY, ℰ (01246) 413971, Fax (01246) 412104 – ⇔ 📺
☎ 📞 ❷ – 🛗 45. 🐠 🖭 𝗩𝗜𝗦𝗔 𝗝𝗖𝗕
closed 25 and 26 December – **Meals** (lunch by arrangement)/dinner 18.95 t. and a la carte
₷ 5.50 – **8 rm** ⊷ 55.00/75.00 t., 2 suites – SB.

**at Holmesfield** Southwest : 2 ¼ m. by B 5056 on B 6054 – ⊠ Dronfield.

🏠 **Horsleygate Hall** ⅁ without rest., Horsleygate Lane, S18 7WD, South : 1 ¼ m. by
B 6054 ℰ (0114) 2890333, « Part Victorian, part Georgian house », ☞, park – ⇔ ❷. ✹
closed 23 to 28 December – **3 rm** ⊷ 27.00/45.00 st.

---

**DRYBROOK** Glos. 🏷️🏷️ M 28 – pop. 2 742.
London 149 – Bristol 34 – Gloucester 12 – Newport 35.

XX **Cider Press**, The Cross, GL17 9EB, ℰ (01594) 544472 – ⇔. 🐠 𝗩𝗜𝗦𝗔
closed Tuesday and first 2 weeks January – **Meals** (lunch by arrangement and Sunday-
Monday) a la carte 19.65/23.85 t. ₷ 5.95.

---

**DUDDENHOE END** Essex 🏷️ U 27 – see Saffron Walden.

---

**DUDLEY** W. Mids. 🏷️🏷️🏷️ N 26 Great Britain G. – pop. 304 615.
See : Black Country Museum★.
🅱 39 Churchill Shopping Centre, DY2 7BL, ℰ (01384) 457494.
London 132 – Birmingham 10 – Wolverhampton 6.

Plan : see Birmingham p. 2

🏨 **Copthorne Merry Hill**, The Waterfront, Level St., Brierley Hill, DY5 1UR, Southwest :
2 ¼ m. by A 461 ℰ (01384) 482882, Fax (01384) 482773, 𝕴𝕬, ≘s, ⃞ – ▐, ⇔ rm, ▤ rest, 📺
☎ ₺ ❷ – 🛗 250. 🐠 🖭 ⑩ 𝗩𝗜𝗦𝗔 ✹                                                  AU z
Meals 17.95/19.50 st. and a la carte ₷ 8.20 – ⊷ 12.75 – **129 rm** 125.00/135.00 st., 9 suites.

🏠 **Ward Arms**, Birmingham Rd, DY1 4RN, Northeast : ¾ m. on A 461 ℰ (01384) 458070,
Fax (01384) 457502 – ⇔ rm, 📺 ☎ ₺ ❷ – 🛗 150. 🐠 🖭 ⑩ 𝗩𝗜𝗦𝗔                    BT a
Meals (carving rest.) a la carte 15.85/19.85 st. – ⊷ 9.75 – **72 rm** 70.00/85.00 st. – SB.

🏠 **Travel Inn**, Dudley Rd, Kingswinford, DY6 8WT, West : 3 m. on A 4101 ℰ (01384) 291290,
Fax (01384) 277593 – ▐, ⇔ rm, ▤ rest, 📺 ₺ ❷ – 🛗 35. 🐠 🖭 ⑩ 𝗩𝗜𝗦𝗔. ✹        AU e
Meals (grill rest.) – **43 rm** 38.00 st.

🏠 **Travelodge** without rest., Dudley Rd, Brierley Hill, DY5 1LQ, Southwest : 2 m. on A 461
ℰ (01384) 481579, Reservations (Freephone) 0800 850950 – ⇔ 📺 ₺ ❷. 🐠 🖭 ⑩ 𝗩𝗜𝗦𝗔
𝗝𝗖𝗕. ✹                                                                              AU c
**32 rm** 39.95/59.95 t.

ATS 125127 Sedgley Rd, Sedgley, Woodsetton ℰ (01902) 662629

---

**DULVERTON** Somerset 🏷️ J 30 The West Country G. – pop. 1 870 (inc. Brushford).
See : Village★.
Env. : Exmoor National Park★★ – Tarr Steps★★, NW : 6 m. by B 3223.
London 198 – Barnstaple 27 – Exeter 26 – Minehead 18 – Taunton 27.

🏠 **Carnarvon Arms**, TA22 9AE, Southeast : 1 ½ m. on B 3222 ℰ (01398) 323302,
Fax (01398) 324022, ☌, ⚲, ☞, park, ⚒ – 📺 ☎ ❷ – 🛗 100. 🐠 🖭 𝗩𝗜𝗦𝗔
Meals (lunch by arrangement Monday to Saturday)/dinner 25.25 t. ₷ 5.90 – **22 rm**
⊷ 45.00/80.00, 1 suite.

🏠 **Ashwick House** ⌖, TA22 9QD, Northwest : 4 ¼ m. by B 3223 turning left after second cattle grid ℰ (01398) 323868, Fax (01398) 323868, ≤, 🏠, « Country house atmosphere », 🌳 – ✲= rest, 🔟 ☎ 🅿. ❄
**Meals** (booking essential for non-residents) (light lunch Monday to Saturday residents only)/dinner 22.00 t. ⏿ 6.00 – **6 rm** ⌕ (dinner included) 76.00/144.00 **t.** – SB.

**DUNCHURCH** Warks. 🟦🟦🟦 Q 26 – pop. 2 251 – ⌧ Rugby.
London 90 – Coventry 12 – Leicester 24 – Northampton 26.

🏠 **Travelodge,** London Rd, Thurlaston, CV23 9LG, Northwest : 2 ½ m. on A 45 ℰ (01788) 521538, Reservations (Freephone) 0800 850950 – ✲= rm, 🔟 ☎ 🅿. ❄ ⏾ ⬛ 🅰🅴 ⓞ 𝘝𝘐𝘚𝘈 🄹🄲🄱. ❄
**Meals** (grill rest.) – **40 rm** 39.95/59.95 **t.**

**DUNSFORD** Devon 🟦🟦🟦 I 31 The West Country G. – pop. 1212.
Env. : Dartmoor National Park★★.
London 206 – Exeter 6 – Plymouth 35.

🏠 **Rock House** ⌖, EX6 7EP, Southeast : 1 ½ m. by B 3212 off Christow rd ℰ (01647) 252514, ≤, 🌳, park – 🅿
**Meals** (by arrangement) 25.00 st. ⏿ 4.00 – **3 rm** ⌕ 37.50/60.00 **st.**

**DUNSLEY** N. Yorks. – see Whitby.

| Les prix | Pour toutes précisions sur les prix indiqués dans ce guide, reportez-vous aux pages de l'introduction. |
|---|---|

**DUNSTABLE** Beds. 🟦🟦🟦 S 28 – pop. 49 666.
🏌 Tilsworth, Dunstable Rd ℰ (01525) 210721/210722.
🅱 The Library, Vernon Pl., LU5 4HA ℰ (01582) 471012.
London 40 – Bedford 24 – Luton 4.5 – Northampton 35.

🏨 **Old Palace Lodge,** Church St., LU5 4RT, ℰ (01582) 662201, Fax (01582) 696422 – 🛗, ✲= rm, 🍽 rest, 🔟 ☎ 🅿 – 🔬 35. ⏾ ⬛ 🅰🅴 ⓞ 𝘝𝘐𝘚𝘈 🄹🄲🄱. ❄
**Meals** 16.00/19.75 **st.** and a la carte ⏿ 7.25 – ⌕ 9.50 – **68 rm** 90.00/125.00 **st.** – SB.

🏠 **Highwayman,** London Rd, LU6 3DX, Southeast : 1 m. on A 5 ℰ (01582) 601122, Fax (01582) 603812 – 🔟 ☎ & 🅿 – 🔬 50. ⏾ ⬛ 🅰🅴 𝘝𝘐𝘚𝘈 🄹🄲🄱. ❄
**Meals** (lunch by arrangement Monday to Saturday)/dinner a la carte 13.95/21.70 **st.** ⏿ 4.95 – **51 rm** ⌕ 55.00/72.00 **st.** – SB.

🏠 **Travel Inn,** 350 Luton Rd, LU5 4LL, Northeast : 1 ¾ m. on A 505 ℰ (01582) 609938, Fax (01582) 664114 – ✲= rm, 🍽 rest, 🔟 & 🅿. ⏾ ⬛ 🅰🅴 ⓞ 𝘝𝘐𝘚𝘈
**Meals** (grill rest.) – **42 rm** 38.00 **t.**

🏠 **Travel Inn,** Watling St., Kensworth, LU6 3QP, Southeast : 2 ½ m. on A 5 ℰ (01582) 840509, Fax (01582) 842811 – ✲= rm, 🔟 & 🅿. ⏾ ⬛ 🅰🅴 ⓞ 𝘝𝘐𝘚𝘈. ❄
**Meals** (grill rest.) – **40 rm** 38.00 **t.**

**at Hockliffe** Northwest : 3 ¼ m. on A 5 – ⌧ Dunstable.

🏠 **Travelodge,** LU7 9LZ, Southeast : ¾ m. on A 5 ℰ (01525) 211177, Fax (01525) 211177, Reservations (Freephone) 0800 850950 – ✲= rm, 🔟 & 🅿. ⏾ ⬛ 🅰🅴 ⓞ 𝘝𝘐𝘚𝘈 🄹🄲🄱. ❄
**Meals** (grill rest.) – **28 rm** 39.95/59.95 **t.**

**DUNSTER** Somerset 🟦🟦🟦 J 30 The West Country G. – pop. 848 – ⌧ Minehead.
See : Town★★ – Castle★★ AC (Upper rooms ≤★) – Dunster Water Mill★ AC – St. George's Church★ – Dovecote★.
Env. : Exmoor National Park★★ (Dunkery Beacon★★★ (≤★★★), Watersmeet★, Valley of the Rocks★, Vantage Point★) – Cleeve Abbey★★ AC, SE : 5 m. by A 39 – Timberscombe (Church★) SW : 3½ m. by A 396.
London 184 – Bristol 61 – Exeter 40 – Taunton 22.

🏨 **Luttrell Arms,** 36 High St., TA24 6SG, ℰ (01643) 821555, Fax (01643) 821567, « Part 15C inn », 🌳 – ✲= 🔟 ☎ ⇔. ⏾ ⬛ 🅰🅴 ⓞ 𝘝𝘐𝘚𝘈
**Meals** 13.00/22.95 **st.** and dinner a la carte ⏿ 6.95 – ⌕ 9.50 – **27 rm** 75.00/95.00 **st.** – SB.

🏠 **The Exmoor House,** West St., TA24 6SN, ℰ (01643) 821268, Fax (01643) 821267, 🌳 – ✲= 🔟 ☎. ⏾ ⬛ 🅰🅴 𝘝𝘐𝘚𝘈 🄹🄲🄱. ❄
– **The Garden Room : Meals** (dinner only) 24.50 **t.** ⏿ 5.00 – **6 rm** ⌕ 50.00/90.00 **t.** – SB.

# DURHAM 401 402 P 19 Great Britain G. – pop. 36 937.

See : City★★★ - Cathedral★★★ (Nave★★★, Chapel of the Nine Altars★★★, Sanctuary Knocker★) B – Oriental Museum★★ AC (at Durham University by A 167) B – City and Riverside (Prebends' Bridge ≤★★★ A , Framwellgate Bridge ≤★★ B) – Monastic Buildings (Cathedral Treasury★, Central Tower≤★) B – Castle★ (Norman chapel★) AC B.

Exc. : Hartlepool Historic Quay★, SE : 14 m. by A 181, A 19 and A 179.

☐₁₈ Mount Oswald, South Rd ℰ (0191) 386 7527.

� Market Pl., DH1 3NJ ℰ (0191) 384 3720.

London 267 – Leeds 77 – Middlesbrough 23 – Sunderland 12.

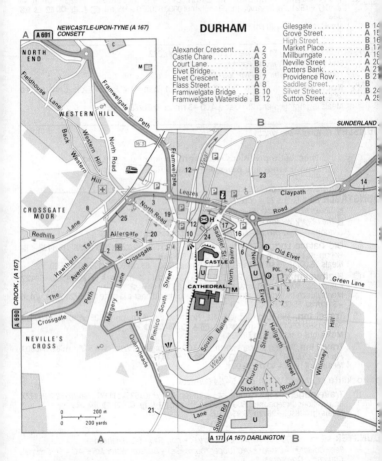

🏨🏨🏨 **Ramside Hall,** Carrville, DH1 1TD, Northeast : 3 m. on A 690 ℰ (0191) 386 5282 Fax (0191) 386 0399, ☐₁₈, ᵴ, park – 🛗, ⇔ rm, 📺 ☎ & ᴾ – 🔬 300. ◑◐ ᴁᴇ ◑ VISA
Meals 22.50 t. and a la carte ᵻ 4.90 – **78 rm** ⇌ 98.00/138.00 t., 2 suites – SB.

🏨🏨🏨 **Royal County,** Old Elvet, DH1 3JN, ℰ (0191) 386 6821, Fax (0191) 386 0704, ᴵ⟳, ⇌, ▨ –
🛗, ⇔ rm, 📺 ☎ & ᴾ – 🔬 120. ◑◐ ᴁᴇ ◑ VISA                                                               B a
**County :** Meals 15.50/24.50 st. and a la carte ᵻ 7.25 – **Bowes :** Meals 14.55/18.50 st. and a la carte ᵻ 7.25 – **150 rm** ⇌ 99.00/135.00 st., 1 suite – SB.

🏨🏨 **Three Tuns Swallow,** New Elvet, DH1 3AQ, ℰ (0191) 386 4326, Fax (0191) 386 1406 –
⇔ rm, 📺 ☎ ᴾ – 🔬 350. ◑◐ ᴁᴇ ◑ VISA                                                                       B e
Meals 11.50/19.95 st. ᵻ 9.00 – **49 rm** ⇌ 95.00/120.00 st., 1 suite – SB.

🏨 **Travel Inn,** Arnison Retail Centre, DH1 5GB, North : 3 m. by A 167 ℰ (0191) 383 9140, *Fax (0191) 383 9107* – 🅿. 🕮 📧 ⑩ 𝑉𝐼𝑆𝐴
40 rm 38.00. t.

✗ **Bistro 21,** Aykley Heads House, Aykley Heads, DH1 5TS, Northwest : 1 ½ m. by A 691 and
🅰 B 6532 ℰ (0191) 384 4354, *Fax (0191) 384 1149,* 🏠 – 🅿. 🕮 📧 ⑩ 𝑉𝐼𝑆𝐴
*closed Sunday and Bank Holidays* – Meals 14.50 t. (lunch) and a la carte 17.50/26.00 t.

**at Croxdale** South : 3 m. on A 167 – B – ✉ Durham.

🏨 **Bridge Toby,** DH1 3SP, ℰ (0191) 378 0524, *Fax (0191) 378 7802* – 📺 ☎ ✆ 🅿 – ⚿ 50. 🕮
📧 𝑉𝐼𝑆𝐴
Meals (grill rest.) a la carte 8.30/15.10 t. ⃒ 4.95 – 46 rm ☲ 52.00/62.00 t. – SB.

🅐 ATS Finchale Rd, Newton Hall ℰ (0191) 384 1810     ATS Mill Rd, Langley Moor ℰ (0191) 378 0262

---

**DUXFORD** *Cambs.* 🔢 U 27 – *see Cambridge.*

---

**EAGLESCLIFFE** *Stockton-on-Tees* 🔢 P 20 – *see Stockton-on-Tees.*

---

**EARL'S COLNE** *Essex* 🔢 W 28 – *pop. 3 420* – ✉ Colchester.
*London 55 – Cambridge 33 – Chelmsford 22 – Colchester 10.*

⌂ **Elm House,** 14 Upper Holt St., CO6 2PG, on A 1124 ℰ (01787) 222197, 🚗 – 🕍 rm. �
*closed Christmas* – Meals (by arrangement) (communal dining) 15.00 s. – 3 rm ☲ 19.00/
50.00 s. – SB.

---

**EASINGTON** *Bucks..*
*London 54 – Aylesbury 13 – Oxford 18.*

🍴 **Mole & Chicken,** The Terrace, HP18 9EY, ℰ (01844) 208387, *Fax (01844) 208387,* « Characterful inn » – 🅿. 🕮 📧 𝑉𝐼𝑆𝐴
*closed 25 December* – Meals (booking essential) a la carte 15.15/23.15 t. ⃒ 6.95.

---

**EASINGWOLD** *N. Yorks.* 🔢 Q 21 – *pop. 2 816* – ✉ York.
🔽 Stillington Rd ℰ (01347) 821486.
🔼 Chapel Lane, YO6 3AE ℰ (01347) 821530 *(summer only).*
*London 217 – Middlesbrough 37 – York 14.*

🏨 **Garth** without rest., York Rd, YO61 3PG, South : 1 ¼ m. ℰ (01347) 822988,
*Fax (01347) 822988,* 🚗 – 🕍 📺 ☎ 🅿. 🕮 𝑉𝐼𝑆𝐴
9 rm ☲ 39.50/49.50 – SB.

⌂ **Old Vicarage** without rest., Market Pl., YO61 3AL, ℰ (01347) 821015, *Fax (01347) 823465,*
🚗 – 🕍 📺 🅿. 🌮
*closed December and January* – 5 rm ☲ 37.00/59.00 s.

**at Raskelf** West : 2 ¾ m. – ✉ York.

🏨 **Old Farmhouse,** YO61 3LF, ℰ (01347) 821971 – 🕍 📺 ☎ 🅿
*March-December* – Meals (dinner only) 17.50 t. ⃒ 4.00 – 10 rm ☲ (dinner included) 47.50/
85.00 t. – SB.

---

**EASTBOURNE** *E. Sussex* 🔢 U 31 *Great Britain G.* – *pop. 94 793.*
See : Seafront★.
Env. : Beachy Head★★★, SW : 3 m. by B 2103 Z.
🔽, 🔽 Royal Eastbourne, Paradise Drive ℰ (01323) 729738 Z – 🔽 Eastbourne Downs, East
Dean Rd ℰ (01323) 720827 – 🔽 Eastbourne Golfing Park, Lottbridge Drove ℰ (01323)
520400.
🔼 3 Cornfield Rd, BN21 4QL ℰ (01323) 411400.
*London 68 – Brighton 25 – Dover 61 – Maidstone 49.*

Plan on next page

🏨🏨 **De Vere Grand,** King Edward's Par., BN21 4EQ, ℰ (01323) 412345, *Fax (01323) 412233,*
<, ⸂⸃, 🛎, ⌇, 🏊, 🚗 – 🕋 📺 ☎ 🅿 – ⚿ 400. 🕮 📧 ⑩ 𝑉𝐼𝑆𝐴                                Z  x
*closed 2 weeks January and 2 weeks August* – **Garden Restaurant :** Meals (dinner only
and lunch Sunday and Monday) 19.50/25.00 st. and a la carte ⃒ 8.00 – (see also **Mirabelle**
below) – 149 rm ☲ 115.00/160.00 st., 15 suites – SB.

🏨🏨 **Cavendish,** 37-40 Grand Par., BN21 4DH, ℰ (01323) 410222, *Fax (01323) 410941,* <, ⸂⸃ –
🕋, 🕍 rm, 📺 ☎ 🅿 – ⚿ 170. 🕮 📧 ⑩ 𝑉𝐼𝑆𝐴 𝐽𝐶𝐵. 🌮                                          X  r
Meals (bar lunch)/dinner 22.00 st. and a la carte ⃒ 6.00 – 108 rm ☲ 90.00/150.00 st.,
4 suites – SB.

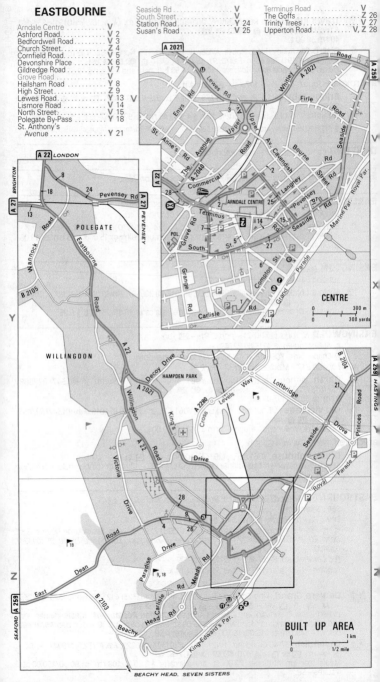

# EASTBOURNE

CENTRE

0    300 m
0    300 yards

BUILT UP AREA

0    1 km
0    1/2 mile

BEACHY HEAD, SEVEN SISTERS

238

🏛 **Albany,** Grand Par., BN21 4DJ, ℘ (01323) 722788, Fax (01323) 410941, ≼ – |₿|, ✸ rest, 📺
🕿 – 🔬 150. 🐠 🖭 ⑩ 𝑽𝑰𝑺𝑨 𝐉𝐂𝐁      X a
Meals (carving rest.) 11.00 **st.** 🍴 6.00 – **60 rm** ⊇ 75.00/90.00 **st.**, 1 suite – SB.

🏛 **Lansdowne,** King Edward's Par., BN21 4EE, ℘ (01323) 725174, Fax (01323) 739721, ≼ –
|₿|, ✸ rest, 📺 🕿 ⟅⟆ – 🔬 120. 🐠 🖭 ⑩ 𝑽𝑰𝑺𝑨 𝐉𝐂𝐁      Z z
closed 1 to 14 January – **Meals** (bar lunch Monday to Saturday)/dinner 16.25 **st.** 🍴 4.85 –
**121 rm** ⊇ 55.00/100.00 **st.** – SB.

🏛 **Chatsworth,** Grand Par., BN21 3YR, ℘ (01323) 411016, Fax (01323) 643270, ≼ – |₿|,
✸ rm, 📺 🕿 – 🔬 100. 🐠 🖭 ⑩ 𝑽𝑰𝑺𝑨      X e
Meals (bar lunch Monday to Saturday)/dinner 16.50 **st.** 🍴 5.25 – **46 rm** ⊇ 48.00/78.00 **st.**,
1 suite – SB.

🏠 **Brownings,** 28 Upperton Rd, BN21 1JS, ℘ (01323) 724358, Fax (01323) 731288, ⤳ – 📺
🕿 🅿 – 🔬 40. 🐠 🖭 ⑩ 𝑽𝑰𝑺𝑨 𝐉𝐂𝐁. ✀      Z a
Meals 12.00/15.00 **st.** and a la carte 🍴 4.50 – **12 rm** ⊇ 35.00/70.00 **st.** – SB.

↑ **Cherry Tree,** 15 Silverdale Rd, BN20 7AJ, ℘ (01323) 722406, Fax (01323) 648838 – ✸ 📺
🕿. 🐠 🖭 ⑩ 𝑽𝑰𝑺𝑨. ✀      Z u
Meals (by arrangement) 12.00 **t.** – **10 rm** ⊇ 27.00/58.00 **t.** – SB.

↑ **Brayscroft,** 13 South Cliff Av., BN20 7AH, ℘ (01323) 647005, Fax (01323) 720705 – ✸
Meals (by arrangement) 10.00 **s.** – **5 rm** ⊇ 24.00/48.00 **st.** – SB.      Z n

↑ **Southcroft,** 15 South Cliff Av., BN20 7AH, ℘ (01323) 729071 – ✸. ✀      Z n
closed Christmas – **Meals** (by arrangement) 9.00 **st.** 🍴 3.00 – **4 rm** ⊇ 25.00/50.00 **st.** – SB.

↑ **Camelot Lodge,** 35 Lewes Rd, BN21 2BU, ℘ (01323) 725207 – ✸ rest, 📺 🅿. 🐠 𝑽𝑰𝑺𝑨.
✀      V u
Meals (by arrangement) 9.00 **st.** – **7 rm** ⊇ 27.00/47.00 **st.** – SB.

XXX **Mirabelle** (at De Vere Grand H.), King Edward's Par., BN21 4EQ, ℘ (01323) 410771,
Fax (01323) 412233 – ▤ 🐠 🖭 ⑩ 𝑽𝑰𝑺𝑨      Z x
closed Sunday, Monday, first 2 weeks January and first 2 weeks August – **Meals** 18.50/
32.50 **st.** and dinner a la carte 🍴 8.00.

**Jevington** Northwest : 6 m. by A 259 – Z – on B 2105 – ✉ Polegate.

XX **Hungry Monk,** The Street, BN26 5QF, ℘ (01323) 482178, Fax (01323) 483989, « Part
Elizabethan cottages », ✿ – ✸ ▤ 🅿. 🖭
closed 24 to 26 December and Bank Holiday Mondays – **Meals** (booking essential) (dinner
only and Sunday lunch)/dinner 24.95 **t.**.

**Wilmington** Northwest : 6½ m. by A 22 on A 27 – Y – ✉ Eastbourne.

XX **Crossways** with rm, Lewes Rd, BN26 5SG, ℘ (01323) 482455, Fax (01323) 487811, ✿ –
✸ rest, 📺 🕿 🅿. 🐠 🖭 𝑽𝑰𝑺𝑨 𝐉𝐂𝐁. ✀
closed 24 December-24 January – **Meals** (closed Sunday and Monday) (dinner only) 27.95 **t.**
🍴 6.95 – **7 rm** ⊇ 48.00/76.00 **st.** – SB.

    ◉ ATS Langney Rise ℘ (01323) 761971

---

**AST BUCKLAND** Devon **403** I 30 – see South Molton.

---

**AST DEREHAM** Norfolk **404** W 25 – pop. 12 974.
    London 109 – Cambridge 57 – King's Lynn 27 – Norwich 16.

↑ **Peacock House** without rest., Peacock Lane, Old Beetley, NR20 4DG, North : 3 ½ m. by
B 1110 ℘ (01362) 860371, « Part 17C farmhouse », ✿ – ✸ 🅿
closed 1 week spring and 1 week autumn – **3 rm** ⊇ 25.00/40.00.

**Wendling** West : 5½ m. by A 47.

↑ **Greenbanks Country H.,** Swaffham Rd, NR19 2AR, ℘ (01362) 687742, ⬳, ✿ –
✸ rest, 📺 🅿. 🐠 𝑽𝑰𝑺𝑨
Meals 12.50 **t.** 🍴 6.50 – **9 rm** ⊇ 48.00/68.00 **st.** – SB.

---

**AST END** Hants. – see Lymington.

---

**AST GRINSTEAD** W. Sussex **404** T 30 – pop. 24 383.
    🇮🇧 Copthorne, Borers Arm Rd ℘ (01342) 712508.
    London 48 – Brighton 30 – Eastbourne 32 – Lewes 21 – Maidstone 37.

🏛 **Jarvis Felbridge,** London Rd, RH19 2BH, Northwest : 1 ½ m. on A 22 ℘ (01342) 326992,
Fax (01342) 410778, 🖟, ☎, 🔟, ✿, ✵ – ✸ 📺 🕿 ♿ 🅿 – 🔬 350. 🐠 🖭 ⑩ 𝑽𝑰𝑺𝑨
Meals (closed Saturday lunch) 12.50/15.95 **st.** 🍴 6.50 – ⊇ 10.50 – **120 rm** 105.00/145.00 –
SB.

🏠 **Woodbury House**, Lewes Rd, RH19 3UD, Southeast : ½ m. on A 22 ℰ (01342) 313657
Fax (01342) 314801, 🌿 – 📺 ☎ 🅿. 🝌 AE ⊙ VISA. 🛠
**The Garden Room :** Meals (closed Sunday dinner) 17.50 **st.** ⅃ 5.50 – **Bistro :** Meal
12.50 **st.** ⅃ 5.50 – **14 rm** ☷ 75.00/110.00 **st.** – SB.

**at Gravetye** Southwest : 4½ m. by B 2110 taking second turn left towards West Hoathly – ⊠ Eas
Grinstead.

🏠 **Gravetye Manor** ⌁, Vowels Lane, RH19 4LJ, ℰ (01342) 810567, Fax (01342) 810080, ≤
❀ « 16C manor house with gardens and grounds by William Robinson », 🐦, park – 🛏 rest
📺 ☎ 🅿. 🝌 VISA. 🛠
Meals (booking essential) 29.00/38.00 **st.** ⅃ 18.00 – ☷ 14.00 – **18 rm** 130.00/300.00 **st.**
**Spec.** Roast scallops with coriander purée and caramelised garlic. Roast rib of Angus bee
girolles and Rossini potatoes. Vanilla panna cotta with poached peaches.

🅐 ATS London Rd, North End ℰ (01342) 410740

---

**EAST HADDON** Northants. 📘📗 Q 27 – pop. 607 – ⊠ Northampton.
London 78 – Birmingham 47 – Leicester 32 – Northampton 6.

🍴 **Red Lion** with rm, High St., NN6 8BU, ℰ (01604) 770223, Fax (01604) 770767, « Par
17C », 🌿 – 📺 ☎ 🅿. 🝌 AE ⊙ VISA JCB
closed 25 December – Meals (closed Sunday dinner) 16.95 **t.** (lunch) and a la carte 24.65
30.65 **t.** ⅃ 7.00 – **5 rm** ☷ 60.00/75.00 **t.**

---

**EASTHAM** Mersey. 📗📘 L 24 – pop. 15 011 – ⊠ Wirral.
London 209 – Birmingham 45 – Chester 13 – Liverpool 7.5 – Manchester 45.

🏠 **Travelodge**, New Chester Rd, L62 9AQ, at junction of A 41 with M 53 ℰ (0151) 327 2489
Fax (0151) 327 2489, Reservations (Freephone) 0800 850950 – 🛏 rm, 📺 ⅃ 🅿. 🝌 AE ⊙
VISA JCB. 🛠
Meals (grill rest.) – **31 rm** 39.95/59.95 **t.**

---

**EAST HOATHLY** E. Sussex 📘 U 31 – pop. 1 206.
London 60 – Brighton 16 – Eastbourne 13 – Hastings 25 – Maidstone 32.

🏡 **Old Whyly** ⌁, BN8 6EL, West : ½ m., turning right after post box on right, taking centr
gravel drive after approx. 400 metres ℰ (01825) 840216, Fax (01825) 840738, ≤, « Georgia
manor house, antiques », 🏊, 🌿, park, 🎾 – 🛏 rm, 🅿. 🛠
Meals (by arrangement) (communal dining) 20.00 – **3 rm** ☷ 67.50/90.00.

---

**EAST HORNDON** Essex.
London 21 – Chelmsford 13 – Southend-on-Sea 17.

🏠 **Travelodge**, CM13 3LL, on A 127 (eastbound carriageway) ℰ (01277) 810819, Reserva
tions (Freephone) 0800 850950 – 📺 ⅃ 🅿. 🝌 AE ⊙ VISA JCB. 🛠
Meals (grill rest.) – **22 rm** 39.95/59.95 **t.**

---

**EAST HORSLEY** Surrey 📘 S 30 – ⊠ Leatherhead.
London 31 – Guildford 8 – Reigate 21.

🏠 **Jarvis Thatchers**, Guildford Rd, KT24 6TB, on A 246 ℰ (01483) 28429
Fax (01483) 284222, 🏊, 🌿 – 🛏 rm, 📺 ☎ 🅿 – 🔔 70. 🝌 AE ⊙ VISA JCB
Meals (closed Saturday lunch) 14.50/19.50 **t.** and a la carte ⅃ 7.75 – ☷ 9.50 – **54 rm** 99.0(
140.00 **st.** – SB.

---

**EASTLEIGH** Devon 📘 H 30 – see Bideford.

---

**EASTLEIGH** Hants. 📘 P 31 – pop. 49 934.
🔖 Fleming Park, Magpie Lane ℰ (01703) 612797.
✈ Southampton (Eastleigh) Airport : ℰ (01703) 620021.
🚩 Town Hall Centre, Leigh Rd, SO50 4DE ℰ (01703) 641261.
London 74 – Winchester 8 – Southampton 4.

🏠 **Travel Inn**, Leigh Rd, SO50 9YX, West : ½ m. on A 335 ℰ (01703) 65054
Fax (01703) 650531 – 🕴, 🛏 rm, 📺 ⅃ 🅿. 🝌 AE ⊙ VISA
Meals (grill rest.) – **60 rm** 38.00 **t.**

🏠 **Travelodge**, Twyford Rd, SO50 4LF, North : 1 m. on A 335 ℰ (01703) 616813, Reserv
tions (Freephone) 0800 850950 – 📺 ⅃ 🅿. 🝌 AE ⊙ VISA JCB. 🛠
Meals (grill rest.) – **32 rm** 39.95/59.95 **t.**

🅐 ATS Dutton Lane, Bishopstoke Rd ℰ (01703) 613027

**EASTLING** Kent **404** W 30 – see Faversham.

**EASTON** Devon **403** I 31 – see Chagford.

**EASTON** Somerset – see Wells.

**EAST RETFORD** Notts. **402 403 404** R 24 – pop. 20 679.
London 148 – Lincoln 23 – Nottingham 31 – Sheffield 27.

⌂ **Old Plough** ⌾ without rest., Top St., North Wheatley, DN22 9DB, Northeast : 5 m. by A 620 ℘ (01427) 880916, ≼, 🌫 – ⭄ 📺 🅿. ℅
*closed Christmas-New Year* – **3 rm** ⊡ 35.00/70.00 **s.**

🏢 ATS Babworth Rd ℘ (01777) 706501

**EAST WITTERING** W. Sussex **404** R 31 – pop. 4 630 – ⊠ Chichester.
London 74 – Brighton 37 – Portsmouth 25.

⅍ **Clifford's Cottage**, Bracklesham Lane, Bracklesham Bay, PO20 8JA, East : 1 m. by B 2179 on B 2198 ℘ (01243) 670250 – 🍽 🅿. 🔟 🎫 ⓞ 🆅
*closed Sunday dinner, Monday, Tuesday, 1 week Spring and 2 weeks November* – **Meals** (dinner only and Sunday lunch)/dinner 18.50 **t.** and a la carte ⓐ 4.50.

**EAST WITTON** N. Yorks. **402** O 21 – pop. 153 – ⊠ Leyburn.
London 238 – Leeds 45 – Middlesbrough 30 – York 39.

⌂ **Holly Tree**, DL8 4SL, ℘ (01969) 622383, « 16C cottage », 🌫 – ⭄ 🅿. ℅
*March-October* – **Meals** (by arrangement) (communal dining) 15.00 **st.** ⓐ 6.50 – **4 rm** ⊡ 88.00 **s.**

⅍⅍ **Blue Lion** with rm, DL8 4SN, ℘ (01969) 624273, Fax (01969) 624189, « Part 18C former coaching inn », 🌫 – 📺 ☎ 🅿. 🔟 🆅
*The Restaurant :* **Meals** *(closed Sunday dinner and Monday)* (dinner only and Sunday lunch)/dinner a la carte 17.95/29.05 **t.** ⓐ 6.15 – (see also *The Bar* below) – **12 rm** ⊡ 47.50/85.00 **t.**

🍴 **The Bar** (at Blue Lion), DL8 4SN, ℘ (01969) 624273, Fax (10969) 624189, 🌫, « Part 18C coaching inn », 🌫 – 🅿. 🔟 🆅
**Meals** (booking essential) a la carte 12.95/27.75 **t.** ⓐ 6.15.

**EBCHESTER** Durham **401 402** O 19 – ⊠ Consett.
🏌 Consett and District, Elmfield Rd, Consett ℘ (01207) 502186.
London 275 – Carlisle 64 – Newcastle upon Tyne 16.

🏨 **Raven Country**, Broomhill, DH8 6RY, Southeast : ¾ m. on B 6309 ℘ (01207) 562562, Fax (01207) 560262, ≼ – 📺 ☎ ও 🅿. 🔟 🎫 ⓞ 🆅
**Meals** (bar lunch Monday to Saturday)/dinner a la carte 9.30/25.95 **st.** ⓐ 4.95 – **28 rm** ⊡ 52.00/69.00 **st.** – SB.

**ECCLES** Gtr. Manchester **402 403 404** M 23 – see Manchester.

**ECCLESTON** Mersey. **402** ㉝ **403** ⑬ – see St. Helens.

---

*Per viaggiare in EUROPA, utilizzate :*

Le **carte** Michelin **Le Grandi Strade**;

Le **carte** Michelin dettagliate;

Le **Guide Rosse** Michelin (alberghi e ristoranti) :
   *Benelux, Deutschland, España Portugal, Europe, France, Great Britain and Ireland, Italia, Svizzera.*

Le **Guide Verdi** Michelin che descrivono
musei, monumenti, percorsi turistici interessanti.

241

**EDENBRIDGE** Kent **404** U 30 Great Britain G. – pop. 7 196.

Env. : Hever Castle★ AC, E : 2½ m. – Chartwell★ AC, N : 3 m. by B 2026.

🔝, 🔝, 🔝 Crouch House Rd ℘ (01732) 867381.

London 35 – Brighton 36 – Maidstone 29.

XXX **Honours Mill,** 87 High St., TN8 5AU, ℘ (01732) 866757, 斎, « Carefully renovated 18C mill » – 🐠 �

closed Saturday lunch, Sunday dinner, Monday, Good Friday and 2 weeks Christmas – Meals 15.50/19.95 t. and a la carte 🖗 9.75.

🔘 ATS Unit 1, Monza House, Fircroft Way ℘ (01732) 867746

---

**EGERTON** Gtr. Manchester **402** ㉑ **403** ② **404** ⑨ – see Bolton.

---

**EGGESFORD** Devon **403** I 31.

London 215 – Barnstaple 18 – Exeter 22 – Taunton 48.

🏠 **Eggesford Country H.,** EX18 7JZ, ℘ (01769) 580345, Fax (01769) 580262, 🔝, 🔈, 🚗 park – 📺 🅿 – 🛃 80. 🐠 🌍 JCB

Meals 13.50 st. and a la carte – **19 rm** ⊡ 36.00/72.00 st. – SB.

---

**EGHAM** Surrey **404** S 29 – pop. 23 816.

London 29 – Reading 21.

🏨 **Runnymede,** Windsor Rd, TW20 0AG, on a 308 ℘ (01784) 436171, Fax (01784) 436340, « Riverside setting », 🔈, ⇌, 🔲, 🚗, 🎾 – 🛗 🗓, 🗱 rm, 🔲 📺 ☎ 🅿 – 🛃 350. 🐠 🅰🅴 🅞 🌍. 🛠

Meals – (see **Leftbank** below) – ⊡ 12.95 – **177 rm** 138.00/190.00 st., 3 suites – SB.

🏛 **Great Fosters,** Stroude Rd, TW20 9UR, South : 1 ¼ m. by B 388 ℘ (01784) 433822, Fax (01784) 472455, « Elizabethan mansion, gardens », ⇌, 🔲, park, 🎾 – 📺 ☎ 🅿 – 🛃 100. 🐠 🅰🅴 🌍. 🛠

Meals 15.50/25.00 st. and a la carte 🖗 5.75 – **42 rm** ⊡ 95.00/225.00 st., 2 suites – SB.

XX **Left Bank** (at Runnymede H.), Windsor Rd, TW20 0AG, ℘ (01784) 437400 – 🐠 🅰🅴 🅞 🌍

closed Saturday lunch and Sunday dinner – Meals a la carte 24.00/29.25 t. 🖗 9.50.

---

**EIGHT ASH GREEN** Essex **404** W 28 – see Colchester.

---

**ELLAND** W. Yorks. **402** O 22 – pop. 10 931 – ⊠ Halifax.

🔝 Hammerstones Leach Lane, Hullen Edge ℘ (01422) 372505.

London 204 – Bradford 12 – Burnley 29 – Leeds 17 – Manchester 30.

X **La Cachette,** 7-10 Town Hall Buildings, HX5 0EU, ℘ (01422) 378833, Fax (01422) 377899 – 🗏. 🐠 🅰🅴 🌍

closed Sunday, 26-27 December and 1 January – Meals 10.95 st. (lunch) and a la carte 13.85/21.85 st. 🖗 5.95.

---

**ELLESMERE PORT** Mersey. **402 403** L 24 – pop. 64 504.

London 211 – Birkenhead 9 – Chester 9 – Liverpool 11 – Manchester 44.

🏨 **Holiday Inn Ellesmere Port Chester,** Centre Island, Waterways, Lower Mersey St., L65 2AL, Northeast : 1 ½ m. by A 5032 (M 53 junction 9) ℘ (0151) 356 8111, Fax (0151) 356 8444, « Marina setting overlooking Boat Museum », 🔈, ⇌, 🔲 – 🛗, 🗱 rm, 🗏 rest, 📺 ☎ & 🅿 – 🛃 120. 🐠 🅰🅴 🅞 🌍 JCB. 🛠

**Waterways :** Meals (closed lunch Saturday and Sunday) 12.95/15.95 t. and a la carte 🖗 9.95 – ⊡ 9.50 – **83 rm** 95.00/120.00 t.

🔘 ATS 1 Rossfield Rd, Rossmore Trading Est. ℘ (0151) 355 8144

---

**ELMDON** Essex **404** U 27 – see Saffron Walden.

---

**ELSING** Norfolk **404** X 25 – pop. 261 – ⊠ East Dereham.

London 118 – Cambridge 66 – King's Lynn 33 – Norwich 15.

🏠 **Bartles Lodge** 🔈 without rest., Church St., NR20 3EA, ℘ (01362) 637177, 🔈, 🚗 – 📺 🅿. 🐠 🌍

**7 rm** ⊡ 35.00/48.00 st.

---

**ELSLACK** N. Yorks. **402** N 22 – see Skipton.

---

**ELSTED** W. Sussex **404** R 31 – see Midhurst.

**ELSTED MARSH** *W. Sussex* 404 R 31 – *see Midhurst.*

**ELSTOW** *Beds.* 404 S 27 – *see Bedford.*

**ELSTREE** *Herts.* 404 T 29 – *pop. 2 196.*
ᵣ₈ *Watling St.* ℰ *(0181) 953 6115.*
*London 10 – Luton 22.*

Plan : see Greater London (North West) pp. 4 and 5

🏨 **Edgwarebury,** Barnet Lane, WD6 3RE, ℰ (0181) 953 8227, Fax (0181) 207 3668, 𝄞, park, ℅ – ⅍ rm, 🖭 ☎ ℗ – 🛦 80. 𝄞 CT **e**
Meals –(see **The Cavendish** below) – ☷ 7.95 – **47 rm** 110.00/190.00 **st.** – SB.

XXX **The Cavendish** (at Edgwarebury H.), Barnet Lane, WD6 3RE, ℰ (0181) 953 8227, Fax (0181) 207 3668, 𝄞, park – ⅍ ℗. 𝄜 🝙 ◑ 𝘝𝘐𝘚𝘈 ᴊᴄʙ
Meals *(closed Saturday lunch)* (booking essential) 29.90 **st.** and a la carte 🖌 6.75.

**ELTERWATER** *Cumbria* – *see Ambleside.*

**ELY** *Cambs.* 404 U 26 *Great Britain G.* – *pop. 10 329.*
See : *Cathedral*★★ *AC.*
Exc. : *Wicken Fen*★, *SE : 9 m. by A 10 and A 1123.*
ᵣ₈ *Cambridge Rd* ℰ *(01353) 662751.*
🄳 *Oliver Cromwells House, 29 St. Mary's St., CB7 4HF* ℰ *(01353) 662062.*
*London 74 – Cambridge 16 – Norwich 60.*

🏨 **Lamb,** 2 Lynn Rd, CB7 4EJ, ℰ (01353) 663574, Fax (01353) 662023 – ⅍ rest, 🖭 ☎ ℗ – 🛦 30. 𝄜 🝙 ◑ 𝘝𝘐𝘚𝘈 ᴊᴄʙ
Meals 11.50/16.95 **st.** and a la carte 🖌 6.50 – **32 rm** ☷ 63.00/84.00 **st.** – SB.

🏠 **Travelodge,** Witchford Rd, CB6 3NN, West : 1 m. on A 10/A 142 roundabout, Ely bypass ℰ (01353) 668499, Reservations (Freephone) 0800 850950 – ⅍ rm, 🖭 ⅋ ℗. 𝄜 🝙 ◑ 𝘝𝘐𝘚𝘈 ᴊᴄʙ
Meals (grill rest.) – **39 rm** 39.95/59.95 **t.**

**at Littleport** *North : 5¾ m. on A 10* – ⊠ *Ely.*

XX **Fen House,** 2 Lynn Rd, CB6 1QG, ℰ (01353) 860645 – ⅍. 𝄜 ◑ 𝘝𝘐𝘚𝘈. ℅
*closed Sunday, Monday and 24 December-6 January* – **Meals** (booking essential) (dinner only) 27.00 **st.** 🖌 6.00.

**at Coveney** *Northwest : 4 m. by West Fen rd* – ⊠ *Ely.*

↥ **Hill House Farm** 🍃 without rest., 9 Main St., CB6 2DJ, ℰ (01353) 778369, 𝄞 – ⅍ 🖭 ℗. ℅
*closed Christmas* – **3 rm** ☷ 36.00/50.00 **s.**

**at Sutton Gault** *West : 8 m. by A 142 off B 1381* – ⊠ *Ely.*

🍴 **Anchor Inn** with rm, CB6 2BD, ℰ (01353) 778537, Fax (01353) 776180, 𝄞, « Part 17C inn » – ⅍ 🖭 ☎ ℗. 𝄜 🝙 𝘝𝘐𝘚𝘈. ℅
Meals a la carte 17.05/22.50 **t.** 🖌 5.95 – **1 rm** ☷ 50.00/62.00 **t.**, 1 suite.

🅐 ATS 11 Broad St. ℰ (01353) 662758/662801

**EMSWORTH** *Hants.* 404 R 31 – *pop. 18 310 (inc. Southbourne).*
*London 75 – Brighton 37 – Portsmouth 10.*

🏨 **Brookfield,** 93-95 Havant Rd, PO10 7LF, East : 1 m. on A 259 ℰ (01243) 373363, Fax (01243) 376342, 𝄞 – ⅍ rm, 🗏 rest, 🖭 ☎ ℗ – 🛦 50. 𝄜 🝙 ◑ 𝘝𝘐𝘚𝘈 ᴊᴄʙ. ℅
*closed 25 December-2 January* – **Hermitage :** Meals 16.95/24.95 **st.** 🖌 5.95 – **40 rm** ☷ 58.00/100.00 **st.** – SB.

🏠 **Travelodge,** PO10 7RB, Northeast : 1 ½ m. on A 27 (eastbound carriageway) ℰ (01243) 370877, Reservations (Freephone) 0800 850950 – ⅍ rm, 🖭 ⅋ ℗. 𝄜 🝙 ◑ 𝘝𝘐𝘚𝘈 ᴊᴄʙ. ℅
Meals (grill rest.) – **36 rm** 39.95/59.95 **t.**

XXX **36 on the Quay** (Farthing), 47 South St., The Quay, PO10 7EG, ℰ (01243) 375592, Fax (01243) 375593, ≤ – 𝄜 🝙 ◑ 𝘝𝘐𝘚𝘈 ᴊᴄʙ
❀ *closed lunch Monday and Saturday, Sunday, 4 to 18 January, 4 to 11 October and Bank Holidays* – **Meals** 19.00/31.95-37.50 **t.** 🖌 7.50
**Spec.** Roast fillet of cod, langoustine fritters, cucumber spaghetti. Fillet of beef, lasagne of mushrooms and spinach, Madeira sauce. Banana ice cream with caramelised banana galette and orange syrup.

XX **Spencer's**, 36 North St., PO10 7DG, ℘ (01243) 372744, Fax (01243) 372744 – ▣. **CO** **AE** **O** **VISA**
closed Sunday, Monday and 24 to 26 December – Meals (dinner only) a la carte 14.00/23.20 t. ⓚ 5.00 – (see also **Downstair's at Spencer's** below).

X **Downstairs at Spencer's**, 36 North St., PO10 7DG, ℘ (01243) 379017, Fax (01243) 372744 – ▣. **CO** **AE** **O** **VISA**
closed Sunday, 24 to 26 December and Bank Holiday Monday – Meals - Brasserie - a la carte 14.00/23.20 t. ⓚ 5.00.

---

**ENSTONE** Oxon. **403** **404** P 28 – pop. 1 523 – ⊠ Chipping Norton.
London 73 – Birmingham 48 – Gloucester 32 – Oxford 18.

⬥ **Swan Lodge** without rest., OX7 4NE, on A 44 ℘ (01608) 678736, Fax (01608) 677963, ⇌ – ⁕⇌ rest., **TV** **P**
3 rm � 35.00/50.00 st.

---

**EPSOM** Surrey **404** ㊴ – pop. 64 405 (inc. Ewell).
🏌 Longdown Lane South, Epsom Downs ℘ (01372) 721666 – 🏌 Horton Park C.C., Hook R℗ ℘ (0181) 393 8400.
London 17 – Guildford 16.

🏠 **Travel Inn**, 2-4 St. Margarets Drive, KT18 7LB, Southwest : ½ m. on A 24 ℘ (01372) 739786, Fax (01372) 739761 – ⁕⇌ rm, **TV** **&** **P**. **CO** **AE** **O** **VISA**
Meals (grill rest.) – 40 rm 38.00.

XX **Le Raj**, 211 Fir Tree Rd, Epsom Downs, KT19 3LB, Southeast : 2 ¼ m. by B 289 and B 284 on B 291 ℘ (01737) 371371, Fax (01737) 211903 – ▣. **CO** **AE** **O** **VISA**
closed 25 and 26 December – Meals - Indian - a la carte 25.50/29.45 t.

---

**ERLESTOKE** Wilts. **403** **404** N 30 – see Devizes.

---

**ERPINGHAM** Norfolk **404** X 25 – pop. 1 871.
London 123 – Cromer 8 – King's Lynn 46 – Norwich 16.

X **The Ark** with rm, The Street, NR11 7QB, ℘ (01263) 761535, ⇌ – ⁕⇌ **TV** **P**. ⁂
closed 25 to 29 December and 2 weeks October – Meals (closed Sunday dinner and Monday) (dinner only and Sunday lunch)/dinner 24.50 t. ⓚ 6.50 – 3 rm ⊇ (dinner included) 67.50/125.00.

🍴 **Saracen's Head** with rm, Wolterton, NR11 7LX, West : 1 ½ m. ℘ (01263) 768909, ⇌ – ⁕⇌ rm, **P**. **CO** **AE** **VISA**
closed 25 December – Meals a la carte 13.85/17.65 t. ⓚ 7.00 – 4 rm ⊇ 40.00/60.00 t.

---

**ESCRICK** N. Yorks. **402** Q 22 – see York.

---

**ESHER** Surrey **404** S 29 – pop. 46 599 (inc. Molesey).
🏌 Thames Ditton & Esher, Portsmouth Rd ℘ (0181) 398 1551 BZ – 🏌 Moore Place Portsmouth Rd ℘ (01372) 463533 BZ – 🏌, 🏌 Sandown Park, More Lane ℘ (01372) 461234 BZ.
London 20 – Portsmouth 58.

Plan : see Greater London (South-West) p. 8

XX **Taste of India**, 104 High St., KT10 9QJ, ℘ (01372) 469555, Fax (01372) 467775 – **CO** **AE** **O** **VISA**
closed Monday – Meals - Indian - a la carte 13.00/22.50 t.

XX **Good Earth**, 14-18 High St., KT10 9RT, ℘ (01372) 462489, Fax (01372) 465588 – ▣. **CO** **AE** **O** **VISA** **JCB**                                                                                      BZ e
closed 24 to 27 December – Meals - Chinese - 12.00/21.80 t. and a la carte ⓚ 6.50.

X **La Orient**, 63 High St., KT10 9RQ, ℘ (01372) 466628 – ▣. **CO** **AE** **O** **VISA**. ⁂               BZ a
closed 25 to 28 December – Meals - South East Asian - 15.50 t. and a la carte ⓚ 4.00.

**at Claygate** Southeast : 1 m. by A 244 – ⊠ Esher.

XX **Monticello's**, 7 High St., KT10 0JW, ℘ (01372) 462200, Fax (01372) 464882 – ▣. **CO** **AE** **O** **VISA**. ⁂                                                                                               BZ r
closed Saturday lunch and Sunday – Meals a la carte 20.00/22.00 st. ⓚ 6.00.

XX **Le Petit Pierrot**, 4 The Parade, KT10 0NU, ℘ (01372) 465105, Fax (01372) 467642 – **CO** **AE** **O** **VISA**                                                                                               BZ r
closed Saturday lunch, Sunday, 1 week Christmas-New Year and Bank Holidays – Meals - French - 18.75/21.75 t. ⓚ 5.15.

**EVERDON** Northants. - see Daventry.

**EVERSHOT** Dorset 403 404 M 31 - pop. 225 - ⊠ Dorchester.
London 149 - Bournemouth 39 - Dorchester 12 - Salisbury 53 - Taunton 30 - Yeovil 10.

🏛 **Summer Lodge** ≫, Summer Lane, DT2 0JR, ℰ (01935) 83424, Fax (01935) 83005, « Part Georgian dower house », ⅃, 🐎, ℀ - ↦ rest, 🖸 ☎ 🅿. 🕼 🗚 🅪 *VISA* JCB
Meals 12.75/36.00 st. and a la carte 21.50/48.00 st. ⅃ 6.50 - **17 rm** ⊇ 125.00/275.00 st. - SB.

⌂ **Rectory House**, Fore St., DT2 0JW, ℰ (01935) 83273, Fax (01935) 83273, 🐎 - ↦ 🖸 🅿. 🕼 *VISA*. ℀
closed January and December - Meals (by arrangement) 18.00 s. - **5 rm** ⊇ 45.00/90.00 s. - SB.

⌂ **Church Farm** ≫ without rest., Stockwood, DT2 0NG, Northeast : 3 ½ m. by The Common and A 37 off Stockwood rd ℰ (01935) 83221, Fax (01935) 83771, « Working farm », 🐎 - ↦ 🖸 🅿
**3 rm** ⊇ 25.00/44.00 st.

**EVESHAM** Worcestershire 403 404 O 27 - pop. 17 823.
🖪 The Almonry, Abbey Gate, WR11 4BG ℰ (01386) 446944.
London 99 - Birmingham 30 - Cheltenham 16 - Coventry 32.

🏛 **Wood Norton Hall**, WR11 4YB, Northwest : 2 ¼ m. on A 4538 ℰ (01386) 420007, Fax (01386) 420190, « Victorian country house », ⅃₆, 🐎, park, ℀, squash - ↦ 🖸 ☎ ℰ 🅿 - 🔏 70. 🕼 🗚 🅪 *VISA*. ℀
closed 25 and 26 December - **Duc's** : Meals (closed Saturday lunch) (booking essential) 21.00/35.00 st. ⅃ 9.75 - **44 rm** ⊇ 110.00/195.00 t., 1 suite - SB.

🏨 **Evesham**, Coopers Lane, WR11 6DA, off Waterside ℰ (01386) 765566, Fax (01386) 765443, Reservations (Freephone) 0800 716969, ⬛, 🐎 - ↦ rest, 🖸 ☎ 🅿. 🕼 🗚 🅪 *VISA*. ℀
closed 25 and 26 December - Meals a la carte 14.75/27.75 st. ⅃ 5.25 - **40 rm** ⊇ 60.00/90.00 st. - SB.

🏨 **Waterside**, 56-59 Waterside, WR11 6JZ, ℰ (01386) 442420, Fax (01386) 446272, ⬟, 🐎 - 🖸 ☎ 🅿. 🕼 🗚 *VISA*. ℀
Meals (grill rest.) a la carte 11.00/15.30 t. - **17 rm** ⊇ 44.80/82.50 - SB.

🏠 **Riverside**, The Parks, Offenham Rd, WR11 5JP, Northeast : 2 m. by Waterside and B 4035 off B 4510 ℰ (01386) 446200, Fax (01386) 40021, ≤, ⬟, 🐎 - ↦ rest, 🖸 ☎ 🅿. 🕼 🗚 *VISA* JCB
closed 25 December - Meals (closed Sunday dinner and Monday) 16.95/26.95 st. and lunch a la carte ⅃ 7.30 - **7 rm** ⊇ 60.00/80.00 st. - SB.

⌂ **Church House** without rest., Greenhill Park Rd, WR11 4NL, ℰ (01386) 40498, 🐎 - 🖸 🅿
closed 20 December-10 January - **3 rm** ⊇ 40.00/50.00 s.

⌂ **The Croft** without rest., 54 Greenhill Park Rd, WR11 4NF, ℰ (01386) 446035, 🐎 - 🖸 🅿
**3 rm** ⊇ 35.00/50.00 s.

**at Harvington** Northeast : 4½ m. by A 4184 and B 4088 off Bidford rd - ⊠ Evesham.

🏨 **Mill at Harvington** ≫, Anchor Lane, WR11 5NR, Southeast : 1 ½ m. ℰ (01386) 870688, Fax (01386) 870686, ≤, « 18C mill with riverside garden », ⅃, ⬟, ℀ - ↦ rest, 🖸 ☎ 🅿. 🕼 🗚 🅪 *VISA* JCB. ℀
closed 1 week Christmas - Meals 14.95/23.00 st. and lunch a la carte ⅃ 6.00 - **21 rm** ⊇ 61.00/115.00 st. - SB.

**at Abbot's Salford** (Warks.) Northeast : 5 m. by A 4184 and B 4088 on Bidford rd - ⊠ Evesham.

🏛 **Salford Hall**, WR11 5UT, ℰ (01386) 871300, Fax (01386) 871301, « Tudor mansion with early 17C extension and gatehouse », ⌂, 🐎, ℀ - ↦ rest, 🖸 ☎ 🅿 - 🔏 50. 🕼 🗚 🅪 *VISA* JCB. ℀
closed 24 to 30 December - Meals (closed Saturday lunch) 15.75/25.00 t. ⅃ 6.50 - ⊇ 8.50 - **33 rm** 80.00/115.00 st. - SB.

🅖 ATS Worcester Rd ℰ (01386) 765313

**EWELL** Surrey 404 T 29 - pop. 4 862.
London 13 - Crawley 26 - Guildford 22.

🏠 **Queen Adelaide - Lodge Inn**, 272 Kingston Rd, KT19 0SH, ℰ (0181) 393 2666, Fax (0181) 394 1780 - ↦ rm, 🖸 ₺ 🅿. 🕼 🗚 🅪 *VISA*. ℀
Meals (grill rest.) 11.45 t. and a la carte - ⊇ 5.50 - **29 rm** 39.00 t.

**EWEN** Glos. 403 404 O 28 - see Cirencester.

**EXETER** Devon **408** J 31 *The West Country G.* – pop. 94 717.

See : *City** - Cathedral** Z – Royal Albert Memorial Museum** Y.*

Exc. : *Killerton** AC, NE : 7 m. by B 3181 V – Ottery St. Mary* (St. Mary's*) E : 12 m. by B 3183 – Y – A 30 and B 3174 – Crediton (Holy Cross Church*), NW : 9 m. by A 377.*

☖ *Downes Crediton, Hookway ℘ (01363) 773991.*

✈ *Exeter Airport : ℘ (01392) 367433, E : 5 m. by A 30 V – Terminal : St. David's and Central Stations.*

🛈 *Civic Centre, Paris St., EX1 IRP ℘ (01392) 265700.*

*London 201 – Bournemouth 83 – Bristol 83 – Plymouth 46 – Southampton 110.*

## EXETER
### BUILT UP AREA

| | | | | | |
|---|---|---|---|---|---|
| Blackboy Road | **V** 8 | Hill Lane | **V** 21 | St. Andrew's Road | **V** 4 |
| Buddle Lane | **X** 9 | Marsh Barton Road | **X** 25 | Summer Lane | **V** 5 |
| Butts Road | **X** 12 | Mount Pleasant Road | **V** 29 | Sweetbriar Lane | **VX** 5 |
| East Wonford Hill | **X** 17 | North Street | | Trusham Road | **X** 5 |
| Heavitree Road | **VX** 20 | HEAVITREE | **X** 32 | Union Road | **V** 5 |
| | | Old Tiverton Road | **V** 35 | Whipton Road | **V** 5 |
| | | Polsloe Road | **V** 39 | Wonford Road | **X** 5 |
| | | Prince Charles Road | **V** 41 | Wonford Street | **X** 5 |
| | | Prince of Wales Road | **V** 42 | Woodwater Lane | **X** 6 |

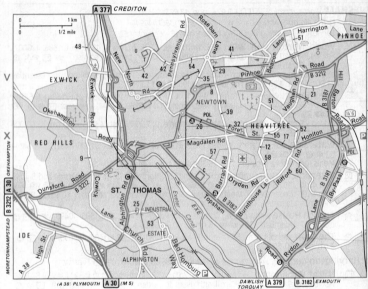

🏨🏨 **Southgate**, Southernhay East, EX1 1QF, ℘ (01392) 412812, Fax (01392) 413549, 🗗, ⇄s ☒ – 🛏, 💱 rm, 📺 ☎ & ➋ – 🔬 150. 🐵 🗚 ⑩ **VISA**
Z
**Meals** *(closed Saturday lunch and Bank Holiday Mondays)* 12.95 **t.** *(lunch)* and a la carte 20.00/29.00 **t.** ⒜ 9.00 – ☑ 10.85 – **109 rm** 99.00 **st.**, 1 suite – SB.

🏨🏨 **Thistle Rougemont**, Queen St., EX4 3SP, ℘ (01392) 254982, Fax (01392) 420928 – 🛗 💱 rm, 🍴 rest, 📺 ☎ ➋ – 🔬 300. 🐵 🗚 ⑩ **VISA**
Y
**Meals** 12.00/18.95 **st.** ⒜ 5.40 – ☑ 9.50 – **88 rm** 95.00/105.00 **st.**, 2 suites – SB.

🏨 **County H. Exeter Royal Clarence**, Cathedral Yard, EX1 1HD, ℘ (01392) 319955, Fax (01392) 439423 – 🛗 💱 📺 ☎ – 🔬 120. 🐵 🗚 ⑩ **VISA**. ⅍
Y
**Meals** 7.00/10.00 **t.** and a la carte ⒜ 6.95 – ☑ 9.95 – **56 rm** 99.00/135.00 **st.**, 1 suite – SB.

🏨 **Gipsy Hill** ⅍, Gipsy Hill Lane, via Pinn Lane, EX1 3RN, East : 2 m. by Honiton Rd (A 30) off Pinhoe rd ℘ (01392) 465252, Fax (01392) 464302, ≼, ☞ – 💱 rm, 📺 ☎ ➋ – 🔬 120. 🐵 🗚 **VISA**
*closed 25 to 30 December* – **Meals** 9.50/16.50 **t.** and a la carte ⒜ 4.50 – **37 rm** ☑ 75.00 95.00 **t.** – SB.

🏨 **Buckerell Lodge**, Topsham Rd, EX2 4SQ, ℘ (01392) 221111, Fax (01392) 441111, ☞ 💱 rm, 📺 ☎ & ➋ – 🔬 50. 🐵 🗚 ⑩ **VISA**
X
**Meals** *(closed Saturday lunch)* 12.50/19.95 **st.** and dinner a la carte ⒜ 6.95 – ☑ 10.50 **53 rm** 45.00/84.00 **t.** – SB.

# EXETER
## CENTRE

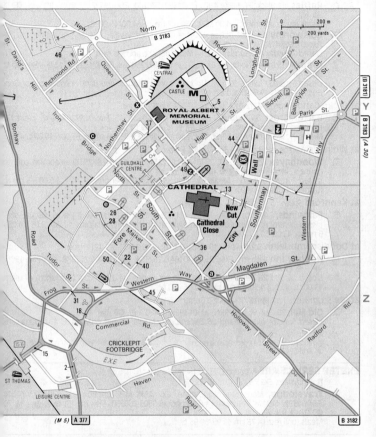

🏠 **St. Olaves Court,** Mary Arches St., EX4 3AZ, ℰ (01392) 217736, *Fax (01392) 413054*, 🌳 –
📺 ☎ 🅿 🚫 AE ① *VISA*. 🛇
Meals – (see ***Golsworthy's*** below) – ☑ 7.00 – **15 rm** 79.00/105.00 **t.** – SB.
Z e

🏠 **Exeter Arms Toby,** Rydan Lane, Middlemoor, EX2 7HL, East: 3 m. on B 3181
ℰ (01392) 435353, *Fax (01392) 453421* – 🍴 rest, 📺 ☎ 🕭 🅿 – 🛎 80. 🚫 AE *VISA*. 🛇
Meals (grill rest.) a la carte 12.45/15.45 **t.** – **37 rm** ☑ 52.50/62.50 **st.** – SB.
X e

🏠 **Devon,** Matford, EX2 8XU, South: 3 m. by A 377 on A 379 ℰ (01392) 259268,
*Fax (01392) 413142* – 🍴 rest, 📺 ☎ 🅿 – 🛎 160. 🚫 AE ① *VISA*
Meals (carving lunch) a la carte 15.25/19.00 **t.** – ☑ 5.00 – **41 rm** 57.00/78.00 **t.** – SB.

🏠 **St. Andrews,** 28 Alphington Rd, EX2 8HN, ℰ (01392) 276784, *Fax (01392) 250249* – 🍴
📺 ☎ 🕭 🅿 🚫 ① *VISA*. 🛇
closed Christmas-New Year – **Meals** (bar lunch)/dinner a la carte 12.65/19.50 **st.** 🍷 3.95 –
**17 rm** ☑ 45.00/67.00 **st.**
X c

🏠 **The Edwardian** without rest., 30-32 Heavitree Rd, EX1 2LQ, ℰ (01392) 276102,
*Fax (01392) 254699* – 📺 ☎. 🚫 AE *VISA*
closed 25 and 26 December – **13 rm** ☑ 26.00/54.00 **st.**
V a

247

🏠 **Travel Inn,** 398 Topsham Rd, EX2 6HE, ℰ (01392) 875441, *Fax (01392) 876174* – ⇔ rm
📺 ⅋ 🅟. ⓂⓈ 🅰 ⓪ *VISA*. ⅏                                                                    X  C
Meals (grill rest.) – **45 rm** 38.00 **t.**

⌂ **The Grange** ⤳ without rest., Stoke Hill, EX4 7JH, North : 1 ¾ m. by Old Tiverton Rd
ℰ (01392) 259723, ⬆, ⌸ – ⇔ 📺 🅟. ⅏
**3 rm** ⊑ 20.00/36.00 **t.**

⌂ **Raffles,** 11 Blackall Rd, EX4 4HD, ℰ (01392) 270200, *Fax (01392) 270200* – 📺 ⇜. ⓂⒶ
⓪ *VISA*                                                                                      V  €
Meals (by arrangement) 14.00 **st.** ⅋ 4.50 – **7 rm** ⊑ 34.00/48.00 **st.** – SB.

XX **Golsworthy's** (at St. Olaves Court H.), Mary Arches St., EX4 3AZ, ℰ (01392) 217736
*Fax (01392) 413054,* ⌸ – 🅟. ⓂⓈ *VISA* ᴊᴄʙ                                                   Z  €
closed Saturday and Sunday lunch – **Meals** 15.00 **t.** and a la carte ⅋ 5.00.

X **Lamb's,** 15 Lower North St., EX4 3ET, ℰ (01392) 254269, *Fax (01392) 431145* – ⇔. ⓂⒶ
*VISA* ᴊᴄʙ                                                                                   Y  C
closed Saturday lunch, Sunday, Monday, 2 weeks August and Bank Holidays except Good
Friday – **Meals** 19.00 **t.** and a la carte ⅋ 5.00.

**at Stoke Canon** North : 5 m. by A 377 off A 396 – V – ⊠ Exeter.

🏠 **Barton Cross** ⤳, Huxham, EX5 4EJ, ℰ (01392) 841245, *Fax (01392) 841942,* « Part 17C
thatched cottages », ⌸ – ⇔ rest, 📺 🅟. ⓂⓈ 🅰 *VISA*. ⅏
Meals (closed Sunday) 20.50/25.00 **t.** and a la carte ⅋ 6.75 – **8 rm** ⊑ 65.00/110.00 **t.** – SB.

**at Whimple** Northeast : 9 m. by A 30 – V – ⊠ Exeter.

🏠 **Woodhayes** ⤳, EX5 2TD, ℰ (01404) 822237, *Fax (01404) 822337,* « Georgian country
house », ⌸ – ⇔ rest, 📺 ☎ 🅟. ⓂⓈ 🅰 *VISA*. ⅏
closed 2 weeks January – **Meals** (booking essential) (dinner only) 30.00 **t.** ⅋ 8.00 – **5 rm** ⊑
(dinner included) 100.00/150.00 **st.**

**at Kennford** South : 5 m. on A 38 – X – ⊠ Exeter.

🏠 **Fairwinds,** EX6 7UD, ℰ (01392) 832911, *Fax (01392) 832911* – ⇔ 📺 ☎ 🅟. ⓂⓈ *VISA*. ⅏
closed December – **Meals** (residents only) (bar lunch)/dinner a la carte 10.90/15.05 ⅋ 4.25 –
**6 rm** ⊑ 42.00/50.00 – SB.

**at Doddiscombsleigh** Southwest : 10 m. by B 3212 off B 3193 – X – ⊠ Exeter.

🍴 **Nobody Inn** with rm, EX6 7PS, ℰ (01647) 252394, *Fax (01647) 252978,* ≤, « Part 16C »
⌸ – ☎ 🅟. ⓂⓈ *VISA*. ⅏
closed 25 and 26 December – **Meals** (in bar Sunday and Monday) (bar lunch) a la carte
11.00/18.45 **t.** ⅋ 4.50 – **7 rm** ⊑ 38.00/64.00 **t.**

**at Ide** Southwest : 3 m. by A 377 – X – ⊠ Exeter.

XX **Old Mill,** 20 High St., EX2 9RN, ℰ (01392) 259480 – 🅟. ⓂⓈ *VISA*
closed Sunday, Monday and 26 December – **Meals** (dinner only) 14.95 **t.** and a la carte
⅋ 4.95.

🔘 ATS 276/280 Pinhoe Road, Polsloe Bridge          ATS Unit 3, Bittern Way, Sowton Ind. Est.
ℰ (01392) 255465                                    ℰ (01392) 216026

---

**EXETER SERVICE AREA** Devon 🔢 J 31 – ⊠ Exeter.
🛈 Sandygate, EX2 7NJ ℰ (01392) 437581.

🏠 **Travelodge,** Moor Lane, Sandygate, EX2 4AR, M 5 junction 30 ℰ (01392) 74044
*Fax (01392) 410406,* Reservations (Freephone) 0800 850950 – ⇔ rm, 📺 ☎ ⅋ 🅟 – ⛪ 70
ⓂⓈ 🅰 ⓪ *VISA* ᴊᴄʙ. ⅏
Meals (grill rest.) – **76 rm** 39.95/59.95 **t.**

---

**EXFORD** Somerset 🔢 J 30 The West Country G..
See : Church★.
Env. : Exmoor National Park★★.
London 193 – Exeter 41 – Minehead 14 – Taunton 33.

🏠 **Crown,** TA24 7PP, ℰ (01643) 831554, *Fax (01643) 831665,* « Attractively furnished country inn, water garden », ⤳ – 📺 ☎ ✆ 🅟. ⓂⓈ 🅰 *VISA* ᴊᴄʙ
Meals (in bar) a la carte 12.25/17.75 **t.** ⅋ 6.00 – (see also **The Restaurant** below) – **17 rm**
⊑ 42.00/110.00 **t.** – SB.

XX **The Restaurant** (at Crown H.), TA24 7PP, ℰ (01643) 831554, *Fax (01643) 831665* – 🅟
ⓂⓈ 🅰 *VISA* ᴊᴄʙ
closed Sunday dinner – **Meals** (dinner only and Sunday lunch)/dinner 27.50 **t.** ⅋ 6.00.

---

**EXMOUTH** Devon 🔢 J 32 The West Country G. – pop. 30 386.
Env. : A la Ronde★ AC, N : 2 m. by B 3180.
🛈 Alexandra Terr., EX8 1NZ ℰ (01395) 222299.
London 210 – Exeter 11.

🏠 **Imperial,** The Esplanade, EX8 2SW, ✆ (01395) 274761, Fax (01395) 265161, ≤, ⚓, 🐾, ✵
– 🛗 ✱⇔ 📺 ☎ 🅿, 🕮 🆎 ① 𝖵𝖨𝖲𝖠
**Meals** (bar lunch Monday to Saturday)/dinner 8.95/16.95 **t.** ₰ 5.95 – **57 rm** ⇆ 65.00/
180.00 **t.**

🏛 **Barn** ◈, Foxholes Hill, EX8 2DF, East : 1 m. via Esplanade and Queens Drive
✆ (01395) 224411, Fax (01395) 225445, ≤, ⚓ – ✱⇔ 📺 ☎ 🅿 – 🔬 50. 🕮 𝖵𝖨𝖲𝖠. ✵
closed mid December-mid January – **Meals** (bar lunch Monday to Saturday) 14.00 ₰ 5.50 –
**11 rm** ⇆ 34.00/68.00 **st.** – SB.

✕✕ **The Seafood,** 9 Tower St., EX8 1NT, ✆ (01395) 269459 – 🕮 🆎 𝖵𝖨𝖲𝖠 𝖩𝖢𝖡
closed 15 February-10 March – **Meals** - Seafood - (dinner only and lunch Wednesday to
Friday) a la carte 20.85/30.40 **t.** ₰ 7.95.

**at Lympstone** North : 3 m. by A 376 – ✉ Exmouth.

✕✕ **River House** with rm, The Strand, EX8 5EY, ✆ (01395) 265147, ≤ Exe Estuary – ✱⇔ rest,
📺, 🕮 🆎 𝖵𝖨𝖲𝖠. ✵
closed 1-2 January, 25 to 27 December and Bank Holiday Monday – **Meals** (closed Sunday
and Monday to non-residents) 35.50 **t.** and lunch a la carte ₰ 6.95 – ⇆ 7.00 – **3 rm** 62.00/
86.00 **t.** – SB.

---

**EYE** Cambs. 402 404 T 26 – see Peterborough.

---

**EYE** Suffolk 404 X 27 – pop. 1 741.
London 94 – Ipswich 19 – Thetford 23.

🏚 **Four Horseshoes** with rm, Thornham Magna, IP23 8HD, Southwest : 5 m. by B 1117 off
A 140 ✆ (01379) 678777, Fax (01379) 678134, « Part 12C inn », ⚓ – ✱⇔ rest, 📺 ☎ 🅿. 🕮
🆎 𝖵𝖨𝖲𝖠 𝖩𝖢𝖡
closed 25 December – **Meals** (closed Sunday dinner) (bar lunch Monday to Saturday)
a la carte 12.95/19.50 **t.** ₰ 7.95 – **7 rm** ⇆ 45.00/65.00 **t.**

---

**EYNSHAM** Oxon. 403 404 P 28 – pop. 4 764.
London 65 – Gloucester 39 – Oxford 7.

✕✕ **Baker's** with rm, 4 Lombard St., OX8 1HT, ✆ (01865) 881888, Fax (01865) 883537 – 📺 ☎.
🕮 𝖵𝖨𝖲𝖠. ✵
closed 26 December, 2 weeks autumn and Bank Holiday Mondays – **Meals** (closed dinner
Sunday, Monday and Bank Holidays except 25 December) 9.50/20.00 **t.** and dinner a la carte
25.00/37.00 **t.** ₰ 7.50 – **2 rm** ⇆ 60.00 **t.** – SB.

---

**EYTON** Herefordshire – see Leominster.

---

**FAKENHAM** Norfolk 404 W 25 – pop. 6 471.
London 111 – Cambridge 64 – Norwich 27.

🏛 **Sculthorpe Mill** ◈, Lynn Rd, Sculthorpe, NR21 9QG, West : 2 ½ m. by A 148
✆ (01328) 856105, Fax (01328) 856651, « Converted late 18C watermill », ⚓ – ✱⇔ rm, 📺
☎ 🅿. 🕮 🆎 𝖵𝖨𝖲𝖠
restricted opening October 1-Good Friday**Meals** (bar lunch Monday to Saturday)/dinner
18.95 **t.** – **6 rm** ⇆ 50.00/75.00 **t.**

---

**FALFIELD** South Gloucestershire 403 404 M 29.
London 132 – Bristol 16 – Gloucester 22.

🏠 **Gables Inn,** Bristol Rd, GL12 8DL, North : ½ m. on A 38 ✆ (01454) 260502,
Fax (01454) 261821, ₷, 🕸 – ✱⇔ rest, 📺 ☎ ♿ 🅿 – 🔬 150. 🕮 🆎 ① 𝖵𝖨𝖲𝖠. ✵
**Meals** 15.00 **st.** (dinner) and a la carte 11.00/19.25 **st.** ₰ 6.00 – ⇆ 5.50 – **32 rm** 58.00 **st.**

---

**FALMOUTH** Cornwall 403 E 33 The West Country G. – pop. 19 217.
See : Town★ – Pendennis Castle★ (≤★★) AC B.
Env. : Glendurgan Garden★★ AC – Trebah Garden★, SW : 4 ½ m. by Swanpool Rd A –
Mawnan Parish Church★ (≤★★) S : 4 m. by Swanpool Rd A – Cruise along Helford River★.
Exc. : Trelissick★★ (≤★★) NW : 13 m. by A 39 and B 3289 A – Carn Brea (≤★★) NW : 10 m. by
A 393 A – Gweek (Setting★, Seal Sanctuary★) SW : 8 m. by A 39 and Treverva rd – Wendron
(Poldark Mine★) AC, SW : 12½ m. by A 39 – A – and A 394.
🛱 Swanpool Rd ✆ (01326) 311262/314296 A – 🛱 Budock Vean Hotel ✆ (01326) 250288.
🛈 28 Killigrew St., TR11 3PN ✆ (01326) 312300.
London 308 – Penzance 26 – Plymouth 65 – Truro 11.

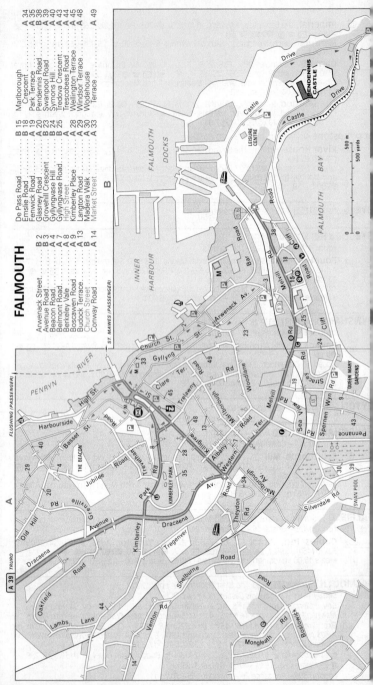

# FALMOUTH

🏨 **Royal Duchy,** Cliff Rd, TR11 4NX, ℰ (01326) 313042, *Fax (01326) 319420*, ≤, ⇔, 🔲, 🎱
– 🛗 📺 ☎ 🅿. ⓐ AE *VISA*                                                                                                   B   a
**Meals** 8.95/20.00 **t.** and a la carte ⅄ 7.00 – **41 rm** ⊑ (dinner included) 67.00/210.00 **t.**,
2 suites.

🏨 **Greenbank,** Harbourside, TR11 2SR, ℰ (01326) 312440, *Fax (01326) 211362*, ≤ harbour,
🕭, ⇔ – 🛗, ⅗ rm, 📺 ☎ ⇔ 🅿 – 🔬 40. ⓐ AE ⓞ *VISA*. ⅍                                    A   a
*closed 24 December-13 January* – **Nightingales :** **Meals** 9.50/17.50 **t.** and dinner a la carte
⅄ 8.75 – **63 rm** ⊑ 95.00/125.00 **t.**

🏨 **Penmere Manor** ⅍, Mongleath Rd, TR11 4PN, ℰ (01326) 211411, *Fax (01326) 317588*,
⇔, 🎱, 🔲, 🍴 – ⅗ rm, 📺 ☎ 🅿 – 🔬 60. ⓐ AE ⓞ *VISA*                                        A   e
*closed 24 to 26 December* – **Bolitho's :** **Meals** (dinner only) 22.00 **t.** and a la carte ⅄ 6.75 –
**37 rm** ⊑ 59.50/93.00 **t.** – SB.

🏚 **Carthion,** Cliff Rd, TR11 4AP, ℰ (01326) 313669, *Fax (01326) 212828*, ≤, 🍴 – 📺 ☎ 🅿. ⓐ
AE ⓞ *VISA*. ⅍                                                                                            B   v
*closed 23 December-31 January* – **Meals** (bar lunch Monday to Saturday)/dinner 14.00 **t.**
and a la carte ⅄ 5.25 – **18 rm** ⊑ 47.00/88.00 **t.** – SB.

🏚 **Broadmead,** 66-68 Kimberley Park Rd, TR11 2DD, ℰ (01326) 315704, *Fax (01326) 311048*
– ⅗ rest, 📺 ☎ 🅿. ⓐ AE *VISA* JCB. ⅍                                                       A   u
*closed 20 December-4 January* – **Meals** (bar lunch)/dinner 12.95 **t.** ⅄ 4.95 – **12 rm** ⊑ 27.00/
54.00 **t.** – SB.

⌂ **Prospect House** without rest., 1 Church Rd, Penryn, TR10 8DA, Northwest : 2 m. by
A 39 on B 3292 ℰ (01326) 373198, *Fax (01326) 373198*, 🍴 – 🅿. ⓐ *VISA*. ⅍
**3 rm** ⊑ 25.00/55.00 **s.**

⌂ **Rosemullion** without rest., Gyllyngvase Hill, TR11 4DF, ℰ (01326) 314690,
*Fax (01326) 210098* – ⅗ 📺 🅿. ⅍                                                             B   c
*June-early October* – **13 rm** ⊑ 21.00/47.00.

⌂ **Melvill House,** 52 Melvill Rd, TR11 4DQ, ℰ (01326) 316645, *Fax (01326) 211608* – ⅗ 📺
🅿. ⓐ *VISA*. ⅍                                                                                  B   o
*closed 23 to 27 December* – **Meals** (by arrangement) 8.50 **st.** ⅄ 3.50 – **7 rm** ⊑ 30.00/
50.00 **st.**

⌂ **Chelsea House,** 2 Emslie Rd, TR11 4BG, ℰ (01326) 212230, ≤, 🍴 – ⅗ rest, 📺 🅿. ⓐ
*VISA* JCB. ⅍                                                                                      B   s
*March-October* – **Meals** (by arrangement) 9.00 **s.** ⅄ 3.95 – **7 rm** ⊑ 32.00/50.00 **s.**

⌂ **Esmond House** without rest., 5 Emslie Rd, TR11 4BG, ℰ (01326) 313214 – ⅗ 📺. ⅍
*closed 25 December* – **7 rm** ⊑ 19.00/38.00.                                                 B   e

⌂ **Trevaylor** without rest., 8 Pennance Rd, TR11 4EA, ℰ (01326) 313041, ≤ – ⅗ rest, 📺 🅿
*Easter-October* – **7 rm** ⊑ 20.00/40.00.                                                     A   r

**at Mylor Bridge** *North : 4½ m. by A 39 and B 3292 on Mylor rd* – A – ✉ *Falmouth.*

🍴 **Pandora Inn,** Restronguet Creek, TR11 5ST, Northeast : 1 m. by Passage Hill off Restron-
guet Hill ℰ (01326) 372678, *Fax (01326) 372678*, ≤, « Thatched inn of 13C origins » – 🔲 🅿.
ⓐ AE *VISA*
**Meals** (bar lunch)/dinner a la carte 17.35/23.95 **st.**

**at Mawnan Smith** *Southwest : 5 m. by Trescobeas Rd* – A – ✉ *Falmouth.*

🏨 **Meudon** ⅍, TR11 5HT, East : ½ m. by Carwinion Rd ℰ (01326) 250541,
*Fax (01326) 250543*, « ≤ Terraced gardens landscaped by Capability Brown », park – 🛗 📺
☎ 🅿. ⓐ AE ⓞ *VISA*
*March-10 November* – **Meals** 15.00/25.00 **st.** and a la carte ⅄ 10.00 – **27 rm** ⊑ (dinner
included) 110.00/200.00 **t.**, 2 suites – SB.

🏛 **Nansidwell Country House** ⅍, TR11 5HU, Southeast : ¼ m. by Carwinion Rd
ℰ (01326) 250340, *Fax (01326) 250440*, ≤, « Country house atmosphere, gardens », park,
⅗ – 📺 ☎ 🅿. ⓐ *VISA* JCB
*closed January* – **Meals** 15.75/27.50 **t.** and dinner a la carte ⅄ 7.95 – ⊑ 5.00 – **12 rm**
95.00/180.00 **t.**

🏚 **Trelawne** ⅍, Maenporth Rd, TR11 5HS, East : ¾ m. by Carwinion Rd ℰ (01326) 250226,
*Fax (01326) 250909*, ≤, 🔲, 🍴 – ⅗ rest, 📺 ☎ 🅿. ⓐ AE ⓞ *VISA*. ⅍
*closed 22 December-12 February* – **The Hutches :** **Meals** *(bar lunch)*/dinner 18.50 **st.**
⅄ 5.95 – **14 rm** ⊑ 62.00/152.00 **st.** – SB.

✕✕ **Pennypots** (Viner), Maenporth Beach, TR11 5HN, East : 1 m. by Carwinion Rd
ℰ (01326) 250251, *Fax (01326) 251040*, ≤ Falmouth Bay – ⅗ 🅿. ⓐ AE ⓞ *VISA* JCB
❀ *closed Sunday, Monday and 4 weeks in winter* – **Meals** (dinner only) 28.50 **t.** ⅄ 5.50
**Spec.** Terrine of smoked red mullet and chargrilled vegetables. Duo of grilled duck breast
and confit of duck leg, peach and Armagnac sauce. "Chocolate temptation".

**at Budock Water** West : 2¼ m. by Trescobeas Rd – A – ⊠ *Falmouth.*

🏨 **Crill Manor** ⌀, TR11 5BL, South : ¾ m. ℰ (01326) 211880, *Fax (01326) 211229*, ⍽, ⌁ –
※ 📺 ☎ ℗, ⬛ ⁂ VISA JCB
**Meals** (bar lunch)/dinner 19.75 st. ⋕ 5.25 – **14 rm** ⍁ 39.00/87.00 st. – SB.

🏨 **Penmorvah Manor** ⌀, TR11 5ED, South : ¾ m. ℰ (01326) 250277,
*Fax (01326) 250509*, ⌁ – 📺 ☎ ℗ – ⅍ 150. ⬛ ⁂ VISA JCB
**Meals** (bar lunch)/dinner 18.50 st. ⋕ 7.50 – **27 rm** ⍁ 45.00/95.00 st. – SB.

⬧ ATS Dracaena Av. ℰ (01326) 319233

---

**FAREHAM** Hants. ⬛⬛⬛ ⬛⬛⬛ Q 31 *Great Britain G.* – pop. 54 866 (inc. Portchester).

Env. : *Portchester castle★ AC, SE : 2½ m. by A 27.*

🛈 *Westbury Manor, West St., PO16 0JJ* ℰ (01329) 221342.

*London 77 – Portsmouth 9 – Southampton 13 – Winchester 19.*

🏨🏨 **Solent,** Rookery Av., Whiteley, PO15 7AJ, Northwest : 5 m. by A 27 ℰ (01489) 880000,
*Fax (01489) 880007*, ⌂, ⌁⌂, ⌂⌂, ⍽, park, ⁂, squash – ⫿, ※ rm, 📺 ☎ ⅋ ℗ – ⅍ 250. ⬛⬛
⁂ ① VISA ⁑
**Meals** (closed Saturday lunch) 10.00/20.00 t. and dinner a la carte ⋕ 9.00 – **117 rm**
⍁ 117.00/160.00 st. – SB.

🏨🏨 **Forte Posthouse Fareham,** Cartwright Drive, Titchfield, PO15 5RJ, West : 2 ¾ m. on
A 27 ℰ (01329) 844644, *Fax (01329) 844666*, ⌂⌂, ⌂⌂, ⍽ – ※ rm, 📺 ☎ ⅋ ℗ – ⅍ 140. ⬛⬛
⁂ ① VISA
**Meals** a la carte 14.65/24.85 t. ⋕ 5.95 – ⍁ 10.95 – **125 rm** 85.00 st. – SB.

🏨 **Red Lion,** East St., PO16 0BP, ℰ (01329) 822640, *Fax (01329) 823579*, ⌂⌂ – 📺 ☎ ⅋ ℗ –
⅍ 80. ⬛⬛ ⁂ ① VISA ⁑
**Meals** (bar lunch Monday to Saturday)/dinner a la carte 16.85/27.65 t. – **42 rm** ⍁ 62.50/
75.00 t.

🏨 **Lysses House,** 51 High St., PO16 7BQ, ℰ (01329) 822622, *Fax (01329) 822762*, ⌁ – ⫿,
※ rest, 📺 ☎ ℗ – ⅍ 100. ⬛⬛ ⁂ ① VISA ⁑
closed 24 to 31 December – **The Richmond :** Meals (closed Saturday lunch, Sunday and
Bank Holidays) 13.95/18.50 st. and a la carte ⋕ 5.50 – **21 rm** ⍁ 60.00/75.00 st.

🏨 **Avenue House** without rest., 22 The Avenue, PO14 1NS, West : ½ m. on A 27
ℰ (01329) 232175, *Fax (01329) 232196*, ⌁ – ※ 📺 ☎ ⅋ ℗. ⬛⬛ ⁂ ① VISA ⁑
– **17 rm** ⍁ 46.00/96.00.

🏨 **Travel Inn,** Southampton Rd, Park Gate, SO3 6AF, West : 4 m. by A 27 ℰ (01489) 579857,
*Fax (01489) 577238* – ※ rm, 📺 ⅋ ℗. ⬛⬛ ⁂ ① VISA ⁑
**Meals** (grill rest.) – **40 rm** 38.00 t.

↑ **Springfield** without rest., 67 The Avenue, PO14 1PE, West : 1 m. on A 27
ℰ (01329) 828325, ⌁ – ※ 📺 ☎ ℗. ⬛⬛ ⁂ ⁑
closed 2 weeks Christmas – **6 rm** ⍁ 40.00/48.00 st.

⬧ ATS Queens Rd ℰ (01329) 234941/280032

---

**FARMBOROUGH** Bath & North East Somerset ⬛⬛⬛ M 29 *The West Country G.* – pop. 1 084 –
⊠ *Bath.*

Exc. : *Bath★★★, NE : 7½ m. by A 39 and A 4.*

*London 137 – Bath 7.5 – Bristol 12 – Wells 13.*

🏨 **Streets,** The Street, BA3 1AR, ℰ (01761) 471452, *Fax (01761) 471452*, ⍽, ⌁ – 📺 ☎ ℗
⬛⬛ ⁂ VISA ⁑
closed 1 week Christmas – **Meals** (residents only) (dinner only) 14.80 st. and a la carte ⋕ 4.50
– **7 rm** ⍁ 46.00/56.00 st.

---

**FARNBOROUGH** Hants. ⬛⬛⬛ R 30 – pop. 52 535.

⛳ *Southwood, Ively Rd* ℰ (01252) 548700.

*London 41 – Reading 17 – Southampton 44 – Winchester 33.*

🏨🏨 **Forte Posthouse Farnborough,** Lynchford Rd, GU14 6AZ, South : 1 ½ m. on Farnborough Rd (A 325) ℰ (01252) 545051, *Fax (01252) 377210*, ⌂⌂, ⌂⌂, ⍽ – ※ rm, ⬛ rest, 📺
☎ ⅋ ⅋ ℗ – ⅍ 110. ⬛⬛ ⁂ ① VISA JCB. ⁑
**Meals** (closed Saturday lunch) a la carte 20.85/30.90 st. ⋕ 7.95 – ⍁ 10.95 – **143 rm**
119.00 st. – SB.

🏨 **Falcon,** 68 Farnborough Rd, GU14 6TH, South : ¾ m. on A 325 ℰ (01252) 545378,
*Fax (01252) 522539* – 📺 ☎ ℗. ⬛⬛ ⁂ ① VISA ⁑
restricted opening Christmas-New Year – **Meals** (closed lunch Saturday and Sunday.
18.50 st. and a la carte ⋕ 5.95 – **30 rm** ⍁ 75.50/92.50 st.

🏨 **Travel Inn**, Ively Rd, Southwood, GU14 0JP, Southwest : 2 m. by A 325 on A 327
    ℘ (01252) 546654, Fax (01252) 546427 – ⚐ rm, 📺 ⅙ 🄿. ⓐⓢ ⒜Ⓔ ⓞ 𝘝𝘐𝘚𝘈 𝙅𝙘𝘽. ℅
    **Meals** (grill rest.) – **40 rm** 38.00 **t.**

✕✕ **Wings Cottage**, 32 Alexandra Rd, GU14 6DA, South : 1 ¼ m. by A 325 off Boundary Rd
    ℘ (01252) 544141, Fax (01252) 549361 – 🄿. ⓐⓢ ⒜Ⓔ ⓞ 𝘝𝘐𝘚𝘈. ℅
    closed Saturday and Sunday lunch – **Meals** - Chinese - 24.50 **t.** (dinner) and a la carte
    16.00/23.50 **t.**

---

**FARNHAM** Surrey 404 R 30 – pop. 36 178.
    🔓 Farnham Park (Par Three) ℘ (01252) 715216.
    🛈 Vernon House, 28 West St., GU9 7DR ℘ (01252) 715109.
    London 45 – Reading 22 – Southampton 39 – Winchester 28.

🏨🏨 **Bush**, The Borough, GU9 7NN, ℘ (01252) 715237, Fax (01252) 733530, � – ⚐ rm, 📺 ☎
    🄿 – 🔔 60. ⓐⓢ ⒜Ⓔ ⓞ 𝘝𝘐𝘚𝘈 𝙅𝙘𝘽
    **Thackeray's :** Meals (dinner only and Sunday lunch) a la carte 20.00/25.00 **st.** ⓙ 7.00 – **Café
    bar Tabac :** Meals a la carte 15.00/21.00 **st.** ⓙ 5.00 – �  10.50 – **65 rm** 105.00 **t.** – SB.

🏨🏨 **Bishop's Table**, 27 West St., GU9 7DR, ℘ (01252) 710222, Fax (01252) 733494, � –
    ⚐ rest, 📺 ☎. ⓐⓢ ⒜Ⓔ ⓞ 𝘝𝘐𝘚𝘈. ℅
    closed 25 December-3 January – **Meals** (closed Saturday lunch) 20.00 **st.** ⓙ 8.25 – **15 rm**
    ⊐ 88.00/105.00 **st.** – SB.

---

*La Grande Londra (GREATER LONDON) è composta dalla City
e da 32 distretti amministrativi (Borough) divisi a loro volta in quartieri
o villaggi che hanno conservato il loro proprio carattere (Area).*

---

**FARRINGTON GURNEY** Bath & North East Somerset 403 404 M 30 The West Country G. –
    pop. 780 – ✉ Bristol.
    **Env. :** Downside Abbey★ (Abbey Church★) SE : 5 m. by A 37 and B 3139.
    **Exc. :** Wells★★ - Cathedral★★★, Vicars' Close★, Bishop's Palace★ AC (≤★★) SW : 8 m. by A 39
    – Chew Magna★ (Stanton Drew Stone Circles★ AC) NW : 9½ m. by A 37 and B 3130.
    London 132 – Bath 13 – Bristol 12 – Wells 8.

🏨 **Country Ways**, Marsh Lane, BS39 6TT, ℘ (01761) 452449, Fax (01761) 452706, � –
    ⚐ rest, 📺 ☎ 🄿. ⓐⓢ 𝘝𝘐𝘚𝘈. ℅
    closed 1 week Christmas – **Meals** (closed Sunday) (dinner only) a la carte 19.70/22.05 **st.**
    ⓙ 8.00 – **6 rm** ⊐ 60.00/95.00 **st.** – SB.

---

**FAR SAWREY** Cumbria 402 L 20 – see Hawkshead.

---

**FAVERSHAM** Kent 404 W 30 – pop. 17 070.
    🛈 Fleur de Lis Heritage Centre, 13 Preston St., ME13 8NS ℘ (01795) 534542.
    London 52 – Dover 26 – Maidstone 21 – Margate 25.

🏠 **Preston Lea** without rest., Canterbury Rd, ME13 8XA, East : 1 m. on A 2
    ℘ (01795) 535266, Fax (01795) 533388, « Late 19C Neo-gothic house », 🌻 – ⚐ 📺 🄿. ⓐⓢ
    𝘝𝘐𝘚𝘈 𝙅𝙘𝘽. ℅
    **3 rm** ⊐ 35.00/48.00 **st.**

🍴 **Albion Tavern**, Front Brents, Faversham Creek, ME13 7DH, ℘ (01795) 591411 – 🄿. ⓐⓢ
    𝘝𝘐𝘚𝘈
    **Meals** a la carte approx. 15.50 **st.**

**at Dargate** East : 6 m. by A 2 off A 299 – ✉ Faversham.

🍴 **Dove Inn**, Plum Pudding Lane, ME13 9HB, ℘ (01227) 751360, Fax (01227) 751360, 🌻 –
🏡 🄿. ⓐⓢ 𝘝𝘐𝘚𝘈 𝙅𝙘𝘽
    closed Sunday dinner and Monday except lunch on Bank Holidays – **Meals** a la carte
    14.50/24.00 **st.** ⓙ 4.00.

**at Boughton** Southeast : 3 m. by A 2 – ✉ Faversham.

🏨 **Garden**, 167-169 The Street, ME13 9BH, ℘ (01227) 751411, Fax (01227) 751801, 🌻 –
    ▤ rest, 📺 ☎ 🄿. ⓐⓢ ⒜Ⓔ 𝘝𝘐𝘚𝘈
    **Meals** (residents only Sunday dinner) 12.50/18.90 **t.** and a la carte ⓙ 6.00 – **10 rm** ⊐ 45.00/
    80.00 **t.** – SB.

**at Plumford** *South : 2½ m. by A 2 and Brogdale Rd on Plumford Lane – ✉ Faversham.*

**The Granary** without rest., Plumford Lane, ME13 0DS, ☏ (01795) 538416, *Fax (01795) 538416*, – TV P. VISA JCB
*closed 25 and 26 December* – **3 rm** 30.00/46.00.

**at Painter's Forstal** *Southwest : 2¼ m. by A 2 and Brogdale Rd – ✉ Faversham.*

XXX ✿ **Read's** (Pitchford), ME13 0EE, ☏ (01795) 535344, *Fax (01795) 591200*, – AE VISA JCB
*closed Sunday, Monday and first week January* – **Meals** 17.50/22.00 **t.** and a la carte 35.00/38.00 **t.** 7.50
**Spec.** Potted crabmeat with bean salad. Aberdeen Angus porterhouse with black pudding and peppercorn sauce. Caramel soufflé with prune and Armagnac ice cream.

**at Eastling** *Southwest : 5 m. by A 2 – ✉ Faversham.*

**Frith Farm House**, Otterden, ME13 0DD, Southwest : 2 m. by Otterden rd on Newnham rd ☏ (01795) 890701, *Fax (01795) 890009*, – TV P. VISA.
**Meals** (by arrangement) (communal dining) 21.00 **s.** – **3 rm** 35.00/60.00 **s.**

ATS 20 North Lane ☏ (01795) 534039

---

**FAWKHAM GREEN** *Kent* 404 ㊹ – *see Brands Hatch.*

---

**FELIXSTOWE** *Suffolk* 404 Y 28 – *pop. 28 606.*
18, 9 *Felixstowe Ferry, Ferry Rd ☏ (01394) 283060.*
*Leisure Centre, Undercliff Road West, IP11 8AB ☏ (01394) 276770.*
*London 84 – Ipswich 11.*

**Orwell,** Hamilton Rd, IP11 7DX, ☏ (01394) 285511, *Fax (01394) 670687*, – rest, TV P – 250. AE VISA.
**Meals** 13.50/16.50 **st.** and a la carte 6.95 – 8.95 – **57 rm** 65.00/85.00 **st.**, 1 suite – SB.

**Waverley,** Wolsey Gdns., IP11 7DF, ☏ (01394) 282811, *Fax (01394) 670185*, – TV P – 70. AE VISA
**Meals** 15.95 **t.** (dinner) and a la carte 14.85/22.85 **t.** 8.95 – 8.50 – **19 rm** 56.95/74.95 **t.** – SB.

ATS 4-8 Sunderland Rd, Carr Rd Ind. Est. ☏ (01394) 675604
ATS Crescent Rd ☏ (01394) 277596/277888

---

**FELSTED** *Essex* 404 V 28 – *pop. 2 512* – ✉ *Great Dunmow.*
*London 39 – Cambridge 31 – Chelmsford 9 – Colchester 24.*

X **Rumbles Cottage,** Braintree Rd, CM6 3DJ, ☏ (01371) 820996 – VISA
*closed Saturday lunch, Sunday dinner, Monday and Tuesday* – **Meals** (lunch by arrangement)/dinner 14.00 **t.** and a la carte 5.00.

---

**FELTON** *Herefordshire* 403 404 M 27 – *pop. 93.*
*London 130 – Birmingham 54 – Hereford 14 – Shrewsbury 50 – Worcester 27.*

**Felton House** without rest., HR1 3PH, ☏ (01432) 820366, *Fax (01432) 820366*, – P
*closed 24 to 27 December* – **5 rm** 22.00/44.00 **s.**

---

**FERMAIN BAY** *Guernsey (Channel Islands)* 403 P 33 and 230 ⑩ – *see Channel Islands.*

---

**FERNDOWN** *Dorset* 403 404 O 31 – *pop. 25 177.*
*London 108 – Bournemouth 6 – Dorchester 27 – Salisbury 23.*

**The Dormy,** New Rd, BH22 8ES, on A 347 ☏ (01202) 872121, *Fax (01202) 895388*, 18, , squash – rm, TV P – 250. AE VISA JCB
**Meals** *(closed Saturday lunch)* (dancing Saturday evening) 14.50/19.50 **st.** and a la carte – **115 rm** 110.00/150.00 **st.**, 5 suites – SB.

**Travel Inn,** Ringwood Rd, Tricketts Cross, BH22 9BB, Northeast : 1 m. on A 347 ☏ (01202) 874210, *Fax (01202) 897794* – rm, TV P. AE VISA.
**Meals** (grill rest.) – **32 rm** 38.00 **t.**

**FERRENSBY** *N. Yorks. – see Knaresborough.*

---

**FERRYBRIDGE SERVICE AREA** *W. Yorks.* 🗺️ Q 22 – ✉️ *Leeds.*
*London 178 – Leeds 14 – Doncaster 14 – Rotherham 28 – York 28.*

🏠 **Travelodge**, WF11 0AF, at junction 33 of M 62 with A 1 *℘ (01977) 672767,*
*Fax (01977) 622529,* Reservations (Freephone) 0800 850950 – ⏚ 📺 ⅋ 🄿. ⑩ ⅍ ① *VISA*
🗾. ℀
**Meals** (grill rest.) – **36 rm** 39.95/59.95 **t.**

---

**FERSFIELD** *Norfolk – see Diss.*

---

**FILEY** *N. Yorks.* 🗺️ T 21 – *pop. 6 619.*
*London 238 – Kingston-upon-Hull 42 – Leeds 68 – Middlesbrough 58.*

🏠 **Downcliffe House**, The Beach, YO14 9LA, *℘ (01723) 513310, Fax (01723) 513773,* ≼ –
⏚ rest, 📺 ☎ ⅋ 🄿. ⑩ *VISA*
*closed January* – **Meals** (bar lunch Monday to Saturday)/dinner a la carte 11.50/16.00 **st.**
⅃ 6.00 – **10 rm** ⊆ 34.00/88.00 **st.** – SB.

*La guida cambia, cambiate la guida ogni anno.*

---

**FINDON** *W. Sussex* 🗺️ S 31 – *pop. 1 776 –* ✉️ *Worthing.*
*London 49 – Brighton 13 – Southampton 50 – Worthing 4.*

🏠 **Findon Manor**, High St., BN14 0TA, off A 24 *℘ (01903) 872733, Fax (01903) 877473,*
« Part 16C stone and flint house », 🌲 – 📺 ☎ ⅋ 🄿 – 🔬 40. ⑩ ⅍ *VISA*. ℀
**Meals** 15.95/17.95 **t.** ⅃ 6.25 – **11 rm** ⊆ 47.50/100.00 **t.** – SB.

---

**FINEDON** *Northants.* 🗺️ S 26 – see Wellingborough.

---

**FLAMSTEAD** *Herts.* 🗺️ S 28 – *pop. 1 399 –* ✉️ *St. Albans.*
*London 32 – Luton 5.*

🏠 **Hertfordshire Moat House**, London Rd, AL3 8HH, on A 5 *℘ (01582) 449988,*
*Fax (01582) 842282,* ⅃₆ – ⏚, ▤ rest, 📺 ☎ 🄿 – 🔬 300. ⑩ ⅍ ① *VISA*. ℀
**Meals** *(closed Saturday lunch)* 16.95/18.95 **st.** ⅃ 6.95 – ⊆ 10.00 – **89 rm** 100.00/130.00 **st.** –
SB.

---

**FLEET** *Hants.* 🗺️ R 30 – *pop. 30 391.*
*London 40 – Basingstoke 11 – Reading 17.*

🏠 **Lismoyne**, Church Rd, GU13 8NA, *℘ (01252) 628555, Fax (01252) 811761,* 🌲 – ⏚ rest,
📺 ☎ 🄿 – 🔬 100. ⑩ ⅍ ① *VISA* 🗾
*closed 31 December* – **Meals** 14.00/21.00 **st.** and a la carte ⅃ 7.95 – ⊆ 9.95 – **44 rm**
75.00/105.00 **st.** – SB.

🄰 ATS 113-115 Kings Rd *℘ (01252) 616412/620028*

---

**FLEET SERVICE AREA** *Hants.* 🗺️ R 30 – ✉️ *Basingstoke.*

🏠 **Welcome Lodge**, Hartley Witney, RG27 8BN, M 3 between junctions 4a and 5 (southbound carriageway) *℘ (01252) 815587, Fax (01252) 815587,* Reservations (Freephone) 0800
7314466 – 📺 ⅋ 🄿. ⑩ ⅍ ① *VISA*
⊆ 7.50 **60 rm** 55.00 **t.**

---

**FLEETWOOD** *Lancs.* 🗺️ K 22 – *pop. 27 227.*
🏌️ Fleetwood, Golf House, Princes Way *℘ (01253) 873114.*
⚓ to the Isle of Man (Douglas) (Isle of Man Steam Packet Co. Ltd) (summer only) (3 h 20
mn).
🄱 Old Ferry Office, The Esplanade, FY7 6DL *℘ (01253) 773953.*
*London 245 – Blackpool 10 – Lancaster 28 – Manchester 53.*

🏨 **North Euston,** The Esplanade, FY7 6BN, ℘ (01253) 876525, Fax (01253) 777842, ← – 📱
📺 ☎ ❷ – 🔬 150. ◍❾ ﴾ﬞ ◍ 𝘝𝘐𝘚𝘈. ⋙
closed 24 and 25 December – **Meals** (bar lunch Saturday) 9.95/17.50 **t.** and dinner a la carte
₴ 5.50 – **53 rm** ⊡ 52.00/77.00 **t.** – SB.

◉ ATS 238 Dock St. ℘ (01253) 771211

---

**FLETCHING** E. Sussex 𝟰𝟬𝟰 U 30/31 – pop. 1 722.
London 45 – Brighton 20 – Eastbourne 24 – Maidstone 20.

🏠 **The Griffin Inn** with rm, TN22 3SS, ℘ (01825) 722890, Fax (01825) 722810, 🏡, « 16C
coaching inn », 🌧 – ⋇ rm, ❷. ◍❾ ﴾ﬞ ◍ 𝘝𝘐𝘚𝘈. ⋙
closed 25 December – **Meals** (closed Sunday dinner September-March) 17.50 **t.**
(lunch) and a la carte 14.40/21.95 **t.** ₴ 4.80 – **8 rm** ⊡ 50.00/75.00 **st.** – SB.

---

**FLITWICK** Beds. 𝟰𝟬𝟰 S 27 – pop. 11 063.
London 45 – Bedford 13 – Luton 12 – Northampton 28.

🏨 **Flitwick Manor** ⤷, Church Rd, MK45 1AE, off Dunstable Rd ℘ (01525) 712242,
Fax (01525) 718753, ←, « 18C manor house », 🌧, park, ⋙ – ⋇ 📺 ☎ ⟍ ❷. ◍❾ ﴾ﬞ ◍ 𝘝𝘐𝘚𝘈
𝘑𝘊𝘉. ⋙
**Meals** 25.00 **st.** and a la carte ₴ 9.00 – ⊡ 12.50 – **17 rm** 55.00/175.00 **t.** – SB.

---

**FLORE** Northants. 𝟰𝟬𝟯 𝟰𝟬𝟰 Q 27 – see Daventry.

---

**FOLKESTONE** Kent 𝟰𝟬𝟰 X 30 Great Britain G. – pop. 45 587.
See : The Leas★ (←★) Z.
Channel Tunnel : Eurotunnel information and reservations ℘ (0990) 353535.
🚢 to France (Boulogne) (Hoverspeed Ltd) 4 daily (55 mn).
🛈 Harbour St., CT20 1QN ℘ (01303) 258594.
London 76 – Brighton 76 – Dover 8 – Maidstone 33.

Plan opposite

🏨 **Clifton,** The Leas, CT20 2EB, ℘ (01303) 851231, Fax (01303) 851231, ←, 🌧 – 📱 📺 ☎ –
🔬 80. ◍❾ ﴾ﬞ ◍ 𝘝𝘐𝘚𝘈 𝘑𝘊𝘉　　　　　　　　　　　　　　　　　　　　　Z　r
**Meals** 10.50/17.00 **t.** and a la carte ₴ 4.95 – ⊡ 8.50 – **80 rm** 51.50/75.00 **t.** – SB.

🏩 **Wards,** 39 Earls Av., CT20 2HB, ℘ (01303) 245166, Fax (01303) 254480 – 📺 ☎ ❷ – 🔬 80.
◍❾ ﴾ﬞ 𝘝𝘐𝘚𝘈. ⋙　　　　　　　　　　　　　　　　　　　　　　　　　　　　　　X　c
closed 1 January – **Meals** (closed Sunday dinner and Bank Holidays) a la carte 10.00/18.95 **t.**
₴ 5.00 – **10 rm** ⊡ 52.00/95.00 **t.**

🏩 **Travel Inn,** Cherry Garden Lane, CT19 4AP, Northwest : 1 ¼ m. by A 259 at junction 13 of
M 20 ℘ (01303) 273620, Fax (01303) 273641 – ⋇ 📺 ⅙ ❷. ◍❾ ﴾ﬞ ◍ 𝘝𝘐𝘚𝘈. ⋙　　X　b
**Meals** (grill rest.) – **40 rm** 38.00 **t.**

🏠 **Harbourside** without rest., 13-14 Wear Bay Rd, CT19 6AT, ℘ (01303) 256528,
Fax (01303) 241299, ←, 🚣, 🌧 – ⋇ 📺. ◍❾ ﴾ﬞ 𝘝𝘐𝘚𝘈. ⋙　　　　　　　　　　　　X　e
**6 rm** ⊡ 40.00/70.00 **t.**

✕✕ **La Tavernetta,** Leaside Court, Clifton Gdns., CT20 2ED, ℘ (01303) 254955,
Fax (01303) 244732 – ◍❾ ﴾ﬞ ◍ 𝘝𝘐𝘚𝘈 𝘑𝘊𝘉　　　　　　　　　　　　　　　　　　　Z　n
closed Sunday, 25-26 December and Bank Holidays – **Meals** - Italian - 9.50 **t.**
(lunch) and a la carte 17.40/30.80 **t.** ₴ 5.55.

**at Sandgate** West : 1 ¾ m. on A 259 – ✉ Folkestone.

🏩 **Sandgate,** The Esplanade, CT20 3DY, West : ½ m. ℘ (01303) 220444, Fax (01303) 220496,
← – 📱 📺 ☎. ◍❾ ﴾ﬞ ◍ 𝘝𝘐𝘚𝘈. ⋙　　　　　　　　　　　　　　　　　　　　　X　a
closed January and first week October – **Meals** – (see **La Terrasse** below) – **15 rm** ⊡ 48.00/
72.00 **t.** – SB.

✕✕✕ **La Terrasse** (Gicqueau) (at Sandgate H.), The Esplanade, CT20 3DY, West : ½ m.
❀ ℘ (01303) 220444, Fax (01303) 220496, ←, 🏡 – ⋇ 📺 ◍❾ ﴾ﬞ ◍ 𝘝𝘐𝘚𝘈　　　　X　a
closed Sunday dinner, Monday, January and first week October – **Meals** - French - (booking
essential) 20.50/29.50 **t.** and a la carte 33.50/42.00 **t.** ₴ 7.50
**Spec.** Warm duck foie gras with pear and kumquat marmalade. Roasted turbot with girolle
mushrooms and a light poultry jus. Valhrona chocolate dessert with almond cream and
coffee ice cream.

◉ ATS 318/324 Cheriton Rd ℘ (01303) 275198/275121

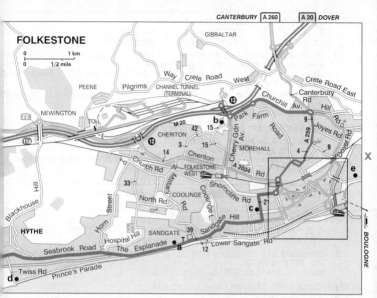

# FOLKESTONE

CANTERBURY A 260    A 20 DOVER

GIBRALTAR

0   1 km
0   1/2 mile

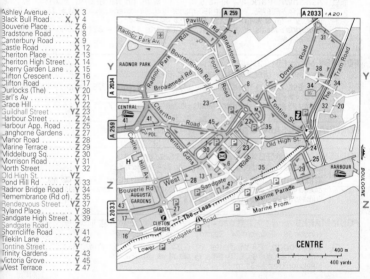

A 259    A 2033 (A 20)

CENTRE
0   400 m
0   400 yards

---

**FONTWELL** W. Sussex 404 S 31 – ⊠ Arundel.
   🛈 Little Chef Complex, BN18 0SD 𝒫 (01243) 543269.
   London 60 – Chichester 6 – Worthing 15.

   🏛 **Travelodge**, BN18 0SB, at A 27/A 29 roundabout 𝒫 (01243) 543973, Reservations (Free-phone) 0800 850950 – ⇤ rm, 📺 ሻ 🅿. 🐵 🜂 ⑩ 𝑽𝑰𝑺𝑨 🇯🇨🇧. ⊗
     **Meals** (grill rest.) – 65 rm 39.95/59.95 t.

---

**FORD** Wilts. – see Castle Combe.

**FORDINGBRIDGE** *Hants.* 403 404 O 31 – *pop. 4 301.*

🛿 *Salisbury St., SP6 1AB* ℘ *(01425) 654560 (summer only).*
*London 101 – Bournemouth 17 – Salisbury 11 – Winchester 30.*

XX **Hour Glass,** Salisbury Rd, Burgate, SP6 1LX, North : 1 m. on A 338 ℘ (01425) 652348
« 14C thatched cottage », 🐴 – 📤 ℗ 🐖 ⓘ 𝘝𝘐𝘚𝘈
*closed Sunday dinner, Monday, 1 week February and 2 weeks November –* **Meals** 19.95 t
(dinner) and a la carte 16.50/24.50 **t.** ⅃ 6.00.

🍴 **The Augustus John** with rm, 116 Station Rd, SP6 1DG, Southwest : ¾ m. on B 3078
℘ (01425) 652098 – 📺 ℗. 🐖 𝘝𝘐𝘚𝘈 𝙅𝘾𝘉
**Meals** a la carte 14.85/18.35 **t.** – **4 rm** 🖙 30.00/60.00 **t.**

*at Stuckton Southeast : 1 m. by B 3078 –* ✉ *Fordingbridge.*

X **Three Lions** 🌦 with rm, Stuckton Rd, SP6 2HF, ℘ (01425) 652489, Fax (01425) 656144
🐴 – 📤 rm, 📺 ℗. 🐖 𝘝𝘐𝘚𝘈 𝙅𝘾𝘉. ✾
*closed 18 January-10 February –* Meals *(closed Sunday dinner and Monday)* a la carte
22.75/28.95 **t.** ⅃ 10.50 – 🖙 5.50 – **3 rm** 65.00/85.00 **st.** – SB.

---

**FOREST** *Guernsey (Channel Islands)* 403 P 33 and 230 ⑨ ⑩ – *see Channel Islands.*

---

**FOREST ROW** *E. Sussex* 404 U 30 – *pop. 3 508.*

🇺⛳, 🇺⛳ *Royal Ashdown Forest, Chapel Lane, Forest Row* ℘ *(01342) 822018.*
*London 35 – Brighton 26 – Eastbourne 30 – Maidstone 32.*

🏨 **Chequers Inn,** The Square, RH18 5ES, ℘ (01342) 823333, Fax (01342) 825454 – 📺 ☎
🚗, 🐖 𝘈𝘌 ⓘ 𝘝𝘐𝘚𝘈. ✾
**Meals** a la carte 12.40/18.45 **st.** – **20 rm** 🖙 55.00/85.00 **st.**

*at Wych Cross South : 2½ m. on A 22 –* ✉ *Forest Row.*

🏨 **Ashdown Park** 🌦, RH18 5JR, East : ¾ m. on Hartfield rd ℘ (01342) 824988,
Fax (01342) 826206, ≤, « Part 19C manor house in extensive gardens », ⌶∂, 🏊, 🏸, 🇺⛳
park, ✾ – 📺 ☎ & ℗ – 🖼 150. 🐖 𝘈𝘌 ⓘ 𝘝𝘐𝘚𝘈 𝙅𝘾𝘉. ✾
*Anderida :* Meals 23.00/33.00 **st.** and a la carte ⅃ 12.50 – **89 rm** 🖙 114.00/304.00 **st.**
6 suites – SB.

---

**FORMBY** *Mersey.* 402 K 23 – ✉ *Southport.*
*London 213 – Liverpool 12 – Manchester 46 – Preston 27.*

X **Est, Est, Est,** 29 Three Tuns Lane, L37 4FB, ℘ (01704) 833775, Fax (01704) 879168 – 🗏
🐖 𝘈𝘌 ⓘ 𝘝𝘐𝘚𝘈
*closed 25 and 26 December –* **Meals** - Italian - a la carte 12.55/21.35 **t.** ⅃ 4.95.

---

**FORNHAM ALL SAINTS** *Suffolk* 404 W 27 – *see Bury St. Edmunds.*

---

**FOULSHAM** *Norfolk* 404 X 25 – *pop. 1 379 –* ✉ *East Dereham.*
*London 121 – Cambridge 69 – King's Lynn 31 – Norwich 18.*

XX **The Gamp,** Claypit Lane, NR20 5RW, ℘ (01362) 684114, 🐴 – 📤 ℗. 🐖 𝘝𝘐𝘚𝘈
*closed Monday and Tuesday lunch and first 2 weeks January –* **Meals** (by arrangement
Sunday) 10.95/11.95 **st.** and a la carte ⅃ 5.75.

---

**FOUR MARKS** *Hants.* 403 404 Q 30 – *pop. 3 843 (inc. Medstead) –* ✉ *Alton.*
*London 56 – Guildford 24 – Reading 29 – Southampton 24.*

🏨 **Travelodge,** 156 Winchester Rd, GU34 5HZ, on A 31 ℘ (01420) 562659, Reservations
(Freephone) 0800 850950 – 📺 & ℗. 🐖 𝘈𝘌 ⓘ 𝘝𝘐𝘚𝘈 𝙅𝘾𝘉. ✾
**Meals** (grill rest.) – **31 rm** 39.95/59.95 **t.**

---

**FOWEY** *Cornwall* 403 G 32 *The West Country G. – pop. 2 123.*
See : *Town*★★.
Env. : *Gribbin Head*★★ (≤★★) *6 m. rtn on foot – Bodinnick* (≤★★) *- Lanteglos Church*★
*E : 5 m. by ferry – Polruan* (≤★★) *SE : 6 m. by ferry – Polkerris*★ *, W : 2 m. by A 3082.*
🛿 *The Post Office, 4 Custom House Hill, PL23 1AA* ℘ *(01726) 833616.*
*London 277 – Newquay 24 – Plymouth 34 – Truro 22.*

🏨 **Fowey Hall** 🌦, Hanson Drive, PL23 1ET, West : ½ m. off A 3082 ℘ (01726) 833866
Fax (01726) 834100, ≤, « Part Victorian country house, special facilities for children », 🏊
🐴 – 📤 rest, 📺 ☎ ℗ – 🖼 40. 🐖 𝘈𝘌 ⓘ
**Meals** (light lunch)/dinner 29.50 **st.** ⅃ 7.50 – **23 rm** 🖙 100.00/160.00 **st.**, 3 suites – SB.

🏨 **Marina,** 17 The Esplanade, PL23 1HY, *℘* (01726) 833315, *Fax (01726) 832779*, ≤ Fowey river and harbour, ☞ – ⤬ rest, 📺 ☎ 🕮 ᴁ 𝖵𝖨𝖲𝖠 ᴶᶜᴮ. ⅏
*closed 20 December-26 February* – **Meals** (dinner only) 18.00 **t.** and a la carte ⏐ 6.95 – 11 rm ⊇ 57.00/98.00 **t.**

🏨 **Carnethic House** ⌂, Lambs Barn, PL23 1HQ, Northwest: ¾ m. on A 3082 *℘* (01726) 833336, *Fax (01726) 833336*, ⚒, ☞, ⅏ – ⤬ rest, 📺 ℗. 🕮 ᴁ ① 𝖵𝖨𝖲𝖠
*closed December and January* – **Meals** (bar lunch)/dinner 15.00 **st.** ⏐ 4.00 – 8 rm ⊇ 40.00/64.00 **st.** – SB.

🏠 **Ocean View** without rest., 24 Tower Park, PL23 1JB, *℘* (01726) 832283, ≤, ☞ – ⤬. ⅏
*April-September* – **4 rm** ⊇ 22.00/42.00 **s.**

⤬⤬ **Food for Thought,** The Quay, PL23 1AT, *℘* (01726) 832221, *Fax (01726) 832077*, « 17C converted coastguard's cottage on quayside » – 🕮 𝖵𝖨𝖲𝖠. ⅏
*closed Sunday, Christmas, January and February* – **Meals** (dinner only) 19.95 **t.** and a la carte 21.50/30.50 ⏐ 5.25.

**at Golant** North : 3 m. by B 3269 – ⊠ Fowey.

🏨 **Cormorant** ⌂, PL23 1LL, *℘* (01726) 833426, *Fax (01726) 833026*, ≤ River Fowey, ⚒, ☞ – 📺 ☎ ℗. 🕮 ᴁ 𝖵𝖨𝖲𝖠 ᴶᶜᴮ
**Meals** (light lunch)/dinner 19.00 **t.** and a la carte ⏐ 8.00 – 11 rm ⊇ 56.50/92.00 **t.** – SB.

---

**FOWNHOPE** Herefordshire **403 404** M 27 – *pop. 900* – ⊠ Hereford.
London 132 – Cardiff 46 – Hereford 6 – Gloucester 27.

🏨 **Green Man Inn,** HR1 4PE, *℘* (01432) 860243, *Fax (01432) 860207*, ⚒, ☞ – ⤬ rest, 📺 ☎ ℗. 🕮 ᴁ ① 𝖵𝖨𝖲𝖠
**Meals** (bar lunch)/dinner a la carte 16.20/20.30 **st.** ⏐ 5.35 – 19 rm ⊇ 35.50/56.00 **st.**

*To visit a town or region: use the **Michelin Green Guides.***

---

**FRADDON** Cornwall **403** F 32 – ⊠ St. Columbus Major.
London 264 – Exeter 77 – Penzance 35 – Newquay 7 – Plymouth 44 – Truro 12.

🏨 **Travel Inn,** Penhale, TR9 6NA, on A 30 (eastbound carriageway) *℘* (01726) 861148, *Fax (01726) 861336* – ⤬ rm, 📺 ⅋ ℗. 🕮 ᴁ ① 𝖵𝖨𝖲𝖠. ⅏
**Meals** (grill rest.) – 40 rm 38.00 **t.**

---

**FRAMLINGHAM** Suffolk **404** Y 27 – *pop. 2 697* – ⊠ Woodbridge.
London 92 – Ipswich 19 – Norwich 42.

🏨 **Crown,** Market Hill, IP13 9AN, *℘* (01728) 723521, *Fax (01728) 724274*, « 16C inn » – ⤬ 📺 ☎ ℗. 🕮 ᴁ 𝖵𝖨𝖲𝖠
**Meals** *(bar lunch Monday to Saturday)*/dinner a la carte 15.00/22.00 **t.** ⏐ 7.95 – 13 rm ⊇ 55.00/65.00 **st.** – SB.

**at Badingham** Northeast : 3¼ m. by B 1120 on A 1120 – ⊠ Woodbridge.

🏠 **Colston Hall** ⌂ without rest., IP13 8LB, East : ¾ m. by A 1120 on Bruisyard rd *℘* (01728) 638375, *Fax (01728) 638875*, ⚒, ☞, park – ⤬ ℗. ⅏
6 rm ⊇ 30.00/50.00 **st.**

---

**FRAMPTON** Dorset **403 404** M 31 – *see Dorchester.*

---

**FRANKLEY SERVICE AREA** W. Mids. **403 404** ⑲ – ⊠ Birmingham.

Plan : see Birmingham p. 2

🏨 **Travelodge,** B32 4AR, M 5 between junctions 3 and 4 *℘* (0121) 550 3131, *Fax (0121) 501 2880*, Reservations (Freephone) 0800 850950 – ⤬ 📺 ☎ ⅋ ℗. 🕮 ᴁ ① 𝖵𝖨𝖲𝖠 ᴶᶜᴮ. ⅏
BU  a
**Meals** (grill rest.) – 62 rm 39.95/59.95 **t.**

---

**FRANT** E. Sussex **404** U 30 – *see Royal Tunbridge Wells.*

---

**FRESHWATER BAY** I.O.W. **403 404** P 31 – *see Wight (Isle of).*

---

**FRILFORD** Oxon. **403 404** P 28-29 – *see Abingdon.*

**FRIMLEY** *Surrey* **404** *R 30 – pop. 5 661 – ⊠ Camberley.*
*London 39 – Reading 17 – Southampton 47.*

🏠 **One Oak Toby,** 114 Portsmouth Rd, GU15 1HS, Northeast : 1 m. on A 325
*℘ (01276) 691939, Fax (01276) 605902* – ↤ 🆉 ☎ ᖷ 🅿 – ᏑᎬ 30. 🐼 🆎 ⓪ 𝘝𝘐𝘚𝘈
*closed 24 December-1 January* – **Meals** *(grill rest.)* a la carte 10.30/15.10 t. ᛜ 4.45 – **40 rm**
⊡ 78.00/88.00 t. – SB.

---

**FRODSHAM** *Ches.* **402 403 404** *L 24 – pop. 8 903 – ⊠ Warrington.*
*London 203 – Chester 11 – Liverpool 21 – Manchester 29 – Stoke-on-Trent 42.*

🏠🏠 **Forest Hills,** Overton Hill, WA6 6HH, South : 1 ¾ m. by B 5152 on Simons Lane
*℘ (01928) 735255, Fax (01928) 735517*, ⩽, 𝄩₆, ≘ₛ, 🔲, squash – ↤ rm, 🆉 ☎ ᖷ 🅿 –
ᏑᎬ 200. 🐼 🆎 ⓪ 𝘝𝘐𝘚𝘈
**Meals** a la carte 14.95/25.00 **st.** ᛜ 6.95 – ⊡ 8.95 – **57 rm** 83.00 **st.** – SB.

🏠 **Old Hall,** Main St., WA6 7AB, *℘ (01928) 732052, Fax (01928) 739046*, 🍃 – ↤ rm, 🆉 ☎ 🅿
– ᏑᎬ 30. 🐼 🆎 ⓪ 𝘝𝘐𝘚𝘈 𝗝𝗖𝗕
**Meals** 11.95/16.95 **st.** and a la carte ᛜ 5.95 – **24 rm** ⊡ 59.50/75.00 **st.**, 1 suite.

🏠 **Heathercliffe Country House** 🌺, Manley Rd, WA6 6HB, South : 1 ½ m. by B 5152
*℘ (01928) 733722, Fax (01928) 735667*, ⩽, 🍃, park – 🆉 ☎ 🅿. 🐼 🆎 𝘝𝘐𝘚𝘈 𝗝𝗖𝗕
*closed 27 to 29 December* – **Meals** *(closed Saturday lunch and Sunday dinner)* a la carte
15.40/33.40 t. ᛜ 6.95 – **9 rm** ⊡ 64.00/95.00 **st.** – SB.

🔧 ATS Brooklyn Garage, Chester Rd *℘ (01928) 733555*

---

**FULBROOK** *Oxon.* **403 404** *P 28 – see Burford.*

---

**FULLETBY** *Lincs.* **402 404** *T 24 – see Horncastle.*

---

**FUNTINGTON** *W. Sussex* **404** *R 31 – see Chichester.*

---

**GALMPTON** *Devon* **403** *J 32 – ⊠ Brixham.*
*London 229 – Plymouth 32 – Torquay 6.*

🏠 **Maypool Park** 🌺, Maypool, TQ5 0ET, Southwest : 1 m. by Greenway Rd
*℘ (01803) 842442, Fax (01803) 845782*, ⩽, 🍃 – ↤ 🆉 ☎ 🅿. 🐼 🆎 𝘝𝘐𝘚𝘈. 🌿
*closed 23 December-2 January* – **Meals** *(residents only) (dinner only and Sunday lunch)*
dinner 20.00 t. ᛜ 7.30 – **10 rm** ⊡ 44.00/94.00 **st.** – SB.

---

**GARFORTH** *W. Yorks.* **402** *P 22 – see Leeds.*

---

**GARSTANG** *Lancs.* **402** *L 22 – pop. 5 697.*
🅱 *Discovery Centre, Council Offices, High St., PR3 1FU ℘ (01995) 602125.*
*London 233 – Blackpool 13 – Manchester 41.*

🏠🏠 **Garstang Country H. and Golf Club,** Bowgreave, PR3 1YE, South : 1 ¼ m. on B 6430
*℘ (01995) 600100, Fax (01995) 600950*, 🝙 – ᛜ ↤ 🆉 ☎ 🅿 – ᏑᎬ 200. 🐼 🆎 ⓪ 𝘝𝘐𝘚𝘈. 🌿
**Meals** 9.95/12.95 **st.** and a la carte ᛜ 4.95 – **32 rm** ⊡ 50.00/65.00 t. – SB.

🏠🏠 **Crofters,** Cabus, PR3 1PH, West : ¾ m. on A 6 *℘ (01995) 604128, Fax (01995) 601646* –
↤ rest, 🆉 ☎ 🅿 – ᏑᎬ 200. 🐼 🆎 ⓪ 𝘝𝘐𝘚𝘈
**Meals** *(dancing Saturday evening) (bar lunch Monday to Saturday)/dinner* a la carte 14.30/
19.80 t. ᛜ 5.25 – ⊡ 6.00 – **19 rm** 38.00/50.00 t.

🏠 **Pickering Park,** Garstang Rd, Catterall, PR3 0HD, South : 1 ½ m. on B 6430
*℘ (01995) 600999, Fax (01995) 602100*, 🍃 – ↤ rest, 🆉 ☎ 🅿 – ᏑᎬ 50. 🐼 🆎 ⓪ 𝘝𝘐𝘚𝘈. 🌿
**Meals** *(closed Monday lunch)* 9.95/14.50 **st.** and a la carte ᛜ 5.50 – **16 rm** ⊡ 55.00/130.00 t.
– SB.

*at Bilsborrow South : 3 ¾ m. by B 6430 on A 6 – ⊠ Preston.*

🏠🏠 **Guy's Thatched Hamlet,** Canalside, St. Michaels Rd, PR3 0RS, off A 6
*℘ (01995) 640010, Fax (01995) 640141* – 🆉 ☎ ᖷ 🅿. 🐼 🆎 𝘝𝘐𝘚𝘈 𝗝𝗖𝗕
*closed 25 December* – **Meals** 10.95 **st.** *(lunch)* and a la carte 11.25/21.00 **st.** ᛜ 4.10 – ⊡ 5.50
– **53 rm** 38.00 **st.** – SB.

🏠 **Olde Duncombe House** without rest., Garstang Rd, PR3 0RE, *℘ (01995) 640336*,
*Fax (01995) 640336* – 🆉 ☎ 🅿. 🐼 🆎 𝘝𝘐𝘚𝘈
**9 rm** ⊡ 35.00/49.00 t.

**GATE SERVICE AREA** Kent 404 X 30 – see Canterbury.

---

**GATESHEAD** Tyne and Wear 401 402 P 19 Great Britain G. – pop. 83 159.

Exc. : Beamish : North of England Open Air Museum★★ AC, SW : 6 m. by A 692 and A 6076 BX.

🇮🇸 Ravensworth, Moss Heaps, Wrekenton ℰ (0191) 487 6014/487 2843 – 🇮🇸 Heworth, Gingling Gate ℰ (0191) 469 2137 BX.

Tyne Tunnel (toll).

🖪 Central Library, Prince Consort Rd, NE8 4LN ℰ (0191) 477 3478 BX – Metrocentre, Portcullis, 7 The Arcade, NE11 9YL ℰ (0191) 460 6345 AX.

London 282 – Durham 16 – Middlesbrough 38 – Newcastle upon Tyne 1 – Sunderland 11.

Plan : see Newcastle upon Tyne

🏨 **Newcastle/Gateshead Marriott,** Cameron Park, Metro Centre, NE11 9XF, ℰ (0191) 493 2233, Fax (0191) 493 2030, ₤₆, ≘s, 🔲 – 📳, 👐 rm, 🔳 🔟 ☎ ✆ ❤ 🅿 – 🔬 450.
🐾 🗛 ⓪ 𝘝𝘐𝘚𝘈. ⌘
AX  e
Meals (bar lunch)/dinner 16.50 st. and a la carte 🍴 8.00 – ⌷ 11.95 – **146 rm** 79.00/94.00 st., 2 suites – SB.

🏨 **Gibside Arms,** Front St., Whickham, NE16 4JG, ℰ (0191) 488 9292, Fax (0191) 488 8000 –
🔳 rest, 🔟 ☎ ✆ 🖐 🛏 – 🔬 100. 🐾 🗛 ⓪ 𝘝𝘐𝘚𝘈
AX  s
closed 23 to 30 December – **Meals** (bar lunch)/dinner 14.95 st. and a la carte – ⌷ 8.50 –
**45 rm** 55.00/66.00 st. – SB.

🏨 **Travel Inn,** Derwenthaugh Rd, NE16 3BL, ℰ (0191) 414 6308, Fax (0191) 414 5032 – 📳 👐
🔟 🛏. 🐾 🗛 ⓪ 𝘝𝘐𝘚𝘈
AX  c
Meals (grill rest.) – **40 rm** 38.00 t.

**at Low Fell** South : 2 m. by A 167 and Belle Vue Bank – BX – ✉ Gateshead.

🏨 **Eslington Villa,** 8 Station Rd, NE9 6DR, ℰ (0191) 487 6017, Fax (0191) 420 0667, 🚗 –
👐 rest, 🔟 ☎ 🅿. 🐾 🗛 ⓪ 𝘝𝘐𝘚𝘈 𝐉𝐂𝐁
closed 25-26 December and 1 January – **Meals** (closed Sunday dinner and Bank Holidays)
15.65/22.45 t. and a la carte 🍴 5.50 – **12 rm** ⌷ 59.50/69.50 t.

🛠 ATS Earlsway, First Av., Team Valley Trading Est. ℰ (0191) 491 0081/182 4797

---

**GATWICK AIRPORT** W. Sussex 404 T 30 – ✉ Crawley.

✈ Gatwick Airport : ℰ (01293) 535353.

🖪 International Arrivals, South Terminal, RH6 0NP ℰ (01293) 560108.

London 29 – Brighton 28.

Plan on next page

🏨 **London Gatwick Airport Hilton,** South Terminal, RH6 0LL, ℰ (01293) 518080, Fax (01293) 528980, ₤₆, ≘s, 🔲 – 📳, 👐 rm, 🔳 🔟 ☎ ✆ ❤ 🅿 – 🔬 500. 🐾 🗛 ⓪ 𝘝𝘐𝘚𝘈 𝐉𝐂𝐁.
⌘
Y  u
Meals 15.95/25.95 t. and a la carte 🍴 9.00 – ⌷ 13.95 – **547 rm** 187.00/220.00 st., 3 suites.

🏨 **Le Meridien London Gatwick,** Gatwick Airport (North Terminal), RH6 0PH, ℰ (01293) 567070, Fax (01293) 567739, ₤₆, ≘s, 🔲 – 📳, 👐 rm, 🔳 🔟 ☎ & 🅿 – 🔬 350. 🐾 🗛 ⓪ 𝘝𝘐𝘚𝘈
Y  e
**Gatwick Oriental :** Meals - Asian - (closed Saturday lunch) a la carte 22.00/34.00 🍴 8.50 –
**Brasserie :** Meals 14.50/18.95 t. and a la carte 🍴 6.95 – ⌷ 10.95 – **468 rm** 175.00 st., 6 suites – SB.

🏨 **Ramada H. Gatwick,** Povey Cross Rd, RH6 0BE, ℰ (01293) 820169, Fax (01293) 820259, ₤₆, ≘s, 🔲, squash – 📳, 👐 rm, 🔳 🔟 ☎ 🅿 – 🔬 180. 🐾 🗛 ⓪ 𝘝𝘐𝘚𝘈. ⌘
Y  a
Meals (closed lunch Saturday and Sunday) 16.50/18.50 st. and dinner a la carte 🍴 7.50 – ⌷ 11.50 – **253 rm** 105.00 st., 2 suites.

🏨 **Forte Posthouse Gatwick,** Povey Cross Rd, RH6 0BA, ℰ (01293) 771621, Fax (01293) 771054 – 📳, 👐 rm, 🔳 rest, 🔟 ☎ 🅿 – 🔬 170. 🐾 🗛 ⓪ 𝘝𝘐𝘚𝘈
Y  c
Meals 14.95 t. (dinner) and a la carte 22.00/30.00. 🍴 7.95 – ⌷ 11.50 – **210 rm** 119.00 st. – SB.

🏨 **Gatwick Moat House,** Longbridge Roundabout, Povey Cross Rd, RH6 0AB, ℰ (01293) 899988, Fax (01293) 785991, ₤₆ – 👐 rm, 🔟 ☎ & 🅿 – 🔬 150. 🐾 🗛 ⓪ 𝘝𝘐𝘚𝘈. ⌘
Y  n
Meals (bar lunch)/dinner a la carte 14.85/21.95 st. 🍴 6.95 – ⌷ 9.95 – **124 rm** 105.00 st. – SB.

🏨 **Travel Inn,** Longbridge Way, Gatwick Airport (North Terminal), RH6 0NX, ℰ (01293) 568158, Fax (01293) 568278 – 📳, 👐 rm, 🔳 rest, 🔟 & 🅿 – 🔬 35. 🐾 🗛 ⓪ 𝘝𝘐𝘚𝘈. ⌘
Y  s
Meals (grill rest.) – **121 rm** 38.00 t.

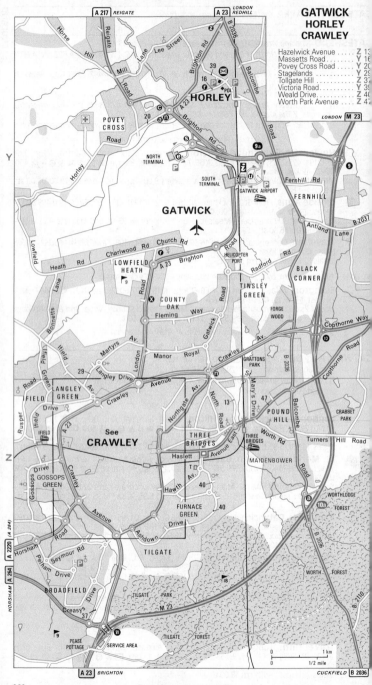

**HORLEY**

**GATWICK**

**CRAWLEY**

See **CRAWLEY**

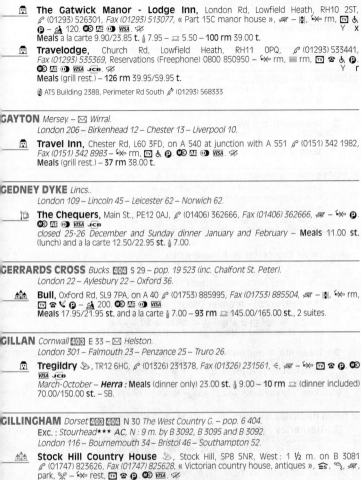

**The Gatwick Manor - Lodge Inn,** London Rd, Lowfield Heath, RH10 2ST, *℘* (01293) 526301, Fax (01293) 513077, « Part 15C manor house », ⏏ – ⫯, ⫯⫯ rm, TV ᵹ **P** – 🛦 120. ⚙ Æ ⓪ *VISA*. ⫯
Meals a la carte 9.90/23.85 t. ⫯ 7.95 – ⫯ 5.50 – **100 rm** 39.00 t.
Y x

**Travelodge,** Church Rd, Lowfield Heath, RH11 0PQ, *℘* (01293) 533441, Fax (01293) 535369, Reservations (Freephone) 0800 850950 – ⫯⫯ rm, 🗏 rm, TV ☎ ᵹ **P**. ⚙ Æ ⓪ *VISA* JCB – ⫯
Meals (grill rest.) – **126 rm** 39.95/59.95 t.
Y r

🅞 ATS Building 238B, Perimeter Rd South *℘* (01293) 568333

---

**GAYTON** Mersey. – ⊠ Wirral.
London 206 – Birkenhead 12 – Chester 13 – Liverpool 10.

**Travel Inn,** Chester Rd, L60 3FD, on A 540 at junction with A 551 *℘* (0151) 342 1982, Fax (0151) 342 8983 – ⫯⫯ rm, TV ᵹ **P**. ⚙ Æ ⓪ *VISA*. ⫯
Meals (grill rest.) – **37 rm** 38.00 t.

---

**GEDNEY DYKE** Lincs..
London 109 – Lincoln 45 – Leicester 62 – Norwich 62.

**The Chequers,** Main St., PE12 0AJ, *℘* (01406) 362666, Fax (01406) 362666, ⏏ – ⫯⫯ **P**. ⚙ Æ ⓪ *VISA* JCB
closed 25-26 December and Sunday dinner January and February – **Meals** 11.00 st. (lunch) and a la carte 12.50/22.95 st. ⫯ 7.00.

---

**GERRARDS CROSS** Bucks. ⓓⓞⓐ S 29 – pop. 19 523 (inc. Chalfont St. Peter).
London 22 – Aylesbury 22 – Oxford 36.

**Bull,** Oxford Rd, SL9 7PA, on A 40 *℘* (01753) 885995, Fax (01753) 885504, ⏏ – ⫯, ⫯⫯ rm, TV ☎ ℂ **P** – 🛦 200. ⚙ Æ ⓪ *VISA*
Meals 17.95/21.95 st. and a la carte ⫯ 7.00 – **93 rm** ⫤ 145.00/165.00 st., 2 suites.

---

**GILLAN** Cornwall ⓓⓞⓑ E 33 – ⊠ Helston.
London 301 – Falmouth 23 – Penzance 25 – Truro 26.

**Tregildry** ⫯, TR12 6HG, *℘* (01326) 231378, Fax (01326) 231561, ≼, ⏏ – ⫯⫯ TV ☎ **P**. ⚙ *VISA* JCB
March-October – **Herra :** Meals (dinner only) 23.00 st. ⫯ 9.00 – **10 rm** ⫤ (dinner included) 70.00/150.00 st. – SB.

---

**GILLINGHAM** Dorset ⓓⓞⓑ ⓓⓞⓐ N 30 The West Country G. – pop. 6 404.
Exc. : Stourhead★★★ AC, N : 9 m. by B 3092, B 3095 and B 3092.
London 116 – Bournemouth 34 – Bristol 46 – Southampton 52.

**Stock Hill Country House** ⫯, Stock Hill, SP8 5NR, West : 1 ½ m. on B 3081 *℘* (01747) 823626, Fax (01747) 825628, « Victorian country house, antiques », ⫯⫯, ⫯, ⏏, park, ⫯ – ⫯⫯ rest, TV ☎ **P**. ⚙ *VISA*. ⫯
Meals (closed Monday lunch) (booking essential) 20.00/35.00 t. and dinner a la carte 30.00/55.00 t. ⫯ 9.50 – **9 rm** ⫤ (dinner included) 120.00/280.00 t. – SB.

---

**GISLINGHAM** Suffolk ⓓⓞⓐ X 27 – pop. 822 – ⊠ Eye.
London 93 – Cambridge 45 – Ipswich 20 – Norwich 30.

**Old Guildhall,** Mill St., IP23 8JT, *℘* (01379) 783361, « 15C former guildhall », ⏏ – ⫯⫯ TV **P**. ⫯
closed January – **Meals** (by arrangement) 12.50 s. ⫯ 3.50 – **3 rm** ⫤ 37.50/55.00 s. – SB.

---

*When travelling for business or pleasure*
*in England, Wales, Scotland and Ireland :*

- use the series of five maps
  (nos ⓓⓞⓐ, ⓓⓞⓑ, ⓓⓞⓒ, ⓓⓞⓐ and ⓠⓩⓑ) at a scale of 1:400 000

- they are the perfect complement to this Guide

**GLENFIELD** *Leicester* 402 403 404 Q 26 – *see Leicester*.

**GLEWSTONE** *Herefordshire* – *see Ross-on-Wye*.

**GLOOSTON** *Leics.* – *see Market Harborough*.

**GLOSSOP** *Derbs.* 402 403 404 O 23 – *pop. 30 771 (inc. Hollingworth)*.

📍 *Sheffield Rd* ℰ *(01457) 865247*.
🚉 *The Gatehouse, Victoria St., SK13 8HT* ℰ *(01457) 855920*.
*London 194 – Manchester 18 – Sheffield 25*.

🏠 **The Wind in the Willows** ⌂, Hurst Rd, Derbyshire Level, SK13 7PT, East : 1 m. by A 57
ℰ *(01457) 868001, Fax (01457) 853354*, 🌲 – ✳ rest, 📺 ☎ ✆ 🅿, 📭 🖭 ① *VISA*. ✀
*closed 1 week Christmas-New Year* – **Meals** *(residents only) (dinner only)* 25.00 st. ₺ 9.50 –
**12 rm** ⇌ 70.00/110.00 st.

**GLOUCESTER** *Glos.* 403 404 N 28 *Great Britain G.* – *pop. 114 003*.

*See : City⋆ - Cathedral⋆⋆* Y *– The Docks⋆* Y *– Bishop Hooper's Lodging⋆ AC* Y M.
📍, 📍 *Gloucester Hotel, Matson Lane* ℰ *(01452) 525653*.
🚉 *St Michael's Tower, The Cross, GL1 1PD* ℰ *(01452) 421188*.
*London 106 – Birmingham 52 – Bristol 38 – Cardiff 66 – Coventry 57 – Northampton 83 –*
*Oxford ◀48 – Southampton 9◔ – Swansea 92 – Swindon 35*.

*Plan opposite*

🏨 **Jarvis Gloucester H. & Country Club**, Robinswood Hill, GL4 6EA, Southeast : 3 m
by B 4073 ℰ *(01452) 525653, Fax (01452) 307212*, ╠6, ⇔, 🔲, 📍, 📍, ✿, squash – ✳ rm
📺 ☎ ✆ 🅿 – 🖾 180. 📭 🖭 ① *VISA*  Z C
*closed 25 and 26 December* – **Meals** *(closed Saturday lunch)* 9.95/17.50 t. and a la carte
₺ 6.50 – ⇌ 8.50 – **102 rm** 99.00/134.00 t., 5 suites – SB.

🏨 **The Twigworth - Premier Lodge**, Tewksbury Rd, Twigworth, GL2 9PG, Northeast
2 ½ m. on A 38 ℰ *(01452) 730266, Fax (01452) 730099*, Reservations (Freephone) 0800
118833 – ✳ rm, 📺 ☎ ♿ 🅿 – 🖾 40. 📭 🖭 ① *VISA JCB*. ✀
*closed 25 December* – **Meals** *(grill rest.)* a la carte 7.85/15.25 t. ₺ 4.55 – ⇌ 5.95 – **52 rm**
44.95 st.

🏨 **Travel Inn**, Tewkesbury Rd, Longford, GL2 9BE, North : 1 ¾ m. on A 38 ℰ *(01452) 523519*
*Fax (01452) 300924* – ✳ rm, 📺 ♿ 🅿. 📭 🖭 ① *VISA*. ✀
**Meals** *(grill rest.)* – **60 rm** 38.00 t.

🍴 **Yeungs**, St. Oswald's Rd, Cattle Market, GL1 2SR, ℰ *(01452) 309957* – 🔳. 📭 🖭 *VISA*
*closed Monday lunch and Sunday* – **Meals** - Chinese - 13.00/23.50 t. and a la carte
₺ 5.50.  Z E

*at Down Hatherley Northeast : 3¼ m. by A 38 – Z – ✉ Gloucester*.

🏠 **Hatherley Manor**, Down Hatherley Lane, GL2 9QA, ℰ *(01452) 730217*
*Fax (01452) 731032*, ╠6, 🌲 – ✳ rest, 📺 ☎ ♿ 🅿 – 🖾 330. 📭 🖭 ① *VISA*. ✀
**Meals** *(bar lunch Monday to Saturday)/dinner* 18.50 st. – ⇌ 9.50 – **57 rm** 80.00/120.00 st. –
SB.

*at Upton St. Leonards Southeast : 3½ m. by B 4073 – Z – ✉ Gloucester*.

🏨 **Hatton Court**, Upton Hill, GL4 8DE, South : ¾ m. on B 4073 ℰ *(01452) 617412*
*Fax (01452) 612945*, ≤, 🔲, 🌲 – ✳ rest, 🍽 rest, 📺 ☎ 🅿 – 🖾 60. 📭 🖭 ① *VISA JCB*.
✀
*Carringtons :* **Meals** 22.50 t. *(dinner)* and a la carte 19.20/31.45 t. – **45 rm** ⇌ 90.00/145.00
– SB.

🏨 **Jarvis Bowden Hall**, Bondend Lane, GL4 8ED, East : 1 m. by Bondend rd
ℰ *(01452) 614121, Fax (01452) 611885*, ≤, ⇔, 🔲, 🌲, park – ✳ 📺 ☎ 🅿 – 🖾 85. 📭 🖭
① *VISA JCB*
**Meals** *(dinner only and Sunday lunch)/dinner* 17.95 st. ₺ 6.00 – ⇌ 8.95 – **72 rm** 99.00/
119.00 st.

↑ **Bullens Manor Farm** *without rest.*, High St., GL4 8DL, Southeast : ½ m.
ℰ *(01452) 616463*, ≤, « Working farm », park – ✳ 📺 🅿. ✀
*closed 1 week Christmas* – **3 rm** ⇌ 22.00/38.00 st.

*at Witcombe Southeast : 7 m. by A 40 on A 417 – Z – off A 46 – ✉ Gloucester*.

🏨 **Travel Inn**, GL3 4SS, ℰ *(01452) 862521, Fax (01452) 864926* – ✳ rm, 📺 ♿ 🅿. 📭 🖭 ①
*VISA*. ✀
*closed 24 to 27 December* – **Meals** *(grill rest.)* – **39 rm** 38.00 t.

🔧 ATS St. Oswalds Rd ℰ *(01452) 527329*

# GLOUCESTER

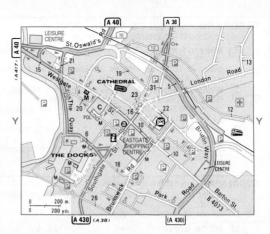

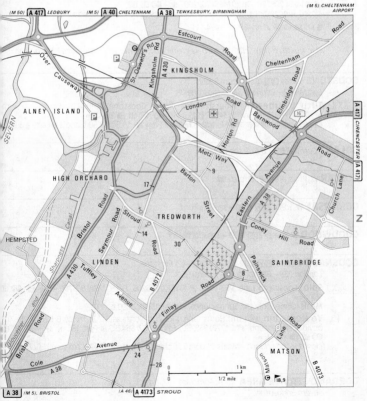

Benutzen Sie auf Ihren Reisen in Europa
die **Michelin-Länderkarten** 1 : 1 000 000.

**GOATHLAND** *N. Yorks.* 402 R 20 – *pop. 444 –* ✉ *Whitby.*
*London 248 – Middlesbrough 36 – York 38.*

🏨 **Mallyan Spout** ⬧, The Common, YO22 5AN, ℘ (01947) 896486, *Fax (01947) 896327,* ≤, ☞ – 📺 ☎ 📞 📫. 🝙🝙 ﬗ *VISA*
*closed 25 December* – **Meals** (bar lunch Monday to Saturday)/dinner 13.50/19.50 **t** and a la carte – **24 rm** ☲ 50.00/130.00 **t.** – SB.

🏠 **Whitfield House** ⬧, Darnholm, YO22 5LA, Northwest : ¾ m. ℘ (01947) 896215 *Fax (01947) 896043,* ☞ – ✦⛬ 📺 ☎ 📞 📫. 🝙🝙 *VISA.* ✦
*closed 24 to 26 December and restricted opening in January* – **Meals** (dinner only) 13.50 **st** ⬥ 4.95 – **9 rm** ☲ 28.00/56.00 **st.**

🏠 **Heatherdene** ⬧, The Common, YO22 5AN, ℘ (01947) 896334, ≤, ☞ – ✦⛬ rest, 📺 📞 📫. 🝙🝙
*closed Christmas* – **Meals** (light lunch)/dinner a la carte approx. 10.55 – **8 rm** ☲ 40.00/ 70.00 **st.**

---

**GODALMING** *Surrey* 404 S 30 – *pop. 20 630.*
🝙 *West Surrey, Enton Green ℘ (01483) 421275 –* 🝙 *Shillinglee Park, Chiddingfold ℘ (01428. 653237.*
*London 38 – Guildford 5 – Southampton 51.*

🍴 **White Horse,** The Street, Hascombe, GU8 4JA, Southeast : 3 ½ m. on B 2130 ℘ (01483) 208258, *Fax (01483) 208200,* ☞ – 🝙🝙 *VISA*
*closed Sunday dinner and 25 December* – **Meals** 22.00 **t.** and a la carte.

🅰 ATS Meadrow ℘ (01483) 421845/422219

*Per visitare una città o una regione : utilizzate le guide verdi Michelin.*

---

**GODSTONE** *Surrey* 404 T 30 – *pop. 2 399.*
*London 22 – Brighton 36 – Maidstone 28.*

XXX **Tutu L'Auberge,** Tilburstow Hill, South Godstone, RH9 8JY, South : 2 ¼ m. ℘ (01342) 892318, *Fax (01342) 893435,* ☞ – 📞. 🝙🝙 ﬗ ⑩ *VISA* *JCB*
*closed Sunday dinner and Monday* – **Meals** - French - 15.50/18.50 **t.** and a la carte ⬥ 6.90.

---

**GOLANT** *Cornwall* 403 G 32 – *see Fowey.*

---

**GOLCAR** *W. Yorks. – see Huddersfield.*

---

**GOMERSAL** *W. Yorks.* 402 O 22 – *see Bradford.*

---

**GOODWOOD** *W. Sussex* 404 R 31 – *see Chichester.*

---

**GOOSNARGH** *Lancs.* 402 L 22 – *pop. 1 087 –* ✉ *Preston.*
*London 238 – Blackpool 18 – Preston 6.*

XX **Solo,** Goosnargh Lane, PR3 2BN, ℘ (01772) 865206, *Fax (01772) 865206* – ✦⛬ 📞. 🝙🝙 ﬗ *VISA* *JCB*
**Meals** (dinner only and Sunday lunch)/dinner 13.90/23.90 **t.**

🍴 **Ye Horns Inn** with rm, Horns Lane, PR3 2FJ, Northeast : 2 ½ m. by B 5269 following obvious signposting ℘ (01772) 865230, *Fax (01772) 864299,* « Part 18C », ☞ – 📺 ☎ 📞. 🝙🝙 ﬗ ⑩ *VISA* *JCB*
*closed Monday lunch* – **Meals** 11.00/16.50 **t.** and a la carte ⬥ 6.00 – **6 rm** ☲ 49.50/75.00 **t.** – SB.

---

**GORDANO SERVICE AREA** *North Somerset –* ✉ *Bristol.*
*Severn Bridge (toll).*

🏨 **Welcome Lodge,** BS20 9XG, M 5 junction 19 ℘ (01275) 373709, *Fax (01275) 374104,* Reservations (Freephone) 0800 7314466 – ✦⛬ rm, 📺 ⬥ 📞. 🝙🝙 ﬗ ⑩ *VISA*
☲ 7.50 **62 rm** 50.00 **t.**

---

**GOREY** *Jersey (Channel Islands)* 403 P 33 and 230 ⑪ – *see Channel Islands.*

**GORING** *Oxon.* [403] [404] Q 29 *The West Country G. – pop. 4 193 (inc. Streatley).*
Exc. : *Ridgeway Path★★.*
*London 56 – Oxford 16 – Reading 12.*

🍴🍴 **Leatherne Bottel,** RG8 0HS, North : 1 ½ m. by B 4009 ☎ (01491) 872667, *Fax (01491) 875308,* ≤, 🏖, « Thames-side setting » – ⚓ 🅿. [MC] [AE] [VISA]
*closed Sunday dinner and 25 December* – **Meals** (booking essential) a la carte 28.50/39.50 **t.**

**GORLESTON-ON-SEA** *Norfolk* [404] Z 26 – *see Great Yarmouth.*

**GOSFORTH** *Cumbria* [402] J 20 – *pop. 1 568* – ✉ *Seascale.*
*London 317 – Kendal 55 – Workington 21.*

🏠 **Westlakes,** Gosforth Rd, CA20 1HP, Southwest : ¼ m. on B 5344 ☎ (019467) 25221, *Fax (019467) 25099,* 🌳 – 📺 ☎ 📞 🅿. [MC] [AE] [VISA] [JCB]. ✂
*closed 24 December-4 January* – **Meals** *(closed Sunday lunch)* a la carte 13.25/23.00 **st.** 🍷 5.00 – **9 rm** 🛏 49.00/56.00 **st.**

**GOSFORTH** *Tyne and Wear* [401] [402] P 18 – *see Newcastle upon Tyne.*

**GOVETON** *Devon* [403] I 33 – *see Kingsbridge.*

**GRAMPOUND** *Cornwall* [403] F 33 *The West Country G.* – ✉ *Truro.*
Env. : *Trewithen★★★ AC, W : 2 m. by A 390 – Probus★ (tower★, Country Demonstration Garden★ AC) W : 2½ m. by A 390.*
*London 287 – Newquay 16 – Plymouth 44 – Truro 8.*

🍴🍴 **Eastern Promise,** 1 Moor View, TR2 4RT, ☎ (01726) 883033 – 🚭 🅿. [MC] [AE] [D] [VISA] [JCB]
*closed Wednesday* – **Meals** - Chinese - (booking essential) (dinner only) 18.90 **st.** and a la carte 🍷 3.90.

**GRANGE-IN-BORROWDALE** *Cumbria* [402] K 20 – *see Keswick.*

**GRANGE-OVER-SANDS** *Cumbria* [402] L 21 *Great Britain G. – pop. 4 473.*
Env. : *Cartmel Priory★, NW : 3 m.*
⛳18 *Meathop Rd ☎ (015395) 33180* – ⛳9 *Grange Fell, Fell Rd ☎ (015395) 32536.*
ℹ *Victoria Hall, Main St., LA11 6PT ☎ (015395) 34026 (restricted opening in winter).*
*London 268 – Kendal 13 – Lancaster 24.*

🏨 **Netherwood,** Lindale Rd, LA11 6ET, ☎ (015395) 32552, *Fax (015395) 34121,* ≤ Morecambe Bay, 🏊, 🌳, park – 🛗 🚭, 🍴 rest, 📺 ☎ 🅿 – 🎤 150. [MC] [VISA]
**Meals** 14.50/22.25 **t.** 🍷 4.95 – **28 rm** 🛏 50.00/120.00 **t.** – SB.

**at Lindale** *Northeast : 2 m. on B 5277* – ✉ *Grange-over-Sands.*

🏠 **Greenacres,** LA11 6LP, ☎ (015395) 34578, *Fax (015395) 34578* – 🚭 📺 🅿. [MC] [VISA] [JCB]. ✂
*closed mid December-mid January* – **Meals** (by arrangement) 12.50 **st.** 🍷 3.50 – **5 rm** 🛏 26.00/52.00 **st.**

**at Witherslack** *Northeast : 5 m. by B 5277 off A 590.*

🏨 **Old Vicarage** 🌿, Church Rd, LA11 6RS, Northwest : ¾ m. ☎ (015395) 52381, *Fax (015395) 52373,* « Part Georgian country house », 🌳, 🎾 – 🚭 rest, 📺 ☎ 🅿. [MC] [AE] [VISA] [JCB]
**Meals** (dinner only and Sunday lunch)/dinner 29.50 **t.** 🍷 6.90 – **14 rm** 🛏 (dinner included) 85.00/200.00 **t.** – SB.

**at Cartmel** *Northwest : 3 m.*

🏨 **Aynsome Manor** 🌿, LA11 6HH, North : ¾ m. by Newby Bridge rd and Wood Broughton rd ☎ (015395) 36653, *Fax (015395) 36016,* 🌳 – 🚭 rest, 📺 ☎ 🅿. [MC] [AE] [VISA] [JCB]
*closed 2 to 30 January* – **Meals** *(closed Sunday dinner to non-residents)* (dinner only and Sunday lunch)/dinner 16.00 **t.** 🍷 6.00 – **12 rm** 🛏 (dinner included) 64.50/110.00 – SB.

🏠 **Uplands** 🌿, Haggs Lane, LA11 6HD, East : 1 m. ☎ (015395) 36248, *Fax (015395) 36848,* ≤, 🌳 – 🚭 rest, 📺 🅿. [MC] [AE] [VISA]
*closed January and February* – **Meals** *(closed Monday and lunch Tuesday to Wednesday)* (booking essential) 16.00/27.00 **t.** 🍷 6.80 – **5 rm** 🛏 (dinner included) 81.00/142.00 **t.** – SB.

**GRANTHAM** Lincs. 402 404 S 25 *Great Britain G. – pop. 33 243.*

See : *St. Wulfram's Church★.*

Env. : *Belton House★ AC, N : 2½ m. by A 607.*

Exc. : *Belvoir Castle★★ AC, W : 6 m. by A 607.*

🖎, 🖎, 🖎 *Belton Park, Belton Lane, Londonthorpe Rd* 🖉 *(01476) 567399 –* 🖎, 🖎, 🖎 *Belto Woods Hotel* 🖉 *(01476) 593200.*

🖎 *The Guildhall Centre, St. Peter's Hill, NG31 6PZ* 🖉 *(01476) 566444.*

*London 113 – Leicester 31 – Lincoln 29 – Nottingham 24.*

🏨 **De Vere Belton Woods,** Belton, NG32 2LN, North : 2 m. on A 607 🖉 *(01476) 593200 Fax (01476) 574547,* ☞, 🖎, 🖎, 🖎, 🖎, 🖎, park, ☜, squash – 🖎 🖎 📺 🖎 🖎 🖎 🖎 275. ⦿ 🖎 ⦿ *VISA*
*Manor :* Meals (dinner only) 24.95 **st.** and a la carte 🖎 15.25 – *Plus Fours :* Meals 18.50 **t** and a la carte 🖎 7.95 – **132 rm** ☞ 115.00/125.00 **t.**, 4 suites – SB.

🏨 **Swallow,** Swingbridge Rd, NG31 7XT, South : 1 ¼ m. at junction of A 607 with A southbound sliproad 🖉 *(01476) 593000, Fax (01476) 592592,* ☞, 🖎, 🖎, 🖎 – 🖎 rm 🖎 rest, 📺 🖎 🖎 🖎 🖎 – 🖎 200. ⦿ 🖎 ⦿ *VISA*
*Tapestry :* Meals 10.25/20.50 **st.** and a la carte – **90 rm** ☞ 95.00/115.00 **st.** – SB.

🏨 **Angel and Royal,** High St., NG31 6PN, 🖉 *(01476) 565816, Fax (01476) 567149,* « Par 13C » – 🖎 📺 🖎 🖎 – 🖎 30. ⦿ 🖎 ⦿ *VISA*
Meals (bar lunch Monday to Saturday)/dinner 15.95 **st.** and a la carte 🖎 5.95 – ☞ 9.25 – **29 rm** 60.00/80.00 **st.** – SB.

**at Hough-on-the-Hill** *North : 6¾ m. by A 607 on Hough Rd –* ✉ *Grantham.*

🍴 **Brownlow Arms** with rm, NG32 2AZ, 🖉 *(01400) 250234, Fax (01400) 250772,* « Part 170 inn », ☞ – 📺 🖎 🖎. ⦿ 🖎 *VISA.* ☜
Meals (closed lunch Monday to Friday, Sunday dinner, 25-26 December and Bank Holidays a la carte 14.35/24.20 **t.** 🖎 4.00 – **7 rm** ☞ 40.00/58.00 **t.**

**at Great Gonerby** *Northwest : 2 m. on B 1174 –* ✉ *Grantham.*

🍴🍴 **Harry's Place** (Hallam), 17 High St., NG31 8JS, 🖉 *(01476) 561780 –* 🖎 🖎. ⦿ 🖎 *VISA*
🌼 *closed Sunday, Monday, 25-26 December and 1 January –* Meals (booking essential a la carte 36.00/50.00 **t.** 🖎 11.25
Spec. Sautéed chicken livers in sherry and black pepper jelly, Cumberland sauce. Fillet o monkfish with basil, coriander, shallots and red wine sauce. Blackcurrant soufflé.

**at Grantham Service Area** *Northwest : 3 m on B 1174 at junction with A 1 –* ✉ *Grantham.*

🏨 **Travelodge,** NG32 2AB, 🖉 *(01476) 577500, Fax (01476) 577500,* Reservations (Free phone) 0800 850950 – 🖎 rm, 📺 🖎 🖎. ⦿ 🖎 ⦿ *VISA* 🖎. ☜
Meals (grill rest.) – **40 rm** 39.95/59.95 **t.**

🏨 ATS East St. 🖉 *(01476) 590222*      ATS Elmer St. South 🖉 *(01476) 590444*

---

**GRASMERE** Cumbria 402 K 20 *Great Britain G. –* ✉ *Ambleside.*

See : *Dove Cottage★ AC* AY A.

Env. : *Lake Windermere★★, SE : by A 591* AZ.

🖎 *Redbank Rd, LA22 9SW* 🖉 *(015394) 35245 (summer only)* BZ.

*London 282 – Carlisle 43 – Kendal 18.*

Plans : see Ambleside

🏨 **Michaels Nook Country House** 🖎, LA22 9RP, Northeast : ½ m. off A 591, turning by
🌼 Swan H. 🖉 *(015394) 35496, Fax (015394) 35645,* ≤ mountains and countryside, « Antiques and gardens », park – 🖎 rest, 📺 🖎 🖎. ⦿ 🖎 ⦿ *VISA* 🖎 AY r
Meals (booking essential) 34.50/45.00 **t.** 🖎 8.00 – **12 rm** ☞ (dinner included) 148.00/296.00 **st.**, 2 suites – SB
Spec. Braised pig's trotter on thyme scented potato cake, Calvados sauce. Best end of lamb with ravioli of sweetbreads and rosemary jus. Pear and praline parfait.

🏨 **Wordsworth,** Stock Lane, LA22 9SW, 🖉 *(015394) 35592, Fax (015394) 35765,* 🖎, 🖎, 🖎 – 🖎 rest, 🖎 rest, 📺 🖎 🖎 – 🖎 130. ⦿ 🖎 ⦿ *VISA.* ☜ BZ s
*Prelude :* Meals 19.50/32.50 **t.** and a la carte 🖎 6.50 – **35 rm** ☞ 65.00/170.00 **t.**, 2 suites – SB.

🏨 **Swan,** LA22 9RF, on A 591 🖉 *(015394) 35551, Fax (015394) 35741,* ≤, 🖎 – 🖎 📺 🖎 🖎 ⦿ 🖎 ⦿ *VISA* AY r
(bar lunch)/dinner a la carte 15.50/18.95 **t.** 🖎 8.00 – ☞ 8.75 – **36 rm** 85.00/120.00 – SB.

🏨 **Thistle Prince of Wales,** Keswick Rd, LA22 9PR, on A 591 🖉 *(015394) 35666, Fax (015394) 35565,* ≤, « Lakeside setting », 🖎, 🖎 – 🖎 📺 🖎 🖎 – 🖎 100. ⦿ 🖎 ⦿ *VISA* 🖎 AY e
Meals (bar lunch)/dinner a la carte approx. 21.50 **st.** 🖎 5.10 – **72 rm** ☞ 85.00/98.00 **st.** – SB.

🏨 **Gold Rill,** Red Bank Rd, LA22 9PU, ✆ (015394) 35486, Fax (015394) 35486, ≼, ⏋, ⌺ –
⌺ rest, 🆃 ☎ 🅿, 🆎 VISA. ⌺
BZ a
*closed 2 weeks January and 1 week mid December* – **Meals** (bar lunch)/dinner 19.00 st.
and a la carte ≬ 6.00 – **24 rm** ⌑ (dinner included) 62.00/114.00 st., 1 suite.

🏨 **White Moss House,** Rydal Water, LA22 9SE, South : 1 ½ m. on A 591 ✆ (015394) 35295,
Fax (015394) 35516, ⌕, ⌺ – ⌺ rest, 🆃 ☎ 🅿, 🆎 VISA JCB. ⌺
BY v
*March-November* – **Meals** *(closed Sunday)* (booking essential) (dinner only) 28.50 t. ≬ 7.95 –
**7 rm** ⌑ (dinner included) 89.00/180.00 st., 1 suite – SB.

🏨 **Red Lion,** Red Lion Sq., LA22 9SS, ✆ (015394) 35456, Fax (015394) 35579, ⌕, ☎ – 🛗,
⌺ rest, 🆃 ☎ 🅿 – ⌺ 60. 🆎 ᴀᴇ ⓪ VISA
BZ c
**Meals** (bar lunch)/dinner 19.00 t. and a la carte – **36 rm** ⌑ 52.50/105.00 t. – SB.

🏨 **Oak Bank,** Broadgate, LA22 9TA, ✆ (015394) 35217, Fax (015394) 35685, ⌺ – ⌺ rest, 🆃
☎ 🅿, 🆎 VISA JCB
BZ e
*closed January and Christmas* – **Meals** (bar lunch)/dinner 18.50 t. – **15 rm** ⌑ (dinner
included) 60.00/140.00 t. – SB.

🏨 **Grasmere,** Broadgate, LA22 9TA, ✆ (015394) 35277, Fax (015394) 35277, ⌺ – ⌺ rest,
🆃 ☎ ⌕ 🅿, 🆎 VISA JCB
BZ r
*closed 2 January-14 February* – **Meals** (dinner only) 17.50 st. ≬ 6.50 – **12 rm** ⌑ (dinner
included) 45.00/90.00 st. – SB.

🏨 **Lancrigg Vegetarian Country House** ⌕, Easedale Rd, LA22 9QN, West : ½ m. on
Easedale Rd ✆ (015394) 35317, Fax (015394) 35058, ≼ Easedale Valley, ⌺, park – ⌺ rest,
🆃 ☎ 🅿, 🆎 VISA JCB
AY u
**Meals** (lunch by arrangement)/dinner 20.00 st. ≬ 8.25 – **13 rm** ⌑ (dinner included) 69.00/
190.00 st. – SB.

🏨 **Bridge House,** Stock Lane, LA22 9SN, ✆ (015394) 35425, Fax (015394) 35523, ⌺ –
⌺ rest, 🆃 ☎ 🅿, 🆎 VISA JCB. ⌺
BZ n
**Meals** (dinner only) 16.00 st. ≬ 5.00 – **18 rm** ⌑ (dinner included) 100.00 st. – SB.

↑ **Rothay Lodge** ⌕ without rest., White Bridge, LA22 9RH, ✆ (015394) 35341, ⌺ – ⌺
🆃 🅿. ⌺
AY o
*March-October* – **3 rm** ⌑ 40.00/55.00.

↑ **Banerigg** without rest., Lake Rd, LA22 9PW, South : ¾ m. on A 591 ✆ (015394) 35204, ≼,
⌺ – 🆃 🅿. ⌺
AY a
*closed 1 week Christmas* – **7 rm** ⌑ 25.00/50.00 st.

---

**GRASSENDALE** Mersey 402 403 L 23 – see Liverpool.

---

**GRASSINGTON** N. Yorks. 402 O 21 – pop. 1 102 – ⌂ Skipton.
🖪 National Park Centre, Colvend, Hebden Rd, BD23 5LB ✆ (01756) 752774 (summer only).
London 240 – Bradford 30 – Burnley 28 – Leeds 37.

↑ **Ashfield House,** Summers Fold, BD23 5AE, ✆ (01756) 752584, Fax (01756) 752584,
« Part 17C », ⌺ – ⌺ 🆃 🅿, 🆎 VISA. ⌺
*restricted opening late November-December, closed 1 week May and 1 week June* – **Meals**
(by arrangement) 15.00 st. ≬ 4.00 – **7 rm** ⌑ 43.00/63.00 st. – SB.

---

**GRAVESEND** Kent 404 V 29 – pop. 51 435.
⌕ to Tilbury (White Horse Ferries Ltd) frequent services daily (6 mn).
🖪 10 Parrock St., DA12 1ET ✆ (01474) 337600.
London 25 – Dover 54 – Maidstone 16 – Margate 53.

🏨 **Manor,** Hever Court Rd, Singlewell, DA12 5UQ, Southeast : 2 ½ m. by A 227 off A 2
✆ (01474) 353100, Fax (01474) 354978, ⌕, ☎, ⌧ – ⌺ rm, ⌸ rest, 🆃 ☎ 🅿 – ⌺ 200. 🆎
ᴀᴇ VISA. ⌺
**Meals** *(closed Saturday, Sunday, Christmas and Bank Holidays)* (bar lunch)/dinner 17.95 t.
and a la carte ≬ 6.50 – ⌑ 7.95 – **53 rm** ⌑ 68.50/75.50 t.

🏨 **Overcliffe,** 15-16 Overcliffe, DA11 0EF, on A 226 (Dartford rd) ✆ (01474) 322131,
Fax (01474) 536737 – 🆃 ☎ 🅿, 🆎 ᴀᴇ ⓪ VISA. ⌺
**Meals** (dinner only) 22.50 t. and a la carte ≬ 8.50 – **28 rm** ⌑ 62.50/85.00 st.

---

**GRAVETYE** W. Sussex – see East Grinstead.

---

**GRAZELEY GREEN** Wokingham – see Reading.

---

*Pas de publicité payée dans ce guide.*

**GREASBY** Mersey. 402 ③② 403 ⑫ – pop. 56 077 (inc. Moreton) – ⊠ Wirral.
London 220 – Liverpool 9.

🏠 **Twelfth Man - Premier Lodge,** Greasby Rd, L49 2PP, on B 5139 ℰ (0151) 677 5445, Fax (0151) 678 5085, Reservations (Freephone) 0800 118833 – ⚖ rm, 📺 ☎ & 🅿. ⓐ ⚫ AE ⬤ VISA. ⌘
**Meals** (grill rest.) 7.25/12.95 **st.** and a la carte – ⌁ 5.95 – **30 rm** 43.95/45.95 **st.**

---

**GREAT BADDOW** Essex 404 V 28 – see Chelmsford.

---

**GREAT BARR** W. Mids. 403 404 O 26 – see Birmingham.

---

**GREAT BROUGHTON** N. Yorks. 402 Q 20 – pop. 937 (inc. Little Broughton) – ⊠ Middlesbrough.
London 241 – Leeds 61 – Middlesbrough 10 – York 54.

🏠 **Wainstones,** 31 High St., TS9 7EW, ℰ (01642) 712268, Fax (01642) 711560 – 📺 ☎ 🅿 – ⚖ 120. ⚫ AE ⬤ VISA JCB. ⌘
**Meals** a la carte 15.45/23.65 **t.** ⓘ 5.95 – **24 rm** ⌁ 62.95/78.95 **t.** – SB.

---

**GREAT DRIFFIELD** East Riding 402 S 21 Great Britain G. – pop. 9 463 – ⊠ York.
Exc. : Burton Agnes Hall★ AC, NE : 6 m. by A 166 – Sledmere House★ AC, NW : 8 m. by A 166 and B 1252.
🏌 Driffield, Sunderlandwick ℰ (01377) 253116 – 🏌 Hainsworth Park, Brandesburton ℰ (01964) 542362.
London 201 – Kingston-upon-Hull 21 – Scarborough 22 – York 29.

XX **Rockingham** with rm, 52 Front St., Lockington, YO25 9SH, South : 9 ¾ m. by A 164 ℰ (01430) 810607, Fax (01430) 810734 – 📺 🅿. ⚫ AE ⬤ VISA
closed 25 December and Bank Holidays – **Meals** (closed Sunday and Monday) (dinner only) 25.95 **t.** – **3 rm** ⌁ 85.00/110.00 **st.**

ⓐ ATS 14 Westgate ℰ (01377) 252386/253628

---

**GREAT DUNMOW** Essex 404 V 28 – pop. 4 907.
London 42 – Cambridge 27 – Chelmsford 13 – Colchester 24.

🏠 **Saracen's Head,** High St., CM6 1AG, ℰ (01371) 873901, Fax (01371) 875743 – ⚖ 📺 ☎ 🅿 – ⚖ 60. ⚫ AE ⬤ VISA
**Meals** 16.95 **t.** and a la carte – ⌁ 9.75 – **24 rm** 70.00/85.00 **t.** – SB.

XXX **The Starr** with rm, Market Pl., CM6 1AX, ℰ (01371) 874321, Fax (01371) 876337 – 📺 ☎ 🅿 – ⚖ 35. ⚫ AE ⬤ VISA
closed first week January – **Meals** (closed Sunday dinner) 22.50/35.00 **t.** ⓘ 6.00 – **8 rm** ⌁ 60.00/110.00 **st.**

---

**GREAT GONERBY** Lincs. 402 404 S 25 – see Grantham.

---

**GREAT GRIMSBY** North East Lincolnshire 402 404 T 23.
🛈 The National Fishing Heritage, Alexandra Docks, DN31 1UZ ℰ (01472) 342422.
London 173 – Boston 51 – Kingston-upon-Hull 33 – Lincoln 37 – Sheffield 73.

🏠 **Travel Inn,** Europa Park, off Gilbey Rd, DN31 2UT, ℰ (01472) 242630, Fax (01472) 250287 – ⚖ rm, 🍽 rest, 📺 & 🅿. ⚫ AE ⬤ VISA. ⌘
**Meals** (grill rest.) – **40 rm** 38.00 **t.**

ⓐ ATS 2 Abbey Rd ℰ (01472) 358151

---

**GREAT LONGSTONE** Derbs. 402 403 404 O 24 – see Bakewell.

---

**GREAT MALVERN** Worcestershire 403 404 N 27 – pop. 31 537.
🛈 Winter Garden Complex, Grange Rd, WR14 3HB ℰ (01684) 892289 B.
London 127 – Birmingham 34 – Cardiff 66 – Gloucester 24.

Plan opposite

🏠 **Red Gate** without rest., 32 Avenue Rd, WR14 3BJ, ℰ (01684) 565013, Fax (01684) 565013, 🌳 – ⚖ 📺 🅿. ⚫ VISA JCB. ⌘                                                                    B r
closed Christmas and New Year – **6 rm** ⌁ 30.00/54.00.

# GREAT MALVERN

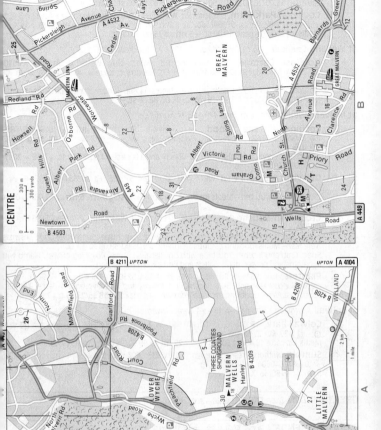

**CENTRE**

B 4211

**Town plans**
roads most used
by traffic and those
on which guide listed
hotels and restaurants
stand are fully drawn;
the beginning only
of lesser roads
is indicated.

271

🏛 **Pembridge**, 114 Graham Rd, WR14 2HX, ℰ (01684) 574813, Fax (01684) 566885, ⚐ – ✠
📺 ☎ 🅿 🐵 🅰🅴 *VISA* ⬜
B
*closed 1 week Christmas* – **Meals** *(closed Sunday dinner)* (lunch by arrangement Monday to Saturday) 13.00/18.00 **st.** ⒤ 7.50 – **8 rm** ⬚ 48.00/68.00 **st.** – SB.

⌂ **Cowleigh Park Farm**, Cowleigh Rd, WR13 5HJ, Northwest : 1½ m. by B 4232 on B 4219
ℰ (01684) 566750, Fax (01684) 566750, « Part 17C farmhouse », ⚐ – ✠ 📺 🅿
A
**Meals** (by arrangement) 10.00 **st.** – **3 rm** ⬚ 35.00/50.00 **st.**

**at Welland** *Southeast : 4½ m. by A 449 on A 4104* – A – ✉ *Great Malvern.*

🏛 **Holdfast Cottage** ⬩, Marlbank Rd, WR13 6NA, West : ¾ m. on A 410⬩
ℰ (01684) 310288, Fax (01684) 311117, « 17C country cottage », ⚐ – ✠ 📺 ☎ 🅿. 🐵
*VISA*
A
*closed Christmas and 2 weeks January* – **Meals** *(closed Sunday dinner)* (booking essential) (dinner only) 22.00 **st.** ⒤ 5.95 – **8 rm** ⬚ 45.00/88.00 **st.** – SB.

**at Malvern Wells** *South : 2 m. on A 449* – ✉ *Malvern.*

🏛🏛 **Cottage in the Wood** ⬩, Holywell Rd, WR14 4LG, ℰ (01684) 575859
Fax (01684) 560662, ⩽ Severn and Evesham Vales, ⚐ – ✠ rest, 🍽 rest, 📺 ☎ 🅿. 🐵 🅰
*VISA* *JCB*
A
*closed 31 December* **Meals** 12.95 **st.** (lunch) and a la carte 14.00/27.00 **st.** ⒤ 7.50 – **20 rm**
⬚ 69.00/139.00 **st.** – SB.

⌂ **Old Vicarage**, Hanley Rd, WR14 4PH, ℰ (01684) 572585, Fax (01684) 572585, ⩽, ⚐ –
✠ rest, 📺 🅿
A
*closed 1 week autumn* – **Meals** (by arrangement) 15.50 **st.** ⒤ 4.50 – **5 rm** ⬚ 32.00/50.00 **st.**
– SB.

✗✗ **Croque-en-Bouche** (Marion Jones), 221 Wells Rd, WR14 4HF, ℰ (01684) 565612 – ✠
🐵 *VISA*
A
⬩
*closed Sunday to Wednesday, 1 week May, 1 week July, 1 week September and Christmas* New Year – **Meals** (booking essential) (dinner only) 25.00/38.00 **st.** ⒤ 7.00
**Spec.** Crab and lobster croustade with bouillabaisse sauce. Roast leg of Welsh lamb with aubergine and braised garlic. Salads and herbs from the garden.

✗ **Planters**, 191-193 Wells Rd, WR14 4HE, ℰ (01684) 575065 – 🐵 *VISA*
A
*closed Sunday, Monday, 25-26 December, 1 January and Tuesdays January-Easter* – **Meals** South East Asian - (booking essential) (dinner only) a la carte 18.35/23.45 **t.** ⒤ 7.80.

**at Colwall** *South East : 3 m. on B 4218* – ✉ *Great Malvern.*

🏛🏛 **Colwall Park**, WR13 6QG, ℰ (01684) 540206, Fax (01684) 540847, ⚐ – ✠ rest, 📺 ☎ ☎
🅿 – ⒜ 120. 🐵 🅰🅴 ⓪ *VISA* *JCB*
A
**Meals** a la carte 18.45/31.50 **t.** ⒤ 7.50 – **22 rm** ⬚ 59.50/95.00 **t.**, 2 suites – SB.

⌂ **Sunfold** without rest., Walwyn Rd, WR13 6PZ, Northeast : ¾ m. on B 4218
ℰ (01684) 540604, ⚐ – ✠ 📺 🅿
A
**3 rm** ⬚ 35.50/53.00.

---

**GREAT MILTON** *Oxon.* 🔢🔢 Q 28 – *see Oxford.*

---

**GREAT MISSENDEN** *Bucks.* 🔢🔢 R 28 – *pop. 7 980 (inc. Prestwood).*
*London 34 – Aylesbury 10 – Maidenhead 19 – Oxford 35.*

✗✗ **La Petite Auberge**, 107 High St., HP16 0BB, ℰ (01494) 865370 – 🐵 *VISA*
*closed Sunday, 2 weeks Christmas and Bank Holidays* – **Meals** - French - (dinner only) a la carte approx. 23.80 **t.**

**at Little Hampden** *Northwest : 2½ m. by Princes Risborough Rd* – ✉ *Great Missenden.*

🏠 **Rising Sun** ⬩ with rm, HP16 9PS, ℰ (01494) 488393, Fax (01494) 488788, ⚐ – 📺. 🐵
*VISA* *JCB*. ⬩
**Meals** *(closed Sunday dinner and Monday except lunch Bank Holidays)* a la carte 15.65/
18.35 **t.** – **4 rm** ⬚ 28.00/60.00 **t.**

---

**GREAT RISSINGTON** *Glos.* – *see Bourton-on-the-Water.*

---

*For the quickest route use the* **Michelin Main Road Maps** :

**970** Europe, **974** Poland, **976** Czech Republic-Slovak Republic, **980** Greece,
**984** Germany, **985** Scandinavia-Finland, **986** Great Britain and Ireland,
**987** Germany-Austria-Benelux, **988** Italy, **989** France,
**990** Spain-Portugal.

**GREAT SNORING** Norfolk 404 W 25 – *pop. 191* – ⊠ *Fakenham.*
*London 115 – Cambridge 68 – Norwich 28.*

🏠 **Old Rectory** ⬧, Barsham Rd, NR21 0HP, ℰ *(01328) 820597, Fax (01328) 820048*, « Part 15C manor house », 🍽 – ⥲ rest, 🆅 ☎ 📵. 🅒🅞 🅐🅔 *VISA* JCB. ⋇
*closed 24 December-4 January* – **Meals** *(booking essential) (dinner only)* 23.50 **t.** ⓖ 5.75 – **6 rm** ☲ 69.50/95.00 **t.** – SB.

**GREAT TEW** Oxon. 403 404 P 28 – *pop. 145.*
*London 75 – Birmingham 50 – Gloucester 42 – Oxford 21.*

🍴 **Falkland Arms** with rm, OX7 4DB, ℰ *(01608) 683653, Fax (01608) 683656*, « 17C inn in picturesque village », 🍽 – ⥲ 🆅. 🅒🅞 *VISA*
*closed 24 to 26 and 31 December* – **Meals** *(closed Sunday dinner) (dinner booking essential)* a la carte 11.20/20.40 **t.** – **6 rm** ☲ 40.00/65.00 **t.**

**GREAT WITLEY** Worcestershire 403 404 M 27 – *pop. 484.*
*London 137 – Birmingham 32 – Hereford 30 – Worcester 11.*

🏠 **Ribston House** ⬧, Bank Rd, Little Witley, WR6 6LS, Southwest : 3 m. by A 443 ℰ *(01886) 888750, Fax (01886) 888925*, 🍽 – 📵. ⋇
*closed 25 and 26 December, booking essential* – **Meals** *(by arrangement) (communal dining)* 18.00 **st.** ⓖ 6.00 – **3 rm** ☲ 30.00/60.00.

**GREAT YARMOUTH** Norfolk 404 Z 26 *Great Britain G.* – *pop. 56 190.*
**Env. :** *The Broads★.*
🏌 *Gorleston, Warren Rd* ℰ *(01493) 661911* – 🏌 *Beach House, Caister-on-Sea* ℰ *(01493) 720421.*
🛈 *Marine Parade, NR30 2EJ* ℰ *(01493) 842195 (summer only).*
*London 126 – Cambridge 81 – Ipswich 53 – Norwich 20.*

🏨 **Imperial,** North Drive, NR30 1EQ, ℰ *(01493) 851113, Fax (01493) 852229* – 🛗, ⥲ rm, 🍽 rest, 🆅 ☎ 📵. 🅒🅞 🅐🅔 *VISA*
**Meals** *(closed lunch Saturday and Bank Holidays)* 13.50/20.50 **st.** and a la carte ⓖ 6.45 – **39 rm** ☲ 68.00/80.00 **st.** – SB.

🏨 **Regency Dolphin,** 14-15 Albert Sq., NR30 3JH, ℰ *(01493) 855070, Fax (01493) 853798*, ☌, 🍽 – ⥲ 🆅 ☎ 📵 – 🔬 120. 🅒🅞 🅐🅔 *VISA*. ⋇
**Meals** 9.95/17.95 **st.** and a la carte ⓖ 8.50 – **48 rm** ☲ 65.00/100.00 **st.** – SB.

🏨 **Star,** Hall Quay, NR30 1HG, ℰ *(01493) 842294, Fax (01493) 330215* – 🛗, ⥲ rm, 🆅 ☎ 📵. 🅒🅞 🅐🅔 🅞 *VISA*. ⋇
**Meals** *(bar lunch)/dinner* 15.75 **t.** ⓖ 5.95 – **40 rm** ☲ 66.00/94.00 **t.**

**at Gorleston-on-Sea** South : 3 m. on A 12 – ⊠ *Great Yarmouth.*

🏨 **Cliff,** Cliff Hill, NR31 6DH, ℰ *(01493) 662179, Fax (01493) 653617*, 🍽 – ⥲ rm, 🆅 ☎ 📵 – 🔬 170. 🅒🅞 🅐🅔 🅞 *VISA*. ⋇
**Meals** 16.50 **t.** and a la carte ⓖ 6.20 – **38 rm** ☲ 69.00/107.00 **t.**, 1 suite – SB.

🔧 ATS Suffling Rd ℰ *(01493) 858211*

**GREAT YELDHAM** Essex 404 V 27 – *pop. 1 513* – ⊠ *Colchester.*
*London 58 – Cambridge 29 – Chelmsford 24 – Colchester 21 – Ipswich 37.*

🍴 **White Hart,** Poole St., CO9 4HJ, ℰ *(01787) 237250, Fax (01787) 238044*, 🍸, « 16C inn », 🍽 – ⥲ 📵. 🅒🅞 🅐🅔 🅞 *VISA* JCB. ⋇
*closed dinner 25-26 December and 1 January* – **Meals** a la carte 11.00/28.75 **t.** ⓖ 7.95.

**GRENOSIDE** S. Yorks. 402 403 404 P 23 – *see Sheffield.*

**GRETA BRIDGE** Durham 402 O 20.
*London 253 – Carlisle 63 – Leeds 63 – Middlesbrough 32.*

🏨 **Morritt Arms,** DL12 9SE, ℰ *(01833) 627232, Fax (01833) 627392*, « 17C former coaching inn », 🍸, 🍽 – ⥲ 🆅 ☎ ⬅ 📵 – 🔬 200. 🅒🅞 🅐🅔 🅞 *VISA*
**Copperfield :** **Meals** 12.95/15.95 **st.** and a la carte ⓖ 4.95 – **26 rm** ☲ 49.50/85.50 **st.** – SB.

**GRÈVE DE LECQ** Jersey (Channel Islands) 403 P 33 and 230 ⑪ – *see Channel Islands.*

**GRIMSBY** North East Lincolnshire 402 404 T 23 – *see Great Grimsby.*

**GRIMSTON** Norfolk 404 V 25 – see King's Lynn.

---

**GRINDLEFORD** Derbs. 402 403 404 P 24 – ⊠ Sheffield (S. Yorks.).
London 165 – Derby 31 – Manchester 34 – Sheffield 10.

🏠 **Maynard Arms,** Main Rd, S32 2HE, on B 6521 ℰ (01433) 630321, Fax (01433) 630445, ≤
⌖ – ⋠ rest, 📺 ☎ 🅿 – 🔬 130. 🅌 🆎 𝗩𝗜𝗦𝗔
**Meals** 18.50 t. ₰ 6.95 – **8 rm** ⊂ 63.00/73.00 t., 2 suites – SB.

---

**GRINDON** Staffs. 403 404 O 24 – pop. 242 – ⊠ Leek.
London 118 – Birmingham 70 – Derby 26 – Manchester 42 – Stoke-on-Trent 20.

⌂ **Porch Farmhouse** ⌂, ST13 7TP, ℰ (01538) 304545, Fax (01538) 304545, « Part 17C »
⌖ – ⋠ 📺 🅿. 🅌 𝗩𝗜𝗦𝗔
closed Christmas-New Year – **Meals** (by arrangement) (communal dining) 18.00 s. – **3 rm**
⊂ 30.00/50.00 s. – SB.

---

**GRINGLEY ON THE HILL** Notts. 402 R 23 – pop. 636 – ⊠ Doncaster.
London 163 – Leeds 52 – Lincoln 25 – Nottingham 43 – Sheffield 29.

⌂ **Old Vicarage,** DN10 4RF, on High St. ℰ (01777) 817248, Fax (01777) 817248, ≤, ⌖, ⋇ –
⋠ 🅿. 🅌 𝗩𝗜𝗦𝗔
closed 24 December-2 January – **Meals** (by arrangement) (communal dining) 20.00 st
₰ 4.60 – **3 rm** ⊂ 33.00/56.00 s.

*Keine bezahlte Reklame im* **Michelin-Führer.**

---

**GRIZEDALE** Cumbria 402 K 20 – see Hawkshead.

---

**GROUVILLE** Jersey (Channel Islands) 403 P 33 and 230 ⑪ – see Channel Islands.

---

**GUERNSEY** 403 OP 33 and 230 ⑨ ⑩ – see Channel Islands.

---

**GUILDFORD** Surrey 404 S 30 – pop. 65 998.
🛈 14 Tunsgate, GU1 3QT ℰ (01483) 444333 Y.
London 33 – Brighton 43 – Reading 27 – Southampton 49.

Plan opposite

🏨 **Angel Posting House and Livery,** High St., GU1 3DP, ℰ (01483) 564555,
Fax (01483) 533770, « 16C coaching inn with 13C vaulted cellar restaurant » – 🛗, ▤ rest
📺 ☎ 👌 – 🔬 70. 🅌 🆎 ⓞ 𝗩𝗜𝗦𝗔                                                            Y e
**No. 1 Angel Gate :** Meals 18.50/21.50 st. and a la carte ₰ 11.50 – ⊂ 9.50 – **14 rm** 135.00/
200.00 st., 7 suites – SB.

🏨 **Forte Posthouse Guildford,** Egerton Rd, GU2 5XZ, ℰ (01483) 574444
Fax (01483) 302960, 🖪, ☎, 🖾, ⌖ – ⋠ rm, 📺 ☎ ✆ 👌 🅿 – 🔬 200. 🅌 🆎 ⓞ 𝗩𝗜𝗦𝗔 𝗝𝗖𝗕
**Meals** (closed Saturday lunch) 12.95 st. (lunch) and a la carte 12.95/25.00 ₰ 6.95 – ⊂ 10.95
– **158 rm** 119.00 st., 4 suites – SB.                                                      Z v

🏠 **Travel Inn,** Parkway, GU1 1UP, North : 1 ½ m. by A 320 on A 25 ℰ (01483) 304932,
Fax (01483) 304935 – ⋠ rm, 📺 👌 🅿. 🅌 🆎 ⓞ 𝗩𝗜𝗦𝗔. ⋇
**Meals** (grill rest.) – **60 rm** 38.00 t.                                                  Z a

🍴🍴 **Café de Paris,** 35 Castle St., GU1 3UQ, ℰ (01483) 534896, Fax (01483) 224340 – 🅌 🆎
𝗩𝗜𝗦𝗔                                                                                         Y u
closed Sunday, last week July-first week August, 25 December and Bank Holidays – **Meals** -
French - 13.95 t. and a la carte ₰ 7.95.

🍴 **The Gate,** No. 3 Milkhouse Gate, GU1 3EZ, ℰ (01483) 576300, Fax (01483) 455068 – ⋠.
🅌 𝗩𝗜𝗦𝗔                                                                                       Y a
closed Saturday lunch, Sunday, 25 December and Bank Holidays – **Meals** 12.95 t.
(lunch) and a la carte 16.40/32.85 t. ₰ 5.95.

**at Shere** East : 6 ¾ m. by A 246 off A 25 – Z – ⊠ Guildford.

🍴🍴 **Kinghams,** Gomshall Lane, GU5 9HB, ℰ (01483) 202168, « 17C cottage » – 🅿. 🅌 🆎 𝗩𝗜𝗦𝗔
𝗝𝗖𝗕
closed Sunday dinner, Monday and 25 December-3 January – **Meals** a la carte 17.85/
22.85 t. ₰ 5.00.

## GUILDFORD



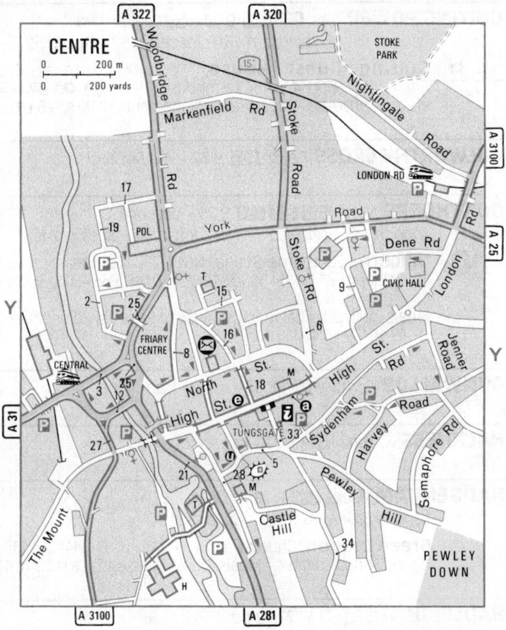

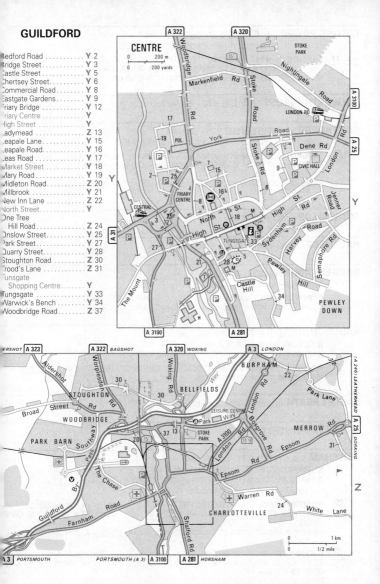

*Se cercate un albergo tranquillo,*
*oltre a consultare le carte dell'introduzione,*
*rintracciate nell'elenco degli esercizi quelli con il simbolo 🐎 o 🐎.*

---

**GUISBOROUGH** *Redcar and Cleveland* 402 *Q 20 – pop. 19 098.*

*Priory Grounds, Church St., TS12 6HL ☎ (01287) 633801.*

*London 264 – Leeds 65 – Middlesbrough 10 – Scarborough 42.*

**Cross Keys - Lodge Inn,** Upsall, TS14 6RW, West : 3 m. on A 171 ☎ (01287) 610035, *Fax (01287) 639037* – ✕ rest, TV P. AE O VISA. ✕
**Meals** (grill rest.) – ☐ 5.50 – **20 rm** 39.00 **t.**

**GUITING POWER** *Glos.* 408 404 O 28 – ⊠ *Cheltenham.*
*London 95 – Birmingham 47 – Gloucester 30 – Oxford 39.*

⌂ **Guiting Guest House,** Post Office Lane, GL54 5TZ, ℘ (01451) 85047C
Fax (01451) 850034, « 16C farmhouse » – ⇔ 🔳. ⚫ 🏧 JCB
*closed Christmas* – **Meals** (by arrangement) 17.00 **s.** – 5 **rm** ⊇ 30.00/54.00 **s.**

---

**GULWORTHY CROSS** *Devon* 408 H 32 – *see Tavistock.*

---

**GUNTHORPE** *Notts.* 402 408 404 R 25 – *pop. 646.*
*London 132 – Lincoln 32 – Nottingham 12 – Sheffield 40.*

🏠 **Unicorn,** Gunthorpe Bridge, NG14 7FB, Southeast : 1 ½ m. by A 6097 and Gunthorpe
(riverside) rd ℘ (0115) 966 3612, Fax (0115) 966 4801, ≤, ⤢ – ▤ rest, 🔳 ☎ 🅿. ⚫ 🄰🄴 🏧
⅜
**Meals** (grill rest.) (bar lunch Monday to Saturday)/dinner a la carte approx. 24.45 **st.** – 16 **rm**
⊇ 49.50/59.50 **st.**

---

**GUNWALLOE** *Cornwall* 408 E 33 – *see Helston.*

---

**HACKNESS** *N. Yorks.* 402 S 21 – *see Scarborough.*

---

**HADDENHAM** *Bucks.* 404 R 28 – *pop. 4 906.*
*London 54 – Aylesbury 8 – Oxford 21.*

🍴 **Green Dragon,** Churchway, HP17 8AA, ℘ (01844) 291403 – 🅿. ⚫ 🄰🄴 🏧
*closed Sunday dinner* – **Meals** (booking essential) a la carte 16.90/26.65 **t.** ⓝ 8.70.

---

**HADLEIGH** *Suffolk* 404 W 27 – *pop. 6 595.*
🄱 *Toppesfield Hall, IP7 5DN ℘ (01473) 823824.*
*London 72 – Cambridge 49 – Colchester 17 – Ipswich 10.*

🏠 **Edgehill,** 2 High St., IP7 5AP, ℘ (01473) 822458, Fax (01473) 827751, 🌲 – ⇔ 🔳 🅿. ⅜
**Meals** (by arrangement) (dinner only) 18.00 **st.** ⓝ 4.50 – 7 **rm** ⊇ 35.00/75.00 **st.** – SB.

---

**HADLEY HEATH** *Worcestershire* – *see Droitwich.*

---

**HAILEY** *Oxon.* 408 404 P 28 – *see Witney.*

---

**HAILSHAM** *E. Sussex* 404 U 31 – *pop. 18 426.*
🄽 *Wellshurst G. & C.C., North St., Hellingly ℘ (01435) 813636.*
🄱 *The Library, Western Rd, BN27 3DN ℘ (01323) 844426.*
*London 57 – Brighton 23 – Eastbourne 7 – Hastings 20.*

🏠 **Boship Farm,** Lower Dicker, BN27 4AT, Northwest : 3 m. by A 295 on A 22
℘ (01323) 844826, Fax (01323) 843945, ≘s, ⤢, 🌲, ⅜ – ⇔ rm, 🔳 ☎ 🅿 – 🔬 120. ⚫ 🄰🄴
⓪ 🏧
**Meals** (bar lunch Monday to Saturday)/dinner 18.00 **t.** ⓝ 5.95 – 45 **rm** ⊇ 60.00/85.00 **t.**
2 suites – SB.

🏠 **Travelodge,** Boship Roundabout, Lower Dicker, BN27 4DT, Northwest : 3 m. by A 295 on
A 22 ℘ (01323) 844556, Reservations (Freephone) 0800 850950 – ⇔ rm, ▤ rest, 🔳 ⅙ 🅿
⚫ 🄰🄴 ⓪ 🏧 JCB. ⅜
**Meals** (grill rest.) – 58 **rm** 39.95/59.95 **t.**

⌂ **Holmbush House** without rest., North St., Hellingly, BN27 4EE, North : 4 m. on A 267
through entrance to Wellshurst Golf Course ℘ (01435) 813078, Fax (01435) 813083, ≤,
« Part Georgian country house », 🌲 – ⇔ 🔳 🅿
*closed 25 and 31 December and 1 January* – 3 **rm** ⊇ 35.00/65.00 **st.**

*at Magham Down Northeast : 2 m. by A 295 on A 271 – ⊠ Hailsham.*

🏠 **Olde Forge,** BN27 1PN, ℘ (01323) 842893, Fax (01323) 842893 – 🔳 ☎ 🅿. ⚫ 🄰🄴 🏧
*closed 25 December-1 January* – **Meals** (dinner only and Sunday lunch)/dinner 14.95 **t.**
and a la carte ⓝ 3.95 – 7 **rm** ⊇ 42.00/68.00 **st.** – SB.

---

**HALE** *Gtr. Manchester* 402 408 404 M 23 – *see Altrincham.*

**HALEBARNS** *Gtr. Manchester* **402** ㉝ **403** ③ **404** ⑨ – *see Altrincham.*

**HALFWAY BRIDGE** *W. Sussex* **404** R 31 – *see Petworth.*

**HALIFAX** *W. Yorks.* **402** O 22 – *pop. 91 069.*
  ᵣ Halifax Bradley Hall, Holywell Green ℘ (01422) 374108 – ᵣ Halifax West End, Paddock Lane, Highroad Well ℘ (01422) 353608, ᵣ Union Lane, Ogden ℘ (01422) 244171 – ᵣ Ryburn, Norland, Sowerby Bridge ℘ (01422) 831355 – ᵣ Elland, Hammerstones Leach Lane, Hullen Edge ℘ (01422) 372505 – ᵣ Lightcliffe, Knowle Top Rd ℘ (01422) 202459.
  🖪 Piece Hall, HX1 1RE ℘ (01422) 368725.
  London 205 – Bradford 8 – Burnley 21 – Leeds 15 – Manchester 28.

🏨 **Holdsworth House,** Holmfield, HX2 9TG, North : 3 m. by A 629 and Shay Lane ℘ (01422) 240024, Fax (01422) 245174, « Part 17C manor house », 🌲 – 🍽 📺 ☎ 🅿 – 🛗 150. 🆚 🆎 ⓪ 𝘝𝘐𝘚𝘈
  closed 26 to 30 December – **Meals** (closed Saturday and Sunday lunch) a la carte 21.20/27.50 **st.** ⅃ 7.50 – ☑ 7.50 – **36 rm** 82.50/120.00 **st.**, 4 suites – SB.

🏨 **Imperial Crown,** 42-46 Horton St., HX1 1QE, ℘ (01422) 342342, Fax (01422) 349866 – 🍽 rm, 📺 ☎ 🅿 – 🛗 150. 🆚 🆎 ⓪ 𝘝𝘐𝘚𝘈
  **Meals** (bar lunch)/dinner 17.95 **st.** and a la carte – **39 rm** ☑ 80.00/90.00 **t.**, 2 suites – SB.

🏨 **The Quays - Premier Lodge,** Salterhebble Hill, Huddersfield Rd, HX3 0QT, South : 2 m. on A 629 ℘ (01422) 347700, Fax (01422) 320793, Reservations (Freephone) 0800 118833, « Canalside setting » – 🍽 rm, 🍽 rest, 📺 ☎ 🕭 🅿 – 🛗 35. 🆚 🆎 ⓪ 𝘝𝘐𝘚𝘈. 🛇
  **Meals** (grill rest.) a la carte 7.45/17.85 **st.** ⅃ 4.25 – ☑ 5.95 – **31 rm** 44.95 **st.** – SB.

✗ **Design House** (Restaurant), Dean Clough (Gate 5), HX3 5AX, ℘ (01422) 383242, Fax (01422) 322732 – 🍽 🅿. 🆚 🆎 𝘝𝘐𝘚𝘈
  closed Saturday lunch, Monday dinner, Sunday, 25 to 27 December and 1-2 January – Meals 13.95 **t.** and a la carte 16.70/27.90 **t.** ⅃ 7.50.

  🅐 ATS Hope St. ℘ (01422) 365892/360819

**HALL GREEN** *W. Mids.* **402 403 404** O 26 – *see Birmingham.*

**HALNAKER** *W. Sussex* – *see Chichester.*

**HALTWHISTLE** *Northd.* **401 402** M 19 *Great Britain G. – pop. 3 773.*
  Env. : Hadrian's Wall★★, N : 4½ m. by A 6079 – Housesteads★★ AC, NE : 6 m. by B 6318 – Roman Army Museum★ AC, NW : 5 m. by A 69 and B 6318 – Vindolanda (Museum★) AC, NE : 5 m. by A 69 – Steel Rig (≤★) NE : 5½ m. by B 6318.
  ᵣ Banktop, Greenhead ℘ (016977) 47367.
  🖪 Church Hall, Main St., NE49 0BE ℘ (01434) 322002 (April-October) – Haltwhistle Swimming and Leisure Club, Greencroft, NE49 9DP ℘ (01434) 322002 (November-March).
  London 335 – Carlisle 22 – Newcastle upon Tyne 37.

↑ **Ashcroft** without rest., Lantys Lonnen, NE49 0DA, ℘ (01434) 320213, Fax (01434) 320213, « Gardens » – 🍽 📺 🅿. 🆚 𝘝𝘐𝘚𝘈. 🛇
  closed 25 December – **7 rm** ☑ 20.00/45.00 **st.**

**HAMBLETON** *Rutland* – *see Oakham.*

**HAMBROOK** *South Gloucestershire* **403 404** M 29 – *see Bristol.*

**HAMSTEAD MARSHALL** *Newbury* **403 404** P29 – *see Newbury.*

**HAMSTERLEY** *Durham* **401 402** O 19 – *pop. 397 –* ✉ *Bishop Auckland.*
  London 260 – Carlisle 75 – Middlesbrough 30 – Newcastle upon Tyne 22.

↑ **Grove House** 🛇, Hamsterley Forest, DL13 3NL, West : 3 ¾ m. via Bedburn on Hamsterley Forest Toll rd ℘ (01388) 488203, Fax (01388) 488174, 🌲 – 🍽 🅿. 🛇
  **Meals** (by arrangement) 18.00 **s.** – **3 rm** ☑ 32.50/60.00 **s.**

**HANDFORTH** *Ches.* **402 403 404** N 23 – *see Wilmslow.*

**HANWOOD** *Shrops.* **402 403** L 25 – *see Shrewsbury.*

277

**HAREWOOD** *W. Yorks.* 402 P 22 – *pop. 3 222 –* ⊠ *Leeds.*
*London 214 – Harrogate 9 – Leeds 10 – York 20.*

🏨 **Harewood Arms**, Harrogate St., LS17 9LH, on A 61 ℰ (0113) 288 6566,
Fax (0113) 288 6064, ☞ – ⅍ 📺 ☎ 🐾 🅿 . 🐠 🅰🅴 ⑩ 𝘝𝘐𝘚𝘈 🅹🅲🅱
**Meals** 10.50/21.50 **t.** and dinner a la carte ᧙ 8.50 – **24 rm** ⊊ 70.00/90.00 **t.** – SB.

---

**HARLOW** *Essex* 404 U 28 – *pop. 74 629.*
☗ᵦ *Nazeing, Middle St.* ℰ (01992) 893798/893915.
*London 22 – Cambridge 37 – Ipswich 60.*

🏨🏨 **Churchgate Manor**, Churchgate St., Old Harlow, CM17 0JT, East : 3 ¼ m. by A 414 and
183 ℰ (01279) 420246, Fax (01279) 437720, Ⅰ₅, ☎, 🔲, ☞ – ⅍ 📺 ☎ 🅿 – 🔏 170. 🐠 🅰
⑩ 𝘝𝘐𝘚𝘈 . 🕸
*closed 27 to 30 December –* **Meals** (bar lunch Saturday) 19.50 **t.** and a la carte ᧙ 7.25 – ⊊
9.75 – **82 rm** 94.00/145.00 **t.**, 3 suites – SB.

🏨 **Harlow Moat House**, Southern Way, CM18 7BA, Southeast : 2 ¼ m. by A 1025 on A 41
ℰ (01279) 829988, Fax (01279) 635094 – ⅍ rm, 📺 ☎ 🅿 – 🔏 150. 🐠 🅰🅴 ⑩ 𝘝𝘐𝘚𝘈 🅹🅲🅱. 🕸
**Meals** (carving rest.) (bar lunch Saturday) a la carte 19.50/25.85 **t.** ᧙ 5.75 – ⊊ 9.50 – **118 rm**
80.00/95.00 **t.** – SB.

🏨 **Travel Inn**, Cambridge Rd, Old Harlow, CM20 2EP, Northeast : 3 ¼ m. by A 414 on A 1188
ℰ (01279) 442545, Fax (01279) 452169 – ⅍ rm, 📺 🛢 🅿 . 🐠 🅰🅴 ⑩ 𝘝𝘐𝘚𝘈 . 🕸
**Meals** (grill rest.) – **38 rm** 38.00 **t.**

🔘 ATS 14 Burnt Mill ℰ (01279) 421965

---

**HARNHAM** *Wilts.* 403 404 O 30 – *see Salisbury.*

---

**HAROME** *N. Yorks. – see Helmsley.*

---

**HARPENDEN** *Herts.* 404 S 28 – *pop. 28 097.*
*London 32 – Luton 6.*

🏨🏨 **Glen Eagle**, 1 Luton Rd, AL5 2PX, ℰ (01582) 760271, Fax (01582) 460819, ☞ – ᛁᛁ, ⅍ rm
■ rest, 📺 ☎ 🐾 🅿 – 🔏 80. 🐠 🅰🅴 ⑩ 𝘝𝘐𝘚𝘈 🅹🅲🅱. 🕸
*closed Christmas and New Year –* **Meals** (bar meals Saturday lunch, Sunday dinner and Bank
Holidays) 12.00 **t.** and a la carte ᧙ 7.50 – ⊊ 9.25 – **58 rm** 105.00/120.00, 2 suites.

🏨🏨 **County H. Harpenden House**, 18 Southdown Rd, AL5 1PE, ℰ (01582) 449955,
Fax (01582) 769858, ☞ – ⅍ rm, 📺 ☎ 🅿 – 🔏 150. 🐠 🅰🅴 ⑩ 𝘝𝘐𝘚𝘈 . 🕸
**Meals** (lunch booking essential) (bar meals Saturday lunch) a la carte 16.70/23.45 **t.** ᧙ 9.50 –
⊊ 10.00 – **53 rm** 115.00/160.00 **st.** – SB.

XX **Chef Peking**, 5-6 Church Green, AL5 2TP, ℰ (01582) 769358, Fax (01582) 462094 – ■. 🐠
🅰🅴 ⑩ 𝘝𝘐𝘚𝘈
**Meals** - Chinese (Peking, Szechuan) - 15.00/19.00 **st.** and a la carte ᧙ 4.00.

---

**HARROGATE** *N. Yorks.* 402 P 22 *Great Britain G. – pop. 66 178.*
**See** : *Town★.*
**Exc.** : *Fountains Abbey★★★ AC :- Studley Royal★★ AC (≤★ from Anne Boleyn's Seat)*
*Fountains Hall (Façade★), N : 13 m. by A 61 and B 6265 AY – Harewood House★★ (The*
*Gallery★) AC, S : 7½ m. by A 61 BZ.*
☗ᵦ *Forest Lane Head* ℰ (01423) 863158 – ☗ᵦ *Follifoot Rd, Pannal* ℰ (01423) 871641 –
☗ᵦ *Oakdale* ℰ (01423) 567162 – ☗ᵦ *Crimple Valley, Hookstone Wood Rd* ℰ (01423) 883485.
🅱 *Royal Baths Assembly Rooms, Crescent Rd, HG1 2RR* ℰ (01423) 537300.
*London 211 – Bradford 18 – Leeds 15 – Newcastle Upon Tyne 76 – York 22.*

Plan opposite

🏨🏨🏨 **Rudding Park**, Rudding Park, Follifoot, HG3 1JH, Southeast : 3 ¾ m. by A 661
ℰ (01423) 871350, Fax (01423) 872286, 🍴, ☗ᵦ, park – ᛁᛁ, ⅍ rm, ■ rest, 📺 ☎ 🐾 🅿 –
🔏 300. 🐠 🅰🅴 𝘝𝘐𝘚𝘈 . 🕸
*The Clocktower Brasserie :* **Meals** 12.95 **st.** (lunch) and a la carte 16.90/25.70 **st.** ᧙ 7.00 –
48 **rm** ⊊ 105.00/150.00 **st.**, 2 suites – SB.

🏨🏨🏨 **Old Swan**, Swan Rd, HG1 2SR, ℰ (01423) 500055, Fax (01423) 501154, ☞ – ᛁᛁ ⅍ 📺 ☎
🅿 – 🔏 400. 🐠 🅰🅴 𝘝𝘐𝘚𝘈                                                                          AY e
*Wedgewood Room :* **Meals** (dinner only and Sunday lunch)/dinner 19.95 **st.** ᧙ 7.70 –
*Library :* **Meals** (closed Sunday and Monday) (dinner only) a la carte 26.00/29.50 **st.** -
**127 rm** ⊊ 107.25/140.50 **st.**, 9 suites.

**St. George,** 1 Ripon Rd, HG1 2SY, ℘ (01423) 561431, *Fax (01423) 530037*, ℐ₅, ⊆s, ☒ – ⊞ ⇥ 🔲 ☎ 🅿 – 🛦 200. 🐠 🄰🄴 🛈 *VISA*
AY O
Meals (bar lunch)/dinner 18.50 st. ₪ 6.00 – **89 rm** ⇌ 95.00/125.00 st., 1 suite – SB.

**Harrogate Moat House,** Kings Rd, HG1 1XX, ℘ (01423) 849988, *Fax (01423) 524435*, ≤ – ⊞, ⇥ rm, ▤ rest, 🔲 ☎ 🅿 – 🛦 400. 🐠 🄰🄴 🛈 *VISA* JᴄB, ⅍
BY X
*Abbey :* Meals (carving rest.) (dinner only) 15.50 t. ₪ 6.50 – *Boulevard :* Meals *(closed Monday lunch)* 15.00/18.00 t. and a la carte ₪ 6.50 – ⇌ 9.95 – **205 rm** 105.00/120.00 st., 9 suites – SB.

**The Crown,** Crown Pl., HG1 2RZ, ℘ (01423) 567755, *Fax (01423) 502284* – ⊞ ⇥ 🔲 ☎ 🅿 – 🛦 300. 🐠 🄰🄴 🛈 *VISA* JᴄB, ⅍
AZ i
Meals (bar lunch Monday to Saturday)/dinner 19.00 t. ₪ 6.75 – ⇌ 11.25 – **116 rm** 90.00/105.00 st., 5 suites – SB.

**The Balmoral,** Franklin Mount, HG1 5EJ, ℘ (01423) 508208, *Fax (01423) 530652*, « Antique furnishings » – ⇥ 🔲 ☎ 🅿. 🐠 🄰🄴 *VISA* JᴄB
BY V
Meals (see *Villu Toots* below) – ⇌ 8.50 – **18 rm** 80.00/105.00 st., 2 suites – SB.

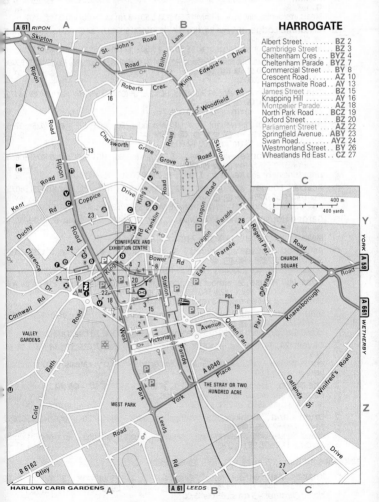

## HARROGATE

ENGLAND

HARROGATE

**Grants,** Swan Rd, HG1 2SS, ℰ (01423) 560666, *Fax (01423) 502550* – |‡|, ≣ rest, 📺 ☎ 🅿
🖴 70. 🐵 🆎 ⑩ 𝗩𝗜𝗦𝗔 ᴊᴄʙ. ⋘
AY
*Chimney Pots Bistro :* Meals 7.00 t. (lunch) and a la carte 13.90/21.40 t. ᐟ 5.75 – **41 rm**
� 101.00/142.00 t., 1 suite.

**White House,** 10 Park Par., HG1 5AH, ℰ (01423) 501388, *Fax (01423) 527973*, « Victoria
house, antique furnishings », 🌲 – ⋙ 📺 ☎. 🐵 🆎 𝗩𝗜𝗦𝗔. ⋘
CZ
Meals (booking essential) (lunch by arrangement)/dinner a la carte 15.75/29.95 t. – **9 rm**
⊋ 75.00/105.00 t., 1 suite – SB.

**Quality Kimberley** without rest., 11-19 Kings Rd, HG1 5JY, ℰ (01423) 505613,
*Fax (01423) 530276* – |‡| 📺 ☎ 🅿 – 🖴 25. 🐵 🆎 ⑩ 𝗩𝗜𝗦𝗔. ⋘
BY
*closed 24 December-4 January* – – ⊋ 7.95 – **48 rm** 64.50/84.50 st.

**Studley,** 28 Swan Rd, HG1 2SE, ℰ (01423) 560425, *Fax (01423) 530967* – |‡| 📺 ☎ 🅿. 🐵 🆎
⑩ 𝗩𝗜𝗦𝗔
AZ
*Le Breton :* Meals 18.00 t. (dinner) and a la carte 12.00/25.00 t. ᐟ 5.60 – **34 rm** ⊋ 70.00/
105.00 t., 2 suites – SB.

**Ruskin,** 1 Swan Rd, HG1 2SS, ℰ (01423) 502045, *Fax (01423) 506131*, 🌲 – ⋙ 📺 ☎ ✆ 🅿
🐵 𝗩𝗜𝗦𝗔. ⋘
AY
Meals (residents only) (dinner only) 18.50 t. ᐟ 5.50 – **6 rm** ⊋ 69.00/110.00 st. – SB.

**Britannia Lodge,** 16 Swan Rd, HG1 2SA, ℰ (01423) 508482, *Fax (01423) 526840* – ⋙ 📺
☎. 🐵 🆎 ⑩ 𝗩𝗜𝗦𝗔. ⋘
AYZ
Meals (residents only) (dinner only) 16.50 t. ᐟ 5.50 – **12 rm** ⊋ 39.00/59.00 st. – SB.

**Alexa House** without rest., 26 Ripon Rd, HG1 2JJ, ℰ (01423) 501988, *Fax (01423) 504086*
– ⋙ 📺 ☎ 🅿. 🐵 🆎 ⑩ 𝗩𝗜𝗦𝗔. ⋘
AY
**13 rm** ⊋ 50.00/70.00 t.

**The Delaine** without rest., 17 Ripon Rd, HG1 2JL, ℰ (01423) 567974, *Fax (01423) 561723*,
🌲 – ⋙ 📺 ☎ 🅿. 🐵 🆎 𝗩𝗜𝗦𝗔 ᴊᴄʙ. ⋘
AY
*closed Christmas* – **10 rm** ⊋ 42.00/60.00 t.

**Alexandra Court** without rest., 8 Alexandra Rd, HG1 5JS, ℰ (01423) 502764,
*Fax (01423) 523151* – ⋙ 📺 ☎ ✆ 🅿. 🐵 🆎 𝗩𝗜𝗦𝗔. ⋘
BY c
*closed Christmas* – **13 rm** ⊋ 38.00/62.00 st.

**Brookfield House** without rest., 5 Alexandra Rd, HG1 5JS, ℰ (01423) 506646,
*Fax (01423) 523151* – ⋙ 📺 ☎ 🅿. 🐵 🆎 ⑩ 𝗩𝗜𝗦𝗔. ⋘
BY s
*closed Christmas and New Year* – **7 rm** ⊋ 38.00/60.00 st.

**Acacia Lodge** without rest., 21 Ripon Rd, HG1 2JL, ℰ (01423) 560752,
*Fax (01423) 503725* – ⋙ 📺 🅿. ⋘
AY v
*closed 2 weeks Christmas and New Year* – **6 rm** ⊋ 55.00/68.00 s.

**Garden House,** 14 Harlow Moor Drive, HG2 0JX, ℰ (01423) 503059, *Fax (01423) 503059* –
⋙ rest, 📺. 🐵 🆎 ⑩ 𝗩𝗜𝗦𝗔. ⋘
AZ u
Meals (by arrangement) 14.00 st. – **7 rm** ⊋ 24.00/48.00 st. – SB.

**Ashwood House** without rest., 7 Spring Grove, HG1 2HS, ℰ (01423) 560081,
*Fax (01423) 527928* – ⋙ 📺. ⋘
AY a
*closed 24 December-2 January* – **8 rm** ⊋ 30.00/56.00 s.

**Knox Mill House** ⊗ without rest., Knox Mill Lane, HG3 2AE, North : 1 ½ m. by A 61
ℰ (01423) 560650, *Fax (01423) 560650*, ≼ – ⋙ 📺 🅿. ⋘
*closed 25 and 31 December* – **3 rm** ⊋ 30.00/42.00.

XX **Villu Toots** (at The Balmoral H.), Franklin Mount, HG1 5EJ, ℰ (01423) 705805,
*Fax (01423) 530652* – ≣ 🅿. 🐵 🆎 𝗩𝗜𝗦𝗔
BY v
*closed Saturday lunch and 26 to 30 December* – Meals 9.50/12.50 t. and a la carte.

X **Olivers 24,** 24 Kings Rd, HG1 5JW, ℰ (01423) 568600, *Fax (01423) 531838* – 🐵 🆎 𝗩𝗜𝗦𝗔
ᴊᴄʙ
BY a
*closed Monday lunch, Sunday, 25-26 December and 1 January* – Meals 10.00 t. and dinner a la carte ᐟ 7.50.

X **The Bistro,** 1 Montpellier Mews, HG1 2TG, ℰ (01423) 530708, 🎨 – 🐵 𝗩𝗜𝗦𝗔
AZ v
*closed Sunday, Monday and 10 days Christmas*
Meals a la carte 18.75/24.25 t. ᐟ 7.25.

X **Drum and Monkey,** 5 Montpellier Gdns., HG1 2TF, ℰ (01423) 502650,
*Fax (01423) 522469* – 🐵 𝗩𝗜𝗦𝗔
AZ v
*closed Sunday and 24 December-2 January* – Meals - Seafood - (booking essential)
a la carte 11.25/25.95 t. ᐟ 5.95.

**at Kettlesing** *West : 6½ m. by A 59* – AY – ✉ Harrogate.

**Knabbs Ash** without rest., Felliscliffe, HG3 2LT, Southwest : 2 m. on A 59
ℰ (01423) 771040, *Fax (01423) 771515*, ≼, 🌲, park – ⋙ 📺 🅿. ⋘
*closed Christmas* – **3 rm** ⊋ 35.00/45.00.

280

**t Markington** *Northwest : 8 ¾ m. by A 61 – AY –* ⊠ *Harrogate.*

🏨 **Hob Green** ⤸, HG3 3PJ, Southwest : ½ m. ℘ (01423) 770031, Fax (01423) 771589, ≤, « Country house in extensive parkland », 🐎 – 🔟 ☎ 🅿. 🕘 🖭 ① 📼
**Meals** 14.95/21.50 **t.** and dinner a la carte 🍷 7.50 – **11 rm** 🖃 80.00/99.00 **t.**, 1 suite – SB.

🚗 ATS Leeds Rd, Pannal ℘ (01423) 879194

---

**ARTFIELD** *E. Sussex* **404** *U 30 – pop. 2 026.*
*London 47 – Brighton 28 – Maidstone 25.*

🏠 **Bolebroke Mill** ⤸ without rest., Edenbridge Rd, TN7 4JP, North : 1 ¼ m. by B 2026 turning right onto unmarked rd ℘ (01892) 770425, Fax (01892) 770425, « Part early 17C cornmill, original features », 🐎 – 💱 🔟 🅿. 🕘 🖭 📼. 🞕
*closed 2 weeks Christmas-New Year and January-12 February* – **5 rm** 🖃 54.00/76.00 **st.**

---

**ARTFORD** *Ches.* **402 403 404** *M 24 – pop. 4 605.*
*London 188 – Chester 15 – Liverpool 31 – Manchester 25.*

🏨 **Hartford Hall**, 81 School Lane, CW8 1PW, ℘ (01606) 75711, Fax (01606) 782285, 🐎 – 🔟 ☎ 🅿 – 🔬 35. 🕘 🖭 ① 📼
**Meals** (dinner only and Sunday lunch)/dinner a la carte 13.00/22.00 **st.** – 🖃 6.95 – **19 rm** 63.00 **st.**, 1 suite – SB.

| Prices | For notes on the prices quoted in this Guide, see the introduction. |
|---|---|

---

**ARTINGTON** *Derbs.* **402 403 404** *O 24 – pop. 1 604 (inc. Dovedale) –* ⊠ *Buxton.*
*London 168 – Derby 36 – Manchester 40 – Sheffield 34 – Stoke-on-Trent 22.*

🏨 **Biggin Hall** ⤸, Biggin, SK17 0DH, Southeast : 2 m. by B 5054 ℘ (01298) 84451, Fax (01298) 84681, ≤, « 17C », 🐎 – 💱 🔟 🅿. 🕘 📼. 🞕
**Meals** (booking essential to non-residents) (dinner only) 14.50 **st.** 🍷 5.50 – 🖃 3.50 – **17 rm** 50.00/75.00 **st.** – SB.

---

**ARTLEBURY** *Worcestershire* **403** *N 26 – pop. 2 253.*
*London 135 – Birmingham 20 – Worcester 11.*

🏨 **Travelodge**, Crossway Green, DY13 9SH, South : 2 ½ m. by B 4193 on A 449 (southbound carriageway) ℘ (01299) 250553, Fax (01299) 251774, Reservations (Freephone) 0800 850950 – 💱 rm, 🔟 ⅍ 🅿. 🕘 🖭 ① 📼 🇯🇵. 🞕
**Meals** (grill rest.) – **32 rm** 39.95/59.95 **t.**

---

**ARTLEPOOL** **402** *Q 19 – pop. 87 310.*

🏌, 🏌 *Seaton Carew, Tees Rd* ℘ (01429) 266249/261040 – 🏌 *Castle Eden & Peterlee* ℘ (01429) 836220 – 🏌 *Hart Warren* ℘ (01429) 274398.
✈ *Teesside Airport :* ℘ (01325) 332811, SW : 20 m. by A 689, A 1027, A 135 and A 67.
🛈 *Hartlepool Art Gallery & Infor, Church Sq., TS24 7EQ* ℘ (01429) 266522.
*London 263 – Durham 19 – Middlesbrough 9 – Sunderland 21.*

🏨 **Grand**, Swainson St., TS24 8AA, ℘ (01429) 266345, Fax (01429) 265217 – ⧉ 🔟 ☎ 📞 🅿 – 🔬 200. 🕘 🖭 ① 📼 🇯🇵
**Meals** (bar lunch Monday to Saturday)/dinner 14.95 **st.** and a la carte 🍷 4.25 – **45 rm** 🖃 49.95/80.00 **st.** – SB.

🏨 **Travel Inn**, Old West Quay, Hartlepool Marina, TS24 0XZ, ℘ (01429) 890115, Fax (01429) 868674, ≤ – 💱 rm, 🔟 ⅍ 🅿. 🕘 🖭 ① 📼. 🞕
**Meals** (grill rest.) – **40 rm** 38.00 **t.**

**at Seaton Carew** *Southeast : 2 m. on A 178.*

🏨 **Marine**, 5-7 The Front, TS25 1BS, ℘ (01429) 266244, Fax (01429) 864144, ≤ – 🔟 ☎ 🅿 – 🔬 50. 🕘 🖭 ① 📼
*closed 25 December* – **Meals** (carving rest.) (bar lunch Saturday) 8.75 **st.** and a la carte 🍷 5.25 – **25 rm** 🖃 48.00/68.00 **st.** – SB.

✗ **Krimo's**, 8 The Front, TS25 1BS, ℘ (01429) 290022 – 🕘 📼
*closed Saturday lunch, Sunday, Monday, last 2 weeks August and 25 December* – **Meals** 9.50/13.95 **st.** and a la carte 🍷 4.50.

🚗 ATS York Rd ℘ (01429) 275552

**HARTSHEAD MOOR SERVICE AREA** *W. Yorks.* 402 O 22 – ⊠ *Brighouse.*
London 213 – Bradford 8 – Burnley 31 – Manchester 35 – Sheffield 39.

🏠 **Welcome Lodge** without rest., Clifton, HD6 4JX, M 62 between junctions 25 and 2 (eastbound carriageway) ℰ (01274) 851706, *Fax* (01274) 855169, Reservations (Freephone) 0800 7314466 – ⚡ rm, 📺 🕭 🅿. 🐵 🗚 ⊙ *VISA*. ⅍
 ⌛ 7.50 **40 rm** 50.00 **t.**

---

**HARVINGTON** *Worcestershire* 403 404 O27 – *see Evesham.*

---

**HARWELL** *Oxon.* 403 404 Q 29 – *pop. 2 236.*
London 64 – Oxford 16 – Reading 18 – Swindon 22.

🏠 **Kingswell,** Reading Rd, OX11 0LZ, South : ¾ m. on A 417 ℰ (01235) 83304 *Fax* (01235) 833193 – 📺 🕭 🕿 🅿 – 🕭 30. 🐵 🗚 ⊙ *VISA*. ⅍
 **Meals** 17.95 **st.** and a la carte ₤ 4.50 – **19 rm** ⌛ 85.00/102.00 **st.** – SB.

---

**HARWICH and DOVERCOURT** *Essex* 404 X 28 – *pop. 18 436 (Harwich).*
 🛏 *Station Rd, Parkeston ℰ (01255) 503616.*
 ⚓ *to Germany (Hamburg) (Scandinavian Seaways) daily (20 h) – to Denmark (Esbjerg) (Scandinavian Seaways) (20 h) – to The Netherlands (Hook of Holland) (Stena Line) 2 daily (3 40 mn) day, (8 h 30 mn) night – to Sweden (Gothenburg) (Scandinavian Seaways) (22 h).*
 🛈 *Iconfield Park, Parkeston, CO12 4SP ℰ (01255) 506139.*
 London 78 – Chelmsford 41 – Colchester 20 – Ipswich 23.

XX **Pier at Harwich** with rm, The Quay, CO12 3HH, ℰ (01255) 241212, *Fax* (01255) 55192 ⇐ – 📺 🕿 🅿. 🐵 🗚 ⊙ *VISA* JCB. ⅍
 **Meals** - Seafood - 17.50/18.50 **st.** and a la carte ₤ 5.95 – ⌛ 4.00 – **6 rm** 52.50/67.50 **t.** – SB
 Ⓜ *ATS 723 Main Rd, Dovercourt ℰ (01255) 508314*

---

**HASLEMERE** *Surrey* 404 R 30 – *pop. 12 218.*
London 47 – Brighton 46 – Southampton 44.

🏠 **Lythe Hill,** Petworth Rd, GU27 3BQ, East : 1 ½ m. on B 2131 ℰ (01428) 651251 *Fax* (01428) 644131, ⇐, ⚲, 🚗, park, ⅍ – ⚡ rest, 📺 🕿 🅿 – 🕭 60. 🐵 🗚 ⊙ *VISA* JCB **Meals** *(closed Sunday lunch and Saturday dinner)* 19.50 **st.** and a la carte ₤ 8.00 – *Auberge de France :* **Meals** - French - *(closed Monday)* (dinner only) 42.75 **t.** and a la carte ₤ 8.00 - ⌛ 11.00 – **28 rm** 94.00/115.00 **t.**, 12 suites – SB.

---

**HASLINGDEN** *Lancs.* 402 N 22.
London 228 – Blackpool 40 – Burnley 9 – Leeds 39 – Manchester 28 – Liverpool 52.

🏠 **Sykeside Country House,** Rawtenstall Road End, BB4 6QE, South : 1 m. by A 680 on A 681 ℰ (01706) 831163, *Fax* (01706) 830090, 🚗 – ⚡ 📺 🕿 🕭 🅿. 🐵 🗚 ⊙ *VISA*. ⅍ closed 26 December and 1 January – **Meals** *(closed Saturday lunch and Sunday dinner)* 10.95/13.95 **t.** and a la carte ₤ 6.50 – **10 rm** ⌛ 57.00/85.00 **t.** – SB.

---

**HASTINGS and ST. LEONARDS** *E. Sussex* 404 V 31 – *pop. 81 139 (Hastings).*
 🛏 *Beauport Park, Battle Rd, St. Leonards-on-Sea ℰ (01424) 852977.*
 🛈 *4 Robertson Terr., TN34 1EZ ℰ (01424) 781111 – Fishmarket, The Stade, TN34 1J ℰ (01424) 781111 (summer only).*
 London 65 – Brighton 37 – Folkestone 37 – Maidstone 34.

Plan opposite

🏠 **Beauport Park** ♨, Battle Rd, TN38 8EA, Northwest : 3 ½ m. at junction of A 2100 with B 2159 ℰ (01424) 851222, *Fax* (01424) 852465, ⇐, « Formal garden », 🏊, 🛏, park, ⅍ – ⚡ ▤ rest, 📺 🕿 🅿 – 🕭 60. 🐵 🗚 ⊙ *VISA* JCB
 **Meals** 16.00/22.00 **t.** and a la carte ₤ 5.60 – **23 rm** ⌛ 80.00/110.00 **t.** – SB.

🏠 **Cinque Ports,** Summerfields, Bohemia Rd, TN34 1ET, ℰ (01424) 439222 *Fax* (01424) 437277 – 📺 🕿 🕭 🅿 – 🕭 250. 🐵 🗚 ⊙ *VISA*. ⅍ AZ a 14.50/17.95 **t.** and a la carte ₤ 6.25 **40 rm** ⌛ 50.00/110.00 **st.** – SB.

🏠 **Tower House,** 26-28 Tower Road West, TN38 0RG, ℰ (01424) 427217 *Fax* (01424) 427217, 🚗 – ⚡ 📺 🕿 🕭. 🐵 🗚 ⊙ *VISA*. ⅍ AY c **Meals** *(residents only)* (dinner only) 13.50 **st.** ₤ 4.50 – **10 rm** ⌛ 36.00/60.00 **st.** – SB.

🏠 **Travel Inn,** 1 John Macadam Way, TN37 7DB, ℰ (01424) 754070, *Fax* (01424) 753139 – 🛗 ⚡ rm, 📺 🕭 🅿. 🐵 🗚 ⊙ *VISA*. ⅍ AY U **Meals** *(grill rest.)* – **44 rm** 38.00 **t.**

# HASTINGS
# AND ST. LEONARDS

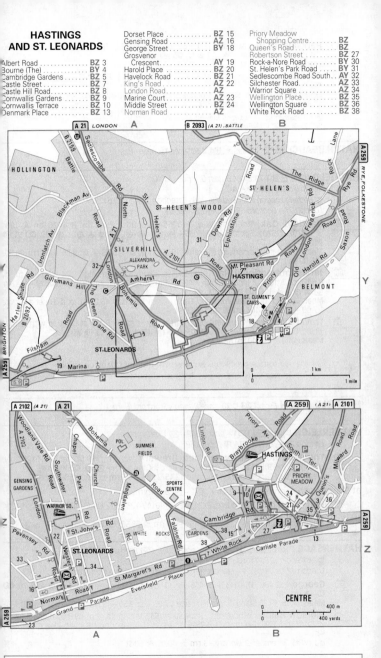

283

↑ **Parkside House** without rest., 59 Lower Park Rd, TN34 2LD, ℰ (01424) 433096, Fax (01424) 421431, ☞ – ❄ 🗹 ☎ ℭ. ⬛ VISA. ⅋
BY e
5 rm ⌂ 27.00/55.00 st.

XX **Röser's**, 64 Eversfield Pl., TN37 6DB, ℰ (01424) 712218, Fax (01424) 712218 – ⬛ AE ⓪ VISA
BZ
closed Saturday lunch, Sunday, Monday, first 2 weeks January and last 2 weeks June – Meals 18.95/21.95 st. and a la carte ℓ 6.50.

⬒ ATS Menzies Rd, Pondswood Ind. Est., St. Leonards-on-Sea ℰ (01424) 427780/424567

---

**HATCH BEAUCHAMP** Somerset ⬛ K 30 – see Taunton.

---

**HATFIELD** Herts. ⬛ T 28 Great Britain G. – pop. 31 104.
See : Hatfield House★★ AC.
🖫 Hatfield London C.C., Bedwell Park, Essendon ℰ (01707) 642624.
London 27 – Bedford 38 – Cambridge 39.

🏨 **Hatfield Oak**, Roehyde Way, AL10 9AF, South : 2 m. by B 6426 on A 100'
ℰ (01707) 275701, Fax (01707) 266033 – ❄ rm, ▤ rest, 🗹 ☎ ﬞ ℗ – ⚴ 120. ⬛ AE ⓪
VISA. ⅋
Meals 17.50 st. (dinner) and a la carte 16.00/21.00 st. ℓ 5.95 – ⌂ 9.25 – **76 rm** 85.00/
105.00 st.

🏨 **Jarvis International Hatfield**, 301 St. Albans Rd West, AL10 9RH, West : 1 m. by B 6426 on A 1057 at junction with A 1001 ℰ (01707) 265411, Fax (01707) 264019 – ❄ rm, 🗹 ☎ ℗ – ⚴ 150. ⬛ AE ⓪ VISA. ⅋
Meals (closed lunch Saturday and Bank Holiday Monday) 16.95 st. and dinner a la carte ℓ 7.00 – ⌂ 8.00 – **101 rm** 89.00/119.00 st. – SB.

🏠 **Travel Inn**, Comet Way, AL10 0DA, Northwest : 1 m. by B 197 at junction with A 1001 ℰ (01707) 268990, Fax (01707) 268293 – ❄ rm, 🗹 ﬞ ℗. ⬛ AE ⓪ VISA. ⅋
Meals (grill rest.) – **40 rm** 38.00 t.

| Les prix | Pour toutes précisions sur les prix indiqués dans ce guide, reportez-vous aux pages de l'introduction. |

---

**HATFIELD HEATH** Essex ⬛ U 28 – see Bishop's Stortford (Herts.).

---

**HATHERLEIGH** Devon ⬛ H 31 – pop. 1 542 – ✉ Okehampton.
London 230 – Exeter 29 – Plymouth 38.

🍴 **The Tally Ho Country Inn and Brewery** with rm, 14 Market St., EX20 3JN, ℰ (01837) 810306, Fax (01837) 811079, « Part 16C inn » – ❄ 🗹 ℗. ⬛ VISA. ⅋
Meals (closed Sunday dinner) a la carte 12.45/21.85 t. – **3 rm** ⌂ 30.00/50.00 t. – SB.

**at Sheepwash** Northwest : 5½ m. by A 3072 – ✉ Beaworthy.

🏠 **Half Moon Inn**, The Square, EX21 5NE, ℰ (01409) 231376, Fax (01409) 231673, « 17C », ⤝ – 🗹 ☎ ℭ ℗. ⬛ VISA
Meals (bar lunch)/dinner 19.50 t. ℓ 4.75 – **14 rm** ⌂ 38.50/75.00 t.

---

**HATHERSAGE** Derbs. ⬛ ⬛ ⬛ P 24 – pop. 2 858 – ✉ Sheffield (S. Yorks.).
🖫 Sickleholme, Bamford ℰ (01433) 651306.
London 177 – Derby 39 – Manchester 34 – Sheffield 11 – Stoke-on-Trent 44.

🏨 **George**, S32 1BB, ℰ (01433) 650436, Fax (01433) 650099 – ❄ rest, 🗹 ☎ ℗ – ⚴ 70. ⬛ AE ⓪ VISA. ⅋
Meals 14.95/19.95 t. and dinner a la carte ℓ 7.95 – ⌂ 9.50 – **19 rm** 59.50/79.50 t. – SB.

↑ **Highlow Hall** ⬙ without rest., Hope Valley, S32 1AX, South : 2 m. by B 6001 on Abney rd ℰ (01433) 650393, Fax (01433) 659505, ⤝, « Part 16C manor house », ☞ – ❄ ℗. ⬛ VISA. ⅋
closed 15 December-2 January – **3 rm** ⌂ 40.00/63.00 st.

---

**HATTON** Warks. – see Warwick.

---

**La HAULE** Jersey (Channel Islands) ⬛ ⑪ – see Channel Islands.

**HAWES** *N. Yorks.* [402] N 21 – *pop. 1 117.*

ℹ *Dales Countryside Museum, Station Yard, DL8 3NT* ✆ *(01969) 667450 (summer only).*
*London 253 – Kendal 27 – Leeds 72 – York 65.*

**Simonstone Hall** ☘, Simonstone, DL8 3LY, North : 1 ½ m. on Muker rd ✆ (01969) 667255, *Fax (01969) 667741*, <, « Part 18C country house », 🌳 – 🚭 [TV] ☎ ☏ [P]. [MC] [AE] VISA JCB. ⊘
Meals (bar lunch Monday to Saturday)/dinner 25.00 **st.** and a la carte 🍷 6.50 – **18 rm** ☕ 50.00/180.00 **st.**, 2 suites – SB.

**Stone House** ☘, Sedbusk, DL8 3PT, North : 1 m. by Muker rd on Askrigg rd ✆ (01969) 667571, *Fax (01969) 667720*, <, 🌳 – 🚭 rest, [TV] ☎ [P]. [MC] VISA JCB
*closed January* – **Meals** (dinner only) 17.50 **t.** 🍷 5.50 – **22 rm** ☕ 35.00/84.00 **t.** – SB.

**Rookhurst Georgian Country House** ☘, Gayle, DL8 3RT, South : ½ m. by Gayle rd ✆ (01969) 667454, *Fax (01969) 667454*, 🌳 – 🚭 [TV] [P]. [MC] VISA. ⊘
*closed 25 to 31 December and 6 January-6 February* – **Meals** (booking essential) (residents only) (dinner only) 20.00 🍷 8.25 – **5 rm** ☕ (dinner included) 60.00/112.00 – SB.

**Cockett's,** Market Pl., DL8 3RD, ✆ (01969) 667312, *Fax (01969) 667162*, 🌳 – 🚭 [TV] ☎. [MC] VISA. ⊘
Meals 9.00/15.95 **t.** and dinner a la carte 🍷 6.75 – **8 rm** ☕ 35.00/59.00 **t.** – SB.

**Herriot's,** Main St., DL8 3QU, ✆ (01969) 667536 – 🚭 rest, [TV]. [MC] VISA. ⊘
*closed Christmas, January and Monday to Wednesday October-Easter* – **Meals** *(closed Monday Easter-October)* 13.95 **t.** (dinner) and a la carte 13.90/20.35 **t.** 🍷 4.95 – **6 rm** ☕ 25.00/55.00 **t.** – SB.

**Brandymires,** Muker Rd, DL8 3PR, North : ¼ m. ✆ (01969) 667482 – 🚭 [P]
*mid February-October* – **Meals** (by arrangement) 12.00 **st.** 🍷 3.95 – **4 rm** ☕ 29.00/38.00 **st.**

**HAWKRIDGE** *Somerset* [403] J 30 *The West Country G.* – ✉ *Dulverton.*

Env. : *Tarr Steps*★★, *NE : 2½ m.*
Exc. : *Exmoor National Park*★★.
*London 203 – Exeter 32 – Minehead 17 – Taunton 32.*

**Tarr Steps** ☘, TA22 9PY, Northeast : 1 ½ m. ✆ (01643) 851293, *Fax (01643) 851218*, <, 🎣, 🌳, park – ☎ [P]. [MC] VISA JCB
*closed 1 to 10 February* – **Meals** (booking essential) (dinner only) 25.00 **t.** 🍷 6.90 – **11 rm** ☕ (dinner included) 68.00/136.00 **t.** – SB.

**HAWKSHEAD** *Cumbria* [402] L 20 *Great Britain G.* – *pop. 570* – ✉ *Ambleside.*

See : *Village*★.
Env. : *Lake Windermere*★★ – *Coniston Water*★ *(Brantwood*★, *on east side), SW : by B 5285.*
ℹ *Main Car Park, LA22 0NT* ✆ *(015394) 36525 (summer only).*
*London 283 – Carlisle 52 – Kendal 19.*

**Highfield House Country H.** ☘, Hawkshead Hill, LA22 0PN, West : ¾ m. on B 5285 (Coniston rd) ✆ (015394) 36344, *Fax (015394) 36793*, < Kirkstone Pass and Fells, 🌳 – 🚭 rest, [TV] ☎ [P]. [MC] VISA JCB
*closed Christmas and last 3 weeks January* – **Meals** (bar lunch)/dinner 18.00 **st.** 🍷 10.00 – **11 rm** ☕ (dinner included) 63.00/130.00 **st.** – SB.

**Rough Close Country House** ☘, LA22 0QF, South : 1 ½ m. on Newby Bridge rd ✆ (015394) 36370, 🌳 – 🚭 [TV] [P]. [MC] VISA. ⊘
*April-October* – **Meals** (by arrangement) – **5 rm** ☕ (dinner included) 52.50/85.00 **t.**

**Ivy House,** Main St., LA22 0NS, ✆ (015394) 36204, 🎣 – 🚭 rest, [TV] [P]. [MC] VISA JCB
*12 March-7 November* – **Meals** 12.50 **t.** 🍷 4.00 – **11 rm** ☕ 30.00/64.00 **t.** – SB.

**Bracken Fell** ☘ without rest., Barngates Rd, Outgate, LA22 0NH, North : 1 m. by B 5286 on Barngates rd ✆ (015394) 36289, 🌳 – 🚭 [P]. ⊘
**6 rm** ☕ 29.00/45.00 **st.**

**at Near Sawrey** *Southeast : 2 m. on B 5285* – ✉ *Ambleside.*

**Sawrey House Country H.** ☘, LA22 0LF, ✆ (015394) 36387, *Fax (015394) 36010*, < Esthwaite Water and Grizedale Forest, 🎣, 🌳 – 🚭 [TV] ☎ [P]. [MC] VISA. ⊘
*closed mid November-February except Christmas* – **Meals** (booking essential) (dinner only) 20.00 **t.** 🍷 5.60 – **10 rm** ☕ (dinner included) 55.00/132.00 **st.** – SB.

**Ees Wyke Country House** ☘, LA22 0JZ, ✆ (015394) 36393, *Fax (015394) 36393*, < Esthwaite Water and Grizedale Forest, 🌳 – 🚭 rest, [TV] [P]. [AE]
*closed January and February* – **Meals** (booking essential) (dinner only) 21.00 **t.** 🍷 6.50 – **8 rm** ☕ (dinner included) 58.00/116.00 **t.**

**at Far Sawrey** *Southeast : 2½ m. on B 5285* – ✉ *Ambleside.*

**West Vale,** LA22 0LQ, ✆ (015394) 42817, < – 🚭 rest, [P]. ⊘
*March-October* – **Meals** (by arrangement) 12.00 **t.** 🍷 4.75 – **6 rm** ☕ 24.00/48.00 **t.**

**at Grizedale** Southwest : 2 ¾ m. – ⊠ Ambleside.

🏛 **Grizedale Lodge** ⌂, LA22 0QL, ℘ (015394) 36532, Fax (015394) 36572 – ⚡ 📺 🅿. ●
AE VISA JCB
Meals (bar lunch)/dinner 23.50 st. ₰ 6.75 – **9 rm** ⌂ (dinner included) 65.00/110.00 st. – SE

---

**HAWNBY** N. Yorks 402 Q 21 – see Helmsley.

---

**HAWORTH** W. Yorks. 402 O 22 Great Britain G. – pop. 4 956 – ⊠ Keighley.
See : Town★.
🏢 2-4 West Lane, BD22 8EF ℘ (01535) 642329.
London 213 – Burnley 22 – Leeds 22 – Manchester 34.

⌂ **Ashmount**, Mytholmes Lane, BD22 8EZ, ℘ (01535) 645726, 🌐 – ⚡ 📺 🅿. ●● VISA
closed 1 week late March, 2 weeks early November and 3 days Christmas – Meals (b
arrangement) (communal dining) 12.50 s. – **6 rm** ⌂ 25.00/39.00 s.

XX **Weaver's** with rm, 15 West Lane, BD22 8DU, ℘ (01535) 643822, Fax (01535) 64483.
⍟ « Former weavers cottages » – ⚡ rest, 📺 ☎. ●● AE ① VISA JCB. ⍟
closed 2 weeks Christmas – Meals (closed Sunday and Monday) (dinner only) 13.50 
and a la carte 12.85/23.85 t. ₰ 6.35 – **3 rm** ⌂ 50.00/75.00 t. – SB.

---

**HAYDOCK** Mersey. 402 403 404 M 23 – pop. 16 705 – ⊠ St Helens.
London 198 – Liverpool 17 – Manchester 18.

🏨 **Haydock Thistle**, Penny Lane, WA11 9SG, Northeast : ½ m. on A 599 ℘ (01942) 272000
Fax (01942) 711092, 🛎, 🍴, 🔲, 🌐 – ⚡ rm, 🍴 rest, 📺 ☎ & 🅿 – 🔥 300. ●● AE ① VIS.
JCB
The Restaurant : Meals (bar lunch Saturday) 13.95/19.50 st. and a la carte ₰ 6.50 – ⌂
10.50 – **135 rm** 95.00/105.00 st., 4 suites – SB.

🏨 **Forte Posthouse Haydock**, Lodge Lane, Newton-le-Willows, WA12 0JG, Northeast :
1 m. on A 49 ℘ (01942) 717878, Fax (01942) 718419, 🛎, 🍴, 🔲, 🌐 – 🛗, ⚡ rm, 🍴 rest
📺 ☎ & 🅿 – 🔥 180. ●● AE ① VISA JCB. ⍟
Meals (closed Saturday lunch) a la carte approx. 19.30 st. ₰ 8.95 – ⌂ 9.95 – **138 rm** 85.00
125.00 st.

🏛 **Travelodge**, Piele Rd, WA11 9TL, on A 580 ℘ (01942) 272055, Fax (01942) 272067, Reser
vations (Freephone) 0800 850950 – ⚡ rm, 📺 & 🅿. ●● AE ① VISA JCB. ⍟
Meals (grill rest.) – **62 rm** 39.95/59.95 t.

---

**HAYFIELD** Derbs. 402 403 404 O 23 – pop. 2 293 – ⊠ Stockport (Ches.).
London 191 – Manchester 22 – Sheffield 29.

🏛 **Waltzing Weasel**, New Mills Rd, Birch Vale, SK22 1BT, West : ½ m. on A 6015
℘ (01663) 743402, Fax (01663) 743402, ≤, 🌐 – 📺 ☎ ✆ 🅿. ●● AE VISA
Meals (bar lunch)/dinner 25.50 st. ₰ 4.75 – **8 rm** ⌂ 38.00/95.00 st.

---

**HAYLING ISLAND** Hants. 404 R 31 – pop. 14 054.
🏌 Links Lane ℘ (01705) 463712/463777.
🏢 Beachlands, Seafront, PO11 0AG ℘ (01705) 467111 (summer only).
London 77 – Brighton 45 – Southampton 28.

⌂ **Cockle Warren Cottage**, 36 Seafront, PO11 9HL, ℘ (01705) 464961
Fax (01705) 464838, 🔲, 🌐 – ⚡ 📺 ☎ ✆ 🅿. ●● AE VISA
closed 1 week April and 1 week October – Meals (by arrangement) 27.50 st. ₰ 5.00 – ⌂ 8.50
– **5 rm** 68.00/108.00 st.

---

**HAYTOR** Devon – see Bovey Tracey.

---

**HAYTOR VALE** Devon – see Bovey Tracey.

---

Bitte beachten Sie die Geschwindigkeitsbeschränkungen in Großbritannien
- 60 mph (= 96 km/h) außerhalb geschlossener Ortschaften
- 70 mph (= 112 km/h) auf Straßen mit getrennten Fahrbahnen und Autobahnen.

**HAYWARDS HEATH** *W. Sussex* 404 T 31 – pop. 28 923.

> 🏌 *Paxhill Park, East Mascalls Lane, Lindfield* ℰ *(01444) 484467.*
> London 41 – Brighton 16.

🏨 **Birch,** Lewes Rd, RH17 7SF, East : ¾ m. on A 272 ℰ (01444) 451565, *Fax (01444) 440109* –
※ rm, 📺 & ℗ – 🕭 60. 🆗 🖭 ① 𝘝𝘐𝘚𝘈. ※
**Meals** (bar lunch Saturday) 17.95 t. ⋆ 4.95 – **51 rm** ☴ 73.00/109.00 t.

@ ATS Gower Rd ℰ (01444) 412640/454189

---

**HEADLAM** *Durham* 402 O 20 – see Darlington.

---

**HEATHROW AIRPORT** *Middx.* 404 S 29 – see Hillingdon (Greater London).

---

**HEBDEN BRIDGE** *W. Yorks.* 402 N 22 – pop. 3 681 – ✉ Halifax.

> 🏌 *Wadsworth* ℰ (01422) 842896.
> 🛈 *1 Bridge Gate, HX7 8EX* ℰ (01422) 843831.
> London 223 – Burnley 13 – Leeds 24 – Manchester 25.

🏨 **Carlton,** Albert St., HX7 8ES, ℰ (01422) 844400, *Fax (01422) 843117* – |≩|, ※ rest, 📺 ☎ –
🕭 150. 🆗 🖭 𝘝𝘐𝘚𝘈 𝘑𝘊𝘉
**Meals** 10.50/13.95 **st.** and dinner a la carte ⋆ 6.95 – **16 rm** ☴ 54.00/79.00 **st.** – SB.

🏨 **The White Lion,** Bridge Gate, HX7 8EX, ℰ (01422) 842197, *Fax (01422) 846619,* « 17C
inn » – ※ rm, 📺 ℗. 🆗 𝘝𝘐𝘚𝘈. ※
*closed 25 December* – **Meals** (in bar Sunday to Thursday) a la carte 7.50/18.40 t. ⋆ 6.75 –
**10 rm** ☴ 35.00/55.00 **t.**

⌂ **Redacre Mill,** Mytholmroyd, HX7 5DQ, Southeast : 1 ½ m. by A646 off Westfield Terr.
ℰ (01422) 885563, *Fax (01422) 885563,* « Converted canalside warehouse », 🌲 – ※ 📺 ℭ
℗. 🆗 𝘝𝘐𝘚𝘈. ※
**Meals** (communal dining) 14.50 **st.** ⋆ 4.80 – **4 rm** ☴ 39.00/58.00 **st.**

> *Le Grand Londres (GREATER LONDON) est composé de la City*
> *et de 32 arrondissements administratifs (Borough)*
> *eux-mêmes divisés en quartiers ou en villages*
> *ayant conservé leur caractère propre (Area).*

---

**HEDON** *East Riding* 402 T 22 – see Kingston-upon-Hull.

---

**HEIGHINGTON** *Durham* 402 P20 – see Darlington.

---

**HELLIDON** *Northants.* 404 Q 27 – see Daventry.

---

**HELMSLEY** *N. Yorks.* 402 Q 21 *Great Britain G.* – pop. 1 833.

> Env. : Rievaulx Abbey★★ *AC,* NW : 2½ m. by B 1257.
> 🏌 *Ampleforth College, 56 High St.* ℰ (01439) 770678.
> 🛈 *Town Hall, Market Pl., YO62 5BL* ℰ (01439) 770173.
> London 239 – Middlesbrough 28 – York 24.

🏨🏨 **Black Swan,** Market Pl., YO62 5BJ, ℰ (01439) 770466, *Fax (01439) 770174,* « Part 16C
inn », 🌲 – ※ 📺 ☎ ℗. 🆗 🖭 ① 𝘝𝘐𝘚𝘈 𝘑𝘊𝘉
**The Rutland Room :** Meals 11.75/24.50 t. and dinner a la carte – ☴ 10.00 – **45 rm**
☴ 85.00/110.00 **t.** – SB.

🏨 **Carlton Lodge,** Bondgate, YO62 5EY, ℰ (01439) 770557, *Fax (01439) 770623,* 🌲 –
※ rest, 📺 ☎ ℗ – 🕭 130. 🆗 𝘝𝘐𝘚𝘈
*closed 1 week January* – **The Stirrings :** Meals (dinner only) 17.50 **st.** and a la carte ⋆ 5.95 –
**11 rm** ☴ 39.50/75.00 **st.** – SB.

🏨 **The Feathers,** Market Pl., YO62 5BH, ℰ (01439) 770275, *Fax (01439) 771101,* 🌲 –
▤ rest, 📺 ☎ ℗. 🆗 𝘝𝘐𝘚𝘈. ※
**Meals** (carving lunch Sunday) (bar lunch Monday to Saturday) a la carte 10.70/20.95 **t.**
⋆ 5.50 – **14 rm** ☴ 43.00/66.00 **t.**

**at Nawton** *East : 3¼ m. on A 170* – ✉ York.

⌂ **Plumpton Court,** High St., YO62 7TT, ℰ (01439) 771223, 🌲 – ※ 📺 ℗. ※
**Meals** (by arrangement) 12.00 **st.** – **7 rm** ☴ 33.50/50.00 **st.** – SB.

**at Harome** Southeast : 2 ¾ m. by A 170 – ⊠ York.

🏠 **The Pheasant**, YO62 5JG, ℘ (01439) 771241, Fax (01439) 771744, ◪, ℛ – ⁕ rest, ☎ 
☎ 🄿, ⬛ⓢ *VISA* JCB, ⌖
mid March-mid November – Meals (bar lunch)/dinner 20.00 t. ⅍ 4.80 – **12 rm** ⌸ (dinner
included) 62.00/130.00 t., 2 suites – SB.

🄰 **The Star Inn**, YO62 5JE, ℘ (01439) 770397, Fax (01439) 771833, ⩨, « Part 14C thatched
inn », ℛ – ⁕ 🄿, ⬛ⓢ *VISA*
closed Sunday dinner. Monday, 3 weeks January and 25 December – Meals (booking
essential) a la carte 18.85/25.85 t. ⅍ 7.25.

**at Wass** Southwest : 6 m. by A 170 – ⊠ Helmsley.

🄰 **Wombwell Arms**, YO61 4BE, ℘ (01347) 868280 – ⁕ 🄿, ⬛ⓢ *VISA*
closed Monday, Sunday dinner September-May and 2 weeks January – Meals a la carte
10.00/20.95 t. ⅍ 7.85.

**at Hawnby** Northwest : 6 ¼ m. by B 1257 – ⊠ Helmsley.

🏠 **Hawnby** ⌖, YO62 5QS, ℘ (01439) 798202, Fax (01439) 798344, ≤, ⩩, ℛ – ⁕ rm, ☎
☎ 🄿, ⬛ⓢ *VISA*, ⌖
closed 25 December – Meals (closed Sunday and Monday to non-residents) (bar lunch),
dinner 12.50 st. ⅍ 4.95 – **6 rm** ⌸ 40.00/60.00 st. – SB.

**at Laskill** Northwest : 6 ¼ m. by B 1257 – ⊠ Hawnby.

🏠 **Laskill Farm**, Easterside, YO62 5BN, ℘ (01439) 798268, Fax (01439) 798268, « Working
farm », ℛ – ⁕ ☎ 🄿, ⬛ⓢ *VISA* JCB, ⌖
closed 25 December – Meals (by arrangement) (communal dining) 12.50 st. ⅍ 5.00 – **6 rm**
⌸ 35.00/64.00 st.

---

**HELSTON** Cornwall 408 E 33 The West Country G. – pop. 8 505.
See : The Flora Day Furry Dance★★.
Env. : Lizard Peninsula★ – Gunwalloe Fishing Cove★, S : 4 m. by A 3083 and minor rd -
Culdrose (Flambards Village Theme Park★), SE : 1 m. – Wendron (Poldark Mine★), NE : 2½ m.
by B 3297 – Gweek (Seal Sanctuary★ – setting★), E : 4 m. by A 394 and minor rd.
London 306 – Falmouth 13 – Penzance 14 – Truro 17.

🏠 **Nansloe Manor** ⌖, Meneage Rd, TR13 0SB, ℘ (01326) 574691, Fax (01326) 564680, ℛ
– ⁕ rest, ☎ ☎ 🄿, ⬛ⓢ *VISA* JCB, ⌖
Meals (bar lunch Monday to Saturday)/dinner a la carte 21.75/27.30 t. ⅍ 11.00 – **7 rm**
⌸ 51.00/120.00 t.

XX **Crahan**, Trevenen, TR13 0ND, Northeast : 2 ¾ m. on A 394 ℘ (01326) 573090, ℛ – 🄿, ⬛ⓢ
*VISA*
closed Monday and 25 and 31 December – Meals (dinner only and lunch Friday and
Saturday)/dinner 21.50 t..

**at Gunwalloe** South : 5 m. by A 394 off A 3083 – ⊠ Helston.

🄰 **The Halzephron Inn** ⌖ with rm, TR12 7QB, ℘ (01326) 240406, ≤, ⩨ – ⁕ rest, ☎
🄿, ⬛ⓢ ⒶⒺ *VISA*
accommodation closed 25 and 26 December – Meals (closed 25 December) a la carte
12.40/21.60 t. ⅍ 3.50 – **2 rm** ⌸ 37.50/64.00 t.

**at Porthleven** Southwest : 2 ¼ m. on B 3304 – ⊠ Helston.

X **Sanders**, Fore St., TR13 9HJ, ℘ (01326) 574145 – ⁕, ⬛ⓢ ⒶⒺ *VISA*
closed Sunday and restricted opening in winter – Meals (booking essential) (dinner only.
18.50 ⅍ 10.00.

🄰 ATS Clodgey Lane ℘ (01326) 562656

---

**HELTON** Cumbria 401 402 L 20 – ⊠ Penrith.
London 287 – Carlisle 26 – Kendal 24 – Workington 43.

🏠 **Beckfoot Country House** ⌖, CA10 2QB, South : 1 ¼ m. ℘ (01931) 713241,
Fax (01931) 713391, ≤, ℛ – ⁕ ☎ 🄿, ⬛ⓢ ⒶⒺ *VISA*
March-November – Meals (dinner only) 15.00 s. – **6 rm** ⌸ 30.00/60.00 – SB.

---

**HEMEL HEMPSTEAD** Herts. 404 S 28 – pop. 79 235.
🛉 Little Hay Golf Complex, Box Lane, Bovingdon ℘ (01442) 833798 – 🛉 Boxmoor, 18 Box
Lane ℘ (01442) 242434.
🄱 Dacorum Information Centre, HP1 1DT ℘ (01442) 234222.
London 30 – Aylesbury 16 – Luton 10 – Northampton 46.

🏨 **Forte Posthouse Hemel Hempstead**, Breakspear Way, HP2 4UA, East : 2 ½ m. on A 414 𝒫 (01442) 251122, Fax (01442) 211812, ₤₅, ⅀, ▨ – ╞╡, ¾⊢ rm, ▥ ☎ ♿ 🅿 – ⌖ 60. 🆖 🆎 ⓪ 𝘝𝘐𝘚𝘈 JCB
Meals a la carte 10.55/25.35 t. – ⌑ 10.95 – **145 rm** 109.00/149.00 t. – SB.

🏨 **Boxmoor Lodge**, London Rd, HP1 2RA, West : 1 m. on A 4251 𝒫 (01442) 230770, Fax (01442) 252230, 🐴 – ¾⊢ rm, ▥ ☎ ♿ 🅿 – ⌖ 35. 🆖 🆎 ⓪ 𝘝𝘐𝘚𝘈 JCB
closed 25 December-4 JanuaryMeals (closed lunch Saturday and Sunday and Monday) 19.00/24.00 t. ⅄ 6.00 – **23 rm** ⌑ 80.00/100.00 t.

🏨 **Travel Inn**, Stoney Lane, Bourne End, HP1 2SB, West : 3 ½ m. by A 4251 off A 41 𝒫 (01442) 879149, Fax (01442) 879147 – ╞╡, ¾⊢ rm, ▥ ♿ 🅿 – ⌖ 35. 🆖 🆎 ⓪ 𝘝𝘐𝘚𝘈. ⌖
Meals (grill rest.) – **60 rm** 38.00 t.

---

**ENFIELD** W. Sussex **404** T 31 – pop. 4 111.
London 47 – Brighton 10 – Worthing 11.

🏨 **Tottington Manor**, Edburton, BN5 9LJ, Southeast : 3 ½ m. by A 2037 on Fulking rd 𝒫 (01903) 815757, Fax (01903) 879331, ≤, 🌳, 🐴 – ▥ ☎ 🅿. 🆖 🆎 ⓪ 𝘝𝘐𝘚𝘈 JCB. ⌖
closed 1 week early January – Meals (closed Sunday dinner) 25.50 t. (dinner) and a la carte 15.25/27.70 t. ⅄ 5.00 – **6 rm** ⌑ 45.00/75.00 t. – SB.

ㄸ **Wineham** Northeast : 3 ½ m. by A 281, B 2116 and Wineham Lane – ✉ Henfield.

↑ **Frylands** 🌿 without rest., BN5 9BP, West : ¼ m. taking left turn at telephone box 𝒫 (01403) 710214, Fax (01403) 711449, ≤, « Part Elizabethan farmhouse », 🛆, 🌿, 🐴, park – ▥ 🅿. ⌖
closed 20 December-1 January – **3 rm** ⌑ 20.00/40.00 s.

*Questa Guida non contiene pubblicità a pagamento.*

---

**ENLADE** Somerset – see Taunton.

---

**ENLEY-IN-ARDEN** Warks. **403** **404** O 27 – pop. 2 803.
London 104 – Birmingham 15 – Stratford-upon-Avon 8 – Warwick 8.5.

🏨 **Ardencote Manor H. & Country Club** 🌿, Lye Green Rd, Claverdon, CV35 8LS, East : 3 ¾ m. by A 4189 on Shrewley rd 𝒫 (01926) 843111, Fax (01926) 842646, ₤₅, ⅀, ▨, ⁏, 🌿, 🐴, park, ⚒, squash – ¾⊢ rest, ▥ ☎ 🅿 – ⌖ 100. 🆖 🆎 ⓪ 𝘝𝘐𝘚𝘈. ⌖
*Oak Room :* Meals (booking essential) 14.95/21.95 t. and a la carte ⅄ 6.50 – **18 rm** ⌑ 87.50/130.00 st.

---

**ENLEY-ON-THAMES** Oxon. **404** R 29 – pop. 10 558.
🏌 Huntercombe, Nuffield 𝒫 (01491) 641207.
🛈 Town Hall, Market Pl., RG9 2AQ 𝒫 (01491) 578034.
London 40 – Oxford 23 – Reading 9.

🏨 **Red Lion**, RG9 2AR, 𝒫 (01491) 572161, Fax (01491) 410039 – ▥ ☎ 🅿 – ⌖ 30. 🆖 🆎 𝘝𝘐𝘚𝘈. ⌖
Meals a la carte 23.75/30.25 t. ⅄ 7.50 – ⌑ 11.00 – **26 rm** 87.50/120.00 st.

✕✕ **Villa Marina**, 18 Thameside, RG9 1BH, 𝒫 (01491) 575262, Fax (01491) 411394 – 🆖 🆎 ⓪ 𝘝𝘐𝘚𝘈
closed 25-26 December and 1 January – Meals - Italian - 12.00 t. (lunch) and dinner a la carte 19.00/23.00 t. ⅄ 5.00.

ㄸ **Stonor** North : 4 m. by A 4130 on B 480 – ✉ Henley-on-Thames.

🏨 **Stonor Arms**, RG9 6HE, 𝒫 (01491) 638866, Fax (01491) 638863, 🐴 – ▥ ☎ 🅿. 🆖 🆎 𝘝𝘐𝘚𝘈
*Stonor :* Meals 21.00 t. (lunch) and a la carte 22.75/38.25 t. ⅄ 8.50 – **10 rm** ⌑ 95.00/140.00 t. – SB.

---

**EREFORD** Herefordshire **403** L 27 Great Britain G. – pop. 54 326.
See : City⋆ – Cathedral⋆⋆ (Mappa Mundi⋆) A A – Old House⋆ A B.
Exc. : Kilpeck (Church of SS. Mary and David⋆⋆) SW : 8 m. by A 465 B.
🏌 Raven's Causeway, Wormsley 𝒫 (01432) 830219 – 🏌 Belmont Lodge, Belmont 𝒫 (01432) 352666 – 🏌 Burghill Valley, Tillington Rd, Burghill 𝒫 (01432) 760456 – 🏌 Hereford Municipal, Holmer Rd 𝒫 (01432) 278178 B.
🛈 1 King St., HR4 9BW 𝒫 (01432) 268430.
London 133 – Birmingham 51 – Cardiff 56.

# HEREFORD

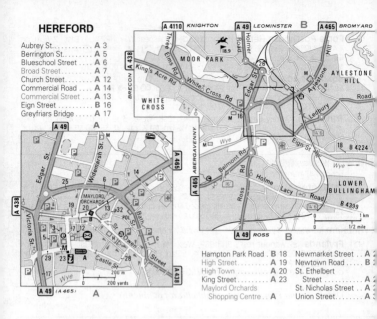

**Green Dragon**, Broad St., HR4 9BG, ℰ (01432) 272506, Fax (01432) 352139 – 🛗 ❄ 📺
🚗 – 🔥 200. 🆔 🆎 ⑨ 𝘝𝘐𝘚𝘈                                                                          A
Meals a la carte 14.50/23.50 **st.** ⓙ 6.50 – ⊊ 8.95 – **80 rm** 70.00/80.00 **st.**, 3 suites – SB.

**Three Counties**, Belmont Rd, HR2 7BP, Southwest : 1 ½ m. on A 465 ℰ (01432) 29995
Fax (01432) 275114 – ❄ rm, 📺 & 🅿 – 🔥 350. 🆔 🆎 ⑨ 𝘝𝘐𝘚𝘈                               B
Meals (bar lunch Monday to Saturday and carving lunch Sunday)/dinner a la carte 15.5(
18.50 **st.** – **60 rm** ⊊ 56.50/74.50 **st.** – SB.

**Aylestone Court**, Aylestone Hill, HR1 1HS, ℰ (01432) 341891, Fax (01432) 267691, 🌾
❄ rest, 📺 ☎ 🅿 – 🔥 60. 🆔 🆎 ⑨ 𝘝𝘐𝘚𝘈 𝘑𝘊𝘉. ※                                             B
Meals (closed Sunday) (dinner only) a la carte 15.50/25.70 **st.** – **9 rm** ⊊ 45.00/60.00 **st.**

**Travel Inn**, Holmer Rd, Holmer, HR4 9RS, North : 1 ¾ m. on A 49 ℰ (01432) 27485
Fax (01432) 343003 – ❄ rm, 📺 & 🅿. 🆔 🆎 ⑨ 𝘝𝘐𝘚𝘈. ※
Meals (grill rest.) – **42 rm** 38.00 **t.**

**Grafton Villa Farm** without rest., Grafton, HR2 8ED, South : 2 ¼ m. on A 4
ℰ (01432) 268689, Fax (01432) 268689, « Working farm », 🌾, park – ❄ 📺 🅿. ※
February-October – **3 rm** ⊊ 25.00/42.00 **st.**

**Collins House** without rest., 19 St. Owen St., HR1 2JB, ℰ (01432) 27241
Fax (01432) 357717 – ❄ 📺 ☎ 🅿. 🆔 𝘝𝘐𝘚𝘈 𝘑𝘊𝘉. ※                                       A
closed 1 week Christmas – ⊊ 3.00 – **3 rm** 30.00/45.00.

**at Marden** North : 5 ¾ m. by A 49 – B – ✉ Hereford.

**The Vauld Farm** ⌲, HR1 3HA, Northeast : 1 ½ m. by Litmarsh rd ℰ (01568) 79789
« 16C timbered farmhouse », 🌾 – ❄ rest, 📺 🅿. ※
Meals (by arrangement) (communal dining) 16.50 **s.** – **3 rm** ⊊ 30.00/50.00 **s.**, 1 suite.

**at Canon Pyon** North : 7 m. on A 4110 – B – ✉ Hereford.

**Hermitage Manor** ⌲ without rest., HR4 8NR, South : 1 m. on A 411
ℰ (01432) 760317, Fax (01432) 760317, ≤ Vale of Hereford, 🌾, park – ❄ 📺 🅿. ※
April-October – **3 rm** ⊊ 30.00/50.00.

**at Ruckhall** West : 5 m. by A 49 off A 465 – B – ✉ Eaton Bishop.

**Ancient Camp Inn** ⌲ with rm, HR2 9QX, ℰ (01981) 250449, Fax (01981) 251581,
River Wye and countryside, ⌇ – ❄ 📺 ☎ 🅿. 🆔 𝘝𝘐𝘚𝘈. ※
Meals (closed Sunday dinner and Monday to non-residents) (booking essential) a la car
18.00/25.00 **t.** ⓙ 6.50 – **5 rm** ⊊ 45.00/65.00 **t.**

# *The traveller's companion*

From the United Kingdom to Japan, from Finland to South Africa, Michelin companies are serving the travelling public.

They produce more than 770,000 tyres a day, from bicycle tyres with a contact patch no bigger than a thumbprint, to the tyres that bring the space shuttle safely to earth after every mission.

Every day, Michelin companies also produce more than 95,000 inner tubes, 1,100 tons of steel, 4 million kilometres of wire, 46,500 wheels and 60,000 tourist maps and guides.

Michelin leads the way in competition, with world championship titles in almost every wheel driven sport, and a commitment to providing faster products, and better service at every stage.

But despite its world beating history, and continual position at the forefront of motoring development, Michelin has always kept close to its customers' needs. So you can be sure that whatever you require, Michelin are committed to find the product that is right for you.

# *Keeping you on track*

The Michelin Hotel and Restaurant Guide
is internationally renowned for directing
travellers to the best places to eat
and sleep.

It offers one of the largest selections
of hotels and restaurants, and every
establishment is visited by Michelin's
expert inspectors, to ensure that
each meets the highest standards
for quality and service.

But there's more to travel with
Michelin than the famous Red Guide.
Michelin publishes a wide range of
literature designed to help you get the
most from your trip.

Michelin Green Tourist Guides are perfect companions for independent sight-seeing with details on history, economy, geography and the arts, including suggested itineraries to help make the most of your time.

As in the Michelin Red Guides, places really worth a visit are marked with Michelin stars and there are town plans, maps and photographs to help you on your way.

For short breaks or package holidays you can get a quick summary of your destination with Michelin In Your Pocket guides, offering a wealth of easy-to-use practical information in a handy sized format.

*New In Your Pocket titles for 1999 are Bruges, Jersey, Malta, San Francisco and Saint Petersburg.*

And to help you reach your destination quickly and easily, Michelin produce a vast range of road maps and atlases which are reviewed and revised meticulously every year. Also available are detailed city/town plans, with new titles for Paris, Amsterdam, Brussels, Lisbon and Milan published this year.

*Michelin publications are available at bookshops throughout Great Britain and Ireland.*

# *Driving forward*

Michelin continually works to offer tyres
with improved safety and better response
levels. Although tyres have developed
enormously over the years, it is often
difficult for drivers to really appreciate the
benefits. Until now.

Imagine a tyre that tells you when it needs
more air; that continues to drive even after
a puncture, and that you really feel offers
an improved ride. These are not dreams.
Thanks to a revolutionary new product
from Michelin, these ideas are set to
become reality.

**The Michelin PAX system is a combined tyre and wheel which at
the very least offers noticeable improvements in cornering,
braking and fuel consumption. More significantly, a pressure
indicator on the dashboard linked to a detector in the wheel tells
the driver of any sudden pressure changes, warning of any
potential problems. And in the unlikely event of a puncture, the
new tyre will continue to run safely for up to 150km at 50km/h.**

These features combine to give the driver
more confidence at the wheel and new
levels of driving pleasure, and led to the
Michelin PAX system winning the
prestigious Autocar magazine 'Innovation
of the Year' award in 1998.

The PAX system is the technology of the
future, but is already being used by Renault
on the new Twingo Initial. In time, it will
make travelling safer, smoother and
ultimately more enjoyable for everyone.

# *The power behind the wheel*

People who enjoy driving face a confusing array of extras to enhance their experience behind the wheel, but none can affect car performance more than the choice of tyre. For the ultimate in control, Michelin Pilot Sport is available for a range of luxury sports cars, and will compliment extreme levels of performance with sure footed handling and unequalled comfort.

*Pilot*

ENERGY

In fact, whatever you drive, a Michelin tyre will bring out the best in your car.

Michelin Energy is designed for a wide range of family and saloon cars and offers outstanding grip, particularly in wet and icy conditions. Michelin Classic on the other hand is designed for medium to small family cars with economy in mind, offering the same grip and mileage as other Michelin tyres but at a lower price.

**For details on all Michelin tyres, contact your nearest tyre dealer.**

CLASSIC

# *Tyre safety checks*

## CONTACT

**Q.**What is the only link between the vehicle and the road?

The contact patch of a car is roughly the same size as the **palm of your hand**, and has to withstand and transmit great forces.

**This is why not only the tyre itself is important, but also fitting and maintenance.**

## CHANGING

**Q.** When should motorists change their car tyres?

**The minimum legal depth of 1.6mm** across the central three quarters of the tyre tread circumferentially is the minimum legal limit, which must be observed.

The **Tread Wear Indicators** moulded into the base of the tread grooves are set at this depth.

The main picture compares the visual difference between a new tyre and one that is worn down to the **Tread Wear Indicators**. The inset picture demonstrates the difference between new and worn tyres in terms of the contact patch:

1.6mm

**New tyre:** Contact patch on the road is **normal** and water evacuation is total.
**Tyre with 3mm tread depth** (within the legal limit): contact patch on the road is **reduced** and water is no longer totally evacuated: starts to aquaplane.

# PRESSURE CHECK

**Q.** How and why should tyre pressures be checked?

The correct pressure is an important factor in both the safety and long life of tyres. Pressures should always be checked when the **tyres are cold.**

Pressure should be checked **regularly** using a proprietary pressure gauge. A drop in pressure could be due to:

- Air leakage through the wheel, bead seal or valve.

- A fall in temperature (particularly if not always checked cold).

- Small penetrations which, in tubeless tyres, do not cause an immediate deflation but may, over a long period, cause the tyre to lose pressure

- Natural diffusion of the air through the components of the tyre.

The **spare tyre** should be checked as well.

# Route planning at the touch of a button

Before you travel make sure you have the most up-to-date route plan for your trip.

Using Michelin's internet route planning service, you can receive a detailed itinerary for your journey*, including which roads to take, where to stop and how much any tolls will cost.

Simply enter your start point and where you're going, and a route map and directions will appear on screen, which you can print out for your journey. You can choose fast routes, or scenic routes, and the site gives you access to thousands of hotels and restaurants, taken from the world famous Michelin Guide.

**Details of the new service, plus information on Michelin's wide range of maps and guides to destinations all over the world are available on**

**www.michelin.travel.com**

*Secure electronic payment is required*

**at Byford** West : 7½ m. by A 438 – B – ⊠ Hereford.

↟ **Old Rectory** without rest., HR4 7LD, ℰ (01981) 590218, Fax (01981) 590499, 🐎 – ⇔ 📺
🅿. ⌖
March-October – **3 rm** ⌑ 27.50/45.00.

    🔧 ATS 6 Kyrle St. ℰ (01432) 265491

---

**HERM** 🔢 P 33 and 🔢 ⑩ – see Channel Islands.

---

**HERMITAGE** Dorset – see Sherborne.

---

**HERSTMONCEUX** E. Sussex 🔢 U 31 – pop. 3 898.
London 63 – Eastbourne 12 – Hastings 14 – Lewes 16.

ⅩⅩ **Sundial,** Gardner St., BN27 4LA, ℰ (01323) 832217, « Converted 16C cottage », 🐎 – ⇔
🅿. 🆎 🆎 🔲 VISA JCB
closed Sunday dinner, Monday, 9 August-early September and 24 December-20 January –
**Meals** - French - 19.50/27.50 **t.** and a la carte ⅄ 6.95.

**at Wartling** Southeast : 3 ¾ m. by A 271 and Wartling rd – ⊠ Herstmonceux.

↟ **Wartling Place,** BN27 1RY, ℰ (01323) 832590, Fax (01323) 832590, 🐎 – ⇔ 📺 🅿. 🆎
VISA JCB
**Meals** (by arrangement) 20.00 **st.** – **3 rm** ⌑ 45.00/85.00 – SB.

---

**HERTFORD** Herts. 🔢 T 28 – pop. 21 665.
🅱 The Castle, SG14 1HR ℰ (01992) 584322.
London 24 – Cambridge 35 – Luton 26.

↟ **Hall House** ⌖, Broad Oak End, SG14 2JA, Northwest : 1 ¾ m. by A 119 and Bramfield Rd
ℰ (01992) 582807, 🐎 – ⇔ 📺 🅿. 🆎 VISA. ⌖
closed Christmas and New Year – **Meals** (by arrangement) 20.00 **s.** – **3 rm** ⌑ 49.00/67.00 **s.**

---

**HERTINGFORDBURY** Herts. 🔢 T 28 – pop. 633 – ⊠ Hertford.
London 26 – Luton 18.

🏨 **White Horse,** Hertingfordbury Rd, SG14 2LB, ℰ (01992) 586791, Fax (01992) 550809, 🐎
– ⇔ 📺 ☎ 🅿 – 🔬 50. 🆎 🆎 🔲 VISA JCB
**Meals** (closed Saturday lunch) 13.95/16.50 **st.** ⅄ 8.00 – ⌑ 9.95 – **42 rm** 100.00/120.00 **st.** –
SB.

---

**HESWALL** Mersey 🔢🔢 K 24 – pop. 16 569.
London 212 – Birkenhead 12 – Chester 14 – Liverpool 14.

Ⅹ **Est, Est, Est,** 146-148 Telegraph Rd, L60 0AH, ℰ (0151) 342 9550, Fax (0151) 342 9551 –
▤. 🆎 🆎 🔲 VISA JCB
closed 25 and 26 December – **Meals** - Italian - 9.95/12.95 **t.** and a la carte ⅄ 5.05.

---

**HETHERSETT** Norfolk 🔢 X 26 – see Norwich.

---

**HETTON** N. Yorks. 🔢 N 21 – see Skipton.

---

**HEVERSHAM** Cumbria 🔢 L 21 – pop. 639 – ⊠ Milnthorpe.
London 270 – Kendal 7 – Lancaster 18 – Leeds 72.

🏨 **Blue Bell,** Princes Way, LA7 7EE, on A 6 ℰ (015395) 62018, Fax (015395) 62455, 🐎 –
⇔ rest, 📺 ☎ 🅿 – 🔬 80. 🆎 🆎 🔲 VISA
**Meals** 12.00/22.00 **t.** and a la carte ⅄ 7.95 – **21 rm** ⌑ 49.50/95.00 **t.** – SB.

*Groß-London (GREATER LONDON) besteht aus der City und 32
Verwaltungsbezirken (Borough). Diese sind wiederum in kleinere
Bezirke (Area) unterteilt, deren Mittelpunkt ehemalige Dörfer
oder Stadtviertel sind, die oft ihren eigenen Charakter bewahrt haben.*

**HEXHAM** Northd. 401 402 N 19 *Great Britain G.* – *pop. 11 008.*

See : *Abbey★ (Saxon Crypt★★, Leschman chantry★ ).*

Env. : *Hadrian's Wall★★, N : 4½ m. by A 6079.*

Exc. : *Housesteads★★, NW : 12½ m. by A 6079 and B 6318.*

🏌 *Spital Park 𝒫 (01434) 602057 – 🏌 Slaley Hall G. & C.C., Slaley 𝒫 (01434) 673350 – 🏌 Tynedale, Tyne Green 𝒫 (01434) 608154.*

🄱 *The Manor Office, Hallgate, NE46 1XD 𝒫 (01434) 605225.*

*London 304 – Carlisle 37 – Newcastle upon Tyne 21.*

🏨 **Beaumont,** Beaumont St., NE46 3LT, 𝒫 (01434) 602331, Fax (01434) 606184 – 📳 ⁜ 📺 ☎ – 🔏 80. 🅾🅾 🅰🅴 🅾 *VISA* �🅲🅱. ✇
closed 25 and 26 December – **Meals** 11.50/17.50 t. and a la carte 🗍 5.00 – ⚌ 6.50 – **25 rm** 60.00/110.00 t. – SB.

↑ **East Peterel Field Farm** ⌂, NE46 2JT, South : by B 6306 off Whiteley Chapel Rc
𝒫 (01434) 607209, Fax (01434) 601753, ≼, ⌖, park – 📺 🄿. ✇
**Meals** (by arrangement) (communal dining) 18.50 st. – **4 rm** ⚌ 35.00/60.00 st.

↑ **West Close House** without rest., Hextol Terr., NE46 2AD, by Allendale Rc
𝒫 (01434) 603307, ⌖ – ⁜ 🄿. ✇
**4 rm** ⚌ 20.00/50.00 st.

**at Slaley** Southeast : 5½ m. by B 6306 – ✉ Hexham.

🏨 **Slaley Hall** ⌂, NE47 0BY, Southeast : 2 ¼ m. 𝒫 (01434) 673350, Fax (01434) 673962, ≼,
🛵, 🚄, 🔲, 🏌, ⌖, park – 📳 ⁜ ▤ 📺 ☎ 🄿 – 🔏 400. 🅾🅾 🅰🅴 🅾 *VISA* 🅼🅲🅱
**Meals** 15.95/19.95 t. and dinner a la carte 🗍 9.75 – **132 rm** ⚌ 110.00/150.00 st., 10 suites –
SB.

🄰 ATS Haugh Lane 𝒫 (01434) 602394

---

**HEYTESBURY** Wilts. 403 404 N 30 – *see Warminster.*

---

**HICKSTEAD** W. Sussex.
*London 40 – Brighton 8.*

🏠 **Travelodge,** Jobs Lane, RH17 5NX, off A 23 𝒫 (01444) 881377, Reservations (Freephone)▶
0800 850950 – 📺 🖰 🄿. 🅾🅾 🅰🅴 🅾 *VISA* 🅼🅲🅱. ✇
**Meals** (grill rest.) – **40 rm** 39.95/59.95 t.

---

**HIGHAM** Suffolk 404 W 28 – *pop. 119* – ✉ Colchester.
*London 55 – Colchester 10 – Ipswich 11.*

↑ **Old Vicarage** ⌂ without rest., CO7 6JY, 𝒫 (01206) 337248, ≼, « 16C former vicarage »,
⊿, ⚘, ⌖, park, ⚒ – 📺 🄿
**3 rm** ⚌ 28.00/58.00.

---

**HIGH CROSBY** Cumbria 401 402 L 19 – *see Carlisle.*

---

**HIGH WYCOMBE** Bucks. 404 R 29 *Great Britain G.* – *pop. 71 718.*

Env. : *Chiltern Hills★ .*

🏌 *Hazlemere G & C.C., Penn Rd, Hazlemere 𝒫 (01494) 714722 – 🏌, 🏌 Wycombe Heights, Rayners Av., Loudwater 𝒫 (01494) 816686.*

🄱 *6 Cashmarket, HP11 2BW 𝒫 (01494) 421892.*

*London 34 – Aylesbury 17 – Oxford 26 – Reading 18.*

🏨 **Forte Posthouse High Wycombe,** Handy Cross, HP11 1TL, Southwest : 1 ½ m. by
A 404 𝒫 (01494) 442100, Fax (01494) 439071 – ⁜ rm, ▤ rest, 📺 ☎ 🖰 🄿 – 🔏 100. 🅾🅾 🅰🅴
🅾 *VISA* 🅼🅲🅱. ✇
**Meals** a la carte 15.15/27.85 st. 🗍 7.50 – ⚌ 10.95 – **106 rm** 109.00/149.00 st. – SB.

🏨 **Alexandra,** Queen Alexandra Rd, HP11 2JX, 𝒫 (01494) 463494, Fax (01494) 463560 –
⁜ rm, 📺 ☎ 🖰 🄿. 🅾🅾 🅰🅴 *VISA*. ✇
**Meals** (closed Friday to Sunday) (dinner only) a la carte 17.00/24.00 st. – ⚌ 8.90 – **29 rm**
75.00 st., 1 suite.

🏠 **Travel Inn,** London Rd, HP10 9YL, Southeast : 3 m. on A 40 𝒫 (01494) 537080 – ⁜ rm,
📺 🖰 🄿. 🅾🅾 🅰🅴 🅾 *VISA*. ✇
**59 rm** 38.00 t.

🄰 ATS Copyground Lane 𝒫 (01494) 525101/          ATS Station Approach, Crendon St.
438019                                                                        𝒫 (01494) 532718

---

**HILLSFORD BRIDGES** Devon – *see Lynton.*

**HILTON PARK SERVICE AREA** W. Mids. – ⊠ Wolverhampton.

🏨 **Travelodge,** WV11 2AT, M 6 between junctions 10A and 11 (southbound carriageway) ℘ (01922) 701997, Fax (01922) 701967, Reservations (Freephone) 0800 850950 – ⁵⁄∗ �📺 ℥ 🅿. 📟 🆎 ① 💳 JCB. ⋇
Meals (grill rest.) – **64 rm** 39.95/59.95 **t.**

---

**HINCKLEY** Leics. 402 403 404 P 26 – pop. 40 608.
🖪 Hinckley Library, Lancaster Rd, LE10 0AT ℘ (01455) 635106.
London 103 – Birmingham 31 – Coventry 12 – Leicester 14.

🏨🏨 **Sketchley Grange,** Sketchley Lane, LE10 3HU, South : 1 ½ m. by B 4109 (Rugby Rd) ℘ (01455) 251133, Fax (01455) 631384, ⅃₆, ≘s, ⃟, ≼ – ⁵⁄∗ �📺 ☎ 🅿 – ⅍ 280. 📟 🆎 ①
💳
Meals (closed Sunday dinner and Bank Holidays) 12.95/19.95 **st.** and a la carte 🅖 8.95 – ⊊ 9.95 – **54 rm** 82.50/99.00 **st.**, 1 suite – SB.

🔘 ATS 5 Leicester Rd ℘ (01455) 632022/635835

---

**HINDON** Wilts. 403 404 N 30 – pop. 493 – ⊠ Salisbury.
London 107 – Exeter 71 – Salisbury 21 – Taunton 47.

🛏 **Grosvenor Arms** with rm, SP3 6DJ, ℘ (01747) 820696, Fax (01747) 820869, 🏦 – ⁵⁄∗ �📺 ☎ 🅿. 📟 💳 JCB
Meals a la carte 13.50/22.50 **t.** 🅖 8.50 – **7 rm** ⊊ 45.00/75.00 **t.** – SB.

*Pour un bon usage des plans de ville, voir les signes conventionnels.*

---

**HINTLESHAM** Suffolk 404 X 27 – see Ipswich.

---

**HINTON CHARTERHOUSE** Bath & North East Somerset – see Bath.

---

**HISTON** Cambs. 404 U 27 – see Cambridge.

---

**HITCHIN** Herts. 404 T 28 – pop. 32 221.
London 40 – Bedford 14 – Cambridge 26 – Luton 9.

🏨 **Lord Lister,** 1 Park St., SG4 9AH, ℘ (01462) 432712, Fax (01462) 438506 – ⁵⁄∗ �📺 ☎ 🅿. 📟 🆎 ① 💳
Meals (dinner only) 8.95 **st.** and a la carte 🅖 4.50 – **19 rm** ⊊ 55.00/70.00 **st.**

✗ **Just 32,** 32 Sun St., SG5 1AH, ℘ (01462) 455666 – 📟 🆎 ① 💳 JCB
closed Monday and Saturday lunch, Sunday and 25 December – Meals a la carte 22.50/ 30.00 **t.**

at Little Wymondley Southeast : 2½ m. by A 602 – ⊠ Hitchin.

🏨🏨 **Blakemore Thistle,** Blakemore End Rd, SG4 7JJ, ℘ (01438) 355821, Fax (01438) 742114, ⃟, ≼ – ⁵⁄∗ rm, �📺 ☎ 🅿 – ⅍ 200. 📟 🆎 ① 💳 JCB
Meals (closed Saturday lunch) 16.95/19.95 **t.** and a la carte 🅖 5.25 – ⊊ 10.75 – **80 rm** 95.00/125.00 **t.**, 2 suites – SB.

✗✗ **Redcoats Farmhouse** with rm, Redcoats Green, SG4 7JR, South : ½ m. ℘ (01438) 729500, Fax (01438) 723322, « Part 15C », ≼ – ⁵⁄∗ rm, �📺 ☎ 🅿. 📟 🆎 ① 💳
closed 1 week Christmas and Bank Holiday Mondays – Meals (closed Sunday dinner and Bank Holiday Mondays) 16.00 **t.** (lunch) and a la carte 22.25/31.00 **t.** 🅖 5.50 – **14 rm** ⊊ 60.00/90.00 **t.** – SB.

🔘 ATS 35 Wilbury Way ℘ (01462) 438262

---

**HOCKLEY HEATH** W. Mids. 403 404 O 26 – pop. 14 538 – ⊠ Solihull.
London 117 – Birmingham 11 – Coventry 17.

🏨🏨 **Nuthurst Grange Country House,** Nuthurst Grange Lane, B94 5NL, South : ¾ m. by A 3400 ℘ (01564) 783972, Fax (01564) 783919, ≼ – ⃟ ☎ 🅿 – ⅍ 80. 📟 🆎 ① 💳. ⋇
closed 25 December – Meals – (see **The Restaurant** below) – **15 rm** ⊊ 125.00/165.00 **t.** – SB.

🏨 **Travel Inn,** Stratford Rd, B94 6NX, on a 3400 ℘ (01564) 782144, Fax (01564) 783197 – ⁵⁄∗ rm, ⃟ & 🅿 – ⅍ 35. 📟 🆎 ① 💳. ⋇
Meals (grill rest.) – **40 rm** 38.00 **t.**

XXX **The Restaurant** (at Nuthurst Grange Country House H.), Nuthurst Grange Lane, B94 5NL, South : ¾ m. by A 3400 &#x1F4DE; (01564) 783972, Fax (01564) 783919, &#x1F6CB; – &#x2716; &#x24C5;. ◍ ⁖ ◍ AE ⓪
*VISA*

closed Saturday lunch and 25 December – **Meals** 29.50 **t.** (dinner) and lunch a la carte 18.50/26.50 **t.** ▯ 8.90.

---

**HOCKLIFFE** Beds. 404 S 28 – see Dunstable.

---

**HOLBROOK** Suffolk 404 X 28 – see Ipswich.

---

**HOLFORD** Somerset 403 K 30 Great Britain G. – pop. 307 – ✉ Bridgwater.
Env. : Stogursey Priory Church★★, W : 4½ m.
London 171 – Bristol 48 – Minehead 15 – Taunton 22.

&#x1F3E0; **Combe House** ⚘, Holford Combe, TA5 1RZ, Southwest : 1 m., turning off A 39 at Elf petrol station &#x1F4DE; (01278) 741382, Fax (01278) 741322, ☎s, ◻, &#x1F6CB;, ⁖ – ⁖ rest, &#x1F4FA; ☎ &#x24C5; ◍ AE VISA
**Meals** (bar lunch)/dinner 20.00 **st.** ▯ 5.80 – **15 rm** ⇌ 35.00/84.00 **st.**, 1 suite – SB.

---

**HOLMES CHAPEL** Ches. 402 403 404 M 24 – pop. 5 465.
London 181 – Chester 25 – Liverpool 41 – Manchester 24 – Stoke-on-Trent 20.

&#x1F3E8; **Old Vicarage**, Knutsford Rd, Cranage, CW4 8EF, Northwest : ½ m. on A 50 &#x1F4DE; (01477) 532041, Fax (01477) 535728 – ⁖ rest, &#x1F4FA; ☎ ✆ &. &#x24C5; – &#x1F4A0; 30. ◍ AE VISA. ⁖
**Church's Brasserie :** Meals 15.50 **st.** and a la carte ▯ 6.40 – **25 rm** ⇌ 69.50/84.00 **st.** – SB.

&#x1F3E8; **Holly Lodge**, 70 London Rd, CW4 7AS, on A 50 &#x1F4DE; (01477) 537033, Fax (01477) 535823 – ⁖ &#x1F4FA; ☎ &#x24C5; – &#x1F4A0; 120. ◍ AE ⓪ VISA
**Meals** (dancing Friday evening) 14.95 **st.** and a la carte – **38 rm** ⇌ 71.50/89.50 **st.**

&#x1F3E8; **Cottage Rest. and Lodge**, London Rd, Allostock, WA16 9LU, North : 3 m. on A 50 &#x1F4DE; (01565) 722470, Fax (01565) 722749 – ⁖ rm, &#x1F4FA; ☎ &#x24C5;. ◍ AE VISA. ⁖
**Meals** (closed Sunday dinner to non-residents) 10.95 **t.** (lunch) and dinner a la carte 9.95/18.00 **t.** – **12 rm** ⇌ 70.00/80.00 **st.**

---

**HOLMESFIELD** Derbs. 402 403 404 P 24 – see Dronfield.

---

**HOLMFIRTH** W. Yorks. 402 404 O 23 – pop. 21 979 (inc. Honley) – ✉ Huddersfield.
🛈 49-51 Huddersfield Rd, HD7 1JP &#x1F4DE; (01484) 687603.
London 195 – Leeds 23 – Manchester 25 – Sheffield 22.

⟰ **Holme Castle**, Holme, HD7 1QG, Southwest : 2 ½ m. on A 6024 &#x1F4DE; (01484) 680680, Fax (01484) 686764, ≼, &#x1F6CB; – ⁖ &#x1F4FA; &#x24C5;. ◍ AE VISA. ⁖
**Meals** (by arrangement) (communal dining) 22.00 ▯ 8.00 – **8 rm** ⇌ 35.00/70.00.

---

**HOLNE** Devon 403 I 32 – see Ashburton.

---

**HOLT** Norfolk 404 X 25 – pop. 2 972.
London 124 – King's Lynn 34 – Norwich 22.

XX **Yetman's**, 37 Norwich Rd, NR25 6SA, &#x1F4DE; (01263) 713320 – ⁖⁖. ◍ AE VISA
closed Monday, Tuesday in winter, 25-26 December, 1 January and 3 weeks late October –
**Meals** (dinner only and Sunday lunch)/dinner 27.00 **t.**.

🅐 ATS Hempstead Rd Ind. Est. &#x1F4DE; (01263) 712015

---

**HOLYWELL** Cambs. 404 T 27 – see St. Ives.

---

**HONILEY** Warks. – see Warwick

---

**HONITON** Devon 403 K 31 The West Country G. – pop. 9 008.
See : All Hallows Museum★ AC.
Env. : Ottery St. Mary★ (St. Mary's★) SW : 5 m. by A 30 and B 3177.
Exc. : Faraway Countryside Park (≼★) AC, SE : 6½ m. by A 375 and B 3174.
🛈 Lace Walk Car Park, EX14 8LT &#x1F4DE; (01404) 43716.
London 186 – Exeter 17 – Southampton 93 – Taunton 18.

**Deer Park** 🔇, Buckerell Village, Weston, EX14 0PG, West : 2 ½ m. by A 30 ☎ (01404) 41266, *Fax (01404) 46598*, ≤, 🏊, 🏊, 🎣, 🌳, park, 🎾, squash – [TV] ☎ [P] – 🎤 70. [MC] [AE] [DC] [VISA] [JCB]. 🐕
**Meals** 17.50/25.00 **st.** and a la carte 🍷 5.00 – **22 rm** 🛏 47.00/200.00 **st.** – SB.

**at Yarcombe** *Northeast : 8 m. on A 30 – ✉ Honiton.*

**Belfry Country H.,** EX14 9BD, on A 30 ☎ (01404) 861234, *Fax (01404) 861579*, ≤ – 🚭 [TV] ☎ 📞 [P]. [MC] [AE] [VISA] [JCB]
**Meals** (dinner only) 18.95 **st.** and a la carte 🍷 7.25 – **6 rm** 🛏 39.00/68.00 **st.** – SB.

**at Wilmington** *East : 3 m. on A 35 – ✉ Honiton.*

**Home Farm,** EX14 9JR, on A 35 ☎ (01404) 831278, *Fax (01404) 831411*, « Part 16C thatched farm », 🌳 – 🚭 rest, [TV] ☎ [P]. [MC] [AE] [DC] [VISA] [JCB]
*closed 25 and 26 December* – **Meals** 14.50 **t.** and a la carte 🍷 5.95 – **13 rm** 🛏 34.00/65.00 **t.** – SB.

**at Payhembury** *Northwest : 7½ m. by A 30 – ✉ Honiton.*

**Cokesputt House** 🔇, EX14 0HD, West : ¼ m. on Tale rd ☎ (01404) 841289, ≤, « Part 17C and 18C, gardens » – 🚭 [P]. [MC] [AE] [VISA]. 🐕
*closed January and Christmas* – **Meals** (booking essential) (communal dining) 21.00 **s.** – **3 rm** 🛏 30.00/60.00 **s.**

---

**HONLEY** *W. Yorks.* [402] [404] O 23 – *see Huddersfield.*

---

**HOO GREEN** *Ches. – see Knutsford.*

---

**HOOK** *Hants.* [404] R 30 – *pop. 6 471* – ✉ *Basingstoke.*
*London 47 – Reading 13 – Southampton 35.*

**Basingstoke Country,** Scures Hill, Nately Scures, RG27 9JS, West : 1 m. on A 30 ☎ (01256) 764161, *Fax (01256) 768341*, 🏋, 🏊, 🏊, 🌳 – 🛗, 🚭 rm, ▤ rest, [TV] ☎ ♿ [P] – 🎤 200. [MC] [AE] [DC] [VISA] [JCB] Y e
**Meals** *(closed Saturday lunch and Sunday dinner)* 15.25/24.50 **st.** and dinner a la carte 🍷 8.50 – 🛏 10.25 – **100 rm** 99.50/139.50 **st.** – SB.

**Hook House,** London Rd, RG27 9EQ, East : ½ m. on A 30 ☎ (01256) 762630, *Fax (01256) 760232*, « Part Georgian house », 🌳 – 🚭 [TV] ☎ 📞 [P]. [MC] [AE] [DC] [VISA] [JCB]. 🐕
*closed Christmas* – **Meals** (residents only) (dinner only) a la carte approx. 15.00 **t.** 🍷 4.00 – **13 rm** 🛏 55.50/74.50 **st.**

**White Hart,** London Rd, RG27 9DZ, on A 30 ☎ (01256) 762462, *Fax (01256) 768351*, 🌳 – [TV] ☎ [P]. [MC] [AE] [DC] [VISA]
**Meals** (in bar) a la carte 8.90/17.85 **t.** – 🛏 6.00 – **21 rm** 59.00 **st.**

**at Rotherwick** *North : 2 m. by A 30 and B 3349 on Rotherwick rd – ✉ Basingstoke.*

**Tylney Hall** 🔇, RG27 9AZ, South : 1 ½ m. by Newnham rd on Ridge Lane ☎ (01256) 764881, *Fax (01256) 768141*, « 19C mansion in extensive gardens by Gertrude Jekyll », 🏋, 🏊, 🏊, 🏊, park, 🎾 – [TV] ☎ [P] – 🎤 100. [MC] [AE] [DC] [VISA] [JCB]. 🐕
**Meals** 23.00/35.00 **st.** and a la carte 🍷 10.00 – **101 rm** 🛏 115.00/190.00 **st.**, 9 suites – SB.

---

**HOOK** *Wilts. – see Swindon.*

---

**HOPE** *Derbs.* [402] [403] [404] O 23 – ✉ *Sheffield.*
*London 180 – Derby 50 – Manchester 31 – Sheffield 15 – Stoke-on-Trent 40.*

**Underleigh** 🔇, Hope Valley, S33 6RF, North : 1 m. by Edale rd ☎ (01433) 621372, *Fax (01433) 621324*, ≤, 🌳 – 🚭 rest, [TV] ☎ [P]. [MC] [VISA]. 🐕
**Meals** (by arrangement) (communal dining) 17.95 **st.** – **5 rm** 🛏 45.00/65.00 **s.**, 1 suite – SB.

---

**HOPE COVE** *Devon* [403] I 33 – *see Salcombe.*

---

**HOPTON WAFERS** *Shrops.* [403] [404] M 26 – *pop. 609* – ✉ *Kidderminster.*
*London 150 – Birmingham 32 – Shrewsbury 38.*

**Crown Inn,** DY14 0NB, on A 4117 ☎ (01299) 270372, *Fax (01299) 271127* – 🚭 rm, [TV] ☎ [P]. [MC] [VISA]. 🐕
*closed 25 December* – **Meals** (in bar lunch Monday to Thursday) 17.95 **t.** (dinner) and a la carte 14.50/19.00 **t.** 🍷 6.50 – **7 rm** 🛏 45.00/75.00 **t.** – SB.

**HOPWOOD** *W. Mids.* 402 ⑨ 403 ㉒ 404 ⑳ – ⊠ *Birmingham.*
*London 131 – Birmingham 8.*

🏨 **Westmead**, Redditch Rd, B48 7AL, on A 441 ℰ (0121) 445 1202, *Fax (0121) 445 6163,* ⇔
– ⋇, ▤ rest, 🔟 ☎ ❖ ❷ – ▵ 250. ⦿⦿ ㏄ ⓪ ⅦⅪ
**Meals** 15.95 **t.** and dinner a la carte ⅋ 5.50 – ⌷ 9.75 – **56 rm** 90.00/105.00 **st.,** 2 suites – SB

---

**HORLEY** *Surrey* 404 T 30 – *pop. 19 267.*
*London 27 – Brighton 26 – Royal Tunbridge Wells 22.*

Plan : see Gatwick

🏨 **Thistle Chequers**, Brighton Rd, RH6 8PH, on A 23 ℰ (01293) 786992
*Fax (01293) 820625* – ⋇, ▤ rest, 🔟 ☎ ❷ – ▵ 60. ⦿⦿ ㏄ Ⅶ ⅥⅪ Ⅰ⼈Ⅾ. ⅍         Y z
**Meals** *(closed Saturday lunch)* 13.50/18.50 **t.** and a la carte ⅋ 5.75 – ⌷ 10.25 – **78 rm**
97.00/120.00 **t.** – SB.

🏠 **Langshott Manor**, Langshott, RH6 9LN, North : by A 23 turning right at Chequers
Thistle onto Ladbroke Rd ℰ (01293) 786680, *Fax (01293) 783905,* « Part Elizabethan manor
house », ⋈ – ⋇ 🔟 ☎ ❷. ⦿⦿ ㏄ ⓪ Ⅶ ⅠⅡⅫ. ⅍
**Meals** *(booking essential)* 19.50/35.00 **t.** ⅋ 8.00 – **14 rm** ⌷ 115.00/175.00 **st.,** 1 suite – SB.

🏠 **Lawn** without rest., 30 Massetts Rd, RH6 7DE, ℰ (01293) 775751, *Fax (01293) 821803,* ⋈
– ⋇ 🔟 ☎ ❷. ⦿⦿ ㏄ Ⅶ ⅠⅡⅫ                                                             Y r
**7 rm** ⌷ 45.00 **st.**

*There is no paid advertising in this Guide.*

---

**HORNCASTLE** *Lincs.* 402 404 T 24 – *pop. 4 994.*
*London 140 – Boston 19 – Great Grimsby 31 – Lincoln 21.*

🏨 **Admiral Rodney**, North St., LN9 5DX, ℰ (01507) 523131, *Fax (01507) 523104* – 📧,
⋇ rm, 🔟 ☎ ❷ – ▵ 140. ⦿⦿ ㏄ ⓪ Ⅶ ⅠⅡⅫ. ⅍
**Meals** *(carving lunch)/dinner* 12.95 **t.** ⅋ 4.95 – **31 rm** ⌷ 49.00/74.00 **st.** – SB.

✕✕ **The Magpies**, 71-75 East St., LN9 6AA, ℰ (01507) 527004, *Fax (01507) 524064* – ⋇, ⦿⦿
Ⅶ
*closed Saturday lunch, Sunday, Monday, 2 weeks August and restricted opening January –*
**Meals** 25.00 **t.** *(dinner)* and lunch a la carte 13.95/25.20 **t.** ⅋ 10.00.

**at Fulletby** *Northeast : 3½ m. by A 153 on Fulletby rd* – ⊠ *Horncastle.*

🏠 **The Old Rectory** ⬙, LN9 6JX, West : ¼ m. ℰ (01507) 533533, *Fax (01507) 533533,* ⬗,
⋈ – ⋇ ❷
*closed Christmas and New Year –* **Meals** *(by arrangement) (communal dining)* 15.00 **t.** –
**4 rm** ⌷ 31.00/52.00 **t.**

---

**HORNDON-ON-THE-HILL** *Essex* 404 V 29.
*London 25 – Chelmsford 22 – Maidstone 34 – Southend-on-Sea 16.*

🍴 **Bell Inn** with rm, High Rd, SS17 8LD, ℰ (01375) 642463, *Fax (01375) 361611,* « 16C coaching inn » – ⋇ rm, ❷. ⦿⦿ ㏄ Ⅶ ⅠⅡⅫ
**Meals** *(closed 25 and 26 December)* a la carte 13.80/23.95 **t.** ⅋ 6.95 – ⌷ 6.50 – **4 rm**
45.00/75.00 **t.**

---

**HORNS CROSS** *Devon* 403 H 31 *The West Country G.* – ⊠ *Bideford.*
Exc. : *Clovelly*★★, *NW : 7 m. by A 39 and B 3237.*
*London 237 – Barnstaple 15 – Exeter 48.*

🏨 **Foxdown Manor** ⬙, Foxdown, EX39 5PJ, South : 1 m. ℰ (01237) 451325,
*Fax (01237) 451525,* ⬗, ⇔, ⟂, ⋈, park, ⋇ 🔟 ☎ ❖ ❷. ⦿⦿ Ⅶ ⅍
*closed February –* **Meals** *(closed Sunday to non-residents) (bar lunch)/dinner* 25.00 **t.** ⅋ 8.00
– **7 rm** ⌷ 45.00/130.00 **t.,** 1 suite – SB.

🏠 **Lower Waytown** without rest., EX39 5DN, Northeast : 1 ¼ m. on A 39
ℰ (01237) 451787, *Fax (01237) 451787,* « Part 17C thatched cottage », ⋈ – ⋇ 🔟 ❷. ⅍
*closed Christmas, New Year and restricted opening in winter –* **3 rm** ⌷ 40.00/55.00 – SB.

---

**HORRINGER** *Suffolk* 404 W 27 – *see Bury St. Edmunds.*

---

**HORSFORTH** *W. Yorks.* 402 P 22 – *see Leeds.*

**HORSHAM** W. Sussex **404** T 30 – pop. 42 552.

Mannings Heath, Fullers, Hammerpond Rd $\mathscr{E}$ (01403) 210228.

**8** 9 Causeway, RH12 1HE $\mathscr{E}$ (01403) 211661.

London 39 – Brighton 23 – Guildford 20 – Lewes 25 – Worthing 20.

**South Lodge** $\gg$, Brighton Rd, Lower Beeding, RH13 6PS, Southeast : 5 m. on A 281 $\mathscr{E}$ (01403) 891711, Fax (01403) 891766, $\leqslant$, « Victorian mansion, gardens », $\overline{\phantom{a}}$, $\gg$, park, $\%$ – $\rightleftharpoons$ rest, $\square$ $\mathbf{\widehat{\pi}}$ $\mathbf{\Theta}$ – $\underline{\mathscr{A}}$ 80. **09** AE $\mathbf{0}$ VISA
**Meals** 18.50/35.00 **t.** and dinner a la carte $\frac{1}{9}$ 9.50 – $\square$ 12.95 – **37 rm** 140.00/205.00 **t.**, 2 suites – SB.

**Cisswood House**, Sandygate Lane, Lower Beeding, RH13 6NF, Southeast : 3 ¾ m. on A 281 $\mathscr{E}$ (01403) 891216, Fax (01403) 891621, $\square$, $\mathscr{R}$ – $\square$ $\mathbf{\widehat{\pi}}$ $\mathbf{\xi}$ $\mathbf{\Theta}$ – $\underline{\mathscr{A}}$ 150. **09** AE $\mathbf{0}$ VISA.
$\%$
closed Easter, Christmas-New Year and August Bank Holiday – **Meals** (closed Sunday) 23.90/26.50 **t.** and a la carte $\frac{1}{9}$ 7.00 – $\square$ 5.50 – **30 rm** 75.00/97.50 **st.**, 2 suites – SB.

**Travel Inn**, The Station, 57 North St., RH12 1RB, $\mathscr{E}$ (01403) 250141, Fax (01403) 270797 – $\rightleftharpoons$ rm, $\square$ $\mathbf{\xi}$ $\mathbf{\Theta}$. **09** AE $\mathbf{0}$ VISA. $\%$
**Meals** (grill rest.) – **40 rm** 38.00 **t.**

**Jeremy's** (at the Crabtree), Brighton Rd, Lower Beeding, RH13 6PT, Southeast : 5 ¼ m. on A 281 $\mathscr{E}$ (01403) 891257, Fax (01403) 891606, $\mathscr{R}$, $\mathscr{R}$ – $\rightleftharpoons$ $\mathbf{\Theta}$ **09** AE VISA
closed dinner Sunday and Bank Holiday Mondays and 25 December – **Meals** 25.00 **t.** (dinner) and lunch a la carte 19.00/21.00 **t.** $\frac{1}{9}$ 10.00.

**at Southwater** South : 3 m. by B 2237 – $\boxtimes$ Horsham.

**Cole's**, Worthing Rd, RH13 7BS, $\mathscr{E}$ (01403) 730456 – $\rightleftharpoons$ $\mathbf{\Theta}$. **09** AE $\mathbf{0}$ VISA JCB
closed Saturday lunch, Sunday dinner and Monday – **Meals** 15.00 **t.** (lunch) and a la carte 19.75/29.40 **t.** $\frac{1}{9}$ 6.50.

**at Slinfold** West : 4 m. by A 281 off A 264 – $\boxtimes$ Horsham.

**Random Hall**, Stane St., RH13 7QX, West : ½ m. on A 29 $\mathscr{E}$ (01403) 790558, Fax (01403) 791046, « Part 16C farmhouse » – $\rightleftharpoons$ rest, $\square$ $\mathbf{\widehat{\pi}}$ $\mathbf{\Theta}$. **09** AE VISA. $\%$
closed 27 December-4 January – **Meals** 14.95/22.00 **st.** $\frac{1}{9}$ 6.00 – **14 rm** $\square$ 74.50/83.00 **st.** – SB.

$\textcircled{1}$ ATS Nightingale Road $\mathscr{E}$ (01403) 267491/251736

---

**HORTON** Northants. **404** R 27 – pop. 574 – $\boxtimes$ Northampton.
London 66 – Bedford 18 – Northampton 6.

**French Partridge**, Newport Pagnell Rd, NN7 2AP, $\mathscr{E}$ (01604) 870033, Fax (01604) 870032 – $\mathbf{\Theta}$
closed Sunday, Monday, 2 weeks Easter, 3 weeks July-August and 2 weeks Christmas – **Meals** (booking essential) (dinner only) 26.00 **st.** $\frac{1}{9}$ 6.00.

---

**HORTON-CUM-STUDLEY** Oxon. **403** **404** Q 28 – pop. 453 – $\boxtimes$ Oxford.
London 57 – Aylesbury 23 – Oxford 7.

**Studley Priory** $\gg$, OX33 1AZ, $\mathscr{E}$ (01865) 351203, Fax (01865) 351613, $\leqslant$, « Elizabethan manor house in park », $\overline{\phantom{a}}$, $\mathscr{R}$, $\%$ – $\rightleftharpoons$ $\square$ $\mathbf{\widehat{\pi}}$ $\mathbf{\Theta}$ – $\underline{\mathscr{A}}$ 30. **09** AE $\mathbf{0}$ VISA. $\%$
**Meals** a la carte 27.50/33.00 **st.** – $\square$ 8.50 – **17 rm** 105.00/200.00 **st.**, 1 suite – SB.

---

**HORWICH** Lancs. **402** **404** M 23 – $\boxtimes$ Bolton.
London 217 – Liverpool 35 – Manchester 21 – Preston 16.

**Holiday Inn Express** without rest., 3 Arena Approach, BL6 6LB, Southeast : 2 ½ m. by A 673 on A 6027 $\mathscr{E}$ (01204) 469111, Fax (01204) 469222 – $\mathbf{|\$\!|}$ $\rightleftharpoons$ $\square$ $\mathbf{\widehat{\pi}}$ $\mathbf{\xi}$ $\mathbf{\Theta}$ – $\underline{\mathscr{A}}$ 30. **09** AE $\mathbf{0}$ VISA JCB. $\%$
**74 rm** 45.00 **st.**

---

**HOTHFIELD** Kent **404** W 30 – see Ashford.

---

**HOUGH-ON-THE-HILL** Lincs. – see Grantham.

---

**HOUGHTON CONQUEST** Beds. **404** S 27 – see Bedford.

---

**HOVE** Brighton and Hove **404** T 31 – see Brighton and Hove.

**HOVINGHAM** N. Yorks. 402 R 21 – pop. 322 – ⊠ York.

London 235 – Middlesbrough 36 – York 25.

🏨 **Worsley Arms,** YO6 4LA, ℘ (01653) 628234, Fax (01653) 628130, « Part 19C coaching inn », ☞ – ⇆ ⊙ ⇔ ☺ – 🛁 25. 🐼 🕮 🚾
**Wyvern :** Meals (dinner only and Sunday lunch)/dinner 25.00 st. ⓘ 7.85 – **Cricketer's Bistro :** Meals a la carte approx. 15.05 st. ⓘ 7.85 – **18 rm** ⊃ 60.00/90.00 – SB.

---

**HOWTOWN** Cumbria – see Ullswater.

---

**HUDDERSFIELD** W. Yorks. 402 404 O 23 – pop. 143 726.

🏌, 🏌 Bradley Park, Bradley Rd ℘ (01484) 223772 – 🏌 Woodsome Hall, Fenay Bridge ℘ (01484) 602971 – 🏌 Outlane, Slack Lane ℘ (01422) 374762 A – 🏌 Meltham, Thick Hollins Hall ℘ (01484) 850227 – 🏌 Fixby Hall, Lightridge Rd ℘ (01484) 420110 B – 🏌 Croslanc Heath, Felks Stile Rd ℘ (01484) 653216 A.

🛈 High Street Building, 3-5 Albion St., HD1 2NW ℘ (01484) 430808.

London 191 – Bradford 11 – Leeds 15 – Manchester 25 – Sheffield 26.

Plans on following pages

🏨 **Hilton National Huddersfield/Halifax,** Ainley Top, HD3 3RH, Northwest : 3 m. at junction of A 629 with A 643 ℘ (01422) 375431, Fax (01422) 310067, 🛌, ≦s, ⃞ – 🖹 ⇆ ⊙ ☎ ⓒ ⓟ – 🛁 400. 🐼 🕮 🚾 🚾 ⎯⎯⎯⎯⎯ A є
Meals (bar lunch Saturday) 12.95/17.95 st. and a la carte ⓘ 6.50 – ⊃ 11.50 – **113 rm** 95.00 st., 1 suite – SB.

🏨 **George,** St. George's Sq., HD1 1JA, ℘ (01484) 515444, Fax (01484) 435056 – 🖹 ⇆ ⊙ ☎ ⓒ ⓟ – 🛁 200. 🐼 🕮 ⓘ 🚾 ⎯⎯⎯⎯⎯ C a
Meals (bar lunch Saturday) 7.95/14.95 st. and a la carte ⓘ 5.25 – ⊃ 9.95 – **59 rm** 80.00/ 110.00 t., 1 suite – SB.

🏨 **The Lodge,** 48 Birkby Lodge Rd, Birkby, HD2 2BG, North : 1 ½ m. by A 629 and Blacker Rd ℘ (01484) 431001, Fax (01484) 421590, ☞ – ⇆ ⊙ ☎ ⓟ – 🛁 30. 🐼 🕮 ⓘ 🚾. ⋘
closed 26 December and Bank Holiday Mondays – Meals (closed Saturday lunch and Sunday dinner to non-residents) 13.95/23.95 t. ⓘ 6.00 – **13 rm** ⊃ 60.00/70.00 t. ⎯⎯⎯⎯⎯ B f

🏨 **Briar Court,** Halifax Rd, Birchencliffe, HD3 3NT, Northwest : 2 m. on A 629 ℘ (01484) 519902, Fax (01484) 431812 – ⇆ rm, ⊙ ☎ & ⓟ – 🛁 150. 🐼 🕮 ⓘ 🚾. ⋘ ⎯⎯⎯⎯⎯ A n
closed 25-26 December, 1 January and Bank Holiday weekends Meals (closed Friday and Saturday) (dinner only) a la carte 9.65/16.45 st. ⓘ 5.75 – **Da Sandro :** Meals – Italian - (closed 25-26 December and 1 January) a la carte 9.85/24.10 t. ⓘ 5.75 – **44 rm** ⊃ 63.00/80.00 t., 4 suites.

🏨 **The Nags Head - Lodge Inn,** New Hey Rd, Fixby, HO2 2EA, Northwest : 3 ½ m. by A 629 off A 643 ℘ (01422) 373758, Fax (01422) 370441 – ⇆ ⊙ ☎ & ⓟ. 🐼 🕮 ⓘ 🚾. ⋘ ⎯⎯⎯⎯⎯ A a
Meals (carving rest.) 11.45 t. – ⊃ 5.50 – **40 rm** 39.00 t.

🏠 **The Mallows** without rest., 55 Spring St., Springwood, HD1 4AZ, ℘ (01484) 544684 – ⇆ ⊙ ⓟ. ⋘ ⎯⎯⎯⎯⎯ C h
closed 21 December-3 January – **6 rm** ⊃ 19.50/40.00 st.

🍴 **Café Pacific,** 3 Viaduct St., HD1 5DL, ℘ (01484) 559055, Fax (01484) 559155 – 🐼 🚾 ⎯⎯⎯⎯⎯ C e
closed Saturday lunch, Sunday, Monday, 25 December and 1 January – Meals 11.50 t. and a la carte ⓘ 4.50.

**at Almondbury** Southeast : 1 ¾ m. by A 629 on Almondbury rd – B – ⊠ Huddersfield.

🍴🍴 **Thorpe Grange Manor,** Thorpe Lane, HD5 8TA, ℘ (01484) 425115, Fax (01484) 425115, ☞ – ⓟ. 🐼 🚾 🚾
closed Saturday lunch, Sunday dinner, Monday and 1 to 12 January – Meals 14.95/19.95 st. and a la carte ⓘ 7.50.

**at Kirkburton** Southeast : 5 m. by A 629 on B 6116 – B – ⊠ Huddersfield.

🏨 **Hanover International H. Huddersfield,** Penistone Rd, HD8 0PE, on A 629 ℘ (01484) 607788, Fax (01484) 607961 – ⇆ rm, ⊙ ☎ ⓟ – 🛁 140. 🐼 🕮 ⓘ 🚾 🚾
Meals a la carte 16.00/27.45 st. ⓘ 6.50 – ⊃ 8.50 – **47 rm** 69.00/89.00 st. – SB.

**at Shelley** Southeast : 6 ¼ m. by A 629 on B 6116 – B – ⊠ Huddersfield.

🏠 **Three Acres Inn,** Roydhouse, HD8 8LR, Northeast : 1 ½ m. on Flockton rd ℘ (01484) 602606, Fax (01484) 608411, ≤ – ⇆ rm, ⊙ ☎ ⓟ. 🐼 🕮 🚾. ⋘
closed 25 December – Meals – (see **The Restaurant** below) – **19 rm** ⊃ 50.00/80.00 t.

## HUDDERSFIELD



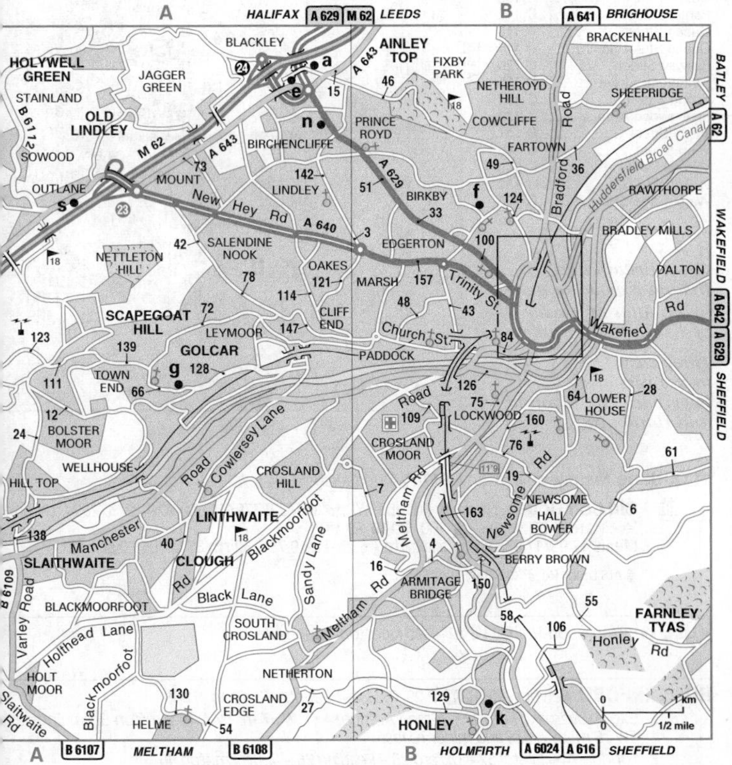


XX **The Restaurant** (at Three Acres Inn H.), Roydhouse, HD8 8LR, Northeast : 1 ½ m. on Flockton rd ✆ (01484) 602606, *Fax (01484) 608411* – ▤ P. MC AE VISA
*closed Saturday lunch* – **Meals** 14.95 **t.** (lunch) and dinner a la carte 17.45/28.15 **t.** 🍷 6.75.

**at Honley** *South : 4 m. by A 616 – ✉ Huddersfield.*

X **Mustard and Punch,** 6 Westgate, HD7 2AA, ✆ (01484) 662066 – MC VISA B k
*closed Saturday lunch, Sunday and Monday* – **Meals** 8.95/13.95 **t.** and a la carte 🍷 4.75.

**at Golcar** *West : 3½ m. by A 62 on B 6111 – ✉ Huddersfield.*

XXX **The Weaver's Shed** with rm, Knowl Rd, via Scar Lane, HD7 4AN, ✆ (01484) 654284, *Fax (01484) 650980,* « Part converted 18C woollen mill » – TV ☎ P. MC AE VISA A g
*closed 25, 26 and 31 December and Bank Holidays* – **Meals** *(closed Saturday lunch, Sunday and Monday)* 13.95 **t.** (lunch) and a la carte 20.45/30.25 **t.** 🍷 5.75 – **5 rm** ☕ 45.00/65.00 **t.**

## HUDDERSFIELD

*Great Britain and Ireland is now covered by an Atlas at a scale of 1 inch to 4.75 miles.*

*Three easy to use versions: Paperback, Spiralbound and Hardback.*

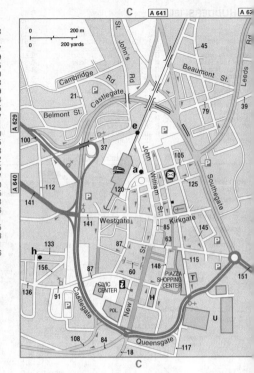

---

**at Outlane** *Northwest : 4 m. on A 640 –* ⊠ *Huddersfield.*

🏠 **Old Golf House,** New Hey Rd, HD3 3YP, ℰ (01422) 379311, *Fax (01422) 372694,* ⌂s, 💨 – ⥮, ▤ rest, 📺 ☎ 🅿 – 🔬 100. 🐧 🗚 ⓪ 𝑉𝐼𝑆𝐴  A
Meals 12.95/17.95 **st.** and a la carte ₰ 6.25 – 🖙 9.75 – **52 rm** 85.00/95.00 **st.** – SB.

🔧 ATS Leeds Rd ℰ (01484) 534441

---

**HULL** *Kingston-upon-Hull* **402** S 22 – *see Kingston-upon-Hull.*

---

**HUNGERFORD** *Newbury* **403 404** P 29 *The West Country G. – pop. 5 046.*
Exc. : *Savernake Forest★★ (Grand Avenue★★★), W : 7 m. by A 4 – Crofton Beam Engines★*
*SW : 8 m. by A 338 and minor roads.*
*London 74 – Bristol 57 – Oxford 28 – Reading 26 – Southampton 46.*

🏠 **Bear at Hungerford,** 17 Charnham St., RG17 0EL, on A 4 ℰ (01488) 682512
*Fax (01488) 684357,* 💨 – ⥮ 📺 ☎ 🅿 – 🔬 75. 🐧 🗚 ⓪ 𝑉𝐼𝑆𝐴 𝐽𝐶𝐵
Meals 14.95/18.95 **st.** and a la carte – 🖙 9.25 – **41 rm** 89.00/135.00 **st.** – SB.

🏠 **Three Swans,** 117 High St., RG17 0LZ, ℰ (01488) 682721, *Fax (01488) 681708 –* ⥮ rm
📺 ☎ 🅿 – 🔬 70. 🐧 🗚 ⓪ 𝑉𝐼𝑆𝐴 𝐽𝐶𝐵
Meals 10.00/15.95 **t.** and a la carte ₰ 4.50 – 🖙 7.95 – **15 rm** 60.00/80.00 **st.** – SB.

⌂ **Marshgate Cottage** without rest., Marsh Lane, RG17 0QX, West : ¾ m. by Church St
ℰ (01488) 682307, *Fax (01488) 685475,* ≤, 💨 – ⥮ 📺 ☎ 🅿. 🐧 𝑉𝐼𝑆𝐴 𝐽𝐶𝐵
**6 rm** 🖙 35.50/55.00 **st.**

✗ **Just William's,** 50 Church St., RG17 0JH, ℰ (01488) 681199 – 🐧 🗚 ⓪ 𝑉𝐼𝑆𝐴
*closed 1 week Christmas –* **Meals** a la carte 12.40/22.95 **t.**

---

*Per usare bene le piante di città, vedere i segni convenzionali.*

**HUNSTANTON** Norfolk 402 404 V 25 – pop. 4 634.
- 🇮🇸 Golf Course Road ℰ (01485) 532811.
- 🇮 Town Hall, The Green, PE36 5BQ ℰ (01485) 532610.
- London 120 – Cambridge 60 – Norwich 45.

🏨 **Le Strange Arms**, Golf Course Rd, PE36 6JJ, North : 1 m. by A 149 ℰ (01485) 534411, Fax (01485) 534724, ≤, 宋 – ᵗᵉ rest, 📺 ☎ 🅿 – 🔬 150. 🐠 🕮 ① 🗚
Meals (bar lunch Monday to Saturday)/dinner 16.50 **t.** and a la carte ≬ 5.50 – **33 rm** ⊡ 54.50/98.00 **t.**, 3 suites – SB.

🏠 **Oriel Lodge** without rest., 24 Homefields Rd, PE36 5HJ, ℰ (01485) 532368, Fax (01485) 535737, 宋 – ᵗᵉ 📺 🅿. 🗚
5 rm ⊡ 38.00/58.00 s.

🏠 **Claremont** without rest., 35 Greevegate, PE36 6AF, ℰ (01485) 533171 – ᵗᵉ 📺
closed 25 December – **7 rm** ⊡ 23.00/46.00 **st.**

---

**HUNSTRETE** Bath & North East Somerset 403 404 M 29 – see Bristol.

---

**HUNTINGDON** Cambs. 404 T 26 – pop. 15 575.
- 🇮🇸 Brampton Park, Buckden Rd ℰ (01480) 434700 – 🇮🇸 Hemingford Abbots, New Farm Lodge, Cambridge Rd ℰ (01480) 495000.
- 🇮 The Library, Princes St., PE18 6PH ℰ (01480) 388588.
- London 69 – Bedford 21 – Cambridge 16.

🏰 **Old Bridge**, 1 High St., PE18 6TQ, ℰ (01480) 452681, Fax (01480) 411017, 宋, 宋 – ᵗᵉ rest, ▤ rm, 📺 ☎ 🅿 – 🔬 50. 🐠 🕮 ① 🗚
Meals a la carte 16.85/26.50 **st.** ≬ 6.50 – **24 rm** ⊡ 79.50/120.00 **st.**

🏰 **Swallow**, Kingfisher Way, Hitchingbrooke Business Park, PE18 8FL, Northwest : by B 1083 at junction with A 14 ℰ (01480) 446000, Fax (01480) 451111, ₭, ☎, ◪ – ▤ ᵗᵉ ▤ 📺 ☎ ✆ ᵭ 🅿 – 🔬 260. 🐠 🕮 ① 🗚
closed 31 December – **Meals** 16.00/20.00 **st.** and a la carte ≬ 6.00 – **146 rm** ⊡ 120.00/180.00 **st.**, 4 suites – SB.

🏨 **George**, George St., PE18 6AB, ℰ (01480) 432444, Fax (01480) 453130 – ᵗᵉ 📺 ☎ 🅿 – 🔬 150. 🐠 🕮 ① 🗚
Meals (bar lunch Monday to Saturday)/dinner 15.95 **t.** and a la carte ≬ 5.95 – ⊡ 9.25 – **24 rm** 79.00/90.00 **st.**

🏡 **Travelodge**, PE18 9JF, Southeast : 5 ½ m. on A 14 (eastbound carriageway) ℰ (01954) 230919, Fax (01954) 230919, Reservations (Freephone) 0800 850950 – ᵗᵉ rm, 📺 ᵭ 🅿. 🐠 🕮 ① 🗚 🗫ᴮ. 🗚
Meals (grill rest.) – **40 rm** 39.95/59.95 **t.**

🅐 ATS Nursery Rd ℰ (01480) 451031/451515

---

**HURLEY-ON-THAMES** Windsor & Maidenhead 404 R 29 – pop. 1 712 – ⊠ Maidenhead.
- London 38 – Oxford 26 – Reading 12.

🏰 **Ye Olde Bell**, High St., SL6 5LX, ℰ (01628) 825881, Fax (01628) 825939, « Part 12C inn », 宋 – 📺 ☎ 🅿 – 🔬 130. 🐠 🕮 ① 🗚
Meals 17.95/23.95 **st.** and a la carte ≬ 9.50 – ⊡ 9.95 – **41 rm** 130.00/150.00 **st.**, 1 suite – SB.

---

**HURSTBOURNE TARRANT** Hants. 403 404 P 30 – pop. 700 – ⊠ Andover.
- London 77 – Bristol 77 – Southampton 33.

🏨 **Esseborne Manor** ⌂, SP11 0ER, Northeast : 1 ½ m. on A 343 ℰ (01264) 736444, Fax (01264) 736725, 宋, 🎾 – 📺 ☎ 🅿. 🐠 🕮 ① 🗚
Meals 17.00 **st.** (lunch) and a la carte 20.00/29.00 **st.** ≬ 9.00 – **15 rm** ⊡ 88.00/135.00 **st.** – SB.

---

**HURST GREEN** Lancs. 402 M 22 – ⊠ Clitheroe.
- London 236 – Blackburn 12 – Burnley 13 – Preston 12.

🏨 **Shireburn Arms**, Whalley Rd, BB7 9QJ, on B 6243 ℰ (01254) 826518, Fax (01254) 826208, 宋 – 📺 ☎ 🅿. 🐠 🕮 🗚
Meals (bar lunch Saturday) a la carte 10.20/19.50 **t.** ≬ 6.50 – **18 rm** ⊡ 40.00/60.00 **t.** – SB.

---

*Pour l'ensemble de la **Grande-Bretagne** et de l'**Irlande**,*
*procurez-vous la **carte Michelin** 986 à 1/1 000 000.*

**HUTTON-LE-HOLE** *N. Yorks.* 402 R 21 – *pop. 162.*
*London 244 – Scarborough 27 – York 33.*

⚐ **Hammer and Hand,** YO62 6UA, ℰ (01751) 417300, *Fax (01751) 417711*, « *18C forme* beer house », 舟 – ✻ ▥ ☎ ✆ ℗. ⬤Ⓞ 𝘃𝘐𝘚𝘈
**Meals** 12.50 **s.** ↥ 4.50 – **3 rm** ⊡ 32.00/44.00 **s.**

⚐ **Quaker Cottage,** YO62 6UA, ℰ (01751) 417300, *Fax (01751) 417711*, « *17C Yorkshir* longhouse », 舟 – ✻ ▥ ☎ ℗. ⬤Ⓞ 𝘃𝘐𝘚𝘈
12.50 **s.** ↥ 4.50 – **4 rm** ⊡ 25.00/44.00 **s.**

---

**HUYTON** *Mersey.* 402 403 L 23 – *see Liverpool.*

---

**HYDE** *Gtr. Manchester* 402 403 404 N 23 – *pop. 30 666.*
*London 202 – Manchester 10.*

🏨 **Village Leisure,** Captain Clarke Rd, Dukinfield, SK14 4QG, Northwest : 1 ¼ m. by A 62 ℰ (0161) 368 1456, *Fax (0161) 367 8343*, ₁₆, ☎, ▨, squash – ▤, ✻ rest, ▥ ☎ ✆ ℗ 🕭 150. ⬤Ⓞ Ⓐⓔ ⓄⒹ 𝘃𝘐𝘚𝘈. ℅
**Meals** (grill rest.) a la carte 10.50/19.40 **st.** – **89 rm** ⊡ 75.00/87.00 **st.**

---

**HYTHE** *Hants.* 403 404 P 31 – *pop. 19 293 (inc. Dibden)* – ✉ *Southampton.*
⛴ to Southampton (White Horse Ferries Ltd) frequent services daily (12 mn).
*London 100 – Bournemouth 22 – Portsmouth 41 – Salisbury 27 – Southampton 17.*

✗ **The Boathouse,** 29 Shamrock Way, Hythe Marina Village, SO45 6DY, ℰ (01703) 845594 *Fax (01703) 846017*, ≼, 舟 – ▤ ℗. ⬤Ⓞ 𝘃𝘐𝘚𝘈
*closed Sunday dinner and Monday* – **Meals** - Brasserie - a la carte 18.00/24.00 **t.**

---

**HYTHE** *Kent* 404 X 30 – *pop. 14 569.*
🏌 Sene Valley, Sene, Folkestone ℰ (01303) 268513.
🅱 En Route Travel, Red Lion Sq., CT21 5AU ℰ (01303) 267799 (summer only).
*London 68 – Folkestone 6 – Hastings 33 – Maidstone 31.*

Plan : see Folkestone

🏨 **Hythe Imperial,** Prince's Par., CT21 6AE, ℰ (01303) 267441, *Fax (01303) 264610*, ≼, ₁₆ ☎, ▨, ₁₆, 舟, ℅, squash – ▤ ✻ ▥ ☎ ♿ ℗ – 🕭 250. ⬤Ⓞ Ⓐⓔ ⓄⒹ 𝘃𝘐𝘚𝘈. ℅ X
**Meals** (bar lunch Saturday) 16.50/23.00 **t.** and a la carte ↥ 13.75 – ⊡ 9.50 – **97 rm** 85.00 105.00 **t.**, 3 suites – SB.

🏨 **Stade Court,** West Par., CT21 6DT, ℰ (01303) 268263, *Fax (01303) 261803*, ≼ – ▤ ✻ rest, ▥ ☎ ℗. ⬤Ⓞ Ⓐⓔ ⓄⒹ 𝘃𝘐𝘚𝘈. ℅
**Meals** (bar lunch Monday to Saturday)/dinner 18.00 **st.** and a la carte ↥ 6.00 – ⊡ 9.50 - **42 rm** 63.00/83.00 **st.** – SB.

---

**IBSTONE** *Bucks* 404 R 29 – *pop. 254* – ✉ *High Wycombe.*
*London 39 – Oxford 20 – Reading 19.*

🏠 **Fox of Ibstone Country,** HP14 3GG, ℰ (01491) 638722, *Fax (01491) 638873*, 舟 – ▥ ☎ ℗. ⬤Ⓞ Ⓐⓔ 𝘃𝘐𝘚𝘈. ℅
*closed 25-26 December and 1 January* – **Meals** (in bar Sunday dinner) a la carte 17.50 25.00 **t.** ↥ 5.00 – **9 rm** ⊡ 59.00/76.00 **st.**

---

**IDE** *Devon* 403 J 31 – *see Exeter.*

---

**IFFLEY** *Oxon* – *see Oxford.*

---

**ILCHESTER** *Somerset* 403 L 30 – *pop. 1 733.*
*London 138 – Bridgwater 21 – Exeter 48 – Taunton 24 – Yeovil 5.*

🏠 **Ilchester Arms,** The Square, BA22 8LN, ℰ (01935) 840220, *Fax (01935) 841353* – ▥ ☎ ℗. ⬤Ⓞ 𝘃𝘐𝘚𝘈 ᴊᴄʙ. ℅
**Meals** a la carte 11.40/22.05 **t.** ↥ 6.50 – **8 rm** ⊡ 55.00/90.00 **t.** – SB.

---

**ILKLEY** *W. Yorks.* 402 O 22 – *pop. 13 530.*
🏌 Myddleton ℰ (01943) 607277.
🅱 Station Rd, LS29 8HA ℰ (01943) 602319.
*London 210 – Bradford 13 – Harrogate 17 – Leeds 16 – Preston 46.*

**Craiglands,** Cowpasture Rd, LS29 8RQ, ✆ (01943) 430001, *Fax (01943) 430000*, – lift, rest, TV ☎ P – 600. MC AE VISA
**Meals** a la carte 10.25/23.50 **st.** 6.95 – **60 rm** 79.00/95.00 **st.** – SB.

**Rombalds,** 11 West View, Wells Rd, LS29 9JG, ✆ (01943) 603201, *Fax (01943) 816586* – TV ☎ P – 70. MC AE DC VISA JCB
*closed 27 to 30 December* – **Meals** 9.95/12.95 **t.** and a la carte 6.75 – **11 rm** 69.50/105.00 **st.**, 4 suites – SB.

**The Grove,** 66 The Grove, LS29 9PA, ✆ (01943) 600298, *Fax (01943) 817426* – rest, TV ☎ P. MC AE DC VISA JCB
**Meals** 12.50/15.50 **st.** and dinner a la carte 4.00 – **6 rm** 42.50/55.00 **st.**

**Box Tree,** 37 Church St., LS29 9DR, ✆ (01943) 608484, *Fax (01943) 607186*, « 18C stone farmhouse, collection of paintings and objets d'art » – MC AE VISA
*closed Sunday dinner, Monday, last 2 weeks January and 26 to 30 December* – **Meals** a la carte 23.50/40.00 **st.** 6.00
**Spec.** Sautéed scallops with a fruit chutney and lemon sauce. Fillet of beef with cep purée and port wine sauce. Croquant of dark chocolate with coffee bean sauce.

---

**LLOGAN** *Cornwall* 403 E 33 *The West Country G. – pop. 13 095 –* ✉ *Redruth.*
Env. : *Portreath★, NW : 2 m. by B 3300 – Hell's Mouth★, SW : 5 m. by B 3301.*
*London 305 – Falmouth 14 – Penzance 17 – Truro 11.*

**Aviary Court**, Mary's Well, TR16 4QZ, Northwest : ¾ m. by Alexandra Rd ✆ (01209) 842256, *Fax (01209) 843744*, – rest, TV ☎ P. MC AE VISA.
**Meals** (dinner only and Sunday lunch)/dinner 13.00 **t.** and a la carte 5.50 – **6 rm** 42.50/60.00 **t.**

---

**LMINSTER** *Somerset* 403 L 31 *The West Country G. – pop. 4 162.*
See : *Town★ – Minster★★.*
Env. : *Barrington Court Gardens★ AC, NE : 3½ m. by B 3168 – Chard (Museum★), S : 6 m. by B 3168 and A 358.*
*London 145 – Taunton 12 – Yeovil 17.*

**Travelodge,** Southfield Roundabout, Horton Cross, TA19 9PT, Northwest : 1 ½ m. at junction of A 303 with A 358 ✆ (01460) 53748, Reservations (Freephone) 0800 850950 – TV P. MC AE DC VISA JCB.
**Meals** (grill rest.) – **32 rm** 39.95/59.95 **t.**

---

**MPINGTON** *Cambs. – see Cambridge.*

---

**NGATESTONE** *Essex* 404 V 28 *– pop. 6 002 –* ✉ *Chelmsford.*
*London 27 – Chelmsford 6.*

**Ivy Hill,** Writtle Rd, Margaretting, CM4 0EH, Northeast : 2 ¼ m. by A 12 ✆ (01277) 353040, *Fax (01277) 355038*, – TV ☎ P – 80. MC AE DC VISA.
**Meals** *(closed Saturday lunch and Sunday dinner)* 21.95 **t.** and a la carte 7.75 – 8.00 – **34 rm** 83.00/150.00 **t.**

---

**NGLEBY GREENHOW** *N. Yorks.* 402 Q 20 *– pop. 391.*
*London 262 – Darlington 28 – Leeds 62 – Middlesbrough 12 – Scarborough 50 – York 49.*

**Manor House Farm**, TS9 6RB, South : 1 m. via lane to manor, next to church ✆ (01642) 722384, <, « Working farm », – P. MC VISA JCB.
*closed Christmas-New Year* – **Meals** – **3 rm** (dinner included) 57.50/95.00 **s.** – SB.

---

**NGLETON** *N. Yorks.* 402 M 21 *– pop. 1 979 –* ✉ *Carnforth (Lancs.).*
*Community Centre Car Park, LA6 3HJ ✆ (015242) 41049 (summer only).*
*London 266 – Kendal 21 – Lancaster 18 – Leeds 53.*

**Pines Country House,** Kendal Rd, LA6 3HN, Northwest : ¼ m. on A 65 ✆ (015242) 41252, *Fax (015242) 41252*, – TV P. MC VISA
*February-October* – **Meals** (booking essential) (residents only) (dinner only) 13.00 **st.** 6.00 – **7 rm** 32.00/48.00 **st.** – SB.

**Ferncliffe House,** 55 Main St., LA6 3HJ, ✆ (015242) 42405 – rest, TV P. MC AE VISA
*March-October* – **Meals** 12.95 **s.** – **5 rm** 28.00/44.00 **st.** – SB.

**Riverside Lodge** without rest., 24 Main St., LA6 3HJ, ✆ (015242) 41359, <, – TV P. MC VISA
**8 rm** 26.00/44.00 **s.**

INSTOW Devon 403 H 30 – see Bideford.

---

IPSWICH Suffolk 404 X 27 Great Britain G. – pop. 130 157.

See : Christchurch Mansion (collection of paintings★) X B.

 craig Rushmere, Rushmere Heath ℘ (01473) 727109 – craig, craig Purdis Heath, Bucklesham R ℘ (01473) 727474 – craig Fynn Valley, Witnesham ℘ (01473) 785267.

🖪 St. Stephens Church, St. Stephens Lane, IP1 1DP ℘ (01473) 258070.

London 76 – Norwich 43.

Plan opposite

🏨 **Swallow Belstead Brook**, Belstead Rd, IP2 9HB, Southwest : 2 ½ m ℘ (01473) 684241, Fax (01473) 681249, I₅, ⇌, ⛱, – 🔟 ☎ ❷ – 🔬 200. 🐶 Aꭆ ❶ 🆅🆂🅰.
Z
Meals (closed Saturday lunch) 19.50 – **86 rm** ⚏ 95.00/105.00 st., 2 suites – SB.

🏨 **Courtyard by Marriott Ipswich**, The Havens, Ransomes Europark, IP3 9SJ, South east : 3 ½ m. by A 1156 and Nacton Rd at junction with A 14 ℘ (01473) 272244 Fax (01473) 272484, I₅ – , rm, 🗐 rest, 🔟 ☎ & ❷ – 🔬 180. 🐶 Aꭆ ❶ 🆅🆂🅰 Jᴄв
Meals 12.95 t. (lunch) and a la carte 17.25/21.00 t. 7.25 – ⚏ 9.50 – **60 rm** 61.00 t. – SB.

🏨 **Marlborough**, Henley Rd, IP1 3SP, ℘ (01473) 257677, Fax (01473) 226927, – rest 🔟 ☎ ❷ – 🔬 50. 🐶 Aꭆ ❶ 🆅🆂🅰 Jᴄв
Y
Meals (closed Saturday lunch) 20.00/23.95 t. and a la carte 8.95 – ⚏ 10.95 – **21 rm** 69.00/85.00 t., 1 suite – SB.

🏨 **Novotel**, Greyfriars Rd, IP1 1UP, ℘ (01473) 232400, Fax (01473) 232414 – , rm, 🔟 ☎ & ❷ – 🔬 180. 🐶 Aꭆ ❶ 🆅🆂🅰 Jᴄв
X
Meals 14.00/16.00 st. and a la carte 8.95 – ⚏ 9.25 – **100 rm** 76.00 st.

🏠 **Highview House**, 56 Belstead Rd, IP2 8BE, ℘ (01473) 601620, Fax (01473) 688659, – 🔟 ☎ ❷. 🐶 🆅🆂🅰 Jᴄв.
Z
Meals (closed Friday to Sunday) (dinner only) a la carte 8.40/13.40 st. – **11 rm** ⚏ 38.50 48.50 st.

🏠 **Travel Inn**, Bourne Hill, Wherstead, IP2 8ND, South : 1 ¾ m. by A 137 (Wherstead Rd ℘ (01473) 692372, Fax (01473) 692283 – rm, 🔟 & ❷. 🐶 Aꭆ ❶ 🆅🆂🅰
Meals (grill rest.) – **40 rm** 38.00 t.

XX **Dhaka**, 6 Orwell Pl., IP4 1BB, ℘ (01473) 251397 – 🐶 Aꭆ 🆅🆂🅰
X
closed 25 and 26 December – Meals - Indian - 6.95/14.95 t. and a la carte 3.95.

X **Mortimer's Seafood**, Wherry Quay, IP4 1AS, ℘ (01473) 230225, Fax (01473) 761611 – 🐶 Aꭆ ❶ 🆅🆂🅰
X
closed Saturday lunch, Sunday and 2 weeks Christmas – Meals - Seafood - a la carte 12.75/25.90 st. 4.50.

X **Galley**, 25 St. Nicholas St., IP1 1TW, ℘ (01473) 281131, Fax (01473) 281131, – . 🐶 Aꭆ ❶ 🆅🆂🅰 Jᴄв
X
closed Sunday, 25-26 December and Bank Holidays – Meals a la carte 18.40/26.40 st. 6.95

**at Claydon** Northwest : 4½ m. by A 1156 off A 14 – Y – ⊠ Ipswich.

🏨 **Claydon Country House**, 16-18 Ipswich Rd, IP6 0AR, ℘ (01473) 830382 Fax (01473) 832476, – 🔟 ☎ ❷. 🐶 Aꭆ 🆅🆂🅰.
Meals (closed Sunday dinner) 12.95 st. and a la carte – **14 rm** ⚏ 54.00/59.00 st. – SB.

🏠 **Travel Inn**, Mockbeggars Hall Farm, Paper Mill Lane, IP6 0AP, Southwest : ½ m. off A 14 roundabout ℘ (01473) 833125, Fax (01473) 833127 – , rm, 🔟 & ❷. 🐶 Aꭆ ❶ 🆅🆂🅰
Meals (dinner only) – **59 rm** 38.00 t.

**at Holbrook** South : 5 ¾ m. by A 137 - Z - and B 1456 on B 1080 – ⊠ Ipswich.

🏠 **Highfield** without rest., Harkstead Rd, IP9 2RA, East : ½ m. by Fishponds Lane ℘ (01473) 328150, ⩽, – 🔟 🔟 ❷.
closed Christmas-New Year – **3 rm** ⚏ 28.00/43.00 st.

**at Copdock** Southwest : 4 m. by A 1214 off A 1071 – Z – ⊠ Ipswich.

🏨 **County H. Ipswich**, London Rd, IP8 3JD, ℘ (01473) 209988, Fax (01473) 730801, I₅, ⇌ – , rm, 🔟 ☎ & ❷ – 🔬 500. 🐶 Aꭆ ❶ 🆅🆂🅰.
Meals 15.00 st. and a la carte 6.00 – ⚏ 8.50 – **76 rm** 75.00/90.00 st. – SB.

**at Burstall** West : 4½ m. by A 1214 off A 1071 – Y – ⊠ Ipswich.

🏠 **Mulberry Hall** , IP8 3DP, ℘ (01473) 652348, Fax (01473) 652110, « 16C farmhouse » , – ❷.
closed 1 week Christmas – Meals (by arrangement) (communal dining) 15.00 st. – **3 rm** ⚏ 20.00/40.00 st.

# IPSWICH

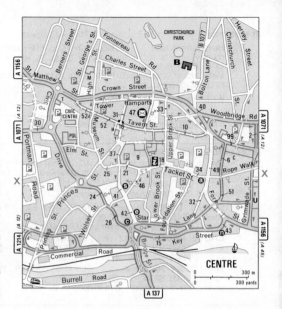

CENTRE

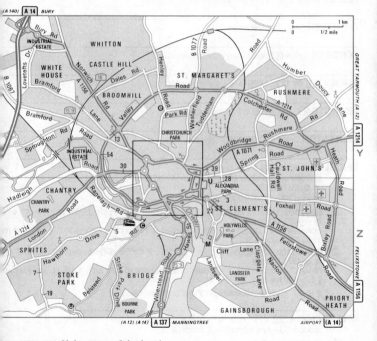

Europe — If the name of the hotel is not in bold type, on arrival ask the hotelier his prices.

305

**at Hintlesham** West : 5 m. by A 1214 on A 1071 – Y – ⊠ Ipswich.

🏰 **Hintlesham Hall** ﹩, IP8 3NS, ℘ (01473) 652334, Fax (01473) 652463, ≤, « Georgian country house of 16C origins », ₤₆, ⓢ, ⊿, ₁₈, ⌕, ☞, park, ✠ – ⓯⌕ rest, 🔟 ☎ ℗ ☒ 60. ◑ ⅍ ⑩ 𝘝𝘐𝘚𝘈
Meals (closed Saturday lunch) 19.50/26.00 **s.** and a la carte 31.00/35.00 **s.** – ⊆ 7.50 – **29 rm** 89.00/220.00 **st.**, 4 suites – SB.

⑩ ATS White Elm St. ℘ (01473) 217157

---

**IREBY** Cumbria ⓓⓞⓘ ⓓⓞⓩ K 19 – see Bassenthwaite.

---

**IRON BRIDGE** Wrekin ⓓⓞⓩ ⓓⓞⓓ M 26 Great Britain G. – pop. 2 184.
See : Ironbridge Gorge Museum★★ AC (The Iron Bridge★★, Coalport China Museum★★, Blists Hill Open Air Museum★★, Museum of the River and visitors centre★).
🛈 4 The Wharfage, TF8 7AW ℘ (01952) 432166.
London 135 – Birmingham 36 – Shrewsbury 18.

⌂ **Severn Lodge** ﹩ without rest., New Rd, TF8 7AS, ℘ (01952) 432148, Fax (01952) 432148, ☞ – ⓯⌕ 🔟 ℗. ✠
closed Christmas-New Year – **3 rm** ⊆ 45.00/55.00 **s.**

⌂ **Bridge House** without rest., Buildwas, TF8 7BN, West : 2 m. on B 4380 ℘ (01952) 432105, Fax (01952) 432105, « 17C cottage », ☞ – 🔟 ℗. ✠
closed Christmas-New Year – **4 rm** ⊆ 35.00/55.00.

⌂ **The Library House** without rest., 11 Severn Bank, TF8 7AN ℘ (01952) 432299, Fax (01952) 433967, ☞ – ⓯⌕ 🔟
closed 24 to 26 December – **4 rm** 40.00/50.00 **st.**

---

**ISLE OF MAN** ⓓⓞⓩ FG 21 – see Man (Isle of).

---

**IVY HATCH** Kent – see Sevenoaks.

---

**IXWORTH** Suffolk ⓓⓞⓓ W 27 – see Bury St. Edmunds.

---

**JERSEY** ⓓⓞⓩ OP 33 and ⓩⓢⓞ ⑩ ⑪ – see Channel Islands.

---

**JEVINGTON** E. Sussex ⓓⓞⓓ U 31 – see Eastbourne.

---

**KEDLESTON** Derbs. ⓓⓞⓩ ⓓⓞⓩ ⓓⓞⓓ P 25 – see Derby.

---

**KEIGHLEY** W. Yorks. ⓓⓞⓩ O 22 – pop. 49 567.
₁₈ Branshaw, Branshaw Moor, Oakworth ℘ (01535) 643235 – ₁₈ Riddlesden, Howden Rough ℘ (01535) 602148.
London 200 – Bradford 10 – Burnley 20.

🏨 **Beeches**, Bradford Rd, BD21 4BB, ℘ (01535) 610611, Fax (01535) 617822 – ⓯⌕ 🔟 ☎ ৬ ℗ – ☒ 40. ◑ ⅍ 𝘝𝘐𝘚𝘈. ✠
closed 24 to 26 December – Meals (carving rest.) a la carte 7.90/15.10 **t.** ₤ 4.45 – **43 rm** ⊆ 60.00/70.00 **t.** – SB.

🏠 **Dalesgate**, 406 Skipton Rd, Utley, BD20 6HP, ℘ (01535) 664930, Fax (01535) 611253 – 🔟 ☎ ℗. ◑ ⅍ ⑩ 𝘝𝘐𝘚𝘈 🄹🄲🄱
closed 2 weeks Christmas – Meals (closed Sunday) (dinner only) 12.25 **st.** and a la carte ₤ 4.75 – **20 rm** ⊆ 45.00/70.00 **st.** – SB.

⑩ ATS 69-73 Bradford Rd, Riddlesden ℘ (01535) 607533/607933

---

**KELLING** Norfolk ⓓⓞⓓ X 25 – pop. 161 – ⊠ Holt.
London 125 – King's Lynn 39 – Norwich 30.

🏨 **The Pheasant**, Coast Rd, NR25 7EG, on A 149 ℘ (01263) 588382, Fax (01263) 588101, ☞ – ⓯⌕ 🔟 ☎ ৬ ℗. ◑ ⅍ 𝘝𝘐𝘚𝘈 🄹🄲🄱
closed 25 December and 2 weeks January – Meals a la carte 12.00/15.00 ₤ 4.95 – **27 rm** ⊆ 48.00/72.00 **t.**

**KELSALE** *Suffolk – pop. 1 309 – ⊠ Saxmundham.*
*London 103 – Cambridge 68 – Ipswich 23 – Norwich 37.*

↑ **Mile Hill Barn,** North Green, IP17 2RG, North : 1½ m. on (main) A 12 ℘ (01728) 668519, ☞ – ⇌ ⊡ ℗
*closed 25 December –* **Meals** (by arrangement) 15.00 **st.** – **3 rm** ⊃ 50.00/70.00 **st.**

✗ **Hedgehogs,** IP17 2RF, North : 1 m. on (main) A 12 ℘ (01728) 604444, *Fax (01728) 604499,* « 16C house » – ⇌ ℗
*closed Tuesday lunch, Sunday dinner, Monday, 1 week January and 1 week October –* **Meals** 9.95 **t.** (dinner) and a la carte 16.40/19.00 **t.**

---

**KEMBLE** *Glos.* 403 404 N 28 – *see Cirencester.*

---

**KEMERTON** *Glos. – see Tewkesbury.*

---

**KENDAL** *Cumbria* 402 L 21 *Great Britain G. – pop. 25 461.*
Env. : *Levens Hall and Garden★ AC, S : 4½ m. by A 591, A 590 and A 6.*
Exc. : *Lake Windermere★★, NW : 8 m. by A 5284 and A 591.*
☈ *The Heights* ℘ (01539) 724079.
🛈 *Town Hall, Highgate, LA9 4DL* ℘ (01539) 725758.
*London 270 – Bradford 64 – Burnley 63 – Carlisle 49 – Lancaster 22 – Leeds 72 – Middlesbrough 77 – Newcastle upon Tyne 104 – Preston 44 – Sunderland 88.*

🏨 **Stonecross Manor,** Milnthorpe Rd, LA9 5HP, South : 1½ m. on A 6 ℘ (01539) 733559, *Fax (01539) 736386,* ☎, ⊡ – ⧉ ⊡ ☎ ⅋ ℗ – 🕍 140. ◉◉ 🗛 *VISA.* ⅋
**Meals** 17.50 **st.** (dinner) and a la carte 16.50/24.50 **st.** ⅃ 6.50 – **30 rm** ⊃ 57.00/140.00 **st.** – SB.

🏨 **Lane Head House,** Helsington, LA9 5RJ, South : 2 m. off A 6 ℘ (01539) 731283, *Fax (01539) 721023,* ≼, ☞ – ⇌ ⊡ ☎ ℗. ◉◉ 🗛 *VISA* JCB. ⅋
**Meals** (dinner only) a la carte 10.50/23.50 **st.** ⅃ 5.00 – **6 rm** ⊃ 41.00/82.00.

↑ **Burrow Hall** without rest., Plantation Bridge, LA8 9JR, Northwest : 3¼ m. by A 5284 on A 591 ℘ (01539) 821711, ☞ – ⇌ ⊡ ℗. ◉◉ *VISA* JCB
*February-November –* **3 rm** ⊃ 35.00/45.00 **st.**, 1 suite.

*at Selside North : 6 m. on A 6 – ⊠ Kendal.*

↑ **Low Jock Scar** ⑤, LA8 9LE, off A 6 ℘ (01539) 823259, *Fax (01539) 823259,* ☞ – ⇌ ℗
*early March-October –* **Meals** (by arrangement) 16.00 **st.** ⅃ 4.00 – **5 rm** ⊃ 30.50/55.00 **st.**

*at Underbarrow West : 3½ m. via All Hallows Lane on Crosthwaite rd – ⊠ Kendal.*

↑ **Tullythwaite House** ⑤, LA8 8BB, South : ¾ m. by Brigster rd ℘ (015395) 68397, ≼, « Georgian house », ☞ – ⇌ rest, ⊡ ℗
*February-October –* **Meals** (by arrangement) 15.00 **st.** – **3 rm** ⊃ 28.00/50.00.

*at Crosthwaite West : 5¼ m. via All Hallows Lane on Crosthwaite rd – ⊠ Kendal.*

↑ **Crosthwaite House,** LA8 8BP, ℘ (015395) 68264, ≼ – ⇌ rest, ⊡. 🗛
*mid January-mid November –* **Meals** (by arrangement) 12.00 **st.** ⅃ 3.25 – **6 rm** ⊃ 22.00/44.00 **st.**

🏮 **Punch Bowl Inn** with rm, LA8 8HR, ℘ (015395) 68237, *Fax (015395) 68875,* ☈ – ⇌ ⊡ ℗. ◉◉ *VISA.* ⅋
*closed 25 December –* **Meals** (booking essential) a la carte 12.00/21.60 **st.** ⅃ 7.50 – **3 rm** ⊃ 40.00/55.00 **t.** – SB.

◎ ATS Mintsfeet Est. ℘ (01539) 721559

---

**KENILWORTH** *Warks.* 403 404 P 26 *Great Britain G. – pop. 21 623.*
See : *Castle★ AC.*
🛈 *The Library, 11 Smalley Pl., CV8 1QG* ℘ (01926) 852595.
*London 102 – Birmingham 19 – Coventry 5 – Warwick 5.*

🏨 **De Montfort,** The Square, CV8 1ED, ℘ (01926) 855944, *Fax (01926) 857830 –* ⧉ ⇌ ⊡ ☎ ℗ – 🕍 300. ◉◉ 🗛 ⓞ *VISA* JCB
**Meals** *(closed Saturday lunch)* 13.50/23.50 **st.** and a la carte ⅃ 6.50 – ⊃ 10.50 – **103 rm** 109.00/120.00 **st.** – SB.

🏨 **Chesford Grange,** Chesford Bridge, CV8 2LD, Southeast : 1¾ m. on A 452 ℘ (01926) 859331, *Fax (01926) 859075,* 📠, ⊡, ☞, park – ⧉, ⇌ rm, ⊡ ☎ ℗ – 🕍 860. ◉◉ 🗛 ⓞ *VISA*
**Meals** 16.50 **st.** (dinner) and a la carte – **154 rm** ⊃ 95.00/105.00 **st.** – SB.

🏠 **Victoria Lodge**, 180 Warwick Rd, CV8 1HU, ℘ (01926) 512020, *Fax (01926) 858703*, 🚗 - ⁵⇔ 📺 ☎ 🄿. 🐵 AE *VISA* JCB. ⁓
*closed 25 December and 1 January* – **Meals** (dinner only) 15.00 **t.** ⅄ 3.50 – **7 rm** ⊆ 37.50/ 57.50 **t.**

🏠 **Castle Laurels**, 22 Castle Rd, CV8 1NG, ℘ (01926) 856179, *Fax (01926) 854954* – ⁵⇔ 📺 ☎ 🄿. 🐵 *VISA*. ⁓
*closed 22 December-3 January and Good Friday-Easter Monday* – **Meals** (residents only) (dinner only) 12.75 **st.** ⅄ 5.00 – **11 rm** ⊆ 33.00/63.00 **t.** – SB.

🏠 **Abbey** without rest., 41 Station Rd, CV8 1JD, ℘ (01926) 512707, *Fax (01926) 859148* – ⁵⇔ 📺. ⁓
*closed 24 December-2 January* – **7 rm** ⊆ 26.00/45.00.

🍴🍴 **Simpson's**, 101-103 Warwick Rd, CV8 1HL, ℘ (01926) 864567, *Fax (01926) 864510* – ▤ 🄿 🐵 AE ① *VISA* JCB
*closed Saturday lunch, Sunday and 24 to 27 December* – **Meals** 15.00/24.95 **t.** ⅄ 5.95.

🍴🍴 **Bosquet**, 97a Warwick Rd, CV8 1HP, ℘ (01926) 852463 – 🐵 AE *VISA*
*closed Sunday, Monday, 3 weeks August and 1 week Christmas* – **Meals** - French - (lunch by arrangement) 23.00 **t.** and a la carte ⅄ 6.00.

---

**KENNFORD** Devon 408 J 32 – *see Exeter.*

---

**KERNE BRIDGE** Herefordshire 408 404 M 28 – *see Ross-on-Wye.*

---

**KESWICK** Cumbria 402 K 20 *Great Britain G.* – pop. 4 836.
Env. : *Derwentwater*★ X – *Thirlmere (Castlerigg Stone Circle*★ ), E : 1½ m. X A.
🐦 Threlkeld Hall ℘ (017687) 79324/79010.
🅱 Moot Hall, Market Sq., CA12 5JR ℘ (017687) 72645 – at Seatoller, Seatoller Barn, Borrow dale, Keswick, CA12 5XN ℘ (017687) 77294 (summer only).
*London 294 – Carlisle 31 – Kendal 30.*

Plan opposite

🏨🏨 **Underscar Manor** ⁓, Applethwaite, CA12 4PH, North : 1 ¾ m. by A 591 on Underscar rd ℘ (017687) 75000, *Fax (017687) 74904*, ≤ Derwent Water and Fells, « Victorian Italianate country house », 🚗, park – 📺 ☎ 🄿. 🐵 AE *VISA*. ⁓
**Meals** – (see *The Restaurant* below) – **11 rm** ⊆ (dinner included) 95.00/250.00 **t.** – SB.

🏠🏠 **Lyzzick Hall** ⁓, Underskiddaw, CA12 4PY, Northwest : 2 ½ m. on A 591 ℘ (017687) 72277, *Fax (017687) 72278*, ≤, ⊆s, 🏊, 🚗 – ⁵⇔ rest, 📺 ☎ 🄿. 🐵 AE *VISA*. ⁓
*closed 24 to 26 December and 4 weeks late January-early February* – **Meals** 11.50/21.50 **st.** and a la carte ⅄ 4.60 – **29 rm** ⊆ 42.50/84.00 **t.**

🏠 **Dale Head Hall Lakeside** ⁓, Thirlmere, CA12 4TN, Southeast : 5 ¾ m. on A 591 ℘ (017687) 72478, *Fax (017687) 71070*, ≤ Lake Thirlmere, « Lakeside setting », 🌲, 🚗 – ⁵⇔ ☎ 🄿. 🐵 AE *VISA* JCB. ⁓
*closed January* – **Meals** (dinner only) 27.50 **st.** ⅄ 8.75 – **9 rm** ⊆ 62.50/90.00 **st.** – SB.

🏠 **Grange Country House** ⁓ without rest., Manor Brow, Ambleside Rd, CA12 4BA, ℘ (017687) 72500, ≤, 🚗 – ⁵⇔ 📺 ☎ 🄿. 🐵 *VISA*    X u
*mnid February-mid November* – **10 rm** ⊆ 28.00/67.00 **st.** – SB.

🏠 **Applethwaite Country House** ⁓, Underskiddaw, CA12 4PL, Northwest : 1 ¾ m. by A 591 on Ormathwaite rd ℘ (017687) 72413, *Fax (017687) 75706*, ≤, 🚗 – ⁵⇔ 📺 ☎ 🄿. 🐵 *VISA*. ⁓
*restricted opening in winter* – **Meals** (dinner only) 17.00 **st.** ⅄ 4.95 – **12 rm** ⊆ 36.00/ 72.00 **t.** – SB.

🏠 **Lairbeck** ⁓, Vicarage Hill, CA12 5QB, ℘ (017687) 73373, 🚗 – ⁵⇔ 📺 ☎ 🄿. 🐵 *VISA* ⁓    X a
*closed January, February and first 2 weeks December* – **Meals** (dinner only) 16.00 **st.** ⅄ 5.25 – **14 rm** ⊆ 36.00/72.00 **st.** – SB.

🏠 **Chaucer House**, Derwentwater Pl., CA12 4DR, ℘ (017687) 72318, *Fax (017687) 75551* – ⁖⁖, ⁵⇔ rest, 📺. 🐵 AE *VISA* JCB    Z a
*5 February-28 November* – **Meals** (dinner only) 17.50 **t.** and a la carte ⅄ 5.95 – **34 rm** ⊆ 40.00/87.00 **t.** – SB.

🏠 **Brackenrigg Country House** ⁓, Thirlmere, CA12 4TF, Southeast : 3 m. on A 591 ℘ (017687) 72258, 🚗 – ⁵⇔ rest, 📺 🄿. ⁓
*Easter-October* – **Meals** (by arrangement) 16.00 – **6 rm** ⊆ 24.00/52.00 – SB.

# KESWICK

*North is at the top on all town plans.*

*Les plans de villes sont disposés le Nord en haut.*

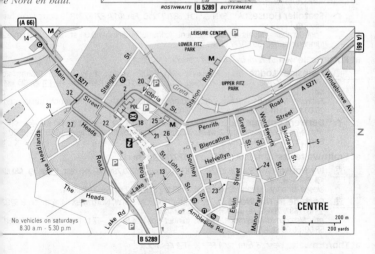

↥ **Acorn House** without rest., Ambleside Rd, CA12 4DL, ℘ (017687) 72553, Fax (017687) 75332 – ⥲ 📺 🅿. 🆎 𝑉𝐼𝑆𝐴. ⚘         Z s
February-November – **10 rm** ⇆ 35.00/65.00 **st.**

↥ **Abacourt House** without rest., 26 Stanger St., CA12 5JU, ℘ (017687) 72967 – ⥲ 📺 🅿. ⚘         Z e
closed January and December – **5 rm** ⇆ 35.00/42.00 **st.**

↥ **Greystones** without rest., Ambleside Rd, CA12 4DP, ℘ (017687) 73108 – ⥲ 📺 🅿. 🆎 𝑉𝐼𝑆𝐴. ⚘         Z n
closed December – **8 rm** ⇆ 24.00/48.00 **st.**

309

XXX **The Restaurant** (at Underscar Manor H.), Applethwaite, CA12 4PH, North : 1 ¾ m. by A 591 on Underscar rd ℘ (017687) 75000, Fax (017687) 74904, ≤ Derwent Water and Fells, « Victorian Italianate country house », ✿, park – ⁴⁄✕ ₱. ⓶ ᴀᴇ 𝘃𝘐𝘚𝘈
**Meals** 25.00 t. and a la carte 25.00/39.00 t. ⁂ 7.00.

**at Threlkeld** East : 4 m. by A 66 – X – ⊠ Keswick.

↑ **Scales Farm** without rest., CA12 4SY, Northeast : 1 ¾ m. off A 66 ℘ (017687) 79660, Fax (017687) 79660, « Part 17C », ✿ – ⁴⁄✕ 𝗧𝗩 ₱
*closed 25 and 26 December* – **5 rm** ⚏ 29.00/52.00 – SB.

**at Borrowdale** South : on B 5289 – ⊠ Keswick.

🏨 **Stakis Keswick Lodore**, CA12 5UX, ℘ (017687) 77285, Fax (017687) 77343, ≤, ♨, ⌚, 🌊, ❄, ✿, park, ⁂, squash – 🔳, ⁴⁄✕ rest, 𝗧𝗩 ☎ ⟵ ₱ – 🔼 70. ⓶ ᴀᴇ ⓪ 𝘃𝘐𝘚𝘈
**Meals** (bar lunch Monday to Saturday)/dinner 17.95 **st.** and a la carte – ⚏ 13.95 – **74 rm** 90.00/132.00 **st.**, 1 suite – SB.                                                                   Y  n

🏠 **Greenbank Country House** ⚝, CA12 5UY, ℘ (017687) 77215, Fax (017687) 77215, ≤, ✿ – ⁴⁄✕ rm, ☏ ₱. ⓶ 𝘃𝘐𝘚𝘈. ❋                                                                               Y  z
*closed January and December* – **Meals** (residents only) (dinner only) 12.00 **t.** ⁂ 4.60 – **11 rm** ⚏ (dinner included) 46.00/90.00 **st.**

**at Grange-in-Borrowdale** South : 4 ¾ m. by B 5289 – ⊠ Keswick.

🏨 **Borrowdale Gates Country House** ⚝, CA12 5UQ, ℘ (017687) 77204, Fax (017687) 77254, ≤ Borrowdale Valley, ✿ – ⁴⁄✕ rest, ₱. ❋
*closed 3 January-5 February and 6 to 16 December* – **Meals** 27.50 (dinner) and a la carte 14.00/35.50 ⁂ 8.25 – **28 rm** ⚏ (dinner included) 77.50/170.00 **st.** – SB.        Y  s

**at Rosthwaite** South : 6 m. on B 5289 – Y – ⊠ Keswick.

🏠 **Hazel Bank** ⚝, CA12 5XB, ℘ (017687) 77248, Fax (017687) 77373, ≤, ✿ – ⁴⁄✕ 𝗧𝗩 ₱. ⓶ 𝘃𝘐𝘚𝘈 ᴊᴄʙ
*April-October* – **Meals** (residents only) (dinner only) – **6 rm** ⚏ (dinner included) 47.50/ 95.00 **st.**

**at Seatoller** South : 8 m. on B 5289 – Y – ⊠ Keswick.

↑ **Seatoller House**, CA12 5XN, ℘ (017687) 77218, Fax (017687) 77218, ≤ Borrowdale, ✿ – ⁴⁄✕ ₱
*April-October* – **Meals** (by arrangement) (communal dining) 10.00 **st.** ⁂ 3.75 – **9 rm** ⚏ (dinner included) 39.50/77.00 **st.**

**at Portinscale** West : 1½ m. by A 66 – ⊠ Keswick.

🏠 **Swinside Lodge** ⚝, Newlands, CA12 5UE, South : 1 ½ m. on Grange Rd ℘ (017687) 72948, Fax (017687) 72948, ≤ Catbells and Causey Pike, ✿ – ⁴⁄✕ 𝗧𝗩 ₱. ⓶ 𝘃𝘐𝘚𝘈. ❋                                                                                                    X  c
*February-November* – **Meals** (set menu only) (booking essential) (dinner only) (unlicensed) 25.00 **t.** – **7 rm** ⚏ (dinner included) 72.00/162.00 **t.** – SB.

↑ **Derwent Cottage** ⚝, CA12 5RF, ℘ (017687) 74838, ✿ – ⁴⁄✕ 𝗧𝗩 ₱. ⓶ 𝘃𝘐𝘚𝘈 ᴊᴄʙ. ❋
*March-October, closed last 2 weeks August* – **Meals** (by arrangement) 14.00 **st.** ⁂ 3.60 – **6 rm** ⚏ 46.00/78.00 **st.**                                                                      X  x

**at Braithwaite** West : 2 m. by A 66 - X - on B 5292 – ⊠ Keswick.

🏠 **Ivy House**, CA12 5SY, ℘ (017687) 78338, Fax (017687) 78113 – ⁴⁄✕ rest, 𝗧𝗩 ☎ ₱. ⓶ ᴀᴇ ⓪ 𝘃𝘐𝘚𝘈 ᴊᴄʙ. ❋                                                                                      X
*closed January* – **Meals** (dinner only) 21.95 **t.** ⁂ 5.25 – **12 rm** 39.00/86.00 **t.**

🏠 **Cottage in The Wood** ⚝, Whinlatter Pass, CA12 5TW, Northwest : 1 ¾ m. on B 5292 ℘ (017687) 78409, ≤, ✿ – ⁴⁄✕ ₱. ⓶ 𝘃𝘐𝘚𝘈 ᴊᴄʙ
*mid March-mid November* – **Meals** (dinner only) 14.50 **st.** – **7 rm** ⚏ (dinner included) 58.00/96.00 **st.** – SB.

**at Thornthwaite** West : 3½ m. by A 66 – X – ⊠ Keswick.

🏠 **Thwaite Howe** ⚝, CA12 5SA, ℘ (017687) 78281, Fax (017687) 78529, ≤ Skiddaw and Derwent Valley, ✿ – ⁴⁄✕ 𝗧𝗩 ☎ ₱. ⓶ 𝘃𝘐𝘚𝘈
*March-October* – **Meals** (residents only) (dinner only) 17.50 **st.** ⁂ 4.50 – **8 rm** ⚏ (dinner included) 69.50/99.00 **st.** – SB.

---

Bitte beachten Sie die Geschwindigkeitsbeschränkungen in Großbritannien
- 60 mph (= 96 km/h) außerhalb geschlossener Ortschaften
- 70 mph (= 112 km/h) auf Straßen mit getrennten Fahrbahnen und Autobahnen.

**KETTERING** Northants. [404] R 26 – pop. 47 186.

🛈 The Coach House, Sheep St., NN16 0AN ℰ (01536) 410266.

London 88 – Birmingham 54 – Leicester 16 – Northampton 24.

🏨 **Kettering Park,** Kettering Parkway, NN15 6XT, South : 2 ¼ m. by A 509 (Wellingborough rd) at junction with A 14 ℰ (01536) 416666, Fax (01536) 416171, ℔₆, ☎, ☒, ☞, squash – ▯
✾ ▤ 🆂 ☎ & 🄿 – ﹙ 200. ◗◗ 🝙 ⓞ 𝘝𝘐𝘚𝘈
*Langberrys :* Meals (bar lunch Saturday) 20.00/30.00 t. and dinner a la carte ⁊ 9.00 –
119 rm ⊊ 120.00/160.00 st.

🏨 **Royal,** Market Pl., NN16 0AJ, ℰ (01536) 520732, Fax (01536) 411036 – ✾ rm, ▥ ☎ 🄿 –
﹙ 170. ◗◗ 🝙 ⓞ 𝘝𝘐𝘚𝘈
Meals (dinner only) 12.95 st. and a la carte ⁊ 5.50 – 40 rm ⊊ 55.00/65.00 st., 1 suite – SB.

🏠 **Travel Inn,** Rothwell Rd, NN16 8XF, Northwest : 1 ¼ m. at junction of A 14 with A 43
ℰ (01536) 310082, Fax (01536) 310104 – ✾ rm, ▥ & 🄿. ◗◗ 🝙 ⓞ 𝘝𝘐𝘚𝘈. ✼
Meals (grill rest.) – 39 rm 38.00 t.

◍ ATS Northfield Av. ℰ (01536) 512832

---

**KETTLESING** N. Yorks. [402] P 21 – see Harrogate.

---

**KETTLEWELL** N. Yorks. [402] N 21 – pop. 297 (inc. Starbotton) – ✉ Skipton.

London 237 – Bradford 33 – Leeds 40.

🏠 **Langcliffe Country House** ⬙, BD23 5RJ, by Church rd on access only rd
ℰ (01756) 760243, ≤, ☞ – ✾ ▥ ☎ 🄿. ◗◗ 𝘝𝘐𝘚𝘈. ✼
Meals (booking essential to non-residents) (dinner only) 17.00 st. ⁊ 4.25 – 6 rm ⊊ 42.00/
64.00 st.

🏠 **High Fold** ⬙, BD23 5RJ, by Church rd on 'Access only' rd ℰ (01756) 760390, « Converted barn », ☞ – ✾ ▥ & 🄿
closed January and February – Meals (by arrangement) (communal dining) 16.00 s. ⁊ 3.50 –
3 rm ⊊ 35.00/56.00 s.

---

**KEXBY** N. Yorks. – see York.

---

**KEYNSHAM** Bristol [403] [404] M 29 – see Bristol.

---

**KEYSTON** Cambs. [404] S 26 – pop. 257 (inc. Bythorn) – ✉ Huntingdon.

London 75 – Cambridge 29 – Northampton 24.

🍴 **Pheasant Inn,** Village Loop Rd, PE18 0RE, ℰ (01832) 710241, Fax (01832) 710340 – ✾
🄿. ◗◗ 🝙 ⓞ 𝘝𝘐𝘚𝘈 🅹🄲🄱
closed dinner 25 December – Meals a la carte 19.00/28.45 st.

---

**KIDDERMINSTER** Worcestershire [403] [404] N 26 – pop. 54 644.

🛈 Severn Valley Railway Station, Comberton Hill, DY10 1QX ℰ (01562) 829400 (summer
only).

London 139 – Birmingham 17 – Shrewsbury 34 – Worcester 15.

🏨 **Stone Manor,** Stone, DY10 4PJ, Southeast : 2 ½ m. on A 448 ℰ (01562) 777555,
Fax (01562) 777834, ≤, ☞, park, ✼ – ✾ ▥ ☎ & 🄿 – ﹙ 150. ◗◗ 🝙 ⓞ 𝘝𝘐𝘚𝘈. ✼
Meals 14.50/18.50 t. and a la carte ⁊ 6.70 – ⊊ 7.95 – 51 rm ⊊ 65.00/115.00 t., 1 suite.

🏨 **Gainsborough House,** Bewdley Hill, DY11 6BS, Southwest : ¾ m. on A 456
ℰ (01562) 820041, Fax (01562) 66179 – ✾ ▥ ☎ 🄿 – ﹙ 240. ◗◗ 🝙 ⓞ 𝘝𝘐𝘚𝘈. ✼
Meals 12.50/16.50 st. and a la carte ⁊ 7.50 – ⊊ 9.50 – 42 rm 65.00/80.00 st. – SB.

**at Chaddesley Corbett** Southeast : 4½ m. by A 448 – ✉ Kidderminster.

🏨 **Brockencote Hall** ⬙, DY10 4PY, on A 448 ℰ (01562) 777876, Fax (01562) 777872, ≤,
« Part 19C mansion in park », ☞ – ✾ rest, ▥ & 🄿 – ﹙ 25. ◗◗ 🝙 ⓞ 𝘝𝘐𝘚𝘈. ✼
Meals (closed Saturday lunch) 19.50/24.50 st. and a la carte ⁊ 8.50 – 17 rm ⊊ 97.00/
150.00 st. – SB.

◍ ATS Park St. ℰ (01562) 744668/744843

---

**KILLINGTON LAKE SERVICE AREA** Cumbria [402] M 21 – ✉ Kendal.

🏠 **RoadChef Lodge** without rest., LA8 0NW, M 6 between junctions 36 and 37 (southbound carriageway) ℰ (01539) 621666, Fax (01539) 621660, Reservations (Freephone) 0800
834719 – ✾ ▥ ☎ & 🄿. ◗◗ 🝙 ⓞ 𝘝𝘐𝘚𝘈. ✼
closed Christmas and New Year – 36 rm 45.95 t.

311

**KIMBOLTON** *Herefordshire* [403] L 27 – *see Leominster.*

**KINGHAM** *Oxon.* [403] [404] P 28 – *pop. 1 434.*
*London 81 – Gloucester 32 – Oxford 25.*

🏨 **Mill House** 🌿, OX7 6UH, ✆ (01608) 658188, *Fax (01608) 658492,* 🎣, 🌳 – 🚭 rest, 📺 ☎ 📞 Ⓟ – 🎤 70. 💳 [AE] [D] [VISA] [JCB]
**Meals** 13.95/22.75 **st.** and a la carte 🍷 8.25 – **23 rm** ☕ (dinner included) 87.75/165.50 **st.** – SB.

**KINGSBRIDGE** *Devon* [403] I 33 *The West Country G. – pop. 5 258.*
See : *Town★ – Boat Trip to Salcombe★★ AC.*
Exc. : *Prawle Point (≤★★★) SE : 10 m. around coast by A 379.*
⛳ *Thurlestone ✆ (01548) 560405.*
ℹ *The Quay, TQ7 1HS ✆ (01548) 853195.*
*London 236 – Exeter 36 – Plymouth 20 – Torquay 21.*

🏨 **Kings Arms,** Fore St., TQ7 1AB, ✆ (01548) 852071, *Fax (01548) 852977,* 🏊 – 🚭 rm, 📺 ☎ Ⓟ – 🎤 250. 💳 [AE] [D] [VISA] [JCB]
**Meals** (light lunch)/dinner a la carte 14.35/21.65 **t.** 🍷 5.30 – **10 rm** ☕ 49.00/85.00 **t.** – SB.

**at Goveton** *Northeast : 2½ m. by A 381 –* ✉ *Kingsbridge.*

🏨 **Buckland-Tout-Saints** 🌿, TQ7 2DS, ✆ (01548) 853055, *Fax (01548) 856261,* ≤ « Queen Anne mansion », 🌳, park – 🚭 rest, 📺 ☎ Ⓟ. 💳 [AE] [D] [VISA]
**Meals** 16.50/30.00 **st.** 🍷 9.75 – **13 rm** ☕ 95.00/195.00 **t.**

**at Chillington** *East : 5 m. on A 379 –* ✉ *Kingsbridge.*

🏨 **White House,** TQ7 2JX, ✆ (01548) 580580, *Fax (01548) 581124,* 🌳 – 🚭 rest, 📺 ☎ 📞 Ⓟ. 💳 [VISA]. 🚫
*March-27 December* – **Meals** (bar lunch residents only)/dinner 19.75 **t.** – **8 rm** ☕ 40.00/115.00 **st.** – SB.

**at Thurlestone** *West : 4 m. by A 381 –* ✉ *Kingsbridge.*

🏨 **Thurlestone** 🌿, TQ7 3NN, ✆ (01548) 560382, *Fax (01548) 561069,* ≤, 🏋, ♨, 🏊, 🏊, ⛳, 🌳, 🎾, squash – 🛗, 🚭 rest, ▤ rest, 📺 ☎ 🚗 Ⓟ – 🎤 100. 💳 [AE] [VISA]. 🚫
**Meals** 11.95/25.00 **t.** and a la carte – **65 rm** ☕ (dinner included) 65.00/196.00 **t.** – SB.

**at Bantham** *West : 5 m. by A 379 –* ✉ *Kingsbridge.*

🍺 **Sloop Inn** with rm, TQ7 3AJ, ✆ (01548) 560489, *Fax (01548) 561940* – 📺 Ⓟ
**Meals** a la carte 11.70/18.90 🍷 4.80 – **5 rm** ☕ 32.00/64.00 **t.** – SB.

ATS Union Rd ✆ (01548) 853247/852699

**KING'S CLIFFE** *Northants.* [404] S 26 – ✉ *Peterborough.*
*London 93 – Leicester 21 – Northampton 19 – Peterborough 7.*

🍴🍴 **King's Cliffe House,** 31 West St., PE8 6XB, ✆ (01780) 470172, 🌳 – 🚭 Ⓟ
*closed Sunday to Tuesday, 1 January, 25-26 December, 2 weeks in spring and 2 weeks in autumn* – **Meals** (booking essential) (dinner only) a la carte 17.45/27.90 **st.** 🍷 4.95.

**KINGSKERSWELL** *Devon* [403] J 32 – *pop. 3 672 –* ✉ *Torquay.*
*London 219 – Exeter 21 – Plymouth 33 – Torquay 4.*

🍴🍴 **Pitt House,** 2 Church End Rd, TQ12 5DS, ✆ (01803) 873374, « 15C thatched dower house », 🌳 – 🚭 Ⓟ. 💳 [VISA]
*closed Sunday dinner, Monday, 2 weeks January, 1 week July and 1 week October* – **Meals** (light lunch) a la carte 21.95/27.25 **t.** 🍷 9.50.

**KINGS LANGLEY** *Herts.* [404] S 28 – *pop. 8 144.*
*London 26 – Luton 14.*

🏨 **Langleys - Lodge Inn,** Hempstead Rd, WD4 8BR, ✆ (01923) 263150, *Fax (01923) 264061* – 🚭 rm, 📺 ♿ Ⓟ. 💳 [AE] [D] [VISA]. 🚫
**Meals** (grill rest.) a la carte 8.50/15.10 **st.** – ☕ 5.50 – **60 rm** 39.00 **st.**

*Keine Aufnahme in den **Michelin-Führer** durch*
*– falsche Information oder*
*– Bezahlung!*

## KING'S LYNN Norfolk 402 404 V 25 Great Britain G. – pop. 41 281.

Exc. : Houghton Hall★★ AC, NE : 14½ m. by A 148 – Four Fenland Churches★ (Terrington St. Clement, Walpole St. Peter, West Walton, Walsoken) SW : by A 47.

🔒 Eagles, School Rd, Tilney All Saints ℰ (01553) 827147.

🖪 The Old Gaol House, Saturday Market Pl., PE30 5DQ ℰ (01553) 763044.

London 103 – Cambridge 45 – Leicester 75 – Norwich 44.

**Knights Hill,** Knights Hill Village, South Wootton, PE30 3HQ, Northeast : 4 ½ m. on A 148 at junction with A 149 ℰ (01553) 675566, Fax (01553) 675568, ₤ₛ, ⇌, 🔲, ☞, ℀ – ✻ 🔟 ☎ 🅿 – 🔏 300. 🐿 🝔 🕦 ₩₸ ⅋
*Garden :* Meals (dinner only and Sunday lunch)/dinner 16.95 st. and a la carte ᛏ 4.50 –
*Farmers Arms :* Meals (carving lunch) a la carte 10.90/19.25 st. ᛏ 4.50 – ☲ 7.50 – **53 rm** 80.00/120.00 st. – SB.

**Duke's Head,** Tuesday Market Pl., PE30 1JS, ℰ (01553) 774996, Fax (01553) 763556 – 🛗 ✻ 🔟 ☎ 🅿 – 🔏 200. 🐿 🝔 🕦 ₩₸ ⅋
*Griffins :* Meals a la carte 9.50/17.50 st. ᛏ 4.95 – *Restaurant :* Meals (dinner only) 15.95 st. and a la carte ᛏ 6.95 – ☲ 9.25 – **71 rm** 75.00/90.00 st. – SB.

**Butterfly,** Beveridge Way, PE30 4NB, Southeast : 2 ¼ m. by Hardwick Rd at junction of A 10 with A 47 ℰ (01553) 771707, Fax (01553) 768027 – ✻ rm, 🔟 ☎ 🅿 – 🔏 40. 🐿 🝔 🕦 ₩₸ ⅋
Meals 15.00 st. and a la carte – ☲ 7.50 – **50 rm** 65.00 st. – SB.

**Old Rectory** without rest., 33 Goodwins Rd, PE30 5QX, ℰ (01553) 768544, ☞ – ✻ 🔟 🅿 **4 rm** ☲ 28.00/42.00 s.

**Fairlight Lodge** without rest., 79 Goodwins Rd, PE30 5PE, ℰ (01553) 762234, Fax (01553) 770280, ☞ – ✻ 🔟 🅿
closed 24 to 26 December – **7 rm** ☲ 25.00/40.00.

**Rococo,** 11 Saturday Market Pl., Old Town, PE30 5DQ, ℰ (01553) 771483, Fax (01553) 771483 – 🐿 🝔 🕦 ₩₸ ⱼ꜀ʙ
closed Monday lunch, Sunday and 24 to 30 December – **Meals** (booking essential) 13.50/ 27.50 st. ᛏ 6.00.

**at Grimston** East : 6 ¼ m. by A 148 – ⊠ King's Lynn.

**Congham Hall** ⌂, Lynn Rd, PE32 1AH, ℰ (01485) 600250, Fax (01485) 601191, ≤, « Part Georgian manor house, herb garden », ⚊, ☞, park, ℀ – ✻ rest, 🔟 ☎ 🅿 – 🔏 25. 🐿 🝔 🕦 ₩₸ ⅋
*Orangery :* Meals 13.50/32.00 t. ᛏ 6.85 – **12 rm** ☲ 80.00/155.00 t., 2 suites – SB.

🔧 ATS 4 Oldmedow Rd, Hardwick Rd Trading Est. ℰ (01553) 774035

---

## KINGS NORTON W. Mids. 402 ⑩ 403 ㉛ 404 ⑳ – see Birmingham.

---

## KINGSTON BAGPUIZE Oxon. 403 404 P 28 – see Abingdon.

---

## KINGSTON-UPON-HULL 402 S 22 Great Britain G. – pop. 310 636.

Exc. : Burton Constable★ AC, NE : 9 m. by A 165 and B 1238 Z.

🔒 Springhead Park, Willerby Rd ℰ (01482) 656309 – 🔒 Sutton Park, Salthouse Rd ℰ (01482) 374242.

Humber Bridge (toll).

✈ Humberside Airport : ℰ (01652) 688456, S : 19 m. by A 63 – **Terminal :** Coach Service.
⛴ to The Netherlands (Rotterdam) (North Sea Ferries) (12 h 30 mn).

🖪 75/76 Carr Lane, HU1 3RQ ℰ (01482) 223559 – King George Dock, Hedon Rd, HU9 5PR ℰ (01482) 702118.

London 183 – Leeds 61 – Nottingham 94 – Sheffield 68.

Plan on next page

**Forte Posthouse Hull Marina,** The Marina, Castle St., HU1 2BX, ℰ (01482) 225221, Fax (01482) 213299, ≤, ₤ₛ, ⇌, 🔲 – 🛗 ✻ rm, 🗏 rest, 🔟 ☎ & 🅿 – 🔏 120. 🐿 🝔 🕦 ⱼ꜀ʙ
Y n
Meals (closed Saturday lunch) 13.00/18.00 st. and a la carte ᛏ 7.95 – ☲ 9.95 – **99 rm** 99.00 st. – SB.

**Quality Royal,** Ferensway, HU1 3UF, ℰ (01482) 325087, Fax (01482) 323172, ₤ₛ, ⇌, 🔲 – 🛗, ✻ rm, 🗏 rest, 🔟 ☎ & 🅿 – 🔏 450. 🐿 🝔 🕦 ₩₸ ⅋
Y a
Meals 14.50 st. and a la carte ᛏ 4.50 – ☲ 9.50 – **155 rm** 66.50/107.00 st.

**Travel Inn,** Kingswood Park, Ennerdale Link Rd, HU7 4HS, North : 5 m. by A 1079 on A 1033 ℰ (01482) 820225, Fax (01482) 820300 – 🛗, ✻ rm, 🗏 rest, 🔟 & 🅿. 🐿 🝔 🕦 ₩₸
Meals (grill rest.) – **42 rm** 38.00 t.

# KINGSTON-UPON-HULL

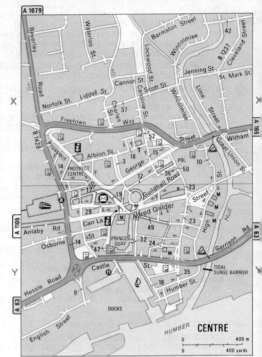

CENTRE

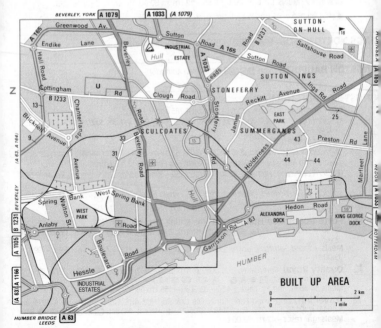

BUILT UP AREA

🏠 **Travel Inn,** Ferriby Rd, Hessle, HU13 0JA, West : 7 m. by A 63 off A 164 ℰ (01482) 645285, *Fax* (01482) 645299 – ▯, ⟵ rm, ▤ rest, ▯ ᴪ 🅿. 🕮 🆎 ① 𝘝𝘐𝘚𝘈. ℅
**Meals** (grill rest.) – **40 rm** 38.00 **t.**

at Hedon *East : 6½ m. by A 63 off A 1033* – Z – ✉ Kingston-upon-Hull.

🏠🏠 **Kingstown,** Hull Rd, HU12 8DJ, West : 1 m. at junction with A 1033 ℰ (01482) 890461, *Fax* (01482) 890713, ⌖ – ⟵ rm, ▤ rest, ▯ ☎ ᴪ 🅿. 🕮 🆎 𝘑𝘤𝘣. ℅
**Meals** (grill rest.) a la carte 7.20/14.65 **t.** – **34 rm** ⊆ 45.00/55.00 **t.**

at Willerby *West : 5 m. by A 1079, Spring Bank - Z - and Willerby Rd* – ✉ Kingston-upon-Hull.

🏠🏠🏠 **Willerby Manor,** Well Lane, HU10 6ER, off Main St. ℰ (01482) 652616, *Fax* (01482) 653901, ℔, ⩲, ▧, ⌖ – ⟵ rm, ▯ ☎ 🅿 – 🕰 500. 🕮 🆎 𝘝𝘐𝘚𝘈. ℅
*closed 25 December* – **Lafite : Meals** *(closed Saturday lunch and Sunday dinner)* 14.00/16.50 **st.** and a la carte ⓙ 5.95 – **Everglades : Meals** a la carte 7.65/15.20 **st.** ⓙ 5.95 – ⊆ 8.75 – **51 rm** 68.50/84.50 **st.**

at Little Weighton *Northwest : 9 m. by A 1079 - Z - and B 1233 via Skidby village* – ✉ Cottingham.

🏠🏠 **Rowley Manor** ⌖, HU20 3XR, Southwest : ½ m. by Rowley Rd ℰ (01482) 848248, *Fax* (01482) 849900, ⟨, « Georgian manor house », ⌖ – ▯ ☎ 🅿 – 🕰 80. 🕮 🆎 ① 𝘝𝘐𝘚𝘈
**Meals** (lunch by arrangement) a la carte approx. 21.50 **t.** ⓙ 6.45 – **16 rm** ⊆ 65.00/90.00 **t.** – SB.

⑩ ATS Great Union St. ℰ (01482) 329044          ATS Waverley St. ℰ (01482) 329370/225502

---

**KINGSTOWN** *Cumbria – see Carlisle.*

---

**KINGSWEAR** *Devon 𝟜𝟘𝟛 J 32 – see Dartmouth.*

---

**KINGTON** *Herefordshire 𝟜𝟘𝟛 K 27 – pop. 2 197.*
*London 152 – Birmingham 61 – Hereford 19 – Shrewsbury 54.*

🏠🏠 **Penrhos Court,** HR5 3LH, East : 1 ½ m. on A 44 ℰ (01544) 230720, *Fax* (01544) 230754, « Part 15C and 16C house with medieval cruck hall », ⌖ – ⟵ ▯ ☎ 🅿 – 🕰 25. 🕮 🆎 𝘝𝘐𝘚𝘈. ℅
*closed January* – **Meals** - Organic produce - (booking essential) (dinner only) 28.50 **t.** – **15 rm** ⊆ 50.00/105.00 **st.** – SB.

at Titley *Northeast : 3½ m. on B 4355* – ✉ Kington.

▯ **Stagg Inn,** HR5 3RL, ℰ (01544) 230221, *Fax* (01544) 230221 – 🅿
**Meals** (booking essential) a la carte 14.00/19.75 **t.** ⓙ 5.95.

⑩ ATS 20-22 Bridge St. ℰ (01544) 230350

---

**KIRKBURTON** *W. Yorks. 𝟜𝟘𝟚 𝟜𝟘𝟜 O 23 – see Huddersfield.*

---

**KIRKBY LONSDALE** *Cumbria 𝟜𝟘𝟚 M 21 – pop. 2 076 – ✉ Carnforth (Lancs.).*
▣₁₈ Scaleber Lane, Barbon ℰ (015242) 76365 – ▣ Casterton, Sedbergh Rd ℰ (015242) 71592.
🅱 24 Main St., LA6 2AE ℰ (015242) 71437 (restricted opening in winter).
*London 259 – Carlisle 62 – Kendal 13 – Lancaster 17 – Leeds 58.*

🏠 **Whoop Hall Inn,** Burrow with Burrow, LA6 2HP, Southeast : 1 m. on A 65 ℰ (015242) 71284, *Fax* (015242) 72154, ⌖ – ▯ ☎ 🅿 – 🕰 140. 🕮 🆎 ① 𝘝𝘐𝘚𝘈 𝘑𝘤𝘣. ℅
**Meals** 15.00 **t.** (dinner) and a la carte 10.00/25.00 **t.** ⓙ 4.95 – **23 rm** ⊆ 60.00/90.00 **t.** – SB.

🏠 **Pheasant Inn,** Casterton, LA6 2RX, Northeast : 1 ¼ m. on A 683 ℰ (015242) 71230, *Fax* (015242) 71230, ⌖ – ⟵ rest, ▯ ☎ ᴪ ᴪ 🅿. 🕮 ① 𝘝𝘐𝘚𝘈 𝘑𝘤𝘣
**Meals** *(closed Sunday November-March and Monday)* (bar lunch)/dinner a la carte 11.50/23.00 **st.** ⓙ 5.45 – **10 rm** ⊆ 37.50/68.00.

▯ **Snooty Fox Tavern** with rm, 33 Main St., LA6 2AH, ℰ (015242) 71308, *Fax* (015242) 72642, « Jacobean inn » – ▯ 🅿. 🕮 🆎 𝘝𝘐𝘚𝘈
*closed 25 December* – **Meals** a la carte 12.50/23.50 **st.** ⓙ 5.00 – **9 rm** ⊆ 30.00/57.50 **st.**

at Cowan Bridge *(Lancs.) Southeast : 2 m. on A 65* – ✉ Carnforth (Lancs.).

🏠 **Hipping Hall,** LA6 2JJ, Southeast : ½ m. on A 65 ℰ (015242) 71187, *Fax* (015242) 72452, « Former 15C hamlet », ⌖ – ⟵ rest, ▯ ☎ 🅿. 🕮 𝘝𝘐𝘚𝘈
*mid March-mid November* – **Meals** (residents only) (communal dining) (dinner only) 24.00 **st.** – **5 rm** ⊆ 72.00/88.00 **st.**, 2 suites – SB.

**KIRKBY MALHAM** N. Yorks. 402 N 21 – pop. 70 – ⊠ Skipton.
*London 235 – Bradford 25 – Burnley 30 – Carlisle 97 – Harrogate 25 – York 47.*

↑ **Holgate Head** ◈, BD23 4BJ, ℰ (01729) 830376, Fax (01729) 830576, ≼, « Part 17C »
🌲 – ⚒ 📺 ℗. ⚘
*March-mid October* – **Meals** (communal dining) 22.00 **st.** ⏶ 4.75 – **3 rm** ⊇ 51.50/73.00 **st.**

---

**KIRKBYMOORSIDE** N. Yorks. 402 R 21 – pop. 2 650.
🏌 *Manor Vale* ℰ (01751) 431525.
*London 244 – Scarborough 26 – York 33.*

🏠 **George and Dragon,** 17 Market Pl., YO62 6AA, ℰ (01751) 433334, Fax (01751) 433334,
« Part 17C coaching inn », ⚘, 🌲 – ⚒ rest, 📺 ☎ ℗. ◍ AE VISA
**Meals** (bar lunch Monday to Saturday) 15.05/20.65 **t.** ⏶ 5.95 – **18 rm** ⊇ 49.00/89.00 **t.** – SB

---

**KIRKBY STEPHEN** Cumbria 402 M 20 – pop. 1 619.
🛈 Market St., CA17 4QN ℰ (017683) 71199 (summer only).
*London 285 – Carlisle 48 – Kendal 24.*

↑ **Ing Hill Lodge** ◈, Mallerstang Dale, CA17 4JT, South : 4 ½ m. on B 6259,
ℰ (017683) 71153, Fax (017683) 71153, ≼ Mallerstang Dale, 🌲 – ⚒ 📺 ℗
*closed January and February* – **Meals** (by arrangement) 12.50 **st.** ⏶ 3.50 – **3 rm** ⊇ 50.00 **st.**
– SB.

**at Crosby Garrett** Northwest : 4½ m. by Silver St. – ⊠ Kirkby Stephen.

↑ **Old Rectory** ◈, CA17 4PW, ℰ (017683) 72074, « Part 17C », 🌲 – ⚒ ℗. ⚘
*closed Christmas and New Year* – **Meals** (by arrangement) (communal dining) 14.00 **st.** –
**3 rm** ⊇ 33.00/48.00 **st.**

---

**KIRKCAMBECK** Cumbria 401 402 L 18 – see Brampton.

---

**KIRKHAM** Lancs. 402 L 22 – pop. 9 038 – ⊠ Preston.
*London 240 – Blackpool 9 – Preston 7.*

🏠 **Fairfield Arms - Premier Lodge,** Fleetwood Rd, PR4 3HE, Northwest : 2 m. by B 5192
on A 585 (M 55 junction 3) ℰ (01772) 685561, Fax (01772) 682464, Reservations (Freephone) 0800 118833 – ⚒ rm, 📺 ☎ ⚒ & ℗. ◍ AE ◍ VISA
**Meals** (grill rest.) a la carte 7.70/14.55 **st.** ⏶ 4.95 – ⊇ 5.95 – **28 rm** 43.95 **st.** – SB.

✗✗ **Cromwellian,** 16 Poulton St., PR4 2AB, ℰ (01772) 685680, Fax (01772) 685680 – ◍ AE
◍ VISA JCB
*closed Sunday, Monday, 1 week spring and 2 weeks summer* – **Meals** (dinner only) 18.00 **st.**
⏶ 5.50.

---

**KIRKWHELPINGTON** Northd. 401 402 N/O 18 Great Britain G. – pop. 353 – ⊠ Morpeth.
Env. : *Wallington House★ AC,* E : 3½ m. by A 696 and B 6342.
*London 305 – Carlisle 46 – Newcastle upon Tyne 20.*

↑ **Shieldhall** ◈, Wallington, NE61 4AQ, Southeast : 2 ½ m. by A 696 on B 6342,
ℰ (01830) 540387, Fax (01830) 540387, 🌲 – ⚒ ℗. ◍ VISA. ⚘
*closed January and December* – **Meals** 15.00 – **4 rm** ⊇ 25.00/47.00.

---

**KIRTLING** Suffolk 404 V 27 – see Newmarket.

---

**KNARESBOROUGH** N. Yorks. 402 P 21 – pop. 13 380.
🏌 *Boroughbridge Rd* ℰ (01423) 863219.
🛈 35 Market Place, HG5 8AL ℰ (01423) 866886 (summer only).
*London 217 – Bradford 21 – Harrogate 3 – Leeds 18 – York 18.*

🏨 **Dower House,** Bond End, HG5 9AL, ℰ (01423) 863302, Fax (01423) 867665, 🛵, 🏋, 🏊,
🌲 – ⚒ 📺 ☎ ℗ – 🔬 65. ◍ AE ◍ VISA. ⚘
**Meals** (bar lunch Monday to Saturday)/dinner 15.00 **st.** and a la carte ⏶ 6.00 – **31 rm**
⊇ 57.50/100.00 **st.**, 1 suite – SB.

**at Ferrensby** Northeast : 3 m. on A 6055.

✗✗ **The General Tarleton Inn** with rm, Boroughbridge Rd, HG5 0QB, ℰ (01423) 340284,
Fax (01423) 340288 – ⚒ rest, 📺 ☎ ℗ – 🔬 40. ◍ ◍ VISA
*closed 25 December* – **The Dining Room :** Meals (dinner only and Sunday lunch)/dinner
25.00 **t.** ⏶ 8.90 – (see also below) – ⊇ 9.95 – **14 rm** 60.00 **t.** – SB.

🏠 **The General Tarleton Inn**, Boroughbridge Rd, HG5 0QB, ℰ (01423) 340284, *Fax (01423) 340288*, « Characterful 18C inn » – ✦ 🅿 🕮 AE VISA
   **Bar/Brasserie :** Meals *(closed 25 December)* (bookings not accepted) 12.45 **t.** (dinner) and a la carte 14.30/25.30 **t.** ⓘ 8.90.

---

**NIGHTWICK** *Worcestershire* 403 404 M 27 – pop. 87 – ⊠ *Worcester.*
   *London 132 – Hereford 20 – Leominster 18 – Worcester 8.*

🏠 **Talbot** with rm, WR6 5PH, on B 4197 ℰ (01886) 821235, *Fax (01886) 821060*, ⇌, ⚲, squash – 🗳 ☎ 🅿 🕮 VISA. ⚘
   *closed dinner 25 December* – **Meals** 12.95/16.95 **st.** – **10 rm** ⊑ 40.00/75.00 **t.** – SB.

---

**KNOWLE** *W. Mids.* 403 404 O 26 – pop. 17 588 – ⊠ *Solihull.*
   *London 108 – Birmingham 9 – Coventry 10 – Warwick 11.*

🏨 **Greswolde Arms**, 1657 High St., B93 0LL, ℰ (01564) 772711, *Fax (01564) 770354* – ✦ rm, 🗳 ☎ & 🅿 – 🔬 150. 🕮 AE ⓞ VISA. ⚘
   **Meals** 15.00/17.50 **t.** and a la carte ⓘ 6.75 – ⊑ 6.75 – **36 rm** 65.00/95.00 **t.** – SB.

---

**KNOWL HILL** *Windsor & Maidenhead* 404 R 29 – ⊠ *Twyford.*
   🏌18, 🏌5, Hennerton, Crazies Hill Rd, Wargrave ℰ (01734) 401000/404778.
   *London 38 – Maidenhead 5 – Reading 8.*

🏨 **Bird in Hand**, Bath Rd, RG10 9UP, ℰ (01628) 826622, *Fax (01628) 826748*, ☞ – 🗳 ☎ & 🅿. 🕮 AE ⓞ VISA
   *closed 23 to 30 December* – **Meals** 16.50 **t.** and a la carte ⓘ 6.00 – **15 rm** ⊑ 90.00/100.00 **st.** – SB.

---

**KNUTSFORD** *Ches.* 402 403 404 M 24 – pop. 13 352.
   🛈 Council Offices, Toft Rd, WA16 6TA ℰ (01565) 632611.
   *London 187 – Chester 25 – Liverpool 33 – Manchester 18 – Stoke-on-Trent 30.*

🏰 **Cottons**, Manchester Rd, WA16 0SU, Northwest : 1 ½ m. on A 50 ℰ (01565) 650333, *Fax (01565) 755351*, 🗲₆, ⇌, 🏊, ⚲, squash – 🗲, ✦ rm, 🗳 ☎ & 🅿 – 🔬 200. 🕮 AE ⓞ VISA. ⚘
   **Magnolia :** Meals *(closed Saturday lunch)* a la carte 20.00/30.00 **t.** ⓘ 9.00 – **90 rm** ⊑ 117.00/161.00 **st.**, 9 suites.

🏨 **Royal George**, King St., WA16 6EE, ℰ (01565) 634151, *Fax (01565) 634955* – 🗲, ✦ rm, 🗳 ☎ 🅿 – 🔬 120. 🕮 AE ⓞ VISA. ⚘
   **Meals** 10.00 **t.** and a la carte – **31 rm** ⊑ 59.45/76.40 **t.**

🏠 **Longview**, 55 Manchester Rd, WA16 0LX, ℰ (01565) 632119, *Fax (01565) 652402* – ✦ rest, 🗳 ☎ 🅿. 🕮 AE VISA
   *closed 24 December-3 January* – **Meals** *(closed Sunday)* (bar lunch)/dinner a la carte 17.80/23.45 **st.** – **23 rm** ⊑ 60.00/88.00 **t.** – SB.

🏠 **Travelodge**, Chester Rd, Tabley, WA16 0PP, Northwest : 2 ¾ m. by A 5033 on A 556 ℰ (01565) 652187, *Fax (01565) 652187*, Reservations (Freephone) 0800 850950 – ✦ rm, 🗳 & 🅿. 🕮 AE ⓞ VISA JCB. ⚘
   **Meals** (grill rest.) – **32 rm** 39.95/59.95 **t.**

XX **Belle Epoque Brasserie** with rm, 60 King St., WA16 6DT, ℰ (01565) 633060, *Fax (01565) 634150*, « Art Nouveau », ☞ – 🗳 ☎ – 🔬 60. 🕮 AE ⓞ VISA. ⚘
   *closed 25-26 December, 1 January and Bank Holidays* – **Meals** *(closed Sunday)* a la carte 17.85/24.15 **st.** ⓘ 6.95 – ⊑ 4.50 – **6 rm** 45.00/55.00 **st.**

XX **Treasure Village**, 84 King St., WA16 6EG, ℰ (01565) 651537, *Fax (01565) 632820* – ▤. 🕮 AE ⓞ VISA
   *closed Saturday lunch and 25-26 December* – **Meals** - Chinese - 5.50/16.00 **t.** and a la carte ⓘ 7.95.

X **Est, Est, Est**, 81 King St., WA16 6DX, ℰ (01565) 755487, *Fax (01565) 651151* – ▤. 🕮 AE VISA
   *closed 25 and 26 December* – **Meals** - Italian - 10.50 **t.** and a la carte.

**at Mobberley** *Northeast : 2½ m. by A 537 on B 5085* – ⊠ *Knutsford.*

🏠 **Hinton**, Town Lane, WA16 7HH, on B 5085 ℰ (01565) 873484, *Fax (01565) 873484*, ☞ – ✦ 🗳 🅿. 🕮 AE ⓞ VISA. ⚘
   **Meals** (by arrangement) 11.00 **st.** – **6 rm** ⊑ 38.00/50.00.

🏠 **Laburnum Cottage** without rest., Knutsford Rd, WA16 7PU, West : ¾ m. on B 5085 ℰ (01565) 872464, *Fax (01565) 872464*, ☞ – ✦ 🗳 🅿. ⚘
   12.00 **st.** – **5 rm** ⊑ 35.00/50.00 **st.**

**at Hoo Green** *Northwest : 3½ m. on A 50 – ✉ Knutsford.*

🏨 **The Kilton Inn - Premier Lodge,** Warrington Rd, WA16 0PZ, ✆ (01565) 830420, *Fax (01565) 830411*, Reservations (Freephone) 0800 118833 – ⊬ rm, [TV] ☎ ♿ [P]. [MC] [AE] [D] [VISA]. ⊁
**Meals** (grill rest.) a la carte 9.50/15.00 **t.** – ☕ 5.95 – **28 rm** 44.95 **t.** – SB.

ATS Malt St. ✆ (01565) 652224

**LACOCK** *Wilts.* [403] [404] N 29 *The West Country G. – pop. 1 068 – ✉ Chippenham.*
See : *Village★★ - Lacock Abbey★ AC – High St.★, St. Cyriac★, Fox Talbot Museum of Photography★ AC.*
*London 109 – Bath 16 – Bristol 30 – Chippenham 3.*

🏨 **Sign of the Angel,** 6 Church St., SN15 2LB, ✆ (01249) 730230, *Fax (01249) 730527*, « Part 14C and 15C former wool merchant's house in National Trust village », 🌳 – [TV] ☎ [P]. [MC] [AE] [D] [VISA] [JCB]
*closed 1 week Christmas* – **Meals** - English - *(closed Monday lunch except Bank Holidays)* a la carte 16.00/30.00 **st.** 🍷 5.50 – **10 rm** ☕ 65.00/105.00 **st.** – SB.

**LAMORNA** *Cornwall* [403] D 33.
*London 303 – Falmouth 30 – Penzance 5 – Plymouth 83 – Truro 32.*

🏨 **The Lamorna Cove** ⊛, TR19 6XH, ✆ (01736) 731411, ⋞, ⛱, 🌳 – 🛗 ⊬ [TV] ☎ [P]. [MC] [AE] [VISA]. ⊁
*March-October and Christmas-New Year* – **Meals** (booking essential to non-residents) (bar lunch)/dinner 17.50 **t.** 🍷 5.00 – **12 rm** ☕ (dinner included) 54.50/120.00 **t.**

**LANCASTER** *Lancs.* [402] L 21 *Great Britain G. – pop. 44 497.*
See : *Castle★ AC.*
⛳ 18 *Ashton Hall, Ashton-with-Stodday ✆ (01524) 752090 –* ⛳ 9 *Lansil, Caton Rd ✆ (01524) 39269.*
[i] *29 Castle Hill, LA1 1YN ✆ (01524) 32878.*
*London 252 – Blackpool 26 – Bradford 62 – Burnley 44 – Leeds 71 – Middlesbrough 97 – Preston 26.*

🏨 **Lancaster House,** Green Lane, Ellel, LA1 4GJ, South : 3 ¼ m. by A 6 ✆ (01524) 844822, *Fax (01524) 844766*, 🏋, ≘s, ⛱ – ⊬, ▤ rest, [TV] ☎ ♿ [P] – 🏛 120. [MC] [AE] [D] [VISA] [JCB]
***Gressingham :*** **Meals** 12.95/21.50 **st.** and a la carte 🍷 6.25 – ☕ 9.45 – **80 rm** 94.00/119.00 **st.** – SB.

🏨 **Forte Posthouse Lancaster,** Waterside Park, Caton Rd, LA1 3RA, Northeast : 1 ½ m. on A 683 at junction 34 of M 6 ✆ (01524) 65999, *Fax (01524) 841265*, 🏋, ≘s, ⛱, 🌳 – 🛗, ⊬ rm, [TV] ☎ ♿ [P] – 🏛 120. [MC] [AE] [D] [VISA] [JCB]
**Meals** a la carte 13.85/24.85 **t.** – ☕ 9.95 – **157 rm** 75.00 **st.** – SB.

🏠 **Edenbreck House** without rest., Sunnyside Lane, off Ashfield Av., LA1 5ED, by Westbourne Rd, near the station ✆ (01524) 32464, 🌳 – [TV] [P]. ⊁
*May-October* – **3 rm** ☕ 30.00/40.00.

**at Carnforth** *North : 6¼ m. on A 6.*

🏠 **New Capernwray Farm** ⊛, Capernwray, LA6 1AD, Northeast : 3 m. by B 6254 ✆ (01524) 734284, *Fax (01524) 734284*, ⋞, « 17C former farmhouse », 🌳 – ⊬ [TV] [P]. [MC] [VISA] [JCB]
*March-October* – **Meals** (by arrangement) (communal dining) 22.50 **s.** – **3 rm** ☕ 45.00/70.00 **s.**

**LANCASTER SERVICE AREA** *Lancs.* [402] L 22 – ✉ *Forton.*
[i] *(M 6) Forton, Bay Horse, LA2 9DU ✆ (01524) 792181.*

🏨 **Travelodge,** LA2 9DU, on M 6 between junctions 32 and 33 ✆ (01524) 792227, *Fax (01524) 791703*, Reservations (Freephone) 0800 850950 – ⊬ [TV] ♿ [P]. [MC] [AE] [D] [VISA] [JCB]. ⊁
**Meals** (grill rest.) – **53 rm** 39.95/59.95 **t.**

**LANCING** *W. Sussex* [404] S 31 – *pop. 29 575 (inc. Sompting).*
*London 59 – Brighton 4 – Southampton 53.*

🏨 **Sussex Pad,** Old Shoreham Rd, BN15 0RH, East : 1 m. off A 27 ✆ (01273) 454647, *Fax (01273) 453010*, 🌳 – ⊬ rest, [TV] ☎ [P]. [MC] [AE] [D] [VISA]
**Meals** 20.50 **t.** and a la carte 🍷 9.00 – **19 rm** ☕ 50.00/90.00 **t.**

**ANGHO** Lancs. 402 M 22 – see Blackburn.

**ANGTON GREEN** Kent – see Royal Tunbridge Wells.

**ANSALLOS** Cornwall 403 G 32 – pop. 1 625 – ⊠ Fowey.
London 273 – Plymouth 30.

⌂ **Carneggan House** ⤺, Lanteglos-by-Fowey, PL23 1NW, Northwest : 2 m. on Polruan rd
ℰ (01726) 870327, Fax (01726) 870327, ≼, ☞ – ⤬ rest, 🆅 🅿. ◑ AE VISA
closed December and January – **Meals** (by arrangement) (communal dining) 12.00 st.
⑃ 3.10 – **3 rm** ⊊ 29.00/56.00 st.

**ARKFIELD** Kent 404 V 30 – see Maidstone.

**ASKILL** N. Yorks. – see Helmsley.

**ASTINGHAM** N. Yorks. 402 R 21 – pop. 87 – ⊠ York.
London 244 – Scarborough 26 – York 32.

🏨 **Lastingham Grange** ⤺, YO62 6TH, ℰ (01751) 417345, Fax (01751) 417358, « Part 17C
farmhouse, country house atmosphere », ☞, park – ⤬ rest, 🆅 ☎ 🅿
March-November – **Meals** (light lunch Monday to Saturday)/dinner 29.75 t. ⑃ 3.75 – **12 rm**
⊊ 82.00/156.00 t. – SB.

*Le Grand Londres (GREATER LONDON) est composé de la City
et de 32 arrondissements administratifs (Borough)
eux-mêmes divisés en quartiers ou en villages
ayant conservé leur caractère propre (Area).*

**AVENHAM** Suffolk 404 W 27 Great Britain G. – pop. 1 231 – ⊠ Sudbury.
See : Town★★ – Church of St. Peter and St. Paul★.
🚹 Lady St., CO10 9RA ℰ (01787) 248207 (summer only).
London 66 – Cambridge 39 – Colchester 22 – Ipswich 19.

🏨 **Swan**, High St., CO10 9QA, ℰ (01787) 247477, Fax (01787) 248286, « Part 14C timbered
inn », ☞ – ⤬ 🆅 ☎ 🅿 – 🛉 45. ◑ AE ⓞ VISA JCB
**Meals** 14.95/24.95 t. and dinner a la carte ⑃ 8.50 – ⊊ 9.95 – **44 rm** 75.00/120.00 t., 2 suites
– SB.

🏨 **Angel**, Market Pl., CO10 9QZ, ℰ (01787) 247388, Fax (01787) 248344, « 15C inn », ☞ – 🆅
☎ 🅿. ◑ AE VISA
closed 25 and 26 December – **Meals** a la carte 11.25/18.00 t. ⑃ 4.95 – **8 rm** ⊊ 42.50/
69.00 t. – SB.

XX **Great House** with rm, Market Pl., CO10 9QZ, ℰ (01787) 247431, Fax (01787) 248007,
« Part 14C timbered house » – 🆅 ☎. ◑ AE VISA JCB
closed 3 weeks January – **Meals** - French - (closed Sunday dinner and Monday to non-
residents) 14.95/17.95 t. and a la carte ⑃ 7.50 – **1 rm** ⊊ 65.00/82.00 t., **3 suites** 70.00/
102.00 t. – SB.

**EA** Lancs. – see Preston.

**EAMINGTON SPA** Warks. 403 404 P 27 – see Royal Leamington Spa.

**EDBURY** Herefordshire 403 404 M 27 – pop. 6 216.
🚹 3 The Homend, HR8 1BN ℰ (01531) 636147.
London 119 – Hereford 14 – Newport 46 – Worcester 16.

🏨 **The Feathers**, High St., HR8 1DS, ℰ (01531) 635266, Fax (01531) 638955, « Timbered
16C inn », ⑃, ◻ – 🆅 ☎ 🅿 – 🛉 120. ◑ AE ⓞ VISA. ✾
**Meals** a la carte 16.00/25.90 st. ⑃ 6.50 – **19 rm** ⊊ 69.50/125.00 t. – SB.

⌂ **The Barn House** without rest., New St., HR8 2DX, ℰ (01531) 632825, « Part 17C », ☞ –
⤬ 🆅 🅿 – 🛉 60. ◑ VISA. ✾
closed 25 and 26 December – **3 rm** ⊊ 38.00/54.00 s.

**LEEDS** *W. Yorks.* 🗺️ P 22 *Great Britain G. – pop. 424 194.*

See : *City★ - Royal Armouries Museum★★★ – City Art Gallery★ AC* GY **M.**

Env. : *Kirkstall Abbey★ AC, NW : 3 m. by A 65* GY *– Temple Newsam★ (decorative arts★) A E : 5 m. by A 64 and A 63* CU **D.**

Exc. : *Harewood House★★ (The Gallery★) AC, N : 8 m. by A 61* CT *– Nostell Priory★, SI 18 m. by A 61 and A 638 – Yorkshire Sculpture Park★, S : 20 m. by M 1 to junction 38 ar 1 m. north off A 637 – Brodsworth Hall★, SE : 25 m. by M 1 to junction 40, A 638 and min rd (right) in Upton.*

🏌️, 🏌️ *Temple Newsam, Temple Newsam Rd, Halton ℘ (0113) 264 5624* CT *–* 🏌️ *Gotts Par Armley Ridge Rd, Armley ℘ (0113) 234 2019* BT *–* 🏌️ *Middleton Park, Ring Rd, Beeston Par Middleton ℘ (0113) 270 9506* CU *–* 🏌️, 🏌️ *Moor Allerton, Coal Rd, Wike ℘ (0113) 266 1154* 🏌️ *Howley Hall, Scotchman Lane, Morley ℘ (01924) 472432 –* 🏌️ *Roundhay, Park Lar ℘ (0113) 266 2695,* CT.

✈️ *Leeds - Bradford Airport : ℘ (0113) 250 9696, NW : 8 m. by A 65 and A 658* BT.

🅱️ *The Arcade, City Station, LS1 1PL ℘ (0113) 242 5242.*

*London 204 – Liverpool 75 – Manchester 43 – Newcastle upon Tyne 95 – Nottingham 74.*

Plans on following pages

🏨 **Oulton Hall,** Rothwell Lane, Oulton, LS26 8HN, Southeast : 5 ½ m. by A 61 and A 639 c A 654 ℘ (0113) 282 1000, *Fax (0113) 282 8066,* ≤, « *Part Victorian mansion* », ʃₐ, ≊, 🗖 🏌️, 🏌️, 🌳 – ᾳ ⚄, 🗐 rest, 🔟 ☎ & 🅿 – 🔬 330. ⓒ🕘 🎴 ⓞ 🈸 CU
*Bronte :* Meals *(closed Saturday lunch)* 15.00/23.00 st. and dinner a la carte ⓝ 8.95
*Blayd's :* Meals 18.00 st. ⓝ 8.95 – **150 rm** ⊇ 130.00/150.00 t., 2 suites – SB.

🏨 **Leeds Marriott,** 4 Trevelyan Sq., Boar Lane, LS1 6ET, ℘ (0113) 236 6366 *Fax (0113) 236 6367,* ʃₐ, ≊, 🗖 – ᾳ, ᾳ⚄ rm, 🗐 🔟 ☎ & 🅿 – 🔬 300. ⓒ🕘 🎴 ⓞ 🈸 🎴🄱 ✻ GZ
*Dyson's (℘ (0113) 236 6444) :* Meals *(dinner only and Sunday lunch)/dinner* 15.95 s and a la carte 16.90/21.90 t. ⓝ 7.50 – *John T's :* Meals 15.95/18.95 st. and a la carte – ⊇ 11.95 – **244 rm** 99.00/105.00 st., 4 suites – SB.

🏨 **Leeds Crown Plaza,** Wellington St., LS1 4DL, ℘ (0113) 244 2200, *Fax (0113) 244 0464,* ʃₐ, ≊, 🗖 – ᾳ, ᾳ⚄ rm, 🗐 🔟 ☎ ✆ 🅿 – 🔬 200. ⓒ🕘 🎴 ⓞ 🈸 🎴🄱. ✻ FZ
Meals 14.95/17.95 st. – *Buongiorno's :* Meals - Italian - a la carte 16.45/27.45 st. ⓝ 5.95 ⊇ 12.50 – **130 rm** 135.00 st., 5 suites – SB.

🏨 **42 The Calls,** 42 The Calls, LS2 7EW, ℘ (0113) 244 0099, *Fax (0113) 234 4100,* ≤, « *Cor verted riverside grain mill* » – ᾳ 🔟 ☎ ✆ ⟷ – 🔬 55. ⓒ🕘 🎴 ⓞ 🈸. ✻ GZ
*closed 5 days Christmas* – Meals – *(see Pool Court at 42 below)* – *(see also Brassera Forty Four below)* – ⊇ 11.50 – **38 rm** 98.00/150.00 st., 3 suites – SB.

🏨 **Queen's,** City Sq., LS1 1PL, ℘ (0113) 243 1323, *Fax (0113) 242 5154* – ᾳ, ᾳ⚄ rm, 🔟 ☎ & ⟷ – 🔬 600. ⓒ🕘 🎴 ⓞ 🈸 🎴🄱 GZ
*Harewood :* Meals *(closed Saturday lunch)* 12.50/17.50 st. and a la carte ⓝ 8.95 – *Th Carvery :* Meals *(carving rest.)* 12.50/15.50 st. ⓝ 7.95 – ⊇ 11.95 – **194 rm** 99.00/130.00 st 5 suites.

🏨 **Hilton National Leeds,** Neville St., LS1 4BX, ℘ (0113) 244 2000, *Fax (0113) 243 3577,* ʃₐ, ≊, 🗖 – ᾳ, ᾳ⚄ rm, 🗐 🔟 ☎ & 🅿 – 🔬 400. ⓒ🕘 🎴 ⓞ 🈸 GZ
Meals 11.95/16.95 t. and dinner a la carte ⓝ 6.50 – ⊇ 11.95 – **176 rm** 120.00/130.00 st 30 suites.

🏨 **Weetwood Hall,** Otley Rd, LS16 5PS, Northwest : 4 m. on A 660 ℘ (0113) 230 6000 *Fax (0113) 230 6095,* ʃₐ, ≊, 🗖, 🌳 – ᾳ ᾳ⚄, 🗐 rest, 🔟 ☎ & 🅿 – 🔬 150. ⓒ🕘 🎴 ⓞ 🈸 🎴🄱. ✻ BT
Meals *(bar lunch Saturday)* 12.95/17.50 st. and dinner a la carte ⓝ 6.95 – ⊇ 9.75 – **108 rm** 89.00/140.00 st. – SB.

🏨 **Village H. and Leisure Club,** Otley Rd, Headingley, LS16 5PR, Northwest : 3 ½ m. on A 660 ℘ (0113) 278 1000, *Fax (0113) 278 1111,* ʃₐ, ≊, 🗖, squash – ᾳ ᾳ⚄ 🗐 🔟 ☎ ✆ & 🅿 – 🔬 250. ⓒ🕘 🎴 ⓞ 🈸 BT
Meals *(grill rest.)* a la carte 10.05/22.20 t. ⓝ 3.90 – **94 rm** ⊇ 88.00/119.00 t.

🏨 **Haley's,** Shire Oak Rd, Headingley, LS6 2DE, Northwest : 2 m. off Otley Rd (A 660 ℘ (0113) 278 4446, *Fax (0113) 275 3342* – ᾳ⚄ 🔟 ☎ 🅿 – 🔬 25. ⓒ🕘 🎴 ⓞ 🈸 🎴🄱. ✻ *closed 26 to 30 December* – Meals *(closed Sunday dinner to non-residents)* (dinner only and Sunday lunch June-August)/dinner a la carte 23.70/29.70 st. ⓝ 6.75 – **29 rm** ⊇ 105.00 140.00 st. – SB. CT

🏨 **Metropole,** King St., LS1 2HQ, ℘ (0113) 245 0841, *Fax (0113) 242 5156* – ᾳ ᾳ⚄ 🔟 ☎ & 🅿 – 🔬 200. ⓒ🕘 🎴 ⓞ 🈸. ✻ FZ
Meals *(closed Sunday lunch)* 12.95/15.95 st. and a la carte ⓝ 6.50 – ⊇ 11.95 – **117 rm** 99.00/119.00 st., 1 suite – SB.

🏨 **Merrion,** Merrion Centre, 17 Wade Lane, LS2 8NH, ✆ (0113) 243 9191, *Fax (0113) 242 3527* – 🛗 ⇖ 🗐 📺 ☎ 🅿 – 🔬 80. 🆄🇸 🇦🇪 ⑩ *VISA* JCB
GZ e
**Meals** 14.95 **st.** and a la carte 🔥 5.10 – ⌧ 10.50 – **109 rm** 109.00/129.00 **t.** – SB.

🏨 **Golden Lion,** 2 Lower Briggate, LS1 4AE, ✆ (0113) 243 6454, *Fax (0113) 242 9327* – 🛗,
⇖ rm, 📺 ☎ 🅿 – 🔬 120. 🆄🇸 🇦🇪 ⑩ *VISA* JCB
GZ v
**Meals** (bar lunch)/dinner 15.95 **st.** and a la carte 🔥 5.50 – **89 rm** ⌧ 99.00 **st.** – SB.

🏨 **Travel Inn,** Citygate, Wellington St., LS3 1LH, ✆ (0113) 242 8104, *Fax (0113) 242 8105* – 🛗,
⇖ rm, 🗐 rest, 📺 🕭 🅿 🆄🇸 🇦🇪 ⑩ *VISA*. ⌀
FZ v
**Meals** (grill rest.) – **84 rm** 38.00 **t.**

🏨 **Holiday Inn Express,** Aberford Rd, Oulton, LS26 8EJ, Southeast : 5 ½ m. by A 61 on
A 639 ✆ (0113) 282 6201, *Fax (0113) 288 7212*, Reservations (Freephone) 0800 897121 –
⇖ rm, 📺 ☎ 🕭 🕭 🅿 – 🔬 40. 🆄🇸 🇦🇪 ⑩ *VISA* JCB. ⌀
FZ e
**Meals** (carving rest.) a la carte 11.55/15.10 **t.** 🔥 6.95 – **49 rm** 45.00 **st.**

321

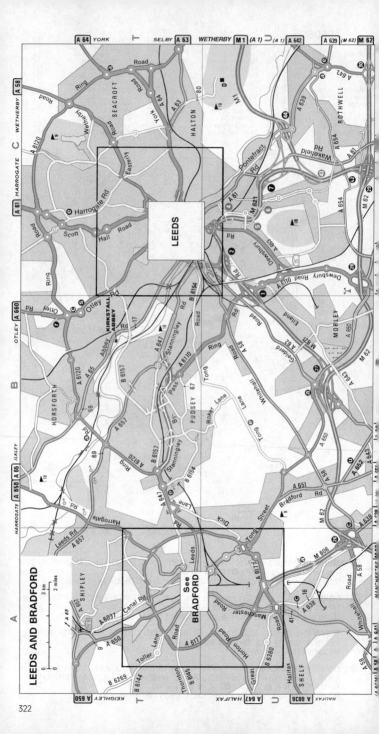

LEEDS AND BRADFORD

# LEEDS

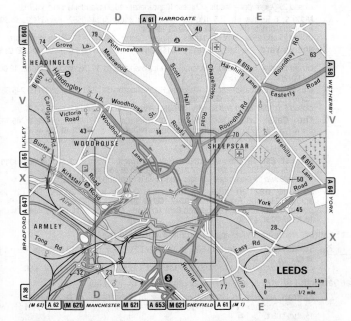

↑ **Pinewood,** 78 Potternewton Lane, LS7 3LW, ✆ (0113) 262 2561, Fax (0113) 262 2561, ⛟
– ⇆ rest, 📺, 🅒🅢 🄰🄴 *VISA*, ⚘
**DV** **a**
*closed Christmas and New Year* – **Meals** (by arrangement) 10.95 **t.** – **10 rm** ⊇ 36.00/
44.00 **t.**

🍴🍴🍴 **Pool Court at 42** (at 42 The Calls H.), 44 The Calls, LS2 7EW, ✆ (0113) 244 4242,
❀ Fax (0113) 234 3332, 🍴, « Riverside setting » – ▤. 🅒🅢 🄰🄴 🄾 *VISA* **GZ** **z**
*closed Saturday lunch, Sunday, Christmas and Bank Holidays* – **Meals** 17.00/29.50 **t.** 🍷 9.15
**Spec.** Salad of caramelised sweetbreads with mint and basil. Nage of wild salmon, scallops
and oysters. Poached squab pigeon in a fumet of ceps and Madeira.

🍴🍴 **Rascasse** (Gueller), Canal Wharf, Water Lane, LS11 5BB, ✆ (0113) 244 6611,
❀ Fax (0113) 244 0736, ≼, « Converted grain warehouse, canalside setting » – ▤. 🅒🅢 🄰🄴 🄾
*VISA* **FZ** **c**
*closed Saturday lunch, Sunday, 1 week after Christmas and Bank Holiday Monday* – **Meals**
17.00 **t.** (lunch) and a la carte 22.00/35.00 **t.** 🍷 7.00
**Spec.** Potage of scallops and oysters, leeks and truffles. Paupiettes of squab pigeon and
foie gras with thyme jus. Caramelised lemon tart, cassis sorbet.

🍴🍴 **Marcell's,** 300 Harrogate Rd, LS17 6LY, North : 3 ¾ m. following signs for A 58 and
Chapeltown area ✆ (0113) 236 9991, Fax (0113) 236 9940, « Collection of contemporary
local art » – ⇆. 🅒🅢 🄰🄴 🄾 *VISA* 🅹🅲🅱 **CT** **e**
*closed Monday and 1 to 14 January* – **Meals** (booking essential) (dinner only and Sunday
lunch)/dinner 15.40/16.40 **t.**.

🍴🍴 **Leodis,** Victoria Mill, Sovereign St., LS1 4BJ, ✆ (0113) 242 1010, Fax (0113) 243 0432, 🍴,
🍷 « Converted riverside warehouse » – 🅒🅢 🄰🄴 *VISA* **GZ** **b**
*closed lunch Saturday and Bank Holidays, Sunday, 25-26 December and 1 January* – **Meals**
13.95 **t.** and a la carte 20.20/26.70 **t.** 🍷 6.85.

🍴🍴 **Brasserie Forty Four** (at 42 The Calls H.), 44 The Calls, LS2 7EW, ✆ (0113) 234 3232,
Fax (0113) 234 3332 – ▤. 🅒🅢 🄰🄴 🄾 *VISA* **GZ** **z**
*closed Saturday lunch, Sunday, Christmas and Bank Holidays* – **Meals** 12.95 **t.**
(lunch) and a la carte 17.20/22.90 **t.** 🍷 7.70.

XX **Fourth Floor** (at Harvey Nichols), 107-111 Briggate, LS1 6AZ, ✆ (0113) 204 8000, *Fax (0113) 204 8080* – ▤. MC AE ◑ VISA JCB GZ s
*closed dinner Monday to Wednesday, Sunday and 25-26 December* – **Meals** (lunch bookings not accepted) 15.00/15.95 **t.** and a la carte 🍷 7.50.

XX **Lucky Dragon,** Templar Lane, LS2 7LP, ✆ (0113) 245 0520, *Fax (0113) 245 0520* – ▤. MC AE ◑ VISA JCB GY u
*closed 25 December* – **Meals** - Chinese (Cantonese) - 16.50 **t.** and a la carte 🍷 4.75.

XX **Maxi's,** 6 Bingley St., LS3 1LX, off Kirkstall Rd ✆ (0113) 244 0552, *Fax (0113) 234 3902,* « Pagoda, ornate decor » – ▤ P. MC AE ◑ VISA DX a
*closed 25 and 26 December* – **Meals** - Chinese (Canton, Peking) - 17.50 **t.** and a la carte.

X **Shears Yard,** The Calls, LS2 7EY, ✆ (0113) 244 4144, *Fax (0113) 244 8102* – ▤. MC AE VISA JCB GZ a
*closed Sunday, Bank Holiday Monday, 1 January and 25 to 30 December* – **Meals** 10.00 **t.** (lunch) and a la carte 15.45/24.10 **t.** 🍷 5.75.

X **L'Escapade,** (basement of Wellesley H.) Wellington St., LS1 4HJ, ✆ (0113) 245 8856, *Fax (0113) 242 6112* – ▤. MC AE VISA FZ n
*closed Saturday lunch and Sunday* – **Meals** - French - 12.50 **t.** and a la carte 🍷 4.80.

X **The Calls Grill,** Calls Landing, 38 The Calls, LS2 7EW, ✆ (0113) 245 3870, *Fax (0113) 243 9035,* « Converted riverside warehouse » – ▤. MC AE ◑ VISA JCB GZ c
*closed Sunday lunch and Christmas-New Year* – **Meals** (grill rest.) 8.75 **t.** (dinner) and a la carte 17.20/25.70 **t.** 🍷 6.50.

X **Est, Est, Est,** 151 Otley Old Rd, LS16 6HN, Northwest : 4 ½ m. by A 660 off Cookridge rd ✆ (0113) 267 2100, *Fax (0113) 267 2100* – ▤ P. MC AE ◑ VISA BT r
*closed 25 and 26 December* – **Meals** - Italian - a la carte approx. 19.00 **t.**

X **Sous le nez en ville,** the basement, Quebec House, Quebec St., LS1 2HA, ✆ (0113) 244 0108, *Fax (0113) 245 0240* – MC AE VISA FZ a
*closed Sunday, 25-26 December and Bank Holidays* – **Meals** 14.95 **st.** (dinner) and a la carte 16.10/27.00 **st.** 🍷 6.50.

**at Seacroft** *Northeast : 5½ m. at junction of A 64 with A 6120* – ✉ *Leeds.*

🏨 **Stakis Leeds,** Ring Rd, LS14 5QF, ✆ (0113) 273 2323, *Fax (0113) 232 3018* – |‡|, ⇔ rm, TV ☎ P – 🎤 250. MC AE ◑ VISA CT a
*(closed Saturday)* a la carte 17.00/26.90 **st.** – ☕ 9.95 **101 rm** 99.00/124.00 **st.** – SB.

**at Garforth** *East : 6 m. by A 63 - CT - at junction with A 642* – ✉ *Leeds.*

XX **Aagrah,** Aberford Rd, LS25 1BA, on A 642 ✆ (0113) 287 6606 – P. MC AE VISA JCB
*closed 25 December* – **Meals** - Indian (Kashmiri) - (booking essential) (dinner only) a la carte 13.70/17.05 **t.**

**at Drighlington** *Southwest : 6 m. by A 62 and A 650 on B 6135* – ✉ *Leeds.*

🏠 **Travel Inn,** The Old Brickworks, Wakefield Rd, BD11 1EA, ✆ (0113) 287 9132, *Fax (0113) 287 9115,* 🌳 – ⇔ rm, ▤ rest, TV ♿ P. MC AE ◑ VISA. ✗ BU a
**Meals** (grill rest.) – **42 rm** 38.00 **t.**

**at Pudsey** *West : 5¾ m. by A 647* – DX – ✉ *Leeds.*

XX **Aagrah,** 483 Bradford Rd, LS28 8ED, on A 647 ✆ (01274) 668818, *Fax (01274) 669803* – ▤ P. MC AE VISA JCB BT e
*closed 25 December* – **Meals** - Indian (Kashmiri) - (booking essential) (dinner only) a la carte 13.70/17.05 **t.**

**at Horsforth** *Northwest : 5 m. by A 65 off A 6120* – ✉ *Leeds.*

X **Paris,** Calverley Bridge, Calverley Lane, Rodley, LS13 1NP, Southwest : 1 m. by A 6120 ✆ (0113) 258 1885, *Fax (0113) 239 0651* – ▤ P. MC AE ◑ VISA BT a
*closed Saturday lunch* – **Meals** 13.95 **t.** and a la carte 14.30/28.40 **t.** 🍷 6.25.

**at Bramhope** *Northwest : 8 m. by A 660* – BT – ✉ *Leeds.*

🏨 **Forte Posthouse Leeds/Bradford,** Leeds Rd, LS16 9JJ, ✆ (0113) 284 2911, *Fax (0113) 284 3451,* ≤, Lδ, ≘s, 🏊, 🌳, park – |‡|, ⇔ rm, TV ☎ P – 🎤 160. MC AE ◑ VISA
**Meals** a la carte 16.85/27.15 **t.** 🍷 7.50 – ☕ 10.95 – **123 rm** 99.00 **t.**, 1 suite – SB.

🏨 **Jarvis Parkway H. and Country Club,** Otley Rd, LS16 8AG, South : 2 m. on A 660 ✆ (0113) 267 2551, *Fax (0113) 267 4410,* Lδ, ≘s, 🏊, 🌳, 🎾 – |‡| ⇔ TV ☎ ♿ P – 🎤 300. MC AE ◑ VISA JCB
**Meals** (carving lunch) (bar lunch Saturday) 12.50/16.80 **t.** and dinner a la carte 🍷 7.95 – ☕ 10.50 – **116 rm** 99.00/109.00 **t.** – SB.

⌂ **The Cottages** without rest., Moor Rd, LS16 9HH, South : ¼ m. on Cookridge rd ✆ (0113) 284 2754, 🌳 – ⇔ TV P. ✗
*closed 24 to 31 December* – **5 rm** ☕ 30.00/44.00.

**at Yeadon** *Northwest : 8 m. by A 65 on A 658 –* BT *–* ⊠ *Leeds.*

🏠 **Travel Inn,** Victoria Av., LS19 7AW, on A 658 ℘ (0113) 250 4284, *Fax (0113) 250 5838 –* ⇔ rm, ▤ rest, 📺 ♿ 🅿. 🐝 AE ⓞ VISA. 🦅
**Meals** (grill rest.) **– 40 rm** 38.00 **t.**

🔧 ATS Cross Green Lane ℘ (0113) 245 9423          ATS 2 Regent St. ℘ (0113) 243 0652

---

**LEEK** *Staffs.* 402 403 404 N 24 *– pop. 18 167.*

🟫 *Westwood, Newcastle Rd, Wallbridge* ℘ (01538) 398385.
🟦 *Market Pl., ST13 5HH* ℘ (01538) 381000.
*London 122 – Derby 30 – Manchester 39 – Stoke-on-Trent 12.*

🏠 **Country Cottage** 🦢, Back Lane Farm, Winkhill, ST13 7PJ, Southeast : 5 ½ m. by A 523 (turning left opposite Little Chef) ℘ (01538) 308273, *Fax (01538) 308098,* ≼, ╤, park – ⇔ 📺 🅿. 🦅
**Meals** 13.00 **st. – 4 rm** ⊑ 21.00/40.00 **st.**

**at Butterton** *East : 8 m. by A 523 off B 5053 –* ⊠ *Leek.*

🏨 **Black Lion Inn** with rm, ST13 7ST, ℘ (01538) 304232, « 18C », ╤ – 📺 🅿. 🐝 VISA. 🦅
**Meals** *(closed Wednesday lunch)* (in bar except Friday and Saturday dinner and Sunday lunch) a la carte 9.10/14.25 **st. – 3 rm** ⊑ 35.00/50.00 **st.**

---

**LEEMING BAR** *N. Yorks.* 402 P 21 *– pop. 1 824 –* ⊠ *Northallerton.*
*London 235 – Leeds 44 – Middlesbrough 30 – Newcastle upon Tyne 52 – York 37.*

🏠 **Little Holtby,** DL7 9LH, Northwest : 2 m. on A 1 (northbound carriageway) ℘ (01609) 748762, ≼, ╤ – 📺 🅿. 🦅
**Meals** (by arrangement) (communal dining) 12.50 **s. – 3 rm** ⊑ 25.00/45.00 **s.** – SB.

---

**LEICESTER** 402 403 404 Q 26 *Great Britain G. – pop. 318 518.*

See : *Guildhall*⋆ BY **B** *– Museum and Art Gallery*⋆ CY **M2** *– St. Mary de Castro Church*⋆ BY **A.**

🟫 *Leicestershire, Evington Lane* ℘ (0116) 273 6035, AY *–* 🟫 *Western Park, Scudamore Rd* ℘ (0116) 287 6158/287 2339 *–* 🟫 *Humberstone Heights, Gipsy Lane* ℘ (0116) 276 1905/ 3680, AX *–* 🟫 *Oadby, Leicester Road Racecourse* ℘ (0116) 270 0215/270 9052, AY.
✈ *East Midlands Airport, Castle Donington :* ℘ (01332) 852852 NW : 22 m. by A 50 *–* AX *– and* M1.
🟦 *7-9 Every St., Town Hall Sq., LE1 6AG* ℘ (0116) 265 0555.
*London 107 – Birmingham 43 – Coventry 24 – Nottingham 26.*

Plans on following pages

🏩 **Stakis Leicester,** Junction 21 Approach, Braunstone, LE3 2WQ, Southwest : 3 ½ m. by A 5460 at junction with A 563 ℘ (0116) 263 0066, *Fax (0116) 263 0627,* ﹝ₛ, ⇌, ⬚, ╤, ⇔ rm, ▤ rest, 📺 ♿ 🅿 – ⬚ 200. 🐝 AE ⓞ VISA. 🦅
**Meals** (bar lunch Saturday) 13.50/20.50 **st.** and a la carte – ⊑ 10.50 **– 168 rm** 135.00/ 170.00 **st.,** 2 suites – SB.                                                                     AY **e**

🏩 **Holiday Inn Leicester,** 129 St. Nicholas Circle, LE1 5LX, ℘ (0116) 253 1161, *Fax (0116) 251 3169,* ﹝ₛ, ⇌, ⬚ – ⬚, ⇔ rm, ▤ 📺 ☎ ♿ 🅿 – ⬚ 280. 🐝 AE ⓞ VISA. 🦅                                                                                          BY **c**
*The Hayloft :* **Meals** 12.95/18.95 **st.** and a la carte ⫯ 8.00 – ⊑ 10.95 **– 187 rm** 115.00/ 125.00 **st.,** 1 suite.

🏩 **Grand,** 73 Granby St., LE1 6ES, ℘ (0116) 255 5599, *Fax (0116) 254 4736* – ⬚, ⇔ rm, 📺 ☎ ☏ 🅿 – ⬚ 450. 🐝 AE ⓞ VISA JCB. 🦅                                                              CY **o**
**Meals** (bar lunch Monday to Saturday)/dinner 16.95 **t.** and a la carte ⫯ 7.00 – ⊑ 8.95 – **91 rm** 99.00/114.00 **t.,** 1 suite – SB.

🏨 **Forte Posthouse Leicester,** Braunstone Lane East, LE3 2FW, Southwest : 2 m. on A 5460 ℘ (0116) 263 0500, *Fax (0116) 282 3623* – ⬚, ⇔ rm, ▤ rest, 📺 ☎ 🅿 – ⬚ 80. 🐝 AE ⓞ VISA JCB                                                                        AY **u**
**Meals** a la carte 15.00/24.00 **t.** ⫯ 7.50 – ⊑ 8.95 **– 170 rm** 75.00 **st.** – SB.

🏨 **Belmont House,** De Montfort St., LE1 7GR, ℘ (0116) 254 4773, *Fax (0116) 247 0804* – ⬚, ⇔ rm, 📺 ☎ 🅿 – ⬚ 100. 🐝 AE ⓞ VISA. 🦅                                                      CY **c**
closed 24 December-2 January – *Cherry's :* **Meals** *(closed Saturday lunch and Bank Holiday Mondays)* 12.95/18.50 **t.** ⫯ 6.00 – ⊑ 8.50 **– 65 rm** 79.00/100.00 **st.** – SB.

# LEICESTER
## BUILT UP AREA

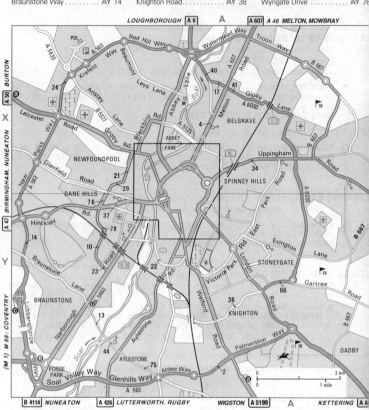

🛏 **Horse and Hounds - Premier Lodge,** Glen Rise, Oadby, LE2 4RG, Southeast : 5 ¾ m on A 6 ℰ (01162) 592229, Fax (01162) 592426, Reservations (Freephone) 0800 118833 – ⇔ rm, 📺 ☎ ✆ & 🅿. 🕮 🆎 ⓪ 𝘝𝘐𝘚𝘈 𝘑𝘊𝘉. ⌘
**Meals** (grill rest.) a la carte 9.05/16.55 **st.** ₰ 4.55 – 🖙 5.95 – **30 rm** 43.95 **st.** – SB.

🛏 **Travel Inn,** Meridian Business Park, Meridian Way, Braunstone, LE3 2LW, Southwest 3 ¾ m. by A 47 off A 563 ℰ (0116) 289 0945, Fax (0116) 282 7486 – ⇔ rm, ▤ rm, 📺 & 🅿 🕮 🆎 ⓪ 𝘝𝘐𝘚𝘈
**Meals** (grill rest.) – **51 rm** 38.00 **t.**
AY c

XX **The Tiffin,** 1 De Montfort St., LE1 7GA, ℰ (0116) 247 0420 – ▤. 🕮 🆎 ⓪ 𝘝𝘐𝘚𝘈
*closed lunch Saturday and Bank Holidays and Sunday* – **Meals** - Indian - 18.00 **t.** (dinner) and a la carte 15.85/21.45 **t.**
CY r

XX **Welford Place,** 9 Welford Pl., LE1 6ZH, ℰ (0116) 247 0758, Fax (0116) 247 1843 – 🕮 🆎 ⓪ 𝘝𝘐𝘚𝘈 𝘑𝘊𝘉
*closed Sunday dinner* – **Meals** 12.50 **st.** and a la carte ₰ 7.00.
CY s

**at Rothley** North : 5 m. by A 6 - AX - on B 5328 – ✉ Leicester.

🛏 **Limes,** 35 Mountsorrel Lane, LE7 7PS, ℰ (0116) 230 2531 – ⇔ rest, ▤ 📺 ☎ 🅿. 🕮 🆎 ⓪ 𝘝𝘐𝘚𝘈 𝘑𝘊𝘉. ⌘
*closed 23 December-4 January* – **Meals** (residents only) (dinner only) a la carte 10.95/18.40 **st.** – **11 rm** 🖙 42.50/55.00 **st.**

326

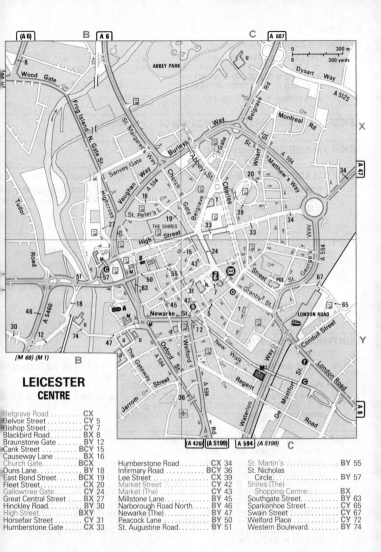

# LEICESTER
## CENTRE

**at Wigston** Southeast : 3 ¼ m. on A 50 – ⊠ Leicester.

🏨 **Leicester Stage H.,** Leicester Rd, LE18 1JW, ℘ (0116) 288 6161, Fax (0116) 281 1874, Ⅰ₅, ≦s, ⏉ – ⁕ rm, 🍴 rest, 📺 ☎ ₺ 🅿 – 🔬 250. 🆎 🆎 ⓪ 𝘝𝘐𝘚𝘈. ⋘                AY a
Meals (carving lunch Sunday) 9.95/15.95 **t.** and a la carte ₰ 4.00 – **75 rm** ⊆ 85.00/99.00 **t.** –
SB.

**at Leicester Forest East** West : 3 m. on A 47 – AY – ⊠ Leicester.

🏨 **Red Cow,** Hinckley Rd, LE3 3PG, ℘ (0116) 238 7878, Fax (0116) 238 6539 – ⁕ rm, 📺 ☎
₺ 🅿. 🆎 🆎 ⓪ 𝘝𝘐𝘚𝘈. ⋘
Meals (grill rest.) a la carte 9.45/17.40 **t.** – ⊆ 4.95 – **31 rm** 39.50 **t.**

🏨 **Travel Inn,** Hinckley Rd, LE3 3GD, ℘ (0116) 239 4677, Fax (0116) 239 3429 – ⁕ rm, 📺 ₺.
🅿. 🆎 🆎 ⓪ 𝘝𝘐𝘚𝘈. ⋘
Meals (grill rest.) – **40 rm** 38.00 **t.**

**at Glenfield** *Northwest : 4 ¾ m. by A 50 – ✉ Leicester.*

**The Gynsills - Premier Lodge,** Leicester Rd, LE3 8HB, Northeast : ¾ m. by Station Rd off A 50 ✆ (0116) 231 3693, *Fax (0116) 321148*, Reservations (Freephone) 0800 118833 – ⇔ rm, TV ☎ ✆ ♿ P. MC AE ① VISA. ✻ AX a
**Meals** (grill rest.) a la carte 8.50/14.55 ₰ 4.55 – ☕ 5.95 – **43 rm** 43.95 **st.**

ATS 16 Wanlip St. ✆ (0116) 262 4281 ATS 31 Woodgate ✆ (0116) 262 5611

**LEICESTER FOREST EAST** *Leics.* 402 403 404 Q26 – *see Leicester.*

**LEIGH** *Dorset* 403 404 M 31 – *see Sherborne.*

**LEIGH DELAMERE SERVICE AREA** *Wilts.* 403 404 N 29 – ✉ *Chippenham.*

**Travelodge,** SN14 6LB, M 4 between junctions 18 and 17 (eastbound carriageway) ✆ (01666) 837691, *Fax (01666) 837112*, Reservations (Freephone) 0800 850950 – ⇔ TV ☎ ♿ P. MC AE ① VISA JCB. ✻
**Meals** (grill rest.) – **51 rm** 39.95/59.95 **t.**

**LEIGHTON BUZZARD** *Beds.* 404 S 28 – *pop. 32 610.*
*Plantation Rd ✆ (01525) 373811/373812 – Aylesbury Vale, Wing ✆ (01525) 240196.*
*London 47 – Bedford 20 – Luton 12 – Northampton 30.*

**Grove Farm** ⛰, Grove, LU7 0QU, South : 3 ½ m. by A 4146, A 505 and B 488 on Grove Church rd ✆ (01525) 372225, *Fax (01525) 854565*, ≤, ≘s, ▣, ⛆, park – TV P. MC AE VISA. ✻
**Meals** (by arrangement) (communal dining) 17.50 **st.** – **3 rm** ☕ 35.00/70.00 **st.**

ATS Grovebury Road ✆ (01525) 376158

**LEINTWARDINE** *Shrops.* 403 L 26 – ✉ *Craven Arms.*
*London 156 – Birmingham 55 – Hereford 24 – Worcester 40.*

**Upper Buckton Farm** ⛰, Buckton, SY7 0JU, West : 2 m. by A 4113 and Buckton rd ✆ (01547) 540634, ≤, « Working farm », ⛆, park – ⇔ P. ✻
**Meals** (by arrangement) 18.00 **s.** – **3 rm** ☕ 40.00/60.00.

**Lower House** ⛰, Adforton, SY7 0NF, South : 2 ¼ m. by A 4113 off B 4530 ✆ (01568) 770223, *Fax (01568) 770592*, ⛆ – ⇔ P. ✻
**Meals** (communal dining) 17.50 – **4 rm** ☕ 27.00/54.00 – SB.

**LENHAM** *Kent* 404 W 30 – *pop. 2 167* – ✉ *Maidstone.*
*London 45 – Folkestone 28 – Maidstone 9.*

**Chilston Park,** Sandway, ME17 2BE, South : 1 ¾ m. off Broughton Malherbe rd ✆ (01622) 859803, *Fax (01622) 858588*, ≤, « Part 13C mansion, antiques », ⛆, ⛆, park, ⚔ – ⇔ rest, TV ☎ ♿ P – 🏛 120. MC AE ① VISA JCB
**Meals** *(closed Saturday lunch)* 19.50/29.95 **st.** and a la carte ₰ 9.75 – ☕ 9.95 – **49 rm** 110.00/125.00 **st.**, 4 suites – SB.

**Lime Tree** with rm, 8-10 The Limes, The Square, ME17 2PQ, ✆ (01622) 859509, *Fax (01622) 850096* – ⇔ rm, TV ☎. MC AE ① VISA JCB. ✻
*closed Monday lunch and Sunday dinner* – **Meals** 17.95/21.95 **t.** and a la carte ₰ 9.50 – **10 rm** ☕ 42.50/75.00 **st.**

**LEOMINSTER** *Herefordshire* 403 L 27 *Great Britain G.* – *pop. 9 543.*
Env. : *Berrington Hall★ AC, N : 3 m. by A 49.*
*Ford Bridge ✆ (01568) 612863.*
*1 Corn Sq., HR6 8LR ✆ (01568) 616460 (summer only).*
*London 141 – Birmingham 47 – Hereford 13 – Worcester 26.*

**Heath House** ⛰, Stoke Prior, HR6 0NF, Southeast : 3 ¾ m. by A 44 on Risbury rd ✆ (01568) 760385, *Fax (01568) 760385*, ⛆ – ⇔ P. ✻
*April-October* – **Meals** (by arrangement) (communal dining) 15.00 **st.** ₰ 3.00 – **3 rm** ☕ 27.00/48.00 **st.** – SB.

**at Kimbolton** *Northeast : 3 m. by A 49 on A 4112.*

**Lower Bache House** ⛰, HR6 0ER, East : 1 ¾ m. by A 4112 ✆ (01568) 750304, « 17C farmhouse », ⛆, park – ⇔ TV P. ✻
**Meals** (by arrangement) 15.50 **st.** ₰ 4.50 – **3 rm** ☕ 31.50/53.00 **st.** – SB.

**at Leysters** *Northwest : 5 m. by A 49 on A 4112 – ✉ Leominster.*

🏠 **The Hills Farm,** HR6 0HP, ☎ (01568) 750205, *Fax (01568) 750205*, ≤, « Working farm », park – 🚭 [TV] [P]. [MC] [VISA] [JCB]
*closed November-late February and 2 weeks June* – **Meals** (by arrangement) 17.00 **s.** – **5 rm** ☕ 34.00/48.00 **s.**

**at Eyton** *Northwest : 2 m. by B 4361 – ✉ Leominster.*

🏠 **The Marsh** 🌿, HR6 0AG, ☎ (01568) 613952, « Part 14C timbered house », 🌳 – 🚭 [TV] ☎ [P]. [MC] [AE] [DC] [VISA]. ✗
*closed 3 weeks January* – **Meals** (booking essential) (dinner only and Sunday lunch)/dinner 26.00 **st.** 🍷 8.75 – **4 rm** ☕ 90.00/130.00 **st.** – SB.

Ⓜ ATS Market Mill, Dishley St. ☎ (01568) 612679/614114

**LETCHWORTH** *Herts.* [404] T 28 – *pop. 31 418.*
*London 40 – Bedford 22 – Cambridge 22 – Luton 14.*

🏨 **Broadway Toby,** The Broadway, SG6 3NZ, ☎ (01462) 480111, *Fax (01462) 473041* – [lift], 🚭 rm, [TV] ☎ [P] – 🎤 200. [MC] [AE] [VISA]. ✗
*closed 25 and 26 December* – **Meals** (grill rest.) a la carte 7.50/16.05 **st.** 🍷 4.45 – **34 rm** ☕ 65.00/75.50 **st.** – SB.

Ⓜ ATS Unit 21, Jubilee Trade Centre, Works Rd ☎ (01462) 670517

***En saison,*** *surtout dans les stations fréquentées,*
*il est prudent de retenir à l'avance.*
*Cependant, si vous ne pouvez pas occuper la chambre*
*que vous avez retenue, prévenez immédiatement l'hôtelier.*

*Si vous écrivez à un hôtel à l'étranger, joignez à votre lettre*
*un coupon-réponse international (disponible dans les bureaux de poste).*

**LEWDOWN** *Devon* [403] H 32 *The West Country G..*
Env. : *Lydford★★, E : 4 m.*
Exc. : *Launceston★ - Castle★ (≤★) St. Mary Magdalene★, W : 8 m. by A 30 and A 388.*
*London 238 – Exeter 37 – Plymouth 22.*

🏨 **Lewtrenchard Manor** 🌿, EX20 4PN, South : ¾ m. by Lewtrenchard rd ☎ (01566) 783256, *Fax (01566) 783332*, « 17C manor house and gardens », 🎣, park – 🚭 rest, [TV] ☎ [P] – 🎤 50. [MC] [AE] [DC] [VISA]. ✗
**Meals** (booking essential to non-residents) (light lunch) 19.50/30.00 **t.** 🍷 6.50 – **9 rm** ☕ 80.00/155.00 **t.**

**LEWES** *E. Sussex* [404] U 31 *Great Britain G. – pop. 15 376.*
See : *Town★ (High Street★, Keere Street★) – Castle (≤★) AC.*
Exc. : *Sheffield Park Garden★ AC, N : 9½ m. by A 275.*
⛳ *Chapel Hill ☎ (01273) 473245.*
[i] *187 High St., BN7 2DE ☎ (01273) 483448.*
*London 53 – Brighton 8 – Hastings 29 – Maidstone 43.*

🏨 **Shelleys,** High St., BN7 1XS, ☎ (01273) 472361, *Fax (01273) 483152*, 🌂, « Part Georgian former inn, antiques », 🌳 – 🚭 rest, [TV] ☎ [P] – 🎤 50. [MC] [AE] [DC] [VISA] [JCB]
**Meals** 17.00/26.00 **t.** and a la carte – ☕ 12.50 – **18 rm** 120.00/149.00 **st.**, 1 suite – SB.

🏠 **Millers** without rest., 134 High St., BN7 1XS, ☎ (01273) 475631, *Fax (01273) 486226*, 🌳 – 🚭 [TV]. ✗
*closed 4-5 November and 19 December-6 January* – **3 rm** ☕ 47.00/52.00.

Ⓜ ATS 18 North St. ☎ (01273) 477972

**LEYBURN** *N. Yorks.* [402] O 21 – *pop. 2 074.*
*London 251 – Darlington 25 – Kendal 43 – Leeds 53 – York 49.*

🏠 **Park Gate House** without rest., Constable Burton, DL8 5RG, East : 3 ½ m. on A 684 ☎ (01677) 450466, 🌳 – 🚭 [TV] [P]. ✗
*closed 25 and 26 December* – **4 rm** ☕ 35.00/56.00 **s.**

**LEYLAND** *Lancs.* 402 L 22 – *pop. 3 729.*

*London 224 – Blackburn 12 – Lancaster 30 – Leeds 68 – Preston 7.*

🏠 **Jarvis Leyland,** Leyland Way, PR5 2JX, East : ¾ m. on B 5256 & (01772) 422922
Fax (01772) 622282, 🚗, ▮ – ❄ rest, 📺 ☎ 🅿 – ⚠ 230. 🐫 🗚 ⓪ 𝘝𝘐𝘚𝘈
**Meals** (bar lunch Saturday) 9.95/13.95 **st.** and dinner a la carte ⅃ 6.50 – 🖙 8.50 – **93 rm**
69.00/79.00 **st.** – SB.

🔘 ATS Leyland Lane & (01942) 674712/674865

---

**LEYSTERS** *Herefordshire* 403 404 M 27 – *see Leominster.*

---

**LICHFIELD** *Staffs.* 402 403 404 O 25 *Great Britain G.* – *pop. 28 666.*

See : *City★ - Cathedral★★ AC.*
📷, 📷 *Seedy Mill, Elmhurst* & (01543) 417333.
🖪 *Donegal House, Bore St., WS13 6NE* & (01543) 252109.
*London 128 – Birmingham 16 – Derby 23 – Stoke-on-Trent 30.*

🏠 **Little Barrow,** Beacon St., WS13 7AR, & (01543) 414500, Fax (01543) 415734 – 📺 ☎ 📞
🅿 – ⚠ 80. 🐫 🗚 ⓪ 𝘝𝘐𝘚𝘈 🗚
**Meals** 10.00/15.50 **st.** and a la carte ⅃ 4.95 – **24 rm** 🖙 60.00/75.00 **st.** – SB.

✕ **Chandlers Grande Brasserie,** Corn Exchange, Conduit St., WS13 6JU
& (01543) 416688, Fax (01543) 417887 – 🐫 🗚
*closed 3 and 31 May and 30 August* – **Meals** 9.95/12.50 **t.** and a la carte.

✕ **Thrales,** 40-44 Tamworth St., WS13 6JJ, (corner of Backcester Lane) & (01543) 255091,
Fax (01543) 415352 – 🐫 𝘝𝘐𝘚𝘈
*closed Sunday dinner, Bank Holiday Monday and 31 December* – **Meals** 9.50/11.50 **t.**
and a la carte ⅃ 5.00.

🔘 ATS Eastern Av. & (01543) 414200

*La **Grande-Bretagne** et l'**Irlande** sont maintenant couvertes
par un **atlas** disponible en trois versions :
broché, relié et à spirale.*

---

**LIFTON** *Devon* 403 H 32 *The West Country G.* – *pop. 964.*

Env. : *Launceston★ – Castle★ (≤★) St. Mary Magdalene★, W : 4½ m. by A 30 and A 388.*
*London 238 – Bude 24 – Exeter 37 – Launceston 4 – Plymouth 32.*

🏠 **Arundell Arms,** Fore St., PL16 0AA, & (01566) 784666, Fax (01566) 784494, 🐟, 🚗 –
❄ rest, 📺 ☎ 🅿 – ⚠ 100. 🐫 🗚 ⓪ 𝘝𝘐𝘚𝘈
*closed 2 days Christmas* – **Meals** – (see **The Restaurant** below) – **28 rm** 🖙 73.00/114.00 **t.**
– SB.

🏡 **Thatched Cottage** 🌭, Sprytown, PL16 0AY, East : 1 ¼ m. by old A 30
& (01566) 784224, Fax (01566) 784334, 🚗 – ❄ rest, 📺 ☎ 🅿 . 🐫 🗚 ⓪ 𝘝𝘐𝘚𝘈 𝘑𝘊𝘉
**Meals** 12.95 **t.** (lunch) and a la carte 18.75/24.40 **t.** ⅃ 5.90 – **5 rm** 🖙 42.50/109.00 **t.** – SB.

✕✕ **The Restaurant** (at Arundell Arms H.), Fore St., PL16 0AA, & (01566) 784666,
Fax (01566) 784494 – ❄
*closed 2 days Christmas* – **Meals** 19.00/29.50 **st.** and a la carte ⅃ 6.50.

---

**LIMPLEY STOKE (LOWER)** *Bath & North East Somerset* 403 404 N 29 – *see Bath.*

---

**LINCOLN** *Lincs.* 402 404 S 24 *Great Britain G.* – *pop. 80 281.*

See : *City★★ – Cathedral and Precincts★★★ AC* Y – *High Bridge★★* Z **9** – *Usher Gallery★ AC*
YZ **M1** – *Jew's House★* Y – *Castle★ AC* Y.
Env. : *Doddington Hall★ AC, W : 6 m. by B 1003 –* Z *– and B 1190.*
Exc. : *Gainsborough Old Hall★ AC, NW : 19 m. by A 57 –* Z *– and A 156.*
📷 *Carholme, Carholme Rd* & (01522) 523725.
✈ *Humberside Airport :* & (01652) 688456, N : 32 m. by A 15 – Y – M 180 and A 18.
🖪 *9 Castle Hill, LN1 3AA* & (01522) 529828.
*London 140 – Bradford 81 – Cambridge 94 – Kingston-upon-Hull 44 – Leeds 73 – Leicester
53 – Norwich 104 – Nottingham 38 – Sheffield 48 – York 82.*

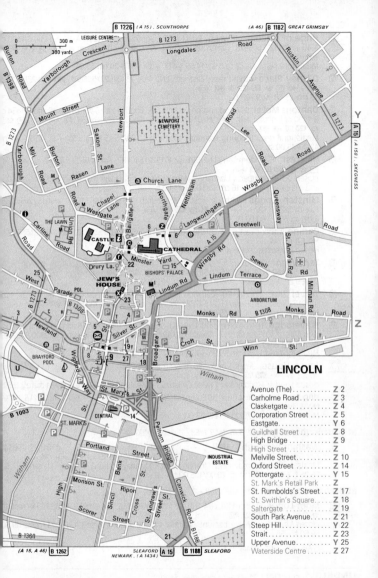

## LINCOLN

🏨 **White Hart**, Bailgate, LN1 3AR, ℘ (01522) 526222, *Fax (01522) 531798*, « Antique furniture » – 🔄 🛏️ ✗⊱ 📺 ☎ 🚗 – 🛎️ 70. 🆎 🆎 ⓘ 🆚🆂🅰 ᴊᴄʙ                                            Y c
*King Richard :* Meals a la carte 20.15/29.15 **t.** ₪ 6.25 – ⊊ 9.50 – **39 rm** 90.00 **t.**, 9 suites – SB.

🏨 **Courtyard by Marriott**, Brayford Wharf North, LN1 1YW, ℘ (01522) 544244, *Fax (01522) 560805*, ℉ᴓ – 🔄, ✗⊱ rm, 🔲 📺 ☎ ℅ & 🅿 – 🛎️ 30. 🆎 🆎 ⓘ 🆚🆂🅰 ᴊᴄʙ, ❄                                                            Z a
Meals a la carte 12.95/25.25 **t.** ₪ 7.25 – ⊊ 9.95 – **95 rm** 72.00 **t.** – SB.

🏨 **Forte Posthouse Lincoln**, Eastgate, LN2 1PN, ℘ (01522) 520341, *Fax (01522) 510780*, 🍴 – 🔄, ✗⊱ rm, 📺 ☎ 🅿 – 🛎️ 90. 🆎 🆎 ⓘ 🆚🆂🅰 ᴊᴄʙ                                            Y z
Meals a la carte 15.35/22.85 **t.** ₪ 7.50 – ⊊ 8.95 – **70 rm** 75.00 **t.** – SB.

331

🏠 **Pride of Lincoln**, off Whisby Rd, LN6 3QZ, Southwest : 6 m. by A 15, A 1434, B 1190 on A 46 ℰ (01522) 686878, *Fax (01522) 500664*, 🚗 – 🛏️, 🔆 rm, 📺 ☎ 🕭 🅿 – 🔬 200. 🆎 🅰
ᵛⁱˢᵃ. ⅋
**Meals** (grill rest.) a la carte 8.90/14.65 ⓐ 4.00 – ⌒ 4.95 – **20 rm** 39.95.

🏠 **D'Isney Place** without rest., Eastgate, LN2 4AA, ℰ (01522) 538881, *Fax (01522) 511132*
🚗 – 🔆 📺 ⚛. 🆎 🅰🅴 ⓪ ᵛⁱˢᵃ ᴶᶜᴮ                                      Y
**17 rm** ⌒ 48.00/92.00 t.

🏠 **Damons Motel**, 997 Doddington Rd, LN6 3SE, Southwest : 4 ¼ m. by A 15 and A 1434 on B 1190 at junction with A 46 ℰ (01522) 887733, *Fax (01522) 887734*, ⅃ⱷ – 🔆 rm, 📺 ☎ 🕭 🅿. 🆎 🅰🅴 ⓪ ᵛⁱˢᵃ. ⅋
**Meals** (grill rest.) (booking essential) a la carte 10.90/25.15 st. ⓐ 6.30 – ⌒ 4.95 – **47 rm** 42.00/45.00 st.

🏠 **Hillcrest**, 15 Lindum Terr., LN2 5RT, ℰ (01522) 510182, *Fax (01522) 510182*, ≤, 🚗 – 🔆
📺 ☎ 🅿. 🆎 🅰🅴 ᵛⁱˢᵃ ᴶᶜᴮ                                            Y
*closed 23 December-4 January* – **Meals** *(closed Sunday)* (bar lunch)/dinner 15.00 t. and a la carte ⓐ 4.50 – **16 rm** ⌒ 50.00/71.00 t. – SB.

🏠 **Minster Lodge** without rest., 3 Church Lane, LN2 1QJ, ℰ (01522) 513220, *Fax (01522) 513220* – 🔆 📺 ☎ ⚛ 🅿. 🆎 ᵛⁱˢᵃ ᴶᶜᴮ. ⅋                       Y
**6 rm** ⌒ 60.00/90.00 st.

🏠 **Carline** without rest., 1-3 Carline Rd, LN1 1HL, ℰ (01522) 530422, *Fax (01522) 530422*
🔆 📺 🅿. ⅋                                                       Y
*closed Christmas and New Year* – **12 rm** ⌒ 32.00/42.00.

🏠 **Tennyson** without rest., 7 South Park Av., LN5 8EN, South : 1 ¼ m. on A 15
ℰ (01522) 521624, *Fax (01522) 521624* – 📺 ☎ 🅿. 🆎 🅰🅴 ⓪ ᵛⁱˢᵃ. ⅋
*closed 22 December-2 January* – **8 rm** ⌒ 29.00/42.00 st.

🏠 **Travel Inn**, Lincoln Rd, Canwick Hill, LN4 2RF, Southeast : 1 ¾ m. on B 1188
ℰ (01522) 525216, *Fax (01522) 542521*, 🚗 – 🔆 rm, 📺 🕭 🅿. 🆎 🅰🅴 ⓪ ᵛⁱˢᵃ. ⅋
**Meals** (grill rest.) – **40 rm** 38.00 t.

🏠 **Travelodge**, Thorpe on the Hill, LN6 9AJ, Southwest : 6 m. by A 15 and A 1434 at junction with A 46 ℰ (01522) 697213, *Fax (01522) 697213*, Reservations (Freephone) 0800 850950 – 🔆 rm, 📺 🕭 🅿. 🆎 🅰🅴 ⓪ ᵛⁱˢᵃ. ⅋
**Meals** (grill rest.) – **32 rm** 39.95/59.95 t.

🍴🍴 **Jew's House**, Jew's House, 15 The Strait, LN2 1JD, ℰ (01522) 524851, « 12C town house » – 🔆. 🆎 🅰🅴 ⓪ ᵛⁱˢᵃ. ⅋                                 YZ
*closed Sunday, Monday and 1 week Christmas* – **Meals** 12.95/25.00 t. and a la carte ⓐ 5.50.

🍴 **Wig and Mitre**, first floor, 30 Steep Hill, LN2 1TL, ℰ (01522) 523705, *Fax (01522) 532402*
🆎 🅰🅴 ⓪ ᵛⁱˢᵃ ᴶᶜᴮ                                                Y
**Meals** a la carte 13.75/21.45 st. ⓐ 7.00.

**at Washingborough** *East : 3 m. by B 1188 - Z - on B 1190 – ✉ Lincoln.*

🏠 **Washingborough Hall** 🏠, Church Hill, LN4 1BE, ℰ (01522) 790340, *Fax (01522) 792936*, ⅃, 🚗 – 🔆 rest, 📺 ☎ 🅿 – 🔬 50. 🆎 🅰🅴 ⓪ ᵛⁱˢᵃ ᴶᶜᴮ. ⅋
**Meals** *(closed Saturday lunch)* (carving lunch Monday to Friday)/dinner a la carte 17.50/26.25 t. ⓐ 6.50 – **14 rm** ⌒ 70.00/125.00 t. – SB.

**at Branston** *Southeast : 3 m. on B 1188 – Z – ✉ Lincoln.*

🏠 **Moor Lodge**, Sleaford Rd, LN4 1HU, ℰ (01522) 791366, *Fax (01522) 794389* – 🔆 rest, 📺 ☎ 🅿 – 🔬 150. 🆎 🅰🅴 ᵛⁱˢᵃ
*closed New Year* – **Meals** (bar lunch)/dinner 12.50 t. and a la carte ⓐ 4.75 – **23 rm** ⌒ 49.50/59.50 t. – SB.

🔧 ATS Crofton Rd, Allenby Trading Est. ℰ (01522) 527225

---

**LINDALE** *Cumbria* 🗺️🗺️ L 21 – *see Grange-over-Sands.*

---

**LINTON** *Kent* 🗺️🗺️ V 30 – *see Maidstone.*

---

**In this guide**

a symbol or a character, printed in red or **black**, in **bold** or light type, does not have the same meaning.
Pay particular attention to the explanatory pages.

332

**IPHOOK** *Hants.* **404** R 30.

> *London 51 – Brighton 48 – Guildford 16 – Portsmouth 30 – Southampton 41 – Winchester 30.*

🏠 **Travelodge,** GU30 7TT, Southwest : 2 m. by B 2131 on A 3 (northbound carriageway) 𝒫 (01428) 727619, Reservations (Freephone) 0800 850950 – ⇄ rm, 📺 ⅏ 🅿. 🆎 AE ① VISA JCB. ⅍
> **Meals** (grill rest.) – **40 rm** 39.95/59.95 **t.**

---

**ISKEARD** *Cornwall* **403** G 32 *The West Country G.* – *pop. 7 044.*

> See : *Church★.*
> Exc. : *Lanhydrock★★, W : 11½ m. by A 38 and A 390 – NW : Bodmin Moor★★ - St. Endellion Church★★ - Altarnun Church★ - St. Breward Church★ - Blisland★ (church★) - Camelford★ – Cardinham Church★ - Michaelstow Church★ - St. Kew★ (church★) - St. Mabyn Church★ - St. Neot★ (Parish Church★★) - St. Sidwell's, Laneast★ - St. Teath Church★ - St. Tudy★ – Launceston★ – Castle★ (≤★) St. Mary Magdalene★, NE : 19 m. by A 390 and A 388.*
> *London 261 – Exeter 59 – Plymouth 18 – Truro 37.*

🏨 **The Well House** ⌂, St. Keyne, PL14 4RN, South : 3 ½ m. by B 3254 on St. Keyne Well rd 𝒫 (01579) 342001, *Fax* (01579) 343891, ≤, « Victorian country house », ⫶, ☞, ⅍ – 📺 ☎ 🅿. 🆎 AE ① VISA JCB
> **Meals** (booking essential to non-residents) 26.95 **t.** ⅃ 5.80 – **9 rm** ⌷ 75.00/165.00 **t.** – SB.

🏠 **Old Rectory** ⌂, Duloe Rd, St. Keyne, PL14 4RL, South : 3 ¼ m. on B 3254 𝒫 (01579) 342617, *Fax* (01579) 342293, ☞ – ⇄ 📺 🅿. 🆎 VISA JCB
> *closed Christmas-New Year* – **Meals** (booking essential) (dinner only) 21.00 **t.** – **8 rm** ⌷ 30.00/70.00 **st.** – SB.

> ⓐ ATS 10 Dean St. 𝒫 (01579) 345489/345247

---

**ITTLEBOURNE** *Kent* **404** X 30 – *see Canterbury.*

---

**ITTLEBURY GREEN** *Essex* **404** O 27 – *see Saffron Walden.*

---

**ITTLE HAMPDEN** *Bucks.* – *see Great Missenden.*

---

**ITTLEHAMPTON** *W. Sussex* **404** S 31 – *pop. 50 408.*

> *London 64 – Brighton 18 – Portsmouth 31.*

🏨 **Bailiffscourt** ⌂, Climping St., Climping, BN17 5RW, West : 2 ¾ m. by A 259 𝒫 (01903) 723511, *Fax* (01903) 723107, « Reconstructed "medieval" house », ☞, park, ⅍ – ⇄ rest, 📺 ☎ 🅿 – 🔥 35. 🆎 AE ① VISA JCB
> **Meals** 18.50/32.50 **st.** – **32 rm** ⌷ 120.00/300.00 **st.** – SB.

🏠 **Travelodge,** Worthing Rd, Rustington, BN17 6JN, East : 1 ¼ m. on B 2187 𝒫 (01903) 733150, Reservations (Freephone) 0800 850950 – ⇄ rm, 📺 ⅏ 🅿. 🆎 AE ① VISA JCB. ⅍
> **Meals** (grill rest.) – **36 rm** 39.95/59.95 **t.**

↟ **Amberley Court** without rest., Crookthorn Lane, Climping, BN17 5QU, West : 1 ¾ m. by B 2187 off A 259 𝒫 (01903) 725131, *Fax* (01903) 734555, ☞ – ⇄ 📺 🅿. ⅍
> *March-September* – **3 rm** ⌷ 35.00/56.00.

> ⓐ ATS Church St. 𝒫 (01903) 713085/716919

---

**ITTLE LANGDALE** *Cumbria* **402** K 20 – *see Ambleside.*

---

**ITTLE LANGFORD** *Wilts.* – *see Salisbury.*

---

**ITTLE PETHERICK** *Cornwall* **403** F 32 – *see Padstow.*

---

**ITTLEPORT** *Cambs.* **404** U 26 – *see Ely.*

---

**ITTLE SHELFORD** *Cambs.* **404** U 27 – *see Cambridge.*

**LITTLE SINGLETON** *Lancs. – see Blackpool.*

---

**LITTLE SUTTON** *Ches.* 402 ⑫ 403 ⑫ – ⊠ *South Wirral.*
*London 208 – Chester 12 – Liverpool 9 – Manchester 48.*

🏨 **Woodhey**, Berwick Rd, L66 4PS, on A 550 ℰ (0151) 339 5121, *Fax (0151) 339 3214*, ⇘
◩ – ⤢, ▤ rest, 📺 ☎ ♿ ℗ – ⊿ 200. ⓬ ⒶⒺ ⓪ *VISA*
**Meals** *(bar lunch)/dinner 17.50* **t.** *and a la carte* ⏐ 8.25 – ⌕ 9.50 – **53 rm** 80.00/100.00 **t.**
SB.

---

**LITTLE THORNTON** *Lancs.* 402 L 22 *– see Blackpool.*

---

**LITTLE WALSINGHAM** *Norfolk* 404 W 25 – ⊠ *Walsingham.*
*London 117 – Cambridge 67 – Cromer 21 – Norwich 32.*

XX **Old Bakehouse** with rm, 33-35 High St., NR22 6BZ, ℰ (01328) 82045
*Fax (01328) 820454* – ⤢ rest, 📺. ⓬ *VISA*. ⋘
*closed 2 weeks February-March, 1 week June, 2 weeks October-November, 25-26 Decem
ber and restricted opening in winter* – **Meals** *(closed Sunday to Tuesday to non-resident.*
*(dinner only) a la carte 21.35/25.25* **t.** ⏐ 8.50 – **3 rm** ⌕ 27.50/47.00 **t.**

---

**LITTLE WEIGHTON** *East Riding* 402 S 22 *– see Kingston-upon-Hull.*

---

**LITTLEWICK GREEN** *Windsor & Maidenhead* 404 R 29 *– see Maidenhead.*

---

**LITTLE WYMONDLEY** *Herts.* 404 T 28 *– see Hitchin.*

---

When visiting London use the Green Guide **"London"**

- Detailed descriptions of places of interest
- Useful local information
- A section on the historic square-mile of the
  City of London with a detailed fold-out plan
- The lesser known London boroughs
  – their people, places and sights
- Plans of selected areas and important buildings.

**LIVERPOOL** *Mersey.* 402 403 L 23 *Great Britain G.* – *pop. 481 786.*

See : *City*★ – *Walker Art Gallery*★★ DY M2 – *Liverpool Cathedral*★★ *(Lady Chapel*★*)* EZ – *Metropolitan Cathedral of Christ the King*★★ EY – *Albert Dock*★ CZ *(Merseyside Maritime Museum*★ AC M1 – *Tate Gallery Liverpool*★ *).*

Exc. : *Speke Hall*★ *AC, SE : 8 m. by A 561 BX.*

🏌, 🏌 *Allerton Municipal, Allerton Rd* 𝒫 *(0151) 428 1046* – 🏌 *Liverpool Municipal, Ingoe Lane, Kirkby* 𝒫 *(0151) 546 5435*, BV – 🏌 *Bowring, Bowring Park, Roby Rd, Huyton* 𝒫 *(0151) 489 1901.*

*Mersey Tunnels (toll)* AX.

✈ *Liverpool Airport :* 𝒫 *(0151) 486 8877, SE : 6 m. by A 561 BX* – **Terminal** *: Pier Head.*

⛴ *to Isle of Man (Douglas) (Isle of Man Steam Packet Co. Ltd) 1-3 daily (2 h 30 mn)* – *to Northern Ireland (Belfast) (Norse Irish Ferries Ltd) (11 h)* – *to Dublin (Isle of Man Steam Packet Co. Ltd) daily 2-3 daily (4 h).*

⛴ *to Birkenhead (Mersey Ferries) frequent services daily* – *to Wallasey (Mersey Ferries) frequent services daily.*

🛈 *Merseyside Welcome Centre, Clayton Square Shopping Centre, L1 1QR* 𝒫 *(0151) 709 3631* – *Atlantic Pavilion, Albert Dock, L3 4AA* 𝒫 *(0151) 708 8854.*

*London 219* – *Birmingham 103* – *Leeds 75* – *Manchester 35.*

Town plans : Liverpool pp. 2-5

🏨 **Swallow,** One Queen Sq., L1 1RH, 𝒫 (0151) 476 8000, *Fax* (0151) 474 5000, 🏋, ⇌s, ◻ – 🛗 ↔ ▤ 🔟 ☎ ✆ & 🅿 – 🕍 250. 🆗 🅰🅴 ⓞ 𝘝𝘐𝘚𝘈. ⋘
DY e
**Meals** *(closed Saturday lunch)* 22.00 **st.** (dinner) and a la carte 21.50/34.00 **st.** 🍷 6.50 – **143 rm** ⊡ 105.00/120.00 **st.**, 3 suites – SB.

🏨 **Liverpool Moat House,** Paradise St., L1 8GT, 𝒫 (0151) 471 9988, *Fax* (0151) 709 2706, 🏋, ⇌s, ◻ – 🛗, ↔ rm, ▤ 🔟 ☎ 🅿 – 🕍 400. 🆗 🅰🅴 ⓞ 𝘝𝘐𝘚𝘈
DZ n
**Meals** 8.95/16.50 **st.** and dinner a la carte 🍷 5.75 – ⊡ 9.50 – **249 rm** 95.00/120.00 **st.**, 2 suites – SB.

🏨 **Thistle Atlantic Tower,** 30 Chapel St., L3 9RE, 𝒫 (0151) 227 4444, *Fax* (0151) 236 3973, ⇐ – 🛗, ↔ rm, ▤ 🔟 ☎ 🅿 – 🕍 100. 🆗 🅰🅴 ⓞ 𝘝𝘐𝘚𝘈 𝘑𝘊𝘉. ⋘
CY r
**Meals** 19.50 **t.** (dinner) and a la carte 15.25/22.75 🍷 5.50 – ⊡ 10.25 – **223 rm** 99.00/110.00 **st.**, 3 suites – SB.

🏦 **Devonshire House,** 293-297 Edge Lane, L7 9LD, East : 2 ¼ m. on A 5047 𝒫 (0151) 280 3903, *Fax* (0151) 263 2109, ☞ – 🛗 🔟 ☎ ✆ & 🅿 – 🕍 300. 🆗 🅰🅴 ⓞ 𝘝𝘐𝘚𝘈
BX a
**Meals** *(closed Saturday lunch)* 13.95/16.95 **st.** and dinner a la carte – **54 rm** ⊡ 80.00/90.00 **st.** – SB.

🏠 **The Park - Premier Lodge,** Dunningsbridge Rd, L30 6YN, North : 6 ¾ m. by A 59 on A 5036 𝒫 (0151) 525 7555, *Fax* (0151) 525 2481, Reservations (Freephone) 0800 118833 – 🛗, ↔ rm, 🔟 ☎ 🅿 – 🕍 200. 🆗 🅰🅴 ⓞ 𝘝𝘐𝘚𝘈. ⋘
**Meals** *(grill rest.)* 7.25/12.95 **st.** and a la carte 🍷 5.40 – ⊡ 6.95 – **60 rm** 43.95 **st.**

🏠 **Travel Inn,** Northern Perimeter Rd, L30 7PT, North : 6 m. by A 59 on A 5036 𝒫 (0151) 531 1497, *Fax* (0151) 520 1842 – ↔ rm, ▤ rest, 🔟 & 🅿. 🆗 🅰🅴 ⓞ 𝘝𝘐𝘚𝘈. ⋘
**Meals** *(grill rest.)* – **43 rm** 38.00 **t.**

🏠 **Travel Inn,** Queens Dr., West Derby, L13 0DL, East : 4 m. on A 5058 (Ringroad) 𝒫 (0151) 228 4724, *Fax* (0151) 220 7610 – ↔ rm, ▤ rest, 🔟 & 🅿. 🆗 🅰🅴 ⓞ 𝘝𝘐𝘚𝘈. ⋘
BV a
**Meals** *(grill rest.)* – **40 rm** 38.00 **t.**

🏠 **Campanile,** Wapping and Chaloner St., L3 4AJ, 𝒫 (0151) 709 8104, *Fax* (0151) 709 8725 – ↔ rm, 🔟 ☎ & 🅿 – 🕍 30. 🆗 🅰🅴 ⓞ 𝘝𝘐𝘚𝘈
CZ a
**Meals** 10.85 **st.** 🍷 6.60 – ⊡ 4.50 – **78 rm** 38.00 **st.**

XX **Becher's Brook,** 29a Hope St., L1 9BQ, 𝒫 (0151) 707 0005, *Fax* (0151) 708 7011 – ↔. 🆗 🅰🅴 ⓞ 𝘝𝘐𝘚𝘈
EZ a
*closed Saturday lunch, Sunday, 25-26 December, 1 January and Bank Holidays* – **Meals** 17.95 **t.** (lunch) and a la carte 20.75/43.00 **t.** 🍷 8.50.

**t Crosby** *North : 5½ m. on A 565* – AV.

🏦 **Carlton Blundellsands,** The Serpentine, Blundellsands, L23 6YB, West : 1 ¼ m. via College Rd, Mersey Rd and Agnes Rd 𝒫 (0151) 924 6515, *Fax* (0151) 931 5364 – 🛗, ↔ rm, 🔟 ☎ 🅿 – 🕍 250. 🆗 🅰🅴 𝘝𝘐𝘚𝘈. ⋘
**Meals** *(bar lunch Saturday and Bank Holidays)* 9.75/13.95 **t.** and a la carte – ⊡ 8.95 – **30 rm** 75.00/110.00 **t.**

**t Huyton** *East : 8¼ m. by A 5047 and A 5080* - BX - *on B 5199* – ✉ *Liverpool.*

🏨 **Village H. and Leisure Club,** Fallows Way, L35 1RZ, Southeast : 3 ¼ m. by A 5080 off Windy Arbor Rd 𝒫 (0151) 449 2341, *Fax* (0151) 449 3832, 🏋, ⇌s, ◻, squash – 🛗, ↔ rm, 🔟 ☎ 🅿 – 🕍 250. 🆗 🅰🅴 ⓞ 𝘝𝘐𝘚𝘈 𝘑𝘊𝘉. ⋘
**Meals** *(closed Saturday lunch)* 15.95 **st.** (lunch) and a la carte 18.50/30.00 **st.** 🍷 6.45 – **62 rm** ⊡ 82.00/107.00 **st.**

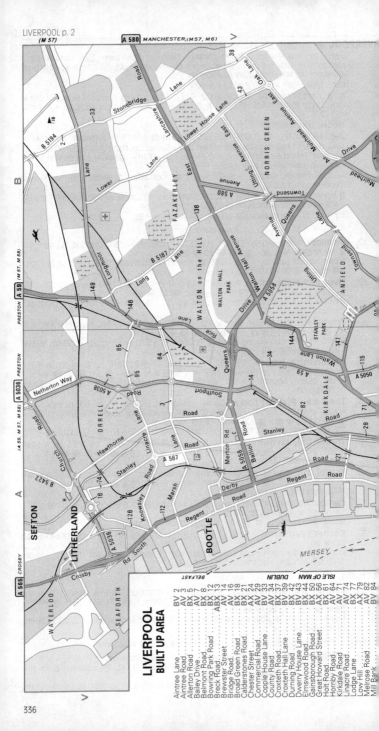

## LIVERPOOL
## BUILT UP AREA

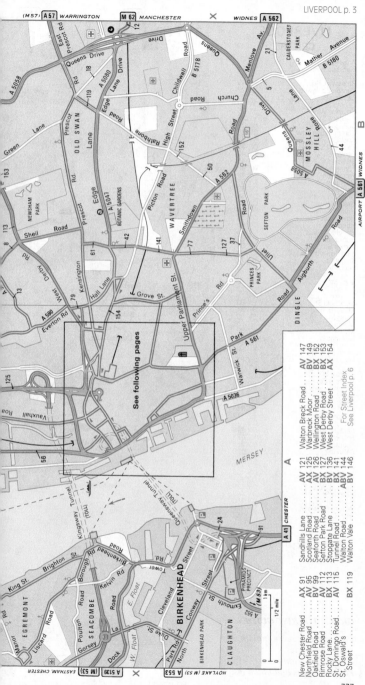

A 5058

East Prescot Rd

Queens Drive

Queens Drive Rd
18
119

A 5080
Edge Lane Drive

OLD SWAN

Prescot Road

Green Lane

153

NEWSHAM PARK

Sheil Road
113
8

West Derby Rd
61
13

Edge Lane

A 5047

Kensington
79
Hall Lane

BOTANIC GARDENS

A 580 Everton Rd

Rathbone Road

High Street

Childwall Road

Picton Road

WAVERTREE

Smithdown Road
141
77

Grove St.
154

Upper Parliament St.

Prince's Rd

PRINCES PARK

Church Road

Menlove Av.
21

CALDERSTONES PARK

Mather Avenue

B 5180

5

MOSSLEY HILL
44

A 5058

SEFTON PARK

50
A 562
127
37

Ullet Road

DINGLE

Aigburth

Road

A 561

Park St.

Warwick St.

A 5036

AIRPORT    A 561 WIDNES    B

See following pages

125

Vauxhall Road

56

MERSEY

A

B

EGREMONT

King St.

Brighton St.

SEACOMBE

Manor Rd

Liscard Road

Poulton Road

Gorsey La.

Dock Rd

W. Float

E. Float

Kingsway Tunnel (TOLL)

Queensway Tunnel (Toll)

Birkenhead Road

Borough Rd

Kelvin Rd

Cleveland Street

Duke St.

Tower Road

Conway Street

BIRKENHEAD

Exmouth St.

PYRAMIDS PRECINCT

BIRKENHEAD PARK

CLAUGHTON

North Rd

Park Rd

A 552

(M53)

24

91

A 41 CHESTER

A 5139

A 553

0    1/2 mile
0    1km

337

# LIVERPOOL
## CENTRE

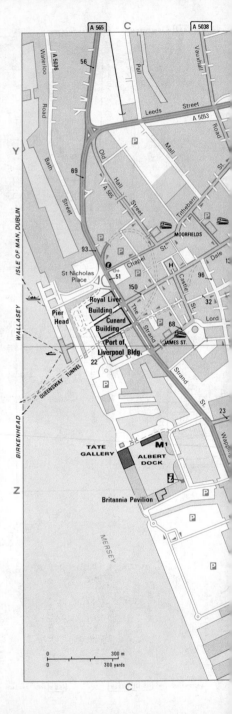

### GREEN TOURIST GUIDES

*Picturesque scenery, buildings*
*Attractive routes*
*Touring programmes*
*Plans of towns and buildings.*

338

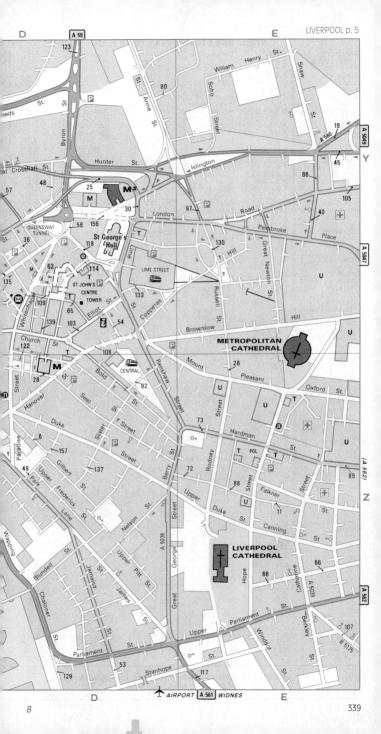

# STREET INDEX TO LIVERPOOL TOWN PLANS

The names of main shopping streets are indicated in red
at the beginning of the list of streets.

🏠 **Derby Lodge - Premier Lodge**, Roby Rd, L36 4HD, Southwest : 1 m. on A 5080 ℘ (0151) 480 4440, *Fax (0151) 443 0952*, Reservations (Freephone) 0800 118833, 🍴 – 🍽 rest, 📺 ☎ 📞 📞 – 🔥 35. 🆎 🅰🅴 ⑩ 𝘝𝘐𝘚𝘈 𝗝𝗖𝗕. ❄
**Meals** (grill rest.) 10.95/12.95 **st.** and a la carte – 🍷 5.95 – **53 rm** 🛏 44.95 **st.**

🏠 **Travel Inn**, Wilson Rd, Tarbock, L36 6AD, Southeast : 2 ¼ m. on A 5080 ℘ (0151) 480 9614, *Fax (0151) 480 9361* – ⁕⁕ rm, 🍽 rest, 📺 ᕁ 📞. 🆎 🅰🅴 ⑩ 𝘝𝘐𝘚𝘈 𝗝𝗖𝗕.
**Meals** (grill rest.) – **40 rm** 38.00 **t.**

**at Grassendale** *Southeast : 4 ½ m. on A 561 – BX – ✉ Liverpool.*

✗✗✗ **Gulshan**, 544-548 Aigburth Rd, L19 3QG, on A 561 ℘ (0151) 427 2273 – 🍽. 🆎 🅰🅴 ⑩ 𝘝𝘐𝘚𝘈 𝗝𝗖𝗕
*closed 25 December* – **Meals** - Indian - (dinner only) 16.95 **t.** and a la carte.

**at Woolton** *Southeast : 6 m. by A 562 – BX – , A 5058 and Woolton Rd – ✉ Liverpool.*

🏛 **Woolton Redbourne**, Acrefield Rd, L25 5JN, ℘ (0151) 421 1500, *Fax (0151) 421 1501*, « Victorian house, antiques », 🍴 – 🍽 rest, 📺 ☎ 📞. 🆎 🅰🅴 ⑩ 𝘝𝘐𝘚𝘈. ❄
**Meals** (residents only) (dinner only) 22.95 **t.** ⅊ 8.95 – **25 rm** 🛏 63.00/92.00 **t.**, 1 suite – SB.

🔧 ATS 15/37 Caryl St. ℘ (0151) 709 8032
ATS Wilson Road, Huyton ℘ (0151) 489 8386
ATS 568-574 Aigburth Rd, Aigburth
℘ (0151) 427 3665
ATS 73-77 Durning Rd, Wavertree
℘ (0151) 263 7604

ATS Musker St., Crosby ℘ (0151) 931 3166
ATS Unit E, Liver Ind. Est., Long Lane, Aintree
℘ (0151) 524 1000

---

**LIZARD** *Cornwall* 𝟰𝟬𝟯 E 34 *The West Country G..*
**Env. :** *Lizard Peninsula★ - Mullion Cove★★ (Church★) - Kynance Cove★★ - Cadgwith★ - Coverack★ – Cury★ (Church★) - Gunwalloe Fishing Cove★ - St. Keverne (Church★) - Landewednack★ (Church★) – Mawgan-in-Meneage (Church★) - Ruan Minor (Church★) - St. Anthony-in-Meneage★.*
*London 326 – Penzance 24 – Truro 29.*

🏠 **Housel Bay** ⌖, Housel Bay, TR12 7PG, ℘ (01326) 290417, *Fax (01326) 290359*, ≤ Housel Cove – 📳, ⁕⁕ rest, 📺 ☎ 📞. 🆎 🅰🅴 𝘝𝘐𝘚𝘈. ❄
**Meals** (bar lunch Monday to Saturday)/dinner 16.50 **t.** ⅊ 6.00 – **21 rm** 🛏 33.00/94.00 **t.** – SB.

🏚 **Landewednack House** ⌖, Church Cove, TR12 7PQ, East : 1 m. by A 3083 ℘ (01326) 290909, *Fax (01326) 290192*, « Part 17C former rectory overlooking Church Cove », 🍴, 🍴 – 🍽 📺 ☎ 📞. 🆎 🅰🅴 𝘝𝘐𝘚𝘈. ❄
*closed 3 days Christmas* – **Meals** (by arrangement) (communal dining) 22.95 **t.** ⅊ 6.00 – **3 rm** 🛏 38.00/84.00 **t.**

🏚 **Penmenner House**, Penmenner Rd, TR12 7NR, ℘ (01326) 290370, ≤, 🍴 – ⁕⁕ 📺 📞. 🆎 𝘝𝘐𝘚𝘈. ❄
**Meals** (by arrangement) 12.50 **s.** – **6 rm** 🛏 27.00/50.00 **st.** – SB.

🏚 **South Parc** without rest., Lighthouse Rd, TR12 7NL, ℘ (01326) 290441, ≤, 🍴 – ⁕⁕ 📺 📞. ❄
*closed Christmas and New Year* – **3 rm** 🛏 32.00/46.00 **st.**

---

**LOFTUS** *Redcar & Cleveland* 𝟰𝟬𝟮 R 20 – pop. 5 931 – ✉ Saltburn-by-the-Sea.
*London 264 – Leeds 73 – Middlesbrough 17 – Scarborough 36.*

🏛 **Grinkle Park** ⌖, Easington, TS13 4UB, Southeast : 3 ½ m. by A 174 on Grinkle rd ℘ (01287) 640515, *Fax (01287) 641278*, ≤, 🍴, park, ✗ – 📺 ☎ 📞. 🆎 🅰🅴 ⑩ 𝘝𝘐𝘚𝘈. ❄
**Meals** 12.75/19.50 **t.** and dinner a la carte ⅊ 5.15 – **20 rm** 🛏 73.95/97.00 **st.** – SB.

---

**LOLWORTH SERVICE AREA** *Cambs.* – *see Cambridge.*

---

The **video cassette**
CHÂTEAUX OF THE LOIRE, from Chambord to Chinon,
is a film to complement the **Michelin Green Guide Châteaux of the Loire**. It portrays the Châteaux and the elegant lifestyle of the Touraine.

Available in six versions:
0751 in French SECAM
0752 in French PAL
1752 in English PAL

2752 in German PAL
3752 in Italian PAL

# LONDON

**404** folds ㊷ to ㊹ – *London G. – pop. 6 679 699*

## PRACTICAL INFORMATION

🅱 *British Travel Centre, 12 Regent St., Piccadilly Circus, SW1Y 4PQ ℘ (0171) 971 0026.*

*🛫 Heathrow, ℘ (0181) 759 4321, p. 10 AX – Terminal : Airbus (A1) from Victoria, Airbus (A2) from Paddington – Underground (Piccadilly line) frequent service daily.*

*🛫 Gatwick, ℘ (01293) 535353, p. 11 : by A 23 EZ and M 23 – Terminal : Coach service from Victoria Coach Station (Flightline 777, hourly service) – Railink (Gatwick Express) from Victoria (24 h service).*

*🛫 London City Airport ℘ (0171) 646 0000, p. 9 : HV.*

*🛫 Stansted, at Bishop's Stortford, ℘ (01279) 680500, NE : 34 m. p. 9 : by M 11 JT and A 120.*

**British Airways, Victoria Air Terminal** : *115 Buckingham Palace Rd, SW1, ℘ (0171) 707 4750, p. 34 BX*

# SIGHTS

## HISTORIC BUILDINGS AND MONUMENTS

*Palace of Westminster*★★★ : *House of Lords*★★, *Westminster Hall*★★ *(hammerbeam roof*★★★*), Robing Room*★, *Central Lobby*★, *House of Commons*★, *Big Ben*★, *Victoria Tower*★ *p. 28* LY – *Tower of London*★★★ *(Crown Jewels*★★★, *White Tower or Keep*★★★, *St. John's Chapel*★★, *Beauchamp Tower*★ *Tower Hill Pageant*★*) p. 29* PVX.

*Banqueting House*★★ *p. 28* LX – *Buckingham Palace*★★ *(Changing of the Guard*★★, *Royal Mews*★★*) p. 34* BVX – *Kensington Palace*★★ *p. 26* FX – *Lincoln's Inn*★★ *p. 35* EV – *London Bridge*★ *p. 29* PVX – *Royal Hospital Chelsea*★★ *p. 33* FU – *St. James's Palace*★★ *p. 31* EP – *Somerset House*★★ *p. 35* EXY – *South Bank Arts Centre*★★ *(Royal Festival Hall*★, *National Theatre*★, *County Hall*★*) p. 28* MX – *The Temple*★★ *(Middle Temple Hall*★*) p. 24* MV – *Tower Bridge*★★ *p. 29* PX.

*Albert Memorial*★ *p. 32* CQ – *Apsley House*★ *p. 30* BP – *Burlington House*★ *p. 31* EM – *Charterhouse*★ *p. 25* NOU – *George Inn*★, *Southwark p. 29* PX – *Gray's Inn*★ *p. 24* MU – *Guildhall*★ *(Lord Mayor's Show*★★*) p. 25* OU – *International Shakespeare Globe Centre*★ *p. 29* OX **T** – *Dr Johnson's House*★ *p. 25* NUV **A** – *Lancaster House*★ *p. 31* EP – *Leighton House*★ *p. 26* EY – *Linley Sambourne House*★ *p. 26* EY – *Lloyds Building*★★ *p. 25* PV – *Mansion House*★ *(plate and insignia*★★*) p. 25* PV **P** – *The Monument*★ *(❅*★*) p. 25* PV **G** – *Old Admiralty*★ *p. 28* KLX – *Royal Albert Hall*★ *p. 32* CQ – *Royal Exchange*★ *p. 25* PV **V** – *Royal Opera Arcade*★ *(New Zealand House) p. 31* FGN – *Royal Opera House*★ *(Covent Garden) p. 35* DX – *Spencer House*★★ *p. 31* DP – *Staple Inn*★ *p. 24* MU **Y** – *Theatre Royal*★ *(Haymarket) p. 31* GM – *Westminster Bridge*★ *p. 28* LY.

## CHURCHES

### The City Churches

*St. Paul's Cathedral*★★★ *(Dome* ⩽★★★*) p. 25* NOV.

*St. Bartholomew the Great*★★ *(choir*★*) p. 25* OU **K** – *St. Dunstan-in-the-East*★★ *p. 25* PV **F** – *St. Mary-at-Hill*★★ *(woodwork*★★, *plan*★*) p. 25* PV **B** – *Temple Church*★★ *p. 24* MV.

*All Hallows-by-the-Tower (font cover*★★ *brasses*★*) p. 25* PV **Y** – *Christ Church*★ *p. 25* OU **E** – *St. Andrew Undershaft (monuments*★*) p. 25* PV **A** – *St. Bride*★ *(steeple*★★*) p. 25* NV **J** – *St. Clement Eastcheap (panelled interior*★★*) p. 25* PV **E** – *St. Edmund the King and Martyr (tower and spire*★*) p. 25* PV **D** – *St-Giles Cripplegate*★ *p. 25* OU **N** – *St. Helen Bishopsgate*★ *(monuments*★★*) p. 25* PUV **R** – *St. James Garlickhythe (tower and spire*★, *sword rests*★*) p. 25* OV **R** – *St. Magnus the Martyr (tower*★, *sword rest*★*) p. 25* PV **K** – *St. Margaret Lothbury*★ *(tower and spire*★, *woodwork*★, *screen*★, *font*★*) p. 25* PU **S** – *St. Margaret Pattens (spire*★, *woodwork*★*) p. 25* PV **N** – *St. Martin-within-Ludgate (tower and spire*★, *door cases*★*) p. 25* NOV **B** – *St. Mary Abchurch*★ *(reredos*★★, *tower and spire*★, *dome*★*) p. 25* PV **X** – *St. Mary-le-Bow (tower and steeple*★★*) p. 25* OV **G** – *St. Michael Paternoster Royal (tower and spire*★*) p. 25* OV **D** – *St. Nicholas Cole Abbey (tower and spire*★*) p. 25* OV **F** – *St. Olave*★ *p. 25* PV **S** – *St. Peter upon Cornhill (screen*★*) p. 25* PV **L** – *St. Stephen Walbrook*★ *(tower and steeple*★, *dome*★*), p. 25* PV **Z** – *St. Vedast (tower and spire*★, *ceiling*★*), p. 25* OU **E**.

### Other Churches

*Westminster Abbey*★★★ *(Henry VII Chapel*★★★, *Chapel of Edward the Confessor*★★, *Chapter House*★★, *Poets' Corner*★*) p. 28* LY.

*Southwark Cathedral*★★ *p. 29* PX.

*Queen's Chapel*★ *p. 31* EP – *St. Clement Danes*★ *p. 35* EX – *St. James's*★ *p. 31* EM – *St. Margaret's*★ *p. 28* LY **A** – *St. Martin-in-the-Fields*★ *p. 35* DY – *St. Paul's*★ *(Covent Garden) p. 35* DX – *Westminster Roman Catholic Cathedral*★ *p. 28* KY **B**.

## PARKS

*Regent's Park*★★★ *p. 23* HI *(terraces*★★*), Zoo*★★.

*Hyde Park – Kensington Gardens*★★ *(Orangery*★*) pp. 26 and 27 – St. James's Park*★★ *p. 28* KXY.

## STREETS AND SQUARES

*The City*★★★ *p. 25* NV

*Bedford Square*★★ *p. 24* KLU – *Belgrave Square*★★ *p. 34* AVX – *Burlington Arcade*★★ *p. 31* DM – *Covent Garden*★★ *(The Piazza*★★*) p. 35* DX – *The Mall*★★ *p. 31* FP – *Piccadilly*★ *p. 31* EM – *The Thames*★★ *pp. 27-29* – *Trafalgar Square*★★ *p. 35* DY – *Whitehall*★★ *(Horse Guards*★*) p. 28* LX.

*Barbican*★ *p. 25* OU – *Bond Street*★ *pp. 30-31* CK-DM – *Canonbury Square*★ *p. 25* NS – *Carlton House Terrace*★ *p. 31* GN – *Cheyne Walk*★ *p. 27* GHZ – *Fitzroy Square*★ *p. 24* KU – *Jermyn Street*★ *p. 31* EN – *Leicester Square*★ *p. 31* GM – *Merrick Square*★ *p. 29* OY – *Montpelier Square*★ *p. 33* EQ – *Neal's Yard*★ *p. 35* DV – *Piccadilly Arcade*★ *p. 31* DEN – *Portman Square*★ *p. 30* AJ – *Queen Anne's Gate*★ *p. 28* KY – *Regent Street*★ *p. 31* EM – *Piccadilly Circus*★ *p. 31* FM – *St. James's Square*★ *p. 31* FN – *St. James's Street*★ *p. 31* EN – *Shepherd Market*★ *p. 30* CN – *Soho*★ *p. 31* – *Trinity Church Square*★ *p. 29* OY – *Victoria Embankment gardens*★ *p. 35* DEXY – *Waterloo Place*★ *p. 31* FN.

## MUSEUMS

*British Museum*★★★ *p. 24* LU – *National Gallery*★★★ *p. 31* GM – *Science Museum*★★★ *p. 32* CR – *Tate Gallery*★★★ *p. 28* LZ – *Victoria and Albert Museum*★★★ *p. 33* DR – *Wallace Collection*★★★ *p. 30* AH.

*Courtauld Institute Galleries*★★ *(Somerset House) p. 35* EXY – *Museum of London*★★ *p. 25* OU M – *National Portrait Gallery*★★ *p. 31* GM – *Natural History Museum*★★ *p. 32* CS – *Sir John Soane's Museum*★★ *p. 24* MU M.

*Clock Museum*★ *(Guildhall) p. 24* OU – *Imperial War Museum*★ *p. 29* NY – *London Transport Museum*★ *p. 35* DX – *Madame Tussaud's*★ *p. 23* IU M – *Museum of Mankind*★ *p. 31* DM – *National Army Museum*★ *p. 33* FU – *Percival David Foundation of Chinese Art*★ *p. 24* KLT M – *Planetarium*★ *p. 23* IU M – *Wellington Museum*★ *(Apsley House) p. 30* BP.

## OUTER LONDON

**Blackheath** *p. 13* HX *terraces and houses*★, *Eltham Palace*★ **A**
**Brentford** *p. 10* BX *Syon Park*★★, *gardens*★
**Bromley** *p. 12* GY *The Crystal Palace Park*★
**Chiswick** *p. 11* CV *Chiswick Mall*★★, *Chiswick House*★ **D**, *Hogarth's House*★ **E**
**Dulwich** *p. 12 Picture Gallery*★ FX **X**
**Greenwich** *pp. 12 and 13 : Cutty Sark*★★ GV **F**, *Footway Tunnel*(≤ ★★*)* – *Fan Museum*★ *p. 8* GV **A**, – *National Maritime Museum*★★ *(Queen's House*★★*)* GV **M**, *Royal Naval College*★★ *(Painted Hall*★, *the Chapel*★*)* GV **G**, *The Park and Old Royal Observatory*★ *(Meridian Building : collection*★★*)* HV **K**, *Ranger's House*★ GX **N**
**Hampstead** *Kenwood House*★★ *(Adam Library*★★, *paintings*★★*) p. 7* EU **P**, *Fenton House*★★, *p. 22* ES
**Hampton Court** *p. 10* BY *(The Palace*★★★, *gardens*★★★, *Fountain Court*★, *The Great Vine*★*)*
**Kew** *p. 11* CX *Royal Botanic Gardens*★★★ : *Palm House*★★, *Temperate House*★, *Kew Palace or Dutch House*★★, *Orangery*★, *Pagoda*★, *Japanese Gateway*★
**Hendon**★ *p. 7, Royal Air Force Museum*★★ CT **M**
**Hounslow** *p. 10* BV *Osterley Park*★★
**Lewisham** *p. 12* GX *Horniman Museum*★ **M**
**Richmond** *pp. 10 and 11 : Richmond Park*★★, ☀★★★ CX, *Richmond Hill*☀★★ CX, *Richmond Bridge*★★ BX **R**, *Richmond Green*★★ BX **S** *(Maids of Honour Row*★★, *Trumpeter's House*★*)*, *Asgill House*★ BX **B**, *Ham House*★★ BX **V**
**Shoreditch** *p. 8* FU *Geffrye Museum*★ **M**
**Tower Hamlets** *p. 8* GV *Canary Wharf*★★ B, *Isle of Dogs*★ St. Katharine Dock*★ **Y**
**Twickenham** *p. 10* BX *Marble Hill House*★ **Z**, *Strawberry Hill*★ **A** .

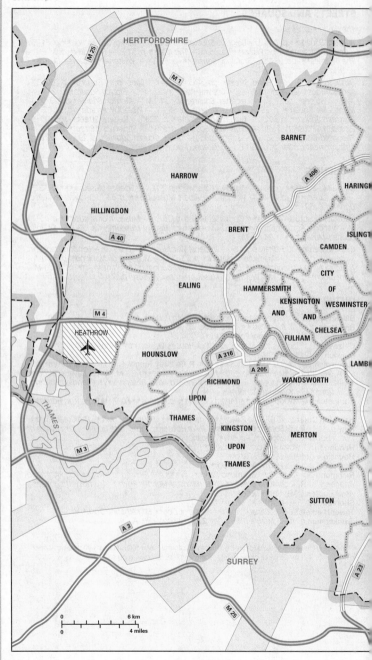

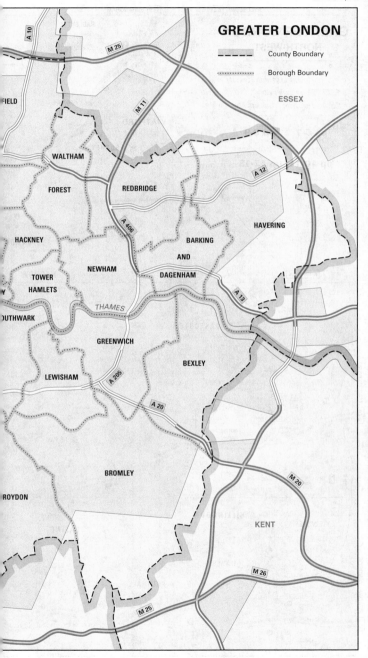

# GREATER LONDON

- – – – County Boundary
- ············ Borough Boundary

ESSEX

A 10

M 25

M 11

FIELD

WALTHAM

FOREST

REDBRIDGE

A 12

HAVERING

HACKNEY

A 406

BARKING

AND

DAGENHAM

TOWER

HAMLETS

NEWHAM

A 13

THAMES

OUTHWARK

GREENWICH

BEXLEY

LEWISHAM

A 205

A 20

BROMLEY

M 20

KENT

ROYDON

M 26

M 25

347

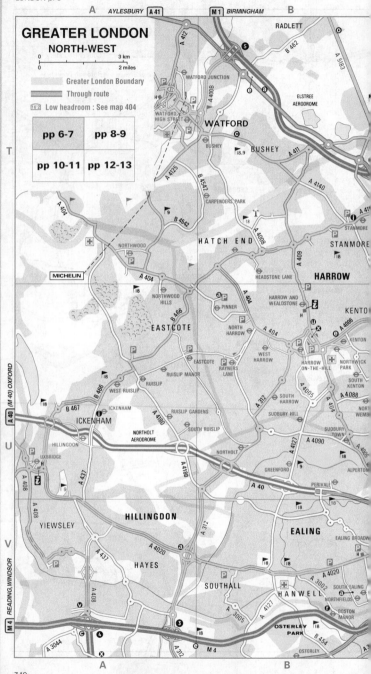

# GREATER LONDON
## NORTH-WEST

0 ____ 3 km
0 ____ 2 miles

Greater London Boundary
Through route
16.2 Low headroom : See map 404

| pp 6-7 | pp 8-9 |
|--------|--------|
| pp 10-11 | pp 12-13 |

AYLESBURY A 41

M 1 BIRMINGHAM

RADLETT

WATFORD JUNCTION

ELSTREE
AERODROME

WATFORD
HIGH STREET

WATFORD

BUSHEY

BUSHEY

CARPENDERS PARK

STANMORE

STANMORE

HATCH END

MICHELIN

NORTHWOOD

HEADSTONE LANE

HARROW

NORTHWOOD
HILLS

PINNER

HARROW AND
WEALDSTONE

KENTO

EASTCOTE

NORTH
HARROW

KENTON

EASTCOTE

WEST
HARROW

HARROW
ON-THE-HILL

NORTHWICK
PARK

RAYNERS
LANE

SOUTH
KENTON

RUISLIP MANOR

RUISLIP

SOUTH
HARROW

A 4088

WEST RUISLIP

RUISLIP GARDENS

SUDBURY HILL

NOR
WEMB

ICKENHAM

SOUTH RUISLIP

SUDBURY
TOWN

ICKENHAM

NORTHOLT
AERODROME

NORTHOLT

HILLINGDON

UXBRIDGE

GREENFORD

ALPERTON

PERIVALE

YIEWSLEY

HILLINGDON

EALING

EALING BROADWAY

HAYES

SOUTHALL

HANWELL

SOUTH EALING

NORTHFIELDS

BOSTON
MANOR

OSTERLEY
PARK

OSTERLEY

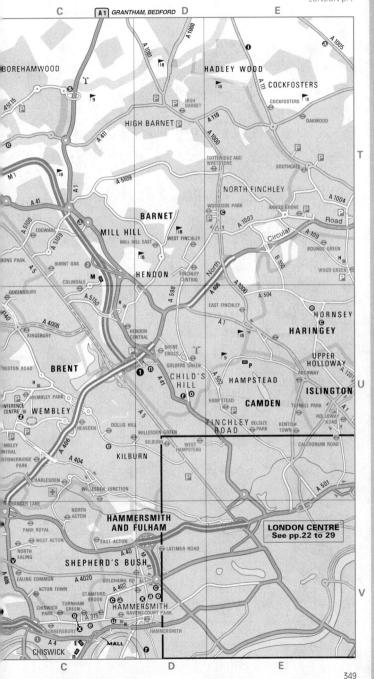

A 10 CAMBRIDGE

HADLEY WOOD

COCKFOSTERS

COCKFOSTERS

OAKWOOD

ENFIELD

TOTTERIDGE AND
WHETSTONE

SOUTHGATE

NORTH FINCHLEY

ARNOS GROVE

WOODSIDE PARK

WALTHAM
FOREST

Road

Circular

BOUNDS GREEN

North

WOOD GREEN

EAST FINCHLEY

TURNPIKE LANE

TOTTENHAM HALE

BLACKHORSE
ROAD

HORNSEY

HARINGEY

SEVEN
SISTERS

WALTHAMSTOW
CENTRAL

UPPER
HOLLOWAY

MANOR HOUSE

6-1999

HAMPSTEAD

ARCHWAY

FINSBURY PARK

HAMPSTEAD

ISLINGTON

CAMDEN

TUFNELL PARK

ARSENAL

CANONBURY

HACKNEY

FINCHLEY
ROAD

BELSIZE
PARK

KENTISH
TOWN

HOLLOWAY
ROAD

DRAYTON PARK

LEYT

CALEDONIAN ROAD

STRATFO
PUDDING
MILL LANE

BETHNAL
GREEN

BOW ROAD

LONDON CENTRE
See pp.22 to 29

SHOREDITCH

STEPNEY
GREEN

MILE END

BROMLEY-
BY-BOW

A 11 WHITECHAPEL

TOWER
HAMLETS

A 13
SHADWELL

WAPPING

CANARY WHARF

BLACKWALL TUNN

ROTHERHITHE

CANADA WATER

BERMONDSEY

ISLE OF DOGS

SURREY QUAYS

A 200

NEW CROSS
GATE

NEW CROSS

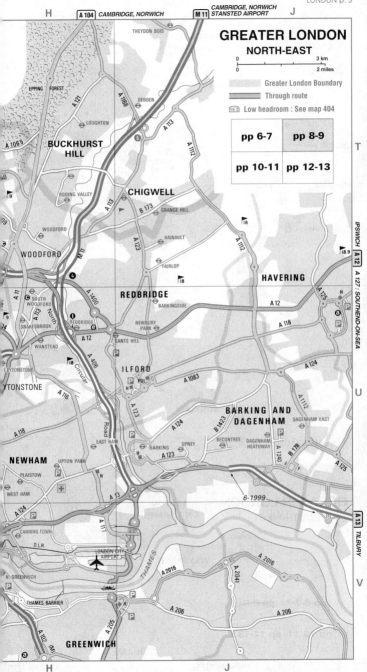

# GREATER LONDON
## NORTH-EAST

0 — 3 km
0 — 2 miles

Greater London Boundary
Through route
16.2 Low headroom : See map 404

| pp 6-7 | pp 8-9 |
| pp 10-11 | pp 12-13 |

A 104 CAMBRIDGE, NORWICH
M 11 CAMBRIDGE, NORWICH STANSTED AIRPORT

THEYDON BOIS

EPPING FOREST

BUCKHURST HILL

DEBDEN

LOUGHTON

A 1069

RODING VALLEY

CHIGWELL

WOODFORD

B 173

GRANGE HILL

HAINAULT

FAIRLOP

WOODFORD

SOUTH WOODFORD

SNARESBROOK

WANSTEAD

REDBRIDGE

BARKINGSIDE

NEWBURY PARK

GANTS HILL

HAVERING

A 12

A 118

LEYTONSTONE

ILFORD

BARKING AND DAGENHAM

DAGENHAM EAST

NEWHAM

UPTON PARK

PLAISTOW

WEST HAM

EAST HAM

BARKING

UPNEY

BECONTREE

DAGENHAM HEATHWAY

6-1999

CANNING TOWN

D.L.R.

LONDON CITY AIRPORT

N GREENWICH

THAMES BARRIER

THAMES

GREENWICH

IPSWICH A 12
A 127 : SOUTHEND-ON-SEA

A 13 TILBURY

351

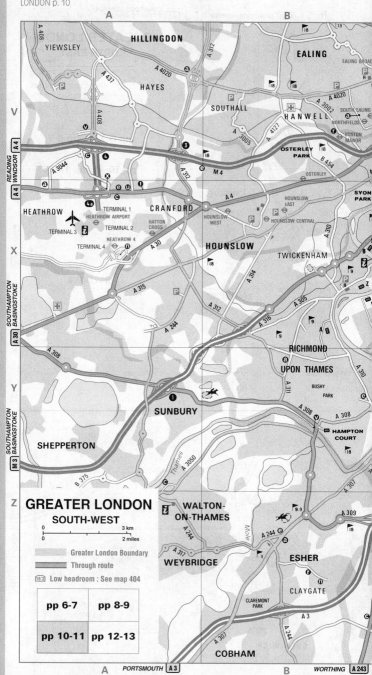

# GREATER LONDON
## SOUTH-WEST

0 ___ 3 km
0 ___ 2 miles

Greater London Boundary
Through route
16:2 Low headroom : See map 404

| pp 6-7 | pp 8-9 |
|---------|---------|
| pp 10-11 | pp 12-13 |

HILLINGDON
YIEWSLEY
EALING
EALING BROAD
HAYES
SOUTHALL
HANWELL
SOUTH EALING
NORTHFIELDS
BOSTON MANOR
OSTERLEY PARK
OSTERLEY
SYON PARK
HEATHROW
HEATHROW AIRPORT
TERMINAL 1
TERMINAL 3
TERMINAL 2
TERMINAL 4
CRANFORD
HATTON CROSS
HOUNSLOW EAST
HOUNSLOW WEST
HOUNSLOW CENTRAL
HOUNSLOW
TWICKENHAM
RICHMOND
UPON THAMES
BUSHY PARK
SUNBURY
SHEPPERTON
HAMPTON COURT
Thames
WALTON-ON-THAMES
Mole
ESHER
WEYBRIDGE
CLAYGATE
CLAREMONT PARK
COBHAM

READING
WINDSOR A4
A4

SOUTHAMPTON
BASINGSTOKE
A 30

SOUTHAMPTON
BASINGSTOKE
M 3

PORTSMOUTH A3
WORTHING A 243

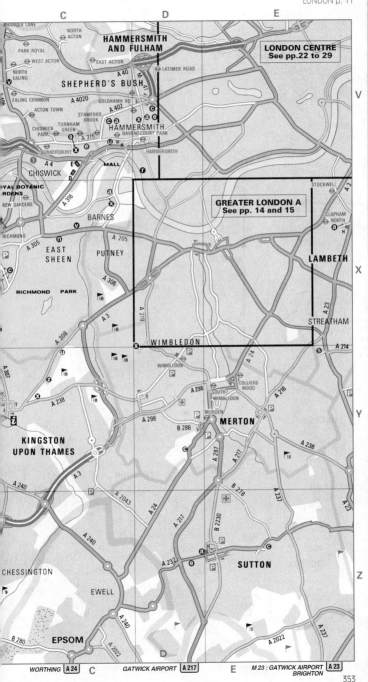

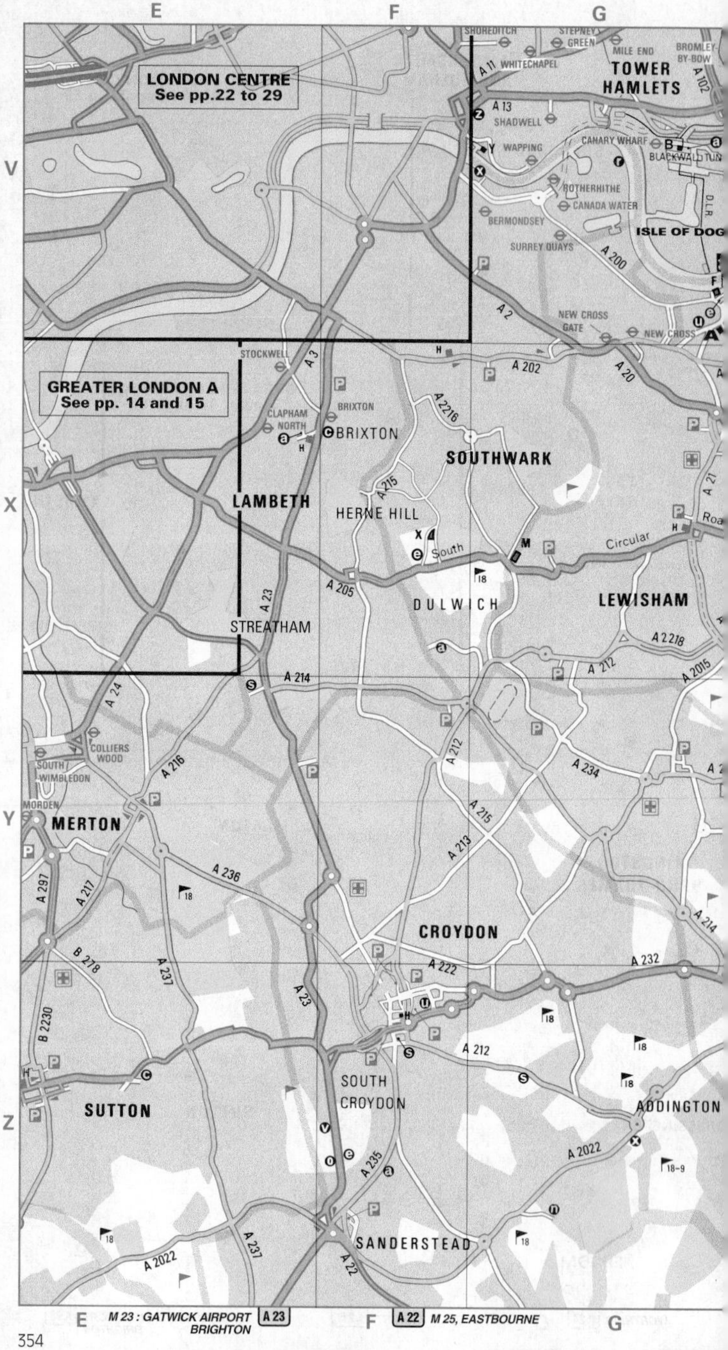

LONDON CENTRE
See pp.22 to 29

GREATER LONDON A
See pp. 14 and 15

E   F   G

V

X

Y

Z

SHOREDITCH
STEPNEY GREEN
MILE END
BROMLEY-BY-BOW
A 11  WHITECHAPEL
A 13  SHADWELL
WAPPING
CANARY WHARF
BLACKWALL TUN.
ROTHERHITHE
CANADA WATER
ISLE OF DOG
BERMONDSEY
SURREY QUAYS
A 200
NEW CROSS GATE
NEW CROSS
A 2
A 20
TOWER HAMLETS

STOCKWELL
A 3
CLAPHAM NORTH
BRIXTON
A 2216
SOUTHWARK
LAMBETH
HERNE HILL
South
A 215
A 205
DULWICH
Circular
LEWISHAM
A 2218
A 212
A 2015
STREATHAM
A 23
A 214

A 24
COLLIERS WOOD
SOUTH WIMBLEDON
A 218
MORDEN
MERTON
A 297
A 217
A 236
A 212
A 215
A 219
A 234
A 214
A 237
B 278
CROYDON
A 222
A 232
B 2230
A 23
SOUTH CROYDON
A 212
ADDINGTON
A 2022
SUTTON
A 235
A 2022
A 237
A 22
SANDERSTEAD

E  M 23 : GATWICK AIRPORT BRIGHTON  A 23    A 22  M 25, EASTBOURNE  F   G

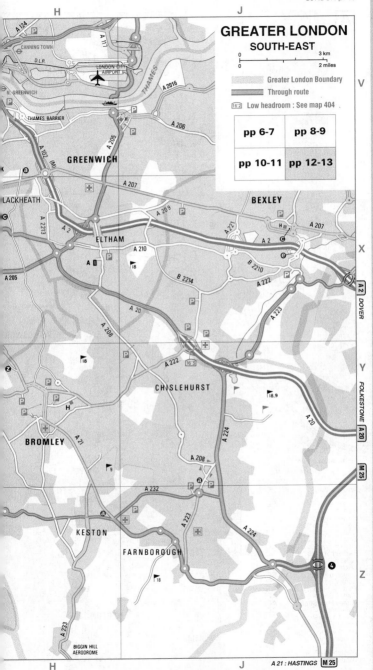

# GREATER LONDON
## SOUTH-EAST

0 — 3 km
0 — 2 miles

Greater London Boundary
Through route
16.2 Low headroom : See map 404

| pp 6-7 | pp 8-9 |
|--------|--------|
| pp 10-11 | pp 12-13 |

A 124
CANNING TOWN
D.L.R.
A 111
LONDON CITY AIRPORT
N. GREENWICH
THAMES
A 2016
A 102 (M)
THAMES BARRIER
A 205
A 206
GREENWICH
A 207
LACKHEATH
A 2213
A 2
A 209
BEXLEY
A 21
A 2
A 207
A 205
ELTHAM
A 210
B 2210
A 208
B 2214
A 222
A 223
A 20
18
18
CHISLEHURST
16.3
A 222
18.9
A 20
BROMLEY
A 21
A 224
A 208
9
A 232
KESTON
A 223
A 224
FARNBOROUGH
18
A 233
BIGGIN HILL AERODROME

V
X
Y
Z

A 2 DOVER
FOLKESTONE A 20
M 25

H
J
A 21 : HASTINGS M 25

355

**A**

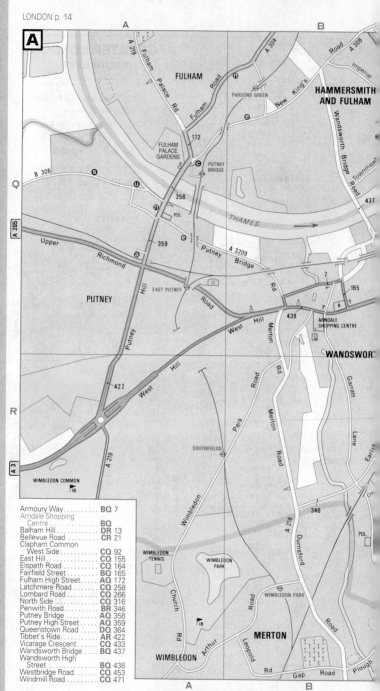

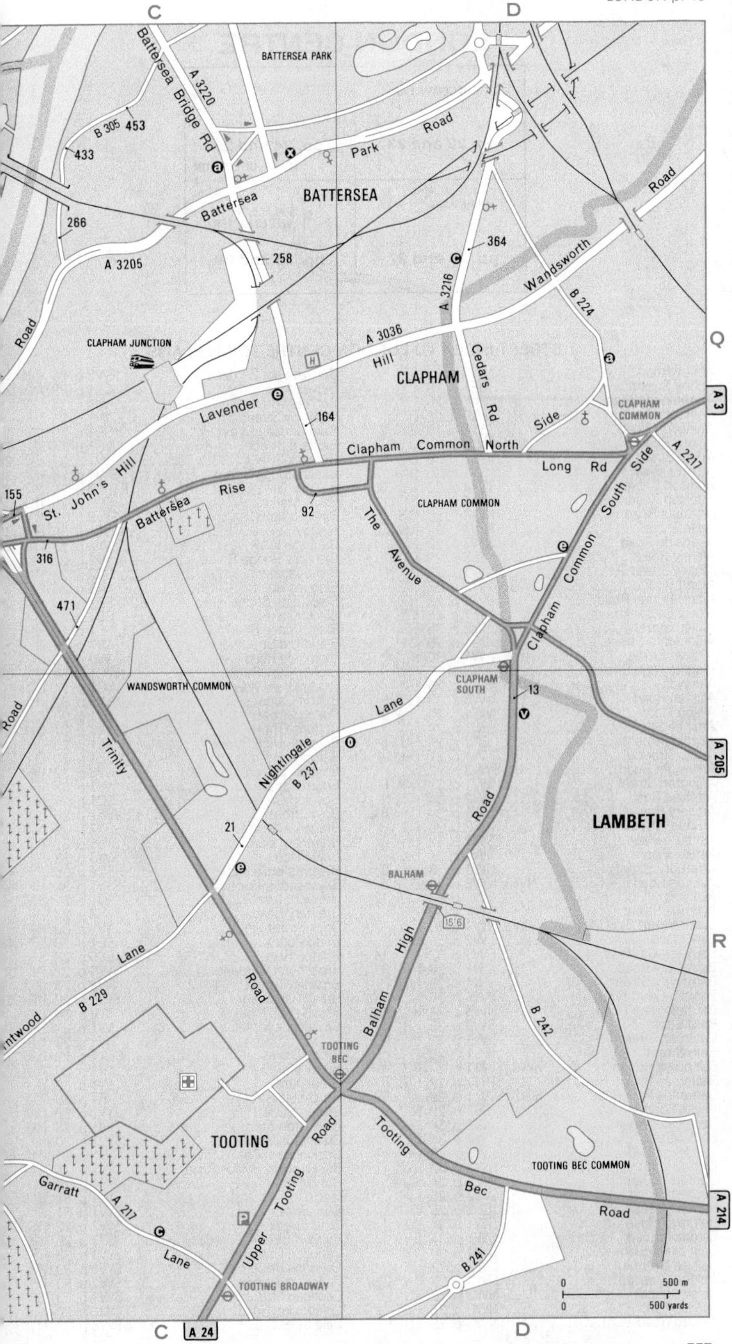
C
D
BATTERSEA PARK
Battersea Bridge Rd
A 3220
B 305
453
433
Park Road
BATTERSEA
Battersea
266
258
364
A 3205
Road
A 3216
Wandsworth
Road
B 224
CLAPHAM JUNCTION
A 3036
Hill
Lavender
CLAPHAM
Cedars Rd
Q
A 3
CLAPHAM COMMON
Side
164
Clapham Common North
Long Rd
A 2217
155
St. John's Hill
Battersea Rise
92
The Avenue
CLAPHAM COMMON
South Side
Clapham Common
316
471
WANDSWORTH COMMON
CLAPHAM SOUTH
13
Lane
Nightingale
B 237
Road
Trinity
A 205
Road
LAMBETH
21
BALHAM
15'6
R
Lane
High
B 229
ntwood
Road
Balham
B 242
TOOTING BEC
TOOTING
Road
Tooting
Bec
TOOTING BEC COMMON
Road
A 214
Garratt
A 217
Upper Tooting
Lane
B 241
TOOTING BROADWAY
0
500 m
500 yards
C
A 24
D

# LONDON CENTRE

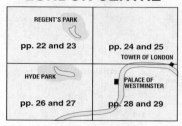

| REGENT'S PARK |  |
|---|---|
| pp. 22 and 23 | pp. 24 and 25<br>TOWER OF LONDON |
| HYDE PARK |  |
| pp. 26 and 27 | pp. 28 and 29<br>PALACE OF<br>WESTMINSTER |

## STREET INDEX TO LONDON CENTRE TOWN PLANS

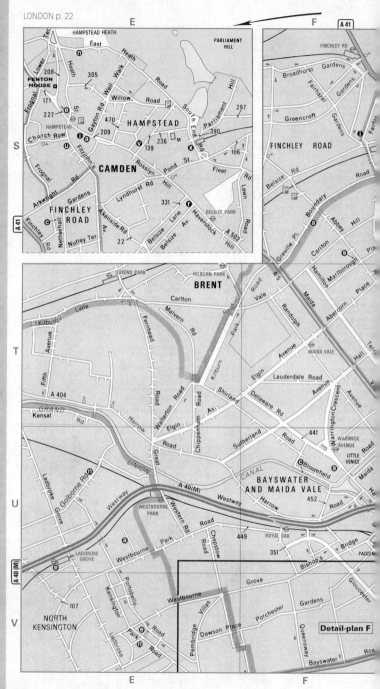

E    F    A 41

HAMPSTEAD HEATH

East

PARLIAMENT
HILL

Heath    Road

FENTON
HOUSE

208
171
227

Lower    Ter.

Frognal

305

Well Walk

Willow    Road

470

209

HAMPSTEAD

South End

Parliament Hill

297

390

106

CAMDEN

Fitzjohn's

Rossiyn

Pond St.

Fleet

236    M

139

X

Church Row

Frognal

Arkwright    Rd

Gardens

FINCHLEY
ROAD

Netherhall

Nutley Ter.

Lyndhurst Rd

Akenside Rd

Belsize    Av.

Belsize    Lane

Haverstock

331

22

BELSIZE PARK

A 502    Hill

FINCHLEY RD

Broadhurst    Gardens

Fairhazel    Gardens    Fairfa

Greencroft    Gardens

FINCHLEY    ROAD

Fairfa

Belsize    Rd    Road

Boundary

Greville Pl.

Carlton

Abbey    Hill

Hamilton    Marlborough    Place

Pla

BRENT

HILBURN PARK

QUEENS PARK

Carlton    Road    A 5    Vale

Malvern    Rd    Park    Randolph    Maida

Abercorn    Terr

Hall

MAIDA VALE

Va

Kilburn    Lane

Fernhead

Avenue

Fifth    A 404    Road    Elgin    Lauderdale Road    Avenue

Kensal    Rd    Harrow    Road    Shirland    Delaware Rd    Road    441    Warrington Crescent

Avenue

WARWICK
AVENUE

GRAND    UNION    Elgin    Chippenham Road    Walterton Road    Great    Sutherland    Road    LITTLE
VENICE

Road    Bloomfield    Maida

Kilburn    Av.

CANAL    BAYSWATER
AND MAIDA VALE

452    Road    Ha

A 40(M)    Westway    Westway    Harrow

Ladbroke Grove    Golborne Rd    Road

WESTBOURNE
PARK

Western Rd    Road    449    ROYAL OAK    Bridge

351    Bishop's    PADDIN

LADBROKE
GROVE    Westbourne    Park    Chepstow Road    Grove    Gloucester

NORTH
KENSINGTON    107    Portobello    Kensington    Road    Westbourne    Pembroke Villas    Dawson Place    Porchester    Gardens    Queensway    Detail-plan F

Ladbroke    Park    Road    Bayswater    Roa

E    F

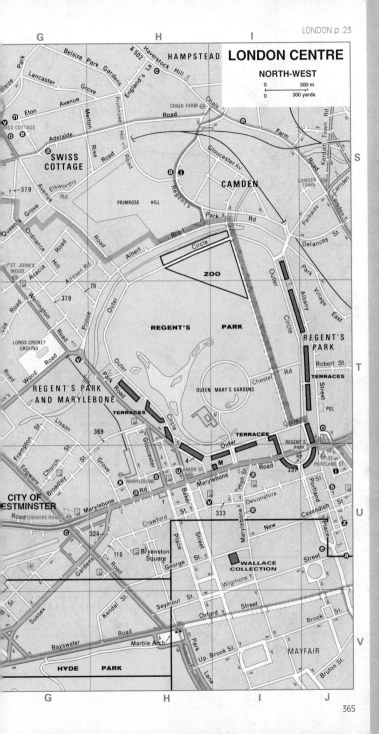

**LONDON CENTRE**

**NORTH-WEST**

| 0 | 300 m |
|---|---|
| 0 | 300 yards |

HAMPSTEAD

Belsize Park Gardens

Haverstock Hill

A 502

England's

Lancaster

Grove

Belsize Park

Eton

Avenue

Merton

Primrose

Hill

CHALK FARM

Rise

CHALK

Adelaide

SWISS COTTAGE

SWISS COTTAGE

Farm

Road

Kentish Town

Rd

Gloucester Av.

CAMDEN

CAMDEN TOWN

Camden

Elsworthy

Rd.

Regent's

PRIMROSE HILL

Park

Rd

Village

Delancey

St.

–379

Queen's

Grove

Avenue

Ordnance

Hill

Road

Acacia

Allitsen Rd.

79

–378

Albert

Circle

ZOO

Outer

Park

Albany

East

REGENT'S PARK

ST. JOHN'S WOOD

Prince

Wellington

Road

Wood

Road

LORDS CRICKET GROUND

REGENT'S

PARK

Outer

Circle

Robert St.

REGENT'S PARK TERRACES

Chester

Rd

Street

POL.

REGENT'S PARK AND MARYLEBONE

Park

Road

Outer

Circle

QUEEN MARY'S GARDENS

TERRACES

Lisson

Frampton

St.

Church

St.

Grove

369

Gloucester

Circle

4

TERRACES

Outer

REGENT'S PARK

GT. PORTLAND ST.

337

Edgware

Broadley

MARYLEBONE

Rd

Baker

St.

M

Marylebone

High St.

Road

a

Portland

St.

CITY OF WESTMINSTER

Road

EDGWARE ROAD

Marylebone

Crawford

St.

Baker

St.

Marylebone

Devonshire

333

New

Cavendish

St.

Place

Z

324

116

Bryanston Square

Place

Street

George

WALLACE COLLECTION

Street

Wigmore

Gardens

Road

Kendal St.

Seymour

St.

Oxford

Street

Brook

St.

Sussex

St.

Bayswater

Road

Marble Arch

Park

Up. Brook St.

MAYFAIR

Bruton St.

HYDE   PARK

Lane

365

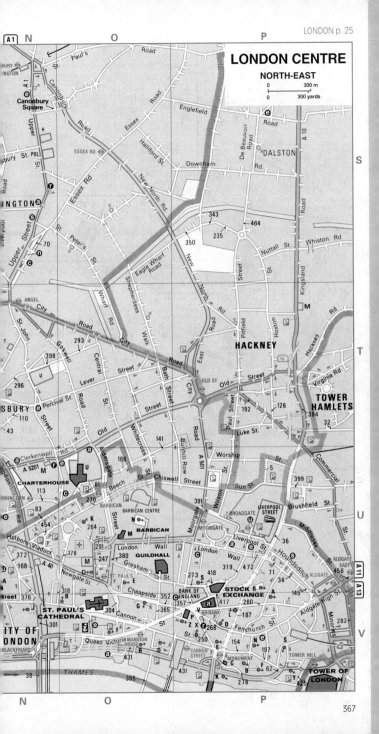

# LONDON CENTRE
## NORTH-EAST

0       300 m
0       300 yards

N      O      P

A1

St. Paul's Road

Canonbury

Canonbury Square

Upper

Road

Essex

Englefield

Road

A 10

De Beauvoir Road

DALSTON

Rd.

Essex Rd

Halliford St.

Downham

Road

ISLINGTON

Essex Rd

New North Rd.

St. Peter's St.

70

Upper Street

St. John

City

ANGEL

Road

Goswell

293

398

296

U

FINSBURY

110

43

Percival St.

Central

Street

Lever

St.

Street

Old

Whitecross

Street

141

Aldersgate

166

Shepherdess

Wharf Rd

Eagle Wharf Road

New North

Road

East

Road

City

Road

Bath

Street

City

Road

Bunhill Row

Worship

343

350

235

464

Nuttall St.

Whiston Rd

Kingsland

Road

Pitfield

Hoxton

Street

HACKNEY

OLD ST

Old

Street

16

Paul Street

Luke St.

192

126

Virginia Rd

TOWER HAMLETS

384

32

Sun St.

St.

Commercial

St.

Clerkenwell Rd

A 5201

CHARTERHOUSE

113

83

454

Holborn Viaduct

372

168

178

247

291

264

270

81

Beech

Street

BARBICAN CENTRE

BARBICAN

London Wall

GUILDHALL

Gresham

St.

A 40

Newgate St.

Cheapside

318

304

301

376

ST. PAUL'S CATHEDRAL

CITY OF LONDON

BLACKFRIARS

38

THAMES

395

431

Queen Victoria

MANSION HOUSE

CANNON STREET

431

Cannon

St.

380

273

352

357

365

418

417

268

250

154

197

278

62

425

BANK OF ENGLAND

STOCK EXCHANGE

260

187

Fenchurch

St.

MONUMENT

TOWER HILL

TOWER OF LONDON

Moorgate

MOORGATE

391

Wilson

5

399

LIVERPOOL STREET

BROADGATE

Liverpool St.

Brushfield St.

Middlesex

36

Houndsditch

71

34

319

472

Wall

London

Aldgate High St.

ALDGATE EAST

456

ALDGATE

145

282

A11

A13

Minories

282

N      O      P

S

T

U

V

367

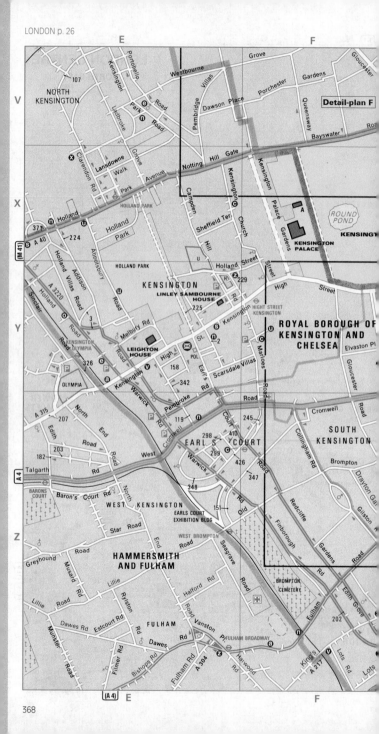

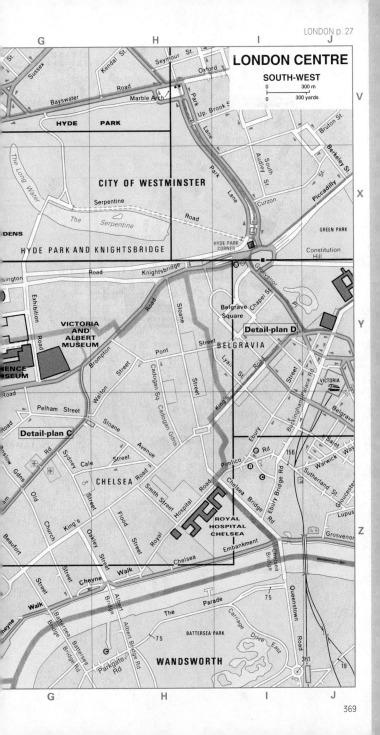

# LONDON CENTRE

## SOUTH-WEST

| 0 | 300 m |
| 0 | 300 yards |

G    H    I    J

V

Sussex

Kendal St.

Seymour  St.

Oxford

Bayswater

Road

Marble Arch

Up. Brook St.

Park

Bruton St.

HYDE    PARK

HYDE

PARK

Lane

Park

South
Audley
St.

Berkeley St.

The Long Water

CITY OF WESTMINSTER

Lane

Curzon

Piccadilly

X

Serpentine

The          Serpentine

Road

GREEN PARK

DENS

HYDE PARK AND KNIGHTSBRIDGE

HYDE PARK
CORNER

Constitution
Hill

Road

Knightsbridge

Grosvenor

Chapel St.

Pl.

sington

Road

Belgrave
Square

Exhibition

Road

Sloane

Detail-plan D

Y

VICTORIA
AND
ALBERT
MUSEUM

Brompton

Pont

Street

BELGRAVIA

VICTORIA

ENCE
SEUM

Street

Walton

Street

Cadogan Sq.

Cadogan Gdns

Lyall
St.

Road

Street

Buckingham Palace Rd.

Belgrave

Road

Pelham  Street

Sloane

King's

Ebury

Detail-plan C

Avenue

Sloane

Rd.

Sydney

Cale

Street

Pimlico

Rd

156

Warwick  Way

Sutherland  St.

Gloucester

nslow

Gdns

Old

CHELSEA

Road

Smith  Street

Hospital

Chelsea

Bridge

Rd

Lupus

Church

King's

Oakley

Street

Flood

Street

Royal

ROYAL
HOSPITAL
CHELSEA

Ebury Bridge Rd.

Grosvenor

Z

Beaufort

Street

Chelsea

Embankment

Chelsea

Bridge

14 9

Cheyne

Walk

Cheyne

Walk

Albert

Bridge

Parade

The

75

Queenstown

Road

19

Walk

Battersea

Bridge

Albert Bridge

Battersea

75

BATTERSEA PARK

Carriage

Drive

East

361

Parkgate
Rd

Bridge Rd

WANDSWORTH

G    H    I    J

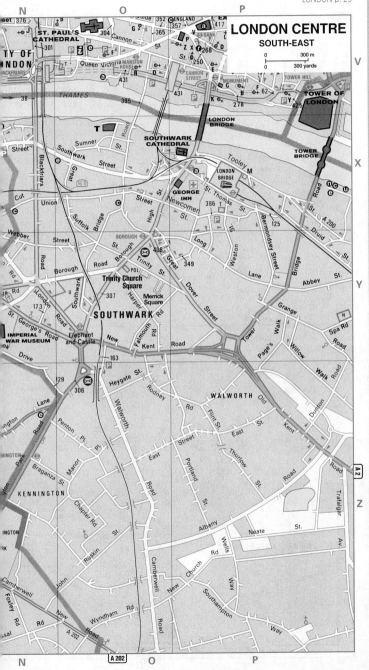

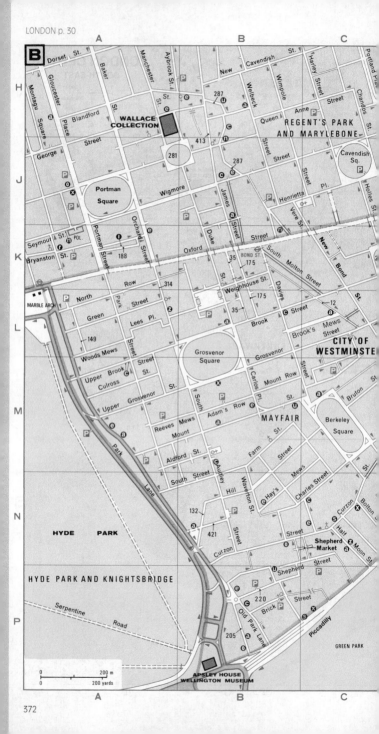

**B**

Dorset St.

Gloucester

Montagu Square

Baker

Manchester

Aybrook St.

New

Cavendish St.

Harley Street

Wimpole

Street

Portland Pla

Chandos St.

H

Blandford

Place

St.

287

Welbeck

Queen Anne

**WALLACE COLLECTION**

**REGENT'S PARK AND MARYLEBONE**

George

Street

413

281

Street

Street

287

Cavendish Sq.

J

Portman Square

Wigmore

Street

James

Henrietta

Pl.

Holles St.

Vere St.

Seymour St.

POL.

Portman Street

Orchard Street

Duke

Street

Street

Bryanston St.

188

Oxford

Street

BOND ST.

35

175

South Molton Street

New Bond

K

Row

314

Weighhouse St.

175

Davies

St.

12

St.

MARBLE ARCH

North

Park

Street

Green

Lees Pl.

Street

35

Brook

Brook's Mews Street

**CITY OF WESTMINSTE**

L

149

Woods Mews

Street

Grosvenor Square

Grosvenor

Carlos Pl.

Mount Row

St.

Bruton

Upper Brook

Culross

St.

South

St.

Adam's Row

St.

**MAYFAIR**

Berkeley Square

M

Upper Grosvenor

Reeves Mews

Mount

Aldford St.

Street

Farm

Street

Hay's

Mews

Charles Street

Curzon

Bolton

South Street

Hill

Waverton St.

Street

N

**HYDE PARK**

132

421

Curzon

Street

**Shepherd Market**

Moon St.

Half

Shepherd

Street

**HYDE PARK AND KNIGHTSBRIDGE**

Serpentine Road

220

Brick

Street

Piccadilly

P

205

Old Park Lane

**GREEN PARK**

0          200 m

0          200 yards

**APSLEY HOUSE WELLINGTON MUSEUM**

Oxford Street is closed to private traffic, Mondays to Saturdays : from 7 am to 9 pm between Portman Street and St. Giles Circus

373

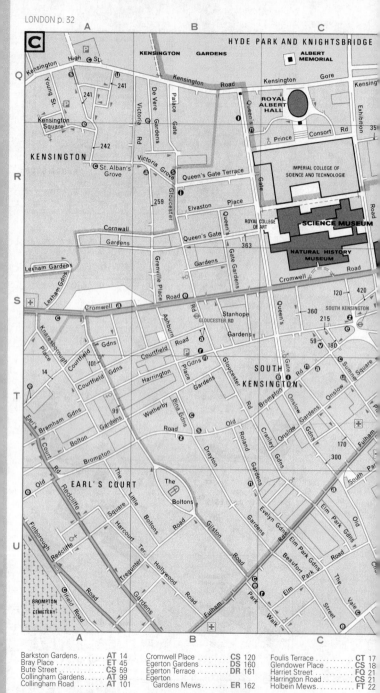

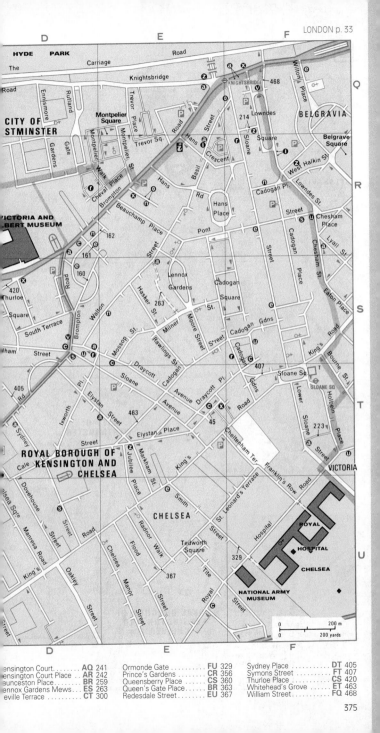

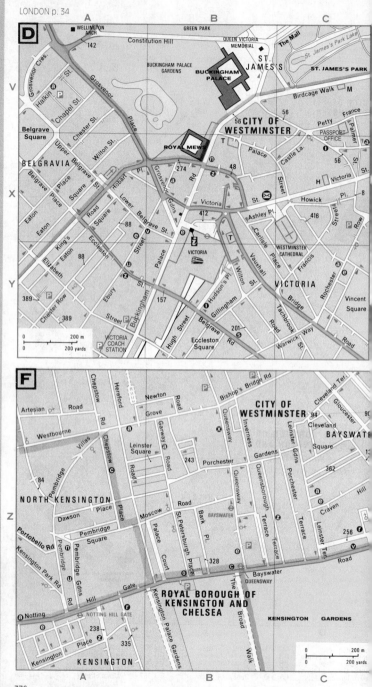

**D**

Wellington Arch

142

GREEN PARK

Constitution Hill

QUEEN VICTORIA MEMORIAL

The Mall

St. James's Park Lake

BUCKINGHAM PALACE

BUCKINGHAM PALACE GARDENS

ST. JAMES'S

ST. JAMES'S PARK

Grosvenor Cres.

Halkin St.

Chapel St.

Grosvenor Pl.

Chester St.

Wilton St.

Birdcage Walk   M

**V**

Belgrave Square

56  CITY OF WESTMINSTER

56

Petty France

Palmer St.

PASSPORT OFFICE

**BELGRAVIA**

Upper Belgrave

Wilton Pl.

ROYAL MEWS

274

Hobart Pl.

Grosvenor Gdns.

48

Palace Street

Castle La.

56

H  Victoria St.

Belgrave Place

Belgrave Square

Road

Lower Belgrave St.

Eccleston

Victoria

St.

Ashley Pl.

Howick Pl.

416

8

**X**

Eaton Place

King's Road

Eaton Square

88

Palace

412

Carlisle Place

WESTMINSTER CATHEDRAL

Street

Row

Elizabeth

Eaton

88

VICTORIA

Francis

**VICTORIA**

Rochester

Chester Row

389

Ebury

Buckingham

157

Hudson's Pl.

Gillingham

Wilton St.

Vauxhall

Bridge

Tachbrook

Vincent Square

389

Street

Belgrave Rd

Eccleston Square

201

Warwick Way

Road

Hugh Street

0    200 m
0    200 yards

VICTORIA COACH STATION

**F**

Chepstow Road

Hereford Road

Newton Road

Bishop's Bridge Rd

Cleveland Ter.

Gloucester

90

Artesian Road

Grove

Queensway

Inverness

CITY OF WESTMINSTER

94

Cleveland Square

BAYSWATER

Westbourne

Leinster Square

Garway Road

Porchester

Leinster Gdns

13

362

Pembroke Villas

Chepstow Rd

243

Queensborough

Porchester Terrace

Leinster Ter.

84

**Z**

**NORTH KENSINGTON**

Dawson Place

Pembridge Place

Moscow Road

St Petersburgh Place

Bark

BAYSWATER

Queensway Terrace

Craven Hill

256

Portobello Rd

Pembridge Square

Palace Court

328

Terrace

Bayswater

Road

Kensington Park Rd

Pembridge Gdns

Pembridge Rd

Hill

Gate

The Broad Walk

QUEENSWAY

Kensington Palace Gardens

ROYAL BOROUGH OF KENSINGTON AND CHELSEA

KENSINGTON     GARDENS

Notting

NOTTING HILL GATE

238

335

Place

**KENSINGTON**

0    200 m
0    200 yards

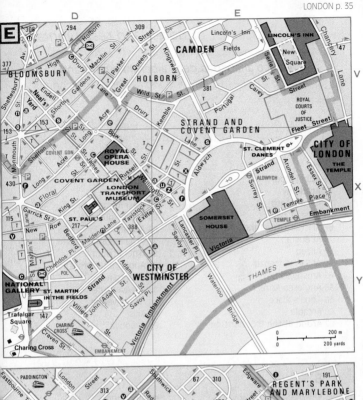

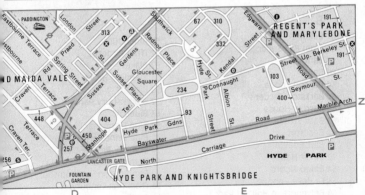

# Alphabetical list of hotels and restaurants
## Liste alphabétique des hôtels et restaurants
### Elenco alfabetico degli alberghi e ristoranti
Alphabetisches Hotel- und Restaurantverzeichnis

## A

66 Abbey Court
52 Academy
75 (L') Accento
84 Alastair Little
67 Alastair Little Lancaster Road
76 Al Bustan
52 Alfred
75 Al San Vincenzo
65 Amsterdam
58 Anglesea Arms
60 Anna's Place
66 Arcadia
82 Ard-Ri at the O'Conor Don

75 Aspects
75 Assaggi
58 (Les) Associés
68 Aster House
82 Asuka
77 Athenaeum
87 (The) Atrium
86 Auberge de Provence
62 Aubergine
82 (L') Aventure
83 (The) Avenue
85 Axis
69 Ayudhya

## B

67 Bailey's
67 (The) Bali Sugar
68 Bangkok
85 Bank
56 Bardon Lodge
64 Barkston Gardens
69 Barrow House
62 Basil Street
62 Beaufort
64 Beit Eddine
72 Belair House
54 Belgo Noord
63 La Belle Epoque
66 Belvedere in Holland Park
71 Bengal Clipper
54 Benihana
63 Benihana
79 Benihana
79 Bentley's
75 (The) Berkeley
80 Berkshire
80 Berners
82 Bertorelli's
85 Bertorelli's

62 Bibendum
52 (The) Birdcage
67 Blakes
53 Bleeding Heart
52 Blooms
52 Bloomsbury Park
63 Bluebird
57 Blue Elephant
72 Blue Print Café
74 Bombay Bicycle Club
68 Bombay Brasserie
52 Bonnington in Bloomsbury
58 (The) Brackenbury
54 Bradley's
54 Brasserie Rocque
63 Brasserie St. Quentin
77 Britannia
51 Bromley Court
77 Brown's
64 Busabong Too
72 Butlers Wharf Chop House
75 Byron
53 Byron's

## C

61 Cadogan
80 (The) Cafe (at Sotheby's)
53 Café des Arts
85 (Le) Café du Jardin
68 Café Lazeez
60 Café Lazeez City
64 Cafe O
83 (The) Café Royal Grill
73 Cafe Spice Namaste
73 Cafe Spice Namaste
81 Caldesi
68 Cambio De Tercio
70 Cannizaro House
62 (The) Canteen
72 Cantina Del Ponte
61 Capital
83 (Le) Caprice
63 Caraffini
71 Carlton Mitre
83 Cave
82 Cavendish
73 Chada
51 Chapter One
57 Chapter Two
71 Chase Lodge
63 Chavot
64 Chelsea Ram
62 Chelsea Village
77 Chesterfield
74 Chez Bruce
65 Chezmax
67 Chez Moi
78 Chez Nico at Ninety Park Lane
58 Chinon
60 (The) Chiswick

79 Chor Bizarre
85 Christopher's
80 Churchill Inter-Continental
63 Chutney Mary
66 Cibo
84 Circus
54 City Rhodes
76 Claridge's
65 Clarke's
62 Claverley
80 Clifton Ford
61 Cliveden Town House
79 Coast
64 (The) Collection
64 (Le) Colombier
75 Comfort Inn
65 Comfort Inn Kensington
74 Commodore
77 Connaught
61 Conrad International London
85 Corney and Barrow
65 Copthorne Tara
54 Coq d'Argent
55 Coulsdon Manor
70 County H. Epping Forest
51 Covent Garden
68 Cranley
81 (The) Crescent
83 Criterion Brasserie
      Marco Pierre White
59 Crowne Plaza Heathrow London
71 Crowther's
55 Croydon Park
53 Cucina
58 Cumberland

## D

64 Dan's
63 Daphne's
74 Del Buongustaio
68 Delhi Brasserie
84 dell'Ugo
75 Delmere
76 Diplomat
86 Dolphin Square
76 Dorchester

60 (La) Dordogne
81 Dorset Square
68 Downstairs at One Ninety
64 Drones of Pont Street
53 Drury Lane Moat House
73 Duke of Cambridge
82 Dukes
61 Durley House
81 Durrants

## E

62 Egerton House
78 1837
62 Eleven Cadogan Gardens
63 English Garden
74 Enoteca Turi
83 (L') Escargot

66 (L') Escargot Doré
85 (L') Estaminet
61 Euphorium
52 Euston Plaza
59 Excelsior Heathrow

## F

63 Fifth Floor (at Harvey Nichols)
68 Five Sumner Place
78 Flemings
58 Florians

59 Forte Crest
50 Forte Posthouse Bexley
52 Forte Posthouse Bloomsbury
55 Forte Posthouse Croydon

# K

64 Kartouche
52 Kenilworth
87 Ken Lo's Memories of China
65 Kensington Park Thistle
66 Kensington Place

68 Khan's of Kensington
69 Kingston Lodge
62 Knightsbridge
76 Knightsbridge Green

# L

80 Landmark London
75 (The) Lanesborough
79 Langan's Brasserie
65 Langan's Coq d'Or
81 Langham Court
80 Langham Hilton
53 Langorf
66 Launceston Place
50 Laurent
67 Leith's
84 Leith's Soho
80 (The) Leonard
84 Lexington
86 Livebait
72 Livebait
69 Lobster Pot
61 Lola's

71 London Bridge
69 London County Hall Travel
   Inn Capital
52 London Euston Travel Inn Capital
77 London Hilton on Park Lane
65 London Kensington Hilton
77 London Marriott Grosvenor Square
69 London Marriott H. County Hall
80 London Marriott Marble Arch
78 London Mews Hilton
62 (The) London Outpost
   of the Carnegie Club
57 London Putney Bridge Travel
   Inn Capital
80 London Regent's Park Hilton
76 Lowndes
72 Luigi's

# M

85 Magno's Brasserie
60 Maison Novelli
66 Malabar
52 Malabar Junction
66 Mandarin
76 Mandarin Oriental Hyde Park
57 Mao Tai
56 Mario
51 Marlborough
79 Marquis
82 Mash
83 Matsuri
56 Maxim
77 May Fair Inter-Continental
66 Memories of China
68 Memories of India
76 (Le) Meridien Piccadilly
85 Meridien Waldorf
57 Mesclun
77 (The) Metropolitan
84 Mezzo

65 (The) Milestone
61 Millenium Chelsea
67 Millenium Gloucester
75 Miller's
78 Mirabelle
55 Miyama
80 Momo
64 Monkey's
52 Mon Plaisir
71 Monsieur Max
51 Montague
80 Montcalm
74 Mornington
79 Morton's – The Restaurant
60 Moro
51 Mountbatten
73 MPW
76 Mr Chow
58 Mr Tang's Mandarin
82 (Le) Muscadet
52 Museum Street Cafe

# N

52 Neal Street
81 Nico Central
79 Nicole's
71 Nightingales
75 Nipa
79 Nobu

75 Norfolk Plaza
57 North Pole
60 Novelli EC1
66 Novelli W8
69 Novotel London Waterloo
68 Number Sixteen

381

79 Scotts
80 Selfridge
56 Selsdon Park
57 755
85 Sheekey's
87 Shepherd's
76 Sheraton Belgravia
59 Sheraton Heathrow
61 Sheraton Park Tower
59 Sheraton Skyline
79 Shogun
60 Simply Nico
63 Simply Nico
72 Simply Nico
87 Simply Nico
59 Simply Nico Heathrow
72 Sixty Two
62 Sloane
58 Snows on the Green
84 Soho Soho
84 Soho Spice
70 Sonny's
79 (Le) Soufflé
57 Soulard

57 Spread Eagle
60 Springbok Café
78 (The) Square
55 Sri India
84 Sri Siam
55 Sri Siam City
82 Stafford
74 Stakis Hyde Park
81 Stakis London Harewood
61 Stakis London Islington
86 Stakis London St. Ermin's
74 Stakis Metropole
68 Star of India
81 Stephen Bull
60 Stephen Bull
85 Stephen Bull St. Martin's Lane
73 (The) Stepping Stone
84 (The) Sugar Club
83 Suntory
64 Swag and Tails
50 Swallow
67 Swallow International
54 Swiss Cottage
62 Sydney House

## T

74 Tabaq
56 Tai Tung
79 Tamarind
58 Tandoori Nights
76 (La) Tante Claire
58 Taste of China
87 Tate Gallery
54 Tatsuso
84 Teatro
79 Teca
54 10
71 Tentazioni
66 (The) Terrace
73 Thatched House
64 Thierry's
86 Thistle Grosvenor
52 Thistle Kingsley
83 Thistle Piccadilly
86 Thistle Royal Horseguards
86 Thistle Royal Westminster

83 Thistle Trafalgar Square
74 Thistle Whites
86 Tophams Ebury Court
64 Toto's
58 Trattoria Sorrentina
55 Travel Inn
58 Travel Inn
59 Travel Inn
59 Travel Inn
69 Travel Inn
70 Travel Inn
60 Travelodge
70 Travelodge
70 Travelodge
73 Travelodge
73 Travelodge
57 Treasure of China
64 T'Su
63 Turner's
82 22 Jermyn Street

## U - V - W

82 Union Café
63 Vama
80 Veeraswamy
53 Vegetarian Cottage
72 (La) Veranda
69 (Le) Versailles
82 Villandry
76 Vong
77 Washington
56 Wellmeadow Lodge
77 Westbury
56 West Lodge Park

54 White House
61 White Onion
55 Willow
58 Wilsons
86 Winchester
69 Windmill on the Common
78 Windows
55 Windsor Castle Toby
66 Wódka
84 Wok Wok
67 Woz

## X - Y - Z

51 Xian
76 Zafferano
53 ZeNW3

80 Zinc Bar & Grill
82 Zoe

# Alphabetical list of areas included
### Liste alphabétique des quartiers cités
### Elenco alfabetico dei quartieri citati
### Liste der erwähnten Bezirke

## Starred establishments in London
### *Les établissements à étoiles de Londres*
### *Gli esercizi con stelle a Londra*
### *Die Stern-Restaurants in London*

❀ ❀ ❀

| | | | | | | |
|---|---|---|---|---|---|---|
| 8 | *Mayfair* | XXXXX | The Oak Room Marco Pierre White (at Le Meridien Piccadilly H.) | 78 | *Mayfair* | XXXXX | Chez Nico at Ninety Park Lane (at Grosvenor House H.) |

❀ ❀

| 8 | *Mayfair* | XXXX | Le Gavroche | 78 | *Mayfair* | XXX | The Square |
|---|---|---|---|---|---|---|---|
| 52 | *Chelsea* | XXXX | Gordon Ramsay | 52 | *Bloomsbury* | XX | Pied à Terre |
| 6 | *Chelsea* | XXXX | La Tante Claire (at The Berkeley H.) | | | | |

❀

| 7 | *Mayfair* | ♙♙♙ | Connaught | 67 | *North Kensington* | XXX | Leith's |
|---|---|---|---|---|---|---|---|
| 1 | *Chelsea* | ♙♙♙ | Capital | 63 | *Chelsea* | XX | Chavot |
| 5 | *Belgravia* | ♙♙ | The Halkin | 79 | *Mayfair* | XX | Nobu (at The Metropolitan H.) |
| 3 | *Soho* | XXXX | The Café Royal Grill | | | | |
| 8 | *Mayfair* | XXXX | Oriental (at Dorchester H.) | 83 | *St James's* | XX | L'Oranger |
| 8 | *Mayfair* | XXXX | Les Saveurs de Jean-Christophe Novelli | 84 | *Soho* | XX | Richard Corrigan at Lindsay House |
| 52 | *Chelsea* | XXX | Aubergine | 57 | *Hammersmith* | XX | River Café |
| 52 | *Chelsea* | XXX | The Canteen | 76 | *Belgravia* | XX | Zafferano |
| 54 | *City of London* | XXX | City Rhodes | 74 | *Wandsworth* | X | Chez Bruce |
| 3 | *Soho* | XXX | L'Escargot | 71 | *Richmond-upon-Thames* | | |
| 1 | *Regent's Park & Marylebone* | XXX | Interlude | | | X | Monsieur Max |

## Good food at moderate prices
### *Repas soignés à prix modérés*
### *Pasti accurati a prezzi contenuti*
### *Sorgfältig zubereitete, preiswerte Mahlzeiten*

😊 "Bib Gourmand"

| 1 | *Farnborough* | XXX | Chapter One | 75 | *Bayswater & Maida Vale* | X | L'Accento |
|---|---|---|---|---|---|---|---|
| 3 | *Wandsworth* | XX | Cafe Spice Namaste | 66 | *Kensington* | X | Malabar |
| 3 | *Whitechapel* | XX | Cafe Spice Namaste | 71 | *Richmond-upon-Thames* | X | Monsieur Max |
| 7 | *Greenwich* | XX | Chapter Two | 51 | *Brent* | X | Sabras |
| 0 | *Richmond-upon-Thames* | XX | Redmond's | 67 | *North Kensington* | X | Woz |

# *Particularly pleasant hotels and restaurants*
### *Hôtels et restaurants agréables*
### *Alberghi e ristoranti ameni*
### *Angenehme Hotels und Restaurants*

🏰🏰

| 76 *Mayfair* | Claridge's | 85 *Strand* | The Savoy |
|---|---|---|---|
| 76 *Mayfair* | Dorchester | *& Covent Garden* | |

🏰

| 77 *Mayfair* | Connaught |
|---|---|

🏰

| 67 *South* | | 86 *Victoria* | Goring |
|---|---|---|---|
| *Kensington* | Blakes | 75 *Belgravia* | The Halkin |
| 61 *Chelsea* | Capital | 85 *Strand &* | |
| 61 *Chelsea* | Cliveden Town | *Covent Garden* | One Aldwych |
| | House | 67 *South* | |
| 51 *Bloomsbury* | Covent Garden | *Kensington* | Pelham |
| 61 *Chelsea* | Durley House | | |

🏠

| 62 *Chelsea* | Sloane | 82 *St. James's* | 22 Jermyn Street |
|---|---|---|---|
| 62 *Chelsea* | Sydney House | | |

XXXXX

| 78 *Mayfair* | The Oak Room Marco Pierre White (at Le Meridien Piccadilly H.) |
|---|---|

XXXX

| 78 *Mayfair* | Grill Room (at Dorchester H.) |
|---|---|

XXX

| 78 *Mayfair* | Goode's at | 72 *Southwark* | Oxo Tower |
|---|---|---|---|
| | Thomas Goode | 71 *Bermondsey* | Le Pont de la Tour |
| 81 *Regent's Park &* | Orrery | | |
| *Marylebone* | | | |

XX

| 83 *St. James's* | Quaglino's |
|---|---|

# Restaurants classified according to type
### Restaurants classés suivant leur genre
### Ristoranti classificati secondo il loro genere
### Restaurants nach Art und Einrichtung geordnet

## Bistros

| | | | |
|---|---|---|---|
| 8 *South Kensington* | ✗ Bangkok | 60 *Finsbury* | ✗ Stephen Bull |

## Chinese

| | | | |
|---|---|---|---|
| 8 *Mayfair* | XXXX ✿ Oriental (at Dorchester H.) | 58 *Stanmore* | XX Mr Tang's Mandarin |
| 9 *Mayfair* | XXX Princess Garden | 75 *Bayswater & Maida Vale* | XX Poons |
| 3 *Chelsea* | XXX L'Oriental (at La Belle Epoque) | 64 *Chelsea* | XX Red of Knightsbridge |
| 1 *Richmond* | XX Four Regions | 73 *Putney* | XX Royal China |
| 0 *Mill Hill* | XX Good Earth | 75 *Bayswater & Maida Vale* | XX Royal China |
| 4 *Chelsea* | XX Good Earth | 58 *Central Harrow* | XX Taste of China |
| 0 *South Woodford* | XX Ho-Ho | 57 *Greenwich* | XX Treasure of China |
| 7 *Victoria* | XX Hunan | 53 *Hampstead* | XX Vegetarian Cottage |
| 5 *City of London* | XX Imperial City | 55 *Addington* | XX Willow |
| 7 *Victoria* | XX Ken Lo's Memories of China | 51 *Orpington* | XX Xian |
| | | 53 *Hampstead* | XX ZeNW3 |
| 7 *Fulham* | XX Mao Tai | 84 *Soho* | ✗ Fung Shing |
| 6 *Ealing* | XX Maxim | 85 *Soho* | ✗ Jen |
| 6 *Kensington* | XX Memories of China | 66 *Kensington* | ✗ Mandarin |
| 6 *Hyde Park & Knightsbridge* | XX Mr Chow | 56 *Croydon* | ✗ Tai Tung |
| | | 84 *Soho* | ✗ Wok Wok |

## English

| | | | |
|---|---|---|---|
| 8 *Mayfair* | XXXX Grill Room (at Dorchester H.) | 85 *Strand & Covent Garden* | XX Rules |
| 7 *Victoria* | XXX Shepherd's | 52 *Bloomsbury* | ✗ Alfred |
| 3 *Chelsea* | XX English Garden | | |

## French

| | | | |
|---|---|---|---|
| 8 *Mayfair* | XXXXX ✿✿✿ Chez Nico at Ninety Park Lane | 86 *Victoria* | XXX Auberge de Provence |
| 8 *Mayfair* | XXXX ✿✿ (Le) Gavroche | 67 *North Kensington* | XXX Chez Moi |
| 8 *Mayfair* | XXXX ✿ (Les) Saveurs de Jean-Christophe Novelli | 58 *Crouch End* | XX (Les) Associés |
| | | 63 *Chelsea* | XX Brasserie St. Quentin |
| | | 63 *Chelsea* | XX ✿ Chavot |
| 6 *Belgravia* | XXXX ✿✿ (La) Tante Claire | 64 *Chelsea* | XX Le Colombier |
| | | 60 *Chiswick* | XX (La) Dordogne |

9

# French

| | | | |
|---|---|---|---|
| 66 *Kensington* | XX (L') Escargot Doré | 53 *Hampstead* | X (La) Grignote |
| 85 *Strand & Covent Garden* | XX (L') Estaminet | 69 *Kensington* | X Lobster Pot |
| 69 *Kingston* | XX Gravier's | 85 *Strand & Covent Garden* | X Magno's Brasserie |
| 63 *Chelsea* | XX Poissonnerie de l'Avenue | 71 *Hampton Hill* | X ✿ Monsieur Ma |
| 55 *City of London* | XX (Le) Quai | 82 *Regent's Park & Marylebone* | X (Le) Muscadet |
| 76 *Belgravia* | XX Vong (French Thai) | 87 *Victoria* | X (La) Poule au Po |
| 82 *Regent's Park & Marylebone* | X (L') Aventure | 57 *Dalston* | X Soulard |
| | | 69 *Brixton* | X Le Versailles |

# Greek

| | |
|---|---|
| 64 *Chelsea* | X Cafe O |

# Hungarian

| | |
|---|---|
| 84 *Soho* | XX Gay Hussar |

# Indian & Pakistani

| | | | |
|---|---|---|---|
| 71 *Bermondsey* | XXX Bengal Clipper | 68 *South Kensington* | XX Memories of India |
| 68 *South Kensington* | XXX Bombay Brasserie | 81 *Regent's Park & Marylebone* | XX (La) Porte des Indes |
| 63 *Chelsea* | XXX Chutney Mary (Anglo-Indian) | 84 *Soho* | XX Red Fort |
| 68 *South Kensington* | XX Café Lazeez | 55 *City of London* | XX Sri India |
| 73 *Battersea* | XX Cafe Spice Namaste | 74 *Wandsworth* | XX Tabaq |
| 73 *Whitechapel* | XX Cafe Spice Namaste | 79 *Mayfair* | XX Tamarind |
| 79 *Mayfair* | XX Chor Bizarre | 58 *Hammersmith* | XX Tandoori Nights |
| 68 *South Kensington* | XX Delhi Brasserie | 63 *Chelsea* | XX Vama |
| 82 *Regent's Park & Marylebone* | XX Gaylord | 74 *Wandsworth* | X Bombay Bicycle Club |
| 56 *Ealing* | XX Gitanjli - Mayfair | 60 *Finsbury* | X Café Lazeez City |
| 84 *Soho* | XX Gopal's | 66 *Kensington* | X Malabar |
| 68 *South Kensington* | XX Khan's of Kensington | 51 *Willesden Green* | X Sabras (Indian Vegetarian) |
| 52 *Bloomsbury* | XX Malabar Junction | 84 *Soho* | X Soho Spice |
| | | 68 *South Kensington* | X Star of India |
| | | 80 *Mayfair* | X Veeraswamy |

# Irish

| | |
|---|---|
| 82 *Regent's Park & Marylebone* | XX Ard-Ri at the O'Conor Don |

## Italian

| | | | |
|---|---|---|---|
| 5 *Belgravia* | 🏛 ✿ (The) Halkin | 58 *Central Harrow* | XX Trattoria Sorrentina |
| 3 *Chelsea* | XXX Grissini | 72 *Carshalton* | XX (La) Veranda |
| 7 *Victoria* | XXX (L') Incontro | 76 *Belgravia* | XX ✿ Zafferano |
| 7 *Victoria* | XXX Santini | 75 *Bayswater & Maida Vale* | X (L') Accento |
| 8 *Mayfair* | XXX Sartoria | 75 *Bayswater & Maida Vale* | X Assaggi |
| 5 *Bayswater & Maida Vale* | XX Al San Vincenzo | 72 *Bermondsey* | X Cantina Del Ponte |
| 2 *Regent's Park & Marylebone* | XX Bertorelli's | 66 *Kensington* | X Cibo |
| 5 *Strand & Covent Garden* | XX Bertorelli's | 71 *Putney* | X Del Buongustaio |
| 1 *Regent's Park & Marylebone* | XX Caldesi | 74 *Putney* | X Enoteca Turi |
| 3 *Chelsea* | XX Caraffini | 58 *Crouch End* | X Florians |
| 3 *Chelsea* | XX Daphne's | 75 *Bayswater & Maida Vale* | X Green Olive |
| 2 *Dulwich* | XX Luigi's | 82 *Regent's Park & Marylebone* | X Ibla |
| 7 *North Kensington* | XX Orsino | 56 *Croydon* | X Mario |
| 7 *Hammersmith* | XX ✿ River Café | 87 *Victoria* | X Olivo |
| 9 *Mayfair* | XX Teca | 70 *Barnes* | X Riva |
| 1 *Bermondsey* | XX Tentazioni | 59 *Ickenham* | X Roberto's |
| 4 *Chelsea* | XX Toto's | | |

## Japanese

| | | | |
|---|---|---|---|
| 3 *St. James's* | XXX Suntory | 79 *Mayfair* | XX ✿ Nobu |
| 4 *City of London* | XXX Tatsuso | 83 *St. James's* | XX Matsuri |
| 2 *Regent's Park & Marylebone* | XX Asuka | 55 *City of London* | XX Miyama |
| 4 *Hampstead* | XX Benihana | 79 *Mayfair* | XX Shogun |
| 3 *Chelsea* | XX Benihana | 55 *City of London* | X Imari |
| 9 *Mayfair* | XX Benihana | 64 *Chelsea* | X T'Su |

## Lebanese

| | | | |
|---|---|---|---|
| 6 *Belgravia* | XX Al Bustan | 66 *Kensington* | XX Phoenicia |
| 4 *Chelsea* | XX Beit Eddine | | |

## Moroccan

| | | | |
|---|---|---|---|
| 8 *South Kensington* | XX Pasha | 80 *Mayfair* | X Momo |

## Polish

| | |
|---|---|
| 6 *Kensington* | X Wódka |

## Pubs

| | | | |
|---|---|---|---|
| 8 *Hammersmith* | Anglesea Arms | 58 *Shepherds Bush* | Havelock Tavern |
| 4 *Chelsea* | Chelsea Ram | 60 *Finsbury* | Peasant |
| 3 *Battersea* | Duke of Cambridge | 53 *Primrose Hill* | (The) Queens |
| | | 64 *Chelsea* | Swag and Tails |

389

# Seafood

| | | | |
|---|---|---|---|
| 63 *Chelsea* | XXX One-O-One | 63 *Chelsea* | XX Poissonnerie de l'Avenue |
| 79 *Mayfair* | XXX Scotts | | |
| 79 *Mayfair* | XX Bentley's | 85 *Strand & Covent Garden* | XX Sheekey's |
| 68 *South Kensington* | XX Downstairs at One Ninety | 69 *Kennington* | X Lobster Pot |
| 69 *Kingston* | XX Gravier's | 72 *Southwark* | X Livebait |
| 75 *Bayswater & Maida Vale* | XX Jason's | 86 *Strand & Covent Garden* | X Livebait |

# South African

| | |
|---|---|
| 60 *Chiswick* | X Springbok Café |

# Spanish

| | |
|---|---|
| 68 *South Kensington* | X Cambio De Tercio |

# Swedish

| | |
|---|---|
| 60 *Canonbury* | X Anna's Place |

# Thai

| | | | |
|---|---|---|---|
| 57 *Fulham* | XX Blue Elephant | 76 *Belgravia* | XX Vong (French Thai) |
| 64 *Chelsea* | XX Busabong Too | 69 *Kingston* | X Ayudhya |
| 73 *Battersea* | XX Chada | 68 *South Kensington* | X Bangkok |
| 75 *Bayswater & Maida Vale* | XX Nipa | 74 *Tooting* | X Oh Boy |
| 55 *City of London* | XX Sri Siam City | 84 *Soho* | X Sri Siam |

# Vegetarian

| | | | |
|---|---|---|---|
| 53 *Hampstead* | XX Vegetarian Cottage | 51 *Willesden Green* | X Sabras (Indian) |

# Vietnamese

| | |
|---|---|
| 85 *Soho* | X Saigon |

# Boroughs and areas

*Greater London* is divided, for administrative purposes, into 32 boroughs plus the City : thes
sub-divide naturally into minor areas, usually grouped around former villages or quarters, whic
often maintain a distinctive character.

---

**BARNET** pp. 6 and 7.

## Brent Cross – ⊠ NW2.

🏨 **Holiday Inn Garden Court**, Tilling Rd, NW2 1LP, ℰ (0181) 201 8686
*Fax (0181) 455 4660* – 🛗, ‰ rm, 🔳 📺 ☎ ᇮ 🅿 – 🔬 50. 🐵 🅰 ⓪ 𝘝𝘐𝘚𝘈 ᴊᴄʙ. ᵟ      DU
**Meals** *(closed Saturday lunch)* (bar lunch)/dinner a la carte 21.00/29.00 st. ⎸ 7.95 – ⌓ 11.9
– **153 rm** 129.00 st. – SB.

## Child's Hill – ⊠ NW2.

Ⅹ **Quincy's**, 675 Finchley Rd, NW2 2JP, ℰ (0171) 794 8499 – 🔳. 🐵 🅰 𝘝𝘐𝘚𝘈      DU
*closed 1 week Christmas* – **Meals** *(booking essential)* (dinner only) 25.00 t. ⎸ 4.50.

Ⅹ **Laurent**, 428 Finchley Rd, NW2 2HY, ℰ (0171) 794 3603 – 🐵 🅰 𝘝𝘐𝘚𝘈      DU (
*closed Sunday, 24-25 December, August and Bank Holidays* – **Meals** - Couscous
a la carte 13.95 t.

## Mill Hill – ⊠ NW7.

🏌 100 Barnet Way, Mill Hill ℰ (0181) 959 2282 CT.

ⅩⅩ **Good Earth**, 143 The Broadway, NW7 4RN, ℰ (0181) 959 7011, *Fax (0181) 959 1464* – 🔳
🐵 🅰 ⓪ 𝘝𝘐𝘚𝘈 ᴊᴄʙ                                                              CT
**Meals** - Chinese - a la carte 10.95/18.25 t. ⎸ 6.00.

---

**BEXLEY** pp. 12 and 13.

## Bexley – ⊠ Kent.

🏨 **Forte Posthouse Bexley**, Black Prince Interchange, Southwold Rd, DA5 1ND, on A 2
ℰ (01322) 526900, *Fax (01322) 526113* – 🛗, ‰ rm, 📺 ☎ ᇮ 🅿 – 🔬 70. 🐵 🅰 ⓪ 𝘝𝘐𝘚𝘈 ᴊᴄʙ
ᵟ                                                                             JX (
**Meals** a la carte 14.45/27.85 t. ⎸ 7.50 – ⌓ 9.95 – **104 rm** 99.00 st.

## Bexleyheath – ⊠ Kent.

🏩 **Swallow**, 1 Broadway, DA6 7JZ, ℰ (0181) 298 1000, *Fax (0181) 298 1234*, 𝐼ᵟ, ⊠ – 🛗
‰ rm, 🔳 📺 ☎ ᇮ 🅿 – 🔬 200. 🐵 🅰 ⓪ 𝘝𝘐𝘚𝘈 ᵟ                                      JX (
**La Galleria :** **Meals** *(closed Saturday and Sunday)* 19.75/26.00 st. and a la carte ⎸ 6.50 -
**Copper :** **Meals** (carving rest.) (dinner only) 19.95 st. and a la carte ⎸ 6.50 – **142 rm**
⌓ 110.00/140.00 st. – SB.

---

**BRENT** p. 7.

## Wembley – ⊠ Middx.

🏩 **Hilton National Wembley**, Empire Way, HA9 8DS, ℰ (0181) 902 8839
*Fax (0181) 900 2201*, 𝐼ᵟ, ≲ᵤ, ⊠ – 🛗, ‰ rm, 🔳 rest, 📺 ☎ ᵛ 🅿 – 🔬 300. 🐵 🅰 ⓪ 𝘝𝘐𝘚𝘈
ᴊᴄʙ                                                                          CU  2
**Celebrities :** **Meals** *(closed Saturday lunch)* (carving rest.) 16.75/19.75 st. ⎸ 6.50 – **Terra
cotta :** **Meals** *(closed Bank Holidays)* (dinner only) a la carte 21.70/33.65 st. ⎸ 6.50 – ⌓
12.00 – **306 rm** 150.00 st. – SB.

## Willesden Green – ⊠ Middx.

※ **Sabras,** 263 High Rd, NW10 2RX, ℘ (0181) 459 0340 – 🕼 AE ⓞ VISA JCB    CU  e
⚶ *closed Monday and 25 December* – **Meals** - Indian Vegetarian - *(dinner only)* a la carte
13.00/19.00 **t.**

## BROMLEY p. 13.

🏌18, 🏌9 *Cray Valley, Sandy Lane, St. Paul's Cray, Orpington ℘ (01689) 831927,* JY.

## Bromley – ⊠ Kent.

🏌9 *Magpie Hall Lane ℘ (0181) 462 7014* HY.

🏨 **Bromley Court,** Bromley Hill, BR1 4JD, ℘ (0181) 464 5011, *Fax (0181) 460 0899,* Ⅰ6, ⇆,
🞷 – 📳, ※ rm, 📺 ☎ 🅿 – 🔬 150. 🕼 AE ⓞ VISA    HY  z
**Meals** *(closed Saturday lunch)* 16.50 **st.** (dinner) and a la carte 10.00/22.45 **st.** ⚶ 6.25 –
**113 rm** ⊇ 90.00/100.00 **st.,** 2 suites – SB.

## Farnborough – ⊠ Kent.

※※※ **Chapter One,** Farnborough Common, Locksbottom, BR6 8NF, ℘ (01689) 854848,
⚶ *Fax (01689) 858439* – 🝙 🅿 🕼 AE ⓞ VISA JCB    HZ  a
**Meals** 19.50/23.45 **t.** ⚶ 7.50.

## Orpington – ⊠ Kent.

🏌18 *High Elms, High Elms Rd, Downe, Orpington ℘ (01689) 858175.*

※※ **Xian,** 324 High St., BR6 0NG, ℘ (01689) 871881 – 🝙. 🕼 AE ⓞ VISA    JY  a
*closed Sunday lunch, 25-26 December and 1 week August* – **Meals** - Chinese (Peking,
Szechuan) - 7.50/13.00 **t.** and a la carte.

## CAMDEN Except where otherwise stated see pp. 22-25.

## Bloomsbury – ⊠ NW1/W1/WC1.

🛈 *34-37 Woburn Pl., WC1H 0JR ℘ (0171) 580 4599.*

🏨 **Holiday Inn Kings Cross,** 1 Kings Cross Rd, WC1X 9HX, ℘ (0171) 833 3900,
*Fax (0171) 917 6163,* ⇜, Ⅰ6, ⇆, 🞷, squash – 📳, ※ rm, 🝙 ☎ 🕭 – 🔬 220. 🕼 AE ⓞ VISA
JCB. ⚸    MT  a
**Meals** *(closed Saturday lunch)* 17.95 **st.** (dinner) and a la carte 15.85/19.85 **st.** ⚶ 6.00 –
**403 rm** ⊇ 170.00 **s.,** 2 suites – SB.

🏨 **Marlborough,** 9-14 Bloomsbury St., WC1B 3QD, ℘ (0171) 636 5601, *Fax (0171) 240 3540*
– 📳, ※ rm, 🝙 rest, 🝙 ☎ 🕭 – 🔬 200. 🕼 AE ⓞ VISA. ⚸    LU  i
*Brasserie Saint Martin :* **Meals** *(bar lunch Saturday)* a la carte approx. 20.50 **st.** ⚶ 8.00 – ⊇
15.00 – **166 rm** 169.00/195.00 **s.,** 7 suites.

🏨 **Russell,** Russell Sq., WC1B 5BE, ℘ (0171) 837 6470, *Fax (0171) 837 2857* – 📳, ※ rm,
🝙 rest, 🝙 ☎ – 🔬 400. 🕼 AE ⓞ VISA JCB. ⚸    LU  o
*Fitzroy Doll's :* **Meals** 14.95/15.95 **t.** and dinner a la carte ⚶ 8.95 – *Virginia Woolf's :*
**Meals** a la carte 13.00/26.70 **t.** ⚶ 7.50 – ⊇ 12.95 – **327 rm** 139.00/204.00 **st.,** 2 suites – SB.

🏨 **Grafton,** 130 Tottenham Court Rd, W1P 9HP, ℘ (0171) 388 4131, *Fax (0171) 387 7394* –
📳, ※ rm, 🝙 rest, 🝙 ☎ 🕭 – 🔬 100. 🕼 AE ⓞ VISA JCB. ⚸    KU  n
*Cliveden Room :* **Meals** 19.50 **t.** and a la carte ⚶ 7.50 – ⊇ 12.00 – **320 rm** 145.00/165.00 **s.,**
4 suites.

🏨 **Montague,** 15 Montague St., WC1B 5BJ, ℘ (0171) 637 1001, *Fax (0171) 637 2516,* 🍴, 🞷
– 📳, ※ rm, 🝙 rest, 🝙 ☎ 🕭 – 🔬 120. 🕼 AE ⓞ VISA JCB. ⚸    LU  c
*Blue Door Bistro :* **Meals** *(closed lunch Saturday and Sunday)* a la carte 16.95/27.85 **t.**
⚶ 15.00 – ⊇ 12.50 – **102 rm** 140.00/210.00 **s.,** 2 suites.

🏨 **Mountbatten,** 20 Monmouth St., WC2H 9HD, ℘ (0171) 836 4300, *Fax (0171) 240 3540* –
📳, ※ rm, 🝙 rest, 🝙 ☎ – 🔬 75. 🕼 AE ⓞ VISA. ⚸    p. 35 DV  o
*The Ad-Lib :* **Meals** 22.50 **t.** and a la carte ⚶ 7.50 – ⊇ 15.00 – **120 rm** 215.00/245.00 **s.,**
7 suites.

🏨 **Covent Garden,** 10 Monmouth St., WC2H 9HB, ℘ (0171) 806 1000, *Fax (0171) 806 1100,*
Ⅰ6 – 📳 🝙 🝙 ☎ 🕭 🕼 AE ⓞ VISA. ⚸    p. 35 DV  n
*Brasserie Max :* **Meals** *(booking essential)* a la carte 25.00/28.95 **t.** – ⊇ 15.50 – **48 rm**
175.00/255.00 **s.,** 2 suites.

🏨🏨 **Thistle Kingsley**, Bloomsbury Way, WC1A 2SD, ℰ (0171) 242 5881, *Fax (0171) 831 022.*
– 劇, ✲ rm, 📺 ☎ ₺ – 🔬 90. 🐵 🆒 ⓪ *VISA* 🎜. 🎬
  LU
**Meals** *(closed lunch Saturday, Sunday and Bank Holidays)* 18.50 **t.** and a la carte ₰ 6.10 – ⊑
12.50 – **138 rm** 150.00/240.00 **st.**

🏨🏨 **Forte Posthouse Bloomsbury**, Coram St., WC1N 1HT, ℰ (0171) 837 1200
*Fax (0171) 837 5374* – 劇, ✲ rm, ▤ rest, 📺 ☎ ₺, – 🔬 300. 🐵 🆒 ⓪ *VISA* 🎜. 🎬
**Meals** 16.95 **t.** (dinner) and a la carte 17.00/28.00 **t.** ₰ 8.95 – ⊑ 11.95 – **281 rm** 139.00
169.00 **st.**, 3 suites – SB.
  LT

🏨🏨 **Kenilworth**, 97 Great Russell St., WC1B 3LB, ℰ (0171) 637 3477, *Fax (0171) 631 3133* – 劇
✲ rm, ▤ rest, 📺 ☎ – 🔬 65. 🐵 🆒 ⓪ *VISA* 🎜. 🎬
**Meals** 14.50 **st.** and a la carte ₰ 9.00 – ⊑ 12.00 – **187 rm** 140.00/165.00 **s.**
  LU

🏨 **Blooms** without rest., 7 Montague St., WC1B 5BP, ℰ (0171) 323 1717
*Fax (0171) 636 6498* – 劇 📺 ☎. 🐵 🆒 ⓪ *VISA* 🎜. 🎬
**27 rm** ⊑ 125.00/195.00 **st.**
  LU r

🏨 **Bonnington in Bloomsbury**, 92 Southampton Row, WC1B 4BH, ℰ (0171) 242 2828
*Fax (0171) 831 9170* – 劇, ✲ rm, ▤ rest, 📺 ☎ ₺, – 🔬 250. 🐵 🆒 ⓪ *VISA* 🎜. LU
**Meals** *(bar lunch Saturday and Sunday)* 11.50/19.75 **st.** and a la carte ₰ 7.80 – **215 rm**
⊑ 110.00/140.00 **st.**

🏨 **Bloomsbury Park**, 126 Southampton Row, WC1B 5AD, ℰ (0171) 430 0434
*Fax (0171) 242 0665* – 劇, ✲ rm, 📺 ☎ – 🔬 25. 🐵 🆒 ⓪ *VISA* 🎜. 🎬
**Meals** a la carte 13.85/17.95 **t.** ₰ 4.95 – ⊑ 11.95 – **95 rm** 110.00/140.00 **st.** – SB.
  LU

🏨 **Academy**, 17-21 Gower St., WC1E 6HG, ℰ (0171) 631 4115, *Fax (0171) 636 3442*, � –
▤ rest, 📺 ☎. 🐵 🆒 ⓪ *VISA* 🎜. 🎬
  KLU
**Alchemy :** **Meals** *(closed Saturday and Sunday)* a la carte 16.25/20.50 **t.** ₰ 8.50 – ⊑ 9.95 –
**47 rm** 100.00/185.00 **st.**

XX **Pied à Terre**, 34 Charlotte St., W1P 1HJ, ℰ (0171) 636 1178, *Fax (0171) 916 1171* – ▤. 🐵
❀❀ 🆒 ⓪ *VISA* 🎜
  KU
*closed Saturday lunch, Sunday, last 2 weeks August, 2 weeks Christmas-New Year and Bank
Holidays* – **Meals** 23.00/35.50-49.00 **t.** ₰ 11.00
**Spec.** Roasted langoustines with tomato and langoustine millefeuille, fennel purée. Venison
son fillet with beetroot gratin and purée, port sauce. Lime parfait with warm ginger savarin
and lime sauce.

XX **Neal Street**, 26 Neal St., WC2H 9PS, ℰ (0171) 836 8368, *Fax (0171) 240 3964* – 🐵 🆒 ⓪
*VISA* 🎜
  p. 35 DV
*closed Sunday, Christmas-New Year and Bank Holidays* – **Meals** 27.00 **t.**
(lunch) and a la carte 25.00/42.00 **t.** ₰ 12.75.

XX **The Birdcage**, 110 Whitfield St., W1P 5RU, ℰ (0171) 383 3346, *Fax (0171) 350 1593* – 🐵
🆒 *VISA*
  KU
*closed Saturday lunch and Sunday* – **Meals** 18.00/32.00 **t.** and a la carte.

XX **Malabar Junction**, 107 Great Russell St., WC1B 3NA, ℰ (0171) 580 5230
*Fax (0171) 436 9942* – ▤. 🐵 🆒 *VISA*
  LU
*closed 25 and 26 December* – **Meals** - South Indian - 8.90 **t.** (lunch) and a la carte 12.00
26.00 **t.** ₰ 8.00.

XX **Mon Plaisir**, 21 Monmouth St., WC2H 9DD, ℰ (0171) 836 7243, *Fax (0171) 240 4774* – 🐵
🆒 ⓪ *VISA* 🎜
  p. 35 DV
*closed Saturday lunch, Sunday, 1 week Christmas-New Year, Easter and Bank Holidays* –
**Meals** - French - 14.95/13.95 **t.** and a la carte ₰ 6.20.

X **Alfred**, 245 Shaftesbury Av., WC2H 8EH, ℰ (0171) 240 2566, *Fax (0171) 497 0672*, 🎋 – ▤
🐵 🆒 ⓪ *VISA*
  p. 35 DV
*closed Sunday, 24 December-2 January and Bank Holidays* – **Meals** - English - 15.90 **t.**
(lunch) and a la carte.

X **Museum Street Cafe**, 47 Museum St., WC1A 1LY, ℰ (0171) 405 3211
*Fax (0171) 405 3211* – ✲. 🐵 🆒 *VISA*
  LU
*closed 1 week in summer and 2 weeks Christmas* – **Meals** *(lunch only)* a la carte 14.00
18.00 **t.** ₰ 9.00.

## Euston – ✉ WC1.

🏨🏨 **Euston Plaza**, 17/18 Upper Woburn Pl., WC1H 0HT, ℰ (0171) 383 4105
*Fax (0171) 383 4106*, ₺, ✥ – 劇, ✲ rm, 📺 ☎ ₺ – 🔬 150. 🐵 🆒 ⓪ *VISA* 🎜. 🎬
**Three Crowns :** **Meals** 13.95/17.95 **t.** and dinner a la carte ₰ 5.90 – **Terrace :** **Meals** a la
carte 11.40/19.05 **t.** ₰ 5.90 – ⊑ 11.95 – **150 rm** 149.00/165.00 **st.** – SB.
  KLT

🏨 **London Euston Travel Inn Capital**, 141 Euston Rd, NW1 2AU, ℰ (0171) 554 3400
*Fax (0171) 554 3419* – 劇, ✲ rm, ▤ rest, 📺 ₺. 🐵 🆒 ⓪ *VISA*. 🎬
  LT
**Meals** *(grill rest.)* – **220 rm** 55.00 **t.**

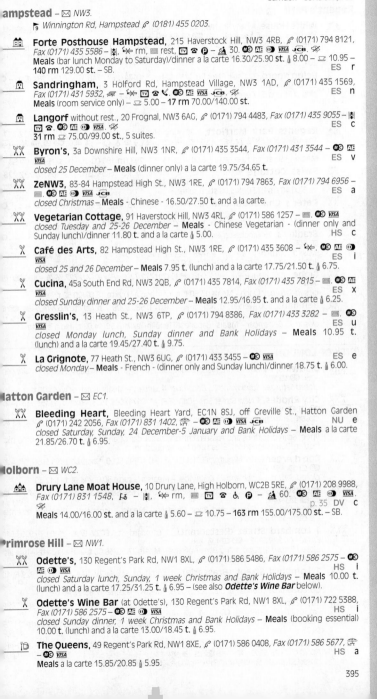

**ampstead** – ⊠ NW3.

🕞 Winnington Rd, Hampstead 𝒫 (0181) 455 0203.

🏦 **Forte Posthouse Hampstead,** 215 Haverstock Hill, NW3 4RB, 𝒫 (0171) 794 8121, Fax (0171) 435 5586 – ▯, 🔆 rm, 🗐 rest, 📺 ☎ 🅿 – 🛆 30. 🐠 🕮 ⑩ 𝗩𝗜𝗦𝗔 𝗝𝗖𝗕. ⋘
**Meals** (bar lunch Monday to Saturday)/dinner a la carte 16.30/25.90 **st.** ⒜ 8.00 – ☲ 10.95 –
**140 rm** 129.00 **st.** – SB.
ES r

🏛 **Sandringham,** 3 Holford Rd, Hampstead Village, NW3 1AD, 𝒫 (0171) 435 1569, Fax (0171) 431 5932, 🐖 – 🔆 📺 ☎ 🕻. 🐠 🕮 𝗩𝗜𝗦𝗔 𝗝𝗖𝗕.
**Meals** (room service only) – ☲ 5.00 – **17 rm** 70.00/140.00 **st.**
ES n

🏠 **Langorf** without rest., 20 Frognal, NW3 6AG, 𝒫 (0171) 794 4483, Fax (0171) 435 9055 – ▯
📺 ☎. 🐠 🕮 ⑩ 𝗩𝗜𝗦𝗔. ⋘
**31 rm** ☲ 75.00/99.00 **st.**, 5 suites.
ES c

🟍🟍 **Byron's,** 3a Downshire Hill, NW3 1NR, 𝒫 (0171) 435 3544, Fax (0171) 431 3544 – 🐠 🕮
𝗩𝗜𝗦𝗔
closed 25 December – **Meals** (dinner only) a la carte 19.75/34.65 **t.**
ES v

🟍🟍 **ZeNW3,** 83-84 Hampstead High St., NW3 1RE, 𝒫 (0171) 794 7863, Fax (0171) 794 6956 –
🗐. 🐠 🕮 ⑩ 𝗩𝗜𝗦𝗔 𝗝𝗖𝗕.
closed Christmas – **Meals** - Chinese - 16.50/27.50 **t.** and a la carte.
ES a

🟍🟍 **Vegetarian Cottage,** 91 Haverstock Hill, NW3 4RL, 𝒫 (0171) 586 1257 – 🗐. 🐠 𝗩𝗜𝗦𝗔
closed Tuesday and 25-26 December – **Meals** - Chinese Vegetarian - (dinner only and
Sunday lunch)/dinner 11.80 **t.** and a la carte ⒜ 5.00.
HS c

🟍 **Café des Arts,** 82 Hampstead High St., NW3 1RE, 𝒫 (0171) 435 3608 – 🔆. 🐠 🕮 ⑩
𝗩𝗜𝗦𝗔
closed 25 and 26 December – **Meals** 7.95 **t.** (lunch) and a la carte 17.75/21.50 **t.** ⒜ 6.75.
ES i

🟍 **Cucina,** 45a South End Rd, NW3 2QB, 𝒫 (0171) 435 7814, Fax (0171) 435 7815 – 🗐. 🐠 🕮
𝗩𝗜𝗦𝗔
closed Sunday dinner and 25-26 December – **Meals** 12.95/16.95 **t.** and a la carte ⒜ 6.25.
ES x

🟍 **Gresslin's,** 13 Heath St., NW3 6TP, 𝒫 (0171) 794 8386, Fax (0171) 433 3282 – 🗐. 🐠
𝗩𝗜𝗦𝗔
closed Monday lunch, Sunday dinner and Bank Holidays – **Meals** 10.95 **t.**
(lunch) and a la carte 19.45/27.40 **t.** ⒜ 9.75.
ES u

🟍 **La Grignote,** 77 Heath St., NW3 6UG, 𝒫 (0171) 433 3455 – 🐠 𝗩𝗜𝗦𝗔
closed Monday – **Meals** - French - (dinner only and Sunday lunch)/dinner 18.75 **t.** ⒜ 6.00.
ES e

**Iatton Garden** – ⊠ EC1.

🟍🟍 **Bleeding Heart,** Bleeding Heart Yard, EC1N 8SJ, off Greville St., Hatton Garden
𝒫 (0171) 242 2056, Fax (0171) 831 1402, 🐖 – 🐠 🕮 ⑩ 𝗩𝗜𝗦𝗔 𝗝𝗖𝗕 – **Meals** a la carte
21.85/26.70 **t.** ⒜ 6.95.
NU e
closed Saturday, Sunday, 24 December-5 January and Bank Holidays

**Iolborn** – ⊠ WC2.

🏰 **Drury Lane Moat House,** 10 Drury Lane, High Holborn, WC2B 5RE, 𝒫 (0171) 208 9988, Fax (0171) 831 1548, 🛵 – ▯, 🔆 rm, 🗐 📺 ☎ 🕭 🅿 – 🛆 60. 🐠 🕮 ⑩ 𝗩𝗜𝗦𝗔.
⋘
**Meals** 14.00/16.00 **st.** and a la carte ⒜ 5.60 – ☲ 10.75 – **163 rm** 155.00/175.00 **st.** – SB.
p. 35 DV c

**Primrose Hill** – ⊠ NW1.

🟍🟍 **Odette's,** 130 Regent's Park Rd, NW1 8XL, 𝒫 (0171) 586 5486, Fax (0171) 586 2575 – 🐠
🕮 ⑩ 𝗩𝗜𝗦𝗔
closed Saturday lunch, Sunday, 1 week Christmas and Bank Holidays – **Meals** 10.00 **t.**
(lunch) and a la carte 17.25/31.25 **t.** ⒜ 6.95 – (see also **Odette's Wine Bar** below).
HS i

🟍 **Odette's Wine Bar** (at Odette's), 130 Regent's Park Rd, NW1 8XL, 𝒫 (0171) 722 5388, Fax (0171) 586 2575 – 🐠 🕮 ⑩ 𝗩𝗜𝗦𝗔
closed Sunday dinner, 1 week Christmas and Bank Holidays – **Meals** (booking essential)
10.00 **t.** (lunch) and a la carte 13.00/18.45 **t.** ⒜ 6.95.
HS i

🏮 **The Queens,** 49 Regent's Park Rd, NW1 8XE, 𝒫 (0171) 586 0408, Fax (0171) 586 5677, 🐖
– 🐠 𝗩𝗜𝗦𝗔
**Meals** a la carte 15.85/20.85 ⒜ 5.95.
HS a

## Regent's Park – ✉ NW1.

🏨 **White House,** Albany St., NW1 3UP, ℘ (0171) 387 1200, Fax (0171) 388 0091, ₤ô, ⬅ –
⅍ rm, ☐ rest, ☑ ☎ – 🔒 110. ◍◙ ᴀᴇ ⓞ ᴠɪѕᴀ ᴊᴄʙ. ℀
JT
*The Restaurant :* Meals a la carte approx. 35.00 t. ⒝ 8.00 – *Garden Cafe :* Meals (close
Saturday lunch and Sunday) a la carte approx. 35.00 t. – ☲ 12.00 – **580 rm** 152.0
201.00 **st.,** 2 suites.

✗ **Belgo Noord,** 72 Chalk Farm Rd, NW1 8AN, ℘ (0171) 267 0718, Fax (0171) 284 4842 – ◍
ᴀᴇ ⓞ ᴠɪѕᴀ ᴊᴄʙ
IS
closed 25 and 31 December – Meals 5.00/12.95 **t.** and a la carte.

## Swiss Cottage – ✉ NW3.

🏨 **Regents Park Marriott,** 128 King Henry's Rd, NW3 3ST, ℘ (0171) 722 771
Fax (0171) 586 5822, ₤ô, ⬅, ▨ – ▤, ⅍ rm, ☰ ☑ ☎ ও ☮ – 🔒 400. ◍◙ ᴀᴇ ⓞ ᴠɪѕᴀ ᴊᴄ
℀
GS
Meals 18.95 **st.** and a la carte ⒝ 6.00 – ☲ 13.95 – **298 rm** 180.00/200.00 **s.,** 5 suites – SB.

🏨 **Swiss Cottage** without rest., 4 Adamson Rd, NW3 3HP, ℘ (0171) 722 228
Fax (0171) 483 4588 – ▤ ☑ ☎ – 🔒 50. ◍◙ ᴀᴇ ⓞ ᴠɪѕᴀ. ℀
GS
☲ 5.00 **48 rm** 87.50/143.00 **st.,** 6 suites.

✗✗ **Peter's Chateaubriand,** 65 Fairfax Rd, NW6 4EE, ℘ (0171) 624 5804 – ☰. ◍
ᴠɪѕᴀ
FS
closed Saturday lunch, 26 December and 1 January – Meals a la carte 17.45/28.40 **t.**

✗✗ **Bradley's,** 25 Winchester Rd, NW3 3NR, ℘ (0171) 722 3457, Fax (0171) 431 4776 – ☰. ◍
ᴀᴇ ᴠɪѕᴀ
GS
closed Saturday lunch, 25-26 December and 1 January – **Meals** 10.00
(lunch) and a la carte 22.00/29.00 **t.** ⒝ 9.00.

✗✗ **Globe,** 100 Avenue Rd, NW3 3HF, ℘ (0171) 722 7200, Fax (0171) 722 7676 – ☰. ◍◙ ᴠɪѕ
ᴊᴄʙ
GS
closed Saturday lunch – Meals 13.50 **t.** (lunch) and a la carte 18.00/20.50 **t.**

✗✗ **Benihana,** 100 Avenue Rd, NW3 3HF, ℘ (0171) 586 9508, Fax (0171) 586 6740 – ☰. ◍◙ ▮
ⓞ ᴠɪѕᴀ ᴊᴄʙ
GS
closed 25 December – Meals - Japanese (Teppan-Yaki) - 8.50/14.00 **t.** and a la carte.

## CITY OF LONDON p. 25.

✗✗✗ **Gladwins,** Minister Court, Mark Lane, EC3R 7AA, ℘ (0171) 444 0004, Fax (0171) 444 00C
– ☰. ◍◙ ᴀᴇ ᴠɪѕᴀ
PV
closed Saturday, Sunday and 23 December-4 January – Meals (lunch only) 33.00 t..

✗✗✗ **City Rhodes,** 1 New Street Sq., EC4A 3BF, ℘ (0171) 583 1313, Fax (0171) 353 1662 – ☰
⸙ ◍◙ ᴀᴇ ⓞ ᴠɪѕᴀ
NU
closed Saturday, Sunday, Christmas, New Year and Bank Holidays – Meals a la carte 29.00
47.00 **t.** ⒝ 9.00
**Spec.** Seared scallops and roasted chicory, sweet carrot and foie gras sauce. Braised pig
trotter "Bourguignonne". Bread and butter pudding.

✗✗✗ **Coq d'Argent,** No.1 Poultry, EC2R 8EJ, ℘ (0171) 395 5000, Fax (0171) 395 5050, ⇞ – ☰
◍◙ ᴀᴇ ⓞ ᴠɪѕᴀ ᴊᴄʙ
PV
closed Saturday lunch and 25 December – Meals a la carte 30.00/43.00 **t.** ⒝ 12.50.

✗✗✗ **Tatsuso,** 32 Broadgate Circle, EC2M 2QS, ℘ (0171) 638 5863, Fax (0171) 638 5864 – ☰. ◍
ᴀᴇ ᴠɪѕᴀ ᴊᴄʙ
PU
closed Saturday, Sunday and Bank Holidays – Meals - Japanese - (booking essentia
a la carte 35.00/80.00 **t.**

✗✗✗ **1 Lombard Street (Restaurant),** 1 Lombard St., EC2V 9AA, ℘ (0171) 929 6611
Fax (0171) 929 6622 – ◍◙ ᴀᴇ ⓞ ᴠɪѕᴀ ᴊᴄʙ
PV
closed Saturday, Sunday and Bank Holidays – Meals 27.50/38.00 **t.** and a la carte – (see als
*1 Lombard Street (Brasserie)* below).

✗✗ **1 Lombard Street (Brasserie),** 1 Lombard St., EC2V 9AA, ℘ (0171) 929 6611
Fax (0171) 929 6622 – ◍◙ ᴀᴇ ⓞ ᴠɪѕᴀ ᴊᴄʙ
PV
closed Saturday, Sunday and Bank Holidays – Meals a la carte 17.95/28.40 **t.**

✗✗ **10,** Cutlers Gardens Arcade, Devonshire Sq., EC2M 4EY, ℘ (0171) 283 7888
Fax (0171) 626 4859 – ☰. ◍◙ ᴀᴇ ⓞ ᴠɪѕᴀ ᴊᴄʙ
PU
closed Saturday, Sunday and Bank Holidays – Meals 15.95 (dinner) and a la carte 21.75
39.75.

✗✗ **Brasserie Rocque,** 37 Broadgate Circle, EC2M 2QS, ℘ (0171) 638 7919
Fax (0171) 628 5899, ⇞ – ☰ ◍◙ ᴀᴇ ⓞ ᴠɪѕᴀ
PU
closed Saturday, Sunday and Bank Holidays – Meals (lunch only) 29.50 **t.** ⒝ 5.00.

XX **Le Quai**, Riverside, 1 Paul's Walk, High Timber St., EC4V 3QH, ℰ (0171) 236 6480, Fax (0171) 236 6479 – ▣. 🕮 🕮 ❶ 𝘝𝘐𝘚𝘈 𝗝𝗖𝗕
OV a
closed Saturday, Sunday, 2 weeks Christmas-New Year and Bank Holidays – **Meals** - French - (dinner booking essential) 32.50 st. ⒤ 13.20.

XX **Miyama**, 17 Godliman St., EC4V 5BD, ℰ (0171) 489 1937, Fax (0171) 236 0325 – ▣. 🕮 🕮 ❶ 𝘝𝘐𝘚𝘈 𝗝𝗖𝗕
OV e
closed Saturday dinner, Sunday, 20 December-3 January and Bank Holidays – **Meals** - Japanese - 35.00/45.00 t. and a la carte.

XX **Imperial City**, Royal Exchange, Cornhill, EC3V 3LL, ℰ (0171) 626 3437, Fax (0171) 338 0125 – ▣. 🕮 🕮 ❶ 𝘝𝘐𝘚𝘈
PV a
closed Saturday, Sunday, 25 and 26 December and Bank Holidays – **Meals** - Chinese - 15.95/30.00 t. and a la carte.

XX **Sri Siam City**, 85 London Wall, EC2M 7AD, ℰ (0171) 628 5772, Fax (0171) 628 3395 – ▣. 🕮 🕮 ❶ 𝘝𝘐𝘚𝘈
PU a
closed Saturday, Sunday, 25-26 December and Bank Holidays – **Meals** - Thai - 15.95/29.95 t. and a la carte ⒤ 8.00.

XX **Sri India**, 7 Bishopgate Churchyard, EC2M 3TJ, ℰ (0171) 628 7888, Fax (0171) 628 8282, 🌤 – ▣. 🕮 🕮 ❶ 𝘝𝘐𝘚𝘈
PU e
closed Saturday, Sunday, 25-26 December and Bank Holidays – **Meals** - Indian - 15.50 t. and a la carte.

X **Imari**, 20 Copthall Av., EC2R 7DN, ℰ (0171) 628 3611, Fax (0171) 431 8071 – ▣. 🕮 🕮 ❶ 𝘝𝘐𝘚𝘈 𝗝𝗖𝗕
PU c
closed Saturday, Sunday and Bank Holidays – **Meals** - Japanese - 9.50/20.00 t. and a la carte.

*When looking for a quiet hotel*
*use the maps found in the introduction*
*or look for establishments with the sign ⏝ or ⏝.*

---

# CROYDON pp. 12 and 13.

**Addington** – ✉ Surrey.
  ▯₈, ▯₈, ▯ Addington Court, Featherbed Lane ℰ (0181) 657 0281/2/3, GZ – ▯ The Addington, Shirley Church Rd ℰ (0181) 777 1055 GZ.

XX **Willow**, 88 Selsdon Park Rd, CR2 8JT, ℰ (0181) 657 4656 – ▣ 𝗣. 🕮 🕮 ❶ 𝘝𝘐𝘚𝘈
closed Sunday lunch and 25 to 27 December – **Meals** - Chinese (Peking, Szechuan) - 16.50 t. and a la carte ⒤ 5.00.
GZ x

**Coulsdon** – ✉ Surrey.
🏨 **Coulsdon Manor** ⏝, Coulsdon Court Rd, via Stoats Nest Rd, CR5 2LL, ℰ (0181) 668 0414, Fax (0181) 668 3118, ▯♣, 🌤, ▯₈, ※, squash – ▯ ⇔ 📺 🕿 𝗣 – 🔬 180. 🕮 🕮 ❶ 𝘝𝘐𝘚𝘈 𝗝𝗖𝗕. ※
EZ e
*Manor House :* Meals (closed Saturday lunch) 17.00/26.00 st. and a la carte ⒤ 7.90 – **35 rm** ☐ 95.00/160.00 st. – SB.

**Croydon** – ✉ Surrey.
  🟦 Croydon Clocktower, Katherine St., CR9 1ET ℰ (0181) 253 1009.

🏨 **Hilton National**, Waddon Way, Purley Way, CR9 4HH, ℰ (0181) 680 3000, Fax (0181) 681 6171, ▯♣, 🌤, ☒ – ▯ ⇔ rm, ▣ 📺 🕿 ♿ 𝗣 – 🔬 400. 🕮 🕮 ❶ 𝘝𝘐𝘚𝘈 – ☐
**Meals** (closed Saturday lunch) 13.50/16.00 t. and dinner a la carte 19.75/29.75 t. ⒤ 6.50 – ☐ 12.00 – **168 rm** 135.00 st.
FZ e

🏨 **Croydon Park**, 7 Altyre Rd, CR9 5AA, ℰ (0181) 680 9200, Fax (0181) 760 0426, ▯♣, 🌤, ☒, ⇔ rm, ▣ 📺 🕿 𝗣 – 🔬 300. 🕮 🕮 ❶ 𝘝𝘐𝘚𝘈 𝗝𝗖𝗕
FZ u
*Oscars :* Meals 14.95/16.95 st. and a la carte ⒤ 5.50 – **211 rm** ☐ 112.00 st.

🏨 **Forte Posthouse Croydon**, Purley Way, CR9 4LT, ℰ (0181) 688 5185, Fax (0181) 681 6438 – ⇔ rm, ▣ rest, 📺 🕿 𝗣 – 🔬 120. 🕮 🕮 ❶ 𝘝𝘐𝘚𝘈
FZ o
closed 31 December and 1 January – **Meals** a la carte 17.35/26.40 st. ⒤ 7.50 – ☐ 9.95 – **83 rm** 109.00 st. – SB.

🏨 **Windsor Castle Toby**, 415 Brighton Rd, South Croydon, CR2 6ES, ℰ (0181) 680 4559, Fax (0181) 649 9801, ⇔ – ⇔ rm, 📺 🕿 𝗣 – 🔬 🕮 𝘝𝘐𝘚𝘈. ※
FZ a
closed 24 to 26 December – **Meals** (carving rest.) a la carte 12.25/14.00 st. – **29 rm** ☐ 64.00/79.00 t. – SB.

🏨 **Travel Inn**, 104 Coombe Rd, CR0 5RB, on A 212 ℰ (0181) 686 2030, Fax (0181) 686 6435, ⇔ – ⇔ rm, 📺 ♿ 𝗣. 🕮 🕮 ❶ 𝘝𝘐𝘚𝘈. ※
GZ s
**Meals** (grill rest.) – **39 rm** 38.00 t.

✕ **Mario**, 299 High St., CR0 1QL, ℰ (0181) 686 5624 – **🕮 🕮 _VISA_** FZ
closed Saturday lunch, Monday dinner, Sunday, last 2 weeks August, 24-26 December a
Bank Holidays – Meals - Italian - 12.95 **t.** and a la carte ⅋ 7.95.

✕ **Tai Tung**, Unit 1A, Wing Yip Centre, 550 Purley Way, CR0 4RF, ℰ (0181) 688 36
Fax (0181) 688 0116 – 🗐 **🅿**. **🕮 🕮** FZ
closed 24 to 26 December – Meals - Chinese (Canton) - a la carte 8.50 **t.** and a la ca
⅋ 5.50.

## Sanderstead – ✉ Surrey.

🏌 Selsdon Park Hotel, Addington Rd, Sanderstead ℰ (0181) 657 8811 GZ.

🏨 **Selsdon Park**, Addington Rd, CR2 8YA, ℰ (0181) 657 8811, Fax (0181) 651 6171, ≼, 🎣
🛥, ⅃, ⬚, 🏌, ⚓, park, ⚹, squash – 📳 ⅏ 📺 ☎ 🅿 – ⚖ 150. **🕮 🕮 ⓞ _VISA_ J**
⚹
GZ
Meals (dancing Friday and Saturday) 19.50/24.95 **st.** and a la carte ⅋ 6.25 – ⚌ 12.95
190 rm 120.00/155.00 **st.**, 4 suites – SB.

---

# EALING pp. 6 and 7.

## Ealing – ✉ W5.

🏌 West Middlesex, Greenford Rd ℰ (0181) 574 3450 BV – 🏌 Horsenden Hill, Woodland R.
ℰ (0181) 902 4555 BU.

🏨 **Jarvis Carnarvon**, Ealing Common, W5 3HN, ℰ (0181) 992 5399, Fax (0181) 992 708₂
📳, ⅏ rm, 📺 ☎ 📟 🅿 – ⚖ 200. **🕮 🕮 ⓞ _VISA_ JCB** CV
Meals 14.95 **st.** (lunch) and a la carte 19.50/30.50 **st.** – ⚌ 10.50 – 189 rm 119.00/134.00
– SB.

🏨 **Holiday Inn**, Western Av., Hanger Lane Gyratory System, W5 1HG, ℰ (0181) 233 32₀
Fax (0181) 233 3201 – 📳, ⅏ rm, 🗐 📺 ☎ & 🅿 – ⚖ 80. **🕮 🕮 ⓞ _VISA_ JCB**. ⚹ CV
Meals a la carte 15.00/29.00 **st.** ⅋ 6.00 – ⚌ 12.50 – 138 rm 140.00 **st.**

✕✕ **Maxim**, 153-155 Northfield Av., W13 9QT, ℰ (0181) 567 1719, Fax (0181) 932 7067 – ▤
**🕮 🕮 ⓞ _VISA_ JCB** BV
closed Sunday lunch and 25 to 28 December – Meals - Chinese (Peking) - 12.00/16.00
and a la carte.

✕✕ **Gitanjli - Mayfair**, 18-19 The Mall, Ealing Broadway, W5 2PJ, ℰ (0181) 810 00₀
Fax (0181) 810 0005 – ▤. **🕮 🕮 ⓞ _VISA_** CV
Meals - North Indian - a la carte 15.00/25.00 **t.**

## Hanwell – ✉ W7.

🏌 Brent Valley, Church Rd, ℰ (0181) 567 1287 BV.

🏠 **Wellmeadow Lodge**, 24 Wellmeadow Rd, W7 2AL, ℰ (0181) 567 729₉
Fax (0181) 566 3468, ⚓ – ⅏ 📺 ☎ ⚘ **🕮 🕮 _VISA_ JCB**. ⚹ BV
Meals (booking essential) (residents only) (communal dining) (dinner only) (unlicense
20.00 **t.** and a la carte – ⚌ 8.00 – 10 rm 70.00/112.00 **t.**

---

# ENFIELD pp. 8 and 9.

🏌 Lee Valley, Picketts Lock Lane, Edmonton ℰ (0181) 803 3611 GT.

## Enfield – ✉ Middx.

🏌 Whitewebbs, Beggars Hollow, Clay Hill ℰ (0181) 363 4454/2951, N : 1 m. FT.

🏨 **Royal Chace**, The Ridgeway, EN2 8AR, ℰ (0181) 366 6500, Fax (0181) 367 7191, ⅃, ⚓
⅏ 📺 ☎ 🅿 – ⚖ 270. **🕮 🕮 ⓞ _VISA_**. ⚹ ET
closed 24 to 31 December – Meals (bar lunch Monday to Saturday)/dinner 19.95 s
and a la carte – 92 rm ⚌ 89.50/184.50 **st.**

## Hadley Wood – ✉ Herts.

🏨 **West Lodge Park** ⚘, off Cockfosters Rd, EN4 0PY, ℰ (0181) 440 831
Fax (0181) 449 3698, ≼, ⚓, park – 📳 ⅏ 📺 ☎ ⚘ 🅿 – ⚖ 80. **🕮 🕮 ⓞ _VISA_**. ⚹ ET
The Cedar : Meals 22.95/25.95 **st.** ⅋ 9.00 – ⚌ 12.00 – 55 rm 95.50/255.00 **st.** – SB.

---

# GREENWICH pp. 12 and 13.

## Blackheath – ✉ SE3.

🏨 **Bardon Lodge**, 15 Stratheden Rd, SE3 7TH, ℰ (0181) 853 4051, Fax (0181) 858 7387, ⚓
– ⅏ rest, 📺 ☎ 🅿 – ⚖ 30. **🕮 🕮 ⓞ _VISA_** HV
Lamplight : Meals (dinner only) 17.50 **st.** ⅋ 4.95 – 32 rm ⚌ 70.00/90.00 **st.**

XX **Chapter Two,** 43-45 Montpelier Vale, SE8 0TJ, ℘ (0181) 333 2666 – ▤. **⑳ ㏂ ⓪ _VISA_**
ⒶⒷ JCB                                                HX  c
   Meals 19.50/23.45 t. ⅃ 8.50.

XX **One Lawn Terrace,** Lawn Terr., SE3 9LJ, ℘ (0181) 355 1110, Fax (0181) 355 0111 – ▤.
**⑳ ㏂ ⓪ _VISA_ JCB**                                       HX  c
   closed Monday lunch, 25-26 December and 1 January – **Meals** 16.50 t. (lunch) and a la carte
   20.50/28.00 t.

**Greenwich** – ✉ SE10.
   🛈 46 Greenwich Church St., SE10 9BL ℘ (0181) 858 6376.

XX **Treasure of China,** 10-11 Nelson Rd, SE10 9JB, ℘ (0181) 858 9884, Fax (0181) 293 5327
   – ▤. **⑳ ㏂ ⓪ _VISA_**                                    GV  e
   **Meals** - Chinese (Peking, Szechuan) - 11.50 t. and a la carte ⅃ 4.00.

XX **Spread Eagle,** 1-2 Stockwell St., SE10 9JN, ℘ (0181) 853 2333, Fax (0181) 305 1666 – ▤.
   **⑳ ㏂ ⓪ _VISA_**                                     GV  c
   closed 25-26 December and Bank Holidays Mondays – **Meals** 15.50 t. and a la carte ⅃ 5.00.

X **North Pole,** 131 Greenwich High Rd, SE10 8JA, ℘ (0181) 853 3020, Fax (0181) 853 3501.
   **⑳ ㏂ _VISA_ JCB**                                    GV  u
   closed Monday lunch – **Meals** 15.00 (lunch) and dinner a la carte 17.00/23.00 t.

---

**HACKNEY** p. 25.

**Dalston** – ✉ N 1.

X **Soulard,** 113 Mortimer Rd, N1 4JY, ℘ (0171) 254 1314 – **⑳ _VISA_**            PS  e
   closed Sunday, Monday, Easter, last 2 weeks August and 1 week Christmas – **Meals** - French
   - (dinner only and lunch in December) 17.95 t..

**Stoke Newington** – ✉ N16.

X **Mesclun,** 24 Stoke Newington Church St., N16 0LU, ℘ (0171) 249 5029 – **⑳ _VISA_ JCB**
   closed 25 and 26 December – **Meals** (dinner only and Sunday lunch) a la carte 14.70/
   20.15 t. ⅃ 7.95.                                        p. 8  FU  c

---

**HAMMERSMITH and FULHAM** Except where otherwise stated see pp. 26 and 27.

**Fulham** – ✉ SW6.

🏠 **La Reserve,** 422-428 Fulham Rd, SW6 1DU, ℘ (0171) 385 8561, Fax (0171) 385 7662 – ▐⃒,
   ✲ rm, 📺 ☎. **⑳ ㏂ ⓪ _VISA_**. ⚘                                 FZ  a
   **Meals** 10.00/12.00 and a la carte ⅃ 9.95 – ⚌ 4.50 – **43 rm** 79.00/110.00 t.

🏠 **London Putney Bridge Travel Inn Capital,** 3 Putney Bridge Approach, SW6 3JD,
   ℘ (0171) 471 8300, Fax (0171) 471 8315 – ▐⃒, ✲ rm, 📺 ♿. **⑳ ㏂ ⓪ _VISA_**. ⚘
   **Meals** (grill rest.) – **154 rm** 55.00 t.                             p. 14 AQ  c

XX **Blue Elephant,** 4-6 Fulham Broadway, SW6 1AA, ℘ (0171) 385 6595, Fax (0171) 386 7665
   – ▤. **⑳ ㏂ ⓪ _VISA_**                                     EZ  z
   closed Saturday lunch and 24 to 27 December – **Meals** - Thai - (booking essential) 29.00 t.
   and a la carte ⅃ 6.25.

XX **755,** 755 Fulham Rd, SW6 5UU, ℘ (0171) 371 0755, Fax (0171) 371 0695 – ▤. **⑳ ㏂ _VISA_**
   closed Sunday dinner, Monday, 2 weeks August and 1 week Christmas – **Meals** 16.00/
   22.00 t. and a la carte ⅃ 9.00.                            p. 14 BQ  n

XX **Mao Tai,** 58 New Kings Rd., Parsons Green, SW6 4UG, ℘ (0171) 731 2520 – ▤. **⑳ ㏂ ⓪**
   **_VISA_**                                           p. 14 BQ  e
   closed 25 and 26 December – **Meals** - Chinese (Szechuan) - a la carte 11.90/17.80 **st.**
   ⅃ 15.00.

**Hammersmith** – ✉ W6/W12/W14.

XX **River Café** (Ruth Rogers/Rose Gray), Thames Wharf, Rainville Rd, W6 9HA,
🎖 ℘ (0171) 381 8824, Fax (0171) 381 6217, 佘 – **⑳ ㏂ ⓪ _VISA_ JCB**        p. 11 DV  r
   closed Sunday dinner, 1 week Christmas-New Year and Bank Holidays – **Meals** - Italian -
   (booking essential) a la carte 33.50/45.00 t. ⅃ 8.50
   **Spec.** Chargrilled squid with red chilli and rocket. Wood roasted tranche of turbot, grilled
   zucchini, peppers and aubergine. "Chocolate nemesis".

XX **Tandoori Nights,** 319-321 King St., W6 9NH, ℰ (0181) 741 4328, *Fax (0181) 741 4328*
■. **◍◎** **AE** **◍** **VISA** **JCB**
p. 11 CV
*closed 25 and 26 December* – **Meals** - Indian - a la carte 12.65/23.25 **t.** ↥ 6.95.

X **Snows on the Green,** 166 Shepherd's Bush Rd, Brook Green, W6 7PP
ℰ (0171) 603 2142, *Fax (0171) 602 7553* – **◍◎** **VISA**
p. 11 DV
*closed Saturday lunch, Sunday dinner, 1 week Christmas and Bank Holiday Mondays* – **Meal**
15.50 **t.** (lunch) and a la carte 20.20/25.95 **t.** ↥ 6.95.

X **The Brackenbury,** 129-131 Brackenbury Rd, W6 0BQ, ℰ (0181) 748 0107
*Fax (0181) 741 0905,* 🍽 – **◍◎** **VISA**
p. 11 CV
*closed Saturday lunch, Sunday dinner and Bank Holidays* – **Meals** 10.50
(lunch) and a la carte 16.00/23.00 **t.** ↥ 8.50.

🍴 **Anglesea Arms,** 35 Wingate Rd, W6 0UR, ℰ (0181) 749 1291, *Fax (0181) 749 1254* – **◍◎**
**VISA**
p. 11 CV
*closed 24 to 31 December* – **Meals** (bookings not accepted) a la carte 15.95/25.70 **t.** ↥ 8.50

## Shepherd's Bush – ✉ W12/W14.

XX **Chinon,** 23 Richmond Way, W14 0AS, ℰ (0171) 602 5968, *Fax (0171) 602 4082* – ■. **◍◎** **A**
**VISA**
p. 11 DV
*closed Sunday, 25 December and 3 days Easter* – **Meals** (dinner only) 20.00 **t.** and a la carte

X **Wilsons,** 236 Blythe Rd, W14 0HJ, ℰ (0171) 603 7267 – ■. **◍◎** **VISA**
p. 11 DV
*closed Saturday lunch and Sunday dinner* – **Meals** a la carte 18.25/24.75 **t.** ↥ 5.25.

🍴 **Havelock Tavern,** 57 Masbro Rd, W14 0LS, ℰ (0171) 603 5374, *Fax (0171) 602 1163,* 🍽
*closed 29-30 August and 21-27 December* – **Meals** (bookings not accepted) a la carte
approx. 16.00 ↥ 4.50.
p. 11 DV

---

# HARINGEY pp. 8 and 9.

## Crouch End – ✉ N 8.

XX **Les Associés,** 172 Park Rd, N8 8JY, ℰ (0181) 348 8944 – **◍◎** **◍** **VISA**
EU
*closed Saturday lunch, Monday, 10 days January and 10 days August-September* – **Meals**
French - 10.50 **t.** (lunch) and dinner a la carte 18.30/22.10 **t.** ↥ 8.20.

X **Florians,** 4 Topsfield Par., Middle Lane, N8 8RP, ℰ (0181) 348 8348, 🍽 – ■. **◍**
**VISA**
EU
*closed 25-26 December and 1 January* – **Meals** - Italian - a la carte 16.50/23.95 **t.** ↥ 5.50.

---

# HARROW pp. 6 and 7.

## Central Harrow – ✉ Middx.

🅱 *Civic Centre, Station Rd, HA1 2XF ℰ (0181) 424 1103/2* BU.

🏨 **Cumberland,** 1 St. John's Rd, HA1 2EF, ℰ (0181) 863 4111, *Fax (0181) 861 5668,* 🈺 -
🍴 rm, **TV** ☎ **🅿** – 🔼 130. **◍◎** **AE** **◍** **VISA**. 🍴
BU
**Meals** 9.50/14.50 **st.** and a la carte ↥ 6.75 – 🖵 8.50 – **84 rm** 91.50/99.00 **st.** – SB.

XX **Taste of China,** 174 Station Rd, HA1 2RH, ℰ (0181) 863 2080 – ■. **◍◎** **AE** **◍** **VISA**
*closed lunch Sunday and Bank Holidays and 25-26 December* – **Meals** - Chinese - 16.80
and a la carte.
BU

XX **Trattoria Sorrentina,** 6 Manor Par., Sheepcote Rd, HA1 2JN, ℰ (0181) 427 9411
*Fax (0181) 427 9411* – ■. **◍◎** **AE** **◍** **VISA**
BU
*closed Saturday lunch and Sunday* – **Meals** - Italian - a la carte 19.25/24.75 ↥ 5.00.

## Kenton – ✉ Middx.

🏨 **Travel Inn,** Kenton Rd, HA3 8AT, ℰ (0181) 907 4069, *Fax (0181) 909 1604* – 🍴 rm, **TV** &
**🅿**. **◍◎** **AE** **◍** **VISA**. 🍴
BU
**Meals** (grill rest.) – **45 rm** 38.00 **t.**

## Pinner – ✉ Middx.

XX **Friends,** 11 High St., HA5 5PJ, ℰ (0181) 866 0286, *Fax (0181) 866 0286* – 🍴. **◍◎** **AE** **◍**
**VISA**
BU
*closed Sunday dinner and Bank Holidays* – **Meals** 16.50/21.50 **t.** and a la carte ↥ 9.50.

## Stanmore – ✉ Middx.

XX **Mr Tang's Mandarin,** 28 The Broadway, HA7 4DW, ℰ (0181) 954 0339 – ■. **◍◎** **AE** **◍**
**VISA** **JCB**
BT
**Meals** - Chinese (Peking) - 7.00/18.00 **st.** and a la carte.

**AVERING** p. 9.

**omford** – ⊠ Essex.
> 🏌 🏌 Havering, Risebridge, Risebridge Chase, Lower Bedfords Rd ℘ (01708) 741429, JT.

🏠 **Travel Inn,** Mercury Gdns., RM1 3EN, ℘ (01708) 760548, Fax (01708) 760456 – 🛗, ⁛ rm, 📺 ⚭ 🅿. 🐵 🆎 ⑩ 𝘷𝘪𝘴𝘢
Meals (grill rest.) – **40 rm** 38.00 t.
JU a

---

**ILLINGDON** pp. 6 and 10.
> 🏌 Haste Hill, The Drive, Northwood ℘ (01923) 825224 AU.

**ayes** – ⊠ Middx.

🏠 **Travel Inn,** 362 Uxbridge Rd, UB4 0HF, ℘ (0181) 573 7479, Fax (0181) 569 1204 – ⁛ rm, 📺 ⚭ 🅿. 🐵 🆎 ⑩ 𝘷𝘪𝘴𝘢. ⁒
Meals (grill rest.) – **62 rm** 38.00 t.
AV a

**eathrow Airport** – ⊠ Middx.

🏨 **Radisson Edwardian,** 140 Bath Rd, Hayes, UB3 5AW, ℘ (0181) 759 6311, Fax (0181) 759 4559, 𝘐𝘴, ⩗, ◨ – 🛗, ⁛ rm, 🔲 📺 ⚭ 🅿 – 🔬 550. 🐵 🆎 ⑩ 𝘷𝘪𝘴𝘢. ⁒
**Henleys :** Meals (closed Saturday and Sunday and Bank Holidays) 30.00 st. and a la carte 🍴 12.00 – **Brasserie :** Meals 16.50 t. (lunch) and a la carte 18.75/24.75 t. 🍴 8.00 – ⌕ 13.50 – **442 rm** 185.00/235.00 st., 17 suites.
AX e

🏨 **Crowne Plaza Heathrow London,** Stockley Rd, West Drayton, UB7 9NA, ℘ (01895) 445555, Fax (01895) 445122, 𝘐𝘴, ⩗, ◨, 🏊 – 🛗, ⁛ rm, 🔲 📺 ⚭ 🅿 – 🔬 200. 🐵 🆎 ⑩ 𝘷𝘪𝘴𝘢 𝘑𝘊𝘉
**Concha Grill :** Meals 18.50 st. and a la carte – (see also **Simply Nico Heathrow** below) – ⌕ 15.00 – **457 rm** 125.00/235.00 st., 1 suite.
AV v

🏨 **Sheraton Skyline,** Bath Rd, Hayes, UB3 5BP, ℘ (0181) 759 2535, Fax (0181) 750 9150, 𝘐𝘴, ◨ – 🛗, ⁛ rm, 🔲 📺 ⚭ ⅋ 🅿 – 🔬 500. 🐵 🆎 ⑩ 𝘷𝘪𝘴𝘢 𝘑𝘊𝘉. ⁒
**Colony Room :** Meals (dinner only) a la carte 25.25/41.75 t. 🍴 11.50 – **Le Jardin :** Meals (lunch only) a la carte 26.00/35.75 st. 🍴 11.50 – ⌕ 15.50 – **346 rm** 198.00/208.00 st., 5 suites.
AX u

🏰 **Hilton Heathrow,** Terminal 4, TW6 3AF, ℘ (0181) 759 7755, Fax (0181) 759 7579, 𝘐𝘴, ⩗, ◨ – 🛗, ⁛ rm, 🔲 📺 ⚭ ⅋ 🅿 – 🔬 240. 🐵 🆎 ⑩ 𝘷𝘪𝘴𝘢 𝘑𝘊𝘉. ⁒
**Brasserie :** Meals 22.50/24.50 st. and a la carte 🍴 12.50 – **Zen Oriental :** Meals - Chinese - 29.00/35.00 t. and a la carte 🍴 14.80 – ⌕ 15.95 – **390 rm** 205.00 st., 5 suites – SB.
AX n

🏰 **Excelsior Heathrow,** Bath Rd, West Drayton, UB7 0DU, ℘ (0181) 759 6611, Fax (0181) 759 3421, 𝘐𝘴, ⩗, ◨ – 🛗, ⁛ rm, 🔲 📺 ⚭ ⅋ 🅿 – 🔬 700. 🐵 🆎 ⑩ 𝘷𝘪𝘴𝘢 𝘑𝘊𝘉. ⁒
Meals (carving rest.) 18.95/19.95 st. and dinner a la carte 🍴 5.50 – **Wheeler's :** Meals - Seafood - (closed lunch Saturday and Sunday and Bank Holidays) a la carte 23.50/38.00 t. 🍴 6.00 – ⌕ 14.95 – **810 rm** 135.00/145.00 st., 20 suites – SB.
AX x

🏰 **Forte Crest,** Sipson Rd, West Drayton, UB7 0JU, ℘ (0181) 759 2323, Fax (0181) 897 8659 – 🛗, ⁛ rm, 🔲 📺 ⚭ ⅋ 🅿 – 🔬 100. 🐵 🆎 ⑩ 𝘷𝘪𝘴𝘢 𝘑𝘊𝘉. ⁒
Meals (closed Saturday lunch) (carving rest.) 17.50 t. 🍴 8.95 – **Sampans :** Meals - Chinese - (dinner only) 18.95 t. and a la carte 🍴 8.75 – ⌕ 11.95 – **604 rm** 155.00/165.00 st., 6 suites – SB.
AV c

🏰 **Renaissance London Heathrow,** Bath Rd, TW6 2AQ, ℘ (0181) 897 6363, Fax (0181) 897 1113, 𝘐𝘴, ⩗ – 🛗, ⁛ rm, 🔲 📺 ⚭ ⅋ 🅿 – 🔬 550. 🐵 🆎 ⑩ 𝘷𝘪𝘴𝘢 𝘑𝘊𝘉. ⁒
Meals 17.50/20.50 st. and a la carte 🍴 6.50 – ⌕ 14.50 – **644 rm** 145.00 st., 6 suites.
AX c

🏰 **Sheraton Heathrow,** Colnbrook bypass, West Drayton, UB7 0HJ, ℘ (0181) 759 2424, Fax (0181) 759 2091 – 🛗, ⁛ rm, 🔲 📺 ⚭ ⅋ 🅿 – 🔬 70. 🐵 🆎 ⑩ 𝘷𝘪𝘴𝘢 𝘑𝘊𝘉. ⁒
Meals 19.95 t. and a la carte 🍴 13.00 – ⌕ 14.95 – **425 rm** 180.00/190.00 t., 6 suites.
AVX a

🏠 **Forte Posthouse Heathrow,** Bath Rd, Hayes, UB3 5AJ, ℘ (0181) 759 2552, Fax (0181) 564 9265 – 🛗, ⁛ rm, 🔲 📺 ⚭ ⅋ 🅿 – 🔬 50. 🐵 🆎 ⑩ 𝘷𝘪𝘴𝘢 𝘑𝘊𝘉. ⁒
Meals a la carte 15.85/24.85 t. – ⌕ 11.50 – **186 rm** 119.00 st.
AX i

🍴🍴 **Simply Nico Heathrow** (at Crowne Plaza Heathrow London H.), Stockley Rd, West Drayton, UB7 9NA, ℘ (01895) 437564, Fax (01895) 437565 – 🛗 🅿. 🐵 🆎 ⑩ 𝘷𝘪𝘴𝘢
closed Saturday lunch, Sunday and 25 December – Meals 25.00 st. 🍴 8.00.
AV v

**ckenham** – ⊠ Middx.

🍴 **Roberto's,** 15 Long Lane, UB10 8AX, ℘ (01895) 632519 – 🔲. 🐵 🆎 𝘷𝘪𝘴𝘢 𝘑𝘊𝘉
closed Monday lunch, Sunday, 2 weeks August and 1 week January – Meals - Italian - a la carte 12.90/31.00 st. 🍴 8.50.
AU i

## HOUNSLOW pp. 10 and 11.

ħₑ *Wyke Green, Syon Lane, Isleworth ℘ (0181) 560 8777* BV – ħₑ *Airlinks, Southall La ℘ (0181) 561 1418* ABV – ħₑ *Hounslow Heath, Staines Rd ℘ (0181) 570 5271* BX.
🛈 *24 The Treaty Centre, Hounslow High St., TW3 1ES ℘ (0181) 572 8279.*

### Chiswick – ⊠ W4.

XX **La Dordogne,** 5 Devonshire Rd, W4 2EU, ℘ (0181) 747 1836, Fax (0181) 994 9144 – ◖
AE ⓞ VISA JCB
CV
*closed lunch Saturday and Sunday and Bank Holidays* – **Meals** - French - a la carte 18.9
30.30 t. ░ 5.10.

X **The Chiswick,** 131 Chiswick High Rd, W4 2ED, ℘ (0181) 994 6887, Fax (0181) 994 550◖
◖Ⓒ AE VISA
CV
*closed Saturday lunch, Sunday dinner and 1 week Christmas* – **Meals** a la carte 20.7⯈
26.00 t. ░ 7.80.

X **Springbok Café,** 42 Devonshire Rd, W4 2HD, ℘ (0181) 742 3149, Fax (0181) 742 85◖
◖Ⓒ VISA
CV
*closed Sunday, 25-26 December and Easter* – **Meals** - South African - (dinner only) a la car▮
17.00/23.50 t.

### Heston Service Area – ⊠ Middx.

🛏 **Travelodge** without rest., TW5 9NB, on M 4 (between junctions 2 and 3 westbou▮
carriageway) ℘ (0181) 580 2000, Fax (0181) 580 2006, Reservations (Freephone) 08▮
850950 – ⬥⬥ ⊡ ☎ ⬥ Ⓟ, ◖Ⓒ AE ⓞ VISA JCB, ⬥
ABV
145 rm 39.95/59.95 t.

---

## ISLINGTON *Except where otherwise stated see pp. 22-25.*

### Canonbury – ⊠ N1.

X **Anna's Place,** 90 Mildmay Park, N1 4PR, ℘ (0171) 249 9379
p. 8 FU
*closed Sunday, Monday, 1 week Easter and 24 December-7 January* – **Meals** - Swedish⯈
(booking essential) a la carte 17.80/26.80.

### Clerkenwell – ⊠ EC1.

XX **Maison Novelli,** 29 Clerkenwell Green, EC1R ODU, ℘ (0171) 251 660◖
Fax (0171) 490 1083 – ◖Ⓒ AE ⓞ VISA
NU
*closed Saturday lunch and Sunday* – **Meals** a la carte 29.75/41.75 t. ░ 12.65.

X **Novelli EC1,** 30 Clerkenwell Green, EC1R ODU, ℘ (0171) 251 6606, Fax (0171) 490 1083▮
◖Ⓒ AE ⓞ VISA
NU
*closed Saturday lunch and Sunday* – **Meals** a la carte 22.50/29.45 t. ░ 10.50.

### Finsbury – ⊠ WC1/EC1/EC2.

XX **Simply Nico,** 7 Goswell Rd, EC1N 7AH, ℘ (0171) 336 7677, Fax (0171) 336 7690 – ▤. ◖◖
AE ⓞ VISA JCB
OUT
*closed Saturday lunch and Sunday* – **Meals** 25.00/27.00 st. ░ 8.00.

X **Stephen Bull,** 71 St. John St., EC1M 4AN, ℘ (0171) 490 1750, Fax (0171) 490 3128 – ▤
◖Ⓒ AE ⓞ VISA
NU
*closed Saturday lunch, Sunday, Easter, 1 week Christmas and Bank Holidays* – **Mea**
a la carte approx. 21.95 t. ░ 6.00.

X **Café Lazeez City,** 88 St. John St., EC1M 4EH, ℘ (0171) 253 2224, Fax (0171) 253 2112▮
▤. ◖Ⓒ AE ⓞ VISA
OU
*closed Sunday and Bank Holidays* – **Meals** - North Indian - a la carte 15.40/23.90 t.

X **Quality Chop House,** 94 Farringdon Rd, EC1R 3EA, ℘ (0171) 837 5093 – ⬥⬥. ◖Ⓒ VISA
*closed Saturday lunch except September and 10 days Christmas* – **Meals** a la carte 18.00
26.25 t. ░ 8.25.
MT

X **Moro,** 34-36 Exmouth Market, EC1R 4QE, ℘ (0171) 833 8336, Fax (0171) 833 9338 – ▤. ◖
AE VISA
NT
*closed Saturday, Sunday, 24 December-2 January and Bank Holidays* – **Meals** a la cart▮
17.50/21.50 t.

X **St. John,** 26 St. John St., EC1M 4AY, ℘ (0171) 251 0848, Fax (0171) 251 4090 – ◖Ⓒ AE ⓞ
VISA JCB
OU
*closed Saturday lunch, Sunday and Christmas-New Year* – **Meals** a la carte 21.50/26.00 ▮
░ 11.00.

🍴 **Peasant,** 240 St. John St., EC1V 4PH, ℘ (0171) 336 7726, Fax (0171) 251 4476 – ◖Ⓒ AE VIS▮
*closed Saturday lunch, Sunday, 24 December-3 January and Bank Holidays* – **Meals** a la cart▮
16.80/22.00 st.
NT

**slington** – ⊠ *N1.*

🏛 **Stakis London Islington**, 53 Upper St., N1 0UY, ℘ (0171) 354 7700, *Fax (0171) 354 7711* – 🛗, ⇔ rm, ▤ 🖵 ☎ 🕭 – 🔬 35. 🐼 🖭 ⓪ 𝗩𝗜𝗦𝗔 𝗝𝗖𝗕. ⌘ NS s
Meals 18.65 t. (dinner) and a la carte 15.40/28.30 t. – ⌑ 12.50 – **177 rm** 160.00/210.00 st.,
6 suites.

🏛 **Jurys London Inn**, 60 Pentonville Rd, N1 9LA, ℘ (0171) 282 5500, *Fax (0171) 282 5511* –
🛗, ⇔ rm, ▤ 🖵 ☎ 🕭 – 🔬 30. 🐼 🖭 ⓪ 𝗩𝗜𝗦𝗔. ⌘ MT e
*closed 24 to 27 December* – **Meals** (carving lunch Monday to Friday)/dinner 15.00 st.
and a la carte 🍷 4.75 – ⌑ 8.00 – **229 rm** 85.00 st.

🍴🍴 **Frederick's**, Camden Passage, N1 8EG, ℘ (0171) 359 2888, *Fax (0171) 359 5173*, 🍸, 🌳
– ▤. 🐼 🖭 ⓪ 𝗩𝗜𝗦𝗔 𝗝𝗖𝗕 NS c
*closed Sunday, Christmas and Bank Holidays* – **Meals** a la carte 25.00/30.00 t. 🍷 6.95.

🍴🍴 **Lola's**, 359 Upper St., N1 0PD, ℘ (0171) 359 1932, *Fax (0171) 359 2209* – 🐼 🖭 ⓪ 𝗩𝗜𝗦𝗔
Meals a la carte 23.25/26.00 t. 🍷 7.75. NS n

🍴🍴 **White Onion**, 297 Upper St., N1 2TU, ℘ (0171) 359 3533, *Fax (0171) 359 3533* – ▤. 🐼 🖭
𝗩𝗜𝗦𝗔 NS r
*closed Monday lunch, 25 December and 1 January* – **Meals** 14.50 t. (lunch) and dinner a la carte 25.00/28.90 t. 🍷 9.50.

🍴 **Granita**, 127 Upper St., N1 1PQ, ℘ (0171) 226 3222, *Fax (0171) 226 4833* – ▤. 🐼 𝗩𝗜𝗦𝗔
*closed Tuesday lunch, Monday, 5 days Easter, 2 weeks summer and 12 days Christmas* –
Meals 13.95 t. (lunch) and dinner a la carte 22.20/25.65 🍷 8.95. NS a

🍴 **Euphorium**, 203 Upper St., N1 1RQ, ℘ (0171) 704 6909, *Fax (0171) 226 0241* – 🐼 🖭 𝗩𝗜𝗦𝗔
*closed Sunday dinner and Bank Holidays* – **Meals** 18.50 t. (lunch) and dinner a la carte
23.00/29.00 🍷 9.50. NS e

---

**KENSINGTON and CHELSEA** *(Royal Borough of).*

**Chelsea** – ⊠ *SW1/SW3/SW10* – *Except where otherwise stated see pp. 32 and 33.*

🏛🏛 **Hyatt Carlton Tower**, 2 Cadogan Pl., SW1X 9PY, ℘ (0171) 235 1234,
*Fax (0171) 235 9129*, ≤, 𝗳𝗼, ≘s, ▤, 🌳, ⌘ – 🛗, ⇔ rm, ▤ 🖵 ☎ 🕭 – 🔬 250. 🐼 🖭
⓪ 𝗩𝗜𝗦𝗔 𝗝𝗖𝗕. ⌘ FR n
**Rib Room** (℘ (0171) 824 7053) : Meals 28.00/34.00 t. and a la carte 🍷 16.00 – (see also
***Grissini*** below) – ⌑ 18.50 – **191 rm** 267.50/372.75 s., 29 suites – SB.

🏛🏛 **Conrad International London**, Chelsea Harbour, SW10 0XG, ℘ (0171) 823 3000,
*Fax (0171) 351 6525*, ≤, 𝗳𝗼, ≘s, 🌳 – 🛗, ⇔ rm, ▤ 🖵 ☎ 🕭 🕭 ⇔ – 🔬 180. 🐼 🖭 ⓪ 𝗩𝗜𝗦𝗔
𝗝𝗖𝗕. ⌘ p. 15 CQ i
**The Brasserie** : Meals 18.00 t. (lunch) and a la carte 28.50/34.00 t. – ⌑ 19.00 –, **159 suites**
160.00/1600.00.

🏛🏛 **Sheraton Park Tower**, 101 Knightsbridge, SW1X 7RN, ℘ (0171) 235 8050,
*Fax (0171) 235 8231*, ≤ – 🛗, ⇔ rm, ▤ 🖵 ☎ 🕭 ⇔ – 🔬 60. 🐼 🖭 ⓪ 𝗩𝗜𝗦𝗔. ⌘ FQ v
Meals – (see ***One-O-One*** below) – ⌑ 18.50 – **267 rm** 285.00/305.00 s., 22 suites.

🏛 **Capital**, 22-24 Basil St., SW3 1AT, ℘ (0171) 589 5171, *Fax (0171) 225 0011* – 🛗 ▤ 🖵 ☎
⇔ – 🔬 25. 🐼 🖭 ⓪ 𝗩𝗜𝗦𝗔 𝗝𝗖𝗕. ⌘ ER a
❀ Meals (booking essential) 28.00/60.00 t. and a la carte 52.50/56.00 t. 🍷 9.00 – ⌑ 16.50 –
**48 rm** 167.00/320.00 s.
**Spec.** Mozzarella and tomato pizza with basil oil. Pigeon pie. Chocolate box with hazelnuts
and cinnamon sauce.

🏛 **Cadogan**, 75 Sloane St., SW1X 9SG, ℘ (0171) 235 7141, *Fax (0171) 245 0994*, 🌳, ⌘ – 🛗,
⇔ rm, ▤ rest, 🖵 ☎ 🕭 – 🔬 40. 🐼 🖭 𝗩𝗜𝗦𝗔. ⌘ FR e
Meals *(closed Saturday lunch)* 17.90/25.50 st. 🍷 6.75 – ⌑ 15.50 – **61 rm** 150.00/230.00 st.,
4 suites – SB.

🏛 **Durley House**, 115 Sloane St., SW1X 9PJ, ℘ (0171) 235 5537, *Fax (0171) 259 6977*, « Georgian town house », 🌳, ⌘ – 🛗 🖵 ☎. 🐼 🖭 𝗩𝗜𝗦𝗔. ⌘ FS e
Meals (room service only) a la carte 20.00/31.50 t. 🍷 19.00 – ⌑ 15.00, **11 suites** 240.00/
435.00.

🏛 **Cliveden Town House**, 26 Cadogan Gdns., SW3 2RP, ℘ (0171) 730 6466,
*Fax (0171) 730 0236*, 🌳 – 🛗, ▤ rm, 🖵 ☎ 🕭. 🐼 🖭 ⓪ 𝗩𝗜𝗦𝗔 𝗝𝗖𝗕 FS c
Meals (room service only) a la carte 35.00/45.00 st. 🍷 20.00 – ⌑ 18.50 – **31 rm** 125.00/
260.00 s., 4 suites.

🏛 **Millenium Chelsea**, 17-25 Sloane St., SW1X 9NU, ℘ (0171) 235 4377,
*Fax (0171) 235 3705* – 🛗, ⇔ rm, ▤ 🖵 ☎ – 🔬 100. 🐼 🖭 ⓪ 𝗩𝗜𝗦𝗔 𝗝𝗖𝗕. ⌘ FR r
**The Restaurant** : Meals *(closed Sunday)* a la carte 23.45/36.45 t. – ⌑ 15.50 – **220 rm**
190.00/230.00 s., 4 suites.

**Franklin,** 22-28 Egerton Gdns., SW3 2DB, ℰ (0171) 584 5533, *Fax (0171) 584 544*
« Tastefully furnished Victorian town house », ☞ – 📳 ≡ 📺 ☎ �, ⓒⓞ ℀Ⓔ ⓞ 𝑉𝐼𝑆𝐴, ⌘
**Meals** (room service only) – ☲ 14.00 – **46 rm** 150.00/295.00 s., 1 suite.
DS

**Basil Street,** 8 Basil St., SW3 1AH, ℰ (0171) 581 3311, *Fax (0171) 581 3693* – 📳 📺 ☎
🅐 55. ⓒⓞ ℀Ⓔ ⓞ 𝑉𝐼𝑆𝐴 JCB.
**Meals** 16.50/19.50 **t.** and a la carte ⒜ 8.50 – ☲ 13.50 – **93 rm** 120.00/179.00 **t.**
FQ

**Chelsea Village,** Fulham Rd, SW6 1HS, ℰ (0171) 565 1400, *Fax (0171) 565 1450*, « Ad
jacent to Chelsea Football Club » – 📳, ⇄ rm, ≡ 📺 ☎ ☏ ☺ ❷ – 🅐 50. ⓒⓞ ℀Ⓔ ⓞ 𝑉𝐼𝑆
⌘
p. 26 FZ
*Kings brasserie :* **Meals** a la carte 20.70/35.50 **t.** ⒜ 14.50 – *Fishnets :* **Meals** - Seafood
a la carte 24.25/30.75 **t.** ⒜ 12.50 – *Arkles :* **Meals** - Irish - 21.00 **t.** (lunch) ar
dinner a la carte 24.50/33.25 **t.** ⒜ 6.50 – ☲ 12.95 – **160 rm** 135.00/155.00 **st.**

**Egerton House,** 17-19 Egerton Terr., SW3 2BX, ℰ (0171) 589 2412, *Fax (0171) 584 654*
« Tastefully furnished Victorian town house » – 📳 ≡ 📺 ☎ ☏, ⓒⓞ ℀Ⓔ ⓞ 𝑉𝐼𝑆𝐴. ⌘
DR
**Meals** (room service only) – ☲ 14.00 – **29 rm** 130.00/210.00 s.

**Sydney House,** 9-11 Sydney St., SW3 6PU, ℰ (0171) 376 7711, *Fax (0171) 376 423*
« Tastefully furnished Victorian town house » – 📳 📺 ☎ ☏. ⓒⓞ ℀Ⓔ ⓞ 𝑉𝐼𝑆𝐴
DT
**Meals** (room service only) – ☲ 14.10 – **21 rm** 150.00/200.00 s.

**The Sloane,** 29 Draycott Pl., SW3 2SH, ℰ (0171) 581 5757, *Fax (0171) 584 1348,* « Victo
ian town house, antiques » – 📳 ≡ 📺 ☎. ⓒⓞ ℀Ⓔ ⓞ 𝑉𝐼𝑆𝐴 JCB. ⌘
ET
**Meals** (room service only) – ☲ 12.00 – **12 rm** 140.00/225.00 s.

**The London Outpost of the Carnegie Club** without rest., 69 Cadogan Gdns., SW
2RB, ℰ (0171) 589 7333, *Fax (0171) 581 4958,* ☞ – 📳 ⇄ rm ≡ 📺 ☎. ⓒⓞ ℀Ⓔ ⓞ 𝑉𝐼𝑆𝐴. ⌘
☲ 16.75 – **11 rm** 150.00/250.00.
FS

**Eleven Cadogan Gardens,** 11 Cadogan Gdns., SW3 2RJ, ℰ (0171) 730 700C
*Fax (0171) 730 5217,* 🄵6 – 📳 📺 ☎. ⓒⓞ ℀Ⓔ ⓞ 𝑉𝐼𝑆𝐴 JCB. ⌘
FS
**Meals** (room service only) – ☲ 11.75 – **55 rm** 160.00/260.00 st., 5 suites.

**Parkes** without rest., 41 Beaufort Gdns., SW3 1PW, ℰ (0171) 581 9994
*Fax (0171) 581 1999* – 📳 ≡ 📺 ☎ ☏. ⓒⓞ ℀Ⓔ ⓞ 𝑉𝐼𝑆𝐴 JCB. ⌘
ER
☲ 5.00 – **18 rm** 130.00/180.00 s., 15 suites 210.00/265.00 s.

**Beaufort** without rest., 33 Beaufort Gdns., SW3 1PP, ℰ (0171) 584 5252
*Fax (0171) 589 2834,* « English floral watercolour collection » – 📳 ≡ 📺 ☎ ☏. ⓒⓞ ℀Ⓔ ⓞ 𝑉𝐼𝑆
JCB. ⌘
ER
**28 rm** 160.00/295.00 s.

**L'Hotel,** 28 Basil St., SW3 1AS, ℰ (0171) 589 6286, *Fax (0171) 823 7826* – 📳 📺 ☎. ⓒⓞ ℀
ⓞ 𝑉𝐼𝑆𝐴 JCB. ⌘
ER
*Le Metro :* **Meals** a la carte 15.00/19.70 **t.** – ☲ 6.50 – **12 rm** 140.00/160.00 s.

**Claverley** without rest., 13-14 Beaufort Gdns., SW3 1PS, ℰ (0171) 589 854
*Fax (0171) 584 3410* – 📳 📺 ☎. ⓒⓞ ℀Ⓔ ⓞ 𝑉𝐼𝑆𝐴 JCB. ⌘
ER
**30 rm** ☲ 85.00/215.00 st.

**Knightsbridge,** 12 Beaufort Gdns., SW3 1PT, ℰ (0171) 589 9271, *Fax (0171) 823 9692*
🄵6, ☎ – 📳 📺 ☎. ⓒⓞ ℀Ⓔ ⓞ 𝑉𝐼𝑆𝐴 JCB. ⌘
ER
**Meals** (room service only) – **44 rm** ☲ 110.00/145.00 **t.**, 6 suites.

**Gordon Ramsay,** 68-69 Royal Hospital Rd, SW3 4HP, ℰ (0171) 352 4441
❀❀❀ *Fax (0171) 352 3334* – ≡. ⓒⓞ ℀Ⓔ ⓞ 𝑉𝐼𝑆𝐴 JCB
EU
*closed Saturday, Sunday, 2 weeks August, 1 week Christmas and Bank Holidays* – **Meal**
(booking essential) 25.00/50.00 **t.** ⒜ 11.00
**Spec.** Panaché of roasted sea scallops with cauliflower purée. Bresse pigeon poached in
bouillon of ceps with chou farci. Crème brûlée with a Granny Smith jus.

**Aubergine,** 11 Park Walk, SW10 0AJ, ℰ (0171) 352 3449, *Fax (0171) 351 1770* – ≡. ⓒⓞ ℀
❀ ⓞ 𝑉𝐼𝑆𝐴
CU
*closed Saturday lunch, Sunday, 2 to 6 April and 23 December-4 January* – **Meals** (booking
essential) 23.50/39.50 **t.** ⒜ 19.00
**Spec.** Brandade of cod with roast scallops and watercress sauce. Roasted veal sweetbread.
with caramelised onion purée and a cep casserole. Millefeuille of caramelised pineappl
with coconut ice cream.

**The Canteen,** Harbour Yard, Chelsea Harbour, SW10 0XD, ℰ (0171) 351 7330
❀ *Fax (0171) 351 6189* – ≡. ⓒⓞ ℀Ⓔ ⓞ 𝑉𝐼𝑆𝐴
p. 15 CQ
*closed Saturday lunch, Sunday dinner, 24 December-4 January and Bank Holidays* – **Meals**
19.50 **t.** (lunch) and a la carte 24.45/27.40 **t.** ⒜ 7.50
**Spec.** Velouté of sweetcorn, coriander and red pepper. Lobster tempura, Asian greens
Chinese noodles and ginger dressing. Chump of lamb with casserole of lentils and
potatoes.

**Bibendum,** Michelin House, 81 Fulham Rd, SW3 6RD, ℰ (0171) 581 5817
❀ *Fax (0171) 823 7925* – ≡. ⓒⓞ ℀Ⓔ ⓞ 𝑉𝐼𝑆𝐴
DS
*closed 24-26 December* – **Meals** 28.00 **t.** (lunch) and dinner a la carte 30.00/51.00 **t.** ⒜ 7.25

XXXX **Fifth Floor** (at Harvey Nichols), Knightsbridge, SW1X 7RJ, $\mathscr{C}$ (0171) 235 5250, Fax (0171) 823 2207 – ■. 🐼 AE ① VISA JCB
FQ a
closed dinner Sunday and Bank Holidays and 24 to 26 December – **Meals** 23.50 **t.** (lunch) and dinner a la carte 29.50/37.50 **t.** 🖡 10.00.

XXXX **La Belle Epoque**, 151 Draycott Av., SW3 3AL, $\mathscr{C}$ (0171) 460 5000, Fax (0171) 460 5001 – ■. 🐼 AE ① VISA JCB
ES c
closed 25-26 December and 1 January – **La Salle : Meals** a la carte 19.00/31.45 **t.** – (see also **L'Oriental** below).

XXXX **L'Oriental** (at La Belle Epoque), 151 Draycott Av., SW3 3AL, $\mathscr{C}$ (0171) 460 5010, Fax (0171) 460 5001 – ■. 🐼 AE ① VISA JCB
ES c
closed Sunday – **Meals** - Eastern specialities - (dinner only) a la carte 29.00/35.00 **t.**

XXXX **Grissini** (at Hyatt Carlton Tower H.), Cadogan Pl., SW1X 9PY, $\mathscr{C}$ (0171) 858 7171, Fax (0171) 235 9129, $\leqslant$ – ■. 🐼 AE ① VISA JCB
FR n
closed Saturday lunch and Sunday – **Meals** - Italian - 22.50/28.50 **t.** 🖡 12.00.

XXX **Turner's**, 87-89 Walton St., SW3 2HP, $\mathscr{C}$ (0171) 584 6711, Fax (0171) 584 4441 – ■. 🐼 AE ① VISA
ES n
closed Saturday lunch, 25 and 26 December and Bank Holidays – **Meals** 15.00/29.50 **t.** and a la carte.

XXX **One-O-One** (at Sheraton Park Tower H.), William St., SW1X 7RN, $\mathscr{C}$ (0171) 290 7101, Fax (0171) 235 6196 – ■. 🐼 AE ① VISA
FQ v
**Meals** - Seafood - 25.00 **t.** (lunch) and a la carte 34.50/47.50 **t.** 🖡 10.95.

XXX **Chutney Mary**, 535 King's Rd, SW10 0SZ, $\mathscr{C}$ (0171) 351 3113, Fax (0171) 351 7694 – ■. 🐼 AE ① VISA JCB
p. 26 FZ v
closed dinner 25 December – **Meals** - Anglo-Indian - a la carte 19.00/28.25 **t.**

XX **Chavot**, 257-259 Fulham Rd, SW3 6HY, $\mathscr{C}$ (0171) 351 7823, Fax (0171) 376 4971 – ■. 🐼 AE ① VISA JCB
CU a
❀
closed Saturday lunch, Sunday and 1 week Christmas – **Meals** - French - 18.50 **t.** (lunch) and a la carte 36.00/43.00 **t.** 🖡 9.50.
**Spec.** Tarte Tatin of endives with pan-fried foie gras. Stuffed saddle of rabbit with squid Provençal, pearl barley risotto. White and dark chocolate marbré.

XX **Bluebird**, 350 King's Rd, SW3 5UU, $\mathscr{C}$ (0171) 559 1000, Fax (0171) 559 1111 – 🐧 ■. 🐼 AE ① VISA JCB
CU e
closed 25 December and lunch 31 December – **Meals** 15.75 **t.** (lunch) and a la carte 19.50/36.90 🖡 5.90.

XX **English Garden**, 10 Lincoln St., SW3 2TS, $\mathscr{C}$ (0171) 584 7272, Fax (0171) 581 2848 – ■. 🐼 AE ① VISA JCB
ET x
closed 25 and 26 December – **Meals** - English - 16.75 **t.** (lunch) and a la carte 25.50/32.50 **t.** 🖡 5.50.

XX **Benihana**, 77 King's Rd, SW3 4NX, $\mathscr{C}$ (0171) 376 7799, Fax (0171) 376 7377 – ■. 🐼 AE ① VISA JCB
EU e
closed 25 December – **Meals** - Japanese (Teppan-Yaki) - 8.50/14.00 **t.** and a la carte.

XX **Brasserie St. Quentin**, 243 Brompton Rd, SW3 2EP, $\mathscr{C}$ (0171) 589 8005, Fax (0171) 584 6064 – ■. 🐼 AE ① VISA JCB
DR a
**Meals** - French - 14.50/16.50 **t.** and a la carte 🖡 8.50.

XX **Daphne's**, 112 Draycott Av., SW3 3AE, $\mathscr{C}$ (0171) 589 4257, Fax (0171) 581 2232 – ■. 🐼 AE ① VISA
DS a
closed 24 December-3 January – **Meals** - Italian - a la carte 26.50/39.50 **t.** 🖡 14.00.

XX **Poissonnerie de l'Avenue**, 82 Sloane Av., SW3 3DZ, $\mathscr{C}$ (0171) 589 2457, Fax (0171) 581 3360 – ■. 🐼 AE ① VISA JCB
DS u
closed Sunday, 24 December-3 January and Bank Holidays – **Meals** - French Seafood - 18.50 **t.** (lunch) and a la carte 28.00/37.00 **t.** 🖡 7.00.

XX **Simply Nico**, 7 Park Walk, SW10 0AJ, $\mathscr{C}$ (0171) 349 8866, Fax (0171) 349 8867 – ■. 🐼 AE ① VISA
BU e
closed lunch Saturday and Monday, Sunday dinner, 25-26 December and Bank Holidays – **Meals** 15.50/25.00 **t.**

XX **Icon**, 21 Elystan St., SW3 3NT, $\mathscr{C}$ (0171) 589 3718, Fax (0171) 584 1789, 🌤 – 🐼 AE ① VISA JCB
DET a
closed Sunday, 24 December-4 January and Bank Holidays – **Meals** 18.00 **t.** (lunch) and a la carte 23.00/36.00 **t.** 🖡 12.50.

XX **Vama**, 438 King's Rd, SW10 0LJ, $\mathscr{C}$ (0171) 351 4118, Fax (0171) 565 8501 – 🐼 AE VISA
p. 27 GZ e
**Meals** - Indian - 10.00 **st.** (lunch) and a la carte 18.50/30.75 **st.**

XX **Caraffini**, 61-63 Lower Sloane St., SW1W 8DH, $\mathscr{C}$ (0171) 259 0235, Fax (0171) 259 0236 – ■. 🐼 AE VISA
FT a
closed Sunday, Easter Saturday and Bank Holidays – **Meals** - Italian - a la carte 18.50/28.00 **t.** 🖡 7.75.

405

XXX **The Collection**, 264 Brompton Rd, SW3 2AS, ℘ (0171) 225 1212, *Fax (0171) 225 1050*
≣. ⓶Ⓞ AE ⑩ VISA JCB
DS
*closed Sunday dinner and 25-26 December* – **Meals** 39.50 t. (dinner) and a la carte 25.00/
33.00 t. 5.75.

XX **Le Colombier**, 145 Dovehouse St., SW3 6LB, ℘ (0171) 351 1155, *Fax (0171) 351 007*
☆. ⓶Ⓞ AE VISA
DT
**Meals** - French - 15.50 t. (lunch) and a la carte 18.60/30.90 t. 5.30.

XX **Pelham Street**, 93 Pelham St., SW7 2NJ, ℘ (0171) 584 4788, *Fax (0171) 584 4796* – ≣
⓶Ⓞ AE ⑩ VISA
DS
*closed Sunday, 25 December and 1 January* – **Meals** 15.95 t. (lunch) and dinner a la carte approx. 28.00 t. 10.50.

XX **Busabong Too**, 1a Langton St., SW10 0JL, ℘ (0171) 352 7414, *Fax (0171) 352 7414* – ≣
⓶Ⓞ AE ⑩ VISA JCB
p. 26 FZ
*closed 24 to 26 December* – **Meals** - Thai - (dinner only) 22.25 t. and a la carte.

XX **Toto's**, Walton House, Walton St., SW3 2JH, ℘ (0171) 589 0075, *Fax (0171) 581 9668* – ≣
⓶Ⓞ AE ⑩ VISA JCB
ES
*closed 25 to 27 December* – **Meals** - Italian - 19.50/33.00 st. and a la carte 11.00.

XX **Red of Knightsbridge**, 8 Egerton Garden Mews, SW3 2EH, ℘ (0171) 584 7007 – ⓶Ⓞ A
⑩ VISA JCB
DR
**Meals** - Chinese - 12.50/15.50 t. and a la carte 4.50.

XX **Good Earth**, 233 Brompton Rd, SW3 2EP, ℘ (0171) 584 3658, *Fax (0171) 823 8769* – ≣
⓶Ⓞ AE ⑩ VISA JCB
DR
*closed 24 to 27 December* – **Meals** - Chinese - 12.25/19.90 st. and a la carte.

XX **Dan's**, 119 Sydney St., SW3 6NR, ℘ (0171) 352 2718, *Fax (0171) 352 3265*, ☆ – ⓶Ⓞ AE VISA
*closed Saturday lunch, Sunday and 25 December-2 January* – **Meals** a la carte 16.00 t
(lunch) and dinner a la carte 20.50/27.00 t.
DU

XX **Beit Eddine**, 8 Harriet St., SW1X 9JW, ℘ (0171) 235 3969, *Fax (0171) 245 6335* – ⓶Ⓞ AE ⑩
VISA
FQ
*closed 25 December* – **Meals** - Lebanese - a la carte approx. 25.00 t. 7.50.

X **Drones of Pont Street**, 1 Pont St., SW1X 9EJ, ℘ (0171) 259 6166, *Fax (0171) 259 617*
– ≣. ⓶Ⓞ AE ⑩ VISA
FR
*closed 24 to 26 December* – **Meals** a la carte 21.95/51.50 t. 9.00.

X **Thierry's**, 342 King's Rd, SW3 5UR, ℘ (0171) 352 3365, *Fax (0171) 352 3365* – ≣. ⓶Ⓞ A
⑩ VISA JCB
CU
*closed Christmas* – **Meals** a la carte 17.75/27.70 t. 8.95.

X **Cafe O**, 163 Draycott Av., SW3 3AJ, ℘ (0171) 584 5950, *Fax (0171) 581 8753* – ⓶Ⓞ AE VISA
*closed Sunday and 25-26 December* – **Meals** - Greek - a la carte 16.75/23.35 t.
DS

X **Kartouche**, 329-331 Fulham Rd, SW10 9QL, ℘ (0171) 823 3515, *Fax (0171) 823 3991* – ≣
⓶Ⓞ AE VISA JCB
BU
*closed 25 to 29 December* – **Meals** a la carte 14.75/21.50 t. 9.00.

X **Foundation** (at Harvey Nichols), Knightsbridge, SW1 7RJ, ℘ (0171) 201 8000
*Fax (0171) 201 8080* – ≣. ⓶Ⓞ AE ⑩ VISA JCB
FQ
*closed Sunday dinner and 25, 26 and 31 December* – **Meals** 16.50/19.50 st. and a la carte
9.00.

X **Monkey's**, 1 Cale St., Chelsea Green, SW3 3QT, ℘ (0171) 352 4711, *Fax (0171) 349 9433* –
≣. ⓶Ⓞ VISA JCB
ET
*closed Saturday, Sunday, 3 weeks August and Christmas* – **Meals** 20.00/25.00 t. 7.50.

X **T'Su**, 118 Draycott Av., SW3 3AE, ℘ (0171) 584 5522, *Fax (0171) 581 8716* – ≣. ⓶Ⓞ AE VISA
**Meals** - Japanese - a la carte 12.00/25.00 t.
DS

🏠 **Chelsea Ram**, 32 Burnaby St., SW10 0PL, ℘ (0171) 351 4008, *Fax (0171) 349 0884* – ⓶Ⓞ
VISA
p. 26 FZ
*closed Christmas* – **Meals** (bookings not accepted) a la carte 12.00/21.00 t.

🏠 **Swag and Tails**, 10-11 Fairholt St., SW7 1EG, ℘ (0171) 584 6926, *Fax (0171) 581 9935* –
⓶Ⓞ AE VISA JCB
DR
*closed Saturday, Sunday and Bank Holidays* – **Meals** a la carte 16.00/21.00 t. 9.75.

**Earl's Court** – ⌧ SW5/SW10 – *Except where otherwise stated see pp. 32 and 33.*

🏨 **Barkston Gardens**, 34-44 Barkston Gdns., SW5 0EW, ℘ (0171) 373 7851
*Fax (0171) 370 6570* – 🛗, ⇙ rm, 📺 ☎ – 🔬 100. ⓶Ⓞ AE ⑩ VISA
AT
**Meals** *(closed Sunday lunch)* 10.00 st. (dinner) and a la carte 14.00/23.00 st. 5.50 – ⌸
8.75 – **93 rm** 85.00/99.00 st.

🏠 **Henley House** without rest., 30 Barkston Gdns., SW5 0EN, ℘ (0171) 370 4111
*Fax (0171) 370 0026*, ☆ – 📺 ☎. ⓶Ⓞ AE ⑩ VISA JCB
AT
⌸ 3.40 – **20 rm** 79.00/109.00 st.

🏠 **Amsterdam** without rest., 7 and 9 Trebovir Rd, SW5 9LS, ℰ (0171) 370 2814, *Fax (0171) 244 7608*, 🌿 – 🛗 📺 ☎. 🐵 🖭 *VISA* *JCB*. ✿
p. 26 EZ c
🖵 2.75 – **20 rm** 75.00/80.00 st., 8 suites.

🏠 **Rushmore** without rest., 11 Trebovir Rd, SW5 9LS, ℰ (0171) 370 3839, *Fax (0171) 370 0274* – 📺 ☎. 🐵 🖭 *VISA* *JCB*. ✿
p. 26 EZ c
**22 rm** 🖵 69.00/85.00 st.

XX **Langan's Coq d'Or**, 254-260 Old Brompton Rd, SW5 9HR, ℰ (0171) 259 2599, *Fax (0171) 370 7735*, 🌴 – 🗐. 🐵 🖭 *VISA* *JCB*. ✿
AU e
*closed Saturday, Easter and 25-26 December* – **Meals** a la carte 22.00/27.50 t.

X **Chezmax**, 168 Ifield Rd, SW10 9AF, ℰ (0171) 835 0874, *Fax (0171) 244 0618* – 🐵 🖭 *VISA*
AU c
*closed Saturday lunch, Sunday, Monday, August and 25-26 December* – **Meals** 15.00/25.00 t. and lunch a la carte 👌 8.00.

**Kensington** – ✉ SW7/W8/W11/W14 – *Except where otherwise stated see pp. 26-29.*

🏨 **Royal Garden**, 2-24 Kensington High St., W8 4PT, ℰ (0171) 937 8000, *Fax (0171) 937 1991*, ≼, ☎ – 🗐, 🌺 rm, 🗐 📺 ☎ ✆ 🕭 🄿 – 🔬 600. 🐵 🖭 ⓪ *VISA* *JCB*. ✿
p. 32 AQ c
*The Tenth* (ℰ (0171) 361 1910) : **Meals** *(closed Saturday lunch, Sunday, 2 weeks August and Bank Holidays)* 21.00 t. (lunch) and a la carte 20.50/38.70 st. 👌 13.75 – *Park Terrace* : **Meals** 14.95 t. (lunch) and a la carte 18.15/31.20 t. 👌 13.75 – 🖵 16.50 – **385 rm** 195.00/295.00, 15 suites.

🏨 **Copthorne Tara**, Scarsdale Pl., W8 5SR, ℰ (0171) 937 7211, *Fax (0171) 937 7100* – 🗐, 🌺 rm, 🗐 📺 ☎ 🕭 🄿 – 🔬 500. 🐵 🖭 *VISA* *JCB*. ✿
FY u
*Brasserie* : **Meals** 19.00 st. and a la carte 👌 6.50 – *Jerome K. Jerome* : **Meals** *(closed Sunday, July and August)* (dinner only) a la carte 19.00/31.00 st. 👌 6.50 – 🖵 13.50 – **815 rm** 170.00/185.00 st., 10 suites – SB.

🏨 **Halcyon**, 81 Holland Park, W11 3RZ, ℰ (0171) 727 7288, *Fax (0171) 229 8516* – 🗐 🗐 📺 ☎ ✆. 🐵 🖭 ⓪ *VISA* *JCB*. ✿
EX u
**Meals** – (see *The Room* below) – 🖵 14.00 – **40 rm** 175.00/270.00 st., 3 suites – SB.

🏨 **The Milestone** without rest., 1-2 Kensington Court, W8 5DL, ℰ (0171) 917 1000, *Fax (0171) 917 1010*, 🛗, ☎ – 🗐 🗐 📺 ☎ ✆. 🐵 🖭 ⓪ *VISA*. ✿
p. 32 AQ u
🖵 15.00 – **47 rm** 220.00/270.00 st., 5 suites.

🏨 **London Kensington Hilton**, 179-199 Holland Park Av., W11 4UL, ℰ (0171) 603 3355, *Fax (0171) 602 9397* – 🗐, 🌺 rm, 🗐 📺 ☎ ✆ 🕭 🄿 – 🔬 300. 🐵 🖭 ⓪ *VISA* *JCB*. ✿
**Meals** 20.50 t. and a la carte 👌 9.50 – *Hiroko* : **Meals** - Japanese - *(closed Monday)* 15.00 t. (lunch) and a la carte 19.50/31.00 👌 7.00 – 🖵 14.95 – **400 rm** 190.00 st.
EX s

🏨 **Kensington Park Thistle**, 16-32 De Vere Gdns., W8 5AG, ℰ (0171) 937 8080, *Fax (0171) 937 7616* – 🗐, 🌺 rm, 🗐 📺 ☎ – 🔬 120. 🐵 🖭 ⓪ *VISA* *JCB*. ✿
**Meals** (buffet lunch) 16.00 st. and a la carte 👌 10.00 – 🖵 14.50 – **346 rm** 150.00/220.00 t., 6 suites – SB.
p. 32 BQ e

🏨 **Hilton National London Olympia**, 380 Kensington High St., W14 8NL, ℰ (0171) 603 3333, *Fax (0171) 603 4846*, 🛗, ☎ – 🗐, 🌺 rm, 🗐 rest, 📺 ☎ 🄿 – 🔬 450. 🐵 🖭 ⓪ *VISA* *JCB*
EY a
**Meals** a la carte 15.50/20.00 st. 👌 12.50 – 🖵 17.50 – **395 rm** 180.00/190.00 st., 10 suites – SB.

🏨 **Forte Posthouse Kensington**, Wrights Lane, W8 5SP, ℰ (0171) 937 8170, *Fax (0171) 937 8289*, 🛗, ☎, 🔍, 🌿 – 🗐, 🌺 rm, 🗐 rest, 📺 ☎ 🄿 – 🔬 180. 🐵 🖭 ⓪ *VISA* *JCB*. ✿
FY c
*Green's* : **Meals** *(closed Sunday lunch)* 17.50 t. and a la carte – *Biancone* : **Meals** - Italian - (dinner only) 17.50 t. and a la carte 👌 8.95 – 🖵 129.00 st. – SB.

🏨 **Comfort Inn Kensington**, 22-32 West Cromwell Rd, SW5 9QJ, ℰ (0171) 373 3300, *Fax (0171) 835 2040* – 🗐, 🌺 rm, 🗐 📺 ☎ – 🔬 80. 🐵 🖭 ⓪ *VISA* *JCB*. ✿
EZ n
**Meals** (bar lunch)/dinner a la carte 14.50/22.00 st. 👌 6.50 – 🖵 9.50 – **125 rm** 83.50/110.00 st.

🏠 **Holland Court** without rest., 31-33 Holland Rd, W14 8HJ, ℰ (0171) 371 1133, *Fax (0171) 602 9114*, 🌿 – 🗐 📺 ☎. 🐵 🖭 ⓪ *VISA*. ✿
EY e
**22 rm** 🖵 85.00/115.00 st.

XXX **The Room** (at Halcyon H.), 129 Holland Park Av., W11 3UT, ℰ (0171) 221 5411, *Fax (0171) 229 8516*, 🌴 – 🗐. 🐵 🖭 ⓪ *VISA* *JCB*
EX u
*closed Saturday lunch and Bank Holidays* – **Meals** 26.00/43.00 t. and a la carte 👌 12.00.

XX **Clarke's**, 124 Kensington Church St., W8 4BH, ℰ (0171) 221 9225, *Fax (0171) 229 4564* – 🗐. 🐵 🖭 *VISA*
EX c
*closed Saturday, Sunday, 2 weeks August and Christmas* – **Meals** (set menu only at dinner) 29.00/42.00 st. 👌 8.50.

XX **Launceston Place,** 1a Launceston Pl., W8 5RL, ✆ (0171) 937 6912, *Fax (0171) 938 24* – ▤. MC AE VISA p. 32 BR
*closed Saturday lunch, Sunday dinner and Bank Holidays* – **Meals** 17.50 **t.** and a la car 🍷 6.00.

XX **Belvedere in Holland Park,** Holland House, off Abbotsbury Rd, W8 6L ✆ (0171) 602 1238, *Fax (0171) 610 4382*, 🏠, « 19C orangery in park » – ▤. MC AE VISA EY
*closed Sunday dinner, 25 December and 1 January* – **Meals** 21.50 **t.** (lunch) and a la car 🍷 5.75.

XX **Arcadia,** Kensington Court, 35 Kensington High St., W8 5EB, ✆ (0171) 937 429 *Fax (0171) 937 4393* – ▤. MC AE DC VISA p. 32 AQ
*closed Saturday lunch and 25 December* – **Meals** 15.95 **t.** (lunch) and dinner a la car 16.75/24.70 **t.** 🍷 6.95.

XX **L'Escargot Doré,** 2-4 Thackeray St., W8 5ET, ✆ (0171) 937 8508, *Fax (0171) 937 8508* ▤. MC AE DC VISA JCB p. 32 AQR
*closed Sunday, last 2 weeks August, 1 week Christmas and Bank Holidays* – **Meals** 16.50 (lunch) and a la carte 27.00/34.40 **t.** 🍷 5.50.

XX **Memories of China,** 353 Kensington High St., W8 6NW, ✆ (0171) 603 695 *Fax (0171) 603 0848* – ▤. MC AE DC VISA EY
*closed Sunday lunch* – **Meals** - Chinese - (booking essential) 20.00/25.00 **t.** and a la cart 🍷 11.00.

XX **The Terrace,** 33c Holland St., W8 4LX, ✆ (0171) 937 3224, *Fax (0171) 937 3323*, 🏠 – ▤ MC AE DC VISA JCB EY
*closed Sunday dinner and 24 December-2 January* – **Meals** 14.50 **t.** (lunch) and a la car 22.50/28.50 **t.** 🍷 7.00.

XX **Phoenicia,** 11-13 Abingdon Rd, W8 6AH, ✆ (0171) 937 0120, *Fax (0171) 937 7668* – ▤ MC AE DC VISA JCB EY
*closed 24 and 25 December* – **Meals** - Lebanese - (buffet lunch) 16.80 (lunch) and a la carte 18.60/23.75 **t.** 🍷 5.80.

X **Kensington Place,** 201 Kensington Church St., W8 7LX, ✆ (0171) 727 318 *Fax (0171) 229 2025* – ▤. MC AE VISA p. 34 AZ
*closed 25 and 26 December* – **Meals** (booking essential) 14.50 **t.** (lunch) and a la cart 24.25/32.50 **t.** 🍷 5.50.

X **Novelli W8,** 122 Palace Gardens Terr., W8 4RT, ✆ (0171) 229 4024, *Fax (0171) 243 182* 🏠 – ▤. MC AE DC VISA p. 34 AZ
*closed Monday lunch* – **Meals** (booking essential) a la carte 24.50/35.00 **t.**

X **Cibo,** 3 Russell Gdns., W14 8EZ, ✆ (0171) 371 6271, *Fax (0171) 602 1371* – MC AE DC VIS JCB EY
*closed Saturday lunch, Sunday dinner and Christmas* – **Meals** - Italian - 12.50 (lunch) and a la carte 25.00/31.50 🍷 6.95.

X **Malabar,** 27 Uxbridge St., W8 7TQ, ✆ (0171) 727 8800 – MC VISA p. 34 AZ
*closed last week August and 4 days Christmas* – **Meals** - Indian - (booking essential) (buffe lunch Sunday) 17.25 **st.** and a la carte 15.80/31.40 **st.** 🍷 4.75.

X **Wódka,** 12 St. Albans Grove, W8 5PN, ✆ (0171) 937 6513, *Fax (0171) 937 8621* – MC AE VISA p. 32 AR
*closed lunch Saturday and Sunday and Bank Holidays* – **Meals** - Polish - 13.50 (lunch) and dinner a la carte 17.30/24.90 **t.**

X **Mandarin,** 197c Kensington High St., W8 6BA, ✆ (0171) 937 1551 – ▤. MC AE DC VIS JCB EY
*closed 24 to 26 December* – **Meals** - Chinese - 7.80/16.50 **t.** and a la carte 🍷 6.50.

## North Kensington – ✉ W2/W10/W11 – *Except where otherwise stated see pp. 22-25.*

**Pembridge Court,** 34 Pembridge Gdns., W2 4DX, ✆ (0171) 229 9977 *Fax (0171) 727 4982*, « Collection of antique clothing » – 🛗, ▤ rest, TV ☎. MC AE DC VISA p. 34 AZ
**Meals** (residents only) (restricted menu) (dinner only) a la carte approx. 25.00 🍷 4.95 – **20 rm** ☕ 115.00/180.00 **st.**

**Abbey Court** without rest., 20 Pembridge Gdns., W2 4DU, ✆ (0171) 221 7518 *Fax (0171) 792 0858*, « Victorian town house » – ⇹ TV ☎. MC AE DC VISA JCB. ✻ ☕ 9.50 **22 rm** 88.00/175.00 **st.** p. 34 AZ

**Portobello,** 22 Stanley Gdns., W11 2NG, ✆ (0171) 727 2777, *Fax (0171) 792 964* « Attractive town house in Victorian terrace » – 🛗 TV ☎. MC AE DC VISA EV
**Meals** a la carte 18.00/24.00 **st.** 🍷 5.95 – ☕ 5.95 – **22 rm** 110.00/225.00.

XXX ✿ **Leith's**, 92 Kensington Park Rd, W11 2PN, ℰ (0171) 229 4481, Fax (0171) 221 1246 – ▤.
**⑩⓪ AE ⓪ VISA JCB**
EV e
*closed lunch Saturday and Monday, Sunday, 2 weeks Christmas-New Year, Bank Holidays and
restricted opening in August* – Meals 24.25/35.00 **t.** and dinner a la carte 34.50/47.75 **t.**
🍷 8.00
**Spec.** Marinated scallops with avocado and clear gazpacho jelly. Noisette of roast pork,
sweetbreads, bacon and potato rösti, truffle jus. Gooseberry and candied ginger soufflé.

XXX **Chez Moi**, 1 Addison Av., Holland Park, W11 4QS, ℰ (0171) 603 8267, Fax (0171) 603 3898
– ▤. **⑩⓪ AE ⓪ VISA**
p. 26 EX n
*closed Saturday lunch, Sunday and Bank Holidays* – Meals - French - 15.00 **t.**
(lunch) and a la carte 22.25/34.25 **t.** 🍷 10.50.

XX **Pharmacy**, 150 Notting Hill Gate, W11 3QG, ℰ (0171) 221 2442, Fax (0171) 243 2345 – ▤.
**⑩⓪ AE ⓪ VISA**
p. 34 AZ a
*closed 25 December and 1 January* – Meals 15.50 **t.** (lunch) and a la carte 20.80/35.00 **t.**

XX **Orsino**, 119 Portland Rd, W11 4LN, ℰ (0171) 221 3299, Fax (0171) 229 9414 – ▤. **⑩⓪ AE**
**VISA**
p. 26 EX x
*closed 24 and 25 December* – Meals - Italian - (booking essential) 15.50 **t.**
(lunch) and a la carte 27.00/31.00 **t.** 🍷 6.00.

X **The Bali Sugar**, 33a All Saints Rd, W11 1HE, ℰ (0171) 221 4477, Fax (0171) 229 2759, 斎
– 🌸❄. **⑩⓪ AE ⓪ VISA JCB**
EU a
*closed 25-26 December and 1 January* – Meals a la carte 24.50/38.10 **t.** 🍷 5.25.

X ☺ **Woz**, 46 Golborne Rd, W10 5PR, ℰ (0181) 968 2200, Fax (0181) 968 0550 – **⑩⓪ AE VISA**
**JCB**
EU n
*closed Monday lunch, Sunday dinner, Easter Saturday, 24 to 30 December and Bank Holi-
days* – Meals (set menu only at dinner) 22.95 **t.** and lunch a la carte approx. 16.70 **t.** 🍷 6.45.

X **Alastair Little Lancaster Road**, 136a Lancaster Rd, W11 1QU, ℰ (0171) 243 2220 – **⑩⓪**
**AE VISA JCB**
EU e
*closed Sunday and Bank Holidays* – Meals 27.50 **t.** (dinner) and lunch a la carte 18.00/
22.00 **t.** 🍷 10.00.

## outh Kensington – ✉ SW5/SW7/W8 – *Except where otherwise stated see pp. 32 and 33.*

🏨 **Millenium Gloucester**, 4-18 Harrington Gdns., SW7 4LH, ℰ (0171) 373 6030,
Fax (0171) 373 0409, 🌡 – 📶, 🌸❄ rm, ▤ 🔲 ☎ 🅿 – 🔬 650. **⑩⓪ AE ⓪ VISA JCB**. 🛇 BS r
*South West 7 :* Meals (dinner only) a la carte 17.50/21.95 **t.** 🍷 8.50 – *Bugis Street Brasse-
rie :* Meals 10.75 **t.** and a la carte – � 15.00 – **602 rm** 225.00/275.00 st., 8 suites.

🏨 **Pelham**, 15 Cromwell Pl., SW7 2LA, ℰ (0171) 589 8288, Fax (0171) 584 8444, « Tastefully
furnished Victorian town house » – 📶 ▤ 🔲 ☎. **⑩⓪ AE VISA**. 🛇 CS z
**t.** *Kemps :* Meals (closed Sunday lunch and Saturday) 12.95/15.95 **t.** and a la carte
19.95/23.95 **t.** 🍷 11.00 – � 13.50 – **46 rm** 145.00/225.00 s., 2 suites.

🏨 **Blakes**, 33 Roland Gdns., SW7 3PF, ℰ (0171) 370 6701, Fax (0171) 373 0442, « Antique
oriental furnishings » – 📶, ▤ rest, 🔲 ☎ 📞 🅿. **⑩⓪ AE ⓪ VISA**. 🛇 BU n
Meals a la carte 35.50/48.00 **t.** 🍷 11.00 – � 17.00 – **46 rm** 130.00/300.00, 5 suites.

🏨 **Harrington Hall**, 5-25 Harrington Gdns., SW7 4JW, ℰ (0171) 396 9696,
Fax (0171) 396 9090, 🌡, 🚭 – 📶, 🌸❄ rm, ▤ 🔲 ☎ 📞 – 🔬 250. **⑩⓪ AE ⓪ VISA JCB**.
🛇
BT n
*Wetherby's :* Meals 20.00 **st.** and a la carte 🍷 14.00 – ⊆ 13.95 – **200 rm** 160.00/195.00 st.

🏨 **Bailey's**, 140 Gloucester Rd, SW7 4QH, ℰ (0171) 373 6000, Fax (0171) 370 3760, 🌡 – 📶,
🌸❄ rm, ▤ 🔲 ☎ 📞 – 🔬 460. **⑩⓪ AE ⓪ VISA**. 🛇 BS a
*Olives :* Meals (dinner only) a la carte 18.70/27.70 **t.** 🍷 6.50 – ⊆ 12.95 – **212 rm** 135.00/
265.00 st.

🏨 **Rembrandt**, 11 Thurloe Pl., SW7 2RS, ℰ (0171) 589 8100, Fax (0171) 225 3363, 🌡, 🚭,
🔲 – 📶, 🌸❄ rm, ▤ rest, 🔲 ☎ – 🔬 250. **⑩⓪ AE ⓪ VISA JCB**. 🛇 DS x
Meals 17.95 **st.** and a la carte 🍷 6.00 – ⊆ 11.95 – **195 rm** 165.00/220.00 st.

🏨 **Swallow International**, Cromwell Rd, SW5 0TH, ℰ (0171) 973 1000,
Fax (0171) 244 8194, 🌡, 🚭, 🔲 – 📶, 🌸❄ rm, ▤ 🔲 ☎ 📞 – 🔬 200. **⑩⓪ AE ⓪ VISA**
🛇
AS c
*closed 23 to 27 December Blayneys :* Meals (dinner only) 22.50 **st.** and a la carte – *Hunter's :* Meals 18.00 **st.** and a la carte – ⊆ 13.00 – **419 rm** 145.00/165.00 st., 2 suites.

🏨 **Jury's Kensington**, 109-113 Queen's Gate, SW7 5LR, ℰ (0171) 589 6300,
Fax (0171) 581 1492 – 📶, 🌸❄ rm, ▤ 🔲 ☎ 📞 – 🔬 80. **⑩⓪ AE ⓪ VISA**. 🛇 CT i
*closed 24 to 26 December* – Meals (bar lunch)/dinner 20.50 **st.** and a la carte 🍷 7.50 – ⊆
14.00 – **172 rm** 170.00/300.00 st.

🏨 **Regency**, 100 Queen's Gate, SW7 5AG, ℰ (0171) 370 4595, Fax (0171) 370 5555, 🚭 –
📶, 🌸❄ rm, ▤ 🔲 ☎ 📞 – 🔬 100. **⑩⓪ AE ⓪ VISA JCB**. 🛇 CT e
Meals (closed lunch Saturday and Sunday) (carving lunch) 18.50 **st.** and a la carte 🍷 6.00 –
⊆ 15.00 – **204 rm** 147.00 s., 6 suites – SB.

🏨🏨🏨 **Holiday Inn Kensington**, 100 Cromwell Rd, SW7 4ER, ℰ (0171) 373 22
Fax (0171) 373 0559, ℔, ⌗, ☞ – ∣🛗∣, ⇜ rm, 🗏 📺 ☎ ♿ – 🔏 130. ◍● ℗ 🅵 🆅🅸🆂🅰 🅹🅲🅱, ⛵
Meals *(closed lunch Saturday and Sunday)* 14.50/14.95 st. and a la carte ♦ 7.95 – � 12.5
**143 rm** 175.00/195.00 st., 19 suites.
BS

🏨🏨 **Gore**, 189 Queen's Gate, SW7 5EX, ℰ (0171) 584 6601, Fax (0171) 589 8127, « Attract
decor » – ∣🛗∣, ⇜ rm, 📺 ☎. ◍● ℗ 🅵 🆅🅸🆂🅰 🅹🅲🅱
BR
*closed 25 and 26 December* – **Bistrot 190 :** Meals (only members and residents may bo
a la carte 17.95/23.75 t. – (see also **Downstairs at One Ninety** below) – ☒ 9.50 – **54 r**
135.00/302.00 st.

🏨🏨 **John Howard**, 4 Queen's Gate, SW7 5EH, ℰ (0171) 581 3011, Fax (0171) 589 8403 –
⇜ rest, 🗏 📺 ☎. ◍● 🆅 ℗ 🅵 🆅🅸🆂🅰 ⛵
BQ
Meals *(closed Sunday)* (dinner only) 20.00 t. and a la carte ♦ 6.50 – ☒ 11.50 – **43 rm**
89.00/119.00 st., 9 suites.

🏨🏨 **Cranley**, 10-12 Bina Gdns., SW5 0LA, ℰ (0171) 373 0123, Fax (0171) 373 9497, « A
tiques » – ∣🛗∣ 🗏 📺 ☎. ◍● 🆅 ℗ 🅵 🆅🅸🆂🅰 🅹🅲🅱. ⛵
BT
Meals (room service only) – ☒ 13.95 – **33 rm** 120.00/160.00 st., 4 suites.

🏨🏨 **Number Sixteen** without rest., 16 Sumner Pl., SW7 3EG, ℰ (0171) 589 52?
Fax (0171) 584 8615, « Attractively furnished Victorian town houses », ☞ – ∣🛗∣ 📺 ☎. ◍●
℗ 🆅🅸🆂🅰. ⛵
CT
☒ 8.00 – **36 rm** 90.00/200.00 st.

🏨 **Five Sumner Place** without rest., 5 Sumner Pl., SW7 3EE, ℰ (0171) 584 758
Fax (0171) 823 9962 – ∣🛗∣ 📺 ☎. ◍● 🆅 🆅🅸🆂🅰 🅹🅲🅱. ⛵
CT
**13 rm** ☒ 88.00/150.00 st.

🏨 **Aster House** without rest., 3 Sumner Pl., SW7 3EE, ℰ (0171) 581 588
Fax (0171) 584 4925, ☞ – ⇜ 📺 ☎. ◍● 🆅🅸🆂🅰 🅹🅲🅱. ⛵
CT
**12 rm** ☒ 60.00/155.00 st.

XXX **Bombay Brasserie**, Courtfield Rd, SW7 4UH, ℰ (0171) 370 4040, Fax (0171) 835 166
« Raj-style decor, conservatory » – 🗏. ◍● 🆅 🆅🅸🆂🅰
BS
*closed 25 and 26 December* – Meals - Indian - (buffet lunch)/dinner a la carte 23.40/34.70
♦ 7.50.

XX **Hilaire**, 68 Old Brompton Rd, SW7 3LQ, ℰ (0171) 584 8993, Fax (0171) 581 2949 – 🗏. ◍
℗ 🆅🅸🆂🅰
CT
*closed Saturday lunch, Sunday, 4 days Easter, 1 week August, 10 days Christmas and Ba
Holidays* – Meals (booking essential) 23.00/36.50 t. ♦ 9.50.

XX **Downstairs at One Ninety**, (at Gore H.), 190 Queen's Gate, SW7 5E
ℰ (0171) 581 5666, Fax (0171) 581 8172 – 🗏. ◍● 🆅 ℗ 🆅🅸🆂🅰 🅹🅲🅱
BR
*closed Sunday and 25-26 December* – Meals - Seafood - (booking essential) (dinner onl
a la carte 25.20/35.90 t.

XX **Café Lazeez**, (first floor), 93-95 Old Brompton Rd, SW7 3LD, ℰ (0171) 581 999
Fax (0171) 581 8200 – 🗏. ◍● 🆅 ℗ 🆅🅸🆂🅰 🅹🅲🅱
CT
Meals - North Indian - 5.75/14.50 t. and a la carte.

XX **Delhi Brasserie**, 134 Cromwell Rd, SW7 4HA, ℰ (0171) 370 7617, Fax (0171) 244 8639
🗏. ◍● 🆅 ℗ 🆅🅸🆂🅰
AS
*closed 25 and 26 December* – Meals - Indian - 6.95/15.95 t. and a la carte.

XX **Khan's of Kensington**, 3 Harrington Rd, SW7 3ES, ℰ (0171) 581 290
Fax (0171) 581 2900 – 🗏. ◍● 🆅 ℗ 🆅🅸🆂🅰
CS
*closed 25 and 26 December* – Meals - Indian - 7.95/14.50 t. and a la carte ♦ 4.95.

XX **Cambio de Tercio**, 163 Old Brompton Rd, SW5 0LJ, ℰ (0171) 244 897
Fax (0171) 373 8817 – ◍● 🆅 🆅🅸🆂🅰
BT
Meals - Spanish - a la carte approx. 19.25 t. ♦ 6.50.

XX **Pasha**, 1 Gloucester Rd, SW7 4PP, ℰ (0171) 589 7969, Fax (0171) 581 9996 – 🗏. ◍● 🆅 ℗
🆅🅸🆂🅰
BR
*closed Sunday except September, 25 December and Bank Holidays* – Meals - Moroccan
14.50 t. (lunch) and dinner a la carte 15.25/26.25 t.

XX **Memories of India**, 18 Gloucester Rd, SW7 4RB, ℰ (0171) 589 645
Fax (0171) 584 4438 – 🗏. ◍● 🆅 ℗ 🆅🅸🆂🅰 🅹🅲🅱
BR
*closed 25 December* – Meals - Indian - 15.50 (dinner) and a la carte 12.90/17.20.

X **Star of India**, 154 Old Brompton Rd, SW5 0BE, ℰ (0171) 373 2901, Fax (0171) 373 5664
🗏. ◍● 🆅 ℗ 🆅🅸🆂🅰 🅹🅲🅱
BT
*closed 25-26 December, 1 January and Bank Holidays* – Meals - Indian - a la carte 22.00
31.50 t.

X **Bangkok**, 9 Bute St., SW7 3EY, ℰ (0171) 584 8529, Fax (0171) 823 7883 – 🗏. ◍● 🆅🅸🆂🅰
*closed Sunday, Christmas and New Year* – Meals - Thai Bistro - a la carte 15.30/29.50
♦ 7.50.
CS

**KINGSTON UPON THAMES** pp. 10 and 11.

 Home Park, Hampton Wick ℰ (0181) 977 6645, BY.

**Chessington** – ⊠ Surrey.

🏠 **Travel Inn,** Leatherhead Rd, KT9 2NE, on A 243 ℰ (01372) 744060, Fax (01372) 720889 –
❦ rm, 🆃 ♿ 🅿. 🕲 🖭 . ❦
Meals (grill rest.) – **42 rm** 38.00 t.
BZ **c**

**Kingston** – ⊠ Surrey.

🏨 **Kingston Lodge,** Kingston Hill, KT2 7NP, ℰ (0181) 541 4481, Fax (0181) 547 1013 –
❦ rm, 🍴 rest, 🆃 ♿ & 🅿 – 🕭 60. 🕲 🖭 ⓪ 🕲 🕲. ❦
Meals 12.95/14.95 t. and a la carte ♦ 7.50 – ⬜ 10.50 – **62 rm** 130.00/150.00 st. – SB.
CY **u**

🍴🍴 **Gravier's,** 9 Station Rd, Norbiton, KT2 7AA, ℰ (0181) 549 5557 – 🕲 🖭 🕲 🕲 🕲
closed Saturday lunch, Sunday, 1 week in spring, 1 week in summer, Christmas and Bank
Holidays – Meals - French Seafood - a la carte 16.95/27.30 t. ♦ 7.50.
CY **x**

🍴 **Ayudhya,** 14 Kingston Hill, KT2 7NH, ℰ (0181) 549 5984, Fax (0181) 549 5984 – 🕲 🖭 ⓪
🕲
closed Monday June-August, 25-26 December, 1 January and Bank Holidays – Meals - Thai -
a la carte 14.55/27.10 t. ♦ 6.00.
CY **z**

**LAMBETH** Except where otherwise stated see pp.12-13 and pp.28-29.

**Brixton** 🕮 ④ – ⊠ SW9.

🍴 **Le Versailles,** 20 Trinity Gdns., SW9 8DP, ℰ (0171) 326 0521, Fax (0171) 733 8701 – 🕲
🕲
closed Sunday – Meals - French - (dinner only) 10.00 t. and a la carte ♦ 5.00.
EX **a**

🍴 **Helter Skelter,** 50 Atlantic Rd, SW9 8JN, ℰ (0171) 274 8600, Fax (0171) 274 8600 – 🕲 🖭
🕲
closed Sunday – Meals (dinner only) a la carte 17.60/23.50 t.
FX **c**

**Clapham Common** – ⊠ SW4.

🏨 **Windmill on the Common,** Clapham Common South Side, SW4 9DE,
ℰ (0181) 673 4578, Fax (0181) 675 1486, ☞ – ❦ rm, 🍴 🆃 🕲 ♿ 🅿. 🕲 🖭 ⓪ 🕲 🕲.
Meals (bar lunch Monday to Saturday)/dinner 16.95 st. and a la carte ♦ 5.50 – **29 rm**
⬜ 90.00/100.00 st.
p. 15 DQ **e**

🍴 **The Grafton,** (first floor), 45 Old Town, SW4 OJL, ℰ (0171) 627 1048, Fax (0171) 627 0255
– 🕲 🖭 🕲 🕲
closed Monday and 24 December-16 January – Meals 14.50/18.50 t. and a la carte ♦ 5.20.
p. 15 DQ **a**

**Kennington** – ⊠ SE11.

🍴 **Lobster Pot,** 3 Kennington Lane, SE11 4RG, ℰ (0171) 582 5556 – 🕲 🖭 ⓪ 🕲 🕲
closed Sunday, Monday and 2 weeks Christmas-New Year – Meals - French Seafood -
15.50/22.50 st. and a la carte ♦ 8.50.
NZ **e**

**Lambeth** – ⊠ SE1.

🏨 **Novotel London Waterloo,** 113 Lambeth Rd, SE1 7LS, ℰ (0171) 793 1010,
Fax (0171) 793 0202, 🛏, �'', – 🔋, ❦ rm, 🍴 🆃 🕲 🕲 ♿ 🚲 – 🕭 40. 🕲 🖭 ⓪ 🕲.
Meals (closed lunch Saturday and Sunday) 15.95 st. and a la carte ♦ 7.00 – ⬜ 11.50 –
**185 rm** 123.00/137.00 st., 2 suites.
LYZ **a**

**Streatham** – ⊠ SW16.

🏠 **Barrow House** without rest., 45 Barrow Rd, SW16 5PE, ℰ (0181) 677 1925,
Fax (0181) 677 1925, « Victoriana », ☞ – ❦. ❦
closed 20 December-3 January – **4 rm** ⬜ 30.00/45.00 t.
EY **s**

**Waterloo** – ⊠ SE1.

Channel Tunnel : Eurostar information and reservations ℰ (0990) 186186.

🏨 **London Marriott H. County Hall,** SE1 7PB, ℰ (0171) 928 5200, Fax (0171) 928 5300,
≤, 🛏, 🚲, 🖾 – 🔋 🍴 🆃 🕲 ♿ & – 🕭 70. 🕲 🖭 ⓪ 🕲 🕲. ❦
County Hall : Meals a la carte 27.50/33.00 t. ♦ 10.50 – ⬜ 13.95 – **195 rm** 205.00/225.00,
5 suites.
LY **a**

🏠 **London County Hall Travel Inn Capital,** Belvedere Rd, SE1 7PB, ℰ (0171) 902 1600,
Fax (0171) 902 1619 – 🔋 ❦, 🍴 rest, 🆃 🕲 &. 🕲 🖭 ⓪ 🕲. ❦
Meals (grill rest.) – **312 rm** 55.00 t.
MX **u**

411

XX **People's Palace,** Level 3, The Royal Festival Hall, SE1 8XX, ℘ (0171) 928 9999, *Fax (0171) 928 2355,* ≤ Victoria Embankment and River Thames – ▤. MC AE ① VISA
**Meals** 17.00 **t.** (lunch) and a la carte 23.00/30.25 **t.** 5.75. MX e

XX **RSJ,** 13a Coin St., SE1 8YQ, ℘ (0171) 928 4554, *Fax (0171) 401 2455* – ▤. MC AE ① VISA
*closed Saturday lunch, Sunday and Christmas* – **Meals** 16.95 **t.** and a la carte. NX e

## LONDON HEATHROW AIRPORT – *see Hillingdon, London p. 59.*

## MERTON *pp. 10 and 11.*

### Morden – ✉ *Morden.*

**Travelodge,** Epsom Rd, SM4 5PH, Southwest : on A 24 ℘ (0181) 640 8227, Reservations (Freephone) 0800 850950 – ⇜ rm, TV ♿ P. MC AE ① VISA JCB. ✈ DY c
**Meals** (grill rest.) – **32 rm** 39.95/59.95 **t.**

### Wimbledon – ✉ *SW19.*

**Cannizaro House** ⑤, West Side, Wimbledon Common, SW19 4UE, ℘ (0181) 879 1464, *Fax (0181) 879 7338,* ≤, « 18C country house in Cannizaro Park », ⛆ – |♦|, ⇜ rm, TV ☎ P – 🅰 60. MC AE ① VISA JCB. ✈ DXY x
**Meals** 28.75 **t.** and a la carte 15.00 – ☕ 13.50 – **44 rm** 182.00/282.00 **t.**, 2 suites – SB.

## REDBRIDGE *pp. 8 and 9.*

*Town Hall, High Rd, IG1 1DD ℘ (0181) 478 3020 ext 2126.*

### Ilford – ✉ *Essex.*

18 *Wanstead Park Rd ℘ (0181) 554 2930,* HU – 18, 9 *Fairlop Waters, Forest Rd, Barkingside ℘ (0181) 500 9911* JT.

**Travel Inn,** Redbridge Lane East, IG4 5BG, ℘ (0181) 550 6451, *Fax (0181) 550 6214* – ⇜ rm, TV ♿ P. MC AE ① VISA. ✈ HU i
**Meals** (grill rest.) – **44 rm** 38.00 **t.**

**Travelodge,** Beehive Lane, IG4 5DR, ℘ (0181) 550 4248, Reservations (Freephone) 0800 850950 – ⇜ rm, TV ♿ P. MC AE ① VISA JCB. ✈ HU e
**Meals** (grill rest.) – **32 rm** 39.95/59.95 **t.**

### South Woodford – ✉ *Essex.*

XX **Ho-Ho,** 20 High Rd, E18 2QL, ℘ (0181) 989 1041 – ▤. MC AE ① VISA JCB HU c
*closed Saturday lunch and 25-26 December* – **Meals** - Chinese (Peking, Szechuan) - a la carte 29.50/43.20 **st.**

### Woodford – ✉ *Essex.*

9 *2 Sunset Av., Woodford Green ℘ (0181) 504 0553/4254.*
*London 13 – Brentwood 16 – Harlow 16.*

**County H. Epping Forest,** 30 Oak Hill, Woodford Green, IG8 9NY, ℘ (0181) 787 9988, *Fax (0181) 506 0941* – |♦|, ⇜ rm, ▤ rest, TV ☎ P – 🅰 150. MC AE ① VISA JCB. ✈
**Meals** 14.95 **st.** (dinner) and a la carte 15.00/24.50 **st.** 5.50 – ☕ 9.50 – **99 rm** 92.00/110.00 **st.** – SB. HT c

## RICHMOND-UPON-THAMES *pp. 10 and 11.*

### Barnes – ✉ *SW13.*

XX **Sonny's,** 94 Church Rd, SW13 0DQ, ℘ (0181) 748 0393, *Fax (0181) 748 2698* – ▤. MC AE ① VISA CX x
*closed Sunday dinner, 25 to 27 December and Bank Holidays* – **Meals** 12.00 **t.** (lunch) and a la carte 19.95/24.85 **t.** 4.75.

X **Riva,** 169 Church Rd, SW13 9HR, ℘ (0181) 748 0434, *Fax (0181) 748 0434* – MC AE ① VISA JCB CX a
*closed Saturday lunch, last 2 weeks August and 1 week Christmas* – **Meals** - Italian - a la carte 18.00/28.50 **t.** 6.95.

### East Sheen – ✉ *SW14.*

XX **Redmond's,** 170 Upper Richmond Road West, SW14 8AW, ℘ (0181) 878 1922, *Fax (0181) 878 1133* – ▤. MC VISA JCB CX v
*closed Saturday lunch and Sunday dinner* – **Meals** 21.50/24.00 **t.** 6.00.

XX **Crowther's**, 481 Upper Richmond Rd West, SW14 7PU, ℰ (0181) 876 6372, *Fax (0181) 876 6372* – ▤. **◍ℬ** *VISA* CX n
*closed Sunday, Monday, 2 weeks August and 1 week Christmas* – **Meals** (booking essential) (lunch by arrangement)/dinner 23.50 **t.** ⓖ 5.25.

## Hampton Court – ✉ Surrey.

🏯 **Carlton Mitre**, Hampton Court Rd, KT8 9BN, ℰ (0181) 979 9988, *Fax (0181) 979 9777*, ≤, 佘, « Riverside setting » – 🛗, ⇔ rm, 🔽 ☎ 🅿 – 🔬 25. **◍ℬ ⅍ ⑩** *VISA* JCB BY v
**Meals** (dinner only) 19.95 **st.** and a la carte ⓖ 6.00 – **Landings :** Meals *(closed Saturday lunch)* a la carte 11.75/17.30 **st.** ⓖ 6.00 – ⊇ 8.95 – **36 rm** 125.00/195.00 **st.**

## Hampton Hill – ✉ Middx.

X **Monsieur Max** (Renzland), 133 High St., TW12 1NJ, ℰ (0181) 979 5546, *Fax (0181) 979 3747* – ▤. **◍ℬ ⅍ ⑩** *VISA* BY a
❀ *closed Saturday lunch and 25-26 December* – **Meals** - French - 14.00/19.50 **t.** ⓖ 5.00
🍸 **Spec.** Ballottine of foie gras, haricot vert salad, nut oil dressing. Cod baked in olive oil, ratatouille, crushed herb potato. Vanilla crème brûlée.

## Hampton Wick – ✉ Surrey.

🏠 **Chase Lodge**, 10 Park Rd, KT1 4AS, ℰ (0181) 943 1862, *Fax (0181) 943 9363* – 🔽 ☎. **◍ℬ** ⅍ *VISA* JCB BY e
**Meals** 9.90/14.00 **t.** and a la carte – **13 rm** ⊇ 62.00/85.00 **t.** – SB.

## Richmond – ✉ Surrey.

🟦, 🟦 Richmond Park, Roehampton Gate ℰ (0181) 876 3205/1795 CX – 🟦 Sudbrook Park ℰ (0181) 940 1463 CX.
🅱 Old Town Hall, Whittaker Av., TW9 1TP ℰ (0181) 940 9125.

🏯 **Petersham**, Nightingale Lane, TW10 6UZ, ℰ (0181) 940 7471, *Fax (0181) 939 1098*, ≤, 帚 – 🛗 🔽 ☎ 🅿 – 🔬 50. **◍ℬ ⅍ ⑩** *VISA*. ⅍ CX c
**Meals** – *(see Nightingales below)* – **57 rm** ⊇ 130.00/170.00 **st.** – SB.

🏯 **Richmond Gate**, 158 Richmond Hill, TW10 6RP, ℰ (0181) 940 0061, *Fax (0181) 332 0354*, 🛠, ☎, 🖂, – 🛗 – ⇔ 🔽 ☎ 🅿 – 🔬 45. **◍ℬ ⅍ ⑩** *VISA*. ⅍ CX c
*Gates On The Park :* **Meals** *(closed Saturday lunch)* 19.25/26.50 **st.** and a la carte ⓖ 8.00 –
*Gates Bistro :* **Meals** *(closed Saturday and Sunday)* (dinner only) a la carte approx. 15.50 **st.** ⓖ 7.50 – **65 rm** ⊇ 129.00/152.00 **st.**, 1 suite.

🏠 **Richmond Hill**, Richmond Hill, TW10 6RW, ℰ (0181) 940 2247, *Fax (0181) 940 5424*, 🛠, ☎, 🖂 – 🛗, ⇔ rm, ▤ rest, 🔽 ☎ 🅿 – 🔬 200. **◍ℬ ⅍ ⑩** *VISA* JCB CX r
*Pembrokes :* **Meals** (dancing Saturday evening) (carving lunch Sunday) 15.00/21.50 **t.** and a la carte ⓖ 7.50 – ⊇ 10.00 – **132 rm** 110.00/155.00 **t.**, 5 suites – SB.

🏠 **Rose of York**, Petersham Rd, TW10 6UY, ℰ (0181) 948 5867, *Fax (0181) 332 6986* – 🔽 ☎ 🅿. **◍ℬ** *VISA*. ⅍ CX z
**Meals** (in bar) a la carte 12.15/20.45 **st.** – **12 rm** ⊇ 68.00/84.00 **st.**

XXX **Nightingales** (at Petersham H.), Nightingale Lane, TW10 6UZ, ℰ (0181) 940 7471, *Fax (0181) 939 1098*, ≤, 帚 – 🅿. **◍ℬ ⅍ ⑩** *VISA* CX c
**Meals** (residents only Sunday dinner) 19.50/28.00 **t.** ⓖ 10.00.

XX **Four Regions**, 102-104 Kew Rd, TW9 2PQ, ℰ (0181) 940 9044, *Fax (0181) 332 6130*, 佘 – ▤ **◍ℬ ⅍** *VISA* CX e
**Meals** - Chinese - 15.00/20.00 **t.** and a la carte ⓖ 5.00.

---

# SOUTHWARK *Except where otherwise stated see pp.12-13 and pp.28-29.*

## Bermondsey – ✉ SE1.

🏠 **London Bridge**, 8-18 London Bridge St., SE1 9SG, ℰ (0171) 855 2200, *Fax (0171) 855 2233* – 🛗, ⇔ rm, ▤ 🔽 ☎ ✆ 🖒 – 🔬 80. **◍ℬ ⅍ ⑩** *VISA* JCB. ⅍ PX a
**Meals** – *(see Simply Nico below)* – ⊇ 11.95 – **119 rm** 150.00/175.00 **st.**

XXX **Le Pont de la Tour**, 36d Shad Thames, Butlers Wharf, SE1 2YE, ℰ (0171) 403 8403, *Fax (0171) 403 0267*, ≤, 佘, « Thames-side setting » – ▤. **◍ℬ ⅍ ⑩** *VISA* JCB PX c
*closed Saturday lunch and dinner 24 December-28 December* – **Meals** 28.50 **t.** (lunch) and dinner a la carte 32.00/46.00 **t.** ⓖ 10.00.

XXX **Bengal Clipper**, Cardamom Building, Shad Thames, Butlers Wharf, SE1 2YR, ℰ (0171) 357 9001, *Fax (0171) 357 9002* – ▤. **◍ℬ ⅍ ⑩** *VISA* JCB PX e
– **Meals** - Indian - 8.75/28.00 **t.** and a la carte ⓖ 8.95.

XX **Tentazioni**, 2 Mill St., Lloyds Wharf, SE1 2BD, ℰ (0171) 237 1100, *Fax (0171) 237 1100*. **◍ℬ ⅍ ⑩** *VISA* JCB GV x
*closed Saturday lunch, Sunday, 1 week August, Christmas and Bank Holidays* – **Meals** - Italian - 26.00 **t.** (dinner) and a la carte 23.50/27.50 **t.**

413

XX **Simply Nico** (at London Bridge H.), 8-18 London Bridge St., SE1 9SG, 𝒫 (0171) 407 4536
Fax (0171) 407 4554 – ▤                                                                      PX a
**Meals** 25.00/27.00 **st.** and a la carte ▵ 8.00.

X **Blue Print Café**, Design Museum, Shad Thames, Butlers Wharf, SE1 2YD
𝒫 (0171) 378 7031, Fax (0171) 357 8810, 😄, « Thames-side setting, ≤ Tower Bridge » -
**◍⑨ ᴀᴇ ⓪ ᴠɪꜱᴀ ᴊᴄʙ**                                                                       PX u
closed Sunday dinner and Christmas – **Meals** a la carte 23.00/29.00 **t.**

X **Butlers Wharf Chop House**, 36e Shad Thames, Butlers Wharf, SE1 2YE
𝒫 (0171) 403 3403, Fax (0171) 403 3414, « Thames-side setting, ≤ Tower Bridge » – ◍⑨ ᴀᴇ
**⓪ ᴠɪꜱᴀ ᴊᴄʙ**                                                                             PX n
closed Saturday lunch, Sunday dinner, dinner 26 December and 1 to 3 January – **Meals**
22.50 **t.** (lunch) and dinner a la carte 24.75/40.25 **t.** ▵ 11.95.

X **Cantina Del Ponte**, 36c Shad Thames, Butlers Wharf, SE1 2YE, 𝒫 (0171) 403 5403,
Fax (0171) 403 0267, ≤, 😄, « Thames-side setting » – ◍⑨ ᴀᴇ ⓪ ᴠɪꜱᴀ                          PX c
closed 25 and 26 December – **Meals** - Italian-Mediterranean - a la carte 15.75/27.15 **t.**
▵ 6.50.

## Dulwich – ⊠ SE19.

XX **Belair House**, Gallery Rd, Dulwich Village, SE21 7AB, 𝒫 (0181) 299 9788
Fax (0181) 299 6793, 😄, « Georgian summer house », � – ℗. ◍⑨ ᴀᴇ ⓪ ᴠɪꜱᴀ ᴊᴄʙ
**Meals** 15.50/24.95 **t.** and dinner a la carte ▵ 10.50.                                  FX e

XX **Luigi's**, 129 Gipsy Hill, SE19 1QS, 𝒫 (0181) 670 1843, Fax (0181) 670 1396 – ▤. ◍⑨ ᴀᴇ ⓪
**ᴠɪꜱᴀ ᴊᴄʙ**                                                                              FX a
**Meals** - Italian - 14.90 **t.** (lunch) and a la carte 16.20/24.65 **t.** ▵ 5.00.

## Rotherhithe – ⊠ SE16.

🏨 **Holiday Inn at Nelson Dock**, 265 Rotherhithe St., Nelson Dock, SE16 1EJ,
𝒫 (0171) 231 1001, Fax (0171) 231 0599, ≤, 😄, « Riverside setting », ℉₆, ≊ₛ, 🔲, ⚒ – ⧉
⧺ rm, ▤ rest, ▣ ☎ ✆ & ℗ – ⚔ 350. ◍⑨ ᴀᴇ ⓪ ᴠɪꜱᴀ ᴊᴄʙ. ⚗                                        GV r
closed 22 to 29 December – **Three Crowns** : **Meals** (bar lunch)/dinner a la carte 19.85/
27.85 **t.** – **Columbia's** : **Meals** (dinner only) 15.00 **st.** ▵ 8.00 – ⚌ 10.50 – **364 rm** 121.00/
143.00 **st.**, 4 suites.

## Southwark – ⊠ SE1.

🏠 **Holiday Inn Express** without rest., 103-109 Southwark St., SE1 0JQ, 𝒫 (0171) 401 2525,
Fax (0171) 401 3322 – ⧉, ⧺ rm, ▤ rest, ▣ ☎ &. ◍⑨ ᴀᴇ ⓪ ᴠɪꜱᴀ ᴊᴄʙ. ⚗                           OX e
**90 rm** 85.00 **st.**

XXX **Oxo Tower**, (8th floor), Oxo Tower Wharf, Barge House St., SE1 9PH, 𝒫 (0171) 803 3888,
Fax (0171) 803 3838, ≤ London skyline and River Thames, 😄 – ⧉ ▤. ◍⑨ ᴀᴇ ⓪ ᴠɪꜱᴀ
**ᴊᴄʙ**                                                                                    NX a
closed Saturday lunch and 25-26 December – **Meals** 26.50 **t.** (lunch) and dinner a la carte
35.00/48.00 **t.** ▵ 22.50 – (see also below).

X **Oxo Tower Brasserie** (at Oxo Tower), (8th floor), Oxo Tower Wharf, Barge House St.,
SE1 9PH, 𝒫 (0171) 803 3888, Fax (0171) 803 3838, ≤ London skyline and River Thames, 😄
– ⧉ ▤. ◍⑨ ᴀᴇ ⓪ ᴠɪꜱᴀ ᴊᴄʙ                                                                    NX a
closed 25 and 26 December – **Meals** a la carte 19.00/32.00 **t.** ▵ 8.50.

X **Livebait**, 43 The Cut, SE1 8LF, 𝒫 (0171) 928 7211, Fax (0171) 928 2279 – ◍⑨ ᴀᴇ ⓪ ᴠɪꜱᴀ
**ᴊᴄʙ**                                                                                    NX c
closed Sunday, 25-26 December and 1 January – **Meals** - Seafood - a la carte 25.00/33.50 **t.**
▵ 8.95.

X **Sixty-Two**, 62 Southwark Bridge Rd, SE1 0AS, 𝒫 (0171) 633 0831, Fax (0171) 261 1271 –
**◍⑨ ᴀᴇ ⓪ ᴠɪꜱᴀ**                                                                           OX c
closed Saturday lunch, Sunday, 2 weeks August and Christmas-New Year – **Meals** a la carte
16.90/22.75 **t.** ▵ 7.95.

## SUTTON pp. 10 and 11.

## Carshalton – ⊠ Surrey.

XX **La Veranda**, 18-19 Beynon Rd, SM5 3RL, 𝒫 (0181) 647 4370 – ▤. ◍⑨ ᴀᴇ ⓪ ᴠɪꜱᴀ            EZ c
closed Sunday and Bank Holidays – **Meals** - Italian - a la carte 20.60/29.10 **t.** ▵ 6.90.

**Sutton** – ✉ *Surrey*.

☐₈, ☐₉ *Oak Sports Centre, Woodmansterne Rd, Carshalton ℰ (0181) 643 8363.*

🏨 **Holiday Inn**, Gibson Rd, SM1 2RF, ℰ (0181) 770 1311, Fax (0181) 770 1539, 🛁, ⛨, ☒ –
🛗 ↤, 🍽 rest, 🆃🆅 ☎ 📞 & 📞 – 🔬 180. 🆀 🆂 ⓞ 🆅🆂🆂 JCB. ※
EZ a
Meals 15.95 st. and a la carte – ⚌ 11.95 – **115 rm** 150.00/175.00 st., 1 suite.

🏠 **Thatched House**, 135-141 Cheam Rd, SM1 2BN, ℰ (0181) 642 3131,
Fax (0181) 770 0684, 🌳 – 🆅 ☎ 📞 – 🔬 50. 🆀 🆂 ⓞ 🆅🆂🆂 JCB. ※
DZ e
Meals *(closed dinner Sunday and Bank Holidays)* 10.95/15.00 t. and a la carte ⅃ 5.75 – **32 rm**
⚌ 45.50/75.00 st. – SB.

---

**TOWER HAMLETS** – *p. 8.*

**Docklands** – ✉ *E14.*

🏠 **Travelodge**, A 13 Coriander Rd, E14 2AA, ℰ (0171) 531 9705, Fax (0171) 515 9178, Reservations (Freephone) 0800 850950 – 🛗, ↤ rm, 🆅 ☎ & 📞. 🆀 🆂 ⓞ 🆅🆂🆂. ※
GV s
Meals *(cafe bar)* – **132 rm** 39.95/59.95 t.

**Canary Wharf** – ✉ *E14.*

XX **MPW**, Second Floor, Cabot Place East, E14 4QT, ℰ (0171) 513 0513, Fax (0171) 513 0551 –
🍽. 🆀 🆂 🆂🆂 🆅🆂🆂
GV a
*closed Christmas and Bank Holidays* – **Meals** 16.95 t. (dinner) and a la carte 24.00/36.00 t.

**Whitechapel** – ✉ *E1.*

XX **Cafe Spice Namaste**, 16 Prescot St., E1 8AZ, ℰ (0171) 488 9242, Fax (0171) 488 9339 –
🍽. 🆀 🆂 🆂🆂 🆅🆂🆂 JCB
GV z
*closed Saturday lunch, Sunday, 24 December-1 January and Bank Holiday Monday* – **Meals** -
Indian - a la carte 17.75/24.40 t. ⅃ 6.90.

---

**WANDSWORTH** *Except where otherwise stated see pp. 14 and 15.*

**Battersea** – ✉ *SW8/SW11.*

🏠 **Travelodge** without rest., 200 York Rd, SW11 3SA, ℰ (0171) 228 5508,
Fax (0171) 228 5508, Reservations (Freephone) 0800 850950 – 🛗 ↤ 🆅 ☎ & 📞. 🆀 🆂 ⓞ
🆅🆂🆂 JCB. ※
CQ r
**80 rm** 39.95/59.95 t.

XX **Ransome's Dock**, 35-37 Parkgate Rd, SW11 4NP, ℰ (0171) 223 1611,
Fax (0171) 924 2614, 🌳 – 🆀 🆂 ⓞ 🆅🆂🆂
p. 27 HZ c
*closed Sunday dinner, 1 week Christmas and August Bank Holiday* – **Meals** a la carte 19.95/
30.50 t. ⅃ 6.50.

XX **Cafe Spice Namaste**, 247 Lavender Hill, SW11 1JW, ℰ (0171) 738 1717,
Fax (0171) 738 1666 – 🍽 rest. 🆀 🆂 ⓞ 🆅🆂🆂 JCB
CQ e
*closed Monday to Wednesday lunch and 25-26 December* – **Meals** - Indian - 10.00 st.
(lunch) and a la carte 16.70/24.70 ⅃ 6.90.

XX **Chada**, 208-210 Battersea Park Rd, SW11 4ND, ℰ (0171) 622 2209, Fax (0171) 924 2178 –
🍽. 🆀 🆂 🆂🆂 🆅🆂🆂 JCB
CQ x
*closed Saturday lunch and Bank Holidays* – **Meals** - Thai - a la carte 16.40/31.40 st.

X **The Stepping Stone**, 123 Queenstown Rd, SW8 3RH, ℰ (0171) 622 0555,
Fax (0171) 622 4230 – 🍽. 🆀 🆂 🆂🆂 🆅🆂🆂
DQ c
*closed Saturday lunch, Sunday dinner, 5 days Christmas and Bank Holidays* – **Meals** 10.75 t.
(lunch) and a la carte 17.25/26.50 t. ⅃ 4.00.

🍴 **Duke of Cambridge**, 228 Battersea Bridge Rd, SW11 3AA, ℰ (0171) 223 5662,
Fax (0171) 801 9684, 🌳 – 🆀 🆂 🆅🆂🆂
CQ a
Meals a la carte 11.40/20.40 t. ⅃ 7.50.

**Putney** – ✉ *SW15.*

XX **Putney Bridge**, Lower Richmond Rd, SW15 1LB, ℰ (0181) 780 1811,
Fax (0181) 780 1211, ≤, « Riverside setting » – 🆀 🆂 🆂🆂 ⓞ 🆅🆂🆂 JCB
AQ u
Meals 17.50 t. (lunch) and a la carte 18.30/34.00 t. ⅃ 5.50.

XX **Royal China**, 3 Chelverton Rd, SW15 1RN, ℰ (0181) 788 0907 – 🍽. 🆂🆂 ⓞ
AQ a
*closed 24 to 26 December* – **Meals** - Chinese - 20.00/26.00 t. and a la carte.

XX **The Phoenix**, Pentlow St., SW15 1LY, ℰ (0181) 780 3131, Fax (0181) 780 1114 – 🍽. 🆀 🆂 🆂🆂
ⓞ 🆅🆂🆂
AQ s
*closed Saturday lunch September-May and Bank Holidays* – **Meals** 12.00 t.
(lunch) and a la carte 18.25/26.00 t.

Ⅹ **Del Buongustaio**, 283 Putney Bridge Rd, SW15 2PT, ☏ (0181) 780 9361, Fax (0181) 789 9659 – ▤. **O9** **AE** **VISA**
AQ e
*closed lunch Saturday and Sunday June-September and Christmas-New Year* – **Meals** Italian - a la carte 18.50/21.40 t. ▯ 7.50.

Ⅹ **Enoteca Turi**, 28 Putney High St., SW15 1SQ, ☏ (0181) 785 4449, Fax (0181) 785 4449 – **O9** **AE** **O** **VISA**
AQ r
*closed Saturday lunch, Sunday and 25 to 30 December* – **Meals** - Italian - a la carte 21.25/ 26.15 t. ▯ 4.75.

**Tooting** – ✉ SW17.

Ⅹ **Oh Boy**, 843 Garratt Lane, SW17 0PG, ☏ (0181) 947 9760, Fax (0181) 879 7867 – ▤. **O9** **AE** **O** **VISA** **JCB**
CR c
**Meals** - Thai - (dinner only) 22.00 t. and a la carte ▯ 4.50.

**Wandsworth** – ✉ SW12/SW17/SW18.

ⅩⅩ **Tabaq**, 47 Balham Hill, SW12 9DR, ☏ (0181) 673 7820, Fax (0181) 673 2701 – ▤. **O9** **AE** **O** **VISA** **JCB**
DR v
*closed Sunday and 25 December* – **Meals** - Indian - a la carte 18.90/29.95 t. ▯ 4.75.

Ⅹ **Chez Bruce** (Poole), 2 Bellevue Rd, SW17 7EG, ☏ (0181) 672 0114, Fax (0181) 767 6648 – ✿ ▤. **O9** **AE** **O** **VISA**
CR e
*closed Sunday dinner, 24 to 30 December and Bank Holidays* – **Meals** 18.00/25.00 t. ▯ 7.00
**Spec.** Boudin noir with caramelised apple and grain mustard sauce. Assiette of rabbit with ceps, Puy lentils and red wine. Crème brûlée.

Ⅹ **Bombay Bicycle Club**, 95 Nightingale Lane, SW12 8NX, ☏ (0181) 673 6217, Fax (0181) 673 9100 – **O9** **AE** **O** **VISA**
DR c
*closed Sunday and Christmas* – **Meals** - Indian - (dinner only) a la carte 20.50/26.00 t. ▯ 7.50

---

**WESTMINSTER (City of).**

**Bayswater and Maida Vale** – ✉ W2/W9 – *Except where otherwise stated see pp. 34 and 35.*

🏨🏨 **Royal Lancaster**, Lancaster Terr., W2 2TY, ☏ (0171) 262 6737, Fax (0171) 724 3191, ≤ – ▣, ≪ rm, ▤ ⁞▩ ☎ ♦ ℗ – ▴ 1400. **O9** **AE** **O** **VISA** **JCB**. ❀
DZ e
*Park :* **Meals** *(closed Saturday lunch and Bank Holidays)* 23.50 st. and a la carte – *Pavement Cafe :* **Meals** 13.50 st. (lunch) and a la carte 17.30/24.30 st. ▯ 6.00 – (see also *Nipa* below) – ☲ 15.00 – **396 rm** 215.00/290.00, 20 suites.

🏨🏨 **Stakis Metropole**, Edgware Rd, W2 1JU, ☏ (0171) 402 4141, Fax (0171) 724 8866, ≤, ⅙ ⇐, ▥ – ▣, ≪ rm, ▤ ⁞▩ ☎ ♦ ℗ – **O9** **VISA**. ❀
p. 23 GU c
**Meals** (buffet rest.) 21.95 t. – (see also *Aspects* below) – ☲ 16.50 – **723 rm** 185.00/ 250.00 st., 26 suites – SB.

🏨🏨 **The Hempel** ⅋, Hempel Garden Sq., 31-35 Craven Hill Gdns., W2 3EA, ☏ (0171) 298 9000, Fax (0171) 402 4666, « Minimalist », ☞ – ▣ ▤ ⁞▩ ☎ ♦ ℅ ℗ – ▴ 40. **O9** **AE** **O** **VISA** **JCB**. ❀
CZ a
*I-Thai :* **Meals** - Thai-Italian - a la carte 30.45/52.75 t. ▯ 16.00 – ☲ 17.00 – **41 rm** 220.00/ 255.00 s., 6 suites.

🏨🏨 **Thistle Whites**, Bayswater Rd, 90-92 Lancaster Gate, W2 3NR, ☏ (0171) 262 2711, Fax (0171) 262 2147 – ▣, ≪ rm, ▤ ⁞▩ ☎ ℗ – ▴ 30. **O9** **AE** **O** **VISA** **JCB**. ❀
CZ v
**Meals** *(closed lunch Saturday and Bank Holidays)* 18.50/22.00 t. and a la carte ▯ 8.60 – ☲ 14.50 – **52 rm** 195.00/245.00 st., 2 suites – SB.

🏨🏨 **Stakis Hyde Park**, 129 Bayswater Rd, W2 4RJ, ☏ (0171) 221 2217, Fax (0171) 229 0557 – ▣, ≪ rm, ▤ rest, ⁞▩ ☎ ♦ – ▴ 40. **O9** **AE** **O** **VISA** **JCB**. ❀
BZ c
**Meals** (bar lunch Saturday and Sunday) 15.95 t. and a la carte – ☲ 10.95 – **128 rm** 145.00/ 205.00 st., 1 suite – SB.

🏨 **Jarvis London Embassy**, 150 Bayswater Rd, W2 4RT, ☏ (0171) 229 1212, Fax (0171) 229 2623 – ▣, ≪ rm, ▤ rest, ⁞▩ ☎ ♦ ℗ – ▴ 100. **O9** **AE** **O** **VISA**
BZ c
**Meals** (carving rest.) 15.95 st. and a la carte ▯ 7.00 – ☲ 9.50 – **212 rm** 135.00/155.00 st., 1 suite.

🏨 **Mornington** without rest., 12 Lancaster Gate, W2 3LG, ☏ (0171) 262 7361, Fax (0171) 706 1028 – ▣, ≪ rm, ⁞▩ ☎. **O9** **AE** **O** **VISA** **JCB**. ❀
DZ s
**66 rm** ☲ 105.00/170.00.

🏨 **Commodore**, 50 Lancaster Gate, W2 3NA, ☏ (0171) 402 5291, Fax (0171) 262 1088 – ▣, ≪ rm, ⁞▩ ☎. **O9** **AE** **O** **VISA** **JCB**. ❀
CZ r
**Meals** - Spanish - *(closed 25 December)* 15.00/20.00 st. and a la carte ▯ 6.50 – ☲ 7.00 – **90 rm** 85.00/110.00 st.

🏠 **Miller's** without rest., 111A Westbourne Grove, W2 4UW, ℘ (0171) 243 1024, Fax (0171) 243 1064, « Antique furnishings » – 📺 ☎. 🕼 AE VISA JCB. 🎇 AZ a
7 rm ⌑ 115.00/130.00 s. – SB.

🏠 **Byron** without rest., 36-38 Queensborough Terr., W2 3SH, ℘ (0171) 243 0987, Fax (0171) 792 1957 – 📳 ▤ 📺 ☎. 🕼 AE ① VISA JCB. 🎇 CZ z
44 rm ⌑ 75.50/105.00, 1 suite.

🏠 **Delmere**, 130 Sussex Gdns., W2 1UB, ℘ (0171) 706 3344, Fax (0171) 262 1863 – 📳 📺 ☎. 🕼 AE VISA JCB. 🎇 DZ v
Meals (dinner only) 12.90 t. ⫕ 8.75 – ⌑ 6.00 – **38 rm** 78.00/98.00 st.

🏠 **Gresham** without rest., 116 Sussex Gdns., W2 1UA, ℘ (0171) 402 2920, Fax (0171) 402 3137 – 📳 📺 ☎. 🕼 AE ① VISA JCB. 🎇 DZ a
⌑ 5.00 – **57 rm** 60.00/85.00 st.

🏠 **Norfolk Plaza** without rest., 29-33 Norfolk Sq., W2 1RX, ℘ (0171) 723 0792, Fax (0171) 224 8770 – 📳 📺 ☎. 🕼 AE ① VISA JCB. 🎇 DZ x
81 rm ⌑ 98.00/118.00 st., 6 suites.

🏠 **Comfort Inn** without rest., 18-19 Craven Hill Gdns., W2 3EE, ℘ (0171) 262 6644, Fax (0171) 260 0673 – 📳 🎇 📺 ☎. 🕼 AE ① VISA. 🎇 CZ e
⌑ 4.50 – **60 rm** 73.00/94.00 st.

XXX **Aspects** (at Stakis London Metropole H.), Edgware Rd, W2 1JU, ℘ (0171) 402 4141, Fax (0171) 724 8866, ≤ London – ▤. 🕼 AE ① VISA p. 23 GU c
closed Saturday lunch and Sunday – Meals 24.15/33.00 t. and a la carte ⫕ 10.50.

XX **Nipa** (at Royal Lancaster H.), Lancaster Terr., W2 2TY, ℘ (0171) 262 6737, Fax (0171) 724 3191 – ▤ 🅿. 🕼 AE ① VISA JCB DZ e
closed Saturday lunch and Sunday – Meals - Thai - 26.00 st..

XX **Al San Vincenzo**, 30 Connaught St., W2 2AE, ℘ (0171) 262 9623 – 🕼 VISA EZ o
closed Saturday lunch, Sunday and 1 week Christmas – Meals - Italian - (booking essential) a la carte 22.50/32.00 t. ⫕ 8.00.

XX **Poons**, Unit 205, Whiteleys, Queensway, W2 4YN, ℘ (0171) 792 2884 – ▤. 🕼 AE ① VISA JCB BZ x
closed 25 and 26 December – Meals - Chinese - 15.00/25.00 t. and a la carte ⫕ 13.00.

XX **Jason's**, Blomfield Rd, Little Venice, W9 2PD, ℘ (0171) 286 6752, Fax (0171) 266 4332, 🎇, « Canalside setting » – 🕼 AE ① VISA JCB p. 22 FU c
closed Sunday dinner, 25-26 December and 1 January – Meals - Seafood - a la carte 28.75/39.85 t. ⫕ 4.95.

XX **Royal China**, 13 Queensway, W2 4QJ, ℘ (0171) 221 2535, Fax (0171) 792 5752 – ▤. 🕼 AE ① VISA BZ e
closed 25-26 December – Meals - Chinese - 23.00 t. (dinner) and a la carte 20.50/80.50 t.

X **Assaggi**, 39 Chepstow Pl., W2 4TS, ℘ (0171) 792 5501 – 🕼 AE ① VISA JCB AZ c
closed Sunday, 2 weeks Christmas and Bank Holidays – Meals - Italian - 35.00 t. and a la carte.

X **L'Accento**, 16 Garway Rd, W2 4NH, ℘ (0171) 243 2201, Fax (0171) 243 2201, 🎇 – 🕼 AE VISA JCB BZ a
Meals - Italian - 15.50 t. and a la carte 20.50/25.00 t. ⫕ 8.00.

X **Green Olive**, 5 Warwick Pl., W9 2PX, ℘ (0171) 289 2469, Fax (0171) 289 4178 – 🕼 AE VISA p. 22 FU a
closed Monday to Friday lunch, 24 to 27 December and Bank Holidays – Meals - Italian - 23.50 t. (dinner) and a la carte 16.50/22.00 t. ⫕ 9.00.

## Belgravia – ✉ SW1 – Except where otherwise stated see pp. 32 and 33.

🏨 **The Lanesborough**, Hyde Park Corner, SW1X 7TA, ℘ (0171) 259 5599, Fax (0171) 259 5606, ℔ – 📳, 🎇 rm, ▤ 📺 ☎ 📞 & 🅿 – 🔏 90. 🕼 AE ① VISA JCB
**The Conservatory :** Meals 24.50/29.50 st. and a la carte ⫕ 8.75 – ⌑ 17.00 – **86 rm** 275.00/ 320.00 s., 9 suites. p. 27 IY a

🏨 **The Berkeley**, Wilton Pl., SW1X 7RL, ℘ (0171) 235 6000, Fax (0171) 235 4330, ℔, ⌔, ▨ – 📳, 🎇 rm, ▤ 📺 ☎ 📞 ⟷ – 🔏 220. 🕼 AE ① VISA JCB. 🎇 FQ e
Meals – (see **La Tante Claire** and **Vong** below) – ⌑ 19.50 – **132 rm** 255.00/465.00 s., 26 suites.

🏨 **The Halkin**, 5 Halkin St., SW1X 7DJ, ℘ (0171) 333 1000, Fax (0171) 333 1100, « Contemporary interior design » – 📳, 🎇 rm, ▤ 📺 ☎ 🅿 – 🔏 25. 🕼 AE ① VISA JCB. 🎇
😊 **Stefano Cavallini Restaurant at The Halkin** : Meals - Italian - (closed lunch Saturday and Sunday and 25-26 December) (booking essential) 25.00 (lunch) and a la carte 42.00/55.00 st. ⫕ 9.50 – ⌑ 16.00 – **36 rm** 255.00/325.00, 5 suites p. 34 AV a
Spec. Stuffed gnocchi with artichoke, white wine and ginger sauce. Mashed cod with potatoes and olive oil, roasted quail, broccoli sauce. Partridge with pomegranate, turnip confit and celeriac purée.

417

**Sheraton Belgravia,** 20 Chesham Pl., SW1X 8HQ, ℰ (0171) 235 604◄
*Fax (0171) 259 6243* – |♦|, ⇔ rm, ▤ 🔟 ☎ ℃ ⊕ 🅿 – 🕍 50. 🐠 🆎 ⓪ 🎫 🇯🇨🇧. ⋘    FR
***Chesham's :*** Meals *(closed Sunday and Bank Holidays)(dinner only)* 30.00 **t.** and a la carte
⧦ 17.00 – **82 rm** 260.00/360.00 **s.**, 7 suites.

**Lowndes,** 21 Lowndes St., SW1X 9ES, ℰ (0171) 823 1234, *Fax (0171) 235 1154* – |♦
⇔ rm, ▤ 🔟 ☎ ℃ ⊕ – 🕍 25. 🐠 🆎 ⓪ 🎫 🇯🇨🇧. ⋘    FR
***Brasserie 21 :*** Meals 17.00 **st.** and a la carte – ⧦ 14.50 – **77 rm** 235.00/245.00 **s.**, 1 suite.

**Diplomat** without rest., 2 Chesham St., SW1X 8DT, ℰ (0171) 235 154◄
*Fax (0171) 259 6153* – |♦| ☎. 🐠 🆎 ⓪ 🎫 🇯🇨🇧. ⋘    FR
**26 rm** ⧦ 90.00/155.00 **t.**

**La Tante Claire** (Koffmann) (at The Berkeley H.), Wilton Pl., SW1X 7RL, ℰ (0171) 823 200?
❀❀ *Fax (0171) 823 2001* – ▤. 🐠 🆎 ⓪ 🎫    FQ
*closed Saturday lunch, Sunday and Christmas-1 January* – Meals - French - *(bookin*
*essential)* 28.00 **t.** (lunch) and a la carte 51.50/77.00 **t.** ⬩ 12.00
**Spec.** Coquille St.Jacques à l'encre. Pied de cochon farci aux morilles. Soufflé aux pistache

**Zafferano** (Locatelli), 15 Lowndes St., SW1X 9EY, ℰ (0171) 235 5800, *Fax (0171) 235 197*
❀ – ▤. 🐠 🆎 🎫 🇯🇨🇧    FR
*closed Sunday, 2 weeks August, 2 weeks Christmas and Bank Holidays* – Meals - Italian
20.50/30.50 **t.** ⬩ 9.50
**Spec.** Tortelli ai gamberi. Filetto d'agnello primaverile alla griglia con peperonata. Tiramisu

**Vong** (at The Berkeley H.), Wilton Pl., SW1X 7RL, ℰ (0171) 235 1010, *Fax (0171) 235 1011*
▤. 🐠 🆎 ⓪ 🎫 🇯🇨🇧    FQ
Meals - French-Thai - 20.00 **t.** (lunch) and a la carte 23.75/45.00 **t.** ⬩ 11.50.

**Al Bustan,** 27 Motcomb St., SW1X 8JU, ℰ (0171) 235 8277, *Fax (0171) 235 1668* – ▤. 🐠
🆎 ⓪ 🎫    FR
Meals - Lebanese - 13.00 **t.** (lunch) and a la carte 18.50/23.50 ⬩ 6.50.

## Hyde Park and Knightsbridge – ✉ *SW1/SW7* – pp. 32 and 33.

**Mandarin Oriental Hyde Park,** 66 Knightsbridge, SW1X 7LA, ℰ (0171) 235 2000
*Fax (0171) 235 4552*, ⩽, 🛁 – |♦|, ⇔ rm, ▤ 🔟 ☎ ℃ ⊕ – 🕍 250. 🐠 🆎 ⓪ 🎫 🇯🇨🇧. ⋘
***The Park :*** Meals 23.50/27.00 **t.** and a la carte ⬩ 17.50 – ⧦ 18.95 – **179 rm** 260.00
290.00 **s.**, 19 suites.    FQ

**Knightsbridge Green** without rest., 159 Knightsbridge, SW1X 7PD, ℰ (0171) 584 6274
*Fax (0171) 225 1635* – |♦| ▤ 🔟 ☎ ℃. 🐠 🆎 ⓪ 🎫. ⋘    EQ
*closed 24 to 26 December* – ⧦ 9.50 – **16 rm** 105.00/140.00 **st.**, 12 suites 165.00 **st.**

**Mr. Chow,** 151 Knightsbridge, SW1X 7PA, ℰ (0171) 589 7347, *Fax (0171) 584 5780* – ▤
🐠 🆎 ⓪ 🎫 🇯🇨🇧    EQ
*closed 24 to 26 December and 1 January* – Meals - Chinese - 9.50 **t.** (lunch) and a la carte
30.00/35.00 **t.**

## Mayfair – ✉ *W1* – pp. 30 and 31.

**Dorchester,** Park Lane, W1A 2HJ, ℰ (0171) 629 8888, *Fax (0171) 409 0114*, 🛁, ⇔ –
⇔ rm, ▤ 🔟 ☎ ℃ ⊛ ⇔ – 🕍 550. 🐠 🆎 ⓪ 🎫 🇯🇨🇧. ⋘    BN
Meals – (see ***The Oriental*** and ***Grill Room*** below) – ⧦ 20.50 – **197 rm** 255.00/315.00 **s.**
47 suites.

**Claridge's,** Brook St., W1A 2JQ, ℰ (0171) 629 8860, *Fax (0171) 499 2210*, 🛁 – |♦|, ⇔ rm
▤ 🔟 ☎ ℃ ℃ – 🕍 200. 🐠 🆎 ⓪ 🎫 🇯🇨🇧. ⋘    BL
***Restaurant :*** Meals 29.50/39.00 **st.** and a la carte 46.00/64.00 **st.** ⬩ 9.50 – ⧦ 18.50 –
**137 rm** 265.00/375.00 **s.**, 60 suites.

**Four Seasons,** Hamilton Pl., Park Lane, W1A 1AZ, ℰ (0171) 499 0888
*Fax (0171) 493 1895*, 🛁 – |♦|, ⇔ rm, ▤ 🔟 ☎ ℃ ⇔ – 🕍 500. 🐠 🆎 ⓪ 🎫 🇯🇨🇧. ⋘
***Lanes :*** Meals 32.00/30.50 **st.** and a la carte ⬩ 18.00 – ⧦ 18.75 – **185 rm** 260.00/315.00 **s.**
35 suites.    BP

**Le Meridien Piccadilly,** 21 Piccadilly, W1V 0BH, ℰ (0171) 734 8000
*Fax (0171) 437 3574*, 🛁, ⇔, ☒, squash – |♦|, ⇔ rm, ▤ 🔟 ☎ ℃ – 🕍 250. 🐠 🆎 ⓪ 🎫
🇯🇨🇧. ⋘    EM
***Terrace Garden :*** Meals 21.50 **t.** and a la carte ⬩ 10.50 – (see also ***The Oak Room Marc***
***Pierre White*** below) – ⧦ 17.50 – **248 rm** 325.00, 18 suites – SB.

**Grosvenor House,** Park Lane, W1A 3AA, ℰ (0171) 499 6363, *Fax (0171) 493 3341*, 🛁
⇔, ☒ – |♦|, ⇔ rm, ▤ 🔟 ☎ ℃ ⇔ – 🕍 1500. 🐠 🆎 ⓪ 🎫 🇯🇨🇧. ⋘    AM
***Café Nico :*** Meals *(closed Monday)* 29.50 **t.** – ***The Italian Restaurant :*** Meals - Italian
*(closed Saturday, Sunday, Easter, 2 weeks August and Christmas* a la carte 31.50/38.50 **t.** -
(see also ***Chez Nico at Ninety Park Lane*** below) – ⧦ 18.50 – **382 rm** 225.00/245.00 **s.**
72 suites – SB.

**London Hilton on Park Lane**, 22 Park Lane, W1Y 4BE, ℘ (0171) 493 8000, Fax (0171) 493 4957, « Panoramic ≤ of London », 𝄽 – 📶, ⅍= rm, 🗏 📺 ☎ ♿ – 🔏 1000.
🕮 AE ① VISA JCB. 🛠
BP e
**Trader Vics** (℘ (0171) 208 4113) : Meals (dinner only) a la carte 20.00/70.00 t. ↓ 7.50 – **Park Brasserie** : Meals 21.50 t. and a la carte ↓ 7.50 – (see also **Windows** below) – ☲ 17.00 –
**394 rm** 270.00/350.00, 52 suites.

**Connaught**, Carlos Pl., W1Y 6AL, ℘ (0171) 499 7070, Fax (0171) 495 3262 – 📶 🗏 📺 ☎ ✆.
🕮 AE ① VISA JCB. 🛠
BM e
✿
**The Restaurant** : Meals (booking essential) 29.00/60.00 t. and a la carte 26.60/69.20 t. ↓ 15.00 – **Grill Room** : Meals (closed Saturday lunch) (booking essential) 29.00/39.00 t. and a la carte 26.60/69.20 t. ↓ 15.00 – ☲ 21.00 – **66 rm** 250.00/365.00 s., 24 suites – SB
Spec. Pâté de turbot froid au homard, sauce pudeur. Filet de boeuf en croûte légère "Strasbourgeoise". Crème brûlée au parfum saisonnier.

**47 Park Street**, 47 Park St., W1Y 4EB, ℘ (0171) 491 7282, Fax (0171) 491 7281 – 📶 🗏 📺 ☎ ✆. 🕮 AE ① VISA JCB. 🛠
AM c
Meals (room service) – (see also **Le Gavroche** below) – ☲ 20.00 –, **52 suites** 260.00/530.00 s.

**Brown's**, Albemarle St., W1X 4BP, ℘ (0171) 493 6020, Fax (0171) 493 9381 – 📶 📺 ☎ ✆ – 🔏 70. 🕮 AE ① VISA. 🛠
DM e
Meals – (see **1837** below) – ☲ 18.00 – **112 rm** 250.00/345.00, 6 suites – SB.

**Park Lane**, Piccadilly, W1Y 8BX, ℘ (0171) 499 6321, Fax (0171) 499 1965 – 📶, ⅍= rm, 🗏 📺 ☎ 🄿 – 🔏 300. 🕮 AE ① VISA JCB. 🛠
CP x
**Brasserie on the Park** (℘ (0171) 290 7364) : Meals 23.50/25.50 t. and a la carte ↓ 10.00 – ☲ 18.50 – **286 rm** 260.00/280.00 s., 20 suites.

**Britannia**, Grosvenor Sq., W1A 3AN, ℘ (0171) 629 9400, Fax (0171) 629 7736, 𝄽 – 📶, ⅍= rm, 🗏 📺 ☎ – 🔏 450. 🕮 AE ① VISA JCB. 🛠
BM x
Meals 16.50 t. (lunch) and a la carte 26.00/30.75 t. – (see also **Shogun** below) – ☲ 16.50 –
**302 rm** 150.00/215.00, 12 suites.

**May Fair Inter-Continental**, Stratton St., W1A 2AN, ℘ (0171) 629 7777, Fax (0171) 629 1459, 𝄽, ☎, ⃞ – 📶, ⅍= rm, 🗏 📺 ☎ ♿ – 🔏 290. 🕮 AE ① VISA JCB. 🛠
DN z
**May Fair Café** (℘ (0171) 915 2842) : Meals (closed Sunday) (lunch only) 15.00 t. and a la carte – (see also **Opus 70** below) – ☲ 17.00 – **275 rm** 269.00/289.00 s., 12 suites.

**Inter-Continental**, 1 Hamilton Pl., Hyde Park Corner, W1V 0QY, ℘ (0171) 409 3131, Fax (0171) 493 3476, ≤, 𝄽, ☎ – 📶, ⅍= rm, 🗏 📺 ☎ ♿ ⇌ – 🔏 1000. 🕮 AE ① VISA. 🛠
BP o
Meals 22.75/26.50 and a la carte – (see also **Le Soufflé** below) – ☲ 20.00 – **416 rm** 280.00/350.00, 42 suites.

**Athenaeum**, 116 Piccadilly, W1V 0BJ, ℘ (0171) 499 3464, Fax (0171) 493 1860, 𝄽, ☎ – 📶, ⅍= rm, 🗏 📺 ☎ ✆ – 🔏 55. 🕮 AE ① VISA JCB. 🛠
CP s
**Bulloch's at 116** : Meals (closed lunch Saturday and Sunday) a la carte 35.90/45.95 t. ↓ 11.00 – ☲ 17.95 – **122 rm** 255.00/325.00 s., 33 suites.

**The Metropolitan**, Old Park Lane, W1Y 4LB, ℘ (0171) 447 1000, Fax (0171) 447 1100, ≤, « Contemporary interior design », 𝄽 – 📶, ⅍= rm, 🗏 📺 ☎ ⇌. 🕮 AE ① VISA JCB. 🛠
BP c
**Met Bar** : Meals (residents and members only) (light lunch) a la carte 16.00/40.50 st. – (see also **Nobu** below) – ☲ 15.00 – **152 rm** 210.00/260.00, 3 suites.

**Westbury**, Bond St., W1A 4UH, ℘ (0171) 629 7755, Fax (0171) 495 1163 – 📶, ⅍= rm, 🗏 📺 ☎ ✆ – 🔏 110. 🕮 AE ① VISA JCB
DM a
Meals (closed Saturday and Sunday lunch) 19.50/21.50 t. and a la carte ↓ 12.00 – ☲ 16.75 –
**231 rm** 210.00/270.00 s., 13 suites.

**London Marriott Grosvenor Square**, Duke St., Grosvenor Sq., W1A 4AW, ℘ (0171) 493 1232, Fax (0171) 491 3201, 𝄽 – 📶, ⅍= rm, 🗏 📺 ☎ – 🔏 600. 🕮 AE ① VISA JCB. 🛠
BL a
**Diplomat** : Meals (closed Saturday lunch) 19.50/12.95 s. and a la carte – ☲ 12.95 – **210 rm** 185.00/260.00, 11 suites.

**Chesterfield**, 35 Charles St., W1X 8LX, ℘ (0171) 491 2622, Fax (0171) 491 4793 – 📶, ⅍= rm, 🗏 rest, 📺 ☎ ✆ – 🔏 110. 🕮 AE ① VISA JCB. 🛠
CN c
**Butlers** : Meals (closed Saturday lunch) 10.50 t. (lunch) and a la carte 22.40/32.85 t. – ☲ 16.50 – **106 rm** 155.00/252.00, 4 suites.

**Washington**, 5-7 Curzon St., W1Y 8DT, ℘ (0171) 499 7000, Fax (0171) 495 6172 – 📶, ⅍= rm, 🗏 📺 ☎ ✆ – 🔏 80. 🕮 AE ① VISA JCB. 🛠
CN s
Meals a la carte 20.40/28.40 t. ↓ 6.95 – ☲ 13.95 – **169 rm** 190.00 s., 4 suites – SB.

**Holiday Inn Mayfair**, 3 Berkeley St., W1X 6NE, ℘ (0171) 493 8282, Fax (0171) 629 2827 – 📶, ⅍= rm, 🗏 📺 ☎ ✆ – 🔏 60. 🕮 AE ① VISA JCB. 🛠
DN r
Meals (closed Saturday lunch) a la carte 19.00/32.00 st. ↓ 8.00 – ☲ 13.95 – **181 rm** 190.00 st., 4 suites.

🏠 **Flemings,** 7-12 Half Moon St., W1Y 7RA, ℘ (0171) 499 2964, *Fax (0171) 629 4063* – 🔊 ▤
📺 ☎ – 🔏 50. 🆎 AE ① VISA JCB. ⅙                  CN z
**Meals** 12.50/23.50 **st.** and a la carte ⌕ 9.00 – ☷ 13.00 – **120 rm** 150.00/180.00, 10 suites.

🏠 **Green Park,** Half Moon St., W1Y 8BP, ℘ (0171) 629 7522, *Fax (0171) 491 8971* – 🔊
⇖ rm, ▤ 📺 ☎ – 🔏 130. 🆎 AE ① VISA JCB. ⅙            CN a
**Meals** 12.95 **st.** (lunch) and a la carte 24.00/40.00 **st.** ⌕ 9.00 – ☷ 11.95 – **160 rm** 150.00/
199.00 **s.,** 1 suite – SB.

🏠 **London Mews Hilton,** 2 Stanhope Row, W1Y 7HE, ℘ (0171) 493 7222
*Fax (0171) 629 4427* – ⇖ rm, ▤ 📺 🆎 ☎ ⇔ – 🔏 50. 🆎 AE ① VISA JCB. ⅙    BP L
**Meals** (dinner only) 18.50 **t.** and a la carte – ☷ 14.50 – **72 rm** 188.00/237.00 **t.**

XXXXX **The Oak Room Marco Pierre White** (at Le Meridien Piccadilly H.), 21 Piccadilly, W1\
❀❀❀ OBH, ℘ (0171) 437 0202 – ▤. 🆎 AE VISA               EM a
*closed Saturday, Sunday, last 2 weeks August and 2 weeks Christmas-New Year -*
**Meals** (booking essential) 29.50/80.00 **t.** ⌕ 25.00
**Spec.** Aspic of oysters with watercress en gelée de Champagne. Pigeon from Bresse er
vessie, sauce Albufera. Soufflé chocolat, glace de lait.

XXXXX **Chez Nico at Ninety Park Lane** (Ladenis) (at Grosvenor House H.), Park Lane, W1A
❀❀❀ 3AA, ℘ (0171) 409 1290, *Fax (0171) 355 4877* – ▤. 🆎 AE VISA      AM e
*closed Saturday lunch, Sunday, 4 days at Easter, 10 days at Christmas and Bank Holida*
*Mondays* – **Meals** - French - (booking essential) 34.00/64.00 **t.**
**Spec.** Seared escalope of foie gras with brioche and caramelised orange. Grilled scallop*
with buttered leeks. Fillet of beef with celeriac and truffle.

XXXX **Le Gavroche** (Roux), 43 Upper Brook St., W1Y 1PF, ℘ (0171) 408 0881
❀❀ *Fax (0171) 409 0939* – ▤. 🆎 AE ① VISA JCB           AM (
*closed Saturday, Sunday, Christmas-New Year and Bank Holidays* – **Meals** - French - (book
ing essential) 40.00 **st.** (lunch) and a la carte 64.80/90.70 **st.** ⌕ 19.00
**Spec.** Foie gras chaud et pastilla de canard à la cannelle. Râble de lapin et galette au
parmesan. Le palet au chocolat amer et praline croustillant.

XXXX **The Oriental** (at Dorchester H.), Park Lane, W1A 2HJ, ℘ (0171) 317 6328
❀ *Fax (0171) 409 0114* – ▤. 🆎 AE ① VISA JCB         BN a
*closed Saturday lunch, Sunday and 3 to 31 August* – **Meals** - Chinese (Canton) - 29.50/
42.00 **st.** and a la carte 43.00/72.50 **st.** ⌕ 12.00
**Spec.** Roasted Peking duck. Double boiled shark's fin with chicken and Chinese cabbage
Stir-fried beef with lemon grass and black pepper.

XXXX **Grill Room** (at Dorchester H.), Park Lane, W1A 2HJ, ℘ (0171) 317 6336
*Fax (0171) 409 0114* – ▤. 🆎 AE ① VISA JCB         BN a
**Meals** - English - 29.50/39.50 **st.** and a la carte 38.00/58.00 **st.** ⌕ 12.00.

XXXX **Les Saveurs de Jean-Christophe Novelli,** 37a Curzon St., W1Y 7AF
❀ ℘ (0171) 491 8919, *Fax (0171) 491 3658* – ▤. 🆎 AE ① VISA JCB     BN c
*closed Saturday lunch, Sunday and Monday* – **Meals** - French - 18.50/31.50 **t.** ⌕ 15.00
**Spec.** Tian of smoked salmon and crab with asparagus and confit tomatoes. Baked sea
bream with polenta, piperade and basil cappuccino. Caramelised apple Tatin with carame
ice cream.

XXXX **Windows** (at London Hilton on Park Lane), 22 Park Lane, W1Y 4BE, ℘ (0171) 208 4021
« Panoramic ⩻ of London » – ▤. 🆎 AE ① VISA JCB        BP e
*closed Saturday lunch and Sunday dinner* – **Meals** 39.50/44.00 **t.** and dinner a la carte.

XXXX **1837** (at Brown's H.), Albemarle St., W1X 4BP, ℘ (0171) 408 1837, *Fax (0171) 493 9381* – 🆎
AE ① VISA JCB                     DM e
*closed Saturday lunch and Sunday* – **Meals** 27.00/45.00 **t.** and a la carte.

XXX **The Square** (Howard), 6-10 Bruton St., W1X 7AG, ℘ (0171) 495 7100, *Fax (0171) 495 7150*
❀❀ – ▤. 🆎 AE ① VISA                  CM v
*closed lunch Saturday and Sunday, 25-26 December and 1 January* – **Meals** 45.00 **t.**
(dinner) and lunch a la carte 34.50/36.00 **t.** ⌕ 13.50
**Spec.** Roast foie gras with caramelised endive and late picked Muscat grapes. Loin of lamb
with artichoke, confit of garlic and rosemary. "A tasting of coffee".

XXX **Mirabelle,** 56 Curzon St., W1Y 8AL, ℘ (0171) 499 4636, *Fax (0171) 499 5449,* ⌗ – ▤. 🆎
AE VISA                        CN X
**Meals** 17.95 **t.** (lunch) and a la carte 28.50/35.50 **t.** ⌕ 12.75.

XXX **Sartoria,** 20 Savile Row, W1X 1AE, ℘ (0171) 534 7000, *Fax (0171) 534 7070* – ▤. 🆎 AE ①
VISA JCB                       DL c
*closed Sunday dinner and 25-26 December* **Meals** - Italian - a la carte 32.50/48.00 **t.** ⌕ 10.25

XXX **Goodes at Thomas Goode,** 19 South Audley St., W1Y 6BN, ℘ (0171) 409 7242
*Fax (0171) 629 4230* – ▤. 🆎 AE ① VISA JCB         BM (
*closed Saturday, Sunday, first 3 weeks August and 1 week Christmas* – **Meals** (lunch only
32.50 **t.** ⌕ 15.20.

XXX **Le Soufflé** (at Inter-Continental H.), 1 Hamilton Pl., Hyde Park Corner, W1V 0QY, ℘ (0171) 409 3131, Fax (0171) 409 7460 – ▤ ⇔, 🆂 AE ① VISA                        BP  o
closed Monday – **Meals** 29.50/35.00 and a la carte.

XXX **Morton's - The Restaurant**, 28 Berkeley Sq., W1X 5HA, ℘ (0171) 493 7171, Fax (0171) 495 3160, ☆ – ✖ ☷ Ⓟ, 🆂 AE ①                        CM  a
closed lunch Saturday and Sunday and 24 to 27 December – **Meals** 19.50/29.50 t. and a la carte ≜ 9.75.

XXX **Princess Garden**, 8-10 North Audley St., W1Y 1WF, ℘ (0171) 493 3223, Fax (0171) 629 3130 – ▤, 🆂 AE ① VISA JCB                        AL  z
closed 23 to 26 December – **Meals** - Chinese (Peking, Szechuan) - 30.00 t. (dinner) and a la carte 29.00/45.00 t. ≜ 9.50.

XXX **Opus 70** (at May Fair Inter-Continental H.), Stratton St., W1A 2AN, ℘ (0171) 915 2842, Fax (0171) 629 1459 – ▤, 🆂 AE ① VISA JCB                        DN  z
closed Saturday lunch – **Meals** 20.00 t. (lunch) and dinner a la carte 28.00/32.50 t. ≜ 7.00.

XXX **Scotts**, 20 Mount St., W1Y 6HE, ℘ (0171) 629 5248, Fax (0171) 499 8246 – ▤, 🆂 AE ① VISA JCB                        BM  a
**Meals** - Seafood - 24.50 t. (lunch) and dinner a la carte 26.25/53.50 t. ≜ 9.50.

XX ❀ **Nobu** (at The Metropolitan H.), 19 Old Park Lane, W1Y 4LB, ℘ (0171) 447 4747, Fax (0171) 447 4749, ← – ▤ ⚿, 🆂 AE ① VISA JCB                        BP  c
closed lunch Saturday and Sunday – **Meals** - New style Japanese with South American influences - a la carte 45.00/90.00 t. ≜ 11.25
**Spec.** Toro tartar with caviar. Black cod with miso. Tiradito.

XX **L'Odéon**, 65 Regent St., W1R 7HH, ℘ (0171) 287 1400, Fax (0171) 287 1300 – ▤, 🆂 AE ① VISA JCB                        EM  r
closed Sunday June-August, 25 to 27 December and Bank Holidays – **Meals** 19.50 t. (lunch) and a la carte 28.50/45.95 t. ≜ 7.50.

XX **Tamarind**, 20 Queen St., W1X 7PJ, ℘ (0171) 629 3561, Fax (0171) 499 5034 – 🆂 AE ① VISA JCB                        CN  e
closed Saturday lunch, 25-26 December and Good Friday – **Meals** - Indian - 16.50 st. (lunch) and a la carte 27.60/35.05 t. ≜ 10.00.

XX **Greenhouse**, 27a Hay's Mews, W1X 7RJ, ℘ (0171) 499 3331, Fax (0171) 499 5368 – ▤, 🆂 AE ① VISA                        BN  e
closed Saturday lunch and 25-26 December and Bank Holidays – **Meals** a la carte 24.40/39.50 t. ≜ 12.50.

XX **Bentley's**, 11-15 Swallow St., W1R 7HD, ℘ (0171) 734 4756, Fax (0171) 287 2972 – ▤, 🆂 AE ① VISA JCB                        EM  i
closed Sunday, 25 December and 1 January – **Meals** - Seafood - 19.50 t. and a la carte 30.40/44.45 t. ≜ 13.50.

XX **Nicole's**, 158 New Bond St., W1V 9PA, ℘ (0171) 499 8408, Fax (0171) 409 0381 – ▤, 🆂 AE ① VISA JCB                        DM  n
closed Saturday dinner, Sunday, 25-26 December, 1 January and Bank Holidays – **Meals** a la carte 26.20/32.75 t. ≜ 11.50.

XX **Teca**, 54 Brooks Mews, W1Y 2NY, ℘ (0171) 495 4774, Fax (0171) 491 3545 – ▤, 🆂 AE ① VISA                        CL  a
**Meals** - Italian - a la carte 24.00/30.00 t. ≜ 12.00.

XX **Langan's Brasserie**, Stratton St., W1X 5FD, ℘ (0171) 491 8822, Fax (0171) 493 8309 – ▤, 🆂 AE ① VISA JCB                        DN  e
closed Saturday lunch, Sunday, Easter, 25-26 December, 1 January and Bank Holidays in May and August – a la carte 20.75/29.85 t. ≜ 7.50.

XX **Marquis**, 121A Mount St., W1Y 5HB, ℘ (0171) 499 1256, Fax (0171) 493 4460 – ▤, 🆂 AE ① VISA JCB                        BM  u
closed Saturday lunch, Sunday, 22 August-5 September, 24 December-6 January and Bank Holidays – **Meals** 17.50 t. and a la carte ≜ 6.30.

XX **Chor Bizarre**, 16 Albemarle St., W1X 3HA, ℘ (0171) 629 9802, Fax (0171) 493 7756, « Authentic Indian decor and furnishings » – 🆂 AE ① VISA JCB                        DM  s
closed 25 and 26 December – **Meals** - Indian - 14.95/23.00 t. and a la carte ≜ 7.95.

XX **Benihana**, 37 Sackville St., Piccadilly, W1X 2DQ, ℘ (0171) 494 2525, Fax (0171) 494 1456 – ▤, 🆂 AE ① VISA JCB                        EM  s
closed 25 December – **Meals** - Japanese (Teppan-Yaki) - 8.50/14.00 t. and a la carte.

XX **Shogun** (at Britannia H.), Adams Row, W1Y 5DE, ℘ (0171) 493 1255, Fax (0171) 629 7736 – ▤, 🆂 AE ① VISA JCB                        BM  x
closed Monday – **Meals** - Japanese - (dinner only) 28.50 and a la carte.

X **Coast**, 26B Albemarle St., W1X 3FA, ℘ (0171) 495 5999, Fax (0171) 495 2999 – 🆂 AE ① VISA                        DM  r
closed 31 December lunch, 25 December, 1 January and Bank Holidays – **Meals** a la carte 25.50/43.50 t.

421

X **The Cafe** (at Sotheby's), 34-35 New Bond St., W1A 2AA, ℘ (0171) 408 5077 – ✂. **AB AE**
**① VISA**
DL €
*closed Saturday, Sunday and Christmas-New Year* – **Meals** (booking essential) (lunch only)
a la carte 18.50/23.45 st.

X **Momo**, 25 Heddon St., W1R 7LG, ℘ (0171) 434 4040, Fax (0171) 287 0404 – ■. **AB AE ①**
**VISA JCB**
EM r
*closed Saturday and Bank Holiday lunch and Sunday*Meals - Moroccan - 15.50 st.
(lunch) and a la carte 19.25/30.00 st.

X **Veeraswamy**, Victory House, 99 Regent St., W1R 8RS, ℘ (0171) 734 1401,
Fax (0171) 439 8434 – ■. **AB AE ① VISA JCB**
EM €
*closed 25 December* – **Meals** - Indian - 14.00 t. (lunch) and a la carte 17.00/23.00 t.

X **Zinc Bar & Grill**, 21 Heddon St., W1R 7LF, ℘ (0171) 255 8899, Fax (0171) 255 8888 – ■. **AB**
**AE ① VISA JCB**
EM x
*closed Sunday dinner, 25-26 December and 1 January* – **Meals** a la carte 18.75/21.95 t.

**Regent's Park and Marylebone** – ⊠ NW1/NW6/NW8/W1 – *Except where otherwise*
*stated see pp. 30 and 31.*

🛈 Basement Services Arcade, Selfridges Store, Oxford St., W1 ℘ (0171) 824 8844.

🏨🏨🏨 **Landmark London**, 222 Marylebone Rd., NW1 6JQ, ℘ (0171) 631 8000,
Fax (0171) 631 8080, « Victorian Gothic architecture, atrium and winter garden », ♨, ≤s
🔲 – 🕸, ✂ rm, ■ 🔟 ☎ ᴖ – 🔏 350. **AB AE ① VISA JCB**. ❀
p. 23 HU a
*The Dining Room :* Meals *(closed Saturday lunch and Sunday dinner)* 26.00/36.95 st.
and a la carte 🕯 14.00 – *Winter Garden :* Meals 23.35 st. and a la carte 🕯 15.00 – ⊆ 18.00 –
**288 rm** 270.00/290.00 s., 9 suites.

🏨🏨🏨 **Churchill Inter-Continental**, 30 Portman Sq., W1A 4ZX, ℘ (0171) 486 5800,
Fax (0171) 486 1255, ❀ – 🕸, ✂ rm, ■ 🔟 ☎ ᴖ 🅿 – 🔏 200. **AB AE ① VISA JCB**. ❀
*Clementine's :* Meals *(closed Saturday lunch)* 23.00 t. and a la carte 🕯 8.00 – ⊆ 17.75 –
**415 rm** 280.00/290.00, 33 suites.
AJ x

🏨🏨🏨 **Langham Hilton**, 1 Portland Pl., Regent St., W1N 4JA, ℘ (0171) 636 1000,
Fax (0171) 323 2340, ♨, ≤s – 🕸, ✂ rm, ■ 🔟 ☎ ᴖ – 🔏 250. **AB AE ① VISA JCB**. ❀
*Memories :* Meals 27.00 st. (lunch) and a la carte 25.00/46.00 st. 🕯 9.50 – *Tsar's :* Meals
*(closed Saturday lunch, Sunday and Bank Holidays)* a la carte 26.50/36.00 st. 🕯 9.50 – ⊆
18.00 – **359 rm** 280.00 s., 20 suites.
p. 23 JU e

🏨🏨🏨 **Selfridge**, Orchard St., W1H 0JS, ℘ (0171) 408 2080, Fax (0171) 629 8849 – 🕸, ✂ rm, ■
🔟 ☎ – 🔏 220. **AB AE ① VISA JCB**. ❀
AK e
*Fletchers :* Meals 19.50 t. and a la carte – *Orchard :* Meals 12.50/16.50 t. and a la carte
🕯 9.95 – ⊆ 14.50 – **290 rm** 180.00/200.00 t., 4 suites.

🏨🏨 **The Leonard**, 15 Seymour St., W1H 5AA, ℘ (0171) 935 2010, Fax (0171) 935 6700, « At-
tractively furnished Georgian town houses », ♨ – 🕸 ■ 🔟 ☎ ᴖ – 🔏 30. **AB AE ① VISA**
JCB. ❀
AK n
Meals (room service only) – ⊆ 16.00 – **6 rm** 170.00/190.00 s., **20 suites** 240.00/410.00 s.

🏨🏨 **Radisson SAS Portman**, 22 Portman Sq., W1H 9FL, ℘ (0171) 208 6000,
Fax (0171) 208 6001, ♨, ≤s, ❀ – 🕸, ✂ rm, ■ 🔟 ☎ ᴖ – 🔏 350. **AB AE ① VISA JCB**.
❀
AJ c
Meals *Portman Corner :* Meals (buffet lunch) 16.50 t. (lunch) and a la carte 19.75/32.50 t.
🕯 9.50 – ⊆ 16.50 – **272 rm** 226.00/245.00 s., 7 suites.

🏨🏨 **Montcalm**, Great Cumberland Pl., W1A 2LF, ℘ (0171) 402 4288, Fax (0171) 724 9180 – 🕸
✂ rm, ■ 🔟 ☎ – 🔏 80. **AB AE ① VISA JCB**. ❀
p. 35 EZ x
Meals – (see *The Crescent* below) – ⊆ 17.95 – **110 rm** 210.00/300.00 s., 10 suites.

🏨🏨 **London Regent's Park Hilton**, 18 Lodge Rd, NW8 7JT, ℘ (0171) 722 7722,
Fax (0171) 483 2408 – 🕸, ✂ rm, ■ 🔟 ☎ ᴖ – 🔏 150. **AB AE ① VISA JCB**. ❀
*Minsky's :* Meals 20.50/21.95 t. and a la carte 🕯 8.50 – *Kashinoki :* Meals - Japanese -
*(closed Monday)* 15.00/32.00 t. and a la carte – ⊆ 16.50 – **376 rm** 180.00/235.00 st., 1 suite
– SB.
p. 23 GT v

🏨🏨 **Clifton Ford**, 47 Welbeck St., W1M 8DN, ℘ (0171) 486 6600, Fax (0171) 486 7492 – 🕸 ■
🔟 ☎ & ᴖ – 🔏 150. **AB AE ① VISA**. ❀
BH a
Meals 24.50/26.00 st. and a la carte 🕯 14.00 – ⊆ 16.00 – **184 rm** 180.00/200.00 s., 2 suites

🏨🏨 **Berners**, 10 Berners St., W1A 3BE, ℘ (0171) 666 2000, Fax (0171) 666 2001 – 🕸, ✂ rm
■ rest, 🔟 ☎ & – 🔏 150. **AB AE ① VISA JCB**. ❀
EJ n
Meals (carving lunch) 16.95/10.25 t. and a la carte 🕯 6.50 – ⊆ 14.95 – **214 rm** 160.00/
240.00 st., 3 suites.

🏨🏨 **London Marriott Marble Arch**, 134 George St., W1H 6DN, ℘ (0171) 723 1277,
Fax (0171) 402 0666, ♨, ≤s, 🔲 – 🕸, ✂ rm, ■ 🔟 ☎ & 🅿 – 🔏 150. **AB AE ① VISA JCB**.
❀
p. 35 EZ x
Meals a la carte 23.95/32.40 st. 🕯 6.50 – ⊆ 13.95 – **240 rm** 190.00/215.00 s.

🏨🏨 **Berkshire**, 350 Oxford St., W1N 0BY, ℘ (0171) 629 7474, Fax (0171) 629 8156 – 🕸, ✂ rm
■ 🔟 ☎ – 🔏 40. **AB AE ① VISA JCB**. ❀
BK n
Meals 22.50/24.00 st. and a la carte – ⊆ 15.00 – **145 rm** 205.00/245.00 s., 2 suites.

🏨🏨 **Forte Posthouse Regent's Park,** Carburton St., W1P 8EE, ℘ (0171) 388 2300, Fax (0171) 387 2806 – |🛗|, ✼ rm, ▤ rest, 📺 ☎ 🗧 ﾖ, – 🔬 320. ◑◎ 📭 ⓪ 𝐕𝐈𝐒𝐀 𝐉𝐂𝐁. 🛇

Meals (closed lunch Saturday and Sunday) a la carte 16.35/22.85 **t.** ⓵ 7.95 – ☲ 12.95 – **324 rm** 149.00/169.00 **st.**, 1 suite – SB.

p. 23 JU · i

🏨 **Saint Georges,** Langham Pl., W1N 8QS, ℘ (0171) 580 0111, Fax (0171) 436 7997, ≼ – |🛗|, ✼ rm, 📺 ☎ – 🔬 25. ◑◎ 📭 𝐕𝐈𝐒𝐀 𝐉𝐂𝐁

p. 23 JU a

Meals 15.00/21.50 **st.** and a la carte ⓵ 7.85 – ☲ 13.95 – **84 rm** 165.00/205.00 **st.**, 2 suites – SB.

🏨 **Dorset Square,** 39-40 Dorset Sq., NW1 6QN, ℘ (0171) 723 7874, Fax (0171) 724 3328, « Attractively furnished Regency town houses », ☞ – |🛗| ▤ 📺 ☎ 🗧. ◑◎ 📭 𝐕𝐈𝐒𝐀. 🛇

**The Potting Shed :** Meals (closed Sunday lunch and Saturday) 14.95/18.95 **t.** and a la carte ⓵ 9.00 – ☲ 13.75 – **38 rm** 98.00/215.00 **s.**

p. 23 HU s

🏨 **Durrants,** 26-32 George St., W1H 6BJ, ℘ (0171) 935 8131, Fax (0171) 487 3510, « Converted Georgian houses with Regency façade » – |🛗|, ▤ rest, 📺 ☎ – 🔬 100. ◑◎ 📭 𝐕𝐈𝐒𝐀. 🛇

AH e

Meals 19.50 **t.** and a la carte ⓵ 9.50 – ☲ 12.50 – **89 rm** 97.50/145.00 **st.**, 3 suites.

🏨 **Savoy Court,** Granville Pl., W1H 0EH, ℘ (0171) 408 0130, Fax (0171) 493 2070 – |🛗|, ✼ rm, 📺 ☎ – 🔬 40. ◑◎ 📭 𝐕𝐈𝐒𝐀 𝐉𝐂𝐁. 🛇

AK i

Meals 12.00 **st.** and a la carte ⓵ 12.00 – ☲ 12.00 – **108 rm** 125.00/150.00 **s.**

🏨 **Langham Court,** 31-35 Langham St., W1N 5RE, ℘ (0171) 436 6622, Fax (0171) 436 2303 – |🛗|, ✼ rm, 📺 ☎ 🗧 – 🔬 80. ◑◎ 📭 ⓪ 𝐕𝐈𝐒𝐀. 🛇

p. 23 JU z

Meals 19.75 **st.** and a la carte ⓵ 6.00 – ☲ 14.50 – **56 rm** 139.00/159.00 **st.**

🏨 **Stakis London Harewood,** Harewood Row, NW1 6SE, ℘ (0171) 262 2707, Fax (0171) 262 2975 – |🛗|, ✼ rm, ▤ rest, 📺 ☎. ◑◎ 📭 ⓪ 𝐕𝐈𝐒𝐀. 🛇

p. 23 HU x

Meals (bar lunch)/dinner 16.50 and a la carte – ☲ 10.50 – **92 rm** 125.00/184.00 **st.** – SB.

🏨 **Rathbone** without rest., Rathbone St., W1P 2LB, ℘ (0171) 636 2001, Fax (0171) 636 3882 – |🛗| ✼ ▤ 📺 ☎. ◑◎ 📭 𝐕𝐈𝐒𝐀 𝐉𝐂𝐁. 🛇

p. 24 KU x

closed 24 to 26 December – ☲ 13.50 – **72 rm** 150.00/225.00 **st.**

🏨 **Hart House** without rest., 51 Gloucester Pl., W1H 3PE, ℘ (0171) 935 2288, Fax (0171) 935 8516 – 📺 ☎. ◑◎ 📭 𝐕𝐈𝐒𝐀 𝐉𝐂𝐁. 🛇

AH a

**16 rm** ☲ 65.00/93.00 **st.**

XXX **Orrery,** 55 Marylebone High St., W1M 3AE, ℘ (0171) 616 8000, Fax (0171) 616 8080, « Converted 19C stables, contemporary interior » – |🛗|. ◑◎ 📭 ⓪ 𝐕𝐈𝐒𝐀 𝐉𝐂𝐁

closed 25 December and Easter Sunday – Meals (booking essential) 26.50 **t.** (lunch) and dinner a la carte 33.50/46.00 **t.**

p. 23 IU a

XXX **Interlude,** 5 Charlotte St., W1P 1HD, ℘ (0171) 637 0222, Fax (0171) 637 0224 – ▤. ◑◎ 📭 ⓪ 𝐕𝐈𝐒𝐀 𝐉𝐂𝐁

❀

p. 24 KU r

closed Saturday lunch, Sunday, last 2 weeks August, 1 week Christmas and Bank Holidays – Meals 24.50/34.50 **st.** and dinner a la carte 24.50/34.50 **t.**

Spec. Langoustine ravioli with crushed coriander. Cumin roasted loin of lamb on smoked aubergine. Chocolate tart with prune and Armagnac ice cream.

XX **The Crescent** (at Montcalm H.), Great Cumberland Pl., W1A 2LF, ℘ (0171) 402 4288, Fax (0171) 724 9180 – ▤. ◑◎ 📭 𝐕𝐈𝐒𝐀 𝐉𝐂𝐁

p. 35 EZ x

closed Saturday lunch and Sunday – Meals 19.00/24.00 **t.**.

XX **Nico Central,** 35 Great Portland St., W1N 5DD, ℘ (0171) 436 8846, Fax (0171) 436 3455 – ▤. ◑◎ 📭 ⓪ 𝐕𝐈𝐒𝐀 𝐉𝐂𝐁

DJ c

Meals 25.00/27.00 **t.** ⓵ 9.00.

XX **La Porte des Indes,** 32 Bryanston St., W1H 7AE, ℘ (0171) 224 0055, Fax (0171) 224 1144 – ▤. ◑◎ 📭 ⓪ 𝐕𝐈𝐒𝐀 𝐉𝐂𝐁

AK r

closed Saturday lunch, 25-26 and 31 December – Meals - Indian - 22.00/31.00 **t.** and a la carte ⓵ 5.50.

XX **Stephen Bull,** 5-7 Blandford St., W1H 3AA, ℘ (0171) 486 9696, Fax (0171) 490 3128 – ▤. ◑◎ 📭 ⓪ 𝐕𝐈𝐒𝐀

BH e

closed Saturday lunch, Sunday, 1 week Christmas-New Year and Bank Holidays – Meals a la carte approx. 27.00 **t.** ⓵ 7.00.

XX **Caldesi,** 15-17 Marylebone Lane, W1M 5FE, ℘ (0171) 935 9226, Fax (0171) 929 0924 – ▤. ◑◎ 📭 ⓪ 𝐕𝐈𝐒𝐀 𝐉𝐂𝐁

BJ e

closed Saturday lunch, Sunday, 25 December and Bank Holidays – Meals - Italian - a la carte 17.00/26.00 **t.** ⓵ 8.00.

XX **Oceana,** Jason Court, 76 Wigmore St., W1H 9DQ, ℘ (0171) 224 2992, Fax (0171) 486 1216 – ▤. ◑◎ 📭 ⓪ 𝐕𝐈𝐒𝐀 𝐉𝐂𝐁

BJ c

closed Saturday lunch, Sunday, 25 December and Bank Holidays – Meals a la carte 19.25/29.00 **t.** ⓵ 8.00.

423

XX **Bertorelli's,** 19-23 Charlotte St., W1P 1HP, *ℰ* (0171) 636 4174, *Fax (0171) 467 8902* – ▤.
**⓪ ㏂ ⓪ ㎹ 亅ᴄʙ** v
p. 24 KU v
*closed Saturday lunch, Sunday, 25-26 December and Bank Holidays* – **Meals** - Italian -
a la carte 17.50/26.75 ⓪ 7.75.

XX **Asuka,** Berkeley Arcade, 209a Baker St., NW1 6AB, *ℰ* (0171) 486 5026, *Fax (0171) 224 1741*
– **⓪ ㏂ ㎹** p. 23 HU u
*closed Saturday lunch, Sunday, Christmas-New Year and Bank Holidays* – **Meals** - Japanese -
14.50/23.90 t. and a la carte ⓪ 13.95.

XX **Gaylord,** 79-81 Mortimer St., W1N 7TB, *ℰ* (0171) 580 3615, *Fax (0171) 636 0860* – ▤. **⓪**
**㏂ ⓪ ㎹ 亅ᴄʙ** p. 24 KU o
**Meals** - Indian - 16.95 t. and a la carte ⓪ 5.95.

XX **Mash,** 19-21 Great Portland St., W1M JD8, *ℰ* (0171) 637 5555, *Fax (0171) 637 7333* – ▤
**⓪ ㏂ ⓪ ㎹** DJ a
*closed 25 December* – **Meals** a la carte approx. 31.50 st.

XX **Ard-Ri at the O'Conor Don,** (first floor), 88 Marylebone Lane, W1M 5FJ,
*ℰ* (0171) 935 9311, *Fax (0171) 486 6706* – **⓪ ㏂ ㎹** BJ n
*closed Saturday lunch, Sunday, Easter, 25-26 December and Bank Holidays* – **Meals** - Irish -
19.00 t. (lunch) and a la carte 22.70/27.30 t.

X **Justin de Blank,** 120-122 Marylebone Lane, W1M 5FZ, *ℰ* (0171) 486 5250,
*Fax (0171) 935 4046* – **⓪ ㏂ ⓪ ㎹** BH u
*closed Sunday, Christmas and Bank Holidays* – **Meals** a la carte 16.15/20.85 t. ⓪ 5.00.

X **L'Aventure,** 3 Blenheim Terr., NW8 0EH, *ℰ* (0171) 624 6232, *Fax (0171) 625 5548*, 佘 –
**⓪ ㏂ ㎹** p. 22 FS s
*closed Saturday lunch, 4 days Easter and first 2 weeks January* – **Meals** - French - a la carte
17.00/24.00 t.

X **Union Café,** 96 Marylebone Lane, W1M 5FP, *ℰ* (0171) 486 4860 – **⓪ ㎹ 亅ᴄʙ** BH c
*closed Sunday, 25-26 and 31 December and 1 January* – **Meals** a la carte 17.00/26.50 t.

X **Villandry,** 170 Great Portland St., W1N 5TB, *ℰ* (0171) 631 3131, *Fax (0171) 631 3030* – 佘
▤. **⓪ ㏂ ㎹** p. 23 JU s
*closed Sunday* – **Meals** a la carte 16.95/28.50 st. ⓪ 9.50.

X **Zoe,** 3-5 Barrett St., St. Christopher's Pl., W1M 5HH, *ℰ* (0171) 224 1122,
*Fax (0171) 935 5444* – ▤. **⓪ ㏂ ⓪ ㎹** BJ a
*closed Sunday* – **Meals** 20.00 t. and a la carte.

X **Le Muscadet,** 25 Paddington St., W1M 3RF, *ℰ* (0171) 935 2883, *Fax (0171) 935 2883* – ▤.
**⓪ ㎹ ㏂** p. 23 HU v
*closed Saturday lunch, Sunday, Easter, 3 weeks August, 1 week Christmas and Bank Holidays*
– **Meals** - French - 18.80 t. (lunch) and a la carte 24.50/26.50 t. ⓪ 10.00.

X **Ibla,** 89 Marylebone High St., W1M 3DE, *ℰ* (0171) 224 3799, *Fax (0171) 486 1370* – **⓪ ㏂**
**㎹** p. 23 IU e
*closed Sunday, 25-26 December, 4 days January and Bank Holidays* – **Meals** - Italian -
17.00/25.00 t..

X **R K Stanleys,** 6 Little Portland St., W1N 5NG, *ℰ* (0171) 462 0099, *Fax (0171) 462 0088* –
▤. **⓪ ㏂ ㎹ 亅ᴄʙ** p. 23 JU a
*closed Sunday, 1 week Christmas and Bank Holidays* – **Meals** - specialising in sausages -
a la carte 18.00/25.00 st. ⓪ 7.80.

## St. James's – ✉ W1/SW1/WC2 – pp. 30 and 31.

🏠🏠🏠🏠 **Ritz,** 150 Piccadilly, W1V 9DG, *ℰ* (0171) 493 8181, *Fax (0171) 493 2687*, 佘, ₭₅ – ▣, 숙 rm,
▤ ▥ ☎ ✆ – 益 50. **⓪ ㏂ ⓪ ㎹ 亅ᴄʙ**. ⅍ DN a
**Italian Garden :** **Meals** (summer only) 35.00/45.00 st. and a la carte ⓪ 18.00 – (see also **The**
**Restaurant** below) – 또 23.50 – **115 rm** 245.00/290.00 s., 15 suites – SB.

🏠🏠🏠 **Dukes** 🐾, 35 St. James's Pl., SW1A 1NY, *ℰ* (0171) 491 4840, *Fax (0171) 491 1264* – ▣
▥ ☎ ✆ – 益 50. **⓪ ㏂ ⓪ ㎹ 亅ᴄʙ**. ⅍ EP x
**Meals** (residents only) a la carte 20.50/41.00 st. ⓪ 7.50 – 또 12.50 – **73 rm** 185.00/205.00 s.,
8 suites.

🏠🏠🏠 **Stafford** 🐾, 16-18 St. James's Pl., SW1A 1NJ, *ℰ* (0171) 493 0111, *Fax (0171) 493 7121* –
▣ ▤ ▥ ☎ ✆ – 益 35. **⓪ ㏂ ⓪ ㎹ 亅ᴄʙ**. ⅍ DN u
**Meals** *(closed Saturday lunch)* 25.50/29.00 st. and a la carte ⓪ 8.50 – 또 15.50 – **76 rm**
199.00/310.00 s., 5 suites – SB.

🏠🏠 **22 Jermyn Street,** 22 Jermyn St., SW1Y 6HL, *ℰ* (0171) 734 2353, *Fax (0171) 734 0750* –
▣ ▤ ▥ ☎ ✆. **⓪ ㏂ ⓪ ㎹ 亅ᴄʙ** FM e
**Meals** (room service only) – 또 16.50 – **6 rm** 199.00 s., **13 suites** 265.00/300.00 s.

🏠🏠🏠 **Cavendish,** 81 Jermyn St., SW1Y 6JF, *ℰ* (0171) 930 2111, *Fax (0171) 839 2125* – ▣,
숙 rm, ▤ rest, ▥ ☎ ⟷ – 益 80. **⓪ ㏂ ⓪ ㎹ 亅ᴄʙ**. ⅍ EN i
**Meals** *(closed lunch Saturday and Sunday)* 21.25 and a la carte ⓪ 6.95 – 또 14.50 – **249 rm**
165.00/195.00 s., 2 suites – SB.

**Pastoria**, 3-6 St. Martin's St., off Leicester Sq., WC2H 7HL, ℘ (0171) 930 8641, Fax (0171) 925 0551 – |≡|, ⧦ rm, ≡ rest, TV ☎ – 🔬 60. 🐼 AE ① VISA JCB. ℅      GM   v
Meals 17.00 and a la carte ♪ 12.50 – ⌑ 12.00 – **58 rm** 175.00/200.00 s.

**Thistle Trafalgar Square**, Whitcomb St., WC2H 7HG, ℘ (0171) 930 4477, Fax (0171) 925 2149 – |≡|, ⧦ rm, TV ☎. 🐼 AE ① VISA JCB. ℅      GM   r
Meals 13.95/16.95 st. and a la carte ♪ 5.95 – ⌑ 13.50 – **108 rm** 150.00/180.00 st. – SB.

**Thistle Piccadilly** without rest., 39 Coventry St., W1V 7EH, ℘ (0171) 930 4033, Fax (0171) 925 2586 – |≡| ⧦ TV ☎. 🐼 AE ① VISA JCB. ℅      FGM   a
⌑ 13.50 – **92 rm** 150.00/190.00 st.

**The Restaurant** (at Ritz H.), 150 Piccadilly, W1V 9DG, ℘ (0171) 493 8181, Fax (0171) 493 2687, 🍽, « Elegant restaurant in Louis XVI style » – ≡. 🐼 AE ① VISA JCB      DN   a
Meals (dancing Friday and Saturday evenings) 35.00/45.00 st. and a la carte 49.00/59.50 st. ♪ 18.00.

**Suntory**, 72-73 St. James's St., SW1A 1PH, ℘ (0171) 409 0201, Fax (0171) 499 0208 – ≡. 🐼 AE ① VISA JCB      EP   z
closed lunch Sunday and Bank Holidays, Easter and Christmas-New Year – **Meals** - Japanese - a la carte 35.50/89.20 st. ♪ 12.00.

**L'Oranger**, 5 St. James's St., SW1A 1EF, ℘ (0171) 839 3774, Fax (0171) 839 4330, 🍽 – ≡. 🐼 AE ① VISA JCB      EP   a
closed Saturday lunch, Sunday and 1 week Christmas – **Meals** 23.50/33.50 s. ♪ 15.00
**Spec.** Goat's cheese parcels in a bouillon of artichoke, hazelnut oil and basil. Roast loin of veal, sautéed girolles, foie gras and truffle sauce. Coconut parfait with pistachio ice cream.

**Quaglino's**, 16 Bury St., SW1Y 6AL, ℘ (0171) 930 6767, Fax (0171) 839 2866 – ≡. 🐼 AE ① VISA JCB      EN   r
Meals (booking essential) 19.00 t. and a la carte 26.00/50.50 t. ♪ 6.00.

**Criterion Brasserie Marco Pierre White**, 224 Piccadilly, W1V 9LB, ℘ (0171) 930 0488, Fax (0171) 930 8190, « 19C Neo-Byzantine decor » – 🐼 AE VISA      FM   c
closed Christmas – **Meals** 17.95 t. (lunch) and a la carte 26.65/29.25 t. ♪ 9.00.

**Le Caprice**, Arlington House, Arlington St., SW1A 1RT, ℘ (0171) 629 2239, Fax (0171) 493 9040 – ≡. 🐼 AE ① VISA      DN   c
closed 25-26 and 31 December, 1 January and 30 August – **Meals** a la carte 22.00/44.25 t. ♪ 8.75.

**Cave** (at Caviar House), 161 Piccadilly, W1V 9DF, ℘ (0171) 409 0445, Fax (0171) 493 1667 – ≡. 🐼 AE ① VISA      DN   s
closed Sunday, 25-26 December and 1 January – **Meals** a la carte 27.95/79.95 t.

**The Avenue**, 7-9 St. James's St., SW1A 1EE, ℘ (0171) 321 2111, Fax (0171) 321 2500 – ≡. 🐼 AE ① VISA      EP   e
closed 25 and 26 December – **Meals** 19.50 t. (lunch) and dinner a la carte 23.15/40.65 t.

**Matsuri**, 15 Bury St., SW1Y 6AL, ℘ (0171) 839 1101, Fax (0171) 930 7010 – ≡. 🐼 AE ① VISA JCB      EN   r
closed Sunday and Bank Holidays – **Meals** - Japanese (Teppan-Yaki, Sushi) - 14.00/40.00 t. and a la carte ♪ 12.50.

## Soho – ✉ W1/WC2 – pp. 30 and 31.

**Hampshire**, Leicester Sq., WC2H 7LH, ℘ (0171) 839 9399, Fax (0171) 930 8122, 🍽, ♠ – |≡|, ⧦ rm, ≡ TV ☎ – 🔬 80. 🐼 AE ① VISA JCB. ℅      GM   s
Meals 22.50 st. and a la carte ♪ 15.25 – ⌑ 15.00 – **119 rm** 280.00 s., 5 suites.

**Hazlitt's** without rest., 6 Frith St., W1V 5TZ, ℘ (0171) 434 1771, Fax (0171) 439 1524, « Early 18C town houses » – TV ☎. 🐼 AE ① VISA JCB. ℅      FK   u
closed Christmas – ⌑ 7.25 – **22 rm** 125.00/163.00, 1 suite.

**The Café Royal Grill**, 68 Regent St., W1R 6EL, ℘ (0171) 437 1177, Fax (0171) 439 7672, « Rococo decoration » – ≡. 🐼 AE VISA      EM   e
closed Saturday lunch and Sunday – **Meals** 24.50 st. (lunch) and a la carte 70.00/90.00 st. ♪ 11.50
**Spec.** Mousseline of lobster, beurre Champagne. Fillet of sea bass with scallops, ratatouille of aubergine and tomato. Bresse pigeon en vessie, ravioli of wild mushrooms, fumet of ceps.

**L'Escargot**, 48 Greek St., W1V 5LQ, ℘ (0171) 437 2679, Fax (0171) 437 0790 – ≡. 🐼 AE ① VISA JCB      GK   e
**Ground Floor :** Meals (closed Saturday lunch, Sunday and Christmas) 17.95 t. (lunch) and a la carte 25.65/31.65 t. ♪ 10.50 – **Picasso Room :** Meals (closed Saturday lunch, Sunday, Monday, August, Christmas and Bank Holidays) 27.50/42.00 t. ♪ 10.50
**Spec.** Tartlet of snails, wild mushrooms, red wine poached eggs. Goosnargh duck, fondant potato, mulled shallots and young vegetables. Iced caramel and apricot crumble.

425

XXX **Quo Vadis,** 26-29 Dean St., W1A 6LL, ☎ (0171) 437 9585, *Fax (0171) 434 9972* – ▤. MC AE VISA FK v
*closed lunch Saturday and Sunday and Christmas* – **Meals** 17.95 **t.** (lunch) and a la carte 25.45/72.90 **t.**

XX ✿ **Richard Corrigan at Lindsay House,** 21 Romilly St., W1V 5TG, ☎ (0171) 439 0450 *Fax (0171) 437 7349* – ▤. MC AE ① VISA GL
*closed Saturday lunch, Sunday, 2 weeks in summer and 1 week Christmas* – **Meals** 26.00/38.00 **t.** 16.00
**Spec.** Chilled lobster with tomato juices, avocado and basil. Saddle of rabbit stuffed with black pudding with root vegetable juices. Marinated cherries with goat's cheese sorbet.

XX **Teatro,** 93-107 Shaftesbury Av., W1V 8BT, ☎ (0171) 494 3040, *Fax (0171) 494 3050* – ▤ MC AE ① VISA JCB GL e
*closed Saturday lunch, Sunday and 25 to 30 December* – **Meals** 18.00 **t.** (lunch) and a la carte 25.75/38.75 11.00.

XX **The Sugar Club,** 21 Warwick St., W1R 5RB, ☎ (0171) 437 7776, *Fax (0171) 437 7778* – ▤. MC AE ① VISA EL r
*closed 25-26 December and 1 January* – **Meals** a la carte 24.10/33.10 **t.**

XX **Circus,** 1 Upper James St., W1R 4BP, ☎ (0171) 534 4000, *Fax (0171) 534 4010* – ▤. MC AE ① VISA EL e
*closed Sunday dinner, 25-26 December and 1 January* – **Meals** a la carte 20.50/34.50 **t.**

XX **Red Fort,** 77 Dean St., W1V 5HA, ☎ (0171) 437 2115, *Fax (0171) 434 0721* – ▤. MC AE ① VISA FJK r
**Meals** - Indian - (buffet lunch) a la carte 24.50/32.35 **t.**

XX **Mezzo,** Lower ground floor, 100 Wardour St., W1V 3LE, ☎ (0171) 314 4000, *Fax (0171) 314 4040* – ▤. MC AE ① VISA JCB FK a
*closed Saturday lunch and 25-26 December* – **Meals** 15.50 **t.** (lunch) and a la carte 23.00/30.25 **t.**

XX **Soho Soho,** (first floor), 11-13 Frith St., W1V 5TS, ☎ (0171) 494 3491, *Fax (0171) 437 3091,* – ▤. MC AE ① VISA JCB FK s
*closed Saturday lunch and Sunday* – **Meals** a la carte 26.50/35.50 **t.** 5.50.

XX **Lexington,** 45 Lexington St., W1R 3LG, ☎ (0171) 434 3401, *Fax (0171) 287 2997* – ▤. MC AE ① VISA JCB EK e
*closed Saturday lunch, Sunday and Bank Holidays* – **Meals** 15.00 **t.** (dinner) and a la carte 20.45/25.70 **t.** 5.00.

XX **Gopal's,** 12 Bateman St., W1V 5TD, ☎ (0171) 434 0840, *Fax (0171) 434 0840* – ▤. MC AE VISA FK e
*closed 25 and 26 December* – **Meals** - Indian - a la carte 13.95/19.50 **t.**

XX **Gay Hussar,** 2 Greek St., W1V 6NB, ☎ (0171) 437 0973, *Fax (0171) 437 4631* – ▤. MC AE ① VISA GJ c
*closed Sunday and Bank Holidays* – **Meals** - Hungarian - 17.50 **t.** (lunch) and a la carte 19.05/27.05 **t.** 7.50.

XX **Leith's Soho,** 41 Beak St., W1R 3LE, ☎ (0171) 287 2057, *Fax (0171) 287 1767* – ▤. MC AE ① VISA JCB EL a
*closed Sunday, 2 weeks Christmas and Bank Holidays* – **Meals** 19.50 **t.** (lunch) and a la carte 18.50/32.50 **t.** 5.75.

X **dell 'Ugo,** 56 Frith St., W1V 5TA, ☎ (0171) 734 8300, *Fax (0171) 734 8784* – MC AE ① VISA
*closed Saturday lunch, Sunday, 25-26 December and Bank Holidays* – **Meals** 12.50 **t.** and a la carte 23.35/27.35 **t.** FK z

X **Sri Siam,** 16 Old Compton St., W1V 5PE, ☎ (0171) 434 3544, *Fax (0171) 287 1311* – ▤. MC AE ① VISA GK r
*closed Sunday lunch, 25-26 December and 1 January* – **Meals** - Thai - 12.95/19.95 **t.** and a la carte 7.75.

X **Soho Spice,** 124-126 Wardour St., W1V 3LA, ☎ (0171) 434 0808, *Fax (0171) 434 0799* – MC AE ① VISA FJ e
**Meals** - Indian - 15.95 **t.** and a la carte.

X **Alastair Little,** 49 Frith St., W1V 5TE, ☎ (0171) 734 5183 – MC AE VISA JCB FK o
*closed Saturday lunch, Sunday and Bank Holidays* – **Meals** (booking essential) 25.00/33.00 **t.**.

X **Wok Wok,** 10 Frith St., W1V 5TZ, ☎ (0171) 437 7080, *Fax (0171) 437 3121* – ▤. MC AE ① VISA JCB FK c
*closed lunch Saturday and Sunday and 25 December* – **Meals** - South East Asian - (bookings not accepted) a la carte 13.65/19.65 **t.**

X **Fung Shing,** 15 Lisle St., WC2H 7BE, ☎ (0171) 734 0284, *Fax (0171) 734 0284* – ▤. MC AE ① VISA GL a
*closed Bank Holiday lunch and 24 to 26 December* – **Meals** - Chinese (Canton) - 16.00 **t.** and a la carte 6.00.

✗ **Saigon,** 45 Frith St., W1V 5TE, ℰ (0171) 437 7109, Fax (0171) 734 1668 – ■. **🗫 AE ① VISA**
*closed Sunday, Easter, 25-26 December and Bank Holidays* – **Meals** - Vietnamese -
a la carte approx. 16.25 **t.**                                                                            FGK x

✗ **Jen,** 7 Gerrard St., W1V 7LJ, ℰ (0171) 287 8193, Fax (0171) 734 9845 – ■. **🗫 AE VISA**
**Meals** - Hong Kong cuisine - 5.50/9.00 **t.** and a la carte.                                   GL e

**Strand and Covent Garden** – ⊠ WC2 - *Except where otherwise stated see p. 35.*

🏛️🏛️🏛️🏛️ **The Savoy,** Strand, WC2R 0EU, ℰ (0171) 836 4343, Fax (0171) 240 6040, ₅₆, ⇌, 🗙 – ⧣,
⇌ rm, ■ 🔟 ☎ ✆ ⇌ – 🔬 500. **🗫 AE ① VISA JCB**. 🛠                            DEY a
*Grill* : **Meals** *(closed Saturday lunch, Sunday and August)* a la carte 40.00/70.00 **t.** ⬧ 9.95 –
*River* : **Meals** 28.50/39.50-43.50 **st.** and a la carte 55.00/75.50 **st.** ⬧ 9.50 – ⌷ 18.75 –
**154 rm** 270.00/325.00 **s.,** 48 suites – SB.

🏛️🏛️🏛️ **Le Meridien Waldorf,** Aldwych, WC2B 4DD, ℰ (0171) 836 2400, Fax (0171) 836 7244 –
⧣, ⇌ rm, ■ rm, 🔟 ☎ – 🔬 450. **🗫 AE ① VISA JCB**                               EX x
*Palm Court* : **Meals** 23.50 **t.** (dinner) and a la carte 26.00/43.00 **st.** ⬧ 13.00 – *Aldwych*
*brasserie* : **Meals** *(closed Sunday dinner)* 15.50 **t.** and a la carte 14.40/19.40 **s.** ⬧ 9.50 – ⌷
17.00 – **286 rm** 225.00/315.00 **s.,** 6 suites – SB.

🏛️🏛️🏛️ **The Howard,** Temple Pl., WC2R 2PR, ℰ (0171) 836 3555, Fax (0171) 379 4547, ≤ – ⧣,
⇌ rm, ■ 🔟 ☎ ✆ ⇌ – 🔬 100. **🗫 AE ① VISA JCB**. 🛠 – **133 rm** 255.00/285.00 **st.,** 2 suites.
**Meals** a la carte 31.95/63.50 **st.** ⬧ 10.50 – ⌷ 19.50 – **133 rm** 255.00/285.00 **st.,** 2 suites.

🏛️🏛️ **One Aldwych,** WC2B 4BZ, ℰ (0171) 300 1000, Fax (0171) 300 1001, « Contemporary interior », ₅₆, ⇌, 🗙 – ⧣, ⇌ rm, ■ 🔟 ☎ ✆ ♿ – 🔬 100. **🗫 AE ① VISA JCB**. 🛠          EX r
*Indigo* : **Meals** a la carte 20.25/34.75 **t.** ⬧ 9.00 – (see also *Axis* below) – ⌷ 16.50 – **96 rm**
245.00/265.00 **s.,** 9 suites.

✗✗✗ **Ivy,** 1 West St., WC2H 9NE, ℰ (0171) 836 4751, Fax (0171) 497 3644 – ■. **🗫 AE ① VISA**
*closed 25-26 and 31 December, 1 January and 30 August* – **Meals** a la carte 23.75/46.25 **t.**
⬧ 8.75.                                                                                       p. 31 GK z

✗✗✗ **Axis,** 1 Aldwych, WC2B 4BZ, ℰ (0171) 300 0300, Fax (0171) 300 0301 – ■. **🗫 AE ① VISA**
**JCB**                                                                                           EX r
**Meals** *(closed Saturday lunch, Sunday and Bank Holidays)* 18.95 **t.** and a la carte ⬧ 10.00.

✗✗ **Rules,** 35 Maiden Lane, WC2E 7LB, ℰ (0171) 836 5314, Fax (0171) 497 1081, « London's
oldest restaurant with collection of antique cartoons, drawings and paintings » – **🗫 AE ①**
**VISA**                                                                                          DX n
*closed 5 days Christmas* – **Meals** - English - a la carte 26.45/31.65 **t.** ⬧ 6.00.

✗✗ **Bank,** 1 Kingsway, Aldwych, WC2B 6UA, ℰ (0171) 379 9797, Fax (0171) 379 9014 – **🗫 AE**
**① VISA JCB**                                                                                     EX s
*closed 25, 27 and 28 December, 1 January and Bank Holidays* – **Meals** 17.50 **t.** and a la carte.

✗✗ **Christopher's,** 18 Wellington St., WC2E 7DD, ℰ (0171) 240 4222, Fax (0171) 836 3506 –
■. **🗫 AE ① VISA JCB**                                                                            EX z
*closed Christmas* – **Meals** a la carte 22.50/41.50 **t.**

✗✗ **L'Estaminet,** 14 Garrick St., off Floral St., WC2 9BJ, ℰ (0171) 379 1432,
Fax (0171) 379 1530 – **🗫 AE VISA JCB**                                                           DX a
*closed Sunday, Easter, 25 December and Bank Holidays* – **Meals** - French - a la carte
20.00/31.40 **t.** ⬧ 8.00.

✗✗ **Sheekey's,** 28-32 St. Martin's Court, WC2N 4AL, ℰ (0171) 240 2565, Fax (0171) 240 8114 –
■. **🗫 AE ① VISA**                                                                               DX v
**Meals** - Seafood - a la carte 35.00/60.00 **t.** ⬧ 9.00.

✗✗ **Bertorelli's,** 44a Floral St., WC2E 9DA, ℰ (0171) 836 3969, Fax (0171) 836 1868 – ■. **🗫**
**AE ① VISA JCB**                                                                                 DX c
*closed 24 December dinner, Sunday and 25-26 December* – **Meals** - Italian - 14.00 **t.**
(lunch) and a la carte 16.85/24.95 **t.** ⬧ 9.25.

✗✗ **Corney and Barrow,** 116 St. Martins Lane, WC2 4AZ, ℰ (0171) 655 9800,
Fax (0171) 655 9801 – ■. **🗫 AE ① VISA**                                                          DY c
*closed Sunday and 25-26 December* **Meals** a la carte 14.95/26.20 **t.**

✗ **Stephen Bull St. Martin's Lane,** 12 Upper St. Martin's Lane, WC2 H9DL,
ℰ (0171) 379 7811 – ■. **🗫 AE ① VISA**                                                            DX r
*closed Saturday lunch, Sunday, 1 week Christmas-New Year and Bank Holidays* – **Meals**
a la carte approx. 27.50 **t.** ⬧ 7.00.

✗ **Le Café du Jardin,** 28 Wellington St., WC2E 7BD, ℰ (0171) 836 8769,
Fax (0171) 836 4123 – ■. **🗫 AE ① VISA JCB**                                                      EX a
*closed 25 December* – **Meals** 13.50 **t.** and a la carte ⬧ 4.50.

✗ **Magno's Brasserie,** 65a Long Acre, WC2E 9JH, ℰ (0171) 836 6077, Fax (0171) 379 6184
– ■. **🗫 AE ① VISA JCB**                                                                         DV e
*closed Saturday lunch, Sunday and 25-26 December* – **Meals** - French - 16.95 **t.**
and a la carte ⬧ 12.50.

&#9987; **Livebait,** 21 Wellington St., WC2E 7DN, &#9742; (0171) 836 7161. &#174; &#174; &#174; &#174; &#174;   EX
*closed Sunday, 1 week Christmas and Bank Holidays* – **Meals** - Seafood - a la carte 21.70
29.85 **t.**

&#9987; **Joe Allen,** 13 Exeter St., WC2E 7DT, &#9742; (0171) 836 0651, *Fax (0171) 497 2148* – &#9776;. &#174; &#174;
*VISA*
EX
*closed 24 and 25 December* – **Meals** 13.00 **t.** (lunch) and a la carte 19.00/25.00 **t.** &#9878; 6.00.

# Victoria – &#9993; SW1 – *Except where otherwise stated see p. 34.*

&#128488; *Victoria Station Forecourt, SW1V 1JU* &#9742; *(0171) 824 8844/(0839) 123456.*

&#127976; **St. James Court,** 45 Buckingham Gate, SW1E 6AF, &#9742; (0171) 834 6655
*Fax (0171) 630 7587,* **f&#x1F6C1;**, &#128701;, &#9776; &#9679;, &#9662;&#9662; rm, &#9776; &#128251; &#9743; &#128216; – &#9910; 180. &#174; &#174; *VISA* JCB, &#9948;
*Café Méditerranée :* **Meals** a la carte 18.50/26.50 **t.** – *Inn of Happiness :* **Meals** - Chinese
- *(closed Saturday lunch)* 16.50/18.50 **t.** – (see also *Auberge de Provence* below) – &#8414;
16.00 – **372 rm** 229.00 **st.,** 18 suites. CX

&#127976; **Thistle Royal Horseguards,** 2 Whitehall Court, SW1A 2EJ, &#9742; (0171) 839 3400
*Fax (0171) 925 2263,* **f&#x1F6C1;** – &#9776;, &#9662;&#9662; rm, &#9776; &#128251; &#9743; &#128216; – &#9910; 180. &#174; &#174; *VISA* JCB, &#9948;
**Meals** 24.00 **st.** and a la carte &#9878; 7.50 – &#8414; 15.00 – **277 rm** 220.00/325.00 **st.,** 3 suites
SB. p. 28 LX

&#127976; **Stakis London St. Ermin's,** Caxton St., SW1H 0QW, &#9742; (0171) 222 7888
*Fax (0171) 222 6914* – &#9776;, &#9662;&#9662; rm, &#9776; rest, &#128251; &#9743; – &#9910; 250. &#174; &#174; &#174; *VISA* JCB, &#9948; CX
*Cloisters brasserie :* **Meals** *(closed Saturday and Sunday)* 18.95/20.95 **st.**
and a la carte – *Caxton Grill :* **Meals** *(closed Saturday lunch, Sunday and Bank Holidays)*
a la carte 19.30/28.75 **st.** &#9878; 7.25 – &#8414; 12.95 – **283 rm** 195.00/245.00 **st.,** 7 suites – SB.

&#127976; **Goring,** 15 Beeston Pl., Grosvenor Gdns., SW1W 0JW, &#9742; (0171) 396 9000
*Fax (0171) 834 4393* – &#9776; &#9776; &#128251; &#9743; – &#9910; 50. &#174; &#174; *VISA*. &#9948;
**Meals** 27.00/35.00 **st.** &#9878; 14.00 – &#8414; 15.00 – **71 rm** 160.00/195.00 **s.,** 4 suites. BX

&#127976; **Thistle Grosvenor,** 101 Buckingham Palace Rd, SW1W 0SJ, &#9742; (0171) 834 9494
*Fax (0171) 630 1978* – &#9776;, &#9662;&#9662; rm, &#128251; &#9743; – &#9910; 200. &#174; &#174; &#174; *VISA* JCB, &#9948; BX
**Meals** (carving rest.) 18.00 **st.** and a la carte &#9878; 7.00 – &#8414; 14.00 – **363 rm** 140.00/203.00 **st**
3 suites.

&#127976; **Thistle Royal Westminster,** 49 Buckingham Palace Rd, SW1W 0QT
&#9742; (0171) 834 1821, *Fax (0171) 931 7542* – &#9776;, &#9662;&#9662; rm, &#9776; &#128251; &#9743; – &#9910; 180. &#174; &#174; &#174; *VISA* JCB
&#9948; BX
**Meals** 11.95/13.95 **t.** and a la carte &#9878; 6.00 – &#8414; 13.95 – **134 rm** 165.00/195.00 **st.**

&#127976; **Dolphin Square,** Dolphin Sq., Chichester St., SW1V 3LX, &#9742; (0171) 834 3800
*Fax (0171) 798 8735,* **f&#x1F6C1;**, &#128701;, &#9635;, &#127939;, &#9987;, squash – &#9776;, &#9662;&#9662; rm, &#9776; rest, &#128251; &#9743; &#9855; &#9854; &#127384;
&#9910; 50. &#174; &#174; &#174; *VISA*. &#9948; p. 28 KZ
**Meals** 12.95 **t.** and a la carte &#9878; 5.00 – (see also *Rhodes in the Square* below) – &#8414; 12.95 –
**15 rm** 100.00/135.00 **st.,** **136 suites** 180.00 **st.**

&#127976; **Rubens,** 39-41 Buckingham Palace Rd, SW1W 0PS, &#9742; (0171) 834 6600
*Fax (0171) 828 5401* – &#9776;, &#9662;&#9662; rm, &#9776; rest, &#128251; &#9743; – &#9910; 75. &#174; &#174; *VISA* JCB, &#9948; BX
**Meals** *(closed Sunday lunch)* (carving lunch) 17.95 **st.** and dinner a la carte &#9878; 10.00 – &#8414;
13.00 – **174 rm** 130.00/210.00 **s.**

&#127977; **Rochester,** 69 Vincent Sq., SW1P 2PA, &#9742; (0171) 828 6611, *Fax (0171) 233 6724* – &#9776;
&#9776; rest, &#128251; &#9743; &#128216; – &#9910; 60. &#174; &#174; &#174; *VISA* JCB, &#9948;
**Meals** 19.75 **st.** and a la carte &#9878; 14.50 – &#8414; 12.95 – **80 rm** 159.00/175.00 **st.** CY

&#127977; **Holiday Inn London Victoria,** 2 Bridge Pl., SW1V 1QA, &#9742; (0171) 834 8123
*Fax (0171) 828 1099,* **f&#x1F6C1;**, &#128701;, &#9635; – &#9776;, &#9662;&#9662; rm, &#9776; &#128251; &#9743; &#128216; – &#9910; 180. &#174; &#174; &#174; *VISA* JCB
&#9948;
**Meals** 17.95/19.50 **t.** and a la carte &#9878; 7.50 – &#8414; 12.75 – **212 rm** 170.00/190.00 **st.** BY

&#127976; **Winchester** without rest., 17 Belgrave Rd, SW1V 1RB, &#9742; (0171) 828 2972
*Fax (0171) 828 5191* – &#128251;. &#9948; BY
*closed 24-25 December* – **18 rm** &#8414; 68.00 **st.**

&#127976; **Tophams Ebury Court,** 28 Ebury St., SW1W 0LU, &#9742; (0171) 730 8147
*Fax (0171) 823 5966* – &#9776; &#128251; &#9743; – &#9910; 30. &#174; &#174; &#174; *VISA* JCB
AX
*closed 24 December-4 January* – **Meals** *(closed lunch Saturday and Sunday)* a la carte
19.00/21.00 **st.** &#9878; 5.00 – **41 rm** &#8414; 110.00/160.00 **t.**

&#9988;&#9988;&#9988; **Rhodes in the Square** (at Dolphin Square H.), Dolphin Sq., Chichester St., SW1V 3LX
&#9742; (0171) 798 6767, *Fax (0171) 798 5685* – &#9776;. &#174; &#174; &#174; *VISA* JCB p. 28 KZ
*closed Saturday lunch and Bank Holidays* – **Meals** 19.50 **t.** (lunch) and a la carte 27.10
38.40 **t.** &#9878; 12.50.

&#9988;&#9988;&#9988; **Auberge de Provence** (at St. James Court H.), 45 Buckingham Gate, SW1E 6AF
&#9742; (0171) 821 1899, *Fax (0171) 630 7587* – &#9776;. &#174; &#174; &#174; *VISA* JCB
CX
*closed Saturday lunch, Sunday, 2 weeks January, 2 weeks August and Bank Holidays* – **Meals**
- French - a la carte 26.50/31.50 **t.**

XXX **L'Incontro,** 87 Pimlico Rd, SW1W 8PH, ℰ (0171) 730 6327, Fax (0171) 730 5062 – 🍽. 🔵🔷
🖭 ⓪ VISA JCB
p. 33  FT  u
*closed lunch Saturday and Sunday and 25-26 December* – **Meals** - Italian - 20.50 **t.**
(lunch) and a la carte 27.50/51.50 **t.** ⓵ 12.50.

XXX **Santini,** 29 Ebury St., SW1W 0NZ, ℰ (0171) 730 4094, Fax (0171) 730 0544 – 🍽. 🔵🔷 🖭 ⓪
VISA JCB
ABX  v
*closed lunch Saturday and Sunday and 25-26 December* – **Meals** - Italian - 19.75 **t.**
(lunch) and a la carte 25.00/51.75 **t.** ⓵ 9.00.

XXX **Shepherd's,**  Marsham  Court,  Marsham  St.,  SW1P  4LA,  ℰ (0171) 834 9552,
Fax (0171) 233 6047 – 🍽. 🔵🔷 🖭 ⓪ VISA JCB
p. 28  LZ  z
*closed Saturday, Sunday, Easter, summer Bank Holidays, 25-26 December and 1 January* –
**Meals** - English - (booking essential) 23.95 **t.** ⓵ 14.75.

XX **Roussillon,** 16 St. Barnabas St., SW1W 8PB, ℰ (0171) 730 5550, Fax (0171) 824 8617 – 🍽.
🔵🔷 ⓪ VISA JCB
p. 27  IZ  c
*closed Sunday, 15 to 29 August, 25-26 December and Bank Holidays* – **Meals** 16.00/24.00 **t.**
and a la carte.

XX **Simply Nico,** 48a Rochester Row, SW1P 1JU, ℰ (0171) 630 8061, Fax (0171) 828 8541 –
🍽. 🔵🔷 🖭 ⓪ VISA JCB
CY  a
*closed Saturday lunch, Sunday, 25-26 December and Bank Holidays* – **Meals** (booking
essential) 25.00/27.00 **st.**.

XX **Tate Gallery,** Tate Gallery, Millbank, SW1P 4RG, ℰ (0171) 887 8877, Fax (0171) 887 8902,
« Rex Whistler murals » – 🍽. 🔵🔷 🖭 ⓪ VISA
p. 28  LZ  c
*closed 25 December* – **Meals** (booking essential) (lunch only) 18.50 **t.** and a la carte ⓵ 8.50.

XX **The Atrium,** 4 Millbank, SW1P 3JA, ℰ (0171) 233 0032, Fax (0171) 233 0010 – 🍽. 🔵🔷 🖭
⓪ VISA
p. 28  LY  s
*closed Saturday, Sunday, Christmas, Easter and Bank Holidays* – **Meals** a la carte 17.40/
29.40 **t.**

XX **Ken Lo's Memories of China,** 67-69 Ebury St., SW1W 0NZ, ℰ (0171) 730 7734,
Fax (0171) 730 2992 – 🍽. 🔵🔷 🖭 ⓪ VISA JCB
AY  u
*closed Sunday lunch, 24 December-1 January and Bank Holidays* – **Meals** - Chinese -
19.00/25.00 **t.** and a la carte.

XX **Hunan,** 51 Pimlico Rd, SW1W 8NE, ℰ (0171) 730 5712, Fax (0171) 730 8265 – 🔵🔷 🖭
VISA
p. 27  IZ  a
*closed Sunday, 4 days Christmas and Bank Holidays* – **Meals** - Chinese (Hunan) - a la carte
11.70/43.80 **t.** ⓵ 10.00.

X **Olivo,** 21 Eccleston St., SW1W 9LX, ℰ (0171) 730 2505, Fax (0171) 824 8190 – 🍽. 🔵🔷 🖭 VISA
*closed lunch Saturday and Sunday, 25 December and Bank Holidays* – **Meals** - Italian -
17.00 **t.** (lunch) and a la carte 24.50/31.00 **t.** ⓵ 7.50.
AY  z

X **La Poule au Pot,** 231 Ebury St., SW1W 8UT, ℰ (0171) 730 7763, Fax (0171) 259 9651, 🏠
– 🍽. 🔵🔷 🖭 ⓪ VISA JCB
p. 27  IZ  e
**Meals** - French - 13.95 **t.** (lunch) and a la carte 26.00/36.35 ⓵ 5.75.

**LONGBRIDGE** Warks. – see Warwick.

---

**LONG CRENDON** Bucks. 403 404 R 28 – pop. 2 505 – ⊠ Aylesbury.
London 50 – Aylesbury 11 – Oxford 15.

X **Angel Inn** with rm, Bicester Rd, HP18 9EE, ℰ (01844) 208268, Fax (01844) 202497, 霜
« Part 16C » – ⇔ rm, ⊡ ☎ ✆ ℗. ⚈ VISA JCB. ⚘
Meals (closed Sunday dinner) a la carte 17.50/25.95 t. ⋔ 7.50 – � 5.00 – **3 rm** 55.00/65.00 t

---

**LONG EATON** Derbs. 402 403 404 Q 25 – see Nottingham (Notts.).

---

**LONGFORD** W. Mids. 403 404 P 26 – see Coventry.

---

**LONG MARSTON** N. Yorks. 402 Q 22 – see York.

---

**LONG MELFORD** Suffolk 404 W 27 Great Britain G. – pop. 2 808.
See : Melford Hall★ AC.
London 62 – Cambridge 34 – Colchester 18 – Ipswich 24.

🏠 **Bull,** Hall St., CO10 9JG, ℰ (01787) 378494, Fax (01787) 880307, « Part 15C coaching inn » –
⇔ rm, ⊡ ☎ ℗ – ⚎ 60. ⚈ ⯒ VISA JCB. ⚘
Meals a la carte 18.50/35.95 t. ⋔ 7.95 – **25 rm** � 65.00/100.00 t. – SB.

🏠 **Countrymen,** The Green, CO10 9DN, ℰ (01787) 312356, Fax (01787) 374557 – ⇔ rest
⊡ ☎ ℗. ⚈ VISA JCB
closed January – **Countrymen :** Meals (closed Sunday dinner and Monday) 9.95 t
and a la carte ⋔ 7.75 – **8 rm** � 60.00/80.00 t., 1 suite – SB.

🏠 **George and Dragon,** Hall St., CO10 9JB, ℰ (01787) 371285, Fax (01787) 312428, 霜 –
⊡ ☎ ℗ – ⚎ 30. ⚈ VISA
Meals a la carte 12.40/21.85 st. ⋔ 6.95 – **7 rm** � 30.00/50.00 st. – SB.

XXX **Chimneys,** Hall St., CO10 9JR, ℰ (01787) 379806, Fax (01787) 312294, « Part 16C cot
tage », 霜 – ⚈ ⓞ VISA
closed Sunday and 24 to 29 December – Meals a la carte 19.65/31.65 st.

X **Scutchers Bistro,** Westgate St., CO10 9DP, on A 1092 ℰ (07000) 728824
Fax (07000) 785443, 霜 – ⚈ ⯒ VISA JCB
closed Sunday, Monday, first week January, Christmas and Bank Holidays – Meals a la carte
14.50/22.00 t.

---

**LONG PRESTON** N. Yorks. 402 N 21 – ⊠ Skipton.
London 232 – Bradford 28 – Kendal 36 – Leeds 47.

🏠 **The Country House,** BD23 4NJ, ℰ (01729) 840246, Fax (01729) 840246, ⬄, 霜 – ⇔
⊡ ℗. ⚘
closed mid December-early February – Meals (residents only) (dinner only) (unlicensed)
16.00 st. – **7 rm** � 35.00/56.00 st.

---

**LONGRIDGE** Lancs. 402 M 22 – pop. 7 351.
London 241 – Blackburn 12 – Burnley 18.

XXX **Paul Heathcote's,** 104-106 Higher Rd, PR3 3SY, Northeast : ½ m. by B 5269 following
🟢 signs for Jeffrey Hill ℰ (01772) 784969, Fax (01772) 785713 – ⇔. ⚈ ⯒ ⓞ VISA
closed Monday – Meals (dinner only and lunch Friday and Sunday) 22.50/30.00 t
and a la carte 32.00/42.00 t. ⋔ 8.00
**Spec.** Avocado, gravadlax and langoustine salad. Roast duck with rhubarb and onions. Wild
strawberry, basil and sherry trifle.

---

**LONG SUTTON** Lincs. 404 U 25 – pop. 4 185.
London 100 – Lincoln 51 – Leicester 67 – Norwich 54.

🏠 **Travelodge,** Wisbech Rd, PE12 9AG, Southeast : 1 m. at junction of A 17 with A 110
ℰ (01406) 362230, Reservations (Freephone) 0800 850950 – ⇔ rm, ⊡ ✆ ℗. ⚈ ⯒ ⓞ VISA
JCB. ⚘
Meals (grill rest.) – **40 rm** 39.95/59.95 t.

**LOOE** Cornwall **403** G 32 *The West Country G. – pop. 5 022.*

See : *Town★ – Monkey Sanctuary★ AC.*

ᵣₛ *Bin Down ℰ (01503) 240239 –* ᵣₛ *Whitsand Bay Hotel, Portwrinkle, Torpoint ℰ (01503) 230276.*

🛈 *The Guildhall, Fore St., PL13 1AA ℰ (01503) 262072 (summer only).*

*London 264 – Plymouth 21 – Truro 39.*

🏦 **Klymiarven** ⬎, Barbican Hill, East Looe, PL13 1BH, East : 2 m. by A 387 off B 3253 or access from town on foot ℰ (01503) 262333, *Fax (01503) 262333*, ≼ Looe and harbour, 🐎 – ☆☆ rest, 📺 ☎ 🅿. 🆎 *VISA* *JCB*
*closed 4 weeks January and 2 weeks November –* **Meals** (dinner only) 14.95 t. and a la carte ⌀ 6.50 – **14 rm** ⬱ 49.00/98.00 st. – SB.

🏦 **Commonwood Manor** ⬎, St. Martins Rd, East Looe, PL13 1LP, Northeast : ½ m. by A 387 on B 3253 ℰ (01503) 262929, *Fax (01503) 262632*, ≼ Looe Valley, 🏊, 🐎 – 📺 ☎ 🅿. 🆎 🅰🅴 *VISA* *JCB*
*closed 1 week Christmas –* **Meals** (bar lunch)/dinner 14.00 st. ⌀ 4.95 – **11 rm** ⬱ 39.00/78.00 st. – SB.

⌂ **Bucklawren Farm** ⬎, St. Martin-by-Looe, PL13 1NZ, Northeast : 3½ m. by A 387 and B 3253 turning right onto single track road signposted to monkey sanctuary ℰ (01503) 240738, *Fax (01503) 240481*, ≼, « Working farm », 🐎, park – ☆☆ rest, 🅿. 🆎 *VISA*. ⌘
*March-October –* **Meals** (by arrangement) 10.50 st. – **6 rm** ⬱ 27.00/44.00 st. – SB.

⌂ **Harescombe Lodge** ⬎ without rest., Watergate, PL13 2NE, Northwest : 2 ¾ m. by A 387 turning right opposite Waylands Farm onto single track road ℰ (01503) 263158, 🐎 – 🅿. ⌘
**3 rm** ⬱ 44.00 s.

**at Sandplace** *North : 2¼ m. on A 387 – ⊠ Polperro.*

🏠 **Polraen Country House**, PL13 1PJ, ℰ (01503) 263956, *Fax (01503) 264389*, 🐎 – ☆☆ rest, 📺 🅿. 🆎 *VISA* *JCB*. ⌘
**Meals** (dinner only and Sunday lunch)/dinner 15.00 st. and a la carte ⌀ 4.95 – **5 rm** ⬱ 35.00/60.00 st. – SB.

**at Widegates** *Northeast : 3½ m. on B 3253 – ⊠ Looe.*

⌂ **Coombe Farm** ⬎, PL13 1QN, on B 3253 ℰ (01503) 240223, *Fax (01503) 240895*, ≼ countryside, 🏊, 🐎, park – ☆☆ 📺 ☎ 🅿. 🆎 🅰🅴 ⓪ *VISA*. ⌘
*March-October –* **Meals** (by arrangement) 16.00 st. ⌀ 3.75 – **10 rm** ⬱ 72.00 st. – SB.

**at Talland Bay** *Southwest : 4 m. by A 387 – ⊠ Looe.*

🏦 **Talland Bay** ⬎, PL13 2JB, ℰ (01503) 272667, *Fax (01503) 272940*, ≼, « Country house atmosphere », ⬱, 🏊, 🐎 – ☆☆ rest, 📺 ☎ 🅿. 🆎 🅰🅴 ⓪ *VISA*. ⌘
*closed January-late February –* **Meals** (bar lunch)/dinner 22.00 t. and a la carte ⌀ 6.10 – **17 rm** ⬱ (dinner included) 67.00/190.00 t., 2 suites – SB.

🏠 **Allhays Country House** ⬎, PL13 2JB, ℰ (01503) 272434, *Fax (01503) 272929*, ≼, 🐎 – ☆☆ 📺 ☎ 🅿. 🆎 🅰🅴 ⓪ *VISA* *JCB*
*closed Christmas-7 January –* **Meals** (bar lunch)/dinner 16.50 st. ⌀ 5.45 – **6 rm** ⬱ 36.00/79.00 st. – SB.

**at Pelynt** *Northwest : 4 m. by A 387 on B 3359 – ⊠ Looe.*

🏠 **Jubilee Inn**, Pelynt, PL13 2JZ, ℰ (01503) 220312, *Fax (01503) 220920*, « Part 16C » – 📺 ☎ ℀ 🅿. 🆎 *VISA* *JCB*
**Meals** a la carte 17.20/25.30 t. ⌀ 5.50 – **9 rm** ⬱ 36.00/59.00 t.

**LORTON** Cumbria **402** K 20 – *see Cockermouth.*

**LOSTWITHIEL** Cornwall **403** G 32 *The West Country G. – pop. 2 452.*

**Env. :** *Lanhydrock★★, N : 4 m. by B 3268 – Restormel Castle★ AC (≼★) N : 1 m. – Bodmin (St. Petroc Church★) NW : 6 m. by B 3268.*

ᵣₛ *Lostwithiel G & C.C., Lower Polscoe ℰ (01208) 873550 –* ᵣₛ *Lanhydrock, Lostwithiel Road, Bodmin ℰ (01208) 73600.*

🛈 *Community Centre, Liddicoat Rd, PL22 0HE ℰ (01208) 872207.*

*London 273 – Plymouth 30 – Truro 23.*

🏠 **Restormel Lodge**, 17 Castle Hill, PL22 0DD, on A 390 ℰ (01208) 872223, *Fax (01208) 873568*, 🏊, 🐎 – 📺 ☎ 🅿. 🆎 🅰🅴 ⓪ *VISA*
**Meals** (bar lunch)/dinner 16.00 st. and a la carte ⌀ 4.50 – **32 rm** ⬱ 50.00/70.00 st. – SB.

**LOUGHBOROUGH** *Leics.* 402 403 404 Q 25 – pop. 46 867.

🐾 *Lingdale, Joe Moore's Lane, Woodhouse Eaves ℰ (01509) 890703.*
🄑 *John Storer House, Wards End, LE11 3HA ℰ (01509) 218113.*
*London 117 – Birmingham 41 – Leicester 11 – Nottingham 15.*

🏤 **Quality**, New Ashby Rd, LE11 0EX, West : 2 m. on A 512 ℰ (01509) 211800
Fax (01509) 211868, *Ⅰ₆, 🖙, 🔲, 🎇 – ✳ rm, 📺 🕿 ఉ 🅿 – 🔏 225.* 🐽 🕮 ⓞ 𝗩𝗜𝗦𝗔
**Meals** 14.50 st. 🍴 4.50 – ☲ 9.50 – **94 rm** 74.25/96.00 st.

🏬 **Cedars**, Cedar Rd, LE11 2AB, Southeast : 1 m. by A 6 ℰ (01509) 214459
Fax (01509) 233573, 🖙, 🔃, 🎇 – 📺 🕿 🅿. 🐽 ⓞ 𝗩𝗜𝗦𝗔
**Meals** *(closed Sunday dinner)* 14.95 t. and a la carte 🍴 7.75 – **36 rm** ☲ 55.00/68.00 st.

⌂ **Charnwood Lodge**, 136 Leicester Rd, LE11 2AQ, Southeast : ¾ m. on A 6
ℰ (01509) 211120 – ✳ rm 🅿. 🐽 ⓞ 𝗩𝗜𝗦𝗔 𝗝𝗖𝗕. 🎇
**Meals** *(by arrangement)* 7.50 s. – **5 rm** ☲ 28.00/38.00.

⌂ **Garendon Park**, 92 Leicester Rd, LE11 2AQ, Southeast : ½ m. on A 6 ℰ (01509) 236557
Fax (01509) 265559 – 📺. 🐽 🕮 ⓞ 𝗩𝗜𝗦𝗔 𝗝𝗖𝗕. 🎇
**Meals** 12.00 st. – **9 rm** ☲ 28.00/50.00 st.

**at Quorndon** *Southeast : 3 m. by A 6 – ⊠ Loughborough.*

🏤 **Quorn Country**, 66 Leicester Rd, LE12 8BB, ℰ (01509) 415050, Fax (01509) 415557, 🎇 –
✳ rm, 🗐 rm, 📺 🕿 ఉ 🅿 – 🔏 120. 🐽 🕮 ⓞ 𝗩𝗜𝗦𝗔
**Shires** : **Meals** *(closed Saturday lunch)* 20.00 t. and a la carte 🍴 5.85 – **Orangery** : **Meals**
*(closed Saturday lunch and dinner Sunday and Monday)* 12.50 t. (lunch) and a la carte
20.65/23.95 t. 🍴 5.85 – ☲ 8.95 – **18 rm** 93.00/104.00 t., 2 suites – SB.

🏨 **Quorn Grange**, 88 Wood Lane, LE12 8DB, Southeast : ¾ m. ℰ (01509) 412167
Fax (01509) 415621, 🎇 – 📺 🕿 ఉ 🅿 – 🔏 100. 🐽 🕮 ⓞ 𝗩𝗜𝗦𝗔 𝗝𝗖𝗕
closed 26 December and 1 January – **Meals** *(closed Saturday lunch and Bank Holidays)*
12.35/20.50 st. and a la carte 🍴 8.95 – ☲ 7.35 – **14 rm** 78.00/92.00 st., 1 suite.

🅐 ATS Bridge St. ℰ (01509) 218447/218472

---

**LOUGHTON** *Essex* 404 U 29.
*London 15 – Cambridge 44 – Ipswich 66 – Luton 30 – Southend-on-Sea 35.*

✕ **Ne'als Brasserie**, 241 High Rd, IG10 1AD, ℰ (0181) 508 3443 – 🗐. 🐽 ⓞ 𝗩𝗜𝗦𝗔 𝗝𝗖𝗕
closed Sunday dinner, Monday and 27 to 31 December – **Meals** a la carte 20.20/28.00 t.
🍴 5.50.

---

**LOUTH** *Lincs.* 402 404 U 23 – pop. 14 248.
*London 156 – Boston 34 – Great Grimsby 17 – Lincoln 26.*

🏤 **Kenwick Park** ⑊, LN11 8NR, Southeast : 2 ¼ m. by B 1520 on A 157 ℰ (01507) 608806
Fax (01507) 608027, ≤, Ⅰ₆, 🖙, 🔲, 🐾, 🎇, park, 🎇, squash – ✳ rest, 📺 🕿 🅿 – 🔏 30. 🐽
🕮 ⓞ 𝗩𝗜𝗦𝗔
**Meals** 18.50 t. and a la carte 🍴 6.95 – **24 rm** ☲ 79.50/120.00 t. – SB.

🏨 **The Beaumont**, 66 Victoria Rd, LN11 0BX, by Eastgate off Ramsgate Rd
ℰ (01507) 605005, Fax (01507) 607768 – 🖞 📺 🕿 🅿 – 🔏 90. 🐽 🕮 𝗩𝗜𝗦𝗔
**Meals** *(closed Sunday lunch)* 12.95 st. and a la carte 🍴 5.50 – **16 rm** ☲ 40.00/75.00 st. – SB

🏨 **Brackenborough Arms**, Cordeaux Corner, Brackenborough, LN11 0SZ, North : 2 m. by
A 16 ℰ (01507) 609169, Fax (01507) 609413 – ✳ rm, 📺 🕿 🅿 – 🔏 30. 🐽 🕮 ⓞ 𝗩𝗜𝗦𝗔 𝗝𝗖𝗕
🎇
closed 25 and 26 December – **Meals** *(closed Sunday dinner)* a la carte 14.25/23.45 t. 🍴 6.95
– **25 rm** ☲ 57.95/69.00 t. – SB.

🅐 ATS 179 Newmarket ℰ (01507) 601975

---

**LOWER ODDINGTON** *Glos.* 403 404 P 28 – see Stow-on-the-Wold.

---

**LOWER SLAUGHTER** *Glos.* 403 404 O 28 – see Bourton-on-the-Water.

---

**LOWESTOFT** *Suffolk* 404 Z 26 *Great Britain G.* – pop. 62 907.
**Env. :** *The Broads★.*
🐾, 🐾 *Rookery Park, Carlton Colville ℰ (01502) 560380.*
🄑 *East Point Pavillion, Royal Plain, NR33 0AP ℰ (01502) 523000.*
*London 116 – Ipswich 43 – Norwich 30.*

🏨 **Hatfield**, Esplanade, NR33 0QP, ℘ (01502) 565337, Fax (01502) 511885, ≤ – 🔟 ☎ 🅿 –
🔏 100. 🆎 🆎 ① VISA JCB. ❄
Meals (closed Saturday lunch) 7.00/14.50 **t.** and a la carte ᗷ 4.95 – **33 rm** ⊇ 49.00/105.00 **t.**
– SB.

🏠 **Travel Inn**, 249 Yarmouth Rd, NR32 4AA, North : 2 ½ m. on A 12 ℘ (01502) 572441 –
❄ rm, 🔟 🕭 🅿. 🆎 🆎 VISA. ❄
Meals (grill rest.) – **41 rm** 38.00 **t.**

**at Oulton Broad** West : 2 m. by A 146 – ⊠ Lowestoft.

🏨 **Ivy House Farm** ⊗, Ivy Lane, NR33 8HY, Southwest : 1 ½ m. by A 146
℘ (01502) 501353, Fax (01502) 501539, 🐦, park – ❄ rest, 🔟 ☎ 🕭 🅿. 🆎 🆎 ① VISA JCB
**Crooked Barn :** Meals 18.95/20.95 **st.** and dinner a la carte ᗷ 7.75 – **12 rm** ⊇ 65.00/
93.00 **t.** – SB.

 🅰 ATS 263 Whapload Rd ℘ (01502) 561581

**LOW FELL** Tyne and Wear – see Gateshead.

**LOW LAITHE** N. Yorks. – see Pateley Bridge.

**LUDLOW** Shrops. 🄰🄾🄱 L 26 Great Britain G. – pop. 9 040.
See : Town★ – Castle★ AC – Feathers Hotel★ – St. Laurence's Parish Church★ (Miser-
icords★ ).
Exc. : Stokesay Castle★ AC, NW : 6½ m. by A 49.
🚹 Castle St., SY8 1AS ℘ (01584) 875053.
London 162 – Birmingham 39 – Hereford 24 – Shrewsbury 29.

🏨 **Feathers**, Bull Ring, SY8 1AA, ℘ (01584) 875261, Fax (01584) 876030, 🏛, « Part Elizabethan house » – 🔋 ❄, 🖿 rest, 🔟 ☎ 🅿 – 🔏 100. 🆎 🆎 ① VISA JCB
Meals 13.50/19.95 **t.** and dinner a la carte – ⊇ 9.25 – **40 rm** 60.00/98.00 **t.** – SB.

🏨 **Dinham Hall**, Dinham, SY8 1EJ, ℘ (01584) 876464, Fax (01584) 876019, 🕭, 🐦 –
❄ rest, 🔟 ☎ 🅿. 🆎 🆎 ① VISA
Meals 18.50/20.50 **t.** ᗷ 7.00 – **13 rm** ⊇ 65.00/125.00 **t.** – SB.

🏨 **Overton Grange**, Hereford Rd, SY8 4AD, South : 1 ¾ m. by B 4361 ℘ (01584) 873500,
Fax (01584) 873524, ≤, 🐦 – ❄ rest, 🔟 ☎ 🅿 – 🔏 160. 🆎 🆎 ① VISA. ❄
**Les Marches :** Meals – French - 20.00 **t.** (dinner) and a la carte 20.00/30.00 **t.** ᗷ 9.00 –
**15 rm** ⊇ 55.00/116.00 **t.** – SB
**Spec.** Pan-fried langoustine scented with curry, velouté of celeriac. John Dory with mille-
feuille of Swiss chard and summer truffles. Chocolate soufflé, star anise ice cream.

🏠 **Cliffe** ⊗, Dinham, SY8 2JE, West : ½ m. via Dinham Bridge ℘ (01584) 872063,
Fax (01584) 873991, 🐦 – ❄ 🔟 ☎ 🅿. 🆎 VISA
Meals (booking essential) (bar lunch Monday to Saturday and Sunday dinner)/dinner
13.95 **t.** ᗷ 4.95 – **9 rm** ⊇ 30.00/60.00 **t.**

⌂ **Number Twenty Eight** without rest., 28 Lower Broad St., SY8 1PQ, ℘ (01584) 876996,
Fax (01584) 876860, 🐦 – ❄ 🔟 ☎ ✆. 🆎 🆎 VISA. ❄
**6 rm** ⊇ 65.00/75.00 **st.**

XX **Oaks**, 17 Corve St., SY8 1DA, ℘ (01584) 872325, Fax (01584) 874024, « 17C oak panelling »
– ❄. 🆎 VISA
closed Sunday, Monday, 1 week early summer and 1 week in autumn – Meals (dinner only)
24.50 **t.** ᗷ 6.50.

XX **Mr. Underhill's at Dinham Weir** (Bradley) with rm, Dinham Bridge, SY8 1EH,
℘ (01584) 874431, Fax (01584) 874431, ≤, 🏛, « Riverside setting », 🐟, 🐦 – ❄ 🔟 ☎ 🅿.
🆎 VISA. ❄
Meals (set menu only) (booking essential) (lunch by arrangement) 22.50/25.00 **t.** ᗷ 6.50 –
**6 rm** ⊇ 50.00/75.00 **t.** – SB
**Spec.** Salmon and brill with leek and tomato. Barbary duck with herbes de Provence. Panna
cotta with red fruit compote.

XX **Merchant House** (Hill), Lower Corve St., SY8 1DU, ℘ (01584) 875438,
Fax (01584) 876927, « Jacobean house » – ❄. 🆎 🆎 JCB
closed Sunday, Monday, 1 week in spring and 1 week Christmas – Meals (dinner only and
lunch Friday and Saturday) 28.50 **st.** ᗷ 8.00
**Spec.** Sautéed scallops with lentil and coriander sauce. Roast hare with celeriac and morel
mushrooms. Chocolate pithiviers.

X **Courtyard**, 2 Quality Sq., SY8 1AR, ℘ (01584) 878080 – ❄ 🖿
closed Sunday, 25-26 and 31 December and 2 weeks January – Meals (light lunch) (dinner
Thursday to Saturday)/dinner a la carte 16.80/21.65 **t.** ᗷ 5.35.

 🅰 ATS Weeping Cross Lane ℘ (01584) 872401

**LUTON** [404] S 28 *Great Britain G. – pop. 171 671.*

See : *Luton Hoo★ (Wernher Collection★★)* **AC X**.

⛳18 *Stockwood Park, London Rd* ☎ *(01582) 413704,* **X** – ⛳18, ⛳9 *South Beds, Warden Hill Ro* ☎ *(01582) 575201.*

✈ *Luton International Airport :* ☎ *(01582) 405100, E : 1 ½ m.* **X** – **Terminal** : Luton Bus Station.

[i] *The Bus Station, 65-67 Bute St., LU1 2EY* ☎ *(01582) 401579.*

*London 35 – Cambridge 36 – Ipswich 93 – Oxford 45 – Southend-on-Sea 63.*

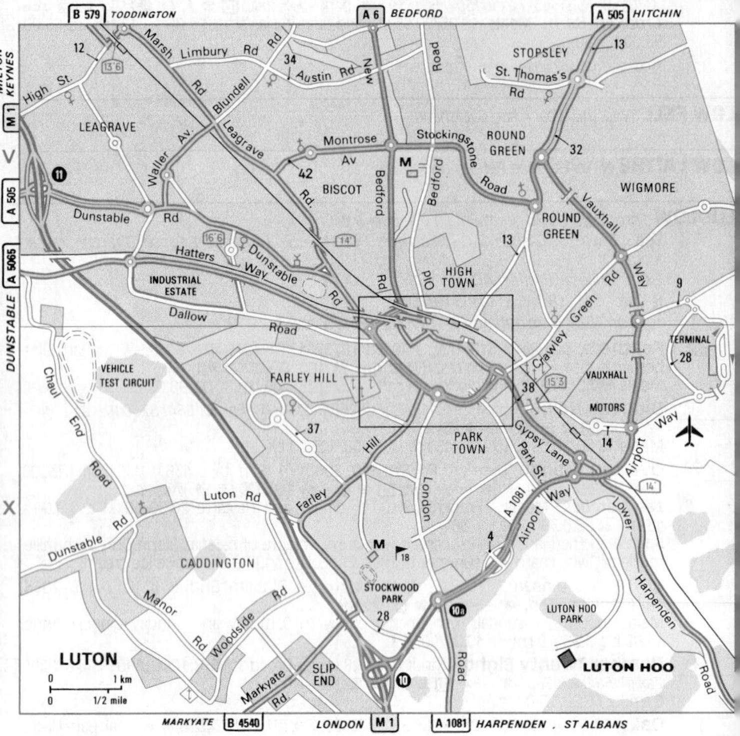


Capability Green .......... **X** 4
Eaton Green Road .......... **V** 9
Grange Avenue .......... **V** 12
Hitchin Road .......... **V** 13
Kimpton Road .......... **X** 14
Newlands Road .......... **X** 23
Percival Way .......... **X** 28
Stopsley Way .......... **X** 32
Trinity Road .......... **V** 34
Whipperley Way .......... **X** 37
Windmill Road .......... **X** 38
Woodland Avenue .......... **V** 42

🏨 **Thistle Strathmore,** Arndale Centre, LU1 2TR, ☎ (01582) 734199, *Fax (01582) 402528* – 🛗, 🚭 rm, ▤ rest, [TV] ☎ ♿ [P] – 🎤 300. [MC] [AE] [D] [VISA] [JCB]. 🚫 Y n
**Meals** a la carte 17.25/32.00 **st.** – ☕ 10.25 – **147 rm** 94.50/112.00 **t.**, 3 suites.

🏨 **The Shannon,** 40a Guildford St., LU1 2PA, ☎ (01582) 482119, *Fax (01582) 482818* – [TV] ☎ [MC] [AE] [D] [VISA] [JCB]. 🚫 Y e
*closed 5 days at Christmas* – **Meals** *(closed Saturday and Sunday)* (meals in bar) a la carte approx. 7.00 **st.** – **28 rm** ☕ 55.50/65.50 **st.**

[M] ATS 67 Kingsway ☎ (01582) 597519
ATS High St., Oakley Rd, Leagrave ☎ (01582) 507020/592381

*When looking for a quiet hotel use the maps found in the introduction or look for establishments with the sign* 🐎 *or* 🐎.

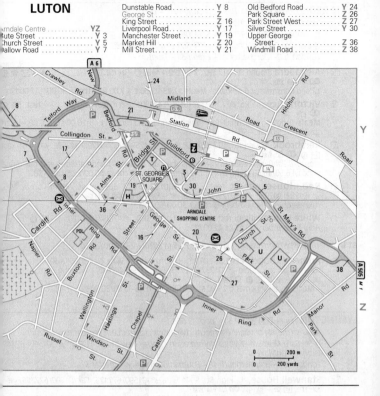

---

**UTTERWORTH** *Leics.* 403 404 Q 26 – *pop. 7 380.*

  Ullesthorpe Court Hotel, Frolesworth Rd ℘ (01455) 209023.
  London 93 – Birmingham 34 – Coventry 14 – Leicester 16.

🏠🏠 **Denbigh Arms**, 24 High St., LE17 4AD, ℘ (01455) 553537, Fax (01455) 556627 – 📺 ☎ 🅿
  – 🔬 50. 🆗 ஊ ⓘ *VISA*. ⅍
  **Meals** (bar lunch Saturday) 8.95/13.95 **t.** and dinner a la carte – ☑ 7.50 – **32 rm** 65.00/
  75.00 **st.** – SB.

---

**UXBOROUGH** *Somerset* 403 J 30 – *pop. 201* – ✉ *Watchet.*
  London 205 – Exeter 42 – Minehead 9 – Taunton 25.

🍴 **Royal Oak** with rm, Exmoor National Park, TA23 0SH, ℘ (01984) 640319, 😤, « Part 14C
  inn », 🖙 – ⅍ rm, ☎ 🅿
  **Meals** a la carte 10.95/21.20 **t.** – **9 rm** ☑ 35.00/65.00 **t.**

---

**YDFORD** *Devon* 403 H 32 *The West Country G.* – *pop. 1 734* – ✉ *Okehampton.*
  See : *Village*★★. – Env. : *Dartmoor National Park*★★.
  London 234 – Exeter 33 – Plymouth 24.

🏠 **Moor View House**, Vale Down, EX20 4BB, Northeast : 1 ½ m. on A 386
  ℘ (01822) 820220, Fax (01822) 820220, 🖙 – ⅍ 📺 🅿
  **Meals** (booking essential to non-residents) (dinner only) 20.00 **st.** ⅙ 4.50 – **4 rm** ☑ 45.00/
  80.00 **st.** – SB.

🍴 **Castle Inn** with rm, EX20 4BH, ℘ (01822) 820242, Fax (01822) 820454, « 16C », 🖙 – 📺
  ☎ 🅿. 🆗 ஊ ⓘ *VISA* 🇯🇨🇧
  closed 25 December – **Meals** (bar lunch)/dinner 15.95 **t.** and a la carte ⅙ 6.85 – **9 rm**
  ☑ 34.50/85.00 **t.** – SB.

**LYME REGIS** Dorset 408 L 31 *The West Country G.* – *pop. 3 566.*

See : *Town★ – The Cobb★.*

🏌 *Timber Hill ℰ (01297) 442963/442043.*

🛈 *Guildhall Cottage, Church St., DT7 3BS ℰ (01297) 442138.*

*London 160 – Dorchester 25 – Exeter 31 – Taunton 27.*

🏨 **Alexandra,** Pound St., DT7 3HZ, ℰ (01297) 442010, Fax (01297) 443229, ≤, 🚗 – 📺 ☎ 🅿
Ⓜ️Ⓞ ⒶⒺ ⓞ VISA. ✾
*closed Christmas and January* – **Meals** 12.95/22.50 **t.** ♦ 7.00 – **27 rm** ⊇ 50.00/117.00 **t.**

🏨 **Victoria,** Uplyme Rd, DT7 3LP, ℰ (01297) 444801, Fax (01297) 422949 – ✝✕ rest, 📺 🅿
Ⓜ️Ⓞ VISA. ✾
**Meals** (booking essential) (bar lunch)/dinner a la carte 11.45/20.00 **st.** ♦ 8.00 – **6 rm**
⊇ 32.50/55.00 **st.** – SB.

🏨 **Kersbrook,** Pound Rd, DT7 3HX, ℰ (01297) 442596, Fax (01297) 442596, 🚗 – ✝✕ rest
📺 🅿. Ⓜ️Ⓞ ⒶⒺ VISA JCB
*closed 4 January-4 February* – **Meals** (bar lunch Monday and Saturday and bar dinne
Sunday) 6.50/16.50 **t.** and dinner a la carte ♦ 5.50 – **10 rm** ⊇ 55.00/82.50 **st.** – SB.

⌂ **Red House** without rest., Sidmouth Rd, DT7 3ES, West : ¾ m. on A 305
ℰ (01297) 442055, Fax (01297) 442055, 🚗 – ✝✕ 📺 🅿
*mid March-mid November* – **3 rm** ⊇ 30.00/50.00 **s.**

⌂ **White House** without rest., 47 Silver St., DT7 3HR, ℰ (01297) 443420, ≤ – 📺 🅿
*April-September* – **7 rm** ⊇ 42.00 **st.**

**at Uplyme** (Devon) *Northwest : 1¼ m. on B 3165 (A 3070)* – ✉ Lyme Regis.

⌂ **Amherst Lodge Farm** ⤢, DT7 3XH, Northwest : 1¼ m. by B 3165 (A 3070), taking left
turn in Yawl to Cathole ℰ (01297) 442773, Fax (01297) 442625, « Working farm », ⤸, 🚗
park – ✝✕ rest, 📺 🅿. Ⓜ️Ⓞ VISA. ✾
– **Meals** (by arrangement) 25.00 **st.** ♦ 8.95 – **4 rm** ⊇ 40.00/80.00 **st.**

**LYMINGTON** Hants. 408 404 P 31 – *pop. 13 508.*

⛴ *to the Isle of Wight (Yarmouth) (Wightlink Ltd) frequent services daily (30 mn).*

🛈 *St. Barb Museum & Visitor Information Centre, New St., SO41 9TW ℰ (01590) 672422.*
*(summer only).*

*London 103 – Bournemouth 18 – Southampton 19 – Winchester 32.*

🏨 **Stanwell House,** 15 High St., SO41 9AA, ℰ (01590) 677123, Fax (01590) 677756, 🚗 –
✝✕ rm, 📺 ☎ – 🔬 40. Ⓜ️Ⓞ ⒶⒺ ⓞ VISA
**Meals** *(closed Sunday dinner and Monday)* 20.00 **st.** (dinner) and a la carte 22.00/28.50 **st**
♦ 9.50 – **Bistro : Meals** 9.25 **st.** (lunch) and a la carte 17.00/31.50 **st.** ♦ 9.50 – **28 rm**
⊇ 60.00/150.00 **t.**, 3 suites.

🏨 **Passford House** ⤢, Mount Pleasant Lane, Mount Pleasant, SO41 8LS, Northwest : 2 m
by A 337 and Sway Rd ℰ (01590) 682398, Fax (01590) 683494, ≤, ℐₔ, ≋, ⊥, ⊠, 🚗, park
✾ – ✝✕ rest, 📺 ☎ 🅿 – 🔬 100. Ⓜ️Ⓞ ⒶⒺ ⓞ VISA
**Meals** 22.50 **t.** and a la carte ♦ 8.50 – **49 rm** ⊇ 75.00/160.00 **t.**, 1 suite – SB.

⌂ **Albany House,** 3 Highfield, SO41 9GB, ℰ (01590) 671900, 🚗 – ✝✕ rest, 📺 🅿. ✾
*closed 23 to 27 December* – **Meals** (by arrangement) 13.50 **s.** – **3 rm** ⊇ 40.00/59.00 **s.**

⌂ **Efford Cottage,** Everton, SO41 0JD, West : 2 m. on A 337 ℰ (01590) 642315
Fax (01590) 642315, 🚗 – ✝✕ rest, 📺 🅿
**Meals** (by arrangement) 30.00 **s.** – **3 rm** ⊇ 44.00/48.00 **s.**

XXX   **Gordleton Mill** with rm, Silver St., Hordle, SO41 6DJ, Northwest : 3½ m. by A 337 and
❀   Sway Rd ℰ (01590) 682219, Fax (01590) 683073, ☆, « Part 17C water mill, gardens » – ✝✕
≡ rest, 📺 ☎ 🅿. Ⓜ️Ⓞ ⒶⒺ ⓞ VISA. ✾
*closed 3 to 31 January* – **Provence : Meals** *(closed Sunday dinner and Monday)* (booking
essential) 16.50-25.00/45.00 **st.** ♦ 13.50 – **8 rm** ⊇ 85.00/160.00 **st.**, 1 suite – SB
**Spec.** Risotto of langoustine. Millefeuille of aubergine and sea bream, ratatouille sauce
Sablé of raspberry, vanilla bavarois, raspberry coulis.

✕ **Limpets,** 9 Gosport St., SO41 9BG, ℰ (01590) 675555, Fax (01590) 675595 – Ⓜ️Ⓞ VISA
*closed Sunday and Monday except Bank Holidays* – **Meals** 14.00/21.00 **t.** and a la carte
♦ 6.00.

**at East End** *Northeast : 4¼ m. by B 3054 off South Baddesley rd* – ✉ Lymington.

🍴 **East End Arms,** Main Rd, SO41 5SY, ℰ (01590) 626223, Fax (01590) 626223, 🚗
*closed Sunday dinner and Monday* – **Meals** a la carte 13.95/23.25 **t.** ♦ 6.00.

Ⓐ ATS Unit 5, Saltmarsh Park, Gosport St. ℰ (01590) 675938/9

**.YMM** Ches. 402 403 404 M 23 – pop. 2 583.
London 197 – Chester 26 – Liverpool 29 – Manchester 15.

🏨 **Lymm**, Whitbarrow Rd, WA13 9AQ, via Brookfield Rd ℰ (01925) 752233, Fax (01925) 756035, 🌳 – 🍴 🔟 ☎ 🅿 – 🔬 120. 🐶 🆎 ⑩ 𝘝𝘐𝘚𝘈. ⋘
**Meals** (bar lunch Monday to Saturday)/dinner 23.50 **st.** ⅙ 6.00 – � 10.50 – **63 rm** 90.00/110.00 – SB.

---

**.YMPSTONE** Devon 403 J 32 – see Exmouth.

---

**.YNDHURST** Hants. 403 404 P 31 Great Britain G. – pop. 2 381.
Env. : New Forest★★ (Bolderwood Ornamental Drive★★, Rhinefield Ornamental Drive★★).
🏌, 🏌 Dibden, Main Rd ℰ (01703) 845596 – 🏌 New Forest, Southampton Rd ℰ (01703) 282752.
🛈 New Forest Museum & Visitor Centre, Main Car Park, SO43 7NY ℰ (01703) 282269.
London 95 – Bournemouth 20 – Southampton 10 – Winchester 23.

🏨🏨 **Parkhill** 🅂, Beaulieu Rd, SO43 7FZ, Southeast : 1 ¼ m. on B 3056 ℰ (01703) 282944, Fax (01703) 283268, ≼, 🍴, « Tastefully furnished country house », 🏊, 🎣, 🌳, park – 🍴 rest, 🔟 ☎ 🅿 – 🔬 50. 🐶 🆎 ⑩ 𝘝𝘐𝘚𝘈. ⋘
**Meals** 16.00/27.00 **t.** and a la carte ⅙ 8.50 – **16 rm** ⊑ 115.00/126.00 **t.**, 3 suites – SB.

🏨🏨 **Crown**, 9 High St., SO43 7NF, ℰ (01703) 282922, Fax (01703) 282751, 🌳 – ₪, 🍴 rest, 🔟 ☎ 🅿 – 🔬 70. 🐶 🆎 ⑩ 𝘝𝘐𝘚𝘈
**Meals** (bar lunch Monday to Saturday)/dinner 18.00 **t.** and a la carte ⅙ 9.50 – **38 rm** ⊑ 72.00/110.00 **t.**, 1 suite – SB.

🏠 **Beaulieu**, Beaulieu Rd, SO42 7YQ, Southeast : 3 ½ m. on B 3056 ℰ (01703) 293344, Fax (01703) 292729, 🏊, 🌳 – 🔟 ☎ 🅿 – 🔬 40. 🐶 🆎 ⑩ 𝘝𝘐𝘚𝘈
**Meals** (dinner only) 20.50 **t.** – **17 rm** ⊑ 70.00/125.00 **st.**, 1 suite – SB.

🏠 **Ormonde House**, Southampton Rd, SO43 7BT, ℰ (01703) 282806, Fax (01703) 282004, 🌳 – 🍴 rest, 🔟 ☎ 🅿. 🐶 🆎 𝘝𝘐𝘚𝘈 𝘑𝘊𝘉
closed Christmas – **Meals** (by arrangement) (residents only) (dinner only) 15.00 ⅙ 5.50 – **17 rm** ⊑ 32.00/78.00 **st.** – SB.

🏠 **Whitemoor House**, Southampton Rd, SO43 7BU, ℰ (01703) 282186, Fax (01703) 282186 – 🍴 🔟 ☎ 🅿. 🐶 𝘝𝘐𝘚𝘈
closed 25 December and 1 January – **Meals** (by arrangement) 12.50 **st.** ⅙ 5.00 – **8 rm** ⊑ 45.00/55.00 **st.** – SB.

---

**.YNMOUTH** Devon 403 I 30 – see Lynton.

---

**.YNTON** Devon 403 I 30 The West Country G. – pop. 1 870 (inc. Lynmouth).
See : Town★ (≼★).
Env. : Valley of the Rocks★, W : 1 m. – Watersmeet★, E : 1½ m. by A 39.
Exc. : Exmoor National Park★★ – Doone Valley★, SE : 7½ m. by A 39 (access from Oare on foot).
🛈 Town Hall, Lee Rd, EX35 6BT ℰ (01598) 752225.
London 206 – Exeter 59 – Taunton 44.

🏨🏨 **Lynton Cottage** 🅂, North Walk Hill, EX35 6ED, ℰ (01598) 752342, Fax (01598) 752597, ≼ bay and Countisbury Hill – 🔟 ☎ 🅿. 🐶 🆎 ⑩ 𝘝𝘐𝘚𝘈. ⋘
closed January and Christmas – **Meals** (light lunch)/dinner 25.00 **t.** and lunch a la carte 9.00/25.00 **t.** ⅙ 6.25 – **16 rm** ⊑ (dinner included) 59.00/118.00 **t.** – SB.

🏨🏨 **Hewitt's** 🅂, North Walk, EX35 6HJ, ℰ (01598) 752293, Fax (01598) 752489, ≼ bay and Countisbury Hill, « Victorian house in wooded cliffside setting », park – 🍴 🔟 ☎ 🅿. 🐶 𝘝𝘐𝘚𝘈 𝘑𝘊𝘉
restricted opening 10 November-10 February – **Meals** (closed Tuesday) (booking essential) (dinner only) 30.00 **st.** and a la carte ⅙ 4.50 – **10 rm** ⊑ 50.00/100.00 **st.** – SB.

🏠 **Highcliffe House**, Sinai Hill, EX35 6AR, ℰ (01598) 752235, Fax (01598) 752235, ≼ bay and Countisbury Hill, « Victorian residence, antiques », 🌳 – 🍴 🔟 🅿. 🐶 𝘝𝘐𝘚𝘈. ⋘
closed January – **Meals** (closed Sunday) (booking essential to non-residents) (dinner only) 27.50 **st.** ⅙ 8.50 – **6 rm** ⊑ 57.00/84.00 **st.**

🏠 **Castle Hill House**, Castle Hill, EX35 6JA, ℰ (01598) 752291, Fax (01598) 752291 – 🍴 rest, 🔟. 🐶 𝘝𝘐𝘚𝘈 𝘑𝘊𝘉
closed January – **Meals** (closed Thursday) (dinner only) a la carte 14.00/16.50 **t.** – **9 rm** ⊑ 30.00/50.00 **st.**

🏠 **Seawood** 🅂, North Walk, EX35 6HJ, ℰ (01598) 752272, ≼ bay and headland – 🍴 rest, 🔟 🅿
April-October – **Meals** (dinner only) 12.50 **st.** ⅙ 4.20 – **12 rm** ⊑ 29.00/59.00 **st.** – SB.

437

🏠 **Chough's Nest** ⚜, North Walk, EX35 6HJ, ℰ (01598) 753315, *Fax (01598) 763529*, ≤ bay
and Countisbury Hill – ✹✹ 📺 🅿. 🐵 ⓪ 𝗩𝗜𝗦𝗔 𝗝𝗖𝗕. ✽
*closed January and December* – **Meals** (dinner only) 19.00 – **12 rm** ☑ 29.00/58.00 **st.**

⌂ **Victoria Lodge**, 30-31 Lee Rd, EX35 6BS, ℰ (01598) 753203, *Fax (01598) 753203*, ☞ –
✹✹ 📺 🅿. 🐵 𝗩𝗜𝗦𝗔. ✽
*restricted opening November-March* – **Meals** (by arrangement) 17.50 **st.** – **9 rm** ☑ 33.00.
64.00 **st.**

⌂ **Longmead House**, 9 Longmead, EX35 6DQ, ℰ (01598) 752523, *Fax (01598) 752523*, ☞
– ✹ 🅿. 🐵 𝗩𝗜𝗦𝗔. ✽
*16 March-31 October* – **Meals** (by arrangement) 14.00 **st.** – **7 rm** ☑ 20.00/44.00.

⌂ **Rockvale** ⚜, Lee Rd, EX35 6HW, off Lee Rd ℰ (01598) 752279, ≤ – ✹✹ 📺 ☎ 🅿. 🐵 𝗩𝗜𝗦𝗔
𝗝𝗖𝗕. ✽
*March-October* – **Meals** (by arrangement) 15.00 **st.** ♦ 5.50 – **8 rm** ☑ 22.00/52.00 **st.** – SB.

**at Lynmouth.**

🏨 **Tors** ⚜, EX35 6NA, ℰ (01598) 753236, *Fax (01598) 752544*, ≤ Lynmouth and bay, ⤫, ☞ –
🔺 📺 ☎ 🅿 – 🔬 80. 🐵 🄰🄴 ⓪ 𝗩𝗜𝗦𝗔
*closed 3 to 31 January and restricted opening in February* – **Meals** (bar lunch Monday to
Saturday)/dinner 24.00 **st.** and a la carte ♦ 7.00 – **35 rm** ☑ 37.00/110.00 **st.** – SB.

🏠 **Rising Sun**, Harbourside, EX35 6EQ, ℰ (01598) 753223, *Fax (01598) 753480*, ≤, « Part 14C
thatched inn », ☞ – ✹✹ 📺 ☎ 🅿. 🐵 🄰🄴 ⓪ 𝗩𝗜𝗦𝗔 𝗝𝗖𝗕. ✽
**Meals** – (see *The Restaurant* below) – **15 rm** ☑ 60.00/140.00 **t.**, 1 suite – SB.

⌂ **Heatherville** ⚜, Tors Park, EX35 6NB, by Tors Rd ℰ (01598) 752327, ≤ – 📺 🅿
*March-October* – **Meals** 16.50 – **8 rm** ☑ 25.00/56.00 **s.** – SB.

⌂ **Seaview Villa**, 6 Summerhouse Path, EX35 6ES, off Watersmeet Rd ℰ (01598) 753460 –
✹✹ 📺
*closed 25 and 26 December* – **Meals** (by arrangement) (communal dining) 13.00 **s.** ♦ 3.50 –
**6 rm** ☑ 19.00/46.00 **s.** – SB.

XX **The Restaurant** (at Rising Sun H.), Harbourside, EX35 6EQ, ℰ (01598) 753223,
*Fax (01598) 753480*, « Part 14C thatched inn », ☞ – ✹✹. 🐵 𝗩𝗜𝗦𝗔 𝗝𝗖𝗕
**Meals** (booking essential) (bar lunch)/dinner 27.50 **t.** and a la carte.

**at Hillsford Bridges** *Southeast : 4½ m. by A 39* – ⊠ *Lynton.*

🏠 **Combe Park** ⚜, EX35 6LE, ℰ (01598) 752356, *Fax (01598) 753484*, ☞ – ✹✹ rest, 🅿
*April-October* – (dinner only) 22.00 **t.** ♦ 8.50 – **9 rm** ☑ (dinner included) 58.00/116.00 **t.**

**at Martinhoe** *West : 4¼ m. via Coast rd (toll)* – ⊠ *Barnstaple.*

🏨 **Old Rectory** ⚜, EX31 4QT, ℰ (01598) 763368, *Fax (01598) 763567*, ☞ – ✹✹ 📺 🅿. ✽
*Easter-October* – **Meals** (dinner only) 26.50 **st.** ♦ 5.00 – **8 rm** ☑ (dinner included) 68.50/
130.00 **st.** – SB.

---

**LYTHAM** *Lancs.* �403 L 22 – *see Lytham St. Anne's.*

---

**LYTHAM ST. ANNE'S** *Lancs.* �403 L 22 – *pop.* 40 866.
🏌 *Fairhaven, Lytham Hall Park, Ansdell* ℰ (01253) 736741 – 🏌 *St. Annes Old Links, Highbur*
*Rd* ℰ (01253) 723597.
🛈 *290 Clifton Drive South, FY8 1LH* ℰ (01253) 725610.
*London 237 – Blackpool 7 – Liverpool 44 – Preston 13.*

🏨 **Dalmeny**, 19-33 South Promenade, FY8 1LX, ℰ (01253) 712236, *Fax (01253) 724447*, ≤,
𝄵, ≦s, 🔲, squash – 🔺 📺 ☎ 🅿 – 🔬 200. 🐵 𝗩𝗜𝗦𝗔. ✽
*closed 24 to 26 December* – **C'est la vie** : **Meals** (dinner only and Sunday lunch)/dinner
a la carte 16.00/22.50 **t.** ♦ 7.00 – **Carvery** : **Meals** (dinner only) 13.00 **t.** ♦ 7.00 – **109 rm**
☑ 49.50/112.00 **t.**

🏨 **The Grand**, South Promenade, FY8 1NB, ℰ (01253) 721288, *Fax (01253) 714459*, ≤ – 🔺
✹✹ rm, 📺 ☎ 🅿 – 🔬 140. 🐵 🄰🄴 𝗩𝗜𝗦𝗔. ✽
*closed 24 to 26 December* – **The Bistro** : **Meals** (bar lunch Monday to Saturday)/dinner
16.50 **t.** and a la carte ♦ 5.75 – **40 rm** ☑ 60.00/110.00 **t.** – SB.

🏨 **Glendower**, North Promenade, FY8 2NQ, ℰ (01253) 723241, *Fax (01253) 723241*, ≤, 𝄵
≦s, 🔲 – 🔺 ✹✹ rest, 📺 ☎ 🅿 – 🔬 150. 🐵 🄰🄴 ⓪ 𝗩𝗜𝗦𝗔
*closed New Year* – **Meals** (bar lunch)/dinner 14.50 **t.** ♦ 4.95 – **58 rm** ☑ 44.00/88.00 **t.** – SB.

🏠 **Bedford**, 307-311 Clifton Drive South, FY8 1HN, ℰ (01253) 724636, *Fax (01253) 729244*
𝄵, ≦s, ✹✹ rest, 📺 ☎ 🅿 – 🔬 120. 🐵 𝗩𝗜𝗦𝗔 𝗝𝗖𝗕
**Meals** (bar lunch)/dinner 17.50 **t.** and a la carte ♦ 4.25 – **36 rm** ☑ 55.00/76.00 **st.** – SB.

**at Lytham** *Southeast : 3 m. by A 584.*

🏫 **Clifton Arms**, West Beach, FY8 5QJ, ℰ (01253) 739898, *Fax (01253) 730657*, ≤ – 📳 📺 ☎ ℗ – 🔬 150. ◐◉ ஊ ◑ *VISA*. ⋇
   **Meals** 15.50/22.50 **t.** and a la carte – **40 rm** ☷ 85.00/110.00 **t.**, 4 suites – SB.

🏠 **The County**, Church Rd, FY8 5LH, ℰ (01253) 795128, *Fax (01253) 795149*, Reservations (Freephone) 0800 118833 – 📺 ☎. ◐◉ ஊ ◑ *VISA*
   **Meals** (grill rest.) 10.95 **t.** and a la carte ₰ 7.95 – ☷ 5.95 – **21 rm** 44.95 **t.**

✗ **The Brasserie**, 9 Clifton St., FY8 5EP, ℰ (01253) 794000, *Fax (01253) 795255* – ◐◉ ஊ ◑ *VISA* ᴊᴄʙ
   *closed 25-26 December and 1 January* – **Meals** (dinner only) a la carte 21.50/27.50 **t.** ₰ 8.00.

   🅐 ATS Hove Rd, Off St. David's Road South ℰ (01253) 721300/711249

---

**MACCLESFIELD** *Ches.* **402 403 404** N 24 – *pop. 50 270.*
   🏌 *The Tytherington Club* ℰ (01625) 434562 – 🏌 *Shrigley Hall, Shrigley Park, Pott Shrigley* ℰ (01625) 575757.
   🔡 *Town Hall, SK10 1DX* ℰ (01625) 504114.
   *London 186 – Chester 38 – Manchester 18 – Stoke-on-Trent 21.*

🏨 **Sutton Hall** ⌂, Bullocks Lane, Sutton, SK11 0HE, *Southeast : 2 m. by A 523* ℰ (01260) 253211, *Fax (01260) 252538*, ☞ – 📺 ☎ ℃ ℗. ◐◉ ஊ *VISA*
   **Meals** 12.95/23.55 ₰ 6.25 – **9 rm** ☷ 75.00/95.00 **t.**

🏠 **Rising Sun - Premier Lodge**, Congleton Rd, Gawsworth, SK11 7XD, *Southwest : 2 m. by A 537 on A 536* ℰ (01625) 422906, *Fax (01625) 434215*, Reservations (Freephone) 0800 118833 – ⋇ rm, 📺 ☎ ₰ ℗. ◐◉ ஊ ◑ *VISA*. ⋇
   **Meals** (grill rest.) a la carte 12.50/15.50 **t.** ₰ 4.25 – ☷ 5.95 – **28 rm** 43.95 **t.** – SB.

🏠 **Chadwick House**, 55 Beech Lane, SK10 2DS, *North : ¼ m. on A 538* ℰ (01625) 615558, *Fax (01625) 610265*, ☞ – ⋇ rm 📺 ℗. ◐◉ *VISA*. ⋇
   **Meals** (residents only) (dinner only) 8.95 **st.** ₰ 4.00 – **13 rm** ☷ 35.00/55.00 **st.**

🏠 **Travel Inn**, Titherington Business Park, Springwood Way, SK10 2XA, *Northeast : 2½ m. by A 523* ℰ (01625) 427809, *Fax (01625) 422874* – ⋇ rm, ▤ rest, 📺 ₰ ℗. ◐◉ ஊ ◑ *VISA*
   **Meals** (grill rest.) – **40 rm** 38.00 **t.**

**at Adlington** *North : 5 m. on A 523* – ✉ *Macclesfield.*

🏠 **Travelodge**, London Road South, SK12 4NA, *on A 523* ℰ (01625) 875292, Reservations (Freephone) 0800 850950 – ⋇ rm, 📺 ₰ ℗. ◐◉ ஊ ◑ *VISA* ᴊᴄʙ. ⋇
   **Meals** (grill rest.) – **32 rm** 39.95/59.95 **t.**

**at Bollington** *Northeast : 3½ m. by A 523 on B 5090* – ✉ *Macclesfield.*

✗✗ **Mauro's**, 88 Palmerston St., SK10 5PW, ℰ (01625) 573898 – ◐◉ ஊ *VISA* ᴊᴄʙ
   *closed Saturday lunch, Sunday and Monday* – **Meals** - Italian - a la carte 18.50/27.00 **t.** ₰ 7.55.

✗ **Beasdales**, 22 Old Market Pl., High St., SK10 5PH, ℰ (01625) 575058 – ◐◉ *VISA* ᴊᴄʙ
   *closed Sunday, Monday and 2 weeks August* – **Meals** - Bistro - (dinner only) a la carte 15.45/22.20 **t.** ₰ 4.75.

**at Pott Shrigley** *Northeast : 4¾ m. by A 523 on B 5090* – ✉ *Macclesfield.*

🏫 **Shrigley Hall** ⌂, Shrigley Park, SK10 5SB, *North : ¼ m.* ℰ (01625) 575757, *Fax (01625) 573323*, « Part 19C country house in park », ℔, ☎, 🏊, 🏌, ✗ – 📳, ⋇ rm, 📺 ☎ ℗ – 🔬 220. ◐◉ ஊ ◑ *VISA*
   *Oakridge :* **Meals** (dinner only) 21.00 **t.** – **150 rm** ☷ 105.00/195.00 **st.**

   🅐 ATS 115 Hurdsfield Rd ℰ (01625) 425481/425233/424237

---

**MACKWORTH** *Derbs.* **402 403 404** P 25 – *see Derby.*

---

**MADINGLEY** *Cambs.* **404** U 27 – *see Cambridge.*

---

**MAGHAM DOWN** *E. Sussex* – *see Hailsham.*

---

**MAIDENCOMBE** *Devon* **403** J 32 – *see Torquay.*

# MAIDENHEAD

*For business
or tourist interest:*
**MICHELIN Red Guide
EUROPE.**

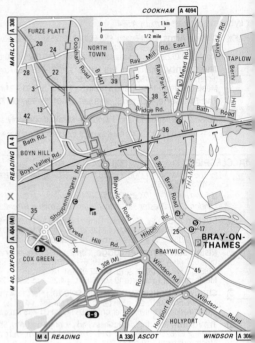

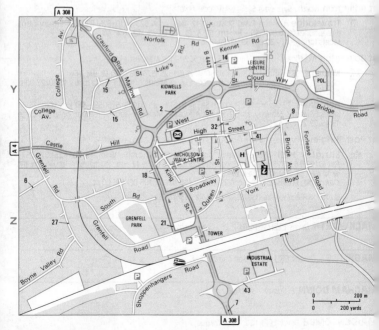

440

**MAIDENHEAD** Windsor & Maidenhead 404 R 29 – pop. 59 605.

🔒 Bird Hills, Drift Rd, Hawthorn Hill ✆ (01628) 771030/75588/26035 – 🔒 Shoppenhangers Rd ✆ (01628) 624693 X.

🚩 The Library, St. Ives Rd, SL6 1QU ✆ (01628) 781110.

London 33 – Oxford 32 – Reading 13.

Plan opposite

🏨 **Holiday Inn Maidenhead,** Manor Lane, SL6 2RA, ✆ (01628) 506000, Fax (01628) 506001, ₤₆, ☎, 🏊, ㈜, squash – 🛗 ♦≒, 🍴 rest, 📺 ☎ ❤ & 🅿 – 🔬 400. ⚙ 🆑 ⓪ VISA. ✲
X n
**Promenade :** Meals (closed Saturday lunch) 23.00 t. and a la carte – 🍷 12.95 – **187 rm** 145.00/180.00 st., 2 suites – SB.

🏨 **Fredrick's,** Shoppenhangers Rd, SL6 2PZ, ✆ (01628) 635934, Fax (01628) 771054, ㈜ – 📺 ☎ ❤ 🅿 – 🔬 150. ⚙ 🆑 ⓪ VISA JCB. ✲
X c
closed Christmas-New Year – Meals – (see **The Restaurant** below) – **36 rm** 🍷 168.00/ 218.00 t., 1 suite – SB.

🏨 **Thames Riviera,** at the bridge, SL6 8DW, ✆ (01628) 674057, Fax (01628) 776586, ≤, ㈜, ㈜ – 📺 ☎ 🅿 – 🔬 50. ⚙ 🆑 ⓪ VISA. ✲
V e
closed 26 to 30 December – **Jerome's :** Meals 19.50 t. and a la carte 🍷 6.50 – 🍷 9.95 – **52 rm** 95.00/120.00 t. – SB.

🏨 **Walton Cottage,** Marlow Rd, SL6 7LT, ✆ (01628) 24394, Fax (01628) 773851 – 🛗, ♦≒ rest, 📺 ☎ 🅿 – 🔬 30. ⚙ 🆑 ⓪ VISA JCB. ✲
Y e
closed 24 December-4 January – Meals (closed Friday to Sunday) (dinner only) 17.50 st. 🍷 6.50 – **64 rm** 🍷 90.00/150.00 t.

🏠 **Beehive Manor** without rest., Cox Green Lane, SL6 3ET, Southwest : 1 ½ m. by Shoppenhangers Rd, off Cox Green Rd ✆ (01628) 620980, Fax (01628) 621840, « Part 16C manor house », ㈜ – ♦≒, ⚙ VISA JCB. ✲
closed 10 days Christmas – **3 rm** 🍷 40.00/60.00 s.

XXX **The Restaurant** (at Fredrick's H.), Shoppenhangers Rd, SL6 2PZ, ✆ (01628) 635934, Fax (01628) 771054, ㈜ – 🍴 🅿. ⚙ 🆑 ⓪ VISA JCB
X c
closed Saturday lunch and Christmas-New Year – Meals 25.50/35.50 t. and a la carte 🍷 9.00.

**at Littlewick Green** West : 3¼ m. by A 4 – V – ✉ Maidenhead.

🏨 **Riders Country House,** Bath Rd, SL6 3RQ, on A 4 ✆ (01628) 822085, Fax (01628) 829211 – 📺 ☎ ❤ 🅿 – 🔬 30. ⚙ 🆑 VISA. ✲
Meals a la carte 13.00/20.00 t. 🍷 5.00 – **20 rm** 🍷 79.50/94.50 st.

🔧 ATS Denmark St., Cordwallis Est. ✆ (01628) 20161

---

**MAIDEN NEWTON** Dorset 403 404 M 31 The West Country G. – pop. 937 – ✉ Dorchester.

Env. : Cerne Abbas★, NE : 5½ m.

London 143 – Bournemouth 35 – Bristol 55 – Taunton 34 – Weymouth 16.

XX **Le Petit Canard,** Dorchester Rd, DT2 0BE, ✆ (01300) 320536 – ♦≒. ⚙ VISA
🍴 closed Sunday, Monday, 1 week January and 1 week May – Meals (booking essential) (dinner only) 24.50 t. 🍷 6.75.

---

**MAIDSTONE** Kent 404 V 30 Great Britain G. – pop. 90 878.

Env. : Leeds Castle★ AC, SE : 4½ m. by A 20 and B 2163.

🔒 Tudor Park Hotel, Ashford Rd, Bearsted ✆ (01622) 734334 – 🔒 Cobtree Manor Park, Chatham Rd, Boxley ✆ (01622) 753276.

🚩 The Gatehouse, The Old Palace Gardens, Mill St., ME15 6YE ✆ (01622) 673581.

London 36 – Brighton 64 – Cambridge 84 – Colchester 72 – Croydon 36 – Dover 45 – Southend-on-Sea 49.

🏨 **Stakis Maidstone,** Bearsted Rd, ME14 5AA, Northeast : 1 ½ m. by A 249 ✆ (01622) 734322, Fax (01622) 734600, ₤₆, ☎, 🏊 – ♦≒ rm, 🍴 rest, 📺 ☎ ❤ 🅿 – 🔬 200. ⚙ 🆑 ⓪ VISA. ✲
Meals 19.75 st. (dinner) and a la carte 22.15/26.40 st. – 🍷 9.50 – **141 rm** 120.00/155.00 st., 3 suites.

🏨 **Travel Inn,** London Rd, ME16 0HG, Northwest : 2 m. on A 20 ✆ (01622) 752515, Fax (01622) 672469 – ♦≒ rm, 📺 & 🅿. ⚙ 🆑 ⓪ VISA. ✲
Meals (grill rest.) – **40 rm** 38.00 t.

**at Bearsted** *East : 3 m. by A 249 off A 20 –* ⊠ *Maidstone.*

🏨 **Marriott Tudor Park H. & Country Club,** Ashford Rd, ME14 4NQ, on A 2
*𝒫 (01622) 734334, Fax (01622) 735360,* ≤, *Ⅰ₆,* ☎, 🏊, 🐎, 🌳, park, ※ – 🛏 ↩ 📺 ☎ & 📶
*– 🔬 300.* 🆎 🆎 ① *VISA*. ※
**Fairviews :** Meals *(closed Saturday lunch)* 15.95/22.50 **st.** and dinner a la carte 🍷 8.00
**LongWeekend :** Meals a la carte 10.45/20.70 **st.** 🍷 8.00 – ☲ 11.95 – **117 rm** 75.0(
81.00 **st.**, 1 suite – SB.

XX **Soufflé,** The Green, ME14 4DN, off Yeoman Lane *𝒫 (01622) 737065, Fax (01622) 737065*
📶 🆎 ① *VISA*
*closed Sunday dinner and Monday –* Meals a la carte approx. 29.70 **t.** 🍷 10.00.

**at Linton** *South : 4 m. on A 229 –* ⊠ *Maidstone.*

↑ **Hill Place** without rest., ME17 4AL, on A 229 *𝒫 (01622) 743834,* ≤, « Part 17C », 🏊, 🐎
※ – ↩ 📺 📶. ※
*closed 1 week Christmas –* **3 rm** ☲ 20.00/50.00 **s.**

**at Boughton Monchelsea** *South : 4½ m. by A 229 on B 2163 –* ⊠ *Maidstone.*

🏠 **Tanyard** 🤚, Wierton Hill, ME17 4JT, South : 1 ½ m. by Park Lane on Wierton F
*𝒫 (01622) 744705, Fax (01622) 741998,* ≤, « 14C tannery », 🐎 – ↩ rest, 📺 ☎ 📶. 🆎 🄱
① *VISA*. ※
*closed 25 December-late January –* Meals *(dinner only and Sunday lunch)/dinner* 29.00
🍷 6.50 – **6 rm** ☲ 65.00/150.00 **t.**

**at Wateringbury** *Southwest : 4½ m. on A 26 –* ⊠ *Maidstone.*

🏠 **Wateringbury - Premier Lodge,** Tonbridge Rd, ME18 5NS, *𝒫 (01622) 81263*
*Fax (01622) 812720,* Reservations (Freephone) 0800 118833, ☎, 🐎 – ↩ rm, 📺 ☎ 📶
🔬 45. 🆎 🆎 *VISA*. ※
Meals (grill rest.) a la carte 12.50/15.50 **t.** 🍷 4.55 – ☲ 5.95 – **40 rm** 44.95 **t.**

**at Larkfield** *West : 3¼ m. on A 20 –* ⊠ *Maidstone.*

🏨 **Larkfield Priory,** 812 London Rd, ME20 6HJ, *𝒫 (01732) 846858, Fax (01732) 846786*
↩ 📺 ☎ 📶 – 🔬 80. 🆎 🆎 🄱 *VISA*
Meals (bar lunch Monday to Saturday)/dinner a la carte 13.50/24.75 **st.** 🍷 5.50 – ☲ 9.75
**51 rm** 65.00/75.00 **st.** – SB.

🔧 ATS 165 Upper Stone St. *𝒫 (01622) 758738/758644*

---

**MAIDSTONE SERVICE AREA** Kent 🆘 V 30 – ⊠ *Maidstone.*

🏠 **Roadchef Lodge,** Hollingbourne, ME17 1SS, junction 8 M 20 (southbound carriagewa
*𝒫 (01622) 631100, Fax (01622) 739535* – ↩ rm, 📺 ☎ & 📶 – 🔬 25. 🆎 🆎 ① *VISA*. ※
*closed Christmas and New Year –* Meals (grill rest.) 49.95 – **40 rm t.**

---

**MALDON** Essex 🆘 W 28 – pop. 15 841.
🏌 Forrester Park, Beckingham Rd, Great Totham *𝒫 (01621) 891406 –* ₅, ₅ Bunsay Down
Little Baddow Rd, Woodham Walter *𝒫 (01245) 412648/412369.*
🅱 Coach Lane, CM9 7UH *𝒫 (01621) 856503.*
London 42 – Chelmsford 9 – Colchester 17.

🏠 **Blue Boar,** Silver St., CM9 4QE, *𝒫 (01621) 852681, Fax (01621) 856202* – ↩ 📺 ☎ 📶
🔬 30. 🆎 🆎 ① *VISA* 🅹🅲🅱
Meals a la carte 16.40/22.50 **t.** 🍷 5.95 – ☲ 9.50 – **28 rm** 70.00/85.00 **t.** – SB.

X **Chigborough Lodge,** Chigborough Rd, Heybridge, CM9 4RE, Northeast : 2 ½ m. b
🏠 A 414 off B 1026 *𝒫 (01621) 853590 –* 📶. 🆎 *VISA*
*closed Saturday lunch, Sunday dinner, Monday, Tuesday, 2 weeks in summer and 1 week*
*winter –* Meals (booking essential) a la carte 17.75/23.25 **st.** 🍷 6.90.

**at Tolleshunt Knights** *Northeast : 7 m. by B 1026 –* ⊠ *Maldon.*

🏨 **Five Lakes H. Golf & Country Club,** Colchester Rd, Tolleshunt Knights, CM9 8H》
North : 1 ¼ m. by B 1026 *𝒫 (01621) 868888, Fax (01621) 869696,* Ⅰ₆, ☎, 🏊, 🐎, par
※indoor/outdoor, squash – 🛏, 🍴 rest, 📺 ☎ & 📶 – 🔬 450. 🆎 🆎 ① *VISA*
**Camelot :** Meals *(closed Sunday dinner)* (dinner only and Sunday lunch)/dinner 23.50 s
and a la carte 🍷 9.75 – **Bejerano's Brasserie :** Meals 17.50 **st.** and a la carte 🍷 9.75 – ☲
9.50 – **110 rm** 95.00/135.00 **st.**, 4 suites – SB.

🔧 ATS 143-147 High St. *𝒫 (01621) 856541*

**MALMESBURY** Wilts. [403] [404] N 29 *The West Country G. – pop. 4 218.*
See : *Town★ – Market Cross★★ – Abbey★.*
🛈 *Town Hall, Market Lane,* ℰ *(01666) 823748.*
*London 108 – Bristol 28 – Gloucester 24 – Swindon 19.*

🏨 **Whatley Manor** ⚜, Easton Grey, SN16 0RB, West : 2 ½ m. on B 4040 ℰ (01666) 822888, *Fax (01666) 826120,* ≤, « Part 18C manor house », ≘s, 🏊, 🐾, 🏖, park, 🎾 – 🖵 ☎ 🅿 – 🔬 40. 🐧 🝙 ⓪ 𝘝𝘐𝘚𝘈
**Meals** 16.00/30.00 t. ₫ 7.00 – **29 rm** � 80.00/130.00 t. – SB.

🏨 **Old Bell,** Abbey Row, SN16 0AG, ℰ (01666) 822344, *Fax (01666) 825145,* « Part 13C former abbots hostel », 🐾 – ⅍ rest, 🖵 ☎ 🅿 – 🔬 35. 🐧 🝙 ⓪ 𝘝𝘐𝘚𝘈 𝘑𝘊𝘉
**Meals** 15.00/26.00 st. – **31 rm** ⊃ 75.00/145.00 st., 1 suite – SB.

🏨 **Knoll House,** Swindon Rd, SN16 9LU, on B 4042 ℰ (01666) 823114, *Fax (01666) 823897,* 🏊, 🐾 – ⅍ rest, 🖵 ☎ 🅿. 🐧 𝘝𝘐𝘚𝘈
*closed 27 to 29 December* – **Meals** (dinner only) 25.00 st. and a la carte ₫ 5.00 – **22 rm** ⊃ 70.00/95.00 st. – SB.

**at Crudwell** *North :* 4 m. on A 429 – ✉ Malmesbury.

🏠 **Mayfield House,** SN16 9EW, on A 429 ℰ (01666) 577409, *Fax (01666) 577977,* 🐾 – ⅍ rest, 🖵 ☎ 🅿 – 🔬 30. 🐧 🝙 ⓪ 𝘝𝘐𝘚𝘈 𝘑𝘊𝘉
**Meals** (bar lunch Monday to Saturday)/dinner 15.95 t. ₫ 4.95 – **23 rm** ⊃ 46.00/69.00 t. – SB.

**MALPAS** Ches. [402] [403] L 24 – *pop. 3 684.*
*London 177 – Birmingham 60 – Chester 15 – Shrewsbury 26 – Stoke-on-Trent 30.*

🏠 **Tilston Lodge** ⚜ without rest., Tilston, SY14 7DR, Northwest : 3 m. on Tilston Rd ℰ (01829) 250223, *Fax (01829) 250223,* « Rare breed farm animals », 🐾 – ⅍ 🖵 🅿. 🐾
**3 rm** ⊃ 45.00/68.00 st.

**MALTON** N. Yorks. [402] R 21 *Great Britain G. – pop. 4 294.*
Env. : *Castle Howard★★ (Park★★★) AC, W :* 6 m.
🏌, 🏌, 🏌 *Malton & Norton, Welham Park, Welham Rd, Norton* ℰ (01653) 692959.
🛈 *58 Market Place, YO17 7LW* ℰ *(01653) 600048.*
*London 229 – Kingston-upon-Hull 36 – Scarborough 24 – York 17.*

🏨 **Talbot,** Yorkersgate, YO17 7AJ, ℰ (01653) 694031, *Fax (01653) 693355,* 🐾 – ⅍ rest, 🖵 ☎ 🅿 – 🔬 35. 🐧 🝙 ⓪ 𝘝𝘐𝘚𝘈. 🐾
*closed New Year* – **Meals** 11.00/17.50 st. ₫ 7.50 – **30 rm** ⊃ 47.50/105.00 st., 1 suite – SB.

🏨 **Green Man,** 15 Market St., YO17 7LY, ℰ (01653) 600370, *Fax (01653) 696006* – ⅍ rest, 🖵 ☎ 🅿 – 🔬 100. 🐧 🝙 ⓪ 𝘝𝘐𝘚𝘈. 🐾
*closed New Year* – **Meals** 16.95 st. ₫ 6.50 – **23 rm** ⊃ 55.00/95.00 st., 1 suite – SB.

🏠 **Newstead Grange,** Beverley Rd, Norton, YO17 9PJ, Southeast : 2 m. on B 1248 ℰ (01653) 692502, *Fax (01653) 696951,* ≤, « Part 18C », 🐾 – ⅍ 🖵 🅿. 🐧 𝘝𝘐𝘚𝘈
*mid March-October* – **Meals** (residents only) (dinner only) 17.50 st. ₫ 4.75 – **8 rm** 45.00/82.00 st. – SB.

🛞 ATS 27 Commercial St., Norton ℰ (01653) 692567/693525

**MALVERN** Worcestershire [403] [404] N 27 – *see Great Malvern.*

**MALVERN WELLS** Worcestershire [403] [404] N 27 – *see Great Malvern.*

**MAN (Isle of)** [402] FG 21 *Great Britain G. – pop. 71 714.*
See : *Laxey Wheel★★ – Snaefell★ (※★★★) – Cregneash Folk Museum★.*
⚓ from Douglas to Belfast (Isle of Man Steam Packet Co. Ltd) (summer only) ( 4 h 30 mn)
– from Douglas to Republic of Ireland (Dublin) (Isle of Man Steam Packet Co. Ltd) (4 h 30mn)
– from Douglas to Fleetwood (Isle of Man Steam Packet Co. Ltd) (summer only) ( 3 h 20 mn)
– from Douglas to Heysham ( Isle of Man Steam Packet Co. Ltd) (3 h 45 mn) – from Douglas to Liverpool (Isle of Man Steam Packet Co. Ltd) (4 h) – from Douglas to Ardrossan (Caledonian MacBrayne Ltd) (summer only) weekly (8 h).

**Ballasalla.**

🍴🍴 **Haworths,** Main Rd, IM9 2DA, ℰ (01624) 822940 – 🐧 𝘝𝘐𝘚𝘈
*closed Saturday lunch, Sunday, Monday and January* – **Meals** 14.95/25.00 t. and a la carte ₫ 9.50.

ENGLAND

# Castletown – pop. 2 958.

🗗 Castletown Civic Centre ℘ (01624) 825005.
Douglas 10.

℀ **Chablis Cellar,** 21 Bank St., IM9 1AT, ℘ (01624) 823527 – ◫◑ 𝖵𝖨𝖲𝖠
closed Sunday dinner – **Meals** a la carte 10.75/25.85 **t.** ᾷ 6.50.

# Douglas – pop. 23 487.

🝖 Douglas Municipal, Pulrose Park ℘ (01624) 661558 – 🝖 King Edward Bay, Groudle Rd
Onchan ℘ (01624) 620430/673821.

✈ Ronaldsway Airport : ℘ (01624) 821600, SW : 7 m. – **Terminal :** Coach service fron
Lord St.

🗗 Sea Terminal Building, IM1 2RA ℘ (01624) 686766.

🏨🏨🏨 **Mount Murray H. & Country Club,** Santon, IM4 2HT, Southwest : 4 ¾ m. by A
℘ (01624) 661111, Fax (01624) 611116, ʃᴁ, ⇌s, ◲, 🝖, park, ℀, squash – 🛗, ⇌× rm, ⊡ ☎
& ℗ – 🖆 300. ◫◑ 🄰🄴 ◐ 𝖵𝖨𝖲𝖠
**Meals** – **Murray's :** Meals (closed Sunday dinner) (dinner only and Sunday lunch)/dinne
15.00 **t.** and a la carte ᾷ 8.00 – **90 rm** ⊡ 88.00/131.00 **t.** – SB.

🏨🏨🏨 **Regency,** Queens Promenade, IM2 4NN, ℘ (01624) 680680, Fax (01624) 680690, ≼ – 🛗
⇌× rm, ⊡ ☎ ☏ – 🖆 70. ◫◑ 🄰🄴 ◐ 𝖵𝖨𝖲𝖠 𝖩𝖢𝖡. ℀
**Five Continents :** Meals 19.95 **st.** and a la carte ᾷ 6.00 – ⊡ 7.50 – **28 rm** 65.00/70.00 st
4 suites.

🏨🏨 **Sefton,** Harris Promenade, IM1 2RW, ℘ (01624) 626011, Fax (01624) 676004, ≼, ʃᴁ, ⇌s
◲ – 🛗, ⇌× rm, ⊡ ☎ & ℗ – 🖆 80. ◫◑ 🄰🄴 ◐ 𝖵𝖨𝖲𝖠 𝖩𝖢𝖡. ℀
**Meals** (bar lunch Monday to Friday/dinner 17.00 **st.** and a la carte ᾷ 7.00 – **109 rm**
⊡ 62.00/95.00 **st.**, 1 suite – SB.

🏨🏨 **Empress,** Central Promenade, IM2 4RA, ℘ (01624) 661155, Fax (01624) 673554, ʃᴁ, ⇌s
◲ – 🛗, ▤ rest, ⊡ ☎ – 🖆 150. ◫◑ 🄰🄴 ◐ 𝖵𝖨𝖲𝖠. ℀
**Meals** a la carte 16.70/24.75 **t.** ᾷ 6.95 – ⊡ 8.50 – **99 rm** 65.00/82.50 **st.**, 3 suites – SB.

🏨🏨 **Admirals House,** 12 Loch Promenade, IM1 2LX, ℘ (01624) 629551, Fax (01624) 675021
🛗 ⊡ ☎. ◫◑ 🄰🄴 ◐ 𝖵𝖨𝖲𝖠. ℀
closed 24 December-5 January – **Meals** - Spanish - (closed Sunday lunch) 15.00/20.00 **t**
and a la carte – **12 rm** ⊡ 75.00/125.00 **t.**

🅐 ATS Mount Vernon, Peel Rd ℘ (01624) 622661    ATS 5-7 South Quay ℘ (01624) 676532

# Peel – pop. 3 819.

🗗 Town Hall, Derby Rd, IM5 1HH ℘ (01624) 842341.
Douglas 11.

↑ **Haven,** 10 Peveril Av., IM5 1QB, ℘ (01624) 842585, Fax (01624) 842585 – ⇌× ⊡. ◫◑ 🄰
𝖵𝖨𝖲𝖠. ℀
**Meals** (by arrangement) (communal dining) 10.00 **st.** – **3 rm** ⊡ 25.00/40.00 **st.** – SB.

# Port Erin – pop. 3 218.

↑ **Rowany Cottier** without rest., Spaldrick, IM9 6PE, ℘ (01624) 832287, ≼ Port Erin Bay
🚗 – ⇌× ⊡ ℗. ℀
**5 rm** ⊡ 33.75/53.50 **st.**

# Ramsey – pop. 6 874.

↑ **The River House** ⌲, IM8 3DA, North : ¼ m. turning left after bridge before Bridge In
on Bowring Rd ℘ (01624) 816412, Fax (01624) 816412, ≼, « Part Georgian house, riversid
setting », 🚗 – ⊡ ℗
closed Christmas – **Meals** (by arrangement) (communal dining) 23.00 – **3 rm** ⊡ 39.50
66.00.

↑ **Rose Cottage** ⌲, St. Judes, IM7 3BX, Northwest : 4 ½ m. off A 13 ℘ (01624) 880610, 🚗
– ⇌× ⊡ ℗. ℀
**Meals** (by arrangement) (communal dining) 13.00 **s.** – **3 rm** ⊡ 25.00/50.00.

---

Particularly pleasant hotels and restaurants
are shown in the Guide by a red symbol.

Please send us the names
of anywhere you have enjoyed your stay.
Your **Michelin Guide** will be even better.

🏨🏨🏨 ... 🏠, ↑

XXXXX ... X, 🍴

# MANCHESTER

Gtr. Manchester **402** **403** **404** N 23 *Great Britain G.* – *pop. 402 889*

*London 202 – Birmingham 86 – Glasgow 221 – Leeds 43 – Liverpool 35 – Nottingham 72.*

## TOURIST INFORMATION

🖪 *Manchester Visitor Centre, Town Hall Extension, M60 2LA* ℘ *(061) 234 3157/8.*
🖪 *Manchester Airport, International Arrivals Hall, Terminal 1, M90 3NY* ℘ *(0161) 436 3344 –*
*Manchester Airport, International Arrivals Hall, Terminal 2, M90 4TU* ℘ *(061) 489 6412.*

## PRACTICAL INFORMATION

🖫 *Heaton Park, Prestwick* ℘ *(0161) 798 0295,* ABV.
🖫 *Houldsworth Park, Houldsworth St., Reddish, Stockport* ℘ *(0161) 442 9611.*
🖫 *Chorlton-cum-Hardy, Barlow Hall, Barlow Hall Rd* ℘ *(0161) 881 3139.*
🖫 *William Wroe, Pennybridge Lane, Flixton* ℘ *(0161) 748 8680.*
✈ *Manchester International Airport :* ℘ *(0161) 489 3000, S : 10 m. by A 5103 –* AX –
**and M 56 – Terminal** : *Coach service from Victoria Station.*

## SIGHTS

See : *City★ - Castlefield Heritage Park★* CZ – *Town Hall★* CZ – *City Art Gallery★* CZ **M2** –
*Cathedral★ (Stalls and Canopies★ )* CY.

# MANCHESTER
## CENTRE

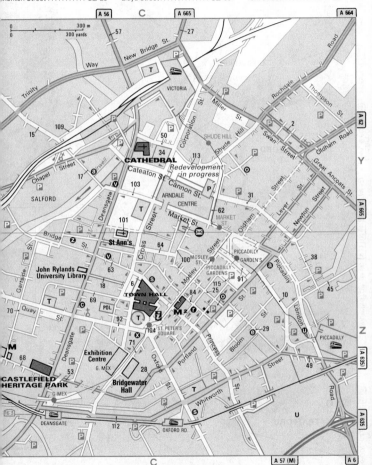

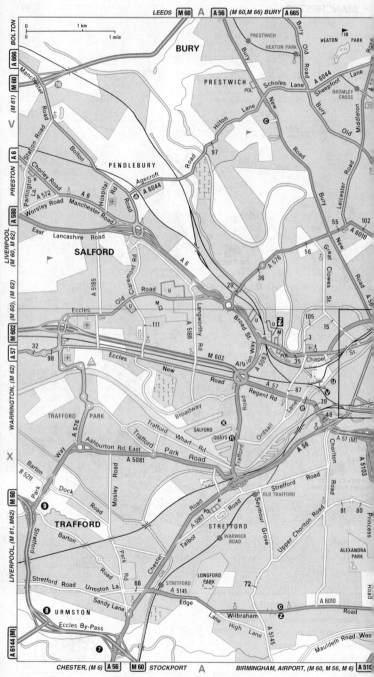

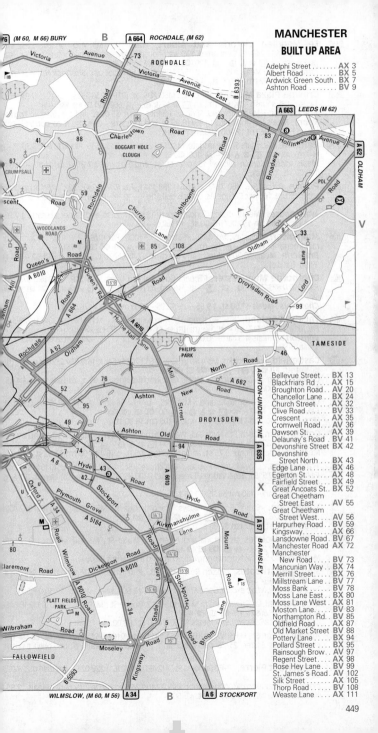

# MANCHESTER
## BUILT UP AREA

449

**Le Meridien Victoria and Albert**, Water St., M3 4JQ, ℰ (0161) 832 118
*Fax (0161) 834 2484*, « Converted 19C warehouse, television themed interior », *f₅*, ⇐
|≜|, ✦ rm, ▤ ⊡ ☎ ❺ ❾ – ⚫ 300. ⒸⒹ ⒶⒺ ⓪ *VISA* ⒿⒸⒷ. ⅏
AX
*Cafe Maigret :* Meals a la carte 22.25/27.25 st. ⅋ 8.50 – (see also *Sherlock Holmes* belov
– ⚏ 10.50 – **152 rm** 149.00 st., 4 suites – SB.

**Crowne Plaza Midland**, Peter St., M60 2DS, ℰ (0161) 236 3333, *Fax (0161) 932 41C*
*f₅*, ⇐, ☒, squash – |≜|, ✦ rm, ▤ ⊡ ☎ ❤ ❾ – ⚫ 600. ⒸⒹ ⒶⒺ ⓪ *VISA* ⒿⒸⒷ CZ
*French rest. :* Meals *(closed Sunday)* (dinner only) 35.00 t. and a la carte – *Traffo*
*Room :* Meals (carving rest.) 14.95/18.95 st. and a la carte – (see also *Nico Central* belov
– ⚏ 13.50 – **296 rm** 120.00/190.00, 7 suites.

**Ramada**, Blackfriars St., Deansgate, M3 2EQ, ℰ (0161) 835 2555, *Fax (0161) 835 3077* – |
✦ rm, ▤ rest, ⊡ ☎ ❺ ❾ – ⚫ 400. ⒸⒹ ⒶⒺ ⓪ *VISA* ⒿⒸⒷ. ⅏ CY
Meals *(closed Sunday dinner)* 15.50/21.50 st. and a la carte ⅋ 7.25 – ⚏ 11.50 – **196 r**
116.00 st., 4 suites.

**Palace**, Oxford St., M60 7HA, ℰ (0161) 288 1111, *Fax (0161) 288 2222*, « Victorian Goth
architecture, former Refuge Assurance building » – |≜| ✦ rm ⊡ ☎ – ⚫ 850. ⒸⒹ ⒶⒺ ⓪ *VIS*
⅏ CZ
*Waterhouses :* Meals *(closed Sunday lunch)* 12.95/17.95 st. and dinner a la carte ⅋ 7.95
⚏ 11.95 – **161 rm** 139.00/165.00 st., 10 suites – SB.

**Malmaison**, Piccadilly, M1 3AQ, ℰ (0161) 278 1000, *Fax (0161) 278 1002*, « Contempo
rary interior », *f₅*, ⇐ – |≜|, ✦ rm, ▤ ⊡ ☎ ❺ ❺ – ⚫ 48. ⒸⒹ ⒶⒺ ⓪ *VISA* CZ
*Brasserie* Meals 12.50 t. (lunch) and a la carte 17.45/25.70 t. ⅋ 3.50 – ⚏ 11.50 – **104 r**
99.00, 8 suites.

**Copthorne Manchester**, Clippers Quay, Salford Quays, M5 2XP, ℰ (0161) 873 732
*Fax (0161) 873 7318*, *f₅*, ⇐, ☒ – |≜|, ✦ rm, ▤ rest, ⊡ ☎ ❺ ❾ – ⚫ 150. ⒸⒹ ⒶⒺ ⓪ *VIS*
⅏ AX
*Chandlers :* Meals 31.50 st. ⅋ 9.95 – ⚏ 12.25 – **166 rm** 140.00/175.00 st.

**Thistle Portland**, 3-5 Portland St., Piccadilly Gdns., M1 6DP, ℰ (0161) 228 340
*Fax (0161) 228 6347*, ⇐ – |≜|, ✦ rm, ⊡ ☎ ❾ – ⚫ 300. ⒸⒹ ⒶⒺ ⓪ *VISA* ⒿⒸⒷ. ⅏ CZ
*Winston's :* Meals a la carte 20.00/31.00 t. ⅋ 6.95 – ⚏ 11.75 – **204 rm** 108.00/143.00 st
1 suite – SB.

**Castlefield**, Liverpool Rd, M3 4JR, ℰ (0161) 832 7073, *Fax (0161) 839 0326*, *f₅*, ⇐, ☒
|≜|, ▤ rest, ⊡ ☎ ❺ ❾ – ⚫ 60. ⒸⒹ ⒶⒺ ⓪ *VISA*. ⅏ AX
closed 25 and 26 December – Meals (bar lunch)/dinner 15.95 t. and a la carte ⅋ 4.15
**48 rm** ⚏ 78.00/84.00 t. – SB.

**Campanile**, 55 Ordsall Lane, M5 4RS, by A 56 off A 57 ℰ (0161) 833 184¹
*Fax (0161) 833 1847* – ✦ rm ⊡ ☎ ❺ ❾ – ⚫ 60. ⒸⒹ ⒶⒺ ⓪ *VISA* AX
Meals 10.85 st. and a la carte – ⚏ 4.50 – **105 rm** 38.00 st.

**Comfort Inn**, Birch St., Hyde Rd, West Gorton, M12 5NT, Southeast : 2 ½ m. by A 5
ℰ (0161) 220 8700, *Fax (0161) 220 8848* – ✦ rm ⊡ ☎ ❺ ❾ – ⚫ 100. ⒸⒹ ⒶⒺ ⓪ *VISA* BX
Meals (bar lunch)/dinner 9.75 st. and a la carte ⅋ 4.50 – ⚏ 6.75 – **90 rm** 42.50 st.

**Travelodge**, Townbury House, Blackfriars St., M3 5AB, ℰ (0161) 834 947£
*Fax (0161) 839 5181*, Reservations (Freephone) 0800 850950 – |≜|, ✦ rm, ▤ rest, ⊡ ❺ ❾
ⒸⒹ ⒶⒺ ⓪ *VISA*. ⅏ CY
Meals (cafe bar) – **160 rm** 39.95/59.95 t.

**Travel Inn**, Basin 8, The Quays, Salford Quays, M5 4SQ, ℰ (0161) 872 402C
*Fax (0161) 876 0094* – ✦ rm, ⊡ ❺ ❾. ⒸⒹ ⒶⒺ ⓪ *VISA*. ⅏ AX
Meals (grill rest.) – **52 rm** 38.00 t.

**Sherlock Holmes** (at Victoria and Albert H.), Water St., M3 4JQ, ℰ (0161) 832 118£
*Fax (0161) 832 2484* – ▤ ❾. ⒸⒹ ⒶⒺ ⓪ *VISA* AX
Meals *(closed Sunday)* (dinner only) 25.00 st. and a la carte ⅋ 9.60.

**Simply Heathcotes**, Jackson Row, M2 5WB, ℰ (0161) 835 3536, *Fax (0161) 835 3534*
▤. ⒸⒹ ⒶⒺ ⓪ *VISA* ⒿⒸⒷ CZ
closed Bank Holidays except Good Friday – Meals 12.50 t. and a la carte 22.50/28.50 t.

**Nico Central** (at Crowne Plaza Midland H.), 2 Mount St., M60 2DS, ℰ (0161) 236 6488
*Fax (0161) 236 8897* – ▤. ⒸⒹ ⒶⒺ ⓪ *VISA* CZ
closed 25 and 26 December – Meals 12.50/24.00 st. ⅋ 8.00.

**Air**, 40 Chorlton St., M1 3HW, ℰ (0161) 661 1111, *Fax (0161) 661 1112* – ▤. ⒸⒹ ⒶⒺ ⓪ *VISA*
closed 2 days Easter, 25-26 December and 1 January – Meals (dinner only) a la cart
25.00/30.00 t. CZ

**Brasserie St Pierre**, 57-63 Princess St., M2 4EQ, ℰ (0161) 228 0231, *Fax (0161) 228 023*
– ▤. ⒸⒹ ⒶⒺ ⓪ *VISA* CZ
closed Saturday lunch, Monday dinner, Sunday and 24 December-2 January – Meals 12.95
(lunch) and a la carte 23.00/32.00 t. ⅋ 5.50.

XX **Est, Est, Est,** 5 Ridgefield, M2 6EG, ℰ (0161) 833 9400 – 🍽 rest. 🕫🕫 ⅍ℰ 𝘝𝘐𝘚𝘈 𝘫𝘤𝘣 CZ v
*closed 25 and 26 December* – **Meals** - Italian - a la carte 18.85/21.40 **t.**

XX **Giulio's Terrazza,** 14 Nicholas St., M1 4EJ, ℰ (0161) 236 4033, *Fax (0161) 228 6501* – 🍽.
🕫🕫 𝘝𝘐𝘚𝘈 𝘫𝘤𝘣 CZ r
*closed Sunday, 25 December, 1 January and Bank Holidays* – **Meals** - Italian - 9.50/12.50 **t.**
and a la carte 🍷 6.90.

XX **Koreana,** Kings House, 40a King St. West, M3 2WY, ℰ (0161) 832 4330,
*Fax (0161) 832 2293* – 🕫🕫 ⅍ℰ ⓪ 𝘝𝘐𝘚𝘈 CZ z
*closed lunch Bank Holidays, Sunday, 25 December and 1 January* – **Meals** - Korean -
5.50/13.50 **t.** and a la carte 🍷 6.95.

XX **Royal Orchid,** 36 Charlotte St., M1 4FD, ℰ (0161) 236 5183, *Fax (0161) 236 8830* – 🕫🕫 ⅍ℰ
⓪ 𝘝𝘐𝘚𝘈 CZ o
*closed lunch Monday and Saturday, Sunday, 25 December and 1 January* – **Meals** - Thai -
7.50/23.00 **t.** and a la carte.

X **Market,** 104 High St., M4 1HQ, ℰ (0161) 834 3743, *Fax (0161) 834 3743* – 🕫🕫 ⅍ℰ ⓪ 𝘝𝘐𝘚𝘈
𝘫𝘤𝘣 CY o
*closed Sunday to Tuesday, 1 week Easter, August and 1 week Christmas* – **Meals** - Bistro -
(dinner only) a la carte 17.05/24.55 **t.** 🍷 5.95.

X **Mash,** 40 Chorlton St., M1 3HW, ℰ (0161) 661 6161, *Fax (0161) 661 6060* – 🍽. 🕫🕫 ⅍ℰ ⓪
𝘝𝘐𝘚𝘈 CZ e
**Meals** a la carte 15.00/20.00 **t.**

**at Northenden** *South : 5¼ m. by A 5103* – AX – ✉ *Manchester.*

🏨 **Forte Posthouse Manchester,** Palatine Rd, M22 4FH, ℰ (0161) 998 7090,
*Fax (0161) 946 0139* – 🛗, 🖚 rm, 📺 ☎ 😊 😊 – 🔏 150. 🕫🕫 ⅍ℰ 𝘝𝘐𝘚𝘈 𝘫𝘤𝘣
**Meals** (bar lunch) a la carte 10.95/20.00 **st.** 🍷 7.50 – ☕ 8.95 – **190 rm** 75.00/115.00 **t.** – SB.

**at Didsbury** *South : 5½ m. by A 5103* - AX - *on a 5145* – ✉ *Manchester.*

X **Est, Est, Est,** 756 Wilmslow Rd, M20 0RN, ℰ (0161) 445 8209 – 🍽. 🕫🕫 ⅍ℰ 𝘝𝘐𝘚𝘈
*closed 25 and 26 December* – **Meals** - Italian - 10.50 **t.** and a la carte.

**at Manchester Airport** *South : 9 m. by A 5103* - AX - *off M 56* – ✉ *Manchester.*

🏨 **Manchester Airport Hilton,** Outwood Lane (Terminal One), M90 4WP,
ℰ (0161) 435 3000, *Fax (0161) 435 3040,* 🛁, ☎, 🔲 – 🛗, 🖚 rm, 🍽 📺 ☎ & 😊 – 🔏 300.
🕫🕫 ⅍ℰ ⓪ 𝘝𝘐𝘚𝘈
**Meals** 18.50 **st.** and a la carte 🍷 7.50 – *Portico :* **Meals** *(closed Sunday)* (dinner only)
30.00 **st.** and a la carte 🍷 8.50 – ☕ 15.00 – **222 rm** 150.00/175.00 **st.,** 1 suite.

🏨 **Forte Posthouse Manchester Airport,** Outwood Lane (Terminal One), M90 3NS,
ℰ (0161) 437 5811, *Fax (0161) 436 2340,* 🛁, ☎, 🔲 – 🛗, 🖚 rm, 🍽 📺 ☎ 😊 – 🔏 75. 🕫🕫
⅍ℰ ⓪ 𝘝𝘐𝘚𝘈 𝘫𝘤𝘣. 🌿
**Meals** (bar lunch Monday to Saturday)/dinner 22.50 **st.** and a la carte 🍷 5.00 – ☕ 11.95 –
**284 rm** 119.00 **st.,** 1 suite – SB.

🏨 **Etrop Grange,** Thorley Lane, M90 4EG, ℰ (0161) 499 0500, *Fax (0161) 499 0790* – 🖚 rm,
📺 ☎ 🔧 & 😊 – 🔏 40. 🕫🕫 ⅍ℰ ⓪ 𝘝𝘐𝘚𝘈 𝘫𝘤𝘣
**Meals** *(closed lunch Saturday amd Bank Holidays)* 17.00/29.00 **st.** 🍷 6.95 – ☕ 12.50 – **37 rm**
120.00/190.00 **st.,** 2 suites – SB.

🏨 **Holiday Inn Garden Court,** Outwood Lane, M90 4HL, ℰ (0161) 498 0333,
*Fax (0161) 498 0222* – 🛗, 🖚 rm, 📺 ☎ & 😊. 🕫🕫 ⅍ℰ ⓪ 𝘝𝘐𝘚𝘈 𝘫𝘤𝘣. 🌿
*closed 31 December* – **Meals** (bar lunch)/dinner 13.95 **t.** and a la carte – ☕ 8.00 – **163 rm**
65.00 **t.**

🏨 **Travel Inn,** Finney Lane, Heald Green, SK8 2QH, East : 2 m. by B 5166 ℰ (0161) 499 1944,
*Fax (0161) 437 4910* – 🖚 rm, 📺 & 😊 – 🔏 70. 🕫🕫 ⅍ℰ ⓪ 𝘝𝘐𝘚𝘈. 🌿
**Meals** (grill rest.) – **60 rm** 38.00 **t.**

XXX **Moss Nook,** Ringway Rd, Moss Nook, M22 5WD, ℰ (0161) 437 4778, *Fax (0161) 498 8089*
– 😊. 🕫🕫 ⅍ℰ 𝘝𝘐𝘚𝘈
*closed Saturday, Sunday, Monday and 2 weeks Christmas* – **Meals** 18.50/29.95 **t.**
and a la carte 🍷 7.00.

**at Chorlton-Cum-Hardy** *Southwest : 5 m. by A 5103 on A 6010* – ✉ *Manchester.*

🏠 **Sabre D'or** without rest., 392 Wilbraham Rd, M21 0UH, ℰ (0161) 881 5055,
*Fax (0161) 881 1546* – 📺 ☎ 😊 AX c
**16 rm** ☕ 30.00/55.00 **st.**

🏠 **Abbey Lodge** without rest., 501 Wilbraham Rd, M21 0UJ, ℰ (0161) 862 9266,
*Fax (0161) 862 9266,* 🌿 – 📺 😊. 🌿 AX z
*closed 22 December-3 January* – **4 rm** ☕ 35.00/45.00 **s.**

**at Eccles** *West : 4 m. by M 602 – AX – ✉ Manchester.*

🏨 **Highbury,** 113 Monton Rd, M30 9HQ, Northwest : 1 ¼ m. by A 576 on B 522 ☎ (0161) 787 8545, *Fax (0161) 787 9023* – ⊬ rest, [TV] ☎ [P]. [MC] [AE] [VISA] [JCB]. ⊬
*closed 23 December-2 January* – **Meals** (by arrangement) (residents only) (dinner only) 8.50 **st.** – **15 rm** ☕ 41.00/46.00 **st.**

**at Worsley** *West : 7 ¼ m. by M 602 - AV - and M 62 (eastbound) on A 572 – ✉ Manchester.*

🏨 **Novotel Manchester West,** Worsley Brow, M28 2YA, at junction 13 of M 6 ☎ (0161) 799 3535, *Fax (0161) 703 8207,* 🏊 – |♦|, ⊬ rm, ▤ rest, [TV] ☎ ☏ ♿ [P] – 🏛 220 [MC] [AE] [D] [VISA]
**Meals** 16.00 **st.** and a la carte 🍷 7.95 – ☕ 8.95 – **119 rm** 69.00 **st.**

🍴🍴 **Tung Fong,** 2 Worsley Rd, M28 4NL, on A 572 ☎ (0161) 794 5331, *Fax (0161) 727 9598* – ▤. [MC] [AE] [D] [VISA]
*closed lunch Saturday and Sunday* – **Meals** - Chinese (Peking) - 6.50/16.50 **st.** and a la carte 🍷 5.50.

**at Pendlebury** *Northwest : 4 m. by A 6 on A 666 – ✉ Manchester.*

🏨 **Henry Boddington - Premier Lodge,** 219 Bolton Rd, M27 8TG, ☎ (0161) 736 5143 *Fax (0161) 737 2786,* Reservations (Freephone) 0800 118833 – [TV] ☎ ♿ [P]. [MC] [AE] [D] [VISA] ⊬ AV
**Meals** (grill rest.) 7.25/10.95 **st.** and a la carte – ☕ 5.95 – **30 rm** 44.95 **st.**

**at Swinton** *Northwest : 4 m. by A 580 - AV - and A 572 on B 5231 – ✉ Manchester.*

🏨 **New Ellesmere - Premier Lodge,** East Lancs Rd, M27 8AA, Southwest : ½ m. on A 580 ☎ (0161) 728 2791, *Fax (0161) 794 8222,* Reservations (Freephone) 0800 118833 – ⊬ rm, [TV] ☎ ☏ ♿ [P]. [MC] [AE] [D] [VISA]. ⊬
**Meals** (grill rest.) 🍷 4.25 – ☕ 5.95 – **27 rm** 44.95 **st.** – SB.

[M] ATS Chester St. ☎ (0161) 236 5505
ATS 98 Wilmslow Rd, Rusholme ☎ (0161) 224 6296
ATS Warren Rd, Trafford Park ☎ (0161) 872 7631
ATS 122 Higher Rd, Urmston ☎ (0161) 748 6990/5923
ATS 20/28 Waterloo Rd ☎ (0161) 832 7752

---

**MANCHESTER AIRPORT** *Gtr. Manchester* [402] [403] [404] N 23 – *see Manchester.*

---

**MANGOTSFIELD** *Bristol* [403] [404] M 29 – *see Bristol.*

---

**MANNINGTREE** *Essex* [404] X 28 – *pop. 5 043* – ✉ *Colchester.*
*London 67 – Colchester 10 – Ipswich 12.*

🏠 **Aldhams** without rest., Bromley Rd, Lawford, CO11 2NE, Southwest : 2 ½ m. by B 1352 and A 137 on Bromley Rd ☎ (01206) 393210, *Fax (01206) 393210,* « Lutyens style house walled garden », 🌳 – ⊬ [TV] [P]. ⊬
*closed 2 weeks in spring and 24 to 26 December* – **3 rm** ☕ 25.00/45.00.

---

**MANSFIELD** *Notts.* [402] [403] [404] Q 24.
*London 145 – Derby 24 – Nottingham 22 – Sheffield 30.*

🏠 **Stoneleigh,** Crow Hill Drive, NG19 7AE, ☎ (01623) 650692, « Victorian Gothic house », 🌳 – ⊬ [P]
*closed 2 weeks in summer and Christmas-New Year* – **Meals** (by arrangement) 19.50 – **3 rm** ☕ 35.00/50.00 – SB.

---

**MARAZION** *Cornwall* [403] D 33 *The West Country G.* – *pop. 1 381* – ✉ *Penzance.*
**Env.** : *St. Michael's Mount★★ (⋞★★) – Ludgvan★ (Church★) N : 2 m. by A 30 – Chysauster Village★, N : 2 m. by A 30 – Gulval★ (Church★) W : 2½ m – Prussia Cove★, SE : 5½ m. by A 30 and minor rd.*
⛳9 *Praa Sands* ☎ *(01736) 763445.*
*London 318 – Penzance 3 – Truro 26.*

🏨 **Mount Haven,** Turnpike Rd, TR17 0DQ, ☎ (01736) 710249, *Fax (01736) 711658* ⋞ St. Michael's Mount and Mount's Bay – ⊬ rest, [TV] ☎ [P]. [MC] [AE] [VISA]
*March-November* – **Meals** (dinner only and Sunday lunch)/dinner 19.50 **st.** and a la carte 🍷 5.00 – **17 rm** ☕ 39.00/80.00 **st.** – SB.

**at St. Hilary** *East : 2½ m. by Turnpike Rd, on B 3280 – ✉ Penzance.*

🏠 **Ennys** 🐚 without rest., Trewhella Lane, TR20 9BZ, ☎ (01736) 740262, *Fax (01736) 740055* « 17C manor house, working farm », 🏊, 🌳, park, 🎾 – [TV] [P]. [MC] [VISA]. ⊬
*mid February-mid November* – **5 rm** ☕ 40.00/65.00 **st.**

**Perranuthnoe** Southeast : 1 ¾ m. by A 394 – ⊠ Penzance.

⌂ **Ednovean Farm** ⤸ without rest., TR20 9LZ, ℰ (01736) 711883, Fax (01736) 710480, « Converted 17C barn », 🐎, park – ⇔ 📺 ➋. ⅏
3 rm � 35.00/55.00 s.

---

**MARCH** Cambs. 402 404 U 26 – pop. 16 221.
🏌 Frogs Abbey, Grange Rd ℰ (01354) 652364.
London 93 – Cambridge 34 – Norwich 63.

🏠 **Olde Griffin**, High St., PE15 9JS, ℰ (01354) 652517, Fax (01354) 650086 – 📺 ☎ ➋ – 🔬 100. 🆎 🎴 ① 💳. ⅏
Meals (bar lunch)/dinner a la carte 18.95/19.95 st. § 4.85 – 20 rm ⊊ 38.50/55.00 st. – SB.

---

**MARDEN** Herefordshire – see Hereford.

---

**MARKET BOSWORTH** Leics. 402 403 404 P 26 – pop. 2 019 – ⊠ Nuneaton.
London 109 – Birmingham 30 – Coventry 23 – Leicester 22.

🏠 **Softleys**, Market Pl., CV13 0JS, ℰ (01455) 290464, Fax (01455) 290464 – ⇔ 📺 ☎. 🆎 🎴 ① 💳. ⅏
closed 25 December – Meals (closed Monday and Sunday) (in bar) a la carte 13.95/22.75 t. § 6.95 – 3 rm ⊊ 45.00/65.00 st.

---

**MARKET HARBOROUGH** Leics. 404 R 26 – pop. 16 563.
🏌 Great Oxendon Rd ℰ (01858) 463684.
🛈 Pen Lloyd Library, Adam and Eve St., LE16 7LT ℰ (01858) 468106.
London 88 – Birmingham 47 – Leicester 15 – Northampton 17.

🏠🏠 **Angel**, High St., LE16 7NL, ℰ (01858) 462702, Fax (01858) 410464 – 📺 ☎ 🕭 ➋ – 🔬 100. 🆎 🎴 💳. ⅏
Meals 12.50/14.95 t. and a la carte – ⊊ 8.50 – 37 rm 70.00/94.00 t. – SB.

**Glooston** Northeast : 7½ m. by B 6047 off Hallaton rd – ⊠ Market Harborough.

🍴 **Old Barn Inn** with rm, LE16 7ST, ℰ (01858) 545215, Fax (01858) 545215 – ⇔ rm, 📺 ➋. 🆎 🎴 💳
Meals (closed lunch Monday to Friday and Sunday dinner) a la carte 14.70/22.50 t. § 4.00 – 2 rm ⊊ 37.50/49.50 t.

**Marston Trussell** (Northants.) West : 3½ m. by A 4304 – ⊠ Market Harborough.

🏠 **Sun Inn**, Main St., LE16 9TY, ℰ (01858) 465531, Fax (01858) 433155 – 📺 ☎ ➋ – 🔬 80. 🆎 🎴 💳
Meals 9.95/19.95 t. and a la carte – 19 rm ⊊ 52.50/90.00 t. – SB.

◎ ATS 47-49 Kettering Rd ℰ (01858) 464535

---

**MARKET RASEN** Lincs. 402 404 T 23 – pop. 2 948.
London 156 – Boston 41 – Great Grimsby 19 – Lincoln 16.

⌂ **Bleasby House** ⤸, Legsby, LN8 3QN, Southeast : 4 ¼ m. by B 1202 ℰ (01673) 842383, Fax (01673) 844808, « Working farm », ⤴, 🐎, park, ⅏ – ⇔ 📺 ➋. ⅏
closed 2 weeks Christmas – Meals (by arrangement) 12.00 st. – 3 rm ⊊ 20.00/40.00 st.

---

**MARKET WEIGHTON** East Riding 402 R/S 22 – pop. 4 371 – ⊠ York.
London 206 – Kingston-upon-Hull 19 – York 20.

🏠🏠 **Londesborough Arms**, 44 High St., YO43 3AH, ℰ (01430) 872214, Fax (01430) 872219 – ⇔ rm, 📺 ☎ ➋ – 🔬 120. 🆎 🎴 💳
Meals (bar lunch Monday to Saturday)/dinner a la carte 13.95/21.75 st. § 6.00 – 18 rm ⊊ 39.00/89.00 st. – SB.

---

**MARKFIELD** Leics. 402 403 404 Q 25 – pop. 3 897.
London 113 – Birmingham 45 – Leicester 6 – Nottingham 24.

🏠🏠 **Field Head**, Markfield Lane, LE67 9PS, on B 5327 ℰ (01530) 245454, Fax (01530) 243740 – ⇔ 📺 ☎ 🕭 ➋ – 🔬 50. 🆎 🎴 ① 💳
Meals (closed Sunday dinner) a la carte 15.50/20.00 t. § 5.50 – 28 rm ⊊ 74.00/84.00 t. – SB.

🏨 **Travelodge,** Littleshaw Lane, LE67 0PP, Northwest : 1 m. on A 50 at junction 22 of M
𝓟 (01530) 244777, Fax (01530) 244580, Reservations (Freephone) 0800 850950 – ᴴ✕ 📺 ◀
& 🄿 �🄌 🄰🄴 ⓪ 𝑉𝐼𝑆𝐴 JCB ⏫
**Meals** (grill rest.) – **40 rm** 39.95/59.95 **t.**

---

**MARKHAM MOOR** Notts. 🟥🟥🟥 – ✉ Retford.
London 143 – Lincoln 18 – Nottingham 28 – Sheffield 27.

🏨 **Travelodge,** DN22 0QU, on A 1 (northbound carriageway) 𝓟 (01777) 83809
Fax (01777) 838091, Reservations (Freephone) 0800 850950 – ᴴ✕ rm, 📺 & 🄿 �🄌 🄰🄴 ◀
𝑉𝐼𝑆𝐴 JCB ⏫
**Meals** (grill rest.) – **40 rm** 39.95/59.95 **t.**

---

**MARKINGTON** N. Yorks. 🟥🟥🟥 P 21 – see Harrogate.

---

**MARKS TEY** Essex 🟥🟥🟥 W 28 – see Colchester.

---

**MARLBOROUGH** Wilts. 🟥🟥🟥 🟥🟥🟥 O 29 The West Country G. – pop. 6 788.
See : Town★.
Env. : Savernake Forest★★ (Grand Avenue★★★), SE : 2 m. by A 4 – Whitehorse (≼★), NW
5 m – West Kennett Long Barrow★, Silbury Hill★, W : 6 m. by A 4.
Exc. : Ridgeway Path★★ – Avebury★★ (The Stones★, Church★), W : 7 m. by A 4 – Croftc
Beam Engines★ AC, SE : 9 m. by A 346 – Wilton Windmill★ AC, SE : 9 m. by A 346, A 338 ar.
minor rd.
🏊 The Common 𝓟 (01672) 512147.
🛈 George Lane Car Park, SN8 1EE 𝓟 (01672) 513989.
London 84 – Bristol 47 – Southampton 40 – Swindon 12.

🏨 **Ivy House,** High St., SN8 1HJ, 𝓟 (01672) 515333, Fax (01672) 515338 – 📺 ☎ 🄿 – 🔏 5️⃣
🄌 🄰🄴 𝑉𝐼𝑆𝐴 ⏫
**Scotts :** Meals 10.95 **t.** (lunch) and a la carte 21.75/28.45 **t.** ⋄ 7.00 – **Courtyard Bar :** Meal
(lunch only) a la carte 9.75/12.50 **t.** ⋄ 7.00 – **30 rm** ☱ 62.00/93.00 **st.** – SB.

🏨 **Castle and Ball,** High St., SN8 1LZ, 𝓟 (01672) 515201, Fax (01672) 515895 – ᴴ✕ 📺 ☎ ◀
– 🔏 45. 🄌 🄰🄴 ⓪ 𝑉𝐼𝑆𝐴
**Meals** 7.95 **t.** (lunch) and a la carte 16.20/18.20 **t.** ⋄ 5.90 – ☱ 10.25 – **34 rm** 65.00/85.00 **t.**
SB.

🅐 ATS 120/121 London Rd 𝓟 (01672) 512274

---

**MARLOW** Bucks. 🟥🟥🟥 R 29 – pop. 17 771.
🛈 Court Garden Leisure Complex, Pound Lane, SL7 2AE 𝓟 (01628) 483597 (summer only).
London 35 – Aylesbury 22 – Oxford 29 – Reading 14.

🏨🏨🏨 **Danesfield House** ⏳, Henley Rd, SL7 2EY, Southwest : 2 ½ m. on A 415
𝓟 (01628) 891010, Fax (01628) 890408, « Italian Renaissance style mansion, ≼ terrace
gardens and River Thames », 🎇, park, 🎾 – 🔄 ⬆, ᴴ✕ rest, ▤ rest, 📺 ☎ ℃ 🄿 – 🔏 80. 🄌
🄰🄴 ⓪ 𝑉𝐼𝑆𝐴 JCB ⏫
**Oak Room :** Meals 24.50/35.50 **t.** and a la carte ⋄ 10.00 – **Orangery :** Meals a la cart
20.95/24.75 **t.** ⋄ 10.00 – **86 rm** ☱ 145.00/175.00 **t.**, 1 suite – SB.

🏨🏨 **Compleat Angler,** Marlow Bridge, Bisham Rd, SL7 1RG, 𝓟 (01628) 484444
Fax (01628) 486388, ≼ River Thames, « Riverside setting », 🎣, 🎾 – 🔄 ᴴ✕ rm, 📺 ☎ & 🄿
– 🔏 120. 🄌 🄰🄴 ⓪ 𝑉𝐼𝑆𝐴 JCB
**Riverside :** Meals 21.50/32.50 **t.** and a la carte ⋄ 9.00 – ☱ 14.50 – **60 rm** 135.00/205.00 **st**
2 suites – SB.

🏨 **Country House** without rest., Bisham Rd, SL7 1RP, 𝓟 (01628) 890606
Fax (01628) 890983, 🌲 – 📺 ☎ 🄿 🄌 🄰🄴 ⓪ 𝑉𝐼𝑆𝐴 JCB ⏫
closed 22 December-3 January – **10 rm** 75.00/99.00 **st.**

🏠 **Holly Tree House** without rest., Burford Close, Marlow Bottom, SL7 3NF, North : 2 m. b
A 4155 and Wycombe Rd, off Marlow Bottom 𝓟 (01628) 891110, Fax (01628) 481278, 🎇
🌲 – 📺 ☎ 🄿. 🄌 🄰🄴 𝑉𝐼𝑆𝐴. ⏫
**5 rm** ☱ 64.50/79.50 **t.**

---

**MARPLE** Gtr. Manchester 🟥🟥🟥 🟥🟥🟥 🟥🟥🟥 N 23 – pop. 19 829.
London 190 – Chesterfield 35 – Manchester 11.

🏨 **Springfield,** 99 Station Rd, SK6 6PA, 𝓟 (0161) 449 0721, Fax (0161) 449 0766, 🌲
ᴴ✕ rm, 📺 ☎ 🄿. 🄌 🄰🄴 𝑉𝐼𝑆𝐴. ⏫
**Meals** (closed Friday to Sunday) (dinner only) 16.00 **t.** – **7 rm** ☱ 35.00/50.00 **st.**

MARSDEN *W. Yorks.* 402 404 O 23 – *pop. 3 873* – ⊠ *Huddersfield.*
*London 195 – Leeds 22 – Manchester 18 – Sheffield 30.*

X **Olive Branch,** Manchester Rd, HD7 6LU, Northeast : 1 m. on A 62 ℰ (01484) 844487 – **P.**
**◍◎** **VISA**
*closed 1 week January, 1 week June and 26 December –* **Meals** *(closed lunch Monday,
Tuesday and Saturday)* a la carte 16.95/28.90 t. ≬ 8.50.

MARSTON MORETAINE *Beds.* 404 S 27 – *see Bedford.*

MARSTON TRUSSELL *Northants.* 404 R 26 – *see Market Harborough.*

MARTINHOE *Devon – see Lynton.*

MARTOCK *Somerset* 403 L 31 *The West Country G. – pop. 4 051.*
See : *Village★ – All Saints★★.*
Env. : *Montacute House★★ AC, SE : 4 m. – Muchelney★★ (Parish Church★★), NW : 4½ m. by
B 3165 – Ham Hill (≤★★), S : 2 m. by minor roads.*
Exc. : *Martock★ – Barrington Court★ AC, SW : 7½ m. by B 3165 and A 303.*
*London 148 – Taunton 19 – Yeovil 6.*

🏠 **Hollies,** Bower Hinton, TA12 6LG, South : 1 m. on B 3165 ℰ (01935) 822232,
*Fax (01935) 822249,* 🌲 – 📺 ☎ ✆ & **P** – 🔏 175. **◍◎** **AE** **①** **VISA**. ✄
**Meals** *(bar lunch Monday to Saturday and Sunday dinner)/dinner* a la carte 18.25/22.20 t.
≬ 5.00 – **28 rm** ⊊ 62.00/80.00 t., 2 suites – SB.

*Si vous cherchez un hôtel tranquille,
consultez d'abord les cartes de l'introduction
ou repérez dans le texte les établissements indiqués avec le signe* ⊰ *ou* ⊱.

MASHAM *N. Yorks.* 402 P 21 – *pop. 1 171 –* ⊠ *Ripon.*
*London 231 – Leeds 38 – Middlesbrough 37 – York 32.*

XX **Floodlite,** 7 Silver St., HG4 4DX, ℰ (01765) 689000 – **◍◎** **AE** **VISA**
*closed Tuesday to Thursday lunch, Monday, 2 weeks in spring and 1 week October –* **Meals**
11.50/15.00 t. and a la carte ≬ 5.25.

MATLOCK *Derbs.* 402 403 404 P 24 *Great Britain G. – pop. 14 680.*
Exc. : *Hardwick Hall★★ AC, E : 12½ m. by A 615 and B 6014.*
🚹 *The Pavilion, DE4 3NR ℰ (01629) 55082.*
*London 153 – Derby 17 – Manchester 46 – Nottingham 24 – Sheffield 24.*

🏠 **Riber Hall** ⊱, Riber Village, DE4 5JU, Southeast : 3 m. by A 615 ℰ (01629) 582795,
*Fax (01629) 580475, « Part Elizabethan manor house »,* 🌲, ✵ – ✥ rest, 📺 ☎ **P**. **◍◎** **AE**
**①** **VISA** **JCB**
**Meals** 16.00/32.00 t. ≬ 7.75 – ⊊ 8.00 – **14 rm** 89.75/157.00 t. – SB.

🏠 **New Bath,** New Bath Rd, Matlock Bath, DE4 3PX, South : 1½ m. on A 6 ℰ (01629) 583275,
*Fax (01629) 580268,* ⇔s, ⊼, ⊠, 🌲, ✵ – ✥ 📺 ☎ ✆ **P** – 🔏 130. **◍◎** **AE** **①** **VISA** **JCB**. ✄
**Meals** *(closed Saturday lunch)* 9.95/19.95 **st.** and a la carte ≬ 7.95 – ⊊ 8.50 – **55 rm** 80.00/
120.00 **st.** – SB.

🏠 **Temple,** Matlock Bath, DE4 3PG, South : 1 ¾ m. by A 6 ℰ (01629) 583911,
*Fax (01629) 580851,* ≤, 🌲 – ✥ rest, 📺 ☎ **P**. **◍◎** **AE** **①** **VISA**. ✄
**Meals** 14.00 **s.** *(dinner)* and a la carte 12.00/22.50 **s.** ≬ 4.70 – **14 rm** ⊊ 39.00/71.00 **st.** – SB.

🏠 **Hodgkinson's,** 150 South Par., Matlock Bath, DE4 3NR, South : 1 ¼ m. on A 6
ℰ (01629) 582170, *Fax (01629) 584891, « Victoriana »* – ✥ rest, 📺 ☎. **◍◎** **AE** **VISA** **JCB**
*closed 25 and 26 December –* **Meals** *(closed Sunday) (dinner only)* 19.50 t. ≬ 5.00 – **7 rm**
⊊ 35.00/95.00 **st.** – SB.

at Tansley *East : 1 ¾ m. on A 615 –* ⊠ *Matlock.*

⌂ **Lane End House** *without rest.,* Green Lane, DE4 5FJ, off Church St. ℰ (01629) 583981,
*Fax (01629) 583981,* 🌲 – ✥ 📺 **P**. **◍◎** **VISA**
*closed Christmas and New Year –* **4 rm** ⊊ 30.00/57.00 **s.**

MATTERDALE END *Cumbria – see Ullswater.*

455

**MAWDESLEY** *Lancs.* [402] L 23 – *pop. 1 750* – ✉ *Ormskirk.*
*London 217 – Liverpool 28 – Manchester 28 – Preston 15.*

🏨 **Mawdesley's Eating House and H.,** Hall Lane, L40 2QZ, North : ½ m ☎ (01704) 822552, *Fax (01704) 822096,* [Lo], [S], [pool] – [TV] ☎ ♿ [P] – 🎤 50. [MC] [AE] [D] [VISA]. ⛔
*accommodation closed 25 and 26 December* – **Meals** (grill rest.) 10.00 **t.** and a la cart
🍾 4.50 – **44 rm** ☕ 45.00/55.00 **t.** – SB.

**MAWNAN SMITH** *Cornwall* [403] E 33 – *see Falmouth.*

**MEADOW HEAD** *S. Yorks.* – *see Sheffield.*

**MEDWAY SERVICE AREA** *Medway* [404] V 29/30 – ✉ *Gillingham.*
*London 39 – Canterbury 22 – Maidstone 11.*

🏨 **Travelodge,** ME8 8PQ, on M 2 between junctions 4 and 5 (westbound carriagewa ☎ (01634) 233343, *Fax (01634) 263187,* Reservations (Freephone) 0800 850950 – 🚭 rm [TV] ☎ ♿ [P]. [MC] [AE] [D] [VISA] [JCB]. ⛔
Meals (grill rest.) – **58 rm** 39.95/59.95 **t.**

**MELBOURN** *Cambs.* [404] U 27 – *pop. 4 006* – ✉ *Royston (Herts.).*
*London 44 – Cambridge 10.*

🏨 **Melbourn Bury** 🌿, Royston Rd, SG8 6DE, Southwest : ¾ m. ☎ (01763) 26115 *Fax (01763) 262375,* ≤, « Country house of Tudor origin », 🌳, park – 🚭 rm, [TV] [P]. [MC] [A [VISA]. ⛔
*closed Easter, 2 weeks August-September and Christmas-New Year* – **Meals** *(closed Sunda dinner)* (booking essential) (residents only) (communal dining) (dinner only) 17.50 **st.** 🍾 6.5 – **3 rm** ☕ 55.00/90.00 **st.**

🏠 **Chiswick House** without rest., 3 Chiswick End, SG8 6LZ, Northwest : 1 m. by Meldret rd, off Whitecroft Rd ☎ (01763) 260242, 🌳 – 🚭 [P]
*closed Christmas and 2 weeks February-March* – **6 rm** ☕ 35.00/45.00.

🍴🍴 **Sheene Mill** with rm, Station Rd, SG8 6DX, ☎ (01763) 261393, *Fax (01763) 261376,* ≤ « Restored 17C water mill », 🌳 – [TV] ☎ [P]. [MC] [AE] [VISA]. ⛔
Meals 14.00 **t.** (lunch) and a la carte 20.00/30.50 **t.** – **8 rm** ☕ 60.00/85.00 **t.** – SB.

🍴🍴 **Pink Geranium,** 25 Station Rd, SG8 6DX, ☎ (01763) 260215, *Fax (01763) 262110,* 🌳 – 🚭 [P]. [MC] [AE] [VISA]
*closed Sunday, Monday and 26 December* – **Meals** 16.00/25.00 **t.** and a la carte.

**MELKSHAM** *Wilts.* [403] [404] N 29 *The West Country G.* – *pop. 13 074.*
Env. : *Corsham Court*★★ *AC, NW : 4½ m. by A 365 and B 3353 – Lacock*★★ *(Lacock Abbey*★ *AC, High Street*★*, St. Cyriac*★*, Fox Talbot Museum of Photography*★ *AC) N : 3½ m. b A 350.*
[i] *Church St., SN12 6LS* ☎ *(01225) 707424.*
*London 113 – Bristol 25 – Salisbury 35 – Swindon 28.*

🏨 **Shurnhold House** without rest., Shurnhold, SN12 8DG, Northwest : 1 m. on A 36 ☎ (01225) 790555, *Fax (01225) 793147,* « Jacobean manor house, gardens » – 🚭 [TV] ☎ [P]. [MC] [AE] [VISA]. ⛔
☕ 5.25 – **4 rm** 50.00/98.00 **s.**

🏠 **Sandridge Park** 🌿, Sandridge Hill, SN12 7QU, East : 2 m. on A 3102 ☎ (01225) 706897 *Fax (01225) 702838,* ≤, « Early Victorian mansion », 🌳, park – 🚭 rm, [TV] [P]. [MC] [VISA] [JCB] ⛔
*closed Christmas and New Year* – **Meals** (booking essential) (communal dining) 20.00 **st.** – **3 rm** ☕ 40.00/80.00.

🍴🍴 **Toxique** with rm, 187 Woodrow Rd, SN12 7AY, Northeast : 1 ¼ m. by A 3102 and Fores Rd ☎ (01225) 702129, *Fax (01225) 742773,* 🌳 – [P]. [MC] [AE] [VISA] [JCB]. ⛔
**Meals** *(closed Sunday dinner, Monday and Tuesday)* (booking essential) (dinner only and Sunday lunch)/dinner 31.00 **t.** 🍾 6.50 – **4 rm** ☕ (dinner included) 95.00/160.00 **t.**

**at Shaw** *Northwest : 1½ m. on A 365* – ✉ *Melksham.*

🏨 **Shaw Country H.,** Bath Rd, SN12 8EF, on A 365 ☎ (01225) 702836, *Fax (01225) 790275* 🌳 – 🚭 rest, [TV] ☎ [P]. [MC] [AE] [D] [VISA] [JCB]
*closed 26 to 28 December* – **Meals** 12.95/17.95 **t.** 🍾 4.25 – **13 rm** ☕ 42.00/82.00 **t.** – SB.

**at Whitley** *Northwest : 2 m. by A 365 on B 3353* – ✉ *Melksham.*

🍺 **Pear Tree,** Top Lane, SN12 8QX, by First Lane ☎ (01225) 709131, 🌳 – 🚭 rest, [P]. [MC] [VISA]
*closed 25 to 28 December* – **Meals** 10.95 **st.** (lunch) and a la carte 16.95/21.65 **st.**

**ELLOR** Lancs. – see Blackburn.

**ELTON MOWBRAY** Leics. **402 404** R 25 – pop. 24 348.

🏌 Waltham Rd, Thorpe Arnold ℘ (01664) 562118.

🛈 Melton Carnegie Museum, Thorpe End, LE13 1RB ℘ (01664) 480992.

London 113 – Leicester 15 – Northampton 45 – Nottingham 18.

🏨 **Stapleford Park** ⸎, LE14 2EF, East : 5 m. by B 676 on Stapleford rd ℘ (01572) 787522, Fax (01572) 787651, ≤, « Part 16C and 19C mansion in park », 𝄞, ≌, 🏊, 🏌, 🐎, ⚒ – 🛗 🖐 🔄 📺 ☎ 🄿 – 🔬 200. 🄼🄾 🄰🄴 🄾 𝗩𝗜𝗦𝗔
**Meals** (booking essential to non-residents) (light lunch Monday to Saturday)/dinner 39.50 **st.** ⅄ 15.00 – **50 rm** ⸗ 165.00/350.00 **s.**, 1 suite.

🏨 **Quorn Lodge,** 46 Asfordby Rd, LE13 0HR, ℘ (01664) 566660, Fax (01664) 480660 – 🖐 📺 ☎ 🄿 – 🔬 80. 🄼🄾 🄰🄴 𝗩𝗜𝗦𝗔. ⚒
**Meals** 9.25/15.75 **t.** and a la carte ⅄ 3.75 – **18 rm** ⸗ 47.50/75.00 **t.** – SB.

**at Old Dalby** Northwest : 8½ m. by A 6006 – ✉ Melton Mowbray.

🏠 **Home Farm** ⸎ without rest., 9 Church Lane, LE14 3LB, ℘ (01664) 822622, Fax (01664) 823155, 🐎 – 🖐 📺 🄿. 🄼🄾 𝗩𝗜𝗦𝗔. ⚒
**5 rm** ⸗ 25.00/42.50 **s.**

🏧 ATS Leicester Rd ℘ (01664) 62072

*Great Britain* and *Ireland* are covered entirely
at a scale of 16 miles to 1 inch by our «*Main roads*» map **986**.

**EMBURY** Devon – see Axminster.

**EMBURY SERVICE AREA** Newbury **403 404** P 29 – ✉ Newbury.

🏨 **Welcome Lodge,** Membury, Lambourn Woodlands, RG16 7TU, M 4 between junctions 14 and 15 (westbound carriageway) ℘ (01488) 72336, Fax (01488) 72336, Reservations (Freephone) 0800 7314466 – 🖐 rm, 📺 ⅄ 🄿. 🄼🄾 🄰🄴 🄾 𝗩𝗜𝗦𝗔
**Meals** (grill rest.) – ⸗ 7.50 – **40 rm** 50.00 **t.**

**ENDLESHAM GREEN** Suffolk **404** W 27 – see Stowmarket.

**ERE** Wilts. **403 404** N 30 The West Country G. – pop. 2 257.

Env. : Stourhead★★★ AC, NW : 4 m. by B 3095 and B 3092.

Exc. : Longleat House★★★ AC, N : 9½ m. by A 303 and B 3092.

🛈 The Square, BA12 6JJ ℘ (01747) 861211.

London 113 – Exeter 65 – Salisbury 26 – Taunton 40.

🏨 **Chetcombe House,** Chetcombe Rd, BA12 6AZ, Northeast : ½ m. by B 3095 ℘ (01747) 860219, Fax (01747) 860111, ≤, 🐎 – 🖐 📺 ☎ 🄿. 🄼🄾 🄰🄴 𝗩𝗜𝗦𝗔 🄹🄲🄱
closed 24 to 26 December and 1 January – **Meals** (lunch by arrangement)/dinner a la carte approx. 14.50 **s.** ⅄ 4.25 – **5 rm** ⸗ 29.00/50.00 **s.** – SB.

**ERIDEN** W. Mids. **403 404** P 26 – see Coventry.

**EVAGISSEY** Cornwall **403** F 33 The West Country G. – pop. 2 272.

See : Town★★.

Env. : NW : Lost Gardens of Heligan★.

London 287 – Newquay 21 – Plymouth 44 – Truro 20.

🏠 **Mevagissey House** ⸎ without rest., Vicarage Hill, PL26 6SZ, ℘ (01726) 842427, Fax (01726) 844327, ≤, 🐎 – 🖐 🄿. 🄼🄾 𝗩𝗜𝗦𝗔 🄹🄲🄱. ⚒
April-October – **4 rm** ⸗ 40.00/56.00 **st.**

**EYSEY HAMPTON** Glos. **403 404** O 28 – ✉ Cirencester.

London 101 – Bristol 44 – Gloucester 26 – Oxford 29.

🏨 **Masons Arms** with rm, High St., GL7 5JT, ℘ (01285) 850164, Fax (01285) 850164, « Part 17C inn » – 🖐 rest, 📺 🄿. 🄼🄾 𝗩𝗜𝗦𝗔 🄹🄲🄱
**Meals** (closed Sunday dinner) a la carte 12.35/17.55 **t.** – **8 rm** ⸗ 34.00/58.00 **t.**

**MICHAELWOOD SERVICE AREA** *Glos.* **403** M 29 – ⊠ *Dursley.*

🏠 **Welcome Lodge** without rest., Lower Wick, GL11 6DD, M 5 between junctions 13 and ' (northbound carriageway) ℘ (01454) 261513, *Fax (01454) 260331,* Reservations (Freephone) 0800 7314466 – ⁜ ᵀⱽ ₰ 🅿. ⬛🅾 🄰🄴 ⑩ ᵛᶦˢᵃ
⊆ 7.50 **40 rm** 50.00 **t.**

---

**MICKLEHAM** *Surrey* **404** ④ – pop. 484.
London 21 – Brighton 32 – Guildford 14 – Worthing 34.

🍴 **The King William IV,** Byttom Hill, RH5 6EL, North : ½ m. by A 24 ℘ (01372) 372590, 
🍽 – ⬛🅾 ᵛᶦˢᵃ
*closed Monday dinner, 25, 26 and 31 December and 1 January* – **Meals** a la carte 13.8'
15.80 **t.**

---

**MICKLEOVER** *Derbs.* **402 403 404** P 25 – see Derby.

---

**MICKLETON** *Glos.* **403 404** O 27 – see Chipping Campden.

---

**MICKLE TRAFFORD** *Ches.* – see Chester.

*Le Grand Londres (GREATER LONDON) est composé de la City*
*et de 32 arrondissements administratifs (Borough)*
*eux-mêmes divisés en quartiers ou en villages*
*ayant conservé leur caractère propre (Area).*

---

**MIDDLE CHINNOCK** *Somerset* **403** L 31 – see Crewkerne.

---

**MIDDLEHAM** *N. Yorks.* **402** O 21 – pop. 754.
London 233 – Kendal 45 – Leeds 47 – York 45.

🏠🏠 **Miller's House,** Market Pl., DL8 4NR, ℘ (01969) 622630, *Fax (01969) 623570,* « 18C »
⁜ rest, ᵀⱽ ☎ 🅿. ⬛🅾 ᵛᶦˢᵃ 🄹🄲🄱, 🍽
*closed 2 to 31 January* – **Meals** (dinner only) 20.50 **t.** ₰ 5.10 – **6 rm** ⊆ 39.00/93.00 **t.** – SB.

🏠 **Waterford House,** 19 Kirkgate, DL8 4PG, ℘ (01969) 622090, *Fax (01969) 624020,* « Pa
17C house, antiques », 🍽 – ⁜ rest, ᵀⱽ ☎ 🅿. ⬛🅾 ᵛᶦˢᵃ 🄹🄲🄱
**Number 19 :** Meals (lunch by arrangement) 17.50/19.50 **st.** and a la carte ₰ 5.50 – **5 r**
⊆ 50.00/90.00 **st.**

**at Carlton-in-Coverdale** *Southwest : 4½ m. on Coverdale Rd* – ⊠ *Leyburn.*

🏠 **Abbots Thorn** ⌂, DL8 4AY, ℘ (01969) 640620, *Fax (01969) 640304,* ≼ – ⁜ ᵀⱽ
**Meals** (by arrangement) (communal dining) 11.00 – **3 rm** ⊆ 24.00/48.00 **st.** – SB.

🍴 **Foresters Arms** with rm, DL8 4BB, ℘ (01969) 640272, *Fax (01969) 640272* – ⁜ rest, 🄻
🅿. ⬛🅾 ᵛᶦˢᵃ. 🍽
*closed 25 December and January* – **Meals** *(closed Sunday dinner and Monday)* (lunch in ba
a la carte 14.25/30.40 **t.** ₰ 5.70 – **3 rm** ⊆ 40.00/70.00 **t.**

---

**MIDDLESBROUGH** **402** Q 20 – pop. 147 430.

🍃 Middlesbrough Municipal, Ladgate Lane ℘ (01642) 315533 – 🍃 Brass Castle Lane, Martc
℘ (01642) 311515.
Cleveland Transporter Bridge (toll) BY.
✈ Teesside Airport : ℘ (01325) 332811, SW : 13 m. by A 66 – AZ – and A 19 on A 67.
🛈 51 Corporation Rd, TS1 1LT ℘ (01642) 243425.
London 246 – Kingston-upon-Hull 89 – Leeds 66 – Newcastle upon Tyne 41.

Plan opposite

🏠🏠 **Baltimore,** 250 Marton Rd, TS4 2EZ, ℘ (01642) 224111, *Fax (01642) 226156* – ᵀⱽ ☎ 🅿
🅰 25. ⬛🅾 🄰🄴 ⑩ ᵛᶦˢᵃ. 🍽                                                                   BZ
**Meals** *(closed lunch Saturday and Sunday)* 14.95 **t.** and a la carte ₰ 6.75 – ⊆ 9.50 – **30 r**
66.50/73.50 **st.**, 1 suite.

🏠 **Highfield,** Marton Rd, TS4 2PA, ℘ (01642) 817638, *Fax (01642) 821219,* 🍽 – ᵀⱽ ☎ 🅿. ⬛🅾
🄰🄴 ⑩ ᵛᶦˢᵃ. 🍽                                                                          BZ
**Meals** (grill rest.) a la carte 9.75/19.95 **t.** – ⊆ 6.95 – **23 rm** 42.50 **t.** – SB.

# MIDDLESBROUGH

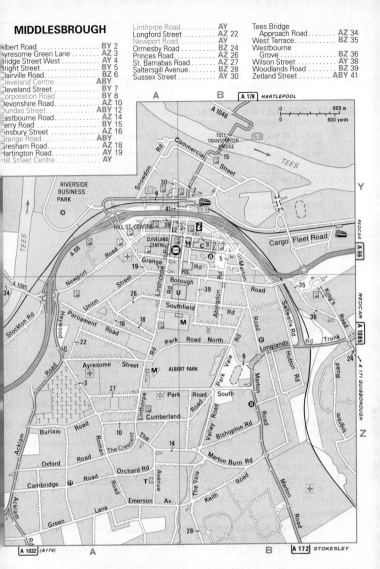

---

🏠 **Grey House,** 79 Cambridge Rd, TS5 5NL, ☎ (01642) 817485, *Fax (01642) 817485*, 🚗 –
⚒ rm, 📺 ☎ 🅿 . 🌐 *VISA*                                                                                                     AZ **n**
Meals (by arrangement) 12.00 t. – **9 rm** ⚏ 40.00/55.00 s.

✗ **The Purple Onion,** 80 Corporation Rd, TS1 2RF, ☎ (01642) 222250, *Fax (01642) 248088*
– ▤, 🌐 *VISA*                                                                                                                BY **a**
*closed 25 December* – **Meals** - Brasserie - (booking essential) a la carte 12.95/27.95 t.
🛢 6.00.

🔧 ATS Murdock Rd (off Sotherby Rd), Cargo St. ☎ (01642) 249245/6

---

**MIDDLETON** *N. Yorks.* – see *Pickering.*

**MIDDLETON** Suffolk – pop. 380 – ⊠ Saxmundham.
London 108 – Cambridge 73 – Ipswich 27 – Norwich 37.

⌂ **Rose Farm** ⌂ without rest., Mill St., IP17 3NG, ℰ (01728) 648456, 🐄 – ⅙⇔ 🖵 🅿. ✦
3 rm ⌑ 45.00/55.00.

⌂ **Little Orchard** ⌂ without rest., IP17 3NT, ℰ (01728) 648385, 🐄 – ⅙⇔ 🖵 🅿. ✦
closed 24 December-1 January – 3 rm ⌑ 21.00/42.00 s.

**MIDDLETON STONEY** Oxon. 🚧🚧 Q 28 – pop. 304.
London 66 – Northampton 30 – Oxford 12.

🏨 **Jersey Arms,** OX6 8SE, ℰ (01869) 343234, Fax (01869) 343565, 🐄 – ⅙⇔ rest, 🖵 ☎ 🅿
🐄 🆎 ⓪ 𝘝𝘐𝘚𝘈 𝘑𝘊𝘉. ✦
Meals a la carte 15.25/26.45 t. ⫪ 4.00 – 13 rm ⌑ 75.00/89.00 t., 3 suites – SB.

**MIDDLE WALLOP** Hants. 🚧🚧 P 30 – ⊠ Stockbridge.
London 80 – Salisbury 11 – Southampton 21.

🏨 **Fifehead Manor,** SO20 8EG, on A 343 ℰ (01264) 781565, Fax (01264) 781400,
« Converted 16C manor house », 🐄 – 🖵 ☎ ☏ 🅿. 🐄 🆎 𝘝𝘐𝘚𝘈. ✦
Meals 19.50/27.00 t. ⫪ 6.00 – 15 rm ⌑ 65.00/135.00 t. – SB.

**MIDGLEY** W. Yorks 🚧 P 22 – see Wakefield.

Les prix    Pour toutes précisions sur les prix indiqués dans ce guide,
reportez-vous aux pages de l'introduction.

**MIDHURST** W. Sussex 🚧 R 31 – pop. 6 451.
London 57 – Brighton 38 – Chichester 12 – Southampton 41.

🏨 **Spread Eagle,** South St., GU29 9NH, ℰ (01730) 816911, Fax (01730) 815668, « 15C hos-
telry, antique furnishings », 🏋, ☎, 🔲 – ⅙⇔ rest, 🖵 ☎ 🅿 – 🕍 50. 🐄 🆎 ⓪ 𝘝𝘐𝘚𝘈
Meals 32.50 t. (dinner) and a la carte 17.50/36.50 t. ⫪ 9.95 – 38 rm ⌑ 95.00/156.00 t.,
2 suites – SB.

🏨 **Angel,** North St., GU29 9DN, ℰ (01730) 812421, Fax (01730) 815928, « 16C coaching inn »
🐄 – ⅙⇔ rm, 🖵 ☎ & 🅿 – 🕍 60. 🐄 🆎 ⓪ 𝘝𝘐𝘚𝘈. ✦
**Cowdray Room :** Meals 17.50/25.00 t. and a la carte ⫪ 6.50 – **Brasserie :** Meals 14.50 st
(dinner) and a la carte 16.25/27.50 t. ⫪ 6.50 – 28 rm ⌑ 85.00/95.00 t. – SB.

✗ **Maxine's,** Red Lion St., GU29 9PB, ℰ (01730) 816271, « 15C timbered cottage » – ⅙⇔. 🐄
🆎 𝘝𝘐𝘚𝘈
closed Sunday dinner, Monday, Tuesday and 2 weeks January – Meals 15.95 st
and a la carte ⫪ 5.95.

**at Bepton** Southwest : 2½ m. by A 286 on Bepton rd – ⊠ Midhurst.

🏨 **Park House** ⌂, South Bepton, GU29 0JB, ℰ (01730) 812880, Fax (01730) 815643, 🏊,
🐄, ✗ – 🖵 ☎ & 🅿 – 🕍 70. 🐄 🆎 ⓪ 𝘝𝘐𝘚𝘈
Meals a la carte 16.50/22.50 t. ⫪ 6.30 – 13 rm ⌑ 70.00/140.00 t., 1 suite.

**at Stedham** West : 2 m. by A 272 – ⊠ Midhurst.

✗ **Nava Thai at Hamilton Arms,** School Lane, GU29 0NZ, ℰ (01730) 812555,
Fax (01730) 817459 – 🅿. 🐄 𝘝𝘐𝘚𝘈 𝘑𝘊𝘉
closed Monday except Bank Holidays – Meals - Thai - 18.50 t. (dinner) and a la carte 15.20/
20.95 t. ⫪ 4.95.

**at Trotton** West : 3¼ m. on A 272 – ⊠ Petersfield (Hants.).

🏨 **Southdowns Country** ⌂, GU31 5JN, South : 1 m. ℰ (01730) 821521,
Fax (01730) 821790, ☎, 🔲, 🐄, ✗ – ⅙⇔, 🔲 rest, 🖵 ☎ 🅿 – 🕍 100. 🐄 🆎 ⓪ 𝘝𝘐𝘚𝘈. ✦
Meals a la carte 7.00/31.95 t. ⫪ 7.50 – 20 rm ⌑ 79.00/119.00 t. – SB.

**at Elsted Marsh** Southwest : 4 m. by A 272 on Elsted rd – ⊠ Midhurst.

🏠 **Elsted Inn** with rm, GU29 0JT, ℰ (01730) 813662, 🐄 – 🖵 🅿. 🐄 𝘝𝘐𝘚𝘈 𝘑𝘊𝘉
closed 25 December – Meals (booking essential) a la carte 13.25/20.00 t. ⫪ 6.00 – 4 rm
⌑ 35.00/50.00 st.

**at Elsted** Southwest : 5 m. by A 272 on Elsted rd – ⊠ Midhurst.

🏠 **Three Horseshoes,** GU29 0JY, ℰ (01730) 825746, « 16C drovers inn » – 🅿. 🐄 𝘝𝘐𝘚𝘈
closed Sunday dinner October-May and 25 December Meals a la carte 16.85/21.85 t.

**MIDSOMER NORTON** *Bath & North East Somerset* 403 M 30 – ✉ *Bath.*
*London 129 – Bath 10 – Bristol 15 – Wells 8.*

**Centurion,** Charlton Lane, BA3 4BD, Southeast : 1 m. by B 3355, Charlton Rd and Fosseway ℘ (01761) 417711, *Fax (01761) 418357*, ←, ☒, ⛳9, ⛱, squash – ⇹ rest, TV ☎ 📞 ♿ P – 🎪 180. MC AE D VISA JCB. ✂
*closed 24 to 27 December* – **Meals** 16.50 **t.** (dinner) and a la carte 🍷 5.90 – **44 rm** ☕ 65.00/75.00 **t.** – SB.

**MILBORNE PORT** *Dorset* 403 404 M 31 – *see Sherborne.*

**MILDENHALL** *Suffolk* 404 V 26 – *pop. 12 827.*
*London 72 – Cambridge 24 – Ipswich 37 – Norwich 45.*

**Riverside,** Mill St., IP28 7DP, ℘ (01638) 717274, *Fax (01638) 715997*, ⛱, ⛱ – 🛗 TV ☎ P – 🎪 60. MC AE D VISA JCB
**Meals** 17.00 **t.** and a la carte 🍷 7.95 – **21 rm** ☕ 53.00/84.00 **t.** – SB.

ATS Southgate Ave. ℘ (01638) 713841

**MILFORD-ON-SEA** *Hants.* 403 404 P 31 – *pop. 4 434* – ✉ *Lymington.*
*London 109 – Bournemouth 15 – Southampton 24 – Winchester 37.*

**Westover Hall** 🐦, Park Lane, SO41 0PT, ℘ (01590) 643044, *Fax (01590) 644490*, ← Christchurch Bay, Isle of Wight and The Needles, « Victorian mansion built by Arnold Mitchell », ⛱ – ⇹ rest, TV ☎ P. MC AE D VISA JCB
**Meals** - Italian - (bar lunch)/dinner 23.50 **st.** 🍷 6.50 – **12 rm** ☕ 70.00/185.00 **st.** – SB.

**South Lawn,** Lymington Rd, SO41 0RF, ℘ (01590) 643911, *Fax (01590) 644820*, ⛱ – ⇹ TV ☎ 📞 P. MC VISA. ✂
*closed 3 weeks Christmas* – **Meals** *(closed Monday lunch)* 18.50 **t.** (dinner) and a la carte 9.50/34.00 **t.** 🍷 6.80 – **24 rm** ☕ 50.00/104.00 **t.** – SB.

**Rocher's,** 69-71 High St., SO41 0QG, ℘ (01590) 642340 – MC AE D VISA
*closed Sunday dinner, Monday, Tuesday and 2 weeks May-June* – **Meals** - French - (dinner only and Sunday lunch)/dinner 23.50 **t.** 🍷 8.50.

**MILNROW** *Gtr. Manchester* 402 404 N 23 – *see Rochdale.*

**MILTON DAMEREL** *Devon* 403 H 31 – *pop. 451.*
*London 249 – Barnstaple 21.*

**Woodford Bridge,** EX22 7LL, North : 1 m. on A 388 ℘ (01409) 261481, *Fax (01409) 261610*, ⛹, ☒s, ☒, ⛱, squash – TV ☎ P. MC AE VISA. ✂
**Meals** (bar lunch Monday to Saturday)/dinner a la carte 10.95/20.40 **t.** – ☕ 7.00 – **8 rm** 55.00/116.00 **t.**

**MILTON KEYNES** 404 R 27 – *pop. 156 148.*
⛳18 *Abbey Hill, Monks Way, Two Mile Ash* ℘ *(01908) 563845* **AV** – ⛳18 *Windmill Hill, Tattenhoe Lane, Bletchley* ℘ *(01908) 648149* **BX** – ⛳18, ⛳9 *Wavendon Golf Centre, Lower End Rd, Wavendon* ℘ *(01908) 281811* **CV.**
🅘 *411 Secklow Gate East, The Food Hall, MK9 3NE* ℘ *(01908) 232525* **FY.**
*London 56 – Birmingham 72 – Bedford 16 – Northampton 18 – Oxford 37.*

Plans on following pages

**Forte Posthouse Milton Keynes,** 500 Saxon Gate West, Central Milton Keynes, MK9 2HQ, ℘ (01908) 667722, *Fax (01908) 674714*, ⛹, ☒s, ☒ – 🛗, ⇹ rm, ▤ TV ☎ ♿ P – 🎪 150. MC AE D VISA JCB — EYZ a
**Meals** a la carte 18.00/22.00 **t.** 🍷 7.50 – ☕ 10.95 – **151 rm** 109.00 **st.**, 2 suites – SB.

**Hilton National Milton Keynes,** Timbold Drive, Kents Hill Park, MK7 6HL, Southeast : 4 m. by B 4034 and A 421 off Brickhill St. (V10) ℘ (01908) 694433, *Fax (01908) 695533*, ⛹, ☒s, ☒ – 🛗, ⇹ rm, ▤ rest, TV ☎ 📞 ♿ P – 🎪 300. MC AE D VISA JCB — CVX d
***New Horizons :*** **Meals** *(closed Saturday and Bank Holiday Mondays)* 12.50/18.50 **st.** and a la carte – ☕ 11.50 – **138 rm** 120.00/130.00 **st.** – SB.

**Courtyard by Marriott Milton Keynes,** London Rd, MK16 0JA, Northeast : 4 ¼ m. on A 509 ℘ (01908) 613688, *Fax (01908) 617335*, ⛹, ⛱ – ⇹ TV ☎ ♿ P – 🎪 200. MC AE D VISA JCB. ✂ — CV r
**Meals** a la carte 17.00/23.00 **t.** 🍷 9.95 – ☕ 9.50 – **49 rm** 90.00/122.00 **t.** – SB.

# MILTON KEYNES

Buckingham Road . . . . . . . . . . . . . . . . . BX
London Road . . . . . . . . . . . . . . . . . CUV
Manor Road . . . . . . . . . . . . . . . . . CX
Marsh End Road . . . . . . . . . . . . . . . CU
Newport Road . . . . . . . . . . . . . . . . BV
Northampton Road . . . . . . . . . . . . . . AU
Stoke Road . . . . . . . . . . . . . . . . . CX
Stratford Road . . . . . . . . . . . . . . . . AV
Whaddon Way . . . . . . . . . . . . . . . . BX
Wolverton Road . . . . . . . . . . . . . . . BU

## « VERTICAL » ROADS

V1 Snelshall Street . . . . . . . . . . . . BX
V2 Tattenhoe Street . . . . . . . . . . ABX
V3 Fulmer Street . . . . . . . . . . . . . . ABX
V4 Watling Street . . . . . . . . . . AV, BX
V5 Great Monks Street . . . . . . . . . . AV
V6 Grafton Street . . . . . . . . . . . . . BVX
V7 Saxon Street . . . . . . . . . . . . . . BVX
V8 Marlborough Street . . . . . . . BV, VX
V9 Overstreet . . . . . . . . . . . . . . . . BV
V10 Brickhill Street . . . . . . . . . BU, CX
V11 Tongwell Street . . . . . . . . . . CVX

## « HORIZONTAL » ROADS

H1 Ridgeway . . . . . . . . . . . . . . . . . AV
H2 Millers Way . . . . . . . . . . . . . . . AV
H3 Monks Way . . . . . . . . . . . . . . ABV
H4 Dansteed Way . . . . . . . . . . . . ABV
H5 Portway . . . . . . . . . . . . . . . . . BCV
H6 Childs Way . . . . . . . . . . . . BX, CV
H7 Chaffron Way . . . . . . . . . . . . . CV
H8 Standing Way . . . . . . . . . . BX, CV
H9 Groveway . . . . . . . . . . . . . . . . CVX
H10 Bletcham Way . . . . . . . . . . . . . CX

*For the quickest route use the*
*Michelin Main Road Maps:*
**970** Europe,
**976** Czech Republic-
    Slovak Republic,
**980** Greece,
**984** Germany,
**985** Scandinavia-Finland,
**986** Great Britain and Ireland,
**987** Germany-Austria-Benelux,
**988** Italy,
**989** France,
**990** Spain-Portugal and
**991** Yugoslavia.

462

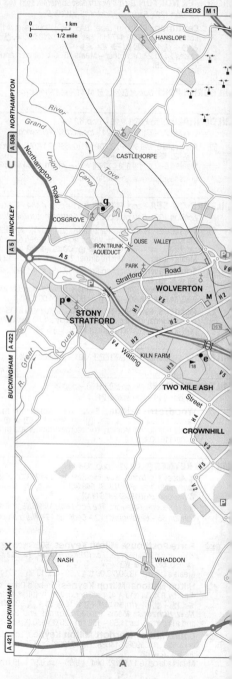

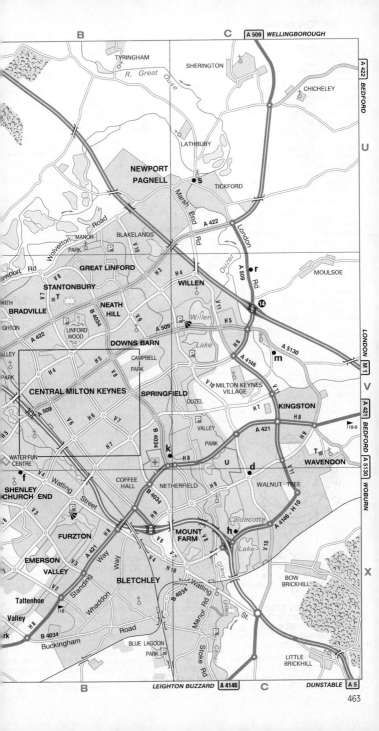

# MILTON KEYNES

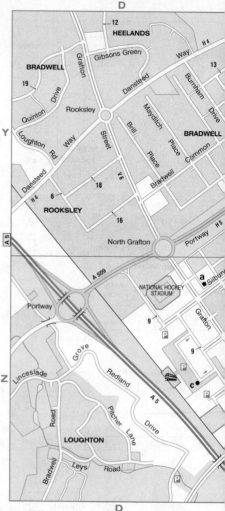

🏠 **Quality,** Monks Way, Two Mile Ash, MK8 8LY, Northwest : 2 m. by A 509 and A 5 at junction with A 422 ℰ (01908) 561666, *Fax (01908) 568303*, ⚡, ⚓ – ⇔ rm, 📺 ☎ & 🅿 – 🔬 120. 🚗 🅰🅴 ⓪ 𝘝𝘐𝘚𝘈. 🛇
AV e
**Meals** *(closed Saturday lunch)* (carving rest.) 14.50 **st.** ⫙ 4.95 – ☑ 9.50 – **88 rm** 74.25/107.00 **st.**

🏠 **Shenley Church Inn,** Burchard Cres., Shenley Church End, MK5 6HQ, Southwest : 2 m. by A 509 and Portway (H5) off Watling St. (V4) ℰ (01908) 505467, *Fax (01908) 340002* – 📳 ⇔ rm, 📺 ☎ & 🅿 – 🔬 100. 🚗 🅰🅴 ⓪ 𝘝𝘐𝘚𝘈. 🛇
BVX
*closed 25 to 31 December* – **Meals** (carving rest.) a la carte 11.15/16.20 **t.** ⫙ 4.45 – **50 rm** ☑ 69.50/79.50 **t.** – SB.

🏠 **Peartree Bridge Inn,** Milton Keynes Marina, Waterside, Peartree Bridge, MK6 3PE, Southeast : 2 m. by B 4034 ℰ (01908) 691515, *Fax (01908) 247982*, « Marina setting beside the Grand Union Canal » – ⇔ 📺 ☎ & 🅿. 🚗 🅰🅴 𝘝𝘐𝘚𝘈. 🛇
BCV k
*closed Christmas* – **Meals** (grill rest.) a la carte 9.35/15.35 **t.** – **39 rm** 68.00/78.00 **t.** – SB.

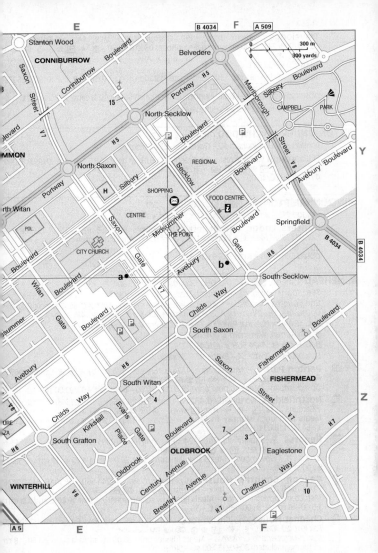

**Broughton,** Broughton Village, MK10 9AA, East : 4 m. by A 509 off A 5130   🏨
 𝒫 (01908) 667726, *Fax (01908) 604844*, ⛟ – 📺 ☎ 🅿. 🆚 ⒶⒺ ⓪ *VISA* JCB.
%      CV m
*closed 24 to 30 December and 1 January* – **Meals** *(closed Sunday dinner)* (bar lunch Monday
to Saturday)/dinner 14.95 **t.** and a la carte ₰ 4.75 – **31 rm** � 90.00/110.00 **t.**

**Caldecotte Arms - Premier Lodge,** Bletcham Way (H10), MK7 8HP, Southeast :   🏨
5 ½ m. by A 509 and A 5, taking 2nd junction left signposted Milton Keynes (South
and East) 𝒫 (01908) 366188, *Fax (01908) 366603*, Reservations (Freephone) 0800 118833,
« Windmill feature, lakeside setting » – ⊱⊱ rm, 📺 ☎ 🕭 🅿. 🆚 ⒶⒺ ⓪ *VISA*. %    CX h
**Meals** (grill rest.) a la carte 10.15/15.15 **t.** ₰ 4.55 – ⊒ 5.95 – **40 rm** 48.95 **st.**

**Travel Inn,** Secklow Gate West, Central Milton Keynes, MK9 3BZ, 𝒫 (01908) 663388,   🏨
*Fax (01908) 607481* – ⊱⊱ rm, 📺 ☎ 🕭 🅿 – 🔬 30. 🆚 ⒶⒺ ⓪ *VISA*. %    FY b
**Meals** (grill rest.) – **38 rm** 38.00 **t.**

465

🏠 **Travelodge** without rest., 199 Grafton Gate, MK9 1AL, ℰ (01908) 241075, *Fax (01908) 241737*, Reservations (Freephone) 0800 850950 – 🛋 ⬚ 📺 ☎ 👌 🅿. 🐶 🆎 ⬚
🆚 🅹🅲🅱. ⬚
**80 rm** 39.95/59.95 **t**.　　　　　　　　　　　　　　　　　　　　DZ

🍴🍴 **Jaipur**, Elder House, 502 Eldergate, Station Sq., MK9 1LR, ℰ (01908) 669979, *Fax (01908) 694464* – 🖥. 🐶 🆎 ⬚ 🆚　　　　　　　　　　　　　　　　DZ
*closed 25 December –* **Meals** - Indian - (buffet lunch Sunday) a la carte 16.95/24.70 **t**.

　　🅰 ATS 38 Victoria Rd, Bletchley ℰ (01908) 640420

---

## MILTON-UNDER-WYCHWOOD *Oxon. – pop. 2 030.*

*London 83 – Birmingham 52 – Gloucester 35 – Oxford 27.*

🏠 **Hillborough** without rest., The Green, OX7 6JH, ℰ (01993) 830501, *Fax (01993) 832005*, 🌳 – ⬚ rest. 📺 ☎ 🅿. 🐶 🆚 🅹🅲🅱. ⬚
**4 rm** ⬚ 28.00/46.00.

---

## MINCHINHAMPTON *Glos.* 🔢🔢 N 28 – *pop. 3 201.*

*London 115 – Bristol 26 – Gloucester 11 – Oxford 51.*

🏠 **Hunters Lodge** without rest., Dr Brown's Rd, GL6 9BT, ℰ (01453) 883588, *Fax (01453) 731449*, ≼, « Cotswold stone house on Minchinhampton common », 🌳 – ⬚
📺 🍴 🅿. ⬚
*closed Christmas –* **3 rm** ⬚ 26.00/46.00.

---

## MINEHEAD *Somerset* 🔢🔢 J 30 *The West Country G. – pop. 9 904.*

See : *Town★ - Higher Town (Church Steps★, St. Michael's★ ).*
Env. : *Dunster★★ - Castle★★ AC (upper rooms ≼★) Water Mill★ AC, St. George's Church★,*
*Dovecote★, SE : 2½ m. by A 39 – Selworthy★ (Church★, ≼★★) W : 4½ m. by A 39.*
Exc. : *Exmoor National Park★★ – Cleeve Abbey★★ AC, SE : 6½ m. by A 39.*
🏌 *The Warren, Warren Rd* ℰ *(01643) 702057.*
🔳 *17 Friday St., TA24 5UB* ℰ *(01643) 702624.*
*London 187 – Bristol 64 – Exeter 43 – Taunton 25.*

🏨 **Periton Park** ⬚, Middlecombe, TA24 8SN, West : 1 ½ m. by A 39 ℰ (01643) 706885, *Fax (01643) 706885*, ≼, 🌳 – ⬚ rest. 📺 ☎ 🅿. 🐶 🆎 🆚 🅹🅲🅱
*closed January –* **Meals** (dinner only) 23.50 **st**. ▯ 6.50 – **8 rm** ⬚ 59.50/99.00 **st**. – SB.

🏨 **Northfield** ⬚, Northfield Rd, TA24 5PU, ℰ (01643) 705155, *Fax (01643) 707715*, ≼ bay, « Gardens », 🏓, 🔲 – 🛋 ⬚ rest. 📺 ☎ 🅿 – 🔺 70. 🐶 🆎 ⬚ 🆚 🅹🅲🅱
**Meals** (bar lunch Monday to Saturday)/dinner 18.95 **t**. and a la carte ▯ 6.95 – **28 rm**
⬚ 54.00/118.00 **t**. – SB.

🏨 **Benares** ⬚, Northfield Rd, TA24 5PT, ℰ (01643) 704911, *Fax (01643) 706373*, ≼ « Gardens » – ⬚ rest. 📺 ☎ 🅿. 🐶 🆎 ⬚ 🆚
*27 March-1 November –* **Meals** (bar lunch)/dinner 20.00 **st**. ▯ 4.95 – **19 rm** ⬚ 50.00/
90.00 **st**. – SB.

🏨 **Beacon Country House** ⬚, Beacon Rd, TA24 5SD, ℰ (01643) 703476, *Fax (01643) 707007*, ≼, 🌳, park – ⬚ rest. 📺 ☎ 🅿. 🐶 🆚 🅹🅲🅱
*restricted opening in winter –* **Meals** (lunch by arrangement)/dinner 16.00 **t**. and a la carte
▯ 5.00 – **8 rm** ⬚ 58.00/138.00 **t**. – SB.

🏨 **Channel House** ⬚, Church Path, TA24 5QG, off Northfield Rd ℰ (01643) 703229, *Fax (01643) 708925*, ≼, 🌳 – 📺 🆚 🅹🅲🅱. ⬚
*March-October and Christmas –* **Meals** (dinner only) 20.00 **st**. and a la carte ▯ 4.50 – **8 rm**
⬚ (dinner included) 80.00/130.00 **st**. – SB.

🏨 **Wyndcott** ⬚, Martlet Rd, TA24 5QE, ℰ (01643) 704522, *Fax (01643) 707577*, ≼, 🌳 – ⬚
☎ 🅿. 🐶 🆎 🆚
**Meals** (booking essential to non-residents) (lunch by arrangement) 11.95/19.95 **st**. ▯ 3.95 –
**10 rm** ⬚ 32.00/80.00 **st**.

🏨 **Beaconwood** ⬚, Church Rd, North Hill, TA24 5SB, ℰ (01643) 702032, *Fax (01643) 702032*, ≼ sea and Minehead, 🏊, 🌳, 🎾 – ⬚ rest. 📺 ☎ 🅿. 🐶 🆚
**Meals** (bar lunch)/dinner 13.95 ▯ 4.25 – **12 rm** ⬚ 40.00/65.00 **st**. – SB.

🏨 **Rectory House**, Northfield Rd, TA24 5QH, ℰ (01643) 702611, 🌳 – ⬚ rest. 📺 🅿. 🐶
🆚
*March-October –* **Meals** (dinner only May-September) 19.50 ▯ 6.95 – **7 rm** ⬚ 25.00/50.00.

　　🅰 ATS Bampton St. ℰ (01643) 704808/9

---

## MINSTER *Kent* 🔢🔢 Y 29 – *see Ramsgate.*

MINSTERLEY *Shrops.* **402 403** L 26 – *pop. 1 397.*
*London 174 – Birmingham 57 – Hereford 55 – Shrewsbury 10.*

⌂ **Cricklewood Cottage** without rest., Plox Green, SY5 0HT, Southwest : 1 m. on A 488
℘ (01743) 791229, 龠 – ⇔ 🅿. ⅍
*closed 24 and 25 December* – **3 rm** � 34.00/47.00.

---

MOBBERLEY *Ches.* **402 403 404** N 24 – *see Knutsford.*

---

MONK FRYSTON *N. Yorks.* **402** Q 22 – *pop. 722* – ⊠ *Lumby.*
*London 190 – Kingston-upon-Hull 42 – Leeds 13 – York 20.*

🏨 **Monk Fryston Hall**, LS25 5DU, ℘ (01977) 682369, Fax (01977) 683544, « Part 16C and
17C manor house, extensive ornamental gardens », park – ⇔ rest, 📺 ☎ 🅿 – 🕯 50. 🐼
AE ◑ VISA
**Meals** 13.45/19.75 **st.** ▯ 7.25 – **28 rm** � 75.00/110.00 **st.** – SB.

---

MONKTON COMBE *Bath & North East Somerset* – *see Bath.*

---

MONKTON FARLEIGH *Wilts.* **403 404** N 29 – *see Bradford-on-Avon.*

---

MONTACUTE *Somerset* **403** L 31 – *see Yeovil.*

---

MORCHARD BISHOP *Devon* **403** I 31 – *pop. 978* – ⊠ *Crediton.*
*London 217 – Barnstaple 28 – Exeter 17 – Taunton 40.*

⌂ **Wigham** ⌂, EX17 6RJ, Northwest : 1 m. on Eastington rd ℘ (01363) 877350,
Fax (01363) 877350, ≤, « 16C longhouse, working farm », ⊐ – ⇔ 📺 ☎ 🅿. 🐼 AE VISA
JCB. ⅍
**Meals** (communal dining) 20.00 **st.** – **5 rm** � (dinner included) 112.50/150.00 **st.** – SB.

---

MORCOTT SERVICE AREA *Rutland* – *see Uppingham.*

---

MORECAMBE *Lancs.* **402** L 21 – *pop. 46 657.*
🏌 Bare ℘ (01524) 418050 – 🏌 Heysham, Trumacar Park, Middleton Rd ℘ (01524) 851011.
🛈 Station Buildings, Central Promenade, LA4 4DB ℘ (01524) 582808/9.
*London 248 – Blackpool 29 – Carlisle 66 – Lancaster 4.*

🏨 **Strathmore**, Marine Rd, East Promenade, LA4 5AP, ℘ (01524) 421234,
Fax (01524) 414242, ≤ – 🛗 📺 ☎ 🅿 – 🕯 200. 🐼 AE ◑ VISA JCB. ⅍
**Meals** 9.95/16.95 **st.** ▯ 4.95 – **51 rm** � 47.50/77.50 **st.** – SB.

🅖 ATS Northgate, White Lund Ind. Est. ℘ (01524) 68075/62011

---

MORETON *Mersey.* **402 403** K 23 – *pop. 12 053.*
*London 225 – Birkenhead 4 – Liverpool 5.*

XX **Lee Ho**, 304-308 Hoylake Rd, L46 6DE, West : ¼ m. on A 553 ℘ (0151) 677 6440 – 🍽. 🐼 AE VISA
*closed Sunday, Monday, 25-26 December and 3 weeks August* – **Meals** - Chinese - (dinner
only) 8.90 **st.** and a la carte ▯ 4.75.

🅖 ATS 83 Hoylake Rd ℘ (0151) 678 2393

---

MORETONHAMPSTEAD *Devon* **403** I 32 *The West Country G.* – *pop. 1 380* – ⊠ *Newton Abbot.*
Env. : Dartmoor National Park★★.
🏌 Manor House Hotel ℘ (01647) 440998.
*London 213 – Exeter 13 – Plymouth 28.*

🏨 **Manor House** ⌂, TQ13 8RE, Southwest : 2 m. on B 3212 ℘ (01647) 440355,
Fax (01647) 440961, ≤, « Part 19C », 🏌, ⌂, 龠, park, ⅏ – 🛗, ⇔ rest, 📺 ☎ 🅿 – 🕯 120.
🐼 AE ◑ VISA
**Meals** (bar lunch Monday to Saturday)/dinner 19.50 **st.** and a la carte ▯ 5.95 – **90 rm**
� 80.00/120.00 **st.** – SB.

467

⤒ **Wray Barton Manor** without rest., TQ13 8SE, Southeast : 1 ½ m. on A 38
*℘ (01647) 440467, Fax (01647) 440628*, ≤, 🚗 - ⇔ 📺 🅿
*April-October* – **6 rm** � 24.00/48.00.

⤒ **Moorcote** without rest., TQ13 8LS, Northwest : ¼ m. on A 382 *℘ (01647) 440966*, 🚗 ⇔ 📺 🅿. ⁂
*March-October* – **5 rm** � 31.00/42.00 t.

---

**MORETON-IN-MARSH** *Glos.* **403 404** O 28 *Great Britain G. – pop. 1 895.*
Env. : *Chastleton House★★, SE : 5 m. by A 44.*
London 86 – Birmingham 40 – Gloucester 31 – Oxford 29.

🏛 **Manor House,** High St., GL56 0LJ, *℘ (01608) 650501, Fax (01608) 651481*, « 16C manor house, gardens », ⇔, 🔲 – 📱, ⇔ rest, 📺 ☎ 🅿 – 🔬 75. 🎫 🅰🄴 ⓪ 𝘝𝘐𝘚𝘈 ⁂
Meals a la carte 20.75/34.65 t. 🍷 11.50 – **37 rm** � 65.00/135.00 **st.**, 1 suite – SB.

🏛 **Redesdale Arms,** High St., GL56 0AW, *℘ (01608) 650308, Fax (01608) 651843*, Reservations (Freephone) 0800 118833 – 📺 ☎ 🅿 – 🔬 80. 🎫 🅰🄴 𝘝𝘐𝘚𝘈. ⁂
Meals a la carte 15.75/21.70 st. – � 4.95 – **16 rm** 42.95 **st.**, 1 suite – SB.

⤒ **Treetops** without rest., London Rd, GL56 0HE, *℘ (01608) 651036, Fax (01608) 651036*, 🚗 – ⇔ 📺 🅿. 🎫 ⁂
**6 rm** � 30.00/45.00.

XX **Marsh Goose,** High St., GL56 0AX, *℘ (01608) 653500, Fax (01608) 653510* – ⇔. 🎫 🅰🄴 ⓪ 𝘝𝘐𝘚𝘈 𝘑𝘊𝘉
*closed Sunday dinner, Monday, 26-27 December and 1-2 January* – **Meals** 14.50/28.00 t and lunch a la carte 20.50/26.50 t. 🍷 6.30.

XX **Annies,** 3 Oxford St., GL56 0LA, *℘ (01608) 651981, Fax (01608) 651981* – 🎫 🅰🄴 ⓪ 𝘝𝘐𝘚𝘈
*closed Sunday and late January-early February* – **Meals** (dinner only) 22.50/32.45 **st.** 🍷 6.25

---

**MORPETH** *Northd.* **401 402** O 18 – pop. 14 393.
🐾 *The Common ℘ (01670) 504942.*
🅱 *The Chantry, Bridge St., NE61 1PJ ℘ (01670) 511323.*
London 301 – Edinburgh 93 – Newcastle upon Tyne 15.

🏛 **Linden Hall** ⊛, Longhorsley, NE65 8XF, Northwest : 7 ½ m. by A 192 on A 697
*℘ (01670) 516611, Fax (01670) 788544*, ≤, « Country house in extensive grounds », 𝑓♨, 🔲 🐾, 🚗, park – 📱, ⇔ rest, 📺 ☎ & 🅿 – 🔬 300. 🎫 🅰🄴 ⓪ 𝘝𝘐𝘚𝘈 𝘑𝘊𝘉. ⁂
Meals a la carte 25.85/33.00 **st.** – **49 rm** � 97.50/185.00 **st.**, 1 suite – SB.

🅐 ATS Coopies Lane Ind. Est. *℘ (01670) 514627*

---

**MORSTON** *Norfolk – see Blakeney.*

---

**MORTEHOE** *Devon* **403** H 30 – *see Woolacombe.*

---

**MOTCOMBE** *Dorset* **403 404** N 30 – *see Shaftesbury.*

---

**MOULSFORD** *Oxon.* **403 404** Q 29 *The West Country G. – pop. 491.*
Exc. : *Ridgeway Path★★.*
London 58 – Oxford 17 – Reading 13 – Swindon 37.

XXX **Beetle and Wedge** with rm, Ferry Lane, OX10 9JF, *℘ (01491) 651381*
*Fax (01491) 651376*, ≤, « Thames-side setting », ⤸, 🚗 – ⬇ ⇔ 📺 ☎ 🅿. 🎫 🅰🄴 ⓪ 𝘝𝘐𝘚𝘈 𝘑𝘊𝘉
*closed 25 December* – **The Dining Room** : Meals *(closed Sunday dinner and Monday) (booking essential)* 27.50/35.00 t. – *(see also Boathouse below)* – **10 rm** � 90.00/150.00 t – SB.

X **Boathouse** (at Beetle and Wedge), Ferry Lane, OX10 9JF, *℘ (01491) 651381*
*Fax (01491) 651376*, ≤, « Thames-side setting », 🚗 – ⬇ 🅿. 🎫 🅰🄴 ⓪ 𝘝𝘐𝘚𝘈 𝘑𝘊𝘉
*closed 25 December* – **Meals** *(booking essential)* a la carte 21.50/30.95 **t.**

---

**MOULSOE** *Bucks. – pop. 251.*
London 57 – Bedford 13 – Luton 21 – Northampton 15.

X **Carrington Arms** with rm, Cranfield Rd, MK16 0HB, *℘ (01908) 218050*
*Fax (01908) 217850* – 📺 🅿. 🎫 🅰🄴 ⓪ 𝘝𝘐𝘚𝘈 𝘑𝘊𝘉
**Meals** *(dinner bookings not accepted)* a la carte 10.00/45.00 t. 🍷 4.70 – � 3.50 – **8 rm** 40.50/50.00 **t.**

**MOULTON** *Northants.* 404 R 27 – *see Northampton.*

---

**MOULTON** *N. Yorks.* 402 P 20 – *pop. 197* – ⊠ *Richmond.*
*London 243 – Leeds 53 – Middlesbrough 25 – Newcastle upon Tyne 43.*

XX **Black Bull Inn**, DL10 6QJ, ℘ (01325) 377289, *Fax* (01325) 377422, « Brighton Belle Pullman coach » – 🅿. ⓂⓄ 🄰🄴 🄾 *VISA* 🄹🄲🄱
*closed Sunday and 24 to 26 December* – **Meals** 14.95 **t.** (lunch) and a la carte 21.75/30.00 **t.** ⒤ 7.00.

---

**MOUSEHOLE** *Cornwall* 403 D 33 *The West Country G.* – ⊠ *Penzance.*
See : *Village*★.
Env. : *Penwith*★★ – *Lamorna (The Merry Maidens and The Pipers Standing Stone*★ *) SW : 3 m. by B 3315.*
Exc. : *Land's End*★ *(cliff scenery*★★★ *) W : 9 m. by B 3315.*
*London 321 – Penzance 3 – Truro 29.*

🏛 **The Old Coastguard**, TR18 6PR, ℘ (01736) 731222, *Fax* (01736) 731720, ≤, 🌳 – ⁕⟶ 📺
🕿 🅿. ⓂⓄ *VISA*
**Meals** 17.95 **st.** (dinner) and a la carte 12.00/18.00 **st.** ⒤ 4.50 – **21 rm** ⊊ 32.00/70.00 **st.** – SB.

---

**MUCH WENLOCK** *Shrops.* 402 403 M 26 *Great Britain G.* – *pop. 1 921.*
See : *Priory*★ *AC.*
Env. : *Ironbridge Gorge Museum*★★ *AC (The Iron Bridge*★★ *- Coalport China Museum*★★ *- Blists Hill Open Air Museum*★★ *– Museum of the River and Visitor Centre*★ *) NE : 4½ m. by A 4169 and B 4380.*
🄱 *The Museum, High St., TF13 6HR* ℘ *(01952) 727679 (summer only).*
*London 154 – Birmingham 34 – Shrewsbury 12 – Worcester 37.*

🏛 **Raven**, Barrow St., TF13 6EN, ℘ (01952) 727251, *Fax* (01952) 728416, � – ⁕⟶ rest, 📺 🕿
🅿. ⓂⓄ 🄰🄴 🄾 *VISA* 🄹🄲🄱. ⁕⁕
*closed 25 December* – **Meals** a la carte approx. 26.50 **t.** ⒤ 7.50 – **15 rm** ⊊ 55.00/120.00 **t.** – SB.

**at Bourton** *Southwest : 2¾ m. on B 4378* – ⊠ *Much Wenlock.*

🏛 **Bourton Manor**, TF13 6QE, ℘ (01746) 785531, *Fax* (01746) 785683, ≤, 🌳 – ⁕⟶ rest, 📺
🕿 🅿 – 🔬 40. ⓂⓄ 🄰🄴 🄾 *VISA* 🄹🄲🄱
**Meals** (bar lunch Monday to Saturday)/dinner a la carte 18.00/28.00 **st.** ⒤ 5.95 – **8 rm**
⊊ 60.00/130.00 **t.** – SB.

---

**MUDEFORD** *Dorset* 403 404 O 31 – *see Christchurch.*

---

**MULLION** *Cornwall* 403 E 33 *The West Country G.* – *pop. 2 040* – ⊠ *Helston.*
See : *Mullion Cove*★★ *(Church*★ *) – Lizard Peninsula*★.
Env. : *Kynance Cove*★★, *S : 5 m. – Cury*★ *(Church*★ *), N : 2 m. by minor roads.*
Exc. : *Helston (The Flora Day Furry Dance*★★ *) (May), N : 7½ m. by A 3083 – Culdrose (Flambards Village Theme Park*★ *) AC, N : 6 m. by A 3083 – Wendron (Poldark Mine*★ *), N : 9½ m. by A 3083 and B 3297.*
*London 323 – Falmouth 21 – Penzance 21 – Truro 26.*

🏛 **Polurrian**, TR12 7EN, Southwest : ½ m. ℘ (01326) 240421, *Fax* (01326) 240083, ≤ Mounts Bay, 🗡, ≘s, 🟰, 🧖, 🌳, 🧺, squash – ⁕⟶ rest, 📺 🕿 ☎ 🅿 – 🔬 120. ⓂⓄ 🄰🄴 🄾 *VISA* 🄹🄲🄱
*closed January* – **Meals** (bar lunch Monday to Saturday)/dinner 22.50 **t.** and a la carte ⒤ 9.50 – **38 rm** ⊊ (dinner included) 50.00/198.00, 1 suite – SB.

---

**MUNGRISDALE** *Cumbria* 401 402 L 19 20 – *pop. 330* – ⊠ *Penrith.*
*London 301 – Carlisle 33 – Keswick 8.5 – Penrith 13.*

🏛 **Mill** ⌂, CA11 0XR, ℘ (017687) 79659, *Fax* (017687) 79155, 🦢, 🌳 – ⁕⟶ rest, 📺 🅿
*March-October* – **Meals** (dinner only) 26.00 **t.** ⒤ 3.95 – **7 rm** ⊊ 39.00/80.00 **t.**

↑ **Mosedale House** ⌂, Mosedale, CA11 0XQ, North : 1 m. by Mosedale rd
℘ (017687) 79371 – ⁕⟶ 📺 ⛱ 🅿
*closed 25 and 26 December* – **Meals** 14.00 **st.** ⒤ 5.40 – **5 rm** ⊊ 25.00/84.00 **st.**

---

**MYLOR BRIDGE** *Cornwall* 403 E 33 – *see Falmouth.*

469

## NAILSWORTH Glos. 403 404 N 28 – pop. 5 242.

London 120 – Bristol 30 – Swindon 41.

🏠 **Egypt Mill**, GL6 0AE, ℰ (01453) 833449, Fax (01453) 836098, « Part 16C converted mill »
🌿 – 📺 ☎ ℗ – 🔬 100. 🐵 🄰🄴 ⓪ 𝘝𝘐𝘚𝘈, ⋇
**Restaurant** : Meals (dinner only) 16.50 t. ⅋ 6.00 – **Cellar Bistro** : Meals a la carte 11.50
19.20 t. ⅋ 6.00 – **16 rm** ⊑ 42.50/75.00 st.

⌂ **Aaron Farm**, Nympsfield Rd, GL6 0ET, West : ¾ m. by Spring Hill ℰ (01453) 833598
Fax (01453) 833598 – ⋇ 📺 ℗
Meals 12.00 st. – **3 rm** ⊑ 28.00/40.00 s.

✕✕ **Waterman's**, Old Market, GL6 0BX, ℰ (01453) 832808 – 🐵 🄰🄴 ⓪ 𝘝𝘐𝘚𝘈 🄹🄲🄱
closed Sunday and Monday – Meals (dinner only and Saturday lunch)/dinner a la carte
17.25/25.50 t. ⅋ 4.50.

✕ **William's Bistro**, 3 Fountain St., GL6 0BL, ℰ (01453) 835507, Fax (01453) 835950 – 🐵
𝘝𝘐𝘚𝘈
closed Sunday, Monday, 2 weeks Christmas and Tuesday following Bank Holidays – Meals
Seafood - (dinner only) a la carte 19.00/30.25 t. ⅋ 6.25.

## NANTWICH Ches. 402 403 404 M 24 – pop. 11 695.

🄱 Church House, Church Walk, CW5 5RG ℰ (01270) 610983/610880.
London 176 – Chester 20 – Liverpool 45 – Stoke-on-Trent 17.

🏨 **Rookery Hall** ⑤, Worleston, CW5 6DQ, North : 2 ½ m. by A 51 on B 5074
ℰ (01270) 610016, Fax (01270) 626027, ≤, « Part 19C country house », 🐾, 🌿, park, ✕ ⋅
🔲 ⋇ 📺 ☎ ఈ ℗ – 🔬 70. 🐵 🄰🄴 ⓪ 𝘝𝘐𝘚𝘈, ⋇
Meals (booking essential) 38.00 st. (dinner) and lunch a la carte 18.40/21.60 st. ⅋ 13.50 – ⊑
9.50 – **42 rm** 130.00/175.00 st., 3 suites – SB.

🏠 **The Peacock - Premier Lodge**, 221 Crewe Rd, CW5 6NE, Northeast : 1 ¼ m. on A 53◄
ℰ (01270) 624069, Fax (01270) 610113, Reservations (Freephone) 0800 118833 – ⋇ rm
📺 ☎ ℗. 🐵 ⓪ 𝘝𝘐𝘚𝘈. ⋇
Meals (grill rest.) a la carte 8.60/14.35 t. ⅋ 4.25 – ⊑ 5.95 – **37 rm** 43.95 t. – SB.

⌂ **Oakland House** without rest., 252 Newcastle Rd, Blakelow, Shavington, CW5 7ET, East
2 ½ m. by A 51 on A 500 ℰ (01270) 567134, Fax (01270) 651752, 🐾 – ⋇ 📺 ℗. 𝘝𝘐𝘚𝘈. ⋇
**5 rm** ⊑ 30.00/39.00.

⌂ **The Limes** without rest., 5 Park Rd, CW5 7AQ, ℰ (01270) 624081, Fax (01270) 624081, 🐾
– ⋇ 📺 ℗
**3 rm** ⊑ 35.00/50.00 st.

✕✕ **Churche's Mansion**, Hospital St., CW5 5RY, East : ¼ m. ℰ (01270) 625933
Fax (01270) 627831, 🌺, « Timbered Elizabethan house », 🐾 – ⋇ ℗. 🐵 ⓪ 𝘝𝘐𝘚𝘈 🄹🄲🄱
closed Monday, Tuesday and 2 weeks January – Meals 29.50 t. (dinner) and lunch a la carte
19.75/23.00 t. ⅋ 9.00.

**at Burland** West : 2½ m. on A 534 – ⊠ Nantwich.

⌂ **Burland Farm** without rest., Wrexham Rd, CW5 8ND, West : ¾ m. on A 534
ℰ (01270) 524210, Fax (01270) 524419, « Working farm », 🐾 – 📺 ℗
closed January and December – **3 rm** ⊑ 25.00/50.00.

## NATIONAL EXHIBITION CENTRE W. Mids. 403 404 O 26 – see Birmingham.

## NAWTON N. Yorks. – see Helmsley.

## NAYLAND Suffolk 404 W 28.

London 64 – Bury St. Edmunds 24 – Cambridge 54 – Colchester 6 – Ipswich 19.

⌂ **Gladwins Farm** ⑤, Harpers Hill, CO6 4NU, Northwest : ½ m. on A 134◄
ℰ (01206) 262261, Fax (01206) 263001, ≤, ☎, 🔲, 🐾, 🐾, park, ✕ – ⋇ rm, 📺 ℗. 🐵 𝘝𝘐𝘚𝘈
closed 24 December-5 January – Meals (by arrangement) 15.00 st. – **3 rm** ⊑ 22.00/
60.00 st.

🏠 **White Hart**, High St., CO6 4JF, ℰ (01206) 263382, Fax (01206) 263638, 🌺 – ℗. 🐵 🄰🄴 ⓪
𝘝𝘐𝘚𝘈
closed dinner 25 December, 26 December and 1 January – Meals 16.00 t. (lunch) and dinner a la carte 17.00/22.00 t.

## NEAR SAWREY Cumbria 402 L 20 – see Hawkshead.

**EEDHAM MARKET** Suffolk 404 X 27 – pop. 4 312.

London 77 – Cambridge 47 – Ipswich 8.5 – Norwich 38.

**Travelodge,** Norwich Rd, IP6 8LP, Beacon Hill Service Area, at junction of A 14 with A 140 ℘ (01449) 721640, Fax (01449) 721640, Reservations (Freephone) 0800 850950 – ℀ rm, 📺 ⅙ 🅿. 🕘 AE ⓞ VISA JCB. ✨
**Meals** (grill rest.) – **40 rm** 39.95/59.95 t.

**Pipps Ford,** Norwich Rd roundabout, IP6 8LJ, Southeast : 1 ¾ m. by B 1078 at junction of A 14 with A 140 ℘ (01449) 760208, Fax (01449) 760561, « Elizabethan farmhouse », ✯, 🐎, ✨ – ℀ 🅿. ✨
closed 22 December-6 January – **Meals** (by arrangement) (communal dining) 18.00 ⌁ 7.00 – **7 rm** ⌑ 42.50/70.00.

**ETTLETON SHRUB** Wilts. 403 404 N 29 – see Castle Combe.

**EWARK-ON-TRENT** Notts. 402 404 R 24 Great Britain G. – pop. 35 129.

See : St. Mary Magdalene★.

📷 Kelwick, Coddington ℘ (01636) 626241.

🖪 The Gilstrap Centre, Castlegate, NG24 1BG ℘ (01636) 78962.

London 127 – Lincoln 16 – Nottingham 20 – Sheffield 42.

**Grange,** 73 London Rd, NG24 1RZ, South : ½ m. on Grantham rd (A 1) ℘ (01636) 703399, Fax (01636) 702328, 🐎 – ℀ 📺 ☎ 🅿. 🕘 AE ⓞ VISA. ✨
closed 24 December-2 January – **Meals** (lunch by arrangement)/dinner a la carte 12.95/19.95 t. – **15 rm** ⌑ 44.95/72.95 t. – SB.

**Travel Inn,** Lincoln Rd, NG24 2DB, ℘ (01636) 640690, Fax (01636) 605135 – 📳 ℀ 📺 ⅙ 🅿. 🕘 AE ⓞ VISA. ✨
**Meals** (grill rest.) – **40 rm** 38.00 t.

**t North Muskham** North : 4½ m. by A 46 and A 1 – ⊠ Newark-on-Trent.

**Travelodge,** NG23 6HT, North : ½ m. on A 1 (southbound carriageway) ℘ (01636) 703635, Fax (01636) 703635, Reservations (Freephone) 0800 850950 – ℀ rm, 📺 ⅙ 🅿. 🕘 AE ⓞ VISA JCB. ✨
**Meals** (grill rest.) – **30 rm** 39.95/59.95 t.

**t Caunton** Northwest : 4½ m. by A 616 – ⊠ Newark-on-Trent.

**Caunton Beck,** Main St., NG23 6AB, ℘ (01636) 636793, Fax (01636) 636828, 😀, 🐎 – 🅿. 🕘 AE ⓞ VISA JCB
**Meals** a la carte 14.50/24.50 st. ⌁ 7.00.

⑩ ATS 70 William St. ℘ (01636) 77531

**EWBURGH** Lancs. 402 L 23.

London 217 – Liverpool 26 – Manchester 39 – Preston 20 – Southport 13.

**Red Lion,** Ash Brow, WN8 7NG, on A 5209 ℘ (01257) 462336, Fax (01257) 462827 – 📺 ☎ 🅿 – ⅍ 45. 🕘 AE VISA JCB
**Meals** (grill rest.) (in bar) a la carte 8.20/19.20 t. ⌁ 3.75 – ⌑ 4.95 – **13 rm** 30.00/39.50 st.

**EWBURY** 403 404 Q 29 – pop. 33 273.

📷 Newbury and Crookham, Bury's Bank Rd, Greenham Common ℘ (01635) 40035 AX – 📷 Donnington Valley, Old Oxford Rd ℘ (01635) 32488 AV.

🖪 The Wharf, RG14 5AS ℘ (01635) 30267.

London 67 – Bristol 66 – Oxford 28 – Reading 17 – Southampton 38.

Plans on following pages

**Donnington Valley H. & Golf Course,** Old Oxford Rd, Donnington, RG14 3AG, North : 1 ¾ m. by A 4 on B 4494 ℘ (01635) 551199, Fax (01635) 551123, 📷, park – 📳 ℀ 📺 ☎ ⅌ ⅙ 🅿 – ⅍ 140. 🕘 AE ⓞ VISA. ✨
**Gallery :** Meals 21.50/23.50 st. and a la carte ⌁ 6.50 – ⌑ 11.50 – **58 rm** 115.00/200.00 st. – SB.
AV a

**Jarvis Elcot Park H. and Country Club,** RG20 8NJ, West : 5 m. by A 4 ℘ (01488) 658100, Fax (01488) 658288, ≼, ⅙, 🛋, 🔲, 🐎, park, ✨ – ℀ rm, 🍽 rest, 📺 ☎ ⅙ 🅿 – ⅍ 110. 🕘 AE ⓞ VISA
**Meals** (closed Saturday lunch) 14.50/18.50 st. and dinner a la carte ⌁ 6.95 – ⌑ 9.50 – **75 rm** 105.00/125.00 t. – SB.

# NEWBURY

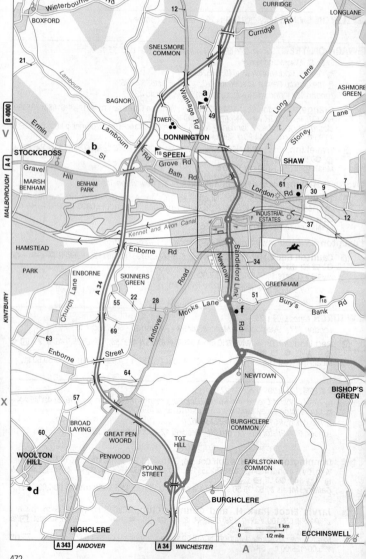

472

# NEWBURY

*There is no paid
advertising in this Guide.*

🏛 **Vineyard,** Stockcross, RG20 8JU, Northwest : 2 m. by A 4 on B 4000 ℰ (01635) 528770,
*Fax (01635) 528398*, 🐾, park – 🛗, ⇔ rm, 🗏 🗐 ☎ ✆ 🅿, 🐿 🆎 ⓪ 𝗩𝗜𝗦𝗔, ✂ AV **b**
**Meals** 33.00 **t.** (lunch) and a la carte 39.50/57.25 **t.** ⱱ 10.00 – ⌑ 24.75 – **29 rm** 120.00/
300.00 **t.**, 4 suites 350.00/500.00 **t.**.

🏛 **Stakis Newbury,** Oxford Rd, RG20 8XY, North : 3 ¼ m. on A 34 ℰ (01635) 247010,
*Fax (01635) 247077*, ₅, ≘ₛ, 🖾 – ⇔ rm, 🗏 rest, 🗐 ☎ ♦ 🅿 – 🔬 100. 🐿 🆎 ⓪ 𝗩𝗜𝗦𝗔 𝗝𝗖𝗕
**Meals** *(closed Saturday lunch)* (carving lunch) 14.95/17.95 **t.** – ⌑ 10.75 – **108 rm** 128.00/
158.00 **st.**, 2 suites – SB.

🏛 **Hilton National,** Pinchington Lane, RG14 7HL, South : 2 m. by A 34 ℰ (01635) 529000,
*Fax (01635) 529337*, ₅, ≘ₛ, 🖾 – ⇔ rm, 🗏 rest, 🗐 ☎ ♦ 🅿 – 🔬 200. 🐿 🆎 ⓪ 𝗩𝗜𝗦𝗔
𝗝𝗖𝗕 AX **f**
**Meals** (bar lunch Saturday) 14.50/18.20 **st.** and dinner a la carte ⱱ 6.50 – ⌑ 11.25 – **109 rm**
119.00/170.00 **st.** – SB.

🏠 **Blue Boar Inn,** North Heath, RG20 8UE, North : 4 ¾ m. by A 4 on B 4494
ℰ (01635) 248236, *Fax (01635) 248506* – 🗐 ☎ 🅿. 🐿 🆎 𝗩𝗜𝗦𝗔 𝗝𝗖𝗕. ✂
**Meals** *(closed 25 and 26 December)* (in bar Sunday dinner) a la carte 12.85/20.20 **t.** – **17 rm**
⌑ 53.00/65.00.

🏠 **Limes,** 368 London Rd, RG14 2QH, East : ½ m. on A 4 ℰ (01635) 33082,
*Fax (01635) 580023*, 🐾 – 🗐 ☎ ✆ 🅿. 🐿 🆎 𝗩𝗜𝗦𝗔 𝗝𝗖𝗕. ✂ AV **n**
*closed Saturday, Sunday and 25 December* – **Meals** (by arrangement) (dinner only) a la carte
14.95/16.70 **st.** – **15 rm** ⌑ 42.00/64.00 **s.**

**at Woolton Hill** *Southwest : 4½ m. by A 34 off A 343 –* ⊠ *Newbury.*

🏛 **Hollington House** 🏞, RG20 9XA, Southwest : ½ m. on East End rd ℰ (01635) 255100,
*Fax (01635) 255075*, ≤, « Edwardian country house, gardens », 🏊, 🖾, park, ⨯ – 🛗 ⇔ 🗐
☎ 🅿 – 🔬 45. 🐿 🆎 ⓪ 𝗩𝗜𝗦𝗔. ✂ AX **d**
**Meals** 29.50 **st.** (dinner) and a la carte 24.00/47.00 **st.** ⱱ 14.00 – **23 rm** ⌑ 105.00/
195.00 **st.**, 1 suite – SB.

473

**at Hamstead Marshall** *Southwest : 5½ m. by A 4 – AV –* ⊠ *Newbury.*

🏠 **White Hart Inn,** Kintbury Rd, RG20 0HW, ℘ *(01488) 658201, Fax (01488) 657192,* 🚗
📺 ☎ 🅿 🌐 VISA 🛇
*closed 2 weeks in summer and 25-26 December –* **Meals** *- Italian - (closed Sunday)* a la cart
14.50/25.50 **t.** – **6 rm** ⊇ 55.00/80.00 **t.**

　🔘 ATS 30 Queens Rd ℘ *(01635) 42250*

---

**NEWBY BRIDGE** *Cumbria* 402 *L 21 Great Britain G. –* ⊠ *Ulverston.*
Env. : *Lake Windermere★★.*
*London 270 – Kendal 16 – Lancaster 27.*

🏨 **Lakeside,** Lakeside, LA12 8AT, Northeast : 1 m. on Hawkshead rd ℘ *(015395) 31207*
*Fax (015395) 31699,* ≤, « *Lakeside setting* », 🔍, 🚗 – 🛗 🌡 📺 ☎ 🅿 – 🔬 100. 🌐 AE ⊕
VISA
**Meals** (bar lunch Monday to Saturday)/dinner 29.00 **t.** – **70 rm** ⊇ 90.00/220.00 **st.** – SB.

🏨 **Whitewater,** The Lakeland Village, LA12 8PX, Southwest : 1 ½ m. by A 590
℘ *(015395) 31133, Fax (015395) 31881,* ₤₅, ≘s, 🔲, 🎾, squash – 🛗 📺 ☎ 🅿 – 🔬 70. 🌐 AE
⊕ VISA 🛇
**Meals** (bar lunch Monday to Saturday)/dinner 19.00 **st.** and a la carte ⌀ 6.95 – **35 rm**
⊇ 70.00/120.00 **st.** – SB.

🏨 **Swan,** LA12 8NB, ℘ *(015395) 31681, Fax (015395) 31917,* ≤, 🔍, 🚗 – ⁴ˣ⁺ rest, 📺 ☎ 🅿 –
🔬 65. 🌐 AE VISA 🛇
**Meals** (bar lunch Monday to Saturday)/dinner 18.75 **t.** and a la carte ⌀ 6.95 – **35 rm**
⊇ 62.00/100.00 **t.**, 1 suite – SB.

**at Cartmell Fell** *Northeast : 3¼ m. by A 590 off A 592 –* ⊠ *Grange-over-Sands.*

⌂ **Lightwood Farmhouse** 🖏, LA11 6NP, ℘ *(015395) 31454, Fax (015395) 31454,* ≤, 🚗
– ⁴ˣ⁺ 🅿 🌐 VISA 🛇
*March-mid December –* **Meals** (by arrangement) 15.00 **st.** ⌀ 5.00 – **4 rm** ⊇ 35.00/56.00 **st**
– SB.

---

**NEWBY WISKE** *N. Yorks.* 402 *P 21 – see Northallerton.*

---

**NEWCASTLE AIRPORT** *Tyne and Wear* 401 402 *O 19 – see Newcastle upon Tyne.*

---

**NEWCASTLE-UNDER-LYME** *Staffs.* 402 403 404 *N 24 Great Britain G. – pop. 73 731.*
Exc. : *Wedgwood Visitor's Centre★ AC, SE : 6½ m. by A 34* Z.
🔚 *Newcastle Municipal, Keele Rd* ℘ *(01782) 627596.*
🅱 *Ironmarket, ST5 1AT* ℘ *(01782) 711964.*
*London 161 – Birmingham 46 – Liverpool 56 – Manchester 43.*

Plan of Built up Area : see Stoke-on-Trent

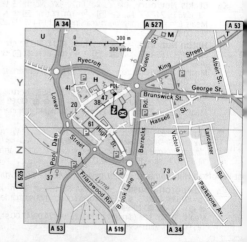

🏨 **Forte Posthouse Newcastle-under-Lyme**, Clayton Rd, Clayton, ST5 4DL, South :
2 m. on A 519 ℘ (01782) 717171, Fax (01782) 717138, ↙₆, ☎, ◨, ☞ – ⋇ rm, ⊡ ☎ ❷ –
🔬 70. ⚿ AE ⓞ VISA JCB             on Stoke-on-Trent town plan   V   n
**Meals** *(closed lunch Saturday)* a la carte 11.90/30.20 **st.** ▯ 7.95 – ⊒ 10.95 – **119 rm** 75.00 **st.**
– SB.

🏨 **Clayton Lodge**, Clayton Rd, Clayton, ST5 4AF, South : 1 ¼ m. on A 519
℘ (01782) 613093, Fax (01782) 711896– ⋇ rm, ⊡ ☎ ❷ – 🔬 280. ⚿ AE ⓞ VISA
**Meals** 15.95 **st.** and a la carte ▯ 6.00 – ⊒ 8.95 – **50 rm** 85.00/115.00 **st.** – SB.
             on Stoke-on-Trent town plan   V   e

✗✗ **Bauhinia**, Parklands, ST4 6NW, ℘ (01782) 719709 – ▤ ❷. ⚿ AE VISA
*closed Sunday and Bank Holiday lunch and 25-26 December* – **Meals** - Chinese - 5.95 **t.**
(lunch) and a la carte 15.75/32.30 **t.** ▯ 6.30.       on Stoke-on-Trent town plan   V   u

   ⓐ ATS Lower St. ℘ (01782) 622431

---

**NEWCASTLE UPON TYNE** Tyne and Wear **401 402** O 19 *Great Britain G.* – pop. 189 150.

See : *City*★★ – *Grey Street*★ CZ – *Quayside*★ CZ : *Composition*★, *All Saints Church*★
*(interior*★*)* – *Castle Keep*★ AC CZ – *Laing Art Gallery and Museum*★ AC CY M1 – *Museum of
Antiquities*★ CY M2.

Env. : *Hadrian's Wall*★★, *W* : by A 69 AV.

Exc. : *Beamish : North of England Open-Air Museum*★★ AC, SW : 7 m. by A 692 and A 6076
AX – *Seaton Delaval Hall*★ AC, NE : 11 m. by A 189 – BV – and A 190.

🛆 Broadway East, Gosforth ℘ (0191) 285 6710, BV – 🛆 City of Newcastle, Three Mile
Bridge, Gosforth ℘ (0191) 285 1775, – 🛆 Wallsend, Rheydt Av., Bigges Main ℘ (0191) 262
1973, NE : by A 1058 BV – 🛆 Whickham, Hollinside Park ℘ (0191) 488 7309.

*Tyne Tunnel (toll).*

✈ Newcastle Airport : ℘ (0191) 286 0966, NW : 5 m. by A 696 AV – **Terminal** : *Bus
Assembly : Central Station Forecourt.*

🛳 *to Norway (Bergen, Haugesund and Stavanger) (Color Line)* – *to Sweden (Gothenburg)
(Scandinavian Seaways) weekly (22 h)* – *to Germany (Hamburg) (Scandinavian Seaways) daily
(21 h)* – *to The Netherlands (Amsterdam) (Scandinavian Seaways) daily (14 h).*

🛈 *Central Library, Princess Sq., NE99 1DX ℘ (0191) 261 0610 – Main Concourse, Central
Station, NE1 5DL ℘ (0191) 230 0030.*

London 276 – Edinburgh 105 – Leeds 95.

Plans on following pages

🏨 **Copthorne Newcastle**, The Close, Quayside, NE1 3RT, ℘ (0191) 222 0333,
Fax (0191) 230 1111, ≤, ↙₆, ☎, ◨ – ▯, ⋇ rm, ▤ rest, ⊡ ☎ ❤ & ❷ – 🔬 200. ⚿ AE ⓞ
VISA JCB. ✺             CZ   z
***Le Rivage :*** **Meals** *(closed Sunday)* (dinner only) a la carte approx. 31.85 **st.** – ***Harry's :***
**Meals** *(closed Saturday lunch)* 14.95 **st.** (dinner) and a la carte 14.80/27.20 **st.** ▯ 7.65 – ⊒
11.50 – **156 rm** 145.00/170.00 **t.** – SB.

🏨 **Vermont**, Castle Garth (off St. Nicholas St.), NE1 1RQ, ℘ (0191) 233 1010,
Fax (0191) 233 1234, ≤, ↙₆ – ▯, ⋇ rm, ⊡ ☎ ❷ – 🔬 200. ⚿ AE ⓞ VISA    CZ   s
***Brasserie :*** **Meals** 14.50/17.50 **st.** and a la carte ▯ 6.50 – (see also ***Blue Room*** below) – ⊒
11.50 – **95 rm** 135.00/155.00 **st.**, 6 suites – SB.

🏨 **Malmaison**, Quayside, NE1 3DX, ℘ (0191) 245 5000, Fax (0191) 245 4545, « Contemporary interior », ↙₆, ☎ – ▯, ⋇ rm, ▤ rest, ⊡ ☎ ❷ – 🔬 60. ⚿ AE ⓞ VISA. ✺    BX   e
**Meals** a la carte 19.50/24.50 **st.** ▯ 13.95 – ⊒ 10.50 – **112 rm** 95.00 **st.**, 4 suites.

🏨 **Imperial Swallow**, Jesmond Rd, NE2 1PR, ℘ (0191) 281 5511, Fax (0191) 281 8472, ↙₆,
☎, ◨ – ▯, ⋇ rm, ▤ rest, ⊡ ☎ ❷ – 🔬 150. ⚿ AE ⓞ VISA          CY   e
**Meals** *(closed Saturday lunch)* 10.25/18.00 **st.** and a la carte ▯ 7.50 – **122 rm** ⊒ 85.00/
105.00 **st.** – SB.

🏨 **Forte Posthouse Newcastle upon Tyne**, 1 New Bridge Street West, NE1 8BS,
℘ (0191) 232 6191, Fax (0191) 261 8529 – ▯, ⋇ rm, ▤ rest, ⊡ ☎ & ❷ – 🔬 400. ⚿ AE
ⓞ VISA JCB                CY   n
**Meals** a la carte 16.85/26.85 **st.** ▯ 7.95 – ⊒ 9.95 – **166 rm** 85.00/109.00 **st.** – SB.

🏨 **Novotel**, Ponteland Rd, Kenton, NE3 3HZ, at junction of A 1(M) with A 696
℘ (0191) 214 0303, Fax (0191) 214 0633, ☎, ◨ – ▯, ⋇ rm, ▤ rest, ⊡ ☎ & ❷ – 🔬 220.
⚿ AE ⓞ VISA              AV   a
**Meals** 13.50 **st.** (dinner) and a la carte 20.00/30.00 ▯ 6.00 – ⊒ 9.00 – **126 rm** 72.00 **st.**

🏨 **Thistle County**, Neville St., NE99 1AH, ℘ (0191) 232 2471, Fax (0191) 232 1285 – ▯,
⋇ rm, ⊡ ☎ ❷ – 🔬 130. ⚿ AE ⓞ VISA JCB           CZ   a
**Meals** *(bar lunch Saturday and Bank Holidays)* 10.95/18.50 **st.** and dinner a la carte ▯ 6.50 –
⊒ 10.95 – **115 rm** 99.00/119.00 **t.** – SB.

# NEWCASTLE
## UPON TYNE

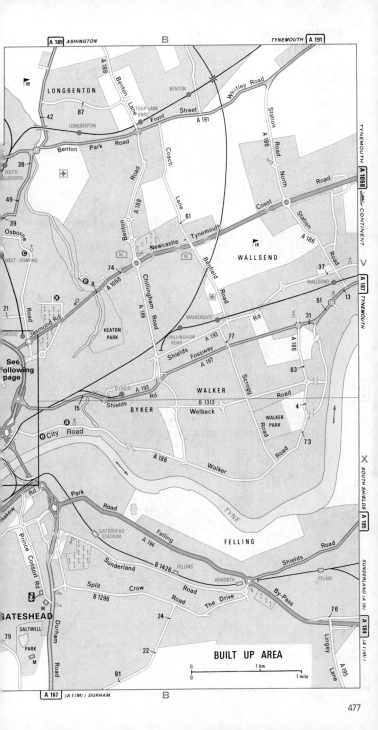

BUILT UP AREA

0       1 km
0       1 mile

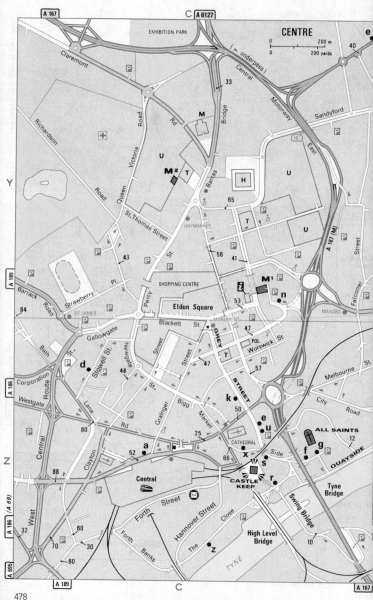

🏨 **Bank Top Toby,** Ponteland Rd., Kenton, NE3 3TY, at junction of A 1(M) with A 696 ℘ (0191) 214 0877, Fax (0191) 214 0095 – ✳️, 🍴 rest, 📺 ☎ & 🅿 – 🔬 50. 🐵 🆎 𝘝𝘐𝘚𝘈. ✳️ closed 24 to 26 December – **Meals** a la carte 7.95/16.20 t. 🍴 4.75 – **30 rm** ⇌ 62.00/72.00 t. – SB.
AV a

🏨 **Surtees,** 12-16 Dean St., NE1 1PG, ℘ (0191) 261 7771, Fax (0191) 230 1322 – 🛗 📺 ☎. 🐵 🆎 ⓪ 𝘝𝘐𝘚𝘈 𝙅𝘾𝘽. ✳️
CZ u
**Meals** - Café-restaurant - (dinner only and Sunday lunch)/dinner a la carte 15.40/20.40 st. – **27 rm** ⇌ 72.50/89.50 st. – SB.

🏨 **Waterside,** 48-52 Sandhill, Quayside, NE1 3JF, ℘ (0191) 230 0111, Fax (0191) 230 1615 – 🛗 📺 ☎. 🐵 🆎 ⓪ 𝘝𝘐𝘚𝘈 𝙅𝘾𝘽. ✳️
CZ r
**Meals** 6.95 st. (lunch) and a la carte 10.45/20.85 st. 🍴 3.95 – ⇌ 10.95 – **36 rm** 52.00/88.00 st.

🏨 **New Kent,** 127 Osborne Rd, Jesmond, NE2 2TB, ℘ (0191) 281 1083, Fax (0191) 281 3369 – 📺 ☎ 🅿. 🐵 🆎 ⓪ 𝘝𝘐𝘚𝘈
BV c
**Meals** (bar lunch)/dinner 12.95 t. and a la carte 🍴 5.00 – **32 rm** ⇌ 69.50/79.50 t. – SB.

🏨 **Travelodge,** Whitemare Pool, NE10 8YB, Southeast : 4 m. at junction of A 194 with A 184 ℘ (0191) 438 3333, Reservations (Freephone) 0800 850950 – ✳️ rm, 📺 & 🅿. 🐵 🆎 ⓪ 𝘝𝘐𝘚𝘈 𝙅𝘾𝘽. ✳️
**Meals** (grill rest.) – **71 rm** 39.95/59.95 t.

🏨 **Travel Inn,** City Rd, Quayside, NE2 2AQ, ℘ (0191) 232 6533, Fax (0191) 232 6557 – 🛗, ✳️ rm, 🍴 rest, 📺 & 🅿. 🐵 🆎 ⓪ 𝘝𝘐𝘚𝘈
BX a
**Meals** (grill rest.) (dinner only) – **82 rm** 38.00 t.

🏠 **Avenue** without rest., 2 Manor House Rd, NE2 2LU, at junction with Osborne Av. ℘ (0191) 281 1396, Fax (0191) 281 6588 – 📺 ☎. 🐵 𝘝𝘐𝘚𝘈 𝙅𝘾𝘽
BV x
**11 rm** ⇌ 29.50/45.00 st.

🏾🏾🏾 **Blue Room** (at Vermont H.), Castle Garth (off St. Nicholas St.), NE1 1RQ, ℘ (0191) 233 1010, Fax (0191) 233 1234 – 🍴 🅿. 🐵 🆎 ⓪ 𝘝𝘐𝘚𝘈
CZ s
closed Sunday – **Meals** (dinner only) a la carte 28.50/38.00 st. 🍴 7.50.

🏾🏾🏾 **Fisherman's Lodge,** Jesmond Dene, Jesmond, NE7 7BQ, ℘ (0191) 281 3281, Fax (0191) 281 6410 – ✳️ 🅿. 🐵 🆎 ⓪ 𝘝𝘐𝘚𝘈 𝙅𝘾𝘽
BV e
closed Saturday lunch, Sunday and Bank Holidays – **Meals** 18.50/30.50 t. and a la carte 🍴 7.50.

🏾🏾 **21 Queen Street** (Laybourne), 21 Queen St., Quayside, NE1 3UG, ℘ (0191) 222 0755, Fax (0191) 221 0761 – 🐵 🆎 ⓪ 𝘝𝘐𝘚𝘈. ✳️
CZ f
😊
closed Saturday lunch, Sunday and Bank Holidays – **Meals** 17.50 t. (lunch) and a la carte 32.50/41.50 t. 🍴 6.50
**Spec.** Terrine of salmon, new potatoes and young leeks. Loin of venison with gingerbread sauce and roasted pears. Warm chocolate cake with coconut ice cream.

🏾🏾 **Vujon,** 29 Queen St., Quayside, NE1 3UG, ℘ (0191) 221 0601, Fax (0191) 221 0602 – 🍴. 🐵 🆎 ⓪ 𝘝𝘐𝘚𝘈
CZ g
closed Sunday lunch – **Meals** - Indian - 20.00/22.00 t. and a la carte.

🏾🏾 **The Blackgate,** The Side, NE1 3JE, ℘ (0191) 261 7356 – 🐵 🆎 ⓪ 𝘝𝘐𝘚𝘈 𝙅𝘾𝘽
CZ x
closed Saturday lunch, Monday dinner, Sunday, 24 to 30 December and Bank Holidays – **Meals** 11.95 t. and a la carte.

🏾🏾 **Leela's,** 20 Dean St., NE1 1PG, ℘ (0191) 230 1261 – ✳️. 🐵 🆎 ⓪ 𝘝𝘐𝘚𝘈
CZ e
closed Sunday, first 2 weeks January and Bank Holidays – **Meals** - South Indian - 9.95/18.95 t. and a la carte 🍴 7.25.

🏾🏾 **King Neptune,** 34-36 Stowell St., NE1 4XB, ℘ (0191) 261 6657, Fax (0191) 261 6657 – 🐵 🆎 ⓪ 𝘝𝘐𝘚𝘈
CZ d
closed 25 December and 1 January – **Meals** - Chinese (Peking) and Seafood - 6.50/16.80 t. and a la carte 🍴 7.50.

🏾 **The Metropolitan,** 35 Grey St., NE1 6EE, ℘ (0191) 230 2306, Fax (0191) 230 2307 – 🐵 🆎 𝘝𝘐𝘚𝘈
CZ k
closed Sunday and 25-26 December – **Meals** 11.95 t. (lunch) and a la carte 12.20/20.15 t.

**at Gosforth** North : 4¾ m. by B 1318 – AV – ✉ Tyneside.

🏨🏨 **Swallow Gosforth Park,** High Gosforth Park, NE3 5HN, on B 1318 ℘ (0191) 236 4111, Fax (0191) 236 8192, ≤, 🏊, ≘s, 🏊, 🎿, park, ✳️, squash – 🛗 ✳️, 🍴 rest, 📺 ☎ & 🅿 – 🔬 600. 🐵 🆎 ⓪ 𝘝𝘐𝘚𝘈
**Brandling :** **Meals** (closed Sunday dinner) 16.00/25.00 st. and a la carte 🍴 8.30 – **Conservatory :** **Meals** 17.50 st. and a la carte 🍴 8.30 – **174 rm** ⇌ 110.00/120.00 st., 4 suites – SB.

**at Seaton Burn** North : 8 m. by B 1318 – AV – ✉ Newcastle upon Tyne.

🏨🏨 **Holiday Inn,** Great North Rd, NE13 6BP, North : ¾ m. at junction with A 1 ℘ (0191) 201 9988, Fax (0191) 236 8091, 🏊, ≘s, 🏊 – ✳️ rm, 🍴 📺 ☎ & 🅿 – 🔬 400. 🐵 🆎 ⓪ 𝘝𝘐𝘚𝘈 𝙅𝘾𝘽
**Meals** 9.95/16.95 t. and dinner a la carte 🍴 8.00 – ⇌ 9.95 – **150 rm** 95.00/105.00 st.

**at Annitsford (Northd.)** *Northeast : 7 m. by B 1318 and A 189 –* ⊠ *Newcastle upon Tyne.*

🏠 **Travel Inn,** Moor Farm Industrial Estate, NE23 7RG, at junction of A 19 and A 18
     *𝒫 (0191) 250 2770, Fax (0191) 250 2216 –* ⍀ rm, 🔲 rest, 📺 🐾 🅿. ⓌⓈ 🄰🄴 ① 𝑽𝑰𝑺𝑨. ⋙
     **Meals** (grill rest.) – **40 rm** 38.00 t.
                                                         AX

**at Boldon** *East : 7 ¾ m. by A 184 –* BX.

🏨 **Quality,** Witney Way, Boldon Business Park, NE35 9PE, 𝒫 (0191) 519 1999
     *Fax (0191) 519 0655,* 🛁, ☎ – ⍀ rm, 🔲 rest, 📺 🐾 🕭 🅿 – 🕭 230. ⓌⓈ 🄰🄴 ① 𝑽𝑰𝑺𝑨 𝐉𝐂𝐁
     **Meals** 14.50 **st.** and a la carte ↑ 4.50 – ⊊ 9.50 – **82 rm** 74.25/96.00 **st.**

🍴🍴 **Forsters,** 2 St. Bedes, Station Rd, East Boldon, NE36 0LE, 𝒫 (0191) 519 0929 – ⍀. ⓌⓈ 🄰
     ① 𝑽𝑰𝑺𝑨
     *closed Sunday, Monday, 2 weeks May, 1 week August, Christmas, New Year and Bank*
     *Holidays –* **Meals** (dinner only) 17.50 **t.** and a la carte 21.00/26.45 **t.** ↑ 4.25.

**at Newcastle Airport** *Northwest : 6 ¾ m. by A 167 off A 696 –* AV – ⊠ *Newcastle upon Tyne.*

🏨 **Airport Moat House,** Woolsington, NE13 8DJ, 𝒫 (0191) 401 9988, *Fax (01661) 860157*
     📳, ⍀ rm, 🔲 rest, 📺 🐾 🅿 – 🕭 400. ⓌⓈ 🄰🄴 ① 𝑽𝑰𝑺𝑨
     **Meals** a la carte 14.75/22.50 **st.** ↑ 5.75 – ⊊ 9.50 – **99 rm** 100.00/115.00 **st.,** 1 suite – SB.

🏠 **Travel Inn,** NE13 0BZ, 𝒫 (01661) 825040, *Fax (01661) 824940,* « Aeronautical theme
     restaurant » – 📳 ⍀ 🔲 📺 🕭 🅿 – 🕭 30. ⓌⓈ 🄰🄴 ① 𝑽𝑰𝑺𝑨. ⋙
     **Meals** (grill rest.) – **86 rm** 38.00 t.

**at Ponteland** *Northwest : 8 ¼ m. by A 167 on A 696 –* AV – ⊠ *Newcastle upon Tyne.*

🍴🍴🍴 **Horton Grange** with rm, Seaton Burn, NE13 6BU, Northeast : 3 ½ m. by Morpeth rd o
     Cramlington rd 𝒫 (01661) 860686, *Fax (01661) 860308,* 🌳 – ⍀ rest, 📺 🐾 🅿. ⓌⓈ 🄰🄴 𝑽𝑰𝑺
     𝐉𝐂𝐁. ⋙
     *closed 1 week Christmas –* **Meals** (booking essential) (dinner only) 34.00 **st.** ↑ 5.50 – **9 rm**
     ⊊ 59.00/90.00 **t.**

🍴 **Café 21,** 35 The Broadway, Darras Hall Estate, NE20 9PW, Southwest : 1 ½ m. by B 632
     and Callerton Lane 𝒫 (01661) 820357, *Fax (01661) 820357 –* ⓌⓈ 🄰🄴 ① 𝑽𝑰𝑺𝑨
     *closed Sunday and Monday –* **Meals** - Bistro - (booking essential) (dinner only and Saturday
     lunch) 12.50 **t.** and a la carte 19.00/24.00 **t.** ↑ 6.50.

     🅰 ATS 80/90 Blenheim St. 𝒫 (0191) 232 3921/       ATS High Street East, Wallsend
     232 5031                                     𝒫 (0191) 262 8878
     ATS Newton Park Garage, Newton Rd, Heaton
     𝒫 (0191) 281 2243

---

**NEWENT** *Glos.* **403 404** M 28 – *pop. 4 111.*
     *London 109 – Gloucester 10 – Hereford 22 – Newport 44.*

🏠 **Orchard House** ⌂, Aston Ingham Rd, Kilcot, GL18 1NP, Southwest : 2 ¼ m. by B 422
     on B 4222 𝒫 (01989) 720417, *Fax (01989) 720770,* 🌳 – 🅿 ⓌⓈ 𝑽𝑰𝑺𝑨 𝐉𝐂𝐁. ⋙
     *closed 24-25 December and 18 January-4 February –* **Meals** (communal dining) 19.50 s
     ↑ 5.50 – **4 rm** ⊊ 29.50/90.00 – SB.

---

**NEWHAVEN** *E. Sussex* **404** U 31 – *pop. 11 208.*
     ⛴ to France (Dieppe) (P &/O Stena Line) 2 daily (2 h 15 mn).
     *London 63 – Brighton 9 – Eastbourne 14 – Lewes 7.*

🏠 **Travel Inn,** Avis Rd, BN9 0AG, East : ½ m. on A 259 𝒫 (01273) 612356, *Fax (01273) 612351*
     – ⍀ rm, 📺 🐾 🅿. ⓌⓈ 🄰🄴 ① 𝑽𝑰𝑺𝑨
     **Meals** (grill rest.) – **40 rm** 38.00 t.

---

**NEWICK** *E. Sussex* **404** U 31 – *pop. 2 445.*
     *London 57 – Brighton 14 – Eastbourne 20 – Hastings 34 – Maidstone 30.*

🏨 **Newick Park** ⌂, BN8 4SB, Southeast : 1 ½ m. following signs for Newick Par
     𝒫 (01825) 723633, *Fax (01825) 723969,* ≼, « Georgian house, extensive grounds », 🏊, 🌳
     park, ⋙ – ⍀ 📺 🐾 🅿. ⓌⓈ 🄰🄴 𝑽𝑰𝑺𝑨. ⋙
     **Meals** (booking essential to non-residents) 19.50/32.00 **t.** and a la carte – **13 rm** ⊊ 95.00
     225.00 **t.** – SB.

*Groß-London (GREATER LONDON) besteht aus der City und 32*
*Verwaltungsbezirken (Borough). Diese sind wiederum in kleinere*
*Bezirke (Area) unterteilt, deren Mittelpunkt ehemalige Dörfer*
*oder Stadtviertel sind, die oft ihren eigenen Charakter bewahrt haben.*

**NEWINGTON** Kent **404** V/W 29 – *pop. 2 454.*
*London 40 – Canterbury 20 – Maidstone 13.*

🏠 **Newington Manor,** Callaways Lane, ME9 7LU, ✆ *(01795) 842053, Fax (01795) 844273,*
« Part 14C and 16C manor house », 🌸 – 📺 ☎ 🅿. 🆆 🎫 ① *VISA*. ⁒
Meals *(closed Friday dinner, Saturday and Bank Holidays)* 16.10 **st.** and a la carte
▮ 6.50 – ⊇ 5.00 – **12 rm** 58.00/99.00 **st.**

---

**NEWLYN** Cornwall **403** D 33 – *see Penzance.*

---

**NEWMARKET** Suffolk **404** V 27 – *pop. 16 498.*
🏌 *Links, Cambridge Rd* ✆ *(01638) 663000.*
🛈 *63 The Rookery, CB8 8HT* ✆ *(01638) 667200.*
*London 64 – Cambridge 13 – Ipswich 40 – Norwich 48.*

🏨 **Bedford Lodge,** Bury Rd, CB8 7BX, Northeast : ½ m. on A 1304 ✆ *(01638) 663175,*
*Fax (01638) 667391,* **F₆**, **⊆s**, 🔲, 🌸 – 🔖 📺 ☎ 🅿 – 🔬 200. 🆆 🎫 ① *VISA* **JCB**.
Meals 18.95 **t.** and a la carte ▮ 6.25 – **49 rm** ⊇ 85.00/108.00 **t.**, 7 suites – SB.

🏨 **Heath Court,** Moulton Rd, CB8 8DY, ✆ *(01638) 667171, Fax (01638) 666533* – 🔖, ⁒ rm,
📺 ☎ 🅿 – 🔬 130. 🆆 🎫 ① *VISA*
Meals *(bar lunch Saturday)* a la carte 14.95/26.25 **t.** ▮ 7.25 – **41 rm** ⊇ 72.00/175.00 **st.** – SB.

✗ **Brasserie 22,** 160 High St., CB8 9AQ, ✆ *(01638) 660646, Fax (01638) 600083* – 🆆 🎫 *VISA*
**JCB**
*closed Sunday, 1 week Christmas-New Year and Bank Holidays* – Meals a la carte 16.65/
23.95 **t.** ▮ 7.45.

**at Kirtling** Southeast : 5 m. by A 1304 off B 1063 – ✉ Newmarket.

🍴 **The Queens Head,** Newmarket Rd, CB8 9PA, ✆ *(01638) 731737, Fax (01284) 830321,*
🌼, « 16C inn » – 🅿. 🆆 🎫 *VISA*
*closed Sunday dinner and 25-26 December* – Meals a la carte 14.25/18.20 **t.**

**at Six Mile Bottom** *(Cambs.) Southwest : 6 m. on A 1304* – ✉ Newmarket.

🏨 **Swynford Paddocks,** CB8 0UE, ✆ *(01638) 570234, Fax (01638) 570283,* ≤, 🌸, park,
⁒ – ⁒ rest, 📺 ☎ 🅿 – 🔬 25. 🆆 🎫 ① *VISA*. ⁒
Meals 26.50 **t.** (dinner) and a la carte 22.95/32.95 **t.** ▮ 10.50 – **15 rm** ⊇ 110.00/188.00 **st.** –
SB.

🔘 ATS 2 Exeter Rd ✆ *(01638) 662521*

---

**NEWMILLERDAM** W. Yorks. – *see Wakefield.*

---

**NEW MILTON** Hants. **403 404** P 31 – *pop. 24 324 (inc. Barton-on-Sea).*
🏌, 🏌 *Barton-on-Sea, Milford Rd* ✆ *(01425) 615308.*
*London 106 – Bournemouth 12 – Southampton 21 – Winchester 34.*

🏨 **Chewton Glen** ⁑, Christchurch Rd, BH25 6QS, West : 2 m. by A 337 and Ringwood Rd
❀ on Chewton Farm Rd ✆ *(01425) 275341, Fax (01425) 272310,* ≤, 🌼, « Gardens », **F₆**, **⊆s**,
🔲, 🔲, 🛝, park, ⁒ indoor/outdoor – ⁒ rest, 🔳 rest, 📺 ☎ 🅿 – 🔬 120. 🆆 🎫 ① *VISA*. ⁒
**Marryat Room and Conservatory :** Meals 18.50/45.00 **t.** ▮ 8.00 – ⊇ 16.50 – **39 rm**
230.00/355.00 **t.**, 13 suites – SB
**Spec.** Salad of French beans with foie gras, shallot and sherry vinaigrette. Braised pork
cheeks and lobster with lemon grass and coriander. Caramelised banana tart with toffee ice
cream.

---

**NEW POLZEATH** Cornwall **403** F 32 – ✉ Wadebridge.
*London 283 – Newquay 27 – Plymouth 49 – Truro 36.*

🏠 **Cornish Cottage,** PL27 6UF, ✆ *(01208) 862213, Fax (01208) 862259,* 🔲 – 📺 ☎ 🅿. 🆆
🎫 *VISA*. ⁒
**The Gourmet :** Meals (dinner only and Sunday lunch)/dinner 29.50 **t.** and a la carte ▮ 4.95 –
**12 rm** ⊇ 48.00/111.00 **t.** – SB.

---

**NEWPORT** Wrekin 402 403 404 M 25 Great Britain G. – pop. 10 964.

Exc. : Weston Park★★, SE : 6½ m. by A 41 and A 5.

London 150 – Birmingham 33 – Shrewsbury 18 – Stoke-on-Trent 21.

🏠 **Royal Victoria**, St. Mary's St., TF10 7AB, ℘ (01952) 820331, Fax (01952) 820209 – 📺 ☎
⊕ – 🔬 140. 🐠 🖭 🖭
Meals (closed dinner Sunday and 25-26 December) 16.50 t. ♦ 6.50 – **24 rm** ⊊ 45.00
59.00 t. – SB.

---

**NEWPORT PAGNELL** Milton Keynes 404 R 27 – pop. 12 285.

London 57 – Bedford 13 – Luton 21 – Northampton 15.

Plan : see Milton Keynes

🏠 **Swan Revived**, High St., MK16 8AR, ℘ (01908) 610565, Fax (01908) 210995 – ☒ 📺 ☎ ⊕
– 🔬 70. 🐠 🖭 🖭 🖭                                on Milton Keynes town plan CU
Meals (closed Saturday lunch) 17.95 st. (dinner) and a la carte 16.85/23.95 st. ♦ 6.50 –
**40 rm** ⊊ 68.00/72.50 t., 2 suites – SB.

---

**NEWQUAY** Cornwall 403 E 32 The West Country G. – pop. 17 390.

Env. : Penhale Point and Kelsey Head★ (≤★★), SW : by A 3075 Y – Trerice★ AC, SE : 3½ n
by A 392 – Y – and A 3058.

Exc. : St. Agnes – St. Agnes Beacon★★ (※★★), SW : 12½ m. by A 3075 – Y – and B 3285.

🏌 Tower Rd ℘ (01637) 872091, Z – 🏌 Treloy ℘ (01637) 878554 – 🏌 Merlin, Mawgan Port.
℘ (01841) 540222.

✈ Newquay Airport : ℘ (01637) 860551 Y.

🛈 Municipal Offices, Marcus Hill, TR7 1BD ℘ (01637) 871345.

London 291 – Exeter 83 – Penzance 34 – Plymouth 48 – Truro 14.

Plan opposite

🏠 **The Bristol**, Narrowcliff, TR7 2PQ, ℘ (01637) 875181, Fax (01637) 879347, ≤, ≦s, ☒ – ☒
📺 ☎ ⊕ – 🔬 200. 🐠 🖭 🖭 🖭 🖭                                                Z
Meals 11.50/19.00 t. and dinner a la carte ♦ 5.75 – **73 rm** ⊊ 60.00/110.00 t., 1 suite – SB.

🏠 **Trebarwith**, Trebarwith Cres., TR7 1BZ, ℘ (01637) 872288, Fax (01637) 875431, ≤ ba
and coast, ≦s, ☒, 🞉 – 🞉 rest, 📺 ☎ ⊕. 🐠 🖭 🖭 ※                              Z
April-October – Meals (bar lunch)/dinner 14.50 st. and a la carte ♦ 7.00 – **41 rm** ⊊ (dinne
included) 45.00/120.00 st. – SB.

🏠 **Kilbirnie**, Narrowcliff, TR7 2RS, ℘ (01637) 875155, Fax (01637) 850769, ≦s, ☒, ☒ – ☒ 📺
☎ ⊕ – 🔬 150. 🐠 🖭 🖭 🖭 🖭
Meals (bar lunch)/dinner 12.50 t. ♦ 3.75 – **66 rm** ⊊ (dinner included) 36.00/78.00 t.

🏠 **Trenance Lodge**, 83 Trenance Rd, TR7 2HW, ℘ (01637) 876702, Fax (01637) 872034, ☒
🞉 – 🞉 rest, 📺 ⊕. 🐠 🖭 ※                                                     Z
Meals (lunch by arrangement)/dinner 17.50 t. and a la carte – 5 rm ⊊ 30.00/60.00 t. – SB

🏠 **Whipsiderry**, Trevelgue Rd, Porth, TR7 3LY, Northeast : 2 m. by A 392 off B 327
℘ (01637) 874777, Fax (01637) 874777, ≤, ≦s, ☒, 🞉 – 🞉 rest, 📺 ⊕. 🐠 🖭 🖭 🖭
closed November-February except Christmas – Meals (bar lunch)/dinner 14.95 t.
and a la carte – **23 rm** ⊊ (dinner included) 45.00/90.00 t.

🏠 **Windward**, Alexandra Rd, Porth Bay, TR7 3NB, ℘ (01637) 873185, Fax (01637) 852436
🞉 rest, 📺 ⊕. 🐠 🖭 ※                                                          Y
Easter-3 October – Meals (residents only) (bar lunch)/dinner 12.00 st. ♦ 5.95 – **14 rm**
⊊ 31.00/54.00 st.

🏠 **Corisande Manor** ⌂, Riverside Av., Pentire, TR7 1PL, ℘ (01637) 872042
Fax (01637) 874557, ≤ Gannel Estuary, 🞉 – 🞉 rest, 📺 ☎ ✆ ⊕. 🐠 🖭                 Y r
Meals (dinner only) 19.50 st. ♦ 5.00 – **15 rm** ⊊ 45.00/90.00 st. – SB.

🏠 **Porth Veor Manor**, Porth Way, TR7 3LW, ℘ (01637) 873274, Fax (01637) 851690, 🞉
🞉 rest, 📺 ⊕. 🐠 🖭 🖭 🖭                                                         Y
Meals (dinner only and Saturday and Sunday lunch)/dinner 11.95 t. and a la carte ♦ 4.95 –
**22 rm** ⊊ (dinner included) 47.50/92.50 st. – SB.

↑ **Wheal Treasure**, 72 Edgcumbe Av., TR7 2NN, ℘ (01637) 874136 – 🞉 rest, 📺 ⊕. ※
June-September – Meals (by arrangement) 7.50 st. ♦ 5.50 – **12 rm** ⊊ (dinner included
29.00/56.00 st.                                                                Z

↑ **Copper Beech**, 70 Edgcumbe Av., TR7 2NN, ℘ (01637) 873376 – 🞉 rest, 📺 ⊕. ※
Easter-October – Meals (residents only) – **15 rm** ⊊ (dinner included) 23.50/47.00 st. Z

↑ **Chynoweth Lodge**, 1 Eliot Gdns., TR7 2QE, ℘ (01637) 876684, 🞉 – 🞉 rest, 📺 ⊕     Z
closed November and December – Meals 6.00 – **9 rm** ⊊ (dinner included) 24.00/48.00
SB.

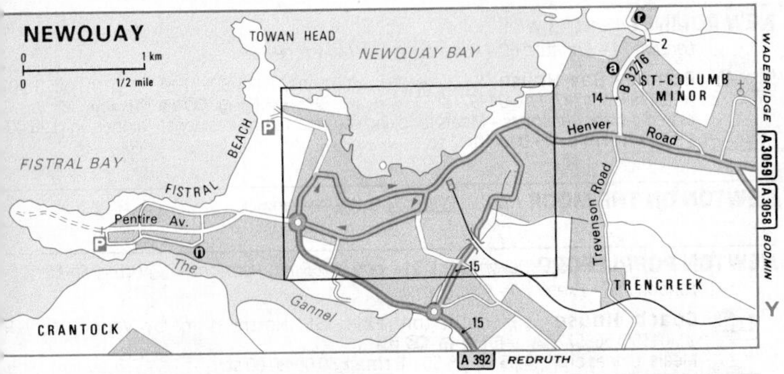
NEWQUAY
0 1 km
0 1/2 mile
TOWAN HEAD
NEWQUAY BAY
FISTRAL BAY
FISTRAL
BEACH
Pentire Av.
The
Gannel
CRANTOCK
B 3276
ST-COLUMB MINOR
14
2
Henver
Road
Trevenson Road
TRENCREEK
15
A 392 REDRUTH
WADEBRIDGE
A 3059
A 3058
BODMIN
Y

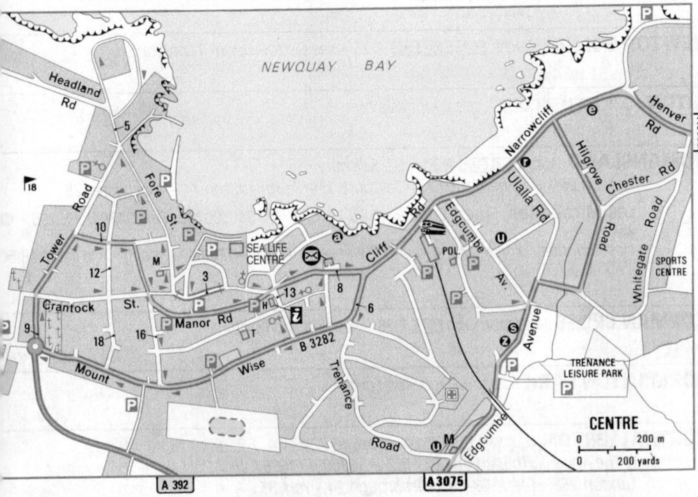
NEWQUAY BAY
Headland Rd
Tower Road
Fore St.
SEA LIFE CENTRE
Crantock St.
Manor Rd
Mount Wise
B 3282
Cliff Rd
Narrowcliff
Edgcumbe Av.
Ulalia Rd
Hilgrove Road
Chester Rd
Whitegate Road
Henver Rd
A3058
Avenue
Trenance Road
Edgcumbe
SPORTS CENTRE
TRENANCE LEISURE PARK
POL
CENTRE
0 200 m
0 200 yards
A 392
A3075
Z

lexandra Road . . . . . . . . . . . . Y 2
ank Street . . . . . . . . . . . . . . Z 3
eacon Road . . . . . . . . . . . . . Z 5
erry Road . . . . . . . . . . . . . . Z 6
ast Street . . . . . . . . . . . . . . Z 8
Fore Street . . . . . . . . . . . . . . Z
Higher Tower Road . . . . . . . . . Z 9
Hope Terrace . . . . . . . . . . . . Z 10
Jubilee Street . . . . . . . . . . . . Z 12
Marcus Hill . . . . . . . . . . . . . . Z 13
Porth Way . . . . . . . . . . . . . . Y 14
Trevemper Road . . . . . . . . . . . Y 15
St. Georges Road . . . . . . . . . . Z 16
St. John's Road . . . . . . . . . . . Z 18

**t St. Newlyn East** *South : 5½ m. by A 392 - Y - off A 3058 – ✉ Newquay.*

⌂ **Trewerry Mill** ⛰ without rest., TR8 5HS, Northeast : 1 ½ m. ☎ (01872) 510345, *Fax (01872) 510345,* 🌳 – ⊁ [P]. 🐕
*closed January and December – (by arrangement)* 8.50 – **6 rm** ☕ 22.00/49.00 **s.** – SB.

**t Crantock** *Southwest : 4 m. by A 3075 – Y – ✉ Newquay.*

🏠 **Crantock Bay** ⛰, West Pentire, TR8 5SE, West : ¾ m. ☎ (01637) 830229, *Fax (01637) 831111,* ≤ Crantock Bay, 🏋, ≘s, 🏊, 🌳, 🎾 – ⊁ rest, 📺 ☎ [P]. 💳 [AE] ⓓ [VISA] [JCB]
*closed January and December and weekends only February, March and November* – **Meals** (buffet lunch)/dinner 17.95 **t.** – **34 rm** ☕ (dinner included) 59.50/119.00 **t.** – SB.

⌂ **Crantock Plains Farmhouse,** Cubert, TR8 5PH, Southeast : 1 ½ m. bearing right at the fork in the road ☎ (01637) 830253, 🌳 – ⊁ [P]. 🐕
*closed January and February* – **Meals** (by arrangement) 9.50 **s.** – **5 rm** ☕ 20.00/45.00 **s.** – SB.

Prices For notes on the prices quoted in this Guide, see the introduction.

**NEW ROMNEY** Kent 404 W 31.

London 71 – Brighton 60 – Folkestone 17 – Maidstone 36.

🏠 **Romney Bay House** ⓈⒷ, Coast Rd, Littlestone, TN28 8QY, East : 2 ¼ m. off B 207
℘ (01797) 364747, Fax (01797) 367156, ≤, ☞, ❀ – 🌤 🗹 🕿 🅿. ⓂⓈ ⒶⒹ 𝑽𝑰𝑺𝑨 𝐉𝐂𝐁. ⫻
closed 1 week Christmas – **Meals** (booking essential to non-residents) (dinner only) 28.00
🍴 9.50 – **11 rm** 🖙 45.00/110.00 **st.**

**NEWTON ON THE MOOR** Northd. 401 402 O 17 – see Alnwick.

**NEWTON POPPLEFORD** Devon 403 K 31 – pop. 1 765 (inc. Harpford) – ✉ Ottery St. Mary.
London 208 – Exeter 10 – Sidmouth 4.

🏠 **Coach House** ⓈⒷ, Southerton, EX11 1SE, North : 1 m. by Venn Ottery R
℘ (01395) 568577, ☞ – 🗹 🕿 🅿. ⓂⓈ 𝑽𝑰𝑺𝑨
**Meals** (dinner only) 14.95 **st.** 🍴 5.50 – **6 rm** 🖙 30.00/80.00 **st.**

**NEWTON SOLNEY** Derbs. 402 403 404 P 25 – see Burton-upon-Trent (Staffs.).

**NITON** I.O.W. 403 404 Q 32 – see Wight (Isle of).

**NOMANSLAND** Wilts. 403 404 P 31 – ✉ Salisbury.
London 96 – Bournemouth 26 – Salisbury 13 – Southampton 14 – Winchester 25.

✗ **Les Mirabelles**, Forest Edge Rd, SP5 2BN, ℘ (01794) 390205, Fax (01794) 390205 – ●
𝑽𝑰𝑺𝑨
closed Sunday dinner, Monday and 2 weeks New Year – **Meals** - French - a la carte 18.50
25.50 **t.** 🍴 7.70.

**NORMAN CROSS** Peterborough 404 T 26 – see Peterborough.

**NORMANTON PARK** Rutland – see Stamford.

**NORTHALLERTON** N. Yorks. 402 P 20 – pop. 13 774.
🅱 The Applegarth Car Park, DL7 8LZ ℘ (01609) 776864.
London 238 – Leeds 48 – Middlesbrough 24 – York 33.

🏠 **Windsor**, 56 South Par., DL7 8SL, ℘ (01609) 774100 – 🌤 🗹. ⓂⓈ 𝑽𝑰𝑺𝑨. ⫻
closed 23 December-2 January – **Meals** (by arrangement) 10.00 **st.** – **6 rm** 🖙 21.00
43.00 **st.**

at Staddlebridge Northeast : 7½ m. by A 684 on A 19 at junction with A 172 – ✉ Northallerton.

🏨 **The Tontine**, DL6 3JB, on southbound carriageway (A 19) ℘ (01609) 88267'
Fax (01609) 882660 – 🍽 rm, 🗹 🕿 ⒶⒺ 𝑽𝑰𝑺𝑨
closed 25-26 December and 1 January – **Meals** – (see **McCoys Bistro** below) – **6 rm**
🖙 75.00/90.00 **t.**

✗ **McCoys Bistro** (at The Tontine H.), DL6 3JB, on southbound carriageway (A 19
℘ (01609) 882671, Fax (01609) 882660 – 🅿. ⓂⓈ ⒶⒺ 𝑽𝑰𝑺𝑨
closed 25-26 December and 1 January – **Meals** - Brasserie - (booking essential) a la cart
23.15/31.70 **t.** 🍴 9.75.

at Newby Wiske South : 2½ m. by A 167 – ✉ Northallerton.

🏨 **Solberge Hall** ⓈⒷ, DL7 9ER, Northwest : 1 ¼ m. on Warlaby rd ℘ (01609) 77919'
Fax (01609) 780472, ≤, ☞, park – 🌤 rest, 🗹 🕿 🅿 – 🔬 100. ⓂⓈ ⒶⒺ ⒶⒹ 𝑽𝑰𝑺𝑨
**Meals** 8.25/22.00 **st.** and dinner a la carte 🍴 6.50 – **23 rm** 🖙 75.00/120.00 **t.**, 1 suite – SB.

**NORTHAMPTON** Northants. 404 R 27 Great Britain G. – pop. 179 596.
Exc. : All Saints, Brixworth★, N : 7 m. on A 508 Y.
🏌, 🏌 Delapre, Eagle Drive, Nene Valley Way ℘ (01604) 764036/763957, Z – 🏌 Collingtre
Park, Windingbrook Lane ℘ (01604) 700000.
🅱 Mr Grant's House, 10 St. Giles Sq., NN1 1DA ℘ (01604) 22677.
London 69 – Cambridge 53 – Coventry 34 – Leicester 42 – Luton 35 – Oxford 41.

# NORTHAMPTON

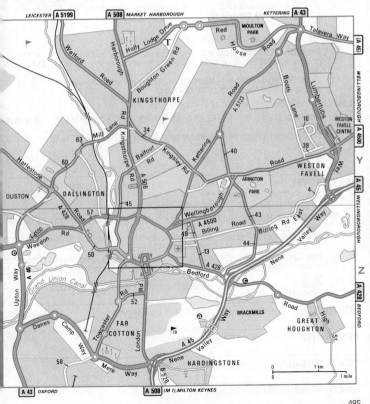

485

**Swallow,** Eagle Drive, NN4 7HW, Southeast : 2 m. by A 428 off A 45 ☎ (01604) 76870 *Fax (01604) 769011*, Lб, ≘s, ▣ – ⇔ rm, ▤ rest, TV ☎ ♿ P – 🏃 220. MC AE ⊙ VISA
**Spires :** Meals *(closed Saturday lunch)* 14.75/21.75 **st.** and a la carte – ***La Fontana :*** **Meals** Italian - *(closed Sunday)* a la carte 24.50/29.15 **st.** – **118 rm** ☕ 110.00/120.00 **st.**, 2 suites SB. Z

**Stakis Northampton,** 100 Watering Lane, Collingtree, NN4 0XW, South : 3 m. on A 50 ☎ (01604) 700666, *Fax (01604) 702850*, Lб, ≘s, ▣, 🌳 – ⇔ rm, ▤ rest, TV ☎ ♿ P – 🏃 300. MC AE ⊙ VISA.
**Meals** *(closed Saturday lunch)* (carving lunch) 14.50/19.95 **t.** and a la carte 🍷 10.95 – 10.95 – **136 rm** 140.00/160.00 **t.**, 3 suites – SB.

**Courtyard by Marriott,** Bedford Rd, NN4 7YF, Southeast : 1 ½ m. on A 42 ☎ (01604) 22777, *Fax (01604) 35454*, Lб – |≑|, ⇔ rm, ▤ TV ☎ ♿ P – 🏃 40. MC AE ⊙ VISA JCB.
**Meals** a la carte 16.00/21.00 **st.** 🍷 7.95 – ☕ 9.50 – **104 rm** 80.00/100.00 **st.** – SB. Z

**Northampton Moat House,** Silver St., NN1 2TA, ☎ (01604) 73998 *Fax (01604) 230614*, Lб, ≘s – |≑|, ⇔ rm, TV ☎ P – 🏃 600. MC AE ⊙ VISA JCB. X
**Meals** (buffet lunch)/dinner 15.50 **st.** and a la carte 🍷 6.25 – ☕ 9.50 – **140 rm** 100.00 110.00 **st.**

**Midway Toby,** London Rd, Wootton, NN4 0TG, South : 2 ½ m. on A 50 ☎ (01604) 769676, *Fax (01604) 769523* – ⇔, ▤ rest, TV ☎ ♿ P – 🏃 100. MC AE VISA.
*closed 24 to 29 December* – **Meals** (grill rest.) a la carte 11.05/14.90 **t.** 🍷 4.45 – **31 rm** ☕ 65.00/75.00 **t.** – SB.

**Travel Inn,** Harpole Turn, Weedon Rd, NN7 4DD, West : 3 ¾ m. on A 45 ☎ (01604) 83234 *Fax (01604) 831807* – ⇔ rm, TV ♿ P – 🏃 60. MC AE ⊙ VISA.
**Meals** (grill rest.) – **51 rm** 38.00 **t.**

**Travelodge,** Upton Way (Ring Rd), NN5 6EG, Southwest : 1 ¾ m. by A 4 ☎ (01604) 758395, *Fax (01604) 758395*, Reservations (Freephone) 0800 850950 – ⇔ rm TV ♿ P. MC AE ⊙ VISA JCB.
**Meals** (grill rest.) – **60 rm** 39.95/59.95 **t.** Z

**at Spratton** *North : 7 m. by A 508 off A 50 – Y – ✉ Northampton.*

**Broomhill Country House** 🐦, Holdenby Rd, NN6 8LD, Southwest : 1 m. on Holdenby rd ☎ (01604) 845959, *Fax (01604) 845834*, ≤, ⛱, 🌳, park, 🎾 – TV ☎ P. MC AE ⊙ VISA JCB.
*closed 25 and 26 December* – **Meals** *(closed Sunday dinner to non-residents)* 14.95/18.95 and a la carte 🍷 7.70 – **13 rm** ☕ 70.00/80.00 **t.**

**at Moulton** *Northeast : 4½ m. by A 43 – Y – ✉ Northampton.*

**Poplars,** 33 Cross St., NN3 7RZ, ☎ (01604) 643983, *Fax (01604) 790233*, 🌳 – TV ☎ P. MC AE VISA
*closed 1 week Christmas* – **Meals** (by arrangement) 15.00 **st.** 🍷 3.50 – **18 rm** ☕ 45.00 55.00 **t.**

ATS Kingsthorpe Rd ☎ (01604) 713303

---

**NORTH BOVEY** *Devon* 403 I 32 *The West Country G. – pop. 254 – ✉ Newton Abbot.*
**Env. :** *Dartmoor National Park*★★.
*London 214 – Exeter 13 – Plymouth 31 – Torquay 21.*

**Blackaller House** 🐦, TQ13 8QY, ☎ (01647) 440322, *Fax (01647) 440322*, ≤, 🌳 ⇔ rest, TV P
*closed January and February* – **Meals** *(closed Monday)* (booking essential to non-residents (dinner only) 22.00 **t.** 🍷 5.25 – **5 rm** ☕ 32.00/74.00 – SB.

**The Gate House** 🐦, TQ13 8RB, just off village green, past "Ring of Bells" public house ☎ (01647) 440479, *Fax (01647) 440479*, ≤, « 15C thatched Devon hallhouse », 🌳 – ⇔ TV P.
**Meals** (by arrangement) (communal dining) 16.00 **s.** – **3 rm** ☕ 34.00/54.00 **s.**

---

**NORTHENDEN** *Gtr. Manchester* 402 403 404 N 23 – *see Manchester.*

---

**NORTHFIELD** *W. Mids.* 403 ㉒ 404 ⑳ – *see Birmingham.*

---

**NORTH MUSKHAM** *Notts.* 402 404 R 24 – *see Newark-on-Trent.*

---

**NORTH NEWINGTON** *Oxon – see Banbury.*

**NORTHREPPS** Norfolk 404 Y 25 – see Cromer.

**NORTH STIFFORD** Essex 404 (44) – ⊠ Grays.
London 22 – Chelmsford 24 – Southend-on-Sea 20.

🏨 **Lakeside Moat House,** High Rd, RM16 5UE, at junction of A 13 with A 1012
*℘* (01708) 719988, Fax (01375) 390426, 👕, ⅋ – ▮, 🔆 rm, 📺 ☎ 🦽 ⅋ 🅿 – 🔬 150. 🐵 🖭
⓪ ☑️ 🎴
Meals (closed Saturday lunch) 17.50 st. and a la carte ▯ 5.95 – ⌸ 9.50 – **96 rm** 85.00/
105.00 st. – SB.

**NORTH STOKE** Oxon. – see Wallingford.

**NORTH WALSHAM** Norfolk 403 404 Y 25 Great Britain G. – pop. 9 534.
Exc. : Blicking Hall★★ AC, W : 8½ m. by B 1145, A 140 and B 1354.
London 125 – Norwich 16.

🏠 **Beechwood,** 20 Cromer Rd, NR28 0HD, *℘* (01692) 403231, Fax (01692) 407284, 👕 – 🔆
📺 ☎ 🅿 🐵 ☑️
Meals (closed lunch Tuesday, Saturday and Bank Holidays) 9.00/20.00 st. ▯ 9.00 – **9 rm**
⌸ 46.00/76.00 st. – SB.

**NORTHWICH** Ches. 402 403 404 M 24 – pop. 4 243.
London 188 – Chester 19 – Liverpool 19 – Manchester 25.

🏠 **Quincey's - Premier Lodge,** London Rd, Leftwich, CW9 8EG, South : 1½ m. on A 533
*℘* (01606) 45524, Fax (01606) 330350, Reservations (Freephone) 0800 118833, 👕 – 🔆 rm,
📺 ☎ 🦽 🅿 – 🔬 35. 🐵 🖭 ⓪ ☑️ ⅋
Meals (grill rest.) a la carte 13.25/20.20 t. – ⌸ 5.95 – **32 rm** 44.95 t. – SB.

🔧 ATS Albion Rd *℘* (01606) 42485/48417

**NORTON** Shrops. – see Telford.

**NORTON ST. PHILIP** Somerset 403 404 N 30 – pop. 820 – ⊠ Bath.
London 113 – Bristol 22 – Southampton 55 – Swindon 40.

🏠 **Monmouth Lodge** without rest., BA3 6LH, on B 3110 *℘* (01373) 834367, 👕 – 🔆 📺
🅿 🐵 ☑️ ⅋
closed 20 December-10 January – **3 rm** ⌸ 55.00/65.00 s.

🏠 **The Plaine** without rest., BA3 6LE, *℘* (01373) 834723, Fax (01373) 834101, « 16C cottages » – 🔆 📺 🅿 🐵 🖭 ☑️ 🎴 ⅋
closed 25 and 26 December – **3 rm** ⌸ 46.00/60.00 st.

**NORWICH** Norfolk 404 Y 26 Great Britain G. – pop. 171 304.
See : City★★ - Cathedral★★ Y – Castle (Museum and Art Gallery★ AC) Z – Market Place★ Z.
Env. : Sainsbury Centre for Visual Arts★ AC, W : 3 m. by B 1108 X.
Exc. : Blicking Hall★★ AC, N : 11 m. by A 140 – V – and B 1354 – NE : The Broads★.
🏌 Royal Norwich, Drayton High Rd, Hellesdon *℘* (01603) 425712, V – 🏌 Sprowston Park,
Wroxham Rd *℘* (01603) 410657 – 🏌 Costessy Park, Costessey *℘* (01603) 746333 – 🏌
Bawburgh, Glen Lodge, Marlingford Rd *℘* (01603) 740404.
✈ Norwich Airport : *℘* (01603) 411923, N : 3½ m. by A 140 V.
🅱 The Guildhall, Gaol Hill, NR2 1NF *℘* (01603) 666071.
London 109 – Kingston-upon-Hull 148 – Leicester 117 – Nottingham 120.

Plans on following pages

🏨 **Swallow Sprowston Manor,** Wroxham Rd, NR7 8RP, Northeast : 3¼ m. on A 1151
*℘* (01603) 410871, Fax (01603) 423911, 👕, 🛁, 🏊, 🏋, 👕, park – ▮ 🔆, 🍽 rest, 📺 ☎
🅿 – 🔬 120. 🐵 🖭 ⓪ ☑️
Meals 16.50/19.95 and a la carte ▯ 9.00 – **93 rm** ⌸ 99.00/140.00 t., 1 suite – SB.

🏨 **Dunston Hall H. Golf & Country Club,** Ipswich Rd, NR14 8PQ, South : 4 m. on A 140
*℘* (01508) 470444, Fax (01508) 471499, 👕, 🛁, 🏊, 🏋, park, ⅋ – ▮ 🔆 rest, 📺 ☎ 🦽
🅿 – 🔬 300. 🐵 🖭 ⓪ ☑️
Meals (carving rest.) a la carte 10.95/13.25 t. ▯ 5.00 – **La Fontaine :** Meals (dinner only)
a la carte approx. 32.80 t. ▯ 5.00 – ⌸ 9.95 – **72 rm** 79.00/135.00 t. – SB.

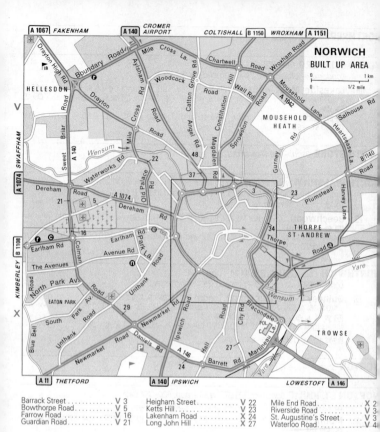

| Barrack Street | V 3 | Heigham Street | V 22 | Mile End Road | X 2 |
| Bowthorpe Road | V 5 | Ketts Hill | V 23 | Riverside Road | V 3 |
| Farrow Road | V 16 | Lakenham Road | X 24 | St. Augustine's Street | V 3 |
| Guardian Road | V 21 | Long John Hill | X 27 | Waterloo Road | V 4 |

**Nelson,** Prince of Wales Rd, NR1 1DX, ℰ (01603) 760260, Fax (01603) 620008, ₤₅, ≘s, 🔲
🝔 – ᇦ, ᭡ rm, ▤ rest, 🆅 ☎ & 🅿 – ⚞ 90. ⬿ 🆎 ⑨ 𝘝𝘐𝘚𝘈. ⬩⬩ Z ⬩
*Trafalgar :* Meals *(closed Saturday lunch)* 9.95/14.95 **st.** and a la carte ⓰ 4.85 – *Quarter deck :* Meals a la carte 11.15/16.95 **st.** ⓰ 4.85 – ⌖ 8.25 – **132 rm** 79.50/98.50 **st.** – SB.

**County H. Norwich Maids Head,** Tombland, NR3 1LB, ℰ (01603) 209955
Fax (01603) 613688 – ᇦ, ᭡ rm, 🆅 ☎ 🅿 – ⚞ 210. ⬿ 🆎 ⑨ 𝘝𝘐𝘚𝘈. ⬩⬩ Y ⬩
Meals 15.00 **t.** *(dinner)* and a la carte – ⌖ 8.75 – **83 rm** 85.00/115.00 **st.**, 1 suite – SB.

**Quality Friendly,** 2 Barnard Rd, Bowthorpe, NR5 9JB, West : 3 ½ m. on A 107⬩
ℰ (01603) 741161, Fax (01603) 741500, ₤₅, ≘s, 🔲 – ᭡ rm, ▤ rest, 🆅 ☎ & 🅿 – ⚞ 180
⬿ 🆎 ⑨ 𝘝𝘐𝘚𝘈
Meals *(carving rest.)* 14.50 **st.** and a la carte ⓰ 5.75 – ⌖ 9.50 – **80 rm** 74.25/96.00 **st.**

**Forte Posthouse Norwich,** Ipswich Rd, NR4 6EP, South : 2 ¼ m. on A 140
ℰ (01603) 456431, Fax (01603) 506400, ₤₅, ≘s, 🔲 – ᭡ rm, 🆅 ☎ 🅿 – ⚞ 100. ⬿ 🆎 ⑨
𝘝𝘐𝘚𝘈 𝗝𝗖𝗕.
Meals *(closed Saturday lunch)* a la carte 14.35/21.35 **st.** ⓰ 5.50 – ⌖ 8.95 – **116 rm** 75.00 **st.**
– SB.

**Jarvis International,** 121 Boundary Rd, NR3 2BA, on A 140 ℰ (01603) 787260
Fax (01603) 400466, ₤₅, ≘s, 🔲 – ᭡ rm, ▤ rest, 🆅 ☎ & 🅿 – ⚞ 300. ⬿ 🆎 ⑨ 𝘝𝘐𝘚𝘈
Meals *(closed lunch Saturday and Bank Holidays)* *(carving lunch)/dinner* 12.50/14.50 **t.**
and a la carte ⓰ 6.00 – ⌖ 7.95 – **106 rm** 79.00/125.00 **st.** – ⬩⬩

**Catton Old Hall,** Lodge Lane, Old Catton, NR6 7HG, North : 3 ¼ m. by Catton Grove Rc⬩
and St. Faiths Rd ℰ (01603) 419379, Fax (01603) 400339, « 17C farmhouse », ⬩⬩ – 🆅 ☎
🅿. ⬿ 🆎 ⑨ 𝘝𝘐𝘚𝘈 𝗝𝗖𝗕. ⬩⬩
closed Christmas and New Year – Meals *(booking essential)* *(residents only)* *(dinner only)*
21.00 **st.** ⓰ 6.00 – **7 rm** ⌖ 48.00/90.00 **st.**

# NORWICH

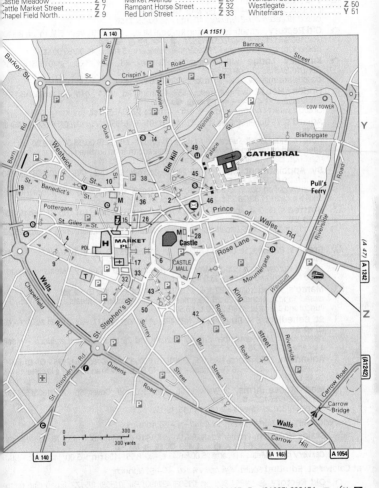

🏠 **Beeches,** 4-6 Earlham Rd, NR2 3DB, ℰ (01603) 621167, *Fax (01603) 620151*, 🌺 – ⚞✕ 📺
VX e
🕿 ﯼ 🅿 . 🄬🅂 🄰🄴 ⓪ 𝘝𝘐𝘚𝘈 𝖩𝖢𝖡 . ℀
*closed 1 week Christmas-New Year* – **Meals** (dinner only) 13.00 **t.** and a la carte ₰ 6.00 –
**25 rm** ⚏ 39.00/76.00 **st.** – SB.

🏠 **Annesley House,** 6 Newmarket Rd, NR2 2LA, ℰ (01603) 624553, *Fax (01603) 621577*, 🌺
– ⚞✕ rest, 📺 🕿 🅿 . 🄬🅂 🄰🄴 ⓪ 𝘝𝘐𝘚𝘈 𝖩𝖢𝖡 . ℀
Z c
*closed 24 to 27 December* – **Meals** (dinner only) 17.50 **t.** and a la carte ₰ 4.25 – **26 rm**
⚏ 65.00/90.00 **t.** – SB.

🏠 **Cumberland,** 212-216 Thorpe Rd, NR1 1TJ, ℰ (01603) 434550, *Fax (01603) 433355* – 📺
X a
🕿 🅿 – ﯼ 60. 🄬🅂 🄰🄴 ⓪ 𝘝𝘐𝘚𝘈 𝖩𝖢𝖡 . ℀
*closed 26 December* – **Meals** *(closed Saturday and Sunday lunch)* (booking essential)
9.95/17.95 **st.** and dinner a la carte ₰ 5.50 – **25 rm** ⚏ 44.95/90.00 **st.** – SB.

489

🏠 **Travel Inn**, Longwater Interchange, New Costessey, NR5 0TL, Northwest : 5 ¼ m. on A 1047 (junction with A 47) *℘* (01603) 749140, *Fax (01603) 749 1219* – ⅍ rm, 📺 & 🅿️. ◉❸ AE ① VISA
Meals (grill rest.) – **40 rm** 38.00 **t.**

🏠 **The Gables** without rest., 527 Earlham Rd, NR4 7HN, *℘* (01603) 456666
*Fax (01603) 250320, ⇗ – ⅍ 📺 ☎ 🅿️. ◉❸ VISA JCB. ✻*                                            X
closed 19 December-2 January – **10 rm** � 35.00/55.00 **st.**

↑ **Old Rectory** without rest., Watton Rd, Little Melton, NR9 3PB, West : 5 ½ m. on B 1108
*℘* (01603) 812121, *Fax (01603) 812521, ⇗ – ⅍ 📺 🅿️. ①. ✻*
closed Saturday, Sunday and 23 December-5 January – **3 rm** ⊒ 45.00/60.00 **st.**

↑ **Kingsley Lodge** without rest., 3 Kingsley Rd, NR1 3RB, *℘* (01603) 615819
*Fax (01603) 615819* – ⅍ 📺. ✻                                                                     Z
closed Christmas-January – **3 rm** ⊒ 25.00/40.00 **s.**

↑ **Linden House** without rest., 557 Earlham Rd, NR4 7HW, *℘* (01603) 451303
*Fax (01603) 250641, ⇗ – ⅍ 📺 🅿️. ◉❸ VISA*                                                       X
closed 2 weeks Christmas and New Year – **4 rm** ⊒ 30.00/42.00 **st.**

XX **Adlard's**, 79 Upper St. Giles St., NR2 1AB, *℘* (01603) 633522, *Fax (01603) 617733* – ◉❸ AE
❀    ① VISA                                                                                      Z  ϵ
closed Monday lunch, Sunday and 1 week Christmas – **Meals** 19.00/33.00 **t.** ⑧ 9.00
**Spec.** Salad of smoked duck with goat's cheese and truffles. Steamed foie gras with honey
roast figs. Iced lime and liquorice parfait with praline biscuits.

XX **By Appointment** with rm, 25-29 St. Georges St., NR3 1AB, *℘* (01603) 630730
*Fax (01603) 630730* – ⅍ 📺 ☎. ◉❸ VISA                                                           Y  a
accommodation closed 25 and 26 December – **Meals** (closed Sunday and Monday) (dinner
only) a la carte 21.80/28.25 **t.** ⑧ 6.75 – **4 rm** ⊒ 65.00/85.00 **t.** – SB.

XX **Brasted's**, 8-10 St. Andrew's Hill, NR2 1AD, *℘* (01603) 625949, *Fax (01603) 766445* – ◉❸
AE ① VISA                                                                                       Y  c
closed Sunday and 25 December-2 January – **Meals** 13.00 **t.** (lunch) and a la carte 25.20/
31.50 **t.** ⑧ 5.50.

XX **Green's**, 82 Upper St. Giles St., NR2 1LT, *℘* (01603) 623733, *Fax (01603) 615268* – ▤. ◉❸
VISA                                                                                            Z  s
closed Saturday lunch, Sunday, Monday, 25 December and 1 January – **Meals** - Seafood -
16.00 **t.** (lunch) and a la carte 23.90/31.30 **t.**

XX **Marco's**, 17 Pottergate, NR2 1DS, *℘* (01603) 624044 – ⅍. ◉❸ AE ① VISA                    Y  ϵ
closed Sunday, Monday, 25-26 December and Bank Holidays – **Meals** - Italian - 14.70 **t.**
(lunch) and a la carte 20.60/28.90 **t.** ⑧ 6.50.

X **St. Benedicts**, 9 St. Benedicts St., NR2 4PE, *℘* (01603) 765377, *Fax (01603) 765377* – ◉❸
AE ① VISA                                                                                       Y  v
closed lunch May-September, Sunday, Monday and 25 to 31 December lunch – **Meals**
a la carte 12.40/17.75 **t.** ⑧ 5.75.

X **Aquarium**, 22 Tombland, NR3 1RF, *℘* (01603) 630090, *Fax (01603) 612195* – ◉❸ AE VISA
closed Sunday and 25-26 December – **Meals** 10.50 **t.** (lunch) and dinner a la carte 19.40/
26.15 **t.** ⑧ 7.50.                                                                            Y  s

▤ **Mad Moose Arms**, 2 Warwick St., NR2 3LD, off Dover St. *℘* (01603) 627687,
*Fax (01603) 766403* – ◉❸ AE VISA                                                                X  n
closed Christmas – **Meals** a la carte 15.15/19.15.

**at Norwich Airport** North : 3½ m. by A 140 – V – ⊠ Norwich.

🏰 **Stakis Norwich**, Cromer Rd, NR6 6JA, *℘* (01603) 410544, *Fax (01603) 789935*, ⚡s, ⊜
☒ – 🛗 ⅍, ▤ rest, 📺 ☎ & 🅿️ – 🔬 450. ◉❸ AE ① VISA. ✻
*Carvery rest.* : Meals a la carte 15.00/16.45 **t.** – ⊒ 8.95 – **108 rm** 105.00/140.00 **st.** – SB.

**at Caistor St. Edmund** South : 4 ¼ m. by A 140 – X – ⊠ Norwich.

↑ **Old Rectory** ⊱, NR14 8QS, *℘* (01508) 492490, *Fax (01508) 495172*, « Georgian rectory », ⇗, park – ⅍ 📺 🅿️. VISA JCB. ✻
restricted opening in winter – **Meals** (by arrangement) (communal dining) 18.00 **st.** – **3 rm**
⊒ 28.00/56.00 **st.**

**at Stoke Holy Cross** South : 5 ¾ m. by A 140 – X – ⊠ Norwich.

▤ **Wildebeest Arms**, 82-86 Norwich Rd, NR14 8QJ, *℘* (01508) 492497, *Fax (01603) 766403*,
⇗ – 🅿️. ◉❸ AE ① VISA
closed 25 December – **Meals** a la carte 18.85/24.85 **t.** ⑧ 6.50.

**at Saxlingham Thorpe** South : 8 m. by A 140 – X – ⊠ Norwich.

↑ **The Lodge**, Cargate Lane, NR15 1TU, *℘* (01508) 471422, *Fax (01508) 471682*, ⇗ – ⅍.
✻
closed 2 weeks Christmas-New Year – **Meals** (by arrangement) (communal dining) 18.50 **st.**
⑧ 4.00 – **3 rm** ⊒ 36.00/62.00 **st.**

**at Hethersett** *Southwest : 6 m. by A 11 – X – ⊠ Norwich.*

🏠 **Park Farm,** NR9 3DL, on B 1172 ℘ (01603) 810264, Fax (01603) 812104, ₤₅, ≋s, ⬚, ☞, park – ✵ rest, 🍴 rest, 📺 ☎ 📞 📶 – 🔏 150. 🆗 🅰🅴 ① 𝗩𝗜𝗦𝗔. 🛇
Meals 12.75/18.50 **t.** and a la carte ⅃ 6.50 – **38 rm** ⊐ 70.00/140.00 **t.** – SB.

🏠 **Travelodge,** Thickthorn Service Area, NR9 3AU, at junction of A 11 with A 47 ℘ (01603) 457549, Reservations (Freephone) 0800 850950 – ✵ rm, 📺 ⅗ 📞. 🆗 🅰🅴 ① 𝗩𝗜𝗦𝗔 𝗝𝗖𝗕. 🛇
Meals (grill rest.) – **40 rm** 39.95/59.95 **t.**

⑩ ATS Mason Rd, Mile Cross Lane ℘ (01603) 423471    ATS Aylsham Way, Aylsham Rd ℘ (01603) 426316

---

**NORWICH AIRPORT** *Norfolk* 𝟜𝟘𝟜 X 25 – *see Norwich.*

*La **Grande-Bretagne** et l'**Irlande** sont maintenant couvertes
par un **atlas** disponible en trois versions :
broché, relié et à spirale.*

---

**NOTTINGHAM** 𝟜𝟘𝟚 𝟜𝟘𝟛 𝟜𝟘𝟜 Q 25 *Great Britain G.* – pop. 270 222.

See : *Castle Museum★ (alabasters★ ) AC, CZ M.*
Env. : *Wollaton Hall★ AC, W : 2½ m. by Ilkeston Rd, A 609 AZ M.*
Exc. : *Southwell Minster★★, NE : 14 m. by A 612 BZ – Newstead Abbey★ AC, N : 11 m. by A 60, A 611 - AY - and B 683 – Mr. Straw's House★, Worksop, N : 20 m. signed from B 6045 (past Bassetlaw Hospital) – St. Mary Magdalene★, Newark-on-Trent, NE : 20 m. by A 612 BZ.*
🏌 *Bulwell Forest, Hucknall Rd ℘ (0115) 977 0576, AY –* 🏌 *Wollaton Park ℘ (0115) 978 7574, AZ –* 🏌 *Mapperley, Central Av., Plains Rd ℘ (0115) 955 6672, BY –* 🏌 *Nottingham City, Lawton Drive, Bulwell ℘ (0115) 927 8021 –* 🏌 *Beeston Fields, Beeston ℘ (0115) 925 7062 –* 🏌 *Ruddington Grange, Wilford Rd, Ruddington ℘ (0115) 984 6141, BZ –* 🏌,🏌 *Edwalton ℘ (0115) 923 4775, BZ –* 🏌, 🏌, 🏌 *Cotgrave Place G & C.C., Stragglethorpe ℘ (0115) 933 3344/5500.*
🛫 *East Midlands Airport, Castle Donington : ℘ (01332) 852852 SW : 15 m. by A 453 AZ.*
🛈 *1-4 Smithy Row, NG1 2BY ℘ (0115) 947 0661 – at West Bridgford : County Hall, Loughborough Rd, NG2 7QP ℘ (0115) 977 3558.*
*London 135 – Birmingham 50 – Leeds 74 – Manchester 72.*

Plans on following pages

🏨 **Forte Posthouse Nottingham City,** St. James's St., NG1 6BN, ℘ (0115) 947 0131, Fax (0115) 948 4366 – 🛗, ✵ rm, 🍴 📺 ☎ 📞 – 🔏 600. 🆗 🅰🅴 ① 𝗩𝗜𝗦𝗔 𝗝𝗖𝗕    CY a
closed 24 to 29 December – Meals a la carte 16.35/28.35 **st.** ⅃ 8.45 – ⊐ 10.95 – **129 rm** 85.00 **st.**, 1 suite – SB.

🏨 **Nottingham Gateway,** Nuthall Rd, NG8 6AZ, ℘ (0115) 979 4949, Fax (0115) 979 4744 – 🛗, ✵ rm, 🍴 rest, 📺 ☎ 📞 📶 – 🔏 250. 🆗 🅰🅴 ① 𝗩𝗜𝗦𝗔. 🛇    AY r
Meals (carving rest.) 7.95/12.95 **st.** and dinner a la carte ⅃ 5.95 – ⊐ 8.50 – **106 rm** 68.00/90.00 **st.**

🏨 **Nottingham Moat House,** 296 Mansfield Rd, NG5 2BT, ℘ (0115) 935 9988, Fax (0115) 969 1506 – 🛗, ✵ rm, 🍴 rest, 📺 ☎ 📞 – 🔏 180. 🆗 🅰🅴 ① 𝗩𝗜𝗦𝗔    BY u
Meals (grill rest.) 7.50/11.75 **st.** and a la carte – ⊐ 9.50 – **169 rm** 95.00/115.00 **st.**, 3 suites – SB.

🏨 **Rutland Square,** St. James's St., NG1 6FJ, ℘ (0115) 941 1114, Fax (0115) 941 0014 – 🛗, ✵ rm, 🍴 rest, 📺 ☎ 📞 – 🔏 150. 🆗 🅰🅴 ① 𝗩𝗜𝗦𝗔    CZ c
Meals (bar meals Monday to Saturday lunch and Sunday dinner)/dinner 15.00 **st.** ⅃ 8.95 – **104 rm** ⊐ 90.00/130.00 **st.**, 1 suite – SB.

🏨 **Thistle Strathdon,** 44 Derby Rd, NG1 5FT, ℘ (0115) 941 8501, Fax (0115) 948 3725 – 🛗, ✵ rm, 🍴 rest, 📺 ☎ 📞 – 🔏 120. 🆗 🅰🅴 ① 𝗩𝗜𝗦𝗔 𝗝𝗖𝗕. 🛇    CY c
Meals (closed Saturday lunch) 15.80/18.10 **st.** and a la carte ⅃ 6.00 – ⊐ 11.25 – **68 rm** 95.00/135.00 **st.** – SB.

🏨 **Holiday Inn Garden Court,** Castle Marina Park, off Castle Boulevard, NG7 1GX, ℘ (0115) 993 5000, Fax (0115) 993 4000 – 🛗, ✵ rm, 🍴 rest, 📺 ☎ 📞 – 🔏 45. 🆗 🅰🅴 ① 𝗩𝗜𝗦𝗔 𝗝𝗖𝗕. 🛇    AZ e
Meals (closed lunch Saturday and Sunday) (bar lunch Monday to Friday)/dinner 14.95 **st.** and a la carte ⅃ 7.95 – ⊐ 8.95 – **97 rm** 82.00 **st.** – SB.

🏨 **Hotel des Clos,** Old Lenton Lane, NG7 2SA, ℘ (0115) 986 6566, Fax (0115) 986 0343, ☞ – 📺 ☎ 📞. 🆗 🅰🅴 ① 𝗩𝗜𝗦𝗔    AZ a
closed 24 December-3 January – Meals (closed Saturday lunch and Sunday dinner) 17.50/26.00 **st.** and a la carte ⅃ 4.95 – ⊐ 9.50 – **7 rm** 85.00/95.00 **st.**, 3 suites – SB.

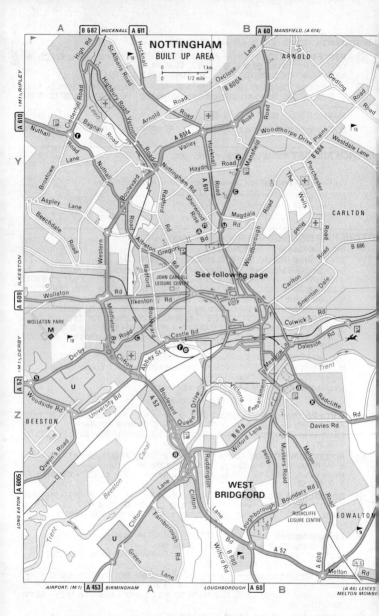

## NOTTINGHAM
### BUILT UP AREA

🏠 **Woodville,** 340 Mansfield Rd, NG5 2EF, ℰ (0115) 960 6436, Fax (0115) 985 6846 – 🔲 res
📺 ☎ 🅿 – 🔬 90. 🔴 ⑨ 🆎 ⑩ 𝘝𝘐𝘚𝘈 𝙹𝘊𝘉. ⚸
BY
**Meals** (closed Sunday and Bank Holidays) (bar lunch)/dinner 14.95 **st.** – **44 rm** ⚌ 52.50
62.50 **st.**

🏠 **Stage,** Gregory Boulevard, NG7 6LB, ℰ (0115) 960 3261, Fax (0115) 969 1040 – ⇘ rm, 🔲
☎ 🅿 – 🔬 40. 🔴 ⑨ 🆎 ⑩ 𝘝𝘐𝘚𝘈 𝙹𝘊𝘉. ⚸
AY
closed 24 December-2 January – **Meals** (closed Sunday) (bar lunch)/dinner 11.95 **st.** ⏧ 4.95
**52 rm** ⚌ 44.50/59.50 **st.**

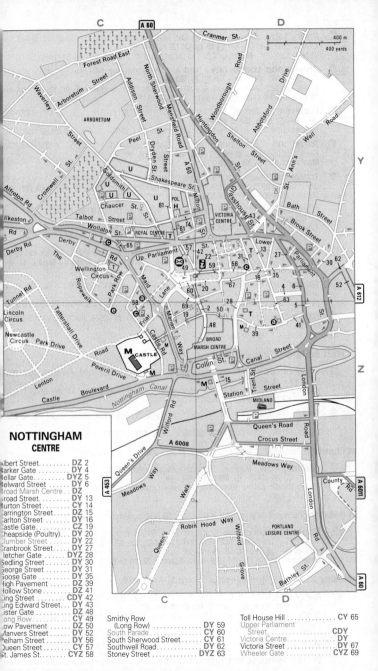

# NOTTINGHAM
## CENTRE

*If you find you cannot take up a hotel booking you have made,*
*please let the hotel know immediately.*

493

🏛 **Priory Toby,** Derby Rd, Wollaton Vale, NG8 2NR, West : 3 m. on A 52 ℘ (0115) 922 169
Fax (0115) 951 8942 – ⤢ 📺 ☎ **📵** **0⃝** AE VISA. ⊁      AZ
June-December – Meals (grill rest.) a la carte approx. 7.95 st. ⊨ 6.95 – **31 rm** ⊑ 59.00 st.

🏠 **Greenwood Lodge City,** Third Av., Sherwood Rise, NG7 6JH, ℘ (0115) 962 120◗
Fax (0115) 962 1206, ☞ – ⤢ 📺 **0⃝** VISA. ⊁      AY
Meals (closed Saturday and Sunday) (residents only) (communal dining) (dinner onl
15.50 s. and a la carte ⊨ 5.25 – **6 rm** ⊑ 32.00/59.00 s.

🏠 **Lucieville St. James,** 349 Derby Rd, NG7 2DZ, ℘ (0115) 978 7389, Fax (0115) 979 034
☞ – ⤢ 📺 ☎ **📵**. **0⃝** AE **0⃝** VISA. ⊁      AZ
Meals (residents only) (dinner only) a la carte 22.00 ⊨ 10.00 – ⊑ 9.50 – **6 rm** 55.00/95.00.

🏠 **Travel Inn,** Castle Marina Park, off Castle Boulevard, NG2 2DG, ℘ (01159) 47341
Fax (01159) 582362 – ⫴ ⤢ 📺 & **📵**. **0⃝** AE **0⃝** VISA. ⊁      AZ
Meals (grill rest.) – **38 rm** 38.00 t.

🏠 **Travel Inn,** Phoenix Centre, Millenium Way West, NG8 6AS, Northwest : 4 m. on A 61
℘ (0115) 951 9971, Fax (0115) 977 0113 – ⫴ ⤢ rm, ▤ rest, 📺 & **📵**. **0⃝** AE **0⃝** VISA. ⊁
Meals (grill rest.) – **60 rm** 38.00 t.      AY

XX **Merchants,** 29-31 High Pavement, NG1 1HE, ℘ (0115) 958 9898, Fax (0115) 941 4322
▤. **0⃝** AE VISA      DZ
closed Sunday dinner, 25-26 December and 1 January – Meals (bar lunch Saturday) 13.5◗
20.00 t. and a la carte 17.70/31.70 t. ⊨ 7.00.

XX **Sonny's,** 3 Carlton St., NG1 1NL, ℘ (0115) 947 3041, Fax (0115) 950 7776 – ▤. **0⃝** AE VISA
closed 25-26 December and Bank Holidays except Good Friday – Meals 11.95 ◗
(lunch) and a la carte 19.25/27.20 t.      DY

XX **Saagar,** 473 Mansfield Rd, Sherwood, NG5 2DR, ℘ (0115) 962 2014 – ▤. **0⃝** AE VISA
JCB      BY
closed Sunday lunch and 25 December – Meals - Indian - a la carte 11.80/22.40 st. ⊨ 5.50.

X **Hart's,** Standard Court, Park Row, NG1 6GN, ℘ (0115) 911 0666, Fax (0115) 911 0611 – **0⃝**
AE VISA      CZ
Meals 13.00 t. (lunch) and a la carte 18.50/25.50 t.

**at West Bridgford** Southeast : 2 m. on A 52 – ✉ Nottingham.

🏛 **Windsor Lodge,** 116 Radcliffe Rd, NG2 5HG, ℘ (0115) 952 8528, Fax (0115) 952 0020
📺 ☎ **📵** – ▵ 40. **0⃝** AE **0⃝** VISA. ⊁      BZ
closed 25 and 26 December – Meals (closed Sunday) (residents only) (dinner only) 11.75 s⬛
⊨ 4.50 – **47 rm** ⊑ 49.50/58.00 st.

🏠 **Swans,** 84-90 Radcliffe Rd, NG2 5HH, ℘ (0115) 981 4042, Fax (0115) 945 5745 – ⫴ 📺 ☎
**📵** – ▵ 50. **0⃝** AE **0⃝** VISA. ⊁      BZ
Meals (closed Sunday dinner) 13.95 st. and a la carte – **30 rm** ⊑ 50.00/65.00 st., 1 suite.

**at Plumtree** Southeast : 5 ¾ m. by A 60 – BZ – off A 606 – ✉ Nottingham.

X **Perkins,** Old Railway Station, Station Rd, NG12 5NA, ℘ (0115) 937 3695
Fax (0115) 937 6405 – **📵**. **0⃝** AE **0⃝** VISA JCB
closed Sunday dinner, Monday and 1 week Christmas – Meals - Bistro - a la carte 18.05
21.65 t. ⊨ 4.80.

**at Beeston** Southwest : 4 ¼ m. on A 6005 – AZ – ✉ Nottingham.

🏨 **Village H. & Leisure Club,** Brailsford Way, Chilwell Meadows, NG9 6DL, Southwest : 2 ¾ m
by A 6005 ℘ (0115) 946 4422, Fax (0115) 946 4428, ₣₅, ☎, 🄓, squash – ⫴ ⤢, ▤ rest, 📺
☎ & **📵** – ▵ 220. **0⃝** AE **0⃝** VISA. ⊁
Meals (grill rest.) 11.50/14.50 s. and a la carte – **92 rm** ⊑ 88.00/101.00 st.

**at Risley** Southwest : 7 ½ m. by A 52 - AZ - on B 5010 – ✉ Derby.

🏨 **Risley Hall,** Derby Rd, DE72 3SS, ℘ (0115) 939 9000, Fax (0115) 939 7766, ₣₅, ☎, 🄓, ☞
– ⫴ ⤢ rest, 📺 ☎ **📵** – ▵ 150. **0⃝** AE **0⃝** VISA. ⊁
Meals (residents only Sunday dinner) a la carte 13.15/32.40 st. ⊨ 8.50 – ⊑ 7.50 – **16 rm**
75.00/115.00 st. – SB.

**at Sandiacre** (Derbs.) Southwest : 7 ½ m. by A 52 - AZ - on B 5010 – ✉ Nottingham.

🏛 **Forte Posthouse Nottingham/Derby,** Bostocks Lane, NG10 5NJ, Southwest : ¾ m
at junction 25 of M 1 ℘ (0115) 939 7800, Fax (0115) 949 0469 – ⤢ rm, ▤ rest, 📺 ☎ **📵** –
▵ 50. **0⃝** AE **0⃝** VISA JCB
Meals a la carte 10.25/19.85 t. ⊨ 8.45 – ⊑ 9.95 – **91 rm** 88.00/119.00 st.

**t Long Eaton** *(Derbs.) Southwest : 8 m. on A 6005 – AZ.*

🏨 **Novotel,** Bostock Lane, NG10 4EP, Northwest : 1 ¾ m. by A 6005 on B 6002 *𝒫* (0115) 946 5111, *Fax (0115) 946 5900*, ⅃, 🐾 – |⌘|, ⅍ rm, 📺 ☎ ✆ ७ ● – 🛣 200. 🕐🕘 🖭 ① 🗺
Meals 14.00 **st.** and a la carte – 🖙 8.25 – **108 rm** 69.50 **st.** – SB.

🏨 **Jarvis Nottingham,** Bostock Lane, NG10 5NL, Northwest : 1 ¾ m. by A 6005 on B 6002 *𝒫* (0115) 946 0000, *Fax (0115) 946 0726* – ⅍ rm, 📺 ☎ ✆ ७ ● – 🛣 60. 🕐🕘 🖭 ① 🗺
*closed 1 week Christmas-New Year* – **Meals** (grill rest.) a la carte 12.95/29.40 **t.** – 🖙 6.50 – **101 rm** 65.00 **t.** – SB.

🏍 ATS 116 Highbury Rd, Bulwell *𝒫* (0115) 927 8824
ATS 66 Castle Boulevard *𝒫* (0115) 947 6678
ATS 126-132 Derby Rd, Stapleford *𝒫* (0115) 939 2986

ATS Oxford St., Long Eaton, Derbs. *𝒫* (0115) 973 2156

---

**NUNEATON** *Warks.* 🔢🔢 P 26 – *pop. 66 715.*

🏌 *Purley Chase, Pipers Lane, Ridge Lane 𝒫 (01203) 393118.*
🅑 *Nuneaton Library, Church St., CV11 4DR 𝒫 (01203) 384027.*
*London 107 – Birmingham 25 – Coventry 10 – Leicester 18.*

🏠 **Travel Inn,** Coventry Rd, CV10 7PJ, South : 2 ½ m. by A 444 on B 4113 *𝒫* (01203) 343584, *Fax (01203) 327156*, 🐾 – ⅍ rm, 📺 ७ ●. 🕐🕘 🖭 ① 🗺. ⅍
**Meals** (grill rest.) – **48 rm** 38.00 **t.**

🏠 **Travelodge,** CV10 7TF, South : 1 ½ m. on A 444 (southbound carriageway) *𝒫* (01203) 382541, *Fax (01203) 382541*, Reservations (Freephone) 0800 850950 – ⅍ 📺 ७. ●. 🕐🕘 🖭 ① 🗺 ᴊᴄʙ. ⅍
**Meals** (grill rest.) – **40 rm** 39.95/59.95 **t.**

🏠 **Travelodge,** St. Nicholas Park Drive, CV11 6EN, Northeast : 1 ½ m. by A 47 (Hinkley Rd) *𝒫* (01203) 353885, *Fax (01203) 353885*, Reservations (Freephone) 0800 850950 – ⅍ 📺 ७. ●. 🕐🕘 🖭 ① 🗺 ᴊᴄʙ. ⅍
**Meals** (grill rest.) – **28 rm** 39.95/59.95 **t.**

**t Sibson** *(Leics.) North : 7 m. on A 444 –* ✉ *Nuneaton.*

🏠 **Millers',** Twycross Rd, CV13 6LB, *𝒫* (01827) 880223, *Fax (01827) 880223* – 📺 ☎ ●. 🕐🕘 🖭 ① 🗺 ᴊᴄʙ
**Meals** *(closed Saturday lunch and Sunday dinner)* 10.95 **st.** ⅃ 4.95 – **40 rm** 🖙 48.50/ 55.50 **st.** – SB.

🏍 ATS Weddington Rd *𝒫* (01203) 341130/341139

---

**OAKHAM** *Rutland* 🔢🔢 R 25 – *pop. 8 691.*

🅑 *Oakham Library, Catimos St., LE15 6HW 𝒫 (01572) 724329.*
*London 103 – Leicester 26 – Northampton 35 – Nottingham 28.*

🏨 **Barnsdale Lodge,** The Avenue, Rutland Water, LE15 8AH, East : 2 ½ m. on A 606 *𝒫* (01572) 724678, *Fax (01572) 724961*, « Converted part 17C farmhouse » – ⅍ 📺 ☎ ● – 🛣 300. 🕐🕘 🖭 ① 🗺 ᴊᴄʙ
**Meals** a la carte 16.85/23.15 **t.** ⅃ 6.95 – **45 rm** 🖙 59.50/99.50 **t.** – SB.

🏨 **Whipper-In,** Market Pl., LE15 6DT, *𝒫* (01572) 756971, *Fax (01572) 757759* – ⅍ rest, 📺 ☎ – 🛣 50. 🕐🕘 🖭 ① 🗺
**Meals** 12.95/18.50 **t.** and a la carte ⅃ 8.95 – **24 rm** 🖙 59.00/84.00 **t.** – SB.

🏠 **Lord Nelson's House,** Market Pl., LE15 6DT, *𝒫* (01572) 723199, *Fax (01572) 723199*, « 17C town house » – ⅍ rm, 📺 ☎. 🕐🕘 🗺. ⅍
*closed Christmas and New Year* – **Meals** (residents only) (light lunch)/dinner 18.50 **st.** ⅃ 5.00 – **5 rm** 🖙 45.00/75.00 **st.**

**t Hambleton** *East : 3 m. by A 606 –* ✉ *Oakham.*

🏨 **Hambleton Hall** 🌸, LE15 8TH, *𝒫* (01572) 756991, *Fax (01572) 724721*, « Victorian ❁ country house », ≤ *Rutland Water* », ⅃, 🐾, park, ⅍ – |⌘|, ⅍ rest, 📺 ☎ ●. 🕐🕘 🗺
**Meals** 19.50/35.00 **st.** and a la carte 39.50/72.50 **st.** ⅃ 14.50 – 🖙 12.00 – **15 rm** 145.00/ 295.00 **st.**
**Spec.** Chilled essence of tomato and basil with langoustine tails. Loin of beef with fondant potato, caramelised shallots and red wine sauce. Caramelised apple tart with blackberry compote and vanilla ice cream.

---

**OAKLEY** *Hants.* 🔢🔢 Q 30 – *see Basingstoke.*

---

**OBORNE** *Dorset* 🔢🔢 M 31 – *see Sherborne.*

**OCKHAM** Surrey 404 S 30 – pop. 407 – ⊠ Ripley.

London 27 – Guildford 9.

🏛 **The Hautboy** ⤢, Ockham Lane, GU23 6NP, ℘ (01483) 225355, Fax (01483) 211176, ⇐
🍽 rest, 📺 ☎ 🅿. 🆊 🆎 ⓪ 𝘝𝘐𝘚𝘈. ⋘
*Oboe* : Meals a la carte 16.70/25.95 t. – (see also *The Chapel* below) – ⊊ 7.50 – 5 r
98.00/125.00 t.

XXX **The Chapel** (at The Hautboy H.), Ockham Lane, GU23 6NP, ℘ (01483) 22535
Fax (01483) 211176, ⇐ – 🍽 🅿. 🆊 🆎 ⓪ 𝘝𝘐𝘚𝘈. ⋘
closed Sunday, Monday and first 2 weeks January – Meals 25.00/35.00 t..

**OCKLEY** Surrey 404 S 30.

London 31 – Brighton 32 – Guildford 23 – Lewes 36 – Worthing 29.

🍴 **Bryce's,** The Old School House, RH5 5TH, ℘ (01306) 627430, Fax (01306) 628274 – 🅿. ●
𝘝𝘐𝘚𝘈
closed Sunday dinner January, February and November and 25-26 December – Meals
Seafood - 20.00/23.50 t. and a la carte ₰ 5.00.

**ODDINGLEY** Worcestershire 403 404 N 27 – see Droitwich.

**ODIHAM** Hants. 404 R 30 – pop. 3 531 – ⊠ Hook.

London 51 – Reading 19 – Winchester 25.

🏛 **George,** 100 High St., RG29 1LP, ℘ (01256) 702081, Fax (01256) 704213, « 15C inn »
⋟ rm, 📺 ☎ 🅿. 🆊 🆎 ⓪ 𝘝𝘐𝘚𝘈
**Meals** (closed Saturday lunch and Sunday dinner) a la carte 18.50/31.50 t. ₰ 7.50 – 26 r
⊊ 70.00/95.00 t.

X **Grapevine,** 121 High St., RG29 1LA, ℘ (01256) 701122 – 🍽. 🆊 𝘝𝘐𝘚𝘈
closed Saturday lunch, Sunday, 1 week Christmas and Bank Holiday Mondays – Mea
a la carte 17.00/23.70 t. ₰ 4.50.

**OKEHAMPTON** Devon 403 H 31 The West Country G. – pop. 4 841.

Exc. : S : Dartmoor National Park★★ – Lydford★★, S : 8 m. by B 3260 and A 386.
🖡 Okehampton ℘ (01837) 52113 – 🖡8, 🖡8, 🖡8 Ashbury, Fowley Cross ℘ (01837) 55453.
🖪 3 West St., EX20 1HQ ℘ (01837) 53020 (summer only).
London 226 – Exeter 25 – Plymouth 30.

🏛 **Travelodge,** Sourton Cross, EX20 4LY, Southwest : 4 ½ m. by B 3260 and A 30 on A 38
℘ (01837) 52124, Reservations (Freephone) 0800 850950 – ⋟ rm, 📺 & 🅿. 🆊 🆎 ⓪ 𝘝𝘐
JCB. ⋘ .
**Meals** (grill rest.) – **42 rm** 39.95/59.95 t.

🏛 **Travelodge,** Whiddon Down, EX20 2QT, East : 7 ¾ m. by A 30 on A 382 ℘ (01837) 23162
Reservations (Freephone) 0800 850950 – ⋟ rm, 📺 & 🅿. 🆊 🆎 ⓪ 𝘝𝘐𝘚𝘈 JCB. ⋘
**Meals** (grill rest.) – **40 rm** 39.95/59.95 t.

🔘 ATS 46 North Rd ℘ (01837) 53277

**OLD** Northants. – pop. 290.

London 77 – Birmingham 58 – Leicester 26 – Northampton 6.

⌂ **Wold Farm** ⤢ without rest., Harrington Rd, NN6 9RJ, ℘ (01604) 781258, « Workin
farm », ⇗, park – ⋟ 🅿. ⋘
**5 rm** ⊊ 25.00/50.00 st.

**OLD BROWNSOVER** Warks. – see Rugby.

**OLD BURGHCLERE** Hants. 404 Q 29 – ⊠ Newbury.

London 77 – Bristol 76 – Newbury 10 – Reading 27 – Southampton 28.

XX **Dew Pond,** RG20 9LH, ℘ (01635) 278408, Fax (01635) 278408, ⇐ – ⋟ 🅿. 🆊 🆎 ⓪ 𝘝𝘐𝘚𝘈
closed Sunday, Monday, 1 week Christmas-New Year and 2 weeks August – Meals (dinne
only) 25.00 st. ₰ 6.75.

**OLDBURY** W. Mids. 402 403 404 N 26 – see Birmingham.

**OLD DALBY** Leics. 402 404 R 25 – see Melton Mowbray.

**OLDHAM** *Gtr. Manchester* **402 404** N 23 – *pop. 103 931.*

🏌 *Crompton and Royton, High Barn, Royton &#9742; (0161) 624 2154 –* 🏌 *Werneth, Green Lane, Garden Suburb &#9742; (0161) 624 1190 –* 🏌 *Lees New Rd &#9742; (0161) 624 4986.*

🛈 *11 Albion St., OL1 3BD &#9742; (0161) 627 1024.*

*London 212 – Leeds 36 – Manchester 7 – Sheffield 38.*

Plan : see Manchester

🏨🏨 **Smokies Park,** Ashton Rd, Bardsley, OL8 3HX, South : 2 ¾ m. on A 627 &#9742; (0161) 624 3405, *Fax (0161) 627 5262,* ♪₆, ☎☞ – 📺 ☎ 🅿 – 🔏 150. **CØ** 🆎 ① **VISA**. ⋘
**Meals** *(closed lunch Saturday and Bank Holidays) (dancing Friday and Saturday evenings) (buffet lunch)* 14.50 t. *(lunch)* and a la carte 11.50/22.65 t. ₆ 4.95 – **47 rm** ⊇ 70.00/80.00 t. – SB.

🏨 **Bower,** Hollinwood Av., Chadderton, OL9 8DE, Southwest : 3 ¼ m. by A 62 on A 6104 &#9742; (0161) 682 7254, *Fax (0161) 683 4605,* 🌺 – ⟊ 📺 ☎ 🅿 – 🔏 200. **CØ** 🆎 **VISA**
**Meals** *(bar lunch)/dinner* 19.95 **st.** and a la carte ₆ 6.50 – ⊇ 10.95 – **63 rm** 85.00/135.00 **st.** – SB.
BV e

🏨 **Avant,** Windsor Rd, off Manchester St., OL8 4AS, &#9742; (0161) 627 5500, *Fax (0161) 627 5896* – 🛗, ⟊ rm, 🍴 rest, 📺 ☎ & 🅿 – 🔏 250. **CØ** 🆎 ① **VISA** **JCB**
**Meals** 9.50/16.95 **st.** and dinner a la carte ₆ 6.00 – ⊇ 8.50 – **101 rm** 75.00/85.00 **st.**, 2 suites – SB.

🏨 **Pennine Way,** Manchester St., OL8 1UZ, &#9742; (0161) 624 0555, *Fax (0161) 627 2031,* ♪₆ – 🛗, ⟊ rm, 📺 ☎ 🅿 – 🔏 320. **CØ** 🆎 **VISA**
**Meals** *(bar lunch Monday to Saturday)/dinner* 15.95 t. ₆ 6.75 – **130 rm** ⊇ 60.00/75.00 t. – SB.

🏨 **Travel Inn,** The Broadway, Chadderton, OL9 8DW, Southwest : 3 ½ m. by A 62 on A 6104 at junction with A 663 &#9742; (0161) 681 1373, *Fax (0161) 682 7974* – ⟊ rm, 🍴 rest, 📺 & 🅿. **CØ** 🆎 ① **VISA**. ⋘
BV e
**Meals** *(grill rest.)* – **40 rm** 38.00 t.

✕✕ **White Hart Inn** with rm, 51 Stockport Rd (1st floor), Lydgate, OL4 4JJ, East : 3 m. by A 669 on A 6050 &#9742; (01457) 872566, *Fax (01457) 875190* – ⟊ 📺 ☎ 🅿. **CØ** 🆎 **VISA**
*closed Sunday dinner and Monday* – **Meals** *(dinner only and Sunday lunch)/dinner* 16.00/ 26.00 t. – (see also *Brasserie* below) – **5 rm** ⊇ 60.00/80.00 t.

✕ **Brasserie** (at White Hart Inn), 51 Stockport Rd, Lydgate, OL4 4JJ, East : 3 m. by A 669 on A 6050 &#9742; (01457) 872566, *Fax (01457) 875190* – 🅿. **CØ** 🆎 **VISA**
🍽 **Meals** *(booking essential)* a la carte 17.50/24.00 t.

🔧 ATS 169-171 Huddersfield Rd &#9742; (0161) 633 1551     ATS Drury Lane/Manchester Rd, Hollinwood
ATS 179-185 Hollins Rd &#9742; (0161) 627 0180/     &#9742; (0161) 681 2281
665 1958

---

**OLD SODBURY** *South Gloucestershire* **403 404** M 29 – ✉ *Bristol.*

🏌, 🏌 *Chipping Sodbury &#9742; (01454) 312024.*
*London 110 – Bristol 14 – Gloucester 30 – Swindon 29.*

🏨 **Sodbury House** without rest., Badminton Rd, BS37 6LU, on A 432 &#9742; (01454) 312847, *Fax (01454) 273105,* 🌺 – ⟊ 📺 🅿 – 🔏 25. **CØ** 🆎 **VISA**. ⋘
*closed 24 December-4 January* – **13 rm** ⊇ 46.00/90.00 **st.**

⚲ **Dornden** ⚲, 15 Church Lane, BS37 6NB, &#9742; (01454) 313325, *Fax (01454) 312263,* ≤, 🌺, ⋘ – 📺 🅿.
*closed 3 weeks September-October and Christmas-New Year* – **Meals** *(by arrangement)* 11.00 t. – **9 rm** ⊇ 27.00/54.00 t.

---

**OLTON** *W. Mids.* **402** ㉒ **403** ⑩ **404** ㉘ – see Solihull.

---

**OMBERSLEY** *Worcestershire* **403 404** N 27 – *pop. 2 089.*
*London 148 – Birmingham 42 – Leominster 33.*

⚲ **Greenlands** ⚲ without rest., Uphampton, WR9 0JP, Northwest : 1 ½ m. by A 449 turning left at the Reindeer pub &#9742; (01905) 620873, ≤, « 16C cottage », 🌺 – ⟊ 📺 🅿. ⋘
**3 rm** ⊇ 19.00/44.00 **st.**

✕✕ **The Venture In,** Main St., WR9 0EW, &#9742; (01905) 620552, « 15C » – ⟊ 🅿. **CØ** **VISA**
🍽 *closed Sunday dinner, Monday, 2 weeks in summer, 2 weeks in winter and 26 December* – **Meals** 15.95/24.95 t. ₆ 5.95.

🍴 **Kings Arms,** Main Rd, WR9 0EW, &#9742; (01905) 620142, *Fax (01905) 620142,* « 15C inn » – 🅿. **CØ** 🆎 **VISA** **JCB**
*closed 25 December* – **Meals** a la carte 13.40/18.00 t.

**ORMSKIRK** *Lancs.* 402 L 23 – *pop. 23 425.*
*London 219 – Liverpool 12 – Preston 18.*

🏠 **Beaufort,** High Lane, Burscough, L40 7SN, Northeast : 1 ¾ m. by B 5319 on A 5
℘ *(01704) 892655, Fax (01704) 895135 –* ⩧ rm, 📺 ☎ & 🅿 – 🔬 40. 🇦🇧🇸 ᴀᴇ ⓞ 𝘝𝘐𝘚𝘈
**Meals** 10.95/15.95 **t.** and a la carte ▯ 5.50 – **21 rm** 🖙 74.50/110.00 **t.** – SB.

**OSMOTHERLEY** *N. Yorks.* 402 Q 20 – *pop. 1 217 –* ⊠ *Northallerton.*
*London 245 – Darlington 25 – Leeds 30 – Middlesbrough 20 – York 36.*

🍴 **Golden Lion,** 6 West End, DL6 3AA, ℘ *(01609) 883526 –* 🇦🇧🇸 𝘝𝘐𝘚𝘈 🇯🇨🇧
*closed dinner 25 December –* **Meals** a la carte 12.00/23.70 **t.**

**OSWESTRY** *Shrops.* 402 403 K 25 – *pop. 15 612.*
🛆 *Aston Park* ℘ *(01691) 610221 –* 🛆 *Llanymynech, Pant* ℘ *(01691) 830542.*
🄑 *Mile End Services, SY11 4JA* ℘ *(01691) 662488 – The Heritage Centre, 2 Church Terr., SY1*
*2TE* ℘ *(01691) 662753.*
*London 182 – Chester 28 – Shrewsbury 18.*

🏠 **Wynnstay,** Church St., SY11 2SZ, ℘ *(01691) 655261, Fax (01691) 670606,* ᴌ₅, 🚢, 🔲, 🦶
*–* ⩧ rm, 🖫 rest, 📺 ☎ 🅿 – 🔬 250. 🇦🇧🇸 ᴀᴇ ⓞ 𝘝𝘐𝘚𝘈
**The Italian :** **Meals** *(closed Sunday dinner)* 10.50/16.95 **st.** and a la carte ▯ 6.00 – 🖙 8.95
**26 rm** 70.00/89.00 **st.**, 1 suite – SB.

🏠 **Travelodge,** Mile End Service Area, SY11 4JA, Southeast : 1 ¼ m. at junction of A 5 with
A 483 ℘ *(01691) 658178,* Reservations (Freephone) 0800 850950 – ⩧ rm, 📺 & 🅿. 🇦🇧🇸 🄰
ⓞ 𝘝𝘐𝘚𝘈 🇯🇨🇧. ⁂
**Meals** (grill rest.) – **40 rm** 39.95/59.95 **t.**

🍴🍴 **Sebastian's** with rm, 45 Willow St., SY11 1AQ, ℘ *(01691) 655444, Fax (01691) 653452*
⩧ 📺 ☎. 🇦🇧🇸 ᴀᴇ 𝘝𝘐𝘚𝘈. ⁂
*closed 25 and 26 December –* **Meals** *(closed Sunday and Monday)* (dinner only) 21.50 **t.**
and a la carte ▯ 5.50 – 🖙 8.95 – **3 rm** 35.00/45.00 **t.**

**at Rhydycroesau** *West :* 3 ¼ m. *on B 4580 –* ⊠ *Oswestry.*

🏠 **Pen-Y-Dyffryn Hall** ⑤, SY10 7JD, Southeast : ¼ m. by B 4580 ℘ *(01691) 653700*
*Fax (01691) 653700,* ≼, 🚢, 🦅 *–* ⩧ rest, 📺 ☎ 🅿. 🇦🇧🇸 ᴀᴇ 𝘝𝘐𝘚𝘈
*closed 20 December-20 January –* **Meals** (booking essential to non-residents) (dinner only
19.00 **t.** ▯ 4.95 – **10 rm** 🖙 54.00/78.00 **t.** – SB.

🔧 ATS Oswald Rd ℘ *(01691) 653540/653256*

**OTLEY** *Suffolk* 404 X 27 – *pop. 1 381 –* ⊠ *Ipswich.*
*London 83 – Ipswich 7.5 – Norwich 43.*

🏠 **Bowerfield House** ⑤ *without rest.,* Helmingham Rd, IP6 9NR, ℘ *(01473) 890742*
*Fax (01473) 890059, « Converted 17C stable and barn »,* 🦅 *–* ⩧ 📺 🅿. ⁂
*15 March-October –* **3 rm** 🖙 36.00/50.00 **st.**

**OTLEY** *W. Yorks.* 402 O 22 – *pop. 13 596.*
🛆 *West Busk Lane* ℘ *(01943) 461015.*
🄑 *Council Offices, 8 Boroughgate, LS21 3AH* ℘ *(0113) 247 7707.*
*London 216 – Harrogate 14 – Leeds 12 – York 28.*

🏠 **Chevin Lodge** ⑤, Yorkgate, LS21 3NU, South : 2 m. by B 6451 off East Chevin Rd
℘ *(01943) 467818, Fax (01943) 850335, « Pine lodge village in extensive woodland »,* ᴌ₅
🚢, 🔲, 🚢, 🦅, park, ⁂ *–* ⩧ rest, 📺 ☎ 🅿 – 🔬 120. 🇦🇧🇸 ᴀᴇ 𝘝𝘐𝘚𝘈
**Meals** 12.50/19.95 **st.** and a la carte ▯ 5.95 – **46 rm** 🖙 89.00/114.00 **st.**, 4 suites – SB.

**OULTON BROAD** *Suffolk* 404 Z 26 – *see Lowestoft.*

**OUNDLE** *Northants.* 404 S 26 – *pop. 3 996 –* ⊠ *Peterborough.*
🛆 *Benefield Rd* ℘ *(01832) 273267.*
🄑 *14 West St., PE8 4EF* ℘ *(01832) 274333.*
*London 89 – Leicester 37 – Northampton 30.*

🏠 **Castle Farm,** Fotheringhay, PE8 5HZ, North : 3 ¾ m. by A 427 off A 605
℘ *(01832) 226200, Fax (01832) 226200, « Riverside garden » –* ⩧ rm, 📺 🅿. ⁂
**Meals** (by arrangement) 12.50 – **6 rm** 🖙 32.00/52.00 **st.**

🍴 **The Falcon Inn,** PE8 5HZ, ℘ *(01832) 226254, Fax (01832) 226046 –* ⩧ 🅿. 🇦🇧🇸 ᴀᴇ ⓞ 𝘝𝘐𝘚𝘈
*closed Monday lunch except Bank Holidays –* **Meals** a la carte 14.00/17.50 **t.** ▯ 7.00.

at **Upper Benefield** West : 4 m. on A 427 – ⊠ Peterborough (Cambs.).

🏠 **Wheatsheaf**, PE8 5AN, 𝒫 (01832) 205254, Fax (01832) 205245, ☞ – 🖵 ☎ 🅿. 🐠 🖭 ⓪ ⅦⅢ ☑ ⒿⒸⒷ. ✿
**Meals** a la carte 10.50/21.40 t. ⏐ 4.25 – **9 rm** ⊊ 49.95/59.95 t. – SB.

---

**OUTLANE** W. Yorks. – see Huddersfield.

---

**OWER** Hants. ⁴⁰³ ⁴⁰⁴ P 31 – see Romsey.

---

**OXFORD** Oxon. ⁴⁰³ ⁴⁰⁴ Q 28 Great Britain G. – pop. 118 795.

See : City★★★ - Christ Church★★ (Hall★★ AC, Tom Quad★, Tom Tower★, Cathedral★ AC - Choir Roof★) BZ – Merton College★★ AC BZ - Magdalen College★★ BZ – Ashmolean Museum★★ BY M2 – Bodleian Library★★ (Ceiling★★, Lierne Vaulting★) AC BZ F – St. John's College★ BY - The Queen's College★ BZ – Lincoln College★ BZ - Trinity College (Chapel★) BY – New College (Chapel★) AC, BZ – Radcliffe Camera★ BZ A – Sheldonian Theatre★ AC, BZ G – University Museum★ BY M3 – Pitt Rivers Museum★ BY M4.

Env. : Iffley Church★ AZ A.

Exc. : Woodstock : Blenheim Palace★★★ (The Grounds★★★) AC, NW : 8 m. by A 4144 and A 34 AY.

Swinford Bridge (toll).

🖪 The Old School, Gloucester Green, OX1 2DA 𝒫 (01865) 726871.

London 59 – Birmingham 63 – Brighton 105 – Bristol 73 – Cardiff 107 – Coventry 54 – Southampton 64.

Plans on following pages

🏯 **Randolph**, Beaumont St., OX1 2LN, 𝒫 (01865) 247481, Fax (01865) 791678 – ⧈, ⅋⩝ rm, 🖵 ☎ – 🔬 250. 🐠 🖭 ⓪ ⅦⅢ ☑ ⒿⒸⒷ       BY n
**Spires :** Meals a la carte 22.00/32.00 st. ⏐ 8.50 – ⊊ 13.25 – **114 rm** 125.00/225.00 st., 5 suites – SB.

🏨 **Oxford Moat House**, Wolvercote Roundabout, OX2 8AL, 𝒫 (01865) 489988, Fax (01865) 310259, ⻗, ☎, 🏊, squash – ⅋⩝ rm, 🍴 rest, 🖵 ☎ 🅿 – 🔬 150. 🐠 🖭 ⓪ ⅦⅢ. ✿       AY e
Meals 12.50/16.50 st. – ⊊ 9.50 – **155 rm** 115.00/140.00 st. – SB.

🏠 **Old Parsonage**, 1 Banbury Rd, OX2 6NN, 𝒫 (01865) 310210, Fax (01865) 311262, ⻗, « Part 17C house », – 🖵 ☎ 🅿. 🐠 🖭 ⓪ ⅦⅢ ⒿⒸⒷ. ✿       BY e
closed 25 and 26 December – **Meals** (room service and meals in bar only) a la carte 17.40/24.65 t. ⏐ 10.80 – **30 rm** ⊊ 125.00/195.00 t.

🏨 **Eastgate**, Merton St., OX1 4BE, 𝒫 (01865) 248244, Fax (01865) 791681 – ⧈ ⅋⩝, 🍴 rest, 🖵 ☎ 🅿. 🐠 🖭 ⓪ ⅦⅢ ☑       BZ c
Meals (bar lunch)/dinner 17.95 st. ⏐ 8.50 – ⊊ 10.95 – **64 rm** 95.00/110.00 t. – SB.

🏨 **Linton Lodge**, Linton Rd, OX2 6UJ, 𝒫 (01865) 553461, Fax (01865) 310365, ☞ – ⧈, ⅋⩝ rm, 🖵 ☎ 🅿 – 🔬 120. 🐠 🖭 ⓪ ⅦⅢ. ✿       AY n
Meals (bar lunch)/dinner a la carte approx. 18.00 st. – ⊊ 10.25 – **71 rm** 105.00/125.00 st.

🏠 **Bath Place**, 4-5 Bath Pl., OX1 3SU, 𝒫 (01865) 791812, Fax (01865) 791834, « 17C Flemish weavers cottages » – ⅋⩝ rest, 🍴 rest, 🖵 ☎ 🅿. 🐠 🖭 ⅦⅢ       BY a
**Meals** (closed Tuesday lunch, Sunday dinner and Monday) 19.50 t. (lunch) and a la carte 31.25/45.00 t. ⏐ 6.95 – ⊊ 9.50 – **11 rm** 95.00/145.00 t., 2 suites.

🏠 **Balkan Lodge**, 315 Iffley Rd, OX4 4AG, 𝒫 (01865) 244524, Fax (01865) 251090 – ⅋⩝ 🖵 ☎ 🅿. 🐠 ⅦⅢ. ✿
closed 23 December-23 January – **Meals** 15.50 st. (dinner) and a la carte 7.50/8.95 st. ⏐ 4.25 – **13 rm** ⊊ 45.50/65.50 t. – SB.

🏠 **Marlborough House** without rest., 321 Woodstock Rd, OX2 7NY, 𝒫 (01865) 311321, Fax (01865) 515329 – ⅋⩝ 🖵 ☎ 🅿. 🐠 🖭 ⓪ ⅦⅢ ⒿⒸⒷ. ✿       AY v
closed 23 December-2 January – **16 rm** 62.50/73.00 st.

🏡 **Cotswold House** without rest., 363 Banbury Rd, OX2 7PL, 𝒫 (01865) 310558, Fax (01865) 310558, ☞ – ⅋⩝ 🖵 🅿. ✿       AY c
closed 1 week Christmas – **7 rm** ⊊ 45.00/65.00 st.

🏡 **Chestnuts** without rest., 45 Davenant Rd, OX2 8BU, 𝒫 (01865) 553375, Fax (01865) 553375 – ⅋⩝ 🖵 🅿. ✿       AY s
closed 22 December-7 January – **5 rm** ⊊ 40.00/69.00.

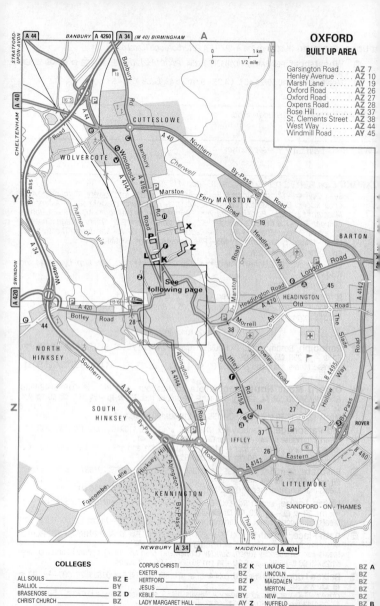

# OXFORD
## BUILT UP AREA

See following page

**COLLEGES**

| | | | | | |
|---|---|---|---|---|---|
| ALL SOULS | BZ E | CORPUS CHRISTI | BZ K | LINACRE | BZ A |
| BALLIOL | BY | EXETER | BZ | LINCOLN | BZ |
| BRASENOSE | BZ D | HERTFORD | BZ P | MAGDALEN | BZ |
| CHRIST CHURCH | BZ | JESUS | BZ | MERTON | BZ |
| | | KEBLE | BY | NEW | BZ |
| | | LADY MARGARET HALL | AY Z | NUFFIELD | BZ B |

⛫ **Mount Pleasant**, 76 London Rd., Headington, OX3 9AJ, ℰ (01865) 762749, Fax (01865) 762749 – ₩ ⚄ 🆃🆅 ☎ 🅿. ⓂⓈ 🅰🅴 ⓄⓄ VISA JCB. ⚘
Meals 10.00 t. and a la carte – **8 rm** ☲ 45.00/75.00 st. – SB.                    AY **a**

⛫ **Dial House** without rest., 25 London Rd, Headington, OX3 7RE, ℰ (01865) 769944, Fax (01865) 769944 – ₩⚄ 🆃🆅 ☎ 🅿. ⚘
**8 rm** ☲ 45.00/65.00 st.                    AY **o**

⛫ **Tilbury Lodge** without rest., 5 Tilbury Lane, Botley, OX2 9NB, West : 2 m. by A 420 off B 4044 ℰ (01865) 862138, Fax (01865) 863700, ⚼ – ₩⚄ 🆃🆅 ☎ 🅿. ⓂⓈ VISA. ⚘
**9 rm** ☲ 45.00/68.00 st.                    AZ **e**

↑ **Pine Castle** without rest., 290-292 Iffley Rd, OX4 4AE, ℰ (01865) 241497, Fax (01865) 727230 – ⇔ 📺 ☎ 🅿. ⫿⑧ 𝘝𝘐𝘚𝘈 𝘑𝘤𝘣. ⫼    Z r
closed 1 week Christmas – **8 rm** ⫼ 57.00/67.00 **st.**

XX **Gee's**, 61 Banbury Rd, OX2 6PE, ℰ (01865) 553540, Fax (01865) 310308, « Conservatory » – 🗐. ⫿⑧ 𝘈𝘌 𝘝𝘐𝘚𝘈 𝘑𝘤𝘣    AY r
closed 25 and 26 December – **Meals** a la carte 19.40/26.15 **t.** ⓓ 8.50.

X    **Le Petit Blanc,** 71-72 Walton St., OX2 6AG, ℘ (01865) 510999, Fax (01865) 510700 – ⟨⟩
🍴    🍽. 🐵 🆎 ⓞ 𝗩𝗜𝗦𝗔                                   AY
        Meals - Brasserie - 15.00 **t.** and a la carte 15.20/25.50 **t.**

X    **Shimla Pinks,** 16 Turl St., OX1 3DH, ℘ (01865) 245564, Fax (01865) 245572 – 🍽. 🐵 🆎 ⓞ
        𝗩𝗜𝗦𝗔                                              BZ
        closed 25-26 December and 1 January – Meals - Indian - 7.50/11.95 **t.** and a la carte.

**at Stanton St. John** Northeast : 7 m. by A 40 – AY – ✉ Oxford.

🍴    **Talkhouse** with rm, OX33 1EX, on B 4027 ℘ (01865) 351648, Fax (01865) 351085, 🍽, ⋆
        – 📺 ☎ 🅿. 🐵 🆎 ⓞ 𝗩𝗜𝗦𝗔 𝗝𝗖𝗕. 🕸
        closed 25 December – Meals (buffet lunch) a la carte 19.50/22.50 **t.** – 4 rm ⊇ 40.00
        49.50 **t.**

**at Wheatley** East : 7 m. by A 40 – AY – ✉ Oxford.

🏠    **Travelodge,** London Rd, OX33 1JH, ℘ (01865) 875705, Reservations (Freephone) 080
        850950 – ⟨⟩ 📺 ♿ 🅿. 🐵 🆎 ⓞ 𝗩𝗜𝗦𝗔 𝗝𝗖𝗕. 🕸
        Meals (grill rest.) – 36 rm 39.95/59.95 **t.**

**at Iffley** Southeast : 2 m. by A 4158 – ✉ Oxford.

🏨    **Hawkwell House,** Church Way, OX4 4DZ, ℘ (01865) 749988, Fax (01865) 748525, ⋆
        ⟨⟩ rest, 📺 ☎ 🅿 – 🔬 200. 🐵 🆎 ⓞ 𝗩𝗜𝗦𝗔 𝗝𝗖𝗕. 🕸             AZ
        17.95 **t.** and a la carte – ⊇ 9.25 49 rm 90.00/150.00 **t.** – SB

🏠    **The Tree,** Church Way, OX4 4EY, ℘ (01865) 775974, Fax (01865) 747554, ⋆ – ⟨⟩ rm, 📺
        ☎ 🅿. 🐵 🆎 𝗩𝗜𝗦𝗔. 🕸                                           AZ
        closed 24 to 27 December – Meals a la carte 9.45/15.45 **t.** ⓙ 4.95 – 8 rm ⊇ 60.00/80.00 **t.**

**at Cowley** Southeast : 2½ m. by B 480 – ✉ Oxford.

🏠    **Travel Inn,** Garsington Rd, OX4 2JZ, ℘ (01865) 779230, Fax (01865) 775887 – 🛗, ⟨⟩ rm
        📺 ♿ 🅿. 🐵 🆎 ⓞ 𝗩𝗜𝗦𝗔. 🕸                                       AZ
        Meals (grill rest.) – 120 rm 38.00 **t.**

**at Great Milton** Southeast : 12 m. by A 40 off A 329 – AY – ✉ Oxford.

🏯    **Le Manoir aux Quat' Saisons** (Blanc) ⟨⟩, Church Rd, OX44 7PD, ℘ (01844) 27888
❀❀    Fax (01844) 278847, ≤, « Part 15C and 16C manor house, gardens », park – ⟨⟩ rest
        🍽 rest, 📺 ☎ 🅿 – 🔬 35. 🐵 🆎 ⓞ 𝗩𝗜𝗦𝗔 𝗝𝗖𝗕. 🕸
        Meals - French - 32.00 **st.** (lunch) and a la carte 70.00/88.50 **st.** ⓙ 14.00 – ⊇ 14.50 – 21 rm
        210.00/310.00 **st.**, 6 suites – SB
        **Spec.** Macaroni in a truffle jus with pan-fried langoustine. Roast rib of milk-fed veal wit
        garden vegetables. Apricot fondue and poached meringue in a nougatine cassolette.

**at Cumnor** West : 4¼ m. by A 420 - AY - on B 4017 – ✉ Oxford.

X    **Bear and Ragged Staff,** Appleton Rd, OX2 9QH, ℘ (01865) 862329
        Fax (01865) 865366 – 🅿. 🐵 🆎 𝗩𝗜𝗦𝗔
        closed 4 days Christmas-New Year – Meals a la carte 16.90/28.95 **t.**

        ⓐ ATS Pony Rd, Horspath Trading Est., Cowley    ATS 2 Stephen Rd, Headington
        ℘ (01865) 777188                                  ℘ (01865) 761732

---

**OXHILL** Warks. 𝟰𝟬𝟯 𝟰𝟬𝟰 P 27 – pop. 303 – ✉ Stratford-upon-Avon.
        London 85 – Birmingham 32 – Oxford 25.

🏠    **Nolands Farm** ⟨⟩, CV35 0RJ, on A 422 ℘ (01926) 640309, Fax (01926) 641662, ⟨⟩, ⋆ -
        ⟨⟩ rest, 📺 🅿. 🐵 𝗩𝗜𝗦𝗔. 🕸
        closed 15 December-15 January – Meals (by arrangement) 16.95 **st.** ⓙ 4.00 – 8 rm
        ⊇ 25.00/44.00 **st.**

---

**PADSTOW** Cornwall 𝟰𝟬𝟯 F 32 The West Country G. – pop. 2 855.
        See : Town★ – Prideaux Place★.
        Env. : Trevone (Cornwall Coast Path★★) W : 3 m. by B 3276 – Trevose Head★ (≤★★) W : 6 m
        by B 3276.
        Exc. : Bedruthan Steps★, SW : 7 m. by B 3276 – Pencarrow★, SE : 11 m. by A 389.
        🏌, 🏌, 🏌 Trevose, Constantine Bay ℘ (01841) 520208.
        🄱 Red Brick Building, North Quay, PL28 8AF ℘ (01841) 533449 (summer only).
        London 288 – Exeter 78 – Plymouth 45 – Truro 23.

🏨 **Metropole,** Station Rd, PL28 8DB, ℘ (01841) 532486, Fax (01841) 532867, ≤ Camel Estuary, ⬚, 🐎 – ⧉ ⁂ 🆃🆅 ☎ 🅿. ⓪⑨ Ⓐ🅔 ① VISA JCB. ※
Meals (bar lunch Monday to Saturday)/dinner a la carte 18.40/23.80 t. ⓵ 6.95 – ⬚ 8.95 –
**50 rm** 85.00/140.00 t. – SB.

🏨 **Cross House** without rest., Church St., PL28 8BG, ℘ (01841) 532391, Fax (01841) 533633
– ⁂, ▥ rm, 🆃🆅 ☎ 🅿. ⓪⑨ VISA. ※
closed January and February – **9 rm** ⬚ 60.00/120.00 t.

🏨 **St. Petroc's House,** 4 New St., PL28 8EA, ℘ (01841) 532700, Fax (01841) 532942 – 🆃🆅 ☎
🅿. ⓪⑨ VISA
closed 20 to 26 December – **St. Petrocs Bistro :** Meals (closed Monday) (booking essential)
19.95 t. ⓵ 7.50 – **13 rm** ⬚ 67.50/130.00 t. – SB.

🏨 **Dower House,** Fentonluna Lane, PL28 8BA, ℘ (01841) 532317, Fax (01841) 532667 – ⁂
🆃🆅 ☎ 🅿. ⓪⑨ VISA
closed January and February – Meals (closed 1 May) a la carte approx. 15.00 st. ⓵ 4.50 –
**6 rm** ⬚ 51.20/80.00 st.

🏨 **Old Custom House Inn,** South Quay, PL28 8ED, ℘ (01841) 532359, Fax (01841) 533372,
≤ Camel Estuary and harbour – ⁂ rest, ▥ rest, 🆃🆅 ☎ ☏, ⓪⑨ Ⓐ🅔 ① VISA
Meals (bar lunch Monday to Saturday) (carving lunch Sunday)/dinner 19.50 st.
and a la carte – **26 rm** ⬚ 71.00/96.00 s. – SB.

↑ **Rick Stein's Café,** Middle St., PL28 8AP, ℘ (01841) 532777, Fax (01841) 533566, �� –
⁂ rest, 🆃🆅. ⓪⑨ VISA
closed 25 and 26 December – Meals (closed Sunday) (light lunch)/dinner 15.50 t. – **3 rm**
⬚ 41.00/75.00 t.

↑ **Woodlands** without rest., Treator, PL28 8RU, West: 1 ¼ m. by A 389 on B 3276
℘ (01841) 532426, Fax (01841) 532426, ≤, 🐎 – ⁂ 🆃🆅 🅿. ※
March-October – **9 rm** ⬚ 30.00/48.00 s.

↑ **Treverbyn House** without rest., Station Rd, PL28 8AD, ℘ (01841) 532855, ≤, 🐎 – 🆃🆅
🅿. ※
closed 14 December-1 February – **3 rm** ⬚ 45.00/80.00 s.

✕✕ **The Seafood** with rm, Riverside, PL28 8BY, ℘ (01841) 532485, Fax (01841) 533574,
« Converted granary overlooking quayside and Carmel estuary » – ⁂ rest, ▥ rest, 🆃🆅 ☎
🅿. ⓪⑨ VISA
closed 20 to 26 December – Meals - Seafood - (closed Sunday) (booking essential) 28.00/
34.00 t. and a la carte 37.90/55.40 t. ⓵ 7.50 – **13 rm** ⬚ 52.50/130.00 t. – SB.

✕✕ **Brocks,** The Strand, PL28 8AJ, ℘ (01841) 532565 – ⁂. ⓪⑨ VISA
closed Monday lunch and Sunday dinner in summer and Monday-Tuesday in winter – Meals
(dinner booking essential in summer) 15.65/19.25 t.

✕ **Bistro Margot Thomas,** 11 Duke St., PL28 8AB, ℘ (01841) 533441 – ⁂. ⓪⑨ VISA
closed November and January – Meals (booking essential) (dinner only) 22.95 t. ⓵ 5.95.

**at Little Petherick** South : 3 m. on A 389 – ⊠ Wadebridge.

🏨 **Molesworth Manor** without rest., PL27 7QT, ℘ (01841) 540292, ≤, « Part 17C and 19C
rectory », 🐎 – 🅿. ※
closed November and December – **10 rm** ⬚ 22.50/65.00 t.

↑ **Old Mill Country House** without rest., PL27 7QT, ℘ (01841) 540388, « Part 16C corn
mill », 🐎 – 🅿. ⓪⑨ Ⓐ🅔 VISA. ※
March-October – **6 rm** ⬚ 60.00/64.00.

**at St. Issey** South : 3½ m. on A 389 – ⊠ Wadebridge.

↑ **Olde Treodore House** ⌾ without rest., PL27 7QS, North : ¼ m. off A 389
℘ (01841) 540291, ≤, 🐎 – ⁂ 🆃🆅 🅿. ※
closed Christmas and New Year and restricted opening in winter – **3 rm** ⬚ 48.00/52.00.

**at Constantine Bay** Southwest : 4 m. by B 3276 – ⊠ Padstow.

🏨 **Treglos** ⌾, PL28 8JH, ℘ (01841) 520727, Fax (01841) 521163, ≤, 🔲, 🐎 – ⧉ ⁂, ▥ rest,
🆃🆅 ☎ ⇦ 🅿. ⓪⑨ VISA
11 March-5 November – Meals 11.90/22.50 t. and a la carte – **41 rm** ⬚ (dinner included)
76.00/152.00 st., 3 suites – SB.

---

**PADWORTH** Newbury 🔳🔳🔳 🔳🔳🔳 Q 29 – pop. 545 – ⊠ Reading.
London 58 – Basingstoke 12 – Reading 10.

🏨 **Courtyard by Marriott Reading,** Bath Rd, RG7 5HT, on A 4 ℘ (01189) 714411,
Fax (01189) 714442, 🛌 – ⁂ ▥ 🆃🆅 ☎ ☾ 🅿 – 🔬 180. ⓪⑨ Ⓐ🅔 ① VISA JCB. ※
Meals (bar lunch Saturday) 12.50/17.00 st. and dinner a la carte ⓵ 7.25 – ⬚ 9.95 – **50 rm**
75.00/85.00 st. – SB.

**PAIGNTON** *Torbay* 403 *J 32 The West Country G.* – pop. 42 989.

See : *Torbay★* - *Kirkham House★ AC* Y B.

Env. : *Paignton Zoo★★ AC*, SW : ½ m. by A 3022 AY *(see Plan of Torbay)* – *Cockington★*, N 3 m. by A 3022 and minor roads.

🛈 *The Esplanade, TQ4 6BN* ✆ *(01803) 558383.*

*London 226 – Exeter 26 – Plymouth 29.*

Plan of Built up Area : see Torbay

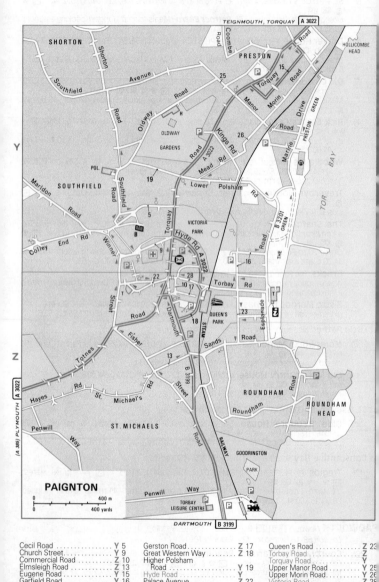

🏛 **Redcliffe,** 4 Marine Drive, TQ3 2NL, ℰ (01803) 526397, Fax (01803) 528030, ≤ Torbay, ₤₅, ⇆, ℥, 🔲, ☞ – ฿, ᴗ rest, 🔟 ☎ ℃ ₽ – 🛓 200. ◍◍ 础 𝘝𝘐𝘚𝘈. ℀
   Y  n
   Meals (bar lunch Monday to Saturday)/dinner 15.75 **t.** and a la carte 🍸 5.50 – **65 rm** ⇌ 54.00/108.00 **t.** – SB.

   ⓐ ATS Orient Rd ℰ (01803) 556888

---

**AINSWICK** Glos. 🟦🟦🟦 🟦🟦🟦 N 28 Great Britain G. – pop. 1 628.
   See : Town★.
   London 107 – Bristol 35 – Cheltenham 10 – Gloucester 7.

🏛 **Painswick** ঌ, Kemps Lane, GL6 6YB, Southeast : ½ m. by Bisley St., St. Marys St. and Tibbiwell ℰ (01452) 812160, Fax (01452) 814059, « Part 18C Palladian house », ☞ – 🔟 ☎ ₽. ◍◍ 础 𝘝𝘐𝘚𝘈 ᴶᴄ᛫ᴮ. ℀
   Meals 14.50/26.00 **st.** and dinner a la carte 🍸 6.00 – **19 rm** ⇌ 85.00/195.00 **st.** – SB.

✕✕ **Country Elephant,** New St., GL6 6XH, ℰ (01452) 813564, Fax (01452) 813564, ☞ – ฿฿.
   ◍◍ 础 ◍ 𝘝𝘐𝘚𝘈 ᴶᴄ᛫ᴮ
   closed Sunday, Monday and 2 weeks Christmas-January – Meals 13.00/18.00 **t.** and a la carte 25.00/29.50 **t.** 🍸 8.75.

---

**AINTER'S FORSTAL** Kent – see Faversham.

---

**ANGBOURNE-ON-THAMES** Newbury 🟦🟦🟦 🟦🟦🟦 Q 29 – ✉ Reading.
   London 53 – Basingstoke 18 – Newbury 16 – Oxford 22 – Reading 6.

🏛 **Copper Inn,** Church Rd, RG8 7AR, ℰ (01189) 842244, Fax (01189) 845542, ☀, ☞ – 🔟 ☎ ₤, – 🛓 60. ◍◍ 础 ◍ 𝘝𝘐𝘚𝘈
   Meals 15.95/19.95 **t.** and a la carte 🍸 7.50 – ⇌ 9.50 – **22 rm** 80.00/115.00 **t.** – SB.

---

**ARBOLD** Lancs. 🟦🟦🟦 L 23 Great Britain G. – pop. 2 872 – ✉ Wigan.
   Env. : Rufford Old Hall★ (Great Hall★) AC, NW : 4 m. by B 5246.
   London 212 – Liverpool 25 – Manchester 24 – Preston 19.

✕✕ **High Moor Inn,** High Moor Lane, WN6 9QA, Northeast : 3 m. by B 5246 and Chorley Rd ℰ (01257) 252364, Fax (01257) 255120 – ฿฿ ₽. ◍◍ 础 ◍ 𝘝𝘐𝘚𝘈
   Meals 12.00 **t.** (lunch) and dinner a la carte 16.20/25.00 **t.**

---

**ARKHAM** Devon 🟦🟦🟦 H 31 – ✉ Bideford.
   London 229 – Barnstaple 14 – Exeter 87 – Plymouth 58.

🏛 **Penhaven Country House** ঌ, Rectory Lane, EX39 5PL, ℰ (01237) 451711, Fax (01237) 451878, ☞, park – ฿฿ rest, 🔟 ☎ ₽. ◍◍ 础 ◍ 𝘝𝘐𝘚𝘈
   Meals 10.50/14.95 **st.** and dinner a la carte 🍸 7.95 – **12 rm** ⇌ (dinner included) 62.95/135.90 **st.** – SB.

🏠 **Old Rectory** ঌ, Rectory Lane, EX39 5PL, ℰ (01237) 451443, ☞ – ฿฿ ₽. ℀
   March-November – Meals (by arrangement) (communal dining) 23.00 **s.** 🍸 5.80 – **3 rm** ⇌ 50.00/80.00 **s.**

---

**ATCHWAY** South Gloucestershire 🟦🟦🟦 🟦🟦🟦 M 29 – see Bristol.

---

**ATELEY BRIDGE** N. Yorks. 🟦🟦🟦 O 21 Great Britain G. – pop. 2 504 – ✉ Harrogate.
   Exc. : Fountains Abbey★★★ AC - Studley Royal★★ AC (≤★ from Anne Boleyn's Seat) - Fountains Hall (Façade★), NE : 8½ m. by B 6265.
   🛈 14 High St., HG3 5AW ℰ (01423) 711147 (summer only).
   London 225 – Leeds 28 – Middlesbrough 46 – York 32.

🏛 **Grassfields Country House** ঌ, Low Wath Rd, HG3 5HL, ℰ (01423) 711412, Fax (01423) 712844, ☀, « Part 18C », ☞ – ฿฿ rest, 🔟 ☎ ₽ – 🛓 60. ◍◍ 𝘝𝘐𝘚𝘈
   Meals 13.95 **t.** (dinner) and a la carte 11.85/23.70 **t.** 🍸 4.95 – **9 rm** ⇌ 31.00/58.00 **st.** – SB.

**t Low Laithe** Southeast : 2 ¾ m. on B 6165 – ✉ Harrogate.

✕✕ **Dusty Miller,** Main Rd, Summerbridge, HG3 4BU, ℰ (01423) 780837 – ₽. ◍◍ 础 𝘝𝘐𝘚𝘈
   closed Sunday, Monday, 25-26 December and 1 January – Meals (dinner only) 24.00 and a la carte 25.30/35.40 🍸 6.45.

✕ **Carters Knox Manor** with rm, Summer Bridge, HG3 4DQ, ℰ (01423) 780607 – ฿฿ rm, 🔟 ₽. ◍◍ 𝘝𝘐𝘚𝘈
   Meals 12.50 **st.** and a la carte 🍸 5.85 – **4 rm** ⇌ 42.50/60.00 **st.** – SB.

505

**at Summerbridge** *Southeast : 3 ¾ m. on B 6165 –* ⊠ *Harrogate.*

⌂ **North Pasture Farm** ⏃, Brimham Rocks, HG3 4DW, Northeast : 2 ¾ m. by Hartw
Bank Rd ℘ (01423) 711470, ≤, « Part 14C and 17C farmhouse, working farm », park – ⏃
**℗**. ⌘
*April-October –* **Meals** 13.50 **s.** – **3 rm** ⌷ 35.00/48.00 **s.**

**at Wath-in-Nidderdale** *Northwest : 2 ¼ m. by Low Wath Rd –* ⊠ *Harrogate.*

ХХ **Sportsman's Arms** ⏃ with rm, HG3 5PP, ℘ (01423) 711306, *Fax (01423) 7125.*
« Part 17C », 🌳 – ⇆ 📺 ☎ **℗**. ⓜ⊘ *VISA*. ⌘
*closed 25 December –* **Meals** (booking essential to non-residents) a la carte 17.45/23.50
▯ 6.90 – **13 rm** ⌷ 40.00/80.00 **t.**

**at Ramsgill-in-Nidderdale** *Northwest : 5 m. by Low Wath Rd –* ⊠ *Harrogate.*

▥▥ **Yorke Arms** ⏃, HG3 5RL, ℘ (01423) 755243, *Fax (01423) 755330,* « Part 17C form
shooting lodge », 🌳 – ⇆ 📺 ☎ ✆ **℗**. ⓜ⊘ ⌷ *VISA*. ⌘
**Meals** *(closed Sunday dinner to non-residents)* a la carte 14.20/23.65 **t.** ▯ 6.50 – **14 ▮**
⌷ 70.00/140.00 **t.**

---

**PATRICK BROMPTON** *N. Yorks.* 402 P 21 – *see Bedale.*

---

**PAULERSPURY** *Northants.* 403 404 R 27 – *see Towcester.*

---

**PAXFORD** *Glos.* 403 404 O 27 – *see Chipping Campden.*

---

**PAYHEMBURY** *Devon – see Honiton.*

---

**PEASMARSH** *E. Sussex* 404 W 31 – *see Rye.*

---

**PEEL** *Isle of Man* 402 F 21 – *see Man (Isle of).*

---

**PELYNT** *Cornwall* 403 G 32 – *see Looe.*

---

**PEMBROKE BAY** *Guernsey (Channel Islands)* 403 P 33 and 230 ⑩ – *see Channel Islands.*

---

**PEMBURY** *Kent* 404 U 30 – *see Royal Tunbridge Wells.*

---

**PENDLEBURY** *Gtr. Manchester* 402 403 404 N 23 – *see Manchester.*

---

**PENRITH** *Cumbria* 401 402 L 19 – *pop. 12 049.*
⌗ *Salkeld Rd ℘ (01768) 891919/865429.*
**🛈** *Robinsons School, Middlegate, CA11 7PT ℘ (01768) 867466.*
*London 290 – Carlisle 24 – Kendal 31 – Lancaster 48.*

▥▥ **North Lakes,** Ullswater Rd, CA11 8QT, South : 1 m. by A 592 at junction 40 of M
℘ (01768) 868111, *Fax (01768) 868291,* ⛱, ⇌, ◰, squash – ▮, ⇆ rm, 📺 ☎ & **℗**
🍴 200. ⓜ⊘ ⌷ ⓞ *VISA*
**Meals** *(closed Saturday lunch)* 12.95/19.50 **t.** and a la carte ▯ 7.95 – **84 rm** ⌷ 102.0
160.00 **t.** – SB.

🏠 **Travelodge,** Redhills, CA11 0DT, Southwest : 1 ½ m. by A 592 on A 66 ℘ (01768) 86695
Reservations (Freephone) 0800 850950 – ⇆ rm, 📺 & **℗**. ⓜ⊘ ⌷ ⓞ *VISA* ᴊᴄʙ. ⌘
**Meals** (grill rest.) – **40 rm** 39.95/59.95 **t.**

Ⓐ ATS Unit 61, Gilwilly Rd, Gilwilly Ind. Est.
℘ (01768) 865656/7

---

**PENSHURST** *Kent* 404 U 30 *Great Britain G. – pop. 1 509.*
*Env. : Hever Castle★ AC, W : 6 m. by B 2176 and B 2027.*
*London 38 – Maidstone 19 – Royal Tunbridge Wells 6.*

⌂ **Swale Cottage** ⏃ without rest., Poundsbridge Lane, TN11 8AH, Southeast : 1 m. by
2176 off Poundsbridge Lane ℘ (01892) 870738, *Fax (01892) 870738,* ≤, 🌳 – ⇆ 📺 **℗**. ⌘
**3 rm** ⌷ 49.00/69.00.

**PENZANCE** *Cornwall* **403** D 33 *The West Country G. – pop. 20 284.*

See : *Town★ - Outlook★★★ – Western Promenade (≼★★★) YZ – National Lighthouse Centre★ AC Y – Chapel St.★ Y – Maritime Museum★ AC Y M1.*

Env. : *St. Buryan★★ (church tower★★), SW : 5 m. by A 30 and B 3283 – Penwith★★ – Trengwainton Garden★★, NW : 2 m. – Sancreed - Church★★ (Celtic Crosses★★) - Carn Euny★, W : 3½ m. by A 30 Z – St. Michael's Mount★★ (≼★★), E : 4 m. by B 3311 – Y – and A 30 – Gulval★ (Church★), NE : 1 m. – Ludgvan★ (Church★), NE : 3½ m. by A 30 – Chysauster Village★, N : 3½ m. by A 30, B 3311 and minor rd – Newlyn★ - Pilchard Works★, SW : 1½ m. by B 3315 Z – Lanyon Quoit★, NW : 3½ m. by St. Clare Street – Men-an-Tol★, NW : 5 m. by B 3312 – Madron Church★, NW : 1½ m. by St. Clare Street Y.*

Exc. : *Morvah (≼★★), NW : 6½ m. by St. Clare Street Y – Zennor (Church★), NW : 6 m. by B 3311 Y – Prussia Cove★, E : 8 m. by B 3311 – Y – and A 394 – Land's End★ (cliff scenery★★★), SW : 10 m. by A 30 Z – Porthcurno★, SW : 8½ m. by A 30, B 3283 and minor rd.*

*Access to the Isles of Scilly by helicopter ☎ (01736) 363871, Fax (01736) 364293.*

*⇌ to the Isles of Scilly (Hugh Town) (Isles of Scilly Steamship Co. Ltd) (summer only) (2 h 40 mn).*

**🛈** *Station Rd, TR18 2NF ☎ (01736) 362207.*

*London 319 – Exeter 113 – Plymouth 77 – Taunton 155.*

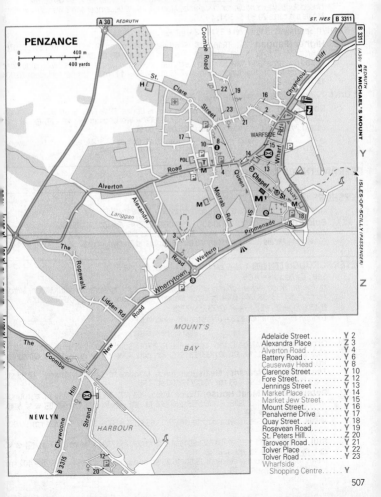

| | |
|---|---|
| Adelaide Street | Y 2 |
| Alexandra Place | Z 3 |
| Alverton Road | Y 4 |
| Battery Road | Y 6 |
| Causeway Head | Y 8 |
| Clarence Street | Y 10 |
| Fore Street | Z 12 |
| Jennings Street | Y 13 |
| Market Place | Y 14 |
| Market Jew Street | Y 15 |
| Mount Street | Y 16 |
| Penalverne Drive | Y 17 |
| Quay Street | Y 18 |
| Rosevean Road | Y 19 |
| St. Peters Hill | Z 20 |
| Taroveor Road | Y 21 |
| Tolver Place | Y 22 |
| Tolver Road | Y 23 |
| Wharfside Shopping Centre | Y |

🏛 **Abbey,** Abbey St., TR18 4AR, ℘ (01736) 366906, *Fax (01736) 351163*, « Attractively furnished 17C house », ☞ – 🆃🆅 . 🐾 🆅🅸🆂🅰 . ℀
Y u
*closed 1 week Christmas* – **Meals** (booking essential) (dinner only) 24.00 **t.** ⓙ 5.00 – **6 rm** ☞ 75.00/140.00 **t.**, 1 suite – SB.

🏛 **Beachfield,** The Promenade, TR18 4NW, ℘ (01736) 362067, *Fax (01736) 331100*, ≼ – 🆃🆅 ☎ 🅲 . 🐾 🆅🅸🆂🅰 🅹🅲🅱
Z a
*closed Christmas-New Year* – **Meals** (bar lunch)/dinner 14.95 **st.** and a la carte ⓙ 4.95 – **18 rm** ☞ 44.50/99.00 **st.**

🏛 **Tarbert,** 11 Clarence St., TR18 2NU, ℘ (01736) 363758, *Fax (01736) 331336* – ⓧ rest, 🆃🆅 ☎ 🅲 . 🐾 🆅🅸🆂🅰 . ℀
Y
*closed 23 December-5 January* – **Meals** (dinner only) 16.50 **t.** and dinner a la carte ⓙ 5.75 – **12 rm** ☞ 36.00/70.00 **st.** – SB.

↑ **Estoril,** 46 Morrab Rd, TR18 4EX, ℘ (01736) 362468, *Fax (01736) 367471* – ⓧ 🆃🆅 ☎ 🅿 . 🐾 🆅🅸🆂🅰 . ℀
Y o
*closed December and January* – **Meals** 15.00 **t.** ⓙ 4.00 – **10 rm** ☞ 27.50/55.00 **t.** – SB.

↑ **Chy-An-Mor** without rest., 15 Regent Terr., TR18 4DW, ℘ (01736) 363441, *Fax (01736) 363441*, ≼, ☞ – ⓧ 🆃🆅 🅿 . ℀
Y e
*March-October* – **10 rm** ☞ 28.00/51.00 **s.**

✗✗ **Harris's,** 46 New St., TR18 2LZ, ℘ (01736) 364408, *Fax (01736) 333273* – 🐾 🅰🅴 🆅🅸🆂🅰
Y a
*closed Sunday except dinner in summer, Monday, 25-26 December and 3 weeks in winter* – **Meals** a la carte 20.80/32.50 **t.** ⓙ 7.50.

**at Newlyn** *Southwest : 1½ m. on B 3315* – Z – ✉ Penzance.

🏨 **Higher Faugan** ⌕, TR18 5NS, Southwest : ¾ m. on B 3315 ℘ (01736) 362076, *Fax (01736) 351648*, ☳, ☞, park, ℀ – ⓧ rest, 🆃🆅 ☎ 🅿 . 🐾 🅰🅴 🅾 🆅🅸🆂🅰 🅹🅲🅱
*closed Christmas and New Year and restricted opening in winter* – **Meals** (by arrangement November-March) (bar lunch)/dinner 17.25 **st.** ⓙ 4.50 – **11 rm** ☞ (dinner included) 70.00/136.00 **t.** – SB.

**at Drift** *Southwest : 2½ m. on A 30* – Z – ✉ Penzance.

↑ **Rose Farm** ⌕ without rest., Chyanhal, Buryas Bridge, TR19 6AN, Southwest : ¾ m. on Chyanhal rd ℘ (01736) 731808, *Fax (01736) 731808*, « Working farm », ☞ – 🆃🆅 🅿 . ℀
*closed 24 and 25 December* – **3 rm** ☞ 25.00/42.00 **st.**

◉ ATS  Jelbert  Way,  Eastern  Green  ATS Units 25-26, Stable Hobba Ind. Est., Newlyn
℘ (01736) 362768 ℘ (01736) 369100

---

**PERRANUTHNOE** *Cornwall* 403 D 33 – *see Marazion.*

---

**PERSHORE** *Worcs.* 404 N 27 – *pop. 7 087.*

London 110 – Birmingham 34 – Cheltenham 27 – Coventry 45.

✗✗✗ **Epicurean,** 76 High St., WR10 1DU, ℘ (01386) 555576, *Fax (01386) 555572*
*closed Saturday to Tuesday, 1 week Easter, 2 weeks late summer and 2 weeks Christmas-New Year* – **Meals** (booking essential) (dinner only and Friday lunch) 27.50/32.50 **st.** ⓙ 14.00.

---

**PETERBOROUGH** 402 404 T 26 *Great Britain G.* – *pop. 134 788.*

**See :** *Cathedral* ★★ AC Y.

🏌 *Thorpe Wood, Nene Parkway* ℘ (01733) 267701, BX – 🏌 *Peterborough Milton, Milton Ferry* ℘ (01733) 380204, BX – 🏌 *Orton Meadows, Ham Lane* ℘ (01733) 237478, BX.
🅱 *45 Bridge St., PE1 1HA* ℘ (01733) 317336.
London 85 – Cambridge 35 – Leicester 41 – Lincoln 51.

Plan on next page

🏨🏨 **Orton Hall,** The Village, Orton Longueville, PE2 7DN, Southwest : 2½ m. by Oundle Rd (A 605) ℘ (01733) 391111, *Fax (01733) 231912*, ☞, park – ⓧ 🆃🆅 ☎ 🅿 – 🛆 120. 🐾 🅰🅴 🅾 🆅🅸🆂🅰 . ℀
BX c
**The Huntly Restaurant :** **Meals** (bar lunch Monday to Saturday)/dinner 17.95 **st.** and a la carte – ☞ 8.95 – **63 rm** 70.00/120.00 **st.** – SB.

🏨🏨 **Peterborough Moat House,** Thorpe Wood, PE3 6SG, Southwest : 2¼ m. at roundabout 33 ℘ (01733) 289988, *Fax (01733) 262737*, ☳, ☎, – 🛗, ⓧ rm, ☰ rest, 🆃🆅 ☎ 🅲 🛆 🅿 – 🛆 400. 🐾 🅰🅴 🅾 🆅🅸🆂🅰
BX s
**Meals** (bar lunch Saturday) a la carte 16.65/23.65 **st.** ⓙ 6.50 – ☞ 9.95 – **121 rm** 90.00/105.00 **st.**, 4 suites – SB.

🏛 **Bull,** Westgate, PE1 1RB, ℘ (01733) 561364, *Fax (01733) 557304* – ⓧ rm, ☰ rest, 🆃🆅 ☎ 🅲 🅿 – 🛆 200. 🐾 🅰🅴 🅾 🆅🅸🆂🅰 🅹🅲🅱 . ℀
Y z
**Meals** (dancing Saturday evening) 15.50/16.75 **st.** and a la carte ⓙ 7.05 – ☞ 7.25 – **102 rm** 67.50/72.50 **st.**, 1 suite – SB.

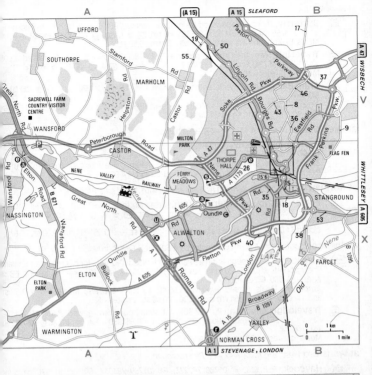

# PETERBOROUGH

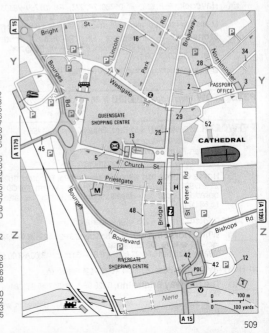

509

**Butterfly,** Thorpe Meadows, off Longthorpe Parkway, PE3 6GA, West : 1 m. by Thorpe R
℘ (01733) 564240, Fax (01733) 565538 – ⇔ rm, ⊡ ☎ ₠ ℗ – 🛦 80. 🌑❾ 🆎 ⓪ 𝘝𝘐𝘚𝘈 𝙅𝘤𝘉. ⅀
**Meals** 15.00 **st.** and a la carte – ⊇ 7.50 – **70 rm** 69.50 **st.**
BX

**Travel Inn,** Ham Lane, Orton Meadows, PE2 0UU, Southwest : 3 ½ m. by Oundle Rd (A 60⁕
℘ (01733) 235794, Fax (01733) 391055 – ⇔ rm, ⊟ rest, ⊡ ₠ ℗. 🌑❾ 🆎 ⓪ 𝘝𝘐𝘚𝘈. ⅀
**Meals** (grill rest.) – **40 rm** 38.00 **t.**
BX

**Grain Barge,** The Quayside, Embankment Rd, PE1 1EG, ℘ (01733) 311967 – ⊟. 🌑❾ 🆎 ⓒ
𝘝𝘐𝘚𝘈 𝙅𝘤𝘉
Z
closed 25 and 26 December – **Meals** - Chinese (Peking) - (buffet lunch Sunday) 14.80 s⁕
(dinner) and a la carte 14.80/21.00 **st.**

**at Eye** Northeast : 4 m. by A 47 – BV – ⊠ Peterborough.

**I Toscanini,** 2 Peterborough Rd, PE6 7YB, ℘ (01733) 223221, Fax (01733) 755355, �
℗. 🌑❾ 🆎 ⓪ 𝘝𝘐𝘚𝘈 𝙅𝘤𝘉
closed Monday lunch and Sunday – **Meals** - Italian - (live music Thursday to Saturda⁕
evening) 14.95 **t.** (lunch) and a la carte 18.20/26.85 **t.** ⅃ 4.90.

**at Norman Cross** South : 5 ¾ m. on A 15 at junction with A 1 – ⊠ Peterborough.

**Forte Posthouse Peterborough,** Great North Rd, PE7 3TB, ℘ (01733) 240209
Fax (01733) 244455, 𝗙⅄, ☎, ◻, – ⇔ rm, ⊟ rest, ⊡ ☎ ₠ ℗ – 🛦 50. 🌑❾ 🆎 ⓪ 𝘝𝘐𝘚
𝙅𝘤𝘉
BX
closed 31 December – **Meals** a la carte 15.35/24.85 **st.** – ⊇ 9.95 – **93 rm** 79.00 **st.** – SB.

**at Alwalton** Southwest : 5 ¾ m. on Oundle Rd (A 605) – ⊠ Peterborough.

**Swallow,** Peterborough Business Park, Lynch Wood, PE2 6GB, (opposite East of Englan⁕
Showground) ℘ (01733) 371111, Fax (01733) 236725, 𝗙⅄, ☎, ◻, 🌲, – ⇔ rm, ⊟ rest, ⊡ ☎
₠ ℗ – 🛦 350. 🌑❾ 🆎 ⓪ 𝘝𝘐𝘚𝘈
AX ☎
**Emperor :** **Meals** (closed Sunday) 21.00 **st.** ⅃ 7.25 – **Laurels :** **Meals** 15.00/17.50 s⁕
and a la carte ⅃ 7.25 – **161 rm** ⊇ 120.00/140.00 **st.**, 2 suites – SB.

**Travelodge,** Great North Rd, PE7 3UR, A 1 (southbound carriageway) ℘ (01733) 231109
Fax (01733) 231109, Reservations (Freephone) 0800 850950 – ⇔ rm, ⊡ ₠ ℗. 🌑❾ 🆎 ⓪
𝘝𝘐𝘚𝘈 𝙅𝘤𝘉. ⅀
AX ⅀
**Meals** (grill rest.) – **32 rm** 39.95/59.95 **t.**

**at Wansford** West : 8 ½ m. by A 47 – ⊠ Peterborough.

**Haycock,** PE8 6JA, ℘ (01780) 782223, Fax (01780) 783031, �, « Part 17C coaching
inn », 🌲, – ⇔ rm, ⊡ ☎ ₠ ℗ – 🛦 150. 🌑❾ 🆎 ⓪ 𝘝𝘐𝘚𝘈
AX ⅀
**Meals** (bar lunch)/dinner 22.95 **st.** and a la carte ⅃ 8.00 – **50 rm** ⊇ 85.00/140.00 **st.** – SB.

**Stoneacre** ⅀ without rest., Elton Rd, PE8 6JT, South : ½ m. on unmarked drive
℘ (01780) 783283, Fax (01780) 783283, 🌲 – ⇔ ⊡ ℗. ⅀
AX ⅀
**5 rm** ⊇ 30.00/50.00 **s.**

🌑 ATS Wareley Rd (off George St.) ℘ (01733) 567112/3

---

**PETERSTOW** Herefordshire 𝟰𝟬𝟯 𝟰𝟬𝟰 M 28 – see Ross-on-Wye.

---

**PETWORTH** W. Sussex 𝟰𝟬𝟰 S 31 Great Britain G. – pop. 2 156.
**See :** Petworth House★★ AC.
🛅 Osiers Farm ℘ (01798) 344097.
London 54 – Brighton 31 – Portsmouth 33.

**Horse Guards Inn** with rm, Upperton Rd, Tillington, GU28 9AF, West : 1 ½ m. by A 272
℘ (01798) 342332, Fax (01798) 344351, 🌲 – ⇔ rm, ⊡. 🌑❾ 🆎 𝘝𝘐𝘚𝘈. ⅀
closed 25 December – **Meals** (booking essential) a la carte 17.50/24.75 **t.** ⅃ 8.95 – **3 rm**
⊇ 68.00 **t.**

**at Sutton** South : 5 m. by A 283 – ⊠ Pulborough.

**White Horse Inn** with rm, The Street, RH20 1PS, ℘ (01798) 869221, Fax (01798) 869291,
🌲 – ⊡ ☎ ₠ ℗. 🌑❾ 🆎 𝘝𝘐𝘚𝘈. ⅀
**Meals** a la carte 13.60/23.00 **t.** ⅃ 6.85 – **6 rm** ⊇ 48.00/68.00 **st.**

**at Halfway Bridge** West : 3 m. on A 272 – ⊠ Petworth.

**The Halfway Bridge Inn,** GU28 9BP, ℘ (01798) 861281, « 17C coaching inn », 🌲 – ℗.
🌑❾ 𝘝𝘐𝘚𝘈. ⅀
closed 25 December – **Meals** (closed Sunday dinner in winter) a la carte 13.45/24.00 **t.**
⅃ 7.95.

**EWSEY** *Wilts.* 408 404 O 29 – *pop. 2 831.*
*London 88 – Bristol 53 – Salisbury 21 – Swindon 19.*

XXX **London House,** Market Pl., SN9 5AB, ℰ (01672) 564775, *Fax (01672) 564785* – ⇌. 🐦 🕮 ⓪ 🆅🆂🅰
*closed Monday lunch, Sunday, 17 to 19 September, 25 to 28 December and Bank Holidays* –
**Meals** 21.00 **t.** and a la carte ₪ 6.50.

🏠 **Seven Stars,** Bottlesford, SN9 6LU, West : 3 ½ m. by Wilcot Rd off Woodborough rd
ℰ (01672) 851325, *Fax (01672) 851583*, « 18C thatched inn », 🍴 – ⓟ. 🐦 🆅🆂🅰 🇯🇨🇧
*closed Sunday dinner, Monday except lunch Bank Holidays and 2 weeks February* – **Meals** -
French - a la carte 15.85/29.45 **t.** ₪ 5.95.

---

**PICKERING** *N. Yorks.* 402 R 21 – *pop. 5 914.*
🖪 *Eastgate Car Park, YO18 7DU* ℰ (01751) 473791.
*London 237 – Middlesbrough 43 – Scarborough 19 – York 25.*

🏨 **Forest and Vale,** Malton Rd, YO18 7DL, ℰ (01751) 472722, *Fax (01751) 472972,* 🍴 – ⇌
📺 ☎ ⓟ – 🔬 40. 🐦 🕮 🆅🆂🅰
**Meals** 9.95/15.50 **t.** ₪ 6.95 – **18 rm** ⊊ 56.00/78.00 **t.** – SB.

🏠 **White Swan,** Market Pl., YO18 7AA, ℰ (01751) 472288, *Fax (01751) 475554* – ⇌ 📺 ☎
ⓟ. 🐦 🕮 🆅🆂🅰
**Meals** a la carte 16.30/21.90 **t.** ₪ 5.25 – **11 rm** ⊊ 40.00/80.00 **t.,** 1 suite – SB.

🏠 **Burgate House,** 17 Burgate, YO18 7AU, ℰ (01751) 473463, *Fax (01751) 473463,* « Part
17C » – ⇌ rest, 📺 ☎ 🕻 ⓟ. 🐦 🆅🆂🅰
*closed 1 week Christmas* – **Meals** (booking essential) 12.00/15.00 **t.** ₪ 4.50 – **6 rm** ⊊ 45.00/
60.00 **t.** – SB.

⌂ **Bramwood,** 19 Hallgarth, YO18 7AW, ℰ (01751) 474066, 🍴 – ⇌ ⓟ. 🐦. 🛇
*closed 24 to 26 December* – **Meals** (by arrangement) 12.50 **s.** – **6 rm** ⊊ 30.00/46.00 **s.**

**at Middleton** *Northwest : 1½ m. on A 170* – ⊠ *Pickering.*

🏠 **Cottage Leas** ⌂, Nova Lane, YO18 8PN, North : 1 m. via Church Lane ℰ (01751) 472129,
*Fax (01751) 474930,* ≤, 🍴 – 📺 ☎ ⓟ. 🐦 🆅🆂🅰 🇯🇨🇧
*closed 25 and 26 December* – **Meals** (lunch by arrangement) a la carte 15.25/24.40 **t.** ₪ 6.50
– **12 rm** ⊊ 42.00/74.00 **t.** – SB.

⌂ **Sunnyside** without rest., Carr Lane, YO18 8PD, ℰ (01751) 476104, *Fax (01751) 476104,*
🍴 – ⇌ 📺. 🐦 🆅🆂🅰
*closed December and January* – **3 rm** ⊊ 28.00/44.00 – SB.

**at Sinnington** *Northwest : 4 m. by A 170* – ⊠ *York.*

🏠 **Fox and Hounds,** Main St., YO62 6SQ, ℰ (01751) 431577, *Fax (01751) 432791,* 🍴 – ⇌
📺 ☎ ⓟ. 🐦 🕮 🆅🆂🅰 🇯🇨🇧
**Meals** a la carte 13.75/20.85 **t.** ₪ 8.40 – **10 rm** ⊊ 40.00/65.00 **t.**

**at Cropton** *Northwest : 4 ¾ m. by A 170* – ⊠ *Pickering.*

⌂ **Burr Bank** ⌂, YO18 8HL, North : ¼ m. ℰ (01751) 417777, *Fax (01751) 417789,* 🍴, park –
⇌ 📺 ⓟ. 🛇
**Meals** (by arrangement) 14.00 **st.** ₪ 4.00 – **3 rm** ⊊ 24.00/48.00 **st.**

---

**PICKHILL** *N. Yorks.* 402 P 21 – *pop. 412* – ⊠ *Thirsk.*
*London 229 – Leeds 41 – Middlesbrough 30 – York 34.*

🏠 **Nags Head Country Inn,** YO7 4JG, ℰ (01845) 567391, *Fax (01845) 567212,* 🍴 – 📺 ☎
ⓟ – 🔬 30. 🐦 🆅🆂🅰 🇯🇨🇧. 🛇
*closed 25 December* – **Meals** 12.00/17.00 **st.** and a la carte ₪ 4.25 – **15 rm** ⊊ 40.00/
55.00 **st.** – SB.

---

**PILLING** *Lancs.* 402 L 22 – *pop. 2 204* – ⊠ *Preston.*
*London 243 – Blackpool 11 – Burnley 43 – Manchester 49.*

🏠 **Springfield House** ⌂, Wheel Lane, PR3 6HL, ℰ (01253) 790301, *Fax (01253) 790907,*
🍴 – ⇌ rest, 📺 ☎ ⓟ. 🐦 🆅🆂🅰 🇯🇨🇧
**Meals** 9.50/10.95 **t.** ₪ 4.95 – **8 rm** ⊊ 35.00/60.00 **t.** – SB.

---

**PIMPERNE** *Dorset* 403 404 N 31 – *see Blandford Forum.*

---

| Die Preise | Einzelheiten über die in diesem Reiseführer angegebenen Preise finden Sie in der Einleitung. |
|---|---|

## PLUCKLEY Kent 404 W 30 – pop. 883.

London 53 – Folkestone 25 – Maidstone 18.

**Elvey Farm Country H.** ⤫, TN27 0SU, West : 2 m. by Smarden rd and Marley Farm re off Mundy Bois rd ℘ (01233) 840442, Fax (01233) 840726, ≤, « Converted oast house an barn », ⊶ – 🆅 **P**. **MO VISA JCB**
**Meals** (booking essential) (residents only) (dinner only) 16.50 t. – **9 rm** ⊇ 55.00/65.00 t.

**Dering Arms,** Station Rd, TN27 0RR, South : 1½ m. on Bethersden rd ℘ (01233) 84037 Fax (01233) 840498, « Mid 19C former hunting lodge », ⊶ – **P**. **MO AE VISA**
closed Sunday dinner, Monday and 26 to 28 December – **Meals** a la carte 13.15/25.85 \
§ 5.45.

---

## PLUMFORD Kent – see Faversham.

---

## PLUMTREE Notts. – see Nottingham.

---

## PLYMOUTH 403 H 32 The West Country G. – pop. 245 295.

See : Town★ – Smeaton's Tower (≤★★) AC BZ **A** – Plymouth Dome★ AC BZ – Royal Citade (ramparts ≤★★) AC BZ – City Museum and Art Gallery★ BZ **M**.

Env. : – Saltram House★★ AC, E : 3½ m. BY **A** – Tamar River★★ – Anthony House★ AC, W 5 m. by A 374 – Mount Edgcumbe (≤★) AC, SW : 2 m. by passenger ferry from Stone house AZ.

Exc. : NE : Dartmoor National Park★★ – Buckland Abbey★★ AC, N : 7½ m. by A 386 ABY.

🏌 Staddon Heights, Plymstock ℘ (01752) 402475 – 🏌 Elfordleigh Hotel G & C.C., Colebroo Plympton ℘ (01752) 336428.

Tamar Bridge (toll) AY.

✈ Plymouth City (Roborough) Airport : ℘ (01752) 772752, N : 3½ m. by A 386 ABY.

⛴ to France (Roscoff) (Brittany Ferries) 1-3 daily (4 h 30 mn) night – to Spain (Santander (Brittany Ferries) 2 weekly (24 h).

🛈 Island House, 9 The Barbican, PL1 2LS ℘ (01752) 264849.

London 242 – Bristol 124 – Southampton 161.

Plans on following pages

**Plymouth Hoe Moat House,** Armada Way, PL1 2HJ, ℘ (01752) 639988 Fax (01752) 673816, ≤ city and Plymouth Sound, ₤₅, ≘s, 🔲 – 📶 ✤, 🗏 rest, 🆅 ☎ ₺ ⟨⟩
– 🔏 400. **MO AE O VISA**. ⋇
BZ 
**Blue Riband :** **Meals** (closed Saturday lunch) 13.95/18.95 **st.** and a la carte § 5.75 – ⊇ 9.9
– **206 rm** 110.00/130.00 **st.** – SB.

**Copthorne Plymouth,** Armada Centre, Armada Way, PL1 1AR, (via Western Approach southbound) ℘ (01752) 224161, Fax (01752) 670688, ₤₅, 🔲 – 📶, ✤ rm, 🗏 rest, 🆅 ☎ ₺ **P** – 🔏 150. **MO AE O VISA JCB**
BZ e
**Meals** (dinner only) 18.50 **st.** and a la carte § 4.95 – **Bentley's :** **Meals** 18.50 **st.** (din ner) and a la carte 14.00/23.00 **st.** § 4.95 – ⊇ 10.95 – **135 rm** 105.00/190.00 **st.** – SB.

**The Duke of Cornwall,** Millbay Rd, PL1 3LG, ℘ (01752) 266256, Fax (01752) 600062 –
📶, ✤ rm, 🆅 ☎ **P** – 🔏 300. **MO AE O VISA**
AZ c
**Meals** (bar lunch Monday to Saturday)/dinner 21.95 **st.** § 6.50 – **67 rm** ⊇ 74.50/89.50 **st.** 5 suites.

**Grand,** Elliot St., The Hoe, PL1 2PT, ℘ (01752) 661195, Fax (01752) 600653, ≤ – 📶 ✤ 🆅
☎ **P** – 🔏 70. **MO AE VISA**
BZ a
**Meals** (residents only Saturday lunch) (dancing Saturday evening) 10.50/18.50 **st.** and din ner a la carte § 8.75 – **77 rm** ⊇ 79.00/139.00 **st.**

**Forte Posthouse Plymouth,** Cliff Rd, The Hoe, PL1 3DL, ℘ (01752) 662828, Fax (01752) 660974, ≤ Plymouth Sound, 🔲 – 📶, ✤ rm, 🆅 ☎ **P** – 🔏 100. **MO AE O VISA JCB**
AZ v
**Meals** (closed Monday lunch) a la carte 19.00/23.00 **t.** § 6.00 – ⊇ 8.95 – **106 rm** 75.00 **t.** – SB.

**New Continental,** Millbay Rd, PL1 3LD, ℘ (01752) 220782, Fax (01752) 227013, ₤₅, ≘s 🔲 – 📶, ✤ rm, 🆅 ☎ **P** – 🔏 400. **MO AE O VISA**
AZ s
closed 24 December-4 January – **Meals** (bar lunch Saturday and Bank Holidays) 9.95/16.25 **t.** and a la carte § 5.50 – **99 rm** ⊇ 72.00/120.00 – SB.

**Travel Inn,** 1 Lockyers Quay, Coxside, PL4 0DX, ℘ (01752) 254180, Fax (01752) 663872, 🍴
– ✤ rm, 🗏 rest, 🆅 ₺ **P** – 🔏 30. **MO AE O VISA**. ⋇
BZ c
**Meals** (grill rest.) – **40 rm** 38.00 **t.**

**Travel Inn,** 300 Plymouth Rd, Crabtree, PL3 6RW, ℘ (01752) 600660 – ✤ rm, 🆅 ₺ **P** –
🔏 30. **MO AE O VISA**. ⋇
BY e
**Meals** (grill rest.) – **40 rm** 38.00 **t.**

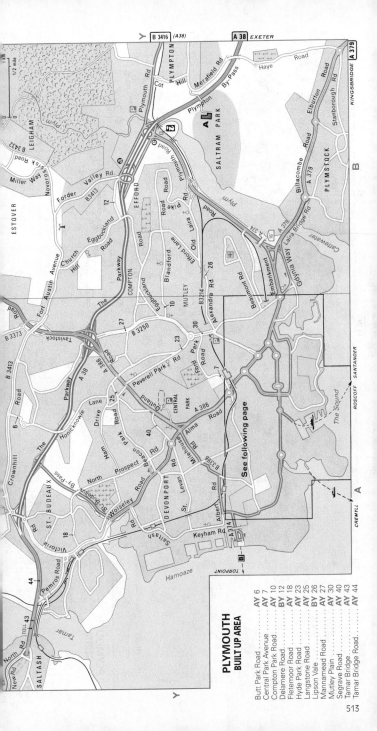

## PLYMOUTH
### BUILT UP AREA

513

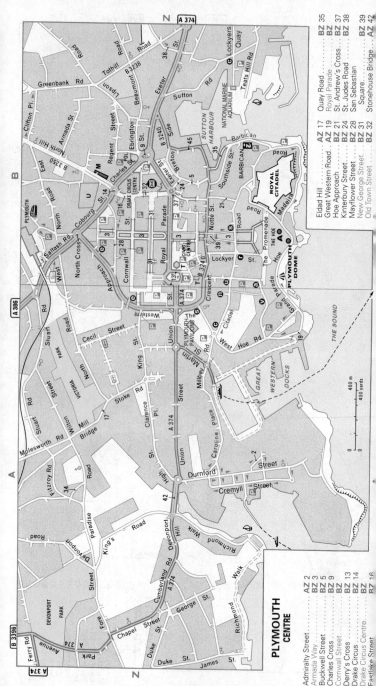

# PLYMOUTH
## CENTRE

514

🏠 **Campanile,** Longbridge Rd, Marsh Mills, PL6 8LD, ℰ (01752) 601087, *Fax (01752) 223213*
– ⇔ rm, 📺 ☎ ﻼ ﻩ – 🔏 30. 🐠🗚 ⑩ 𝘝𝘐𝘚𝘈        BY a
**Meals** 10.85 st. and a la carte – ⌷ 4.50 – **50 rm** 36.50 st.

🏠 **Bowling Green** without rest., 9-10 Osborne Pl., Lockyer St., The Hoe, PL1 2PU,
ℰ (01752) 209090, *Fax (01752) 209092* – 📺 ☎. 🐠🗚 ⑩ 𝘝𝘐𝘚𝘈        BZ r
*closed 24 to 26 December* – **12 rm** ⌷ 36.00/50.00 st.

🏠 **Berkeley's of St. James** without rest., 4 St. James Place East, The Hoe, PL1 3AS,
ℰ (01752) 221654, *Fax (01752) 221654* – ⇔ 📺. 🐠🗚 𝘝𝘐𝘚𝘈. ⅏        AZ n
**5 rm** ⌷ 25.00/50.00.

🏠 **Athenaeum Lodge** without rest., 4 Athenaeum St., The Hoe, PL1 2RQ,
ℰ (01752) 665005 – ⇔ 📺 ﻼ. 🐠 𝘝𝘐𝘚𝘈. ⅏        BZ u
*closed 24 December-2 January* – **9 rm** ⌷ 22.00/40.00 st.

✕ **Chez Nous** (Marchal), 13 Frankfort Gate, PL1 1QA, ℰ (01752) 266793, *Fax (01752) 266793*
🕄 – 🐠🗚 ⑩ 𝘝𝘐𝘚𝘈        AZ e
*closed Saturday lunch, Sunday, Monday, 3 weeks February, 3 weeks September and Bank
Holidays* – **Meals** - French - 30.50 t. ﹩ 9.00
**Spec.** Coquilles St. Jacques au gingembre. La petite salade de cailles aux raisin. Flétan grillé
aux câpres.

**at Plympton** *Northeast : 5 m. by A 374 on B 3416* – BY – ✉ *Plymouth.*

🏛 **Boringdon Hall** ♨, Boringdon Hill, PL7 4DP, North: 1 ½ m. by Glen Rd
ℰ (01752) 344455, *Fax (01752) 346578*, « Part 16C manor », ⓩ, 🔲, park, ⅏ – ⇔ 📺 ☎
ﻼ – 🔏 150. 🐠🗚 𝘝𝘐𝘚𝘈 🗚𝘊𝘉. ⅏
*The Gallery :* **Meals** (bar lunch Saturday) (carving lunch Sunday) 15.00/18.95 st.
and a la carte ﹩ 6.65 – **40 rm** ⌷ 75.00/95.00 st. – SB.

🏠 **The Barn** ♨, Hemerdon, PL7 5BU, Northeast : 2 ½ m. by Glen Rd following signs for
Newnham industrial estate then Hemerdon, turning left beside telephone box after Miners
Arms in Hemerdon ℰ (01752) 347016, *Fax (01752) 335670*, « Converted 19C barn », 🌱 –
⇔ ﻼ. ⅏
*closed Christmas and New Year* – **Meals** (by arrangement) (communal dining) 19.50 ﹩ 5.60 –
**3 rm** ⌷ 30.00/64.00.

🏠 **Windwhistle Farm** ♨, Hemerdon, PL7 5BU, Northeast : 2 ½ m. by Glen Rd following
signs for Newnham industrial estate then Hemerdon, turning left beside telephone box
after Miners Arms in Hemerdon ℰ (01752) 340600, *Fax (01752) 340600*, 🌱 – ⇔ 📺 ﻼ. ⅏
*closed Christmas and New Year* – **Meals** (by arrangement) (communal dining) 15.00 s. –
**3 rm** ⌷ 23.00/46.00.

**at Yealmpton** *East : 8 m. by A 374 on A 379* – BY – ✉ *Plymouth.*

🏛 **Kitley** ♨, The Kitley Estate, PL8 2NW, West : ½ m. on A 379 ℰ (01752) 881555,
*Fax (01752) 881667*, ⩽, « 17C mansion », 🌱, park – 📺 ☎ ﻼ – 🔏 150. 🐠🗚 𝘝𝘐𝘚𝘈
**Meals** (bar lunch Monday to Saturday)/dinner 22.50 t. and a la carte ﹩ 7.00 – **10 rm**
⌷ 89.50/135.00 st., 1 suite.

🆎 ATS Strode Rd, Newnham Ind. Est., Plympton ℰ (01752) 331001

---

**PLYMPTON** *Plymouth* 𝟺𝟶𝟹 H 32 – *see Plymouth.*

---

**PODIMORE** *Somerset* – *see Yeovil.*

---

**POLPERRO** *Cornwall* 𝟺𝟶𝟹 G 33 *The West Country G.* – ✉ *Looe.*
See : *Village★*.
*London 271 – Plymouth 28.*

🏠 **Trenderway Farm** ♨ without rest., Pelynt, PL13 2LY, Northeast : 2 m. by A 387
ℰ (01503) 272214, *Fax (01503) 272991*, ⩽, « 16C farmhouse, working farm », 🌱, park –
⇔ 📺 ﻼ. ⅏
*closed Christmas and New Year* – **4 rm** ⌷ 45.00/70.00 st.

✕ **Kitchen,** The Coombes, PL13 2RQ, ℰ (01503) 272780 – ⇔. 🐠 𝘝𝘐𝘚𝘈
*Easter-October* – **Meals** *(closed Sunday)* (dinner only) a la carte 18.00/23.00 st. ﹩ 6.50.

---

**PONTEFRACT** *N. Yorks.* 𝟺𝟶𝟸 Q 22.
*London 194 – Leeds 16 – Manchester 53 – Nottingham 64 – Sheffield 29 – York 25.*

🏠 **Travel Inn,** Knottingley Rd, Knottingley, WF11 0BU, Northeast : 2 ½ m. by A 645
ℰ (01977) 607946, *Fax (01977) 607954* – ⇔ rm, 🍽 rest, 📺 ﻼ ﻩ. 🐠🗚 ⑩ 𝘝𝘐𝘚𝘈
**Meals** (grill rest.) – **40 rm** 38.00 t.

**POOLE** **403 404** O 31 *The West Country G. –* pop. 133 050.

See : *Town★ (Waterfront* **M1** *, Scaplen's Court* **M2** *).*

Env. : *Compton Acres★★, (English Garden ≼★★★) AC, SE : 3 m. by B 3369* **BX** *(on Bourne* mouth town plan) – *Brownsea Island★ (Baden-Powell Stone ≼★★) AC, by boat from Poo* Quay or Sandbanks **BX** *(on Bournemouth town plan).*

▟ₙ *Parkstone, Links Rd* ℰ *(01202) 707138 –* ▟ₙ *Bulbury Woods, Lytchett Matravers* ℰ *(0192* 459574.

⛴ *to France (Cherbourg) (Brittany Ferries Truckline) 1-2 daily (4 h 15 mn) day (5 h 45 m* night – *to France (St. Malo) (Brittany Ferries) (winter only) 4 weekly (8 h) – to France (S* Malo) via Jersey (St. Helier) (Condor Ferries Ltd) daily – *to Guernsey (St. Peter Port) an* Jersey (St. Helier) (Condor Ferries Ltd).

🛈 *The Quay, BH15 1HE* ℰ *(01202) 673322 – Dolphin Shopping Centre, BH15 1SZ.*

*London 116 – Bournemouth 4 – Dorchester 23 – Weymouth 28.*

Plan of Built up Area : see Bournemouth

**POOLE**

| | |
|---|---|
| Church Street | 3 |
| Dolphin Shopping Centre | |
| Emerson Road | 4 |

| | |
|---|---|
| Falkland Sq. | 6 |
| Fishermans Rd. | 7 |
| Furnell Rd. | 8 |
| High Street | |
| Holes Bay Rd | 10 |
| Labrador Drive | 12 |
| Longfleet Rd. | 13 |

| | |
|---|---|
| Market St. | 1 |
| New Orchard | 1 |
| New Street | 1 |
| Serpentine Rd | 1 |
| Thames St. | 1 |
| Towngate Bridge | 2 |
| Westons Lane | 2 |

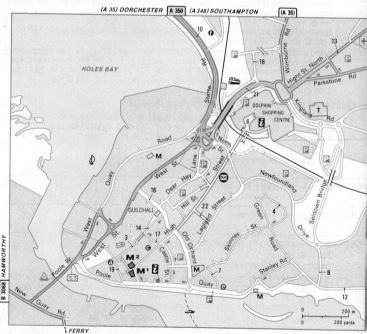

▟▟▟ **Haven,** Banks Rd, Sandbanks, BH13 7QL, Southeast : 4 ¼ m. on B 3369 ℰ (01202) 707333 Fax (01202) 708796, ≼ Ferry, Old Harry Rocks and Poole Bay, ᏝᏮ, ≅≊, ⌇, 🔲, ※, squash – ⌸ 🔟 ☎ 🅿 – 🔥 160. 🐽 ᴬᴱ ① 𝘝𝘐𝘚𝘈, ⅏ on Bournemouth town plan **BX** ◖ Meals 15.00/23.00 **t.** and dinner a la carte ⌗ 6.25 – **Brasserie :** Meals (lunch only) a la carte 20.00/31.00 **st.** ⌗ 6.25 – **92 rm** 🖵 79.00/245.00 **st.,** 2 suites – SB.

🏛 **Salterns,** 38 Salterns Way, Lilliput, BH14 8JR, ℰ (01202) 707321, *Fax (01202) 707488*, ≤, « Harbourside setting », ℛ – ⇚ rm, 🗏 rest, 🗐 ☎ 🅿 – 🔏 80. 🕮 🕮 🕮 *VISA*. ⟨⟨
*Waterside :* Meals 15.50/25.00 **t.** and a la carte ↥ 6.50 – *Shellies :* Meals a la carte 14.00/
21.00 **t.** ↥ 7.50 – 🖵 10.00 – **20 rm** 86.00/106.00 **t.** – SB.

on Bournemouth town plan **BX** **e**

🏛 **Mansion House,** 7-11 Thames St., BH15 1JN, off Poole Quay ℰ (01202) 685666, *Fax (01202) 665709*, « 18C town house » – 🗏 rest, 🗐 ☎ 🅿 – 🔏 40. 🕮 🕮 🕮 *VISA* 🕮
⟨⟨
**a**
*Benjamin's :* Meals *(closed Saturday lunch and Sunday dinner and restricted opening Bank Holidays)* 16.50 **t.** (lunch) and dinner a la carte 21.70/23.75 **t.** ↥ 6.50 – *JJ's Bistro :* Meals *(closed Sunday lunch and Bank Holiday Monday)* (residents only) 13.85 **t.** (dinner) and lunch a la carte 10.25/18.00 **t.** ↥ 4.50 – **28 rm** 🖵 85.00/115.00 **st.** – SB.

🏛 **Thistle Quay,** The Quay, BH15 1HD, ℰ (01202) 666800, *Fax (01202) 684470*, ≤ – 🛗,
⇚ rm, 🗐 ☎ 🅿 – 🔏 60. 🕮 🕮 🕮 *VISA* 🕮. ⟨⟨
**e**
*Octagon :* Meals 18.00/23.00 **t.** and a la carte ↥ 10.00 – 🖵 11.50 – **68 rm** 104.00/120.00 **t.**
– SB.

🏛 **Arndale Court,** 62-66 Wimborne Rd, BH15 2BY, ℰ (01202) 683746, *Fax (01202) 668838* –
🗐 ☎ 🅿 – 🔏 30. 🕮 🕮 🕮 *VISA*. ⟨⟨         on Bournemouth town plan **ABX** **r**
Meals (in bar Monday to Saturday lunch and Sunday dinner)/dinner a la carte 15.20/
20.35 **t.** ↥ 4.50 – **32 rm** 🖵 61.00/70.00 **st.**

🏛 **Travel Inn,** Holesbay Rd, BH15 2BD, ℰ (01202) 669944, *Fax (01202) 669954* – ⇚ rm, 🗐
🕭 🅿. 🕮 🕮 🕮 *VISA*. ⟨⟨
**r**
Meals (grill rest.) – **40 rm** 38.00 **t.**

✗ **John B's,** 20 High St., Old Town, BH15 1BP, ℰ (01202) 672440, *Fax (01202) 672440* – 🕮 🕮
🕮 *VISA*
**c**
*closed Saturday lunch and Sunday except Bank Holidays* – Meals a la carte 21.20/27.40 **t.**
↥ 6.50.

✗ **Isabel's,** 32 Station Rd, Lower Parkstone, BH14 8UD, ℰ (01202) 747885 – 🕮 🕮 🕮 *VISA*
*closed Sunday, Monday, 26 December and 1 January* – Meals (dinner only) 18.00 **t.**
and a la carte ↥ 6.50.           on Bournemouth town plan **BX** **a**

🅐 ATS 1 Fernside Rd ℰ (01202) 733301/733326

---

**POOLEY BRIDGE** *Cumbria* 🔢🔢 L 20 – *see Ullswater.*

---

**PORLOCK** *Somerset* 🔢 J 30 *The West Country G. – pop. 1 395 (inc. Oare) –* ✉ *Minehead.*
See : *Village★ – Porlock Hill (≤★★) – St. Dubricius Church★.*
Env. : *Dunkery Beacon★★★ (≤★★★), S : 5 ½ m. – Exmoor National Park★★ – Selworthy★
(≤★★, Church★), E : 2 m. by A 39 and minor rd – Luccombe★ (Church★), E : 3 m. by A 39 –
Culbone★ (St. Beuno), W : 3½ m. by B 3225, 1½ m. on foot – Doone Valley★, W : 6 m. by
A 39, access from Oare on foot.*
*London 190 – Bristol 67 – Exeter 46 – Taunton 28.*

🏛 **Oaks,** TA24 8ES, ℰ (01643) 862265, *Fax (01643) 862265*, ≤ Porlock Bay, ℛ – ⇚ 🗐 ☎ 🅿.
🕮 *VISA*
*mid March-October* – Meals (booking essential to non-residents) (dinner only) 26.00 **st.**
↥ 5.00 – **9 rm** 🖵 55.00/95.00 **st.** – SB.

⌂ **Bales Mead** ⟨⟨ *without rest.,* West Porlock, TA24 8NX, Northwest : 1 m. on B 3225
ℰ (01643) 862565, ≤, ℛ – ⇚ 🗐 🅿. ⟨⟨
*closed Christmas and New Year* – **3 rm** 🖵 48.00/58.00 **st.**

**at Porlock Weir** *Northwest : 1½ m. –* ✉ *Minehead.*

🏛 **Anchor and Ship Inn,** TA24 8PB, ℰ (01643) 862753, *Fax (01643) 862843*, ≤, ℛ – 🗐 ☎
🕭 🅿. 🕮 *VISA*
*closed January* – Meals (bar lunch)/dinner 20.75 **st.** and a la carte ↥ 8.75 – **20 rm** 🖵 (dinner included) 97.50/177.00 **st.** – SB.

---

**PORLOCK WEIR** *Somerset* 🔢 J 30 – *see Porlock.*

---

**PORT ERIN** *Isle of Man* 🔢 F 21 – *see Man (Isle of).*

---

**PORTHLEVEN** *Cornwall* 🔢 E 33 – *see Helston.*

---

**PORTINSCALE** *Cumbria – see Keswick.*

## PORT ISAAC *Cornwall* 408 F 32 *The West Country G..*

Env. : *St. Endellion (church★★), S : 2 ½ m. by B 3267 on B 3314 – St. Kew★ (church★, SE : 3 m. by B 3267, B 3314 and minor roads.*
Exc. : – *Pencarrow★, SE : 12 m. by B 3267, B 3314 and A 389.*
*London 266 – Newquay 24 – Tintagel 14 – Truro 32.*

🏛 **Port Gaverne,** Port Gaverne, PL29 3SQ, South : ½ m. ℘ (01208) 880244, *Fax* (01208) 880151, « Retaining 17C features » – ⚡ rest, 📺 ☎ ℗, 💳 AE ⓞ VISA JCB, closed 9 January-19 February – **Meals** (bar lunch)/dinner a la carte 19.50/28.20 **t.** ¼ 4.70 – **17 rm** � (dinner included) 61.00/136.00 **t.** – SB.

🏛 **Castle Rock,** 4 New Rd, PL29 3SB, ℘ (01208) 880300, *Fax* (01208) 880219, ≤ Port Isaac Bay and Tintagel Head – ⚡ rest, 📺 ☎ ℗, 💳 AE VISA, closed January – **Meals** (bar lunch)/dinner 16.00 **t.** and a la carte ¼ 4.95 – **17 rm** � 32.00/ 74.00 **t.** – SB.

🏠 **Archer Farm** 🌿 without rest., Trewetha, PL29 3RU, Southeast : ½ m. by B 3267, ℘ (01208) 880522, ≤, 🛖 – ℗ ☎ ℗, *April-October* – **5 rm** ⊫ 30.00/65.00.

🏨 **Slipway** with rm, Harbour Front, PL29 3RH, ℘ (01208) 880264, *Fax* (01208) 880264, �️ « Part 16C inn » – ℗, 💳 AE ⓞ VISA JCB, 🌿 closed 4 January-12 February – **Meals** (restricted opening in winter) (bar lunch)/dinner a la carte 16.20/24.75 **t.** ¼ 4.95 – **12 rm** ⊫ 28.00/88.00 **t.** – SB.

## PORTLOE *Cornwall* 408 F 33 – ✉ *Truro.*

*London 296 – St. Austell 15 – Truro 15.*

🏛 **Lugger,** TR2 5RD, ℘ (01872) 501322, *Fax* (01872) 501691, ≤, ⚡, ⚡ rest, 📺 ☎ ℗, 💳 AE ⓞ VISA JCB, 🌿 *9 March-October* – **Meals** (bar lunch Monday to Saturday)/dinner 25.00 **t.** – **19 rm** ⊫ (dinner included) 75.00/150.00 **t.** – SB.

## PORTREATH *Cornwall* 408 E 33 – *pop. 1 251.*

*London 309 – Falmouth 20 – Penzance 23 – Truro 14.*

XX **Tabb's,** Tregea Terr., TR16 4LD, ℘ (01209) 842488, *Fax* (01209) 842488 – 💳 VISA *closed Tuesday, 2 weeks January and 2 weeks November* – **Meals** (dinner only and Sunday lunch)/dinner 14.50 **t.** and a la carte ¼ 5.75.

## PORTSCATHO *Cornwall* 408 F 33 *The West Country G.* – ✉ *Truro.*

Env. : *St. Just-in-Roseland Church★★, W : 4 m. by A 3078 – St. Anthony-in-Roseland (≤★★, S : 3½ m.*
*London 298 – Plymouth 55 – Truro 16.*

🏛 **Roseland House** 🌿, Rosevine, TR2 5EW, North : 2 m. by A 3078 ℘ (01872) 580644, *Fax* (01872) 580801, ≤ Gerrans Bay, 🛖 – ⚡ 📺 ☎ ℗, 💳 AE VISA, 🌿 *restricted opening November-February* – **Meals** (booking essential) (bar lunch)/dinner 18.50 **t.** ¼ 7.00 – **10 rm** ⊫ (dinner included) 84.50/130.00 **t.** – SB.

🏛 **Gerrans Bay,** 12 Tregassick Rd, TR2 5ED, ℘ (01872) 580338, *Fax* (01872) 580250, ≤, 🛖 – ⚡ rest, 📺 ℗, 💳 AE ⓞ VISA, 🌿 *February-October* – **Meals** (bar lunch Monday to Saturday)/dinner 19.00 **st.** – **14 rm** ⊫ (dinner included) 53.00/106.00 **st.** – SB.

See : City★ – *Naval Portsmouth BY : H.M.S. Victory*★★★ *AC, The Mary Rose*★★, *Royal Naval Museum*★★ *AC* – *Old Portsmouth*★ BYZ : *The Point* (≤★★) - *St. Thomas Cathedral*★ – *Southsea (Castle*★ *AC)* AZ – *Royal Marines Museum, Eastney*★ *AC*, AZ M1.

Env. : *Portchester Castle*★ *AC, NW : 5½ m. by A 3 and A 27 AY.*

🔼 *Great Salterns, Portsmouth Golf Centre, Burrfields Rd* 🔎 *(01705) 664549 AY –* 🔼 *Crookhorn Lane, Widley* 🔎 *(01705) 372210 –* 🔼 *Southwick Park, Pinsley Drive, Southwick* 🔎 *(01705) 380131.*

🚢 *to France (Cherbourg) (P & O European Ferries Ltd) 2 daily (5 h) day, (7 h) night – to France (Le Havre) (P & O European Ferries Ltd) 2-3 daily (2 h 45 mn) – to France (St. Malo) (Brittany Ferries) 2-3 daily (5 h 30 mn) day (7 h 30 mn) night – to the Isle of Wight (Fishbourne) (Wightlink Ltd) frequent services daily (35 mn) – to Spain (Santander) (Brittany Ferries) winter only (24 h) – to Spain (Bilbao) (P & O European Ferries Ltd) 1-2 weekly (37 h).*

🚢 *to the Isle of Wight (Ryde) (Wightlink Ltd) frequent services daily (15 mn) – from Southsea to the Isle of Wight (Ryde) (Hovertravel Ltd) frequent services daily (10 mn).*

🅱 *The Hard, PO1 3QJ* 🔎 *(01705) 826722 – Clarence Esplanade, PO5 3ST* 🔎 *(01705) 832464 (summer only) – Terminal Building, Portsmouth Ferryport* 🔎 *(01705) 838635 – 102 Commercial Rd, PO1 1EJ* 🔎 *(01705) 838382.*

*London 78 – Brighton 48 – Salisbury 44 – Southampton 21.*

Plans on following pages

🏨 **Hilton National,** Eastern Rd, Farlington, PO6 1UN, Northeast : 5 m. on A 2030 🔎 (01705) 219111, *Fax (01705) 210762,* 🛁, 🚿, 🔲, 🎾 – ⇆ rm, 🔟 ☎ 🕭 🅟 – 🔬 230. 🔢 AZ Ⓞ 𝘝𝘐𝘚𝘈 𝙅𝘾𝘽. ⬚ AY c
**Meals** *(bar lunch Saturday)* 14.50/18.50 **st.** and dinner a la carte ⁜ 6.50 – ⊇ 11.50 – **118 rm** 95.00/105.00 **st.** – SB.

🏨 **Forte Posthouse Portsmouth,** Pembroke Rd, PO1 2TA, 🔎 (01705) 827651, *Fax (01705) 756715,* 🛁, 🚿, 🔲 – 🛗 ⇆ 🔟 ☎ 📞 🅟 – 🔬 250. 🔢 AZ Ⓞ 𝘝𝘐𝘚𝘈 𝙅𝘾𝘽 CZ o
**Meals** a la carte 16.00/24.95 **t.** ⁜ 7.50 – ⊇ 9.95 – **163 rm** 85.00/125.00 **t.** – SB.

🏨 **Innlodge,** Burrfields Rd, PO3 5HH, 🔎 (01705) 650510, *Fax (01705) 693458,* 🚗 – ⇆ rm, ▤ rest, 🔟 ☎ 🕭 🅟 – 🔬 150. 🔢 AZ Ⓞ 𝘝𝘐𝘚𝘈. ⬚ AY u
*Beiderbecks :* **Meals** *(closed Saturday lunch)* (grill rest.) a la carte 14.20/20.65 **t.** – ⊇ 7.00 – **73 rm** 50.00/60.00 **t.**

🏨 **Green Farm Toby,** Copnor Rd, Hilsea, PO3 5HS, 🔎 (01705) 654645, *Fax (01705) 626060 –* ⇆, ▤ rest, 🔟 ☎ 🕭 🅟 – 🔬 35. 🔢 AZ Ⓞ 𝘝𝘐𝘚𝘈. ⬚ AY e
**Meals** *(grill rest.)* a la carte 9.35/15.40 ⁜ 4.95 – ⊇ 5.50 – **30 rm** 49.50 **t.** – SB.

🏨 **Beaufort,** 71 Festing Rd, Southsea, PO4 0NQ, 🔎 (01705) 823707, *Fax (01705) 870270 –* ⇆ rm, 🔟 ☎ 🅟. 🔢 AZ Ⓞ 𝘝𝘐𝘚𝘈. ⬚ AZ n
**Meals** *(dinner only)* 14.95 **st.** and a la carte ⁜ 4.50 – **20 rm** ⊇ 50.00/75.00 **st.** – SB.

🏨 **Seacrest,** 11-12 South Par., Southsea, PO5 2JB, 🔎 (01705) 733192, *Fax (01705) 832523,* ≤ – 🛗 ⇆ 🔟 ☎ 🅟. 🔢 𝘝𝘐𝘚𝘈 AZ e
**Meals** *(residents only) (dinner only)* 14.95 **st.** ⁜ 4.50 – **27 rm** ⊇ 48.00/75.00 **st.** – SB.

🏨 **Westfield Hall,** 65 Festing Rd, Southsea, PO4 0NQ, 🔎 (01705) 826971, *Fax (01705) 870200 –* 🔟 ☎ 🅟. 🔢 AZ Ⓞ 𝘝𝘐𝘚𝘈. ⬚ AZ a
*closed 24 December-4 January –* **Meals** *(dinner only)* 14.95 **t.** and a la carte ⁜ 4.95 – **27 rm** ⊇ 46.00/75.00 **t.**

🏠 **Fortitude Cottage** without rest., 51 Broad St., Old Portsmouth, PO1 2JD, 🔎 (01705) 823748, *Fax (01705) 823748 –* ⇆ 🔟. 🔢 AZ Ⓞ 𝘝𝘐𝘚𝘈 𝙅𝘾𝘽. ⬚ BY c
*closed 25 and 26 December –* **3 rm** ⊇ 40.00/46.00 **st.**

🏠 **Glencoe** without rest., 64 Whitwell Rd, Southsea, PO4 0QS, 🔎 (01705) 737413, *Fax (01705) 737413 –* ⇆ 🔟. 🔢 𝘝𝘐𝘚𝘈. ⬚ AZ u
**7 rm** ⊇ 18.50/38.00.

XX **Bistro Montparnasse,** 103 Palmerston Rd, Southsea, PO5 3PS, 🔎 (01705) 816754, *Fax (01705) 816754 –* 🔢 AZ 𝘝𝘐𝘚𝘈 CZ a
*closed Sunday, Monday and 25-26 December –* **Meals** *(dinner only)* 14.90 **t.** and a la carte ⁜ 6.95.

XX **Tang's,** 127 Elm Grove, Southsea, PO5 1LJ, 🔎 (01705) 826000, *Fax (01705) 838323 –* ▤. 🔢 AZ Ⓞ 𝘝𝘐𝘚𝘈 𝙅𝘾𝘽 AZ c
*closed Monday and lunch 25 December –* **Meals** - Chinese - *(dinner only)* 15.00 **st.** and a la carte.

X **Lemon Sole,** 123 High St., Old Portsmouth, PO1 2HW, 🔎 (01705) 811303, *Fax (01705) 862064 –* 🔢 AZ Ⓞ 𝘝𝘐𝘚𝘈 BY a
*closed 25 December and 1 January –* **Meals** - Seafood - 9.95 **t.** and a la carte ⁜ 4.15.

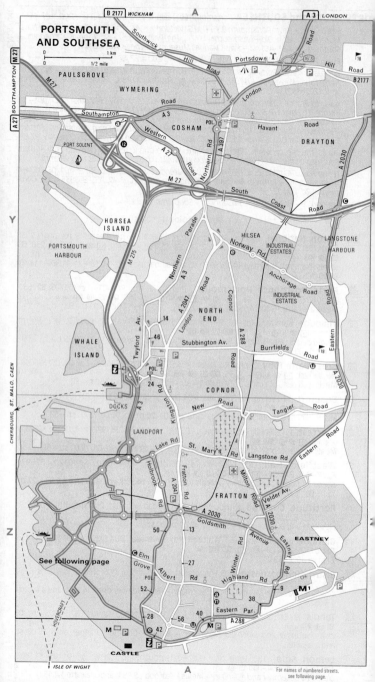

# PORTSMOUTH AND SOUTHSEA

For names of numbered streets,
see following page.

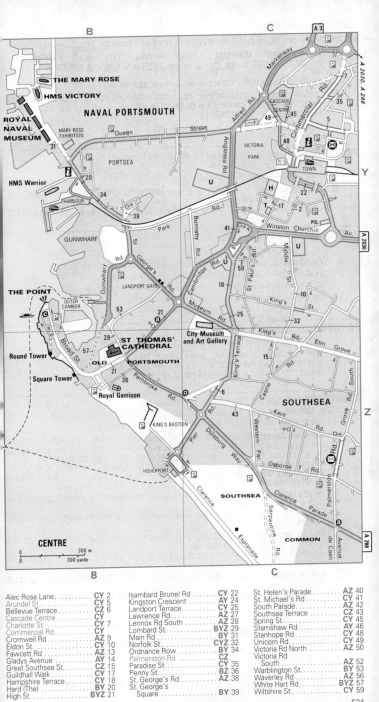

521

**at Cosham** North : 4½ m. by A 3 and M 275 on A 27 – ⊠ Portsmouth.

🏨🏨 **Portsmouth Marriott,** North Harbour, PO6 4SH, ℰ (01705) 383151, Fax (01705) 388701, ₤₅, ⌕, ⬚, ☐ – ⫮, ⇒ rm, ▤ ⚟ ☎ ℰ & 🅿 – 🔏 300. 🐠 🕮 ⓞ 𝘝𝘐𝘚𝘈 🗪 ⋙
Meals 19.95 st. ⫞ 8.25 – **172 rm** ⊇ 86.00/125.00 st. – SB.
AY

🏨 **Travel Inn,** 1 Southampton Rd, North Harbour, PO6 4SA, ℰ (01705) 321122, Fax (01705) 324895 – ⇒ rm, �📺 🅿 🅿. 🐠 🕮 ⓞ 𝘝𝘐𝘚𝘈. ⋙
Meals (grill rest.) – **64 rm** 38.00 t.
AY

🏭 ATS Sharps Close, off Williams Rd ℰ (01705) 665959

---

**POSTBRIDGE** Devon 🔢🔢🔢 I 32 The West Country G. – ⊠ Yelverton.
Env. : Dartmoor National Park★★.
London 205 – Exeter 21 – Plymouth 19.

🏨 **Lydgate House** ⌘, PL20 6TJ, ℰ (01822) 880209, Fax (01822) 880202, ≤, ⌇, ⌰, park – ⇒ rest, �📺 🅿. 🐠 𝘝𝘐𝘚𝘈
closed 4 January-1 March – **Meals** (dinner only) 16.50 t. ⫞ 5.50 – **8 rm** ⊇ 31.00/65.00 t.

---

**POTT SHRIGLEY** Ches. – see Macclesfield.

---

*Le Grand Londres (GREATER LONDON) est composé de la City et de 32 arrondissements administratifs (Borough) eux-mêmes divisés en quartiers ou en villages ayant conservé leur caractère propre (Area).*

---

**POYNTON** Ches. 🔢🔢 🔢🔢🔢 N 23 – pop. 14 768.
London 193 – Chester 44 – Manchester 12 – Stoke-on-Trent 28.

🏨 **The Spinney** without rest., 59-61 Chester Rd, SK12 1HB, West : ¼ m. on A 5149, ℰ (01625) 871397, Fax (01625) 872143, ⌰ – ⇒ �📺 🅿. 🐠 🕮 ⓞ 𝘝𝘐𝘚𝘈 🗪
closed 19 December-5 January – **13 rm** ⊇ 49.50/59.50 st.

---

**PRESTBURY** Ches. 🔢🔢 🔢🔢🔢 🔢🔢🔢 N 24 – pop. 3 346.
🛝 Mottram Hall Hotel, Wilmslow Rd, Mottram St. Andrews ℰ (01625) 828135.
London 184 – Liverpool 43 – Manchester 17 – Stoke-on-Trent 25.

🏨🏨 **De Vere Mottram Hall,** Wilmslow Rd, Mottram St. Andrew, SK10 4QT, Northwest : 2¼ m. on A 538 ℰ (01625) 828135, Fax (01625) 829284, ≤, « Part 18C mansion », ₤₅, ⌕, ⬚, 🛝, ⌰, park, ⚞, squash – ⫮, ⇒ rm, ⚟ ☎ & 🅿 – 🔏 275. 🐠 🕮 ⓞ 𝘝𝘐𝘚𝘈. ⋙
Meals (dancing Friday and Saturday evenings) (bar lunch Saturday) 19.00/26.00 st. ⫞ 9.00 –
**Oak :** Meals (closed Saturday lunch) 19.00/26.00 **st.** and a la carte ⫞ 9.00 – **129 rm** ⊇ 135.00/160.00 st., 3 suites – SB.

🏨 **White House Manor,** The Village, SK10 4HP, ℰ (01625) 829376, Fax (01625) 828627, ⌰ – 📺 ☎ 🅿. 🐠 𝘝𝘐𝘚𝘈. ⋙
closed 24 and 25 December – **Meals** – (room service or see **White House** below) – ⊇ 8.50 – **11 rm** 70.00/120.00 t.

🏨 **The Bridge,** The Village, SK10 4DQ, ℰ (01625) 829326, Fax (01625) 827557, ⌰ – 📺 ☎ ℰ & 🅿 – 🔏 100. 🐠 🕮 ⓞ 𝘝𝘐𝘚𝘈 🗪. ⋙
Meals (closed Sunday dinner) a la carte 21.55/29.10 t. ⫞ 6.50 – ⊇ 8.50 – **23 rm** 45.00/90.00 st.

XX **White House,** The Village, SK10 4DG, ℰ (01625) 829376, Fax (01625) 828627 – 🅿. 🐠 🕮 ⓞ 𝘝𝘐𝘚𝘈
closed Monday lunch, Sunday dinner and 24-25 December – **Meals** 13.50/17.95 t. and a la carte ⫞ 6.50.

---

**PRESTON** Lancs. 🔢🔢 L 22 – pop. 177 660.
🛝 Fulwood Hall Lane, Fulwood ℰ (01772) 700436 – 🛝 Ingol, Tanterton Hall Rd, Ingol ℰ (01772) 734556 – 🛝 Aston & Lea, Tudor Av., Blackpool Rd ℰ (01772) 726480 – 🛝 Penwortham, Blundell Lane ℰ (01772) 743207.
🛈 The Guildhall, Lancaster Rd, PR1 1HT ℰ (01772) 253731.
London 226 – Blackpool 18 – Burnley 22 – Liverpool 30 – Manchester 34 – Stoke-on-Trent 65.

**Forte Posthouse Preston,** The Ringway, PR1 3AU, ✆ (01772) 259411, *Fax (01772) 201923* – |♦|, ⇔ rm, TV ☎ P – 🅰 120. MC AE ⓓ VISA. ✱
**Meals** a la carte 14.00/25.00 **st.** – ☐ 8.95 – **119 rm** 69.00/119.00 **st.** – SB.

**Claremont,** 516 Blackpool Rd, Ashton, PR2 1HY, Northwest : 2 m. by A 6 on A 5085 ✆ (01772) 729738, *Fax (01772) 726274*, ⛲ – ⇔ rest, TV ☎ ✆ P. MC AE ⓓ VISA
**Meals** (lunch by arrangement)/dinner 11.95 **st.** and a la carte 5.00 – **14 rm** ☐ 37.50/54.00 **st.**

**Heathcotes Brasserie,** 23 Winckley Sq., PR1 3JJ, ✆ (01772) 252732, *Fax (01772) 203433* – ▤. MC AE ⓓ VISA
**Meals** 10.50 **t.** (lunch) and a la carte 19.00/27.00 **t.**

**t Broughton** *North : 3 m. on A 6 – ✉ Preston.*

**Preston Marriott,** 418 Garstang Rd, PR3 5JB, ✆ (01772) 864087, *Fax (01772) 861728*, Fð, ≘s, 🔲, ⛲ – |♦| ⇔ TV ☎ P – 🅰 200. MC AE ⓓ VISA JCB. ✱
***Broughton Park :* Meals** *(closed Saturday lunch)* 13.00/18.95 **st.** and dinner a la carte 6.00 – ☐ 11.95 – **97 rm** 95.00 **t.**, 1 suite – SB.

**t Samlesbury** *East : 2½ m. by A 59 – ✉ Preston.*

**Tickled Trout,** Preston New Rd, PR5 0UJ, West : 1 m. on A 59 ✆ (01772) 877671, *Fax (01772) 877463*, ≤, ≘s, ⛲ – ⇔ TV ☎ P – 🅰 150. MC AE ⓓ VISA
**Meals** *(closed Saturday lunch)* 13.95/23.95 **st.** and dinner a la carte 6.75 – ☐ 10.50 – **72 rm** 98.00/120.00 **st.** – SB.

**Swallow,** Preston New Rd, PR5 0UL, East : 1 m. at junction of A 59 with A 677 ✆ (01772) 877351, *Fax (01772) 877424*, ≘s, 🔲, squash – |♦| ⇔, ▤ rest, TV ☎ P – 🅰 250. MC AE ⓓ VISA JCB. ✱
**Meals** (bar lunch Saturday) 12.95/19.25 **st.** – **78 rm** ☐ 85.00/110.00 **st.** – SB.

**t Walton le Dale** *Southeast : 2 m. by A 6, A 675, B 6230 (Bamber Bridge rd) on B 6258 – ✉ Preston.*

**The Vineyard,** Cinnamon Hill, PR5 4JN, ✆ (01772) 254646, *Fax (01772) 258967* – TV ☎ P – 🅰 100. MC AE ⓓ VISA. ✱
**Meals** *(closed dinner 25 December)* (grill rest.) 14.00 **t.** and a la carte – ☐ 6.95 – **16 rm** 47.50 **t.**

**t Bamber Bridge** *South : 5 m. by A 6 on B 6258 – ✉ Preston.*

**Novotel,** Reedfield Place, Walton Summit, PR5 8AA, Southeast : ¾ m. by A 6 at junction 29 of M 6 ✆ (01772) 313331, *Fax (01772) 627868*, 🏊, ⛲ – |♦|, ⇔ rm, ▤ rest, TV ☎ ✆ P – 🅰 180. MC AE ⓓ VISA JCB
**Meals** a la carte 9.95/21.75 **st.** – ☐ 9.00 – **98 rm** 60.00 **st.** – SB.

**The Poachers Tavern - Lodge Inn,** Lobstock Lane, PR5 6BA, South : ½ m. on A 6 ✆ (01772) 324100, *Fax (01772) 629525* – ⇔ rm, TV ✆ ♿ P. MC AE ⓓ VISA. ✱
**Meals** (grill rest.) a la carte 9.50/15.00 **st.** 3.75 – ☐ 5.50 – **40 rm** 39.00 **st.**

**t Lea** *West : 3½ m. on A 583 – ✉ Preston.*

**Travel Inn,** Blackpool Rd, PR4 0XL, on A 583 ✆ (01772) 720476, *Fax (01772) 729971* – ⇔ rm, ▤ rest, TV ♿ P. MC AE ⓓ VISA. ✱
**Meals** (grill rest.) – **38 rm** 38.00 **t.**

ATS 296-298 Aqueduct St, Ashton ✆ (01772) 257688

**PRESTWICH** *Gtr. Manchester* 402 403 404 N 23 – *pop. 31 801* – ✉ *Manchester.*
*London 205 – Leeds 40 – Liverpool 30 – Manchester 5.*

Plan : see Manchester

**Village H & Leisure Club,** George St., M25 9WS, South : 1 ¾ m. by A 56 ✆ (0161) 798 8905, *Fax (0161) 773 5562*, Fð, ≘s, squash – ⇔, ▤ rest, TV ☎ ✆ P – 🅰 120. MC AE ⓓ VISA. ✱ AV c
**Meals** (grill rest.) a la carte 9.05/23.50 **st.** 3.90 – **39 rm** ☐ 69.00/80.00 **st.**, 1 suite.

**Travel Inn,** Bury New Rd, M25 3AJ, Northwest : ½ m. on A 56 ✆ (0161) 798 0827, *Fax (0161) 773 8099* – ⇔ rm, TV ♿ P. MC AE ⓓ VISA. ✱
**Meals** (grill rest.) – **60 rm** 38.00 **t.**

**PRIDDY** *Somerset* 403 L 30 – *see Wells.*

**PUCKRUP** *Glos. – see Tewkesbury.*

**PUDDINGTON** *Ches.* 402 403 K 24 – *see Chester.*

**PUDSEY** W. Yorks. 402 P 22 – see Leeds.

**PULBOROUGH** W. Sussex 404 S 31 – pop. 3 497.
  ⓘₛ, ⓘₛ West Chiltington, Broadford Bridge Rd ℘ (01798) 813574.
  London 49 – Brighton 25 – Guildford 25 – Portsmouth 35.

  🏨 **Chequers,** Church Pl., RH20 1AD, Northeast : ¼ m. on A 29 ℘ (01798) 87248❚
  Fax (01798) 872715, � – ⇌ 📺 ☎ 🅿. 🐵 🖭 ⓞ 🎴
  Meals (dinner only) 22.95 t. ▯ 6.50 – **11 rm** � 59.50/92.00 t. – SB.

  ✕✕ **Stane Street Hollow,** Codmore Hill, RH20 1BG, Northeast : 1 m. on A 2❚
  ℘ (01798) 872819 – ⇌ 🅿. 🐵 🖭 🎴
  closed Saturday lunch, Sunday dinner, Monday and Tuesday – Meals - Swiss - (bookin❚
  essential) 15.50 t. (lunch) and a la carte 21.50/26.00 t. ▯ 7.50.

at West Chiltington : 2¾ m. by A 283 on West Chiltington rd – ✉ Pulborough.

  ⌂ **New House Farm** without rest., Broadford Bridge Rd, RH20 2LA, ℘ (01798) 812215, 🌑
  – ⇌ 📺 🅿. 🎇
  **3 rm** � 35.00/50.00.

**La PULENTE** Jersey (Channel Islands) 403 P 33 and 230 ⑪ – see Channel Islands.

**PULHAM MARKET** Norfolk 404 X 26 – pop. 919 – ✉ Diss.
  London 106 – Cambridge 58 – Ipswich 29 – Norwich 16.

  ⌂ **Old Bakery,** Church Walk, IP21 4SJ, ℘ (01379) 676492, Fax (01379) 676492, « Part 16❚
  timbered house », � – ⇌ 📺. 🎇
  closed Christmas and New Year – Meals (by arrangement) 15.00 st. ▯ 4.00 – **3 rm** � 45.00❚
  52.00 st.

**PURFLEET** Essex 404 ⑭.
  Dartford Tunnel and Bridge (toll).
  London 16 – Hastings 56 – Maidstone 26 – Southend-on-Sea 24.

  🏨 **Travel Inn,** High St., RM16 1QA, ℘ (01708) 865432, Fax (01708) 860852 – ⇌ rm, 📺 & ⑥❚
  🐵 🖭 ⓞ 🖭. 🎇
  Meals (grill rest.) – **30 rm** 38.00 t.

**PURTON** Wilts. 403 404 O 29 – pop. 3 879 – ✉ Swindon.
  London 94 – Bristol 41 – Gloucester 31 – Oxford 38 – Swindon 5.

  🏨 **Pear Tree at Purton,** Church End, SN5 9ED, South : ½ m. by Church St. on Lydiar❚
  Millicent rd ℘ (01793) 772100, Fax (01793) 772369, ≤, « Conservatory restaurant », �
  📺 ☎ 🅿 – 🔏 60. 🐵 🖭 ⓞ 🎴
  closed 26 to 30 December – Meals (closed Saturday lunch) 17.50/29.50 st. ▯ 5.50 – **16 rr**❚
  � 95.00 st., 2 suites.

**QUORNDON** Leics. 402 403 404 Q 25 – see Loughborough.

**RAINHILL** Mersey. 402 ㉝ 403 ⑬ – see St. Helens.

**RAMSBOTTOM** Gtr. Manchester 402 N 23 – pop. 17 318.
  London 223 – Blackpool 39 – Burnley 12 – Leeds 46 – Manchester 13 – Liverpool 39.

  ✕ **Village,** 18 Market Pl., BL0 9HT, ℘ (01706) 825070, Fax (01706) 822005 – ⇌. 🐵 🖭 ⓞ 🖭❚
  🎴
  closed Sunday dinner, Monday, Tuesday, 26 December and 1 January – Meals 8.00/19.50 s❚
  ▯ 4.75.

**RAMSEY** Isle of Man 402 G 21 – see Man (Isle of).

**RAMSGATE** Kent 404 Y 30 – pop. 37 895.
  ⚓ – to Belgium (Ostend) (Holyman Sally Ferries) 2 daily (4 h) – to France (Dunkerque❚
  (Holyman Sally Ferries) 3-4 daily (1 h 15 mn).
  ⚓ to Belgium (Ostend) (Holyman Sally Ferries) 5-7 daily (1 h 40 mn).
  ⓘ 19-21 Harbour St., CT11 8HA ℘ (01843) 583333.
  London 77 – Dover 19 – Maidstone 45 – Margate 4.5.

🏠 **Jarvis Marina**, Harbour Par., CT11 8LJ, 𝓟 *(01843) 588276, Fax (01843) 586866*, ≤, ⇔, ▧ – 🛗 ⅍, ▤ rest, 📺 ☎ – 🛦 120. 🕮 AE ⓪ VISA
**Meals** (bar lunch Monday to Saturday)/dinner 14.00 **st.** and a la carte ₰ 6.00 – **58 rm** ⊑ 69.00/94.00 **st.** – SB.

**t Minster** *West : 5½ m. by A 253 on B 2048 –* ⊠ *Ramsgate.*

🍴 **Morton's Fork** with rm, 42 Station Rd, CT12 4BZ, 𝓟 *(01843) 823000, Fax (01843) 821224* – ⅍ 📺 🅿 🕮 AE ⓪ VISA
*closed 25 and 26 December –* **Meals** (closed Sunday dinner and Monday) 11.95/14.95 **t.** and a la carte ₰ 5.75 – ⊑ 5.75 – **6 rm** 39.00/63.00 **t.** – SB.

🔧 ATS 82-84 Bellevue Rd 𝓟 *(01843) 595829*

---

**RAMSGILL-IN-NIDDERDALE** *N. Yorks.* 402 O 21 *– see Pateley Bridge.*

---

**RASKELF** *N. Yorks.* 402 Q 21 *– see Easingwold.*

---

**RAVENSTONEDALE** *Cumbria* 402 M 20 *– pop. 886 –* ⊠ *Kirkby Stephen.*
*London 280 – Carlisle 43 – Kendal 19 – Kirkby Stephen 5.*

🏠 **Black Swan**, CA17 4NG, 𝓟 *(015396) 23204, Fax (015396) 23604*, ⤢, 🐾 – ⅍ rest, 📺 ☎ & 🅿. 🕮 VISA
**Meals** 10.50/21.00 **t.** and a la carte ₰ 5.00 – **15 rm** ⊑ 50.00/85.00 **t.** – SB.

🏠 **Fat Lamb Inn** ⤷, Crossbank, CA17 4LL, Southeast : 2 m. by Sedbergh rd on A 683 𝓟 *(015396) 23242, Fax (015396) 23285*, ≤, 🐾, park – ⅍ 🅿. 🕮 VISA
**Meals** 12.00/18.00 **t.** and a la carte ₰ 3.75 – **12 rm** ⊑ 38.00/64.00 **t.** – SB.

---

**READING** 403 404 Q 29 *– pop. 213 474.*
🏌 *Calcot Park, Bath Rd, Calcot* 𝓟 *(0118) 942 7124.*
*Whitchurch Bridge (toll).*
🛈 *Town Hall, Blagrave St., RG1 1QH* 𝓟 *(01734) 566226.*
*London 43 – Brighton 79 – Bristol 78 – Croydon 47 – Luton 62 – Oxford 28 – Portsmouth 67 – Southampton 46.*

*Plan on next page*

🏨🏨 **Holiday Inn Reading**, Caversham Bridge, Richfield Av., RG1 8BD, 𝓟 *(01189) 259988, Fax (01189) 391665*, ≤, « Thames-side setting », ₖ₆, ⇔, ▧ – 🛗, ⅍ rm, 📺 ☎ & 🅿 – 🛦 250. 🕮 AE ⓪ VISA                    X e
**Meals** 15.95/18.95 **t.** and a la carte ₰ 6.00 – ⊑ 9.25 – **109 rm** 115.00 **st.**, 2 suites – SB.

🏨🏨 **Ramada**, Oxford Rd, RG1 7RH, 𝓟 *(01189) 586222, Fax (01189) 597842*, ₖ₆, ⇔, ▧ – 🛗, ⅍ rm, ▤ 📺 ☎ & 🅿 – 🛦 220. 🕮 AE ⓪ VISA JCB. ⅍                    Z i
**Meals** (buffet lunch Monday to Saturday)/dinner a la carte approx. 20.65 **st.** – ⊑ 11.95 – **195 rm** 125.00 **st.**, 1 suite.

🏨 **Forte Posthouse Reading**, 500 Basingstoke Rd, RG2 0SL, South : 2 ½ m. on A 33 𝓟 *(01189) 875485, Fax (01189) 311958*, ₖ₆, ⇔, ▧ – ⅍ rm, 📺 ☎ 🅿 – 🛦 100. 🕮 AE ⓪ VISA                    X a
**Meals** a la carte 16.45/28.65 **t.** ₰ 7.50 – ⊑ 9.95 – **202 rm** 119.00/139.00 **st.** – SB.

🏠 **Upcross**, 68 Berkeley Av., RG1 6HY, 𝓟 *(01189) 590796, Fax (01189) 576517*, 🐾 – ⅍ rest, 📺 ☎ 🅿 – 🛦 45. 🕮 AE ⓪ VISA                    X o
**Meals** (closed Saturday lunch) 15.00/17.50 **st.** and a la carte ₰ 5.75 – **22 rm** ⊑ 67.50/115.00 **st.** – SB.

🏠 **Hillingdon Prince**, 39 Christchurch Rd, RG2 7AN, 𝓟 *(01189) 311391, Fax (01189) 756357* – 🛗 📺 ☎ 🅿 – 🛦 100. 🕮 AE VISA. ⅍                    X v
**Meals** a la carte approx. 19.45 **st.** – **40 rm** ⊑ 72.50/95.00 **st.**

🏠 **Rainbow Corner**, 132-138 Caversham Rd, RG1 8AY, 𝓟 *(01189) 588140, Fax (01189) 586500* – 📺 ☎ 🅿. 🕮 ⓪ VISA                    X u
**Meals** (closed Friday dinner and Sunday) 12.95/13.95 **t.** and a la carte – ⊑ 5.95 – **32 rm** 69.00/79.00 **st.**

🏠 **Travelodge**, 387 Basingstoke Rd, RG2 0JE, South : 2 m. on A 33 𝓟 *(01189) 750618*, Reservations (Freephone) 0800 850950 – ⅍ rm, 📺 & 🅿. 🕮 AE ⓪ VISA JCB. ⅍                    X c
**Meals** (grill rest.) – **36 rm** 39.95/59.95 **t.**

🏠 **Dittisham** without rest., 63 Tilehurst Rd, RG30 2JL, 𝓟 *(01189) 569483*, 🐾 – 📺 🅿. 🕮 VISA. ⅍                    X s
**5 rm** ⊑ 27.50/50.00 **st.**

🍴🍴 **Old Siam**, King's Walk, King St., RG1 2HG, 𝓟 *(01189) 512600, Fax (01189) 596300* – 🕮 AE ⓪ VISA JCB                    Z a
*closed Sunday, 2 weeks Christmas-New Year and Bank Holidays –* **Meals** - Thai - 14.50/22.50 **t.** and a la carte.

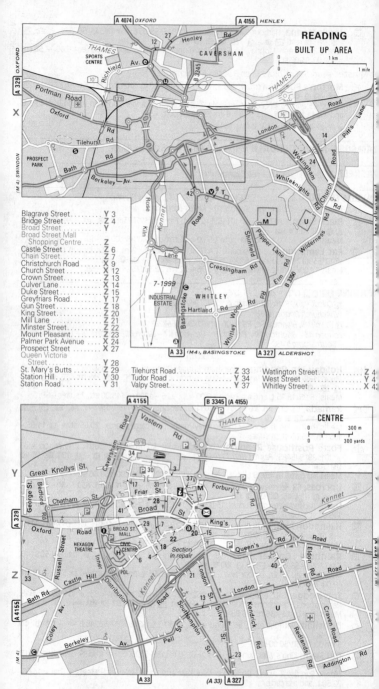

## READING
### BUILT UP AREA

0 ____ 1 km
0 ____ 1 mile

A 4074 OXFORD
A 4155 HENLEY
THAMES
SPORTS CENTRE
Henley Rd
CAVERSHAM
Richfield Av.
Portman Road
Oxford Rd
Tilehurst Rd
PROSPECT PARK
Bath Rd
Berkeley — Av.
London Road
Wokingham Road
Whiteknights
Church Rd
Pitt's Lane
Rose Kiln Lane
Kennet
Shinfield Rd
Pepper Lane
Elm Rd
Wilderness
7-1999 INDUSTRIAL ESTATE
WHITLEY
Cressingham Rd
Basingstoke Rd
Hartland Rd
Whitley Wood Rd
A 33 (M4), BASINGSTOKE
A 327 ALDERSHOT

Blagrave Street........ Y 3
Bridge Street.......... Z 4
Broad Street........... Y
Broad Street Mall
  Shopping Centre...... Z
Castle Street.......... Z 6
Chain Street........... Z 7
Christchurch Road...... X 9
Church Street.......... X 12
Crown Street........... Z 13
Culver Lane............ X 14
Duke Street............ Z 15
Greyfriars Road........ Y 17
Gun Street............. Z 18
King Street............ Z 20
Mill Lane.............. Z 21
Minster Street......... Z 22
Mount Pleasant......... Z 23
Palmer Park Avenue .... X 24
Prospect Street ....... X 27
Queen Victoria
  Street............... Y 28
St. Mary's Butts ...... Z 29
Station Hill........... Y 30
Station Road .......... Y 31

Tilehurst Road......... Z 33
Tudor Road............. Y 34
Valpy Street........... Y 37

Watlington Street...... Z 4
West Street............ Y 4
Whitley Street......... X 42

### CENTRE

0 ____ 300 m
0 ____ 300 yards

A 4155
B 3345 (A 4155)
THAMES
Vastern Rd
Caversham Road
Great Knollys St.
George St.
Bedford Rd
Chatham St
Friar St
Forbury Rd
Broad St
King's Rd
Oxford Road
BROAD ST MALL
HEXAGON THEATRE
CIVIC CENTRE
Section in repair
Queen's Rd
Russell Street
Castle Hill
Inner Distribution
Kennet
London Road
Southampton St
Pell St
Silver St
Kendrick Rd
Redlands Rd
Craven Road
Eldon Rd
Addington Rd
Coley Av.
Berkeley Av.
Bath Rd
A 329
A 4155 (M 4)
A 33
(A 33) A 327

526

t **Sindlesham** Southeast : 5 m. by A 329 on B 3030 – X – ✉ Wokingham.

🏨 **Reading Moat House,** Mill Lane, RG41 5DF, Northwest : ½ m. by Mole Rd
℘ (01189) 499988, Fax (01189) 666530, ₤₅, ⇌ – ⁆, ╳ rm, ⓣⓥ ☎ & ℗ – 🔏 80. ⬛⬛ ⒶⒺ ⓪
⬛⬛⬛ ⬛⬛⬛
Meals (closed Saturday lunch) 18.95 t. – ⊑ 10.00 – **100 rm** 125.00/145.00 st. – SB.

t **Shinfield** South : 4¼ m. on A 327 – X – ✉ Reading.

🎍🎍🎍 **L'Ortolan** (Burton-Race), The Old Vicarage, Church Lane, RG2 9BY, ℘ (01189) 883783,
😳😳 Fax (01189) 885391, ⩘ – ℗. ⬛⬛ ⒶⒺ ⓪ ⬛⬛⬛
closed Sunday dinner and Monday – Meals - French - 23.00/42.00 t. (except Saturday dinner) and a la carte 46.00/64.50 t. ₰ 10.00
**Spec.** Queue de homard rôti, sauce Sauternes. Filet de veau et ses béatilles aux deux
saveurs. Assiette chocolatière.

t **Grazeley Green** Southwest : 5½ m. by A 33 – X – ✉ Reading.

🏠 **Old Bell - Premier Lodge,** RG7 1LS, ℘ (01189) 883115, Fax (01189) 886225, Reservations (Freephone) 0800 118833 – ╳ rm, ⓣⓥ ☎ & ℗. ⬛⬛ ⒶⒺ ⓪ ⬛⬛⬛. ⬛
**Meals** a la carte 12.85/20.00 st. – ⊑ 5.95 – **32 rm** 44.95 st.

🔧 ATS Basingstoke Rd ℘ (01189) 759500

**READING SERVICE AREA** Newbury ⬛⬛⬛ ⬛⬛⬛ Q 29 – ✉ Reading.

🏠 **Travelodge,** RG30 3UQ, M 4 eastbound between junctions 11 and 12 ℘ (01189) 566966,
Fax (01189) 508427, Reservations (Freephone) 0800 850950 – ╳ ⓣⓥ ☎ & ℗. ⬛⬛ ⒶⒺ ⓪ ⬛⬛⬛
⬛⬛⬛. ⬛
Meals (grill rest.) – **45 rm** 39.95/59.95 t.

*The Guide is updated annually so renew your Guide every year.*

**REDDITCH** Worcestershire ⬛⬛⬛ ⬛⬛⬛ O 27 – pop. 73 372.
📍 Abbey Park G & C.C., Dagnell End Rd ℘ (01527) 63918 – 📍 Lower Grinsty, Green Lane,
Callow Hill ℘ (01527) 543309 – 📍 Pitcheroak, Plymouth Rd ℘ (01527) 541054.
🛈 Civic Square, Alcester St., B98 8AH ℘ (01527) 60806.
London 111 – Birmingham 15 – Cheltenham 33 – Stratford-upon-Avon 15.

🏨🏨 **Quality Friendly** ⬛, Pool Bank, Southcrest, B97 4JS, ℘ (01527) 541511,
Fax (01527) 402600, ⩘ – ⓣⓥ ☎ ℗ – 🔏 100. ⬛⬛ ⒶⒺ ⓪ ⬛⬛⬛ ⬛⬛⬛
**Meals** (closed Saturday lunch) 11.50/14.50 st. and a la carte – ⊑ 9.50 – **58 rm** 90.00/
105.00 st. – SB.

🏠 **Foxlydiate Arms - Premier Lodge,** Birchfield Rd, B97 6PX, West : 4 ¾ m. by A 441
and A 448 off Tardebigge rd ℘ (01527) 542934, Fax (01527) 547727, Reservations (Freephone) 0800 118833, ⩘ – ╳ rm, ⓣⓥ ☎ ✆ & ℗ – 🔏 150. ⬛⬛ ⒶⒺ ⬛⬛⬛. ⬛
**Meals** (closed dinner 25 December) (grill rest.) a la carte 8.50/14.55 t. ₰ 4.55 – ⊑ 5.95 –
**33 rm** ⊑ 44.95 t. – SB.

🏠 **Old Rectory** ⬛, Ipsley Lane, Ipsley, B98 0AP, ℘ (01527) 523000, Fax (01527) 517003, ⩘
– ╳ ☎ ✆ ℗. ⬛⬛ ⒶⒺ ⓪ ⬛⬛⬛ ⬛⬛⬛
closed 25 December – Meals (booking essential to non-residents) (dinner only) 16.95 t. –
**10 rm** ⊑ 60.00/90.00 st.

🏠 **Campanile,** Far Moor Lane, Winyates Green, B98 0SD, East : 2 ½ m. by A 4023
℘ (01527) 510710, Fax (01527) 517269 – ╳ rm, ⓣⓥ & ℗ – 🔏 25. ⬛⬛ ⒶⒺ ⓪ ⬛⬛⬛
**Meals** 10.85 st. and a la carte – ⊑ 4.50 – **47 rm** 36.50 st.

🔧 ATS Pipers Rd, Park Farm Ind. Est., Park Farm
South ℘ (01527) 502002

**REDHILL** Surrey ⬛⬛⬛ T 30 – pop. 47 602 (inc. Reigate).
📍 Redhill & Reigate, Clarence Lodge, Pendleton Rd ℘ (01737) 244626/244433.
London 22 – Brighton 31 – Guildford 20 – Maidstone 34.

🏨🏨 **Nutfield Priory,** Nutfield, RH1 4EN, East : 2 m. on A 25 ℘ (01737) 822066,
Fax (01737) 823321, ≤, ₤₅, ⇌, ⬛, ⩘, park, squash – ⁆ ╳ ⓣⓥ ☎ ✆ ℗ – 🔏 80. ⬛⬛ ⒶⒺ ⓪
⬛⬛⬛. ⬛
**Cloisters :** Meals (closed Saturday lunch) 16.00/24.50 t. and a la carte – ⊑ 12.00 – **59 rm**
115.00/140.00 st., 1 suite – SB.

🏠 **Ashleigh House** without rest., 39 Redstone Hill, RH1 4BG, on A 25 ℘ (01737) 764763,
Fax (01737) 780308, ⬛, ⩘ – ⓣⓥ ℗. ⬛⬛ ⬛⬛⬛. ⬛
closed Christmas – **8 rm** ⊑ 30.00/55.00 st.

**at Salfords** South : 2½ m. on A 23 – ⊠ Redhill.

🏨 **Travel Inn,** Brighton Rd, RH1 5BT, ℘ (01737) 767277, Fax (01737) 778099 – ﹩ rm, 📺 ♲
&, 🅿, 🐵 AE ⓪ VISA. ✻
**Meals** (grill rest.) – 48 rm 38.00 t.

---

**REDMILE** Leics. 402 404 R 25 – pop. 697.
London 140 – Leicester 20 – Lincoln 37 – Nottingham 17 – Sheffield 52.

XX **The Peacock Inn** with rm, Church Corner, NG13 0GA, ℘ (01949) 84255–
Fax (01949) 843746, 佘, « Part 17C » – ﹩ 📺 ☎ ✆ 🅿, 🐵 VISA. ✻
**Meals** a la carte 14.70/24.40 st. ⅟ 5.25 – (see also below) – 10 rm ☲ 75.00/130.00 st.

🍴 **The Peacock Inn,** Church Corner, NG13 0GA, ℘ (01949) 842554, Fax (01949) 84374◀
佘, « Part 17C » – ﹩ 🅿, 🐵 VISA
**Meals** a la carte 14.70/18.85 st. ⅟ 5.25.

---

**REDRUTH** Cornwall 403 E 33 The West Country G. – pop. 12 111.
Env. : Carn Brea (﹩ ★★) SW : 1½ m. and 500 yds south of Carnbrea or Brea village, last 15
yds up a field track.
Exc. : Poldark Mine★, Wendron, S : 7 m. on B 3297.
London 303 – Falmouth 15 – Penzance 20 – Truro 12.

XX **The Basset Count House,** Carnkie, Southwest : 2 m. by A 393 and B 3297 on Carnkie r
℘ (01209) 215181 – ﹩ 🅿, 🐵 VISA
closed Sunday dinner, Monday and Tuesday – Meals (dinner only and Sunday lunch
25.00 st. ⅟ 6.00.

---

**REDWORTH** Durham – see Darlington.

---

**REEPHAM** Norfolk 404 X 25 – pop. 2 405 – ⊠ Norwich.
London 125 – Cromer 26 – King's Lynn 34 – Norwich 14.

⌂ **Westwood Barn** ⑤, Crabgate Lane South, Wood Dalling, NR11 6SW, North : 3 m. b
Station Rd and Wood Dalling Rd ℘ (01263) 584108, ﹩, « Converted barn », 舜 – ﹩ rm, 📺
🅿, ✻
**Meals** (by arrangement) 16.00 st. – 3 rm ☲ 32.00/50.00 st. – SB.

---

**REETH** N. Yorks. 402 O 20 – pop. 939 – ⊠ Richmond.
London 253 – Leeds 53 – Middlesbrough 36.

🏨 **Burgoyne,** On The Green, DL11 6SN, ℘ (01748) 884292, Fax (01748) 884292, ﹩, 舜 – ﹩
📺 ☎ &, 🅿, 🐵 VISA
closed 2 January-mid February – Meals (dinner only) 23.00 t. ⅟ 6.00 – 8 rm ☲ 60.00
135.00 t. – SB.

🏨 **Arkleside,** DL11 6SG, Northeast corner of the green ℘ (01748) 88420◀
Fax (01748) 884200, ﹩, 舜 – ﹩ 📺 🅿, 🐵 VISA
closed 1 January-13 February – Meals (dinner only) 18.00 t. ⅟ 6.50 – 8 rm ☲ 37.00/64.00 t
1 suite.

---

**REIGATE** Surrey 404 T 30 – pop. 47 602 (inc. Redhill).
London 26 – Brighton 33 – Guildford 20 – Maidstone 38.

🏨 **Bridge House,** Reigate Hill, RH2 9RP, North : 1 ¼ m. on A 217 ℘ (01737) 24680◀
Fax (01737) 223756, ﹩ – 📺 ☎ 🅿 – 🔏 50. 🐵 AE ⓪ VISA. ✻
**Meals** (dancing Wednesday to Saturday evenings) 17.15/23.40 t. and a la carte ⅟ 6.00 – ☲
11.50 – 39 rm 55.00/125.00 t. – SB.

🏨 **Cranleigh,** 41 West St., RH2 9BL, ℘ (01737) 223417, Fax (01737) 223734, ⊒, 舜 – 📺 ☎
🅿, 🐵 AE ⓪ VISA JCB. ✻
closed 1 week Christmas – Meals (closed Friday to Sunday) (dinner only) a la carte 19.00
24.00 st. ⅟ 5.00 – 9 rm ☲ 70.00/90.00 st.

XX **The Dining Room,** 59a High St., RH2 9AE, ℘ (01737) 226650 – ﹩ ▤, 🐵 AE ⓪ VISA
closed Saturday lunch, Sunday, 1 week Easter, 2 weeks August, 1 week Christmas and Ban
Holidays – Meals 13.95 t. (lunch) and a la carte 29.95/31.95 t. ⅟ 9.50.

X **La Barbe,** 71 Bell St., RH2 7AN, ℘ (01737) 241966, Fax (01737) 226387 – 🐵 AE ⓪ VISA JCB
closed Saturday lunch, Sunday, 25-26 December, 1 January and Bank Holidays – Meals
French - 18.95/24.95 st. ⅟ 7.95.

**RETFORD** Notts. 402 403 404 R 24 – see East Retford.

---

**REYDON** Suffolk – see Southwold.

---

**RHYDYCROESAU** Shrops. 402 403 K 25 – see Oswestry.

---

**RICHMOND** N. Yorks. 402 O 20 Great Britain G. – pop. 7 862.

See : Town★ – Castle★ AC – Georgian Theatre Royal and Museum★.

Exc. : Josephine and John Bowes Museum★, Barnard Castle, NW : 15 m. by B 6274, A 66 and minor rd (right) – Raby Castle★, NE : 6 m. of Barnard Castle by A 688.

🅱 Bend Hagg ℰ (01748) 825319 – 🅱 Catterick, Leyburn Rd ℰ (01748) 833401.

🛈 Friary Gardens, Victoria Rd, DL10 4AJ ℰ (01748) 850252.

London 243 – Leeds 53 – Middlesbrough 26 – Newcastle upon Tyne 44.

🏨 **King's Head,** Market Pl., DL10 4HS, ℰ (01748) 850220, Fax (01748) 850635 – ⇔ 🆃🆅 ☎ 🅿
– 🔬 150. 🆀🅾 🅰🅴 🅾 𝘝𝘐𝘚𝘈
Meals (bar lunch Monday to Saturday)/dinner 18.95 **t.** and a la carte ⓘ 4.95 – **30 rm**
⬜ 55.00/86.00 **t.** – SB.

⌂ **West End,** 45 Reeth Rd., DL10 4EX, West : ½ m. on A 6108 ℰ (01748) 824783, ☞ – ⇔ 🆃🆅
🅿
closed Christmas and New Year – **Meals** (by arrangement) 12.00 **st.** ⓘ 4.30 – **5 rm** ⬜ 21.00/
42.00 **st.**

⌂ **The Old Brewery,** 29 The Green, DL10 4RG, via Victoria Rd off Cravengate
ℰ (01748) 822460, Fax (01748) 825561, ☞ – ⇔ 🆃🆅. 🆀🅾 𝘝𝘐𝘚𝘈 𝗝𝗖𝗕. ⁂
closed December and January – **Meals** (by arrangement) 13.00 – **5 rm** ⬜ 30.00/44.00.

**at Whashton** Northwest : 4½ m. by Ravensworth rd – ⊠ Richmond.

⌂ **Whashton Springs Farm** ⤸ without rest., DL11 7JS, South : 1 ½ m. on Richmond rd
ℰ (01748) 822884, Fax (01748) 826285, « Working farm », ☞, park – ⇔ 🆃🆅 ☎ 🅿. ⁂
closed mid December-February – **8 rm** ⬜ 28.00/44.00 **s.**

🍴 **The Hack and Spade,** DL11 7JL, ℰ (01748) 823721 – ⇔ 🅿. 𝘝𝘐𝘚𝘈
closed Sunday dinner, Monday, 2 weeks January and 25-26 December – **Meals** (dinner only
and Sunday lunch) a la carte 13.00/21.70 **st.** ⓘ 5.00.

**at Dalton** Northwest : 6¾ m. by Ravensworth rd and Gayles rd – ⊠ Richmond.

🍴 **The Travellers Rest,** DL11 7HU, ℰ (01833) 621225 – 🅿. 🆀🅾 𝘝𝘐𝘚𝘈
closed Sunday, 25-26 December and 1 January – **Meals** (dinner only) a la carte approx.
17.95 **t.** ⓘ 4.95.

🏧 ATS Reeth Rd ℰ (01748) 824182/3

---

**RIDGEWAY** Derbs. – see Sheffield (S. Yorks.).

---

**RINGWOOD** Hants. 403 404 O 31 – pop. 11 959.

🛈 The Furlong, BH24 1AZ ℰ (01425) 470896 (summer only).

London 102 – Bournemouth 11 – Salisbury 17 – Southampton 20.

🏨 **Moortown Lodge,** 244 Christchurch Rd, BH24 3AS, South : 1 m. on B 3347
ℰ (01425) 471404, Fax (01425) 476052 – ⇔ 🆃🆅 ☎ 🅿. 🆀🅾 🅰🅴 🅾 𝘝𝘐𝘚𝘈. ⁂
closed 24 December-mid January – **Meals** (closed Sunday to non residents) (dinner only)
19.95 **t.** ⓘ 5.95 – **6 rm** ⬜ 35.00/80.00 **t.** – SB.

🏧 ATS 9 Carvers Ind Est. ℰ (01425) 477961

---

**RIPLEY** N. Yorks. 402 P 21 – pop. 193 – ⊠ Harrogate.

London 213 – Bradford 21 – Leeds 18 – Newcastle upon Tyne 79.

🏨 **The Boar's Head,** HG3 3AY, ℰ (01423) 771888, Fax (01423) 771509, « 18C coaching inn
within estate village of Ripley Castle », ⬧, ⁂ – ⇔ rm, 🆃🆅 ☎ 📞 🅿. 🆀🅾 🅰🅴 🅾 𝘝𝘐𝘚𝘈. ⁂
**The Restaurant :** Meals 17.50/27.50 **st.** ⓘ 5.50 – **The Bistro :** Meals 11.95 **st.**
and a la carte ⓘ 5.50 – **25 rm** ⬜ 90.00/110.00 **st.** – SB.

**at Burnt Yates** West : 2 ¾ m. on B 6165 – ⊠ Harrogate.

   🏛 **Bay Horse Inn**, HG3 3EJ, on B 6165 ℘ (01423) 770230, Fax (01423) 771894, 🛲 – ⇔ 📺
      ☎ ✆ 🅿. 🐵🐵 VISA. ⋘
      Meals (bar lunch Monday to Saturday)/dinner 15.95 t. and a la carte ⏐ 5.95 – 16 rr
      �驿 45.00/60.00 t. – SB.

   ⌂ **High Winsley Cottage** ⌂, HG3 3EP, Northwest : 1 m. by Brimham Rocks r◀
      ℘ (01423) 770662, ≤, 🛲 – ⇔ 🅿. ⋘
      closed January and February – Meals (communal dining) 12.50 t. – 4 rm ⊒ 36.50/52.00 t. ◀
      SB.

---

**RIPLEY** Surrey 404 S 30 – pop. 1 697.
    London 28 – Guildford 6.

   XXX **Michels'**, 13 High St., GU23 6AQ, ℘ (01483) 224777, Fax (01483) 222940, 🛲 – 🅿 AE VISₐ
      JCB
      closed Saturday lunch, Sunday dinner, Monday and early January – Meals 21.00 t◀
      and a la carte ⏐ 4.30.

---

**RIPON** N. Yorks. 402 P 21 Great Britain G. – pop. 13 806.
    See : Town★ - Cathedral★ (Saxon Crypt★★) AC.
    Env. : Fountains Abbey★★★ AC :- Studley Royal★★ AC (≤★ from Anne Boleyn's Seat)
    Fountains Hall (Facade★), SW : 2½ m. by B 6265 – Newby Hall (Tapestries★) AC, SE : 3½ m
    by B 6265.
    🛝 Ripon City, Palace Rd ℘ (01765) 603640.
    🛈 Minster Rd, HG4 1QT ℘ (01765) 604625 (summer only).
    London 222 – Leeds 26 – Middlesbrough 35 – York 23.

   🏨 **Ripon Spa**, Park St., HG4 2BU, ℘ (01765) 602172, Fax (01765) 690770, 🛲 – ⌗, 🍴 rest, 📺
      ☎ 🅿 – 🔬 150. 🐵🐵 AE ① VISA JCB
      Meals 14.75/19.25 st. and a la carte ⏐ 5.95 – ⊒ 4.95 – 40 rm 70.00/95.00 st. – SB.

   XX **Old Deanery** with rm, Minster Rd, HG4 1QS, ℘ (01765) 603518, Fax (01765) 603518
      « 17C former deanery », 🛲 – ⇔ rest, 📺 🅿. 🐵🐵 AE ① VISA JCB. ⋘
      closed 25 to 30 December – Meals (closed Sunday dinner and Monday) 13.95/19.95 t
      and a la carte ⏐ 6.25 – 3 rm ⊒ (dinner included) 75.00/130.00 st.

**at Aldfield** Southwest : 3 ¾ m. by B 6265 – ⊠ Ripon.

   ⌂ **Bay Tree Farm** ⌂, HG4 3BE, ℘ (01765) 620394, Fax (01765) 620394, 🛲 – ⇔ 📺 🅿. VISₐ
      Meals (by arrangement) (communal dining) 12.00 st. – 6 rm ⊒ 27.50/45.00 st.

      🅐 ATS Dallamires Lane ℘ (01765) 601579

---

**RISLEY** Notts. – see Nottingham.

---

**ROADE** Northants. 404 R 27 – pop. 2 239.
    London 66 – Coventry 36 – Northampton 5.5.

   XX **Roade House** with rm, 16 High St., NN7 2NW, ℘ (01604) 863372, Fax (01604) 862421 –
      ⇔, 🍴 rest, 📺 ☎ 🅿. 🐵🐵 AE VISA. ⋘
      Meals (closed Monday lunch and Sunday dinner) 17.00 st. (lunch) and dinner a la carte
      21.00/26.00 st. ⏐ 7.50 – 6 rm ⊒ 65.00/85.00 st.

---

**ROCHDALE** Gtr. Manchester 402 N 23 – pop. 94 313.
    🛝 Edenfield Rd, Bagslate ℘ (01706) 646024 – 🛝 Marland, Springfield Park, Bolton R◀
    ℘ (01706) 649801 – 🛝, 🛝 Castle Hawk, Chadwick Lane, Castleton ℘ (01706) 640841.
    🛈 The Clock Tower, Town Hall, OL16 1AB ℘ (01706) 356592.
    London 224 – Blackpool 40 – Burnley 11 – Leeds 45 – Manchester 12 – Liverpool 40.

   🏨🏨 **Norton Grange**, Manchester Rd, Castleton, OL11 2XZ, Southwest : 3 m. by A 58 on A 664
      ℘ (01706) 30788, Fax (01706) 49313, 🛲 – ⌗, ⇔ rm, 🍴 rest, 📺 ☎ ✆ 🅿 – 🔬 150. 🐵🐵
      AE ① VISA JCB
      Meals (closed Saturday lunch) 9.95/23.95 st. and a la carte – ⊒ 10.00 – 50 rm 100.00/
      125.00 st., 1 suite – SB.

   🏨 **Royal Toby Lodge**, Manchester Rd, Castleton, OL11 3HF, Southwest : 2 m. by A 58 on A
      664 ℘ (01706) 861861, Fax (01706) 868428, 🛲 – ⌗, 🍴 rest, 📺 ☎ ✆ 🅿. 🐵🐵 AE ① VISA
      JCB
      Meals 8.25/10.50 t. and a la carte ⏐ 5.25 – **Fallen Angel** : Meals - Italian - (dinner only
      a la carte 16.25/24.85 t. ⏐ 5.25 – 41 rm 57.50/82.50 st.

🏠 **Castleton,** Manchester Rd, Castleton, OL11 2XX, Southwest : 3 m. by A 58 on A 664 *𝒫* (01706) 357888, *Fax* (01706) 525757, *☞* – �📺 ☎ ✆ **🅿**. **◍ⓞ** **AE** **①** **VISA**. *✻*
**Meals** *(closed lunch Monday, Saturday and Bank Holidays)* 9.70/14.90 **t.** and a la carte ₰ 4.65 – 13 **rm** �ⴰ 60.00/70.00 **t.**

XX **Nutters,** Edenfield Rd, Cheesden, Norden, OL12 7TY, West : 5 m. on A 680 *𝒫* (01706) 650167, *Fax* (01706) 650167, *≼* – *✻* 🅿. **◍ⓞ** **AE** **①** **VISA**
*closed Tuesday and first 2 weeks August* – **Meals** 29.50 **t.** *(dinner)* and a la carte 22.35/27.85 **t.** ₰ 7.95.

XX **After Eight,** 2 Edenfield Rd, OL11 5AA, West : 1 m. on A 680 *𝒫* (01706) 646432, *Fax* (01706) 861493 – *✻*. **◍ⓞ** **AE** **①** **VISA**
*closed Sunday, Monday, 1 week spring, 25-26 December and 1 January* – **Meals** *(dinner only)* a la carte 15.90/24.40 **st.** ₰ 6.90.

**at Milnrow** *Southeast : 3 m. by A 640* – ✉ *Rochdale.*

🏠 **Travel Inn,** Newhey Rd, OL16 4JF, *𝒫* (01706) 299999, *Fax* (01706) 299074 – *✻* rm, ▤ rest, 📺 & **🅿**. **◍ⓞ** **AE** **①** **VISA**. *✻*
**Meals** *(grill rest.)* – **40 rm** 38.00 **t.**

◍ ATS Yorkshire St. *𝒫* (01706) 32411/49935   ATS Castleton Moor, Nixon St. (ASDA) *𝒫* (01706) 57068

---

**ROCHESTER** *Medway* **404** V 29 *Great Britain G.* – *pop. 23 971* – ✉ *Chatham.*
See : *Castle★ AC* – *Cathedral★ AC.*
Env. : *The Historic Dockyard★, Chatham, NE : 2 m. of the Cathedral.*
Exc. : *Leeds Castle★, SE : 11 m. by A 229 and M 20.*
🛈 *95 High St., ME1 1EW* *𝒫* (01634) 843666.
*London 30 – Dover 45 – Maidstone 8 – Margate 46.*

🏯 **Bridgewood Manor,** Bridgewood Roundabout, ME5 9AX, Southeast : 3 m. by A 2 and A 229 on Walderslade rd *𝒫* (01634) 201333, *Fax* (01634) 201330, *Iₐ*, *≘s*, *◻*, *✺* – *⧚* *✻*, ▤ rest, 📺 ☎ & **🅿** – *⌀* 200. **◍ⓞ** **AE** **①** **VISA**. *✻*
*Squires :* **Meals** *(closed Saturday lunch)* 17.50/25.00 **t.** and a la carte – ⊐ 9.95 – **96 rm** 93.00/129.00 **st.**, 4 suites – SB.

🏨 **Forte Posthouse Rochester,** Maidstone Rd, ME5 9SF, Southeast : 2½ m. by A 2 on A 229 *𝒫* (01634) 687111, *Fax* (01634) 864876, *Iₐ*, *≘s*, *◻*, *☞* – *⧚*, *✻* rm, ▤ rest, 📺 ☎ & **🅿** – *⌀* 110. **◍ⓞ** **VISA**. *✻*
**Meals** a la carte 16.35/22.85 **t.** ₰ 7.50 – ⊐ 9.95 – **145 rm** 95.00 **st.** – SB.

◍ ATS 82 King St. *𝒫* (01634) 820100

---

**ROCHFORD** *Essex* **404** W 29 – *pop. 15 081.*
*London 46 – Chelmsford 19 – Colchester 39 – Southend-on-Sea 3.*

🏨 **Renouf,** Bradley Way, SS4 1BU, *𝒫* (01702) 541334, *Fax* (01702) 549563, *☞* – ▤ rest, 📺 ☎ **🅿** – *⌀* 30. **◍ⓞ** **AE** **①** **VISA**. *✻*
*closed 26 to 30 December* – **Meals** *(closed Saturday lunch)* *(residents only Sunday dinner and Bank Holidays)* 17.50/28.50 **t.** ₰ 5.80 – **23 rm** ⊐ 59.50/109.50 **t.**

---

**ROCK** *Cornwall* **403** F 32 *The West Country G.* – *pop. 4 593* – ✉ *Wadebridge.*
Exc. : *Pencarrow★, SE : 8½ m. by B 3314 and A 389.*
*London 266 – Newquay 24 – Tintagel 14 – Truro 32.*

🏨 **St. Enodoc,** PL27 6LA, *𝒫* (01208) 863394, *Fax* (01208) 863970, *≼*, *斋*, *Iₐ*, *≘s*, *◻*, *☞*, squash – *✻* rm, 📺 ☎ ✆ **🅿**. **◍ⓞ** **AE** **①** **VISA**. *✻*
*closed 5 January-12 February* – *Porthilly Grill :* **Meals** *(light lunch)/dinner* 22.00 **st.** and a la carte – ⊐ 5.00 – **18 rm** 90.00/120.00 **st.**, 3 suites.

---

**ROGATE** *W. Sussex* **404** R 30 – *pop. 1 785* – ✉ *Petersfield (Hants.).*
*London 63 – Brighton 42 – Guildford 29 – Portsmouth 23 – Southampton 36.*

⌂ **Mizzards Farm** *≫ without rest.*, GU31 5HS, Southwest : 1 m. by Harting rd *𝒫* (01730) 821656, *Fax* (01730) 821655, *≼*, *« 17C farmhouse »*, *◻*, *☞*, park – *✻* 📺 **🅿**. *✻*
*closed Christmas* – **3 rm** ⊐ 38.00/62.00 **st.**

---

**ROLLESTON-ON-DOVE** *Staffs.* **402 403 404** P 25 – *see Burton-upon-Trent.*

---

**ROMALDKIRK** *Durham* **402** N 20 – *see Barnard Castle.*

**ROMSEY** Hants. 403 404 P 31 *Great Britain G.* – pop. 17 032.

See : *Abbey★ (interior★★).*

Env. : *Broadlands★ AC, S : 1 m.*

🏌 *Dunwood Manor, Shootash Hill ℘ (01794) 340549* – 🏌 *Nursling ℘ (01703) 732218* – 🏌, *Wellow, Ryedown Lane, East Wellow ℘ (01794) 322872.*

🏢 *1 Latimer St., SO51 8DF ℘ (01794) 512987.*

*London 82 – Bournemouth 28 – Salisbury 16 – Southampton 8 – Winchester 10.*

🏨 **White Horse,** Market Pl., SO51 8ZJ, ℘ (01794) 512431, *Fax (01794) 517485* – ↤↦ rm, [
☎ ℗ – 🛎 30. ⓦ ᴀᴇ ⓞ ⱽⁱˢᴬ ᴊᴄʙ
**Meals** 6.95 t. (lunch) and dinner a la carte 12.70/19.95 t. ᵈ 7.50 – ☲ 8.95 – **33 rm** 65.00/
100.00 t. – SB.

🏠 **Spursholt House** ⤳, Salisbury Rd, SO51 6DJ, West : 1 ¼ m. by A 3090 (old A 31) on A 2
℘ (01794) 512229, *Fax (01794) 523142,* « *Part 17C mansion, gardens* » – ↤↦ ℗
*closed 24 December-2 January* – **Meals** (by arrangement) (communal dining) – **3 r**
☲ 28.00/50.00 st.

🏠 **Highfield House** ⤳, Newtown Rd, Awbridge, SO51 0GG, Northwest : 3 ½ m. by A 309
(old A 31) and A 27 ℘ (01794) 340727, *Fax (01794) 341450,* 🌳 – ↤↦ rm, ⱶⱽ ℗. ✿
**Meals** (by arrangement) (communal dining) 15.00 s. – **3 rm** ☲ 55.00 s.

XXX **Old Manor House,** 21 Palmerston St., SO51 8GF, ℘ (01794) 517353, « *Timbered 16*
*house* » – ℗. ⓦ ᴀᴇ ⱽⁱˢᴬ
*closed Sunday dinner and Monday* – **Meals** a la carte 21.50/29.50 st. ᵈ 6.00.

🍴 **The Old Horse and Jockey,** 23 Mainstone, SO51 8HG, Southwest : ½ m. on A 309
℘ (01794) 519515, *Fax (01794) 814632,* 🌳 – ℗. ⓦ ⱽⁱˢᴬ
*closed 25 December* – **Meals** a la carte 16.25/22.50 t. ᵈ 6.00.

**at Ower** *Southwest : 3½ m. by A 3090 (old A 31) on A 36* – ✉ *Romsey.*

🏩 **Vine Inn - Premier Lodge,** Romsey Rd, SO51 6ZJ, ℘ (01703) 81433
*Fax (01703) 812123,* Reservations (Freephone) 0800 118833 – ↤↦ rm, ⱶⱽ ☎ ✆ ℗ – 🛎 15
ⓦ ᴀᴇ ⓞ ⱽⁱˢᴬ. ✿
**Meals** (grill rest.) a la carte 10.45/15.20 st. ᵈ 4.25 – ☲ 5.95 – **50 rm** 44.95 st. – SB.

---

**ROSEDALE ABBEY** N. Yorks. 402 R 20 *Great Britain G.* – pop. 332 (Rosedale) – ✉ *Pickering.*

Env. : *≼★ on road to Hutton-le-Hole.*

*London 247 – Middlesbrough 27 – Scarborough 25 – York 36.*

🏨 **Blacksmith's Arms,** Hartoft End, YO18 8EN, Southeast : 2 ½ m. on Pickering r
℘ (01751) 417331, *Fax (01751) 417167,* « *Part 16C* », 🌳 – ↤↦ rest, ⱶⱽ ☎ ℗. ⓦ ᴀᴇ ⓞ ⱽ
ᴊᴄʙ
**Meals** a la carte 12.15/18.15 st. ᵈ 5.95 – **13 rm** ☲ 45.00/70.00 t. – SB.

🏨 **Milburn Arms,** YO18 8RA, ℘ (01751) 417312, *Fax (01751) 417312,* 🌳 – ↤↦ rest, ⱶⱽ ☎
℗. ⓦ ⓞ ⱽⁱˢᴬ
*closed last 2 weeks January* – **Priory : Meals** (bar lunch Monday to Saturday)/dinne
19.50 t. and a la carte ᵈ 5.80 – **11 rm** ☲ 45.50/94.00 t. – SB.

---

**ROSS-ON-WYE** Herefordshire 403 404 M 28 *Great Britain G.* – pop. 9 606.

See : *Market House★ – Yat Rock (≼★).*

Env. : *SW : Wye Valley★ – Goodrich Castle★ AC, SW : 3½ m. by A 40.*

🏢 *Swan House, Edde Cross St., HR9 7BZ ℘ (01989) 562768.*

*London 118 – Gloucester 15 – Hereford 15 – Newport 35.*

🏨 **The Chase,** Gloucester Rd, HR9 5LH, ℘ (01989) 763161, *Fax (01989) 768330,* 🌳 – ⱶⱽ ☎
℗ – 🛎 250. ⓦ ᴀᴇ ⓞ ⱽⁱˢᴬ
*closed 26, 27 and 31 December* – **Meals** 15.00/25.00 st. ᵈ 4.50 – **38 rm** ☲ 60.00/115.00 sw
– SB.

🏨 **Royal,** Palace Pound, HR9 5HZ, ℘ (01989) 565105, *Fax (01989) 768058,* ≼, 🌳 – ↤↦ ⱶⱽ ☎
℗ – 🛎 80. ⓦ ᴀᴇ ⓞ ⱽⁱˢᴬ
**Meals** (bar lunch Monday to Saturday)/dinner 19.95 **st.** and a la carte ᵈ 8.95 – ☲ 9.75 –
**39 rm** 65.00/85.00 st. – SB.

🏠 **Travel Inn,** Ledbury Rd, HR9 7QJ, Northeast : 1 ½ m. by A 40 at junction with A 449 and
M 50 ℘ (01989) 563861, *Fax (01989) 566124* – ↤↦ rm, ⱶⱽ & ℗. ⓦ ᴀᴇ ⓞ ⱽⁱˢᴬ. ✿
**Meals** (grill rest.) – **43 rm** 38.00 t.

🏠 **Arches,** Walford Rd, HR9 5PT, on B 4234 ℘ (01989) 563348, 🌳 – ↤↦ ⱶⱽ ℗. ⓦ ⱽⁱˢᴬ. ✿
**Meals** (by arrangement) 12.00 st. ᵈ 3.00 – **5 rm** ☲ 25.00/46.00 st.

XX **Pheasants,** 52 Edde Cross St., HR9 7BZ, ℘ (01989) 565751 – ↤↦. ⓦ ᴀᴇ ⓞ ⱽⁱˢᴬ
*closed Sunday, Monday, 25 December-3 January and 1 to 7 June* – **Meals** (dinner only)
27.00 st..

**at Kerne Bridge** *South : 3 ¾ m. on B 4234 – ✉ Ross-on-Wye.*

**Lumleys** without rest., HR9 5QT, ✆ (01600) 890040, – – ✆ **P**
**3 rm** 25.00/50.00.

**at Glewstone** *Southwest : 3 ¼ m. by A 40 – ✉ Ross-on-Wye.*

**Glewstone Court,** HR9 6AW, ✆ (01989) 770367, *Fax (01989) 770282*, ≤, « Part Georgian and Victorian country house », – **P**. VISA JCB
*closed 25 to 27 December* – **Meals** (bar lunch Monday to Saturday)/dinner 25.00 **st.** 5.75 – **7 rm** 50.00/105.00 **st.** – SB.

**at Peterstow** *West : 2½ m. on A 49 – ✉ Ross-on-Wye.*

**Pengethley Manor**, HR9 6LL, Northwest : 1 ½ m. on A 49 ✆ (01989) 730211, *Fax (01989) 730238*, ≤, , , , park – **P** – 50. VISA
**Meals** 16.50/25.00 **t.** and dinner a la carte 9.95 – **22 rm** 75.00/160.00 **t.**, 3 suites – SB.

ATS Ind. Est., Alton Rd ✆ (01989) 564638

---

**ROSTHWAITE** *Cumbria* 402 K 20 – *see Keswick.*

---

**ROTHBURY** *Northd* 401 402 O 18 *Great Britain G. – pop. 1 805 –* ✉ *Morpeth.*

See : *Cragside House★ (interior★) AC.*

*National Park Information Centre, Church House, Church St., NE65 7UP ✆ (01669) 620887 (summer only).*

*London 311 – Edinburgh 84 – Newcastle upon Tyne 29.*

**Orchard** without rest., High St., NE65 7TL, ✆ (01669) 620684, – .
*Easter-October* – **6 rm** 21.00/46.00 **t.**

---

**ROTHERHAM** *S. Yorks.* 402 403 404 P 23 – *pop. 121 380.*

*Thrybergh Park ✆ (01709) 850466 – Grange Park, Upper Wortley Rd, Kimberworth ✆ (01709) 558884 – Phoenix, Pavilion Lane, Brinsworth ✆ (01709) 363788.*

*Central Library, Walker Pl., S65 1JH ✆ (01709) 823611.*

*London 166 – Kingston-upon-Hull 61 – Leeds 36 – Sheffield 6.*

**Hellaby Hall,** Old Hellaby Lane, Hellaby, S66 8SN, East : 5 ¼ m. by A 6021 off A 631 ✆ (01709) 702701, *Fax (01709) 700979*, « Part 17C hall with Dutch colonial influences », – , rm, **P** – 140. VISA JCB
***Attic* : Meals** (dancing Friday and Saturday evenings) (bar lunch Saturday) 12.50/20.00 **t.** and a la carte – **51 rm** 90.00/105.00 **t.**, 1 suite – SB.

**Swallow,** West Bawtry Rd, S60 4NA, South : 2 ¼ m. on A 630 ✆ (01709) 830630, *Fax (01709) 830549*, , – **P** – 300. VISA
**Meals** (bar lunch Monday to Saturday)/dinner 17.00 **st.** and a la carte 20.50/32.50 **st.** – **98 rm** 90.00/115.00 **st.**, 2 suites – SB.

**County H. Rotherham Carlton Park,** 102-104 Moorgate Rd, S60 2BG, ✆ (01709) 849955, *Fax (01709) 368960*, , – , rm, rest, **P** – 250. VISA.
**Meals** a la carte 11.70/21.65 **t.** 5.75 – 9.50 – **76 rm** 80.00/110.00 **st.** – SB.

**Travel Inn,** Bawtry Rd, S65 3JB, East : 2 m. by A 6021 on A 631 ✆ (01709) 543216, *Fax (01709) 531546* – rm, rest, **P**. VISA.
**Meals** (grill rest.) – **37 rm** 38.00 **t.**

**Campanile,** Lowton Way, Hellaby Ind. Est., S66 8RY, East : 5 m. by A 6021 and A 631 off Denby Way ✆ (01709) 700255, *Fax (01709) 545169* – rm, **P** – 30. VISA
**Meals** (grill rest.) 10.85 **st.** and a la carte – 4.50 – **50 rm** 36.50 **st.**

**at Bramley** *East : 4½ m. by A 6021 off A 631 – ✉ Rotherham.*

**Elton,** Main St., off Cross St., S66 2SF, ✆ (01709) 545681, *Fax (01709) 549100* – rm, **P** – 40. VISA JCB
**Meals** 11.50/20.00 **st.** and a la carte 5.95 – 8.95 – **29 rm** 53.00/75.00 **st.** – SB.

ATS Eastwood Works, Fitzwilliam Rd ✆ (01709) 371556/372391

---

**ROTHERWICK** *Hants – see Hook.*

---

**ROTHLEY** *Leics.* 402 403 404 Q 25 – *see Leicester.*

**ROUGHAM GREEN** Suffolk – *see Bury St. Edmunds.*

**ROWDE** Wilts. 403 404 N 29 – *see Devizes*

**ROWNHAMS SERVICE AREA** Hants. 403 404 P 31 – ⊠ *Southampton.*
🛈 M 27 Services (westbound), SO1 8AW 𝒫 (01703) 730345.

🏠 **RoadChef Lodge** without rest., SO16 8AP, M 27 between junctions 3 and 4 (southbour carriageway) 𝒫 (01703) 741144, Fax (01703) 740204, Reservations (Freephone) 080 834719 – ⚒ 📺 ☎ 🔥 🅿. 🚫 🆎 ⓪ 🚫 ⚒
closed Christmas and New Year – **39 rm** 45.95 **t.**

**ROWSLEY** Derbs. 402 403 404 P 24 *Great Britain G.* – *pop. 451* – ⊠ *Matlock.*
Env. : *Chatsworth★★★ (Park and Garden★★★) AC, N : by B 6012.*
London 157 – Derby 23 – Manchester 40 – Nottingham 30.

🏠🏠 **The Peacock,** Bakewell Rd, DE4 2EB, 𝒫 (01629) 733518, Fax (01629) 732671, « 17C stor house, antiques », ⛵, ☞ – ⚒ rest, 📺 ☎ 🅿. 🚫 🆎 ⓪ 🚫 🇯🇨🇧. ⚒
**Meals** 15.50/23.50 **t.** ⅄ 9.00 – ⊊ 9.50 – **16 rm** 90.00/110.00 **t.** – SB.

🏠🏠 **East Lodge,** DE4 2EF, 𝒫 (01629) 734474, Fax (01629) 733949, ☞, park – ⚒ rest, 📺 ◀ 🔥 🅿. 🚫 🆎 🚫, ⚒
**Meals** 22.95 **t.** (dinner) and lunch a la carte 14.60/25.00 **t.** – **15 rm** ⊊ 68.00/124.00 **t.** – SB

**ROWTON** Ches. 402 403 L 24 – *see Chester.*

**ROYAL LEAMINGTON SPA** Warks. 403 404 P 27 – *pop. 55 396.*
🏌 Leamington and County, Golf Lane, Whitnash 𝒫 (01926) 425961 (on plan of Warwick).
🛈 Jephson Lodge, Jephson Gardens, The Parade, CV32 4AB 𝒫 (01926) 311470.
London 99 – Birmingham 23 – Coventry 9 – Warwick 3.

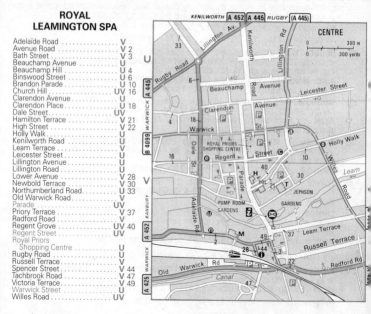

**ROYAL LEAMINGTON SPA**

| | |
|---|---|
| Adelaïde Road | V |
| Avenue Road | V 2 |
| Bath Street | V 3 |
| Beauchamp Avenue | U |
| Beauchamp Hill | U 4 |
| Binswood Street | U 6 |
| Brandon Parade | U 10 |
| Church Hill | UV 16 |
| Clarendon Avenue | U |
| Clarendon Place | U 18 |
| Dale Street | UV |
| Hamilton Terrace | V 21 |
| High Street | V 22 |
| Holly Walk | U |
| Kenilworth Road | V |
| Leam Terrace | V |
| Leicester Street | U |
| Lillington Avenue | U |
| Lillington Road | U |
| Lower Avenue | V 28 |
| Newbold Terrace | V 30 |
| Northumberland Road | U 33 |
| Old Warwick Road | V |
| Parade | UV |
| Priory Terrace | V 37 |
| Radford Road | V |
| Regent Grove | UV 40 |
| Regent Street | V |
| Royal Priors Shopping Centre | U |
| Rugby Road | U |
| Russell Terrace | V |
| Spencer Street | V 44 |
| Tachbrook Road | V 47 |
| Victoria Terrace | V 49 |
| Warwick Street | V |
| Willes Road | UV |

🏠🏠🏠 **Mallory Court** ⚓, Harbury Lane, Bishop's Tachbrook, CV33 9QB, South : 2 ¼ m. by 4087 (Tachbrook Rd) 𝒫 (01926) 330214, Fax (01926) 451714, ≤, ☞, « Country house i extensive gardens », ⚒ – ⚒ rest, 📺 ☎ ⇔ 🅿. 🚫 🚫. ⚒
**Meals** (booking essential) 27.00/38.00 **st.** and a la carte – ⊊ 12.50 – **10 rm** 150.00 265.00 **st.** – SB.

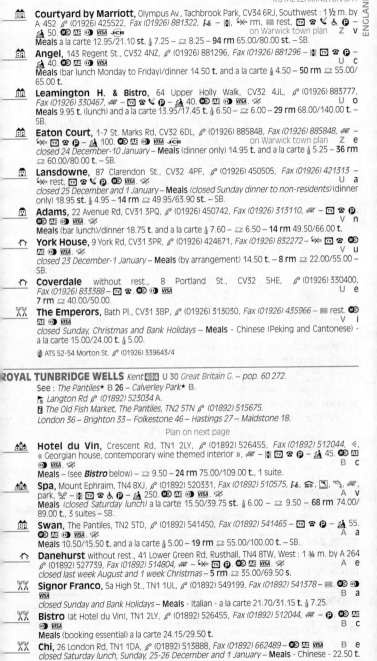

**Courtyard by Marriott,** Olympus Av., Tachbrook Park, CV34 6RJ, Southwest : 1 ½ m. by A 452 ℘ (01926) 425522, Fax (01926) 881322, ₭ – ₪, ₩ rm, ▤ rest, ▥ ☎ ✆ ₺ ₱ – ₳ 50. ₥ ℻ ① VISA JCB
on Warwick town plan  Z  v
Meals a la carte 12.95/21.10 **st.** ₰ 7.25 – ☲ 8.25 – **94 rm** 65.00/80.00 **st.** – SB.

**Angel,** 143 Regent St., CV32 4NZ, ℘ (01926) 881296, Fax (01926) 881296 – ₪ ▥ ☎ ₱ –
₳ 40. ₥ ℻ ① VISA
U  c
**Meals** (bar lunch Monday to Friday)/dinner 14.50 **t.** and a la carte ₰ 4.50 – **50 rm** ☲ 55.00/
65.00 **t.**

**Leamington H. & Bistro,** 64 Upper Holly Walk, CV32 4JL, ℘ (01926) 883777, Fax (01926) 330467, ☞ – ▥ ☎ ✆ ₱ – ₳ 40. ₥ ℻ ① VISA. ℅
U  o
**Meals** 9.95 **t.** (lunch) and a la carte 13.95/17.45 **t.** ₰ 6.50 – ☲ 6.00 – **29 rm** 68.00/140.00 **t.** –
SB.

**Eaton Court,** 1-7 St. Marks Rd, CV32 6DL, ℘ (01926) 885848, Fax (01926) 885848, ☞ –
₩ ▥ ☎ ₱ – ₳ 100. ₥ ℻ ① VISA JCB
on Warwick town plan  Z  e
closed 24 December-10 January – **Meals** (dinner only) 14.95 **t.** and a la carte ₰ 5.25 – **36 rm**
☲ 60.00/80.00 **t.** – SB.

**Lansdowne,** 87 Clarendon St., CV32 4PF, ℘ (01926) 450505, Fax (01926) 421313 –
₩ rest. ▥ ☎ ✆ ₱. ₥ ℻ ① VISA. ℅
U  a
closed 25 December and 1 January – **Meals** (closed Sunday dinner to non-residents) (dinner
only) 18.95 **st.** ₰ 4.95 – **14 rm** ☲ 49.95/63.90 **st.** – SB.

**Adams,** 22 Avenue Rd, CV31 3PQ, ℘ (01926) 450742, Fax (01926) 313110, ☞ – ▥ ☎ ₱.
₥ ℻ ① VISA
V  n
**Meals** (bar lunch)/dinner 18.75 **t.** and a la carte ₰ 7.60 – ☲ 6.50 – **14 rm** 49.50/66.00 **t.**

**York House,** 9 York Rd, CV31 3PR, ℘ (01926) 424671, Fax (01926) 832272 – ₩ ▥ ☎. ₥
℻ ① VISA. ℅
V  u
closed 23 December-1 January – **Meals** (by arrangement) 14.50 **t.** – **8 rm** ☲ 22.00/55.00 –
SB.

**Coverdale** without rest., 8 Portland St., CV32 5HE, ℘ (01926) 330400,
Fax (01926) 833388 – ▥ ☎. ₥ ℻ ① VISA
U  e
**7 rm** ☲ 40.00/50.00.

**The Emperors,** Bath Pl., CV31 3BP, ℘ (01926) 313030, Fax (01926) 435966 – ▤ rest. ₥
℻ ① VISA
V  i
closed Sunday, Christmas and Bank Holidays – **Meals** - Chinese (Peking and Cantonese) -
a la carte 15.00/24.00 **t.** ₰ 5.00.

 ⓐ ATS 52-54 Morton St. ℘ (01926) 339643/4

---

**ROYAL TUNBRIDGE WELLS** Kent ▧▨▨ U 30 Great Britain G. – pop. 60 272.
See : The Pantiles★ B 26 – Calverley Park★ B.
₮ₛ Langton Rd ℘ (01892) 523034 A.
🛈 The Old Fish Market, The Pantiles, TN2 5TN ℘ (01892) 515675.
London 36 – Brighton 33 – Folkestone 46 – Hastings 27 – Maidstone 18.

Plan on next page

**Hotel du Vin,** Crescent Rd, TN1 2LY, ℘ (01892) 526455, Fax (01892) 512044, ≤,
« Georgian house, contemporary wine themed interior », ☞ – ₪ ▥ ☎ ₱ – ₳ 45. ₥ ℻
① VISA. ℅
B  c
**Meals** – (see **Bistro** below) – ☲ 9.50 – **24 rm** 75.00/109.00 **t.**, 1 suite.

**Spa,** Mount Ephraim, TN4 8XJ, ℘ (01892) 520331, Fax (01892) 510575, ₭, ≋, ◫, ⍩, ☞,
park, ℅ – ₪ ▥ ☎ ₺ ₱ – ₳ 250. ₥ ℻ ① VISA. ℅
A  v
**Meals** (closed Saturday lunch) a la carte 15.50/39.75 **st.** ₰ 6.00 – ☲ 9.50 – **68 rm** 74.00/
89.00 **t.**, 3 suites – SB.

**Swan,** The Pantiles, TN2 5TD, ℘ (01892) 541450, Fax (01892) 541465 – ▥ ☎ ₱ – ₳ 55.
₥ ℻ ① VISA. ℅
A  a
**Meals** 10.50/15.50 **t.** and a la carte ₰ 5.00 – **19 rm** ☲ 55.00/100.00 **t.** – SB.

**Danehurst** without rest., 41 Lower Green Rd, Rusthall, TN4 8TW, West : 1 ¾ m. by A 264
℘ (01892) 527739, Fax (01892) 514804, ☞ – ₩ ▥ ₱. ₥ ℻ ① VISA. ℅
A  e
closed last week August and 1 week Christmas – **5 rm** ☲ 35.00/69.50 **s.**

**Signor Franco,** 5a High St., TN1 1UL, ℘ (01892) 549199, Fax (01892) 541378 – ▤. ₥ ①
VISA
B  a
closed Sunday and Bank Holidays – **Meals** - Italian - a la carte 21.70/31.15 **t.** ₰ 7.25.

**Bistro** (at Hotel du Vin), TN1 2LY, ℘ (01892) 526455, Fax (01892) 512044, ☞ – ₱. ₥ ℻
① VISA
B  c
**Meals** (booking essential) a la carte 24.15/29.50 **t.**

**Chi,** 26 London Rd, TN1 1DA, ℘ (01892) 513888, Fax (01892) 662489 – ₥ ℻ VISA
B  e
closed Saturday lunch, Sunday, 25-26 December and 1 January – **Meals** - Chinese - 22.50 **t.**
and a la carte.

## ROYAL TUNBRIDGE WELLS

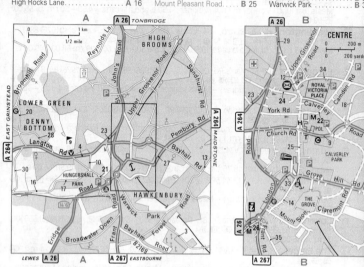

**at Pembury** *Northeast : 4 m. by A 264 off B 2015* – A – ⊠ *Royal Tunbridge Wells.*

🏨 **Jarvis International**, 8 Tonbridge Rd, TN2 4QL, ℰ (01892) 823567, *Fax (01892) 82393*
⇔, 🔲 – ⇔ 📺 ☎ ᕦ 🅿 – 🔬 200. 🅐🅒 🅐🅔 ⓪ 𝘝𝘐𝘚𝘈
**Meals** (bar lunch Saturday) 12.50/17.95 **st.** and a la carte ₤ 7.95 – ☷ 9.50 – **82 rm** 109.00
120.00 **st.**, 2 suites – SB.

**at Frant** *South : 2½ m. on A 267* – A – ⊠ *Royal Tunbridge Wells.*

⌂ **Old Parsonage** ⤳ *without rest.*, Church Lane, TN3 9DX, ℰ (01892) 750773
*Fax (01892) 750773*, ≼, « Georgian rectory », ☞ – ⇔ 📺 🅿. 🅐🅒 𝘝𝘐𝘚𝘈
**3 rm** ☷ 55.00/72.00 **st.**

XX **Restaurant 37**, 37 High St., TN3 9DT, ℰ (01892) 750635, *Fax (01892) 750635*, « 15C » –
⇔. 🅐🅒 🅐🅔 𝘝𝘐𝘚𝘈 🅹🅲🅱
*closed Saturday lunch, Sunday dinner and Monday* – **Meals** 17.00/24.00 **st.** and a la carte
₤ 8.00.

**at Langton Green** *West : 2 m. on A 264* – ⊠ *Royal Tunbridge Wells.*

🍴 **Hare**, Langton Rd, TN3 0JA, ℰ (01892) 862419, *Fax (01892) 861275*, 佘 – 🅿. 🅐🅒 🅐🅔 𝘝𝘐𝘚𝘈
*closed 25 December and 1 January* – **Meals** a la carte 14.40/23.85 **t.**

---

**ROZEL BAY** *Jersey (Channel Islands)* 𝟜𝟘𝟛 P 33 and 𝟚𝟛𝟘 ⑪ – *see Channel Islands.*

---

**RUAN-HIGH-LANES** *Cornwall* 𝟜𝟘𝟛 F 33 – *see Veryan.*

---

**RUCKHALL** *Herefordshire – see Hereford.*

---

**RUGBY** *Warks.* 𝟜𝟘𝟛 𝟜𝟘𝟜 Q 26 – *pop.* 61 106.
🔟 *Whitefields Hotel, Coventry Rd, Thurlaston* ℰ (01788) 521800.
🔼 *The Library, St. Matthews St., CV21 3BZ* ℰ (01788) 535348.
*London 88 – Birmingham 33 – Leicester 21 – Northampton 20 – Warwick 17.*

🏨 **Rugby Grosvenor**, 81-87 Clifton Rd, CV21 3QQ, on B 5414 ℘ (01788) 535686, *Fax (01788) 541297*, ₤₅, ≋, 🔲 – 🔟 ☎ 🅿. 🕮 🕮 🕦 *VISA* *JCB*
*closed Christmas, New Year and Bank Holidays* – **Meals** *(closed Sunday lunch)* a la carte 18.15/24.40 **t.** – ☲ 6.50 – **26 rm** 69.50/79.50 **t.**

XX **Imperial**, 3-5 Castle St., CV21 2TP, ℘ (01788) 542326, *Fax (01788) 542326* – 🔳. 🕮 🕮 *VISA*
**Meals** - Chinese - (buffet lunch Sunday) a la carte 14.50/16.50 **t.**

🔹**t Old Brownsover** *North : 2 m. by A 426 and Brownsover Rd* – ✉ *Rugby.*

🏨 **Brownsover Hall**, Brownsover Lane, CV21 1HU, ℘ (01788) 546100, *Fax (01788) 579241*, « 19C Gothic style hall », 🌲, park – ✸ rm, 🔟 ☎ 🅿 – 🔬 80. 🕮 🕮 🕦 *VISA*
**Meals** *(closed Saturday lunch)* 12.95/19.95 **st.** and dinner a la carte ⅙ 6.85 – ☲ 9.25 – **31 rm** 90.00/105.00 **st.** – SB.

🔹**t Crick** *Southeast : 6 m. on A 428.*

🏨 **Forte Posthouse Rugby/Northampton**, NN6 7XR, West : ½ m. on A 428 ℘ (01788) 822101, *Fax (01788) 823955*, ₤₅, ≋, 🔲 – ✸ rm, 🔳 rest, 🔟 ☎ 🅿 – 🔬 200. 🕮 🕮 🕦 *VISA* *JCB*
**Meals** a la carte 17.65/26.85 **st.** – ☲ 8.95 – **88 rm** 89.00 **st.** – SB.

🔹**t West Haddon** *(Northants.) Southeast : 10 m. on A 428.*

🏠 **Pytchley Inn**, 23 High St., NN6 7AP, ℘ (01788) 510426, *Fax (01788) 510209*, 🌲 – 🔟 ☎ 🅿. 🕮 🕮 *VISA*. ✸
*closed 25 and 26 December* – **Meals** (grill rest.) a la carte 8.60/18.70 **t.** ⅙ 6.25 – **17 rm** ☲ 39.00/80.00 **t.**

⑩ ATS 73 Bath St. ℘ (01788) 574705

---

**Les prix**   Pour toutes précisions sur les prix indiqués dans ce guide, reportez-vous aux pages de l'introduction.

---

**RUGELEY** *Staffs.* 🕮🕮🕮 O 25 – *pop. 22 975.*
*London 134 – Birmingham 31 – Derby 29 – Stoke-on-Trent 22.*

🏠 **Travelodge**, Western Springs Rd, WS15 2AS, at junction of A 51 with A 460 ℘ (01889) 570096, *Fax (01889) 570096*, Reservations (Freephone) 0800 850950 – ✸ rm, 🔟 ₺ 🅿. 🕮 🕮 🕦 *VISA* *JCB*. ✸
**Meals** (grill rest.) – **32 rm** 39.95/59.95 **t.**

⑩ ATS Mill Lane ℘ (01889) 582500/578600

---

**RUMWELL** *Somerset* – see Taunton.

---

**RUNCORN** *Ches.* 🕮🕮 🕮🕮 L 23 – *pop. 64 154.*
🏌 *Clifton Rd* ℘ (01928) 572093.
*London 202 – Liverpool 14 – Manchester 29.*

🏨 **Forte Posthouse Warrington/Runcorn**, Wood Lane, Beechwood, WA7 3HA, Southeast : ½ m. off junction 12 of M 56 ℘ (01928) 714000, *Fax (01928) 714611*, ₤₅, ≋, 🔲, 🌲 – 🛗, ✸ rm, 🔟 ☎ 🅿 – 🔬 500. 🕮 🕮 🕦 *VISA* *JCB*
**Meals** *(closed Saturday lunch)* a la carte 18.80/25.80 **st.** – ☲ 9.95 – **136 rm** 89.00 **st.** – SB.

🏠 **Campanile**, Lowlands Rd, WA7 5TP, beside the railway station ℘ (01928) 581771, *Fax (01928) 581730* – ✸ rm, 🔟 ☎ ₺ 🅿 – 🔬 30. 🕮 🕮 🕦 *VISA*
**Meals** 10.85 **st.** and a la carte – ☲ 4.50 – **53 rm** 36.50 **t.**

🏠 **Travel Inn**, Chester Rd, Preston Brook, WA7 3BB, Southeast : 6 m. by A 533 on A 56 ℘ (01928) 716829, *Fax (01928) 719852* – ✸ rm, 🔳 rest, 🔟 ₺ 🅿 – 🔬 40. 🕮 🕮 🕦 *VISA*. ✸
**Meals** (grill rest.) – **40 rm** 38.00 **t.**

⑩ ATS Walkers Island Garage, Greenway Rd ℘ (01928) 567715

---

**RUSHDEN** *Northants.* 🕮🕮🕮 S 27 – *pop. 23 854.*
*London 74 – Cambridge 42 – Northampton 14 – Peterborough 25.*

🏠 **Travelodge**, NN10 9EP, on A 45 (eastbound carriageway) ℘ (01933) 357008, *Fax (01933) 411325*, Reservations (Freephone) 0800 850950 – ✸ rm, 🔟 ₺ 🅿. 🕮 🕮 🕦 *VISA* *JCB*. ✸
**Meals** (grill rest.) – **40 rm** 39.95/59.95 **t.**

**RUSHLAKE GREEN** E. Sussex 404 U 31 – ⊠ Heathfield.
London 54 – Brighton 26 – Eastbourne 13.

🏠 **Stone House** ⤴, TN21 9QJ, Northeast corner of the green ℰ (01435) 83055
Fax (01435) 830726, ⩽, « Part 15C, part Georgian country house, antiques », ⬝, ⛳, park
📺 ☎ 🅿. ⚘
closed 24 December-29 January – Meals (residents only) (dinner only) 24.95 st. 🛈 5.50
6 rm ⚏ 80.00/195.00 st., 1 suite.

**RUSHYFORD** Durham 401 402 P 20.
London 269 – Carlisle 82 – Middlesbrough 14 – Newcastle upon Tyne 26 – Sunderland 22.

🏨 **Eden Arms,** DL17 0LL, ℰ (01388) 720541, Fax (01388) 721871, 🛵, ⬮, 🔲 – ⅙ rm, 📺
🅿 – 🔬 100. 🆗 🆎 ① 𝗩𝗜𝗦𝗔
Meals (closed Saturday lunch) 22.00 t. and a la carte 🛈 5.50 – 45 rm ⚏ 92.00/130.00 st.
SB.

**RYDE** I.O.W. 403 404 Q 31 – see Wight (Isle of).

**RYE** E. Sussex 404 W 31 Great Britain G. – pop. 3 708.
See : Old Town★★ : Mermaid Street★, St. Mary's Church (⩽★).
🛈 The Heritage Centre, Strand Quay, TN31 7AY ℰ (01797) 226696.
London 61 – Brighton 49 – Folkestone 27 – Maidstone 33.

🏨 **Mermaid Inn,** Mermaid St., TN31 7EY, ℰ (01797) 223065, Fax (01797) 225069, « 15C »
📺 ☎ 🅿. 🆗 🆎 ① 𝗩𝗜𝗦𝗔 ⚘
Meals 16.00/29.00 t. and a la carte 🛈 10.95 – 30 rm ⚏ 68.00/154.00 st. – SB.

🏨 **George,** High St., TN31 7JP, ℰ (01797) 222114, Fax (01797) 224065 – ⅙ rm 📺 ☎ – 🔬 6
🆗 🆎 ① 𝗩𝗜𝗦𝗔
Meals (residents only 25 and 26 December) (bar lunch Monday to Saturday)/(dinner 18.00 s
🛈 6.90 – ⚏ 8.95 – 22 rm 75.00/95.00 – SB.

🏨 **Rye Lodge,** Hilders Cliff, TN31 7LD, ℰ (01797) 223838, Fax (01797) 223585 – ⅙ rest, 🔲
☎ 🅿. 🆗 🆎 ① 𝗩𝗜𝗦𝗔 𝗝𝗖𝗕
Meals (bar lunch)/dinner 19.50 t. and a la carte 🛈 5.75 – 20 rm ⚏ 49.50/110.00 t. – SB.

🏠 **Jeake's House** without rest., Mermaid St., TN31 7ET, ℰ (01797) 22282⟨
Fax (01797) 222623, « Part 17C » – 📺 ☎. 🆗 𝗩𝗜𝗦𝗔
12 rm ⚏ 25.50/89.00 st.

🏠 **Old Vicarage** without rest., 66 Church Sq., TN31 7HF, ℰ (01797) 22211
Fax (01797) 227466, « Part 14C », ⛐ – ⅙ 📺 🅿. ⚘
closed 24 to 26 December – 5 rm ⚏ 38.00/62.00 st.

🏠 **Little Orchard House** without rest., West St., TN31 7ES, ℰ (01797) 22383⟨
Fax (01797) 223831, ⛐ – ⅙ 📺. 🆗 𝗩𝗜𝗦𝗔. ⚘
3 rm ⚏ 45.00/84.00 st.

✗✗ **Flushing Inn,** 4 Market St., TN31 7LA, ℰ (01797) 223292, « 15C inn with 16C mural »
⅙ ⩽. 🆗 🆎 ① 𝗩𝗜𝗦𝗔
closed Monday dinner, Tuesday and 31 December-third week January – Meals - Seafood
15.00/27.00 t. and a la carte 🛈 5.40.

✗ **Landgate Bistro,** 5-6 Landgate, TN31 7LH, ℰ (01797) 222829 – 🆗 🆎 ① 𝗩𝗜𝗦𝗔 𝗝𝗖𝗕
closed Sunday, Monday, 1 week in summer, 1 week in autumn and 1 week Christmas
Meals (dinner only) 16.50 st. and a la carte 🛈 4.50.

**at Rye Foreign** Northwest : 2 m. on A 268 – ⊠ Rye.

🏠 **Broomhill Lodge,** TN31 7UN, on A 268 ℰ (01797) 280421, Fax (01797) 280402, 🛵, ⬮
⛐ – 📺 ☎ ⛾ 🅿 – 🔬 40. 🆗 𝗩𝗜𝗦𝗔. ⚘
Meals (dinner only) 23.50 – 10 rm ⚏ 48.00/140.00 – SB.

**at Peasmarsh** Northwest : 4 m. on A 268 – ⊠ Rye.

🏨 **Flackley Ash,** London Rd, TN31 6YH, on A 268 ℰ (01797) 230651, Fax (01797) 23051⟨
🛵, ⬮, 🔲, ⛐ – ⅙ rest, 📺 ☎ ♿ 🅿 – 🔬 100. 🆗 🆎 ① 𝗩𝗜𝗦𝗔 𝗝𝗖𝗕
Meals (bar lunch)/dinner 22.50 st. 🛈 5.95 – 40 rm ⚏ 75.00/145.00 st., 2 suites – SB.

**RYE FOREIGN** E. Sussex – see Rye.

**RYLSTONE** N. Yorks. 402 N 21 – see Skipton.

**RYTON ON DUNSMORE** W. Mids. 403 404 P 28 – see Coventry.

**AFFRON WALDEN** *Essex* **404** U 27 *Great Britain G. – pop. 13 201.*

See : *Audley End★★ AC.*

🖪 *1 Market Pl., Market Sq., CB10 1HR* ℰ *(01799) 510444.*

*London 46 – Cambridge 15 – Chelmsford 25.*

⭕ **Bridge End Orchard** without rest., 35 Bridge St., CB10 1BT, ℰ *(01799) 522001,* Fax *(01799) 524576,* 🌳 – ❄ 📺 🅿. 🕮 *VISA*. ⚸
**3 rm** ⚌ 50.00/56.00 st.

⭓ **Littlebury Green** *West : 4½ m. by B 1383 –* ⊠ *Saffron Walden.*

⭕ **Elmdon Lee**, CB11 4XB, ℰ *(01763) 838237,* Fax *(01763) 838237,* 🌳 – 📺 🅿. 🕮 ⓞ *VISA.* ⚸
*closed 25 December –* **Meals** *(by arrangement) (communal dining)* 18.00 s. ⓐ 9.00 – **4 rm** ⚌ 32.00/70.00 s.

⭓ **Duddenhoe End** *West : 7½ m. by B 1052 and B 1383 off B 1039 –* ⊠ *Saffron Walden.*

⭕ **Duddenhoe End Farm** without rest., CB11 4UU, ℰ *(01763) 838258,* 🌳, park – ❄ 📺 🅿. ⚸
*closed 20 December-20 January –* **3 rm** ⚌ 28.00/48.00.

⭓ **Elmdon** *West : 7½ m. by B 1052 and B 1383 off B 1039 –* ⊠ *Saffron Walden.*

⭕ **Elmdon Bury** ⚜, CB11 4NF, ℰ *(01763) 838220,* Fax *(01763) 838504,* ◩, 🌳, park, ⚹ – ❄ rm, 🅿. ⚸
*closed 22 December-6 January –* **Meals** *(by arrangement) (communal dining) (dinner only) (unlicensed)* 18.00 s. – **3 rm** ⚌ 30.00/50.00 s.

🔘 *ATS Station Rd* ℰ *(01799) 521426*

*When looking for a quiet hotel*
*use the maps found in the introduction*
*or look for establishments with the sign* ⚜ *or* ⚜*.*

**T. AGNES** *Cornwall* **403** E 33 *The West Country G. – pop. 2 899.*

See : *St. Agnes Beacon★★ (❄★★).*

Env. : *Portreath★, SW : 5½ m.*

📛 *Perranporth, Budnic Hill* ℰ *(01872) 572454.*

*London 302 – Newquay 12 – Penzance 26 – Truro 9.*

🏠 **Rose-in-Vale** ⚜, Mithian, TR5 0QD, East : 2 m. by B 3285 ℰ *(01872) 552202,* Fax *(01872) 552700,* ◪, 🌳 – ❄ rest, 📺 ☎ 🅿. 🕮 🜉 ⓞ *VISA*
*closed January –* **Meals** *(bar lunch)/dinner* 21.95 st. and a la carte ⓐ 4.50 – **18 rm** ⚌ 48.00/88.00 st. – SB.

**T. ALBANS** *Herts.* **404** T 28 *Great Britain G. – pop. 80 376.*

See : *City★ - Cathedral★ - Verulamium★ (Museum★ AC).*

Env. : *Hatfield House★★ AC, E : 6 m. by A 1057.*

📛 *Batchwood Hall, Batchwood Drive* ℰ *(01727) 833349 –* 📛, 📛 *Kinsbourne Green Lane, Redbourn* ℰ *(01582) 793493.*

🖪 *Town Hall, Market Pl., AL3 5DJ* ℰ *(01727) 864511.*

*London 27 – Cambridge 41 – Luton 10.*

🏨 **Sopwell House** ⚜, Cottonmill Lane, AL1 2HQ, Southeast : 1½ m. by A 1081 and Mile House Lane ℰ *(01727) 864477,* Fax *(01727) 844741,* 🌫, Ⓕ₆, ☎ₛ, ◪, 🌳, park – ⧈ 📺 ☎ 🅿 – 🔬 400. 🕮 🜉 ⓞ
***Bejerano's Brasserie :*** Meals a la carte 13.70/20.85 t. – (see also **Magnolia Conservatory** below) – ⚌ 11.50 – **90 rm** 114.75/144.75 t., 2 suites – SB.

🏨 **Thistle Noke**, Watford Rd, AL2 3DS, Southwest : 2½ m. at junction of A 405 with B 4630 ℰ *(01727) 854252,* Fax *(01727) 841906,* Ⓕ₆ – ❄ rm, ▤ rest, 📺 ☎ 🅿 – 🔬 50. 🕮 🜉 ⓞ *VISA* 🇯🇨🇧
**Meals** *(closed lunch Saturday and Bank Holidays and 27 to 30 December)* 19.50/24.00 t. and a la carte ⓐ 6.50 – ⚌ 11.00 – **109 rm** 109.00/121.00 t., 2 suites.

🏨 **The Manor 'St. Michael's Village'**, Fishpool St., AL3 4RY, ℰ *(01727) 864444,* Fax *(01727) 848909,* ≼, « *Part 16C, part William and Mary manor house, lake and gardens* » – ❄ rm, 🅿. 🕮 🜉 ⓞ ⚸
**Meals** 19.95/29.50 t. ⓐ 10.00 – **22 rm** ⚌ 105.00/225.00 t., 1 suite – SB.

🏠 **Pré**, Redbourn Rd, AL3 6JZ, Northwest : 1¼ m. on A 5183 ℰ *(01727) 855259,* Fax *(01727) 852239,* 🌳 – ❄ rest, 📺 ☎ 🅿. 🕮 🜉 *VISA*. ⚸
*closed 25 December –* **Meals** *(grill rest.)* a la carte 10.80/17.00 t. ⓐ 6.00 – **11 rm** ⚌ 55.00/65.00 t.

🏛 **Nonna Rosa,** 3 Manor Rd, AL1 3ST, ℰ (01727) 853613, Fax (01727) 853613, 斧 – 📺 ☎
🅿 🕮 AE ⓪ VISA ⚇
Meals a la carte 15.50/18.50 t. – 10 rm ⌷ 30.00/55.00 st.

🏛 **Ardmore House,** 54 Lemsford Rd, AL1 3PR, ℰ (01727) 859313, Fax (01727) 859313,
– 📺 ☎ 🅿 🕮 AE VISA JCB. ⚇
Meals (dinner only) a la carte 10.45/22.00 st. – 40 rm ⌷ 49.50/85.00 st.

🏛 **Black Lion Inn,** 198 Fishpool St., AL3 4SB, ℰ (01727) 851786, Fax (01727) 859243 – 📺
🕭 🅿 🕮 AE VISA JCB
Meals - Italian - (closed Monday lunch and Sunday) 20.75/25.25 t. ⓵ 6.00 – ⌷ 5.95 – 16 rm
50.00/52.00 t.

⌂ **Orchard House** ⚇ without rest., Orchard House Lane, Holywell Hill, AL1 1E
ℰ (01727) 856520, Fax (01727) 840957 – ⚇ 📺 🅿. ⚇
3 rm ⌷ 40.00/60.00 s.

XXX **Magnolia Conservatory** (at Sopwell House H.), Cottonmill Lane, AL1 2HQ, Southeas
1 ½ m. by A 1081 and Mile House Lane ℰ (01727) 864477, Fax (01727) 844741 – ⚇ 🅿. 🕮
AE ⓪ VISA
closed Saturday lunch, Sunday dinner and Bank Holiday Mondays – Meals 16.95/24.00
and a la carte ⓵ 10.50.

X **Sukiyaki,** 6 Spencer St., AL3 5EG, ℰ (01727) 865009 – 🕮 AE ⓪ VISA JCB
closed Sunday, Monday, 25 December, 1 January, 2 weeks in summer and Bank Holidays
Meals - Japanese - (dinner only) 17.50 t. and a la carte 13.00/24.00 t.

🅖 ATS 163 Victoria St. ℰ (01727) 835174          ATS Lyon Way, Hatfield Rd ℰ (01727) 852314

*Le Guide change, changez de guide Michelin tous les ans.*

---

**ST. ANNE** Alderney (Channel Islands) 403 Q 33 and 230 ⑨ – see Channel Islands.

---

**ST. AUBIN** Jersey (Channel Islands) 403 P 33 and 230 ⑪ – see Channel Islands.

---

**ST. AUSTELL** Cornwall 403 F 32 The West Country G. – pop. 21 622.
See : Holy Trinity Church★.
Env. : St. Austell Bay★★ (Gribbin Head★★) E : by A 390 and A 3082 – Carthew : Wheal Martu
China Clay Heritage Centre★★ AC, N : 2 m. by A 391 – Mevagissey★★ - Lost Gardens
Heligan★, S : 5 m. by B 3273 – Charlestown★, SE : 2 m. by A 390.
Exc. : Trewithen★★★ AC, NE : 7 m. by A 390 – Lanhydrock★★, NE : 11 m. by A 390 an
B 3269 – Polkerris★, E : 7 m. by A 390 and A 3082.
🝉 Carlyon Bay ℰ (01726) 814250.
London 281 – Newquay 16 – Plymouth 38 – Truro 14.

🏛 **White Hart,** Church St., PL25 4AT, ℰ (01726) 72100, Fax (01726) 74705 – 📺 ☎ ⚇
🕭 45. 🕮 AE ⓪ VISA ⚇
closed 25 and 26 December – Meals 7.75/12.50 t. ⓵ 6.50 – 18 rm ⌷ 44.00/69.50 t. – SB.

⌂ **Poltarrow Farm** without rest., St. Mewan, PL26 7DR, Southwest : 1 ¾ m. by A 39
ℰ (01726) 67111, Fax (01726) 67111, « Working farm », 斧, park – ⚇ 📺 🅿. 🕮 VISA ⚇
closed 25 December – 5 rm ⌷ 25.00/46.00.

at Tregrehan East : 2½ m. by A 390 – ✉ St. Austell.

🏠 **Boscundle Manor,** PL25 3RL, ℰ (01726) 813557, Fax (01726) 814997, « Converted 18
manor, gardens », ⚇, 🝉, park – ⚇ rest, 📺 ☎ 🅿. 🕮 AE VISA JCB
mid March-October – Meals (closed Sunday to non-residents) (dinner only) 25.00 st. ⓵ 5.0
– 10 rm ⌷ 75.00/130.00 st., 2 suites.

⌂ **Anchorage House,** Nettles Corner, Boscundle, PL25 3RH, ℰ (01726) 814071, 斧 – ⚇
📺 🅿. 🕮 VISA ⚇
Meals (by arrangement) (communal dining) 22.50 s. – 3 rm ⌷ 38.00/64.00 s.

at Carlyon Bay East : 2½ m. by A 3601 – ✉ St. Austell.

🏛🏛 **Carlyon Bay,** PL25 3RD, ℰ (01726) 812304, Fax (01726) 814938, ≤ Carlyon Bay, « Exten
sive gardens », ⚇s, 🝉, 🝉, 🝉, ※ –📗 📺 ☎ 🅿 – 🕭 65. 🕮 AE ⓪ VISA ⚇
Meals 13.95/24.00 t. and a la carte ⓵ 6.95 – 72 rm ⌷ (dinner included) 94.00/230.00 t. – SE

🏛 **Cliff Head,** Sea Rd, PL25 3RB, ℰ (01726) 812345, Fax (01726) 815511, ⚇s, 🝉, 斧 – 📺 ☎
🅿 – 🕭 230. 🕮 AE ⓪ VISA ⚇
Meals 7.95/18.95 t. and a la carte ⓵ 4.95 – 59 rm ⌷ 42.00/72.00 t. – SB.

⌂ **Wheal Lodge** without rest., 91 Sea Rd, PL25 3SH, ℰ (01726) 815543, Fax (01726) 81554.
斧 – 📺 🅿. 🕮 VISA ⚇
closed 25 December-3 January – 6 rm ⌷ 35.00/75.00 s.

t **Charlestown** *Southeast : 2 m. by A 390 –* ⊠ *St. Austell.*

🏨 **Pier House**, PL25 3NJ, ℰ *(01726) 67955, Fax (01726) 69246,* ≤ – 📺 ☎ 🅿. 🕦 *VISA*. ✸
Meals a la carte 10.45/23.40 t. 🍷 3.65 – **26 rm** ☑ 35.00/69.00 t.

⤒ **T' Gallants** without rest., 6 Charlestown Rd, PL25 3NJ, ℰ *(01726) 70203,* 🌾 – 📺 🅿. 🕦
*VISA*. ✸
8 rm ☑ 25.00/38.00 s.

@ ATS Gover Rd ℰ *(01726) 65685/6*

**ST. BLAZEY** *Cornwall* 📗 *F 32 – pop. 8 837 (inc. Par).*
*London 276 – Newquay 21 – Plymouth 33 – Truro 19.*

⤒ **Nanscawen House** ⌇ without rest., Prideaux Rd, PL24 2SR, West : ¾ m. following
signs for Luxulyan ℰ *(01726) 814488, Fax (01726) 814488,* ≤, ⊐, 🌾 – ✸ 📺 ☎ 🅿. 🕦 *VISA*
JCB. ✸
*closed 25 and 26 December –* **3 rm** ☑ 50.00/78.00.

**ST. BRELADE'S BAY** *Jersey (Channel Islands)* 📗 *P 33 and* 📙 ⑪ *– see Channel Islands.*

**ST. CLEMENT** *Jersey (Channel Islands)* 📗 *P 33 and* 📙 ⑪ *– see Channel Islands.*

**ST. HELENS** *Mersey.* 📗📗 *L 23 – pop. 106 293.*
📷 *Sherdley Park Municipal, Sherdley Park* ℰ *(01744) 813149.*
*London 207 – Liverpool 12 – Manchester 27.*

🏰 **Stakis St. Helens**, Linkway West, WA10 1NG, ℰ *(01744) 453444, Fax (01744) 454655,* ℟,
⬆, 🔲 – 🛏, ✸ rm, 🔲 ☎ 🅿 – 🛎 200. 🕦 🎫 ⑩ *VISA*
*The Chalon :* Meals *(dancing Friday and Saturday evenings) (bar lunch)/dinner 18.95* st.
and a la carte – ☑ 9.95 – **81 rm** 100.00/135.00 st., 3 suites – SB.

🏨 **Waterside - Premier Lodge**, East Lancashire Rd, WA11 7LX, North : 1 ¾ m. at junction
of A 580 with A 571 ℰ *(01744) 23333, Fax (01744) 454231,* Reservations (Freephone) 0800
118833 – ✸ rm, 📺 ☎ ℅ �& 🅿 – 🛎 80. 🕦 🎫 ⑩ *VISA*. ✸
Meals *(grill rest.) 7.25/10.95* st. and a la carte 🍷 3.80 – ☑ 5.95 – **43 rm** 44.95 st.

t **Rainhill** *Southwest : 3½ m. by A 58 and B 5413 –* ⊠ *St. Helens.*

🏨 **The Ship - Premier Lodge**, 804 Warrington Rd, L35 6PE, Southeast : 1 m. on A 57
ℰ *(0151) 426 4165, Fax (0151) 426 2831,* Reservations (Freephone) 0800 118833, 🌾 –
✸ rm, 📺 ☎ �& 🅿 🕦 🎫 ⑩ *VISA*. ✸
Meals *(closed dinner 24 December) (grill rest.) 7.25/12.95* st. and a la carte – ☑ 5.95 –
**34 rm** 42.25 st.

t **Eccleston** *West : 3 m. by A 570 on B 5201 –* ⊠ *St. Helens.*

🏨 **Griffin - Premier Lodge**, Church Lane, WA10 5AD, on B 5201 ℰ *(01744) 27907,*
*Fax (01744) 453475,* Reservations (Freephone) 0800 118833, 🌾 – ✸ rm, 📺 ☎ 🅿. 🕦 🎫
*VISA*. ✸
Meals *(grill rest.) 10.95/12.95* st. and a la carte – ☑ 4.95 – **11 rm** 42.95 st. – SB.

@ ATS Sutton Rd ℰ *(01744) 613434*                    ATS Blackbrook Rd, Blackbrook
                                                        ℰ *(01744) 754175*

**ST. HELIER** *Jersey (Channel Islands)* 📗 *P 33 and* 📙 ⑪ *– see Channel Islands.*

**ST. HILARY** *Cornwall – see Marazion.*

**ST. ISSEY** *Cornwall* 📗 *F 32 – see Padstow.*

*Great Britain* and *Ireland* is now covered
by an *Atlas* at a scale of 1 inch to 4.75 miles.

*Three easy to use versions: Paperback, Spiralbound and Hardback.*

**ST. IVES** *Cambs.* **404** T 27 – *pop. 15 312 –* ⊠ *Huntingdon.*
*London 75 – Cambridge 14 – Huntingdon 6.*

🏨 **Slepe Hall**, Ramsey Rd, PE17 4RB, ℘ (01480) 463122, Fax (01480) 300706 – ⅍ rest, 📺
🅿 – 🔬 40. 🆗 🕮 ⓪ 𝘝𝘐𝘚𝘈. ⋘
*closed 25 to 28 December* – **Meals** 13.95/14.95 st. and a la carte ⅄ 4.50 – **16 rm** ⊇ 68.00
89.00 st.

🏨 **Dolphin**, Bridge Foot, London Rd, PE17 4EP, ℘ (01480) 466966, Fax (01480) 495597 – [
☎ ₺ 🅿 – 🔬 150. 🆗 🕮 ⓪ 𝘝𝘐𝘚𝘈. ⋘
*restricted opening 24 December-5 January* – **Meals** (bar lunch Monday to Saturday)/dinne
17.50 t. and a la carte ⅄ 5.95 – **47 rm** ⊇ 65.00/85.00 t. – SB.

🏨 **Oliver's Lodge**, Needingworth Rd, PE17 4JP, ℘ (01480) 463252, Fax (01480) 461150
▤ rest, 📺 ☎ ☏ 🅿 – 🔬 65. 🆗 🕮 𝘝𝘐𝘚𝘈 𝐉𝐂𝐁
**Meals** a la carte 15.00/27.00 t. ⅄ 4.95 – **15 rm** ⊇ 65.00/90.00 t. – SB.

**at Holywell** *East : 3 m. by A 1123 –* ⊠ *Huntingdon.*

🏨 **Old Ferryboat Inn**, PE17 3TG, ℘ (01480) 463227, Fax (01480) 494885, 🌧 – ⅍ rest, [
☎ 🅿. 🆗 𝘝𝘐𝘚𝘈. ⋘
*closed 25 December* – **Meals** a la carte approx. 14.15 – **7 rm** ⊇ 49.50/80.00 t.

🅐 ATS East St. ℘ (01480) 465572

---

*Groß-London (GREATER LONDON) besteht aus der City und 32*
*Verwaltungsbezirken (Borough). Diese sind wiederum in kleinere*
*Bezirke (Area) unterteilt, deren Mittelpunkt ehemalige Dörfer*
*oder Stadtviertel sind, die oft ihren eigenen Charakter bewahrt haben.*

---

**ST. IVES** *Cornwall* **403** D 33 *The West Country G. – pop. 10 092.*
See : Town★★ - *Barbara Hepworth Museum*★★ AC Y M1 – *Tate Gallery*★★ (≤★★)
*St. Nicholas Chapel* (≤★★) Y – *Parish Church*★ Y A.
Env. : *S : Penwith*★★ Y.
Exc. : *St. Michael's Mount*★★ (≤★★) *S : 10 m. by B 3306 –* Y – B 3311, B 3309 and A 30.
🏌 *Tregenna Castle Hotel* ℘ (01736) 795254 ext: 121 Y – 🏌 *West Cornwall, Lelant* ℘ (0173
753401.
🛈 *The Guildhall, Street-an-Pol, TR26 2DS* ℘ (01736) 796297.
*London 319 – Penzance 10 – Truro 25.*

Plan opposite

🏨 **Porthminster**, The Terrace, TR26 2BN, ℘ (01736) 795221, Fax (01736) 797043, ≤, ⬚
≘s, ⏚, ⬚, 🌧 – 🕪 📺 🅿. 🆗 🕮 ⓪ 𝘝𝘐𝘚𝘈
*closed 2 to 8 January* – **Meals** (bar lunch Monday to Saturday)/dinner 15.00 st
and a la carte ⅄ 4.95 – **46 rm** ⊇ 55.00/132.00 st. – SB.

🏨 **Countryman at Trink**, Old Coach Rd, TR26 3JQ, South : 2 ½ m. by B 3306 and B 3311 o
Hayle rd ℘ (01736) 797571, Fax (01736) 797571, 🌧 – ⅍ 📺 🅿. 🆗 🕮 ⓪ 𝘝𝘐𝘚𝘈 𝐉𝐂𝐁. ⋘
**Meals** (dinner only) a la carte 15.20/16.00 s. ⅄ 3.50 – **6 rm** ⊇ 35.00/60.00 s. – SB.

🏠 **Old Vicarage** without rest., Parc-an-Creet, TR26 2ET, ℘ (01736) 79612
Fax (01736) 796124, 🌧 – ⅍ 📺 🅿. 🆗 🕮 𝘝𝘐𝘚𝘈 𝐉𝐂𝐁
*April-October* – **8 rm** ⊇ 27.00/52.00.

🏠 **Blue Hayes**, Trelyon Av., TR26 2AD, ℘ (01736) 797129, ≤, 🌧 – ⅍ rest, 📺 🅿. 🆗 𝘝𝘐𝘚
𝐉𝐂𝐁. ⋘
*mid March-mid October* – **Meals** 16.50 st. – **9 rm** ⊇ 37.00/86.00 st. – SB.

🏠 **Trewinnard**, 4 Parc Av., TR26 2DN, ℘ (01736) 794168, Fax (01736) 798161, ≤ – ⅍ 📺 🅿
🆗 𝘝𝘐𝘚𝘈 𝐉𝐂𝐁. ⋘
*April-October* – **Meals** (by arrangement) a la carte 9.40/15.85 st. ⅄ 2.75 – **7 rm** ⊇ 28.00
55.00 st.

🏠 **The Pondarosa**, 10 Porthminster Terr., TR26 2DQ, ℘ (01736) 79587
Fax (01736) 795875 – ⅍ 📺 🅿. 🆗 🕮 𝘝𝘐𝘚𝘈. ⋘
**Meals** 9.00 st. ⅄ 3.95 – **9 rm** ⊇ 20.00/42.00 st. – SB.

🍴 **Pig'n'Fish**, Norway Lane, TR26 1LZ, ℘ (01736) 794204, 🏝 – ⅍. 🆗 𝘝𝘐𝘚𝘈 𝐉𝐂𝐁
*closed Sunday, Monday, late December-mid February and restricted opening November*
*December* – **Meals** - Seafood - 15.00/21.00 t. and a la carte 23.15/27.15 t. ⅄ 6.00.

**at Carbis Bay** *South : 1 ¾ m. on A 3074 –* ⊠ *St. Ives.*

🏨 **Boskerris**, Boskerris Rd, TR26 2NQ, ℘ (01736) 795295, Fax (01736) 798632, ≤, ⬚, 🌧
⅍ rest, 📺 ☎ 🅿. 🆗 🕮 ⓪ 𝘝𝘐𝘚𝘈 𝐉𝐂𝐁. ⋘
*Easter-October* – **Meals** (bar lunch)/dinner 18.50 ⅄ 6.00 – **18 rm** ⊇ 51.20/102.40 – SB.

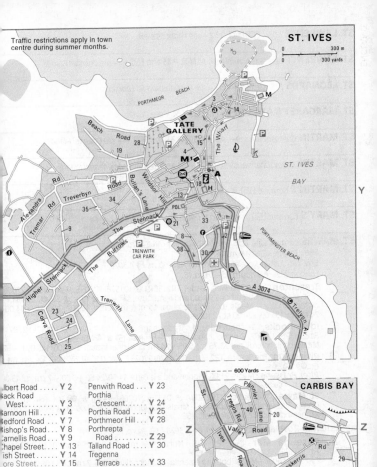

ST. IVES

Traffic restrictions apply in town centre during summer months.

PORTHMEOR BEACH

TATE GALLERY

ST. IVES BAY

PORTHMINSTER BEACH

TRENWITH CAR PARK

CARBIS BAY

*Pour un bon usage des plans de ville, voir les signes conventionnels.*

**ST. JUST** *Cornwall* 403 C 33 *The West Country G. – pop. 2 092.*

See : *Church★.*

Env. : *Penwith★★ – Sancreed – Church★★ (Celtic Crosses★★), SE : 3 m. by A 3071 – St. Buryan★★ (Church Tower★★), SE : 5 ½ m. by B 3306 and A 30 – Land's End★ (cliff scenery★★★), S : 5½ m. by B 3306 and A 30 – Cape Cornwall★ (≤★★), W : 1½ m. – Morvah (≤★★), NE : 4½ m. by B 3306 – Geevor Tin Mine★ AC, N : 3 m. by B 3306 – Carn Euny★, SE : 3 m. by A 3071 – Wayside Cross★ – Sennen Cove★ (≤★), S : 5½ m. by B 3306 and A 30.*

Exc. : *– Porthcurno★, S : 9½ m. by B 3306, A 30 and B 3315.*

≈₁₈ *Cape Cornwall G & C.C., ℘ (01736) 788611.*

*London 325 – Penzance 7.5 – Truro 35.*

**Boscean Country** ≫, TR19 7QP, Northwest : ½ m. by Bosweddon Rd
℘ (01736) 788748, Fax (01736) 788748, ≤, 룕 – ✹ rest, ℗. ◑⑬ VISA. ✁
*closed 1 week Christmas –* **Meals** *(dinner only) (residents only)* 13.00 st. – **12 rm** ☷ 26.00/ 44.00 st.

**ST. JUST IN ROSELAND** *Cornwall* 403 E 33 – see St. Mawes.

543

**ST. LAWRENCE** *I.O.W.* [403] [404] Q 32 – *see Wight (Isle of).*

**ST. LAWRENCE** *Jersey (Channel Islands)* [403] P 33 and [230] ⑪ – *see Channel Islands.*

**ST. LEONARDS** *E. Sussex* [404] V 31 – *see Hastings and St. Leonards.*

**ST. MARGARET'S AT CLIFFE** *Kent* [404] Y 30 – *see Dover.*

**ST. MARTIN** *Guernsey (Channel Islands)* [403] P 33 and [230] ⑩ – *see Channel Islands.*

**ST. MARTIN** *Jersey (Channel Islands)* [403] P 33 and [230] ⑪ – *see Channel Islands.*

**ST. MARTIN'S** *Cornwall* [403] ㉚ – *see Scilly (Isles of).*

**ST. MARY'S** *Cornwall* [403] ㉚ – *see Scilly (Isles of).*

**ST. MAWES** *Cornwall* [403] E 33 *The West Country G.* – ✉ *Truro.*
See : *Town★ - Castle★ AC (≤★).*
Env. : *St. Just-in-Roseland Church★★, N : 2½ m. by A 3078.*
*London 299 – Plymouth 56 – Truro 18.*

🏨 **Tresanton** 🐚, 27 Lower Castle, TR2 5DR, ☎ (01326) 270055, *Fax (01326) 27005*
≤ St. Mawes bay, St. Anthony's head and lighthouse, 🌳 – [TV] ☎ [P] – 🏛 50. [MC] [AE] [VISA]
*closed January* – **Meals** (booking essential to non-residents) 18.00/30.00 **st.** 🍷 14.00
**24 rm** 🛏 153.00/220.00 **st.**, 2 suites.

🏨 **Idle Rocks,** Harbourside, 1 Tredenham Rd, TR2 5AN, ☎ (01326) 27077
*Fax (01326) 270062,* ≤ harbour and estuary – 🚭 rest, [TV] ☎. [MC] [AE] [VISA]
**Meals** (bar lunch)/dinner 23.75 **t.** 🍷 5.95 – **24 rm** 🛏 (dinner included) 74.00/148.00 **t.** – SB

🏨 **Rising Sun,** The Square, TR2 5DJ, ☎ (01326) 270233, *Fax (01326) 270198* – 🚭 rm, [TV]
[P]. [MC] [VISA]. 🐕
***Riser Brasserie :*** **Meals** 21.00 (dinner) and a la carte 11.50/24.50 🍷 6.50 – **7 rm** 🛏 45.0
90.00 **t.**, 1 suite – SB.

🏨 **St. Mawes,** The Seafront, TR2 5DW, ☎ (01326) 270266, ≤ – [TV] ☎. [MC] [VISA] [JCB]
*closed 7 November-21 February* – **Meals** (bar lunch)/dinner 17.00 **st.** 🍷 6.00 – **7 rm** 🛏
(dinner included) 62.00/128.00 **st.** – SB.

**at St. Just in Roseland** *North : 2½ m. on A 3078* – ✉ *Truro.*

🏨 **Rose da Mar** 🐚, TR2 5JB, North : ¼ m. on B 3289 ☎ (01326) 27045
*Fax (01326) 270450,* ≤, 🌳 – 🚭 [P]
*Easter-October* – **Meals** (booking essential) (dinner only) 13.50 – **7 rm** 🛏 30.00/69.00.

**ST.MICHAELS-ON-WYRE** *Lancs.* [402] L 22.
*London 235 – Blackpool 24 – Burnley 35 – Manchester 43.*

🏠 **Compton House** without rest., Garstang Rd, PR3 0TE, ☎ (01995) 67937
*Fax (01995) 679378,* 🌳 – [TV] [P]
*closed 2 weeks Christmas* – **3 rm** 🛏 30.00/40.00.

🍴 **Mallards,** Garstang Rd, PR3 0TE, ☎ (01995) 679661 – [P]. [MC] [VISA]
*closed Sunday dinner and 1 week January, June and October* – **Meals** (dinner only an
Sunday lunch)/dinner 19.00 **t.** 🍷 5.95.

**ST. NEOTS** *Cambs.* [404] T 27 *Great Britain G.* – *pop. 13 471.*
See : *Town★.*
Env. : *Parish Church★★.*
⛳18, ⛳18 *Abbotsley, Eynesbury Hardwicke* ☎ *(01480) 474000/210033.*
*London 60 – Bedford 11 – Cambridge 17 – Huntingdon 9.*

🏨 **Eaton Oak,** Crosshall Rd, PE19 4AG, Northwest : 1 m. on B 1048 at junction with A
☎ (01480) 219555, *Fax (01480) 407520* – 🚭 rest, [TV] ☎ 📞 [P]. [MC] [AE] [VISA] [JCB]. 🐕
**Meals** (grill rest.) a la carte 13.00/20.95 **t.** – **9 rm** 🛏 40.00/50.00 **t.**
🛞 ATS Brook St. ☎ (01480) 472920

**ST. NEWLYN EAST** *Cornwall* [403] E 32 – *see Newquay.*

**T. PETER** *Jersey (Channel Islands)* 403 P 33 and 230 ⑪ – *see Channel Islands.*

**T. PETER PORT** *Guernsey (Channel Islands)* 403 P 33 and 230 ⑩ – *see Channel Islands.*

**T. SAVIOUR** *Guernsey (Channel Islands)* 403 P 33 and 230 ⑨ – *see Channel Islands.*

**T. SAVIOUR** *Jersey (Channel Islands)* 403 P 33 and 230 ⑪ – *see Channel Islands.*

**SALCOMBE** *Devon* 403 I 33 *The West Country G. – pop. 2 189.*
 **Env.** : Sharpitor (Overbecks Museum and Garden★) (≤★★) *AC, S : 2 m. by South Sands* Z.
 **Exc.** : Prawle Point (≤★★★) *E : 16 m. around coast by A 381 –* Y *– and A 379.*
 🛈 *Council Hall, Market St., TQ8 8DE ℘ (01548) 843927 (summer only).*
 *London 243 – Exeter 43 – Plymouth 27 – Torquay 28.*

## SALCOMBE

Allenhayes Road . . . . . . . . **Y** 2
Bonaventure Road . . . . . . . **Y** 3
Buckley Street . . . . . . . . . **Y** 4
Camperdown Road . . . . . **Y** 7
Church Street . . . . . . . . . **Y** 8
Coronation Road. . . . . . . . **Y** 9
Devon Road . . . . . . . . . . **Y** 13
Fore Street . . . . . . . . . . . **Y**
Fortescue Road. . . . . . . . **Z** 14
Grenville Road . . . . . . . . **Y** 15
Herbert Road. . . . . . . . . . **Y** 18
Knowle Road. . . . . . . . . . **Y** 19
Moult Road . . . . . . . . . . **Z** 20
Newton Road . . . . . . . . . **Y** 23
Sandhills Road. . . . . . . . . **Z** 24
Shadycombe Road. . . . . . **Y** 25

**Town plans**
roads most used
by traffic and those
on which guide listed
hotels and restaurants
stand are fully drawn;
the beginning only
of lesser roads
is indicated.

🏨🏨🏨 **Tides Reach,** South Sands, TQ8 8LJ, ℘ (01548) 843466, Fax (01548) 843954, ≤ estuary, ♨, ≘s, 🏊, 🌳, squash – 🖗 📠, ⤬ rest, 📺 ☎ 🅿, ⓬ 🅰🅴 ⓪ 𝑽𝑰𝑺𝑨 𝐉𝐂𝐁          Z **x**
 *closed December and January –* **Meals** (bar lunch)/dinner 27.25 **st.** and a la carte ⓵ 6.45 –
 38 **rm** ⊑ (dinner included) 104.00/210.00 **st.** – SB.

🏨🏨🏨 **Marine,** Cliff Rd, TQ8 8JH, ℘ (01548) 844444, Fax (01548) 843109, ≤ estuary, ♨, ≘s, 🏊 –
 🖗, ⤬ rest, 📺 ☎ 🅿, ⓬ 🅰🅴 ⓪          Y **e**
 **Meals** 26.50 **t.** (dinner) and lunch a la carte approx. 16.95 **t.** ⓵ 8.00 – 51 **rm** ⊑ (dinner included) 105.00/250.00 **t.** – SB.

🏨🏨 **South Sands,** South Sands, TQ8 8LL, ℘ (01548) 843741, Fax (01548) 842112, ≤, 🏊 – 🛗,
 ⤬ rest, 📺 ☎ 🅿, ⓬ 🅰🅴 𝑽𝑰𝑺𝑨 𝐉𝐂𝐁          Z **a**
 *mid March-October –* **Meals** (bar lunch)/dinner 20.00 **st.** and a la carte – 30 **rm** ⊑ (dinner
 included) 91.00/172.00 **st.** – SB.

🏨🏨 **Bolt Head** ⤸, South Sands, TQ8 8LL, ℘ (01548) 843751, Fax (01548) 843060, ≤ estuary,
 🏊 – 📺 ☎ 🅿, ⓬ 🅰🅴 ⓪ 𝑽𝑰𝑺𝑨, ⫽          Z **z**
 *15 March-4 November –* **Meals** (buffet lunch)/dinner 26.00 **t.** ⓵ 8.50 – 28 **rm** ⊑ 55.00/
 110.00 **t.** – SB.

SALCOMBE

🏬 **Grafton Towers**, Moult Rd, TQ8 8LG, ℘ (01548) 842882, Fax (01548) 842857, ⇐ estuar
⚘ – ⅍ rest, 📺 🅿. ⓪ 𝘝𝘐𝘚𝘈
Z
*mid March-October* – **Meals** (dinner only) 17.50 t. ⓐ 4.95 – **12 rm** ⧠ (dinner include
48.00/108.00 t. – SB.

⌂ **The Wood** ⤳, De Courcy Rd, Moult Hill, TQ8 8LQ, by Moult Rd ℘ (01548) 84277
Fax (01548) 844277, ⇐ estuary, ⚘ – ⅍ 📺 🅿. ⒜
Z
*May-October* – **Meals** (by arrangement) 17.00 – **3 rm** ⧠ 31.00/41.00.

**at Soar Mill Cove** *Southwest : 4¼ m. by A 381 via Malborough village* – Y – ✉ *Salcombe.*

🏯 **Soar Mill Cove** ⤳, TQ7 3DS, ℘ (01548) 561566, Fax (01548) 561223, ⇐, ⅏, ☒, ⚘, ✄
⅍ rest, 📺 ☎ 🅿. ⓪ ⒜ 𝘝𝘐𝘚𝘈 𝘑𝘊𝘉. ✄
*closed 2 November.-12 February* – **Meals** (booking essential to non-residents) (light lunch
dinner 34.00 t. ⓐ 8.50 – **19 rm** ⧠ 115.00/231.00 t. – SB.

**at Hope Cove** *West : 4 m. by A 381 via Malborough village* – Y – ✉ *Kingsbridge.*

🏬 **Lantern Lodge** ⤳, TQ7 3HE, by Grand View Rd ℘ (01548) 561280, Fax (01548) 56173
⇐, ⅏, ☒, ⚘ – ⅍ rest, 📺 ☎ 🅿. ⓪ 𝘝𝘐𝘚𝘈 𝘑𝘊𝘉. ✄
*March-November* – **Meals** (bar lunch)/dinner 15.00 t. ⓐ 5.95 – **14 rm** ⧠ (dinner include
55.00/130.00 t. – SB.

*Keine Aufnahme in den **Michelin-Führer** durch*
- *falsche Information oder*
- *Bezahlung!*

---

**SALE** *Gtr. Manchester* 𝟜𝟘𝟚 𝟜𝟘𝟛 𝟜𝟘𝟜 N 23 – pop. 56 052 – ✉ *Manchester.*
🏌 *Sale Lodge, Golf Rd ℘ (0161) 973 3404.*
*London 212 – Liverpool 36 – Manchester 6 – Sheffield 43.*

🏨 **Amblehurst**, 44 Washway Rd, M33 7QZ, on a 56 ℘ (0161) 973 8800, Fax (0161) 905 169
⚘ – ⅍ rm, ▤ rest, 📺 ☎ 🅿. ⓪ ⒜ ⓪ 𝘝𝘐𝘚𝘈. ✄
**Meals** *(closed Saturday lunch, Sunday dinner and Bank Holidays)* 13.95 t. and a la cart
ⓐ 6.25 – **42 rm** ⧠ 90.00/125.00 st.

🏬 **Lennox Lea**, Irlam Rd, M33 2BH, ℘ (0161) 973 1764, Fax (0161) 969 6059, ⚘ – ⅍ res
📺 ☎ ✆ 🅿. ⓪ ⒜ ⓪ 𝘝𝘐𝘚𝘈. ✄
*closed 25-26 December, Easter Sunday and 1 January* – **Meals** *(closed Sunday)* (dinner onl
12.95 st. and a la carte ⓐ 4.95 – **29 rm** ⧠ 49.95/59.95 st.

🏬 **Cornerstones**, 230 Washway Rd, M33 4RA, ℘ (0161) 283 6909, Fax (0161) 283 6909, ⚘
– ⅍ 📺 ☎ ✆ 🅿. ⓪ 𝘝𝘐𝘚𝘈. ✄
*closed 2 weeks Christmas-New Year* – **Meals** *(closed Friday to Sunday)* (residents onl
(dinner only) 15.00 s. – ⧠ 4.50 – **9 rm** 27.00/50.00 s. – SB.

🏬 **Travel Inn**, Carrington Lane, Ashton-upon-Mersey, M33 5BL, Northwest : 1 ½ m. by
5166 on A 6144 ℘ (0161) 962 8113, Fax (0161) 905 1742 – ⅍ rm, 📺 ⅚ 🅿 – ⚛ 40. ⓪ ⒜
⓪ 𝘝𝘐𝘚𝘈. ✄
**Meals** (grill rest.) – **40 rm** 38.00 t.

---

**SALFORDS** *Surrey* 𝟜𝟘𝟜 T 30 – see Redhill.

---

**SALISBURY** *Wilts.* 𝟜𝟘𝟛 𝟜𝟘𝟜 O 30 *The West Country G.* – pop. 39 268.
See : *City** – Cathedral*** AC Z – Salisbury and South Wiltshire Museum* AC Z M2
Close* Z : Mompesson House* AC Z A – Sarum St. Thomas Church* Y B – Royal Glouc
estershire, Berkshire and Wiltshire Regiment Museum*.*
Env. : *Wilton Village* (Wilton House** AC, Wilton Carpet Factory* AC), W : 3 m. by A 30
– Old Sarum* AC, N : 2 m. by A 345 Y – Woodford (Heale House Garden*) AC, NW : 4½ n
by Stratford Rd Y.*
Exc. : *Stonehenge*** AC, NW : 10 m. by A 345 – Y – and A 303 – Wardour Castle* AC
W : 15 m. by A 30 Y.*
🏌, 🏌 *Salisbury & South Wilts., Netherhampton ℘ (01722) 742645 – 🏌 High Post, Grea
Durnford ℘ (01722) 782231.*
🧭 *Fish Row, SP1 1EJ ℘ (01722) 334956.*
*London 91 – Bournemouth 28 – Bristol 53 – Southampton 23.*

Plan opposite

🏨 **White Hart**, 1 St. John's St., SP1 2SD, ℘ (01722) 327476, Fax (01722) 412761 – ⅍ 📺 ☎
🅿 – ⚛ 80. ⓪ ⒜ ⓪ 𝘝𝘐𝘚𝘈. ✄
Z
**Meals** *(closed Saturday lunch)* 9.95 st. (lunch) and dinner a la carte 17.45/27.45 st. ⓐ 8.70
⧠ 10.25 – **68 rm** 80.00/130.00 st. – SB.

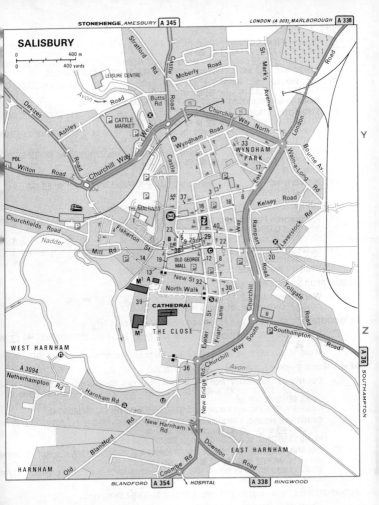

**Red Lion**, 4 Milford St., SP1 2AN, ℰ (01722) 323334, *Fax* (01722) 325756 – ▯, ⤧ rest, 📺 ☎ – 🔬 100. 🅼🅞 🄰🄴 🅞 *VISA*. ⌘
Z c
**Meals** 18.50 **t.** (dinner) and lunch a la carte 10.75/16.10 **t.** – ⌓ 9.00 – **54 rm** 79.50/115.00 **t.** – SB.

**Milford Hall**, 206 Castle St., SP1 3TE, ℰ (01722) 417411, *Fax* (01722) 419444 – 📺 ☎ 🅿 – 🔬 25. 🅼🅞 *VISA*. ⌘
Y a
**Meals** a la carte 15.50/25.00 **t.** ▯ 6.00 – **35 rm** ⌓ 60.00/85.00 **t.** – SB.

**Travel Inn**, Pearce Way, Bishopdown, SP1 3YU, Northeast : 2 ½ m. on A 338 ℰ (01722) 339836, *Fax* (01722) 337889 – ⤧ rm, 📺 ⅋ 🅿. 🅼🅞 🄰🄴 🅞 *VISA*. ⌘
**Meals** (grill rest.) – **40 rm** 38.00 **t.**

547

🏠 **Cricket Field Cottage**, Wilton Rd, SP2 7NS, West : 1 ¼ m. on A 36 ℘ (01722) 32259
Fax (01722) 322595 – ⊁✕ 📺 🄿. 🆗 *VISA*. ✄
*closed 24 and 25 December* – Meals *(closed Monday and Friday)* (booking essentia
(residents only) (dinner only) (unlicensed) 17.00 st. – **13 rm** ⊑ 35.00/55.00 st.

↑ **Old House**, 161 Wilton Rd, SP2 7JQ, West : 1 m. on A 36 ℘ (01722) 33343
Fax (01722) 416144, ☞ – ⊁✕ 📺 🄿. ✄
**Meals** (by arrangement) 18.00 ¼ 2.50 – **7 rm** ⊑ 30.00/50.00 st. – SB.

↑ **Stratford Lodge**, 4 Park Lane, SP1 3NP, off Castle Rd ℘ (01722) 32517
Fax (01722) 325177, ☞ – ⊁✕ 📺 ☎ 🄿. 🆗 🄰🄴 🄾 *VISA*. ✄
*closed 1 week Christmas* – Meals (by arrangement) 18.00 st. ¼ 4.50 – **8 rm** ⊑ 38.5
58.50 st. – SB.

↑ **Glen Lyn** without rest., 6 Bellamy Lane, Milford Hill, SP1 2SP, ℘ (01722) 32788C
Fax (01722) 327880 – ⊁✕ 📺 🄿. 🆗 🄰🄴 🄾 *VISA* *JCB*. ✄                    YZ
**6 rm** ⊑ 28.50/49.50 st.

↑ **Malvern** without rest., 31 Hulse Rd, SP1 3LU, ℘ (01722) 327995, ☞ – ⊁✕ 📺. ✄    Y
**3 rm** ⊑ 30.00/44.00 st.

**at Whiteparish** *Southeast : 7½ m. by A 36 - Z - on A 27 –* ⊠ *Salisbury.*

↑ **Brickworth Farmhouse** without rest., Brickworth Lane, SP5 2QE, Northwest : 1 ½ m
off A 36 ℘ (01794) 884663, *Fax (01794) 884186,* ☞ – 📺 🄿. ✄
*closed 22 December-2 January* – **4 rm** ⊑ 28.00/46.00 st.

↑ **Newton Farmhouse**, Southampton Rd, SP5 2QL, Southwest : 1 ½ m. on A 3
℘ (01794) 884416, ☞ – ⊁✕ 📺 🄿. ✄
**Meals** (by arrangement) 16.00 s. – **7 rm** ⊑ 25.00/50.00 s.

**at Downton** *South : 6 m. by A 338 - Z - on B 3080.*

↑ **Warren** without rest., 15 High St., SP5 3PG, ℘ (01725) 510263, ☞ – 🄿
*closed 20 December-6 January* – **5 rm** ⊑ 32.00/48.00 st.

**at Woodfalls** *South : 7¾ m. by A 338 - Z - on B 3080 –* ⊠ *Salisbury.*

🏠 **Woodfalls Inn**, The Ridge, SP5 2LN, ℘ (01725) 513222, *Fax (01725) 513220* – ⊁✕ 📺 ☎
🄿 – 🕃 150. 🆗 *VISA*
**Meals** 14.95/19.95 t. and a la carte ¼ 7.95 – **10 rm** ⊑ 54.95/80.00 st., 1 suite – SB.

**at Harnham** *Southwest : 1½ m. by A 3094 –* ⊠ *Salisbury.*

🏨 **County H. Salisbury Rose & Crown**, Harnham Rd, SP2 8JQ, ℘ (01722) 399955
Fax (01722) 339816, ≼, 🏛, « Part 13C inn, riverside setting », ☞ – ⊁✕ rest, 📺 ☎ 🄿.
🕃 80. 🆗 🄰🄴 🄾 *VISA*. ✄                                                      Z
**Meals** 9.95/19.50 st. and a la carte ¼ 5.00 – ⊑ 9.50 – **28 rm** 110.00/145.00 st.

🏠 **Grasmere House**, 70 Harnham Rd, SP2 8JN, ℘ (01722) 338388, Fax (01722) 333710, ≼
🏛, ☞ – 📺 ☎ 🄿 – 🕃 80. 🆗 🄰🄴 🄾 *VISA* *JCB*.                                Z
**Meals** 12.50/21.50 st. ¼ 6.50 – **20 rm** ⊑ 57.50/135.00 st. – SB.

🏠 **Old Mill**, Town Path, SP2 8EU, ℘ (01722) 327517, Fax (01722) 333367, ≼, « Part 12C wate
mill », 🔽, 📺 ☎ 🄿. 🆗 🄾 *VISA* *JCB*. ✄                                      Z  r
**Meals** *(closed Sunday dinner)* 16.50 t. (dinner) and a la carte 15.45/21.00 t. ¼ 4.00 – **10 rm**
⊑ 52.50/85.00 st. – SB.

**at Teffont** *West : 10¼ m. by A 36 - Y - and A 30 on B 3089 –* ⊠ *Salisbury.*

🏠 **Howard's House** ⌖, Teffont Evias, SP3 5RJ, on lane opposite Black Horse
℘ (01722) 716392, *Fax (01722) 716820,* ≼, « Part 17C former dower house », ☞ – 
⊁✕ rest, 📺 ☎ 🄿. 🆗 🄰🄴 🄾 *VISA*
*closed 25 to 27 December* – Meals (dinner only and Sunday lunch)/dinner 25.00 t. ¼ 9.25 –
**1 rm** ⊑ 75.00/145.00 t. – SB.

**at Stapleford** *Northwest : 7 m. by A 36 - Y - on B 3083 –* ⊠ *Salisbury.*

↑ **Elm Tree Cottage** without rest., SP3 4LH, ℘ (01722) 790507, ☞ – 📺 🄿
*restricted opening November-February* – **3 rm** ⊑ 33.00/46.00.

**at Little Langford** *Northwest : 8 m. by A 36 - Y - and Great Wishford rd –* ⊠ *Salisbury.*

↑ **Little Langford Farmhouse** without rest., SP3 4NR, ℘ (01722) 790205
Fax (01722) 790086, ≼, « Working farm », ☞, park – ⊁✕ 🄿. ✄
*closed 25 December and January* – **3 rm** ⊑ 32.00/48.00 st.

🅐 ATS 155 Wilton Rd ℘ (01722) 336789        ATS 28 St. Edmund's Church St.
                                             ℘ (01722) 322390

*Wenn Sie ein ruhiges Hotel suchen,*
*benutzen Sie zuerst die Karte in der Einleitung*
*oder wählen Sie im Text ein Hotel mit dem Zeichen ⌖ oder ⌖.*

**ALTASH** *Cornwall* 403 H 32 *The West Country G.* – *pop. 14 139.*
   Env. : *Tamar River*★★.
   Exc. : *St. Germans Church*★, *SW : 7 m. by A 38 and B 3249.*
   ⓘ, ⓘ *St. Mellion* ℘ *(01579) 351351* – ⓘ *China Fleet C.C.* ℘ *(01752) 848668.*
   *London 246 – Exeter 38 – Plymouth 5 – Truro 49.*

   🏨 **Travelodge,** Callington Rd, Carkeel, PL12 6LF, Northwest : 1 ½ m. by A 388 on A 38 at
   Saltash Service Area ℘ *(01752) 848408,* Reservations *(Freephone)* 0800 850950 – ⇔ rm, 📺 ☎
   ⓖ ⓟ. ⓒ 🄰🄴 ⓞ 𝗩𝗜𝗦𝗔 🄹🄲🄱. ❌
   **Meals** *(grill rest.)* – **31 rm** 39.95/59.95 **t.**

   ⓐ ATS 99 St. Stephens Rd ℘ *(01752) 848469*

---

**ALTFORD** *Bath & North East Somerset* 403 404 M 29 – *see Bristol.*

---

**AMLESBURY** *Lancs.* 402 M 22 – *see Preston.*

---

**AMPFORD PEVERELL** *Devon* 403 J 31 *The West Country G.* – *pop. 1 091* – ✉ *Tiverton.*
   Env. : *Uffculme (Coldharbour Mill*★★*), SE : 3 m. by A 373, A 38 and minor roads.*
   Exc. : *Knightshayes Court*★, *W : 7 m. by A 373 and minor roads.*
   *London 184 – Barnstaple 34 – Exeter 20 – Taunton 19.*

   🏨 **Parkway House,** EX16 7BJ, ℘ *(01884) 820255,* Fax *(01884) 820780,* ☞ – 📺 ☎ ⓟ –
   🔬 150. ⓒ 🄰🄴 ⓞ 𝗩𝗜𝗦𝗔 🄹🄲🄱. ❌
   **Meals** a la carte 14.15/22.75 **t.** ⓘ 4.25 – **10 rm** ⌐ 42.50/60.00 **t.** – SB.

   🏨 **Waterloo Cross Inn,** ✉ Uffculme, EX15 3ES, East : 1 ¾ m. by A 361 on A 38
   ℘ *(01884) 840328,* Fax *(01884) 840908* – 📺 ⓟ. ⓒ 🄰🄴 𝗩𝗜𝗦𝗔. ❌
   **Meals** *(in bar)* a la carte 9.75/15.90 **st.** – ⌐ 4.95 – **10 rm** 45.00 **t.**

---

| Les prix | Pour toutes précisions sur les prix indiqués dans ce guide, reportez-vous aux pages de l'introduction. |

---

**AMPFORD PEVERELL SERVICE AREA** *Devon* 403 J 31 – ✉ *Tiverton.*
   *London 184 – Barnstaple 34 – Exeter 20 – Taunton 19.*

   🏨 **Travelodge,** EX16 7HD, M 5 junction 27 ℘ *(01884) 821087,* Reservations *(Freephone)*
   0800 850950 – ⇔ rm, 📺 ⓖ ⓟ. ⓒ 🄰🄴 ⓞ 𝗩𝗜𝗦𝗔 🄹🄲🄱. ❌
   **Meals** *(grill rest.)* – **40 rm** 39.95/59.95 **t.**

---

**SANDBACH** *Ches.* 402 403 404 M 24 – *pop. 15 839.*
   ⓘ *Malkins Bank* ℘ *(01270) 765931.*
   *London 177 – Liverpool 44 – Manchester 28 – Stoke-on-Trent 16.*

   🏨 **Chimney House,** Congleton Rd, CW11 0ST, East : 1 ½ m. on A 534 ℘ *(01270) 764141,*
   Fax *(01270) 768916,* ⟲s, ☞ – ⇔ 📺 ☎ ⓟ – 🔬 100. ❌
   **Meals** a la carte 22.50/29.00 **st.** ⓘ 5.95 – ⌐ 9.75 – **49 rm** 90.00/105.00 **st.** – SB.

   🏨 **Old Hall,** High St., CW11 1AL, ℘ *(01270) 761221,* Fax *(01270) 762551,* « *17C coaching
   inn* », ☞ – ⇔ rest, 📺 ☎ ⓟ – 🔬 30. ⓒ 🄰🄴 𝗩𝗜𝗦𝗔 🄹🄲🄱. ❌
   **Meals** *(closed Sunday)* (dinner only) a la carte approx. 21.45 **t.** ⓘ 5.95 – **14 rm** ⌐ 64.00/
   82.00 **t.**

   🏨 **Saxon Cross,** Holmes Chapel Rd, CW11 1SE, East : 1 ¼ m. by A 534 ℘ *(01270) 763281,*
   Fax *(01270) 768723* – 📺 ☎ ⓟ – 🔬 80. ⓒ 🄰🄴 ⓞ 𝗩𝗜𝗦𝗔
   **Meals** *(closed Saturday lunch and Sunday dinner)* 8.60/15.75 **t.** and dinner a la carte ⓘ 5.75
   – **52 rm** ⌐ 62.50/70.00 **t.** – SB.

   *at Wheelock South : 1½ m. by A 534 – ✉ Sandbach.*

   XX **Grove House** with rm, Mill Lane, CW11 4RD, ℘ *(01270) 762582,* Fax *(01270) 759465* – 📺
   ☎ ⓟ. ⓒ 🄰🄴 𝗩𝗜𝗦𝗔 🄹🄲🄱
   *closed 27 to 30 December* – **Meals** *(closed Sunday dinner)* (dinner only and Sunday
   lunch)/dinner 18.00 **t.** and a la carte ⓘ 6.50 – **8 rm** ⌐ 47.50/75.00 **t.**

---

**SANDGATE** *Kent* 404 X 30 – *see Folkestone.*

---

**SANDIACRE** *Derbs.* 402 403 404 Q 25 – *see Nottingham (Notts.).*

**SANDIWAY** Ches. 402 403 404 M 24 – ✉ Northwich.
London 191 – Liverpool 34 – Manchester 22 – Stoke-on-Trent 26.

🏠 **Nunsmere Hall** ⮬, Tarporley Rd, CW8 2ES, Southwest : 1 ½ m. by A 556 on A 4
𝒫 (01606) 889100, Fax (01606) 889055, ≤, ♨, « Part Victorian house on wooded peni
sula », 🐎, park – 🖺 ⁝✕ 📺 ☎ ℃ 🅿 – 🛦 50. 🆀 AE ① VISA JCB. ℅
Meals (bar lunch Saturday) 19.50 st. (lunch) and dinner a la carte 32.00/40.00 st. 🍷 10.00
35 rm ⮰ 130.00/190.00 st., 1 suite.

---

**SANDPLACE** Cornwall – see Looe.

---

**SANDRINGHAM** Norfolk 402 404 V 25 Great Britain G. – pop. 430 – ✉ King's Lynn.
See : Sandringham House★ AC.
London 111 – King's Lynn 8 – Norwich 50.

🏠 **Park House** ⮬, PE35 6EH, 𝒫 (01485) 543000, Fax (01485) 540663, ≤, « Former Roy
residence » Restricted to physically disabled and their companions, ♨, 🐎 – 🖺 ⁝✕ 📺 ☎
🅿. 🆀 VISA. ℅
Meals (buffet lunch)/dinner 14.50 st. – 16 rm ⮰ 68.00/118.00 st.

---

**SANDWICH** Kent 404 Y 30 Great Britain G. – pop. 4 164.
See : Town★.
🛈 The Guildhall, Cattle Market, CT13 9AH 𝒫 (01304) 613565 (summer only).
London 72 – Canterbury 13 – Dover 12 – Maidstone 41 – Margate 9.

🏠 **Bell,** The Quay, CT13 9EF, 𝒫 (01304) 613388, Fax (01304) 615308 – ⁝✕ 📺 ☎ 🅿 – 🛦 120
🆀 AE ① VISA JCB
accommodation closed 25 December – Meals 9.95 t. and a la carte 🍷 5.70 – 33 rm
⮰ 75.00/145.00 – SB.

*La guida cambia, cambiate la guida ogni anno.*

---

**SANDY** Beds. 404 T 27 – pop. 8 554.
London 49 – Bedford 8 – Cambridge 24 – Peterborough 35.

🏠 **Holiday Inn Garden Court,** Girtford Bridge, London Rd, SG19 1DH, West : ¾ m. by
1042 at junction of A 1 with A 603 𝒫 (01767) 692220, Fax (01767) 680452 – ⁝✕ rm, 📺 ☎ 🅿
– 🛦 200. 🆀 AE ① VISA JCB. ℅
Meals (dinner only) 15.00 st. and a la carte 🍷 6.00 – ⮰ 8.50 – 56 rm 64.00 st.

🏠 **Highfield Farm** without rest., Great North Rd, SG19 2AQ, North : 2 m. by B 1042 on A
(southbound carriageway) 𝒫 (01767) 682332, Fax (01767) 692503, park – ⁝✕ 🅿. 🆀 VISA
JCB
6 rm ⮰ 40.00/50.00 s.

---

**SANDYPARK** Devon 403 I 31 – see Chagford.

---

**SARISBURY** Hants. 403 404 Q 31 – pop. 5 805 – ✉ Southampton.
London 90 – Portsmouth 16 – Southampton 6.

🏠 **Dormy House,** 21 Barnes Lane, Sarisbury Green, SO31 7DA, South : 1 m
𝒫 (01489) 572626, Fax (01489) 573370, 🐎 – 📺 ☎ ℃ 🅿. 🆀 VISA JCB
Meals (by arrangement) 10.95 st. 🍷 6.95 – 12 rm ⮰ 37.60/46.00 st.

---

**SARK** 403 P 33 and 230 ⑩ – see Channel Islands.

---

**SAUNTON** Devon 403 H 30 – ✉ Braunton.
Env. : Braunton★ – St. Brannock's Church★, E : 2½ m. on B 3231 – Braunton Burrows★, E
½ m. on B 3231.
🛆, 🛆 Saunton 𝒫 (01271) 812436.
London 230 – Barnstaple 8 – Exeter 48.

🏠 **Preston House,** EX33 1LG, 𝒫 (01271) 890472, Fax (01271) 890555, ≤ Saunton Sands
⮬s, ♨, 🐎 – 📺 ☎ 🅿. 🆀 VISA JCB. ℅
closed January and February – Meals (bar lunch)/dinner 19.50 st. 🍷 6.00 – 14 rm ⮰ 60.00/
95.00 st. – SB.

**SAWBRIDGEWORTH** Herts. 🗺️404 U 28 – pop. 9 432.

London 26 – Cambridge 32 – Chelmsford 17.

XX **The Shoes**, 52 Bell St., CM21 9AN, 𝄞 (01279) 722554, Fax (01279) 832494 – 🆎 AE VISA
closed lunch Monday and Saturday, Sunday, 2 weeks August and 2 weeks after Christmas –
**Meals** 13.25/21.50 t. and a la carte 🍷 7.25.

**SAWLEY** Lancs. 🗺️402 M 22 – pop. 237.

London 242 – Blackpool 39 – Leeds 44 – Liverpool 54.

X **Spread Eagle** with rm, BB7 4NH, 𝄞 (01200) 441202, Fax (01200) 441973 – ⭐ rest, 📺 ☎
℗, 🆎 AE VISA. ⊗
closed 25 December – **Meals** a la carte 12.00/19.95 st. 🍷 7.80 – **10 rm** ⊒ 35.00/60.00 t.

**SAXLINGHAM THORPE** Norfolk – see Norwich.

**SAXTON** N. Yorks. – see Tadcaster.

**SCALBY** N. Yorks. 🗺️402 S 21 – see Scarborough.

**SCARBOROUGH** N. Yorks. 🗺️402 S 21 Great Britain G. – pop. 38 809.

Exc. : Robin Hood's Bay★, N : 16 m. on A 171 and minor rd to the right (signposted) –
Whitby Abbey★, N : 21 m. on A 171 – Sledmere House★, S : 21 m. on A 645, B 1249 and B
1253 (right).

🏌️ Scarborough North Cliff, North Cliff Av., Burniston Rd 𝄞 (01723) 360786, NW : 2 m. by A
165 Y – 🏌️ Scarborough South Cliff, Deepdale Av., off Filey Rd 𝄞 (01723) 360522, S : 1 m. by
A 165 Z.

🛈 Unit 3, Pavilion House, Valley Bridge Rd, YO11 1UZ 𝄞 (01723) 373333.

London 253 – Kingston-upon-Hull 47 – Leeds 67 – Middlesbrough 52.

Plan on next page

🏨🏨 **The Crown**, 7-11 Esplanade, YO11 2AG, 𝄞 (01723) 373491, Fax (01723) 362271, ≤ – 🛗 ⭐
📺 ☎ – 🔬 160. 🆎 AE ⓪ VISA JCB                                                        Z i
**Meals** (bar lunch Monday to Saturday)/dinner 16.95 st. and a la carte 🍷 6.75 – ⊒ 9.75 –
**77 rm** 69.00/92.00 st., 1 suite.

🏨 **Palm Court**, St. Nicholas Cliff, YO11 2ES, 𝄞 (01723) 368161, Fax (01723) 371547, 🖼️ – 🛗
📺 ☎ 🌊 🔬 150. 🆎 AE ⓪ VISA. ⊗                                                       Z e
**Meals** (dancing Saturday evening) 13.50 st. (dinner) and a la carte 18.00/20.00 st. 🍷 5.00 –
**47 rm** ⊒ 40.00/84.00 st.

🏨 **The Mount**, Cliff Bridge Terr., YO11 2HA, 𝄞 (01723) 360961, Fax (01723) 375850, ≤ – 🛗
📺 ☎. 🆎 VISA. ⊗                                                                     Z r
**Meals** (dinner only and Sunday lunch)/dinner 15.50 t. 🍷 5.50 – **50 rm** ⊒ 40.00/110.00 t. –
SB.

🏨 **Ox Pasture Hall** ⊗, Lady Edith's Drive, Raincliffe Woods, YO12 5TD, West : 3 ¼ m. by A
171 following signs for Raincliffe Woods 𝄞 (01723) 365295, Fax (01723) 355156, ≤, « Part
17C », 🌾, 🐎, park – ⭐ rest, 📺 ☎ ℗, 🆎 VISA
**Meals** (dinner only and Sunday lunch)/dinner 16.50 st. and a la carte 🍷 5.25 – **16 rm**
⊒ 44.50/78.00 st., 1 suite.

🏨 **Old Mill**, Mill St., YO11 1SZ, by Victoria Rd 𝄞 (01723) 372735, Fax (01723) 372735, « Restored 18C windmill, toy museum » – ⭐ rest, 📺 ☎. 🆎 VISA                           Z u
**Meals** (light lunch) (dinner by arrangement to residents only)/dinner 12.50 t. 🍷 4.00 –
**12 rm** ⊒ 27.50/47.00 st.

XX **Jade Garden**, 121 Falsgrave Rd, YO12 5EG, 𝄞 (01723) 369099, Fax (01723) 375193 – 🆎
AE VISA                                                                            Z v
**Meals** - Chinese - (dinner only) a la carte 8.20/15.30 t.

**at Scalby** Northwest : 3 m. by A 171 – Z – ✉️ Scarborough.

🏨🏨 **Wrea Head Country House** ⊗, Barmoor Lane, YO13 0PB, North : 1 m. by A 171 on
Barmoor Lane 𝄞 (01723) 378211, Fax (01723) 355936, ≤, « Victorian country house », 🌾,
park – ⭐ rest, 📺 ☎ ℗ – 🔬 25. 🆎 AE ⓪ VISA. ⊗
**Meals** 12.50/24.50 t. 🍷 12.95 – **19 rm** ⊒ 67.50/140.00 st., 1 suite – SB.

**at Hackness** Northwest : 7 m. by A 171 – Z – ✉️ Scarborough.

🏨 **Hackness Grange** ⊗, YO13 0JW, 𝄞 (01723) 882345, Fax (01723) 882391, « 18C country house », 🖼️, 🌊, 🌾, park, ⚽ – ⭐ rest, 📺 ☎ ℗, 🆎 AE ⓪ VISA. ⊗
closed 31 December – **Meals** 12.50/22.50 st. 🍷 7.95 – **28 rm** ⊒ 77.50/165.00 st. – SB.

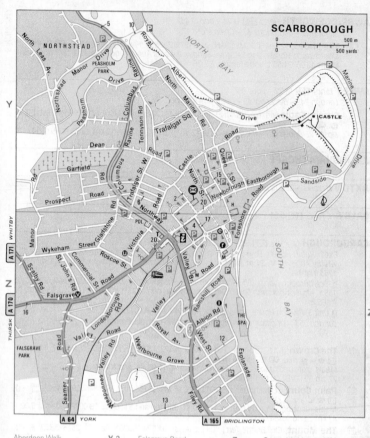

SCARBOROUGH

*Per spostarvi più rapidamente utilizzate le* **carte Michelin "Grandi Strade"**

nº **970** Europa, nº **976** Rep. Ceca/Slovacchia, nº **980** Grecia,
nº **984** Germania, nº **985** Scandinavia-Finlandia,
nº **986** Gran Bretagna-Irlanda, nº **987** Germania-Austria-Benelux,
nº **988** Italia, nº **989** Francia, nº **990** Spagna-Portogallo.

---

**SCILLY (Isles of)** *Cornwall* **403** ③ *The West Country G.* – pop. 2 048.

See : *Islands★ - The Archipelago* (≤★★★).

Env. : *St. Agnes : Horsepoint★.*

*Helicopter service from St. Mary's and Tresco to Penzance :* ℰ *(01736) 363871.*

✈ *St. Mary's Airport :* ℰ *(01720) 422677, E : 1½ m. from Hugh Town.*

⏴ *from Hugh Town to Penzance (Isles of Scilly Steamship Co. Ltd) (summer only) (2 h 40 mn).*

🛈 *Porthcressa Bank, St. Mary's, TR21 0JY* ℰ *01720 (Scillonia) 422536.*

552

**ryher** *The West Country G. – pop. 78 – ⊠ Scillonia.*
See : Watch Hill (≤ ★) – Hell Bay★.

🏨 **Hell Bay** ⌂, TR23 0PR, ℰ (01720) 422947, Fax (01720) 423004, 🍽 – ⍥ rest, 📺 ☎, 🆗 ⑨ *VISA* JCB, ⋇
*26 March-October* – **Meals** (bar lunch)/dinner 23.00 **t.** ⅄ 7.50, **13 suites** ⫐ (dinner included) 114.00/156.00 **st.** – SB.

🏠 **Bank Cottage** ⌂, TR23 0PR, ℰ (01720) 422612, Fax (01720) 422612, ≤, 🍽 – ⍥ rest, 📺, ⋇
*April-October* – **5 rm** ⫐ (dinner included) 38.00/80.00 **st.**

**t. Martin's** *The West Country G. – pop. 113.*
See : St. Martin's Head (≤ ★★).

🏨 **St. Martin's on the Isle** ⌂, TR25 0QW, ℰ (01720) 422092, Fax (01720) 422298, ≤ Tean Sound and islands, 📺, 🍽, ⋇ – ⍥ rest, 📺 ☎, 🆗 ⑨ *VISA*
*April-October* – *Tean* : **Meals** (bar lunch)/dinner a la carte 25.00/40.00 **st.** ⅄ 10.00 – **28 rm** ⫐ (dinner included) 80.00/260.00 **st.**, 2 suites.

**t. Mary's** *The West Country G. – pop. 1 607.*
See : Gig racing★★ – Garrison Walk★ (≤ ★★) – Peninnis Head★ – Hugh Town - Museum★.
🏌 ℰ (01720) 422692.

🏨 **Star Castle** ⌂, TR21 0JA, ℰ (01720) 422317, Fax (01720) 422343, « Elizabethan fortress », 📺, 🍽, ⋇ – ⍥ rest, 📺 ☎ 🆗 ⑨ *VISA*
*March-October* – **Meals** (bar lunch)/dinner 25.00 **t.** ⅄ 6.00 – **31 rm** ⫐ (dinner included) 79.00/178.00 **t.**, 3 suites – SB.

🏨 **Atlantic**, Hugh St., Hugh Town, TR21 0PL, ℰ (01720) 422417, Fax (01720) 423009, ≤ St. Mary's Harbour – ⍥ rest, 📺 ☎, 🆗 *VISA*
*closed 7 November-mid February* – **Meals** (dinner only) 21.50 **t.** ⅄ 6.50 – **24 rm** ⫐ (dinner included) 70.00/170.00 **t.**

🏠 **Carnwethers Country House** ⌂, Pelistry Bay, TR21 0NX, ℰ (01720) 422415, Fax (01720) 422415, ⍾, 🍽, 🍽 – ⍥ 📺
*May-September* – **Meals** ⅄ 3.60 – **9 rm** ⫐ (dinner included) 52.00/110.00 **st.**

🏠 **Crebinick House**, Church St., TR21 0JT, ℰ (01720) 422968, Fax (01720) 422968 – ⍥, ⋇
*March-October* – **Meals** – **6 rm** ⫐ (dinner included) 90.00 **t.**

🏠 **Evergreen Cottage** without rest., Parade, High Town, TR21 0LP, ℰ (01720) 422711 – ⍥
**5 rm** ⫐ 28.50/57.00 **st.**

**resco** *The West Country G. – pop. 167 – ⊠ New Grimsby.*
See : Island★ - Abbey Gardens★★ AC (Lighthouse Way ≤ ★★).

🏨 **The Island** ⌂, Old Grimsby, TR24 0PU, ℰ (01720) 422883, Fax (01720) 423008, ≤ St. Martin's and islands, « Idyllic island setting, sub-tropical gardens », 🍽, park, ⋇ – 📺 ☎, 🆗 ⑨ ⌷ *VISA*, ⋇
*March-October* – **Meals** (bar lunch)/dinner 33.00 **t.** ⅄ 8.00 – **46 rm** ⫐ (dinner included) 90.00/314.00 **t.**, 2 suites.

🏨 **New Inn**, TR24 0QQ, ℰ (01720) 422844, Fax (01720) 423200, ≤, 🍽, 🍽 – ⍥ rest, 📺 ☎, 🆗 ⑨ *VISA*
**Meals** (booking essential) (bar lunch)/dinner 21.50 **st.** ⅄ 6.60 – **14 rm** ⫐ (dinner included) 86.00/172.00 **st.** – SB.

---

**SCOTCH CORNER** *N. Yorks.* 402 P 20 – ⊠ Richmond.
🄳 Granada Services, A 1, DL10 6PQ ℰ (01325) 377677.
London 235 – Carlisle 70 – Middlesbrough 25 – Newcastle upon Tyne 43.

🏨 **Quality H. Scotch Corner**, DL10 6NR, ℰ (01748) 850900, Fax (01748) 825417, 🍽, ⍾, 📺 – 🛗, ⍥ rm, 📺 ☎ 🄿 – 🔏 350, 🆗 ⑨ ⌷ *VISA* JCB
**Meals** 9.75/14.50 **st.** and a la carte ⅄ 5.50 – ⫐ 9.50 – **90 rm** 63.25/84.25 **st.** – SB.

🏨 **Travelodge**, Middleton Tyas Lane, D10 6PQ, ℰ (01325) 377719, Fax (01325) 377890, Reservations (Freephone) 0800 850950 – ⍥ rm, 🍽 rest, 📺 ⍾ 🄿, 🆗 ⑨ ⌷ *VISA* JCB, ⋇
**Meals** (grill rest.) – **50 rm** 39.95/59.95 **t.**

🏨 **Travelodge**, Skeeby, DL10 5EQ, South : 1 m. on A 1 (northbound carriageway) ℰ (01748) 823768, Fax (01748) 823768, Reservations (Freephone) 0800 850950 – ⍥ rm, 🍽 rest, 📺 ⍾ 🄿, 🆗 ⑨ ⌷ *VISA* JCB, ⋇
**Meals** (grill rest.) – **40 rm** 39.95/59.95 **t.**

**SCUNTHORPE** North Lincolnshire 402 S 23 – pop. 75 982.

  ॊ Ashby Decoy, Burringham Rd ℰ (01724) 842913 – ॊ Kingsway ℰ (01724) 840945 – ॊ₉,
  Grange Park, Butterwick Rd, Messingham ℰ (01724) 762945.
  ✈ Humberside Airport : ℰ (01652) 688456, E : 15 m. by A 18.
  London 167 – Leeds 54 – Lincoln 30 – Sheffield 45.

🏨🏨🏨 **Briggate Lodge Inn,** Ermine St., Broughton, DN20 0AQ, Southeast : 5 m. by A 1029 c
  A 18 ℰ (01652) 650770, Fax (01652) 650495, ॊ – 📳 ⁴⁄× 📺 ☎ ✆ ❷ – 🔬 300. 🐠 🖭 ⓪ 🕅
  ᴊᴄʙ, ⅍
  Meals 12.95/19.50 st. and a la carte ₰ 7.45 – **84 rm** ⊑ 79.00/94.00 st., 2 suites.

🏨🏨 **Royal,** Doncaster Rd, DN15 7DE, ℰ (01724) 282233, Fax (01724) 281826 – ⁴⁄× 📺 ☎ ❷
  🔬 240. 🐠 🖭 ⓪ 𝘝𝘐𝘚𝘈
  Meals (closed Saturday lunch) 8.95/14.95 st. and dinner a la carte ₰ 5.25 – ⊑ 7.95 – **33 r**
  64.50/74.50 st. – SB.

🏨 **Travel Inn,** Lakeside Retail Park, Lakeside Parkway, DN16 3NA, Southeast : 2 ½ m. C
  A 1029 at junction with A 18 ℰ (01724) 870030, Fax (01724) 851809 – ⁴⁄× rm, 🍴 rest, 📺
  ❷. 🐠 🖭 ⓪ 𝘝𝘐𝘚𝘈. ⅍
  Meals (grill rest.) – **40 rm** 38.00 t.

  🅐 ATS Grange Lane North ℰ (01724) 868191

---

**SEACROFT** W. Yorks. 402 ⑩ – see Leeds.

---

*To visit a town or region: use the Michelin Green Guides.*

---

**SEAFORD** E. Sussex 404 U 31 – pop. 19 622.

  ॊ Seaford Head, Southdown Rd ℰ (01323) 890139.
  🛈 Station Approach, BN25 2AR ℰ (01323) 897426.
  London 65 – Brighton 14 – Folkestone 64.

🍴🍴 **Quincy's,** 42 High St., BN25 1PL, ℰ (01323) 895490 – 🐠 🖭 𝘝𝘐𝘚𝘈 ᴊᴄʙ
  closed Sunday dinner and Monday – **Meals** (dinner only and Sunday lunch)/dinner 24.00
  ₰ 5.00.

**at Westdean** East : 3 ¼ m by A 259.

🏠 **Old Parsonage** ॐ without rest., BN25 4AL, ℰ (01323) 870432, Fax (01323) 87043
  « 13C King John house », ◄⁼ – ⁴⁄× ❷. ⅍
  closed Christmas and New Year – **3 rm** ⊑ 37.50/70.00.

---

**SEAHOUSES** Northd 401 402 P 17 Great Britain G..

  Env. : Farne Islands★ (by boat from harbour).
  ॊ Beadnell Rd ℰ (01665) 720794.
  🛈 Car Park, Seafield Rd, NE68 7SR ℰ (01665) 720884 (summer only).
  London 328 – Edinburgh 80 – Newcastle upon Tyne 46.

🏨 **Olde Ship,** 9 Main St., NE68 7RD, ℰ (01665) 720200, Fax (01665) 721383, « Nautical men
  orabilia » – 📺 ☎ ❷. 🐠 𝘝𝘐𝘚𝘈 ᴊᴄʙ. ⅍
  closed Christmas and New Year – **Meals** (bar lunch)/dinner 14.50 st. ₰ 5.35 – **12 rm**
  ⊑ 39.00/78.00 st., 4 suites – SB.

🏨 **Beach House,** 12a St. Aidans, Seafront, NE68 7SR, ℰ (01665) 72033?
  Fax (01665) 720921, ≤, ◄⁼ – ⁴⁄× 📺 ☎ ✆ ⅙ ❷. 🐠 🖭 ⓪ 𝘝𝘐𝘚𝘈 ᴊᴄʙ. ⅍
  closed January – **Meals** (dinner only) 14.75 st. ₰ 5.25 – **14 rm** ⊑ (dinner included) 49.0C
  106.00 st.

---

**SEALAND** Flintshire 402 403 L 24 – see Chester (Ches.).

---

**SEATOLLER** Cumbria – see Keswick.

---

**SEATON BURN** Tyne and Wear 402 P 18 – see Newcastle upon Tyne.

---

**SEATON CAREW** Hartlepool 402 Q 20 – see Hartlepool.

---

**SEAVIEW** I.O.W. 403 404 Q 31 – see Wight (Isle of).

**SEAVINGTON ST. MARY** Somerset **403** L 31 The West Country G. – pop. 367 – ⊠ Ilminster.
Env. : Ilminster★ - Minster★★, W : 2 m.
London 142 – Taunton 14 – Yeovil 11.

🏨 **Pheasant,** Water St., TA19 0QH, 𝒫 (01460) 240502, Fax (01460) 242388, 🌧 – 🌱 rest, 📺
☎ 🅿 📶 🄰🄴 💳. 🍴
Meals (dinner only and Sunday lunch)/dinner a la carte 20.00/33.95 t. – 6 rm ⊊ 70.00/
90.00 st., 2 suites – SB.

---

**SEDGEFIELD** Durham **401 402** P 20 – pop. 90 530.
London 270 – Carlisle 83 – Middlesbrough 15 – Newcastle upon Tyne 27 – Sunderland 23.

🏠 **Travelodge,** A 689 Roundabout, TS21 2JX, Southeast : ¾ m. on A 689 𝒫 (01740) 623399,
Fax (01740) 623540, Reservations (Freephone) 0800 850950 – 🌱 rm, 📺 🅿. 📶 🄰🄴 🄾 💳
🄹🄲🄱. 🍴
Meals (grill rest.) – 40 rm 39.95/59.95 t.

---

**SEDGEMOOR SERVICE AREA** Somerset **403** L 30.
🅗 Somerset Visitor Centre, M 5 South, BS26 2UF 𝒫 (01934) 750833.

🏠 **Welcome Lodge** without rest., BS24 0JL, M 5 (northbound carriageway) between
junctions 22 and 21 𝒫 (01934) 750831, Fax (01934) 750808, Reservations (Freephone) 0800
7314466 – 🌱 rm, 📺 🕭 🅿. 📶 🄰🄴 💳
⊊ 7.50 40 rm 50.00 t.

*Pour visiter une ville ou une région : utilisez les Guides Verts Michelin.*

---

**SEDLESCOMBE** E. Sussex **404** V 31 – pop. 1 631 (inc. Whatlington) – ⊠ Battle.
London 56 – Hastings 7 – Lewes 26 – Maidstone 27.

🏨 **Brickwall,** The Green, TN33 0QA, 𝒫 (01424) 870253, Fax (01424) 870785, 🌧, 🏊, 🌧 – 📺
☎ 🅿. 📶 🄰🄴 🄾 💳 🄹🄲🄱
Meals 15.00/20.50 t. 🅹 5.50 – 23 rm ⊊ 50.00/78.00 t. – SB.

---

**SELBY** N. Yorks. **402** Q 22 Great Britain G. – pop. 12 600.
See : Abbey Church★.
🅗 Park St., YO8 0AA 𝒫 (01732) 844785.
London 201 – Doncaster 21 – Kingston-upon-Hull 37 – Leeds 22 – York 14.

🏠 **Barff Lodge** without rest., Mill Lane, Brayton, YO8 9LB, Southwest : 2 ¾ m. by A 19 on
Gateforth rd 𝒫 (01757) 213030, Fax (01757) 212313, 🌧 – 🌱 📺 🅿. 📶 💳. 🍴
5 rm ⊊ 28.00/40.00 st.

🕮 ATS Unit 1, Canal Rd, Bawtry Rd 𝒫 (01757) 703245/702147

---

**SELSIDE** Cumbria – see Kendal.

---

**SEMINGTON** Wilts. **403 404** N 29 – see Trowbridge.

---

**SETTLE** N. Yorks. **402** N 21 – pop. 3 082.
🏌 Giggleswick 𝒫 (01729) 825288.
🅗 Town Hall, Cheapside, BD24 9EJ 𝒫 (01729) 825192.
London 238 – Bradford 34 – Kendal 30 – Leeds 41.

🏨 **Falcon Manor,** Skipton Rd, BD24 9BD, 𝒫 (01729) 823814, Fax (01729) 822087, 🌧 –
🌱 rest, 📺 ☎ 🅿 – 🕭 50. 📶 🄰🄴 🄾 💳
Meals (bar lunch Monday to Saturday)/dinner 24.50 st. and a la carte 🅹 7.25 – 19 rm
⊊ 55.00/104.00 st. – SB.

---

**SEVENOAKS** Kent **404** U 30 Great Britain G. – pop. 24 489.
Env. : Knole★★ AC, SE : ½ m. – Ightham Mote★ AC, E : 5 m. by A 25.
🏌 Woodlands Manor, Tinkerpot Lane 𝒫 (01959) 523805 – 🏌 Darenth Valley, Station Rd,
Shoreham 𝒫 (01959) 522944.
🅗 Buckhurst Lane, TN13 1LQ 𝒫 (01732) 450305.
London 26 – Guildford 40 – Maidstone 17.

**Royal Oak,** Upper High St., TN13 1HY, ℰ (01732) 451109, *Fax (01732) 740187*, ℁ – 📺 ☜
🄿 – 🛦 35. 🚳 🄰🄴 🕦 *VISA*. ℀
**Sycamore :** Meals 7.50/16.95 **t.** and a la carte 🛭 6.95 – ☲ 8.95 – **36 rm** 79.00/90.00 **st.**
SB.

⋇⋇ **Sun Do,** 61 High St., TN13 1JF, ℰ (01732) 453299, *Fax (01732) 461289* – 🗏. 🚳 🄰🄴 🕦 *VISA*
*closed 25 and 26 December* – **Meals** - Chinese - 7.50/13.50 **t.** and a la carte 🛭 6.60.

**at Ivy Hatch** *East : 4¾ m. by A 25 on Coach Rd* – ✉ *Sevenoaks.*

🄳 **The Plough,** High Cross Rd, TN15 0NL, ℰ (01732) 810268, *Fax (01732) 810268*, 🍃, � –
🗏 🄿. 🚳 *VISA*
**Meals** a la carte 15.30/23.65 **t.** 🛭 8.50.

---

**SEVERN STOKE** *Worcestershire* 🕮🕮 **N 27** – *see Worcester.*

---

**SEVERN VIEW SERVICE AREA** *South Gloucestershire* 🕮🕮 **M 29** – ✉ *Bristol.*
*Severn Bridge (toll).*

🄵 **Travelodge,** BS12 3BH, M 48 junction 1 ℰ (01454) 633199, *Fax (01454) 632482*, Reservations (Freephone) 0800 850950 – ᵗ✗= 📺 ☎ 🕹 🄿. 🚳 🄰🄴 🕦 *VISA* 🄹🄲🄱. ℀
**Meals** (grill rest.) – **51 rm** 39.95/59.95 **t.**

---

**SHAFTESBURY** *Dorset* 🕮🕮 **N 30** *The West Country G.* – pop. 6 203.
See : *Gold Hill*★ (≼★) – *Local History Museum*★ *AC*.
Env. : *Wardour Castle*★ *AC*, NE : 5 m.
🄱 *8 Bell St., SP7 8AE* ℰ (01747) 853514.
London 115 – Bournemouth 31 – Bristol 47 – Dorchester 29 – Salisbury 20.

**Royal Chase,** Royal Chase Roundabout, SP7 8DB, Southeast : at junction of A 30 with
A 350 ℰ (01747) 853355, *Fax (01747) 851969*, ⊠, � – ᵗ✗= 📺 ☎ 🄿 – 🛦 130. 🚳 🄰🄴 🕦 *VISA*
**Meals** a la carte 17.40/32.65 **t.** 🛭 7.30 – ☲ 8.50 – **32 rm** 75.00/95.00 **st.** – SB.

↑ **Paynes Place Barn** without rest., New Rd, SP7 8QL, Northwest : ½ m. off B 3081
ℰ (01747) 855016, *Fax (01747) 855016*, ✗= Vale of Blackmore, � – ᵗ✗= 📺 🄿. ℀
*closed 25 December* – **2 rm** ☲ 35.00/52.00 **t.**, 1 suite.

⋇⋇ **La Fleur de Lys,** 25 Salisbury St., SP7 8EL, ℰ (01747) 853717, 🍃 – 🚳 🄰🄴 🕦 *VISA* 🄹🄲🄱
*closed Monday lunch, Sunday dinner and 7 to 21 January* – **Meals** 23.50 **t.** (dinner) and a la carte 24.00/31.00 **t.** 🛭 6.50.

**at Compton Abbas** *South : 4 m. on A 350* – ✉ *Shaftesbury.*

↑ **Old Forge** without rest., Chapel Hill, SP7 0NQ, ℰ (01747) 811881, *Fax (01747) 811881*,
« Blacksmiths forge museum », 🌧 – ᵗ✗= 🄿. ℀
**3 rm** ☲ 30.00/50.00 **s.**

**at Motcombe** *Northwest : 2½ m. by B 3081* – ✉ *Shaftesbury.*

**Coppleridge Inn** ⮥, SP7 9HW, North : 1 m. on Mere rd ℰ (01747) 851980,
*Fax (01747) 851858*, 🌧, park, ℁ – 📺 ☎ 🄿 – 🛦 50. 🚳 🄰🄴 🕦 *VISA*
**Meals** 10.00 **t.** and a la carte 🛭 4.75 – **10 rm** ☲ 42.50/75.00 **t.** – SB.

🄰 ATS New Rd ℰ (01747) 853354

---

**SHALDON** *Devon* 🕮 **J 32** – *see Teignmouth.*

---

**SHANKLIN** *I.O.W.* 🕮🕮 **Q 32** – *see Wight (Isle of).*

---

**SHAW** *Wilts.* 🕮🕮 **N 29** – *see Melksham.*

---

**SHEDFIELD** *Hants.* 🕮🕮 **Q 31** – pop. 3 558 – ✉ *Southampton.*
🄸, 🄵 *Meon Valley Hotel, Sandy Lane,* ℰ (01329) 833455, off A 334.
London 75 – Portsmouth 13 – Southampton 10.

**Marriot Meon Valley H. and Country Club,** Sandy Lane, SO32 2HQ, off A 334
ℰ (01329) 833455, *Fax (01329) 834411*, 🛵, ≘s, ⊠, 🄸, park, ℁ – 🗄 ᵗ✗=, 🗏 rest, 📺 ☎ 🕹 🕹
🄿 – 🛦 120. 🚳 🄰🄴 🕦 *VISA* 🄹🄲🄱. ℀
**Meals** (bar lunch Saturday) 14.00 **st.** (lunch) and a la carte 21.00/31.00 **st.** 🛭 7.50 – ☲ 10.00
– **113 rm** ☲ 70.00/100.00 **st.** – SB.

*Benutzen Sie den Hotelführer des laufenden Jahres.*

SHEFFIELD S. Yorks. 402 403 404 P 23 Great Britain G. – pop. 431 607.

See : Cutlers' Hall★ CZ A – Cathedral Church of SS. Peter and Paul CZ B : Shrewsbury Chapel (Tomb★).

₁₈ Tinsley Park, High Hazel Park, Darnall ℰ (0114) 256 0237, BY – ₁₈ Beauchief Municipal, Abbey Lane ℰ (0114) 236 7274/262 0040, AZ – ₁₈ Birley Wood, Birley Lane ℰ (0114) 264 7262, BZ – ₁₈ Concord Park, Shiregreen Lane ℰ (0114) 257 0274/257 0053, BY – ₁₈ Hillsborough, Worrall Rd ℰ (0114) 234 3608, AY – ₁₈ Abbeydale, Twentywell Lane, Dore ℰ (0114) 236 0763, AZ – ₁₈ Lees Hall, Hemsworth Rd, Norton ℰ (0114) 255 4402, AZ.

🖪 Peace Gdns., S1 2HH ℰ (0114) 273 4671/2.

London 174 – Leeds 36 – Liverpool 80 – Manchester 41 – Nottingham 44.

Plans on following pages

🏨 **Stakis Sheffield,** Victoria Quays, Furnival Rd, S4 7YA, ℰ (0114) 252 5500, Fax (0114) 252 5511, ≤, 佘, « Canalside setting », ₤ᴤ, ≘ˢ, ☒ – ⵉ⵩ 🛎, ≣ rest, 📺 ☎ & 🅿 –
🛦 300. 🕮 🖼 ⓞ 𝑉𝐼𝑆𝐴 𝐽𝐶𝐵.
DY e
**Meals** (grill rest.) a la carte 15.40/20.15 st. – ⍁ 10.50 – **128 rm** 115.00/160.00 st. – SB.

🏨 **Swallow,** Kenwood Rd, S7 1NQ, ℰ (0114) 258 3811, Fax (0114) 250 0138, ₤ᴤ, ≘ˢ, ☒, ⍨,
𝕒𝕣, park – ⵉ⵩ 🛎 📺 ☎ 🅿 – 🛦 200. 🕮 🖼 ⓞ 𝑉𝐼𝑆𝐴
AZ r
**Meals** 14.00/20.00 st. and a la carte – **117 rm** ⍁ 105.00/120.00 st.

🏨 **Holiday Inn Royal Victoria Sheffield,** Victoria Station Rd, S4 7YE, ℰ (0114) 276 8822, Fax (0114) 272 4519 – ⵉ⵩, 🛎 rm, 📺 ☎ 🅿 – 🛦 400. 🕮 🖼 ⓞ 𝑉𝐼𝑆𝐴 𝐽𝐶𝐵.
❀
DY a
**Meals** 12.95/17.00 st. and a la carte ⑂ 5.95 – ⍁ 10.50 – **100 rm** 95.00/115.00 st.

🏨 **Beauchief,** 161 Abbeydale Road South, S7 2QW, Southwest : 3 ½ m. on A 621 ℰ (0114) 262 0500, Fax (0114) 235 0197 – 🛎 rm, 📺 ☎ 🅿 – 🛦 100. 🕮 🖼 ⓞ 𝑉𝐼𝑆𝐴. ❀
**Meals** 10.95/18.00 t. and a la carte ⑂ 8.75 – ⍁ 8.95 – **41 rm** 85.00 t. – SB.

🏨 **Charnwood,** 10 Sharrow Lane, S11 8AA, ℰ (0114) 258 9411, Fax (0114) 255 5107 – 📺 ☎ 🅿 – 🛦 100. 🕮 🖼 ⓞ 𝑉𝐼𝑆𝐴. ❀
CZ u
closed 24 to 30 December – **Meals** (closed Sunday) (dinner only) 12.00 t. and a la carte ⑂ 4.75 – **22 rm** ⍁ 75.00/90.00 t.

🏨 **Forte Posthouse Sheffield,** Manchester Rd, Fulwood, S10 5DX, ℰ (0114) 267 0067, Fax (0114) 268 2620, ≤, ₤ᴤ, ≘ˢ, ☒ – ⵉ⵩, 🛎 rm, 📺 ☎ 🅿 – 🛦 300. 🕮 🖼 ⓞ 𝑉𝐼𝑆𝐴 𝐽𝐶𝐵.
❀
AZ a
**Meals** a la carte 15.95/28.95 t. – ⍁ 9.95 – **134 rm** 75.00 t., 2 suites – SB.

🏨 **Novotel,** Arundel Gate, S1 2PR, ℰ (0114) 278 1781, Fax (0114) 278 7744, ☒ – ⵉ⵩, 🛎 rm, ≣ rest, 📺 ☎ & 🅿 – 🛦 200. 🕮 🖼 ⓞ 𝑉𝐼𝑆𝐴
DZ a
**Meals** 15.00 st. (dinner) and a la carte 15.00/19.00 st. ⑂ 6.00 – ⍁ 9.00 – **144 rm** 75.00/120.00 st.

🏠 **Westbourne House** without rest., 25 Westbourne Rd, S10 2QQ, ℰ (0114) 266 0109, Fax (0114) 266 7778, 𝕒𝕣 – 📺 ☎ 🅿. 🕮 🖼 ⓞ 𝑉𝐼𝑆𝐴
AZ c
**10 rm** ⍁ 38.00/78.00 st.

🏠 **Travel Inn,** Attercliffe Common Rd, S9 2LU, ℰ (0114) 242 2802, Fax (0114) 242 3703 – ⵉ⵩, 🛎 rm, 📺 & 🅿. 🕮 🖼 ⓞ 𝑉𝐼𝑆𝐴. ❀
BY a
**Meals** (grill rest.) – **61 rm** 38.00 t.

🏠 **Travelodge,** 340 Prince of Wales Rd, S2 1FF, ℰ (0114) 253 0935, Fax (0114) 253 0935, Reservations (Freephone) 0800 850950 – 🛎 rm, 📺 & 🅿 – 🛦 80. 🕮 🖼 ⓞ 𝑉𝐼𝑆𝐴 𝐽𝐶𝐵.
❀
BZ a
**Meals** (grill rest.) – **60 rm** 39.95/59.95 t.

🏠 **The Cooke House,** 78 Brookhouse Hill, Fulwood, S10 3TB, West : 3 ½ m. by A 57 off Fulwood Rd ℰ (0114) 230 8186, Fax (0114) 263 0241 – 🛎 rm, 📺 ☎ 🅿. 🕮 🖼 𝑉𝐼𝑆𝐴
closed 1 week Christmas – **Meals** 25.00 s. ⑂ 6.00 – **3 rm** ⍁ 45.00/60.00 st.

XX **Smith's of Sheffield,** 34 Sandygate Rd, S10 5RY, West : 2 ¼ m. by A 57, turning left at Crosspool Tavern ℰ (0114) 266 6096 – 🕮 🖼 𝑉𝐼𝑆𝐴
closed Sunday, Monday, 25 December and 1 January – **Meals** (booking essential) (dinner only) a la carte 21.50/26.00 st. ⑂ 7.50.

XX **Rafters,** 220 Oakbrook Rd, Nether Green, S11 7ED, Southwest : 2 ½ m. by A 625 and Rustlings Rd, turning left at roundabout ℰ (0114) 230 4819, Fax (0114) 230 4819 – 🖼
closed Sunday, Tuesday, 9 to 19 August and Bank Holidays – **Meals** (dinner only) 21.50 t. ⑂ 6.95.

X **Nonna's,** 539-541 Ecclesall Rd, S11 8PR, ℰ (0114) 268 6166, Fax (0114) 266 6122 – 🕮 𝑉𝐼𝑆𝐴
AZ e
closed dinner Sunday, Monday and 25 December-1 January – **Meals** - Italian - a la carte 13.40/21.45 t. ⑂ 4.95.

Barrow Road............ **BY** 4
Bawtry Road........... **BY** 5
Bradfield Road.......... **AY** 7
Brocco Bank........... **AZ** 8

Broughton Lane ......... **BY** 10
Burngreave Road ........ **AY** 12
Handsworth Road ....... **BZ** 24
Holywell Road........... **BY** 29
Main Road.............. **BZ** 32
Meadow Hall Road ...... **BY** 33
Meadowhall
  Shopping Centre ...... **BY**

Middlewood Road ........ **AY** 3
Newhall Road........... **BY** 3
Westbourne
  Road................ **AZ** 4
Western Bank ......... **AZ** 4
Whitham Road .......... **AZ** 4
Woodbourn Road ....... **BYZ** 5
Woodhouse Road........ **BZ** 5

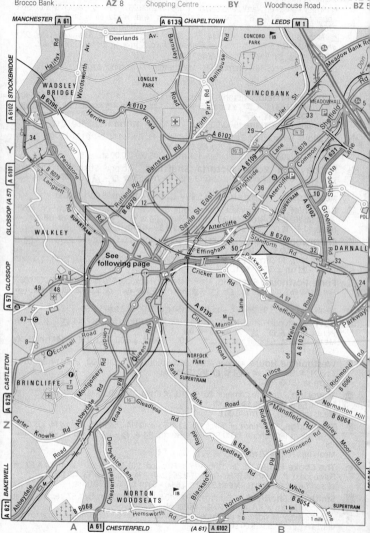

**Ne confondez pas :**

Confort des hôtels        : 🏨🏨🏨 ... 🏚, ↰
Confort des restaurants : XXXXX ..... X, 🍴
Qualité de la table       : ❀❀❀, ❀❀, ❀, Meals ᧗

ngel Street .............. **DY** 3
lonk Street .............. **DY** 6
astle Gate .............. **DY** 13
harter Row .............. **CZ** 14
hurch Street ............. **CZ** 15

Commercial Street ........ **DZ** 16
Cumberland
   Street ................ **CZ** 17
Fargate ................. **CZ**
Fitzwilliam Gate .......... **CZ** 19
Flat Street .............. **DZ** 20
Furnival Gate ............ **CZ** 21
Furnival Street ........... **CZ** 22
Haymarket ............... **DY** 25
High Street .............. **DZ**

Leopold Street ........... **CZ** 31
Moorfields ............... **CY** 35
Pinstone Street .......... **CZ** 37
Queen Street ............ **CY** 38
St. Mary's Gate .......... **CZ** 40
Shalesmoor .............. **CY** 41
Snig Hill ................ **DY** 42
Waingate ................ **DY** 44
West Bar Green .......... **CY** 45
West Street .............. **CZ**

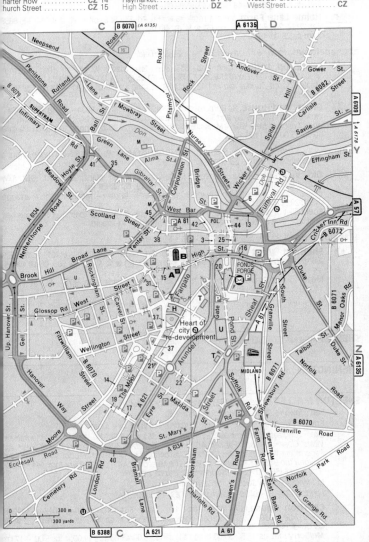

**No confondete :**

Confort degli alberghi : 🏨🏨🏨 ... 🏠, 🏚
Confort dei ristoranti : XXXXX ..... X 🏠
Qualità della tavola : ❀❀❀, ❀❀, ❀, Meals 🍴

**at Grenoside** North : 4½ m. on A 61 – AY – ⊠ Sheffield.

🏛 **Whitley Hall** ⮳, Elliott Lane, S35 8NR, East : 1 m. off Whitley Lane ℘ (0114) 245 4444
Fax (0114) 245 5414, « Part 16C Elizabethan manor house », ☞, park – ⅍ rest, 📺 ☎ ✆ (
– ⅍ 70. ◍ ▫ ① VISA
closed 25 December and 1 January – **Meals** (closed Saturday lunch) 12.95/19.95
and a la carte ⅃ 6.45 – **18 rm** ⌱ 65.00/99.00 st.

⌂ **Holme Lane Farm** without rest., 38 Halifax Rd, S35 8PB, on A 61 ℘ (0114) 246 8858
Fax (0114) 246 8858, ☞ – ⅍ 📺 ☎ ✆ ℗. ◍ VISA. ⅍
**7 rm** ⌱ 28.00/45.00 s.

**at Chapeltown** North : 6 m. on A 6135 – AY – ⊠ Sheffield.

🏛 **Staindrop Lodge,** Lane End, S35 3UH, Northwest : ½ m. on High Green r
℘ (0114) 284 6727, Fax (0114) 284 6783, ☞ – 📺 ☎ ℗ – ⅍ 90. ◍ ▫ VISA
**Meals** (closed Sunday dinner) 12.50/21.50 st. and a la carte ⅃ 6.00 – **13 rm** ⌱ 59.00
74.00 st. – SB.

XX **Greenhead House,** 84 Burncross Rd, S35 1SF, ℘ (0114) 246 9004 – ⅍ ℗. ◍ ▫ VISA
closed lunch Wednesday and Saturday, Sunday to Tuesday, 2 weeks Easter, 2 weeks Augus
and Christmas-New Year – **Meals** (booking essential) 29.00 t. (dinner) and lunch a la carte
10.00/15.00 t. ⅃ 11.75.

**at Ridgeway** (Derbs.) Southeast : 6 ¾ m. by A 6135 (signed Manor Park) on B 6054 turning right a
Ridgeway Arms – BZ – ⊠ Sheffield.

XXX **Old Vicarage** (Tessa Bramley), Ridgeway Moor, on Marsh Lane rd, S12 3XW
✿ ℘ (0114) 247 5814, Fax (0114) 247 7079, ☞ – ⅍ ℗. ◍ ▫ ① VISA
closed Sunday dinner, Monday and 30 December-5 January – **Meals** (lunch by arrange
ment) 29.00/40.00 t. ⅃ 8.00
**Spec.** Fillet of grey mullet, roasted coconut and light curry sauce. Roast fillet of Angus bee
with tapenade crust. Caramelised apple tart, cinnamon ice cream.

**at Meadow Head** South : 5¼ m. on A 61 – AZ – ⊠ Sheffield.

🏛 **Sheffield Moat House,** Chesterfield Rd South, S8 8BW, ℘ (0114) 282 9988
Fax (0114) 237 8140, ₤₰, ☎, ◲, ☞ – ▯ ⅍, ▤ rest, 📺 ☎ ✆ ₺ ℗ – ⅍ 500. ◍ ▫ ① VISA
⅍
**Meals** (closed Saturday lunch) 11.75/17.25 st. and a la carte – ⌱ 9.75 – **89 rm** 115.00.
140.00 st., 5 suites – SB.

◉ ATS Unit 9, Surbiton St. ℘ (0114) 244 9750/    ATS Herries Rd ℘ (0114) 234 3986/7
244 9759

---

**SHELLEY** W. Yorks. 402 404 O 23 – see Huddersfield.

---

**SHENINGTON** Oxon. – see Banbury.

---

**SHEPTON MALLET** Somerset 403 404 M 30 The West Country G. – pop. 7 581.
See : Town★ - SS. Peter and Paul's Church★.
Env. : – Downside Abbey★ (Abbey Church★) N : 5½ m. by A 37 and A 367.
Exc. : Longleat House★★★ AC, E : 15 m. by A 361 and B 3092 – Wells★★ - Cathedral★★★
Vicars' Close★, Bishop's Palace★ AC (⇐★★) W : 6 m. by A 371 – Wookey Hole★ (Caves★ AC
Papermill★) W : 6 ½ m. by B 371 – Glastonbury★★ - Abbey★★ (Abbot's Kitchen★) AC
St. John the Baptist★★, Somerset Rural Life Museum★ AC – Glastonbury Tor★ (⇐★★★) SW
9 m. by B 3136 and A 361 - Nunney★, E : 8½ m. by A 361.
🟢 Mendip, Gurney Slade ℘ (01749) 840570.
London 127 – Bristol 20 – Southampton 63 – Taunton 31.

🏛 **Charlton House,** BA4 4PR, East : 1 m. on A 361 (Frome rd) ℘ (01749) 342008
✿ Fax (01749) 346362, ⌂, « Part Georgian country house », ☎, ☞, ⅍ – ⅍ rest, 📺 ☎ ℗
◍ ▫ ① VISA JCB. ⅍
**Mulberry : Meals** 17.50/30.00 t. and a la carte 26.00/43.00 t. ⅃ 11.00 – ⌱ 5.00 – **17 rm**
90.00/200.00 st. – SB
**Spec.** Mosaic of rabbit and duck foie gras with hazelnut oil. Roast loin of tuna, confit of
onion and pimento. Summer fruit terrine, Génoise, pistachio ice cream.

🏛 **Shrubbery,** Commercial Rd, BA4 5BU, ℘ (01749) 346671, Fax (01749) 346581, ☞ –
⅍ rest, 📺 ☎ ℗ ◍ ▫ ① VISA
**Meals** (closed Sunday dinner) 14.95/21.00 t. and a la carte ⅃ 4.75 – **7 rm** ⌱ 43.00/75.00 t. –
SB.

XX **Bowlish House** with rm, Wells Rd, BA4 5JD, West : ½ m. on A 371 ℰ (01749) 342022, Fax (01749) 342022, ⌘ – 🆃🆅 🅿. ⫶⫶ 🆅🅸🆂🅰. ⫶
closed 1 week in spring and 1 week in autumn – Meals (booking essential) (dinner only) 22.50 t. ﹟ 5.00 – ⚏ 3.50 – **3 rm** 48.00/58.00 t.

t Doulting East : 1½ m. on A 361 – ⊠ Shepton Mallet.

XX **Brottens Lodge** ⟩ with rm, BA4 4RB, South : 1 m. turning right at Abbey Barn Inn, following sign for Evercreech ℰ (01749) 880352, Fax (01749) 880601, ⟨, ⌘ – ⟨𝕩 rest, 🆃🆅 🅿. ⫶⫶ 🆅🅸🆂🅰. ⫶
Meals (closed Sunday, Monday, 26 December and 1 January) (dinner only) a la carte 12.45/21.45 t. ﹟ 9.50 – **3 rm** ⚏ 45.00/65.00 st.

# HERBORNE Dorset 403 404 M 31 The West Country G. – pop. 7 606.

See : Town★ - Abbey★★ – Castle★ AC.

Env. : Sandford Orcas Manor House★ AC, NW : 4 m. by B 3148 – Purse Caundle Manor★ AC, NE : 5 m. by A 30.

Exc. : Cadbury Castle (⩽★★) N : 8 m. by A 30 – Parish Church★, Crewkerne, W : 14 m. on A 30.

📍 Clatcombe ℰ (01935) 812475.

🅱 3 Tilton Court, Digby Rd, DT9 3NL ℰ (01935) 815341.

London 128 – Bournemouth 39 – Dorchester 19 – Salisbury 36 – Taunton 31.

🏨 **Eastbury,** Long St., DT9 3BY, ℰ (01935) 813131, Fax (01935) 817296, ⌘ – 🆃🆅 ☎ 🅿 – 🅰 60. ⫶⫶ 🅰🅴 🆅🅸🆂🅰. ⫶
Meals 12.95/16.95 t. and dinner a la carte ﹟ 7.90 – **15 rm** ⚏ 49.50/89.00 t. – SB.

XX **Pheasants** with rm, 24 Greenhill, DT9 4EW, ℰ (01935) 815252, Fax (01935) 815252 – 🆃🆅 ☎ 🅿. ⫶⫶ 🆅🅸🆂🅰. ⫶
closed 2 weeks mid January – Meals (closed lunch Tuesday to Friday, Sunday dinner and Monday) 15.00/24.00 t. ﹟ 6.20 – **6 rm** ⚏ 40.00/55.00 t. – SB.

t Oborne Northeast : 2 m. by A 30 – ⊠ Sherborne.

XX **Grange** ⟩ with rm, DT9 4LA, ℰ (01935) 813463, Fax (01935) 817464, ⟨, ⌘, ⫶⫶ – 🆃🆅 ☎ 🅿. ⫶⫶ 🅰🅴 🆅🅸🆂🅰 🅹🅲🅱. ⫶
closed 1 to 7 January and first 2 weeks September – Meals - Italian - (closed Sunday dinner) (dinner only and Sunday lunch)/dinner a la carte 17.50/24.55 t. ﹟ 6.00 – **10 rm** ⚏ 53.00/70.00 t. – SB.

t Milborne Port Northeast : 3 m. on A 30 – ⊠ Sherborne.

🏠 **Old Vicarage,** Sherborne Rd, DT9 5AT, ℰ (01963) 251117, Fax (01963) 251515, ⟨, ⌘ – 🆃🆅 ☎ 🅿. ⫶⫶ 🅰🅴 🆅🅸🆂🅰. ⫶
closed 2 January-5 February – Meals (closed Sunday to Thursday) (dinner only) 21.30 t. ﹟ 7.20 – **7 rm** ⚏ 28.00/90.00 st. – SB.

t Hermitage South : 7½ m. by A 352 – ⊠ Sherborne.

↑ **Almshouse Farm** ⟩ without rest., DT9 6HA, ℰ (01963) 210296, Fax (01963) 210296, ⟨, « Former monastery, working farm », ⌘ – 🆃🆅 🅿. ⫶
closed December-January – **3 rm** ⚏ 25.00/50.00.

t Yetminster Southwest : 5½ m. by A 352 and Yetminster rd – ⊠ Sherborne.

↑ **Manor Farmhouse,** DT9 6LF, ℰ (01935) 872247, Fax (01935) 872247, « 17C », ⌘ – ⟨𝕩 🆃🆅 🅿. ⫶⫶ 🆅🅸🆂🅰. ⫶
Meals (by arrangement) 15.00 – **3 rm** ⚏ 30.00/50.00.

t Leigh Southwest : 6¼ m. by A 352 – ⊠ Sherborne.

↑ **Huntsbridge Farm** ⟩ without rest., DT9 6JA, Southeast : ¼ m. on Batcombe rd ℰ (01935) 872150, Fax (01935) 872150, ⟨, « Working farm », ⌘ – ⟨𝕩 🆃🆅 🅿. ⫶⫶ 🆅🅸🆂🅰. ⫶
February-mid December – **3 rm** ⚏ 30.00/50.00 s.

# HERBOURNE Warks. – see Warwick.

# HERE Surrey 404 S 30 – see Guildford.

---

*Für Ihre Reisen in Großbritannien*

- 5 Karten (Nr. 401, 402, 403, 404, 923) im Maßstab 1 : 400 000
- Die auf den Karten rot unterstrichenen Orte sind im Führer erwähnt, benutzen Sie deshalb Karten und Führer zusammen.

**SHIFNAL** Shrops. 402 403 404 M 25 – pop. 5 893 – ✉ Telford.
London 150 – Birmingham 28 – Shrewsbury 16.

🏨 **Park House**, Park St., TF11 9BA, ℘ (01952) 460128, Fax (01952) 461658, ☎s, 🔲, 🐎 –
≒ 📺 ☎ 🕭 ♿ 🅿 – 🏛 180. 🐵 🖭 ① 𝘝𝘐𝘚𝘈
**Meals** (closed Saturday lunch) 13.50/23.50 **st.** and a la carte 🍴 6.25 – 🖙 10.50 – **52 r**
113.00/148.00 **st.**, 2 suites – SB.

---

**SHINFIELD** Wokingham 404 R 29 – see Reading.

---

**SHIPBOURNE** Kent 404 U 30 – pop. 1 129 – ✉ Tonbridge.
London 35 – Maidstone 14 – Royal Tunbridge Wells 14.

🍴 **Chaser Inn** with rm, Stumble Hill, TN11 9PE, ℘ (01732) 810360, Fax (01732) 810941, 🎪
🐎 – 📺 ☎ 🕭 🅿. 🐵 🖭 𝘝𝘐𝘚𝘈
**Meals** (in bar Sunday dinner and Monday) 14.95/22.50 **t.** 🍴 6.75 – **15 rm** 🖙 45.00/65.00 **t.**

---

**SHIPHAM** Somerset 403 L 30 The West Country G. – pop. 1 094 – ✉ Winscombe.
Env. : Cheddar Gorge★★ (Gorge★★, Caves★, Jacobs's Ladder ☀★) – Axbridge★★ – Kir
John's Hunting Lodge★ – St. John the Baptist★, SW : 5 m. on A 38 – St. Andrew's Church
S : 2½ m.
🛅, 🛅 Mendip Spring, Honeyhall Lane, Congresbury, Avon ℘ (01934) 853337/852322.
London 135 – Bristol 14 – Taunton 20.

🏨 **Daneswood House**, Cuck Hill, BS25 1RD, ℘ (01934) 843145, Fax (01934) 843824, ≤, 🐎
– ≒ rest, 📺 ☎ 🅿. 🐵 🖭 ① 𝘝𝘐𝘚𝘈. 🕸
closed 26 December-4 January – **Meals** 29.95 **st.** 🍴 4.50 – **9 rm** 🖙 65.00/89.50 **t.**, 3 suites
SB.

---

**SHIPLEY** W. Yorks. 402 O 22 – pop. 28 165.
🛅 Northcliffe, High Bank Lane ℘ (01274) 584085.
London 216 – Bradford 4 – Leeds 12.

🏨 **Marriott Hollins Hall H. and Country Club** ॐ, Hollins Hill, Baildon, BD17 7QW
Northeast : 2 ½ m. on A 6038 ℘ (01274) 530053, Fax (01274) 530187, ≤, 🕭, ☎s, 🔲, 🐎
park – 🛗 ≒ 📺 ☎ 🕭 🅿 – 🏛 200. 🐵 🖭 ① 𝘝𝘐𝘚𝘈. 🕸
**Meals** a la carte 13.95/23.40 **st.** 🍴 7.75 – 🖙 11.95 – **121 rm** 75.00/125.00 **st.**, 1 suite – SB.

✗ **Aagrah**, 27 Westgate, BD18 3QX, ℘ (01274) 530880 – 🔲. 🐵 🖭 𝘝𝘐𝘚𝘈 𝘫𝘤𝘣
closed 25 December – **Meals** - Indian (Kashmiri) - (booking essential) (dinner only) a la carte
13.70/17.05 **t.**

---

**SHIPTON GORGE** Dorset – see Bridport.

---

**SHIPTON-UNDER-WYCHWOOD** Oxon. 403 404 P 28 – pop. 1 154.
London 81 – Birmingham 50 – Gloucester 37 – Oxford 25.

🏠 **Lamb Inn**, High St., OX7 6DQ, ℘ (01993) 830465, Fax (01993) 832025 – ≒ 📺 ☎ 🅿. 🐵
🖭 𝘝𝘐𝘚𝘈. 🕸
**Meals** (closed Sunday dinner and Monday) (dinner only and Sunday lunch)/dinner a la carte
18.40/26.85 **t.** – **5 rm** 🖙 65.00/95.00 **t.** – SB.

---

**SHIRLEY** W. Mids. 403 404 O 26 – see Solihull.

---

**SHOBDON** Herefordshire 403 L 27 – pop. 741 – ✉ Leominster.
London 158 – Birmingham 55 – Hereford 18 – Shrewsbury 37 – Worcester 33.

🏠 **The Paddock**, HR6 9NQ, West : ¼ m. on B 4362 ℘ (01568) 708176, Fax (01568) 708176
≒ 📺 🅿. 🕸
**Meals** (by arrangement) 15.00 **st.** – **5 rm** 🖙 25.00/44.00 **st.**

---

**SHOTTISHAM** Suffolk 404 X 27 – see Woodbridge.

---

**SHREWLEY** Warks. 403 404 P 27 – see Warwick.

**HREWSBURY** *Shrops.* 402 403 L 25 *Great Britain G.* – pop. 64 219.

See : *Abbey*★ **D.**

Exc. : *Ironbridge Gorge Museum*★★ *AC (The Iron Bridge*★★ - *Coalport China Museum*★★ -
*Blists Hill Open Air Museum*★★ – *Museum of the River and Visitor Centre*★ ) *SE : 12 m. by A 5
and B 4380.*

📷18 *Condover* ℘ *(01743) 872976 –* 📷9 *Meole Brace* ℘ *(01743) 364050.*

🅱 *The Music Hall, The Square, SY1 1LH* ℘ *(01743) 350761.*

*London 164 – Birmingham 48 – Chester 43 – Derby 67 – Gloucester 93 – Manchester 68 –
Stoke-on-Trent 39 – Swansea 124.*

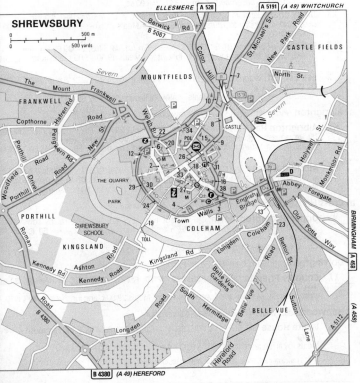

🏨 **Lion,** Wyle Cop, SY1 1UY, ℘ *(01743) 353107, Fax (01743) 352744* – 📶 ⇆ 📺 ☎ 🅿 –
🔔 200. **CB** AE ① **VISA** JCB
**Meals** 10.00/17.95 **st.** and dinner a la carte 🍷 6.50 – ⊊ 9.75 – **59 rm** 70.00/90.00 **st.** – SB.
**c**

🏨 **Prince Rupert,** Butcher Row, SY1 1UQ, ℘ *(01743) 499955, Fax (01743) 357306,* 📠, ⇔ –
📶, 🍴 rest, 📺 ☎ 🅿 – 🔔 70. **CB** AE ① **VISA**
**Meals** 11.00/17.00 **st.** and a la carte 🍷 7.50 – **67 rm** ⊊ 75.00/85.00 **st.**, 2 suites – SB.
**n**

🏨 **Fieldside** without rest., 38 London Rd, SY2 6NX, East : 1 ¼ m. by Abbey Foregate on
A 5064 (via Shirehall) ℘ *(01743) 353143, Fax (01743) 358645,* 🌳 – ⇆ 📺 ☎ 🧹 🅿. **CB** **VISA**
🈺
closed 2 weeks November – **4 rm** ⊊ 32.00/46.00 **st.**

**Travelodge,** Bayston Hill Service Area, SY3 0DA, South : 2 ¾ m. by Belle Vue Rd (A 519 and A 5112 at junction with A 5 ℘ (01743) 874256, Reservations (Freephone) 0800 85095C
※ rm, ⊡ & ₧ ⬤ ☎ ⓐ ⑩ *VISA* ᴊᴄʙ ⁒
Meals (grill rest.) – **40 rm** 39.95/59.95 **t.**
⌧ 38.00/54.00 **s.**

↑ **Pinewood House** without rest., Shelton Park, The Mount, SY3 8BL, Northwest : 1 ½ m. on A 458 ℘ (01743) 364200, ☞ – ⊡ ₧
*closed 25-26 December, January, 3 weeks in spring and restricted opening in winter* – **4 r**

↑ **Tudor House** without rest., 2 Fish St., SY1 1UR, ℘ (01743) 351735, « 15C » – ⊡ ⁒
*closed 24 and 25 December* – **3 rm** ⌧ 34.00/48.00 **st.**

XX **Jacky Chan,** Barracks Passage, Wyle Cop, SY1 1XA, ℘ (01743) 242188 – ⬤ *VISA* ᴊᴄʙ
*closed lunch Monday to Thursday and Sunday* – **Meals** - Chinese (Peking) - 5.70/13.00 and a la carte.

X **Sol,** 82 Wyle Cop, SY1 1UT, ℘ (01743) 340560, Fax (01743) 340552 – ⬤ ⓐ *VISA* ᴊᴄʙ
*closed Sunday, Monday and 2 weeks in winter* – **Meals** 19.50/25.00 **t.** and lunch a la cart ₰ 6.50.

X **Est, Est, Est,** Victoria Quay, Victoria Av., SY1 1HH, ℘ (01743) 233222, Fax (01743) 236671
⬤ ⓐ ⑩ *VISA* ᴊᴄʙ
*closed 25 and 26 December* – **Meals** - Italian - a la carte 11.75/22.95 **t.** ₰ 5.75.

**at Albrighton** North : 3 m. on A 528 – ⊠ Shrewsbury.

🏛 **Albrighton Hall,** Ellesmere Rd, SY4 3AG, ℘ (01939) 291000, Fax (01939) 291123, *ʄₛ,* ≊
▣, ☞, squash – ▐, ※ rm, ⊡ ☎ ℃ & ₧ – ₰ 400. ⬤ ⓐ ⑩ *VISA* ᴊᴄʙ
**Meals** *(closed Saturday lunch)* 14.00/27.00 **t.** and a la carte ₰ 7.50 – ⌧ 11.00 – **71 r**
116.00 **t.** – SB.

🏛 **Albright Hussey** ⍟, Ellesmere Rd, SY4 3AF, ℘ (01939) 290571, Fax (01939) 291143,
« 16C moated manor house », ☞ – ※ ⊡ ☎ ℃ & ₧ – ₰ 300. ⬤ ⓐ ⑩ *VISA* ᴊᴄʙ ⁒
**Meals** 12.50/24.50 **t.** and a la carte ₰ 6.50 – **13 rm** ⌧ 73.00/135.00 **t.**, 1 suite – SB.

**at Cross Houses** Southeast : 5 m. on A 458 – ⊠ Shrewsbury.

↑ **Upper Brompton Farm** ⍟ without rest., SY5 6LE, East : ½ m. by Lower Cro℘ (01743) 761629, Fax (01743) 761679, « Working farm », ☞, park – ※ ⊡ ₧. ⬤ *VI*
ᴊᴄʙ. ⁒
*closed Christmas* – **3 rm** ⌧ 40.00/65.00 **s.**

**at Dorrington** South : 7 m. on A 49 – ⊠ Shrewsbury.

XX **Country Friends,** SY5 7JD, ℘ (01743) 718707, Fax (01743) 718707, ☞ – ※ ₧. ⬤ *VI*
ᴊᴄʙ
*closed Sunday, Monday and 2 weeks mid July* – **Meals** 29.00 **t.** and lunch a la carte ₰ 6.50.

**at Hanwood** Southwest : 4 m. on A 488 – ⊠ Shrewsbury.

↑ **White House,** SY5 8LP, ℘ (01743) 860414, Fax (01743) 860414, « 16C farmouse », ☞
※ ₧. ⁒
**Meals** (by arrangement) 19.00 **s.** ₰ 6.00 – **6 rm** ⌧ 28.00/60.00 – SB.

🅐 ATS Lancaster Rd, Harlescott ℘ (01743) 443954/442231

---

**SHURDINGTON** Glos. 🆘🆘 N 28 – see Cheltenham.

---

**SIBSON** Leics. – see Nuneaton (Warks.).

---

**SIDFORD** Devon 🆘 K 31 – see Sidmouth.

---

*When visiting Great Britain,*
*use the Michelin Green Guide* **"Great Britain".**

- *Detailed descriptions of places of interest*
- *Touring programmes*
- *Maps and street plans*
- *The history of the country*
- *Photographs and drawings of monuments,*
  *beauty spots, houses...*

**SIDMOUTH** Devon 🗾 K 31 *The West Country G. – pop. 12 982.*

Env. : *Bicton★ (Gardens★) AC, SW : 5 m.*

🏌 *Cotmaton Rd ℘ (01395) 513023.*

🛈 *Ham Lane, EX10 8XR ℘ (01395) 516441.*

*London 176 – Exeter 14 – Taunton 27 – Weymouth 45.*

🏠🏠 **Riviera,** The Esplanade, EX10 8AY, ℘ (01395) 515201, *Fax (01395) 577775,* ≤ – 📶, 🖛 rest,
📺 ☎ ♿ 🚗 – 🔬 85. 🕮 🕮 🕮 *VISA*
**Meals** 15.00/25.00 t. and a la carte ♿ 5.50 – **27 rm** ⚏ (dinner included) 90.00/210.00 t. – SB.

🏠🏠 **Belmont,** The Esplanade, EX10 8RX, ℘ (01395) 512555, *Fax (01395) 579101,* ≤, 🌺 – 📶,
🖛 rest, 📺 ☎ ♿. 🕮 🕮 🕮 *VISA*. ⛞
**Meals** (dancing Saturday evening) 13.00/23.50 **st.** and a la carte ♿ 7.00 – **51 rm** ⚏ (dinner
included) 105.00/240.00 **st.** – SB.

🏠 **Salcombe Hill House** ⛞, Beatlands Rd, EX10 8JQ, ℘ (01395) 514697,
*Fax (01395) 578310,* 🏊, 🌺, ❀ – 📶, 🖛 rest, 📺 ☎ ♿. 🕮 *VISA* JCB
*March-October* – **Meals** (bar lunch Monday to Saturday)/dinner 15.95 **t.** and a la carte ♿ 4.25
– **28 rm** ⚏ (dinner included) 58.50/120.00 **t.** – SB.

🏠 **Fortfield** ⛞, Station Rd, EX10 8NU, ℘ (01395) 512403, *Fax (01395) 512403,* 🕿, 🔲, 🌺 –
📶, 🖛 rest, 📺 ☎ ♿. 🕮 🕮 🕮 *VISA* JCB
**Meals** 5.50/16.50 **st.** and dinner a la carte ♿ 5.50 – **55 rm** ⚏ (dinner included) 59.50/
120.00 **st.** – SB.

🏠 **Hunters Moon,** Sid Rd, EX10 9AA, ℘ (01395) 513380, *Fax (01395) 514270,* 🌺 – 🖛 rest,
📺 ☎ ♿. 🕮 *VISA* JCB
*March-October* – **Meals** (booking essential to non-residents) (dinner only) 15.95 **st.** ♿ 3.75 –
**18 rm** ⚏ (dinner included) 47.00/94.00 **st.**

🏠 **Littlecourt,** Seafield Rd, EX10 8HF, ℘ (01395) 515279, *Fax (01395) 578373,* 🌺 – 🖛 rm,
📺 ♿. 🕮 🕮 *VISA* JCB. ⛞
*closed January and February* – **Meals** (bar lunch Monday and Tuesday) 15.00 **t.** (dinner) and lunch a la carte approx. 13.70 **t.** ♿ 4.10 – **19 rm** ⚏ (dinner included) 54.00/
108.00 **st.** – SB.

🏠 **Abbeydale,** Manor Rd, EX10 8RP, ℘ (01395) 512060, *Fax (01395) 515566,* 🌺 – 📶,
🖛 rest, 📺 ☎ ♿. 🕮 *VISA*. ⛞
*March-October* – **Meals** (bar lunch)/dinner 14.00 **st.** ♿ 4.25 – **18 rm** ⚏ 28.00/100.00 **st.** –
SB.

🏠 **Mount Pleasant,** Salcombe Rd, EX10 8JA, ℘ (01395) 514694, 🌺 – 🖛 📺 ♿. ⛞
*March-October* – **Meals** (residents only) (dinner only) 14.50 **st.** ♿ 5.25 – **16 rm** ⚏ (dinner
included) 45.50/91.00 **st.** – SB.

🏠 **Woodlands,** Station Rd, Cotmaton Cross, EX10 8HG, ℘ (01395) 513120,
*Fax (01395) 513348,* 🌺 – 🖛 rest, 📺 ♿. 🕮 *VISA* JCB
**Meals** 5.95/9.95 **st.** and a la carte ♿ 4.95 – **31 rm** ⚏ 32.00/64.00 – SB.

**at Sidford** *North : 2 m.* – ✉ *Sidmouth.*

🏠 **Salty Monk,** Church St., EX10 9QP, on A 3052 ℘ (01395) 513174, « *Part 16C* », 🌺 –
🖛 rest, 📺 ☎ ♿. 🕮 🕮 *VISA*. ⛞
**Meals** (light lunch)/dinner 12.50 **st.** ♿ 4.50 – **7 rm** ⚏ 20.00/45.00 **st.** – SB.

🔧 ATS Vicarage Rd ℘ (01395) 512433

---

**SILCHESTER** Hants. 🗾🗾 Q 29 – *pop. 1 428 – ✉ Reading (Berks.).*
*London 62 – Basingstoke 8 – Reading 14 – Winchester 26.*

🏠 **Romans,** Little London Rd, RG7 2PN, ℘ (01189) 700421, *Fax (01189) 700691,* 🌿, 🕿, 🏊,
🌺 – 🖛 rest, 📺 ☎ ♿ – 🔬 80. 🕮 🕮 *VISA*
*closed 25 to 31 December* – **Meals** (closed Saturday lunch) (booking essential Sunday
dinner) 15.50 **st.** and a la carte ♿ 6.25 – **25 rm** ⚏ 75.00/115.00 **st.**

---

**SIMONSBATH** Somerset 🗾 I 30 *The West Country G. – ✉ Minehead.*
Env. : *Exmoor National Park★★ – Exford (Church★) E : 5½ m. by B 3223 and B 3224.*
*London 200 – Exeter 40 – Minehead 19 – Taunton 38.*

🏠 **Simonsbath House,** TA24 7SH, ℘ (01643) 831259, *Fax (01643) 831557,* ≤, « *17C country house* », 🌺 – 🖛 rest, 📺 ☎ ♿. 🕮 🕮 🕮 *VISA* JCB. ⛞
*closed December and January* – **Meals** (dinner only) 22.50 **t.** ♿ 4.75 – **7 rm** ⚏ 56.00/96.00 **t.**
– SB.

**SINDLESHAM** *Wokingham – see Reading.*

**SINGLETON** *Lancs.* 402 L 22 *– see Blackpool.*

**SINNINGTON** *N. Yorks.* 402 R 21 *– see Pickering.*

**SISSINGHURST** *Kent* 404 V 30 *– see Cranbrook.*

**SITTINGBOURNE** *Kent* 404 W 29.
    *London 44 – Canterbury 18 – Maidstone 15 – Sheerness 9.*

   🏠 **Hempstead House**, London Rd, Bapchild, ME9 9PP, East : 2 m. on A 2
     𝒫 (01795) 428020, *Fax (01795) 428020*, 🏡, « Victorian country house », ☐, 🐎 – ↤ 📺
     ☎ 📞 🅿. ⑩ 🆎 ⓪ *VISA* Jᴄʙ
     **Meals** 15.50/29.50 **st.** ↑ 6.50 **– 13 rm** ⊇ 62.00/72.00 **st.**

   ↥ **Beaumont** without rest., 74 London Rd, ME10 1NS, West : ¼ m. on A 2
     𝒫 (01795) 472536, *Fax (01795) 425921* – ↤ 📺 ☎ 📞 🅿. ⑩ 🆎 ⓪ *VISA* Jᴄʙ
     **9 rm** ⊇ 34.00/55.00 **st.**

     🅐 ATS Crown Quay Lane 𝒫 (01795) 472384/472472

     *En saison, surtout dans les stations fréquentées,*
     *il est prudent de retenir à l'avance.*
     *Cependant, si vous ne pouvez pas occuper la chambre*
     *que vous avez retenue, prévenez immédiatement l'hôtelier.*

     *Si vous écrivez à un hôtel à l'étranger, joignez à votre lettre*
     *un coupon-réponse international (disponible dans les bureaux de poste).*

**SIX MILE BOTTOM** *Cambs. – see Newmarket (Suffolk).*

**SKELTON** *N. Yorks.* 402 Q 22 *– see York.*

**SKELWITH BRIDGE** *Cumbria* 402 K 20 *– see Ambleside.*

**SKIPTON** *N. Yorks.* 402 N 22 *Great Britain G. –* pop. 13 583.
    See : *Castle*★ *AC.*
    🏌 𝒫 (01756) 795657.
    🅱 *The Old Town Hall, 9 Sheep St., BD23 1JH* 𝒫 (01756) 792809.
    *London 217 – Kendal 45 – Leeds 26 – Preston 36 – York 43.*

   🏠 **Hanover International**, Keighley Rd, BD23 2TA, South : 1 ¼ m. on A 629
     𝒫 (01756) 700100, *Fax (01756) 700107*, ≼, 🏋, 🚝, ☒, squash – ⧚ ↤ 📺 ☎ 🕭 🅿 – 🕭 350
     ⑩ 🆎 ⓪ *VISA*
     *closed 25 and 26 December* – **Meals** (bar lunch Monday to Saturday)/dinner 16.00 **st.** ↑ 7.80
     – ⊇ 9.50 **– 75 rm** 78.00/88.00 **st.** – SB.

   🏨 **The Unicorn**, Devonshire Pl., Keighley Rd, BD23 2LP, 𝒫 (01756) 794146
     *Fax (01756) 793376* – 📺 ☎. ⑩ 🆎 *VISA*. 🍴
     **Meals** (residents only) (dinner only) a la carte 11.50/13.80 **st.** ↑ 3.25 **– 9 rm** ⊇ 44.00/
     51.00 **st.** – SB.

   🏨 **Travelodge**, Gargrave Rd, BD23 1UD, West : 1 ¾ m. by Water St. at A 65/A 59 roundabout
     𝒫 (01756) 798091, *Fax (01756) 798091*, Reservations (Freephone) 0800 850950 – ↤ rm.
     📺 🕭 🅿. ⑩ 🆎 ⓪ *VISA* Jᴄʙ. 🍴
     **Meals** (grill rest.) **– 32 rm** 39.95/59.95 **t.**

   ✗ **Aagrah**, Unit 4, Unicorn House, Devonshire Pl., Keighley Rd, BD23 2LP, 𝒫 (01756) 790807
     – ⑩ 🆎 *VISA* Jᴄʙ
     *closed 25 December* – **Meals** - Indian (Kashmiri) - (booking essential) (dinner only) a la carte
     13.70/17.05 **t.**

**at Rylstone** *North : 5 m. on B 6265 –* ✉ *Skipton.*

   ↥ **The Manor House** without rest., BD23 6LH, 𝒫 (01756) 730226, ≼, 🏡, park – 📺 🅿. 🍴
     **3 rm** ⊇ 45.00/80.00.

**at Hetton** *North : 5 ¾ m. by B 6265 and Hetton rd on Settle rd –* ✉ *Skipton.*

🍴🍴 **Angel Inn,** BD23 6LT, ☎ (01756) 730263, *Fax (01756) 730363,* « Characterful 18C inn » – 🚭 ▤ [P]. [MC] [AE] [VISA]
*closed Sunday and second week January* – ***The Restaurant :*** **Meals** (dinner only) 19.50/30.95 **t.** 🍷 5.25 – (see also below).

🍺 **Angel Inn,** BD23 6LT, ☎ (01756) 730263, *Fax (01756) 730363,* 🏞, « Characterful 18C inn » – 🚭 [P]. [MC] [AE] [VISA]
*closed second week January* – Meals ***Bar/Brasserie :*** **Meals** a la carte 12.00/21.95 **t.** 🍷 5.25.

**at Elslack** *West : 4 ½ m. by A 59 off A 56 –* ✉ *Skipton.*

🏠 **The Tempest Arms,** BD23 3AY, ☎ (01282) 842450, *Fax (01282) 843331* – [TV] ☎ [P] – 👥 50. [MC] [AE] [VISA]. ✗
**Meals** a la carte 10.75/21.45 **t.** – **10 rm** ☕ 49.50/57.50 **t.** – SB.

ATS Carleton Rd Garage, Carleton Rd ☎ (01756) 795741/2

---

**SLAIDBURN** *Lancs.* [402] M 22 – *pop. 302* – ✉ *Clitheroe.*
*London 249 – Burnley 21 – Lancaster 19 – Leeds 48 – Preston 27.*

🏠 **Parrock Head** 🌿, Woodhouse Lane, BB7 3AH, Northwest : 1 m. ☎ (01200) 446614, *Fax (01200) 446313,* ≤ Bowland Fells, 🌳 – 🚭 rest, [TV] ☎ [P]. [MC] [VISA]. ✗
*closed January* – **Meals** (bar lunch Monday to Saturday)/dinner 21.50 **t.** 🍷 6.75 – **9 rm** ☕ 45.00/70.00 **t.** – SB.

---

**SLALEY** *Northd.* [401] [402] N 19 – *see Hexham.*

---

**SLEAFORD** *Lincs.* [402] [404] S 25 – *pop. 10 388.*
⛳18 *Willoughby Rd, South Rauceby* ☎ *(01529) 488273.*
ℹ *The Mill, Money's Yard, Carre St., NG34 7TW* ☎ *(01529) 414294.*
*London 119 – Leicester 45 – Lincoln 17 – Nottingham 39.*

🏠 **Lincolnshire Oak,** East Rd, NG34 7EH, Northeast : ¾ m. on B 1517 ☎ (01529) 413807, *Fax (01529) 413710,* 🌳 – 🚭 rest, [TV] ☎ [P] – 👥 140. [MC] [AE] [VISA]. ✗
**Meals** (booking essential) a la carte 15.50/20.00 **st.** 🍷 5.95 – **17 rm** ☕ 47.00/65.00 **st.** – SB.

🏠 **Travelodge,** NG34 8NP, Northwest : 1 m. on A 15 at junction with A 17 ☎ (01529) 414752, *Fax (01529) 414752,* Reservations (Freephone) 0800 850950 – 🚭 rm, [TV] ♿ [P]. [MC] [AE] [O] [VISA] [JCB]. ✗
**Meals** (grill rest.) – **40 rm** 39.95/59.95 **t.**

🍺 **Tally Ho Inn** with rm, Aswarby, NG34 8SA, South : 4 ½ m. on A 15 ☎ (01529) 455205, *Fax (01529) 455205,* ≤, 🌳 – [TV] [P]. [MC] [O] [VISA]
**Meals** (bar lunch Monday to Saturday) (in bar Sunday dinner) a la carte 10.25/17.95 **t.** 🍷 3.75 – **6 rm** ☕ 33.00/48.00 **st.**

ATS 40 Albion Terr., off Boston Rd ☎ (01529) 302908

---

**SLINFOLD** *W. Sussex – see Horsham.*

---

**SLOUGH** [404] S 29 – *pop. 110 708.*
*London 29 – Oxford 39 – Reading 19.*

🏨 **Copthorne,** Cippenham Lane, SL1 2YE, Southwest : 1 ¼ m. by A 4 on A 355 off M 4 junction 6 ☎ (01753) 516222, *Fax (01753) 516237,* 🏋, ♨, 🏊 – 🛗, 🚭 rm, ▤ [TV] ☎ 📞 ♿ [P] – 👥 200. [MC] [AE] [O] [VISA]. ✗
***Reflections :*** **Meals** *(closed Sunday and August)* (dinner only) 19.50 **st.** and a la carte 🍷 8.50 – ***Veranda :*** **Meals** *(closed lunch Saturday and Sunday)* (dancing Saturday evening) 19.50 **st.** and a la carte 🍷 8.50 – ☕ 11.50 – **217 rm** 150.00/185.00 **st.**, 2 suites.

🏨 **Slough/Windsor Marriott,** Ditton Rd, Langley, SL3 8PT, Southeast : 2 ½ m. on A 4 ☎ (01753) 544244, *Fax (01753) 540272,* 🏋, ♨, 🏊, 🎾 – 🛗, 🚭 rm, ▤ [TV] ☎ ♿ [P] – 👥 300. [MC] [AE] [O] [VISA]. ✗
**Meals** (bar lunch Saturday and Sunday) 16.95/19.95 **t.** and a la carte – ☕ 11.95 – **379 rm** 135.00/160.00 **st.**, 1 suite – SB.

🏨 **Courtyard by Marriott,** Church St., Chalvey, SL1 2NH, Southwest : 1 ¼ m. by A 4 on A 355 off M 4 junction 6 ☎ (01753) 551551, *Fax (01753) 553333,* 🏋 – 🛗, 🚭 rm, ▤ [TV] ☎ 📞 ♿ [P] – 👥 40. [MC] [AE] [O] [VISA] [JCB]. ✗
**Meals** (bar lunch Saturday) a la carte 12.95/21.75 **st.** 🍷 7.25 – ☕ 9.50 – **148 rm** 115.00 **st.**

ATS 1A Furnival Av. ☎ (01753) 524214/538555 ATS Poyle Rd, Colnbrook ☎ (01753) 682901/2

**SMITE** *Worcestershire – see Droitwich.*

---

**SNAPE** *Suffolk* 404 Y 27 – *pop. 1 509.*
*London 113 – Ipswich 19 – Norwich 50.*

🍴 **Crown Inn** with rm, Bridge Rd, IP17 1SL, ℘ (01728) 688324, « 15C inn », ☞ – ⇔ rm, 🅿
🚗 *VISA*
*closed 25 December –* **Meals** a la carte 14.00/23.20 t. ↕ 5.80 – **3 rm** ⊇ 35.00/50.00 t.

---

**SOAR MILL COVE** *Devon – see Salcombe.*

---

| Prices | For notes on the prices quoted in this Guide, see the introduction. |
|---|---|

---

**SOLIHULL** *W. Mids.* 403 404 O 26 – *pop. 94 531.*
🛈 *Central Library, Homer Rd, B91 3RG* ℘ *(0121) 704 6130/704 6134.*
*London 109 – Birmingham 7 – Coventry 13 – Warwick 13.*

🏨 **Solihull Moat House,** Homer Rd, B91 3QD, ℘ (0121) 623 9988, Fax (0121) 711 2696, 🔒
🔒, 🔲 – 🛗, ⇔ rm, 🔳 rest, 🔲 ☎ 🅿 – 🔬 200. 🚗 🅰🄴 ⑩ *VISA JCB*
**Meals** (bar lunch Saturday) 14.50/18.00 **st.** and a la carte ↕ 7.95 – ⊇ 9.50 – **113 rm** 140.00
170.00 **st.,** 2 suites – SB.

🏨 **St. John's Swallow,** 651 Warwick Rd, B91 1AT, ℘ (0121) 711 3000, Fax (0121) 705 6629
🔒, 🔒, 🔲, ☞ – 🛗, ⇔ rm, 🔲 rest, 🔲 ☎ 🅿 – 🔬 700. 🚗 🅰🄴 ⑩ *VISA*
**Conservatory :** **Meals** *(closed Saturday dinner)* (buffet lunch) 14.50/21.50 **st.** and a la carte
↕ 6.50 – **Warwick :** **Meals** 15.00/21.50 **st.** and a la carte ↕ 6.50 – **176 rm** ⊇ 135.00
150.00 **st.,** 1 suite – SB.

🏨 **Jarvis International,** The Square, B91 3RF, ℘ (0121) 711 2121, Fax (0121) 711 3374
🛗, ⇔ rm, 🔲 ☎ 🕓 🅿 – 🔬 200. 🚗 🅰🄴 ⑩ *VISA*
**Meals** 13.50/19.50 **st.** ↕ 6.50 – ⊇ 10.50 – **135 rm** 120.00/145.00 **st.,** 10 suites – SB.

🍴🍴 **Shimla Pinks,** 44 Station Rd, B91 3RX, ℘ (0121) 704 0344, Fax (0121) 704 0344 – 🔲. 🚗
🅰🄴 ⑩ *VISA*
*closed lunch Saturday and Sunday, 25-26 December, 1 January and Bank Holidays –* **Meals**
Indian - 6.95/12.95 **t.** and a la carte.

**at Shirley** *West : 2½ m. by B 4102 on A 34 – ⊠ Solihull.*

🏨 **Regency,** Stratford Rd, B90 4EB, Southeast : 1 m. on A 34 ℘ (0121) 745 6119
Fax (0121) 733 3801, 🔒, 🔒, 🔲 – 🛗, ⇔ rm, 🔲 rest, 🔲 ☎ 🅿 – 🔬 150. 🚗 🅰🄴 ⑩
*VISA*
**Meals** (bar lunch Saturday) 18.95 **st.** and dinner a la carte ↕ 5.95 – ⊇ 11.95 – **110 rm**
140.00/150.00 **st.,** 2 suites – SB.

🏠 **Travel Inn,** Stratford Rd, B90 4EP, Southeast : 1 ½ m. on A 34 ℘ (0121) 744 2942
Fax (0121) 733 7075 – ⇔ rm, 🔲 🕓 🅿. 🚗 🅰🄴 ⑩ *VISA.* ⚘
**Meals** (grill rest.) – **51 rm** 38.00 **t.**

🍴🍴 **Chez Julien,** 1036 Stratford Rd, Monkspath, B90 4EE, Southeast : 1 ½ m. on A 34
℘ (0121) 744 7232, Fax (0121) 745 4775, ☞ – 🅿. 🚗 🅰🄴 ⑩ *VISA JCB*
*closed Saturday lunch, Sunday and Bank Holidays –* **Meals** - French - 12.90 **t.** and a la carte
↕ 5.50.

**at Olton** *Northwest : 2½ m. on A 41 – ⊠ Solihull.*

🍴🍴 **Rajnagar,** 256 Lyndon Rd, B92 7QW, ℘ (0121) 742 8140, Fax (0121) 743 3147 – ⇔ 🔲. 🚗
🅰🄴 ⑩ *VISA JCB*
**Meals** - Indian - (dinner only) 17.95 **t.** and a la carte ↕ 5.00.

---

**SOMERTON** *Somerset* 403 L 30 *The West Country G. – pop. 4 489.*
See : *Town* ⭐ - *Market Place* ⭐ *(cross* ⭐ *) – St. Michael's Church* ⭐ .
Env. : *Long Sutton* *(Church* ⭐⭐ *) SW : 2½ m. by B 3165 – Huish Episcopi (St. Mary's Church*
*Tower* ⭐⭐ *) SW : 4½ m. by B 3153 – Lytes Cary* ⭐, *SE : 3½ m. by B 3151 – Street - The Shoe*
*Museum* ⭐, *N : 5 m. by B 3151.*
Exc. : *Muchelney* ⭐⭐ *(Parish Church* ⭐⭐ *) SW : 6½ m. by B 3153 and A 372 – High Ham (≤* ⭐⭐
*St. Andrew's Church* ⭐ *), NW : 9 m. by B 3153, A 372 and minor rd – Midelney Manor* ⭐ *AC*
*SW : 9 m. by B 3153 and A 378.*
*London 138 – Bristol 32 – Taunton 17.*

**Lynch Country House** without rest., 4 Behind Berry, TA11 7PD, ℰ (01458) 272316, Fax (01458) 272590, ≤, « Attractively converted Regency house », 🚗, park – 📺 ☎ 🅿, 🚳 🖭 *VISA*. 🛇
*closed Christmas and New Year* – **5 rm** 🖙 49.00/75.00 **t.**

🔘 ATS Bancombe Rd Trading Est. ℰ (01458) 273467

---

**SONNING-ON-THAMES** Wokingham **404** R 29 – *pop. 1 354.*
*London 48 – Reading 4.*

XXX **French Horn** with rm, Thames St., RG4 6TN, ℰ (01189) 692204, Fax (01189) 442210, ≤ River Thames and gardens – 📺 ☎ ❤ 🅿, 🚳 🖭 ⑩ *VISA*. 🛇
*closed 25-26 December and Good Friday* – **Meals** (booking essential) 19.50/32.00 **st.** and a la carte – **15 rm** 🖙 100.00/125.00 **st.**, 5 suites.

---

**SOUTHAMPTON** **403 404** P 31 *Great Britain G.* – *pop. 210 138.*
See : *Old Southampton* AZ : *Bargate\** **B** - *Tudor House Museum\** **M1.**
🏌️, 🏌️ Southampton Municipal, Golf Course Rd, Bassett ℰ (01703) 768407, AY – 🏌️ Stoneham, Monks Wood Close, Bassett ℰ (01703) 768151, AY – 🏌️ Chilworth Golf Centre, Main Rd, Chilworth ℰ (01703) 740544, AY.
*Itchen Bridge (toll)* AZ.
✈ Southampton/Eastleigh Airport : ℰ (01703) 620021, N : 4 m. BY.
🚢 to France (Cherbourg) (Stena Line) 1-2 daily (5 h) – to the Isle of Wight (East Cowes) (Red Funnel Ferries) frequent services daily (55 mn).
🚢 to Hythe (White Horse Ferries Ltd) frequent services daily (12 mn).
🛈 9 Civic Centre Rd, SO14 7LP ℰ (01703) 221106.
*London 87 – Bristol 79 – Plymouth 161.*

Plans on following pages

🏨 **De Vere Grand Harbour**, West Quay Rd, SO15 1AG, ℰ (01703) 633033, Fax (01703) 633066, 🏋️, ☎s, 🏊 – 🕴 🍴 ≡ 📺 ☎ ❤ 🕭 🅿 – 🕍 500. 🚳 🖭 *VISA*. 🛇
*Allerton's :* **Meals** *(closed Sunday lunch)* (booking essential) 15.50 **t.** (lunch) and a la carte 26.65/35.75 **st.** 🍷 9.00 – *Brewster's :* Meals (dinner only and Sunday lunch)/dinner 24.00 **t.** 🍷 8.95 – **169 rm** 🖙 140.00/185.00 **t.**, 3 suites – SB.　　　　　　　AZ **a**

🏨 **Hilton National**, Bracken Pl., Chilworth, SO16 3RB, ℰ (01703) 702700, Fax (01703) 767233, 🏋️, ☎s, 🏊 – 🕴 🍴 rm, ≡ rest, 📺 ☎ ❤ 🕭 🅿 – 🕍 200. 🚳 🖭 ⑩ *VISA* 🄹🄲🄱　　　　　　　　　　　　　　　　　　　　　　　　　　　　　　　　　　　　AY **e**
**Meals** *(closed Saturday lunch)* 14.00/18.50 **t.** and a la carte – 🖙 11.95 – **133 rm** 120.00 **st.**, 2 suites.

🏨 **Forte Posthouse Southampton**, Herbert Walker Av., SO15 1HJ, ℰ (01703) 330777, Fax (01703) 332510, ≤, 🏋️, ☎s, 🏊 – 🕴 🍴 rm, 📺 ☎ ❤ 🕭 🅿 – 🕍 200. 🚳 🖭 ⑩ *VISA*
**Meals** a la carte 16.40/26.60 **t.** – 🖙 9.95 – **126 rm** 85.00/150.00 **st.**, 2 suites – SB.　AZ **o**

🏨 **Novotel**, 1 West Quay Rd, SO15 1RA, ℰ (01703) 330550, Fax (01703) 222158, ≤, 🏋️, ☎s, 🏊 – 🕴, 🍴 rm, ≡ 📺 ☎ ❤ 🕭 🅿 – 🕍 450. 🚳 🖭 ⑩ *VISA*　　　　　　　AZ **x**
**Meals** 14.95 **st.** and a la carte 🍷 5.95 – 🖙 9.50 – **121 rm** 72.50/75.00 **st.**

🏨 **Southampton Park**, 12-13 Cumberland Pl., SO15 2WY, ℰ (01703) 343343, Fax (01703) 332538, 🏋️, ☎s, 🏊 – 🕴, 🍴 rm, ≡ rest, 📺 ☎ – 🕍 150. 🚳 🖭 ⑩ *VISA*
*closed 24 to 26 December* – *Number 12 Cumberland Place :* Meals (dinner only) 16.95 **t.** 🍷 6.45 – 🖙 7.50 – **72 rm** 70.00/80.00 **st.** – SB.　　　　　　　　　　　AZ **u**

🏨 **Travel Inn**, Romsey Rd, Nursling, SO16 0XJ, Northwest : 4 m. on A 3057 ℰ (01703) 732262 – 🍴 rm, 📺 🕭 🅿. 🚳 🖭 ⑩ *VISA*. 🛇　　　　　　　　　　　AY **a**
**Meals** (grill rest.) – **32 rm** 38.00 **t.**

🔘 ATS West Quay Rd ℰ (01703) 333231　　　　　　　ATS 88-94 Portswood Rd ℰ (01703) 582727

---

When visiting London use the **Green Guide "London"**

- Detailed descriptions of places of interest
- Useful local information
- A section on the historic square-mile of the City of London with a detailed fold-out plan
- The lesser known London boroughs
  - their people, places and sights
- Plans of selected areas and important buildings.

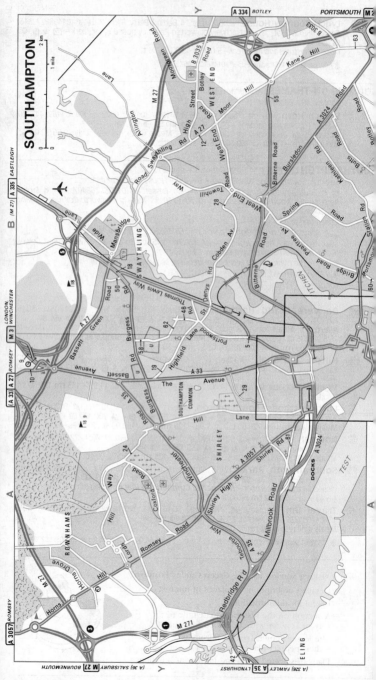

# SOUTHAMPTON

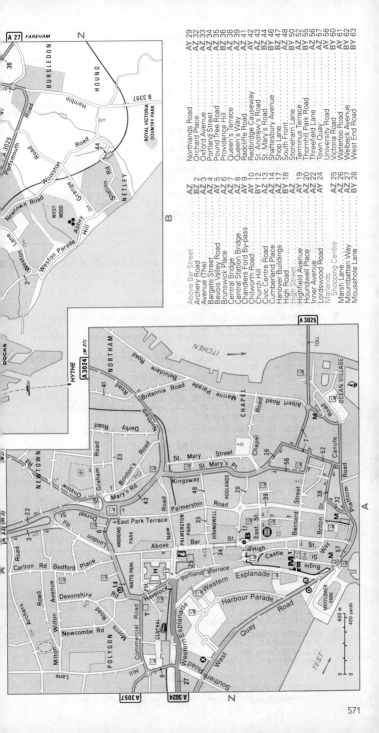

**SOUTHBOURNE** Bournemouth 403 404 O 31 – see Bournemouth.

---

**SOUTH BRENT** Devon 403 I 32 The West Country G. – pop. 2 087.
Env. : Dartmoor National Park★★.
London 227 – Exeter 29 – Plymouth 16 – Torquay 16.

🏠 **Brookdale House** ⌂, North Huish, TQ10 9NR, Southeast : 4 ½ m. by B 3210 via Avonwick village ℘ (01548) 821661, Fax (01548) 821606, 霖 – ⇔ rm, 🔟 ☎ 🄿. ◲ 歴 ₩₪ JCB. ⁊
Meals a la carte 11.80/15.00 t. ░ 8.50 – **8 rm** ⋤ 65.00/100.00 t. – SB.

---

**SOUTH CAVE** East Riding 402 S 22 – pop. 2 669.
📙 Cave Castle Hotel ℘ (01430) 421286/422245.
London 176 – Kingston-upon-Hull 12 – Leeds 40 – York 30.

🏠 **Travelodge,** Beacon Service Area, HU15 1RZ, Southwest : 2 ½ m. on A 63 (eastbound carriageway) ℘ (01430) 424455, Fax (01430) 424455, Reservations (Freephone) 0800 850950 – ⇔ rm, 🔟 ₫ 🄿. ◲ 歴 ⓪ ₩₪ JCB. ⁊
Meals (grill rest.) – **40 rm** 39.95/59.95 t.

---

**SOUTHEND-ON-SEA** Southend 404 W 29 – pop. 158 517.
📙 Belfairs, Eastwood Rd North, Leigh-on-Sea ℘ (01702) 525345 – 📙 Ballards Gore G & C.C Gore Rd, Canewdon, Rochford ℘ (01702) 258917.
⤬ Southend-on-Sea Airport : ℘ (01702) 340201, N : 2 m.
🄱 19 High St., SS1 1JE ℘ (01702) 215120.
London 39 – Cambridge 69 – Croydon 46 – Dover 85.

🏠 **Balmoral,** 32-36 Valkyrie Rd, Westcliff-on-Sea, SS0 8BU, ℘ (01702) 342947, Fax (01702) 337828 – 🔟 ☎ 🄿. ◲ 歴 ₩₪. ⁊
closed 31 December – Meals (closed Sunday dinner) (bar lunch)/dinner 12.95 t. ░ 4.25 – **28 rm** ⋤ 39.00/72.00 t., 1 suite.

🏠 **Camelia,** 178 Eastern Esplanade, SS1 3AA, ℘ (01702) 587917, Fax (01702) 585704 – ⧈ rest, 🔟 ☎ ☎. ◲ 歴 ₩₪ JCB
Meals (dinner only and Sunday lunch)/dinner 12.95 st. ░ 3.50 – **16 rm** ⋤ 46.00/60.00 st. – SB.

🏠 **Travel Inn,** Thanet Grange, SS2 6GB, Northwest : 2 ½ m. by A 127 off B 1013 ℘ (01702) 338787, Fax (01702) 337436 – 🅗, ⇔ rm, 🔟 ₫ 🄿. ◲ 歴 ⓪ ₩₪. ⁊
Meals (grill rest.) – **60 rm** 38.00 t.

↑ **Pebbles,** 190 Eastern Esplanade, SS1 3AA, ℘ (01702) 582329, Fax (01702) 582329 – ⇔ rest, 🔟. ◲ ₩₪. ⁊
Meals (by arrangement) 18.00 st. – **5 rm** ⋤ 30.00/45.00 st.

↑ **Moorings** without rest., 172 Eastern Esplanade, SS1 3AA, ℘ (01702) 587575 – 🔟. ⁊
**3 rm** ⋤ 27.50/40.00 s.

✕✕ **Paris,** 719 London Rd, Westcliff-on-Sea, SS0 9ST, ℘ (01702) 344077, Fax (01702) 344077 – ◲ 歴 ₩₪ JCB
closed Sunday dinner, Monday and Bank Holidays – Meals 15.95/24.95 st. ░ 6.50.

---

**SOUTH LEIGH** Oxon. 403 404 P 28 – see Witney.

---

**SOUTH MIMMS SERVICE AREA** Herts. 404 T 28 – ✉ Potters Bar.
🄱 Welcome Break, M 25 Motorway Services, EN6 3QQ ℘ (01707) 643233.
London 21 – Luton 17.

🏠 **Forte Posthouse South Mimms,** Bignells Corner, EN6 3NH, M 25 junction 23 at junction with A 1 (M) ℘ (01707) 643311, Fax (01707) 646728, Ϝ₅, ☎, ⬚ – ⇔ rm, 🔟 ☎ 🄿 – 🔬 100. ◲ 歴 ⓪ ₩₪
Meals 13.00/18.00 t. and a la carte ░ 7.50 – ⋤ 10.95 – **144 rm** 109.00 t. – SB.

🏠 **Welcome Lodge,** Bignells Corner, EN6 3QQ, M 25 junction 23 at junction with A 1(M) ℘ (01707) 665440, Fax (01707) 660189, Reservations (Freephone) 0800 7314466 – ⇔ rm 🔟 ₫ 🄿. ◲ 歴 ⓪ ₩₪
Meals (grill rest.) – ⋤ 7.50 – **52 rm** 60.00 t.

---

*"Un atlante della Gran Bretagna e dell' Irlanda*
*è disponibile in tre versioni : rilegato, in brossura e a spirale."*

**OUTH MOLTON** Devon 403 I 30 – pop. 4 066.

🛈 1 East St., EX36 3BU ℰ (01769) 574122 (summer only).

London 210 – Exeter 35 – Taunton 39.

🏛 **Whitechapel Manor** ⌂, EX36 3EG, East : 4 m. by B 3227 and Whitechapel rd ℰ (01769) 573377, Fax (01769) 573797, ≤, « Elizabethan manor house built by Robert de Bassett, gardens », park – ❄ rest, 📺 ☎ 🅿 – 🔬 30. 🐵 🆎 ① 𝘝𝘐𝘚𝘈 𝗝𝗖𝗕. ❄
**Meals** (booking essential to non-residents) (dinner only) 34.00 **st.** ⑧ 8.00 – **11 rm** 🖃 70.00/170.00 **st.** – SB.

🏠 **Marsh Hall Country House** ⌂, EX36 3HQ, Northeast : 1 ½ m. on North Molton rd ℰ (01769) 572666, Fax (01769) 574230, ≤, 🌲 – ❄ rest, 📺 ☎ 🅿. 🐵 𝘝𝘐𝘚𝘈 𝗝𝗖𝗕. ❄
**Meals** (dinner only) 20.00 **st.** ⑧ 6.00 – **7 rm** 🖃 50.00/100.00 **st.** – SB.

t **East Buckland** Northwest : 6 ¼ m. by B 3226 and Filleigh rd, turning right at Stags Head – ✉ Barnstaple.

✕✕ **Lower Pitt** ⌂ with rm, EX32 0TD, ℰ (01598) 760243, Fax (01598) 760243, 🌲 – ❄ 🅿. 🐵 🆎 𝘝𝘐𝘚𝘈. ❄
closed 25 December and 1 January – **Meals** (closed Sunday and Monday in winter) (booking essential) (dinner only) a la carte 16.25/22.00 **t.** ⑧ 8.90 – **3 rm** 🖃 (dinner included) 65.00/120.00 **t.** – SB.

**SOUTH NORMANTON** Derbs. 402 403 404 Q 24 – pop. 13 044 (inc. Pinxton).

London 130 – Derby 17 – Nottingham 15 – Sheffield 31.

🏨 **Swallow,** Carter Lane East, DE55 2EH, on A 38 ℰ (01773) 812000, Fax (01773) 580032, 🅵🅴, ≦s, 🏊, – ❄ rm, 📺 ☎ 🅦 ♿ 🅿 – 🔬 200. 🐵 🆎 ① 𝘝𝘐𝘚𝘈 𝗝𝗖𝗕
**Meals** (closed Saturday lunch) 18.00/24.00 **st.** – **157 rm** 🖃 110.00/120.00 **st.** – SB.

**SOUTHPORT** Mersey. 402 K 23 – pop. 90 959.

🏌 Southport Municipal, Park Road West ℰ (01704) 535286.

🛈 112 Lord St., PR8 1NY ℰ (01704) 533333.

London 221 – Liverpool 20 – Manchester 38 – Preston 19.

🏨 **Scarisbrick,** 239 Lord St., PR8 1NZ, ℰ (01704) 543000, Fax (01704) 533335 – 🛗 📺 ☎ 🅿 – 🔬 180. 🐵 🆎 ① 𝘝𝘐𝘚𝘈
**Meals** (dancing Saturday evening) 8.95/12.95 **st.** and a la carte ⑧ 5.00 – **77 rm** 🖃 72.00/120.00 **st.** – SB.

🏠 **Stutelea,** Alexandra Rd, PR9 0NB, ℰ (01704) 544220, Fax (01704) 500232, 🅵🅴, ≦s, 🏊, 🌲 – 🛗 📺 ☎ 🅿. 🐵 🆎 ① 𝘝𝘐𝘚𝘈 𝗝𝗖𝗕. ❄
**Meals** (bar lunch)/dinner 14.00 **st.** and a la carte ⑧ 5.00 – **22 rm** 🖃 65.00/120.00 **st.** – SB.

🏠 **Cambridge House,** 4 Cambridge Rd, PR9 9NG, Northeast : 1 m. on A 565 ℰ (01704) 538372, Fax (01704) 547183, 🌲 – ❄ 📺 ☎ 🅿. 🐵 🆎 𝘝𝘐𝘚𝘈
**Meals** (dinner only and Sunday lunch)/dinner 14.50 **t.** and a la carte ⑧ 5.75 – **18 rm** 🖃 33.00/60.00 **t.** – SB.

🏠 **Ambassador,** 13 Bath St., PR9 0DP, ℰ (01704) 543998, Fax (01704) 536269 – ❄ 📺 🅿. 🐵 🆎 𝘝𝘐𝘚𝘈
closed 24 December-1 February – **Meals** 10.00 ⑧ 4.00 – **8 rm** 🖃 30.00/50.00.

✕✕ **Warehouse Brasserie,** 30 West St., PR8 1QN, ℰ (01704) 544662, Fax (01704) 500074 – ▤. 🐵 🆎 𝘝𝘐𝘚𝘈
closed Sunday and 25 December – **Meals** (light lunch)/dinner 10.95 **t.** and a la carte ⑧ 6.95.

✕✕ **Ho'Lee Chow's,** Rotton Row, Victoria Park, PR8 2BZ, ℰ (01704) 551167, Fax (01704) 550519 – ▤ 🅿. 🐵 𝘝𝘐𝘚𝘈 𝗝𝗖𝗕
**Meals** - Chinese - (dinner only) 10.00 **st.** and a la carte.

🅐 ATS 69 Shakespeare St. ℰ (01704) 534434

**SOUTHSEA** Portsmouth 403 404 Q 31 – see Portsmouth and Southsea.

**SOUTHWAITE SERVICE AREA** Cumbria 401 402 L 19 – ✉ Carlisle.

🛈 M 6 Service Area, CA4 0NS ℰ (016974) 73445/73446.

London 300 – Carlisle 14 – Lancaster 58 – Workington 48.

🏠 **Travelodge,** CA4 0NT, M 6 between junctions 41 and 42 ℰ (016974) 73131, Fax (016974) 73669, Reservations (Freephone) 0800 850950 – ❄ 📺 ☎ ♿ 🅿. 🐵 🆎 ① 𝘝𝘐𝘚𝘈 𝗝𝗖𝗕. ❄
**Meals** (grill rest.) – **39 rm** 39.95/59.95 **t.**

**SOUTH WALSHAM** *Norfolk* **404** Y 26 *Great Britain G. – pop. 1 612 –* ⊠ *Norwich.*
Env. : *The Broads*★.
*London 120 – Great Yarmouth 11 – Norwich 9.*

🏨 **South Walsham Hall** ♨, The Street, NR13 6DQ, ℰ *(01603) 270378*
Fax *(01603) 270519*, ≤, 🔼, ⌇, 🐎, park, ℀ – 📺 ☎ 🅿 – 🔬 25. 🆑 ℀ ⑩ 𝘝𝘐𝘚𝘈 𝐉𝐂𝐁. ℀
Meals 18.50 t. and a la carte ⅟ 5.00 – **17 rm** ⊇ 50.00/180.00 st. – SB.

---

**SOUTHWATER** *W. Sussex* **404** T 30 – *see Horsham.*

---

**SOUTHWELL** *Notts.* **402 404** R 24 *Great Britain G. – pop. 6 498.*
See : *Minster*★★ *AC.*
*London 135 – Lincoln 24 – Nottingham 14 – Sheffield 34.*

🏨 **Saracen's Head,** Market Pl., NG25 0HE, ℰ *(01636) 812701,* Fax *(01636) 815408*, 🈺
℀ rm, 📺 ☎ 🅿 – 🔬 120. 🆑 ℀ 𝘝𝘐𝘚𝘈
Meals (bar lunch)/dinner 13.95 t. and a la carte ⅟ 5.95 – ⊇ 8.95 – **27 rm** 65.00/75.00 st. –
SB.

↑ **Old Forge** without rest., 2 Burgage Lane, NG25 0ER, ℰ *(01636) 812809*
Fax *(01636) 816302*, 🐎 – ℀ 📺 ☎ 🅿. 🆑 ℀ 𝘝𝘐𝘚𝘈
**5 rm** ⊇ 35.00/56.00.

---

**SOUTHWOLD** *Suffolk* **404** Z 27 – *pop. 3 905.*
🏌 *The Common* ℰ *(01502) 723234.*
🅑 *Town Hall, Market Pl., IP18 6EF* ℰ *(01502) 724729 (summer only).*
*London 108 – Great Yarmouth 24 – Ipswich 35 – Norwich 34.*

🏨 **Swan,** Market Pl., IP18 6EG, ℰ *(01502) 722186,* Fax *(01502) 724800*, 🐎 – ⃒, ℀ rest, 📺
☎ 🅿 – 🔬 40. 🆑 ℀ ⑩ 𝘝𝘐𝘚𝘈
Meals (bar lunch Monday to Friday November-March) 16.50/22.50 t. ⅟ 5.00 – **43 rm**
⊇ 60.00/130.00 t., 2 suites.

🏠 **Crown,** 90 High St., IP18 6DP, ℰ *(01502) 722275,* Fax *(01502) 727263* – 📺 ☎ 🅿 – 🔬 40.
🆑 ℀ ⑩ 𝘝𝘐𝘚𝘈 𝐉𝐂𝐁. ℀
closed 1 week January – Meals 17.00/23.00 t. – ⊇ 5.50 – **12 rm** 45.00/68.00 t.

**at Reydon** *Northwest : 1 m. by A 1095 on B 1126 –* ⊠ *Southwold.*

🏠 **Cricketers** with rm, Wangford Rd, IP18 6PZ, ℰ *(01502) 723603,* Fax *(01502) 722194*, 🐎
℀ rest, 📺 ☎ ✆ 🅿. 🆑 ℀ 𝘝𝘐𝘚𝘈 𝐉𝐂𝐁. ℀
Meals a la carte 11.80/14.35 t. ⅟ 5.85 – **8 rm** ⊇ 39.00/58.00 st. – SB.

---

**SPALDING** *Lincs.* **402 404** T 25 – *pop. 18 731.*
🅑 *Ayscoughfee Hall, Churchgate, PE11 2RA* ℰ *(01775) 725468/761161.*
*London 111 – Lincoln 40 – Leicester 56 – Norwich 65.*

↑ **Bedford Court** without rest., 10 London Rd, PE11 2TA, ℰ *(01775) 722377*
Fax *(01775) 722377*, 🐎 – ℀ 📺 🅿. ℀
**4 rm** ⊇ 25.00/40.00.

🅐 ATS 10 Gosberton Rd, Surfleet ℰ *(01775) 680251*

---

**SPEEN** *Bucks.* **404** R 28 – ⊠ *Princes Risborough.*
*London 41 – Aylesbury 15 – Oxford 33 – Reading 25.*

℀℀ **Old Plow** (Restaurant), Flowers Bottom, HP27 0PZ, West : ½ m. by Chapel Hill and
Highwood Bottom ℰ *(01494) 488300,* Fax *(01494) 488702*, 🐎 – 🅿. 🆑 ℀ 𝘝𝘐𝘚𝘈
closed Sunday dinner, Monday, 3 days Christmas, Bank Holidays and 2 weeks late August –
Meals 19.95/25.00 t. and a la carte ⅟ 8.95.

---

**SPORLE** *Norfolk – see Swaffham.*

---

**SPRATTON** *Northants.* **404** R 27 – *see Northampton.*

---

**STADDLEBRIDGE** *N. Yorks. – see Northallerton.*

---

*The Guide is updated annually so renew your Guide every year.*

ENGLAND

**STADHAMPTON** *Oxon.* 403 404 Q 28 – *pop. 718.*
*London 53 – Aylesbury 18 – Oxford 10.*

🍽 **Crazy Bear** with rm, Bear Lane, OX44 7UR, off Wallingford rd ℰ (01865) 890714, Fax (01865) 400481, 佘 – ≣ rest, ⊡ 🅟, ⓪ 🆎 *VISA*, ⅍
Meals 16.95/19.95 t. and a la carte 15.85/32.40 t. – � 8.50 – **5 rm** ⊆ 50.00/100.00 t. – SB.

---

**STAFFORD** *Staffs.* 402 403 404 N 25 – *pop. 61 885.*
🏌 Brocton Hall, Brocton ℰ (01785) 662627 – 🏌 Stafford Castle, Newport Rd ℰ (01785) 223821.
🛈 The Ancient High House, Greengate St., ST16 2HS ℰ (01785) 240204.
*London 142 – Birmingham 26 – Derby 32 – Shrewsbury 31 – Stoke-on-Trent 17.*

🏨 **Tillington Hall,** Eccleshall Rd, ST16 1JJ, Northwest : 1 ½ m. by A 34 on A 5013 ℰ (01785) 253531, Fax (01785) 259223, 🛵, 😑, 🏊, 🐎, ⅍ – 📱 ⅍, ≣ rest, ⊡ ☎ ⅙ 🅟 – 🔬 200. ⓪ 🆎 ⓪ *VISA* *JCB*
Meals (carving lunch) 10.50/15.25 st. and a la carte – **92 rm** ⊆ 75.00/120.00 st. – SB.

🏨 **Garth,** Wolverhampton Rd, ST17 9JR, South : 2 m. on A 449 ℰ (01785) 256124, Fax (01785) 255152, 🐎 – ⅍ rm, ≣ rest, ⊡ ☎ 🅟 – 🔬 175. ⓪ 🆎 ⓪ *VISA* *JCB*
Meals (bar lunch Monday to Saturday) (carving rest.) a la carte 18.00/29.50 st. ⅙ 5.25 – ⊆ 9.50 – **60 rm** 75.00/90.00 st. – SB.

🏠 **Holiday Inn Express** without rest., Acton Court, Acton Gate, ST18 9AR, South : 3 m. on A 449 ℰ (01785) 212244, Fax (01785) 212377 – 📱, ⅍ rm, ≣ rest, ⊡ ☎ ⅙ 🅟 – 🔬 55. ⓪ 🆎 ⓪ *VISA*, ⅍
**103 rm** 49.95 t.

◉ ATS Kenworthy Rd, Astonfields Ind. Est.   ◉ ATS Sandon Rd ℰ (01785) 253200 ℰ (01785) 223832

---

**STAFFORD SERVICE AREA** *Staffs.* 403 404 N 25 – ✉ *Stafford.*

🏠 **Travelodge,** Stone, ST15 0EU, M6 between junctions 14 and 15 (northbound carriageway) ℰ (01785) 811188, Fax (01785) 810500, Reservations (Freephone) 0800 850950 – ⅍ ⊡ ☎ ⅙ 🅟, ⓪ 🆎 ⓪ *VISA* *JCB*, ⅍
Meals (grill rest.) – **49 rm** 39.95/59.95 t.

---

**STAINES** *Middx.* 404 S 29 – *pop. 51 167.*
*London 26 – Reading 25.*

🏨 **Thames Lodge,** Thames St., TW18 4SF, ℰ (01784) 464433, Fax (01784) 454858, ≤, « Riverside setting » – ⅍, ≣ rest, ⊡ ☎ 🅟 – 🔬 50. ⓪ 🆎 ⓪ *VISA* *JCB*
Meals 10.95/17.95 st. and dinner a la carte ⅙ 7.45 – ⊆ 10.75 – **79 rm** 125.00/145.00 st. – SB.

---

**STAITHES** *Redcar & Cleveland* 402 R 20 – ✉ *Saltburn (Cleveland).*
*London 269 – Middlesbrough 22 – Scarborough 31.*

🍴 **Endeavour,** 1 High St., TS13 5BH, ℰ (01947) 840825 ⅍
closed Sunday except Bank Holidays, July and August and restricted opening in winter – Meals - Seafood - (lunch booking essential) a la carte 18.65/23.65 t. ⅙ 4.50.

---

**STAMFORD** *Lincs.* 402 404 S 26 *Great Britain G.* – *pop. 17 492.*
See : Town★★ – St. Martin's Church★ – Lord Burghley's Hospital★ – Browne's Hospital★ AC.
Env. : Burghley House★★ AC, SE : 1½ m. by B 1443.
🛈 Stamford Arts Centre, 27 St. Mary's St., PE9 2DL ℰ (01780) 755611.
*London 92 – Leicester 31 – Lincoln 50 – Nottingham 45.*

🏨 **The George of Stamford,** 71 St. Martin's, PE9 2LB, ℰ (01780) 750750, Fax (01780) 750701, 佘, « Part 16C coaching inn with walled monastic garden » – ⊡ ☎ 🅟 – 🔬 50. ⓪ 🆎 ⓪ *VISA*
Meals 16.50 st. (lunch) and a la carte 27.10/44.35 st. ⅙ 6.75 – **46 rm** ⊆ 78.00/175.00 st., 1 suite – SB.

🏨 **Garden House,** 42 High St., St. Martin's, PE9 2LP, ℰ (01780) 763359, Fax (01780) 763339, 佘, 🐎 – ⊡ ☎ 🅟, ⓪ 🆎 *VISA*
Meals (bar dinner Sunday) 15.00 t. and a la carte ⅙ 4.50 – **20 rm** ⊆ 55.00/79.50 st. – SB.

🏨 **Ram Jam Inn,** Great North Rd, Stretton, LE15 7QX, Northwest : 8 m. by B 1081 on A 1 (northbound carriageway) ℰ (01780) 410776, Fax (01780) 410361, 🐎 – ⊡ ☎ ⅙ 🅟 – 🔬 30. ⓪ 🆎 *VISA*, ⅍
closed 25 December – Meals a la carte 11.20/22.65 t. ⅙ 7.50 – ⊆ 4.75 – **7 rm** 45.00/55.00 t. – SB.

575

STAMFORD

🏛 **Lady Anne's**, 37-38 High St., St. Martin's Without, PE9 2LJ, ℰ (01780) 481184
*Fax* (01780) 765422, 🖾 – 💥 rest, 📺 ☎ 🅿 – 🔬 100. 🐼 🅰🅴 ① 🆅🅸🆂🅰
*closed 27 to 30 December* – **Meals** (booking essential Saturday lunch) 12.95/19.50 **st.** ▮ 5.3
– **28 rm** ⚏ 52.00/90.00 **t.** – SB.

✗✗ **Raj of India**, 2 All Saints St., PE9 2PA, ℰ (01780) 753556 – ▤. 🐼 🅰🅴 ① 🆅🅸🆂🅰
*closed 25 December* – **Meals** - Indian - a la carte 10.95/15.80 **t.** ▮ 4.80.

✗✗ **The Bombay Cottage**, 52 Scotgate, PE9 2YQ, ℰ (01780) 480138 – ▤. 🐼 🅰🅴 ① 🆅🅸🆂.
🅹🅲🅱
**Meals** - Indian - a la carte 23.70/44.60 **t.**

**at Tallington** *East : 5 m. by A 6121 on A 16* – ⊠ *Stamford*.

⌂ **Old Mill** 🈸 without rest., Mill Lane, PE9 4RR, ℰ (01780) 740815, *Fax* (01780) 740280
« Converted 17C mill », park – 💥 📺 🅿
**6 rm** ⚏ 30.00/55.00 **st.**

**at Normanton Park** *(Leics.) West : 6½ m. by A 606 on Edith Weston Rd* – ⊠ *Oakham*.

🏛 **Normanton Park** 🈸, South Shore, LE15 8RP, ℰ (01780) 720315, *Fax* (01780) 721086
<, « Converted Georgian stables on shores of Rutland Water », ☜, 🖾 – 💥 rm, ▤ rest
📺 ☎ 🅿 – 🔬 30. 🐼 🅰🅴 🆅🅸🆂🅰 🅹🅲🅱
**Meals** *(closed Sunday dinner)* a la carte 14.75/23.75 **t.** ▮ 5.25 – **23 rm** ⚏ 58.00/85.00 **t.**
SB.

---

**STANDISH** *Gtr. Manchester* � � *M 23* – *pop. 12 196* – ⊠ *Wigan*.
*London 210 – Liverpool 22 – Manchester 21 – Preston 15.*

🏛 **Kilhey Court**, Chorley Rd, WN1 2XN, East : 1 ¾ m. by B 5239 on A 5106
ℰ (01257) 472100, *Fax* (01257) 422401, 𝄜, ☎, 🅻, 🖾 – 🛏 💥, ▤ rest, 📺 ☎ 🅿 – 🔬 180
🐼 🅰🅴 ① 🆅🅸🆂🅰
**Laureate : Meals** *(closed Saturday lunch)* 13.25/24.50 **st.** and dinner a la carte ▮ 8.25
**Kilhey's Brasserie : Meals** a la carte approx. 13.00 **st.** ▮ 8.25 – **62 rm** ⚏ 95.00/165.00 – SB

🏛 **Wigan/Standish Moat House**, Almond Brook Rd, WN6 0SR, West : 1 m. on A 5209
ℰ (01257) 499988, *Fax* (01257) 427327, 𝄜, ☎, 🅻 – 🛏, 💥 rm, ▤ rest, 📺 ☎ 🅿
🔬 150. 🐼 🅰🅴 ① 🆅🅸🆂🅰
**Meals** *(closed Saturday lunch)* (carving rest.) 10.50/11.25 **st.** and a la carte ▮ 5.75 – ⚏ 9.50 –
**124 rm** 80.00/95.00 **st.** – SB.

🏛 **Ashfield House**, Ashfield Park Drive, WN6 0EQ, Southeast : ¾ m. by A 49
ℰ (01257) 473500, *Fax* (01257) 400311, 🖾 – 📺 ☎ ✆ 🅿. 🐼 🅰🅴 ① 🆅🅸🆂🅰. 🎘
**Meals** *(closed Saturday lunch)* 17.95 **st.** (dinner) and a la carte 20.85/30.85 **st.** ▮ 7.95
**15 rm** ⚏ 65.00/85.00 **st.**

⊚ ATS 23 Market St. ℰ (01257) 423146/423732

---

**STANNERSBURN** *Northd.* � � *M 18* – ⊠ *Hexham*.
*London 363 – Carlisle 56 – Newcastle upon Tyne 46.*

🍴 **Pheasant Inn** 🈸 with rm, Falstone, NE48 1DD, ℰ (01434) 240382, *Fax* (01434) 240382
💥 📺 🅿. 🐼 🆅🅸🆂🅰 🅹🅲🅱
*closed 25-26 December and Monday January-February* – **Meals** a la carte 13.95/20.15 **t.**
▮ 4.50 – **8 rm** ⚏ 40.00/58.00 **t.** – SB.

---

**STANSTEAD ABBOTTS** *Herts.* � *U 28* – *pop. 1 909* – ⊠ *Ware*.
🅻 Briggens House Hotel, Briggens Park, Stanstead Rd ℰ (01279) 793742.
*London 22 – Cambridge 37 – Luton 32 – Ipswich 66.*

🏛 **County H. Stanstead Abbotts Briggens House**, Stanstead Rd, SG12 8LD, East :
2 m. by A 414 ℰ (01279) 829955, *Fax* (01279) 793685, <, 🔟, 🅻, 🖾, park, ✗ – 🛏 📺 ☎ 🅿 –
🔬 100. 🐼 🅰🅴 ① 🆅🅸🆂🅰. 🎘
**Bridgemans : Meals** 18.25/23.50 **st.** and a la carte ▮ 7.50 – ⚏ 9.50 – **53 rm** 110.00/
158.00 **st.**, 1 suite – SB.

---

**STANSTED AIRPORT** *Essex* � *U 28* – ⊠ *Stansted Mountfitchet*.
*London 37 – Cambridge 29 – Chelmsford 32 – Colchester 29.*

🏛 **Hilton National**, Round Coppice Rd, CM24 8SE, ℰ (01279) 680800, *Fax* (01279) 680890,
𝄜, ☎, 🔟 – 🛏, 💥 rm, ▤ 📺 ☎ 🅻 🅿 – 🔬 250. 🐼 🅰🅴 ① 🆅🅸🆂🅰 🅹🅲🅱
**Meals** *(bar lunch Saturday)* 16.50/21.00 **t.** and dinner a la carte ▮ 7.50 – ⚏ 12.75 – **235 rm**
137.00/184.00 **st.**, 5 suites.

🏛 **Welcome Lodge** without rest., Birchanger Green Service Area, Old Dunmow Rd, CM23
5QZ, at junction 8 of M 11 ℰ (01279) 656477, *Fax* (01279) 656590, Reservations (Freephone)
0800 7314466 – 💥 📺 🅻 🅿. 🐼 🅰🅴 ① 🆅🅸🆂🅰
⚏ 6.50 **60 rm** 60.00 **t.**

**at Broxted** Northeast : 3 ¾ m. by Broxted rd – ⊠ Great Dunmow.

🏛 **Whitehall,** Church End, CM6 2BZ, on B 1051 ℘ (01279) 850603, Fax (01279) 850385, ≼,
« Part 12C and 15C manor house, walled garden », ℀ – 🆃🆅 ☎ ℃ 🅿 – 🛓 100. 🐠 🆀 ⑩
𝑉𝐼𝑆𝐴. ℀
closed 26 to 31 December – Meals – (see **The Restaurant** below) – ⬓ 9.50 – **25 rm**
80.00/140.00 **t.** – SB.

XXX **The Restaurant** (at Whitehall H.), Church End, CM6 2BZ, on B 1051 ℘ (01279) 850603,
Fax (01279) 850385 – 🅿 🐠 🆀 ⑩ 𝑉𝐼𝑆𝐴
closed Saturday lunch and 26 to 31 December – Meals 17.50/20.00 **t.** and dinner a la carte
� 8.50.

---

**STANTON** Suffolk 𝟒𝟎𝟒 W 27 – pop. 2 490.
London 88 – Cambridge 38 – Ipswich 40 – King's Lynn 38 – Norwich 39.

X **Leaping Hare,** Wyken Vineyards, IP31 2DW, South : 1 ¼ m. by Wyken Rd
℘ (01359) 250287, Fax (01359) 252256, « Converted 17C barn, vineyard », � – ʕᘔᑎ 🅿. 🐠
𝑉𝐼𝑆𝐴
closed Monday to Wednesday and January – Meals (booking essential) a la carte 15.15/
21.85 **st.**

---

**STANTON FITZWARREN** Wilts. – see Swindon.

---

**STANTON ST. JOHN** Oxon. 𝟒𝟎𝟑 𝟒𝟎𝟒 Q 28 – see Oxford.

---

**STANTON WICK** Bath & North East Somerset 𝟒𝟎𝟑 𝟒𝟎𝟒 M 29 – see Bristol.

---

**STAPLEFORD** Wilts. 𝟒𝟎𝟑 𝟒𝟎𝟒 O 30 – see Salisbury.

---

**STAVERTON** Devon 𝟒𝟎𝟑 I 32 – pop. 682 – ⊠ Totnes.
London 220 – Exeter 20 – Torquay 33.

🏛 **Kingston House** ⤸, TQ9 6AR, Northwest : 1 m. on Kingston rd ℘ (01803) 762235,
Fax (01803) 762444, ≼, « Georgian mansion, antiques and marquetry staircase », 🌾, park
– ʕᘔᑎ ☎ 🅿. 🐠 🆀 ⑩ 𝑉𝐼𝑆𝐴 JCB. ℀
Meals (residents only) (lunch by arrangement)/dinner 32.50 **st.** ♾ 7.95 – **3 rm** ⬓ 77.50/
135.00 **st.** – SB.

🍴 **Sea Trout Inn** with rm, TQ9 6PA, ℘ (01803) 762274, Fax (01803) 762506, ⤸ – ʕᘔᑎ rest,
🆃🆅 ☎ 🅿. 🐠 🆀 🆀
accommodation closed 25 and 26 December – Meals (bar meals Monday to Saturday and
Sunday dinner)/dinner 18.95 and a la carte ♾ 4.25 – **10 rm** ⬓ 46.50/70.00 **st.** – SB.

---

**STAVERTON** Glos. – see Cheltenham.

---

**STEDHAM** W. Sussex 𝟒𝟎𝟒 R 31 – see Midhurst.

---

**STEEPLE ASTON** Oxon. 𝟒𝟎𝟑 𝟒𝟎𝟒 Q 28 – pop. 874 – ⊠ Bicester.
London 69 – Coventry 38 – Oxford 10.

🏛 **Hopcrofts Holt,** OX6 3QQ, Southwest : 1 ¼ m. at junction of A 4260 with B 4030
℘ (01869) 340259, Fax (01869) 340865, 🌾 – ʕᘔᑎ 🆃🆅 ☎ 🅿 – 🛓 120. 🐠 🆀 ⑩ 𝑉𝐼𝑆𝐴
Meals (bar lunch Saturday) 12.95/23.00 **st.** and a la carte ♾ 5.50 – **86 rm** ⬓ 85.00/115.00 **st.**
– SB.

---

**STEVENAGE** Herts. 𝟒𝟎𝟒 T 28 Great Britain G. – pop. 76 064.
Env. : Knebworth House★ AC, S : 2½ m.
🏌ᵦ, 🏌ᵦ Aston Lane ℘ (01438) 880424 – 🏌ᵦ, 🏌ᵦ Chesfield Downs Golf Centre, Jack's Hill,
Graveley ℘ (01462) 482929.
London 36 – Bedford 25 – Cambridge 27.

🏛 **County H. Stevenage Cromwell,** High St., Old Town, SG1 3AZ, ℘ (01438) 779954,
Fax (01438) 742169, 🌾 – ʕᘔᑎ rm, 🍽 rest, 🆃🆅 ☎ 🅿 – 🛓 200. 🐠 🆀 ⑩ 𝑉𝐼𝑆𝐴. ℀
Meals 11.00 **st.** (lunch) and dinner a la carte 12.40/25.00 **st.** ♾ 5.75 – ⬓ 9.50 – **56 rm** 95.00/
115.00 **st.** – SB.

🏨 **County H. Stevenage Hertfordpark,** Danestrete, SG1 1EJ, ℰ (01438) 779955
Fax (01438) 741880 – 📶, ✦≒ rm, 🍴 ☎ – 🔬 200. ➍➒ 🆎 ➀ 𝒱𝒾𝒮𝒜
**Meals** 14.50 **st.** (dinner) and a la carte 11.25/18.95 **st.** ⅋ 4.95 – ☑ 9.00 – **98 rm** 80.00
90.00 **st.** – SB.

🏨 **Novotel Stevenage,** Knebworth Park, SG1 2AX, Southwest : 1 ½ m. by A 602 at junction
with A 1 (M) ℰ (01438) 742299, Fax (01438) 723872, ☒ – 📶, ✦≒ rm, 🍴 rest, 🔟 ☎ 🕭 🅿
🔬 120. ➍➒ 🆎 ➀ 𝒱𝒾𝒮𝒜
**Meals** 17.00 **st.** and a la carte – ☑ 10.45 – **100 rm** 85.00 **st.**

🏨 **Travel Inn,** Corey's Mill Lane, SG1 4AA, Northwest : 2 m. on A 602 ℰ (01438) 351318
Fax (01438) 721609 – 📶, ✦≒ rm, 🍴 rest, 🔟 🕭 🅿. ➍➒ 🆎 ➀ 𝒱𝒾𝒮𝒜. ✦
**Meals** (grill rest.) – **39 rm** 38.00 **t.**

🅐 ATS 4-8 Norton Rd ℰ (01438) 313262

---

**STEYNING** W. Sussex 🔢🔢🔢 T 31 – pop. 8 692 (inc. Upper Beeding).
London 52 – Brighton 12 – Worthing 10.

🏨 **The Old Tollgate,** The Street, Bramber, BN44 3WE, Southwest : 1 m. ℰ (01903) 879494
Fax (01903) 813399, ✦ – 📶 🔟 ☎ 🕭 🅿. ➍➒ 🆎 ➀ 𝒱𝒾𝒮𝒜 𝙹𝙲𝙱. ✦
**Meals** (carving rest.) 12.95/18.95 **t.** ⅋ 6.30 – ☑ 6.95 – **31 rm** 64.00/86.00 **t.** – SB.

🏨 **Springwells** without rest., 9 High St., BN44 3GG, ℰ (01903) 812446, Fax (01903) 879823
≘s, ☒, ✦ – 🔟 ☎ 🅿. ➍➒ 🆎 ➀ 𝒱𝒾𝒮𝒜. ✦
closed 1 week Christmas-New Year – **10 rm** ☑ 40.00/83.00.

*Le Grand Londres (GREATER LONDON) est composé de la City*
*et de 32 arrondissements administratifs (Borough)*
*eux-mêmes divisés en quartiers ou en villages*
*ayant conservé leur caractère propre (Area).*

---

**STILTON** Cambs. 🔢🔢🔢 T 26 – pop. 2 219 – ✉ Peterborough.
London 76 – Cambridge 30 – Northampton 43 – Peterborough 6.

🏨 **Bell Inn,** Great North Rd, PE7 3RA, ℰ (01733) 241066, Fax (01733) 245173, « Part 16C »
✦ – ✦≒ rm, 🔟 ☎ 🅿 – 🔬 100. ➍➒ 🆎 ➀ 𝒱𝒾𝒮𝒜 𝙹𝙲𝙱. ✦
closed 25 December – **Meals** (bar lunch Saturday) 19.95 **t.** – **19 rm** ☑ 67.00/107.00 **t.**

---

**STOCKBRIDGE** Hants. 🔢🔢🔢 🔢🔢🔢 P 30 – pop. 570.
London 75 – Salisbury 14 – Winchester 9.

🏠 **Carbery,** Salisbury Hill, SO20 6EZ, on A 30 ℰ (01264) 810771, Fax (01264) 811022, ☒, ✦ –
🔟 🅿. ✦
closed 2 weeks Christmas – **Meals** (by arrangement) 13.00 **st.** – **11 rm** ☑ 26.00/52.00.

🍴 **Peat Spade Inn** with rm, Longstock, SO20 6DR, North : 1 ½ m. on A 305
ℰ (01264) 810612, Fax (01264) 810612, « 18C inn », ✦ – 🔟 🕭 🅿
closed Sunday dinner, Monday, 1 week in spring, 1 week in autumn and 25-26 December –
**Meals** a la carte 13.20/18.20 **t.** – **2 rm** ☑ 54.25/58.75 **st.**

---

**STOCKPORT** Gtr. Manchester 🔢🔢🔢 🔢🔢🔢 🔢🔢🔢 N 23 – pop. 132 813.
🔟 Heaton Moor, Mauldeth Rd ℰ (0161) 432 2134 - 🔟 Romiley, Goosehouse Green ℰ (0161)
430 2392 – 🔟 Ladythorn Rd, Bramhall ℰ (0161) 439 4057 – 🔟 Hazel Grove ℰ (0161) 48
3217 – 🔟 Offerton Rd, Offerton ℰ (0161) 427 2001.
🗓 Graylaw House, Chestergate, SK1 1NG ℰ (0161) 474 3320/1.
London 201 – Liverpool 42 – Manchester 6 – Sheffield 37 – Stoke-on-Trent 34.

🏨 **Jarvis Alma Lodge,** 149 Buxton Rd, SK2 6EL, South : 1 ¼ m. on A 6 ℰ (0161) 483 4431
Fax (0161) 483 1983 – ✦≒ rm, 🔟 ☎ ✆ 🅿 – 🔬 200. ➍➒ 🆎 ➀ 𝒱𝒾𝒮𝒜
**Meals** (carving rest.) (bar lunch Saturday) 11.50 **t.** and a la carte ⅋ 6.75 – ☑ 8.00 – **52 rm**
75.00/110.50 **st.**

🏨 **Old Rectory - Premier Lodge,** Churchgate, SK1 1YG, East : ¼ m. by Wellington St
ℰ (0161) 429 0060, Fax (0161) 474 0076, Reservations (Freephone) 0800 118833 – 📶
🍴 rest, 🔟 ☎ 🕭 🅿. ➍➒ 🆎 ➀ 𝒱𝒾𝒮𝒜
**Meals** (closed 25 December) 10.95/12.95 and a la carte – ☑ 5.95 – **46 rm** 44.95 **st.**

🏨 **Saxon Holme,** 230 Wellington Rd North, SK4 2QN, North : 1 m. on A
ℰ (0161) 432 2335, Fax (0161) 431 8076 – 📶 ✦≒ 🔟 ☎ 🕭 🅿. ➍➒ 🆎 ➀ 𝒱𝒾𝒮𝒜. ✦
**Meals** (closed Sunday and 1 week Christmas) 8.95/12.95 **t.** and a la carte ⅋ 3.95 – **33 rm**
☑ 48.00/58.00 **t.** – SB.

🛏 **Wycliffe,** 74 Edgeley Rd, Edgeley, SK3 9NQ, West : 1 m. on B 5465 ℘ (0161) 477 5395, Fax (0161) 476 3219 – 📺 ☎ 🅿 – 🛄 30. ◍ 🅰🅴 🆅🆂🅰. %
closed 26 to 28 December – **Meals** - Italian - (closed Saturday lunch and Bank Holiday Mondays) 8.00/15.50 **t.** and a la carte ↥ 5.75 – **20 rm** ☑ 44.00/58.00 **st.**

🛏 **Travel Inn,** Buxton Rd, SK2 6NB, South : 1 m. on A 6 ℘ (0161) 480 2968, Fax (0161) 477 8520 – ⤢ rm, 🍴 rest, 📺 ⚒ 🅿. ◍ 🅰🅴 🆅🆂🅰. %
**Meals** (grill rest.) – **40 rm** 38.00 **t.**

⊕ ATS Hollingworth Rd, Bredbury      ATS Long Lane, Chapel en la Frith
℘ (0161) 430 5221          ℘ (01298) 813231/813145

---

**STOCKTON-ON-TEES** 402 P 20 – pop. 83 576.

🏌 Eaglescliffe, Yarm Rd ℘ (01642) 780098 – 🏌, 🏌 Knotty Hill Golf Centre, Sedgefield ℘ (01740) 620320 – 🏌 Norton, Junction Rd ℘ (01642) 676385.
✈ Teesside Airport : ℘ (0345) 554554, SW : 6 m. by A 1027, A 135 and A 67.
🛈 Theatre Yard, off High St., TS18 1AT ℘ (01642) 615080.
London 251 – Leeds 61 – Middlesbrough 4.

🏨 **Swallow,** 10 John Walker Sq., TS18 1AQ, ℘ (01642) 679721, Fax (01642) 601714, ↕5, ≘s, 🔲 – 🛗, ⤢ rm, 📺 ☎ 🅿 – 🛄 300. ◍ 🅰🅴 🆅🆂🅰
**Portcullis :** Meals (dinner only) 19.75 **st.** – **Matchmaker Brasserie :** Meals (closed Sunday) a la carte 11.95/28.95 **st.** – **125 rm** ☑ 90.00/130.00 **st.** – SB.

🛏 **Travel Inn,** Yarm Rd, TS18 3RT, Southwest : 1 ¾ m. on A 135 at junction with A 66 ℘ (01642) 633354, Fax (01642) 633339 – ⤢ rm, 🍴 rest, 📺 ⚒ 🅿. ◍ 🅰🅴 🆅🆂🅰. %
**Meals** (grill rest.) – **40 rm** 38.00 **t.**

**at Eaglescliffe** South : 3½ m. on A 135 – ⊠ Stockton-on-Tees.

🏨 **Parkmore,** 636 Yarm Rd, TS16 0DH, ℘ (01642) 786815, Fax (01642) 790485, ↕5, ≘s, 🔲, 🎾 – ⤢ 📺 ☎ 🅿 – 🛄 140. ◍ 🅰🅴 🆅🆂🅰 🅹🅲🅱
**Carlton Room :** Meals a la carte 14.00/24.50 **st.** ↥ 5.20 – ☑ 7.50 – **54 rm** 60.00/82.00 **st.**, 1 suite – SB.

⊕ ATS 112 Norton Rd ℘ (01642) 604477

---

**STOKE BRUERNE** Northants. 404 R 27 – pop. 347 – ⊠ Towcester.
London 69 – Coventry 33 – Northampton 9 – Oxford 33.

✗ **Bruerne's Lock,** 5 The Canalside, NN12 7SB, ℘ (01604) 863654, Fax (01604) 863654, « Canalside setting » – ◍ 🅰🅴 🆅🆂🅰. %
closed Saturday lunch, Sunday dinner, Monday and 26 December-5 January – **Meals** 17.00 **t.** (lunch) and dinner a la carte 20.70/29.95 **t.** ↥ 6.95.

---

**STOKE BY NAYLAND** Suffolk 404 W 28.
London 70 – Bury St. Edmunds 24 – Cambridge 54 – Colchester 11 – Ipswich 14.

⚲ **Ryegate House** without rest., CO6 4RA, ℘ (01206) 263679, ≤, 🎾 – ⤢ 📺 🅿
closed 25 to 27 December and 1 week spring and autumn – **3 rm** ☑ 32.00/46.00 **t.**

✗✗ **Angel Inn** with rm, Polstead St., CO6 4SA, ℘ (01206) 263245, Fax (01206) 263373, « Part timbered 17C inn » – 📺 ☎ 🅿. ◍ 🅰🅴 🆅🆂🅰. %
.closed 25 and 26 December – **Meals** a la carte 12.70/22.95 **t.** ↥ 4.80 – **6 rm** ☑ 47.50/61.00 **st.**

---

**STOKE CANON** Devon 403 J 31 – see Exeter.

---

**STOKE D'ABERNON** Surrey 404 ⑫ – see Cobham.

---

**STOKE FLEMING** Devon 403 J 33 – see Dartmouth.

---

Les prix   Pour toutes précisions sur les prix indiqués dans ce guide, reportez-vous aux pages de l'introduction.

**STOKE GABRIEL** Devon **403** J 32 – see Totnes.

**STOKE HOLY CROSS** Norfolk **404** X 26 – see Norwich.

**STOKE-ON-TRENT** **402** **403** **404** N 24 Great Britain G. – pop. 266 543.

See : The Potteries Museum and Art Gallery★ Y **M** – Gladstone Pottery Museum★ AC V.

Env. : Wedgwood Visitor Centre★ AC, S : 7 m. on A 500, A 34 and minor rd V.

Exc. : Little Moreton Hall★★ AC, N : 10 m. by A 500 on A 34 U.

⊞ Greenway Hall, Stockton Brook ℘ (01782) 503158, U – ⊞ Parkhall, Hulme Rd, Westo
Coyney ℘ (01782) 599584, V.

🛈 Potteries Shopping Centre, Quadrant Rd, Hanley, ST1 1RZ ℘ (01782) 284600.

London 162 – Birmingham 46 – Leicester 59 – Liverpool 58 – Manchester 41 – Sheffield 53

### STOKE-ON-TRENT
### NEWCASTLE-UNDER-LYME
### BUILT UP AREA

| | | | | | |
|---|---|---|---|---|---|
| Alexandra Road | U 3 | Cobridge Road | U 21 | Mayne Street | V 45 |
| Bedford Road | U 4 | Davenport Street | U 23 | Moorland Road | U 46 |
| Brownhills Road | U 12 | Elder Road | U 24 | Porthill Road | U 59 |
| Church Lane | U 19 | Etruria Vale Road | U 27 | Snow Hill | U 63 |
| | | Grove Road | V 30 | Stoke Road | V 66 |
| | | Hanley Road | U 31 | Strand (The) | V 69 |
| | | Heron Street | U 34 | Victoria Park Road | U 75 |
| | | High Street | U 35 | Victoria Place Link | V 76 |
| | | Higherland | V 37 | Watlands View | U 77 |
| | | Manor Street | U 44 | Williamson Street | U 78 |

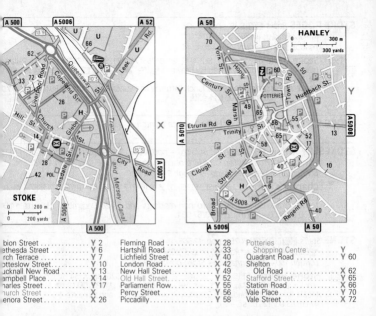

**Stoke-on-Trent Moat House**, Etruria Hall, Festival Park, Etruria, ST1 5BQ, ℰ (01782) 609988, *Fax (01782) 284500*, ⅃ᵟ, ☎, ◩ – ⅁, ⅍ rm, ▤ ⅏ ☎ ℗ – ⅍ 600. ⍟⑨ ᴬᴱ ⓪ 𝗩𝗜𝗦𝗔 JCB, ⅍
U  n
Meals *(bar lunch Saturday)* 18.95 st. (dinner) and a la carte 12.40/24.65 st. ⅃ 5.95 – ⌻ 10.00 – **143 rm** 110.00/130.00 st. – SB.

**Stakis Stoke-on-Trent**, 66 Trinity St., Hanley, ST1 5NB, ℰ (01782) 202361, *Fax (01782) 286464*, ⅃ᵟ, ☎, ◩ – ⅁, ⅍ rm, ⅏ ☎ ℥ ℗ – ⅍ 300. ⍟⑨ ᴬᴱ ⓪ 𝗩𝗜𝗦𝗔
Y  c
*(closed Saturday lunch)* 11.00/17.45 st. and dinner a la carte – ⌻ 9.50 **122 rm** 110.00/ 140.00 st., 3 suites – SB.

**North Stafford**, Station Rd, ST4 2AE, ℰ (01782) 744477, *Fax (01782) 744580* – ⅁ ⅏ ☎ ℗ – ⅍ 450. ⍟⑨ ᴬᴱ ⓪ 𝗩𝗜𝗦𝗔
X  a
Meals *(closed Saturday lunch)* 9.95/16.95 st. and a la carte ⅃ 5.95 – ⌻ 8.50 – **69 rm** 99.00/ 109.00 st. – SB.

t Burslem *North : 3½ m. by A 500 and A 53 on A 50 –* ⊠ *Stoke-on-Trent.*

**The George**, Swan Sq., ST6 2AE, ℰ (01782) 577544, *Fax (01782) 837496* – ⅁ ⅏ ☎ ℗ – ⅍ 200. ⍟⑨ ᴬᴱ ⓪ 𝗩𝗜𝗦𝗔 JCB, ⅍
U  e
*closed 24 to 26 December –* Meals 10.95/15.95 t. and a la carte – **38 rm** ⌻ 65.00/85.00 st. – SB.

t Basford *Northwest : 1¾ m. by A 500 off A 53 –* ⊠ *Stoke-on-Trent.*

**Haydon House**, 9 Haydon St., ST4 6JD, ℰ (01782) 711311, *Fax (01782) 717470* – ⅏ ☎ ℗ – ⅍ 80. ⍟⑨ ᴬᴱ ⓪ 𝗩𝗜𝗦𝗔
U  a
*Townhouse :* Meals *(closed lunch Saturday and Sunday)* 10.50/14.90 st. and a la carte ⅃ 14.00 – ⌻ 6.00 – **24 rm** 55.50/75.00 t., 6 suites.

t Talke *Northwest : 4 m. on A 500 at junction with A 34 –* ⊠ *Stoke-on-Trent.*

**Travelodge**, Newcastle Rd, ST7 1UP, ℰ (01782) 777000, *Fax (01782) 777000*, Reserva-tions (Freephone) 0800 850950 – ⅍ rm, ⅏ ☎ ℥ ℗. ⍟⑨ ᴬᴱ ⓪ 𝗩𝗜𝗦𝗔 JCB, ⅍
U  s
Meals (grill rest.) – **62 rm** 39.95/59.95 t.

⒨ ATS 25 Smithpool Rd, Fenton ℰ (01782) 847081        ATS 87/89 Waterloo Rd, Burslem ℰ (01782) 838493/836591

*Si vous cherchez un hôtel tranquille,*
*consultez d'abord les cartes de l'introduction*
*ou repérez dans le texte les établissements indiqués avec le signe ⑊ ou ⑊.*

**STOKE POGES** Bucks. 404 S 29 – pop. 4 508.
🏗 Park Road ℘ (01753) 717170.
London 30 – Aylesbury 28 – Oxford 44.

🏠 **Stoke Park** ⟲, Park Rd, SL2 4PG, ℘ (01753) 717171, Fax (01753) 717181, « Palladian mansion in parklands by Capability Brown », 🏗, ⟋, ⊸, ⚓ – 🛗 📺 ☎ ✆ 🅿 – 🕍 80. 🆗 🅰
🆗 VISA JCB. ⌘
*Stoke's Brasserie :* Meals (bar lunch Saturday and Sunday) a la carte 27.80/43.45 t. ⅄ 7.2
– ⚏ 10.75 – **20 rm** 195.00 t., 1 suite.

**STOKE ST. GREGORY** Somerset 403 L 30 – see Taunton.

**STOKESLEY** N. Yorks. 402 Q 20 Great Britain G. – pop. 4 008 – ✉ Middlesbrough.
Env. : Great Ayton (Captain Cook Birthplace Museum★ AC), NE : 2½ m. on A 173.
London 239 – Leeds 59 – Middlesbrough 8 – York 52.

✗ **Chapter's** with rm, 27 High St., TS9 5AD, ℘ (01642) 711888, Fax (01642) 713387 – ⟿ rm
📺 ☎. 🆗 🅰 🅾 VISA
Meals (closed Sunday dinner to non-residents and 25-26 December) a la carte 14.00
25.00 t. ⅄ 7.00 – **13 rm** ⚏ 54.00/67.00 t.

**STONE** Staffs. 402 403 404 N 25 – pop. 12 305.
🏗 Barlaston, Meaford Rd ℘ (01782) 372867.
London 150 – Birmingham 36 – Stoke-on-Trent 9.

🏠 **Stone House**, ST15 0BQ, South : 1 ¼ m. by A 520 on A 34 ℘ (01785) 81553
Fax (01785) 814764, ₤₅, ⊛, ◲, ⟋, ⊸ – ⟿ 📺 ☎ 🅿 – 🕍 180. 🆗 🅰 🅾 VISA. ⌘
Meals (bar lunch Monday to Saturday)/dinner 16.95 st. and a la carte ⅄ 6.95 – ⚏ 8.95
**47 rm** 85.00/120.00 st. – SB.

**STON EASTON** Somerset 403 404 M 30 – pop. 579 – ✉ Bath (Bath & North East Somerset).
London 131 – Bath 12 – Bristol 11 – Wells 7.

🏠 **Ston Easton Park** ⟲, BA3 4DF, ℘ (01761) 241631, Fax (01761) 241377, ≤, « Palladian mansion », ⊸, park, ⚓ – ⟿ 📺 ☎ 🅿 – 🕍 30. 🆗 🅰 🅾 VISA. ⌘
Meals 16.00 st. (lunch) and a la carte 37.00/48.00 st. ⅄ 10.00 – ⚏ 12.50 – **20 rm** 145.00
330.00 t., 2 suites – SB.

**STONOR** Oxon. 404 R 29 – see Henley-on-Thames.

**STONY STRATFORD** Milton Keynes 404 R 27 – pop. 55 733 (inc. Wolverton).
London 58 – Birmingham 68 – Northampton 14 – Oxford 32.

Plans : see Milton Keynes

✗✗ **Peking**, 117 High St., MK11 1AT, ℘ (01908) 563120, Fax (01908) 560084 – ▤. 🆗 🅰 VISA
JCB
on Milton Keynes town plan AV
Meals - Chinese (Peking, Szechuan) - a la carte 14.50/25.50 t.

**at Cosgrove** (Northants.) North : 2½ m. by A 508 – ✉ Milton Keynes.

🏠 **Old Bakery**, Main St., MK19 7JL, ℘ (01908) 262255, Fax (01908) 263620 – 📺 ☎ 🅿. 🆗 🅰
🅾 VISA JCB. ⌘
on Milton Keynes town plan AU
Meals (by arrangement Friday to Sunday) (residents only) (dinner only) 12.50
and a la carte – **8 rm** ⚏ 55.00/65.00 t.

**STORRINGTON** W. Sussex 404 S 31 – pop. 7 429.
London 54 – Brighton 20 – Portsmouth 36.

🏠 **Little Thakeham** ⟲, Merrywood Lane, Thakeham, RH20 3HE, North : 1 ¾ m. by B 213
℘ (01903) 744416, Fax (01903) 745022, ≤, « Lutyens house with gardens in the style of
Gertrude Jekyll » – 📺 ☎ ✆ 🅿. 🆗 🅰 🅾 VISA JCB. ⌘
closed Christmas and New Year – Meals (closed Monday lunch and Sunday dinner
non-residents) (lunch by arrangement) 20.00/30.00 s. ⅄ 6.50 – **7 rm** ⚏ 95.00/150.00 s
2 suites – SB.
✗✗✗ **Fleur de Sel**, Manley Hill, RH20 4BT, East : ¼ m. on A 283 ℘ (01903) 74233
Fax (01903) 740649 – 🅿. 🆗 🅰 VISA
closed Sunday and Tuesday dinner, Monday and 2 weeks January – Meals 15.50/19.50
⅄ 7.50.

🍴🍴 **Old Forge,** 6 Church St., RH20 4LA, ☎ (01903) 743402, *Fax (01903) 742540* – [MC] [AE] [D] [VISA] [JCB]
*closed Saturday lunch, Sunday dinner, Monday, Tuesday, 2 weeks in spring, 2 weeks in autumn and 25 to 30 December* – **Meals** 14.50/22.50-27.50 **t.** 🍷 6.00.

**STOURBRIDGE** *W. Mids.* [403] [404] N26 – *pop. 55 624.*
*London 147 – Birmingham 14 – Wolverhampton 10 – Worcester 21.*
Plan : see Birmingham p. 2

🏠 **Travel Inn,** Birmingham Rd, Hagley, DY9 9JS, Southeast : 3 ½ m. by A 491 on A 456 (eastbound carriageway) ☎ (01562) 883120, *Fax (01562) 884416* – 🚭 rm, [TV] ♿ [P]. [MC] [AE] [D] [VISA]. 🐕 AU r
**Meals** (grill rest.) – **40 rm** 38.00 **t.**

**STOURPORT-ON-SEVERN** *Worcestershire* [403] [404] N 26 – *pop. 18 283.*
*London 137 – Birmingham 21 – Worcester 12.*

🏨 **Stourport Manor,** Hartlebury Rd, DY13 9JA, East : 1 ¼ m. on B 4193 ☎ (01299) 289955, *Fax (01299) 878520*, 🏋, 🧖, 🏊, 🏊, 🌳, 🎾, squash – 🚭 [TV] ☎ [P] – 🪑 350. [MC] [AE] [D] [VISA]
**Meals** (bar lunch Saturday) 10.95/19.95 **t.** and a la carte 🍷 6.25 – ☕ 9.25 – **66 rm** 85.00/95.00 **st.**, 2 suites – SB.

**STOWMARKET** *Suffolk* [404] W/X 27 – *pop. 13 229.*
[i] *Wilkes Way, IP14 1DE ☎ (01449) 676800.*
*London 81 – Cambridge 42 – Ipswich 12 – Norwich 38.*

🏠 **Gipping Heights,** Creeting Rd, IP14 5BT, East : 1 m. by Station Rd East (B 1113) ☎ (01449) 675264 – [TV] [P]. [MC] [VISA]. 🐕
**Meals** (bar lunch)/dinner 12.50 **s.** and a la carte 🍷 5.40 – **5 rm** ☕ 35.00/46.00 **s.**

🏠 **Travelodge,** IP14 3PY, Northwest : 2 m. by A 1038 on A 14 (westbound) ☎ (01449) 615347, Reservations (Freephone) 0800 850950 – 🚭 rm, [TV] ♿ [P]. [MC] [AE] [D] [VISA] [JCB]. 🐕
**Meals** (grill rest.) – **40 rm** 39.95/59.95 **t.**

**at Mendlesham Green** *Northeast : 6 ¼ m. by B 1115, A 1120 and Mendlesham rd – ✉ Stowmarket.*

🏡 **Cherry Tree Farm,** Mendlesham Green, IP14 5RQ, ☎ (01449) 766376, « Part Elizabethan house », 🌳 – 🚭 [P]. 🐕
*closed Christmas, New Year and January* – **Meals** (by arrangement) (communal dining) 16.00 **s.** – **3 rm** ☕ 48.00 **s.**

**STOW-ON-THE-WOLD** *Glos.* [403] [404] O 28 *Great Britain G. – pop. 1 999.*
Exc. : *Chastleton House★★, NE : 6½ m. by A 436 and A 44.*
[i] *Hollis House, The Square, GL54 1AF ☎ (01451) 831082.*
*London 86 – Birmingham 44 – Gloucester 27 – Oxford 30.*

🏨 **Wyck Hill House** 🐎, GL54 1HY, South : 2 ¼ m. by A 429 on A 424 ☎ (01451) 831936, *Fax (01451) 832243*, ≤, « Part Victorian country house », 🌳, park – 🛗, 🚭 rest, [TV] ☎ [P] – 🪑 50. [MC] [AE] [D] [VISA]
**Meals** 15.25/33.75 **t.** 🍷 10.50 – **29 rm** ☕ 100.00/175.00 **t.**, 1 suite – SB.

🏨 **Grapevine,** Sheep St., GL54 1AU, ☎ (01451) 830344, *Fax (01451) 832278*, « Mature grapevine in restaurant » – 🚭 rest, [TV] ☎ 📞 [P] – 🪑 25. [MC] [AE] [D] [VISA] [JCB]. 🐕
**Meals** 14.95/26.00 **t.** 🍷 6.75 – **22 rm** ☕ 87.00/174.00 **t.** – SB.

🏨 **Fosse Manor,** Fosse Way, GL54 1JX, South : 1 ¼ m. on A 429 ☎ (01451) 830354, *Fax (01451) 832486*, 🧖, 🌳 – 🚭 rest, [TV] ☎ [P] – 🪑 40. [MC] [AE] [D] [VISA] [JCB]
*closed 22 to 30 December* – **Meals** 14.50/24.00 **t.** and a la carte 🍷 6.95 – **20 rm** ☕ 57.00/150.00 **t.** – SB.

🏨 **Unicorn,** Sheep St., GL54 1HQ, ☎ (01451) 830257, *Fax (01451) 831090* – 🚭 [TV] ☎ [P]. [MC] [AE] [D] [VISA] [JCB]
**Meals** (bar lunch Monday to Saturday)/dinner 17.95 **t.** and a la carte 🍷 6.95 – ☕ 8.75 – **20 rm** ☕ 50.00/110.00 **t.** – SB.

🏠 **Stow Lodge,** The Square, GL54 1AB, ☎ (01451) 830485, *Fax (01451) 831671*, 🌳 – 🚭 [TV] ☎ [P]. [MC] [D] [VISA] [JCB]. 🐕
*closed Christmas and January* – **Meals** (bar lunch)/dinner 17.50 **t.** and a la carte 🍷 8.00 – **21 rm** ☕ 70.00/110.00 **t.** – SB.

🏡 **Wyck Hill Lodge** without rest., Wyck Hill, GL54 1HT, South : 2 m. by A 429 on A 424 ☎ (01451) 830141, ≤, 🌳 – 🚭 [TV] [P]. 🐕
*March-November* – **3 rm** ☕ 46.00 **s.**

**at Broadwell** Northeast : 1 ¾ m. by A 429 – ⊠ Moreton-in-Marsh.

↑ **College House**, Chapel St., GL56 0TW, ℘ (01451) 832351, « 17C », 無 – ⁙⁘ 🗺 ℗. ⁙⁙
closed 24 to 27 December – **Meals** (by arrangement) (communal dining) 18.50 st. – **3 rm**
⊴ 63.00/68.00 st.

**at Lower Oddington** East : 3 m. by A 436 – ⊠ Stow-on-the-Wold.

🍴 **Fox**, GL56 0UR, ℘ (01451) 870555, 無 – ℗. ◍◍ 𝘝𝘐𝘚𝘈
closed 25-26 December and dinner 31 December – **Meals** a la carte 12.40/17.15 t.

**at Bledington** Southeast : 4 m. by A 436 on B 4450 – ⊠ Kingham.

🏠 **Kings Head**, OX7 6XQ, ℘ (01608) 658365, Fax (01608) 658902, « Part 15C inn » – ⁙⁘ rm,
🗺 ☎ ℗. ◍◍ ① 𝘝𝘐𝘚𝘈 𝗝𝗖𝗕. ⁙⁙
closed 24 and 25 December – **Meals** 10.95 t. (lunch) and dinner a la carte 11.40/19.70 t.
🍴 4.50 – **12 rm** ⊴ 45.00/75.00 st.

---

**STRATFIELD TURGIS** Hants. 𝟰𝟬𝟯 𝟰𝟬𝟰 Q 29 – pop. 94 – ⊠ Basingstoke.
London 46 – Basingstoke 8 – Reading 11.

🏨 **Wellington Arms**, RG27 0AS, on A 33 ℘ (01256) 882214, Fax (01256) 882934, 無 –
⁙⁘ rm, 🗺 ☎ ℗ – 🔬 80. ◍◍ 𝖠𝖤 ① 𝘝𝘐𝘚𝘈
**Meals** (closed Saturday lunch and Sunday dinner) 19.95 t. and a la carte 🍴 5.95 – **33 rm**
⊴ 85.00/125.00 t., 2 suites.

*Wenn Sie ein ruhiges Hotel suchen,*
*benutzen Sie zuerst die Karte in der Einleitung*
*oder wählen Sie im Text ein Hotel mit dem Zeichen ⑊ oder ⑊.*

---

**STRATFORD-UPON-AVON** Warks. 𝟰𝟬𝟯 𝟰𝟬𝟰 P 27 Great Britain G. – pop. 22 231.
See : Town★ - Shakespeare's Birthplace★ AC, AB.
Env. : Mary Arden's House★ AC, NW : 4 m. by A 3400 A.
Exc. : Ragley Hall★ AC, W : 9 m. by A 422 A.
🐦 Tiddington Rd ℘ (01789) 297296, B – 🐦 Welcombe Hotel, Warwick Rd ℘ (01789) 299012,
B – 🐦 Stratford Oaks, Bearley Rd, Snitterfield ℘ (01789) 731982, B.
🎫 Bridgefoot, CV37 6GW ℘ (01789) 293127.
London 96 – Birmingham 23 – Coventry 18 – Oxford 40.

## STRATFORD-UPON-AVON

*For maximum information*
*from town plans:*
*consult the*
*conventional signs key.*

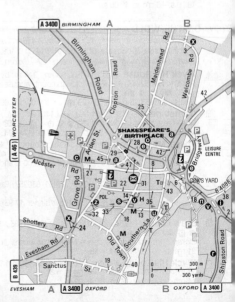

🏨🏨🏨 **Welcombe H. & Golf Course**, Warwick Rd, CV37 0NR, Northeast : 1 ½ m. on A 439 *ℰ* (01789) 295252, *Fax (01789) 414666*, ≤, « 19C Jacobean style mansion in park », 🏊, ⚓, 🌳, ⚒ – 🍴 rest, 📺 ☎ & 🅿 – 🔬 80. 🐾 🝤 ① 𝘝𝘐𝘚𝘈 🛐🅲🅱 🌮
**Meals** a la carte 29.00/61.00 t. ⓘ 9.00 – **64 rm** ⊊ 135.00/375.00 t., 3 suites – SB.

🏨🏨🏨 **Ettington Park** 🌭, Alderminster, CV37 8BU, Southeast : 6 ¼ m. on A 3400 *ℰ* (01789) 450123, *Fax (01789) 450472*, ≤, « Victorian Gothic mansion », ⚒, 🔲, 🌳, ⚓, park, ⚒ – 🛗, ⚒ rest, 📺 ☎ 🅿 – 🔬 60. 🐾 🝤 ① 𝘝𝘐𝘚𝘈 🌮
**Meals** 17.50/30.50 t. and a la carte – **43 rm** ⊊ 130.00/185.00 t., 5 suites.

🏨🏨 **Stratford Moat House**, Bridgefoot, CV37 6YR, *ℰ* (01789) 279988, *Fax (01789) 298589*, 🔬, ⚓, 🔲, ⚒ – 🛗 rm, ▤ 📺 ☎ & 🅿 – 🔬 450. 🐾 🝤 ① 𝘝𝘐𝘚𝘈 🌮        B  e
**Meals** (bar lunch Monday to Saturday)/dinner 14.50 **st.** and a la carte ⓘ 7.25 – ⊊ 9.50 – **245 rm** 115.00/145.00 st., 2 suites – SB.

🏨🏨 **Alveston Manor**, Clopton Bridge, CV37 7HP, *ℰ* (01789) 204581, *Fax (01789) 414095*, « Part Elizabethan house », ⚒ – ⚒ rm, 📺 ☎ 🅿 – 🔬 150. 🐾 🝤 ① 𝘝𝘐𝘚𝘈 🌮      B  i
*Manor :* **Meals** a la carte 17.00/27.00 **st.** – ⊊ 10.95 – **105 rm** 105.00/140.00 st., 1 suite – SB.

🏨🏨 **Shakespeare**, Chapel St., CV37 6ER, *ℰ* (01789) 294771, *Fax (01789) 415411*, « 17C timbered inn » – 🛗 ⚒ 📺 ☎ 🅿 – 🔬 100. 🐾 🝤 ① 𝘝𝘐𝘚𝘈 🛐🅲🅱        A  v
**Meals** a la carte 17.00/48.45 st. ⓘ 8.75 – ⊊ 10.50 – **62 rm** 95.00/135.00 st., 1 suite – SB.

🏨🏨 **The Thistle Stratford-Upon-Avon**, 44 Waterside, CV37 6BA, *ℰ* (01789) 294949, *Fax (01789) 415874*, 😋, ⚓, ⚒ – ⚒ 📺 ☎ 🅿 – 🔬 50. 🐾 🝤 ① 𝘝𝘐𝘚𝘈 🛐🅲🅱 🌮     B  u
*Bards :* **Meals** a la carte 19.40/26.85 st. ⓘ 5.50 – ⊊ 10.50 – **62 rm** 96.00/134.00 st. – SB.

🏨🏨 **Stratford Manor**, Warwick Rd, CV37 0PY, Northeast : 3 m. on A 439 *ℰ* (01789) 731173, *Fax (01789) 731131*, 🔬, ⚓, 🔲, park, ⚒ – 🛗 ⚒, ▤ rest, 📺 ☎ & 🅿 – 🔬 350. 🐾 🝤 ① 𝘝𝘐𝘚𝘈
**Meals** (bar lunch Saturday) 13.50/23.00 t. and a la carte ⓘ 7.60 – ⊊ 9.50 – **103 rm** 94.00/140.00 t. – SB.

🏨🏨 **Stratford Victoria**, Arden St., CV37 6QQ, *ℰ* (01789) 271000, *Fax (01789) 271001*, 🔬 – 🛗, ⚒ rm, ▤ rest, 📺 ☎ & 🅿 – 🔬 140. 🐾 🝤 ① 𝘝𝘐𝘚𝘈        A  c
**Meals** (carving lunch Sunday and carving dinner Saturday) a la carte 18.50/26.75 st. ⓘ 7.95 – **99 rm** ⊊ 85.00/120.00 st., 1 suite – SB.

🏨 **Grosvenor**, 12-14 Warwick Rd, CV37 6YT, *ℰ* (01789) 269213, *Fax (01789) 266087* – 📺 ☎ & 🅿 – 🔬 100. 🐾 🝤 ① 𝘝𝘐𝘚𝘈        B  a
**Meals** 10.95/15.50 st. and a la carte ⓘ 9.95 – ⊊ 7.25 – **67 rm** 75.00/85.00 st. – SB.

🏨 **Forte Posthouse Stratford-upon-Avon**, Bridgefoot, CV37 7LT, *ℰ* (01789) 266761, *Fax (01789) 414547*, ⚒ – ⚒ rm, 📺 ☎ 🅿 – 🔬 150. 🐾 🝤 ① 𝘝𝘐𝘚𝘈 🌮     B  v
**Meals** a la carte 17.85/24.85 st. ⓘ 8.45 – ⊊ 9.95 – **68 rm** 89.00 st. – SB.

🏨 **Dukes**, Payton St., CV37 6UA, *ℰ* (01789) 269300, *Fax (01789) 414700*, ⚒ – 📺 ☎ 🅿. 🐾 🝤 𝘝𝘐𝘚𝘈 🛐🅲🅱 🌮            AB  o
*closed Christmas and New Year* – **Meals** *(closed Sunday)* a la carte 16.15/25.40 t. ⓘ 5.50 – **22 rm** ⊊ 52.50/115.00 t. – SB.

🏠 **Stratford Court**, Avenue Rd, CV37 6UX, *ℰ* (01789) 297799, *Fax (01789) 262449*, « Edwardian house », ⚒ – 📺 ☎ 🅿. 🐾 𝘝𝘐𝘚𝘈        B  x
**Meals** (booking essential) (residents only) (dinner only) 17.50 st. ⓘ 6.50 – **13 rm** ⊊ 57.50/140.00 st.

🏠 **Sequoia House** without rest., 51-53 Shipston Rd, CV37 7LN, *ℰ* (01789) 268852, *Fax (01789) 414559*, ⚒ – ⚒ 📺 ☎ 🅿 – 🔬 40. 🐾 🝤 ① 𝘝𝘐𝘚𝘈 🛐🅲🅱 🌮     B  r
*closed 22 to 29 December* – **24 rm** ⊊ 45.00/79.00 st.

🏠 **Caterham House** without rest., 58-59 Rother St., CV37 6LT, *ℰ* (01789) 267309, *Fax (01789) 414836* – 📺 🅿. 🐾 𝘝𝘐𝘚𝘈        A  z
**10 rm** ⊊ 60.00/75.00 st.

🏠 **Stratheden** without rest., 5 Chapel St., CV37 6EP, *ℰ* (01789) 297119, *Fax (01789) 297119* – 📺 ☎. 🐾 𝘝𝘐𝘚𝘈 🌮        A  s
*closed 15 December-2 January* – **9 rm** ⊊ 45.00/70.00 st.

🏡 **Twelfth Night** without rest., Evesham Pl., CV37 6HT, *ℰ* (01789) 414595 – ⚒ 📺 🅿. 🐾 𝘝𝘐𝘚𝘈 🌮        A  x
**6 rm** ⊊ 35.00/58.00.

🏡 **Payton** without rest., 6 John St., CV37 6UB, *ℰ* (01789) 266442, *Fax (01789) 266442* – ⚒ 📺 🝤 🝤 🌮        A  e
*closed 25 and 26 December* – **5 rm** ⊊ 40.00/64.00 s.

🏡 **Victoria Spa Lodge** without rest., Bishopton Lane, CV37 9QY, Northwest : 2 m. by A 3400 on Bishopton Lane turning left at roundabout with A 46 *ℰ* (01789) 267985, *Fax (01789) 204728*, ⚒ – ⚒ 📺 🅿. 🐾 𝘝𝘐𝘚𝘈 🌮
**7 rm** ⊊ 45.00/60.00 t.

⌂ **Virginia Lodge,** 12 Evesham Pl., CV37 6HT, ☎ (01789) 292157, 🌳 – ⊁ [TV] [P]. ✕ A
*closed 24 to 26 December* – **Meals** (by arrangement) 14.00 **st.** – **7 rm** ☐ 22.00/48.00 **t.**

XX **Desport's,** 13-14 Meer St., CV37 6QB, ☎ (01789) 269304, *Fax (01789) 269304* – [MC] [AE] [VISA] [JCB] A
*closed Sunday dinner, Monday, 25 to 26 December, 2 weeks January and Bank Holidays* – **Meals** 14.50 **t.** (lunch) and a la carte 22.85/35.90 **t.** 🍷 10.00.

XX **Hussain's,** 6a Chapel St., CV37 6EP, ☎ (01789) 267506, *Fax (01789) 415341* – ▤. [MC] [AE] [D] [VISA] [JCB] A
*closed 25 December* – **Meals** - Indian - 5.95 **t.** (lunch) and a la carte 10.25/19.70 **t.** 🍷 6.95.

X **The Boathouse,** Swan's Nest Lane, CV37 7LS, ☎ (01789) 297733, *Fax (01789) 297733*, ≤ « Riverside setting » – [MC] [VISA] B
*closed lunch Monday and Saturday, Sunday, 25-26 December, 1 January and restricted opening in winter* – **Meals** 14.95 **t.** (lunch) and a la carte 18.50/25.00 **t.** 🍷 8.50.

**at Charlecote** *East : 4 ¾ m. by B 4086* – **B** – ✉ *Stratford-upon-Avon.*

🏨 **County H. Stratford Charlecote Pheasant,** CV35 9EW, ☎ (01789) 279954, *Fax (01789) 470222*, 🏊, 🌳, 🎾 – ⊁ rm, [TV] ☎ ♿ [P] – 🏛 120. [MC] [AE] [D] [VISA]. ✕
**Meals** 11.50/16.95 **st.** and a la carte 🍷 5.25 – ☐ 9.50 – **67 rm** 90.00/125.00 **st.** – SB.

**at Wellesbourne** *East : 5 ¾ m. on B 4086* – **B** – ✉ *Warwick.*

🏨 **Chadley House** 🐦, Loxley Rd, CV35 9JL, Southwest : 1 ¼ m. by A 429, ☎ (01789) 840994, *Fax (01789) 842977*, « Part Georgian farmhouse », 🌳 – [TV] [P]. [MC] [D] [VISA]. ✕
*closed 1 week Christmas* – **Meals** (lunch by arrangement) (light dinner Sunday residents only)/dinner a la carte 17.65/22.00 **t.** 🍷 4.90 – **9 rm** ☐ 50.00/90.00 **t.** – SB.

**at Binton** *Southwest : 4½ m. by B 439* – **A** – ✉ *Stratford-upon-Avon.*

⌂ **Gravelside Barn** 🐦 without rest., CV37 9TU, Northwest : ¾ m. by Binton Hi ☎ (01789) 750502, *Fax (01789) 298056*, ≤, « Converted barn », 🌳, 🎾 – ⊁ [TV] [P]. [MC]. ✕
**3 rm** ☐ 35.00/60.00 **st.**

**at Billesley** *West : 4½ m. by A 422* - **A** - *off A 46* – ✉ *Stratford-upon-Avon.*

🏨 **Billesley Manor** 🐦, B49 6NF, ☎ (01789) 279955, *Fax (01789) 764145*, ≤, « Part Elizabethan manor, topiary garden », 🏊, park, 🎾 – ⊁ rest, [TV] ☎ [P] – 🏛 90. [MC] [AE] [D] [VISA]. ✕
**Meals** *(bar lunch)/dinner* 30.00 **st.** and a la carte 🍷 7.00 – ☐ 9.75 – **39 rm** 125.00/190.00 **st.** 2 suites – SB.

**at Wilmcote** *Northwest : 3½ m. by A 3400* – **A** – ✉ *Stratford-upon-Avon.*

⌂ **Pear Tree Cottage** 🐦 without rest., 7 Church Rd, CV37 9UX, ☎ (01789) 205889, *Fax (01789) 262862*, « Part Elizabethan », 🌳 – ⊁ [TV] [P]. ✕
*closed Christmas-2 January* – **5 rm** ☐ 35.00/50.00 **s.**

ATS Western Rd ☎ (01789) 205591

**STRATTON** *Glos.* [403] [404] O 28 – *see Cirencester.*

**STREATLEY** *Newbury* [403] [404] Q 29 *Great Britain G.* – *pop. 4 193 (inc. Goring)* – ✉ *Goring.*
Env. : *Basildon Park★ AC, SE : 2½ m. by A 329* – *Mapledurham★ AC, E : 6 m. by A 329, B 47 and B 4526.*
Exc. : *Ridgeway Path★★.*
⛳ [18] *Goring & Streatley, Rectory Rd* ☎ *(01491) 872688.*
*London 56* – *Oxford 16* – *Reading 11.*

🏨 **Swan Diplomat,** High St., RG8 9HR, ☎ (01491) 873737, *Fax (01491) 872554*, 🏠, « Thames-side setting », 🏋, 🧖, 🏊, 🌳 – [TV] ☎ ♿ [P] – 🏛 80. [MC] [AE] [D] [VISA] [JCB]
**Meals** (bar lunch Monday to Saturday)/dinner 32.00 **t.** and a la carte 🍷 10.50 – ☐ 9.50 – **45 rm** 99.00/156.00 **t.**, 1 suite – SB.

**STRETTON** *Ches.* [402] [403] [404] M 23 – *see Warrington.*

**STRETTON** *Staffs.* [402] [403] [404] P 25 – *see Burton-upon-Trent.*

Les prix — Pour toutes précisions sur les prix indiqués dans ce guide, reportez-vous aux pages de l'introduction.

**STROUD** *Glos.* 403 404 N 28 – *pop. 38 835.*

☐₁₈, ☐₁₈, ☐₁₈ *Minchinhampton* ℘ *(01453) 832642 (old course) (01453) 833866 (new course)* – ☐₁₈ *Painswick* ℘ *(01452) 812180.*

🛈 *Subscription Rooms, George St., GL5 1AE* ℘ *(01453) 765768.*
*London 113 – Bristol 30 – Gloucester 9.*

🏨 **Stonehouse Court,** Stonehouse, GL10 3RA, West : 4 m. on A 419 ℘ *(01453) 825155,* *Fax (01453) 824611,* « *Part 16C manor house* », � – 📺 ☎ 🅿 – 🔬 150. 🕮 🆎 ① 𝘝𝘐𝘚𝘈 JᴄB. 🍸
**Meals** *(closed Saturday lunch)* 14.95/28.95 **t.** and dinner a la carte ₰ 5.50 – **36 rm** ☲ 84.00/ 145.00 **t.,** 1 suite – SB.

🏠 **Old Nelson - Premier Lodge,** Stratford Lodge, Stratford Rd, GL5 4AF, North : ½ m. by A 46 ℘ *(01453) 765821, Fax (01453) 765964,* Reservations (Freephone) 0800 118833 – ⛝ rm, 📺 ☎ 🅴 ⅙ 🅿. 🕮 🆎 ① 𝘝𝘐𝘚𝘈 JᴄB. 🍸
**Meals** *(grill rest.)* a la carte 9.05/14.65 **st.** – ☲ 5.95 – **30 rm** 43.95 **st.** – SB.

**at Brimscombe** *Southeast : 2¼ m. on A 419 –* ⊠ *Stroud.*

🏨 **Burleigh Court** ⤢, Burleigh Lane, GL5 2PF, South : ½ m. by Burleigh rd via The Roundabouts ℘ *(01453) 883804, Fax (01453) 886870,* ≤, ⬛, 🌫 – ⛝ rest, 📺 ☎ 🅿. 🕮 ① 𝘝𝘐𝘚𝘈 JᴄB
*closed 28 December-7 January –* **Meals** *(light dinner Sunday)* 17.50/24.50 **t.** ₰ 6.50 – **17 rm** ☲ 68.50/145.00 **t.** – SB.

**at Amberley** *South : 3 m. by A 46 –* ⊠ *Stroud.*

🏠 **Amberley Inn,** GL5 5AF, ℘ *(01453) 872565, Fax (01453) 872738,* 🌫 – 📺 ☎ 🅴 🅿. 🕮 🆎 𝘝𝘐𝘚𝘈
**Meals** 11.85/15.95 **t.** and dinner a la carte – **15 rm** ☲ 30.00/70.00 **t.** – SB.

🔘 ATS Dudbridge Rd ℘ *(01453) 758156/752191*

---

**STUCKTON** *Hants. – see Fordingbridge.*

---

**STUDLEY** *Warks.* 403 404 O 27 – *pop. 5 883 –* ⊠ *Redditch.*
*London 109 – Birmingham 15 – Coventry 33 – Gloucester 39.*

✗✗ **Pepper's,** 45 High St., B80 7HN, ℘ *(01527) 853183 –* ▤. 🕮 🆎 𝘝𝘐𝘚𝘈
*closed 25 December –* **Meals** - Indian - *(dinner only)* 22.50 **t.** and a la carte.

---

**STURMINSTER NEWTON** *Dorset* 403 404 N 31 *The West Country G. – pop. 2 155.*
See : *Mill★ AC.*
*London 123 – Bournemouth 30 – Bristol 49 – Salisbury 28 – Taunton 41.*

🏠 **Stourcastle Lodge,** Gough's Close, DT10 1BU, (off the Market Place) ℘ *(01258) 472320, Fax (01258) 473381,* 🌫 – ⛝ 📺 ☎ 🅿. 𝘝𝘐𝘚𝘈. 🍸
**Meals** 17.00 **st.** – **5 rm** ☲ 44.00/70.00 **st.**

✗✗✗ **Plumber Manor** ⤢ with rm, DT10 2AF, Southwest : 1¾ m. by A 357 on Hazelbury Bryan rd ℘ *(01258) 472507, Fax (01258) 473370,* ≤, « *18C manor house* », 🌫, park, 🏌 – 📺 ☎ 🅿 – 🔬 25. 🕮 🆎 ① 𝘝𝘐𝘚𝘈
*closed February –* **Meals** *(dinner only and Sunday lunch)/dinner* 19.50 **st.** ₰ 6.50 – **16 rm** ☲ 75.00/140.00 **st.** – SB.

🔘 ATS Bults Pond Ind Est. ℘ *(01258) 473083*

---

**SUDBURY** *Suffolk* 404 W 27 *Great Britain G. – pop. 19 512.*
See : *Gainsborough's House★ AC.*
🛈 *Town Hall, Market Hill, CO10 6TL* ℘ *(01787) 881320 (summer only).*
*London 59 – Cambridge 37 – Colchester 15 – Ipswich 21.*

🏨 **Mill,** Walnut Tree Lane, CO10 6BD, ℘ *(01787) 375544, Fax (01787) 373027,* ≤, « *Converted 19C mill* » – ▤ rest, 📺 ☎ 🅿 – 🔬 70. 🕮 🆎 ① 𝘝𝘐𝘚𝘈 JᴄB
**Meals** *(residents only 24-26 and 31 December)* 14.50 **t.** *(lunch)* and dinner a la carte 20.15/ 30.50 **t.** ₰ 6.95 – ☲ 8.50 – **56 rm** ☲ 55.00/89.00 **st.** – SB.

✗ **Red Onion Bistro,** 57 Ballingdon St., CO10 6DA, Southwest : ¾ m. on A 131 ℘ *(01787) 376777, Fax (01787) 883156,* 🌤 – 🅿. 🕮 𝘝𝘐𝘚𝘈 JᴄB
*closed Sunday dinner and 25 December-1 January –* **Meals** *(booking essential)* 7.75/9.75 **t.** and a la carte ₰ 3.75.

🔘 ATS Edgeworth Rd ℘ *(01787) 374227*

---

**SUMMERBRIDGE** *N. Yorks.* 402 O 21 – *see Pateley Bridge.*

# SUNDERLAND

*Town plans:* the names
of main shopping streets
are indicated in red
at the beginning
of the list of streets.

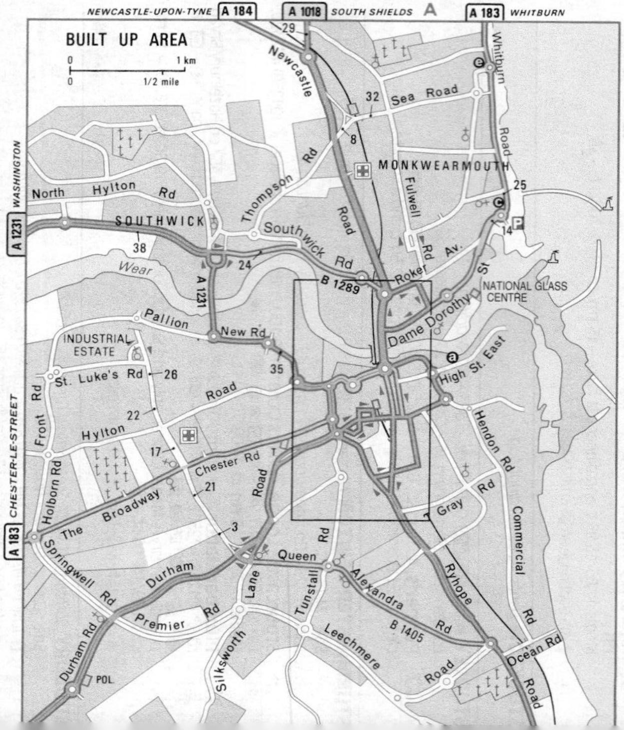

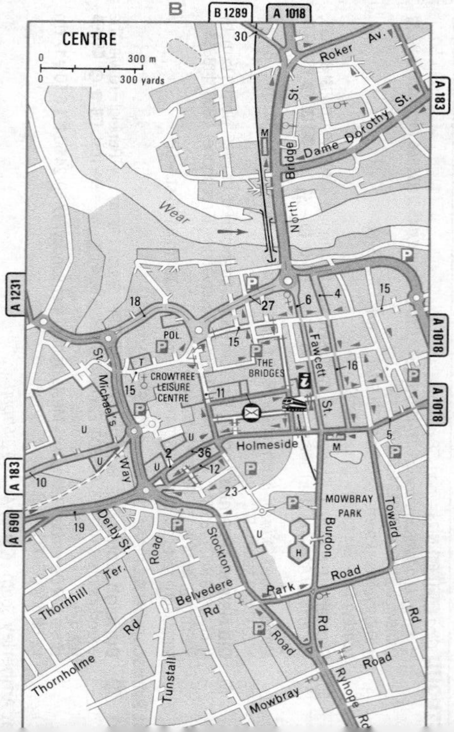

**SUNDERLAND** Tyne and Wear **401 402** P 19 – pop. 183 310.

⌐ Whitburn, Lizard Lane ℰ (0191) 529 2144.

🚹 Unit 3 Crowtree Rd, SR1 3EL ℰ (0191) 565 0990.

London 272 – Leeds 92 – Middlesbrough 29 – Newcastle upon Tyne 12.

Plan opposite

**Swallow Sunderland,** Queens Par., Seaburn, SR6 8DB, ℰ (0191) 529 2041, Fax (0191) 529 4227, ≤, ⌐ℰ, ⌐, ⌐, ⌐ rm, ▤ ⌐ ☎ ✆ ℰ ℗ – ⌐ 300. ◖◗ ஊ ◑ ፵ℑ. ⌐
Meals 15.95/24.00 st. and a la carte ⌐ 6.50 – **65 rm** ⌐ 99.00/135.00 **st.** – SB.
A e

**Roker,** Roker Terrace, Roker, SR6 0PH, ℰ (0191) 567 1786, Fax (0191) 510 0289, ≤ – ⌐ ☎ ℗ – ⌐ 300. ◖◗ ஊ ◑ ፵ℑ. ℘
A c
Meals (grill rest.) a la carte 8.75/18.45 **t.** – ⌐ 6.95 – **44 rm** 45.00/55.00 **t.**

**Travel Inn,** Wessington Way, SR5 3HR, Northwest: 3 ¾ m. by A 1231 ℰ (0191) 548 9384, Fax (0191) 548 4148 – ⌐ rm, ⌐ ℰ ℗ – ⌐ 25. ◖◗ ஊ ◑ ፵ℑ. ℘
Meals (grill rest.) – **41 rm** 38.00 **t.**

**Brasserie 21,** Wylam Wharf, Low St., SR1 2AD, ℰ (0191) 567 6594, Fax (0191) 510 3994, « Converted 17C warehouse » – ℗. ◖◗ ஊ ◑ ፵ℑ
A a
closed Sunday and Bank Holidays – Meals (booking essential) 14.50 **t.** (lunch) and dinner a la carte 18.50/23.00 **t.**

⌐ ATS Monkwearmouth Bridge ℰ (0191) 565 7694

---

**SUNNINGHILL** Windsor & Maidenhead **404** S 29 – see Ascot.

---

| Prices | For notes on the prices quoted in this Guide, see the introduction. |
|---|---|

---

**SUTTON** W. Sussex – see Petworth.

---

**SUTTON COLDFIELD** W. Mids. **403 404** O 26 – pop. 106 001.

⌐ Pype Hayes, Eachelhurst Rd, Walmley ℰ (0121) 351 1014, DT – ⌐ Boldmere, Monmouth Drive ℰ (0121) 354 3379, DT – ⌐ 110 Thornhill Rd ℰ (0121) 353 2014, DT – ⌐, ⌐ The Belfry, Lichfield Rd, Wishaw ℰ (01675) 470301 DT.

London 124 – Birmingham 8 – Coventry 29 – Nottingham 47 – Stoke-on-Trent 40.

Plan : see Birmingham pp. 2 and 3

**The Belfry,** Wishaw, B76 9PR, East: 6 ½ m. by A 453 on A 446 ℰ (01675) 470301, Fax (01675) 470178, ≤, ⌐ℰ, ⌐ℰ, ⌐, ⌐, ⌐, park, ℀, squash – ⌐, ⌐ rm, ▤ rest, ⌐ ☎ ✆ ℰ, ℗ – ⌐ 450. ◖◗ ஊ ◑ ፵ℑ. ℘
**Garden Room :** Meals (carving rest.) 15.95/21.95 **t.** ⌐ 10.50 – **French Restaurant :** Meals (closed Saturday lunch and Sunday dinner) 18.00/31.50 **t.** ⌐ 10.50 – **Riley's :** Meals (buffet lunch)/dinner 21.95 **t.** ⌐ 10.50 – **315 rm** ⌐ 150.00/175.00 **st.,** 9 suites – SB.

**New Hall** ⌐, Walmley Rd, B76 1QX, Southeast : 1 ½ m. by Coleshill St., Coleshill Rd and Reddicap Hill on B 4148 ℰ (0121) 378 2442, Fax (0121) 378 4637, ≤, ⌐, « Part 13C moated manor house, gardens », ⌐, park, ℀ – ⌐ rm ⌐ ☎ ℰ ℗ – ⌐ 50. ◖◗ ஊ ◑ ፵ℑ ⌐.
DT i
℘
Meals (closed Saturday lunch) 20.50/36.50 **st.** ⌐ 7.50 – ⌐ 13.50 – **55 rm** 135.00/180.00 **st.,** 5 suites – SB.

**Moor Hall,** Moor Hall Drive, B75 6LN, Northeast : 2 m. by A 453 and Weeford Rd ℰ (0121) 308 3751, Fax (0121) 308 8974, ⌐ℰ, ⌐ℰ, ⌐, ⌐ – ⌐, ⌐ rm, ⌐ ☎ ℗ – ⌐ 250. ◖◗ ஊ ◑ ፵ℑ ⌐.
DT r
Meals (carving lunch)/dinner 19.50 **t.** and a la carte ⌐ 3.95 – **75 rm** ⌐ 95.00/118.00 **t.** – SB.

**Penns Hall,** Penns Lane, Walmley, B76 1LH, Southeast : 2 ¾ m. by A 5127 ℰ (0121) 351 3111, Fax (0121) 313 1297, ⌐ℰ, ⌐ℰ, ⌐, ⌐, ⌐, park, squash – ⌐, ⌐ rm, ⌐ ☎ ℰ ℗ – ⌐ 400. ◖◗ ஊ ◑ ፵ℑ
DT v
Meals (closed Saturday lunch) 10.95/17.95 **st.** and a la carte ⌐ 7.00 – ⌐ 9.95 – **132 rm** 115.00/135.00 **st.,** 3 suites – SB.

**Royal,** High St., B72 1UD, ℰ (0121) 355 8222, Fax (0121) 355 1837 – ⌐ ☎ ℗ – ⌐ 40. ◖◗ ஊ ◑ ፵ℑ. ℘
DT c
Meals (grill rest.) 6.00/9.95 **st.** and a la carte ⌐ 6.00 – **22 rm** ⌐ 54.95/76.90 **st.** – SB.

**Sutton Court,** 60-66 Lichfield Rd, B74 2NA, North : ½ m. at junction of A 5127 with A 453 ℰ (0121) 354 4991, Fax (0121) 355 0083 – ⌐ rm, ⌐ ☎ ℰ ℗ – ⌐ 90. ◖◗ ஊ ◑ ፵ℑ
DT x
Meals (bar lunch)/dinner 9.50/16.95 **st.** and dinner a la carte ⌐ 6.00 – **64 rm** ⌐ 89.00/118.00 **st.** – SB.

**Parson and Clerk,** Chester Rd North, Streetly, B73 6SP, West : 3 ½ m. by A 453 on A 452 ℰ (0121) 580 7700, Fax (0121) 352 1340 – ⌐ ☎ ℗. ◖◗ ஊ ◑ ፵ℑ ⌐. ℘
CT s
Meals (grill rest.) a la carte 10.70/18.85 **t.** – ⌐ 6.00 – **36 rm** 37.95 **st.**

🏨 **Travelodge,** Boldmere Rd, B72 5UP, Southwest : 1 ¼ m. by A 5127 and A 453 on B 4114
    𝒫 (0121) 355 0017, Reservations (Freephone) 0800 850950 – ❄ rm, 📺 ⅀ 🅿. 🐵 🆎 ⓘ
    𝚅𝙸𝚂𝙰 𝙹𝙲𝙱. ⅍
    **Meals** (grill rest.) – **32 rm** 39.95/59.95 **t.**
    DT

🍴🍴 **La Truffe,** 65 Birmingham Rd, B72 1QF, 𝒫 (0121) 355 5836, Fax (0121) 314 9955 – 🐵 🅰
    𝚅𝙸𝚂𝙰
    DT
    closed Saturday lunch, Sunday, Monday, 3 days Easter, last 2 weeks August, 25-26 December
    and 1 January – **Meals** 17.95 **t.** (dinner) and a la carte 22.10/27.20 **t.** ⅃ 6.95.

**at Curdworth** Southeast : 6½ m. by A 5127, A 452 and A 38 - DT - on A 4097 – ✉ Sutton Coldfield

🏠 **Old School House,** Kingsbury Rd, B76 7DR, on A 4097 𝒫 (01675) 470177
    Fax (01675) 470177, 🐎 – 📺 🅿. 🐵 𝚅𝙸𝚂𝙰
    **Meals** (by arrangement) 14.00 – **7 rm** ⅃ 42.00/54.00.

---

**SUTTON COURTENAY** Oxon. **403 404** Q 29 – ✉ Abingdon.
    London 57 – Newbury 21 – Oxford 11 – Swindon 27.

🍴🍴 **The Fish** with rm, 4 Appleford Rd, OX14 4NQ, 𝒫 (01235) 848242, Fax (01235) 848014, 🐎
    – 📺 🅿. 🐵 🆎 ⓘ 𝚅𝙸𝚂𝙰. ⅍
    **Meals** 16.95/19.95 **t.** and a la carte ⅃ 5.00 – ⅀ 7.50 – **2 rm** 35.00/45.00 **t.**

---

**SUTTON GAULT** Cambs. **404** U 26 – see Ely.

---

**SUTTON SCOTNEY SERVICE AREA** Hants. **403 404** P 30 – ✉ Winchester.
    London 66 – Reading 32 – Salisbury 21 – Southampton 19.

🏨 **Travelodge,** SO21 3JY, on A 34 𝒫 (01962) 761016 (northside), (01962) 760779 (south
    side), Reservations (Freephone) 0800 850950 – ❄ rm, 📺 ⅀ 🅿. 🐵 🆎 ⓘ 𝚅𝙸𝚂𝙰 𝙹𝙲𝙱. ⅍
    **Meals** (grill rest.) – **71 rm** 39.95/59.95 **t.**

---

**SWAFFHAM** Norfolk **404** W 26 Great Britain G. – pop. 5 332.
    Exc. : Oxburgh Hall★★ AC, SW : 7½ m.
    London 97 – Cambridge 46 – King's Lynn 16 – Norwich 27.

🏨 **Strattons,** Ash Close, PE37 7NH, off Market Sq. 𝒫 (01760) 723845, Fax (01760) 720458
    « Part Queen Anne house », 🐎 – ❄ 📺 ☎ 🅿. 🐵 𝚅𝙸𝚂𝙰
    closed 24 to 26 December – **Meals** (booking essential to non-residents) (dinner only)
    28.00 **st.** ⅃ 6.40 – **7 rm** ⅀ 70.00/150.00 **st.**

**at Sporle** Northeast : 3¼ m. by A 1065 and A 47 – ✉ King's Lynn.

🏠 **Corfield House,** PE32 2EA, on Necton rd 𝒫 (01760) 723636, 🐎 – ❄ 📺 🅿. 🐵 𝚅𝙸𝚂𝙰
    April-mid December – **Meals** 12.50 **s.** ⅃ 4.00 – **4 rm** ⅀ 30.00/43.00 **s.**

    🔘 ATS Unit 2a, Tower Meadow (off Station St.) 𝒫 (01760) 722543

---

**SWANAGE** Dorset **403 404** O 32 The West Country G. – pop. 9 037.
    See : Town★.
    Env. : St. Aldhelm's Head★★ (≤★★★), SW : 4 m. by B 3069 – Durlston Country Park (≤★★,
    S : 1 m. – Studland (Old Harry Rocks★★, Studland Beach (≤★), St. Nicholas Church★,
    N : 3 m. – Worth Matravers (Anvil Point Lighthouse ≤★★), S : 2 m. – Great Globe★, S : 1¼m.
    Exc. : Corfe Castle★ (≤★★) AC, NW : 6 m. by A 351 – Blue Pool★, NW : 9 m. by A 351 and
    minor roads – Lulworth Cove★, W : 18 m. by A 351 and B 3070.
    🏌₁₈, 🏌₉ Isle of Purbeck, Studland 𝒫 (01929) 450361.
    🛈 The White House, Shore Rd, BH19 1LB 𝒫 (01929) 422885.
    London 130 – Bournemouth 22 – Dorchester 26 – Southampton 52.

🍴 **Cauldron Bistro,** 5 High St., BH19 2LN, 𝒫 (01929) 422671 – 🐵 🆎 ⓘ 𝚅𝙸𝚂𝙰
    closed Tuesday lunch, Monday, 2 weeks November and 2 weeks January – **Meals** a la carte
    18.30/24.75 **t.** ⅃ 7.50.

🍴 **The Galley,** 9 High St., BH19 2LN, 𝒫 (01929) 427299 – 🐵 🆎 ⓘ 𝚅𝙸𝚂𝙰 𝙹𝙲𝙱
    closed 3 weeks November and 31 December-Easter – **Meals** (dinner only) 18.50 **t.** ⅃ 4.25.

    🔘 ATS Unit 4, Ind Est., Victoria Ave. 𝒫 (01929) 424741

---

**SWAVESEY SERVICE AREA** Cambs. **404** U 27 – see Cambridge.

---

**SWAY** Hants. **403 404** P 31 – see Brockenhurst.

**SWINDON** 403 404 O 29 *The West Country G. – pop. 145 236.*

**See** : *Great Western Railway Museum★ AC – Railway Village Museum★ AC* Y **M.**

**Env.** : *Lydiard Park (St. Mary's★ ) W : 4 m.* U.

**Exc.** : *Ridgeway Path★★ , S : 8½ m. by A 4361 – Whitehorse (≼★ )E : 7½ m. by A 4312, A 420 and B 400 off B 4057.*

☗, ☗ *Broome Manor, Pipers Way ☏ (01793) 532403 –* ☗ *Shrivenham Park, Penny Hooks ☏ (01793) 783853 –* ☗ *Wootton Bassett ☏ (01793) 849999 –* ☗ *Wrag Barn G & C.C., Shrivenham Rd, Highworth ☏ (01793) 861327.*

🛈 *37 Regent St., SN1 1JL ☏ (01793) 2530328.*

*London 83 – Bournemouth 69 – Bristol 40 – Coventry 66 – Oxford 29 – Reading 40 – Southampton 65.*

## SWINDON

| | | | | | |
|---|---|---|---|---|---|
| Beechcroft Road | U 4 | Devises Road | V 18 | Rodbourne Road | U 48 |
| Bridge End Road | U 6 | Gipsy Lane | U 25 | Slade Drive | U 51 |
| Cheney Manor Road | U 10 | Hobley Drive | U 28 | Swindon Road | U 57 |
| Cirencester Way | U 12 | Kingsdown Road | U 30 | Vicarage Road | U 61 |
| | | Newport Street | V 36 | Westcott Place | U 64 |
| | | Oxford Road | U 42 | Whitworth Road | U 66 |
| | | Park Lane | U 43 | Wootton Basset Road | U 69 |

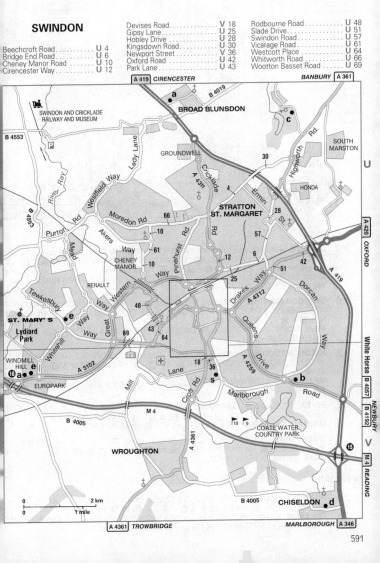

# SWINDON

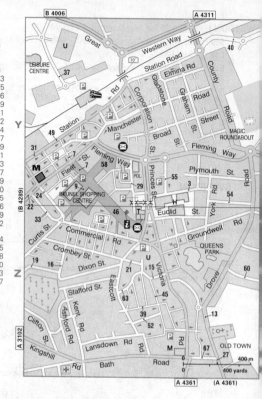

**De Vere,** Shaw Ridge Leisure Park, Whitehill Way, SN5 7DW, West : 2 ¾ m. by A 3102 and Tewkesbury Way (at Mannington junction) ℰ (01793) 878785, Fax (01793) 877822, ℔, ⇌s, ◲ – ⅋ ℀, ▤ rest, ▣ ☎ ℄ ᴋ ℗ – ⚹ 400. ⦿ ஊ ⓪ ⱱᴎˢᴬ ᴊᴄʙ           U  e
Meals (bar lunch Saturday) (carving lunch) 14.25 **t.** (lunch) and a la carte approx. 22.85 – 146 rm ⊇ 120.00 **t.**, 8 suites – SB.

**Swindon Marriott,** Pipers Way, SN3 1SH, Southeast : 1½ m. by Marlborough Road off B 4006 ℰ (01793) 512121, Fax (01793) 513114, ℔, ⇌s, ◲, ℀, squash – ⅋ ℀ rm, ▤ ▣ ☎ ℄ ᴋ ℗ – ⚹ 250. ⦿ ஊ ⓪ ⱱᴎˢᴬ           V  s
Meals (closed Saturday and Sunday lunch) 15.00/17.20 **st.** and a la carte ⅄ 7.45 – ⊇ 10.95 – 153 rm 95.00 **st.** – SB.

**Hilton National,** Lydiard Fields, Great Western Way, SN5 8UZ, M 4 junction 16 ℰ (01793) 881777, Fax (01793) 881881, ℔, ⇌s, ◲ – ⅋, ℀ rm, ▤ ▣ ☎ ᴋ ℗ – ⚹ 350. ⦿ ஊ ⓪ ⱱᴎˢᴬ           V  a
Meals (bar lunch Saturday) 14.20/19.20 **st.** and a la carte ⅄ 6.00 – ⊇ 12.25 – 150 rm 155.00/180.00 **st.** – SB.

**Forte Posthouse Swindon,** Marlborough Rd, SN3 6AQ, ℰ (01793) 524601, Fax (01793) 512887, ℔, ⇌s, ◲ – ℀ rm, ▣ ☎ ℗ – ⚹ 70. ⦿ ஊ ⓪ ⱱᴎˢᴬ ᴊᴄʙ           V  b
Meals a la carte 15.95/23.90 **t.** ⅄ 8.95 – ⊇ 9.95 – 98 rm 85.00/125.00 **t.** – SB.

**Travel Inn,** Lydiard Fields, Great Western Way, SN5 8UY, M 4 junction 16 ℰ (01793) 881490, Fax (01793) 886890 – ℀ rm, ▣ ᴋ ℗. ⦿ ஊ ⓪ ⱱᴎˢᴬ           V  e
Meals (grill rest.) – 63 rm 38.00 **t.**

**at Blunsdon** North : 4½ m. on A 419 – ✉ Swindon.

**Blunsdon House,** SN2 4AD, ℰ (01793) 721701, Fax (01793) 721056, ℔, ⇌s, ◲, ℞, 🏊, park, ℀, squash – ⅋, ℀ rm, ▣ ☎ ᴋ ℗ – ⚹ 300. ⦿ ஊ ⓪ ⱱᴎˢᴬ ᴊᴄʙ. ℀           U  a
The Ridge : Meals (closed Saturday lunch) 15.50/21.50 **st.** and a la carte – **Carrie's** : Meals (carving rest.) 11.50/15.00 **st.** – 86 rm ⊇ 92.00/140.00 **st.**, 1 suite – SB.

SWINDON
ENGLAND

**at Stanton Fitzwarren** Northeast : 5¼ m. by A 4312 and A 419 off A 361 – ⊠ Swindon.

🏠 **Stanton House** ⤷, The Avenue, SN6 7SD, 𝓅 (01793) 861777, Fax (01793) 861857, 🌳, park, 🎾 – 📱, ✲ rm, ▤ rest, 📺 ☎ & 🅿 – 🔬 110. ◑ 🅰 ◑ 𝘝𝘐𝘚𝘈 ᴊᴄʙ. 🎝 U c
Meals - Japanese - 15.00 t. (lunch) and a la carte 25.00/33.00 t. – **86 rm** ⊒ 65.00/105.00 t.

**at Chiseldon** South : 6¼ m. by A 4312, A 4259 and A 345 on B 4005 – ⊠ Swindon.

🏠 **Chiseldon House** ⤷, New Rd, SN4 0NE, 𝓅 (01793) 741010, Fax (01793) 741059, ☑, 🌳 – 📺 ☎ 🅿. 🎝 V d
closed 1 week Christmas – **Orangery :** Meals (closed lunch Saturday and Sunday) 9.95/24.95 st. ⅙ 5.30 – **21 rm** ⊒ 75.50/100.00 st.

**at Wootton Bassett** West : 6¼ m. on A 3102 - V - ⊠ Swindon.

🏠 **Marsh Farm,** Coped Hall, SN4 8ER, North : 1 m. by A 3102 on Purton rd 𝓅 (01793) 848044, Fax (01793) 851528, 🌳 – ✲ rest, 📺 ☎ 🅿 – 🔬 150. ◑ 🅰 𝘝𝘐𝘚𝘈. 🎝
Meals (closed Saturday lunch) 21.00/23.00 st. and dinner a la carte ⅙ 5.85 – **33 rm** ⊒ 92.00/115.00 st.

**at Hook** West : 6¼ m. by A 3102 - V - , B 4534 and Hook rd – ⊠ Swindon.

🏠 **The School House,** Hook St., SN4 8EF, 𝓅 (01793) 851198, Fax (01793) 851025, 🌳 – ✲ rest, 📺 ☎ 📞 🅿. ◑ 🅰 𝘝𝘐𝘚𝘈. 🎝
Meals 18.95/25.95 t. ⅙ 8.95 – **12 rm** ⊒ 75.00/115.00 st.

🔧 ATS Cheney Manor Ind. Est. 𝓅 (01793) 521171    ATS 86 Beatrice St. 𝓅 (01793) 534867/431620

---

**SWINTON** Gtr.Manchester 402 403 404 N 23 – see Manchester.

---

**SYMONDS YAT WEST** Herefordshire 403 404 M 28 Great Britain G. – ⊠ Ross-on-Wye.
See : Town★ – Yat Rock (≼★).
Env. : S : Wye Valley★.
London 126 – Gloucester 23 – Hereford 17 – Newport 31.

🏠 **Norton House,** Whitchurch, HR9 6DJ, 𝓅 (01600) 890046, Fax (01600) 890045, « 18C farmhouse of 15C origins », 🌳 – ✲ 📺 🅿
Meals (by arrangement) (communal dining) 14.95 s. – **3 rm** ⊒ 30.00/44.00 s.

---

**TADCASTER** N. Yorks. 402 Q 22 – pop. 6 915.
London 206 – Harrogate 16 – Leeds 14 – York 11.

🏨 **Hazlewood Castle** ⤷, Paradise Lane, Hazlewood, LS24 9NJ, Southwest : 2 ¾ m. by A 659 (A 64) 𝓅 (01937) 535353, Fax (01937) 530630, ≼, « Part 13C fortified manor house in parkland », 🌳 – ✲ rest, 📺 ☎ 🅿 – 🔬 120. ◑ 🅰 ◑ 𝘝𝘐𝘚𝘈 ᴊᴄʙ. 🎝
**1086** (𝓅 (01937) 535354) : Meals (closed Saturday lunch, Sunday dinner and Monday) 15.00 st. and a la carte – **Prickly Pear Café** 12.00/15.95 st. and lunch a la carte – **10 rm** ⊒ 95.00/165.00 st., **11 suites** 195.00/300.00 st. – SB.

XX **Aagrah,** York Rd, Steeton, LS24 8EG, Northeast : 2 ½ m. on A 64 𝓅 (01937) 530888 – ▤ 🅿. ◑ 🅰 𝘝𝘐𝘚𝘈 ᴊᴄʙ
closed 25 December – Meals - Indian - (dinner only) a la carte 13.70/17.05 t.

**at Saxton** South : 5 m. by A 162 – ⊠ Tadcaster.

X **The Plough Inn,** Headwell Lane, LS24 9PX, 𝓅 (01937) 557242 – ✲ 🅿. ◑ 🅰 𝘝𝘐𝘚𝘈. 🎝
closed Sunday dinner, Monday and 1 to 15 January – Meals a la carte 16.25/22.45 t. ⅙ 7.50.

🔧 ATS Station Road Ind. Est. 𝓅 (01937) 832626/833969

---

**TADWORTH** Surrey 404 T 30 – pop. 37 245 (inc. Banstead).
London 23 – Brighton 36 – Guildford 22 – Maidstone 41.

XX **Gemini,** 28 Station Approach, KT20 5AH, 𝓅 (01737) 812179 – ✲. ◑ 🅰 𝘝𝘐𝘚𝘈
closed Saturday lunch, Sunday dinner, Monday, 2 weeks in summer and 2 weeks Christmas – Meals 25.50 t. ⅙ 7.90.

---

**TALKE** Staffs. 402 403 404 N 24 – see Stoke-on-Trent.

---

**TALLAND BAY** Cornwall 403 G 32 – see Looe.

---

**TALLINGTON** Lincs. – see Stamford.

593

**TAMWORTH** Staffs. 402 403 404 O 26 – pop. 68 440.

⌐ Eagle Drive, Amington ℰ (01827) 53850.

🚹 Town Hall, Market St., B79 7LY ℰ (01827) 59134 (summer only).

London 128 – Birmingham 12 – Coventry 29 – Leicester 31 – Stoke-on-Trent 37.

🏠 **Travel Inn,** Bitterscote, Bonehill Rd, B78 3HQ, on A 51 ℰ (01827) 54414
Fax (01827) 310420 – ↤ rm, 🖸 ċ 🅿. 🐠 🆎 ⓪ 🚺 .ṣ
**Meals** (grill rest.) – **40 rm** 38.00 **t.**

at Bodymoor Heath South : 6 ¾ m. by A 4091 – ⊠ Sutton Coldfield.

🏠🏠 **Marston Farm,** B76 9JD, ℰ (01827) 872133, Fax (01827) 875043, ⁓ – ↤ rest, 🖸 🕿 ċ
🅿 – 🔬 50. 🐠 🆎 ⓪ 🚺
**Meals** 9.95/17.95 **st.** and a la carte ≬ 4.50 – **36 rm** ⌐ 85.00/110.00 **st.** – SB.

⊚ ATS Tame Valley Ind. Est., Watling St., Wilnecote ℰ (01827) 281983

---

**TAMWORTH SERVICE AREA** Staffs. 402 403 404 P 26 – ⊠ Tamworth.

🏠 **Travelodge,** Green Lane, B77 5PS, at junction 10 of M 42 ℰ (01827) 260120
Fax (01827) 260145, Reservations (Freephone) 0800 850950 – ↤ 🖸 🕿 ċ 🅿. 🐠 🆎 ⓪ 🚺
ᴊᴄʙ. ṣ
**Meals** (grill rest.) – **63 rm** 39.95/59.95 **t.**

---

**TANSLEY** Derbs. – see Matlock.

*Se cercate un albergo tranquillo,*
*oltre a consultare le carte dell'introduzione,*
*rintracciate nell'elenco degli esercizi quelli con il simbolo* ⏛ *o* ⏛.

---

**TAPLOW** Windsor & Maidenhead 404 R 29.

London 33 – Maidenhead 2 – Reading 12.

🏠🏠🏠 **Cliveden** ⏛, SL6 0JF, North : 2 m. by Berry Hill ℰ (01628) 668561, Fax (01628) 661837
« Mid-Victorian stately home, ≤ National Trust Gardens, parterre and River Thames », ℱ❺
≋⇘, ⏛, ⏛, ⸙, park, ⁓ indoor/outdoor, squash – 🖚 ↤ 🖸 🕿 🅿 – 🔬 40. 🐠 🆎 ⓪ 🚺
**Terrace :** Meals 26.00/39.00 **st.** and a la carte 41.50/64.50 **st.** ≬ 12.00 – (see also **Waldo's**
below) – ⌐ 17.00 – **33 rm** 235.00/425.00, 5 suites – SB.

XXXX **Waldo's** (at Cliveden H.), SL6 0JF, North : 2 m. by Berry Hill ℰ (01628) 668561,
✿ Fax (01628) 661837 – ↤ 🗏 🅿. 🐠 🆎 ⓪ 🚺
closed Sunday and Monday – **Meals** (booking essential) (dinner only) 52.00 **st.** ≬ 12.00
**Spec.** Ginger scented ravioli of crab with scallops. Roast breast of duck with celeriac and
Calvados sauce. Orange muscat terrine with bittersweet chocolate sorbet.

---

**TARPORLEY** Ches. 402 403 404 M 24 – pop. 2 308.

⌐ Portal G & C.C., Cobblers Cross Lane ℰ (01829) 733933 – ⌐ Portal Premier, Forest Rc
ℰ (01829) 733884.

London 186 – Chester 11 – Liverpool 36 – Shrewsbury 36.

🏠 **Swan,** 50 High St., CW6 0AG, ℰ (01829) 733838, Fax (01829) 732932 – 🖸 🕿 ċ 🅿 –
🔬 100. 🐠 🆎 🚺 ᴊᴄʙ
**Bohars Brasserie :** Meals a la carte 11.00/17.00 **t.** ≬ 7.50 – **20 rm** ⌐ 55.00/75.00 **t.**

at Bunbury South : 3 ¼ m. by A 49 – ⊠ Tarporley.

🍴 **Dysart Arms,** Bowes Gate Rd, CW6 9PH, by Bunbury Mill rd ℰ (01829) 260183,
Fax (01829) 261286, ⁓ – 🅿. 🐠 🆎 🚺
closed 25 December – **Meals** a la carte 15.85/20.15.

---

**TATTENHALL** Ches. 402 403 404 L 24 – pop. 1 854.

London 200 – Birmingham 71 – Chester 10 – Manchester 38 – Stoke-on-Trent 30.

⌂ **Higher Huxley Hall** ⏛, CH3 9BZ, North : 2 ¼ m. on Huxley rd ℰ (01829) 781484,
Fax (01829) 781142, ≤, « Working farm », 🔲, ⁓ – ↤ 🖸 🕿 🅿. 🐠 🚺 ᴊᴄʙ. ṣ
booking essential – **Meals** (by arrangement) (communal dining) 22.50 **s.** ≬ 8.00 – **3 rm**
⌐ 40.00/70.00 **s.** – SB.

⌂ **Newton Hall** ⏛ without rest., CH3 9AY, North : 1 m. by Huxley rd on Gatesheath rd
ℰ (01829) 770153, Fax (01829) 770655, « Working farm », ⁓ – ↤ 🖸 🅿
closed 1 January – **3 rm** ⌐ 25.00/50.00 **s.**

**TAUNTON** Somerset [403] K 30 *The West Country G. – pop. 55 855.*

See : *Town★ – St. Mary Magdalene★* V *– Somerset County Museum★ AC* U *– St. James'★* U *– Hammett St.★* V **25** *– The Crescent★* V *– Bath Place★* V **3**.

Env. : *Trull (Church★), S : 2½ m. by A 38.*

Exc. : *Bishops Lydeard★ (Church★), NW : 6 m. – Wellington : Church★, Wellington Monument (≤★★), SW : 7½ m. by A 38 – Combe Florey★, NW : 8 m. – Gaulden Manor★ AC, NW : 10 m. by A 358 and B 3227.*

🐾, 🐾 *Taunton Vale, Creech Heathfield ✆ (01823) 412220 –* 🐾 *Vivary, Vivary Park ✆ (01823) 289274 –* 🐾 *Taunton and Pickeridge, Corfe ✆ (01823) 421240.*

🖪 *Paul St., TA1 3PF ✆ (01823) 336344.*

*London 168 – Bournemouth 69 – Bristol 50 – Exeter 37 – Plymouth 78 – Southampton 93 – Weymouth 50.*

Plan on next page

🏛 **The Castle,** Castle Green, TA1 1NF, ✆ (01823) 272671, Fax (01823) 336066, « Part 12C castle with Norman garden » – 🛗, ⇸ rest, 📺 ☎ 🚗 🅿 – 🔏 100. 🕮 🈺 ⑩ 𝘝𝘐𝘚𝘈 𝘑𝘊𝘉. ⅏
Meals 19.00/20.00 st. ᐧ 12.50 – **44 rm** ⊇ 85.00/210.00 – SB.
V a

🏛 **Forte Posthouse Taunton,** Deane Gate Av., TA1 2UA, East : 2½ m. by A 358 at junction with M 5 ✆ (01823) 332222, Fax (01823) 332266, 🗝 – 🛗, ⇸ rm, 🍽 rest, 📺 ☎ 🅿 – 🔏 300. 🕮 🈺 ⑩ 𝘝𝘐𝘚𝘈
BY h
Meals a la carte 15.35/27.35 t. ᐧ 7.50 – ⊇ 9.95 – **97 rm** 85.00 st. – SB.

🏨 **Holiday Inn Express,** Blackbrook Business Park, TA1 2RW, ✆ (01823) 624000, Fax (01823) 624024, 🌿 – 🛗, ⇸ rm, 🍽 rest, 📺 ☎ 🍴 🅿 – 🔏 30. 🕮 🈺 ⑩ 𝘝𝘐𝘚𝘈 𝘑𝘊𝘉
Meals (grill rest.) a la carte 16.00/22.00 st. – **92 rm** 47.50 st.
BY a

🏨 **Travel Inn,** 81 Bridgwater Rd, TA1 2DU, East : 1¾ m. by A 358 ✆ (01823) 321112, Fax (01823) 322054 – 🛗 rm, 📺 🅿 🅿 🕮 🈺 ⑩ 𝘝𝘐𝘚𝘈. ⅏
BY e
Meals (grill rest.) – **40 rm** 38.00 t.

🏠 **Orchard House** without rest., Fons George, Middleway, TA1 3JS, off Wilton St. ✆ (01823) 351783, Fax (01823) 351785, « Georgian house », 🌿 – ⇸ 📺 🅿. 🕮 𝘝𝘐𝘚𝘈. ⅏
closed New Year – **6 rm** ⊇ 35.00/60.00 s.
AZ d

🏠 **Forde House** without rest., 9 Upper High St., TA1 3PX, ✆ (01823) 279042, Fax (01823) 279042, 🌿 – 📺 🅿. ⅏
closed Christmas and New Year – **5 rm** ⊇ 27.00/50.00.
V b

✗ **Brazz,** Castle Bow, TA1 1NF, ✆ (01823) 252000, Fax (01823) 336066 – 🕮 🈺 ⑩ 𝘝𝘐𝘚𝘈
Meals a la carte 15.40/25.50 st.
V e

**at Henlade** East : 3½ m. on A 358 – BZ – ✉ Taunton.

🏛 **Mount Somerset** ⑂, TA3 5NB, South : ½ m. by Stoke Rd and Ash Cross rd ✆ (01823) 442500, Fax (01823) 442900, ≤, « Regency country house », 🌿 – 🛗 📺 ☎ 🍴 🅿 – 🔏 60. 🕮 🈺 ⑩ 𝘝𝘐𝘚𝘈 𝘑𝘊𝘉. ⅏
Meals 16.95/24.50 st. ᐧ 6.80 – **11 rm** ⊇ 85.00/170.00 st. – SB.

**at Hatch Beauchamp** Southeast : 6 m. by A358 – BZ – ✉ Taunton.

🏛 **Farthings** ⑂, TA3 6SG, ✆ (01823) 480664, Fax (01823) 481118, « Georgian country house », 🌿 – ⇸ 📺 ☎ 🍴 🅿. 🕮 🈺 𝘝𝘐𝘚𝘈 𝘑𝘊𝘉. ⅏
Meals (closed Sunday dinner) (dinner only and Sunday lunch)/dinner 18.95 t. ᐧ 5.95 – **9 rm** ⊇ 60.00/95.00 t. – SB.

🏠 **Frog Street Farm** ⑂, Beercrocombe, TA3 6AF, Southeast : 1¼ m. by Beercrocombe Rd ✆ (01823) 480430, Fax (01823) 480430, « 15C farmhouse, working farm », 🌿 – ⇸ 🅿. ⅏
March-October – Meals (by arrangement) 16.00 st. – **3 rm** ⊇ 30.00/60.00 st. – SB.

**at Rumwell** Southwest : 2½ m. on A 38 – AZ – ✉ Taunton.

🏛 **Rumwell Manor,** TA4 1EL, ✆ (01823) 461902, Fax (01823) 254861, 🌿 – ⇸ rest, 📺 ☎ 🅿 – 🔏 40. 🕮 🈺 𝘝𝘐𝘚𝘈.
Meals (bar lunch Monday to Saturday)/dinner 17.50 t. and dinner a la carte ᐧ 6.50 – **20 rm** ⊇ 59.00/105.00 t. – SB.

**at Bishop's Hull** West : 1¾ m. by A 38 – ✉ Taunton.

🏨 **Meryan House,** Bishop's Hull Rd, TA1 5EG, ✆ (01823) 337445, Fax (01823) 322355, 🌿 – ⇸ 📺 ☎ 🅿. 🕮 𝘝𝘐𝘚𝘈 𝘑𝘊𝘉
AZ c
Meals (closed Sunday) (dinner only) 18.00 st. and a la carte ᐧ 8.00 – **12 rm** ⊇ 49.00/70.00 st. – SB.

**at Stoke St. Gregory** Northeast : 10¼ m. by A 358 - BZ - and A 378 on Stoke St. Gregory rd – ✉ Taunton.

🏠 **Slough Court** ⑂ without rest., Slough Lane, TA3 6JQ, ✆ (01823) 490311, Fax (01823) 490311, « 14C moated manor house, working farm », 🏊, 🌿, ⅏ – ⇸ 📺 🅿. ⅏
April-October – **3 rm** ⊇ 30.00/58.00 st.

# TAUNTON

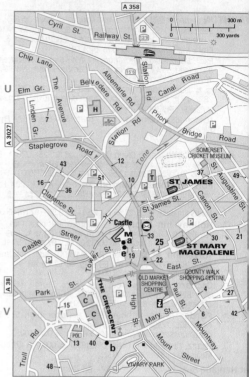

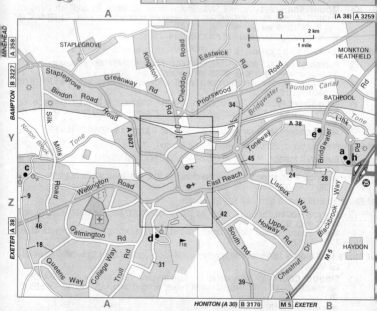

**at West Bagborough** Northwest : 10½ m. by A 358 – AY – ⊠ Taunton.

⌂ **Bashfords Farmhouse** ⊱ without rest., TA4 3EF, *Fax (01823) 432520, « 18C », 🚗 – ⅍⊷ 📺 🅿. ⅍
3 rm ⊑ 22.50/45.00.

⌂ **Tilbury Farm** ⊱, Cothelstone, TA4 3DY, East : ¾ m. *ℰ (01823) 432391, ≤ Vale of Taunton, « 18C », 🚗, park – ⅍⊷ 📺 🅿. ⅍
**Meals** (by arrangement) 17.50 – 3 rm ⊑ 25.00/50.00.

🔘 ATS 138 Bridgwater Rd, Bathpool *ℰ (01823) 412826

---

**TAUNTON DEANE SERVICE AREA** Somerset 🔢 K 31 – ⊠ Taunton.

🏠 **RoadChef Lodge** without rest., TA3 7PF, (southbound carriageway) *ℰ (01823) 332228, *Fax (01823) 338131, Reservations (Freephone) 0800 834719 – ⅍⊷ 📺 ☎ & 🅿. 🆎 🆎 ⓪ 𝘝𝘐𝘚𝘈. ⅍
*closed Christmas and New Year* – 39 rm 45.95 t.

---

**TAVISTOCK** Devon 🔢 H 32 The West Country G. – pop. 10 222.
   Env. : Morwellham★ AC, SW : 4½ m.
   Exc. : E : Dartmoor National Park★★ – Buckland Abbey★★ AC, S : 7 m. by A 386 – Lydford★★, N : 8½ m. by A 386.
   🏌 Down Rd *ℰ (01822) 612049 – 🏌 Hurdwick, Tavistock Hamlets *ℰ (01822) 612746.
   🛈 Town Hall, Bedford Sq., PL19 0AE *ℰ (01882) 612938 (restricted opening in winter).
   London 239 – Exeter 38 – Plymouth 15.

⌂ **Quither Mill** ⊱, PL19 0PZ, Northwest : 5 ¾ m. by Chillaton rd on Quither rd *ℰ (01822) 860160, ≤, « 18C converted water mill », 🚗, park – ⅍⊷ 📺 🅿. 🆎 𝘝𝘐𝘚𝘈
**Meals** (communal dining) 17.50 ‖ 4.50 – 3 rm ⊑ 35.00/70.00, 1 suite.

⌂ **April Cottage** without rest., Mount Tavy Rd, PL19 9JB, *ℰ (01822) 613280 – ⅍⊷ 🅿. ⅍
*closed 1 week Christmas* – 3 rm ⊑ 24.00/36.00.

✕ **Neils,** 27 King St., PL19 0DT, *ℰ (01822) 615550 – ⅍⊷. 🆎 🆎 𝘝𝘐𝘚𝘈
*closed Sunday and Monday* – **Meals** (dinner only) 18.00 t. and a la carte ‖ 6.00.

**at Gulworthy Cross** West : 3 m. on A 390 – ⊠ Tavistock.

✕✕✕ **Horn of Plenty** ⊱ with rm, PL19 8JD, Northwest : 1 m. by Chipshop rd
❁ *ℰ (01822) 832528, Fax (01822) 832528, ≤ Tamar Valley and Bodmin Moor, 🚗 – ⅍⊷ 📺 ☎ ℂ 🅿. 🆎 🆎 𝘝𝘐𝘚𝘈
*closed 25 and 26 December* – **Meals** (closed Monday lunch) 19.50/32.50 st. and a la carte approx. 40.50 t. ‖ 6.00 – ⊑ 7.50 – 6 rm 78.00/110.00 t. – SB
**Spec.** Smoked salmon millefeuille with goat's cheese cream. Grilled loin of lamb with olives, tomato and saffron potatoes. Chocolate and raspberry mousse cake, raspberry sauce.

🔘 ATS 2 Parkwood Rd *ℰ (01822) 612545

---

**TEFFONT** Wilts. – see Salisbury.

---

**TEIGNMOUTH** Devon 🔢 J 32 – pop. 13 403.
   🛈 The Den, Sea Front, TQ14 8BE *ℰ (01626) 779769.
   London 216 – Exeter 16 – Torquay 8.

🏨 **Cliffden,** Dawlish Rd, TQ14 8TE, *ℰ (01626) 770052, Fax (01626) 770594, ≤, Restricted to the blind and their companions, ▨, 🚗 – ᛗ ⅍⊷ 📺 ☎ & 🅿. 🆎 𝘝𝘐𝘚𝘈
*closed 5 January-6 February* – **Meals** (residents only) (dinner only) a la carte 11.25/16.90 st. – 21 rm ⊑ (dinner included) 36.50/82.00 st. – SB.

🏠 **Thomas Luny House** without rest., Teign St., TQ14 8EG, follow signs for the Quays, off the A 381 *ℰ (01626) 772976, « Georgian house built by Thomas Luny », 🚗 – 📺 ☎ 🅿. ⅍
*closed January* – 4 rm ⊑ 35.00/70.00 st.

**at Shaldon** South : 1 m. on B 3199 – ⊠ Teignmouth.

🏠 **Ness House,** Marine Drive, TQ14 0HP, *ℰ (01626) 873480, Fax (01626) 873486, ≤, 🚗 – ⅍⊷ 📺 ☎ 🅿. 🆎 🆎 𝘝𝘐𝘚𝘈 𝘑𝘊𝘉.
*closed 24 and 25 December* – **Meals** (carving lunch Sunday) 17.50 t. and a la carte ‖ 5.95 – 12 rm ⊑ 39.00/95.00 t. – SB.

⌂ **Glenside,** Ringmore Rd, TQ14 0EP, West : ½ m. on B 3195 *ℰ (01626) 872448, 🚗 – 📺 🅿
**Meals** (by arrangement) 15.00 st. ‖ 7.50 – 8 rm ⊑ 24.00/56.00 st. – SB.

**TELFORD** Wrekin 402 403 404 M 25 Great Britain G. – pop. 119 340.

Env.: Ironbridge Gorge Museum★★ AC (The Iron Bridge★★, Coalport China Museum★★, Blists Hill Open Air Museum★★, Museum of the River and Visitor Centre★) S : 5 m. by B 4373.

Exc.: Weston Park★★ AC, E : 7 m. by A 5.

🛐, 🛐 Telford G & C.C. Moat House, Great Hay, Sutton Heights ℰ (01952) 429977 – 🛐 Wrekin, Wellington ℰ (01952) 244032 – 🛐, 🛐, 🛐 The Shropshire, Muxton Grange, Muxton ℰ (01952) 677866.

🖪 The Telford Centre, Management Suite, TF3 4BX ℰ (01952) 291370.

London 152 – Birmingham 33 – Shrewsbury 12 – Stoke-on-Trent 29.

🏛️ **Madeley Court** ⋙, Castlefields Way, Madeley, TF7 5DW, South : 4 ½ m. by A 442 and A 4169 on B 4373 ℰ (01952) 680068, Fax (01952) 684275, « Part 16C manor house », 🐴 – ✤ rest, 📺 ☎ & 🅿 – 🕍 200. 🆗 🖭 ⓪ 🆅🅸🆂🅰 🅹🅲🅱
Meals 11.50/17.50 st. and dinner a la carte ↓ 6.50 – **Priory :** Meals (closed Sunday dinner) (dinner only and Sunday lunch)/dinner 17.50 st. and a la carte ↓ 6.50 – ☑ 9.50 – **47 rm** 95.00/150.00 st. – SB.

🏛️ **Holiday Inn Telford/Ironbridge**, Telford International Centre, St. Quentin Gate, TF3 4EH, Southeast : ½ m. ℰ (01952) 292500, Fax (01952) 291949, 🎏, 🚘, 🖾, 🎾, squash – 🛗, ✤ rm, 🗏 rest, 📺 ☎ & 🅿 – 🕍 250. 🆗 🖭 ⓪ 🆅🅸🆂🅰 🅹🅲🅱
Meals (bar lunch Saturday) 10.95/13.95 st. and a la carte ↓ 8.50 – ☑ 9.95 – **100 rm** 110.00/ 140.00 st. – SB.

🏛️ **Telford Moat House**, Forgegate, Telford Centre, TF3 4NA, ℰ (01952) 429988, Fax (01952) 292012, 🎏, 🚘, 🖾 – 🛗 ✤, 🗏 rest, 📺 ☎ & 🅿 – 🕍 400. 🆗 🖭 ⓪ 🆅🅸🆂🅰
**Casa Med :** Meals (bar lunch Monday to Saturday)/dinner 15.95 t. and a la carte ↓ 5.95 – ☑ 9.50 – **143 rm** 100.00/115.00 t., 4 suites – SB.

🏠 **Travel Inn**, Euston Way, TF3 4LY, North : ½ m. by Cannock rd at jucntion with A 442 ℰ (01952) 201075, Fax (01952) 290742 – 🛗, ✤ rm, 🗏 rest, 📺 ☎ 🅿 – 🕍 30. 🆗 🖭 ⓪ 🆅🅸🆂🅰. ✼
Meals (grill rest.) – **60 rm** 38.00 t.

🏠 **Travelodge**, Shawbirch Crossroads, Shawbirch, TF1 3QA, Northwest : 5 ½ m. by A 442 at junction with B 5063 ℰ (01952) 251244, Fax (01952) 246534, Reservations (Freephone) 0800 850950 – ✤ rm, 📺 & 🅿. 🆗 🖭 ⓪ 🆅🅸🆂🅰 🅹🅲🅱. ✼
Meals (grill rest.) – **40 rm** 39.95/59.95 t.

🏠 **White House**, Wellington Rd, Muxton, TF2 8NG, North : 4 ½ m. by A 442 off A 518 ℰ (01952) 604276, Fax (01952) 670336, 🐴 – 📺 ☎ 🅿. 🆗 🆅🅸🆂🅰
Meals (bar lunch Saturday and Bank Holidays) 8.50/13.50 t. and a la carte ↓ 4.60 – **32 rm** ☑ 57.50/69.50 t. – SB.

**at Norton** South : 7 m. on A 442 – ✉ Shifnal.

🏠 **Hundred House** with rm, Bridgnorth Rd, TF11 9EE, ℰ (01952) 730353, Fax (01952) 730355, « Characterful inn », 🐴 – 📺 ☎ 🅿. 🆗 🖭 🆅🅸🆂🅰 🅹🅲🅱
closed 1 January and 31 December – Meals a la carte 15.80/27.85 t. ↓ 6.50 – **10 rm** ☑ 69.00/109.00 t. – SB.

**at Wellington** West : 6 m. by M 54 on B 5061 – ✉ Telford.

🏠 **Charlton Arms**, Church St., TF1 1DG, ℰ (01952) 251351, Fax (01952) 222077, Reservations (Freephone) 0800 118833 – ✤ 📺 ☎ 🅿 – 🕍 150. 🆗 🖭 ⓪ 🆅🅸🆂🅰. ✼
Meals (grill rest.) 10.95 st. (dinner) and a la carte 13.70/16.65 – ☑ 4.95 – **22 rm** 42.95 st.

🔘 ATS Queen St., Madeley ℰ (01952) 582820 ⏐ ATS Kensington Way, Oakengates ℰ (01952) 613810/612198

---

**TEMPLE SOWERBY** Cumbria 401 402 M 20 – pop. 329 – ✉ Penrith.
London 297 – Carlisle 31 – Kendal 38.

🏛️ **Temple Sowerby House**, CA10 1RZ, ℰ (017683) 61578, Fax (017683) 61958, « Early 18C farmhouse with Georgian additions », 🐴 – ✤ rest, 📺 ☎ 🅿. 🆗 🖭 🆅🅸🆂🅰 🅹🅲🅱
Meals a la carte 23.25/28.45 t. ↓ 6.25 – **12 rm** ☑ 65.00/110.00 t. – SB.

---

**TENBURY WELLS** Worcestershire 403 404 M 27 – pop. 2 219.
London 144 – Birmingham 36 – Hereford 20 – Shrewsbury 37 – Worcester 28.

🏠 **Cadmore Lodge** ⋙, St. Michaels, WR15 8TQ, Southwest : 2 ¾ m. by A 4112 ℰ (01584) 810044, Fax (01584) 810044, ≼, 🖾, 🛐, 🢤, park, 🎾 – ✤ rest, 📺 ☎ 🕈 🅿 – 🕍 100. 🆗 🖭 ⓪ 🆅🅸🆂🅰 🅹🅲🅱. ✼
closed 25 December – Meals 12.00/17.00 t. and a la carte ↓ 4.00 – **14 rm** ☑ 30.00/100.00 t. – SB.

**TENTERDEN** Kent ₄₀₄ W 30 – *pop. 6 803.*

> 🖪 *Town Hall, High St., TN30 6AN ℰ (01580) 763572 (summer only).*
> *London 57 – Folkestone 26 – Hastings 21 – Maidstone 19.*

🏠 **Little Silver Country**, Ashford Rd, St. Michaels, TN30 6SP, North : 2 m. on A 28 ℰ (01233) 850321, Fax (01233) 850647, 🌲 – ⇌ rest, 📺 ☎ ⭐ 🅿 – 🕰 150. 🐵 🖭 JCB. ⅍
> **Meals** (booking essential) (lunch residents only) a la carte 20.25/24.45 t. ₰ 6.00 – **10 rm** ⊇ 60.00/110.00 t. – SB.

🏠 **Collina House**, 5 East Hill, TN30 6RL, ℰ (01580) 764852, Fax (01580) 762224 – ⇌ rm, 📺 ☎ 🅿. 🐵 🖭 ⓪ *VISA*. ⅍
> *closed 23 December-15 January* – **Meals** (dinner only) 15.50 **st.** and a la carte ₰ 5.00 – **14 rm** ⊇ 40.00/65.00 **st.** – SB.

↥ **Brattle House**, Watermill Bridges, TN30 6UL, West : 1 m. by A 28 on Cranbrook Rd ℰ (01580) 763565, ≤, 🌲 – ⇌ 🅿. ⅍
> *closed Christmas and New Year* – **Meals** (by arrangement) (communal dining) 20.00 **s.** – **3 rm** ⊇ 45.00/70.00 **s.**

---

**TETBURY** Glos. ₄₀₃ ₄₀₄ N 29 *Great Britain G. – pop. 4 618.*

> Env. : *Westonbirt Arboretum★ AC, SW : 2½ m. by A 433.*
> 🏌 *Westonbirt ℰ (01666) 880242.*
> 🖪 *The Old Court House, 63 Long St., GL8 8AA ℰ (01666) 503552 (summer only).*
> *London 113 – Bristol 27 – Gloucester 19 – Swindon 24.*

🏨 **The Close**, 8 Long St., GL8 8AQ, ℰ (01666) 502272, Fax (01666) 504401, « 16C town house with walled garden » – ⇌ rest, 📺 ☎ 🅿 – 🕰 30. 🐵 🖭 *VISA*. ⅍
> **Meals** 18.50/29.50 **t.** and a la carte – **15 rm** ⊇ 100.00/180.00 **t.** – SB.

🏠 **Snooty Fox**, Market Pl., GL8 8DD, ℰ (01666) 502436, Fax (01666) 503479 – ⇌ rest, 📺 ☎. 🐵 🖭 ⓪ *VISA* JCB. ⅍
> **Meals** (bar lunch)/dinner a la carte 14.95/24.95 **t.** ₰ 6.50 – **12 rm** ⊇ 65.00/90.00 **t.**

**at Willesley** Southwest : 4 m. on A 433 – ⊠ Tetbury.

↥ **Tavern House** without rest., GL8 8QU, ℰ (01666) 880444, Fax (01666) 880254, « Part 17C former inn and staging post », 🌲 – ⇌ 📺 ☎ 🅿. 🐵 *VISA*. ⅍
> **4 rm** ⊇ 45.00/65.00.

**at Calcot** West : 3½ m. on A 4135 – ⊠ Tetbury.

🏨 **Calcot Manor** ⑤, GL8 8YJ, ℰ (01666) 890391, Fax (01666) 890394, 🏡, « Converted Cotswold farm buildings », ⌇, 🌲, ℀ – ⇌ rest, 📺 ☎ ⭐ 🅿 – 🕰 65. 🐵 🖭 ⓪ *VISA*. ⅍
> *Conservatory :* **Meals** a la carte 21.00/35.00 **st.** ₰ 6.00 – (see also *The Gumstool Inn* below) – **23 rm** ⊇ 95.00/110.00 **st.**, 4 suites – SB.

🍴 **The Gumstool Inn** (at Calcot Manor H.), GL8 8YJ, ℰ (01666) 890391, Fax (01666) 890394, 🏡, 🌲 – 🅿. 🐵 🖭 ⓪ *VISA*
> **Meals** (booking essential) a la carte 13.45/21.20 **st.** ₰ 4.50.

---

**TEWKESBURY** Glos. ₄₀₃ ₄₀₄ N 28 *Great Britain G. – pop. 9 488.*

> See : *Town★ – Abbey★★ (Nave★★, vault★).*
> Env. : *St. Mary's, Deerhurst★, SW : 4 m. by A 38 and B 4213.*
> 🏌 *Tewkesbury Park Hotel, Lincoln Green Lane ℰ (01684) 295405.*
> 🖪 *64 Barton St., GL20 5PX ℰ (01684) 295027.*
> *London 108 – Birmingham 39 – Gloucester 11.*

🏨 **Tewkesbury Park H. & Country Club**, Lincoln Green Lane, GL20 7DN, South : 1 ¼ m. by A 38 ℰ (01684) 295405, Fax (01684) 292386, ≤, 🏋, ≘s, ⌇, 🏌, park, ℀, squash – ⇌ 📺 ☎ 🅿 – 🕰 150. 🐵 🖭 ⓪ *VISA*. ⅍
> **Meals** *(closed lunch Sunday and Bank Holidays)* 12.50/18.75 **t.** and a la carte ₰ 7.25 – ⊇ 9.50 – **78 rm** 90.00/105.00 **t.** – SB.

🏨 **Bell**, Church St., GL20 5SA, ℰ (01684) 293293, Fax (01684) 295938 – ⇌ rest, 📺 ☎ 🅿 – 🕰 40. 🐵 🖭 *VISA*
> **Meals** (bar lunch)/dinner 18.95 **t.** and a la carte ₰ 5.95 – **24 rm** ⊇ 60.00/105.00 **t.** – SB.

🏠 **Jessop House**, 65 Church St., GL20 5RZ, ℰ (01684) 292017, Fax (01684) 273076 – 📺 ☎ 🅿. 🐵 🖭 *VISA*. ⅍
> *closed 24 December-2 January* – **Meals** *(closed Sunday)* (bar lunch)/dinner 19.95 **st.** ₰ 5.95 – **8 rm** ⊇ 57.50/78.00 **st.** – SB.

🍴 **Bistrot André**, 78 Church St., GL20 5RX, ℰ (01684) 290357 – 🐵 *VISA*
> *closed Sunday, Monday, 1 week September and February* – **Meals** - French - (dinner only) a la carte 15.65/23.95 ₰ 7.50.

**at Puckrup** *North : 2½ m. on A 38 –* ⊠ *Tewkesbury.*

🏨 **Stakis Puckrup Hall,** GL20 6EL, ℘ (01684) 296200, Fax (01684) 850788, ᠘ᠪ, ⇔, 🔲, ᠓ᠪ
�, park – ᠄᠄, ᠄᠄ rm, 🔲 ☎ 🄿 – 🄰 200. 🕮
Meals *(closed Saturday lunch)* 12.50/18.50 **t.** and a la carte – � 9.50 – **82 rm** 125.00
155.00 **st.**, 2 suites.

**at Kemerton** *Northeast : 5¼ m. by A 46 –* ⊠ *Tewkesbury.*

🏠 **Upper Court** ⌂, GL20 7HY, take right turn at stone cross in village ℘ (01386) 725351
Fax (01386) 725472, ≼, « Georgian manor house, antique furnishings, gardens », ⌇, park
⌘ – 🔲 🄿. 🚾
closed 24 to 26 December – **Meals** (by arrangement) 30.00 **st.** ᠗ 4.50 – **5 rm** ⊻ 65.00
110.00 **st.**

**at Corse Lawn** *Southwest : 6 m. by A 38 and A 438 on B 4211 –* ⊠ *Gloucester.*

🏨 **Corse Lawn House** ⌂, GL19 4LZ, ℘ (01452) 780771, Fax (01452) 780840, « Queen
Anne house », 🔲, ⌘, ⌘ – 🔲 🄿 – 🄰 40. 🕮
closed 25 and 26 December – **Bistro : Meals** a la carte 16.85/22.85 **st.** ᠗ 5.00 – (see also **The
Restaurant** below) – **17 rm** ⊻ 70.00/100.00 **st.**, 2 suites – SB.

🍴 **The Restaurant** (at Corse Lawn House H.), GL19 4LZ, ℘ (01452) 780771
Fax (01452) 780840, ⌘ – 🄿. 🕮
Meals 16.95/25.00 **st.** and a la carte 27.40/32.40 ᠗ 5.00.

🅰 ATS Oldbury Rd ℘ (01684) 292461

*Le Guide change, changez de* **guide Michelin** *tous les ans.*

---

**THAME** *Oxon.* 🄐🄐🄐 *R 28 The West Country G. – pop. 10 806.*
Exc. : *Ridgeway Path★★.*
🄱 *Market House, North St., OX9 3HH ℘ (01844) 212834.*
*London 48 – Aylesbury 9 – Oxford 13.*

🏨 **Spread Eagle,** 16 Cornmarket, OX9 2BW, ℘ (01844) 213661, Fax (01844) 261380 – 🔲 ☎
🄿 – 🄰 250. 🕮 🄰🄴 🕮 🚾 🄹🄲🄱. 🌣
closed 28 to 30 December – **Meals** *(closed lunch Bank Holiday Monday)* 17.95/21.95 **st.**
and a la carte ᠗ 5.60 – ⊻ 8.95 – **31 rm** 90.25/122.80 **st.**, 2 suites – SB.

🏠 **Travelodge,** OX9 3XA, Northwest : 1 m. by B 4445 on B 4011 at junction with A 418
℘ (01844) 218740, Fax (01844) 218740, Reservations (Freephone) 0800 850950 – ᠄᠄ rm
☰ rest, 🔲 ᠘ 🄿. 🕮 🄰🄴 🕮 🚾 🌣
Meals (grill rest.) – **31 rm** 39.95/59.95 **t.**

🍴 **The Old Trout,** 29-30 Lower High St., OX9 2AA, ℘ (01844) 212146, Fax (01844) 212614
« 15C thatched inn » – 🄿. 🕮 🚾
closed Sunday, 2 weeks August and 2 weeks December – **Meals** 9.75 **st.**
(lunch) and a la carte 17.50/26.25 **st.** ᠗ 6.50.

**at Towersey** *East : 2 m. by A 4129 –* ⊠ *Thame.*

🏠 **Upper Green Farm** ⌂ without rest., Manor Rd, OX9 3QR, ℘ (01844) 212496
Fax (01844) 260399, « Part 15C and 16C thatched farmhouse, 18C barn », ⌘ – ᠄᠄ 🔲 ᠘
🄿. 🌣
closed Christmas-New Year – **10 rm** ⊻ 40.00/60.00 **st.**

---

**THANET WAY SERVICE AREA** *Kent* 🄐🄐 *W 30 – see Whitstable.*

---

**THATCHAM** *Newbury* 🄐🄐🄐 🄐🄐🄐 *Q 29 – pop. 20 726 –* ⊠ *Newbury.*
*London 69 – Bristol 68 – Oxford 30 – Reading 15 – Southampton 40.*

🏨 **Regency Park,** Bowling Green Rd, RG18 3RP, Northwest : 1 ¾ m. by A 4 and Northfield
Rd ℘ (01635) 871555, Fax (01635) 871571, ⌘, ⌘ – ᠄᠄ ᠄᠄, ☰ rest, 🔲 ☎ ᠘ 🄿 – 🄰 110
🕮 🄰🄴 🕮 🚾 🄹🄲🄱. 🌣
Meals *(closed Saturday lunch)* 16.95/24.50 **st.** and a la carte ᠗ 6.95 – ⊻ 10.50 – **45 rm**
110.00/160.00 **st.** – SB.

🏠 **Berkshire Arms - Premier Lodge,** Bath Rd, Midgham, RG7 5UX, East : 2 m. on A 4
℘ (0181) 971 4114, Fax (0181) 971 2077, Reservations (Freephone) 0800 118833 – ᠄᠄ rm
🔲 ᠘ 🄿. 🕮 🄰🄴 🕮 🚾
Meals (grill rest.) a la carte 9.55/14.65 **t.** – ⊻ 5.95 – **29 rm** 44.95 **t.** – SB.

🅰 ATS 29 High St. ℘ (01635) 865551

**THAXTED** Essex 🄴🄰🄴 V 28 – pop. 1 899.
London 44 – Cambridge 24 – Colchester 31 – Chelmsford 20.

🏠 **Four Seasons**, Walden Rd, CM6 2RE, Northwest : ½ m. on B 184 ℘ (01371) 830129, Fax (01371) 830835 – ⇄ 📺 ☎ 📵. ✇ 🅰🄴 VISA JCB. ⬦
Meals (closed Sunday dinner and Bank Holidays) a la carte 13.20/24.25 t. ⬦ 8.00 – ⊏ 8.50 – 9 rm 55.00/65.00 t. – SB.

🏠 **Crossways** without rest., 32 Town St., CM6 2LA, ℘ (01371) 830348, 🌿 – ⇄ 📺
restricted opening in winter – 3 rm ⊏ 35.00/50.00 t.

**THEBERTON** Suffolk – pop. 334.
London 109 – Cambridge 75 – Ipswich 30 – Norwich 36.

🏠 **Theberton Grange Country House** ⬦, Theberton, IP16 4RR, Southwest : ½ m. off B 1122 ℘ (01728) 830625, Fax (01728) 830625, 🌿 – ⇄ 📺 📵. ✇✇ VISA. ⬦
closed 1 week Christmas – Meals (closed Sunday) (residents only) (dinner only) 19.50 st. ⬦ 6.50 – 6 rm ⊏ 50.00/80.00 st.

**THIRSK** N. Yorks. 🄸🄾🄸 P 21 – pop. 6 860.
🏌 Thornton-Le-Street ℘ (01845) 522170.
🛈 14 Kirkgate, YO7 1PQ ℘ (01845) 522755 (summer only).
London 227 – Leeds 37 – Middlesbrough 24 – York 24.

🏠🏠 **Golden Fleece**, 42 Market Pl., YO7 1LL, ℘ (01845) 523108, Fax (01845) 523996 – ⇄ rest, 📺 ☎ 📵 – ⚖ 80. ✇✇ 🅾🄳
closed 31 December Meals (closed Saturday lunch) 7.50/17.50 t. and dinner a la carte ⬦ 6.95 – 18 rm ⊏ 60.00/80.00 t. – SB.

🏠 **Sheppard's**, Front St., Sowerby, YO7 1JF, South : ½ m. ℘ (01845) 523655, Fax (01845) 524720 – ⇄ rm, 📺 ☎ 📵. ✇✇ VISA. ⬦
closed first week January – Restaurant : Meals (dinner only) a la carte 16.15/25.15 st. ⬦ 5.50 – Bistro : Meals a la carte 14.70/25.15 st. ⬦ 5.50 – 8 rm ⊏ 62.00/84.00 st.

🏠 **Spital Hill**, York Rd, YO7 3AE, Southeast : 1 ¾ m. on A 19, entrance between 2 white posts ℘ (01845) 522273, Fax (01845) 542970, 🌿, park – ⇄ ☎ 📵. ✇✇ 🅰🄴 VISA. ⬦
Meals (by arrangement) (communal dining) 22.50 t. ⬦ 3.60 – 3 rm ⊏ 44.75/69.50 t.

🏠 **Thornborough House Farm**, YO7 2NP, North : 1 ¾ m. following signs for A 19 Teesside, entrance off A 19 Teesside sliproad ℘ (01845) 522103, Fax (01845) 522103, « Working farm », 🌿 – ⇄ 📺 📵. ✇✇ VISA. ⬦
Meals (by arrangement) (communal dining) 10.00 s. – 3 rm ⊏ 16.00/36.00 s.

**at Topcliffe** Southwest : 4½ m. by A 168 – ✉ Thirsk.

🏠 **Angel Inn**, Long St., YO7 3RW, ℘ (01845) 577237, Fax (01845) 578000, 🌿 – 📺 ☎ 📵 – ⚖ 150. ✇✇ VISA. ⬦
Meals a la carte 14.75/21.25 t. – 14 rm ⊏ 42.50/59.50 st.

**at Asenby** Southwest : 5¼ m. by A 168 – ✉ Thirsk.

🍴🍴 **Crab and Lobster**, Dishforth Rd, YO7 3QL, ℘ (01845) 577286, Fax (01845) 577109, « Thatched inn, memorabilia », 🌿 – ⇄ 📵. ✇✇ 🅰🄴 VISA
The Restaurant : Meals – Seafood - (booking essential) 14.50/21.50 st. and a la carte – 8 rm ⊏ 55.00/90.00 st. – SB.

🍴 **Crab and Lobster**, Dishforth Rd, YO7 3QL, ℘ (01845) 577286, Fax (01845) 577109, 🍴, « Thatched inn, memorabilia », 🌿 – 📵. ✇✇ 🅰🄴 VISA
The Brasserie : Meals – Seafood - (bookings not accepted) 14.50/21.50 st. and a la carte ⬦ 4.50.

🔘 ATS Long St. ℘ (01845) 522982/522923

**THORALBY** N. Yorks. 🄸🄾🄸 N/O 21 – pop. 160 – ✉ Leyburn.
London 245 – Kendal 41 – Leeds 64 – York 57.

🏠 **Littleburn** ⬦, DL8 3BE, West : ½ m. by unmarked lane taking left fork after ¼ m. ℘ (01969) 663621, <, « 17C country house », 🌿 – ⇄ 📵. ⬦
Meals (by arrangement) (communal dining) 20.00 st. – 3 rm ⊏ 42.00/64.00 s.

🏠 **Low Green House** ⬦, DL8 3SZ, Southeast : ¼ m. on unmarked lane ℘ (01969) 663623, <, 🌿 – ⇄ 📺 📵
restricted opening in winter – Meals (by arrangement) 14.00 s. – 3 rm ⊏ 30.00/48.00 s. – SB.

🏠 **High Green House**, DL8 3SU, ℘ (01969) 663420, Fax (01969) 663420, <, 🌿 – ⇄ 📺 ⬥ 📵. ✇✇ VISA
April-October – Meals (by arrangement) 16.00 s. ⬦ 3.00 – 3 rm ⊏ 38.00/56.00 s. – SB.

**THORNABY-ON-TEES** *Stockton-on-Tees* [402] Q 20 – *pop. 12 108* – ✉ *Middlesbrough.*
*London 250 – Leeds 62 – Middlesbrough 3 – York 49.*

**Forte Posthouse Teesside,** Low Lane, Stainton Village, TS17 9LW, Southeast : 3 ½ m by A 1045 on A 1044 ✆ (01642) 591213, *Fax (01642) 594989,* 🌳 – ⊬ rm, [TV] ☎ [P] – 🎤 120. [MC] [AE] [D] [VISA]
Meals a la carte 15.35/24.85 **st.** 🍷 7.50 – ☕ 8.95 – **136 rm** 69.00 **st.** – SB.

**Travel Inn,** White Water Way, TS17 6QB, Northeast : 1 ½ m. by A 66 following signs to Teeside Park ✆ (01642) 671573, *Fax (01642) 671464* – ⊬ rm, ▤ rest, [TV] ♿ [P]. [MC] [AE] [D] [VISA]. ✗
Meals (grill rest.) – **40 rm** 38.00 **t.**

**THORNBURY** *South Gloucestershire* [403] [404] M 29 – *pop. 12 108* – ✉ *Bristol.*
*London 128 – Bristol 12 – Gloucester 23 – Swindon 43.*

**Thornbury Castle** ⛰, Castle St., BS35 1HH, ✆ (01454) 281182, *Fax (01454) 416188,* « 16C castle, antiques, gardens and vineyard », park – ⊬ rest, [TV] ☎ [P]. [MC] [AE] [D] [VISA]. ✗
*closed 4 days January* – **Meals** 19.50/39.50 **t.** – ☕ 8.95 – **18 rm** 85.00/335.00 **t.**, 2 suites – SB.

*Per spostarvi più rapidamente utilizzate le carte Michelin "Grandi Strade":*
*n°* [970] Europa, *n°* [976] Rep. Ceca/Slovacchia, *n°* [980] Grecia,
*n°* [984] Germania, *n°* [985] Scandinavia-Finlandia,
*n°* [986] Gran Bretagna-Irlanda, *n°* [987] Germania-Austria-Benelux,
*n°* [988] Italia, *n°* [989] Francia, *n°* [990] Spagna-Portogallo.

**THORNTHWAITE** *Cumbria* [402] K 20 – *see Keswick.*

**THORNTON CLEVELEYS** *Lancs.* [402] L 22 – *pop. 28 061.*
*London 244 – Blackpool 6 – Lancaster 20 – Manchester 44.*

**Didier's,** Victorian House, Trunnah Rd, Thornton, FY5 4HF, ✆ (01253) 860619, *Fax (01253) 865350,* ☂, 🌳 – [P]. [MC] [AE] [VISA] [JCB]
*closed 1 January, 26 December and 1 week February* – **Meals** (bookings not accepted) 8.50 **st.** (lunch) and a la carte 12.70/19.10 **st.**

**THORNTON HOUGH** *Mersey.* [402] [403] K 24 – ✉ *Wirral.*
*London 215 – Birkenhead 12 – Chester 17 – Liverpool 14.*

**Thornton Hall,** L63 1JF, on B 5136 ✆ (0151) 336 3938, *Fax (0151) 336 7864,* [Ls], ≘s, 🏊, 🌳 – [TV] ☎ [P] – 🎤 250. [MC] [AE] [D] [VISA] [JCB]
*closed 24 and 25 December* – ***The Italian Room :*** **Meals** (bar lunch Saturday) 10.95/22.00 **st.** and dinner a la carte 🍷 7.75 – ☕ 7.95 – **62 rm** 75.00/85.00 **t.**, 1 suite – SB.

**THORPE** *Derbs.* [402] [403] [404] O 24 *Great Britain G.* – *pop. 201* – ✉ *Ashbourne.*
See : *Dovedale★★ (Ilam Rock★).*
*London 151 – Derby 16 – Sheffield 33 – Stoke-on-Trent 26.*

**Peveril of the Peak** ⛰, DE6 2AW, ✆ (01335) 350333, *Fax (01335) 350507,* ≤, 🌳, 🎾 – ⊬ [TV] ☎ [P] – 🎤 50. [MC] [AE] [D] [VISA] [JCB]
Meals 11.95/21.95 **st.** 🍷 9.50 – ☕ 9.75 – **46 rm** 80.00/120.00 **st.** – SB.

**THORPE MARKET** *Norfolk* [404] X 25 – *pop. 303* – ✉ *North Walsham.*
*London 130 – Norwich 21.*

**Elderton Lodge** ⛰, Gunton Park, NR11 8TZ, South : 1 m. on A 149 ✆ (01263) 833547, *Fax (01263) 834673,* ≤, 🌳 – ⊬ [TV] ☎ [P]. [MC] [D] [VISA]
*closed 28 December-10 January* – **Meals** a la carte 15.40/21.50 **st.** 🍷 6.25 – **11 rm** ☕ 55.00/95.00 **st.** – SB.

**Green Farm,** North Walsham Rd, NR11 8TH, ✆ (01263) 833602, *Fax (01263) 833163* – ⊬ [TV] ☎ [P]. [MC] [AE] [D] [VISA] [JCB]
Meals (bar lunch)/dinner 18.95 **st.** and a la carte 🍷 5.25 – **12 rm** ☕ 48.00/90.00 **st.** – SB.

**'HRAPSTON SERVICE AREA** Northants. **404** S 26 – ✉ Kettering.

🏠 **Travelodge**, NN14 4UR, at junction of A 14 with A 605 and A 45 ℰ (01832) 735199, Fax (01832) 735199, Reservations (Freephone) 0800 850950 – ⇔ rm, 🗺 ♿ 🅿. 🕔 🕮 ⓪ 𝗩𝗜𝗦𝗔 𝗝𝗖𝗕. ✇
Meals (grill rest.) – **40 rm** 39.95/59.95 **t.**

---

**'HREE BRIDGES** W. Sussex – see Crawley.

---

**'HRELKELD** Cumbria **402** K 20 – see Keswick.

---

**'HRUSSINGTON** Leics. **402 403 404** Q 25 – pop. 512 – ✉ Leicester.
London 101 – Leicester 10 – Nottingham 22 – Lincoln 34.

🏠 **Travelodge**, Green Acres Filling Station, LE7 8TF, on A 46 (southbound carriageway) ℰ (01664) 424525, Fax (01664) 424525, Reservations (Freephone) 0800 850950 – ⇔ rm, 🍽 rest, 🗺 ♿ 🅿. 🕔 🕮 ⓪ 𝗩𝗜𝗦𝗔 𝗝𝗖𝗕. ✇
Meals (grill rest.) – **32 rm** 39.95/59.95 **t.**

---

**'HURLESTONE** Devon **403** I 33 – see Kingsbridge.

---

**'HURROCK SERVICE AREA** Thurrock **404** V 29 – ✉ West Thurrock.
⛳ Belhus Park, South Ockendon ℰ (01708) 854260.
🔼 Granada Motorway Service Area (M 25), RM16 3BG ℰ (01708) 863733.

🏠 **Travelodge**, RM16 3BG, ℰ (01708) 891111, Fax (01708) 860971, Reservations (Freephone) 0800 850950 – ⛛ ⇔ 🗺 ☎ ♿ 🅿. 🕔 🕮 ⓪ 𝗩𝗜𝗦𝗔 𝗝𝗖𝗕. ✇
Meals (grill rest.) – **44 rm** 39.95/59.95 **t.**

🔧 ATS Units 13/14, Eastern Av., Waterglade Ind. Park, West Thurrock, Grays ℰ (01708) 862237

---

**'ICEHURST** E. Sussex **404** V 30 – pop. 3 118 – ✉ Wadhurst.
⛳ Dale Hill Hotel, Ticehurst ℰ (01580) 200112.
London 49 – Brighton 44 – Folkestone 38 – Hastings 15 – Maidstone 24.

🏠🍽 **Dale Hill**, TN5 7DQ, Northeast : ½ m. on A 268 ℰ (01580) 200112, Fax (01580) 201249, ✺, ⇔s, ▨, ⛳, park – ⛛ 🗺 ☎ 🅿 – 🔬 30. 🕔 🕮 𝗩𝗜𝗦𝗔
Meals (dinner only and Sunday lunch)/dinner 17.95 **st.** ♦ 12.95 – **31 rm** ⌧ 64.00/148.00 **t.**, 1 suite – SB.

---

**'ICKTON** East Riding – see Beverley.

---

**'ILTON ON THE HILL** Leics. **402 404** R 26.
London 113 – Leicester 13 – Northampton 35 – Nottingham 30.

🍽 **Rose and Crown**, Main St., LE7 9LF, ℰ (0116) 259 7234, Fax (0116) 259 7234 – 🅿. 🕔 𝗩𝗜𝗦𝗔
closed Sunday dinner – Meals a la carte 12.50/30.00 **t.**

---

**'INTAGEL** Cornwall **403** F 32 The West Country G. – pop. 1 721.
See : Arthur's Castle (site★★★) AC – Church★ – Old Post Office★ AC.
Env. : Boscastle★ , E : off B 3263 – W : Hell's Mouth★.
Exc. : Camelford★, SE : 6½ m. by B 3263 and B 3266.
London 264 – Exeter 63 – Plymouth 49 – Truro 41.

🏠 **Trebrea Lodge** ≫, Trenale, PL34 0HR, Southeast : 1 ¼ m. by Boscastle Rd (B 3263) and Trenale Lane on Trewarmett rd ℰ (01840) 770410, Fax (01840) 770092, ≤, « Part 18C manor house, 14C origins », ☞ – ⇔ 🗺 ♿ 🅿. 🕔 🕮 𝗩𝗜𝗦𝗔
closed 1 January-12 February – Meals (booking essential to non-residents) (dinner only) 22.00 **t.** ♦ 6.00 – **7 rm** ⌧ 57.50/90.00 **t.** – SB.

🏠 **Wootons Country H.**, Fore St., PL34 0DD, ℰ (01840) 770170, Fax (01840) 770978 – 🗺 ☎ 🅿. 🕔 🕮 ⓪ 𝗩𝗜𝗦𝗔 𝗝𝗖𝗕. ✇
Meals (bar lunch)/dinner 9.00 **st.** and a la carte ♦ 3.95 – **11 rm** ⌧ 35.00/70.00 **st.**

🏡 **Polkerr**, Molesworth St., PL34 0BY, ℰ (01840) 770382, ☞ – 🗺 🅿. ✇
closed 25 December – Meals (by arrangement) 10.00 – **7 rm** ⌧ 22.00/50.00 **s.**

⌂ **Old Borough House,** Bossiney Rd, PL34 0AY, Northeast : ½ m. on B 326
*℘* (01840) 770475 – 𝕏 rest, **Ⓟ**. 𝕏
**Meals** (by arrangement) 12.50 **st.** – **6 rm** � 27.00/44.00 **s.**

⌂ **Old Millfloor** 𝒮, Trebarwith, PL34 0HB, South : 1 ¾ m. by B 3263 *℘* (01840) 77023
« Former flour mill », 🌲, park – 𝕏 **Ⓣ Ⓥ Ⓟ**. 𝕏
*Easter-November* – **Meals** (by arrangement) 12.50 – **3 rm** ⊆ 20.00/40.00 – SB.

---

**TITCHWELL** Norfolk 𝟰𝟬𝟰 V 25 – pop. 99 – ⊠ Brancaster.
London 130 – Cambridge 82 – Norwich 48.

🏨 **Titchwell Manor,** PE31 8BB, *℘* (01485) 210221, Fax (01485) 210104, 🌲 – **Ⓣ Ⓥ ☎ Ⓟ**. **◎**
**Æ ① VISA JCB**
*closed 17 January-1 February* – **Meals** (bar lunch)/dinner 24.00 **t.** ♭ 6.50 – **16 rm** ⊆ 55.00
110.00 **t.** – SB.

---

**TITLEY** Herefordshire 𝟰𝟬𝟯 L 27 – see Kington.

---

**TODDINGTON SERVICE AREA** Beds. 𝟰𝟬𝟰 S 28 – pop. 4 500 – ⊠ Luton.

🏨 **Travelodge,** LU5 6HR, M 1 (southbound carriageway) *℘* (01525) 878424
Fax (01525) 878452, Reservations (Freephone) 0800 850950 – 𝕏 **Ⓣ Ⓥ ☎ & Ⓟ**. **◎ Æ ① VIS**
**JCB**. 𝕏
**Meals** (grill rest.) – **43 rm** 39.95/59.95 **t.**

---

**TODWICK** S. Yorks. 𝟰𝟬𝟮 𝟰𝟬𝟯 𝟰𝟬𝟰 Q 23 – pop. 1 639 – ⊠ Sheffield.
London 165 – Derby 39 – Lincoln 37 – Nottingham 37 – Sheffield 12.

🏨 **The Red Lion Inn,** Worksop Rd, S26 1DJ, (on A 57) *℘* (01909) 771654
Fax (01909) 773704, 🌲 – 𝕏 rm, ▤ rest, **Ⓣ Ⓥ ☎ Ⓟ** – 🖕 100. **◎ VISA**. 𝕏
**Meals** (grill rest.) a la carte 11.95/15.40 **t.** ♭ 7.95 – **29 rm** ⊆ 46.00/56.00 **t.**

---

**TOFT** Lincs. – see Bourne.

---

**TOLLESHUNT KNIGHTS** Essex – see Maldon.

---

**TONBRIDGE** Kent 𝟰𝟬𝟰 U 30 – pop. 34 260.
🅱, 🅱 Poult Wood, Higham Lane *℘* (01732) 364039.
🅱 Tonbridge Castle, Castle St., TN9 1BG *℘* (01732) 770929.
London 33 – Brighton 37 – Hastings 31 – Maidstone 14.

🏨 **Langley,** 18-20 London Rd, TN10 3DA, North : on B 245 *℘* (01732) 353311
Fax (01732) 771471, 🌲 – |≡|, ▤ rest, **Ⓣ Ⓥ ☎ Ⓟ**. **◎ Æ ① VISA**. 𝕏
**Meals** (bar lunch Monday to Friday)/dinner 18.00 **t.** and a la carte ♭ 5.00 – **34 rm** ⊆ 65.00/
110.00 **st.** – SB.

⌂ **Starvecrow Place** without rest., Starvecrow Hill, Shipbourne Rd, TN11 9NL, North : 2 m
on A 227 *℘* (01732) 356863, 🔊, 🌲 – 𝕏 **Ⓣ Ⓥ Ⓟ**. 𝕏
*closed Christmas and New Year* – **3 rm** ⊆ 30.00/44.00 **s.**

🔘 ATS Unit 4, Sovereign Way *℘* (01732) 353800/352231

---

**TOPCLIFFE** N. Yorks. 𝟰𝟬𝟮 P 21 – see Thirsk.

---

**TORQUAY** Torbay 𝟰𝟬𝟯 J 32 The West Country G. – pop. 59 587.
See : Torbay★ – Kent's Cavern★ **AC** CX A.
Env. : Paignton Zoo★★ **AC**, SE : 3 m. by A 3022 – Cockington★, W : 1 m. AX.
🅱 Petitor Rd, St. Marychurch *℘* (01803) 327471, B.
🅱 Vaughan Parade, TQ2 5JG *℘* (01803) 297428.
London 223 – Exeter 23 – Plymouth 32.

Plans on following pages

🏨 **Imperial,** Parkhill Rd, TQ1 2DG, *℘* (01803) 294301, Fax (01803) 298293, ⩽ Torbay, ♭ͦ, ⩬
🔊, 🔲, 🌲, 𝕏, squash – |≡|, 𝕏 rm, ▤ rest, **Ⓣ Ⓥ ☎ & ⬅ Ⓟ** – 🖕 350. **◎ Æ ① VISA JCB**
𝕏
CZ a
*Regatta :* **Meals** (dinner only) 25.00 **t.** and a la carte ♭ 11.00 – *Sundeck Brasserie :* **Meals**
a la carte 16.25/31.00 **t.** ♭ 9.50 – ⊆ 13.50 – **138 rm** 85.00/168.00 **st.**, 17 suites – SB.

**Palace**, Babbacombe Rd, TQ1 3TG, ℰ (01803) 200200, *Fax (01803) 299899*, ≤, « Extensive gardens », ≦s, ⬓, ▤, ⅓, park, ﹪indoor/outdoor, squash – ⦚, ﹪rm, �📺 ☎ ⇐ ⦿ – CX u
🛦 350. ◎ 쪼 ⓪ 𝘝𝘐𝘚𝘈. ﹪
**Meals** 15.00/23.00 t. and a la carte ₰ 6.25 – **135 rm** ⊃ 67.00/154.00 s., 6 suites – SB.

**Grand**, Sea Front, TQ2 6NT, ℰ (01803) 296677, *Fax (01803) 213462*, ≤, 𝕝δ, ≦s, ⬓, ▤, ﹪ – ⦚, ﹪rest, ⏶ ☎ ⇐ – 🛦 300. ◎ 쪼 ⓪ 𝘝𝘐𝘚𝘈 𝘑𝘊𝘉
BZ z
**Meals** 15.50/23.50 st. and dinner a la carte ₰ 6.50 – **100 rm** ⊃ 67.00/116.00 st., 11 suites – SB.

**Osborne**, Hesketh Cres., Meadfoot, TQ1 2LL, ℰ (01803) 213311, *Fax (01803) 296788*, ≤, « Regency town houses », 𝕝δ, ≦s, ⬓, ▤, ﹐, ﹪ – ⦚, ﹪rest, ⏶ ☎ ⦿ – 🛦 80. ◎ 쪼
𝘝𝘐𝘚𝘈. ﹪ CX n
**Langtry's :** **Meals** (dinner only) 17.95 st. and a la carte ₰ 6.95 – **The Brasserie :** **Meals** a la carte 13.45/20.00 st. ₰ 6.95 – **29 rm** ⊃ (dinner included) 78.00/186.00 st. – SB.

**Livermead House**, Seafront, TQ2 6QJ, ℰ (01803) 294361, *Fax (01803) 200758*, ≤, ≦s, ⬓, ﹐, squash – ⦚, ﹪rest, ⏶ ☎ ⦿ – 🛦 350. ◎ 쪼 ⓪ 𝘝𝘐𝘚𝘈. ﹪ BZ e
**Meals** (bar lunch Monday to Saturday)/dinner 19.75 t. and a la carte ₰ 4.75 – **65 rm** ⊃ 41.00/150.00 t. – SB.

**Livermead Cliff**, Seafront, TQ2 6RQ, ℰ (01803) 299666, *Fax (01803) 294496*, ≤, ⬓, ﹐ – ⦚ ⏶ ☎ ⦇ ⦿ – 🛦 70. ◎ 쪼 ⓪ 𝘝𝘐𝘚𝘈 𝘑𝘊𝘉. ﹪ BX r
**Meals** 9.75/17.75 st. and a la carte ₰ 5.75 – **64 rm** ⊃ 49.00/159.00 st. – SB.

**Albaston House**, 27 St. Marychurch Rd, TQ1 3JF, ℰ (01803) 296758 – ⏶ ☎ ⦿. ◎ 쪼
⓪ 𝘝𝘐𝘚𝘈 𝘑𝘊𝘉 CY a
*closed Christmas* – **Meals** (dinner only) 12.00 st. ₰ 4.50 – **13 rm** ⊃ 32.00/72.00 st. – SB.

**Fairmount House**, Herbert Rd, Chelston, TQ2 6RW, ℰ (01803) 605446,
*Fax (01803) 605446*, ﹐ – ﹪rest, ⏶ 𝘝𝘐𝘚𝘈 AX a
*early March-October* – **Meals** (*closed Sunday dinner September*) (residents only) (bar lunch)/dinner 13.50 t. ₰ 5.25 – **8 rm** ⊃ 33.00/66.00 t. – SB.

**Cranborne**, 58 Belgrave Rd, TQ2 5HY, ℰ (01803) 298046, *Fax (01803) 298046* – ﹪rest, ⏶. ◎ 쪼 𝘝𝘐𝘚𝘈. ﹪ BY i
**Meals** (by arrangement) 9.50 st. ₰ 3.00 – **13 rm** ⊃ 20.00/50.00 st. – SB.

**Belmont**, 66 Belgrave Rd, TQ2 5HY, ℰ (01803) 295028, *Fax (01803) 211668* – ﹪rest, ⏶ ⦿. ◎ 쪼 ⓪ 𝘝𝘐𝘚𝘈 𝘑𝘊𝘉 BY i
**Meals** (by arrangement) 8.50 st. ₰ 5.00 – **13 rm** ⊃ 18.00/50.00 st. – SB.

**Glenorleigh**, 26 Cleveland Rd, TQ2 5BE, ℰ (01803) 292135, *Fax (01803) 292135*, ⬓, ﹐ – ⏶ ⦿. ◎ 𝘝𝘐𝘚𝘈 BY n
**Meals** (by arrangement) 9.50 st. ₰ 3.75 – **16 rm** ⊃ 25.00/50.00 st. – SB.

**Cedar Court**, 3 St. Matthews Rd, Chelston, TQ2 6JA, ℰ (01803) 607851 – ⏶ ⦿. ﹪
*closed 30 November-2 January* – **Meals** (by arrangement) 6.50 st. – **9 rm** ⊃ 20.00/38.00 – BY a
SB.

**Remy's**, 3 Croft Rd, TQ2 5UF, ℰ (01803) 292359 – ﹪. ◎ 𝘝𝘐𝘚𝘈 𝘑𝘊𝘉 CY x
*closed Sunday and Monday* – **Meals** - French - (booking essential) (dinner only) 17.85 t.
₰ 4.50.

**Mulberry House** with rm, 1 Scarborough Rd, TQ2 5UJ, ℰ (01803) 213639 – ﹪ ⏶. ﹪
**Meals** (*closed Monday and Tuesday to non-residents*) (booking essential) 7.95 st.
(lunch) and a la carte 12.50/16.50 st. ₰ 7.00 – **3 rm** ⊃ 35.00/55.00 st. – SB. CY x

**at Maidencombe** North : 3½ m. by B 3199 – BX – ⊠ Torquay.

**Orestone Manor** ⌂, Rockhouse Lane, TQ1 4SX, ℰ (01803) 328098, *Fax (01803) 328336*, ≤, ⬓, ﹐ – ﹪rest, ⏶ ☎ ⦿. ◎ 쪼 ⓪ 𝘝𝘐𝘚𝘈
*closed first 2 weeks January* – **Meals** (lunch by arrangement)/dinner 27.50 t. ₰ 6.75 – **18 rm** ⊃ 70.00/160.00 t. – SB.

**Barn Hayes** ⌂, Brim Hill, TQ1 4TR, ℰ (01803) 327980, *Fax (01803) 327980*, ≤, ﹐ – ﹪rest, ⏶ ⦿. ◎ 𝘝𝘐𝘚𝘈
*booking essential November-March, closed 30 December-5 February* – **Meals** (bar lunch)/dinner 15.00 st. ₰ 3.65 – **12 rm** ⊃ 32.00/64.00 st. – SB.

**at Babbacombe** Northeast : 1½ m. – ⊠ Torquay.

**Table**, 135 Babbacombe Rd, TQ1 3SR, ℰ (01803) 324292, *Fax (01803) 324292* – ◎ 쪼 𝘝𝘐𝘚𝘈
*closed lunch Saturday and Sunday May-September, 2 weeks early February and 2 weeks late April* – **Meals** 26.50/28.50 t. ₰ 5.50. CX a

🅐 ATS 100 Teignmouth Rd ℰ (01803) 329495

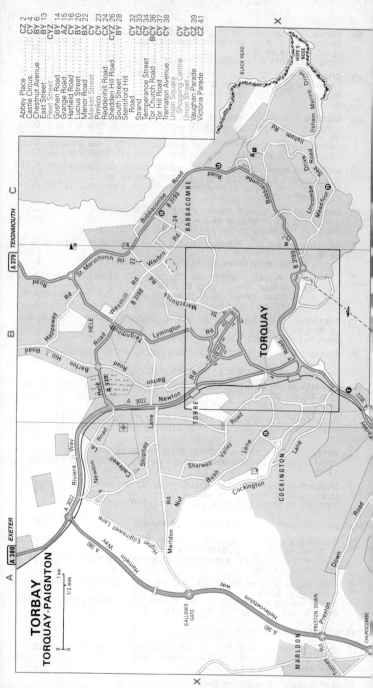

TORBAY
TORQUAY-PAIGNTON

606

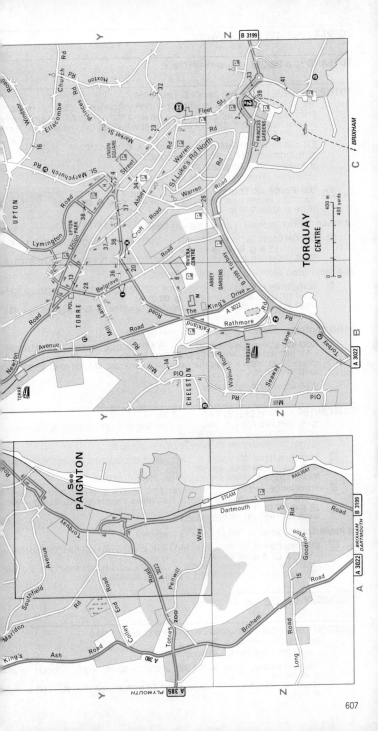

TORQUAY
CENTRE

See PAIGNTON

**TORVER** Cumbria 402 K 20 – see Coniston.

**TOTLAND** I.O.W. 403 404 P 31 – see Wight (Isle of).

**TOTNES** Devon 403 I 32 The West Country G. – pop. 7 018.
See : Town★ – Elizabethan Museum★ – St. Mary's★ – Butterwalk★ – Castle (≤★★★) AC.
Env. : Paignton Zoo★★ AC, E : 4½ m. by A 385 and A 3022 – British Photographic Museum, Bowden House★ AC, S : 1 m. by A 381 – Dartington Hall (High Cross House★ ), NW : 2 m. by A 385 and A 384.
Exc. : Dartmouth★★ (Castle ≤★★★) SE : 12 m. by A 381 and A 3122.
🏌18, 🏌18 Dartmouth G & C.C., Blackawton ℘ (01803) 712686.
🛈 The Plains, TQ9 5EJ ℘ (01803) 863168.
London 224 – Exeter 24 – Plymouth 23 – Torquay 9.

⌂ **Old Forge at Totnes** without rest., Seymour Pl., TQ9 5AY, ℘ (01803) 862174, Fax (01803) 865385, « 14C working forge », 🐎 – 🖐 🗹 ☎ 🅿. 🕮 VISA. ⋘
10 rm ⊇ 42.00/72.00 st.

**at Stoke Gabriel** Southeast : 4 m. by A 385 – ⌗ Totnes.

🏨 **Gabriel Court** ⤸, Stoke Hill, TQ9 6SF, ℘ (01803) 782206, Fax (01803) 782333, ⏉, 🐎, ⋘ – 🖐 rest, 🗹 ☎ 🅿. 🕮 🆎 ① VISA JCB
Meals (dinner only and Sunday lunch)/dinner 25.00 st. ⬩ 6.75 – **19 rm** ⊇ 55.00/80.00 st.

**at Ashprington** South : 3½ m. by A 381 – ⌗ Totnes.

🏠 **Waterman's Arms,** Bow Bridge, TQ9 7EG, ℘ (01803) 732214, Fax (01803) 732214, « Part 15C inn », 🐎 – 🖐 rest, 🗹 ☎ 🅿. 🕮 🆎 VISA
Meals (bar lunch Monday to Saturday)/dinner a la carte 13.95/30.40 t. ⬩ 8.25 – **15 rm** ⊇ 46.00/80.00 st.

**at Dartington** Northwest : 2 m. by A 385 on A 384 – ⌗ Totnes.

🏠 **Cott Inn** with rm, TQ9 6HE, South : ½ m. off A 385 ℘ (01803) 863777, Fax (01803) 866629, « 14C thatched inn », 🐎 – 🖐 🗹 ☎ 🅿. 🕮 🆎 VISA JCB
closed 25 December – **Meals** (bar lunch)/dinner a la carte 14.50/21.00 st. ⬩ 5.50 – **6 rm** ⊇ 47.50/65.00 st. – SB.

⒜ ATS Babbage Rd ℘ (01803) 862086

**TOWCESTER** Northants. 403 404 R 27 – pop. 7 006.
🏌18, 🏌18 West Park G. & C.C., Whittlebury, Towcester ℘ (01327) 858092 – 🏌18 Farthingstone Hotel, Farthingstone ℘ (01327) 361291.
London 70 – Birmingham 50 – Northampton 9 – Oxford 36.

🏨 **Saracens Head,** 219 Watling St., NN12 7BX, ℘ (01327) 350414, Fax (01327) 359879 – 🗹 ☎ 🅿 – 🔬 100. 🕮 🆎 VISA JCB. ⋘
Meals 11.95/14.50 st. and dinner a la carte – **21 rm** ⊇ 62.50/85.00 st.

🏨 **Travelodge,** East Towcester bypass, NN12 6TQ, Southwest : ½ m. by Brackley rd on A 43 ℘ (01327) 359105, Fax (01327) 359105, Reservations (Freephone) 0800 850950 – 🖐 rm 🗹 ⛐ 🅿. 🕮 🆎 ① VISA JCB. ⋘
Meals (grill rest.) – **33 rm** 39.95/59.95 t.

**at Paulerspury** Southeast : 3¼ m. by A 5 – ⌗ Towcester.

XX **Vine House** with rm, 100 High St., NN12 7NA, ℘ (01327) 811267, Fax (01327) 811309, 🐎 – 🖐 rest, 🗹 ☎ 🅿. 🕮 VISA. ⋘
closed 2 weeks Christmas-New Year – **Meals** (closed Sunday) (dinner only and lunch Thursday and Friday)/dinner 24.95 t. – **6 rm** ⊇ 45.00/66.00.

**TOWERSEY** Oxon. 404 R 28 – see Thame.

**TREGONY** Cornwall 403 F 33 The West Country G. – pop. 729 – ⌗ Truro.
Env. : Trewithen★★★ AC, N : 2½ m.
London 291 – Newquay 18 – Plymouth 53 – Truro 10.

⌂ **Tregony House,** 15 Fore St., TR2 5RN, ℘ (01872) 530671, Fax (01872) 530671, 🐎 – 🖐 🅿. 🕮 VISA. ⋘
closed mid November-mid February – **Meals** (by arrangement) 11.50 st. – **5 rm** ⊇ 19.00/46.00 st.

**REGREHAN** Cornwall 403 F 32 – see St. Austell.

**RESCO** Cornwall 403 ㉚ – see Scilly (Isles of).

**RING** Herts. 404 S 28 – pop. 11 455.
London 38 – Aylesbury 7 – Luton 14.

🏛 **Pendley Manor,** Cow Lane, HP23 5QY, East : 1 ½ m. by B 4635 off B 4251 *ℰ* (01442) 891891, *Fax* (01442) 890687, ≤, *Ⅰぉ*, *ℛ*, park, *%* – |創, *⅙*⊷ rest, *Ⅲ* ☎ 💪 🄿 – 📇 220. 🐵 🝙 ⓪ *ⱽⁱˢᴬ* *Ｊᴄʙ*
**Meals** 21.00 t. and a la carte ⅃ 6.50 – **68 rm** ⊃ 90.00/120.00 st., 2 suites.

🏛 **Rose and Crown,** High St., HP23 5AH, *ℰ* (01442) 824071, *Fax* (01442) 890735 – *⅙*⊷ rm, *Ⅲ* ☎ 🄿. 🐵 🝙 ⓪ *ⱽⁱˢᴬ*
**Meals** (bar meals Monday to Saturday lunch and Sunday dinner)/dinner 17.50 t. and a la carte ⅃ 5.50 – ⊃ 9.75 – **27 rm** 90.00/100.00 t. – SB.

🏠 **Travel Inn,** Tring Hill, HP23 4LD, West : 1 ½ m. on A 41 *ℰ* (01442) 824819, *Fax* (01442) 890787 – *⅙*⊷ rm, *Ⅲ* 💪 🄿. 🐵 🝙 ⓪ *ⱽⁱˢᴬ*. *%*
**Meals** (grill rest.) – **30 rm** 38.00 t.

**@TRINITY**æ Jersey (Channel Islands) 403 P 33 and 230 ⑪ – see Channel Islands.

**ROTTON** W. Sussex – see Midhurst.

**ROUTBECK** Cumbria 402 L 20 – see Windermere.

**ROWBRIDGE** Wilts. 403 404 N 30 The West Country G. – pop. 25 279.
Env. : Westwood Manor★, NW : 3 m. by A 363 – Farleigh Hungerford★ (St. Leonard's Chapel★) AC, W : 4 m.
Exc. : Longleat House★★★ AC, SW : 12 m. by A 363, A 350 and A 362 - Bratton Castle (≤★★) SE : 7 ½ m. by A 363 and B 3098 – Steeple Ashton★ (The Green★) E : 6 m. – Edington (St. Mary, St. Katherine and All Saints★) SE : 7 ½ m.
🖪 St. Stephen's Pl., BA14 8AH *ℰ* (01225) 777054.
London 115 – Bristol 27 – Southampton 55 – Swindon 32.

🏛 **Old Manor** ⌂, Trowle, BA14 9BL, Northwest : 1 m. on A 363 *ℰ* (01225) 777393, *Fax* (01225) 765443, « Queen Anne house of 15C origins », *ℛ* – *⅙*⊷ *Ⅲ* ☎ 🄿. 🐵 🝙 ⓪ *ⱽⁱˢᴬ* *Ｊᴄʙ*. *%*
closed 4 days Christmas – **Meals** (closed Sunday) (residents only) (dinner only) 15.00 t. and a la carte ⅃ 3.95 – **14 rm** ⊃ 48.50/85.00 t.

🏠 **Hilbury Court,** Hilperton Rd, BA14 7JW, Northeast : ¼ m. on A 361 *ℰ* (01225) 752949, *Fax* (01225) 777990, *ℛ* – *⅙*⊷ rest, *Ⅲ* ☎ 🄿. 🐵 *ⱽⁱˢᴬ*. *%*
**Meals** (dinner only) a la carte 15.25/18.25 st. ⅃ 3.50 – **13 rm** ⊃ 45.00/60.00 st. – SB.

🏠 **Brookfield House** ⌂ without rest., Vaggs Hill, Wingfield, BA14 9NA, Southwest : 4 m. by A 366 on B 3109 *ℰ* (01373) 830615, *Fax* (01373) 830615, « Working farm », *ℛ*, park – *⅙*⊷ *Ⅲ* 🄿. *%*
closed 25 December – **3 rm** ⊃ 30.00/50.00 st.

🏠 **Welam House** without rest., Bratton Rd, West Ashton, BA14 6AZ, Southeast : 2 m. by A 361 on West Ashton Rd *ℰ* (01225) 755908, *ℛ* – *⅙*⊷ 🄿. *%*
March-November – **3 rm** ⊃ 20.00/32.00.

**at Semington** Northeast : 2½ m. by A 361 – ⊠ Trowbridge.

🍴 **Lamb on the Strand,** 99 The Strand, BA14 6LL, East : 1 ½ m. on A 361 *ℰ* (01380) 870263, *Fax* (01380) 870815, *ℛ* – 🄿. 🐵 🝙 *ⱽⁱˢᴬ*
closed Sunday dinner and 25 December – **Meals** a la carte 13.20/17.50 t. ⅃ 5.00.

@ ATS Canal Rd, Ladydown Trading Est. *ℰ* (01225) 753469

**ROWELL SERVICE AREA** Notts. 404 Q 25 – ⊠ Ilkeston.

🏠 **Travelodge,** NG9 3PL, at junction 25/6 on M 1 (northbound carriageway) *ℰ* (0115) 932 0291, *Fax* (0115) 930 7261, Reservations (Freephone) 0800 850950 – *⅙*⊷ *Ⅲ* ☎ 💪 🄿. 🐵 🝙 ⓪ *ⱽⁱˢᴬ* *Ｊᴄʙ*. *%*
**Meals** (grill rest.) – **35 rm** 39.95/59.95 t.

**TRURO** Cornwall **403** E 33 The West Country G. – pop. 16 522.

See : Royal Cornwall Museum★★ AC.

Env. : Trelissick Garden★★ (≤★★) AC, S : 4 m. by A 39 – Feock (Church★) S : 5 m. by A 39 and B 3289.

Exc. : Trewithen★★★, NE : 7½ m. by A 39 and A 390 – Probus★ (tower★ - garden★) NE : 9 m. by A 39 and A 390.

🏌 Treliske ℰ (01872) 272640 – 🏌 Killiow Golf Park, Killiow, Kea ℰ (01872) 270246.

🛈 Municipal Buildings, Boscawen St., TR1 2NE ℰ (01872) 274555.

London 295 – Exeter 87 – Penzance 26 – Plymouth 52.

🏨 **Alverton Manor**, Tregolls Rd, TR1 1XQ, ℰ (01872) 276633, Fax (01872) 222989, « M 19C manor house, former Bishop's residence and convent », 🐾 – 📶, 🛏 rest, 📺 ☎ 📵 🔥 200. 🐠 🗛 ① 𝒱𝐼𝑆𝐴 𝐽𝐶𝐵
Meals 16.25/19.50 **st.** and dinner a la carte ⏐ 5.25 – **30 rm** � 67.00/114.00 **st.**, 4 suites SB.

🏨 **Royal**, Lemon St., TR1 2QB, ℰ (01872) 270345, Fax (01872) 242453 – 🛏 rm, 📺 ☎ 📵. 🐠 🗛 ① 𝒱𝐼𝑆𝐴 𝐽𝐶𝐵. 🛇
closed 25 and 26 December – Meals (closed Sunday lunch) (grill rest.) a la carte 14.00/21.70 **t.** ⏐ 7.00 – **35 rm** ⊂ 52.00/100.00 **t.** – SB.

↑ **Laniley House** ⌂ without rest., Newquay Rd, nr. Trispen, TR4 9AU, Northeast : 3 ½ m. by A 39 and A 3076 on Frogmore rd ℰ (01872) 275201, 🐾 – 🛏 📺 📵. 🛇
Easter-September – **3 rm** ⊂ 38.00.

↑ **Blue Haze** without rest., The Parade, Malpas Rd, TR1 1QE, ℰ (01872) 22355 Fax (01872) 223553, 🐾 – 🛏 📺 📵. 🛇
**3 rm** ⊂ 39.00/41.00 **s.**

↑ **Conifers** without rest., 36 Tregolls Rd, TR1 1LA, ℰ (01872) 279925 – 🛏 📺 📵. 🛇
**4 rm** ⊂ 22.00/38.00 **s.**

**at Carnon Downs** Southwest : 3¼ m. by A 39 – ✉ Truro.

🏨 **Travel Inn**, Old Carnon Hill, TR3 6JT, ℰ (01872) 863370, Fax (01872) 865620, 🐾 – 🛏 rm ▤ rest, 📺 🔥 📵. 🐠 🗛 ① 𝒱𝐼𝑆𝐴. 🛇
Meals (grill rest.) – **40 rm** 38.00 **t.**

**at Blackwater** West : 7 m. by A 390 – ✉ Truro.

↑ **Rock Cottage** without rest., TR4 8EU, ℰ (01872) 560252, Fax (01872) 560252 – 🛏 📺 📵. 🐠 𝒱𝐼𝑆𝐴 𝐽𝐶𝐵.
closed Christmas and New Year – **3 rm** ⊂ 28.00/48.00 **s.**

🔧 ATS Tabernacle St. ℰ (01872) 274083          ATS Newham Rd ℰ (01872) 240353

---

**TUNBRIDGE WELLS** Kent **404** U 30 – see Royal Tunbridge Wells.

---

**TURNERS HILL** W. Sussex **404** T 30 – pop. 1 534.

London 33 – Brighton 24 – Crawley 7.

🏨 **Alexander House** ⌂, East St., RH10 4QD, East : 1 m. on B 2110 ℰ (01342) 714914 Fax (01342) 717328, ≤, « Part 17C country house in extensive parkland », 🐾, 🎾 – 📶 🛏 rest, 📺 ☎ 📵. 🐠 🗛 ① 𝒱𝐼𝑆𝐴 𝐽𝐶𝐵. 🛇
Meals 22.00/28.00 **st.** and a la carte ⏐ 9.50 – **9 rm** ⊂ 120.00/155.00 **st.**, 6 suites – SB.

---

**TURVEY** Beds. **404** S 27 – see Bedford.

---

**TUTBURY** Staffs. **402 403 404** O 25 Great Britain G. – pop. 5 646 (inc. Hatton) – ✉ Burton-upon-Trent.

Env. : Sudbury Hall★★ AC, NW : 5½ m. by A 50.

London 132 – Birmingham 33 – Derby 11 – Stoke-on-Trent 27.

🏨 **Ye Olde Dog and Partridge**, High St., DE13 9LS, ℰ (01283) 81303C Fax (01283) 813178, « Part 15C timbered inn », 🐾 – 🛏 rm, 📺 ☎ 📵. 🐠 🗛 𝒱𝐼𝑆𝐴. 🛇
closed 25-26 December and 1 January – Meals (carving rest.) 6.95/7.95 **t.** and a la carte ⏐ 5.95 – **14 rm** ⊂ 55.00/90.00 **t.**

↑ **Mill House** without rest., Cornmill Lane, DE13 9HA, Southeast : ¾ m. ℰ (01283) 813634 « Georgian house and watermill », 🐾 – 🛏 📺 📵. 🛇
closed 25 December – **3 rm** ⊂ 35.00/55.00 **s.**

*The Guide is updated annually so renew your Guide every year.*

**WO BRIDGES** *Devon* [403] I 32 *The West Country G.* – ✉ *Yelverton.*
*Env. : Dartmoor National Park★★.*
*London 226 – Exeter 25 – Plymouth 17.*

🏨 **Prince Hall** 🛌, PL20 6SA, East : 1 m. on B 3357 ☎ (01822) 890403, *Fax (01822) 890676*, ⩽, 🐕, 🌳 – 🚭 rest, [TV] ☎ [P]. [MC] [AE] [D] VISA JCB
*closed January and first week February* – **Meals** (booking essential to non-residents) (dinner only) 24.00 **t.** 🍷 5.10 – **9 rm** ☕ (dinner included) 59.50/129.00 **t.** – SB.

**WO MILLS** *Ches. – see Chester.*

**YNEMOUTH** *Tyne and Wear* [401] [402] P 18 – *pop. 17 422.*
*London 290 – Newcastle upon Tyne 8 – Sunderland 7.*

🏨 **Grand,** Grand Par., NE30 4ER, ☎ (0191) 293 6666, *Fax (0191) 293 6665*, ⩽, « Victorian mansion » – [lift] [TV] ☎ [P] – 🎤 75. [MC] [AE] [D] VISA. 🚫🐕
**Meals** (bar meals Sunday dinner) 11.75/14.75 **t.** and dinner a la carte 🍷 4.75 – **44 rm** ☕ 70.00/150.00 **t.**

**CKFIELD** *E. Sussex* [404] U 31 – *pop. 13 531.*
*London 45 – Brighton 17 – Eastbourne 20 – Maidstone 34.*

🏨 **Horsted Place** 🛌, Little Horsted, TN22 5TS, South : 2 ½ m. by B 2102 and A 22 on A 26 ☎ (01825) 750581, *Fax (01825) 750459*, ⩽, 🌳, « Victorian Gothic country house and gardens », [pool], [18], park, 🎾 – [lift], 🚭 rest, [TV] ☎ [P] – 🎤 100. [MC] [AE] [D] VISA JCB. 🚫🐕
*closed 3 to 7 January* – **Meals** 17.95/32.00 **t.** and a la carte – ☕ 3.00 – **15 rm** 140.00 **t.**, 5 suites – SB.

🏨 **Hooke Hall,** 250 High St., TN22 1EN, ☎ (01825) 761578, *Fax (01825) 768025*, « Queen Anne town house », 🌳 – [TV] ☎ [P]. [MC] [AE] VISA. 🚫🐕
*closed 24 to 31 December* – **Meals** – (see ***La Scaletta*** below) – ☕ 7.75 – **9 rm** 50.00/120.00 **st.**

🍴🍴 **La Scaletta** (at Hooke Hall H.), 250 High St., TN22 1EN, ☎ (01825) 766844, *Fax (01825) 768025* – 🚭 [air]. [MC] [AE] VISA
*closed Saturday lunch, Sunday, 24 to 31 December and Bank Holidays* – **Meals** - Italian - 12.95 **t.** (lunch) and a la carte 21.00/30.00 **t.** 🍷 6.50.

**FFINGTON** *Oxon.* [403] [404] P 29.
*London 75 – Oxford 29 – Reading 32 – Swindon 17.*

🏠 **Craven** 🛌, Fernham Rd, SN7 7RD, ☎ (01367) 820449, « 17C thatched house », 🌳 – 🚭 [P]. [MC] [AE] VISA. 🚫🐕
**Meals** (by arrangement) (communal dining) 16.50 🍷 3.50 – **6 rm** ☕ 30.00/70.00.

**LLINGSWICK** *Herefordshire* [403] [404] M 27 – *pop. 237* – ✉ *Hereford.*
*London 134 – Hereford 12 – Shrewsbury 52 – Worcester 19.*

🏨 **Steppes Country House** 🛌, HR1 3JG, ☎ (01432) 820424, *Fax (01432) 820042*, « Converted farmhouse of 14C origins », 🌳 – 🚭 [TV] ☎ [P]. [MC] [AE] VISA JCB
*closed 2 weeks before Christmas and first 2 weeks January* – **Meals** (booking essential) (dinner only) 26.00 **st.** 🍷 4.95 – **6 rm** ☕ 60.00/90.00 **st.** – SB.

**LLSWATER** *Cumbria* [402] L 20 – *pop. 1 199* – ✉ *Penrith.*
[i] *Main Car Park, Glenridding, CA11 0PA ☎ (017684) 82414 (summer only).*
*London 296 – Carlisle 25 – Kendal 31 – Penrith 6.*

**at Matterdale End** *North : 2 ¾ m. on A 5091* – ✉ *Penrith.*

🏠 **Bank House Farm** 🛌 without rest., CA11 0LF, West : ¾ m. turning left after telephone box in village centre ☎ (017684) 82040, *Fax (017684) 82040*, ⩽, 🌳 – 🚭 [TV] [P]
*Easter-October* – **3 rm** ☕ 55.00 **s.**

**at Howtown** *Southwest : 4 m. of Pooley Bridge* – ✉ *Penrith.*

🏨 **Howtown** 🛌, CA10 2ND, ☎ (017684) 86514, ⩽, 🌳 – [P]. 🚫🐕
*26 March-October* – **Meals** (light lunch)/dinner 14.00 **t.** 🍷 5.20 – **14 rm** ☕ (dinner included) 44.00/88.00 **t.**

**at Pooley Bridge** on B 5320 – ⊠ Penrith.

🏛🏛    **Sharrow Bay Country House** ⓢ, CA10 2LZ, South : 2 m. on Howtown
❀    ℰ (017684) 86301, Fax (017684) 86349, ≼ Ullswater and fells, « Lakeside setting, gardens
    » – ५⊁, 🗏 rest, 🆃🆅 ☎ 🅿. ◍◐ 𝘝𝘐𝘚𝘈. ⊀
    closed 6 December-26 February – **Meals** (booking essential) 37.00/47.00 **st.** ⓘ 8.50 – **24 r**
    ⊑ (dinner included) 145.00/380.00 **st.**, 2 suites
    **Spec.** Suissesse soufflé of Stilton, onion and spinach. Fillet steak with steak and kidne
    pudding, Burgundy sauce. Francis Coulson's syllabub.

**at Watermillock** on A 592 – ⊠ Penrith.

🏛🏛    **Leeming House** ⓢ, CA11 0JJ, on A 592 ℰ (017684) 86622, Fax (017684) 86443,
    « Lakeside country house and gardens », ❧, park – ५⊁ 🆃🆅 ☎ & 🅿 – ⚰ 35. ◍◐ 🅰🅴 ◐ 𝙑
    🅹🅲🅱
    **Meals** 13.95/23.50 **st.** ⓘ 10.45 – ⊑ 11.50 – **40 rm** 105.00/160.00 **st.** – SB.

🏛🏛    **Rampsbeck Country House** ⓢ, CA11 0LP, ℰ (017684) 86442, Fax (017684) 86688,
    Ullswater and fells, « Lakeside setting », ❧, park – 🆃🆅 ☎ 🅿. ◍◐ 🅰🅴 𝘝𝘐𝘚𝘈. ⊀
    closed January-mid February – **Meals** – (see **The Restaurant** below) – **19 rm** ⊑ 55.0
    150.00 **t.**, 1 suite – SB.

🏛    **Old Church** ⓢ, CA11 0JN, ℰ (017684) 86204, Fax (017684) 86368, ≼ Ullswater and fell
    « Lakeside setting », ❧, ❀ – ५⊁ rest, 🆃🆅 ☎ 🅿. ◍◐ 🅰🅴 𝘝𝘐𝘚𝘈. ⊀
    restricted opening November-March – **Meals** (closed Sunday) (booking essential) (dinn
    only) a la carte 18.20/26.90 **st.** ⓘ 8.50 – **10 rm** ⊑ 65.00/135.00 **st.** – SB.

✗✗    **The Restaurant** (at Rampsbeck Country House H.), CA11 0LP, ℰ (017684) 8644
    Fax (017684) 86688, ❀, park – ५⊁ 🅿. ◍◐ 𝘝𝘐𝘚𝘈
    **Meals** (booking essential) (lunch by arrangement Monday to Saturday)/dinner 26.0∎
    39.00 **t.** ⓘ 6.75.

---

**ULVERSTON** Cumbria 𝟰𝟬𝟮 K 21 – pop. 11 866.
    🛅 Bardsea Park ℰ (01229) 582824.
    🔟 Coronation Hall, County Sq., LA12 7LZ ℰ (01229) 587120.
    London 278 – Kendal 25 – Lancaster 36.

🏛    **Trinity House,** 1 Princes St., LA12 7NB, off A 590 ℰ (01229) 587639, Fax (01229) 588552
    ५⊁ rest, 🆃🆅 ☎ ℂ 🅿. ◍◐ 🅰🅴 ◐ 𝘝𝘐𝘚𝘈
    **Meals** 15.95 **t.** (dinner) and a la carte 13.50/21.15 **t.** – **6 rm** ⊑ 51.00/62.00 **t.** – SB.

⌂    **Church Walk House** without rest., Church Walk, LA12 7EW, ℰ (01229) 582211 – ५⊁
    closed 2 weeks Christmas and New Year – **3 rm** ⊑ 22.00/44.00 **st.**

✗✗    **Bay Horse** ⓢ with rm, Canal Foot, LA12 9EL, East : 2 ¼ m. by A 5087, Morecambe Rd an
    beyond Industrial area, on the coast ℰ (01229) 583972, Fax (01229) 580502, ≼ Morecamb
    bay – ५⊁ rest, 🆃🆅 ☎ 🅿. ◍◐ 𝘝𝘐𝘚𝘈
    **Meals** (closed lunch Sunday and Monday) (booking essential) 16.75 **t.** (lunch) and a la cart
    23.65/27.85 **t.** ⓘ 8.50 – **7 rm** ⊑ (dinner included) 85.00/160.00 **t.** – SB.

    ⓐ ATS The Gill ℰ (01229) 583442

---

**UMBERLEIGH** Devon 𝟰𝟬𝟯 I 31.
    London 218 – Barnstaple 7 – Exeter 31 – Taunton 49.

🏛    **Rising Sun,** EX37 9DU, on A 377 ℰ (01769) 560447, Fax (01769) 560764, ❧ – ५⊁ rm, 🖵
    ☎ 🅿. ◍◐ 𝘝𝘐𝘚𝘈
    **Meals** 10.00/15.00 **st.** and a la carte ⓘ 4.50 – **9 rm** ⊑ 40.00/77.00 **st.** – SB.

---

**UNDERBARROW** Cumbria 𝟰𝟬𝟮 L 21 – see Kendal.

---

**UP HOLLAND** Lancs. 𝟰𝟬𝟮 M 23 – see Wigan.

---

**UPLYME** Devon 𝟰𝟬𝟯 L 31 – see Lyme Regis.

---

**UPPER BENEFIELD** Northants. – see Oundle.

---

**UPPER CLATFORD** Hants. 𝟰𝟬𝟯 𝟰𝟬𝟰 P 30 – see Andover.

**PPER QUINTON** *Warks.* – ⊠ *Stratford-upon-Avon.*
*London 95 – Cheltenham 24 – Oxford 43 – Stratford-upon-Avon 6.*

↑ **Winton House** without rest., The Green, CV37 8SX, ℰ (01789) 720500, « Victorian farmhouse », 涼 – ⅍ 🄿. 
*closed 25 December* – **3 rm** ⊆ 40.00/52.00 st.

---

**PPER SLAUGHTER** *Glos.* ᐫᐫᐫ ᐫᐫᐫ O 28 – *see Bourton-on-the-Water.*

---

**PPINGHAM** *Rutland* ᐫᐫᐫ R 26 – *pop. 3 140.*
*London 101 – Leicester 19 – Northampton 28 – Nottingham 35.*

↑ **Rutland House** without rest., 61 High St. East, LE15 9PY, ℰ (01572) 822212, *Fax (01572) 822497,* 涼 – 🄣 🄿. 🄌 🄴 🄸
**5 rm** ⊆ 30.00/40.00 t.

XX **Lake Isle** with rm, 16 High St. East, LE15 9PZ, ℰ (01572) 822951, *Fax (01572) 822951* – 🄣 ☎ 🄿. 🄌 🄴 🄸
**Meals** *(closed Monday lunch)* (Sunday dinner residents only) 14.00/23.00 t. ⅟ 6.50 – **10 rm** ⊆ 52.00/74.00 st., 2 suites – SB.

**t Morcott Service Area** *East : 4¼ m. by A 6003 on A 47* – ⊠ *Uppingham.*

🏠 **Travelodge**, Glaston Rd, LE15 8SA, ℰ (01572) 747719, *Fax (01572) 747719,* Reservations (Freephone) 0800 850950 – ⅍ rm, 🄣 & 🄿. 🄌 🄴 🄸 🄥🄘🄢. ✸
**Meals** (grill rest.) – **40 rm** 39.95/59.95 t.

---

**PTON ST. LEONARDS** *Glos.* – *see Gloucester.*

---

**PTON SNODSBURY** *Worcestershire* ᐫᐫᐫ ᐫᐫᐫ N 27 – *see Worcester.*

---

**PTON-UPON-SEVERN** *Worcestershire* ᐫᐫᐫ ᐫᐫᐫ N 27 – *pop. 1 756.*
🖪 *4 High St., WR8 0HB ℰ (01684) 594200 (summer only).*
*London 116 – Hereford 25 – Stratford-upon-Avon 29 – Worcester 11.*

↑ **Welland Court** ⤳ without rest., WR8 0ST, West : 3 ¾ m. by A 4104 ℰ (01684) 594426, *Fax (01684) 594426,* ≼ The Malvern Hills, « Georgian manor house of 13C origins », ⤳, 涼, park – 🄣 🄿. ✸
*closed 25 December* **3 rm** ⊆ 45.00/70.00.

↑ **Tiltridge Farm** ⤳ without rest., Upper Hook Rd, WR8 0SA, West : 1½ m. by A 4104 and Greenfields Rd off Hyde Lane ℰ (01684) 592906, *Fax (01684) 594142,* « Part 17C farmhouse, working vineyard », 涼 – ⅍ 🄣 🄿
*closed Christmas-New Year* – **3 rm** ⊆ 30.00/44.00 s.

**t Welland Stone** *Southwest : 3¼ m. by A 4104* – ⊠ *Upton-upon-Severn.*

↑ **Bridge House** ⤳, WR8 0RW, ℰ (01684) 593046, *Fax (01684) 593046,* ≼, 涼 – ⅍ 🄣 🄿. ✸
**Meals** (by arrangement) 20.00 – **3 rm** ⊆ 28.00/50.00 – SB.

---

**TTOXETER** *Staffs.* ᐫᐫᐫ ᐫᐫᐫ ᐫᐫᐫ O 25 *Great Britain G.* – *pop. 10 329.*
*Env. : Sudbury Hall*★★ *AC, E : 5 m. by A 518 and A 50.*
🏌 *Wood Lane ℰ (01889) 565108.*
*London 145 – Birmingham 33 – Derby 19 – Stafford 13 – Stoke-on-Trent 16.*

🏠 **White Hart**, Carter St., ST14 8EU, ℰ (01889) 562437, *Fax (01889) 565099* – ⅍ rest, 🄣 ☎ 📞 🄿 – 🕍 50. 🄌 🄴 🄸 🄥🄘🄢. ✸
**Meals** (grill rest.) 7.95 t. and a la carte ⅟ 5.50 – ⊆ 6.00 – **20 rm** 49.00 t.

🏠 **Travelodge**, Ashbourne Rd, ST14 5AA, at junction of A 50 with B 5030 ℰ (01889) 562043, *Fax (01889) 562043,* Reservations (Freephone) 0800 850950 – ⅍ rm, 🄣 & 🄿. 🄌 🄴 🄸 🄥🄘🄢. ✸
**Meals** (grill rest.) – **32 rm** 39.95/59.95 t.

**t Doveridge** *(Derbs.) Northeast : 2½ m. by Derby rd on A 50* – ⊠ *Ashbourne.*

XX **Beeches Farmhouse** ⤳ with rm, Waldley, DE6 5LR, Northeast : 2 m. by Marston Lane ℰ (01889) 590288, *Fax (01889) 590559,* « Working farm », 涼 – 🄣 ☎ 🄿. 🄌 🄴 🄸 🄥🄘🄢. ✸
*closed 1 week Christmas* – **Meals** 11.95 t. (lunch) and a la carte 14.00/18.45 t. ⅟ 4.25 – **10 rm** ⊆ 42.00/64.00 t.

🛞 ATS Smithfield Rd ℰ (01889) 563848/565201

**VAZON BAY** *Guernsey (Channel Islands)* 403 P 33 and 230 ⑨ – *see Channel Islands.*

**VENN OTTERY** *Devon* 403 K 31 – ✉ *Ottery St. Mary.*

*London 209 – Exeter 11 – Sidmouth 5.*

**Venn Ottery Barton** ⛺, EX11 1RZ, ☏ (01404) 812733, *Fax (01404) 814713,* « P 16C », – rest, TV ☎ P. MC VISA JCB
Meals (lunch booking essential) 13.50/17.50 **t.** 6.75 – **16 rm** 34.00/80.00 **st.** – SB.

**VENTNOR** *I.O.W.* 403 404 Q 32 – *see Wight (Isle of).*

**VERYAN** *Cornwall* 403 F 33 *The West Country G. – pop. 877 –* ✉ *Truro.*

See : *Village*★.

*London 291 – St. Austell 13 – Truro 13.*

**Nare** ⛺, Carne Beach, TR2 5PF, Southwest : 1 ¼ m. ☏ (01872) 50127 *Fax (01872) 501856,* ≤ Carne Bay, , , , , , , – TV ☎ P. MC VISA
*closed 4 January-1 February* – **Meals** 15.00/30.00 **t.** and a la carte 7.25 – **34 rm** 93.C 252.00 **t.**, 2 suites.

**Crugsillick Manor** ⛺, TR2 5LJ, West : 1 m. on St. Mawes rd ☏ (01872) 50121 *Fax (01872) 501228,* « Queen Anne manor house of Elizabethan origins », – rm, MC VISA
Meals (by arrangement) (communal dining) 32.50 **st.** 8.00 – **3 rm** 45.00/96.00 **st.**

**at Ruan High Lanes** *West : 1 ¼ m. on A 3078 –* ✉ *Truro.*

**Hundred House,** TR2 5JR, ☏ (01872) 501336, *Fax (01872) 501151,* – rest, TV P. MC AE VISA
*March-November* – **Meals** (dinner only) 24.00 **t.** 5.50 – **10 rm** (dinner include 60.00/120.00 **t.** – SB.

**VIRGINSTOW** *Devon* 403 H 31.

*London 227 – Bideford 25 – Exeter 41 – Launceston 11 – Plymouth 35.*

**Percy's at Coombeshead** with rm, EX21 5EA, Southwest : 1 ¼ m. on Tower Hill ☏ (01409) 211236, *Fax (01409) 211275,* ≤, , park – TV P. MC AE VISA
Meals 22.00 **t.** 4.00 – **8 rm** 49.50/79.50 **t.**

**WADDESDON** *Bucks.* 404 R 28 *Great Britain G. – pop. 1 864 –* ✉ *Aylesbury.*

See : *Chiltern Hills*★.

Env. : *Waddesdon Manor*★★, *S : ½ m. by a 41 and minor rd – Claydon House*★, *N :* *minor rd.*

*London 51 – Aylesbury 5 – Northampton 32 – Oxford 31.*

**Five Arrows** with rm, High St., HP18 0JE, ☏ (01296) 651727, *Fax (01296) 658596,* TV ☎ P. MC VISA.
**Meals** a la carte 15.85/23.90 **t.** – **8 rm** 60.00/80.00 **t.**

**WADDINGTON** *Lancs.* 402 M 22 – *see Clitheroe.*

**WADHURST** *E. Sussex* 404 U 30 – *pop. 4 248.*

*London 44 – Hastings 21 – Maidstone 24 – Royal Tunbridge Wells 6.*

**Newbarn** ⛺ without rest., Wards Lane, TN5 6HP, East : 3 m. by B 2099 on Wards Lar ☏ (01892) 782042, *Fax (01892) 782042,* ≤ Bewl Water and countryside, – P.
**3 rm** 23.00/50.00.

**WAKEFIELD** *W. Yorks.* 402 P 22 *Great Britain G. – pop. 73 955.*

Env. : *Nostell Priory*★ *AC, SE : 4½ m. by A 638.*

*18 City of Wakefield, Lupset Park, Horbury Rd ☏ (01924) 367442 – 18 28 Woodthorpe Lane Sandal ☏ (01924) 255104 – 9 Normanton, Snydale Rd ☏ (01924) 892943 – 9 Painthorp House, Painthorpe Lane, Crigglestone ☏ (01924) 255083.*

*Town Hall, Wood St., WF1 2HQ ☏ (01924) 305000/1.*

*London 188 – Leeds 9 – Manchester 38 – Sheffield 23.*

**Cedar Court,** Denby Dale Rd., Calder Grove, WF4 3QZ, Southwest : 3 m. on A 636 at junction with M 1 ℰ (01924) 276310, Fax (01924) 280221, ₤₅ – ₪, ⅏ rm, ▤ rest, ▥ ☎ ◗ – 🅐 400. ⬛ 🄰🄴 ⓪ 🆅🅸🆂🅰
Meals (bar lunch Saturday) 12.75/19.00 **t.** and a la carte – ⚏ 9.50 – **146 rm** 92.50 **t.**, 5 suites – SB.

**Forte Posthouse Wakefield,** Queen's Drive, Ossett, WF5 9BE, West : 2 ½ m. on A 638 ℰ (01924) 276388, Fax (01924) 276437 – ₪, ⅏ rm, ▤ rest, ▥ ☎ ◗ – 🅐 150. ⬛ 🄰🄴 ⓪ 🆅🅸🆂🅰
Meals a la carte 11.65/24.85 **st.** ₪ 6.45 – ⚏ 9.95 – **99 rm** 69.00 **st.** – SB.

**Travel Inn,** Denby Dale Rd, Thornes Park, WF2 8DY, West : ½ m. on A 636 ℰ (01924) 367901, Fax (01924) 373620, 🌧 – ⅏, ▤ rest, ▥ ⅙ ◗ – 🅐 60. ⬛ 🄰🄴 ⓪ 🆅🅸🆂🅰. ⅏
Meals (grill rest.) – **42 rm** 38.00 **t.**

**Aagrah,** 108 Barnsley Rd, South : 1 ¼ m. on A 61 ℰ (01924) 242222, Fax (01924) 240562 – ▤ ◗. ⬛ 🆅🅸🆂🅰 🄹🄲🄱
closed 25 December – Meals - Indian - (booking essential) (dinner only) a la carte 14.15/19.80 **t.**

**at Newmillerdam** South : 3½ m. on A 61 – ✉ Wakefield.

**St. Pierre,** Barnsley Rd, WF2 6QG, ℰ (01924) 255596, Fax (01924) 252746, ₤₅ – ₪ ⅏, ▤ rest, ▥ ☎ ◗ – 🅐 120. ⬛ 🄰🄴 ⓪ 🆅🅸🆂🅰 🄹🄲🄱. ⅏
Meals (bar lunch Saturday and carving lunch Sunday) 9.95/15.95 **t.** and a la carte ₪ 5.95 – ⚏ 7.50 – **52 rm** 67.50/77.50 **t.**, 2 suites.

**at Midgley** Southwest : 6¼ m. by A 636 on A 637 – ✉ Wakefield.

**Midgley Lodge Motel** without rest., Barr Lane, WF4 4JJ, ℰ (01924) 830069, Fax (01924) 830087, ≤ – ▥ ☎ ◗. ⬛ 🄰🄴 ⓪ 🆅🅸🆂🅰 🄹🄲🄱. ⅏
⚏ 4.50 – **25 rm** 38.00 **t.**

⑩ ATS Bethel Pl., Thornes Lane ℰ (01924) 371638

---

**WALBERSWICK** Suffolk 🈶🈚🈯 Y 27 – pop. 1 648 – ✉ Southwold.
London 97 – Great Yarmouth 28 – Ipswich 32 – Norwich 32.

**Anchor,** The Street, IP18 6UA, ℰ (01502) 722112, 🌧 – ⅏ rest, ▥ ◗. ⬛ 🆅🅸🆂🅰 🄹🄲🄱
Meals (bar lunch)/dinner 13.95 **t.** and a la carte Wednesday to Sunday ₪ 6.25 – **6 rm** ⚏ 45.00/60.00 **st.** – SB.

---

**WALBERTON** W. Sussex – see Arundel.

---

**WALKINGTON** East Riding 🈯 S 22 – see Beverley.

---

**WALLASEY** Mersey. 🈯🈯 K 23 – pop. 15 642 – ✉ Wirral.
London 222 – Birkenhead 3 – Liverpool 4.

**Grove House,** Grove Rd, L45 3HF, ℰ (0151) 639 3947, Fax (0151) 639 0028 – ▥ ☎ ◗ – 🅐 100. ⬛ 🄰🄴 🆅🅸🆂🅰. ⅏
Meals (closed Saturday lunch and Bank Holiday Mondays) 12.95/15.95 **t.** and a la carte ₪ 5.25 – ⚏ 5.95 – **14 rm** 54.50/59.00 **t.**

⑩ ATS 40 Mill Lane ℰ (0151) 638 1949/8606

---

**WALLINGFORD** Oxon. 🈯🈯 Q 29 The West Country G. – pop. 9 315.
Exc. : Ridgeway Path★★.
🄱 Town Hall, Market Place, OX10 0EG ℰ (01491) 7826972.
London 54 – Oxford 12 – Reading 16.

**George Thistle,** 84 High St., OX10 0BS, ℰ (01491) 836665, Fax (01491) 825359 – ⅏ rm, ▥ ☎ ◗ – 🅐 120. ⬛ 🄰🄴 ⓪ 🆅🅸🆂🅰 🄹🄲🄱
Meals (dinner only and Sunday lunch)/dinner 19.95 **st.** and a la carte ₪ 6.75 – ⚏ 10.50 – **39 rm** 79.00/145.00 **st.** – SB.

**at North Stoke** South : 2¾ m. by A 4130 and A 4074 on B 4009 – ✉ Wallingford.

**Springs** ≫, Wallingford Rd, OX10 6BE, ℰ (01491) 836687, Fax (01491) 836877, ≤, ⚎, ⌇, 🌧 – ▥ ☎ ◗ – 🅐 50. ⬛ 🄰🄴 ⓪ 🆅🅸🆂🅰 🄹🄲🄱. ⅏
Meals 15.50/27.50 **st.** and a la carte ₪ 9.50 – ⚏ 9.00 – **28 rm** 80.00/135.00 **st.**, 2 suites – SB.

---

**WALMERSLEY** Gtr. Manchester 🈯② 🈯③ 🈯⑨ – see Bury.

## WALSALL W. Mids. 403 404 O 26 – pop. 174 739.

🛍 Calderfields, Aldridge Rd ℰ (01922) 640540 CT.
London 126 – Birmingham 9 – Coventry 29 – Shrewsbury 36.

Plan of enlarged area : see Birmingham pp. 2 and 3

🏨 **Quality,** 20 Wolverhampton Rd West, Bentley, WS2 0BS, West : 2 ½ m. by A 45
ℰ (01922) 724444, Fax (01922) 723148, ⅃₅, ⇔, ◻ – ⋆ rm, 🖭 ☎ & 🅿 – 🔬 180. ◗◗ 🝗
◗ VISA JCB ⅍
Meals (carving rest.) 13.15/24.25 st. ⅃ 4.50 – � 9.50 – **155 rm** 74.25/107.00 st. – SB.

🏨 **Boundary,** Birmingham Rd, WS5 3AB, Southeast : 1 ½ m. on A 34 ℰ (01922) 63355
Fax (01922) 612034, ⅍ – ⌑, ⋆ rm, ▤ rest, 🖭 ☎ 🅿 – 🔬 65. ◗◗ ◭ ◗ VISA   CT
Meals (carving rest.) (bar lunch Monday to Saturday)/dinner 15.95 st. and a la carte ⅃ 5.75
⊑ 9.95 – **94 rm** 75.00/90.00 st. – SB.

🏨 **Travel Inn,** Bentley Rd North, Darlaston, WS2 0WB, West : 2 ¾ m. by A 454 and Bentle
South rd ℰ (01922) 724485, Fax (01922) 724098 – ⋆ rm, ▤ rest, 🖭 & 🅿. ◗◗ ◭ ◖
VISA   BT
Meals (grill rest.) – **40 rm** 38.00 t.

⑭ ATS Leamore Trading Est., Fryers Rd, Bloxwich ℰ (01922) 478631

## WALSGRAVE W. Mids. – see Coventry.

## WALTHAM ABBEY Essex 404 U 28 – pop. 15 629.

London 15 – Cambridge 44 – Ipswich 66 – Luton 30 – Southend-on-Sea 35.

🏩 **Swallow,** Old Shire Lane, EN9 3LX, Southeast : 1 ½ m. on A 121 ℰ (01992) 71717◖
Fax (01992) 711841, ⅃₅, ⇔, ◻ – ⋆ rm, ▤ rest, 🖭 ☎ ⌕ & 🅿 – 🔬 220. ◗◗ ◭ ◗ VISA
Meals 15.50/23.50 st. and a la carte ⅃ 7.00 – **163 rm** ⊑ 110.00/135.00 st. – SB.

⑭ ATS Unit 17, Lea Rd Ind. Park, Lea Rd ℰ (01992) 788050

## WALTON LE DALE Lancs. 402 M 22 – see Preston.

## WANSFORD Peterborough 404 S 26 – see Peterborough.

## WANTAGE Oxon. 403 404 P 29 – pop. 9 452.

London 71 – Oxford 16 – Reading 24 – Swindon 21.

🍴 **Boar's Head,** Church St., Ardington, OX12 8QA, East : 2 ½ m. by A 417 ℰ (01235) 833254
Fax (01235) 833254 – 🅿. ◗◗ VISA JCB
closed Sunday dinner and 25 December – **Meals** a la carte 14.00/19.75 t. ⅃ 4.45.

⑭ ATS 76 Grove St. ℰ (01235) 776 6466/7

## WARE Herts. 404 T 28 – pop. 17 000.

🛍 Whitehill, Dane End ℰ (01920) 438495.
London 24 – Cambridge 30 – Luton 22.

🏰 **Marriott Hanbury Manor H. & Country Club,** Thundridge, SG12 0SD, North : 1 ¾ m
by A 1170 on A 10 ℰ (01920) 487722, Fax (01920) 487692, ≤, ⌖, « Jacobean style mansion
in extensive grounds, walled garden », ⅃₅, ⇔, ◻, 🛍, ⅍ – ⌑, ⋆ rm, ▤ rest, 🖭 ☎ 🅿 –
🔬 100. ◗◗ ◭ ◗ VISA JCB
**Vardon :** Meals 19.50/20.00 st. and a la carte ⅃ 8.50 – (see also **Zodiac** below) – ⊑ 14.50 –
**85 rm** 145.00/200.00 st., 9 suites – SB.

XXXX **Zodiac** (at Marriott Hanbury Manor H. & Country Club), Thundridge, SG12 0SD, North :
1 ¾ m. by A 1170 on A 10 ℰ (01920) 487722, Fax (01920) 487692 – ⋆ 🅿. ◗◗ ◭ ◗ VISA
JCB
Meals 25.00/33.50 st. and a la carte ⅃ 15.00.

## WAREHAM Dorset 403 404 N 31 The West Country G. – pop. 5 644.

See : Town★ – St. Martin's★★.
Env. : Blue Pool★ AC, S : 3 ½ m. by A 351 – Bovington Tank Museum★ AC, Woolbridge
Manor★, W : 5 m. by A 352.
Exc. : Moreton Church★★, W : 9½ m. by A 352 – Corfe Castle★ (≤★★) AC, SE : 6 m. by A 351
– Lulworth Cove★, SW : 10 m. by A 352 and B 3070 – Bere Regis★ (St. John the Baptist
Church★), NW : 6½ m. by minor rd.
🛈 Trinity Church, South St., BH20 4LU ℰ (01929) 552740.
London 123 – Bournemouth 13 – Weymouth 19.

🏛 **Priory** ⌖, Church Green, BH20 4ND, ℰ (01929) 551666, Fax (01929) 554519, ≤, 斎, « Part 16C priory, riverside gardens », ⌖ – ⬇, ⅙ rest, 📺 ☎ 🅿. 🆀🅾 🅰🄴 ⓪ 𝘝𝘐𝘚𝘈, ⅍
Meals 15.95/26.50 **t.** and a la carte 32.50/44.75 **t.** ⫯ 10.00 – **17 rm** ⌖ 80.00/240.00 **t.**, 2 suites – SB.

🏛 **Springfield Country,** Grange Rd, BH20 5AL, South : 1 ¼ m. by South St. and West Lane ℰ (01929) 552177, Fax (01929) 551862, ℹ️, ⌖s, ⛴, 🄽, 🐾, 🌳, 🎾, squash – 📳, ⅙ rest, 📺 ☎ 🅿 – 🔏 200. 🆀🅾 🅰🄴 ⓪ 𝘝𝘐𝘚𝘈
Meals (bar lunch)/dinner 19.50 **st.** and a la carte ⫯ 5.50 – **46 rm** ⌖ 55.00/140.00 **st.** – SB.

🏛 **Kemps Country House,** East Stoke, BH20 6AL, West : 2 ¾ m. on A 352 ℰ (01929) 462563, Fax (01929) 405287, 🌳 – ⅙ rest, 📺 ☎ 📞 🅿 – 🔏 70. 🆀🅾 🅰🄴 ⓪ 𝘝𝘐𝘚𝘈, ⅍
Meals (closed Saturday lunch) 9.95/19.95 **t.** and a la carte ⫯ 6.50 – **14 rm** ⌖ 59.00/86.00 **t.** – SB.

🏠 **Gold Court House** without rest., St. John's Hill, BH20 4LZ, ℰ (01929) 553320, Fax (01929) 553320, « Georgian house », 🌳 – 📺 🅿. ⅍
closed Christmas-New Year – **Meals** – **3 rm** ⌖ 28.00/45.00.

---

**WAREN MILL** Northd. **401 402** O 17 – see Bamburgh.

---

**WARMINSTER** Wilts. **403 404** N 30 The West Country G. – pop. 16 379.

Env. : Longleat House★★★ AC, SW : 3 m.

Exc. : Stonehenge★★★ AC, E : 18 m. by A 36 and A 303 – Bratton Castle (≤★★) NE : 6 m. by A 350 and B 3098.

🅱 Central Car Park, BA12 9BT ℰ (01985) 218548.

London 111 – Bristol 29 – Exeter 74 – Southampton 47.

🏛 **Bishopstrow House,** BA12 9HH, Southeast : 1 ½ m. on B 3414 ℰ (01985) 212312, Fax (01985) 216769, ≤, 斎, ℹ️, ⛴, 🄽, 🐾, 🌳, park, 🎾indoor/outdoor – ⅙ rest, 📺 ☎ 🅿 – 🔏 60. 🆀🅾 🅰🄴 ⓪ 𝘝𝘐𝘚𝘈, ⅍
Meals 35.00 **t.** (dinner) and a la carte approx. 19.00 **t.** ⫯ 7.50 – ⌖ 5.50 – **28 rm** 105.00/187.00 **t.**, 3 suites – SB.

🏛 **Travelodge,** BA12 7RU, Northwest : 1 ¼ m. by B 3414 at junction of A 36 and A 350 ℰ (01985) 219539, Fax (01985) 214380, Reservations (Freephone) 0800 850950 – ⅙ rm, 📺 ⅙ 🅿. 🆀🅾 🅰🄴 ⓪ 𝘝𝘐𝘚𝘈 𝘑𝘊𝘉, ⅍
Meals (grill rest.) – **33 rm** 39.95/59.95 **t.**

**at Heytesbury** Southeast : 3 ¾ m. by B 3414 – ✉ Warminster.

🍴 **Angel Inn,** High St., BA12 0ED, ℰ (01985) 840330, Fax (01985) 840931, « 17C » – 🅿. 🆀🅾 🅰🄴 𝘝𝘐𝘚𝘈
closed 25 December – **Meals** (bar lunch Monday to Saturday)/dinner a la carte 13.75/19.75 **t.** ⫯ 7.95.

**at Crockerton** South : 1 ¾ m. by A 350 – ✉ Warminster.

🏠 **Springfield House,** BA12 8AU, on Potters Hill rd ℰ (01985) 213696, 🌳, 🎾 – ⅙ 🅿. ⅍
closed 24 to 26 December – **Meals** (by arrangement) (communal dining) 15.00 **s.** – **3 rm** ⌖ 36.00/55.00.

---

**WARRINGTON 402 403 404** M 23 – pop. 82 812.

🟢 Hill Warren, Appleton ℰ (01925) 261620 – 🟢 Walton Hall, Warrington Rd, Higher Walton ℰ (01925) 266775 – 🟢 Birchwood, Kelvin Close ℰ (01925) 818819 – 🟢 Leigh, Kenyon Hall, Culcheth ℰ (01925) 763130 – 🟢 Alder Root, Alder Root Lane, Winwick ℰ (01925) 291919.

🅱 21 Rylands St., WA1 1EJ ℰ (01925) 442180.

London 195 – Chester 20 – Liverpool 18 – Manchester 21 – Preston 28.

🏛 **Village H. and Leisure Club,** Centre Park, WA1 1QA, ℰ (01925) 240000, Fax (01925) 445240, ℹ️, ⌖s, 🄽, 🎾, squash – 📳 ⅙, 🍽 rest, 📺 ☎ ⅙ 🅿 – 🔏 250. 🆀🅾 🅰🄴 ⓪ 𝘝𝘐𝘚𝘈
Meals 12.50 **t.** (dinner) and a la carte 13.50/24.00 **t.** **87 rm** ⌖ 88.00/116.00 **t.**

🏛 **Holiday Inn Garden Court,** Woolston Grange Av., Woolston, WA1 4PX, East : 3 ¼ m. by A 57 on B 5210 at junction 21 of M 6 ℰ (01925) 838779, Fax (01925) 838859 – 📳, ⅙ rm, 🍽 rest, 📺 ☎ ⅙ 🅿. 🆀🅾 🅰🄴 ⓪ 𝘝𝘐𝘚𝘈 𝘑𝘊𝘉
Meals (closed lunch Saturday and Sunday) 13.95 **st.** (dinner) and a la carte 16.50/19.75 **st.** ⫯ 6.95 – ⌖ 9.75 – **98 rm** 75.00 **st.** – SB.

🏠 **Travel Inn,** 1430 Centre Park, Park Boulevard, WA1 1QA, ℰ (01925) 24269
Fax (01925) 244259 – |฿|, ⁑ rm, ▤ rest, 📺 ₺, ⬛⬥ ㏂ ⓪ 𝐕𝐈𝐒𝐀 ⁒
Meals (grill rest.) – 42 rm 38.00 t.

🏠 **Travel Inn,** Woburn Rd, WA2 8RN, North : 2 ¼ m. on A 49 ℰ (01925) 41441
Fax (01925) 414544 – ⁑ rm, ▤ rest, 📺 ₺ 🅿. ⬛⬥ ㏂ ⓪ 𝐕𝐈𝐒𝐀. ⁒
Meals (grill rest.) – 40 rm 38.00 t.

**at Stretton** South : 3½ m. by A 49 on B 5356 – ✉ Warrington.

🏨 **Park Royal International,** Stretton Rd, WA4 4NS, ℰ (01925) 73070
Fax (01925) 730740, ↯₆, ⤺s, ▨, ⁒ – |฿|, ⁑ rm, ▤ rest, 📺 ☎ ✆ 🅿 – 🔏 400. ⬛⬥ ㏂ ⓪ 𝐕𝐈
𝐉𝐂𝐁. ⁒
*The Harlequin :* Meals 12.95/17.95 t. and a la carte – ⌂ 8.95 – **137 rm** 106.50/116.50 t
3 suites – SB.

🏠 **Cat and Lion - Premier Lodge,** Tarporley Rd, WA4 4NB, ℰ (01925) 73045
Fax (01925) 730709, Reservations (Freephone) 0800 118833 – ⁑, ▤ rest, 📺 ☎ ✆ ₺ 🅿
⬛⬥ ㏂ ⓪ 𝐕𝐈𝐒𝐀. ⁒
Meals a la carte 10.95/13.05 t. ₰ 4.25 – ⌂ 5.95 **29 rm** 44.95 t. – SB.

🔧 ATS Grange Av., Latchford ℰ (01925) 632613

---

**WARTLING** E. Sussex 𝟒𝟎𝟒 V 31 – see Herstmonceux.

---

**WARWICK** Warks. 𝟒𝟎𝟑 𝟒𝟎𝟒 P 27 Great Britain G. – pop. 22 476.
See : Town⋆ - Castle⋆⋆ AC Y – Leycester Hospital⋆ AC Y B – Collegiate Church o
St. Mary⋆ (Tomb⋆) Y A.
🅖 Warwick Racecourse ℰ (01926) 494316 Y.
🄳 The Court House, Jury St., CV34 4EW ℰ (01926) 492212.
London 96 – Birmingham 20 – Coventry 11 – Oxford 43.

Plan opposite

🏠 **Old Fourpenny Shop,** 27-29 Crompton St., CV34 6HJ, ℰ (01926) 491360
Fax (01926) 411892 – ⁑ 📺 ☎ ✆ 🅿. ⬛⬥ ㏂ ⓪ 𝐕𝐈𝐒𝐀 𝐉𝐂𝐁. ⁒                          Y
Meals (closed Sunday and Monday) (bar lunch)/dinner 15.00 t. and a la carte ₰ 4.75 – **11 rm**
⌂ 39.50/75.00 t. – SB.

🏠 **Charter House** without rest., 87 West St., CV34 6AH, ℰ (01926) 496965
Fax (01926) 411910, « 15C », ⛱ – ⁑ 📺 ☎ 🅿. ⬛⬥ ⓪ 𝐕𝐈𝐒𝐀 𝐉𝐂𝐁. ⁒                 Y
closed 31 December and 1 January – **3 rm** ⌂ 55.00/75.00.

🏠 **Park Cottage** without rest., 113 West St., CV34 6AH, ℰ (01926) 410319
Fax (01926) 410319 – ⁑ 📺 ☎ ✆ 🅿. ⬛⬥ 𝐕𝐈𝐒𝐀. ⁒                                   Y
**4 rm** ⌂ 45.00/60.00.

**at Barford** South : 3½ m. on A 429 – Z – ✉ Warwick.

🏨 **Glebe,** Church St., CV35 8BS, on B 4462 ℰ (01926) 624218, Fax (01926) 624625, ↯₆, ⤺s
▨, ⛱ – |฿|, ▤ rest, 📺 ☎ ✆ 🅿 – 🔏 120. ⬛⬥ ㏂ ⓪ 𝐕𝐈𝐒𝐀
Meals 16.95/20.95 t. and a la carte ₰ 8.00 – **39 rm** ⌂ 100.00/150.00 st., 1 suite – SB.

**at Longbridge** Southwest : 2 m. on A 429 – Z – ✉ Warwick.

🏨 **Hilton National,** Stratford Rd, CV34 6RE, on A 429 at junction 15 of M 40
ℰ (01926) 499555, Fax (01926) 410020, ↯₆, ⤺s, ▨ – |฿|, ⁑ rm, ▤ rest, 📺 ☎ ₺ 🅿 –
🔏 300. ⬛⬥ ㏂ ⓪ 𝐕𝐈𝐒𝐀. ⁒
Meals (closed Saturday lunch) (carving lunch) 13.95/20.50 st. and dinner a la carte ₰ 7.50 –
⌂ 12.00 – **181 rm** 130.00 st. – SB.

🏠 **Holiday Inn Express** without rest., Stratford Rd, CV34 6TW, on A 429 at junction 15 of
M 40 ℰ (01926) 483033, Fax (01926) 483000 – |฿| ⁑ ▤ 📺 ☎ ✆ ₺ 🅿 – 🔏 50. ⬛⬥ ㏂ ⓪ 𝐕𝐈𝐒𝐀
𝐉𝐂𝐁. ⁒
**117 rm** 52.50 st.

**at Sherbourne** Southwest : 2¾ m. by A 429 – Z – ✉ Warwick.

🏠 **Old Rectory,** Vicarage Lane, CV35 8AB, at junction with A 46 ℰ (01926) 624562
Fax (01926) 624995, ⛱ – 📺 ☎ 🅿. ⬛⬥ ⓪ 𝐕𝐈𝐒𝐀 𝐉𝐂𝐁
Meals (dinner only) a la carte 13.00/19.50 st. ₰ 4.00 – **14 rm** ⌂ 35.00/65.00 st. – SB.

**at Hatton** Northwest : 3½ m. by A 425 on A 4177 – Z – ✉ Warwick.

🏠 **Northleigh House** without rest., Five Ways Rd, CV35 7HZ, Northwest : 2½ m. by A 4177,
turning left at roundabout with A 4141 ℰ (01926) 484203, Fax (01926) 484006, ⛱ – ⁑ 📺
🅿. ⬛⬥ 𝐕𝐈𝐒𝐀. ⁒
closed mid December-January – **7 rm** ⌂ 33.00/58.00 st.

# WARWICK
## ROYAL
## LEAMINGTON SPA

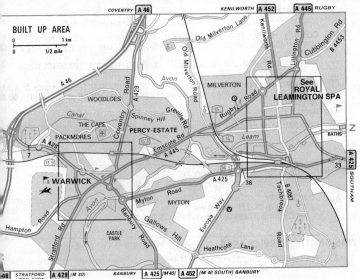

**at Shrewley** Northwest : 4 ¾ m. by A 425 and A 4177 - Z - on B 4439 – ⊠ Warwick.

  ⚚ **Shrewley House** without rest., Hockley Rd, CV35 7AT, on B 4439 ℘ (01926) 842549, Fax (01926) 842216, « Part 17C farmhouse », ☞ – ⑭ ⑳ ☎ ℗. ⓜ❸ ⓪ 𝘝𝘐𝘚𝘈. ⌘
  **3 rm** ⚁ 47.00/75.00 **st.**

**at Honiley** Northwest : 6 ¾ by A 425 on A 4177 – Z – ⊠ Warwick.

  🏨 **Honiley Court**, CV8 1NP, on A 4177 ℘ (01926) 484234, Fax (01926) 484474 – ▯, ⛶ rm,
  ⑭ ☎ ℅ ℗ – 🕭 150. ⓜ❸ ⒶⒺ ⓪ 𝘝𝘐𝘚𝘈
  **Meals** (bar lunch Saturday) 10.00/17.50 **t.** and dinner a la carte ╿ 6.25 – ⚁ 9.25 – **62 rm**
  85.00 **t.** – SB.

*Le Guide change, changez de **guide Michelin** tous les ans.*

**WARWICK SERVICE AREA** Warks. 404 P 27.

🖪 The Court House, Jury St., CV34 4EW ℘ (01926) 492212.

🏠 **Welcome Lodge,** Banbury Rd, Ashorn, CV35 0AA, M 40 (northbound) between junction 12 and 13 ℘ (01926) 651681, Fax (01926) 651634, Reservations (Freephone) 0800 73144 – 铉 rm, 📺 ሴ 🅿. 🕮 🖭 ⑩ 𝘝𝘐𝘚𝘈
Meals (grill rest.) – 🖙 7.50 – **56 rm** 50.00 **t.**

🏠 **Welcome Lodge** without rest., Banbury Rd, Ashorn, CV35 0AA, M 40 (southbour between junctions 12 and 13 ℘ (01926) 651699, Fax (01926) 651601, Reservations (Fre phone) 0800 7314466 – 铉 📺 ሴ 🅿. 🕮 🖭 ⑩ 𝘝𝘐𝘚𝘈
🖙 7.50 **40 rm** 50.00 **t.**

---

**WASDALE HEAD** Cumbria 402 K 20 – ✉ Gosforth.
London 324 – Kendal 72 – Workington 30.

🏠 **Wasdale Head Inn** ⌂, CA20 1EX, ℘ (019467) 26229, Fax (019467) 26334, ≼ Wasda Head, 🐎 – 铉 rest, ☎ 🅿. 🕮 🖭 𝘝𝘐𝘚𝘈 𝗝𝗖𝗕
Meals (bar lunch)/dinner 18.00 **st.** 🍷 5.50 – **10 rm** 🖙 39.00/78.00 **st.**, 3 suites.

---

**WASHINGBOROUGH** Lincs. 402 404 S 24 – see Lincoln.

---

**WASHINGTON** Tyne and Wear 401 402 P 19 – pop. 56 848.
🖪ᵢ₈ Washington Moat House, Stone Cellar Rd , Usworth ℘ (0191) 402 9988.
London 278 – Durham 13 – Middlesbrough 32 – Newcastle upon Tyne 7.

🏠🏠🏠 **County H. George Washington,** Stone Cellar Rd, District 12, NE37 1P ℘ (0191) 402 9988, Fax (0191) 415 1166, 🖪♨, ≋, 🗔, 🖪ᵢ₈, squash – 铉 📺 ☎ 🅿 – 🕿 200. 🕮 🖭 ⑩ 𝘝𝘐𝘚𝘈. 🕉
Meals 10.00/15.95 **st.** and a la carte 🍷 6.00 – 🖙 9.95 – **102 rm** 110.00/160.00 **st.**, 1 suite SB.

🏠🏠 **Forte Posthouse Washington,** Emerson, District 5, NE37 1LB, at junction of A 1(M with A 195 ℘ (0191) 416 2264, Fax (0191) 415 3371 – 🖪, 铉 rm, 📺 ☎ 🅿 – 🕿 100. 🕮 🖭 ⑩ 𝘝𝘐𝘚𝘈 𝗝𝗖𝗕
Meals a la carte 16.85/27.35 **st.** 🍷 7.95 – 🖙 8.95 – **138 rm** 75.00 **st.** – SB.

🏠 **Campanile,** Emerson Rd, Emerson, District 5, NE37 1LE, at junction of A 1(M) with A 19 ℘ (0191) 416 5010, Fax (0191) 416 5023 – 铉 rm, 📺 ☎ 🅿 – 🕿 30. 🕮 🖭 ⑩ 𝘝𝘐𝘚𝘈
Meals 10.85 **st.** and a la carte – 🖙 4.50 – **77 rm** 38.00 **st.**

---

**WASHINGTON** W. Sussex 404 S 31 – pop. 1 035.
London 47 – Brighton 14 – Portsmouth 32 – Worthing 6.

✕✕ **Chardonnay,** Old London Rd, RH20 3BN, North : 1 ¼ m. off A 24 (northbound carriage way) ℘ (01903) 892271 – 🕮 🖭 𝘝𝘐𝘚𝘈
closed Sunday and Monday – Meals 21.50/23.50 **t.** 🍷 6.25.

---

**WASHINGTON SERVICE AREA** Tyne and Wear 401 402 P 19 – ✉ Washington.

🏠 **Travelodge,** DH3 2SJ, on A 1(M) (southbound carriageway) ℘ (0191) 410 343₆ Fax (0191) 410 0057, Reservations (Freephone) 0800 850950 – 铉 📺 ☎ ሴ 🅿. 🕮 🖭 ⑩ 𝘝𝘐𝘚 𝗝𝗖𝗕. 🕉
Meals (grill rest.) – **36 rm** 39.95/59.95 **t.**

🏠 **Travelodge,** DH3 2SJ, on A 1(M) northbound carriageway ℘ (0191) 410 343₆ Fax (0191) 410 9258, Reservations (Freephone) 0800 850950 – 铉 rm, 📺 ሴ 🅿. 🕮 🖭 ⑩ 𝘝𝘐𝘚𝘈 𝗝𝗖𝗕. 🕉
Meals (grill rest.) – **31 rm** 39.95/59.95 **t.**

---

**HELMSLEY** N. Yorks. – see Helmsley.

---

**WATERHEAD** Cumbria 402 L 20 – see Ambleside.

---

*When looking for a quiet hotel*
*use the maps found in the introduction*
*or look for establishments with the sign* ⌂ *or* ⌂.

**WATERHOUSES** Staffs. 402 403 404 O 24 *Great Britain G.* – *pop. 1 182* – ⊠ *Stoke-on-Trent.*
Env. : *Dovedale*★★ *(Ilam Rock*★*) E : 6 m. by A 523.*
*London 115 – Birmingham 63 – Derby 23 – Manchester 39 – Stoke-on-Trent 17.*

🍴🍴  **Old Beams** (Wallis) with rm, Leek Rd, ST10 3HW, ℰ *(01538) 308254, Fax (01538) 308157,*
☸  *🖈 – ⇒ 📺 🕿 🕻 🅿, ⚙ ⚙ ⓞ VISA. ⚙*
*closed 3 weeks January and 1 week September – Meals (closed lunch Saturday and Tuesday, Sunday dinner and Monday) (booking essential) 21.00 t. (lunch) and dinner a la carte 30.40/39.65 t. ◊ 9.45 – ⊆ 6.50 – 5 rm 65.00/120.00 t.*
**Spec.** Wild mushrooms with truffle scented cappuccino sauce. Noisettes of veal, sweetbreads, asparagus and wild mushrooms. Hot chocolate gateau with clotted cream.

**WATERINGBURY** Kent 404 V 30 – see Maidstone.

**WATERMILLOCK** Cumbria 402 L 20 – see Ullswater.

**WATER YEAT** Cumbria – see Coniston.

**WATFORD** Herts. 404 S 29 – pop. 113 080.
🛇 Bushey Hall, Bushey Hall Drive ℰ *(01923) 222253, BT –* 🛇 *Bushey G. & C.C., High St.* ℰ *(0181) 950 2283, BT –* 🛇 *Oxhey Park, Prestwick Rd, South Oxhey* ℰ *(01923) 248312, AT.*
*London 21 – Aylesbury 23.*

Plan : see Greater London (North-West) p. 4

🏨  **Hilton National,** Elton Way, WD2 8HA, Watford Bypass, East : 3 ½ m. on A 41 at junction with B 462 ℰ *(01923) 235881, Fax (01923) 220836,* ⅙, ≋, ▨ – ≣, ⇒ rm, ≣ rest, 📺 🕿 🕻 🅿 – ⚙ 500. ⚙ ⚙ ⓞ VISA JCB. ⚙
BT  e
*Patio rest. : Meals (closed Saturday lunch) 14.95/19.25 st. and dinner a la carte ◊ 6.30 –*
*Patio Brasserie : Meals (closed Friday to Sunday) (dinner only) a la carte 18.70/30.25 t.*
*◊ 6.50 – ⊆ 11.25 – 194 rm 149.00/169.00 st., 1 suite – SB.*

🏨  **Jarvis International,** Watford Bypass, WD2 8HQ, East : 4 m. on A 41 ℰ *(0181) 950 6211, Fax (0181) 950 5804,* ⅙, ≋, ▨, ⚙ – ⇒, ≣ rest, 📺 🕿 🅿 – ⚙ 200. ⚙ ⚙ ⓞ VISA
*Meals (closed lunch Bank Holiday Mondays) (carving rest.) (bar lunch Saturday) 12.50/15.50 st. – ⊆ 10.50 – 217 rm 125.00/140.00 st. – SB.*
BT  a

**WATH-IN-NIDDERDALE** N. Yorks. – see Pateley Bridge.

**WEAVERHAM** Ches. 402 403 404 M 24 – pop. 6 604.
*London 191 – Chester 15 – Liverpool 28 – Manchester 28.*

🏠  **Oaklands,** Millington Lane, Gorstage, CW8 2SU, Southwest : 2 m. by A 49
ℰ *(01606) 853249, Fax (01606) 852419,* ☸ – 📺 🕿 🅿. ⚙ ⚙ ⓞ VISA
*Meals 14.95 st. (dinner) and a la carte 10.65/21.85 st. – 11 rm ⊆ 49.00/65.00 st. – SB.*

🏠  **Tall Trees Lodge** without rest., Tarporley Rd, Lower Whitley, WA4 4EZ, North : 2 ¾ m. on A 49 at junction with A 533 ℰ *(01928) 790824, Fax (01928) 791330 –* ⇒ 📺 🕿 🕻 🕹 🅿 –
⚙ 40. ⚙ ⚙ VISA
*20 rm 38.00 st.*

**WELLAND** Worcestershire 403 404 N 27 – see Great Malvern.

**WELLAND STONE** Worcestershire 403 404 N 27 – see Upton-upon-Severn.

**WELLESBOURNE** Warks. 403 404 P 27 – pop. 5 230 – see Stratford-upon-Avon.

**WELLINGBOROUGH** Northants. 404 R 27 – pop. 41 602.
🅱 *Wellingborough Library, Pebble Lane, NN8 1AS* ℰ *(01933) 228101.*
*London 73 – Cambridge 43 – Leicester 34 – Northampton 10.*

🏨  **Hind,** Sheep St., NN8 1BY, ℰ *(01933) 222827, Fax (01933) 441921 –* ⇒, ≣ rest, 📺 🕿 🅿 –
⚙ 80. ⚙ ⚙ ⓞ VISA. ⚙
*Meals 8.95/14.50 t. and a la carte ◊ 5.25 – ⊆ 8.25 – 34 rm 75.00/95.00 t. – SB.*

🏠  **Travel Inn,** London Rd, NN8 2DP, Southeast : ¾ m. on A 5193 ℰ *(01933) 278606, Fax (01933) 275947 –* ⇒ rm, 📺 🕹 🅿. ⚙ ⚙ ⓞ VISA
*Meals (grill rest.) – 40 rm 38.00 t.*

**at Finedon** Northeast : 3½ m. by A 510 – ⊠ Wellingborough.

🏠 **Tudor Gate**, High St., NN9 5JN, ℰ (01933) 680408, Fax (01933) 680745 – ✤ 🔟 ☎ 🅿
🔥 45. ⓦⓞ ◯ℰ ⓞ 🆅🅸🆂🅰 🅹🅲🅱
**Meals** 18.50 **t.** (dinner) and a la carte 21.85/43.45 **t.** ₰ 4.95 – **27 rm** ⊆ 70.00/85.00 **t.** – SB

---

**WELLINGTON** Wrekin 🟦🟦🟦 M 25 – see Telford.

---

**WELLINGTON** Somerset 🟦🟦 K 31 – pop. 11 302.
London 176 – Barnstaple 42 – Exeter 27 – Taunton 10.

🏠 **Bindon Country House** ⤳, Langford Budville, TA21 0RU, Northwest : 4 ½ m.
B 3187 following signs for Wiveliscombe from Longford Budville village ℰ (01823) 40007
Fax (01823) 400071, ≤, 🛱, « Part 17C country house with distinctive Flemish gables », ▭
🛲, ⌘ – 🔟 ☎ 🅿 – 🔥 45. ⓦⓞ ◯ℰ ⓞ 🆅🅸🆂🅰
**The Wellesley :** Meals 14.95/29.50 **st.** and a la carte 40.00/46.10 **st.** ₰ 8.50 – **12 r**
⊆ 75.00/155.00 **st.** – SB.

---

**WELLS** Somerset 🟦🟦 🟦🟦 M 30 The West Country G. – pop. 9 763.
See : City★★ – Cathedral★★★ – Vicars' Close★ – Bishop's Palace★ (≤★★) AC – St. Cuthbert
Env. : Glastonbury★★ – Abbey★★ (Abbot's Kitchen★) AC, St. John the Baptist★★, Somers
Rural Life Museum★ AC, Glastonbury Tor★ (≤★★★), SW : 5½ m. by A 39 – Wookey Hole
(Caves★ AC, Papermill★), NW : 2 m.
Exc. : Cheddar Gorge★★ (Gorge★★, Caves★, Jacob's Ladder ⚹★) – St. Andrew's Church
NW : 7 m. by A 371 – Axbridge★★ (King John's Hunting Lodge★, St. John the Bapt.
Church★), NW : 8½ m. by A 371.
🖥 East Horrington Rd ℰ (01749) 672868.
🅱 Town Hall, Market Pl., BA5 2RB ℰ (01749) 672552.
London 132 – Bristol 20 – Southampton 68 – Taunton 28.

🏠 **Swan**, 11 Sadler St., BA5 2RX, ℰ (01749) 678877, Fax (01749) 677647 – ✤ rest, 🔟 ☎ 🅿
🔥 150. ⓦⓞ ◯ℰ ⓞ 🆅🅸🆂🅰
**Meals** 13.50/17.50 **t.** ₰ 4.95 – **38 rm** ⊆ 72.50/97.50 **t.** – SB.

🏠 **The Market Place**, BA5 2RW, ℰ (01749) 672616, Fax (01749) 679670, 🛱 – 🔟 ☎ 🅿. ⓦ
◯ℰ 🆅🅸🆂🅰
closed 31 December – **Meals** (closed Sunday lunch) (booking essential) a la carte 18.0C
27.00 **t.** ₰ 7.65 – **34 rm** ⊆ 72.50/97.50 **t.** – SB.

🏠 **Beryl** ⤳, BA5 3JP, East : 1 ¼ m. by B 3139 off Hawkers Lane ℰ (01749) 67873
Fax (01749) 670508, ≤, « Victorian Gothic country house, antique furnishings », 🛋, 🛲
park – ✤ 🔟 ☎ 🅿. ⓦⓞ 🆅🅸🆂🅰
closed 24 and 25 December – **Meals** (closed Sunday) (booking essential) (residents onl
(communal dining) (dinner only) 20.00 **t.** ₰ 4.00 – **7 rm** ⊆ 50.00/85.00 **t.**

🏠 **White Hart**, Sadler St., BA5 2RR, ℰ (01749) 672056, Fax (01749) 672056 – ✤ 🔟 ☎ 🅿
🔥 60. ⓦⓞ ◯ℰ 🆅🅸🆂🅰
**Meals** (grill rest.) 15.00 **t.** (dinner) and a la carte 13.15/17.25 **t.** – **13 rm** ⊆ 50.00/70.00 **t.**
SB.

🏠 **Infield House**, 36 Portway, BA5 2BN, ℰ (01749) 670989, Fax (01749) 679093, 🛲 – ✤
🔟 🅿. ⓦⓞ 🆅🅸🆂🅰 ⌘
closed 15 to 23 January – (by arrangement) 9.50 **s.** – **3 rm** ⊆ 34.50/49.00 **s.** – SB.

🏠 **Littlewell Farm**, Coxley, BA5 1QP, Southwest : 1½ m. on A 39 ℰ (01749) 677914, 🛲
✤ 🔟 🅿. ⌘
**Meals** (by arrangement) (communal dining) 18.75 **st.** – **5 rm** ⊆ 25.00/48.00 **st.** – SB.

**at Wookey Hole** Northwest : 1¾ m. by A 371 – ⊠ Wells.

🏠 **Glencot House** ⤳, Glencot Lane, BA5 1BH, ℰ (01749) 677160, Fax (01749) 67021
« Victorian mansion built in Jacobean style », ⌂s, ⤳, 🛲, park – ✤ 🔟 ☎ 🅿 – 🔥 30. ⓦ
◯ℰ 🆅🅸🆂🅰
**Meals** (dinner only) 26.50 **st.** ₰ 5.60 – **13 rm** ⊆ 62.00/100.00 **st.** – SB.

**at Easton** Northwest : 3 m. on A 371 – ⊠ Wells.

🏠 **Beaconsfield Farm** without rest., BA5 1DU, on A 371 ℰ (01749) 870308
Fax (01749) 870166, 🛲 – ✤ 🔟 ☎ 🅿. ⌘
April-October – **3 rm** ⊆ 30.00/44.00 **st.**

**at Priddy** Northwest : 6¼ m. by A 39 – ⊠ Wells.

🏠 **Highcroft** without rest., Wells Rd, BA5 3AU, Southeast : 1¼ m. ℰ (01749) 673446, ≤, 🛲
park – ✤ 🅿. ⌘
February-October – **4 rm** ⊆ 19.00/40.00 **st.**

**WELWYN** *Herts.* 404 T 28 – *pop. 10 512 (inc. Codicote).*
London 31 – Bedford 31 – Cambridge 31.

🏠 **Tewin Bury Farm,** AL6 OJB, Southeast : 3 ½ m. by A 1000 on B 1000 ℰ (01438) 717793, Fax (01438) 840440, 綜, park – 🕥 ☎ 🅿 – 🔬 70. 🐵 🖭 *VISA*
closed Christmas-New Year – **Meals** 18.75 **st.** (dinner) and lunch a la carte 10.65/14.65 **st.** ⓘ 6.10 – **25 rm** � 70.00/99.00 **st.** – SB.

---

**WELWYN GARDEN CITY** *Herts.* 404 T 28.
🏌 *Panshanger, Old Herns Lane,* ℰ (01707) 333312 – 🏌 *Mannicotts, High Oaks Rd* ℰ (01707) 322722.
London 22 – Luton 21.

XXX **Auberge du Lac,** Brocket Hall, AL8 7XG, West : 3 m. by A 6129 on B 653 ℰ (01707) 368888, Fax (01707) 368898, ≼, 綜, « Part 18C former hunting lodge, lakeside setting », park – 🗐 🅿. 🐵 *VISA*
closed Sunday dinner and Monday – **Meals** 18.50/38.00 **t.** ⓘ 8.00.

ⓐ ATS 17 Tewin Rd ℰ (01707) 371619

---

**WEM** *Shrops.* 402 403 L 25 – *pop. 4 882* – ⊠ *Shrewsbury.*
London 167 – Birmingham 50 – Chester 32 – Stoke-on-Trent 36 – Shrewsbury 8.

🏠 **Soulton Hall,** SY4 5RS, East : 2 m. on B 5065 ℰ (01939) 232786, Fax (01939) 234097, « Part 15C manor house », ≤∿, 綜, park – ⤢ 🕥 ☎ 🅿. 🐵 ⓿ *VISA* 🅹🅲🅱. ⌦
**Meals** (booking essential) (dinner only) 25.00 **t.** ⓘ 4.95 – **5 rm** � 34.50/70.00 **t.,** 1 suite.

---

**WENDLING** *Norfolk* 404 W 25 – *see East Dereham.*

---

**WENTBRIDGE** *W. Yorks.* 402 404 Q 23 – ⊠ *Pontefract.*
London 183 – Leeds 19 – Nottingham 55 – Sheffield 28.

🏨 **Wentbridge House,** Old Great North Rd, WF8 3JJ, ℰ (01977) 620444, Fax (01977) 620148, 綜, park – 🕥 ☎ 🅿 – 🔬 120. 🐵 🖭 ⓿ *VISA*. ⌦
closed 25 December – **Meals** 14.50/21.00 **t.** and a la carte ⓘ 8.75 – **18 rm** � 69.50/105.00 **t.**

---

**WEOBLEY** *Herefordshire* 403 L 27 – *pop. 1 076* – ⊠ *Hereford.*
London 145 – Brecon 30 – Hereford 12 – Leominster 9.

🏠 **Red Lion,** HR4 8SE, ℰ (01544) 318220, Fax (01544) 319075, « 14C former inn » – 🕥 🅿. 🐵 *VISA*. ⌦
closed Christmas-February – **Meals** (residents only) (dinner only) 19.50 **st.** ⓘ 5.00 – **5 rm** � 42.50/62.50 – SB.

XX **Ye Olde Salutation Inn** with rm, Market Pitch, HR4 8SJ, ℰ (01544) 318443, Fax (01544) 318216, « Part 13C former cider house » – ⤢ 🕥 🅿. 🐵 ⓿ *VISA* 🅹🅲🅱. ⌦
**Meals** (bar meals Sunday dinner and Monday) a la carte 19.70/27.45 **t.** ⓘ 5.00 – **4 rm** � 40.00/70.00.

---

**WEST BAGBOROUGH** *Somerset* 403 K 30 – *see Taunton.*

---

**WEST BEXINGTON** *Dorset* 403 404 M 31 – ⊠ *Dorchester.*
London 150 – Bournemouth 43 – Bridport 6 – Weymouth 13.

🏨 **Manor,** Beach Rd, DT2 9DF, ℰ (01308) 897616, Fax (01308) 897035, ≼, 綜 – 🕥 ☎ 🅿. 🐵 🖭 ⓿ *VISA*. ⌦
**Meals** 15.95/22.95 **t.** – **13 rm** � 54.00/90.00 **t.** – SB.

---

**WEST BRIDGFORD** *Nottingham* 403 404 Q 25 – *see Nottingham.*

---

**WEST BROMWICH** *W. Mids.* 403 404 O 26 – *see Birmingham.*

---

**WEST BURTON** *N. Yorks.* 402 O 21 – ⊠ *Leyburn.*
London 260 – Carlisle 81 – Darlington 34 – Kendal 40 – Leeds 62 – York 58.

🏠 **The Grange,** DL8 4JR, ℰ (01969) 663348, 綜 – ⤢ rm, 🕥 🅿
**Meals** (by arrangement) (communal dining) 15.00 **st.** – **3 rm** � 30.00/50.00 – SB.

**WESTBURY** Wilts. 📖📖 N 30 – pop. 9 939 (inc. Storridge).
🖼 The Library, Edward St., BA13 3BD 🕿 (01373) 827158.
London 110 – Bristol 32 – Salisbury 24 – Swindon 38 – Yeovil 40.

🏠 **Cedar**, Warminster Rd, BA13 3PR, 🕿 (01373) 822753, Fax (01373) 858423, 🐾 – ⅙ res
📺 🕿 📵 📠 AE VISA
closed 27 December-2 January – Meals a la carte 12.95/19.50 st. ⓐ 3.95 – **16 rm** ⊇ 43.0
60.00 st.

**WEST CHILTINGTON** W. Sussex 📖 S 31 – see Pulborough.

**WESTDEAN** E. Sussex – see Seaford.

**WEST DOWN** Devon 📖 H 30.
Env. : Exmoor National Park★★ – Ilfracombe : Hillsborough (≤★★) AC, Capstone Hill★ (≤★
St. Nicholas' Chapel (≤★) AC, N : 3 m. by A 361 and minor rd.
London 221 – Exeter 52 – Taunton 59.

🏠 **Long House**, The Square, EX34 8NF, 🕿 (01271) 863242, 🐾 – 📺. ⅍
March-October – Meals (by arrangement) 14.00 st. ⓐ 4.00 – **3 rm** ⊇ 30.00/52.00 st. – SB.

**WEST HADDON** Northants. 📖📖 Q 26 – see Rugby.

> **Les prix** Pour toutes précisions sur les prix indiqués dans ce guide,
> reportez-vous aux pages de l'introduction.

**WEST ILSLEY** Newbury 📖📖 Q 29 – pop. 334 – ✉ Newbury.
London 56 – Oxford 21 – Reading 20 – Swindon 31 – Southampton 50.

🍴 **Harrow Inn**, RG20 7AR, 🕿 (01635) 281260, 🐾 – 📵 VISA
Meals (booking essential) a la carte 14.60/23.90 t.

**WESTLETON** Suffolk 📖 Y 27 – pop. 1 317 – ✉ Saxmundham.
London 97 – Cambridge 72 – Ipswich 28 – Norwich 31.

🏠 **Crown**, IP17 3AD, 🕿 (01728) 648777, Fax (01728) 648239, 🐾 – ⅙ 📺 🕿 📵 📵 AE ⓒ
VISA JCB
accommodation closed Christmas – Meals (bar lunch)/dinner 16.50 t. and a la carte ⓐ 6.45
**19 rm** ⊇ 59.50/112.50 t. – SB.

🏠 **Pond House** without rest., The Hill, IP17 3AN, 🕿 (01728) 648773, 🐾 – ⅙ 📵. ⅍
closed 23 December-1 January – **3 rm** ⊇ 44.00 st.

**WEST LULWORTH** Dorset 📖📖 N 32 The West Country G. – pop. 838 – ✉ Wareham.
See : Lulworth Cove★.
London 129 – Bournemouth 21 – Dorchester 17 – Weymouth 19.

🏠 **Cromwell House**, Main Rd, BH20 5RJ, 🕿 (01929) 400253, Fax (01929) 400566, ≤, ⊃, 🐾
– ⅙ rest, 📺 🕿 📵 AE VISA
closed Christmas and New Year – Meals (bar lunch)/dinner 15.00 t. and a la carte ⓐ 5.00
**14 rm** ⊇ 38.50/70.00 t. – SB.

🏠 **Gatton House** without rest., Main Rd, BH20 5RU, 🕿 (01929) 400252, Fax (01929) 400252
🐾 – 📺 📵. 📵 VISA
March-October – **8 rm** ⊇ 35.00/59.00 st.

**WEST MALLING** Kent 📖 V 30 – pop. 2 479.
🖼 Addington, Maidstone 🕿 (01732) 844785.
London 35 – Maidstone 7 – Royal Tunbridge Wells 14.

🏠 **Travel Inn**, Leybourne, ME19 5TR, Northwest : 1 m. on A 228 🕿 (01732) 521630
Fax (01732) 521609 – 📵. 📵 AE ① VISA. ⅍
Meals (grill rest.) – **40 rm** 38.00 t.

🏠 **Scott House** without rest., 37 High St., ME19 6QH, 🕿 (01732) 84138C
Fax (01732) 870025, « Part Georgian town house » – ⅙ 📺. 📵 AE ① VISA JCB. ⅍
closed Christmas – **3 rm** ⊇ 49.00/69.00 s.

**WESTON-SUPER-MARE** *North Somerset* 403 K 29 *The West Country G. – pop. 69 372.*

**See :** *Seafront (≤★★)* BZ.

**Exc. :** *Axbridge★★ (King John's Hunting Lodge★, St. John the Baptist Church★) SE : 9 m. by A 371 – BY – and A 38 – Cheddar Gorge★★ (Gorge★★, Caves★, Jacob's Ladder ※★) – Clevedon★ (≤★★, Clevedon Court★), NE : 10 m. by A 370 and M 5 – St. Andrew's Church★, SE : 10½ m. by A 371.*

Worlebury, Monks Hill ℘ (01934) 623214, BY – Uphill Road North ℘ (01934) 626968 AZ.

🛈 *Beach Lawns, BS23 1AT ℘ (01934) 626838.*

*London 147 – Bristol 24 – Taunton 32.*

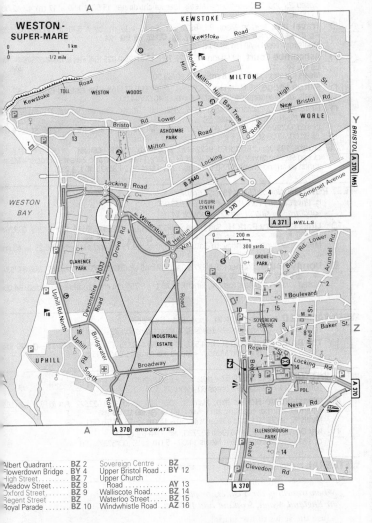

**Old Colonial,** 30 Knightstone Rd, BS23 2AW, ℘ (01934) 620739, *Fax (01934) 642725,* ≤ – TV ☎ 🅿 ⓦ AE *VISA* ⫽
BZ a
*accommodation closed 24 to 26 December –* **Meals** (in bar) 13.95 **t.** and a la carte ⓘ 5.50 – **10 rm** ⊇ 50.00/67.50 **t.** – SB.

🏛 **Commodore**, Beach Rd, Sand Bay, Kewstoke, BS22 9UZ, by Kewstoke rd (to ℰ (01934) 415778, Fax (01934) 636483 – 📺 ☎ 🅿 – 🔏 120. 🆘 🆎 *VISA*
AY
**Meals** (carving lunch Monday to Saturday)/dinner a la carte 11.00/18.50 t. 🛈 6.50 – **18 rr**
🖾 50.00/75.00 t. – SB.

🏛 **Beachlands**, 17 Uphill Rd North, BS23 4NG, ℰ (01934) 621401, Fax (01934) 621966, 🕾
🔽, 🌱 – ✦ rest, 📺 ☎ 🅿 – 🔏 25. 🆘 🆎 *VISA*. ✦
AZ
closed 24 December-5 January – **Meals** (bar lunch Monday to Saturday)/dinner 19.50 s
🛈 8.25 – **25 rm** 🖾 38.00/77.00 t. – SB.

🏛 **Queenswood**, Victoria Park, BS23 2HZ, off Upper Church Rd ℰ (01934) 41614
Fax (01934) 621759 – ✦ rest, 📺 ☎. 🆘 🆎 ① *VISA* 🇯🇨🇧
BZ
closed 25 and 26 December – **Meals** (bar lunch)/dinner 15.50 🛈 4.50 – **17 rm** 🖾 42.00
75.00 t.

🏛 **Travel Inn**, Hutton Moor Rd, BS22 8LY, East : 1 ½ m. by A 370 ℰ (01934) 62262
Fax (01934) 627401, 🌱 – ✦ rm, 📺 🕭 🅿. 🆘 🆎 ① *VISA*. ✦
BY
**Meals** (grill rest.) – **40 rm** 38.00 t.

🏠 **Ashcombe Court**, 17 Milton Rd, BS23 2SH, ℰ (01934) 625104, Fax (01934) 625104 – ✦
📺 🅿. ✦
AY
**Meals** (by arrangement) – **6 rm** 🖾 19.50/39.00.

🏠 **Milton Lodge**, 15 Milton Rd, BS23 2SH, ℰ (01934) 623161 – ✦ rest, 📺 🅿. AY
**Meals** (by arrangement) 10.00 st. – **6 rm** 🖾 40.00/44.00.

🏠 **Braeside**, 2 Victoria Park, BS23 2HZ, off Upper Church Rd ℰ (01934) 626642
Fax (01934) 626642 – ✦ rest, 📺
BZ
closed October, Christmas and New Year – **Meals** (by arrangement) 12.00 st. – **9 rm**
🖾 24.00/48.00 st.

XX **Duets**, 103 Upper Bristol Rd, BS22 8ND, ℰ (01934) 413428 – 🆘 *VISA*
BY
closed Sunday dinner, Monday, 1 week February, 1 week June and 2 weeks October – **Meal**
(lunch by arrangement) 17.50 t. (dinner) and a la carte 21.85/23.40 t. 🛈 7.95.

---

**WEST RUNTON** Norfolk 404 X 25 – ✉ Cromer.
🟦 Links Country Park Hotel ℰ (01263) 838383.
London 135 – King's Lynn 42 – Norwich 24.

🏛 **Links Country Park H.**, Sandy Lane, NR27 9QH, ℰ (01263) 838383, Fax (01263) 838264
🕾, 🔽, 🟦, 🌱, ✦ – 🛗, ✦ rest, 🍴 rest, 📺 ☎ 🅿 – 🔏 200. 🆘 *VISA*
**Meals** (bar lunch Monday to Saturday)/dinner 19.75 t. and a la carte 🛈 6.25 – **40 rm**
🖾 77.50/185.00 t. – SB.

🏛 **Dormy House**, Cromer Rd, NR27 9QA, on A 149 ℰ (01263) 837537, Fax (01263) 837537
🌱 – 🛗 📺 ☎ 🕭 🅿. 🆘 🆎 *VISA*. ✦
closed January – **Meals** (carving lunch) 10.75 t. 🛈 5.75 – **14 rm** 🖾 (dinner included) 64.00
124.00 t. – SB.

---

**WEST TANFIELD** N. Yorks. 402 P 21 – pop. 551 – ✉ Ripon.
London 237 – Darlington 29 – Leeds 32 – Middlesbrough 39 – York 36.

🍽 **The Bruce Arms**, Main St., HG4 5JJ, ℰ (01677) 470325, Fax (01677) 470796 – 🅿. 🆘 *VISA*
closed Sunday dinner and Monday – **Meals** a la carte 13.50/22.95 t.

---

**WEST WITTON** N. Yorks. 402 O 21 – pop. 325 – ✉ Leyburn.
London 241 – Kendal 39 – Leeds 60 – York 53.

🏛 **Wensleydale Heifer Inn**, Main St., DL8 4LS, ℰ (01969) 622322, Fax (01969) 624183
« Part 17C former coaching inn », 🌱 – 📺 ☎ 🅿. 🆘 🆎 ① *VISA*
**Meals** 12.50/23.50 t. and a la carte 🛈 6.50 – **14 rm** 🖾 55.00/76.00 t. – SB.

🏠 **Ivy Dene**, DL8 4LP, ℰ (01969) 622785, 🌱 – ✦ 📺 🅿. ✦
closed 24 to 26 December – **Meals** 14.00 – **5 rm** 🖾 37.00/52.00 – SB.

---

**WETHERAL** Cumbria 401 402 L 19 – see Carlisle.

---

*When travelling for business or pleasure*
*in England, Wales, Scotland and Ireland:*

- use the series of five maps
  (nos 401, 402, 403, 404 and 923) at a scale of 1:400 000

- they are the perfect complement to this Guide

**WETHERBY** W. Yorks. 402 P 22 *Great Britain G.* – pop. 8 154.

Env. : *Harewood House*★★ *(The Gallery*★*) AC*, SW : 5½ m. by A 58 and A 659.

ඕ Linton Lane, ℘ (01937) 580089.

🛈 *Council Offices, 24 Westgate, LS22 6NL ℘ (01937) 582706.*

*London 208 – Harrogate 8 – Leeds 13 – York 14.*

🏰 **Wood Hall** ⌂, Trip Lane, Linton, LS22 4JA, Southwest : 3 m. by A 661 and Linton Rd ℘ (01937) 587271, *Fax (01937) 584353*, ≼, « Part Jacobean and Georgian country house in park », ⌂, 🔲, ⌂, 🚗 – 🛗, ⇔ rest, 📺 ☎ 🅿 – 🔬 140. 🆗 🆎 ① 🝙
**Meals** *(closed Saturday lunch)* 14.95/29.95 **st.** ⅄ 9.00 – 🝙 9.95 – **41 rm** 105.00/155.00 **st.**, 1 suite – SB.

🏩 **Linton Springs** ⌂, Sicklinghall Rd, LS22 4AF, West : 1 ¾ m. by A 661 ℘ (01937) 585353, *Fax (01937) 587579*, 🚗, park, ⌂ – 📺 ☎ 🅿 – 🔬 70. 🆗 🆎 ① 🝙 ⌂
*The Gun Room :* **Meals** *(closed Sunday dinner and Monday)* (dinner only and Sunday lunch)/dinner a la carte 17.65/21.85 **t.** ⅄ 5.50 – **11 rm** 🝙 70.00/95.00 **st.**, 1 suite.

🏩 **Jarvis Wetherby,** Leeds Rd, LS22 5HE, West : ½ m. on A 58 ℘ (01937) 583881, *Fax (01937) 580062* – ⇔ 📺 ☎ ⌂ 🅿 – 🔬 150. 🆗 🆎 ① 🝙
**Meals** (carving lunch) (bar lunch Saturday) 11.50/14.95 **t.** and dinner a la carte ⅄ 6.50 – 10.95 – **103 rm** 85.00/110.00 **st.** – SB.

---

**WETHERSFIELD** Essex 404 V 28 – pop. 1 204 – ⊠ Braintree.

*London 52 – Cambridge 31 – Chelmsford 19 – Colchester 22.*

✗✗ **Dicken's,** The Green, CM7 4BS, ℘ (01371) 850723, *Fax (01371) 850723*, « Part 17C house » – 🅿. 🆗 🝙
*closed Sunday dinner, Monday, Tuesday, 25-26 December and Bank Holidays –* **Meals** 10.00 **t.** (lunch) and a la carte 19.20/26.70 **t.** ⅄ 7.00.

---

**WEYBRIDGE** Surrey 404 S 29 – pop. 52 802 *(inc. Walton).*

*London 23 – Crawley 27 – Guildford 17 – Reading 33.*

🏰 **Oatlands Park,** Oatlands Drive, KT13 9HB, Northeast : ¾ m. by A 317 on A 3050 ℘ (01932) 847242, *Fax (01932) 842252*, ⌂, 🚗, park, ⌂ – 🛗, ⇔ rm, 📺 ☎ ⌂ 🅿 – 🔬 300. 🆗 🆎 ① 🝙
**Meals** (bar lunch Saturday) 19.00/25.00 **st.** and a la carte ⅄ 6.00 – 🝙 11.50 – **125 rm** 🝙 100.00/140.00 **st.**, 5 suites – SB.

🏩 **Ship Thistle,** Monument Green, High St., KT13 8BQ, off A 317 ℘ (01932) 848364, *Fax (01932) 857153* – ⇔ rm, 🗖 rest, 📺 ☎ 🅿 – 🔬 150. 🆗 🆎 ① 🝙 🝙
**Meals** (bar lunch Saturday) 13.75/19.75 **t.** and a la carte ⅄ 6.75 – 🝙 11.00 – **39 rm** 110.00/125.00 **st.** – SB.

✗✗✗ **Casa Romana,** 2 Temple Hall, Monument Hill, KT13 8RH, on A 317 ℘ (01932) 843470, *Fax (01932) 845221* – 🗖 🅿. 🆗 🆎 ① 🝙
*closed Saturday lunch, 25-26 December and Bank Holidays –* **Meals** - Italian - 14.95/18.95 **st.** and a la carte ⅄ 6.95.

---

**WEYMOUTH** Dorset 403 404 M 32 *The West Country G.* – pop. 46 065.

See : *Town*★ – *Timewalk*★ *AC* – *Nothe Fort* (≼★) *AC* – *Boat Trip*★ *(Weymouth Bay and Portland Harbour) AC.*

Env. : *Chesil Beach*★★ – *Portland*★ – *Portland Bill* (⁂★★) S : 2½ m. by A 354.

Exc. : *Maiden Castle*★★ (≼★) N : 6 ½ m. by A 354 – *Abbotsbury*★★ *(Swannery*★ *AC, Sub-Tropical Gardens*★ *AC, St. Catherine's Chapel*★*) NW : 9 m. by B 3157.*

ඕ Links Road ℘ (01305) 773981.

🛈 *The King's Statue, The Esplanade, DT4 7AN ℘ (01305) 785747.*

*London 142 – Bournemouth 35 – Bristol 68 – Exeter 59 – Swindon 94.*

🏩 **Moonfleet Manor** ⌂, DT3 4ED, Northwest : 4 ½ m. by B 3157 ℘ (01305) 786948, *Fax (01305) 774395*, ≼, ⌂, 🔲, 🚗, ⌂, squash – ⇔ rest, 📺 ☎ 🅿 – 🔬 60. 🆗 🆎 ① 🝙 🝙 ⌂
**Meals** (bar lunch Monday to Saturday)/dinner 18.50 **t.** and a la carte – **38 rm** 🝙 60.00/175.00 **t.**, 2 suites – SB.

🏩 **Rex,** 29 The Esplanade, DT4 8DN, ℘ (01305) 760400, *Fax (01305) 760500* – 🛗 📺 ☎ ⌂. 🆗 🆎 ① 🝙
*closed 24 to 30 December –* **Meals** (bar lunch)/dinner 11.25 **t.** and a la carte – **31 rm** 🝙 51.50/89.50 **t.** – SB.

🏠 **Bay Lodge,** 27 Greenhill, DT4 7SW, ℘ (01305) 782419, *Fax (01305) 782828* – ⇔ rest, 📺 ☎ 🅿. 🆗 🆎 ① 🝙 ⌂
**Meals** *(closed Friday and Saturday)* (dinner only) a la carte 13.95/23.95 **st.** ⅄ 4.95 – **12 rm** 🝙 31.00/62.00 **st.** – SB.

↑ **Chatsworth**, 14 The Esplanade, DT4 8EB, ℰ (01305) 785012, Fax (01305) 766342 – 📺 📶
⏱ 🐝 *VISA*. ✇
**Meals** 16.00 st. – **9 rm** ☲ 32.00/64.00 t., 1 suite – SB.

✕ **Perry's**, The Old Harbour, 4 Trinity Rd, DT4 8TJ, ℰ (01305) 785799 – 🐝 *VISA*
*closed lunch Monday and Saturday, Sunday dinner September-March, 1 January an*
*25-26 December* – **Meals** a la carte 15.50/24.50 t. ⓘ 6.00.

---

**WHALLEY** Lancs. 402 M 22 – pop. 5 364 – ⊠ Blackburn.
🔂 Long Leese Barn, Clerkhill ℰ (01254) 822236.
London 233 – Blackpool 32 – Burnley 12 – Manchester 28 – Preston 15.

🏛 **Foxfields Country**, Whalley Rd, Billington, BB7 9HY, Southwest : 1 ¼ m
ℰ (01254) 822556, Fax (01254) 824613, ▮₆, 🈺, 🔲, 🚿 – 🐝, 📇 rest, 📺 ☎ 🕭 🕐 – 🔬 15⓪
🐝 🅰🅴 ⓪ *VISA*
**Expressions :** **Meals** (bar lunch Saturday) (dancing Saturday evening) 10.50/18.95 s⓪
and a la carte – **18 rm** ☲ 90.00/120.00 st., **26 suites** 120.00 st. – SB.

---

**WHAPLODE** Lincs. 402 404 T 25 – pop. 1 929 – ⊠ Spalding.
London 106 – Lincoln 45 – Leicester 61 – Norwich 60.

↑ **Guy Wells** ⟫, Eastgate, PE12 6TZ, East : ½ m. by A 151 ℰ (01406) 422239⓪
Fax (01406) 422239, « Queen Anne house », 🚿 – 🚿 🕐. ✇
*closed 25-26 and 31 December and 1 January* – **Meals** (by arrangement) 12.00 st. – **3 rm**
☲ 25.00/44.00 st.

---

**WHASHTON** N. Yorks. – see Richmond.

---

**WHEATLEY** Oxon. 403 404 Q 28 – see Oxford.

---

**WHEELOCK** Ches. – see Sandbach.

---

**WHIMPLE** Devon 403 J 31 – see Exeter.

---

**WHITBY** N. Yorks. 402 S 20 Great Britain G. – pop. 13 640.
See : Abbey★.
🔂 Sandsend Rd, Low Straggleton ℰ (01947) 602768.
🅱 Langborne Rd, YO21 1YN ℰ (01947) 602674.
London 257 – Middlesbrough 31 – Scarborough 21 – York 45.

🏠 **Bagdale Hall**, 1 Bagdale, YO21 1QL, ℰ (01947) 602958, Fax (01947) 820714, « Part 16C »
– 🚿 rest, 📺 ☎ 🕐. 🐝 🅰🅴 ⓪ *VISA*. ✇
**Meals** (dinner only and Sunday lunch)/dinner a la carte 13.30/29.40 t. ⓘ 5.50 – **6 rm**
☲ 54.00/98.00 t.

↑ **Crescent House**, 6 East Cres., YO21 3HD, ℰ (01947) 600091, Fax (01947) 600091, ≼ –
🚿 📺
*19 March-13 November* – **Meals** (by arrangement) 9.00 s. – **6 rm** ☲ 38.00/42.00 s.

**at Dunsley** West : 3 ¼ m. by A 171 – ⊠ Whitby.

🏛 **Dunsley Hall** ⟫, YO21 3TL, ℰ (01947) 893437, Fax (01947) 893505, ≼, ▮₆, 🈺, 🔲, 🚿
🚿 – 🚿 📺 ☎ 🕐. 🐝 🅰🅴 ⓪. ✇
**Meals** (light lunch Monday to Saturday) 14.95/24.95 t. and a la carte ⓘ 7.95 – **18 rm**
☲ 65.00/119.90 t. – SB.

---

**WHITEPARISH** Wilts. 403 404 P 30 – see Salisbury.

---

**WHITEWELL** Lancs. 402 M 22 – pop. 5 617 – ⊠ Clitheroe.
London 281 – Lancaster 31 – Leeds 55 – Manchester 41 – Preston 13.

🏛 **Inn at Whitewell**, Forest of Bowland, BB7 3AT, ℰ (01200) 448222, Fax (01200) 448298,
≼, « Memorabilia », 🐟, 🚿 – 📺 ☎ 🕐. 🐝 🅰🅴 ⓪ *VISA* 🇯🇨🇧
**Meals** (bar lunch)/dinner a la carte 14.30/31.80 t. ⓘ 4.60 – **14 rm** ☲ 50.00/83.00 st.,
1 suite.

---

**WHITLEY** W. Yorks. 402 P 23 – see Dewsbury.

**WHITLEY** Wilts. – see Melksham.

---

**WHITLEY BAY** Tyne and Wear 401 402 P 18 – pop. 33 335.
🛈 Park Rd, NE26 1EJ ℘ (0191) 200 8535.
London 295 – Newcastle upon Tyne 10 – Sunderland 10.

🏨 **Windsor,** South Par., NE26 2RF, ℘ (0191) 251 8888, Fax (0191) 297 0272 – 🛗, 🍽 rest, 📺
☎ 🅿 – 🔬 100. 🐵 🅰🅴 ⑩ 𝘝𝘐𝘚𝘈
Meals (bar lunch)/dinner a la carte 11.95/23.45 st. ⑧ 5.00 – **63 rm** ⥁ 59.00/70.00 st.

◎ ATS John St., Cullercoats ℘ (0191) 253 3903

---

**WHITNEY-ON-WYE** Herefordshire 403 K 27 – pop. 133 – ✉ Hereford.
London 150 – Birmingham 56 – Cardiff 73 – Hereford 17.

🏨 **Rhydspence Inn,** HR3 6EU, West : 1 ½ m. on A 438 ℘ (01497) 831262,
Fax (01497) 831751, « Part 14C », 🍴 – 📺 🅿. 🐵 🅰🅴 𝘝𝘐𝘚𝘈. 🦅
closed 25 December and 2 weeks January – Meals a la carte 19.95/31.95 ⑧ 4.95 – **7 rm**
⥁ 37.50/75.00 t. – SB.

---

**WHITSTABLE** Kent 404 X 29 – pop. 28 907 – ✉ Whitstable.
London 68 – Dover 24 – Maidstone 37 – Margate 12.

🏨 **Continental,** Beach Walk, CT5 2BP, ℘ (01227) 280280, Fax (01227) 280257, ≤ – ⇄ rm,
📺 🅿. 🐵 🅰🅴 ⑩ 𝘝𝘐𝘚𝘈. 🦅
Meals 9.50/12.50 t. and a la carte – **23 rm** ⥁ 35.00/70.00.

🏨 **Travel Inn,** Thanet Way, CT5 3OB, Southwest : 2 m. by A 290 ℘ (01227) 272459 – ⇄ rm,
📺 🅿. 🐵 🅰🅴 ⑩ 𝘝𝘐𝘚𝘈. 🦅
Meals (grill rest.) – **40 rm** 38.00 t.

↑ **Barnfield at Windyridge** 🦢, Wraik Hill, CT5 3BY, Southwest : 2 m. off A 290
℘ (01227) 263506, Fax (01227) 771191, ≤, 🍴 – 📺 🅿. 🐵 𝘝𝘐𝘚𝘈. 🦅
Meals (by arrangement) 15.00 s. ⑧ 5.00 – **8 rm** ⥁ 20.00/60.00 st. – SB.

✗ **Whitstable Oyster Fishery Co.,** Royal Native Oyster Stores, The Horsebridge, CT5
1BU, ℘ (01227) 276856, Fax (01227) 770666, ≤, « Converted warehouse on beach » – 🐵
🅰🅴 ⑩ 𝘝𝘐𝘚𝘈
closed Sunday dinner, Monday and 25, 26 and 31 December – Meals - Seafood - a la carte
18.45/28.95 t. ⑧ 6.50.

---

**at Thanet Way Service Area** Southwest : 3 ¼ m. by A 290 on A 299 – ✉ Faversham.

🏨 **Travelodge,** ME13 9EL, (eastbound carriageway) ℘ (01227) 770980, Reservations (Freephone) 0800 850950 – ⇄ rm, 📺 🅿. 🐵 🅰🅴 ⑩ 𝘝𝘐𝘚𝘈 𝘑𝘊𝘉. 🦅
Meals (grill rest.) – **40 rm** 39.95/59.95 t.

---

**WHITTLE-LE-WOODS** Lancs. 402 M 23 – see Chorley.

---

**WHITWELL-ON-THE-HILL** N. Yorks. 402 R 21 – pop. 136 – ✉ York.
London 229 – Leeds 39 – Middlesbrough 60 – Scarborough 29.

🏠 **The Stone Trough Inn,** Kirkham Abbey, YO6 7JJ, East : 1 m. ℘ (01653) 618713,
Fax (01653) 618819, 🏡, 🍴 – ⇄ 🅿. 🐵 𝘝𝘐𝘚𝘈 𝘑𝘊𝘉
closed Monday and 25 December – Meals (in bar Tuesday to Saturday lunch and Sunday
dinner) a la carte 17.20/20.00 t. ⑧ 5.25.

---

**WICKFORD** Essex 404 V 29 – see Basildon.

---

**WICKHAM** Hants. 403 404 Q 31 – pop. 2 941.
London 74 – Portsmouth 12 – Southampton 11 – Winchester 16.

🏨 **Old House,** The Square, PO17 5JG, ℘ (01329) 833049, Fax (01329) 833672, « Queen Anne
house », 🍴 – 📺 🅿. 🐵 🅰🅴 ⑩ 𝘝𝘐𝘚𝘈. 🦅
closed 2 weeks August, 2 weeks Christmas and Bank Holidays Meals (closed Sunday and
Monday) 20.00/30.00 t. ⑧ 7.75 – **8 rm** 75.00/90.00 t.

---

**WIDEGATES** Cornwall 403 G 32 – see Looe.

**WIDNES** Halton 402 403 404 L 23 – pop. 57 162.

🏕 Highfield Rd ℘ (0151) 424 2440.

London 205 – Liverpool 19 – Manchester 27 – Stoke-on-Trent 42.

🏨 **Everglades Park,** Derby Rd, WA8 3UJ, Northeast : 3 m. by A 568 on A 508
℘ (0151) 495 2040, Fax (0151) 424 6536 – � rm, 🍴 rest, 📺 ☎ 🅿 – 🕍 200. 🌕🔟 🖭 ⓞ 𝗩𝗜.
JCB. ⚘
Meals (closed Saturday lunch) (bar lunch)/dinner 15.95 **t.** and a la carte 🝙 5.85 – ⌑ 8.95
**65 rm** 70.00/80.00 **t.** – SB.

**at Cronton** Northwest : 2 m. by A 568 on A 5080 – ⊠ Widnes.

🏨 **Hillcrest,** Cronton Lane, WA8 9AR, ℘ (0151) 424 1616, Fax (0151) 495 1348 – ▐ 📺 ☎ 🅿
🕍 120. 🌕🔟 🖭 ⓞ 𝗩𝗜𝗦𝗔
Meals (bar lunch Saturday) (carving lunch Sunday)/dinner 14.95 **t.** and a la carte 10.85
27.20 🝙 5.95 – **50 rm** ⌑ 64.00/125.00 **st.** – SB.

ⓘ ATS Tanhouse Lane ℘ (0151) 424 3011/2945

---

**WIGAN** Gtr. Manchester 402 M 23 – pop. 85 819.
London 203 – Liverpool 18 – Manchester 24 – Preston 18.

🏨 **The Bellingham,** 149 Wigan Lane, WN1 2NB, North : 1 ¼ m. on A 49 ℘ (01942) 243893
Fax (01942) 821027 – ▐ ⇔axe 📺 ☎ 🅿 – 🕍 100. 🌕🔟 🖭 ⓞ 𝗩𝗜𝗦𝗔 ⚘
Meals (lunch by arrangement) 15.75 **t.** and a la carte 🝙 6.50 – **32 rm** ⌑ 59.50/89.50 **st.** – SB

🏨 **Wigan Oak,** Riverway, WN1 3SS, access by Orchard St. ℘ (01942) 826888
Fax (01942) 825800 – ▐, ⇔axe rm, 📺 ☎ 🅿 – 🕍 200. 🌕🔟 🖭 ⓞ 𝗩𝗜𝗦𝗔. ⚘
Meals (closed 26 December and 1 January) 15.95 **st.** (dinner) and a la carte 16.45/22.95 **st**
🝙 5.95 – **88 rm** ⌑ 82.00/98.00 **st.** – SB.

🏨 **Travel Inn,** Warrington Rd, Marus Bridge, WN3 6XB, South : 2 ¾ m. on A 49
℘ (01942) 493469, Fax (01942) 498679 – ⇔axe rm, 📺 ⚳ 🅿. 🌕🔟 🖭 ⓞ 𝗩𝗜𝗦𝗔
Meals (grill rest.) – **41 rm** 38.00 **t.**

🏨 **Travel Inn,** Orrell Rd, Orrell, WN5 8HQ, West : 3 ½ m. on A 577 ℘ (01942) 211516
Fax (01942) 215002 – ⇔axe 📺 ⚳ 🅿 – 🕍 80. 🌕🔟 🖭 ⓞ 𝗩𝗜𝗦𝗔. ⚘
Meals (grill rest.) – **40 rm** 38.00 **t.**

**at Up Holland** West : 4 ¾ m. on A 577 – ⊠ Wigan.

🏨 **Quality Hotel Skelmersdale,** Prescott Rd, WN8 9PU, Southwest : 2 ¾ m. by A 577 and
Stannanought Rd ℘ (01695) 720401, Fax (01695) 50953 – ⇔axe rm, 🍴 rest, 📺 ☎ ⚳ 🅿 –
🕍 200. 🌕🔟 🖭 ⓞ 𝗩𝗜𝗦𝗔. ⚘
9.50/16.95 **st.** and a la carte 🝙 4.50 – ⌑ 9.50 – **55 rm** 63.25/96.00 **st.** – SB.

ⓘ ATS 98 Warrington Rd, Newtown ℘ (01942) 242017/242442

---

**WIGHT (Isle of)** 403 404 PQ 31 32 Great Britain G. – pop. 124 577.

See : Island★★.

Env. : Osborne House, East Cowes★★ AC – Carisbrooke Castle, Newport★★ AC (Keep ⩽★ ) –
Brading★ (Roman Villa★ AC, St. Mary's Church★, Nunwell House★ AC) – Shorwell
St. Peter's Church★ (wall paintings★ ).

🚢 from East Cowes to Southampton (Red Funnel Ferries) frequent services daily (55 mn.
– from Yarmouth to Lymington (Wightlink Ltd) frequent services daily (30 mn) – from
Fishbourne to Portsmouth (Wightlink Ltd) frequent services daily (35 mn).

🚤 from Ryde to Portsmouth (Hovertravel Ltd) frequent services daily (10 mn) – from Ryde
to Portsmouth (Wightlink Ltd) frequent services daily (15 mn).

**Alverstone** – ⊠ Isle of Wight.

🏠 **Grange** ⧇ without rest., PO36 0EZ, ℘ (01983) 403729, Fax (01983) 403729, 🎠 – ⇔axe 🅿
⚘
closed December and January – **6 rm** ⌑ 20.00/48.00 **st.**

**Chale** – pop. 717 – ⊠ Isle of Wight.
Newport 9.

🏨 **Clarendon H. and Wight Mouse Inn,** Newport Rd, PO38 2HA, ℘ (01983) 730431,
Fax (01983) 730431, ⩽, 🎠 – 📺 ☎ 🅿. 🌕🔟 𝗩𝗜𝗦𝗔 ⚘
Meals 10.00/15.00 **st.** and a la carte 🝙 5.00 – **14 rm** ⌑ 39.00/78.00 **st.**, 1 suite – SB.

🏨 **Chale Bay Farm,** PO38 2JF, ℘ (01983) 730950, Fax (01983) 730395, ⩽, 🎠 – ⇔axe rest, 📺
☎ 🅿. 🌕🔟 𝗩𝗜𝗦𝗔. ⚘
Meals (closed Tuesday lunch and Sunday to Wednesday dinner) a la carte 10.90/16.90 **st.**
🝙 5.00 – **10 rm** ⌑ 39.00/78.00 **st.**

**Cowes** – *pop. 16 335* – ✉ *Isle of Wight.*

⛳9 *Osborne, Osborne House Estate, East Cowes* ℘ *(01983) 295421.*

[i] *The Arcade, Fountain Quay, PO31 7AR* ℘ *(01983) 291914.*

*Newport 4.*

🏨 **New Holmwood,** Queens Rd, Egypt Point, PO31 8BW, ℘ (01983) 292508, *Fax (01983) 295020,* < – ▤ rest, [TV] ☎ [P] – 🎤 150. [MC] [AE] [D] VISA JCB
**Meals** (carving lunch Sunday) 11.50/16.50 **t.** 🍷 4.50 – **24 rm** ☕ 67.50/95.00 **st.**, 2 suites – SB.

**Freshwater** – *pop. 7 317 (inc. Totland)* – ✉ *Isle of Wight.*

*Newport 13.*

⌂ **Rockstone Cottage,** Colwell Chine Rd, PO40 9NR, Northwest : ¾ m. by A 3055 off A 3054 ℘ (01983) 753723, 🌳 – 🚭 rm, [TV] [P]
**Meals** (by arrangement) 12.00 **st.** 🍷 5.00 – **5 rm** ☕ 25.00/50.00 **st.** – SB.

🍴 **Red Lion,** Church Pl., PO40 9BP, ℘ (01983) 754925, *Fax (01983) 754925,* ⛱, « Part 14C » – [P]. [MC] VISA
*closed 25 December* – **Meals** a la carte 14.90/21.00 **t.**

**Niton** – ✉ *Isle of Wight.*

🏨 **Windcliffe Manor** 🐌, Sandrock Rd, Undercliff, PO38 2NG, ℘ (01983) 730215, *Fax (01983) 730215,* 🏊, 🌳 – 🚭 rest, [TV] ☎ 📞 [P]. [MC] [AE] [D] VISA JCB
**Meals** (light lunch Monday to Saturday)/dinner a la carte approx. 17.95 **t.** 🍷 5.85 – **14 rm** ☕ (dinner included) 61.85/109.70 **t.** – SB.

**Ryde** – ✉ *Isle of Wight.*

⛳9 *Binstead Rd* ℘ *(01983) 614809.*

[i] *81-83 Union St., PO33 2LW* ℘ *(01983) 562905.*

*Newport 7.*

⌂ **Little Upton Farm** 🐌 without rest., Gatehouse Rd, Ashey, PO33 4BS, Southwest : 2 m. by West St. ℘ (01983) 563236, *Fax (01983) 563236,* <, « 17C farmhouse, working farm », 🌳, park – 🚭 [TV] [P]
*closed 25 and 26 December* – **3 rm** ☕ 20.00/40.00 **s.**

**St. Lawrence** – ✉ *Isle of Wight.*

*Newport 16.*

⌂ **Little Orchard** without rest., Undercliffe Drive, PO38 1YA, West : 1 m. on A 3055 ℘ (01983) 731106, 🌳 – 🚭 [TV] [P]. 🚫
**3 rm** ☕ 25.00/38.00.

**Seaview** – *pop. 2 181* – ✉ *Isle of Wight.*

🏨 **Seaview,** High St., PO34 5EX, ℘ (01983) 612711, *Fax (01983) 613729* – 🚭 [TV] ☎ [P]. [MC] [AE] [D] VISA JCB
*closed Christmas* – **Meals** – (see ***The Restaurant and Sunshine Room*** below) – **14 rm** ☕ 55.00/88.00 **t.**, 2 suites – SB.

XX **The Restaurant and Sunshine Room** (at Seaview H.), High St., PO34 5EX, ℘ (01983) 612711, *Fax (01983) 613729,* ⛱ – 🚭 ▤ [P]. [MC] [AE] [D] VISA JCB
**Meals** (in bar Sunday dinner) a la carte 18.95/25.85 **t.** 🍷 4.50.

**Shanklin** – *pop. 17 305 (inc. Sandown)* – ✉ *Isle of Wight.*

⛳18 *Fairway Lake, Sandown* ℘ *(01983) 403217.*

[i] *67 High St., PO37 6JJ* ℘ *(01983) 862942.*

*Newport 9.*

🏨 **Brunswick,** Queens Rd, PO37 6AN, ℘ (01983) 863245, *Fax (01983) 868398,* ≘, 🏊, [🏊], 🌳 – 🚭 rest, [TV] ☎ [P]. [MC] VISA
*closed January and December* – **Meals** (dinner only) 14.50 **st.** 🍷 4.50 – **32 rm** ☕ 40.00/80.00 **st.** – SB.

🏨 **Bourne Hall Country** 🐌, Luccombe Rd, PO37 6RR, ℘ (01983) 862820, *Fax (01983) 865138,* ≘, 🏊, [🏊], 🌳, 🎾 – 🚭 rest, [TV] ☎ 📞 [P]. [MC] [AE] VISA. 🚫
*closed mid November-24 December and 1 January-mid February* – **Meals** (bar lunch)/dinner a la carte 19.75/26.75 **t.** 🍷 4.75 – **30 rm** ☕ 40.00/75.00 **t.**

🏨 **Rylstone Manor** 🐌, Rylstone Gdns., PO37 6RG, ℘ (01983) 862806, « Part Victorian », 🌳 – 🚭 [TV] [P]. [MC] [AE] [D] VISA JCB. 🚫
*closed January and November* – **Meals** (residents only) (dinner only) 14.50 **t.** 🍷 5.50 – **9 rm** ☕ 34.00/68.00 **st.**

**Luccombe Chine Country House** 🐦, Luccombe Chine, PO37 6RH, South : 2 ¼ m. b
A 3055 ☎ (01983) 862037, *Fax (01983) 862037*, ←, 🌳 – 🚭 rest, [TV] [P]. [MC] [VISA]. 🐕
*closed January and December* – **Meals** (dinner only) 15.00 **t.** 🍷 6.00 – **6 rm** ☕ (dinne
included) 70.00/100.00 **t.** – SB.

**Grange Bank,** Grange Rd, PO37 6NN, ☎ (01983) 862337, *Fax (01983) 862737* – 🚭 [TV] ☎
[P]. 🐕
*April-October* – **Meals** (booking essential) (residents only) (dinner only) (unlicensed) 6.00 **s.** -
**9 rm** ☕ 22.00/44.00 **s.** – SB.

## Totland – *pop. 7 317 (inc. Freshwater)* – ✉ *Isle of Wight.*

*Newport 13.*

**Sentry Mead,** Madeira Rd, PO39 0BJ, ☎ (01983) 753212, *Fax (01983) 753212*, 🌳 –
🚭 rest, [TV] [P]. [MC] [VISA] [JCB]
*closed last week December-first week January* – **Meals** (bar lunch)/dinner 15.00 **t.** 🍷 5.00 -
**14 rm** ☕ 35.00/70.00 **t.** – SB.

**Littledene Lodge,** Granville Rd, PO39 0AX, ☎ (01983) 752411 – 🚭 rest, [P]. [MC] [VISA]
**Meals** (by arrangement) 12.00 **st.** 🍷 3.00 – **7 rm** ☕ 19.50/44.00 **st.** – SB.

## Ventnor – *pop. 5 978* – ✉ *Isle of Wight.*

*⛳9 Steephill Down Rd ☎ (01983) 853326.*
*[i] 34 High St., PO38 1RZ ☎ (01983) 853625 (summer only).*
*Newport 10.*

**Royal,** Belgrave Rd, PO38 1JJ, ☎ (01983) 852186, *Fax (01983) 855395*, 🌳 – [lift] 🚭 [TV] ☎ 📞
[P] – 🧑‍🏫 40. [MC] [AE] [DC] [VISA]
**Meals** (light lunch Monday to Saturday)/dinner 22.00 **t.** and a la carte 🍷 6.00 – **54 rm**
☕ 60.00/136.00 **t.**, 1 suite – SB.

**Winterbourne** 🐦, Bonchurch, PO38 1RQ, via Bonchurch Shute ☎ (01983) 852535,
*Fax (01983) 853056*, « Country house ← gardens and sea », 🏊 – 🚭 rest, [TV] ☎ [P]. [MC] [AE]
[VISA]
*April-November* – **Meals** (dinner only) 16.95 **t.** 🍷 8.70 – **13 rm** ☕ (dinner included) 59.00/
155.00 **t.**, 1 suite.

**Lake** 🐦, Shore Rd, Bonchurch, PO38 1RF, ☎ (01983) 852613, 🌳 – 🚭 [TV] [P]
*March-October* – **Meals** (dinner only) 8.00 **st.** 🍷 4.80 – **20 rm** ☕ 27.00/54.00 – SB.

## Yarmouth – ✉ *Isle of Wight.*

*Newport 10.*

**The George,** Quay St., PO41 0PE, ☎ (01983) 760331, *Fax (01983) 760425*, ←, ⛱, « 17C
former governors residence », 🌳 – ▤ rest, [TV] ☎ 📞 – 🧑‍🏫 40. [MC] [AE] [DC] [VISA]
✿ ***The Restaurant* : Meals** *(closed Sunday dinner and Monday)* (booking essential) (dinner
only and Sunday lunch)/dinner 36.75 **t.** 🍷 5.95 – (see also below) – **15 rm** ☕ 80.00/185.00 **t.**,
1 suite – SB
**Spec.** Red mullet with couscous and tomato dressing. Pan-fried loin of lamb, black olive
and lamb sausage. Rhubarb and almond tart, cranberry sorbet.

🍴 **The Brasserie** (at The George H.), Quay St., PO41 0PE, ☎ (01983) 760331,
*Fax (01983) 760425* – [MC] [AE] [VISA]
**Meals** a la carte 16.65/25.85 **t.** 🍷 5.95.

---

**WIGSTON** *Leics.* [402] [403] [404] Q 26 – *see Leicester.*

---

**WILLERBY** *East Riding* [402] S 22 – *see Kingston-upon-Hull.*

---

**WILLERSEY** *Glos.* [403] [404] O 27 – *see Broadway (Worcestershire).*

---

**WILLERSEY HILL** *Glos.* [403] [404] O 27 – *see Broadway (Worcestershire).*

---

**WILLESLEY** *Glos.* [403] [404] N 29 – *see Tetbury.*

*Wenn Sie ein ruhiges Hotel suchen,*
*benutzen Sie zuerst die Karte in der Einleitung*
*oder wählen Sie im Text ein Hotel mit dem Zeichen 🐦 oder 🐦.*

**WILLITON** Somerset **403** K 30 *The West Country G. – pop. 2 025 –* ✉ *Taunton.*
Env. : *Exmoor National Park*★★ *– Cleeve Abbey*★★ *AC, W : 2 m. by A 39.*
*London 177 – Minehead 8 – Taunton 16.*

🏠 **White House,** 11 Long St., TA4 4QW, ℰ (01984) 632306 – ⇜ rest, 📺 ☎ 🅿
*mid May-early November –* **Meals** *(dinner only)* 31.00 **t.** ⓘ 8.50 – **10 rm** ⊇ 58.00/94.00 **t.** –
SB.

🏠 **Curdon Mill** ⬎, Lower Yellow, TA4 4LS, Southeast : 2 ½ m. by A 358 on Stogumber rd
ℰ (01984) 656522, Fax (01984) 656197, ≼, « Converted water mill on working farm », ⬥,
⬥, 🐎, park – ⇜ 📺 🅿 🕮 🆎 VISA ⬥
**Meals** *(closed Monday lunch and Sunday dinner)* (booking essential to non-residents)
24.00 **st.** (dinner) and lunch a la carte 12.25/18.20 **st.** ⓘ 4.50 – **6 rm** ⊇ 40.00/70.00 **st.** – SB.

---

**WILMCOTE** Warks. **403 404** O 27 *– see Stratford-upon-Avon.*

---

**WILMINGTON** Devon **403** K 31 *– see Honiton.*

---

**WILMINGTON** East Sussex **404** U 31 *– see Eastbourne.*

---

**WILMSLOW** Ches. **402 403 404** N 24 *– pop. 28 604.*
🏌 *Great Warford, Mobberley* ℰ (01565) 872148.
*London 189 – Liverpool 38 – Manchester 12 – Stoke-on-Trent 27.*

🏨 **Stanneylands,** Stanneylands Rd, SK9 4EY, North : 1 m. by A 34 ℰ (01625) 525225,
Fax (01625) 537282, « Gardens » – ⇜ rm, 📺 ☎ ⬥ 🅿 – 🛦 100. 🕮 🆎 ⓸ VISA ⬥
**Meals** *– (see **The Restaurant** below) –* ⊇ 10.50 – **32 rm** 78.00/107.00 **s.** – SB.

🏨 **Manchester Airport Moat House,** Oversley Ford, Altrincham Rd, SK9 4LR, Northwest : 2 ¾ m. on A 538 ℰ (01625) 889988, Fax (01625) 531876, ⒡₆, ☎s, 🔲, squash – ⧢,
⇜ rm, 📺 ☎ ⬥ 🅿 – 🛦 300. 🕮 🆎 ⓸ VISA
**Meals** *(closed Saturday lunch)* 17.95 **st.** (dinner) and a la carte 13.55/30.20 **st.** ⓘ 6.75 – ⊇
9.50 – **126 rm** 105.00/155.00 **st.** – SB.

🏠 **Boddington Arms - Premier Lodge,** Racecourse Rd, SK9 5LR, West : 1 m. by A 538
ℰ (01625) 525849, Fax (01625) 548382, Reservations (Freephone) 0800 118833 – ⧢ ⇜,
🔲 rest, 📺 ☎ ⬥ ⬥ 🅿 🕮 🆎 ⓸ VISA ⬥
**Meals** *(grill rest.)* 7.50 **st.** and a la carte – ⊇ 5.95 – **37 rm** 44.95 **st.** – SB.

XXX **The Restaurant** (at Stanneylands H.), Stanneylands Rd, SK9 4EY, North : 1 m. by A 34
ℰ (01625) 525225, Fax (01625) 537282, « Gardens » – 🅿. 🕮 🆎 ⓸ VISA
*closed Sunday dinner to non-residents –* **Meals** *(buffet dinner Sunday)* 14.00/32.00 **st.**
ⓘ 7.50.

X **Bank Square,** 4-6 Bank Sq., SK9 1AN, ℰ (01625) 539754 – 🔲. 🕮 🆎 ⓸ VISA
*closed Sunday –* **Meals** *(booking essential)* 9.95/12.50 **t.** and a la carte.

**at Handforth** *North : 3 m. on A 34 –* ✉ *Wilmslow.*

🏨 **Thistle Pinewood,** 180 Wilmslow Rd, SK9 3LG, South : 1 m. on A 34 ℰ (01625) 529211,
Fax (01625) 536812, 🐎 – ⧢ ⇜, 🔲 rest, 📺 ☎ 🅿 – 🛦 200. 🕮 🆎 ⓸ VISA JCB. ⬥
**Meals** 14.00/18.50 **st.** and dinner a la carte ⓘ 5.50 – ⊇ 10.50 – **58 rm** 94.00/110.00 **st.** – SB.

🏨 **Belfry,** Stanley Rd, SK9 3LD, ℰ (0161) 437 0511, Fax (0161) 499 0597 – ⧢, ⇜ rm, 📺 ☎ ⬥
🅿 – 🛦 180. 🕮 🆎 ⓸ VISA ⬥
**Meals** *(dancing Friday and Saturday evening)* 16.00/19.50 **t.** and a la carte – **78 rm**
⊇ 79.00/99.00 **t.**, 2 suites – SB.

---

**WIMBORNE MINSTER** Dorset **403 404** O 31 *The West Country G. – pop. 15 274.*
See : *Town*★ *– Minster*★ *– Priest's House Museum*★ *AC.*
Env. : *Kingston Lacy*★★ *AC, NW : 3 m. by B 3082.*
🛈 *29 High St., BH21 1HR* ℰ (01202) 886116.
*London 112 – Bournemouth 10 – Dorchester 23 – Salisbury 27 – Southampton 30.*

🏠 **Beechleas,** 17 Poole Rd, BH21 1QA, ℰ (01202) 841684, Fax (01202) 849344, « Georgian
town house » – ⇜ rest, 📺 ☎ 🅿. 🕮 🆎 ⓸ VISA ⬥
*closed 24 December-2 January –* **Meals** *(dinner only)* 19.75 **t.** ⓘ 7.95 – **9 rm** ⊇ 69.00/
99.00 **t.** – SB.

XX **Les Bouviers,** Oakley Hill, Merley, BH21 1RJ, South : 1 ¼ m. on A 349 ℰ (01202) 889555,
Fax (01202) 889555 – 🅿. 🕮 🆎 ⓸ VISA
*closed Saturday lunch –* **Meals** 12.75/23.95 **st.** a la carte ⓘ 8.25.

**WINCHCOMBE** *Glos.* 403 404 O 28 – *pop. 4 243.*
*London 100 – Birmingham 43 – Gloucester 26 – Oxford 43.*

⚿ **Isbourne Manor House** without rest., Castle St., GL54 5JA, ℰ (01242) 602281
Fax (01242) 602281, « Part Georgian and Elizabethan manor house », ☞ – ⇄ 🆃🆅 ℗. ✻
closed 24 to 26 December and Easter – **3 rm** ☑ 40.00/65.00.

⚿ **Sudeley Hill Farm** ⊰ without rest., GL54 5JB, East : 1 m. by Castle St
ℰ (01242) 602344, Fax (01242) 602344, ≤, « Part 15C house, working farm », ☞, park –
⇄ 🆃🆅 ℗. ✻
closed Christmas – **3 rm** ☑ 28.00/44.00 st.

XX **Wesley House** with rm, High St., GL54 5LJ, ℰ (01242) 602366, « Part 15C » – ⇄ 🆃🆅 ☎
◍③ 🆎 𝗩𝗜𝗦𝗔, ✻
closed 14 January-10 February – **Meals** (closed Sunday dinner except at Bank Holidays
16.50/28.50 t. ₰ 7.95 – **5 rm** ☑ 48.00/80.00 st. – SB.

---

**WINCHELSEA** *E. Sussex* 404 W 31 *Great Britain G.*.
See : *Town★ – St. Thomas Church (effigies★).*
*London 64 – Brighton 46 – Folkestone 30.*

⚿ **Strand House,** TN36 4JT, East : ¼ m. on A 259 ℰ (01797) 226276, Fax (01797) 224806
« Part 14C and 15C », ☞ – ⇄ 🆃🆅 ℗. ◍③ 𝗩𝗜𝗦𝗔 𝗝𝗖𝗕
**Meals** (by arrangement) 16.00 st. ₰ 6.00 – **10 rm** ☑ 34.00/54.00 st. – SB.

*La guida cambia, cambiate la guida ogni anno.*

---

**WINCHESTER** *Hants.* 403 404 P 30 *Great Britain G.* – *pop. 36 121.*
See : *City★★ – Cathedral★★★ AC* B – *Winchester College★ AC* B – *Castle Great Hall★* B D –
*God Begot House★* B A.
Env. : *St. Cross Hospital★★ AC* A.
🅱 Guildhall, The Broadway, SO23 9LJ ℰ (01962) 840500.
*London 72 – Bristol 76 – Oxford 52 – Southampton 12.*

## WINCHESTER

| | | | | | | |
|---|---|---|---|---|---|---|
| Alresford Road | A 2 | City Road | B 10 | Park Road | A 26 |
| Andover Road | B 3 | Clifton Terrace | B 12 | St. George's Street | B 32 |
| Bereweeke Road | A 5 | East Hill | B 15 | St. Paul's Hill | B 33 |
| Bridge Street | B 6 | Eastgate Street | B 16 | St. Peter's Street | B 34 |
| Broadway (The) | B 7 | Easton Lane | A 18 | Southgate Street | B 35 |
| Brooks Shopping Centre | B 8 | Friarsgate | B 19 | Stoney Lane | A 36 |
| Chilbolton Avenue | A 9 | High Street | B | Stockbridge Road | B 37 |
| | | Kingsgate Road | B 22 | Sussex Street | B 38 |
| | | Magdalen Hill | B 23 | Union Street | B 39 |
| | | Middle Brook Street | B 24 | Upper High Street | B 40 |

**Lainston House** ⚛, Sparsholt, SO21 2LT, Northwest : 3 ½ m. by B 3049 (old A 272)
&#8466; (01962) 863588, *Fax* (01962) 776672, ≤, « 17C manor house », ☞, park, ✵ – ⇆ rest,
📺 ☎ 🅿 – 🔥 80. 🐵 🆎 ① 🆅🅸🆂🅰 🅹🅲🅱
**Meals** 18.50/36.50 **st.** and dinner a la carte ⑂ 8.00 – ⳤ 14.00 – **37 rm** 100.00/150.00 **st.**,
1 suite – SB.

**Wessex**, Paternoster Row, SO23 9LQ, &#8466; (01962) 861611, *Fax* (01962) 841503, ≤ – 🛗,
⇆ rm, 🍽 rest, 📺 ☎ 🅿 – 🔥 100. 🐵 🆎 ① 🆅🅸🆂🅰 🅹🅲🅱
B c
*Wessex :* **Meals** 15.50 **t.** (lunch) and a la carte 14.45/27.15 **t.** ⑂ 7.95 – ⳤ 10.95 – **93 rm**
94.00/99.00 **t.**, 1 suite – SB.

**Hotel du Vin**, 14 Southgate St., SO23 9EF, &#8466; (01962) 841414, *Fax* (01962) 842458, « Ge-
orgian town house, wine themed interior », ☞ – 📺 ☎ 🅿 – 🔥 40. 🐵 🆎 ① 🆅🅸🆂🅰
B i
✵
**Meals** – (see *Bistro* below) – ⳤ 10.00 – **22 rm** 79.00/115.00 **t.**, 1 suite.

**Royal**, St. Peter St., SO23 8BS, &#8466; (01962) 840840, *Fax* (01962) 841582, ☞ – ⇆, 🍽 rest,
📺 ☎ 🕿 🅿 – 🔥 100. 🐵 🆎 ① 🆅🅸🆂🅰 🅹🅲🅱
B n
**Meals** 21.00 **t.** (dinner) and a la carte 19.00/26.50 ⑂ 5.75 – ⳤ 10.50 – **75 rm** 78.00/110.00 –
SB.

**Winchester Moat House**, Worthy Lane, SO23 7AB, &#8466; (01962) 709988,
*Fax* (01962) 840862, 🗲, ⇌, 🏊 – ⇆ 📺 ☎ ❺ 🅿 – 🔥 200. 🐵 🆎 ① 🆅🅸🆂🅰
B e
**Meals** (closed lunch Saturday and Sunday) 16.00 **t.** and a la carte ⑂ 5.75 – ⳤ 9.50 – **72 rm**
95.00/110.00 – SB.

**Wykeham Arms** with rm, 75 Kingsgate St., SO23 9PE, &#8466; (01962) 853834,
*Fax* (01962) 854411, « Traditional 18C inn, memorabilia », ⇌, ☞ – ⇆ rm, 📺 ☎ 🅿. 🐵 🆎
① 🆅🅸🆂🅰 🅹🅲🅱
B u
closed 25 December – **Meals** (closed Sunday) (booking essential) (in bar) a la carte 17.85/
21.95 **st.** ⑂ 5.75 – **12 rm** ⳤ 45.00/92.00 **st.**, 1 suite.

**Dawn Cottage** without rest., Romsey Rd, SO22 5PQ, &#8466; (01962) 869956,
*Fax* (01962) 869956, ≤, ☞ – ⇆ 📺 🅿. 🐵 🆅🅸🆂🅰 ✵
A c
**3 rm** ⳤ 44.00/52.00 **s.**

**East View** without rest., 16 Clifton Hill, SO22 5BL, &#8466; (01962) 862986, ≤, ☞ – ⇆ 📺 🅿.
🐵 🆅🅸🆂🅰 ✵
B v
closed Christmas and New Year – **3 rm** ⳤ 40.00/50.00 **st.**

**Portland House** without rest., 63 Tower St., SO23 8TA, &#8466; (01962) 865195,
*Fax* (01962) 865195 – 📺. ✵
B a
**4 rm** ⳤ 38.00/48.00 **st.**

**Florum House**, 47 St. Cross Rd, SO23 9PS, &#8466; (01962) 840427, *Fax* (01962) 862287, ☞ –
⇆ 📺 ☎ 🅿. 🐵 🆅🅸🆂🅰
A a
closed 24 to 26 December – **Meals** (by arrangement) 13.70 **st.** – **9 rm** ⳤ 44.00/61.00 **st.** –
SB.

**Nine The Square**, 9 Great Minster St., The Square, SO23 9HA, &#8466; (01962) 864004,
*Fax* (01962) 879586 – 🐵 🆎 ① 🆅🅸🆂🅰
B s
closed Sunday, 1 January and 25 to 28 December – **Meals** a la carte 14.10/29.15 **t.**

**Old Chesil Rectory**, Chesil St., SO23 8HU, &#8466; (01962) 851555, *Fax* (01962) 869704,
« 15C » – 🐵 ① 🆅🅸🆂🅰 🅹🅲🅱
B r
closed Sunday, Monday, dinner 24 to 30 December, 1 to 4 January and 16 to 30 August –
**Meals** 20.00/30.00 **st.** and a la carte.

**Bistro** (at Hotel du Vin), 14 Southgate St., SO23 9EF, &#8466; (01962) 841414,
*Fax* (01962) 842458, ☞ – 🅿. 🐵 🆎 ① 🆅🅸🆂🅰
B i
**Meals** a la carte 26.00/32.00 ⑂ 9.00.

**at Crawley** Northwest : 6 m. by B 3049 – A – ✉ Winchester.

**Vistro** (at the Fox and Hounds), SO21 2PR, &#8466; (01962) 776285, *Fax* (01962) 776005 – 🅿. 🐵
🆎 🆅🅸🆂🅰 🅹🅲🅱
closed Sunday dinner, Monday and Bank Holidays – **Meals** - French - 12.50/17.50 **t.**
and a la carte.

🅐 ATS 61 Bar End Rd &#8466; (01962) 865021

---

**WINDERMERE** Cumbria 🔟🔟🔟 L 20 *Great Britain G.* – pop. 6 847.
Env. : Lake Windermere★★ – Brockhole National Park Centre★ *AC*, NW : 2 m. by A 591.
🏌 Cleabarrow &#8466; (015394) 43123, E : 1½ m. by A 5074 – Z – on B 5284.
🅱 Victoria St., LA23 1AD &#8466; (015394) 46499.
*London 274 – Blackpool 55 – Carlisle 46 – Kendal 10.*

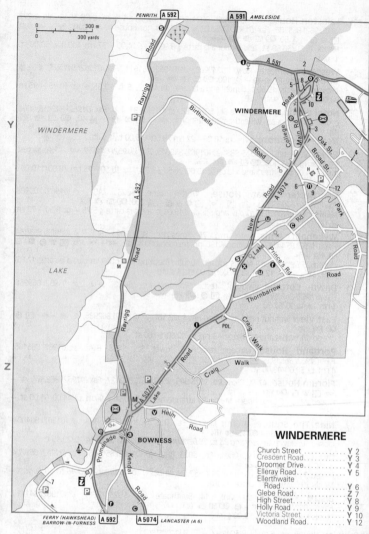

**Langdale Chase** 🦢, LA23 1LW, Northwest : 3 m. on A 591 ℰ (015394) 32201, Fax (015394) 32604, ≤ Lake Windermere and mountains, « Victorian country house in lakeside setting, carvings and artefacts », 🏸, 🐎, ✗ – ✗ rest, 🍴 rest, 📺 ☎ 🅿 – 🕭 25
**Meals** a la carte 13.50/17.50 st. 🍷 6.50 – **29 rm** 😊 60.00/170.00 st., 1 suite – SB.

**Holbeck Ghyll** 🦢, Holbeck Lane, LA23 1LU, Northwest : 3 ¼ m. by A 591 ℰ (015394) 32375, Fax (015394) 34743, ≤ Lake Windermere and mountains, « Former Victorian hunting lodge, gardens », 🛌, ≘s, ✗ – ✗ rest, 📺 ☎ 🅿. 🕮 🅮 🛈 🆅🆂🅰 🅹🅲🅱
**Meals** (light lunch)/dinner 32.50 t. 🍷 7.95 – **19 rm** 😊 (dinner included) 100.00/280.00 t., 1 suite – SB.

**Miller Howe**, Rayrigg Rd, LA23 1EY, ℰ (015394) 42536, Fax (015394) 45664, ≤ Lake Windermere and mountains, 🐎 – ✗ rest, 🍴 rest, 📺 ☎ 🅲 🅿 🕮 🅰🅴 🛈 🆅🆂🅰. 🍽 Y s
closed 3 January-11 February – **Meals** (booking essential) 15.00/32.00 t. 🍷 13.00 – **12 rm**
😊 (dinner included) 95.00/250.00 t. – SB.

636

🏠 **Quarry Garth,** Troutbeck Bridge, LA23 1LF, Northwest : 2 m. on A 591 ℰ (015394) 88282, *Fax (015394) 46584,* 🚗 – ⤙ rest, 📺 ☎ 🅿. 🐷 🆎 ⑩ 𝘝𝘐𝘚𝘈
**Meals** (light lunch Monday to Saturday)/dinner a la carte 21.40/25.95 **st.** ⋀ 7.95 – **14 rm** ⚌ (dinner included) 55.00/140.00 **st.** – SB.

🏠 **Glenburn,** New Rd, LA23 2EE, ℰ (015394) 42649, *Fax (015394) 88998* – ⤙ 📺 ☎ 📞 🅿. 🐷 𝘝𝘐𝘚𝘈 𝐉𝐂𝐁. ⌘
**Meals** (dinner only) 16.50 **st.** ⋀ 5.75 – **16 rm** ⚌ 35.00/64.00 **st.**
Y u

🏠 **Cedar Manor,** Ambleside Rd, LA23 1AX, ℰ (015394) 43192, *Fax (015394) 45970,* 🚗 – ⤙ rest, 📺 ☎ 🅿. 🐷 𝘝𝘐𝘚𝘈. ⌘
**Meals** (light lunch)/dinner 18.50 **t.** and a la carte ⋀ 6.00 – **12 rm** ⚌ (dinner included) 60.00/120.00 **t.** – SB.
Y i

🏠 **Woodlands,** New Rd, LA23 2EE, ℰ (015394) 43915, *Fax (015394) 48558* – ⤙ 📺 🅿. 🐷 𝘝𝘐𝘚𝘈. ⌘
*restricted opening in winter* – **Meals** (residents only) (dinner only) 14.50 **t.** ⋀ 4.00 – **14 rm** ⚌ 40.00/90.00 **t.**
Y u

⛫ **Archway,** 13 College Rd, LA23 1BU, ℰ (015394) 45613 – ⤙ 📺 ☎ 📞. 🐷 𝘝𝘐𝘚𝘈 𝐉𝐂𝐁. ⌘
*closed 2 weeks January* – **Meals** (by arrangement) 13.50 **st.** ⋀ 4.50 – **4 rm** ⚌ 50.00/56.00 **st.** – SB.
Y e

⛫ **Braemount House** without rest., Sunny Bank Rd, LA23 2EN, by Queens Drive ℰ (015394) 45967, *Fax (015394) 45967* – ⤙ 📺 🅿. 🐷 𝘝𝘐𝘚𝘈. ⌘
**6 rm** ⚌ 32.00/54.00.
Z u

⛫ **Hawksmoor,** Lake Rd, LA23 2EQ, ℰ (015394) 42110, 🚗 – ⤙ 📺 🅿. 🐷 𝘝𝘐𝘚𝘈 𝐉𝐂𝐁. ⌘
*closed December and January* – **Meals** (dinner only) 12.25 **st.** ⋀ 4.50 – **10 rm** ⚌ 38.00/62.00 **st.**
Z s

⛫ **Beaumont** without rest., Holly Rd, LA23 2AF, ℰ (015394) 47075, *Fax (015394) 47075* – ⤙ 📺 🅿. 🐷 𝘝𝘐𝘚𝘈. ⌘
*closed December and January* – **10 rm** ⚌ 35.00/84.00 **t.**
Y n

⛫ **Fir Trees** without rest., Lake Rd, LA23 2EQ, ℰ (015394) 42272, *Fax (015394) 42272* – ⤙ 📺 🅿. 🐷 🆎 𝘝𝘐𝘚𝘈. ⌘
**8 rm** ⚌ 45.00/56.00 **st.**
Z x

⛫ **Glencree,** Lake Rd, LA23 2EQ, ℰ (015394) 45822, *Fax (015394) 45822* – ⤙ 📺 🅿. 🐷 𝘝𝘐𝘚𝘈. ⌘
**Meals** (by arrangement) 12.00 **s.** ⋀ 4.00 – **5 rm** ⚌ 30.00/60.00 – SB.
Z s

⛫ **Kirkwood** without rest., Prince's Rd, LA23 2DD, ℰ (015394) 43907, *Fax (015394) 43907* – ⤙ 📺. 🐷 𝘝𝘐𝘚𝘈 𝐉𝐂𝐁
*closed 25 December* – **7 rm** ⚌ 56.00.
YZ r

⛫ **Oldfield House** without rest., Oldfield Rd, LA23 2BY, ℰ (015394) 88445, *Fax (015394) 43250* – ⤙ 📺 ☎ 🅿. 🐷 🆎 𝘝𝘐𝘚𝘈 𝐉𝐂𝐁. ⌘
*closed January* – **8 rm** ⚌ 32.50/64.00 **st.**
Y c

✕✕ **Roger's,** 4 High St., LA23 1AF, ℰ (015394) 44954 – 🐷 🆎 ⑩ 𝘝𝘐𝘚𝘈
*closed Sunday* – **Meals** (dinner only) 16.50 **t.** and a la carte ⋀ 5.50.
Y o

**at Bowness-on-Windermere** South : 1 m. – Z – ✉ Windermere.

🏨 **Old England,** Church St., LA23 3DF, ℰ (015394) 42444, *Fax (015394) 43432,* ≤ Lake Windermere, ⤡, 🚗 – 📱, ⤙ rm, 📺 ☎ 🅿 – 🔔 120. 🐷 🆎 ⑩ 𝘝𝘐𝘚𝘈
**Meals** (bar lunch Monday to Saturday)/dinner a la carte 17.85/24.85 **st.** ⋀ 7.95 – ⚌ 8.95 – **76 rm** 55.00/160.00 **st.** – SB.
Z e

🏨 **Linthwaite House** ⌘, Crook Rd, LA23 3JA, South : ¾ m. by A 5074 on B 5284 ℰ (015394) 88600, *Fax (015394) 88601,* ≤ Lake Windermere and fells, « Extensive grounds and private lake », ⤡ – ⤙ 📺 ☎ 🅿. 🐷 🆎 ⑩ 𝘝𝘐𝘚𝘈. ⌘
**Meals** (light lunch Monday to Saturday)/dinner 33.50 **st.** ⋀ 7.50 – **18 rm** ⚌ (dinner included) 120.00/230.00 **st.** – SB.

🏨 **Gilpin Lodge** ⌘, Crook Rd, LA23 3NE, Southeast : 2 ½ m. by A 5074 on B 5284 ℰ (015394) 88818, ≤, 🚗, park – ⤙ rest, 📺 ☎ 🅿. 🐷 🆎 ⑩ 𝘝𝘐𝘚𝘈 𝐉𝐂𝐁. ⌘
**Meals** (booking essential) 29.50 **st.** (dinner) and lunch a la carte 13.00/22.00 **st.** ⋀ 10.95 – **14 rm** ⚌ 85.00/180.00 **st.** – SB.

🏨 **Lindeth Fell** ⌘, Lyth Valley Rd, LA23 3JP, South : 1 m. on A 5074 ℰ (015394) 43286, *Fax (015394) 47455,* ≤ Lake Windermere and mountains, « Country house atmosphere, gardens », ⤡ – ⤙ rest, 📺 ☎ 🅿. 🐷 𝘝𝘐𝘚𝘈. ⌘
*closed 4 January-12 February* – **Meals** (light lunch Monday to Saturday)/dinner 19.00 **st.** ⋀ 6.00 – **15 rm** ⚌ (dinner included) 63.00/150.00 **st.** – SB.

🏨 **Burnside**, Kendal Rd, LA23 3EP, ℰ (015394) 42211, *Fax (015394) 43824*, ⅃₆, ☎s, ◪, ◭ squash – ⊉ ⅍ ⊡ ☎ ₰ ₱ – ℳ 100. ⬤❸ ⅄Ε ❿ *VISA* ᴊᴄʙ. – SB.
Meals (bar lunch Monday to Saturday) (carving lunch Sunday and dinner Monday-Tuesda⸜ dinner 18.00 st. and a la carte ₰ 6.00 – **57 rm** ⊇ 80.00/120.00 **st.** – SB.

🏨 **Fayrer Garden House** ⅍, Lyth Valley Rd, LA23 3JP, South : 1 m. on A 50 ℰ (015394) 88195, *Fax (015394) 45986*, ≤, ☞ – ⅍ rest, ☰ rest, ⊡ ☎ ₱. ⬤❸ ⅄Ε *VISA* closed 3 to 23 January – **Meals** (bar lunch)/dinner 24.00 **t.** ₰ 6.95 – **18 rm** ⊇ (dinn⸜ included) 70.00/180.00 **t.** –

🏨 **Craig Manor**, Lake Rd, LA23 2JF, ℰ (015394) 88877, *Fax (015394) 88878*, ≤ – ⅍ rest, ⎙ ☎ ₱. ⬤❸ ⅄Ε *VISA* ᴊᴄʙ.
Meals (dinner only and Sunday lunch) (carving lunch Sunday) 19.50 **st.** and a la carte ₰ 11.0⸜ – **16 rm** ⊇ 64.00/108.00 **st.** – SB.

🏨 **Burn How Garden House**, Back Belsfield Rd, LA23 3HH, ℰ (015394) 4622⸜ Fax (015394) 47000, ☞ – ⅍ rest, ⊡ ☎ ₱. ⬤❸ ⅄Ε ❿ *VISA* ᴊᴄʙ. ⅍
Meals (bar lunch)/dinner 19.50 **t.** ₰ 6.50 – **26 rm** ⊇ 86.00/98.00 **st.** – SB.

🏨 **Wild Boar**, Crook Rd, LA23 3NF, Southeast : 4 m. by A 5074 on B 5284 ℰ (015394) 4522⸜ Fax (015394) 42498, ☞ – ⅍ rest ⊡ ☎ ₱. ₱ – ℳ 35. ⬤❸ ⅄Ε ❿ *VISA*
Meals 19.95 **t.** (dinner) and a la carte 25.45/36.00 **t.** ₰ 5.95 – **36 rm** ⊇ (dinner include⸜ 82.00/166.00 **t.** – SB.

🏨 **Crag Brow Cottage**, Helm Rd, LA23 3BU, ℰ (015394) 44080, *Fax (015394) 46003*, ☞ ⅍ ⊡ ☎ ₱. ⬤❸ ⅄Ε *VISA* ᴊᴄʙ. ⅍
Meals 7.95/12.95 **st.** and dinner a la carte ₰ 7.95 – **11 rm** ⊇ (dinner included) 65.0⸜ 120.00 **st.** – SB.

🏨 **Lindeth Howe** ⅍, Storrs Park, LA23 3JF, South : 1 ¼ m. by A 592 off B 528⸜ ℰ (015394) 45759, *Fax (015394) 46368*, ≤, ☎s, ☞ – ⅍ rest, ⊡ ☎ ₱. ⬤❸ *VISA* ᴊᴄʙ. ⅍
Meals (dinner only and Sunday lunch)/dinner 19.50 **st.** ₰ 5.95 – **15 rm** ⊇ (dinner include⸜ 68.00/170.00 **st.** – SB.

🏠 **White Foss** ⅍ without rest., Longtail Hill, LA23 3JD, South : ¾ m. by A 592 on B 528⸜ ℰ (015394) 46593, ≤, ☞ – ₱. ⅍
March-October – **3 rm** ⊇ 35.00/56.00 **st.**

🏠 **Laurel Cottage** without rest., St. Martins Sq., Kendal Rd, LA23 3EF, ℰ (015394) 4559⸜ Fax (015394) 45594 – ⊡ ₱. ⅍
**14 rm** ⊇ 24.00/56.00 **st.**

**at Troutbeck** North : 4 m. by A 592 – Y – ✉ Windermere.

🏨 **Broadoaks** ⅍, Bridge Lane, LA23 1LA, South : 1 m. ℰ (015394) 4556⸜ Fax (015394) 88766, ☞ – ⅍ rest ⊡ ☎ ₱. ⬤❸ *VISA*
Meals (lunch by arrangement)/dinner a la carte 19.45/39.95 **st.** ₰ 6.25 – **13 rm** ⊇ 62.00⸜ 170.00 **st.**

🏨 **Mortal Man** ⅍, LA23 1PL, ℰ (015394) 33193, *Fax (015394) 31261*, ≤ Garburn Hill an⸜ Troutbeck Valley, ☞ – ⅍ rest, ⊡ ☎ ₱. ⬤❸ ⅄Ε *VISA*
Meals (bar lunch Monday to Saturday) a la carte 10.95/26.25 **t.** ₰ 7.50 – **12 rm** ⊇ 70.00⸜ 90.00 **t.** – SB.

🍴 **Queens Head** with rm, LA23 1PW, East : ¼ m. on A 592 ℰ (015394) 32174 Fax (015394) 31938, ≤, « 17C inn » – ⅍ rm, ⊡ ₱. ⬤❸ *VISA* ᴊᴄʙ closed 25 December – **Meals** (lunch in bar) a la carte 11.95/22.40 **t.** ₰ 6.00 – **8 rm** ⊇ 45.00⸜ 70.00 **t.**

---

**WINDLESHAM** Surrey ⏢⬜⬜ S 29 – pop. 4 525.
London 37 – Basingstoke 26 – Reading 16 – Southampton 55.

🍴 **Brickmakers Arms**, Chertsey Rd, GU20 6HT, ℰ (01276) 472267, *Fax (01276) 451014* – ₱. ⬤❸ ⅄Ε ❿ *VISA*. ⅍
Meals 13.90/17.95 **t.** and a la carte ₰ 6.75.

---

**WINDSOR** Windsor & Maidenhead ⏢⬜⬜ S 29 Great Britain G. – pop. 30 136 (inc. Eton).
See : Town★ – Castle★★★ : St. George's Chapel★★★ AC (stalls★★★), State Apartments★★ AC, North Terrace (≤★★)Z – Eton College★★ AC (College Chapel★★, Wall paintings★)Z.
Env. : Windsor Park★ ACY.
🛈 24 High St., SL4 1LH ℰ (01753) 852010.
London 28 – Reading 19 – Southampton 59.

*Plan opposite*

🏨 **Oakley Court** ⅍, Windsor Rd, Water Oakley, SL4 5UR, West : 3 m. on A 308 ℰ (01753) 609988, *Fax (01628) 637011*, ≤, « Part Gothic mansion on banks of River Thames », ⅃₆, ☎s, ◪, ⌗, ⌐, ☞, ⅍ – ⅍ rm, ⊡ ☎ ₺ ₱ – ℳ 160. ⬤❸ ⅄Ε ❿ *VISA*
**Le Boulestin** : Meals 24.00/29.50 **st.** and a la carte ₰ 14.95 – **Boaters Brasserie** : Meals (closed Sunday lunch) a la carte 15.00/45.00 **st.** ₰ 14.95 – ⊇ 16.00 – **114 rm** 180.00⸜ 205.00 **st.**, 1 suite – SB.

# WINDSOR

North is at the top
on all town plans.

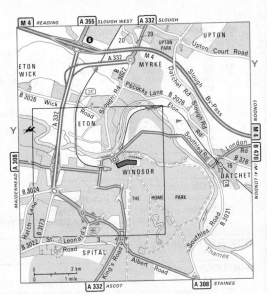

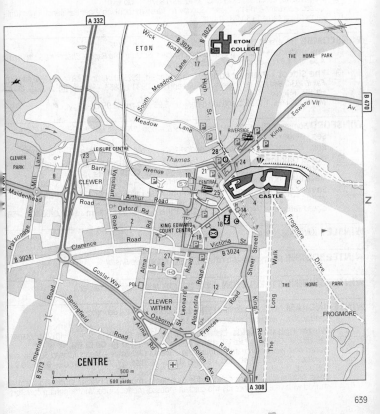

CENTRE

500 m
500 yards

🏰 **Castle**, High St., SL4 1LJ, ✆ (01753) 851011, *Fax* (01753) 830244 – 🛗 ⁵⁄₄ 🗤 ☎ 🄿 – 🔬 400
🐵 🄰🄴 🄓 *VISA* 🄹🄲🄱. ❀
**Castle restaurant** : Meals a la carte 14.85/24.40 **st.** – **Grand Cafe** : Meals a la carte 15.00
20.00 **st.** – ☲ 11.95 – **110 rm** 135.00/195.00 **t.**, 1 suite – SB.

🏛 **Sir Christopher Wren's House**, Thames St., SL4 1PX, ✆ (01753) 861354
*Fax* (01753) 860172, ⌂ – 🄳. ⁵⁄₄ rm, 🗤 ☎ 🄿 – 🔬 90. 🐵 🄰🄴 🄓 *VISA*. ❀
**Meals** 18.50 **t.** (lunch) and a la carte 21.15/39.90 **t.** ◊ 9.00 – ☲ 10.50 – **52 rm** 125.00
175.00 **st.**, 5 suites – SB.

🏛 **Aurora Garden**, 14 Bolton Av., SL4 3JF, ✆ (01753) 868686, *Fax* (01753) 831394, ⌨ – 🗤
☎ 🄿 – 🔬 90. 🐵 🄰🄴 *VISA*
closed 1 week Christmas**Meals** 8.95/12.95 **t.** and dinner a la carte ◊ 7.95 – **19 rm** ☲ 80.00
100.00 **t.** – SB.

---

**WINEHAM** W. Sussex 🗺 T 31 – see Henfield.

---

**WINFORTON** Herefordshire 🗺 K 27 – ✉ Hereford.
London 155 – Birmingham 71 – Cardiff 66 – Hereford 15.

🍴 **Sun Inn** with rm, HR3 5EA, ✆ (01544) 327677, « Part 17C », ⌨ – ⁵⁄₄ rm, 🗤 🄿
closed Tuesday – **Meals** a la carte 13.80/22.35 **t.** ◊ 5.60 – **3 rm** ☲ 32.00/60.00 **t.**

---

**WINGFIELD** Suffolk – see Diss.

---

**WINKLEIGH** Devon 🗺 I 31 – pop. 1 063.
London 218 – Barnstaple 25 – Exeter 23 – Plymouth 43 – Truro 76.

🍴 **Pophams**, Castle St., EX19 8HQ, ✆ (01837) 83767 – 🐵 *VISA*
closed February – Meals (closed Sunday to Tuesday) (booking essential) (lunch only) (unlicensed) a la carte 18.30/28.00.

---

**WINSCOMBE** Somerset 🗺 L 30 The West Country G. – pop. 4 192.
Env. : Axbridge★★ (King John's Hunting Lodge★, St. John the Baptist Church★), S : 1¾m. by
A 38 and A 371 – London 137 – Bristol 16 – Taunton 22.

🏛 **The Sidcot - Premier Lodge**, Bridgwater Rd, BS25 1NN, on A 38 ✆ (01934) 844145,
*Fax* (01934) 844192, ≼, Reservations (Freephone) 0800 118833 – ⁵⁄₄ rm, 🗤 ☎ 🕭 🄿. 🐵 🄰🄴
🄓 *VISA* 🄹🄲🄱. ❀
**Meals** (grill rest.) 10.95 **t.** and a la carte – ☲ 5.95 – **32 rm** 44.95 **t.** – SB.

---

**WINSFORD** Somerset 🗺 J 30 The West Country G. – pop. 270 – ✉ Minehead.
See : Village★.
Env. : Exmoor National Park★★ – London 194 – Exeter 31 – Minehead 10 – Taunton 32.

🏛 **Royal Oak Inn**, Exmoor National Park, TA24 7JE, ✆ (01643) 851455, *Fax* (01643) 851009,
« Attractive part 12C thatched inn », ⌨ – 🗤 ☎ 🄿. 🐵 🄰🄴
**Meals** (bar lunch Monday to Saturday)/dinner 25.00 **t.** – ☲ 10.00 – **14 rm** 80.00/90.00 **t.** – SB.

🍴🍴 **Savery's at Karslake House** with rm, Halse Lane, Exmoor National Park, TA24 7JE,
✆ (01643) 851242, *Fax* (01643) 851242, ⌨ – ⁵⁄₄ 🗤 🄿. 🐵 *VISA* 🄹🄲🄱
closed February – Meals (closed Sunday) (dinner only) 24.95 **t.** – **7 rm** ☲ 40.00/80.00 **t.** – SB.

---

**WINSLEY** Wilts. 🗺 N 29 – see Bradford-on-Avon.

---

**WINTERBOURNE** South Gloucestershire 🗺 M 29 – see Bristol.

---

**WINTERBOURNE STEEPLETON** Dorset 🗺 M 31 – see Dorchester.

---

**WINTERINGHAM** North Lincolnshire 🗺 S 22 – pop. 4 714 – ✉ Scunthorpe.
London 176 – Kingston-upon-Hull 16 – Sheffield 67.

🍴🍴🍴🍴 **Winteringham Fields** (Schwab) with rm, Silver St., DN15 9PF, ✆ (01724) 733096,
❀❀ *Fax* (01724) 733898, « Part 16C manor house » – ⁵⁄₄ 🗤 ☎ 🄿. 🐵 🄰🄴 *VISA*. ❀
closed first week March and August and 2 weeks Christmas – Meals (closed Sunday and
Monday) 20.00/29.00 **st.** and a la carte 49.40/58.70 **st.** ◊ 6.75 – ☲ 9.50 – **9 rm** 70.00/
105.00 **st.**, 1 suite
**Spec.** Millefeuille of lobster and truffle oil polenta, morel and lobster sauce. Pig's trotter
stuffed with veal sweetbreads and chicken mousse, merlot sauce. Winteringham corn tart.

**WITCOMBE** *Glos. – see Gloucester.*

---

**WITHERSLACK** *Cumbria* **402** L 21 – *see Grange-over-Sands.*

---

**WITHINGTON** *Glos.* **403 404** O 28 – *pop. 486.*
London 91 – Gloucester 15 – Oxford 35 – Swindon 24.

⚐ **Halewell** ॐ, GL54 4BN, ℰ (01242) 890238, *Fax* (01242) 890332, ≤, « Part 15C monastery », ⅃, �’, ☞, park – ⅋⅋ rest, 🆅 & 🅿. ◓⑨ 🆎 🆅🆂🅰. ⅍
**Meals** (by arrangement) (communal dining) 25.00 st. – **6 rm** ⊆ 60.00/87.00 st.

---

**WITHYPOOL** *Somerset* **403** J 30 *The West Country G.* – *pop. 196* – ⊠ *Minehead.*
Env. : *Exmoor National Park*★★ – *Tarr Steps*★★, SE : 4 m. *by B 3223 and minor roads* – *Exford (Church*★*) NE : 4 m. by B 3223 and B 3224.*
London 204 – Exeter 34 – Taunton 36.

⏛ **Royal Oak Inn** with rm, TA24 7QP, ℰ (01643) 831506, *Fax* (01643) 831659, « Part 17C », �’ – 🆅 ☎ 🅿. ◓⑨ 🆎 🆅🆂🅰 🅹🅲🅱 – **Meals** (bar lunch Monday to Saturday)/dinner 19.50 t. and a la carte � 6.00 – **8 rm** ⊆ 33.00/90.00 st.

---

**WITNEY** *Oxon* **403 404** P 28 – *pop. 20 377.*
🇿 Town Hall, 51A Market Sq., OX8 6AG ℰ (01993) 775802.
London 69 – Gloucester 39 – Oxford 13.

🏨 **Witney Four Pillars**, Ducklington Lane, OX8 7TJ, South : 1 ½ m. *on A 415* ℰ (01993) 779777, *Fax* (01993) 703467, 🇮♭, ☎, ⬜ – ⅋⅋ rm, 🆅 ☎ & 🅿 – 🔬 160. ◓⑨ 🆎 ⓘ 🆅🆂🅰 – **Meals** 12.95/15.95 st. and a la carte – ⊆ 7.95 – **74 rm** 76.00/86.00 st. – SB.

**at Hailey** *North : 1¼ m. on B 4022* – ⊠ *Witney.*

🏠 **Bird in Hand**, White Oak Green, OX8 5XP, North : 1 m. *on B 4022* ℰ (01993) 868321, *Fax* (01993) 868702 – ⅋⅋ 🆅 ☎ & 🅿. ◓⑨ ⓘ 🆅🆂🅰 – *closed 25 and 26 December* – **Meals** a la carte 12.70/21.15 t. ᵉ 5.50 – **16 rm** ⊆ 60.00/75.00 t. – SB.

**at Barnard Gate** *East : 3¼ m. by B 4022 off A 40* – ⊠ *Eynsham.*

⏛ **The Boot Inn**, OX8 6XE, ℰ (01865) 881231, *Fax* (01865) 358910, « Collection of celebrities boots » – 🅿. ◓⑨ 🆅🆂🅰 – **Meals** a la carte 15.95/23.50 t. ᵉ 4.75.

**at South Leigh** *Southeast : 3 m. by A 4022* – ⊠ *Witney.*

✗ **Mason Arms** with rm, OX8 6XN, ℰ (01993) 702485, « 15C thatched inn », ☞ – 🆅 🅿. 🆎. ⅍
*closed 25 and 26 December* – **Meals** *(closed Sunday dinner and Monday)* a la carte 21.90/48.95 t. ᵉ 6.00 – **2 rm** 35.00/50.00 t.

◖ ATS Orchard Way, off Corn St. ℰ (01993) 704273

---

**WITTERSHAM** *Kent* **404** W 30 – *pop. 1 431* – ⊠ *Tenterden.*
London 59 – Brighton 54 – Folkestone 22 – Maidstone 28.

⚐ **Wittersham Court** ॐ, The Street, TN30 7EA, ℰ (01797) 270425, *Fax* (01797) 270425, « Part 17C », ☞, ✗ – ⅋⅋ rm, 🅿. ◓⑨ 🆅🆂🅰. ⅍
*closed Christmas and New Year* – **Meals** (by arrangement) (communal dining) 20.00 st. ᵉ 6.00 – **3 rm** ⊆ 45.00/70.00 s.

---

**WIVELISCOMBE** *Somerset* **403** K 30 *The West Country G.* – *pop. 1 753* – ⊠ *Taunton.*
Env. : *Gaulden Manor*★ *AC, NE : 3 m. by B 3188.*
London 185 – Barnstaple 38 – Exeter 37 – Taunton 14.

🏨 **Langley House**, Langley Marsh, TA4 2UF, North : ¾ m. ℰ (01984) 623318, *Fax* (01984) 624573, ☞ – ⅋⅋ rest, 🆅 ☎ 🅿. ◓⑨ 🆎 🆅🆂🅰
**Meals** (booking essential to non-residents) (dinner only) 25.00 st. ᵉ 6.25 – **8 rm** ⊆ 77.50/127.50 st. – SB.

---

**WIX** *Essex* **404** X 28 – ⊠ *Manningtree.*
London 70 – Colchester 10 – Harwich 7 – Ipswich 16.

⚐ **Dairy House Farm** ॐ without rest., Bradfield Rd, CO11 2SR, Northwest : 1 m. ℰ (01255) 870322, *Fax* (01255) 870186, ≤, ☞, park – ⅋⅋ 🆅 🅿. ⅍
*closed 25 and 26 December* – **3 rm** ⊆ 27.00/40.00.

**WOBURN** *Beds.* 404 S 28 *Great Britain G.* – *pop. 1 534* – ✉ *Milton Keynes.*
See : *Woburn Abbey*★★ – *London 49* – *Bedford 13* – *Luton 13* – *Northampton 24.*

**Thistle Bedford Arms,** 1 George St., MK17 9PX, ✆ (01525) 290441, *Fax (01525) 29043*
– ⇹ rm, ▤ rest, TV ☎ ♿ P – 🎓 60. MC AE ① VISA JCB. ✂
Meals 16.95/19.95 **st.** and a la carte 6.00 – ☕ 11.00 – **51 rm** 105.00/148.00 **st.**, 2 suites – SB

**Paris House,** Woburn Park, MK17 9QP, Southeast : 2 ¼ m. on A 4012 ✆ (01525) 290692
*Fax (01525) 290471,* « Reconstructed timbered house in park », – P. MC AE ① VISA
*closed Sunday dinner, Monday and February* – **Meals** 26.00/48.00 **t.** and a la carte 6.00.

**WOKINGHAM** 404 R 29 – *pop. 38 063* – 18 *Sand Martins, Finchampstead Rd* ✆ *(0118) 979 2711* -
9 *Hurst, Sandford Lane* ✆ *(01734) 344355* – *London 43* – *Reading 7* – *Southampton 52.*

**Stakis St. Anne's Manor,** London Rd, RG40 1ST, East : 1 ½ m. on A 32
✆ (01189) 772550, *Fax (01189) 772526,* Lö, ≘s, 🏊, park, 🎾 – |‡|, ⇹ rm, ▤ rest, TV ☎
♿ P – 🎓 200. MC AE ① VISA. ✂
*closed 26 to 30 December* – **Meals** *(closed Saturday lunch)* (carving lunch) 14.95/22.50 **t**
and dinner a la carte – ☕ 13.45 – **156 rm** 175.00/245.00 **st.**, 3 suites – SB.

**Edward Court,** Wellington Rd, RG40 2AN, ✆ (0118) 9775886, *Fax (0118) 9772018* – TV ☎
☎ P – 🎓 40. MC AE ① VISA. ✂
13.95/15.00 **t.** and a la carte 5.40 – **27 rm** ☕ 75.00/120.00 **t.** – SB.

**Rose Street,** 6 Rose St., RG40 1XU, ✆ (01189) 788025 – MC AE VISA – *closed Sunday*
*dinner, 25-26 December and 1 January* – Meals a la carte 18.65/29.15 **t.** 6.70.

## WOLVERHAMPTON


Alfred Squire Road . . . . . . . . . . A 2
Birmingham New Road . . . . . A 3
Bridgnorth Road. . . . . . . . . . . . A 6
Cleveland Street . . . . . . . . . . . . B 7
Darlington Street . . . . . . . . . . . B
Garrick Street. . . . . . . . . . . . . . B 8
High Street. . . . . . . . . . . . . . . . A 9
Lichfield Road . . . . . . . . . . . . . A 10
Lichfield Street . . . . . . . . . . . . B 12
Mander Centre . . . . . . . . . . . . . B
Market Street. . . . . . . . . . . . . . B 14
Princess Street . . . . . . . . . . . . B 15
Queen Square . . . . . . . . . . . . . B 17
Railway Drive . . . . . . . . . . . . . B 20
Salop Street . . . . . . . . . . . . . . B 22
Thompson Avenue . . . . . . . . . A 23
Victoria Street . . . . . . . . . . . . B 24
Wulfrun Centre . . . . . . . . . . . B


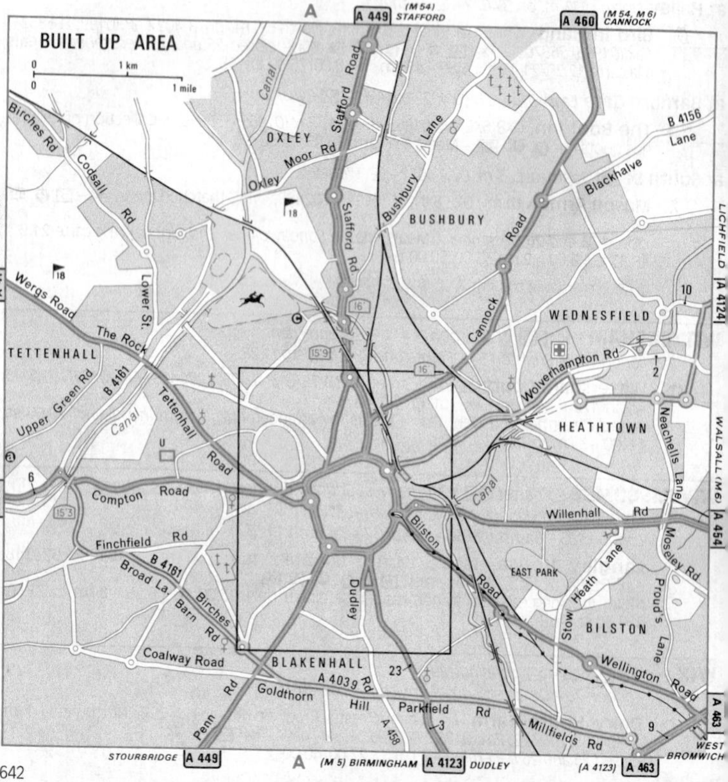

A
A 449 (M 54) STAFFORD
A 460 (M 54, M 6) CANNOCK
BUILT UP AREA
0 1 km
0 1 mile
Birches Rd
Codsall Rd
Canal
Stafford Road
OXLEY
Oxley Moor Rd
Bushbury Lane
BUSHBURY
B 4156 Lane
Blackhalve
Cannock Road
Stafford Rd
WEDNESFIELD
LICHFIELD A 4124
WHITCHURCH A 41
Wergs Road
The Rock
Lower St.
TETTENHALL
Upper Green Rd
B 4161
Tettenhall Road
Wolverhampton Rd
HEATHTOWN
Neachells Lane
BRIDGNORTH A 454
Compton Road
Finchfield Rd
Broad La.
Barn Rd
Birches Rd
Willenhall Rd
WALSALL (M 6) A 454
Bilston Road
Moseley Rd
EAST PARK
Stow Heath Lane
Proud's Lane
BILSTON
Coalway Road
Dudley
BLAKENHALL
Wellington Road
Penn Rd
Goldthorn Hill
A 4039 Rd
Parkfield Rd
Millfields Rd
A 458
A 463
WEST BROMWICH
STOURBRIDGE A 449
(M 5) BIRMINGHAM A 4123 DUDLEY
(A 4123) A 463

**WOLVERHAMPTON** *W. Mids.* [402] [403] [404] N 26 – *pop. 257 943.*

[i] *18 Queen Sq., WV1 1TQ* ☎ *(01902) 312051.*

*London 132 – Birmingham 15 – Liverpool 89 – Shrewsbury 30.*

Plan of Enlarged Area : see Birmingham pp. 2 and 3

🏨 **Mount** 🐎, Mount Rd, Tettenhall Wood, WV6 8HL, West : 2 ½ m. by A 454 ☎ (01902) 752055, *Fax (01902) 745263,* 🌳 – ⇐ [TV] ☎ [P] – 🎤 200. [MC] [AE] [D] [VISA] [JCB]
*closed 31 December* – **Meals** 12.95/18.95 **st.** and dinner a la carte 🍷 7.00 – ☕ 8.50 – **55 rm** 79.00/95.00 **st.**, 1 suite – SB. A a

🏨 **Goldthorn,** 126 Penn Rd, WV3 0ER, ☎ (01902) 429216, *Fax (01902) 710419,* 🏋, ≘s, 🏊 – ⇐ [TV] ☎ [P] – 🎤 120. [MC] [AE] [D] [VISA] [JCB]. 🚫 B c
**Meals** (bar lunch Saturday) 11.95/16.95 **st.** and a la carte 🍷 6.50 – ☕ 9.50 – **92 rm** 79.00/104.00 **st.** – SB.

🏨 **Novotel,** Union St., WV1 3JN, ☎ (01902) 871100, *Fax (01902) 870054,* 🏊 – 🛗, ⇐ rm, ▤ rest, [TV] ☎ 📞 ♿ [P] – 🎤 200. [MC] [AE] [D] [VISA] B a
**Meals** 9.95/15.50 **st.** and a la carte – ☕ 8.50 – **132 rm** 69.00 **st.**

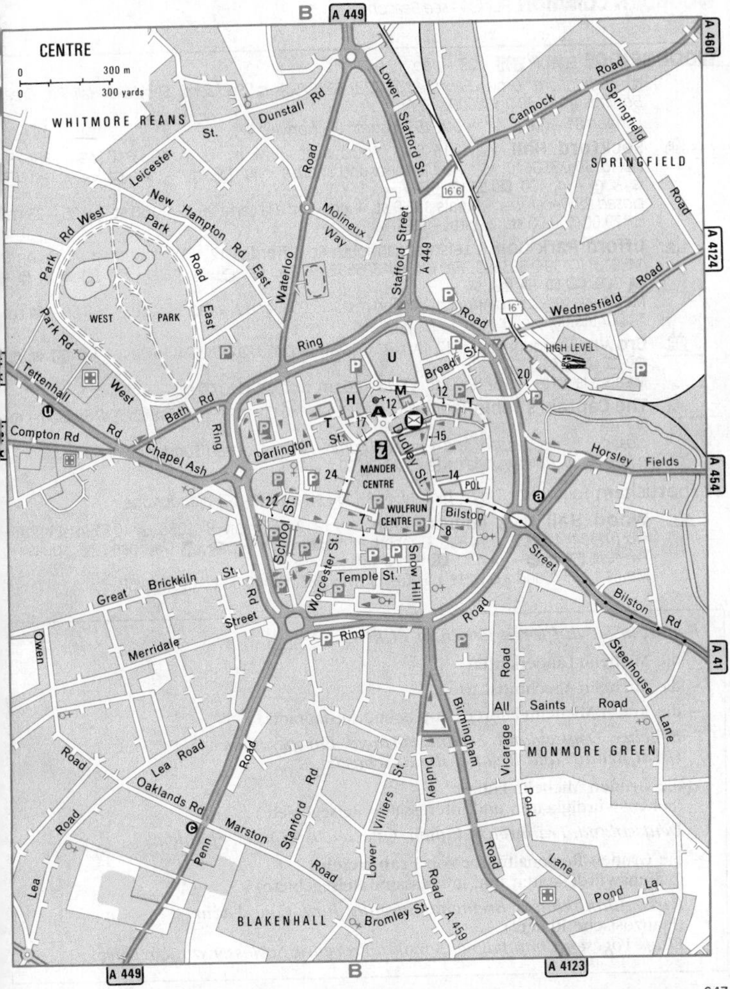

🏨 **Holiday Inn Garden Court,** Dunstall Park, WV6 0PE, North : 1 ¾ m. by A 44⬛
℘ (01902) 713313, Fax (01902) 714364, ⅙ – 🕸, ✲ rm, 📺 ☎ ♿ ⍟. ⬛⚫ 🅐🅔 ⓪ 🆅🅸🆂🅰 🅹🅲🅱. ✄
**Meals** (bar lunch)/dinner 14.75 **st.** and a la carte ⅊ 6.50 – ⌓ 9.50 – **54 rm** 60.00 **st.**     A  ◖

🏠 **Ely House,** 53 Tettenhall Rd, WV3 9NB, ℘ (01902) 311311, Fax (01902) 421098 – 📺 ☎ ♿
⬛⚫ 🅐🅔 ⓪ 🆅🅸🆂🅰. ✄     B  ∪
*closed 24 to 27 December* – **Meals** (lunch by arrangement) 12.95 **t.** and a la carte ⅊ 6.95 –
**18 rm** ⌓ 48.00/70.00 **t.**

⑩ ATS 35-39 Wednesfield Rd ℘ (01902) 455055          ATS 2 Willenhall Rd ℘ (01902) 871417

---

**WOLVISTON** Cleveland 📟 Q 20 – pop. 2 482 – ⌧ Stockton-on-Tees.
London 280 – Carlisle 93 – Middlesbrough 8 – Newcastle upon Tyne 37 – Sunderland 23.

🏠 **Holiday Inn Express** without rest., Coal Lane, TS22 5PZ, on A 689 at junction with A 19⬛
℘ (01740) 644000, Fax (01740) 644111 – ✲ 📺 ☎ ♿ ⍟ – 🛃 40. ⬛⚫ 🅐🅔 ⓪ 🆅🅸🆂🅰. ✄
**49 rm** 45.00 **t.**

---

**WOOBURN COMMON** Bucks. – see Beaconsfield.

---

**WOODBRIDGE** Suffolk 📟 X 27 – pop. 10 950.
🏌 Cretingham, Grove Farm ℘ (01728) 685275 – ⓖ Seckford, Seckford Hall Rd, Great
Bealings ℘ (01394) 388000.
London 81 – Great Yarmouth 45 – Ipswich 8 – Norwich 47.

🏰 **Seckford Hall** ⑊, IP13 6NU, Southwest : 1 ¼ m. by A 12 ℘ (01394) 385678,
Fax (01394) 380610, ≤, « Part Tudor country house », ⅙, 🏊, ⓖ, ⍩, 🐎, park – ▤ rest, 📺
☎ ♿ ⍟ – 🛃 100. ⬛⚫ 🅐🅔 ⓪ 🆅🅸🆂🅰 🅹🅲🅱
*closed 25 December* – **Meals** 13.50 **st.** (lunch) and a la carte 25.45/40.50 **st.** ⅊ 6.85 – **25 rm**
⌓ 79.00/150.00 **st.,** 7 suites – SB.

🏰 **Ufford Park Golf & Leisure,** Yarmouth Rd, Ufford, IP12 1QW, Northeast : 2 m. on B
1438 ℘ (01394) 383555, Fax (01394) 383582, ≤, ⅙, ≦ₛ, 🏊, ⓖ, park – ✲ 📺 ☎ ♿ ⍟ –
🛃 200. ⬛⚫ 🅐🅔 ⓪ 🆅🅸🆂🅰. ✄
**Meals** *(closed Saturday lunch)* (carving rest.) 16.00 **t.** and a la carte ⅊ 7.50 – ⌓ 8.50 – **44 rm**
75.00/115.00 **t.** – SB.

🏨 **Crown,** Thoroughfare, IP12 1AD, ℘ (01394) 384242, Fax (01394) 387192 – ✲ 📺 ☎ ♿.
⬛⚫ 🅐🅔 ⓪ 🆅🅸🆂🅰
**Meals** a la carte 10.75/18.90 **st.** ⅊ 5.75 – **20 rm** ⌓ 75.00/110.00 **st.** – SB.

✗ **The Captain's Table,** 3 Quay St., IP12 1BX, ℘ (01394) 383145, Fax (01394) 388508 – ♿.
⬛⚫ 🆅🅸🆂🅰
*closed 2 weeks January and 1 week autumn* – **Meals** *(closed Sunday dinner and Monday
except Bank Holidays)* a la carte 13.20/20.00 **t.** ⅊ 6.75.

**at Shottisham** Southeast : 5 ¾ m. by B 1438, A 1152 on B 1083 – ⌧ Woodbridge.

🏰 **Wood Hall H. & Country Club** ⑊, IP12 3EG, on B 1083 ℘ (01394) 411283,
Fax (01394) 410007, ≤, « Part Elizabethan manor house », ≦ₛ, 🏊, 🐎, park, ✗, squash –
✲ rest, 📺 ☎ ♿ – 🛃 150. ⬛⚫ 🅐🅔 ⓪ 🆅🅸🆂🅰
**Meals** 17.95 **t.** and a la carte ⅊ 5.00 – **13 rm** ⌓ 83.00/140.00 **t.,** 1 suite – SB.

---

**WOODFALLS** *Wilts. – see Salisbury.*

**WOODHALL SERVICE AREA** *S. Yorks.* [402] [403] [404] Q 24 – ✉ *Sheffield.*

🏨 **Welcome Lodge,** S31 8XR, M1 between junctions 30 and 31 ℘ (01142) 487992, *Fax (01142) 485634*, Reservations (Freephone) 0800 7314466 – 🚭 rm, [TV] ♿ [P]. [MC] [AE] [D] [VISA]
**Meals** (grill rest.) – ☕ 7.50 – **40 rm** 50.00 **t.**

**WOODHALL SPA** *Lincs.* [402] [404] T 24 *Great Britain G. – pop. 3 337.*
Env. : *Tattershall Castle★ AC, SE : 4 m. by B 1192 and A 153.*
⛳ *Woodhall Spa ℘ (01526) 352511.*
ℹ *The Cottage Museum, Iddlesleigh Rd, LN10 6SH ℘ (01526) 353775 (summer only).*
*London 138 – Lincoln 18.*

🏨 **The Petwood** 🐴, Stixwould Rd, LN10 6QF, ℘ (01526) 352411, *Fax (01526) 353473*, <, « Gardens », park – 🛗 🚭 [TV] ☎ [P] – 👥 150. [MC] [AE] [D] [VISA]
**Meals** (bar lunch Monday to Saturday)/dinner 16.95 **t.** and a la carte 🍷 6.50 – **46 rm** ☕ 70.00/110.00 **t.**, 1 suite – SB.

🏨 **Golf,** The Broadway, LN10 6SG, ℘ (01526) 353535, *Fax (01526) 353096*, 🌳, 🎾 – 🚭 rest, [TV] ☎ [P] – 👥 150. [MC] [AE] [D] [VISA] [JCB]
**Meals** (bar lunch Monday to Saturday)/dinner 16.95 **t.** and a la carte 🍷 5.25 – **50 rm** ☕ 65.00/80.00 **t.** – SB.

**WOODSTOCK** *Oxon.* [403] [404] P 28 *Great Britain G. – pop. 2 898.*
See : *Blenheim Palace★★★ (The Grounds★★★) AC.*
ℹ *Hensington Rd, OX20 1JQ ℘ (01993) 811038.*
*London 65 – Gloucester 47 – Oxford 8.*

🏨 **Bear,** Park St., OX20 1SZ, ℘ (01993) 811511, *Fax (01993) 813380*, « Part 16C inn » – 🚭 [TV] ☎ [P] – 👥 30. [MC] [AE] [D] [VISA] [JCB]
**Meals** a la carte 22.00/34.00 **t.** 🍷 7.00 – ☕ 10.50 – **41 rm** 120.00/135.00 **t.**, 3 suites – SB.

🏨 **Feathers,** Market St., OX20 1SX, ℘ (01993) 812291, *Fax (01993) 813158*, « Restored 17C houses » – 🚭 rest, ❄ rest, [TV] ☎. [MC] [AE] [D] [VISA] [JCB]
**Meals** 21.00 **t.** (lunch) and a la carte 34.10/43.60 **t.** 🍷 9.00 – ☕ 8.25 – **19 rm** 75.00/169.00 **t.**, 2 suites – SB.

**WOOKEY HOLE** *Somerset* [403] L 30 – *see Wells.*

**WOOLACOMBE** *Devon* [403] H 30 *The West Country G..*
Env. : *Exmoor National Park★★ – Mortehoe★★ (St. Mary's Church★, Morte Point – vantage point★) N : ½ m – Ilfracombe : Hillsborough (<★★) AC, Capstone Hill★ (<★), St. Nicholas' Chapel (<★) AC, NE : 5½ m. by B 3343 and A 361.*
Exc. : *Braunton★ (St. Braunton's Church★, Braunton Burrows★), S : 8 m. by B 3343 and A 361.*
ℹ *Red Barn Cafe Car Park, Barton Rd ℘ (01271) 870553 (summer only).*
*London 237 – Barnstaple 15 – Exeter 55.*

🏨 **Woolacombe Bay,** South St., EX34 7BN, ℘ (01271) 870388, *Fax (01271) 870613*, <, 🏋, 🧖, 🏊, 🏊, 🌳, 🎾, squash – 🛗 [TV] ☎ [P] – 👥 200. [MC] [AE] [D] [VISA] [JCB]. 🚫🐕
*closed 3 January-14 February* – **Meals** (dancing Tuesday evening) (light lunch Monday to Saturday)/dinner 20.00 **st.** and a la carte 🍷 7.00 – **62 rm** ☕ (dinner included) 99.00/190.00 **st.**

🏨 **Little Beach,** The Esplanade, EX34 7DJ, ℘ (01271) 870398, *Fax (01271) 870051*, < – 🚭 [TV] ☎ 📞 [P]. [MC] [VISA]
*March-October* – **Meals** (residents only) (dinner only) 10.00 **st.** 🍷 3.75 – **10 rm** ☕ 26.00/76.00 **s.**

**at Mortehoe** *North : ½ m. – ✉ Woolacombe.*

🏨 **Watersmeet,** The Esplanade, EX34 7EB, ℘ (01271) 870333, *Fax (01271) 870890*, < Morte Bay, 🏊, 🏊, 🌳, 🎾 – 🚭 rest, [TV] ☎ [P]. [MC] [AE] [D] [VISA]. 🚫🐕
*closed December and January* – **Meals** (bar lunch Monday to Saturday)/dinner 22.00 **t.** and a la carte 🍷 5.25 – **24 rm** ☕ (dinner included) 117.00/204.00 **t.** – SB.

🏨 **Cleeve House,** EX34 7ED, ℘ (01271) 870719, *Fax (01271) 870719*, 🌳 – 🚭 rest, [TV] [P]. [MC] [VISA] [JCB]. 🚫🐕
*April-October* – **Meals** (dinner only) 14.50 **st.** 🍷 4.60 – **7 rm** ☕ 28.50/57.50 **st.** – SB.

🏨 **Sunnycliffe,** Chapel Hill, EX34 7EB, ℘ (01271) 870597, *Fax (01271) 870597*, < Morte Bay – 🚭 [TV] [P]. [MC] [VISA] [JCB]. 🚫🐕
*March-October* – **Meals** (dinner only) (residents only) 15.00 **st.** 🍷 4.05 – **8 rm** ☕ (dinner included) 51.00/92.00 **st.** – SB.

**WOOLLEY EDGE SERVICE AREA** *W. Yorks.* 402 404 P 23 – ⊠ *Wakefield.*

🏠 **Travelodge,** WF4 4LQ, M 1 between junctions 38 and 39 ℘ (01924) 830371 Fax (01924) 830609, Reservations (Freephone) 0800 850950 – ⇄ 🖵 🕭 **P**. 🐠 🖭 ⑩ 🚾 JCB. ⅏
Meals (grill rest.) – **32 rm** 39.95/59.95 **t.**

---

**WOOLSTASTON** *Shrops.* 402 403 L 26 – *see Church Stretton.*

---

**WOOLSTONE** *Glos.* – *see Cheltenham.*

---

**WOOLTON** *Newbury* 402 403 L 23 – *see Liverpool.*

---

**WOOLTON HILL** *Newbury* – *see Newbury.*

---

**WOOTTON BASSETT** *Wilts.* 403 404 O 29 – *see Swindon.*

---

**WOOTTON WAWEN** *Warks.* 403 404 O 27 – *pop. 2 056.*
London 105 – Birmingham 18 – Stratford-upon-Avon 5 – Warwick 11 – Worcester 23.

🏠 **Bull's Head,** Stratford Rd, B95 6BD, ℘ (01564) 792511, 🛱, 🚗 – **P**. 🐠 🚾
Meals - Seafood specialities - a la carte 19.00/33.00 **t.**

---

**WORCESTER** *Worcestershire* 403 404 N 27 Great Britain G. – *pop. 82 661.*
See : City★ – Cathedral★★ – Royal Worcester Porcelain Works★ (Dyson Perrins Museum★) M.
Exc. : The Elgar Trail★ – ⅊ Perdiswell Municipal, Bilford Rd ℘ (01905) 754668.
🛈 The Guildhall, High St., WR1 2EY ℘ (01905) 726311.
London 124 – Birmingham 26 – Bristol 61 – Cardiff 74.

Plan opposite

🏛 **Diglis House,** Severn St., WR1 2NF, ℘ (01905) 353518, Fax (01905) 767772, ≤, 🛱, « Georgian house on banks of River Severn », 🚗 – ⇄ rest, 🖵 ☎ **P**. 🐠 🖭 ⑩ 🚾. ⅏     o
Meals (bar lunch)/dinner 19.50 **st.** and a la carte ⅊ 6.95 – **24 rm** ⊇ 75.00/110.00 **st.**, 1 suite – SB.

🏠 **Travel Inn,** Wainwright Way, Warndon, WR4 9FA, Northeast : 5 ½ m. by A 449 (at junction 6 of M 5) ℘ (01905) 451240, Fax (01905) 756601 – ⇄ rm, 🖵 🕭. 🐠 🖭 ⑩ 🚾. ⅏
Meals (grill rest.) – **60 rm** 38.00 **t.**

⌂ **Number 40** without rest., 40 Britannia Sq., WR1 3DN, ℘ (01905) 611920, Fax (01905) 27152, « Regency townhouse », 🚗 – ⇄ 🖵. 🐠 🖭 🚾. ⅏     n
**3 rm** ⊇ 50.00/65.00 **s.**

XX **Brown's,** 24 Quay St., WR1 2JJ, ℘ (01905) 26263, Fax (01905) 25768, « Converted riverside corn mill » – 🐠 🖭 🚾     c
closed Saturday lunch, Sunday dinner, Monday and 1 week Christmas – Meals 18.50/34.50 **st.** ⅊ 6.00.

XX **Il Pescatore,** 34 Sidbury, WR1 2HZ, ℘ (01905) 21444, Fax (01905) 21444 – ⇄. 🐠 ⑩ 🚾     e
closed Sunday, Monday, 25-26 December, 1 week in summer and 1 week in autumn – Meals - Italian - a la carte 16.20/23.00 **t.** ⅊ 5.25.

**at Upton Snodsbury** East : 6 m. by A 44 on A 422 – ⊠ Worcester.

⌂ **Upton House,** WR7 4NR, on B 4082 (beside church) ℘ (01905) 381226, Fax (01905) 381226, « Part 13C timbered house », 🏊, 🚗 – ⇄ 🖵 **P**. ⅏
closed Easter, Christmas and New Year – Meals (by arrangement) (communal dining) 20.00 **st.** – **3 rm** ⊇ 40.00/70.00.

**at Severn Stoke** South : 7 m. on A 38 403 404 N 27 – ⊠ Worcester.

🏛 **Old Schoolhouse,** Severn Stoke, WR8 9JA, ℘ (01905) 371368, Fax (01905) 371591, 🏊, 🚗 – ⇄ 🖵 ☎ **P** – ⅍ 100. 🐠 🖭 🚾 JCB
Meals (closed Saturday lunch) 11.50/16.50 **t.** and a la carte ⅊ 5.25 – **13 rm** ⊇ 45.00/75.00 – SB.

🛞 ATS Little London, Barbourne ℘ (01905) 24009/28543

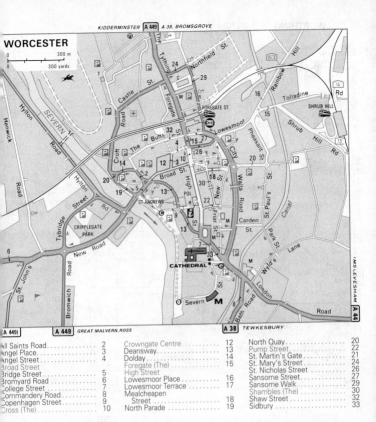

WORCESTER

KIDDERMINSTER A 449 A 38. BROMSGROVE

*Si vous cherchez un hôtel tranquille,*
*consultez d'abord les cartes de l'introduction*
*ou repérez dans le texte les établissements indiqués avec le signe ⓢ ou ⓢ.*

---

**WORFIELD** Shrops. − see Bridgnorth.

---

**WORKSOP** Notts. **402 403 404** Q 24 Great Britain G. − pop. 37 247.

See : Mr. Straw's House★.

⬚ Kilton Forest, Blyth Rd ℘ (01909) 472488 − ⬚ Windmill Lane ℘ (01909) 472696.

🖪 Worksop Library, Memorial Av., S80 2BP ℘ (01909) 501148.

London 163 − Derby 47 − Lincoln 28 − Nottingham 30 − Sheffield 19.

🏨 **Clumber Park,** Clumber Park, S80 3PA, Southeast : 6 ½ m. by B 6040 and A 57 on A 614 ℘ (01623) 835333, Fax (01623) 835525 − ⓧ 🔟 ☎ 🅿 − 🔏 180. 🐯 AE ⓪ VISA JCB. ⌘
Meals 11.95/16.00 t. a la carte − ⌑ 9.75 − **47 rm** 65.00/80.00 t., 1 suite − SB.

🏠 **Travelodge,** Dukeries Mill, St. Anne's Drive, S80 3QD, West : ½ m. by A 57 ℘ (01909) 501528, Fax (01909) 501528, Reservations (Freephone) 0800 850950 − ⓧ rm, 🔟 & 🅿 🐯 AE ⓪ VISA JCB. ⌘
Meals (grill rest.) − **40 rm** 39.95/59.95 t.

⑩ ATS 44-46 Carlton Rd ℘ (01909) 501818

---

**WORMINGTON** Glos. **403 404** O 27 − see Broadway (Worcestershire).

---

**WORSLEY** Gtr. Manchester **402 403 404** MN 23 − see Manchester.

647

# WORTHING

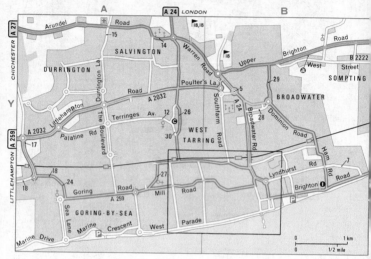

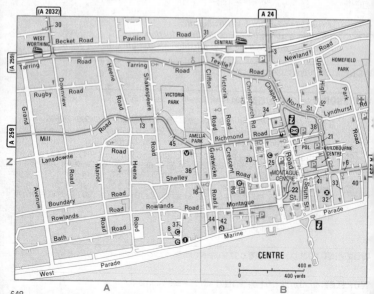

648

**WORTHING** W. Sussex 404 S 31 – pop. 95 732.

🏌18 Hill Barn, Hill Barn Lane ℰ (01903) 237301, BY – 🏌18, 🏌18 Links Rd ℰ (01903) 260801 AY.

✈ Shoreham Airport : ℰ (01273) 296900, E : 4 m. by A 27 BY.

🖪 Chapel Rd, BN11 1HL ℰ (01903) 210022 – Marine Parade, BN11 3PX ℰ (01903) 210022 (summer only).

London 59 – Brighton 11 – Southampton 50.

Plan opposite

🏨🏨 **Beach,** Marine Par., BN11 3QJ, ℰ (01903) 234001, Fax (01903) 234567, ← – 🛗 🖵 ☎ 🅿 – 🔬 60. 🆎 🆎 ① 𝖵𝖨𝖲𝖠. 🕸
AZ e
Meals (bar lunch except Sunday and Bank Holidays)/dinner 18.95 **t.** and a la carte – **75 rm** ⊑ 55.75/89.00 **t.**, 4 suites – SB.

🏨 **Chatsworth,** Steyne, BN11 3DU, ℰ (01903) 236103, Fax (01903) 823726 – 🛗, ✹ rest, 🖵
BZ x
☎ 🅿 – 🔬 150. 🆎 🆎 ① 𝖵𝖨𝖲𝖠
Meals (carving lunch) 10.95/16.95 **t.** – **107 rm** ⊑ 59.00/84.00 **t.**

🏨🏨 **Berkeley,** 86-95 Marine Par., BN11 3QD, ℰ (01903) 820000, Fax (01903) 821333, ← – 🛗 🖵
BZ a
☎ 🅿 – 🔬 150. 🆎 🆎 ① 𝖵𝖨𝖲𝖠. 🕸
Meals (bar lunch Monday to Saturday)/dinner 14.95 **t.** and a la carte ⓵ 6.00 – **84 rm** ⊑ 59.00/92.00 **t.** – SB.

🏨 **Windsor House,** 14-20 Windsor Rd, BN11 2LX, ℰ (01903) 239655, Fax (01903) 210763,
BY i
– ✹ rest, ▤ rest, 🖵 ☎ 🅿 – 🔬 120. 🆎 🆎 ① 𝖵𝖨𝖲𝖠. 🕸
closed 26 December – Meals (buffet lunch)/dinner 17.50 **t.** and a la carte ⓵ 5.95 – **32 rm** ⊑ 57.00/110.00 **st.** – SB.

🏨 **Kingsway,** 117-119 Marine Par., BN11 3QQ, ℰ (01903) 237542, Fax (01903) 204173 – 🛗,
AZ i
✹ rest, 🖵 ☎ 🅿 – 🔬 40. 🆎 🆎 ① 𝖵𝖨𝖲𝖠
Meals (bar lunch Monday to Saturday)/dinner a la carte 15.00/25.00 **t.** ⓵ 6.60 – **29 rm** ⊑ 52.50/98.00 **t.** – SB.

↑ **Beacons** without rest., 18 Shelley Rd, BN11 1TU, ℰ (01903) 230948, Fax (01903) 230948 –
BZ e
✹ 🖵 ☎ 🅿. 🆎 🆎 ① 𝖵𝖨𝖲𝖠 𝖩𝖢𝖡
**8 rm** ⊑ 29.00/58.00.

↑ **Bonchurch House,** 1 Winchester Rd, BN11 4DJ, ℰ (01903) 202492 – ✹ rest, 🖵 🅿. 🆎
AZ v
𝖵𝖨𝖲𝖠 𝖩𝖢𝖡. 🕸
closed 28 December-13 February – Meals (by arrangement) 14.50 **t.** ⓵ 5.00 – **7 rm** ⊑ 21.00/42.00 **st.**

↑ **Upton Farm House** without rest., Upper Brighton Rd, Sompting Village, BN14 9JU,
BY a
ℰ (01903) 233706, 🌳 – ✹ 🖵 🅿
**3 rm** ⊑ 20.00/45.00 **st.**

✕✕ **Trenchers,** 118-120 Portland Rd, BN11 1QA, ℰ (01903) 820287, Fax (01903) 820287 – 🆎
BZ c
𝖵𝖨𝖲𝖠
closed Sunday dinner – Meals 26.00 **t.** (dinner) and a la carte 31.00/42.00 **t.** ⓵ 6.00.

✕✕ **Parsonage,** 6-10 High St., Tarring, BN14 7NN, ℰ (01903) 820140, Fax (01903) 523233,
AY c
🌳, « 15C cottages » – 🆎 🆎 ① 𝖵𝖨𝖲𝖠
closed Saturday lunch, Sunday, 1 week Christmas and Bank Holidays – Meals 19.50 **t.** and a la carte ⓵ 7.50.

✕✕ **Paragon,** 9-11 Brunswick Rd, BN11 3NG, ℰ (01903) 233367, Fax (01903) 233367 – 🆎 🆎
AZ c
① 𝖵𝖨𝖲𝖠 𝖩𝖢𝖡
closed Sunday, Monday and 2 to 16 January – Meals 15.50/19.50 **t.** and a la carte ⓵ 6.00.

🅐 ATS Units 1/2, Hazelwood Trading Est., Dominion Way ℰ (01903) 237640/820971

---

**WRESSLE** East Riding 402 R 22 Great Britain G. – ✉ Selby (N. Yorks.).

Env. : Selby (Abbey Church★), W : 5 m. by minor road and A 63.

London 208 – Kingston-upon-Hull 31 – Leeds 31 – York 19.

🏨 **Loftsome Bridge Coaching House,** YO8 6EN, South : ½ m. ℰ (01757) 630070,
Fax (01757) 630070, 🌳 – ✹, ▤ rest, 🖵 ☎ 🅿. 🆎 ① 𝖵𝖨𝖲𝖠. 🕸
Meals (closed Sunday dinner) (dinner only and Sunday lunch)/dinner 16.95 **t.** ⓵ 4.25 – **17 rm** ⊑ 42.50/52.50 **t.**

---

**WROTHAM HEATH** Kent 404 U 30 – pop. 1 767 – ⊠ Sevenoaks.
London 35 – Maidstone 10.

🏚 **Forte Posthouse Maidstone/Sevenoaks,** London Rd, TN15 7R
℘ (01732) 883311, Fax (01732) 885850, 🛵, ☎, 🔲, ☞ – ⅓ rm, 🔲 ☎ ໓ ❷ – 🔬 60. ◍ ◪
◍ 𝗩𝗜𝗦𝗔 𝗝𝗖𝗕
closed 31 December – Meals a la carte 19.85/28.85 st. ⅟ 8.95 – ☲ 9.95 – **107 rm** 95.00 st.
SB.

🏠 **Travel Inn,** London Rd, TN15 7RX, ℘ (01732) 884214, Fax (01732) 780368 – ⅓ rm, 🔲 ໓
❷ ◍◪ 🗚 ◍ 𝗩𝗜𝗦𝗔 🗳
Meals (grill rest.) – **40 rm** 38.00 t.

---

**WROXHAM** Norfolk 404 Y 25 Great Britain G. – pop. 3 247 (inc. Hoveton).
Env.: The Broads★.
London 118 – Great Yarmouth 21 – Norwich 7.

↑ **Garden Cottage,** 96 Norwich Rd, NR12 8RY, ℘ (01603) 784376, Fax (01603) 783192
🗳 🔲 ❷. ◍◪ 𝗩𝗜𝗦𝗔
closed 24 December-2 January – Meals (by arrangement) 12.50 st. ⅟ 4.50 – **3 rm** ☲ 35.00
55.00 st. – SB.

---

**WROXTON** Oxon. 403 404 P 27 – see Banbury.

---

**WYCH CROSS** E. Sussex 404 U 30 – see Forest Row.

---

**WYE** Kent 404 W 30 – pop. 1 608 – ⊠ Ashford.
London 60 – Canterbury 10 – Dover 28 – Hastings 34.

XX **Wife of Bath** with rm, 4 Upper Bridge St., TN25 5AW, ℘ (01233) 812540
Fax (01233) 813630, ☞ – ⅓ rm, 🔲 ☎ ❷. ◍◪ 🗚 ◍ 𝗩𝗜𝗦𝗔 𝗝𝗖𝗕. 🗳
Meals (closed Sunday and Monday) 13.75/23.50 t. and lunch a la carte ⅟ 6.50 – ☲ 5.00 –
**6 rm** 40.00/80.00 t.

---

**WYMONDHAM** Norfolk 404 X 26 – pop. 10 869.
London 102 – Cambridge 55 – King's Lynn 49 – Norwich 12.

🏚 **Wymondham Consort,** 28 Market St., NR18 0BB, ℘ (01953) 606721
Fax (01953) 601361, ☞ – ⅓ 🔲 ☎ 📞 ❷. ◍◪ 🗚 ◍ 𝗩𝗜𝗦𝗔 𝗝𝗖𝗕
Meals 11.95/17.95 t. and a la carte ⅟ 6.25 – **20 rm** ☲ 55.00/80.00 t. – SB.

---

**YARCOMBE** Devon 403 K 31 – see Honiton.

---

**YARM** Stockton-on-Tees 402 P 20 – pop. 8 929.
London 242 – Middlesbrough 8.

🏛 **Crathorne Hall** ⑤, Crathorne, TS15 0AR, South : 3 ½ m. by A 67 ℘ (01642) 700398,
Fax (01642) 700814, ≼, « Converted Edwardian mansion », ⌕, ☞, park – ⅓ 🔲 ☎ ❷ –
🔬 90. ◍◪ 🗚 ◍ 𝗩𝗜𝗦𝗔
Leven : Meals 38.50 st. (dinner) and a la carte 25.00/38.00 st. – **37 rm** ☲ 115.00/175.00 t.
– SB.

🏚 **Judges at Kirklevington Hall** ⑤, Kirklevington, TS15 9LW, South : 1 ½ m. on A 67
℘ (01642) 789000, Fax (01642) 782878, ≼, « Former Victorian judges residence », ☞, park
– ⅓ rest, 🔲 ☎ ❷ – 🔬 70. ◍◪ 🗚 ◍ 𝗩𝗜𝗦𝗔
Meals (bar lunch Saturday) 14.95/25.00 and a la carte ⅟ 11.95 – **21 rm** ☲ 120.00/152.00 t. –
SB.

---

**YARMOUTH** I.O.W. 403 404 P 31 – see Wight (Isle of).

---

**YATELEY** Hants. 404 R 29 – pop. 15 663 – ⊠ Camberley.
London 37 – Reading 12 – Southampton 58.

🏛 **Casa Dei Cesari,** Handford Lane, Cricket Hill, GU46 6BT, ℘ (01252) 873275,
Fax (01252) 870614, ☞ – 🔲 ☎ 📞 ❷. ◍◪ 🗚 ◍ 𝗩𝗜𝗦𝗔 🗳
closed 26 December and 1 January – Meals - Italian - 16.95 t. and a la carte ⅟ 5.25 – **40 rm**
☲ 72.50/87.50 t., 2 suites.

**YATTENDON** Newbury [403] [404] Q 29 – pop. 288 – ⊠ Newbury.
London 61 – Oxford 23 – Reading 12.

XX **Royal Oak** with rm, The Square, RG18 0UG, ℘ (01635) 201325, Fax (01635) 201926, « Part 17C coaching inn », 佘 – ⇔ rest, ▥ ☎ ఈ ℗. 🆎 ⒶⒺ ⓪ 𝘝𝘐𝘚𝘈
Meals (closed lunch Monday and Saturday and Sunday dinner) (booking essential) 29.50 t. (dinner) and lunch a la carte 20.50/26.25 t. – (see also below) – ☲ 9.50 – 5 rm 90.00/110.00 – SB.

▯D **Royal Oak,** The Square, RG18 0UG, ℘ (01635) 201325, Fax (01635) 201926, 佘 – ఈ ℗. 🆎 ⒶⒺ ⓪ 𝘝𝘐𝘚𝘈 𝘑𝘊𝘉
Meals 14.00 t. (lunch) and a la carte approx. 21.00 t. ⑧ 8.00.

**YEADON** W. Yorks. [402] O 22 – see Leeds.

**YEALMPTON** Devon [403] I 32 – see Plymouth.

**YELVERTON** Devon [403] H 32 The West Country G. – pop. 3 609 (inc. Horrabridge).
See : Yelverton Paperweight Centre★.
Env. : Buckland Abbey★★ AC, SW : 2 m.
Exc. : E : Dartmoor National Park★★.
🛅 Golf Links Rd ℘ (01822) 853618.
London 234 – Exeter 33 – Plymouth 9.

▦ **Moorland Links** ♨, PL20 6DA, South : 2 m. on A 386 ℘ (01822) 852245, Fax (01822) 855004, ≼, 佘, ⁒ – ⇔ ▥ ☎ ℗ – 🔬 200. 🆎 ⒶⒺ ⓪ 𝘝𝘐𝘚𝘈
Meals (closed 25 and 26 December) (bar lunch Saturday and Bank Holidays) 21.00 t. ⑧ 6.45 – 43 rm ☲ 75.00/107.00 t., 1 suite – SB.

⌂ **Harrabeer Country House,** Harrowbeer Lane, PL20 6EA, ℘ (01822) 853302, Fax (01822) 853302, 佘 – ⇔ rm, ▥ ☎ ℗. 🆎 𝘝𝘐𝘚𝘈
closed 24 December-2 January – Meals (by arrangement) 12.50 s. ⑧ 3.95 – 7 rm ☲ 20.00/53.00 s. – SB.

**YEOVIL** Somerset [403] [404] M 31 The West Country G. – pop. 28 317.
See : St. John the Baptist★.
Env. : Monacute House★★ AC, W : 4 m. on A 3088 – Fleet Air Arm Museum, Yeovilton★★ AC, NW : 5 m. by A 37 – Tintinhull House Garden★ AC, NW : 5½ m. – Ham Hill (≼★★) W : 5½ m. by A 3088 – Stoke sub-Hamdon (parish church★) W : 5¼m. by A 3088.
Exc. : Muchelney★★ (Parish Church★★) NW : 14 m. by A 3088, A 303 and B 3165 – Lytes Cary★, N : 7½ m. by A 37, B 3151 and A 372 – Sandford Orcas Manor House★, NW : 8 m. by A 359 – Cadbury Castle (≼★★) NE : 10½ m. by A 359 – East Lambrook Manor★ AC, W : 12 m. by A 3088 and A 303.
🛅, 🛅 Sherborne Rd ℘ (01935) 75949.
🅱 Petter's House, Petter's Way, BA20 1SH ℘ (01935) 471279 – at Podimore, South Somerset Visitor Centre, Forte Services (A 303), BA22 8JG ℘ (01935) 841302 (summer only).
London 136 – Exeter 48 – Southampton 72 – Taunton 26.

▦ **Yeovil Court,** West Coker Rd., BA20 2NE, Southwest : 2 m. on A 30 ℘ (01935) 863746, Fax (01935) 863990 – ⇔ rm, ▥ ☎ ℗ – 🔬 60. 🆎 ⒶⒺ ⓪ 𝘝𝘐𝘚𝘈 𝘑𝘊𝘉
Meals (closed Saturday lunch and Sunday dinner) a la carte 15.00/23.00 t. ⑧ 5.30 – 25 rm ☲ 62.50/72.50 t., 1 suite – SB.

⌂ **Holywell House** ♨ without rest., Holywell, East Coker, BA22 9NQ, Southwest : 2 ¾ m. by A 30 on Hardington rd ℘ (01935) 862612, Fax (01935) 863035, « Georgian manor house », 佘, ⁒ – ▥ ℗. ⁒
closed 2 weeks Christmas and New Year – 2 rm ☲ 40.00/65.00 s., 1 suite – SB.

**at Podimore** North : 9½ m. by A 37 off A 303 – ⊠ Yeovil.

▥ **Travelodge,** BA22 8JG, West : ½ m. ℘ (01935) 840074, Reservations (Freephone) 0800 850950 – ⇔ rm, ▥ ᙖ ℗. 🆎 ⒶⒺ ⓪ 𝘝𝘐𝘚𝘈 𝘑𝘊𝘉. ⁒
Meals (grill rest.) – 31 rm 39.95/59.95 t.

**at Barwick** South : 2 m. by A 30 off A 37 – ⊠ Yeovil.

XX **Little Barwick House** ♨ with rm, BA22 9TD, ℘ (01935) 423902, Fax (01935) 420908, « Georgian dower house », 佘 – ⇔ ▥ ☎ ℗. 🆎 ⒶⒺ 𝘝𝘐𝘚𝘈 𝘑𝘊𝘉
closed Christmas-New Year – Meals (closed Sunday to non-residents) (booking essential) (dinner only) 27.90 st. ⑧ 5.00 – 6 rm ☲ 57.50/95.00 st.

**at Montacute** West : 5½ m. by A 3088 – ⊠ Martock.

🏠 **Kings Arms,** Bishopston, TA15 6UU, ℰ (01935) 822513, Fax (01935) 826549, 🌤 – ⊱ [
☎ 🅿. 🐿 AE 𝗩𝗜𝗦𝗔. ⅌
**Meals** (buffet lunch Monday to Saturday and bar dinner Sunday)/dinner 19.50
and a la carte ⅃ 5.95 – **15 rm** ⊑ 53.00/85.00 **t.** – SB.

🔘 ATS Lyde Rd., Penmill Trading Est.
ℰ (01904) 475580

---

**YETMINSTER** Dorset 𝟺𝟶𝟹 𝟺𝟶𝟺 M 31 – see Sherborne.

---

**YORK** N. Yorks. 𝟺𝟶𝟸 Q 22 Great Britain G. – pop. 124 609.

See : City★★★ – Minster★★★ (Stained Glass★★★, Chapter House★★, Choir Screen★★ ) CDY
National Railway Museum★★★ CY – The Walls★★ CDXYZ – Castle Museum★ AC DZ **M2**
Jorvik Viking Centre★ AC DY **M1** – Fairfax House★ AC DY A – The Shambles★ DY **54.**

🏌 Lords Moor Lane, Strensall ℰ (01904) 491840, BY – 🏌 Heworth, Muncaster Hous
Muncastergate ℰ (01904) 424618 BY.

🛈 The De Grey Rooms, Exhibition Sq., YO1 2HB ℰ (01904) 621756 – York Railway Statio
Outer Concourse, YO2 2AY ℰ (01904) 621756 – TIC Travel Office, 6 Rougier St., YO2 1.
ℰ (01904) 620557.

London 203 – Kingston-upon-Hull 38 – Leeds 26 – Middlesbrough 51 – Nottingham 88
Sheffield 62.

Plan opposite

🏛🏛 **Middlethorpe Hall,** Bishopthorpe Rd, YO23 2GB, South : 1 ¾ m. ℰ (01904) 64124
Fax (01904) 620176, ≤, « William and Mary house, gardens », park – 🖗, ⅌ rest, 🆃 ☎ 🅿
🅿 50. 🐿 𝗩𝗜𝗦𝗔. ⅌
**Meals** (closed to non-residents on 25 December) (booking essential to non-resident
14.50/27.95 **st.** ⅃ 7.50 – **Grill :** Meals (May-September) (dinner only Friday and Saturda
23.95 **st.** ⅃ 7.50 – ⊑ 12.50 – **23 rm** 99.00/155.00 **st.,** 7 suites.

🏛🏛 **The Grange,** Clifton, YO30 6AA, ℰ (01904) 644744, Fax (01904) 612453, « Regency tow
house » – 🆃 ☎ 🅿 – 🅿 45. 🐿 🅰🅴 𝗩𝗜𝗦𝗔                                                CX
**The Brasserie :** Meals a la carte 15.85/19.25 **t.** ⅃ 7.50 – (see also **The Ivy** below) – **29 r**
⊑ 99.00/175.00 **t.,** 1 suite – SB.

🏛🏛 **Swallow,** Tadcaster Rd, YO24 1QQ, ℰ (01904) 701000, Fax (01904) 702308, 🖎, 🚲, 🖫
🌤 – 🖗, ⅌ rm, 🆃 ☎ ☏ 🕭 🅿 – 🅿 170. 🐿 🅰🅴 ⓪ 𝗩𝗜𝗦𝗔                               AZ
**Meals – Ridings :** Meals 14.75/20.75 **st.** and a la carte ⅃ 10.00 – **111 rm** ⊑ 110.00/150.0
1 suite – SB.

🏛🏛 **York Viking Moat House,** North St., YO1 6JF, ℰ (01904) 459988, Fax (01904) 64179.
≤, 🖎, 🖫 – 🖗 ⅌, 🗏 rest, 🆃 ☎ ☐ 🕭 🅿 – 🅿 300. 🐿 🅰🅴 ⓪ 𝗩𝗜𝗦𝗔 𝗝𝗖𝗕. ⅌         CY
**Meals** (dinner only and Sunday lunch)/dinner 15.25 **st.** and a la carte ⅃ 6.80 – ⊑ 9.50
**199 rm** 120.00/150.00 **st.,** 1 suite – SB.

🏠 **York Pavilion,** 45 Main St., Fulford, YO10 4PJ, South : 1 m. on A 19 ℰ (01904) 622099
Fax (01904) 626939 – ⅌ 🆃 ☎ ☏ – 🅿 100. 🐿 🅰🅴 ⓪ 𝗩𝗜𝗦𝗔 𝗝𝗖𝗕. ⅌
**Langtons Brasserie :** Meals a la carte 17.65/27.90 **st.** – **44 rm** ⊑ 90.00/115.00 **st.** – SB.

🏠 **Ambassador,** 123-125 The Mount, YO24 1DU, ℰ (01904) 641316, Fax (01904) 64025.
🌤 – 🖗, ⅌ rest, 🆃 ☎ 🅿 – 🅿 50. 🐿 🅰🅴 ⓪ 𝗩𝗜𝗦𝗔. ⅌                               AZ
**Gray's :** Meals (dinner only) a la carte 22.50/26.50 **st.** ⅃ 6.50 – **25 rm** ⊑ 98.00/128.00 **st.**
SB.

🏠 **Dean Court,** Duncombe Pl., YO1 7EF, ℰ (01904) 625082, Fax (01904) 620305 – 🖗, ⅌ rm
🆃 ☎ 🅿 – 🅿 40. 🐿 🅰🅴 ⓪ 𝗩𝗜𝗦𝗔 𝗝𝗖𝗕. ⅌                                        CY
**Meals** 13.50/21.00 **st.** and dinner a la carte ⅃ 6.35 – **40 rm** ⊑ 77.50/155.00 **st.** – SB.

🏠 **Judges' Lodging,** 9 Lendal, YO1 8AQ, ℰ (01904) 638733, Fax (01904) 679947, « Forme
18C judges residence » – 🆃 ☎ 🅿 🐿 🅰🅴 ⓪ 𝗩𝗜𝗦𝗔. ⅌
**Meals** 8.95 **t.** (dinner) and a la carte 6.70/24.40 **t.** – **12 rm** ⊑ 80.00/150.00 **t.,** 2 suites.

🏠 **Novotel,** Fishergate, YO10 4FB, ℰ (01904) 611660, Fax (01904) 610925, 🖎 – 🖗 ⅌
🗏 rest, 🆃 ☎ 🅿 – 🅿 210. 🐿 🅰🅴 ⓪ 𝗩𝗜𝗦𝗔 𝗝𝗖𝗕                                     DZ
**Meals** 16.00 **st.** (dinner) and a la carte 17.75/23.20 **st.** ⅃ 4.35 – ⊑ 9.00 – **124 rm** 80.00
99.00 **st.** – SB.

🏠 **Monkbar,** St. Maurice's Rd, YO31 7JA, ℰ (01904) 638086, Fax (01904) 629195 – 🖗 🆃 ☏
🅿 – 🅿 200. 🐿 🅰🅴 ⓪ 𝗩𝗜𝗦𝗔 𝗝𝗖𝗕. ⅌                                              DX
**Meals** 10.95 **st.** (lunch) and a la carte 16.75/25.45 **st.** ⅃ 7.00 – **47 rm** ⊑ 82.00/164.00 **st.**
SB.

🏠 **Forte Posthouse York,** Tadcaster Rd, YO24 1QF, ℰ (01904) 70792
Fax (01904) 702804, 🌤 – 🖗, ⅌ rm, 🆃 ☎ 🅿 – 🅿 80. 🐿 🅰🅴 ⓪ 𝗩𝗜𝗦𝗔             AZ
**Meals** a la carte 18.85/25.90 **t.** ⅃ 6.00 – ⊑ 8.95 – **143 rm** 69.00 **st.** – SB.

# YORK

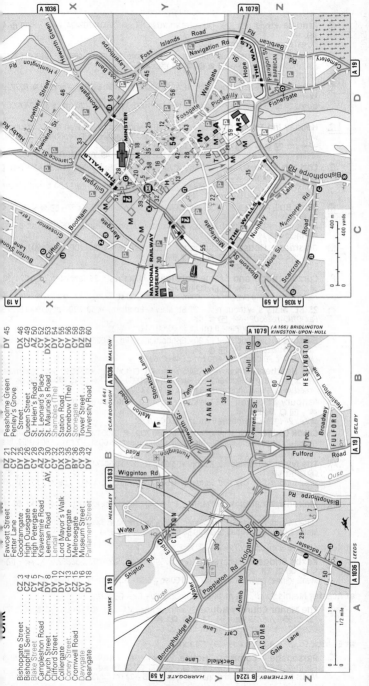

653

🏠 **Arndale** without rest., 290 Tadcaster Rd, YO24 1ET, ✆ (01904) 702424, 🚗 – ⅙⇐ 📺 🅿️. 🅼
*VISA*. ⌘
AZ
*closed Christmas* – **10 rm** ⊃ 49.00/75.00 **st.** – SB.

🏠 **Holmwood House** without rest., 114 Holgate Rd, YO24 4BB, ✆ (01904) 62618
*Fax (01904) 670899* – ⅙⇐ 📺 ☎ 🅿️. 🅼🅾 🆎 *VISA*. ⌘
AZ
**12 rm** ⊃ 40.00/75.00 **t.**

🏠 **Savages,** St. Peter's Grove, Clifton, YO30 6AQ, ✆ (01904) 610818, *Fax (01904) 627729*
⅙⇐ rest, 📺 ☎ 🅿️. 🅼🅾 🆎 🅾 *VISA*. ⌘
CX
*closed 24 to 26 December* – **Meals** (dinner only) 11.50 **st.** ₰ 4.95 – **20 rm** ⊃ 32.00/64.00 **s**
– SB.

🏠 **Holiday Inn Express,** Malton Rd, YO32 9TE, Northeast : 2 ¾ m. on A 1036 at junctic
with A 1237 ✆ (01904) 438660, *Fax (01904) 438660*, Reservations (Freephone) 0800 89712
– ⅙⇐ rm, 📺 ☎ 🕻 ⅙ 🅿️ – ⅍ 30. 🅼🅾 🆎 🅾 *VISA*. ⌘
**Meals** (grill rest.) 4.95 and a la carte 8.50/11.50 **st.** ₰ 7.45 – **49 rm** ⊃ 40.00 **st.**

🏠 **Cottage,** 3 Clifton Green, YO30 6LH, ✆ (01904) 643711, *Fax (01904) 611230* – ⅙⇐ rest, 📺
☎ 🅿️. 🅼🅾 🆎 🅾 *VISA*. ⌘
AY
*closed 25 and 26 December* – **Meals** (residents only) (dinner only) 12.00 **t.** and a la car
₰ 5.95 – **20 rm** ⊃ 40.00/65.00 **t.** – SB.

🏠 **Black Bull,** Hull Rd, YO10 3LF, ✆ (01904) 411856, *Fax (01904) 430667* – 📺 ☎ 🕻 ⅙ 🅿️. 🅼
🆎 *VISA*. ⌘
BZ
**Meals** (grill rest.) (bar lunch Monday to Saturday)/dinner a la carte 12.95/18.45 **st.** ₰ 4.00
**40 rm** ⊃ 49.50/59.50 **st.**

🏠 **Grasmead House** without rest., 1 Scarcroft Hill, YO24 1DF, ✆ (01904) 62999
*Fax (01904) 629996* – ⅙⇐ 📺 🅼🅾 🆎 🅾 *VISA* *JCB*. ⌘
CZ
**5 rm** ⊃ 65.00/70.00 **st.**

🏠 **Curzon Lodge and Stable Cottages** without rest., 23 Tadcaster Rd, YO24 1Q
✆ (01904) 703157 – ⅙⇐ 📺 🅿️. 🅼🅾 *VISA* *JCB*. ⌘
AZ
*restricted opening December* – **10 rm** ⊃ 47.00/75.00 **st.**

↑ **23 St. Mary's** without rest., 23 St. Mary's, Bootham, YO30 7DD, ✆ (01904) 62273
*Fax (01904) 628802* – ⅙⇐ 📺 ☎. ⌘
CX
*closed 2 weeks Christmas* – **9 rm** ⊃ 32.00/60.00 **t.**

↑ **Eastons's** without rest., 90 Bishopthorpe Rd, YO23 1JS, ✆ (01904) 62664
*Fax (01904) 626646* – ⅙⇐ 📺 🅿️. ⌘
CZ
*closed 24 to 26 December* – **10 rm** ⊃ 44.00/69.00.

↑ **The Heathers** without rest., 54 Shipton Rd, Clifton-without, YO30 5RQ, Northwest
1 ½ m. on A 19 ✆ (01904) 640989, *Fax (01904) 640989*, 🚗 – ⅙⇐ 📺 🅿️. 🅼🅾 🆎 *VISA*. ⌘
AY
*closed January and Christmas* – **8 rm** ⊃ 28.85/32.90.

↑ **Ashbury** without rest., 103 The Mount, YO24 1AX, ✆ (01904) 647339, *Fax (01904) 64733*
🚗 – 📺 🅿️. 🅼🅾 *VISA*. ⌘
CZ
*closed 24 to 26 December* – **6 rm** ⊃ 35.00/55.00 **st.**

↑ **Crook Lodge,** 26 St. Mary's, Bootham, YO30 7DD, ✆ (01904) 655614 – ⅙⇐ 📺 🅿️. ⌘
*closed Christmas and January* – **Meals** (by arrangement) 13.00 **st.** – **7 rm** ⊃ 30.00/52.00 **s**
– SB.
CX

🞤🞤🞤 **The Ivy** (at The Grange H.), Clifton, YO3 6AA, ✆ (01904) 644744, *Fax (01904) 612453* – 🅿
🅼🅾 🆎 🅾 *VISA*
CX
*closed lunch Saturday and Sunday* – **Meals** 11.50/25.00 **t.** and a la carte 28.25/31.70
₰ 7.50.

🞤🞤 **Melton's,** 7 Scarcroft Rd, YO23 1ND, ✆ (01904) 634341, *Fax (01904) 635115* – ⅙⇐. 🅼🅾 *VIS*
⌘
CZ
*closed Monday lunch, Sunday dinner, 1 week summer and 3 weeks Christmas-New Year*
**Meals** (booking essential) 16.00/20.50 **st.** and a la carte ₰ 6.50.

**at Kexby** *East : 6 ¾ m. on A 1079* – B – ✉ York.

🏠 **Kexby Bridge,** Hull Rd, YO4 5LD, ✆ (01759) 388223, *Fax (01759) 388822*, 🤽, 🚗 – 📺 ☎
🕻 🅿️. 🅼🅾 🆎 *VISA*. ⌘
**Meals** (dinner only) a la carte 12.00/23.00 **st.** ₰ 5.50 – **32 rm** ⊃ 50.00/75.00 **st.** – SB.

**at Acaster Malbis** *South : 4 ¾ m. by Bishopthorpe Rd* – BZ – ✉ York.

🏠 **The Manor Country House** ⌕ without rest., Mill Lane, YO23 2UL, ✆ (01904) 70672
*Fax (01904) 706723*, 🚗 – ⅙⇐ 📺 ☎ 🅿️. 🅼🅾 *VISA*. ⌘
*closed 1 week Christmas* – **10 rm** ⊃ 40.00/64.00 **st.**

**at Escrick** *South : 5 ¾ m. on A 19* – B – ✉ York.

🏠🏠 **Parsonage Country House,** Main St., YO19 6LF, ✆ (01904) 72811
*Fax (01904) 728151*, 🚗 – ⅙⇐ 📺 ☎ 🅿️ – ⅍ 200. 🅼🅾 🆎 🅾 *VISA*. ⌘
**Meals** 12.00/19.50 **st.** and dinner a la carte ₰ 7.25 – **22 rm** ⊃ 75.00/140.00 **st.** – SB.

at **Bilbrough** *Southwest : 5½ m. by A 1036 – AZ - off A 64 – ⊠ York.*

**Travel Inn,** Bilbrough Top, Colton, YO2 3PP, South : ½ m. on A 64 (westbound carriageway) ℘ (01937) 835067, *Fax (01937) 835934* – |≢|, ⁵⁄₈ rm, ⛁ ♿ 🅿 – 🔬 30. ◉ ⅍ ⓪ 𝘝𝘐𝘚𝘈. ⅏
**Meals** (grill rest.) – **60 rm** 38.00 **t.**

**Travelodge,** Steeton, LS24 8EG, Southwest : ¾ m. on A 64 (eastbound carriageway) ℘ (01937) 531823, *Fax (01937) 531823*, Reservations (Freephone) 0800 850950 – ⁵⁄₈ rm, ⛁ ♿ 🅿. ◉ ⅍ ⓪ 𝘝𝘐𝘚𝘈 𝘑𝘤𝘣. ⅏
**Meals** (grill rest.) – **62 rm** 39.95/59.95 **t.**

at **Long Marston** *West : 7 m. on B 1224 – AZ – ⊠ York.*

**Gill House Farm** without rest., Tockwith Rd, YO26 7PJ, North : ½ m. ℘ (01904) 738379, « Working farm », 🐎 – ⁵⁄₈ ⛁ 🅿. ◉ 𝘝𝘐𝘚𝘈. ⅏
**4 rm** ⊇ 35.00/48.00 **st.**

at **Skelton** *Northwest : 3 m. on A 19 – AY – ⊠ York.*

**Jarvis International,** Shipton Rd, YO30 1XW, ℘ (01904) 670222, *Fax (01904) 670311*, 🐎 – |≢| ⁵⁄₈, ▤ rest, ⛁ ☎ 🅿 – 🔬 200. ◉ ⅍ ⓪ 𝘝𝘐𝘚𝘈
**Meals** 8.50/16.30 **st.** and a la carte ⅃ 7.75 – ⊇ 8.50 – **84 rm** 99.00/119.00 **st.**, 6 suites – SB.

at **York Business Park** *Northwest : 3¾ m. by A 59 - AY - on A 1237 – ⊠ York.*

**Travel Inn,** White Rose Close, YO2 7NY, ℘ (01904) 787630, *Fax (01904) 787663* – |≢|, ⁵⁄₈ rm, ⛁ ♿ 🅿. ◉ ⅍ ⓪ 𝘝𝘐𝘚𝘈. ⅏
**Meals** (grill rest.) – **44 rm** 38.00 **t.**

ⓐ ATS 2 James St. ℘ (01904) 412372/410375          ATS 110 Layerthorpe ℘ (01904) 628479/625884

---

**GREEN TOURIST GUIDES**
Picturesque scenery, buildings
Attractive routes
Touring programmes
Plans of towns and buildings.

# *Scotland*

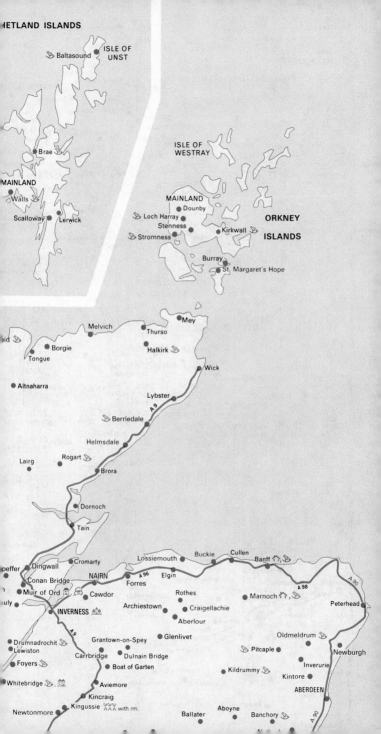

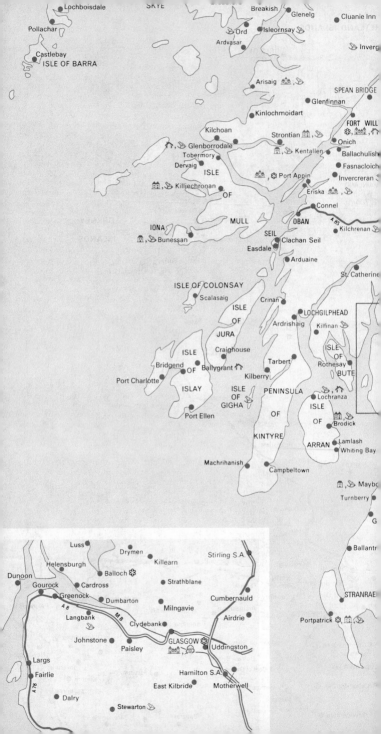

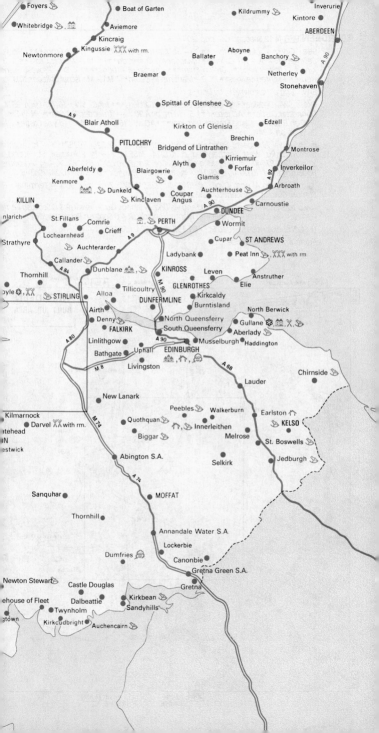

# ABERDEEN 🎯 N 12 *Scotland G.* – pop. 204 885.

**See** : *City★★ – Old Aberdeen★★* X – *St. Machar's Cathedral★★ (West Front★★★, Heraldic Ceiling★★★)* X A – *Art Gallery★★ (Macdonald Collection★★)* Y M – *Mercat Cross★★* Y B – *King's College Chapel★ (Crown Spire★★★, medieval fittings★★★)* X D – *Provost Skene House★ (painted ceilings★★)* Y E – *Maritime Museum★* Z M1 – *Marischal College★* Y U.

**Env.** : *Brig o' Balgownie★, by Don St.* X.

**Exc.** : *SW : Deeside★★ – Crathes Castle★★ (Gardens★★★) AC, SW : 16 m. by A 93* X – *Dunnottar Castle★★ AC (site★★★), S : 18 m. by A 90* X – *Pitmedden Garden★★, N : 14 m. by A 90 on B 999* X – *Castle Fraser★ (exterior★★) AC, W : 16 m. by A 944* X – *Fyvie Castle★, NW : 26½ m. on A 947.*

🏌, 🏌 *Royal Aberdeen, Balgownie, Bridge of Don* ℰ *(01224) 702571,* X – 🏌 *Auchmill, Bomyview Rd, West Heatheryfold* ℰ *(01224) 715214,* X – 🏌 *Balnagask, St. Fitticks R*℘ ℰ *(01224) 876407,* X – 🏌 *King's Links, Golf Rd* ℰ *(01224) 632269,* X – 🏌 *Portlethen, Badentoy Rd* ℰ *(01224) 781090,* X–🏌, 🏌 *Murcar, Bridge of Don* ℰ *(01224) 704345,* X.

✈ *Aberdeen Airport, Dyce :* ℰ *(01224) 722331, NW : 7 m. by A 96* X – **Terminal :** *Bus Station, Guild St. (adjacent to Railway Station).*

🚢 *to Shetland Islands (Lerwick) and via Orkney Islands (Stromness) (P & O Scottish Ferries) – to Norway (Bergen) via Shetland Islands (Lerwick) (P & O Scottish Ferries) weekly.*

🛈 *St. Nicholas House, Broad St., AB9 1DE* ℰ *(01224) 632727.*

*Edinburgh 130 – Dundee 67.*

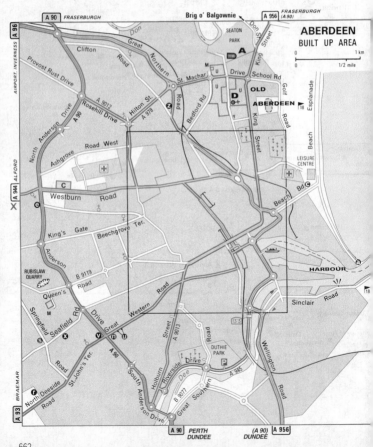

## ABERDEEN

| | | |
|---|---|---|
| on Accord Centre | Y | |
| road Street | Y | 6 |
| astle Street | Y | 7 |
| ollege Street | Z | 9 |
| raigie Loanings | Y | 12 |
| enburn Road | YZ | 14 |
| ast North Street | Y | 16 |
| eorge Street | Y | |
| reat Southern Road | Z | 18 |
| Guild Street | Z | 19 |
| Justice Street | Y | 21 |
| Millburn Street | Z | 23 |
| Rosemount Terrace | Y | 25 |
| Rosemount Viaduct | Y | 26 |
| St. Andrew Street | Y | 28 |
| St. Nicholas Centre | Y | 29 |
| St. Nicholas Street | YZ | 30 |
| School Hill | YZ | 32 |
| South Esplanade West | Z | 33 |
| South Mount Street | Y | 34 |
| Springbank Terrace | Z | 35 |
| Spring Garden | Y | 36 |
| Trinity Centre | Z | |
| Trinity Quay | Z | 37 |
| Union Street | Z | |
| Union Terrace | Z | 39 |
| Upperkirkgate | Y | 40 |
| Victoria Street | Z | 42 |
| Waverley Place | Z | 43 |
| Wellington Place | Z | 45 |
| Wellington Road | Z | 47 |
| Woolmanhill | Y | 48 |

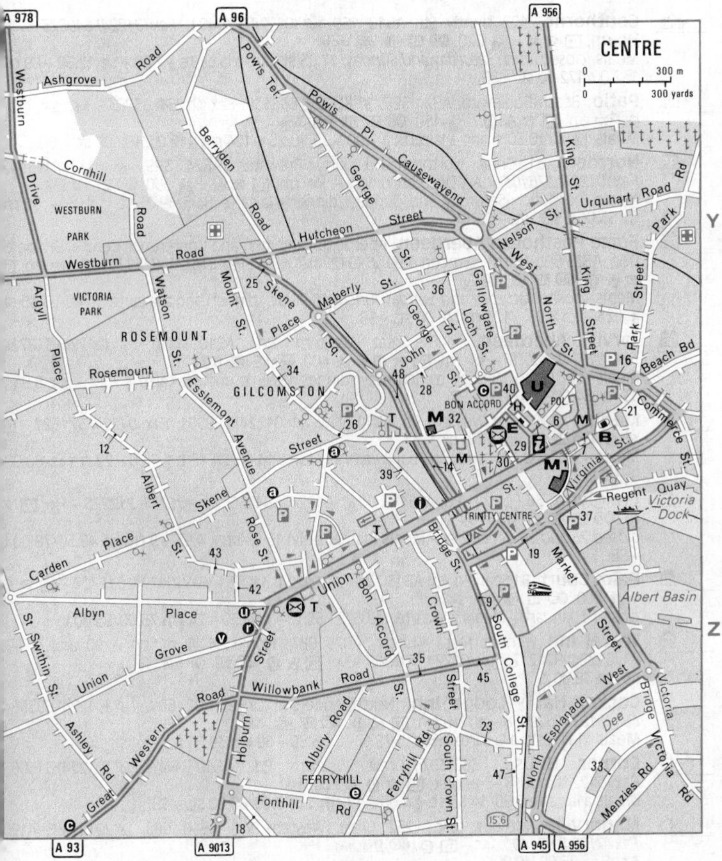


**Marcliffe at Pitfodels,** North Deeside Rd, AB15 9YA, ☎ (01224) 861000, *Fax (01224) 868860,* – rest, ☎ – 400. MC AE VISA JCB X r
***Invery Room :*** Meals (dinner only) a la carte 32.50/43.50 **st.** 10.50 – ***Conservatory :*** Meals a la carte 22.50/32.50 **st.** 7.50 – **42 rm** 145.00/255.00 **st.** – SB.

**Skene House Holborn** without rest., 6 Union Grove, AB10 6SY, ☎ (01224) 580000, *Fax (01224) 585193* – ☎ MC AE VISA JCB. Z v
8.50, **35 suites** 99.00/110.00 **st.**.

**Ardoe House**, South Deeside Rd, Blairs, AB12 5YP, Southwest : 5 m. on B 9077 ☎ (01224) 867355, *Fax (01224) 861283*, « Part 19C baronial mansion », park – ☎ – 120. MC AE VISA
Meals *(closed Saturday lunch)* 37.50 **t.** (dinner) and a la carte 20.00/32.00 **t.** 7.50 – 12.50 – **69 rm** 140.00/165.00 **t.**, 2 suites – SB.

**Thistle Caledonian,** 10-14 Union Terr., AB10 1WE, ℰ (01224) 640023
Fax (01224) 641627 – ⁅, ⁂ rm, ⚏ ☎ ℗ – ⚿ 35. ⬛⬛ ⒶⒺ ⬤ 𝕍𝕀𝕊𝔸. ⁓
**Meals** (closed lunch Saturday and Sunday) 12.95/20.50 **st.** and a la carte ⓙ 5.25 – ⚌ 11.75
**75 rm** 119.00/135.00 **st.**, 2 suites – SB.

**Stakis Aberdeen Tree Tops,** 161 Springfield Rd, AB15 7AQ, ℰ (01224) 313377
Fax (01224) 312028, ⌊₅, ⁼⁼s, ⬛, ⌗, ⌗, ⁂ – ⁅, ⁂ rm, ⚏ ☎ ℃ ℗ – ⚿ 900. ⬛⬛ ⒶⒺ ⬤ 𝕍𝕀𝕊𝔸
⁓
X
**Meals** 10.95/17.50 **t.** and dinner a la carte – ⚌ 9.95 – **111 rm** 120.00/140.00 **st.**, 1 suite
SB.

**Copthorne,** 122 Huntly St., AB10 1SU, ℰ (01224) 630404, Fax (01224) 640573 – ⁅
⁂ rm, ⚏ ☎ ℃ – ⚿ 220. ⬛⬛ ⒶⒺ ⬤ 𝕍𝕀𝕊𝔸 𝕁𝕔𝕓
Z
**Meals** (closed lunch Saturday and Sunday) 17.95 **st.** and a la carte ⓙ 7.50 – ⚌ 12.50 – **89 rm**
132.00/172.00 **st.** – SB.

**Patio,** Beach Boulevard, AB24 5EF, ℰ (01224) 633339, Fax (01224) 638833, ⌊₅, ⁼⁼s, ⬛
⁅, ⁂ rm, ⚏ ☎ ℗ – ⚿ 150. ⬛⬛ ⒶⒺ ⬤ 𝕍𝕀𝕊𝔸 𝕁𝕔𝕓
**Meals** 12.50/15.50 **s.** and a la carte ⓙ 7.90 – ⚌ 10.25 – **124 rm** 112.00/182.00 **st.** – SB.

**Northern,** 1 Great Northern Rd, Kitty Brewster, AB24 3PS, ℰ (01224) 483342
Fax (01224) 276103, « Art Deco building » – ⁂ rm, ⚏ ☎ ⅋, – ⚿ 350. ⬛⬛ ⒶⒺ ⬤ 𝕍𝕀𝕊𝔸
**Meals** (bar lunch Saturday and Sunday)/dinner a la carte 8.95/19.25 **st.** ⓙ 4.25 – **32 rm**
⚌ 55.00/65.00 **st.** – SB.
X

**Forte Posthouse Aberdeen,** Aberdeen Exhibition and Conference Centre, Bridge c
Don, AB23 8BL, North : 3 m. on A 90 ℰ (01224) 706707, Fax (01224) 823923 – ⁅, ⁂ rm, ⚏
☎ ⅋ ℗. ⬛⬛ ⒶⒺ ⬤ 𝕍𝕀𝕊𝔸
**Meals** (closed Saturday and Sunday lunch) 16.95 **st.** (dinner) and a la carte 14.40/23.35 **st.**
ⓙ 7.25 – ⚌ 8.95 – **123 rm** 79.00 **st.** – SB.

**Jarvis Aberdeen,** 448 Great Western Rd, AB10 6NP, ℰ (01224) 318724
Fax (01224) 312716 – ⁂ rm, ⚏ ☎ ℗ – ⚿ 400. ⬛⬛ ⒶⒺ ⬤ 𝕍𝕀𝕊𝔸
X
**Meals** (bar lunch Monday to Saturday)/dinner 13.95 **t.** and a la carte ⓙ 7.50 – ⚌ 8.95 –
**53 rm** 84.00/104.00 **t.** – SB.

**Mariner,** 349 Great Western Rd, AB10 6NW, ℰ (01224) 588901, Fax (01224) 571621 – ⚏
☎ ℗. ⬛⬛ ⒶⒺ ⬤ 𝕍𝕀𝕊𝔸 𝕁𝕔𝕓. ⁓
X
**Meals** - Seafood - (closed Saturday lunch) a la carte 14.50/24.75 **t.** ⓙ 7.00 – **22 rm** ⚌ 60.00
95.00 **t.**

**Craiglynn,** 36 Fonthill Rd, AB11 6UJ, ℰ (01224) 584050, Fax (01224) 212225 – ⁂ ⚏ ☎
℗. ⬛⬛ ⒶⒺ ⬤ 𝕍𝕀𝕊𝔸 𝕁𝕔𝕓. ⁓
Z
closed 25 and 26 December – **Meals** (dinner only) 15.95 **st.** ⓙ 4.95 – **9 rm** ⚌ 49.50/78.00 **t.**
– SB.

**Palm Court,** 81 Seafield Rd, AB15 7YU, ℰ (01224) 310351, Fax (01224) 312707 – ⚏ ☎ ℗
– ⚿ 100. ⬛⬛ ⒶⒺ ⬤ 𝕍𝕀𝕊𝔸. ⁓
X
closed 1 January – **Meals** a la carte 11.05/21.55 **t.** – ⚌ 9.50 – **24 rm** 75.00/95.00 **t.**

**Travel Inn** without rest., Murcar, AB23 8BP, North : 4 ½ m. on A 90 and B 99
ℰ (01224) 821217, Fax (01224) 706869 – ⁂ ⚏ ⅋ ℗. ⬛⬛ ⒶⒺ ⬤ 𝕍𝕀𝕊𝔸. ⁓
40 rm 38.00 **t.**

**Cocket Hat - Lodge Inn,** North Anderson Drive, AB2 6DW, ℰ (01224) 695684
Fax (01224) 692438 – ⁅, ⁂ rm, ⚏ ⅋ ℗. ⬛⬛ ⒶⒺ 𝕍𝕀𝕊𝔸. ⁓
X
**Meals** (grill rest.) a la carte 8.50/15.75 **t.** – ⚌ 5.50 – **60 rm** 39.00 **t.**

**Corner House,** 385-387 Great Western Rd, AB10 6NY, ℰ (01224) 313063
Fax (01224) 313063 – ⁂ rest, ⚏ ☎ ℗. ⬛⬛ ⒶⒺ 𝕍𝕀𝕊𝔸
X
**Meals** a la carte 8.90/14.55 **st.** ⓙ 4.00 – **17 rm** ⚌ 48.00/60.00 **st.** – SB.

**Manorville** without rest., 252 Great Western Rd, AB10 6PJ, ℰ (01224) 594190
Fax (01224) 594190, ⌗ – ⚏ ℗. ⬛⬛ 𝕍𝕀𝕊𝔸. ⁓
Z
3 rm ⚌ 25.00/40.00.

**Fourways** without rest., 435 Great Western Rd, AB10 6NJ, ℰ (01224) 310218
Fax (01224) 310218 – ⚏ ℗. ⬛⬛ ⒶⒺ 𝕍𝕀𝕊𝔸. ⁓
X
6 rm ⚌ 25.00/45.00 **s.**

**Q Brasserie,** 9 Alford Pl., AB1 1YD, ℰ (01224) 595001, Fax (01224) 582245 – ⬛⬛ ⒶⒺ ⬤
𝕍𝕀𝕊𝔸
Z
closed Saturday lunch and Sunday – **Meals** and a la carte 19.00/27.50 **st.** ⓙ 5.50.

**Rendezvous,** 210-212 George St., AB1 1BS, ℰ (01224) 633610, Fax (01224) 649389 – ☰
⬛⬛ ⒶⒺ 𝕍𝕀𝕊𝔸
Y
closed lunch Monday to Friday – **Meals** - Chinese (Peking) and Thai - 8.90/17.00 **t.**
and a la carte ⓙ 6.00.

**Courtyard on the Lane,** 1 Alford Lane, AB1 1YD, ℰ (01224) 213795
Fax (01224) 212961 – ⬛⬛ ⒶⒺ 𝕍𝕀𝕊𝔸 𝕁𝕔𝕓. ⁓
Z
closed Sunday, Monday, 25-26 December and 1-2 January – **Meals** a la carte 17.75/26.70 **t.**
ⓙ 6.95.

XX **Nargile,** 77-79 Skene St., AB10 1QD, ℰ (01224) 636093, *Fax (01224) 636202* – 🆆🆂 🆀🅴 🅾️
*VISA*
                                                                      Y  a
*closed 25-26 December and 1 January* – **Meals** - Turkish - (dinner only) 20.95 **t.**
and a la carte ⓘ 7.50.

X **Silver Darling,** Pocra Quay, North Pier, AB11 5DQ, ℰ (01224) 576229, *Fax (01224) 791275*
– 🆀🅴 🅰🅴 🅾️ *VISA* 🅹🅲🅱                                        X  a
*closed Saturday lunch, Sunday, 25-26 December and 1-2 January* – **Meals** - French Seafood
- (booking essential) a la carte 20.95/30.50 **t.** ⓘ 7.00.

**at Altens** *(Aberdeenshire) South : 3 m. on A 956* – X – ⊠ *Aberdeen.*

🏨🏨🏨 **Thistle Aberdeen,** Souter Head Rd, AB12 3LF, ℰ (01224) 877000, *Fax (01224) 896964*,
⤓ – ⓘ, ⇔ rm, ▤ rest, 📺 ☎ & 🅿 – 🔬 400. 🆀🅴 🅰🅴 🅾️ *VISA*
**Meals** 18.50 **t.** (dinner) and a la carte 18.50/25.00 **t.** ⓘ 6.00 – ⏞ 11.00 – **210 rm** 99.00/
105.00 **st.**, 1 suite – SB.

**at Portlethen** *(Aberdeenshire) South : 6 m. on A 90* – X – ⊠ *Aberdeen.*

🏨 **Travel Inn,** Mains of Balquuarn, AB12 4QS, ℰ (01224) 783856, *Fax (01224) 783836* – 🆀🅴 🅰🅴
🅾️ *VISA*
**Meals** (grill rest.) – **40 rm** 38.00 **t.**

**at Cults** *(Aberdeenshire) Southwest : 4 m. on A 93* – X – ⊠ *Aberdeen.*

X **Faraday's,** 2 Kirk Brae, AB1 9SQ, ℰ (01224) 869666, *Fax (01224) 869666* – 🅿. 🆀🅴 🅰🅴 *VISA*
*closed Sunday, Monday and 1 week Christmas* – **Meals** (booking essential) 18.00/
26.95 **t.** 7.10

**at Bankhead** *(Aberdeenshire) Northwest : 3½ m. by A 96* – X – ⊠ *Aberdeen.*

🏨 **Craighaar,** Waterton Rd, AB21 9HS, ℰ (01224) 712275, *Fax (01224) 716362* – ⇔ rm, 📺
☎ 🅿 – 🔬 90. 🆀🅴 🅰🅴 🅾️ *VISA*. 🅪
*closed 26 December and 1-2 January* **Meals** *(closed Saturday lunch)* 12.95/17.95 **t.**
and a la carte ⓘ 7.25 – ⏞ 9.50 – **49 rm** 75.00/95.00 **t.**, 6 suites.

**at Bucksburn** *(Aberdeenshire) Northwest : 4 m. by A 96* - X - on A 947 – ⊠ *Aberdeen.*

🏨🏨🏨 **Aberdeen Moat House,** Malcolm Rd, AB21 9LN, ℰ (01224) 409988,
*Fax (01224) 714020*, ⤓, ⇔, ⬚ – ⓘ, ⇔ rm, 📺 ☎ 🅿 – 🔬 180. 🆀🅴 🅰🅴 🅾️ *VISA*. 🅪
**Meals** *(bar lunch Monday to Saturday)/dinner* 19.50 **st.** and a la carte ⓘ 6.50 – ⏞ 10.95 –
**144 rm** 105.00/120.00 **st.** – SB.

**at Dyce** *(Aberdeenshire) Northwest : 5½ m. by A 96* - X - on A 947 – ⊠ *Aberdeen.*

🏨🏨🏨 **Aberdeen Marriott,** Overton Circle, AB21 7AZ, ℰ (01224) 770011, *Fax (01224) 722347*,
⤓, ⇔, ⬚ – ⇔ rm, ▤ 📺 ☎ & 🅿 – 🔬 400. 🆀🅴 🅰🅴 🅾️ *VISA* 🅹🅲🅱. 🅪
*closed 6 to 9 September, 31 December and 1 January* – **Meals** *(bar lunch)/dinner* a la carte
20.85/29.65 **st.** ⓘ 7.75 – ⏞ 11.95 – **154 rm** 105.00/118.00 **st.**, 1 suite.

🏨 **Travel Inn,** Burnside Drive, AB21 7HW, off Riverview Drive via Wellheads Rd
ℰ (01224) 772787, *Fax (01224) 772968*, ⇔ – ⇔ rm, 📺 & 🅿. 🆀🅴 🅰🅴 🅾️ *VISA*. 🅪
**Meals** (grill rest.) – **40 rm** 38.00 **t.**

**at Aberdeen Airport** *(Aberdeenshire) Northwest : 6 m. by A 96* – X – ⊠ *Aberdeen.*

🏨🏨🏨 **Thistle Aberdeen Airport,** Argyll Rd, AB21 7DU, ℰ (01224) 725252,
*Fax (01224) 723745*, ⤓ – ⇔ rm, 📺 ☎ & 🅿 – 🔬 550. 🆀🅴 🅰🅴 🅾️ *VISA* 🅹🅲🅱
**Meals** *(closed lunch Saturday and Sunday)* 13.95/20.50 **st.** and a la carte ⓘ 6.40 – ⏞ 12.00 –
**146 rm** 105.00/135.00 **st.**, 1 suite – SB.

🏨 **Speedbird Inn,** Argyll Rd, AB21 0AF, ℰ (01224) 772884, *Fax (01224) 772560* – ⇔ rm, 📺
☎ & 🅿 – 🔬 35. 🆀🅴 🅰🅴 🅾️ *VISA*
**Meals** *(closed Saturday lunch)* (bar lunch)/dinner 15.75 **st.** and a la carte ⓘ 4.00 – ⏞ 3.95 –
**99 rm** 45.50 **st.** – SB.

Ⓐ ATS Beach Boulevard ℰ (01224) 592727        ATS 214 Hardgate ℰ (01224) 589461

---

**ABERDEEN AIRPORT** *Aberdeenshire* 🆂🅾🆂 N 12 – *see Aberdeen.*

---

**ABERFELDY** *Perthshire and Kinross* 🆂🅾🆂 I 14 *Scotland G.* – *pop. 4 083.*
See : *Town★.*
Env. : *St. Mary's Church (painted ceiling★ ) NE : 2 m. by A 827.*
Exc. : *Loch Tay★★, SW : 6 m. by A 827 – Ben Lawers★★, SW : 16 m. by A 827 – Blair Castle★★
AC, N : 20½ m. by A 827 and A 9.*
🏌 *Taybridge Rd ℰ (01887) 820535.*
🅱 *The Square, PH15 2DD ℰ (01887) 820276.*
*Edinburgh 76 – Glasgow 73 – Oban 77 – Perth 32.*

ABERFELDY

🏨 **Farleyer House** ⌂, PH15 2JE, West : 2 m. on B 846 ℘ (01887) 82033⌂
Fax (01887) 829430, ≤, ⌂, 🛋, park – 📺 ☎ 🅿. 🐾 🆎 ⑩ 𝘝𝘐𝘚𝘈. ⌂
**Glen Lyon** : Meals 29.50 st. (dinner) and a la carte 15.90/24.40 st. ⌂ 8.50 – **19 r**⌂
⌂ 105.00/180.00 st.

🏨 **Guinach House** ⌂, Urlar Rd, PH15 2ET, off Crieff Rd ℘ (01887) 82025⌂
Fax (01887) 829607, ≤, ⌂ – ⌂ rest, 📺 🅿. 🐾 𝘝𝘐𝘚𝘈. ⌂
closed 4 days Christmas – Meals (dinner only) 25.00 st. ⌂ 8.45 – **7 rm** ⌂ 45.50/91.00 st.

---

**ABERFOYLE** Stirling 𝟰𝟬𝟭 G 15 Scotland G. – pop. 936 – ⌂ Stirling.
Env. : The Trossachs★★★ (Loch Katherine★★) N : 5 m. by A 821 – Hilltop Viewpoint★★
(⌂★★★) N : 2½ m. by A 821 – Inchmahone Priory (double effigy★) AC, E : 4 m. by A 81.
Exc. : Ben Lomond★★, W : 9 m. by B 829 – Loch Lomond★★, SW : 14 m. by A 81, A 811 an⌂
B 837.
🏌 Braeval ℘ (018772) 382493.
🛈 Main St., ℘ (01877) 382352 (summer only).
Edinburgh 56 – Glasgow 27.

XX **Braeval**, FK8 3UY, East : 1 m. by A 821 on A 81 ℘ (01877) 382711, Fax (01877) 38240⌂
⌂ « Converted mill », ⌂ – 🅿. 🐾 𝘝𝘐𝘚𝘈.
closed Sunday dinner, Monday, Tuesday, 1 week February, 1 week June, 2 weeks Octobe⌂
25-26 December and 1-2 January – Meals (set menu only) (booking essential) 19.50-22.5⌂
31.50 t. ⌂ 10.00
Spec. Warm salad of seared tuna with sesame oil. Breast of wood pigeon with beetroot an⌂
celeriac purée. Banana parfait, rhubarb ice cream.

---

**ABERLADY** East Lothian 𝟰𝟬𝟭 L 15 – pop. 1 033.
Edinburgh 16 – Haddington 5 – North Berwick 7.5.

🏨 **Green Craigs** ⌂, EH32 0PY, Southwest : 1 m. on A 198 ℘ (01875) 87030⌂
Fax (01875) 870440, ≤, 🛋, park – 📺 ☎ 🅿. 🐾 🆎 ⑩ 𝘝𝘐𝘚𝘈 𝘑𝘊𝘉
closed 1 January – Meals 27.50 t. (dinner) and a la carte 13.75/27.00 t. ⌂ 6.00 – **6 rr**⌂
⌂ 65.00/130.00 t. – SB.

🏨 **Kilspindie House**, Main St., EH32 0RE, ℘ (01875) 870682, Fax (01875) 870504 – 📺 ☎ 🅿⌂
🐾 ⑩ 𝘝𝘐𝘚𝘈 𝘑𝘊𝘉
Meals a la carte 9.80/16.00 t. ⌂ 5.90 – **26 rm** ⌂ 40.00/72.00 t. – SB.

---

**ABERLOUR** Aberdeenshire 𝟰𝟬𝟭 K 11 Scotland G. – pop. 1 780.
Env. : Dufftown (Glenfiddich Distillery★), SE : 6 m. by A 95 and A 941.
Edinburgh 192 – Aberdeen 60 – Elgin 15 – Inverness 55.

🏨 **Dowans**, AB38 9LS, Southwest : ¾ m. by A 95 ℘ (01340) 871488, Fax (01340) 871038, ⌂
🛋 – 📺 ☎ 🅿. 🐾 🆎 𝘝𝘐𝘚𝘈
closed 20 December-10 March – Meals (bar lunch)/dinner 22.95 st. and a la carte ⌂ 4.75
**19 rm** ⌂ 40.00/80.00 st.

---

**ABINGTON SERVICE AREA** South Lanarkshire 𝟰𝟬𝟭 I 17 – ⌂ Biggar.
Edinburgh 43 – Dumfries 37 – Glasgow 38.

🏨 **Welcome Lodge**, ML12 6RG, at junction 13 of M 74 ℘ (01864) 502782⌂
Fax (01864) 502759, Reservations (Freephone) 0800 7314466 – 📺 ⌂ 🅿. 🐾 🆎 ⑩ 𝘝𝘐𝘚𝘈
Meals (grill rest.) – ⌂ 7.50 – **56 rm** 50.00 t.

---

**ABOYNE** Aberdeenshire 𝟰𝟬𝟭 L 12 Scotland G. – pop. 3 793 (inc. Cromar).
Exc. : Craigievar Castle★ AC, NE : 12 m. by B 9094, B 9119 and A 980.
🏌 Formanston Park ℘ (013398) 86328.
🛈 Ballater Road Car Park ℘ (013398) 86060 (summer only).
Edinburgh 131 – Aberdeen 30 – Dundee 68.

🏨 **Birse Lodge** ⌂, Charleston Rd, AB34 5EL, ℘ (013398) 86253, Fax (013398) 87796, 🛋
📺 ☎ 🅿. 🐾 𝘝𝘐𝘚𝘈
Meals (closed lunch Monday to Wednesday) a la carte 13.00/23.00 t. ⌂ 4.50 – **12 rr**⌂
⌂ 40.00/70.00 st. – SB.

⌂ **Hazlehurst Lodge**, Ballater Rd, AB34 5HY, ℘ (013398) 86921, Fax (013398) 8666⌂
« Contemporary art collection », ⌂ – ⌂ 📺 🅿. 🐾 𝘝𝘐𝘚𝘈
March-November – Meals (by arrangement) 25.00 t. ⌂ 7.50 – **3 rm** ⌂ 45.00/80.00 t. – SB.

⌂ **Struan Hall** without rest., Ballater Rd, AB34 5HY ℘ (013398) 87241, Fax (013398) 8724⌂
🛋 – ⌂ 📺 🅿. 🐾 𝘝𝘐𝘚𝘈. ⌂
March-October – **3 rm** ⌂ 25.00/50.00 t.

⭡ **Arbor Lodge** without rest., Ballater Rd, AB34 5HY, ℰ (013398) 86951,
  *Fax (013398) 86951*, 🚿 – 🕪 📺 🅿. 🕦 *VISA*
  *March-November* – **3 rm** ⚏ 32.00/64.00 **st.**

✗ **White Cottage**, AB34 5BP, East : ½ m. on A 93 ℰ (013398) 86265, *Fax (013398) 86265* –
  🅿. 🕦 *VISA*
  *closed Sunday, Monday, 25-26 December, 1 week in spring, 2 weeks in summer and 1 week
  in autumn* – **Meals** 29.50 **t.** (dinner) and lunch a la carte 15.10/28.00 **t.** 🍷 7.00.

---

**CHILTIBUIE** *Highland* 401 D 9.
  *Edinburgh 243 – Inverness 84 – Ullapool 25.*

🏨 **Summer Isles** 🦢, IV26 2YG, ℰ (01854) 622282, *Fax (01854) 622251*, « Picturesque set-
❀  ting ≤ Summer Isles », 🔍 – 🕪 rest, 🕿 🅿. 🕦 *VISA*
  *Easter-mid October* – **Meals** (booking essential) (light seafood lunch)/dinner 37.00 **st.**
  🍷 8.50 – **11 rm** ⚏ 62.00/112.00 **st.**, 1 suite
  **Spec.** Roulade of Stilton and hazelnuts on a herb leaf salad. Pan-fried goujons of monkfish
  with lime, ginger and coriander. Roast rib of beef, caramelised garlic and red wine sauce.

---

**IRDRIE** *North Lanarkshire* 401 I 16.
  🏌 *Rochsoles* ℰ (01236) 762195.
  *Edinburgh 34 – Glasgow 14 – Perth 54 – Stirling 22.*

✗ **Bouzy Rouge**, 1 Rochsolloch Rd, Coatdyke, ML6 9BB, Southwest : 1 m. off A 89
  ℰ (01236) 763853, *Fax (01236) 770340* – 🍽 🅿. 🕦 🆎 ① *VISA*
  *closed 1 January* – **Meals** 7.95/12.95 **t.** and a la carte 🍷 6.95.

  ⓐ ATS 122 Coity Rd ℰ (01656) 658775/6

---

  *When looking for a quiet hotel*
  *use the maps found in the introduction*
  *or look for establishments with the sign* 🦢 *or* 🦢.

---

**IRTH** *Falkirk* 401 I 15 – pop. 1 519 – ✉ *Falkirk*.
  *Edinburgh 30 – Dunfermline 14 – Falkirk 7 – Stirling 8.*

🏨 **Radisson SAS Airth Castle** 🦢, FK2 8JF, ℰ (01324) 831411, *Fax (01324) 831419*, ≤,
  « Part 13C and 17C castle and stables in extensive grounds », 🛁, �, 🏊, 🚿, park – 🛗,
  🕪 rm, 📺 🕿 🅿 – 🔬 380. 🕦 🆎 ① *VISA* 🅹🅲🅱. 🛂
  **Meals** *(closed Sunday dinner)* (light lunch)/dinner 24.50 **st.** and a la carte – **123 rm**
  ⚏ 98.00/140.00 **st.** – SB.

---

**LLOA** *Clackmannanshire* 401 I 15 *Scotland G.* – pop. 26 691.
  Exc. : *Culross★★ (Village★★★, Palace★★ AC, Study★ AC), SE : 7 m. by A 907, A 977 and B
  9037 – Castle Campbell★ (site★★★, ≤★) AC, NE : 8 m. by A 908 and A 91 – Stirling★★, W : 8
  m. by A 907.*
  *Edinburgh 33 – Dundee 48 – Glasgow 35.*

🏨 **Gean House** 🦢, Gean Park, Tullibody Rd, FK10 2HS, Northwest : 1 m. on B 9096
  ℰ (01259) 219275, *Fax (01259) 213827*, ≤, 🚿 – 🕪 rest, 📺 🕿 🅿 – 🔬 50. 🕦 🆎 ① *VISA*
  🅹🅲🅱. 🛂
  **Meals** 15.00/25.00 **st.** 🍷 7.00 – **7 rm** ⚏ 90.00/165.00 **st.**

  ⓐ ATS Union St. ℰ (01259) 724253

---

**LLOWAY** *South Ayrshire* 401 402 G 17 – see Ayr.

---

**LTENS** *Aberdeenshire* – see Aberdeen.

---

**LTNAHARRA** *Highland* 401 G 9 *Scotland G.* – ✉ *Lairg*.
  Exc. : *Ben Loyal★★, N : 10 m. by A 836 – Ben Hope★ (≤★★★) NW : 14 m.*
  *Edinburgh 239 – Inverness 83 – Thurso 61.*

🏨 **Altnaharra** 🦢, IV27 4UE, ℰ (01549) 411222, *Fax (01549) 411222*, ≤, 🔍 – 🕪 rest, 🅿.
  🕦 *VISA*. 🛂
  *March-October* – **Meals** (bar lunch)/dinner 25.00 **st.** – **15 rm** ⚏ (dinner included) 66.00/
  132.00 **st.** – SB.

**ALYTH** Perthshire and Kinross **401** J 14 – pop. 4 650.

⌐ Pitcrocknie ℰ (01828) 632268.

*Edinburgh 63 – Aberdeen 69 – Dundee 16 – Perth 21.*

🏨 **Lands of Loyal** ⌂, Loyal Rd, PH11 8JQ, North : ½ m. by B 952 ℰ (01828) 63315
Fax (01828) 633313, ≤, ⇗ – ⊡ ☎ 🅿. ⬤🟑 Æ 🆅🆂🅰
**Meals** 21.95 t. (dinner) and a la carte 12.95/24.40 t. ⚡ 5.95 – **14 rm** �@ 49.50/79.00 t. – SB

🏛 **Drumnacree House**, St. Ninians Rd, PH11 8AP, ℰ (01828) 632194, Fax (01828) 63219
⇗ – ⇘⇙ ⊡ 🅿. ⬤🟑 Æ 🆅🆂🅰
*April-November* – **Meals** *(closed Sunday and Monday to non-residents)* (booking essenti
(dinner only) a la carte 18.00/23.50 t. ⚡ 6.50 – **6 rm** �@ 43.50/80.00 t. – SB.

---

**ANNANDALE WATER SERVICE AREA** Dumfries and Galloway **401** J 18 – ✉ Lockerbie.

🏛 **Annandale Water Lodge**, Johnstonebridge, DG11 1HD, junction 16 A 74 (N
ℰ (0800) 470870, Fax (01576) 470644, ≤ – ⇙⇘ rm, ⊡ ☎ & 🅿. ⬤🟑 Æ ⓞ 🆅🆂🅰
**Meals** (grill rest.) a la carte 10.45/13.00 st. – �@ 4.80 – **42 rm** 42.95 st.

---

**ANSTRUTHER** Fife **401** L 15 Scotland G. – pop. 1 307.

See : Scottish Fisheries Museum★★ AC.

Env. : The East Neuk★★ – Crail★★ (Old Centre★★, Upper Crail★) NE : 4 m. by A 917.

Exc. : Kellie Castle★ AC, NW : 7 m. by B 9171, B 942 and A 917.

⌐ Marsfield Shore Rd ℰ (01333) 310956.

🖪 Scottish Fisheries Museum ℰ (01333) 311073 (summer only).

Edinburgh 46 – Dundee 23 – Dunfermline 34.

↥ **Spindrift**, Pittenweem Rd, KY10 3DT, ℰ (01333) 310573, Fax (01333) 310573 – ⇙⇘ ⊡
🅿. ⬤🟑 Æ 🆅🆂🅰. ⋘
*closed 15 November-15 December and Christmas* – **Meals** (by arrangement) 15.00 t. ⚡ 4.
– **8 rm** �@ 35.00/62.00 st. – SB.

✗ **Cellar**, 24 East Green, KY10 3AA, ℰ (01333) 310378, Fax (01333) 312544 – ⇙⇘. ⬤🟑 Æ (
🆅🆂🅰
*closed Wednesday to Sunday lunch in summer, Sunday and Monday in winter* – **Meals**
Seafood - (booking essential) 28.50 t. (dinner) and a la carte 12.50/18.00 ⚡ 9.25.

---

**ARBROATH** Angus **401** M 14 Scotland G. – pop. 24 002 (inc. St. Vigeans).

See : Town★ – Abbey★ AC.

Env. : St. Vigeans★, N : 1½ m. by A 92.

⌐ Elliot ℰ (01241) 872069.

🖪 Market Pl., DD11 1HR ℰ (01241) 872609.

Edinburgh 72 – Aberdeen 51 – Dundee 16.

✗ **But 'n' Ben**, Auchmithie, DD11 5SQ, Northeast : 3 m. by A 92 ℰ (01241) 87722
« Converted fishermens cottages » – ⇙⇘. ⬤🟑 🆅🆂🅰 🅹🅲🅱
*closed Sunday dinner and Tuesday* – **Meals** (light lunch) a la carte 11.10/21.30 t. ⚡ 7.50.

---

**ARCHIESTOWN** Moray **401** K 11 – ✉ Aberlour (Aberdeenshire).

Edinburgh 194 – Aberdeen 62 – Inverness 49.

🏛 **Archiestown**, AB38 7QX, ℰ (01340) 810218, Fax (01340) 810239, ⚲, ⇗ – ☎ 🅿. ⬤🟑 🆅🆁
10 February-September – **Meals** – (see *Bistro* below) – **8 rm** �@ 45.00/90.00 t.

✗ **Bistro** (at Archiestown H.), AB38 7QL, ℰ (01340) 810218, Fax (01340) 810239 – 🅿. ⬤🟑 (
🆅🆂🅰
10 February-September – **Meals** a la carte 13.75/27.50 t. ⚡ 8.50.

---

**ARDEONAIG** Perthshire and Kinross **401** H 14 – see Killin (Stirling).

---

**ARDRISHAIG** Argyll and Bute **401** D 15 – pop. 1 315 – ✉ Lochgilphead.

Edinburgh 132 – Glasgow 86 – Oban 40.

↥ **Allt-na-Craig**, Tarbert Rd, PA30 8EP, on A 83 ℰ (01546) 603245, ≤, ⇗ – 🅿
*closed mid December-mid January* – **Meals** (by arrangement) 16.00 s. ⚡ 5.50 – **6 r**
⊚ 30.00/60.00 s. – SB.

*There is no paid advertising in this Guide.*

SCOTLAND

**RDUAINE** Argyll and Bute **401** D 15 Scotland G. – ⊠ Oban.
Exc. : Loch Awe★★, E : 12 m. by A 816 and B 840.
Edinburgh 142 – Oban 20.

🏠 **Loch Melfort** ⤷, PA34 4XG, ℘ (01852) 200233, Fax (01852) 200214, ≤ Sound of Jura, 🛲, park – ✝⊱ rest, 🔟 ☎ 🄿. 🕮 🄰🄴 🆅🅸🆂🅰. ⋘
closed 4 January-15 February – **Meals** (bar lunch)/dinner 32.50 t. ⌀ 6.95 – **26 rm** ⥮ 81.00/123.00 t. – SB.

**RDVASAR** Highland **401** C 12 – see Skye (Isle of).

**RDVOURLIE** Western Isles (Outer Hebrides) **401** Z 10 – see Lewis and Harris (Isle of).

**RISAIG** Highland **401** C 13 Scotland G..
See : Village★.
Env. : Silver Sands of Morar★, N : 5½ m. by A 830.
🏌 Traigh ℘ (01687) 450337.
Edinburgh 172 – Inverness 102 – Oban 88.

🏠 **Arisaig House** ⤷, Beasdale, PH39 4NR, Southeast : 3 ¼ m. on A 830 ℘ (01687) 450622, Fax (01687) 450626, ≤ Loch nan Uamh and Roshven, « Gardens », park – ✝⊱ rest, 🔟 ☎ 🄿. 🕮 🆅🅸🆂🅰. ⋘
April-October – **Meals** (dinner booking essential to non-residents) 40.00 t. (dinner) and lunch a la carte 15.15/18.25 t. ⌀ 8.50 – **12 rm** ⥮ 80.00/240.00 t., 2 suites – SB.

🏠 **Arisaig**, PH39 4NH, ℘ (01687) 450210, Fax (01687) 450310, ≤ – ✝⊱ rest, 🔟 ☎ 🄿. 🕮 🆅🅸🆂🅰
closed 24 to 26 December – **Meals** (bar lunch)/dinner a la carte 13.85/22.40 st. ⌀ 5.75 – **13 rm** ⥮ 35.00/70.00 st.

✗ **Old Library Lodge** with rm, High St., PH39 4NH, ℘ (01687) 450651, Fax (01687) 450219, ≤ Loch nan Ceall and Inner Hebridean Isles – 🔟 ☎. 🕮 🄰🄴 🆅🅸🆂🅰 🅹🅲🄱. ⋘
April-October – **Meals** (closed Tuesday lunch) 25.00 st. (dinner) and lunch a la carte approx. 13.15 – **6 rm** ⥮ 48.00/74.00 st.

**RRAN (Isle of)** North Ayrshire **401 402** DE 16 17 Scotland G. – pop. 4 474.
See : Island★★ - Brodick Castle★★ AC.
⤼ from Brodick to Ardrossan (Caledonian MacBrayne Ltd) 4-6 daily (30 mn) – from Lochranza to Kintyre Peninsula (Claonaig) (Caledonian MacBrayne Ltd) frequent services daily (30 mn) – from Brodick to Isle of Bute (Rothesay) via Largs (Mainland) (Caledonian MacBrayne Ltd) 3 weekly (2 h 5 mn).

**rodick** – pop. 822.
🏌 Brodick ℘ (01770) 302349 – 🏌 Machrie Bay ℘ (01770) 850232.
🄱 The Pier KA27 8AU ℘ (01770) 302140/302401.

🏠 **Auchrannie Country House** ⤷, KA27 8BZ, ℘ (01770) 302234, Fax (01770) 302812, 🛵, 🖃, 🔲, 🛲 – ✝⊱ rest, 🔟 ☎ 🕭 🄿. 🕮 🆅🅸🆂🅰
**Meals** 24.00 st. (dinner) and lunch a la carte 10.00/25.00 st. ⌀ 7.25 – **26 rm** ⥮ 67.50/115.00 st., 2 suites – SB.

🏠 **Kilmichael Country House** ⤷, Glen Cloy, KA27 8BY, West : 1 m. by Shore Rd, taking left turn opposite Golf Club ℘ (01770) 302219, Fax (01770) 302068, 🛲, park – ✝⊱ 🔟 ☎ 🄿. 🕮 🆅🅸🆂🅰
closed 1 week Christmas – **Meals** (booking essential) (dinner only) 26.50 t. ⌀ 8.95 – **7 rm** ⥮ 68.00/125.00 t., 2 suites.

🏠 **Dunvegan House**, Shore Rd, KA27 8AJ, ℘ (01770) 302811, Fax (01770) 302811, ≤, 🛲 – ✝⊱ rm, 🔟 🄿. ⋘
**Meals** 15.00 st. – **9 rm** ⥮ 30.00/60.00 st.

**amlash** – pop. 900 – ⊠ Brodick.
🏌 Lamlash ℘ (01770) 600296.

🏠 **Glenisle**, Shore Rd, KA27 8LS, ℘ (01770) 600559, Fax (01770) 600966, ≤, 🛲 – 🔟 ☎ 🄿. 🕮 🆅🅸🆂🅰
closed 4 January-1 March – **Meals** 15.00 t. (dinner) and lunch a la carte 10.00/15.00 t. ⌀ 4.60 – **13 rm** ⥮ 34.50/69.00 t.

🏠 **Lilybank**, Shore Rd, KA27 8LS, ℘ (01770) 600230, Fax (01770) 600230, ≤, 🛲 – ✝⊱ 🔟 🄿. ⋘
March-October – **Meals** 15.00 – **8 rm** ⥮ 25.00/55.00 st. – SB.

✗✗ **Carraig Mhor**, Shore Rd, KA27 8LS, ℘ (01770) 600453, Fax (01770) 600453 – ✝⊱. 🕮 🆅🅸🆂🅰
closed Sunday, Monday and mid January-mid February – **Meals** (dinner only) 22.50 t. ⌀ 8.50.

669

ARRAN (Isle of)

## Lochranza.

🏌 *Lochranza* ℰ *(01770) 830273.*

🛈 *The Pier* ℰ *(01770) 830320 (summer only).*

⌂ **Apple Lodge**, KA27 8HJ, South : ½ m. on Brodick rd ℰ *(01770) 8302*
*Fax (01770) 830229*, ≤, *☞* – ⇔ 🔟 🅿. ⋇
*minimum stay 2 nights May-October, closed 22 to 27 December –* **Meals** 16.00 st. – 3 ■
⊐ 45.00/58.00 **st.**, 1 suite.

⌂ **Butt Lodge Country House** ⌂, KA27 8JF, Southeast : ¾ m. by Brodick
ℰ *(01770) 830240, Fax (01770) 830240,* ≤, *☞* – ⇔ 🔟 🅿. ⦿③ VISA JCB. ⋇
*March-October –* **Meals** (by arrangement) 14.00 **t.** – **5 rm** ⊐ 38.00/60.00.

## Whiting Bay – ⊠.

🏌 *Whiting Bay, Golf Course Rd* ℰ *(017707) 487.*

⌂ **Argentine House**, Shore Rd, KA27 8PZ, ℰ *(01770) 700662, Fax (01770) 700693,* ≤, *☞*
⇔ rest, 🔟 🅿. ⦿③ VISA JCB
*closed 3 weeks January and 2 weeks February –* **Meals** (by arrangement) 19.00 **st.** – **6** ■
⊐ 56.00/96.00 **st.** – SB.

⌂ **Grange House** without rest., Shore Rd, KA27 8QH, ℰ *(01770) 7002*
*Fax (01770) 700263,* ≤, ⇔s, *☞* – ⇔ 🔟 ⅙ 🅿. ⦿③ VISA. ⋇
*Easter-October –* **7 rm** ⊐ 35.00/70.00 **s.**

⌂ **Royal**, Shore Rd, KA27 8PZ, ℰ *(01770) 700286, Fax (01770) 700286,* ≤, *☞* – ⇔ rest, 🔟
🅿
*March-October –* **Meals** (by arrangement) 14.00 **st.** – **6 rm** ⊐ 24.00/48.00 **st.**

*Le Grand Londres* (GREATER LONDON) *est composé de la City
et de 32 arrondissements administratifs (Borough)
eux-mêmes divisés en quartiers ou en villages
ayant conservé leur caractère propre (Area).*

---

**AUCHENCAIRN** *Dumfries and Galloway* 401 402 I 19 – ⊠ *Castle Douglas.*
*Edinburgh 94 – Dumfries 21 – Stranraer 60.*

🏛 **Balcary Bay** ⌂, DG7 1QZ, Southeast : 2 m. on Balcary rd ℰ *(01556) 6402*
*Fax (01556) 640272,* ≤, *☞* – 🔟 ☎ 🅿. ⦿③ AE VISA
*5 March-3 November –* **Meals** (bar lunch Monday to Saturday)/dinner 23.50
and a la carte ₪ 5.75 – **17 rm** ⊐ 57.00/114.00 **st.** – SB.

---

**AUCHTERARDER** *Perthshire and Kinross* 401 I 15 *Scotland G. – pop. 3 910.*
Env. : *Tullibardine Chapel*, NW : 2 m.*
🏌 *Ochil Rd* ℰ *(01764) 662804,* 🏌 *Dunning, Rollo Park* ℰ *(01764) 684747.*
🛈 *90 High St. PH3 1BJ* ℰ *(01764) 663450.*
*Edinburgh 55 – Glasgow 45 – Perth 14.*

🏨🏨🏨🏨 **Gleneagles**, PH3 1NF, Southwest : 2 m. by A 824 on A 823 ℰ *(01764) 6622.*
*Fax (01764) 662134,* ≤, 🍴, « Championship golf courses and extensive leisure facilities
₪, ⇔s, ⬛, 🏌, 🏌, ⬟, *☞*, park, ⚒, squash – ⫿, ⇔ rm, ≡ rest, 🔟 ☎ ⚲ ⅙ 🅿 – 🔬 360.
AE ① VISA
**Meals** (light lunch) a la carte 19.00/54.95 **t.** ₪ 8.00 – **Strathearn** : **Meals** (dinner only a
Sunday lunch)/dinner 41.00 **t.** and a la carte ₪ 12.00 – **215 rm** ⊐ 180.00/380.00
14 suites.

🏛🏛 **Auchterarder House** ⌂, PH3 1DZ, North : 1 ½ m. on B 8062 ℰ *(01764) 6636*
*Fax (01764) 662939,* ≤, « Scottish Jacobean house », *☞*, park – ⇔ rest, 🔟 ☎ 🅿. ⦿③
① VISA. ⋇
**Meals** 16.50/32.50 **t.** and a la carte ₪ 8.50 – **13 rm** ⊐ 120.00/250.00 **t.**, 2 suites – SB.

🏛 **Duchally House** ⌂, PH3 1PN, South : 4 m. by A 824 off A 823 ℰ *(01764) 6630*
*Fax (01764) 662464,* ≤, *☞*, park – 🔟 ☎ 🅿 – 🔬 40. ⦿③ AE ① VISA
*closed 3 weeks Christmas –* **Meals** 24.50/33.50 **t.** and a la carte ₪ 5.75 – **10 rm** ⊐ 65.0
110.00 **t.**, 1 suite – SB.

🏛 **Cairn Lodge**, Orchil Rd, PH3 1LX, ℰ *(01764) 662634, Fax (01764) 664866,* *☞* – ⇔ re
🔟 ☎ 🅿. ⦿③ AE VISA JCB. ⋇
**Meals** (bar lunch)/dinner a la carte 14.50/35.00 **t.** ₪ 8.00 – **7 rm** ⊐ 65.00/126.00 **t.**

🏛 **Collearn House**, PH3 1DF, ℰ *(01764) 663553, Fax (01764) 662376,* *☞* – ⇔ rm, 🔟 ☎
– 🔬 60. ⦿③ AE ① VISA. ⋇
**Meals** 26.50 **t.** ₪ 5.75 – **8 rm** ⊐ 65.00/100.00 **t.** – SB.

**AUCHTERHOUSE** *Angus* 401 K 14 – *pop. 794* – ⊠ *Dundee.*
*Edinburgh 69 – Dundee 7 – Perth 24.*

XXX **Old Mansion House** � with rm, DD3 0QN, ℰ (01382) 320366, *Fax (01382) 320400*, ≼,
« Part 15C and 17C country house », ⌁, ☞, ※, squash – � ☎ ☎ 👤. ⚙⚙ 🅰🅴 ⓞ 𝘝𝘐𝘚𝘈. ※
**Meals** 33.00 t. (dinner) and lunch a la carte 15.45/25.40 t. ᐃ 6.50 – **6 rm** ⌑ 85.00/110.00.
– SB.

**AULDEARN** *Highland* 401 I 11 – *see Nairn.*

**AULTBEA** *Highland* 401 D 10 *Scotland G..*
Env. : *Wester Ross*★★★ – *Inverewe Gardens*★★★ *AC, S : 5½ m. by A 832.*
Exc. : *Loch Maree*★★★, *S : 10 m. by A 832.*
*Edinburgh 234 – Inverness 79 – Kyle of Lochalsh 80.*

🏠 **Aultbea**, IV22 2HX, ℰ (01445) 731201, *Fax (01445) 731214*, ≼ Loch Ewe, ☞ – 📺 ☎ 👤. ⚙⚙
🅰🅴 𝘝𝘐𝘚𝘈 𝘑𝘊𝘉
**Meals** (bar lunch)/dinner 21.50 t. and a la carte ᐃ 4.50 – **11 rm** ⌑ 36.00/82.00 t.

🏠 **Cartmel** without rest., Birchburn Rd, IV22 2HZ, ℰ (01445) 731375, ☞ – ⍬� 👤
*April-October* – **4 rm** ⌑ 18.00/42.00 st.

**AVIEMORE** *Highland* 401 I 12 *Scotland G.* – *pop. 2 214 – Winter sports.*
See : *Town*★.
Exc. : *The Cairngorms*★★ (≼★★★) – ⚘★★★ *from Cairn Gorm, SE : 11 m. by B 970 – Landmark
Visitor Centre (The Highlander*★*) AC, N : 7 m. by A 9 – Highland Wildlife Park*★ *AC, SW : 7 m.
by A 9.*
🅱 Grampian Rd, PH22 1PP ℰ (01479) 810363.
*Edinburgh 129 – Inverness 29 – Perth 85.*

🏨 **Stakis Four Seasons**, PH22 1PF, ℰ (01479) 810681, *Fax (01479) 810534*, ≼ Cairngorms,
ᵴ, ≘, ⍐ – ⫶, ⍬� rm, 📺 ☎ 👤 – 🔬 110. ⚙⚙ 🅰🅴 ⓞ 𝘝𝘐𝘚𝘈 𝘑𝘊𝘉
**Meals** (dancing Saturday evening) (bar lunch)/dinner 21.90 t. and a la carte – ⌑ 9.50 –
**98 rm** 95.00/125.00 st. – SB.

🏠 **Corrour House** �, Inverdruie, PH22 1QH, Southeast : 1 m. on B 970 ℰ (01479) 810220,
*Fax (01479) 811500*, ≼, ⌁, ☞ – ⍬� rest. 📺 ☎ 👤. ⚙⚙ 𝘝𝘐𝘚𝘈
*closed November-26 December* – **Meals** (dinner only) 22.00 st. ᐃ 7.00 – **7 rm** ⌑ 38.00/
76.00 st. – SB.

🏠 **Lynwilg House**, Lynwilg, PH22 1PZ, South : 2 m. by B 9152 on A 9 ℰ (01479) 811685,
*Fax (01479) 811685*, ≼, ⌁, ☞ – ⍬⍴ endash 📺 👤. ⚙⚙ 𝘝𝘐𝘚𝘈
*closed November-27 December* – **Meals** (by arrangement) 25.00 s. – **4 rm** ⌑ 28.00/
70.00 st.

**AYR** *South Ayrshire* 401 402 G 17 *Scotland G.* – *pop. 47 872.*
Env. : *Alloway*★ *(Burns Cottage and Museum*★ *AC) S : 3 m. by B 7024 BZ.*
Exc. : *Culzean Castle*★ *AC (setting*★★★*, Oval Staircase*★★*) SW : 13 m. by A 719 BZ.*
🇬 Belleisle, Bellisle Park, Doonfoot Rd ℰ (01292) 441258, BZ – 🇬 Dalmilling, Westwood Av.
ℰ (01292) 263893, BZ – 🇬 Doon Valley, Hillside, Patna ℰ (01292) 531607, BZ.
🅱 Burns House, Burns Statue Square, KA7 1UD ℰ (01292) 288688.
*Edinburgh 81 – Glasgow 35.*

Plan on next page

🏨 **Fairfield House**, 12 Fairfield Rd, KA7 2AR, ℰ (01292) 267461, *Fax (01292) 261456*, ᵴ,
≘, ⍐ – ⍬⍴ endash 📺 ☎ 👤 – 🔬 150. ⚙⚙ 🅰🅴 ⓞ 𝘝𝘐𝘚𝘈. ※
**Meals** 9.50 (lunch) and a la carte 13.00/25.00 st. ᐃ 7.00 – **45 rm** ⌑ 95.00/180.00 st. – SB.  AY a

🏨 **Kylestrome**, 11 Miller Rd, KA7 2AX, ℰ (01292) 262474, *Fax (01292) 260863* – 📺 ☎ ☏ 👤 –
🔬 25. ⚙⚙ 🅰🅴 ⓞ 𝘝𝘐𝘚𝘈. ※
*closed 26 December and 1 January* – **Meals** 9.95/17.95 t. and a la carte – **12 rm** ⌑ 50.00/
80.00 t. – SB.  AY e

🏠 **No. 26 The Crescent** without rest., 26 Bellevue Cres., KA7 2DR, ℰ (01292) 287329,
*Fax (01292) 286779* – ⍬⍴ endash 📺 👤. ⚙⚙ 🅰🅴 𝘝𝘐𝘚𝘈. ※
*closed mid November-5 January* – **4 rm** ⌑ 30.00/54.00.  BZ c

🏠 **Coila** without rest., 10 Holmston Rd, KA7 3BB, ℰ (01292) 262642 – 📺 👤. ⚙⚙ 𝘝𝘐𝘚𝘈. ※
**4 rm** ⌑ 25.00/40.00 st.  AY u

🏠 **Langley Bank** without rest., 39 Carrick Rd, KA7 2RD, ℰ (01292) 264246,
*Fax (01292) 282628*, ☞ – 📺 ☎ 👤. ⚙⚙ 🅰🅴 𝘝𝘐𝘚𝘈. ※
**6 rm** ⌑ 45.00/50.00 t.  BZ a

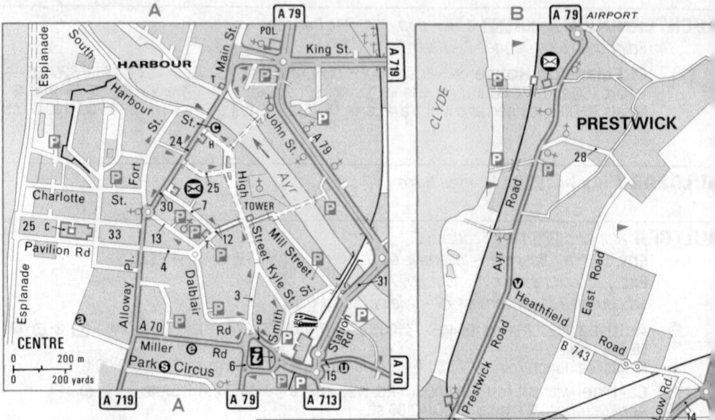


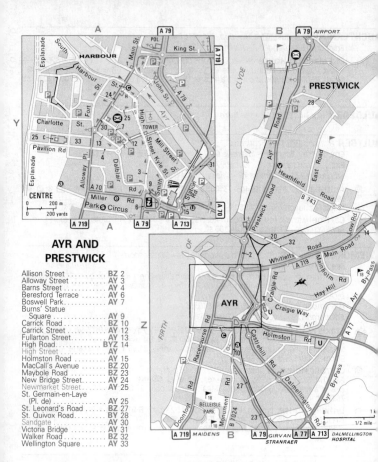

# AYR AND PRESTWICK

Allison Street . . . . . . . . . . BZ 2
Alloway Street . . . . . . . . . AY 3
Barns Street . . . . . . . . . . . AY 4
Beresford Terrace . . . . . . AY 6
Boswell Park . . . . . . . . . . . AY 7
Burns' Statue
Square . . . . . . . . . . . . . . AY 9
Carrick Road . . . . . . . . . . . BZ 10
Carrick Street . . . . . . . . . . AY 12
Fullarton Street . . . . . . . . . AY 13
High Road . . . . . . . . . . . BYZ 14
High Street . . . . . . . . . . . . AY
Holmston Road . . . . . . . . AY 15
MacCall's Avenue . . . . . . . BZ 20
Maybole Road . . . . . . . . . . BZ 23
New Bridge Street . . . . . . AY 24
Newmarket Street . . . . . . AY 25
St. Germain-en-Laye
(Pl. de) . . . . . . . . . . . . . . AY 25
St. Leonard's Road . . . . . BZ 27
St. Quivox Road . . . . . . . . BY 28
Sandgate . . . . . . . . . . . . . . AY 30
Victoria Bridge . . . . . . . . . AY 31
Walker Road . . . . . . . . . . . BZ 32
Wellington Square . . . . . . . AY 33

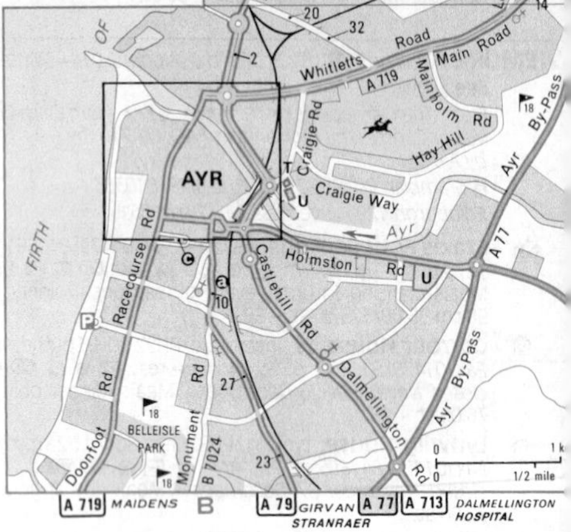


**Chaz-Ann** without rest., 17 Park Circus, KA7 2DJ, ℘ (01292) 611215, *Fax (01292) 285491*
AY
3 rm ⊐ 25.00/40.00.

**Fouters,** 2a Academy St., KA7 1HS, ℘ (01292) 261391, *Fax (01292) 619323* – MC AE ⓓ VISA
*closed Sunday, Monday, 25 to 27 December, 1 to 3 January and first 2 weeks July* – **Mea**
15.00 **t.** (dinner) and a la carte 16.85/22.35 **t.** 6.95.
AY

**at Alloway** *South : 3 m. on B 7024* – BZ – ✉ *Ayr.*

**Brig O'Doon House,** KA7 4PQ, ℘ (01292) 442466, *Fax (01292) 441999,* – TV ☎
220. MC AE VISA.
Meals a la carte 14.95/21.50 **st.** 7.50 – **5 rm** ⊐ 80.00/100.00 **st.**

**Northpark House,** 2 Alloway, KA7 4NL, ℘ (01292) 442336, *Fax (01292) 445572* –
☎ P. MC AE ⓓ VISA JCB.
**Meals** 17.95/21.50 **t.** and a la carte 5.95 – **5 rm** ⊐ 69.50/135.00 **t.** – SB.

Besonders angenehme Hotels oder Restaurants
sind im Führer rot gekennzeichnet.

Sie können uns helfen, wenn Sie uns die Häuser angeben,
in denen Sie sich besonders wohl gefühlt haben.

Jährlich erscheint eine komplett überarbeitete Ausgabe
aller Roten **Michelin-Führer.**

**BALLACHULISH** *Highland* 401 E 13 *Scotland G..*

Exc. : *Glen Coe★★, E : 6 m. by A 82.*

*PA39 4JR (01855) 811296 (summer only).*

*Edinburgh 117 – Inverness 80 – Kyle of Lochalsh 90 – Oban 38.*

**Ballachulish,** PA39 4JY, West : 2 ¼ m. by A 82 on A 828 (01855) 811606, *Fax (01855) 821463,* ≤, – . VISA
*restricted opening in winter* – **Meals** (bar lunch)/dinner 25.50 **t.** and a la carte 7.00 – **53 rm** (dinner included) 75.00/150.00 **t.**, 1 suite – SB.

**Isles of Glencoe,** PA39 4HL, (01855) 811602, *Fax (01855) 821463,* ≤ Loch Leven and the Pap of Glencoe, « Lochside setting », , , , park – . VISA
**Meals** 5.95/21.00 **t.** and a la carte 7.95 – **39 rm** (dinner included) 94.00/173.00 **t.** – SB.

**Ballachulish House**, PA39 4JX, West : 2 ½ m. by A 82 on A 828 (01855) 811266, *Fax (01855) 811498,* ≤, – . VISA JCB
*restricted opening in winter* – **Meals** 25.00 **st.** 7.50 – **6 rm** 42.00/84.00 **st.**

**Lyn Leven,** White St., PA39 4JP, (01855) 811392, *Fax (01855) 811600,* ≤, – rest, . VISA
*closed 25 December* – **Meals** (by arrangement) 9.00 **t.** 3.80 – **8 rm** 26.00/46.00 **t.** – SB.

**BALLANTRAE** *South Ayrshire* 401 402 E 18 – *pop. 672* – *Girvan.*

*Edinburgh 115 – Ayr 33 – Stranraer 18.*

**Cosses Country House**, KA26 0LR, East : 2 ¼ m. by A 77 (south) taking first turn left after bridge (01465) 831363, *Fax (01465) 831598,* « Part 16C former shooting lodge », , park – . VISA
**Meals** (by arrangement) (communal dining) 25.00 5.10 – **1 rm, 2 suites** 42.00/76.00 – SB.

**BALLATER** *Aberdeenshire* 401 K 12 – *pop. 1 362.*

*Victoria Rd (013397) 55567.*

*Station Sq. (013397) 55306 (summer only).*

*Edinburgh 111 – Aberdeen 41 – Inverness 70 – Perth 67.*

**Stakis Craigendarroch,** Braemar Rd, AB35 5XA, on A 93 (013397) 55858, *Fax (013397) 55447,* ≤ Dee Valley and Grampians, , , , , , squash – – 110. VISA JCB.
**Meals** 21.95 **t.** (dinner) and lunch a la carte 8.80/16.50 **t.** 7.00 – (see also ***Oaks*** below) – 10.50 – **38 rm** 130.00/155.00 **st.**, 6 suites.

**Darroch Learg,** Braemar Rd, AB35 5UX, (013397) 55443, *Fax (013397) 55252,* ≤ Dee Valley and Grampians, – . VISA JCB
*closed 3 weeks January and Christmas* – **Meals** - (see ***Conservatory*** below) – **18 rm** 75.00/190.00 **st.** – SB.

**Balgonie Country House**, Braemar Pl., AB35 5NQ, (013397) 55482, *Fax (013397) 55482,* ≤, – rest, . VISA JCB
*closed 5 January-12 February* – **Meals** (booking essential) 17.50/28.50 **t.** 9.95 – **9 rm** 65.00/110.00 **t.** – SB.

**Glen Lui**, Invercauld Rd, AB35 5RP, (013397) 55402, *Fax (013397) 55545,* ≤, – . VISA JCB
*closed February* – **Meals** 8.50 **st.** (lunch) and a la carte 13.20/19.75 **st.** 7.50 – **17 rm** 38.00/76.00 **st.**, 2 suites.

**Auld Kirk,** Braemar Rd, AB35 5RQ, (013397) 55762, *Fax (013397) 55707,* « Former 19C church » – . VISA
*closed 25-26 December and 1, 2 and 31 January* – **Meals** 16.00 **t.** (dinner) and a la carte 10.20/15.00 **t.** 4.50 – **6 rm** 35.00/54.00 **st.** – SB.

**Alexandra,** 12 Bridge Sq., AB35 5QJ, (013397) 55376, *Fax (013397) 55466* – . VISA JCB.
**Meals** (bar lunch)/dinner 17.50 **t.** and a la carte 4.95 – **7 rm** 24.00/60.00 **t.** – SB.

**Moorside House** without rest., 26 Braemar Rd, AB35 5RL, (013397) 55492, *Fax (013397) 55492,* – . VISA.
*April-October* – **9 rm** 40.00 **s.**

**Oaklands House** without rest., 30 Braemar Rd, AB35 5RL, (013397) 55013, –
*May-September* – **3 rm** 30.00/48.00 **st.**

**Oaks** (at Stakis Craigendarroch H.), Braemar Rd, AB35 5XA, on A 93 (013397) 55858, *Fax (013397) 55447* – . VISA JCB
**Meals** (dinner only) 27.50 **t.** and a la carte 7.00.

**Conservatory** (at Darroch Learg H.), Braemar Rd, AB35 5UX, (013397) 55443, *Fax (013397) 55252,* – . VISA
*closed 3 weeks January and Christmas* – **Meals** (light lunch Monday to Saturday)/dinner 29.00 **st.** 8.00.

BALLATER

XX **Green Inn** with rm, 9 Victoria Rd, AB35 5QQ, ℘ (013397) 55701, *Fax (013397) 55701 –* 
TV, ⬛ AE VISA JCB
*closed Sunday October-March, 2 weeks October and 24 to 26 December* – Meals (dinner
only and Sunday lunch in summer)/dinner 25.00 t. ≬ 7.50 – **3 rm** ⊑ (dinner included)
65.00/108.00 t. – SB.

---

**BALLOCH** *West Dunbartonshire* 401 G 15 *Scotland G.* – ✉ *Alexandria.*
Env. : N : *Loch Lomond*★★.
🄱 *Balloch Rd, JH3 8LQ ℘ (01389) 753533 (summer only).*
*Edinburgh 72 – Glasgow 20 – Stirling 30.*

🏨 **Cameron House** ♨, Loch Lomond, G83 8QZ, Northwest : 1 ½ m. by A 811 on A 82
℘ (01389) 755565, *Fax (01389) 759522,* ≤ Loch Lomond, « Lochside setting », *f₆,* ≋, ⬜
🏡, ♨, ⩩, park, ⅋, squash – 🔋 🔄, ¾⊷ rm, ⬛ rest, TV ☎ ❷ – 🔏 300. ⬛ AE ⓞ VISA. ⅋
*Smolletts :* Meals (dinner only, Saturday and Sunday lunch)/dinner 19.50/21.50 st.
and dinner a la carte ≬ 10.50 – *Breakers :* Meals a la carte 16.15/22.15 t. – (see also *Georgian Room* below) – 89 rm ⊑ 145.00/195.00 t., 7 suites – SB.

🏠 **Sheildaig Farm** ♨, Upper Stoneymollen Rd, G83 8QX, West : 1 m. by A 811 off A 82
℘ (01389) 752459, *Fax (01389) 752459,* ⩩, park – ¾⊷ TV ❷. ⬛ VISA
Meals (by arrangement) 15.00 t. ≬ 5.00 – **4 rm** ⊑ 45.00/60.00 s. – SB.

XXXX **Georgian Room** (at Cameron House H.), Loch Lomond, G83 8QZ, Northwest : 1 ½ m. by
🏵️ A 811 on A 82 ℘ (01389) 755565, *Fax (01389) 759522,* ≤ Loch Lomond, « Lochside setting », ⩩ – ¾⊷ ⬛ ❷. ⬛ AE ⓞ VISA
*closed lunch Saturday and Sunday* – Meals (booking essential) 21.00/38.50 t. and a la carte
42.00/57.95 t. ≬ 7.50
Spec. Charlotte of Arbroath smokie, fennel and coriander dressing. Pot roast squab pigeon
and venison, roast garlic, port and elderflower jus. Strawberry soufflé, Champagne and
basil sorbet.

*Groß-London (GREATER LONDON) besteht aus der City und 32
Verwaltungsbezirken (Borough). Diese sind wiederum in kleinere
Bezirke (Area) unterteilt, deren Mittelpunkt ehemalige Dörfer
oder Stadtviertel sind, die oft ihren eigenen Charakter bewahrt haben.*

---

**BALLYGRANT** *Argyll and Bute* 401 B 16 – *see Islay (Isle of).*

---

**BALTASOUND** *Shetland Islands* 401 R 1 – *see Shetland Islands (Island of Unst).*

---

**BANAVIE** *Highland* 401 E 13 – *see Fort William.*

---

**BANCHORY** *Aberdeenshire* 401 M 12 *Scotland G.* – *pop. 6 230.*
Env. : *Crathes Castle*★★ *(Gardens*★★★*) AC, E : 3 m. by A 93 – Cairn o'Mount Road*★ *(≤*★★*)
S : by B 974.*
Exc. : *Dunnottar Castle*★★ *(site*★★★*) AC, SW : 15 ½ m. by A 93 and A 957 – Aberdeen*★
*NE : 17 m. by A 93.*
🄻₈ *Kinneskie ℘ (01330) 822365 –* 🄻 *Torphins ℘ (013398) 82115.*
🄱 *Bridge St. AB31 3SX ℘ (01330) 822000.*
*Edinburgh 118 – Aberdeen 17 – Dundee 55 – Inverness 94.*

🏰 **Raemoir House** ♨, AB31 4ED, North : 2 ½ m. on A 980 ℘ (01330) 824884,
*Fax (01330) 822171,* ≤, « 18C mansion with 16C Ha-House », ⩩, park, ⅋ – ¾⊷ rest, TV
📞 ❻ ❷ – 🔏 50. ⬛ ⓞ VISA
Meals 18.50/26.50 t. ≬ 9.40 – **19 rm** ⊑ 60.00/120.00 t. – SB.

🏰 **Banchory Lodge** ♨, Dee St., AB31 5HS, ℘ (01330) 822625, *Fax (01330) 825019,*
« Part 18C house on River Dee », ♨, ⩩ – TV ☎ ❷ – 🔏 30. ⬛ AE ⓞ VISA
*closed 1 week January* – Meals (bar lunch Monday to Saturday)/dinner 25.50 st. ≬ 5.50 –
22 rm ⊑ 75.00/140.00 st. – SB.

🏛️ **Tor-na-Coille,** Inchmarlo Rd, AB31 4AB, ℘ (01330) 822242, *Fax (01330) 824012,* ⩩ –
TV ☎ ❷ – 🔏 90. ⬛ AE VISA
*closed 25 to 28 December* – Meals (bar lunch Monday to Saturday)/dinner 26.00 t. ≬ 8.50 –
22 rm ⊑ 69.00/115.00 t. – SB.

🏠 **Old West Manse,** 71 Station Rd, AB31 5UD, ℘ (01330) 822202, *Fax (01330) 822202,* ≤
¾⊷ TV ⬛ VISA. ⅋
Meals (by arrangement) 18.00 t. ≬ 6.50 – **3 rm** ⊑ 35.00/50.00 t.

**BANFF** Aberdeenshire **401** M 10 Scotland G. – pop. 4 402.

See : Town★ – Duff House★★ (baroque exterior★ ) AC – Mercat Cross★.

🏌 Royal Tarlair, Buchan St., Macduff 𝒫 (01261) 832897 – 🏌 Duff House Royal, The Barnyards 𝒫 (01261) 812062.

🛈 Collie Lodge, AB45 1AU 𝒫 (01261) 812419 (summer only).

Edinburgh 177 – Aberdeen 47 – Fraserburgh 26 – Inverness 74.

⚲ **Eden House** ⏃, AB45 3NT, South : 5 m. by A 98 and A 947 on Scatterty Dunlugas rd 𝒫 (01261) 821282, Fax (01261) 821283, « Part 18C former shooting lodge overlooking River Deveron Valley », ☜, 🗶, park, ✕ – ✕⊱ ⓟ
closed 10 December-mid January – Meals (by arrangement) (communal dining) 18.00 – 5 rm ⯒ 36.00/72.00 s.

🔘 ATS Carmelite St. 𝒫 (01261) 812234

**BANKHEAD** Aberdeenshire **401** N 12 – see Aberdeen.

**BARRA (Isle of)** Western Isles **401** X 12/13 – pop. 1 316 – ⊠ Castlebay.

⚓ from Castlebay to Oban and South Uist (Lochboisdale) (Caledonian MacBrayne Ltd) (summer only).

**Castlebay.**

🏛 **Castlebay**, HS9 5XD, 𝒫 (01871) 810223, Fax (01871) 810455, ≤ Kisimul Castle and Island of Vatersay, ☜ – ✕⊱ rest, 📺 ☎ ⓟ. 🆗 𝑉𝐼𝑆𝐴
closed Christmas and New Year – Meals a la carte 11.45/24.50 st. – 12 rm ⯒ 40.00/70.00 st.

⚲ **Tigh na Mara** without rest., HS9 5XD, 𝒫 (01871) 810304, Fax (01871) 810304, ≤ – ✕⊱ 📺 ⓟ. ⌗
April-October – 5 rm ⯒ 22.00/44.00 s.

**BATHGATE** West Lothian **401** J 16 – pop. 23 368.

Edinburgh 24 – Dundee 62 – Glasgow 29 – Perth 50.

🏛 **Holiday Inn Express**, Starlaw Rd, EH48 1LQ, 𝒫 (01506) 650650, Fax (01506) 650651 – |≑|, ✕⊱ rm, ▤ rest, 📺 ☎ ✆ & ⓟ – ⚠ 40. 🆗 ᴬᴱ ⓞ 𝑉𝐼𝑆𝐴 ᴶᴄᴮ. ⌗
Meals (grill rest.) a la carte 7.95/23.90 t. – 74 rm 45.00 st.

**BEATTOCK** Dumfries and Galloway **401 402** J 18 – see Moffat.

**BEAULY** Highland **401** G 11 – pop. 1 154.

Edinburgh 169 – Inverness 13 – Wick 125.

🏨 **Lovat Arms**, High St., IV4 7BS, 𝒫 (01463) 782313, Fax (01463) 782862 – ✕⊱ rest, 📺 ☎ ⓟ – ⚠ 30. 🆗 𝑉𝐼𝑆𝐴 ᴶᴄᴮ
Meals 21.00 t. (dinner) and a la carte 8.00/24.00 t. ⅃ 4.50 – 22 rm ⯒ 48.00/110.00 st. – SB.

🏨 **Priory**, The Square, IV4 7BX, 𝒫 (01463) 782309, Fax (01463) 782531 – |≑| 📺 ☎. 🆗 ᴬᴱ ⓞ 𝑉𝐼𝑆𝐴
Meals 17.50 t. (dinner) and a la carte 6.50/24.00 t. ⅃ 5.50 – 36 rm ⯒ 42.50/99.00 t. – SB.

⚲ **Chrialdon House**, Station Rd, IV4 7EH, 𝒫 (01463) 782336, Fax (01463) 782336, 🗲 – ✕⊱ 📺 ⓟ. 🆗 𝑉𝐼𝑆𝐴
April-October – Meals 20.00 st. ⅃ 4.95 – 9 rm ⯒ 40.00/60.00 st.

**BENBECULA** Western Isles **401** X/Y 11 – see Uist (Isles of).

**BERRIEDALE** Highland **401** J 9.

Edinburgh 251 – Inverness 94 – Thurso 28 – Wick 14.

⚲ **The Factor's House** ⏃, Langwell, KW7 6HD, take private road to Langwell House - 2.9 m. 𝒫 (01593) 751280, Fax (01593) 751251, ≤, 🗲, park – ✕⊱ ⓟ. ⌗
Meals (communal dining) 20.00 t. – 3 rm ⯒ 45.00/70.00 t.

*Si vous cherchez un hôtel tranquille,*
*consultez d'abord les cartes de l'introduction*
*ou repérez dans le texte les établissements indiqués avec le signe ⏃ ou ⏃.*

**BIGGAR** South Lanarkshire **401** J 17 – pop. 2 238.
  ┌₁₈ The Park, Broughton Rd ℰ (01899) 220618/220319.
  🛈 155 High St. ℰ (01899) 221066.
  Edinburgh 31 – Dumfries 49 – Glasgow 40.

  ⚑ **Lindsaylands** ⌂, Lindsaylands Rd, ML12 6NR, Southwest : ¾ m. via Park Place and The
    Wynd ℰ (01899) 220033, Fax (01899) 221009, ≤, ⌨, park, ℅ – 🅿. ℅
    March-November – **Meals** (by arrangement) 14.00 st. – **3 rm** ⊠ 28.00/50.00 st.

**BLAIR ATHOLL** Perthshire and Kinross **401** I 13 – pop. 906.
  ┌₉ Blair Atholl ℰ (01796) 481407.
  Edinburgh 79 – Inverness 83 – Perth 35.

  ✗✗ **The Loft,** Golf Course Rd, PH18 5TE, ℰ (01796) 491377, Fax (01796) 481511, « Converted
    hayloft » – 🅿. ⓒⓢ 💳 JCB
    **Meals** 26.50 st. (dinner) and a la carte 12.75/26.75 st.

**BLAIRGOWRIE** Perthshire and Kinross **401** J 14 Scotland G. – pop. 5 208.
  Exc. : Scone Palace★★ AC, S : 12 m. by A 93.
  🛈 26 Wellmeadow, PH10 6AS ℰ (01250) 872960.
  Edinburgh 60 – Dundee 19 – Perth 16.

  ⌂⌂⌂ **Kinloch House** ⌂, PH10 6SG, West : 3 m. on A 923 ℰ (01250) 884237,
    Fax (01250) 884333, ≤, « Victorian country house », ₤₅, ⊜, ⊠, ⌨, park – ℅ rest, 📺 ☎
    🅿. ⓒⓢ ☃ ① 💳 JCB. ℅
    **Meals** (bar lunch Monday to Saturday)/dinner 29.90 st. ⅙ 6.70 – **21 rm** ⊠ (dinner included)
    95.00/195.00 st. – SB.

  ⌂ **Altamount House** ⌂, Coupar Angus Rd, PH10 6JN, on A 923 ℰ (01250) 873512,
    Fax (01250) 876200, ⌨ – ℅ rest, 📺 ☎ 🅿. ⓒⓢ ☃ 💳
    closed 1 to 7 December – **Meals** 22.50 t. (dinner) and a la carte 19.75/29.65 t. ⅙ 8.00 – **7 rm**
    ⊠ 50.00/94.00 t. – SB.

  ⚑ **Laurels,** PH10 6LH, Southwest : 1 ¼ m. on A 93 ℰ (01250) 874920, ⌨ – ℅ 📺 🅿. ⓒⓢ ☃
    ① 💳. ℅
    closed December-first 2 weeks January – **Meals** (by arrangement) 10.50 s. ⅙ 3.50 – **6 rm**
    ⊠ 19.50/39.00.

  ✗ **Cargills,** Lower Mill St., PH10 6AQ, ℰ (01250) 876735, Fax (01250) 876735 – 🅿. ⓒⓢ 💳
    closed Monday – **Meals** a la carte 14.65/19.80 t. ⅙ 7.75.

**BLAIRLOGIE** Stirling – see Stirling.

**BOAT OF GARTEN** Highland **401** I 12.
  ┌₁₈ Boat of Garten ℰ (01479) 831282.
  Edinburgh 133 – Inverness 28 – Perth 89.

  ⌂⌂ **The Boat,** PH24 3BH, ℰ (01479) 831258, Fax (01479) 831414, ⌨ – ℅ rest, 📺 ☎ 🅿 –
    ⚑ 30. ⓒⓢ ☃ ① 💳 JCB
    **Meals** (bar lunch)/dinner 23.00 st. ⅙ 6.00 – **30 rm** ⊠ 45.00/90.00 st. – SB.

  ⚑ **Heathbank - The Victorian House,** Drumvillie Rd, PH24 3BD, ℰ (01479) 831234, ⌨
    – ℅ 🅿. ℅
    closed February, 1 week before Easter and 1 November-25 December – **Meals** 22.00 s.
    ⅙ 5.00 – **7 rm** ⊠ 30.00/80.00 s.

**BONNYRIGG** Midlothian **401** K 16 – see Edinburgh.

**BORGIE** Highland **401** H 8.
  Edinburgh 262 – Inverness 93 – Thurso 31.

  ⌂ **Borgie Lodge** ⌂, KW14 7TH, ℰ (01641) 521332, Fax (01641) 521332, ≤, ⌇, ⌨ –
    ℅ rest, 🅿. ⓒⓢ 💳
    closed January and December – **Meals** (bar lunch)/dinner 22.50 t. ⅙ 5.00 – **8 rm** ⊠ 50.00/
    150.00 st.

**BRAE** Shetland Islands **401** P 2 – see Shetland Islands (Mainland).

**BRAEMAR** Aberdeenshire **401** J 12 Scotland G..
Env. : Lin O'Dee★, W : 5 m.
🇮🇸 Cluniebank Rd ℘ (013397) 41618.
🇮🇸 The Mews, Mar Rd ℘ (013397) 41600.
Edinburgh 85 – Aberdeen 58 – Dundee 51 – Perth 51.

🏨 **Invercauld Arms,** Invercauld rd, AB35 5YR, ℘ (013397) 41605, Fax (013397) 41428 – 🛗,
✱ rm, 📺 ☎ & 🅿 – 🔏 60. 🆗 🆎 ⓪ 𝑽𝑰𝑺𝑨 𝐉𝐂𝐁
Meals (bar lunch Monday to Saturday)/dinner 19.50 st. and a la carte ▯ 7.50 – **66 rm**
☑ 83.00/109.00 st. – SB.

🏠 **Braemar Lodge,** Glenshee Rd, AB35 5YQ, ℘ (013397) 41627, Fax (013397) 41627, 🏤 –
✱ 📺 🅿. 🆗 𝑽𝑰𝑺𝑨 𝐉𝐂𝐁
Meals (dinner only) a la carte 14.00/20.00 t. ▯ 5.00 – **7 rm** ☑ 35.00/70.00 t.

**BREAKISH** Highland **401** C 12 – see Skye (Isle of).

**BREASCLETE** Western Isles (Outer Hebrides) **401** Z 9 – see Lewis and Harris (Isle of).

**BRECHIN** Angus **401** M 13 – pop. 8 315.
Exc. : Aberlemno Stones★, SW : 1 m. by B 966 on B 9134 – Cairn O'Mount Road★, N : 1 m.
by B 9667 on A 94.
🇮🇸 Trinity ℘ (01356) 622383.
🇮🇸 St. Ninians Pl. ℘ (01356) 623050 (summer only).
Edinburgh 83 – Aberdeen 42 – Dundee 28 – Perth 44.

🏠 **Doniford,** 26 Airlie St., DD9 6JX, ℘ (01356) 622361, 🏤 – ✱ 📺 🅿
Meals (by arrangement) 9.00 st. – **3 rm** ☑ 17.50/40.00 st.

🏠 **Blibberhill Farmhouse** ❧, DD9 6TH, Southwest : 5 m. by A 935 and B 9134 off
Melgund rd ℘ (01307) 830323, Fax (01307) 830323, « Working farm », 🏤, park – ✱ 📺
🅿. ❧
closed 25 December – Meals (by arrangement) 11.00 st. – **3 rm** ☑ 29.00/50.00.

**BRIDGEND** Argyll and Bute **401** B 16 – see Islay (Isle of).

**BRIDGEND OF LINTRATHEN** Angus **401** K 13.
Edinburgh 80 – Aberdeen 60 – Dundee 22 – Perth 34.

❌❌ **Lochside Lodge and Roundhouse Restaurant** with rm, DD8 5JJ,
℘ (01575) 560340 – 📺 🅿. 🆗 𝑽𝑰𝑺𝑨. ❧
closed Sunday dinner November-February, Monday, 26 December and 1 January – Meals
a la carte 12.65/24.85 t. ▯ 7.00 – **2 rm** ☑ 40.00/60.00 t.

**BROADFORD** Highland **401** C 12 – see Skye (Isle of).

**BRODICK** North Ayrshire **401 402** E 17 – see Arran (Isle of).

**BRORA** Highland **401** I 9 – pop. 1 687.
🇮🇸 Golf Rd ℘ (01408) 621417.
Edinburgh 234 – Inverness 78 – Wick 49.

🏨 **Royal Marine,** Golf Rd, KW9 6QS, ℘ (01408) 621252, Fax (01408) 621181, ⌘, ☎s, 🏊, ♒,
🏤 – ✱ rest, 📺 ☎ & 🅿 – 🔏 50. 🆗 🆎 ⓪ 𝑽𝑰𝑺𝑨
Meals a la carte 17.00/24.00 t. ▯ 6.00 – **16 rm** ☑ 60.00/110.00 t. – SB.

🏨 **Links** ❧, Golf Rd, KW9 6QS, ℘ (01408) 621225, Fax (01408) 621383, ≤, ♒, 🏤 – 📺 ☎ 🅿.
🆗 🆎 ⓪ 𝑽𝑰𝑺𝑨
April-October – Meals (bar lunch)/dinner 20.00 t. and a la carte ▯ 6.00 – **20 rm** ☑ 60.00/
110.00 t., 2 suites – SB.

🏠 **Lynwood,** Golf Rd, KW9 6QS, ℘ (01408) 621226, Fax (01408) 621226, 🏤 – ✱ 📺 🅿. 🆗
𝑽𝑰𝑺𝑨. ❧
closed Christmas-1 March – Meals (by arrangement) 12.50 st. – **4 rm** ☑ 27.00/46.00 st. –
SB.

🏠 **Tigh Fada** without rest., Golf Rd, KW9 6QS, ℘ (01408) 621332, Fax (01408) 621332, ≤, 🏤
– ✱ 🅿. ❧
**3 rm** ☑ 19.50/39.00 s.

**BROUGHTY FERRY** Dundee City **401** L 14 – see Dundee.

**BUCKIE** Moray **401** L 10 – pop. 8 324.

    🔞 Buckpool, Barhill Rd ℘ (01542) 832236 – 🔞 Strathlene ℘ (01542) 31798.
    🎫 Cluny Sq. ℘ (01542) 834853 (summer only).
    Edinburgh 195 – Aberdeen 66 – Inverness 56.

   XX  **Old Monastery,** Drybridge, AB56 5JB, Southeast : 3 ½ m. by A 942 on Deskford
    ℘ (01542) 832660, Fax (01542) 832660, ≤, « Former chapel overlooking Spey Bay » – ❶
    🆎 🆎 𝘝𝘐𝘚𝘈
    closed Sunday, Monday, 25-26 December, 1-2 January, first 2 weeks November and la
    3 weeks January – **Meals** a la carte 16.45/30.00 t. ⓙ 5.50.

---

**BUCKSBURN** Aberdeenshire **401** N 12 – see Aberdeen.

---

**BUNCHREW** Highland – see Inverness.

---

**BUNESSAN** Argyll and Bute **401** B 15 – see Mull (Isle of).

---

**BURNTISLAND** Fife **401** K 15 Scotland G. – pop. 5 951.

    Env. : Aberdour★ – Aberdour Castle★ AC, W : 3 m. by A 921.
    🔞 Burntisland Golf House Club, Dodhead ℘ (01592) 874093 – 🔞 Kinghorn Municipa
    McDuff Cres., Kingham ℘ (01592) 890345.
    🎫 4 Kirkgate, KY3 9BB ℘ (01592) 872667.
    Edinburgh 20 – Dunfermline 10 – Kirkcaldy 6.

   🏠  **Kingswood,** Kinghorn Rd, KY3 9LL, East : 1 m. on A 921 ℘ (01592) 872329
    Fax (01592) 873123, 🌼 – ✣ rest, 📺 ☎ ❶ – 🛗 100. 🆎 🆎 𝘝𝘐𝘚𝘈
    **Meals** (bar lunch)/dinner 20.00 t. ⓙ 4.95 – **9 rm** �-⃞ 48.00/70.00 t. – SB.

---

**BURRAY** Orkney Islands **401** L 7 – see Orkney Islands.

---

**BUSBY** East Renfrewshire **401 402** H 16 – see Glasgow.

---

**BUTE (Isle of)** Argyll and Bute **401 402** E 16 – pop. 7 354.

    🚢 from Rothesay to Wemyss Bay (Mainland) (Caledonian MacBrayne Ltd) frequent ser
    vices daily (30 mn) – from Rhubodach to Colintraive (Mainland) (Caledonian MacBrayne Ltd
    frequent services daily (5 mn) – from Rothesay to Isle of Arran (Brodick) via Largs (Mainland
    (Caledonian MacBrayne Ltd) 3 weekly (2 h 5 mn).

**Rothesay.**

    🔞 Canada Hill ℘ (01700) 502244.
    🎫 15 Victoria St., Rothesay, PA20 0AJ ℘ (01700) 502151.

   🏠  **Ardmory House,** Ardmory Rd, Ardbeg, PA20 0PG, North : 1 ¾ m. by A 866
    ℘ (01700) 502346, Fax (01700) 505596, ≤, 🌼 – ✣ 📺 ☎ ❶ 🆎 🆎 ❶ 𝘝𝘐𝘚𝘈 𝘑𝘊𝘉
    **Meals** (carving lunch Sunday) (bar lunch Monday to Saturday)/dinner 17.50 t. and a la carte
    ⓙ 4.95 – **5 rm** �-⃞ 45.00/70.00 t. – SB.

---

**CAIRNBAAN** Argyll and Bute **401** D 15 – see Lochgilphead.

---

**CALLANDER** Stirling **401** H 15 Scotland G. – pop. 3 268.

    See : Town★.
    Exc. : The Trossachs★★★ (Loch Katrine★★) – Hilltop Viewpoint★★★ (✳★★★) W : 10 m. by
    A 821.
    🔞 Aveland Rd ℘ (01877) 330090.
    🎫 Rob Roy & Trossachs Visitor Centre, Ancaster Sq., FK17 8ED ℘ (01877) 330342.
    Edinburgh 52 – Glasgow 43 – Oban 71 – Perth 41.

   🏠  **Roman Camp** ⚜, Main St., FK17 8BG, ℘ (01877) 330003, Fax (01877) 331533, ≤, « Part
    17C hunting lodge in extensive gardens », 🎣, park – ✣ rest, 📺 ☎ ✆ & ❶. 🆎 🆎 ❶ 𝘝𝘐𝘚𝘈
    🌼
    **Meals** 19.00/34.00 st. and a la carte ⓙ 13.00 – **11 rm** �-⃞ 90.00/160.00 st., 3 suites – SB.

   🏠  **Arran Lodge** without rest., Leny Rd, FK17 8AJ, ℘ (01877) 330976, 🎣, 🌼 – ✣ 📺 ❶. 🌼
    12 March-September – **4 rm** �-⃞ 63.00/85.00.

🏠 **Invertrossachs Country House** ⊗, Invertrossachs Rd, FK17 8HG, Southwest :
5 ½ m. by A 81 and Invertrossachs rd taking no through road after 1 ¾ m.
𝒫 (01877) 331126, *Fax (01877) 331229*, ≤, « Edwardian hunting lodge in extensive
grounds », ♈, 🐎 – ⤢ rest, 📺 ☎ 🄿, 🆗 🄰🄴 *VISA*
*closed mid December-8 January* – **Meals** (by arrangement) (dinner only) (unlicensed)
22.50 **st.** – **3 rm** ⊇ 65.00/170.00 **st.** – SB.

🏠 **Lubnaig**, Leny Feus, FK17 8AS, 𝒫 (01877) 330376, *Fax (01877) 330376*, 🐎 – ⤢ rest, 📺
🄿 🆗 *VISA* **JCB**. ⚘
*Easter-October* – **Meals** (residents only) (dinner only) a la carte 12.45/18.25 **t.** 🛈 7.25 –
**10 rm** ⊇ 45.00/66.00 **t.** – SB.

🏠 **Priory** ⊗, Bracklinn Rd, FK17 8EH, 𝒫 (01877) 330001, *Fax (01877) 330001*, 🐎 – ⤢ 📺
🄿. ⚘
*Easter-mid October* – **Meals** (by arrangement) 15.00 **t.** 🛈 4.50 – **8 rm** ⊇ 27.00/54.00 **t.** – SB.

🏠 **Brook Linn** ⊗ without rest., Leny Feus, FK17 8AU, 𝒫 (01877) 330103,
*Fax (01877) 330103*, ≤, 🐎 – ⤢ 📺 🄿. 🆗 *VISA*
*March-October* – – **7 rm** ⊇ 26.00/52.00 **st.**

🏠 **East Mains House** without rest., Bridgend, FK17 8AG, 𝒫 (01877) 330535,
*Fax (01877) 330535*, 🐎 – ⤢ 📺 🄿. 🆗 *VISA*. ⚘
**4 rm** ⊇ 29.00/48.00 **s.**

🏠 **Dunmore** without rest., Leny Rd, FK17 8AL, 𝒫 (01877) 330756 – ⤢ 📺 🄿. ⚘
*May-September* – **4 rm** ⊇ 27.00/44.00 **t.**

**CAMPBELTOWN** *Argyll and Bute* **401** D 17 – *see Kintyre (Peninsula).*

**CANNICH** *Highland* **401** F 11 – ⊠ *Beauly.*
*Edinburgh 184 – Inverness 28 – Kyle of Lochalsh 54.*

🏠 **Mullardoch House** ⊗, IV4 7LX, West : 8 ½ m. 𝒫 (01456) 415460, *Fax (01456) 415460*,
≤ Loch Sealbanach and Affric Hills, « Former hunting lodge », ♈, 🐎 – ⤢ 📺 ☎ 🄿. 🆗 🄰🄴
*VISA*
**Meals** (booking essential to non-residents) (bar lunch)/dinner 24.00 **t.** 🛈 6.25 – **6 rm**
⊇ 57.00/102.00 – SB.

**CANONBIE** *Dumfries and Galloway* **401** **402** L 18 – *pop. 1 144.*
*Edinburgh 80 – Carlisle 15 – Dumfries 34.*

✗ **Riverside Inn** with rm, DG14 0UX, 𝒫 (013873) 71295 – ⤢ rest, 📺 🄿. 🆗 *VISA* **JCB**
*closed 25 and 26 December, 1 January, 2 weeks February and 2 weeks November* – **Meals**
(booking essential) 19.50 **t.** (dinner) and a la carte 12.65/22.40 **t.** 🛈 6.95 – **7 rm** ⊇ 55.00/
90.00 **t.** – SB.

**CARBOST** *Highland* **401** A 12 – *see Skye (Isle of).*

**CARDROSS** *Argyll and Bute* **401** G 16 *Scotland G..*
**Env. :** *The Clyde Estuary*∗.
*Edinburgh 63 – Glasgow 17 – Helensburgh 5.*

🏠 **Kirkton House** ⊗, Darleith Rd, G82 5EZ, 𝒫 (01389) 841951, *Fax (01389) 841868*, ≤, 🐎
– 📺 ☎ 🄿. 🆗 🄰🄴 🄳 *VISA* **JCB**
*closed January and December* – **Meals** 19.00 **st.** – **6 rm** ⊇ 40.00/65.00 **st.** – SB.

**CARNOUSTIE** *Angus* **401** L 14 – *pop. 12 337.*
🛅, 🛅 Monifieth Golf Links, Medal Starter's Box, Princes St., Monifieth 𝒫 (01382) 532767 –
🛅 Panmure, Barry 𝒫 (01241) 853120.
🄱 *1b High St., DD7 6AN 𝒫 (01241) 852258 (summer only).*
*Edinburgh 68 – Aberdeen 59 – Dundee 12.*

✗✗ **11 Park Avenue**, 11 Park Av., DD7 7JA, 𝒫 (01241) 853336, *Fax (01241) 853336* – 🆗 🄰🄴
*VISA* **JCB**
*closed Sunday and Monday* – **Meals** a la carte 17.65/25.70 **t.** 🛈 7.80.

*Halten Sie beim Betreten des Hotels oder des Restaurants*
*den Führer in der Hand.*
*Sie zeigen damit, daß Sie aufgrund dieser Empfehlung gekommen sind.*

**CARRBRIDGE** Highland **401** I 12.

◻ Carrbridge ℘ (01479) 841623.

🛈 Main St. ℘ (01479) 841630 (summer only).

Edinburgh 135 – Aberdeen 92 – Inverness 23.

🏠 **Fairwinds,** PH23 3AA, ℘ (01479) 841240, Fax (01479) 841240, ✿ – ✵ rest, 📺 ☎ 🅿. ◍
**VISA** ⠀

closed 29 October-18 December – **Meals** (booking essential) (dinner only) 16.00 st
and a la carte ◊ 6.75 – **5 rm** � 24.00/56.00 st.

↑ **Feith Mho'r Country House** ⌖ without rest., Station Rd, PH23 3AP, West : 1 ¼ m
℘ (01479) 841621, ≤, ✿ – 📺 🅿
closed 1 to 26 December – **6 rm** ⊐ 26.00/52.00.

---

**CASTLEBAY** Western Isles **401** X 12/13 – see Barra (Isle of).

---

**CASTLE DOUGLAS** Dumfries and Galloway **401 402** I 19 Scotland G. – pop. 4 187.

Env. : Threave Garden★★ AC, SW : 2½ m. by A 75 – Threave Castle★ AC, W : 1 m.

◻ Abercromby Rd ℘ (01556) 502801.

🛈 Markethill Car Park ℘ (01556) 502611 (summer only).

Edinburgh 98 – Ayr 49 – Dumfries 18 – Stranraer 57.

↑ **Longacre Manor** ⌖, Ernespie Rd, DG7 1LE, Northeast : ¾ m. on A 745
℘ (01556) 503576, Fax (01556) 503886, ≤, ✿ – ✵ rest, 📺 ☎ 🅿
**Meals** (by arrangement) (communal dining) 17.50 s. ◊ 4.20 – **4 rm** ⊐ 40.00/80.00 s.

◉ ATS Station Yard ℘ (01556) 503121/2

---

**CAWDOR** Highland **401** I 11 – pop. 812 – ✉ Inverness.

Edinburgh 170 – Aberdeen 100 – Inverness 14.

🍴 **Cawdor Tavern,** The Lane, IV12 5XP, ℘ (01667) 404777, Fax (01667) 404777, ☂ – 🅿
◍ AE ◔ VISA
**Meals** (booking essential Saturday and Sunday) a la carte 12.00/23.35 t. ◊ 5.95.

---

**CHIRNSIDE** Borders **401** N 16 – pop. 1 680 – ✉ Duns.

Edinburgh 52 – Berwick-upon-Tweed 8 – Glasgow 95 – Newcastle-upon-Tyne 70.

🏨 **Chirnside Hall** ⌖, TD11 3LD, Southeast : 1 ¼ m. on A 6105 ℘ (01890) 818219
Fax (01890) 818231, ≤, ℔, ⇌, ⟍, ✿ – ✵ rest, 📺 ☎ 🅿. ◍ AE ◔ VISA JCB
**Meals** 15.95/22.50 t. and dinner a la carte ◊ 5.75 – **10 rm** ⊐ 60.00/100.00 t. – SB.

---

**CLACHAN SEIL** Argyll and Bute **401** D 15 – see Seil (Isle of).

---

**CLEISH** Perthshire and Kinross **401** J 15 – see Kinross.

---

**CLUANIE INN** Highland – ✉ Glenmoriston.

Edinburgh 176 – Inverness 39 – Kyle of Lochalsh 32 – Oban 135.

🏠 **Cluanie Inn,** IV3 6YW, ℘ (01320) 340238, Fax (01320) 340293, ≤, ⇌ – ☎ ℃ 🅿. ◍ ◔
**VISA**
**Meals** (bar lunch)/dinner 18.50 st. – **13 rm** ⊐ 35.50/87.00 st.

---

**CLYDEBANK** West Dunbartonshire **401** G 16 – pop. 45 717.

◻ Clydebank Municipal, Overtoun Rd, Dalmuir ℘ (0141) 952 8698 – ◻ Clydebank & District,
Hardgate ℘ (01389) 873289.

Edinburgh 52 – Glasgow 6.

🏨 **Beardmore,** Beardmore St., G81 4SA, off A 814 ℘ (0141) 951 6000, Fax (0141) 951 6018,
℔, ⇌, ⬚, ✿ – 🛗, ✵ rm, 🖷 📺 ☎ ℃ & 🅿 – 🔬 170. ◍ AE ◔ VISA ⠀
**Citrus :** Meals (closed Saturday and Sunday lunch) 15.50/20.50 t. and a la carte ◊ 8.50 – ⊐
12.95 – **162 rm** 90.00 st., 6 suites.

---

**COLONSAY (Isle of)** Argyll and Bute **401** B 15 – pop. 106 (inc. Oronsay).

◻ Isle of Colonsay ℘ (01951) 200316.

⛴ – from Scalasaig to Oban (Caledonian MacBrayne Ltd) 4 weekly (2 h 10 mn) – from
Scalasaig to Kintyre Peninsula (Kennacraig) via Isle of Islay (Port Askaig) (Caledonian Mac-
Brayne Ltd) weekly (2 h 35 mn).

**:alasaig** – ✉ *Colonsay.*

**Isle of Colonsay**, PA61 7YP, ☎ (01951) 200316, *Fax (01951) 200353*, ≤, – rest, TV P. MC AE VISA.
**Meals** (booking essential) (bar lunch)/dinner 25.00 **t.** – **11 rm** (dinner included) 80.00 **st.** – SB.

**OMRIE** *Perthshire* 401 I 14 – *pop. 1 926.*
*Edinburgh 66 – Glasgow 56 – Oban 70 – Perth 24.*

**The Royal**, Melville Sq., PH6 2DN, ☎ (01764) 679200, *Fax (01764) 679219*, « Attractively furnished », – TV ☎ P. MC AE VISA JCB.
**Meals** 12.75 **t.** and a la carte – **11 rm** 80.00/130.00 – SB.

**ONAN BRIDGE** *Highland* 401 G 11.
*Edinburgh 168 – Inverness 12.*

**Kinkell House**, Easter Kinkell, IV7 8HY, Southeast : 3 m. by B 9163 and A 835 on B 9169 ☎ (01349) 861270, *Fax (01349) 865902*, ≤, – TV ☎ & P. MC VISA
**Meals** (booking essential) (residents only Saturday lunch and Sunday dinner) a la carte 11.00/23.75 **st.** 5.95 – **9 rm** 50.00/80.00 **st.** – SB.

**ONNEL** *Argyll and Bute* 401 D 14 – ✉ *Oban.*
*Edinburgh 118 – Glasgow 88 – Inverness 113 – Oban 5.*

**Ards House**, PA37 1PT, on A 85 ☎ (01631) 710255, ≤, – P. MC VISA JCB.
*March-November* – **Meals** 21.00 **t.** 9.90 – **6 rm** (dinner included) 40.00/100.00 **t.** – SB.

**Ronebhal** without rest., PA37 1PJ, on A 85 ☎ (01631) 710310, *Fax (01631) 710310*, ≤, – TV P. MC VISA.
*mid March-October* – **6 rm** 18.00/60.00.

**ONTIN** *Highland* 401 G 11 – *pop. 1 194* – ✉ *Strathpeffer.*
*Edinburgh 175 – Inverness 19.*

**Coul House**, IV14 9EY, ☎ (01997) 421487, *Fax (01997) 421945*, ≤, – rest, TV ☎ P. MC AE VISA JCB
**Meals** (lunch by arrangement)/dinner 28.50 **st.** (dinner) and a la carte 18.65/29.75 **st.** 8.90 – **19 rm** 63.25/112.50 **st.**, 1 suite.

**Achilty**, IV14 9EG, Northwest : ¾ m. on A 835 ☎ (01997) 421355, *Fax (01997) 421923* – TV ☎ P. MC VISA
**Meals** a la carte 10.70/26.95 **st.** – **12 rm** 47.00/69.00 **st.** – SB.

**:OUPAR ANGUS** *Perthshire and Kinross* 401 K 14 – *pop. 3 844* – ✉ *Blairgowrie.*
*Edinburgh 63 – Dundee 14 – Perth 13.*

**Moorfield House**, Myreiggs Rd, PH13 9HS, Northwest : 2 ½ m. by A 923 ☎ (01828) 627303, *Fax (01828) 627339*, – rm, TV ☎ P – 120. MC AE VISA
*closed 4 day Christmas* – **Meals** (booking essential) (bar lunch)/dinner 25.50 **t.** 6.50 – **11 rm** 50.00/94.00 **t.**

**:RAIGELLACHIE** *Moray* 401 K 11 *Scotland G..*
Env. : *Dufftown (Glenfiddich Distillery★), SE : 5 m. by A 941.*
*Edinburgh 190 – Aberdeen 58 – Inverness 53.*

**Craigellachie**, Victoria St., AB38 9SR, ☎ (01340) 881204, *Fax (01340) 881253*, – TV ☎ P – 35. MC AE VISA JCB
**Meals** 14.95/27.50 **t.** and a la carte – **26 rm** 92.50/185.00 **t.** – SB.

**CRAIGHOUSE** *Argyll and Bute* 401 C 16 – *see Jura (Isle of).*

**CRIANLARICH** *Stirling* 401 G 14.
*Edinburgh 82 – Glasgow 52 – Perth 53.*

**Allt-Chaorain House**, FK20 8RU, Northwest : 1 m. on A 82 ☎ (01838) 300283, *Fax (01838) 300238*, ≤, – TV ☎ P. MC AE VISA JCB
*April-October* – **Meals** (residents only) (communal dining) (dinner only) 18.00 **t.** – **7 rm** 48.00/78.00 **t.** – SB.

**CRIEFF** *Perthshire and Kinross* **401** I 14 *Scotland G.* – pop. 6 096.

See : *Town★*.

Env. : *Drummond Castle Gardens★ AC, S : 2 m. by A 822 – Comrie (Scottish Tartan Museum★ ) W : 6 m. by A 85.*

Exc. : *Scone Palace★★ AC, E : 16 m. by A 85 and A 93.*

🇳 , 🇳 *Perth Rd ℰ (01764) 652909 – 🇳 Muthill, Peat Rd ℰ (01764) 681523.*

🇧 *Town Hall, High St., PH7 3HU ℰ (01764) 652578.*

*Edinburgh 60 – Glasgow 50 – Oban 76 – Perth 18.*

🏠 **Murraypark,** Connaught Terr., PH7 3DJ, ℰ (01764) 653731, Fax (01764) 655311, 🚗
✯ rest, 📺 ☎ & 🅿 – 🛎 25. 🆎 🆎 🆎 *VISA*
**Meals** (bar lunch)/dinner a la carte 14.40/18.85 t. ♦ 4.95 – **19 rm** 🖙 50.00/80.00 t., 1 suite SB.

---

**CRINAN** *Argyll and Bute* **401** D 15 *Scotland G.* – ⊠ *Lochgilphead.*

See : *Hamlet★*.

Exc. : *Kilmory Knap (Macmillan's Cross★ ) SW : 14 m.*

*Edinburgh 137 – Glasgow 91 – Oban 36.*

🏨 **Crinan,** PA31 8SR, ℰ (01546) 830261, Fax (01546) 830292, « Commanding setting, ≤ Loch Crinan and Sound of Jura », 🍴 – 🛗, ✯ rest, 📺 ☎ 🅿. 🆎 🆎 *VISA*
**Meals** (bar lunch)/dinner 35.00 t. ♦ 7.50 – (see also **Lock 16** below) – **22 rm** 🖙 (dinner included) 95.00/240.00 t.

✕✕ **Lock 16** (at Crinan H.), PA31 8SR, ℰ (01546) 830261, Fax (01546) 830292, « Commanding setting, ≤ Loch Crinan and Sound of Jura » – ✯ 🅿. 🆎 🆎 *VISA*
*closed Sunday, Monday and October-May* – **Meals** - Seafood - (booking essential) (dinner only) 35.00 t. ♦ 7.95.

**THE CHANNEL TUNNEL Map Guide**

**260** *French edition*
    *with tourist sights in England*

**261** *English edition*
    *with tourist sights on the Continent*

---

**CROMARTY** *Highland* **401** H 10 *Scotland G.* – pop. 865.

See : *Town★*.

Exc. : *Fortrose (Cathedral Church setting★ ), SW : 10 m. by A 832.*

🇳 *Fortrose & Rosemarkie, Ness Road East ℰ (01381) 620529.*

*Edinburgh 182 – Inverness 26 – Wick 126.*

🏠 **Royal,** Marine Terr., IV11 8YN, ℰ (01381) 600217, ≤ – 📺 🅿. 🆎 🆎 *VISA*
**Meals** 12.50/16.90 t. and a la carte ♦ 5.00 – **10 rm** 🖙 35.00/60.00 t. – SB.

---

**CROSSFORD** *Fife* **401** J 15 – *see Dunfermline.*

---

**CULLEN** *Moray* **401** L 10 *Scotland G.* – pop. 1 522.

See : *Cullen Auld Kirk★ (Sacrament house★, panels★ ).*

Env. : *Deskford Church (Sacrament house★ ) S : 4 m. by A 98 and B 9018 – Portsoy★, E 5½ m. by A 98.*

🇳 *The Links ℰ (01542) 840685.*

🇧 *20 Seafield St., AB56 2FH ℰ (01542) 840757 (summer only).*

*Edinburgh 189 – Aberdeen 59 – Banff 12 – Inverness 61.*

🏠 **Bayview,** Seafield St., AB56 4SU, ℰ (01542) 841031, Fax (01542) 841731, ≤ – ✯ 📺 ☎
🆎 🆎 🆎 *VISA*
**Meals** a la carte 9.75/24.15 t. ♦ 4.75 – **6 rm** 🖙 35.00/70.00 t.

---

**CULLODEN** *Highland* **401** H 11 – *see Inverness.*

---

**CULNAKNOCK** *Highland* **401** B 11 – *see Skye (Isle of).*

---

**CULTS** *Aberdeenshire* **401** N 12 – *see Aberdeen.*

**CUMBERNAULD** *North Lanarkshire* [401] I 16 – *pop. 62 412.*
*Edinburgh 40 – Glasgow 11 – Stirling 13.*

**Westerwood H. Golf and Country Club,** St. Andrews Drive, G68 0EW, North : 2 m. by A 8011 and off Eastfield rd ☎ (01236) 457171, *Fax (01236) 738478,* [Lб], [☐], [18], ✂ – [|$|], ⚡ rm, ▤ rest, [TV] ☎ [P] – 🏛 180. [MC] [AE] [O] [VISA]. ✂
**Meals** (bar lunch Saturday) 9.95/16.50 **t.** and a la carte – **49 rm** ☐ 82.50/155.00 **st.** – SB.

**Travel Inn,** 4 South Muirhead Rd, G67 1AX, off A 8011 ☎ (01236) 725339, *Fax (01236) 736380* – ⚡ rm, ▤ rest, [TV] ♿ [P]. [MC] [AE] [O] [VISA]. ✂
**Meals** (grill rest.) – **37 rm** 38.00 **t.**

**CUPAR** *Fife* [401] K 15 – *pop. 8 174.*
[i] *The Granary, Coal Rd, PY15 5YQ ☎ (01334) 652874 (summer only).*
*Edinburgh 45 – Dundee 15 – Perth 23.*

**Todhall House** ⚘, Dairsie, KY15 4RQ, East : 2 m. by A 91 ☎ (01334) 656344, *Fax (01334) 656344,* ⩽, 🌳 – ⚡ [TV] [P]. [MC] [VISA]. ✂
*mid March-October* – **Meals** (by arrangement) (communal dining) 18.00 **st.** – **3 rm** ☐ 32.00/60.00 **st.**

**Ostler's Close,** Bonnygate, KY15 4BU, ☎ (01334) 655574, *Fax (01334) 654036* – [MC] [AE] [VISA] [JCB]. ✂
*closed Sunday, Monday, 1 January, 25-26 December, 2 weeks January, last 2 weeks May and first week June* – **Meals** (1unch by arrangement) a la carte 15.95/31.15 **t.** 🍷 5.95.

ATS St. Catherine St. ☎ (01334) 654003

**DALBEATTIE** *Dumfries and Galloway* [401] [402] I 19 *Scotland G.* – *pop. 4 421.*
Env. : *Kippford*★, *S : 5 m. by A 710.*
[9] *Dalbeattie ☎ (01556) 611421.*
[i] *Town Hall, DJ5 ☎ (01556) 610117 (summer only).*
*Edinburgh 94 – Ayr 56 – Dumfries 14 – Stranraer 62.*

**Auchenskeoch Lodge** ⚘, DG5 4PG, Southeast : 5 m. on B 793 ☎ (01387) 780277, *Fax (01387) 780277,* ⚘, 🌳, park – ⚡ rest, [TV] ♿ [P]. [MC] [VISA]
*Easter-October* – **Meals** (by arrangement) (communal dining) 16.00 **st.** 🍷 6.10 – **2 rm** ☐ 39.00/62.00 **st.**, 1 suite – SB.

**Broomlands House** ⚘, Haugh Rd, DG5 4AR, West : ½ m. by Auchencairn rd (A 711) ☎ (01556) 611463, *Fax (01556) 611462,* 🌳 – ⚡ [TV] [P]
*March-October* – **Meals** (by arrangement) 10.00 – **3 rm** ☐ 32.00/44.00.

**Briardale House,** 17 Haugh Rd, DG5 4AR, West : ½ m. by Auchencairn rd (A 711) ☎ (01556) 611468, 🌳 – ⚡ [TV] [P]
*closed November and December* – **Meals** (by arrangement) 12.50 **st.** – **3 rm** ☐ 48.00 **st.**

**DALCROSS** *Highland* – *see Inverness.*

**DALRY** *North Ayrshire* [401] [402] F 16.
*Edinburgh 70 – Ayr 21 – Glasgow 25.*

**Braidwoods** ⚘, Drumastle Mill Cottage, KA24 4LN, Southwest : 1 ½ m. by A 737 on Saltcoats rd ☎ (01294) 833544, *Fax (01294) 833553* – ⚡ [P]. [MC] [AE] [VISA]
*closed Tuesday lunch, Sunday dinner, Monday, 25 December, first 3 weeks January, last 2 weeks September and first week October* – **Meals** (booking essential) 16.00/26.00 **st.** 🍷 8.95.

**DARVEL** *East Ayrshire* [401] [402] H 17.
*Edinburgh 60 – Ayr 22 – Glasgow 21.*

**Scoretulloch House** ⚘ with rm, KA17 0LR, Southeast : 2 m. by A 71 ☎ (01560) 323331, *Fax (01560) 323441,* ⩽, 🌳 – ⚡ [TV] ☎ [P]. [MC] [AE] [VISA] [JCB]
*closed 25 December and 1 January* – **Meals** 15.00/25.00 **t.** and lunch a la carte 25.00/27.50 **t.** 🍷 5.60 – **4 rm** ☐ 55.00/125.00 **t.**

**DENNY** *Falkirk* [401] I 15 *Scotland G.* – *pop. 11 061.*
Exc. : *Stirling*★★, *N : 8 m. by A 872.*
*Edinburgh 34 – Glasgow 25 – Stirling 7.*

**Topps Farm** ⚘, Fintry Rd, FK6 5JF, West : 4 m. on B 818 ☎ (01324) 822471, *Fax (01324) 823099,* ⩽ – ⚡ [TV] ☎ ♿ [P]. [MC] [VISA]. ✂
*closed 24 to 26 December* – **Meals** (by arrangement) 24.50 **st.** – **8 rm** ☐ 32.00/44.00 **st.**

**DERVAIG** Argyll and Bute **401** B 14 – see Mull (Isle of).

---

**DINGWALL** Highland **401** G 11 – pop. 5 572.
Edinburgh 172 – Inverness 14.

XX **Cafe India Brasserie**, Lockhart House, Tulloch St., IV15 9JZ, ℰ (01349) 862552 – **MC AE** **VISA**
Meals - Indian - 6.95/26.00 **t**. and a la carte.

---

**DORNIE** Highland **401** D 12 Scotland G. – ⊠ Kyle of Lochalsh.
See : Eilean Donan Castle★ AC (site★★).
Env. : Glen Shiel★, SE : 4 m. on A 87.
Edinburgh 212 – Inverness 74 – Kyle of Lochalsh 8.

🏠 **Conchra House** ⟨⟩, Ardelve, IV40 8DZ, North : 1 ¾ m. by A 87 on Conchra ro
ℰ (01599) 555233, Fax (01599) 555433, ≼ Loch Long, « Part Georgian country house », 🐎
– ⚒ **℗** – 🔥 40. **MC AE** **VISA**. ⚒
Meals (booking essential to non-residents) (dinner only) 15.00 **t**. ⬧ 4.50 – **6 rm** ⊂⊃ 42.00/
74.00 **s**. – SB.

---

**DORNOCH** Highland **401** H 10 Scotland G. – pop. 2 042.
See : Town★.
🏌, 🏌 Royal Dornoch, Golf Rd ℰ (01862) 810219.
🄱 The Square, IV25 3SD ℰ (01862) 810400.
Edinburgh 219 – Inverness 63 – Wick 65.

🏠 **Highfield** without rest., Evelix Rd, IV25 3HR, ℰ (01862) 810909, Fax (01862) 810909, ≼,
🐎 – ⚒ 📺 **℗**
**3 rm** ⊂⊃ 35.00/50.00.

XX **2 Quail** with rm, Castle St., IV25 3SN, ℰ (01862) 811811 – ⚒ rm, 📺. **MC AE** **VISA**. ⚒
restricted opening in winter – Meals (closed Sunday) (dinner only) 24.00 **st**. ⬧ 6.50 – **2 rm**
⊂⊃ 40.00/60.00 **st**.

---

**DOUNBY** Orkney Islands **401** K 6 – see Orkney Islands (Mainland).

---

**DRUMBEG** Highland **401** E 9 – ⊠ Lairg.
Edinburgh 262 – Inverness 105 – Ullapool 48.

🏠 **Drumbeg**, Assynt, IV27 4NW, ℰ (01571) 833236, Fax (01571) 833333, ≼ – ⚒ rest, 📺 **℗**.
**MC** **VISA**. ⚒
April-October – Meals (booking essential to non-residents) (bar lunch) a la carte 9.50/
13.50 **st**. – **6 rm** ⊂⊃ 50.00/66.00 **st**.

🏠 **Taigh Druimbeag** ⟨⟩, IV27 4NW, ℰ (01571) 833209, 🐎 – ⚒ **℗**. **VISA**. ⚒
Easter-October – Meals (by arrangement) (communal dining) 12.50 **st**. – **3 rm** ⊂⊃ 30.00/
55.00 **st**.

---

**DRUMNADROCHIT** Highland **401** G 11 Scotland G. – pop. 852 – ⊠ Milton.
Env. : Loch Ness★★ – Loch Ness Monster Exhibition★ AC – The Great Glen★.
Edinburgh 172 – Inverness 16 – Kyle of Lochalsh 66.

🏨 **Polmaily House** ⟨⟩, IV3 6XT, West : 2 m. on A 831 ℰ (01456) 450343,
Fax (01456) 450813, « Special facilities for young children », 🔲, 🐎, park, ⚒ – ⚒ 📺 ☎
**℗**. **MC** **VISA** **JCB**
closed Christmas, 2 weeks January and 2 weeks December – Meals (bar lunch)/dinner
24.00 **t**. and a la carte ⬧ – **11 rm** ⊂⊃ 55.00/130.00 **t**. – SB.

🏠 **Drumbuie Farm** without rest., Drumbuie, IV3 6XP, East : ¾ m. by A 82
ℰ (01456) 450634, Fax (01456) 450595, ≼, « Working farm », park – ⚒ 📺 **℗**. ⚒
**3 rm** ⊂⊃ 44.00 **st**.

---

**DRYMEN** Stirling **401** G 15 Scotland G. – pop. 1 565.
Env. : Loch Lomond★★, W : 3 m.
🄱 Drymen Library, The Square, J63 OBL ℰ (01360) 660068 (summer only).
Edinburgh 64 – Glasgow 18 – Stirling 22.

🏨 **Buchanan Arms**, Main St., G63 0BQ, ℰ (01360) 660588, Fax (01360) 660943, 🏋, ⚒, 🔲,
🐎, squash – ⚒ 📺 ☎ **℗** – 🔥 150. **MC AE ⓞ** **VISA** **JCB**
Meals 10.50/20.50 **st**. and a la carte ⬧ 5.95 – ⊂⊃ 8.95 – **52 rm** 79.00/116.00 **st**. – SB.

**DULNAIN BRIDGE** Highland [401] J 12 – ⊠ Grantown-on-Spey.
Edinburgh 140 – Inverness 31 – Perth 96.

🏨 **Muckrach Lodge** ⤴, PH26 3LY, ℰ (01479) 851257, Fax (01479) 851325, ≤, 🐎, park –
⇔ rest, 📺 🕿 ⭑ 🅿, 🚳 🅰🅴 ① 𝗩𝗜𝗦𝗔 JCB
**Meals** (bar lunch Monday to Saturday)/dinner 26.00 **st.** 🛊 7.00 – **11 rm** ⌷ 49.50/99.00 **st.**,
2 suites – SB.

🏠 **Auchendean Lodge**, PH26 3LU, South : 1 m. on A 95 ℰ (01479) 851347,
Fax (01479) 851347, ≤ Spey Valley and Cairngorms, 🐎 – ⇔ rest, 📺 🅿, 🚳 🅰🅴 ① 𝗩𝗜𝗦𝗔
closed January – **Meals** (dinner only) 26.00 **st.** 🛊 4.00 – **6 rm** ⌷ 41.00/78.00 **st.** – SB.

---

**DUMBARTON** West Dunbartonshire [401] G 16 Scotland G. – pop. 77 173.

See : Dumbarton Castle (site★) AC.
Env. : Loch Lomond★★, N : 5½ m. by A 82.
🏌 Vale of Leven, Northfield Rd, Bonhill ℰ (01389) 752351.
🄳 Milton, by Dumbarton A 82 (northbound) ℰ (01389) 742306 (summer only).
Edinburgh 64 – Glasgow 12 – Greenock 17.

🏠 **Travelodge**, Milton, G82 2TY, East : 3 m. by A 814 on A 82 ℰ (01389) 65202, Reservations
(Freephone) 0800 850950 – ⇔ rm, 📺 ⭑ 🅿, 🚳 🅰🅴 ① 𝗩𝗜𝗦𝗔 JCB, 🛠
**Meals** (grill rest.) – **32 rm** 39.95/59.95 **t.**

*En saison, surtout dans les stations fréquentées,*
*il est prudent de retenir à l'avance.*
*Cependant, si vous ne pouvez pas occuper la chambre*
*que vous avez retenue, prévenez immédiatement l'hôtelier.*

*Si vous écrivez à un hôtel à l'étranger, joignez à votre lettre*
*un coupon-réponse international (disponible dans les bureaux de poste).*

---

**DUMFRIES** Dumfries and Galloway [401] [402] J 18 Scotland G. – pop. 21 164.

See : Town★ – Midsteeple★ A A.
Env. : Lincluden College (Tomb★) AC, N : 1½ m. by College St. A.
Exc. : Drumlanrig Castle★★ (cabinets★) AC, NW : 16½ m. by A 76 A – Shambellie House
Museum of Costume (Costume Collection★) S : 7¼m. by A 710 A – Sweetheart Abbey★ AC,
S : 8 m. by A 710 A – Caerlaverock Castle★ (Renaissance façade★★) AC, SE : 9 m. by B 725 B
– Glenkiln (Sculptures★) W : 9 m. by A 780 – A – and A 75 – Ruthwell Cross★, SE : 12 m. by A
780 – B – A 75 and B 724.
🏌 Dumfries & Galloway, 2 Laurieston Av., Maxwelltown ℰ (01387) 253582 A – 🏌 Crichton,
Bankend Rd ℰ (01387) 247894, B.
🄳 64 Whitesands, DG1 4TH ℰ (01387) 253862, A.
Edinburgh 80 – Ayr 59 – Carlisle 34 – Glasgow 79 – Manchester 155 – Newcastle upon Tyne
91.

Plan on next page

🏨🏨 **Cairndale**, English St., DG1 2DF, ℰ (01387) 254111, Fax (01387) 250555, ₤ₔ, �cs, ⬚ – ⬛,
⇔ rm, 🍽 rest, 📺 🕿 🅿 – 🖄 160. 🚳 🅰🅴 ① 𝗩𝗜𝗦𝗔, 🛠                                           B a
**Meals** 9.95/17.50 **st.** and dinner a la carte 🛊 5.95 – **76 rm** ⌷ 85.00/119.00 **st.** – SB.

🏨 **Station**, 49 Lovers Walk, DG1 1LT, ℰ (01387) 254316, Fax (01387) 250388 – ⬚ 📺 🕿 🅿 –
🖄 70. 🚳 🅰🅴 ① 𝗩𝗜𝗦𝗔 JCB                                                                              B e
**Meals** (bar lunch)/dinner 16.50 **st.** and a la carte 🛊 5.95 – **32 rm** ⌷ 80.00/110.00 **st.** – SB.

🏠 **Travelodge**, Annan Rd, DG1 3SE, East : 2 ¼ m. on A 75 ℰ (01387) 750658,
Fax (01387) 750658, Reservations (Freephone) 0800 850950 – ⇔ rm, 📺 ⭑ 🅿, 🚳 🅰🅴 ①
𝗩𝗜𝗦𝗔 JCB, 🛠
**Meals** (grill rest.) – **40 rm** 39.95/59.95 **t.**

🏠 **Orchard House** without rest., 298 Annan Rd, DG1 3JE, East : 1½ m. on A 780 (Carlisle rd)
ℰ (01387) 255099, 🐎 – ⇔ 📺 ⭑ 🅿, 🛠
**3 rm** ⌷ 25.00/40.00.

✗ **Wishart's**, The Robert Burns Centre, Mill Rd, DG2 7BE, ℰ (01387) 259679 – 🚳 ① 𝗩𝗜𝗦𝗔
🍴 closed Sunday, Monday, 25 to 29 December and 2 weeks early January – **Meals** (dinner only)
a la carte 19.50/25.00 **t.** 🛊 8.95.                                                              A e

🄰 ATS Glasgow St. ℰ (01387) 266154                          ATS 4 Downsway Ind. Est., Heathall
                                                             ℰ (01387) 263837/8

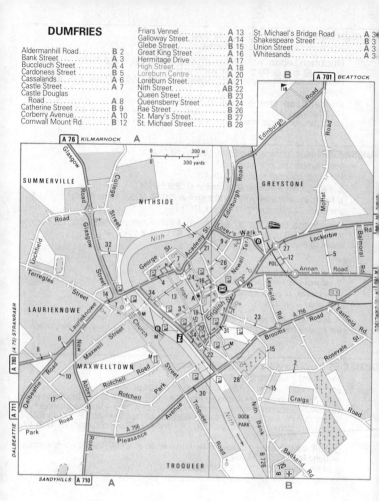

## DUMFRIES

*When looking for a quiet hotel*
*use the maps found in the introduction*
*or look for establishments with the sign 🦢 or 🦢.*

---

**DUNAIN PARK** Highland – see Inverness.

---

**DUNBLANE** Stirling 🔟🔟 I 15 Scotland G. – pop. 8 007 (inc. Lecropt).

See : Town★ – Cathedral★ (west front★★).

Env. : Doune★ (castle★ AC) W : 4½ m. by A 820 – Doune Motor Museum★ AC, W : 5½ m.
by A 820 and A 84.

🛈 Stirling Rd ℘ (01786) 824428 (summer only).

Edinburgh 42 – Glasgow 33 – Perth 29.

🏛 **Cromlix House** 🦢, Kinbuck, FK15 9JT, North : 3 ½ m. on B 8033 ℘ (01786) 822125,
Fax (01786) 825450, ≤, « Antique furnishings, 19C chapel », 🎣, 🛥, park, 🎿 – ﹣✸ rest, 📺
☎ 🅿. 🆎 🖭 🗚 💳 💳
closed January – **Meals** (booking essential) (lunch by arrangement) 25.00/37.75 **st.** 💧 12.50
– 6 rm 🖙 185.00/295.00 **st.**, 8 **suites** 240.00/295.00 **st.** – SB.

686

**UNDEE** 401 L 14 *Scotland G. – pop. 165 873.*

See : *Town★ – The Frigate Unicorn★ AC Y A – Discovery Point★ AC Y B – Verdant Works★ – McManus Galleries★.*

18, 9, 9 *Caird Park, Mains Loan* ℰ *(01382) 453606 –* 18 *Camperdown, Camperdown Park* ℰ *(01382) 623398.*

*Tay Road Bridge (toll)* Y.

✈ *Dundee Airport :* ℰ *(01382) 643242, SW : 1½ m.* Z.

🛈 *4 City Sq., DD1 3BA* ℰ *(01382) 434664.*

*Edinburgh 63 – Aberdeen 67 – Glasgow 83.*

## DUNDEE

| | |
|---|---|
| Albert Street | Z 2 |
| Ancrum Road | Z 5 |
| Bell Street | Y 6 |
| City Square | Y 7 |
| Commercial Street | Y 8 |
| Coupar Angus Road | Z 9 |
| Douglas Road | Z 10 |
| Drumgeith Road | Z 12 |
| Dudhope Terrace | Y 13 |
| East Dock Street | Y 14 |
| East Marketgait | Y 15 |
| Greendykes Road | Z 16 |
| High Street | Z 17 |
| Logie Street | Z 18 |
| Longtown Road | Z 20 |
| Mains Road | Z 21 |
| Meadowside | Z 23 |
| Moncur Crescent | Z 24 |
| Murraygate | Y 25 |
| Nethergate | Y 26 |
| Old Glamis Road | Z 32 |
| Overgate Centre | Y |
| Provost Road | Y 34 |
| Reform Street | Y 35 |
| St. Andrews Street | Y 36 |
| South Union Street | Y 39 |
| Strathmartine Road | Y 40 |
| Trades Lane | Y 41 |
| Ward Road | Y 42 |
| Wellgate Centre | Y |
| West Bell Street | Y 43 |
| West Marketgait | Y 44 |

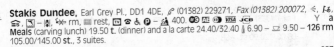

🏨 **Stakis Dundee**, Earl Grey Pl., DD1 4DE, ℰ *(01382) 229271, Fax (01382) 200072,* ≤, Ⅰ₅, ⇌s, ⬛ – 📶, ↤ rm, ☰ rest, 📺 ☎ & ℗ – 🔬 *400.* 🆎 🆎 ① *VISA* ᴶᶜᴮ
**Meals** (carving lunch) 19.50 **t.** (dinner) and a la carte 24.40/32.40 ᵭ 6.90 – ⊐ 9.50 – **126 rm** 105.00/145.00 **st.**, 3 suites.                                                                   Y a

687

🏨 **Swallow,** Kingsway West (Dundee Ring Rd), DD2 5JT, West : 4 ¾ m. at junction of A 8⬛ with A 90 ℰ (01382) 641122, Fax (01382) 568340, ↳, ⇌, ☒, ⟲ – ⟲, ☰ rest, 🔲 ☎ 🅿 ⚒ 80. 🐵 🆀 🅴 𝘝𝘐𝘚𝘈
**Meals** (bar lunch)/dinner 20.50 st. ♬ 7.00 – **106 rm** ⟷ 105.00/145.00 st., 1 suite – SB.

🏨 **Shaftesbury,** 1 Hyndford St., DD2 1HQ, ℰ (01382) 669216, Fax (01382) 641598 ⟲ rest, 🔲 ☎ 🆀 🅴 𝘝𝘐𝘚𝘈
closed Christmas-New Year – **Meals** (lunch by arrangement) (Sunday dinner residents onl⬛ a la carte 11.10/20.90 t. ♬ 5.00 – **12 rm** ⟷ 51.00/80.00 t. – SB. 

🏨 **Travel Inn,** Discovery Quay, Riverside Drive, DD1 4XA, ℰ (01382) 20324⬛ Fax (01382) 203237, ≤ – ⟲ rm, 🔲 ♿ 🅿 🆀 🅴 ① 𝘝𝘐𝘚𝘈 ⟲
**Meals** (grill rest.) – **40 rm** 38.00 t. 

🏨 **Travel Inn,** Kingsway West, Invergowrie, DD2 5JU, Northwest : on A 90 ℰ (01382) 56111⬛ Fax (01382) 568431 – ⟲ rm, 🔲 ♿ 🅿 🆀 🅴 ① 𝘝𝘐𝘚𝘈 ⟲
**Meals** (grill rest.) – **64 rm** 38.00 t.

🏨 **Travelodge,** Kingsway West, Invergowrie, DD2 4TD, Northwest : on A 9⬛ ℰ (01382) 610488, Reservations (Freephone) 0800 850950 – 🔲 ☎ ♿ 🅿 🆀 🅴 ① 𝘝𝘐𝘚𝘈 ⟲
**Meals** (grill rest.) – **30 rm** 39.95/59.95 t.

🏠 **Hillside** without rest., 43 Constitution St., DD3 6JH, ℰ (01382) 22344⬛ Fax (01382) 223443 – ⟲ 🔲 🅿 🆀 𝘝𝘐𝘚𝘈 ⟲
**4 rm** ⟷ 22.00/48.00.

**at Broughty Ferry** East : 4½ m. by A 930 - Z - (Dundee Rd) – ✉ Dundee.

🏨 **Broughty Ferry,** 16 West Queen St., DD5 1AR, ℰ (01382) 480027, Fax (01382) 47766⬛ ↳, ⇌, ☒ – ⟲ rm, 🔲 ☎ 🅿 🆀 🅴 𝘝𝘐𝘚𝘈 ⟲
**Meals** – (see **Bombay Brasserie** below) – **15 rm** ⟷ 59.00/74.00 t.

🏠 **Beach House,** 22 Esplanade, DD5 2EN, ℰ (01382) 776614, Fax (01382) 480241 – ⟲ res⬛ 🔲 ☎ 🆀 𝘝𝘐𝘚𝘈 ⟲
**Meals** 12.50 st. ♬ 4.50 – **5 rm** ⟷ 38.00/48.00 st.

🏠 **Invermark House** without rest., 23 Monifieth Rd, DD5 2RN, ℰ (01382) 739430, ⟲ ⟲ 🔲 🅿 🆀 𝘝𝘐𝘚𝘈 ⟲
closed Christmas and New Year – **4 rm** ⟷ 30.00/45.00 s.

✗ **Bombay Brasserie** (at Broughty Ferry H.), 16 West Queen St., DD5 1AR ℰ (01382) 480490, Fax (01382) 477660 – 🅿 🆀 🅴 𝘝𝘐𝘚𝘈
closed Sunday lunch – **Meals** - Indian - (dinner only) a la carte 13.15/21.95 t. ♬ 6.20.

✗ **Cafe Montmartre,** 98 Gray St., DD5 2DN, ℰ (01382) 739313, Fax (01382) 521324 – ☰ 🆀 🅴 𝘝𝘐𝘚𝘈 𝘑𝘊𝘉
closed Sunday and Monday – **Meals** - French - a la carte 13.45/21.15 t. ♬ 4.95.

Ⓐ ATS 332 Clepington Rd ℰ (01382) 858327

---

**DUNDONNELL** Highland 🗺️⬛ E 10 Scotland G. – ✉ Garve.
Env. : Wester Ross★★★ – Loch Broom★★, N : 4½ m. via Allt na h–Airbhe.
Exc. : Falls of Measach★★, SE : 10 m. by A 832 – Corrieshalloch Gorge★, SE : 11 ½ m. by⬛ A 832 and A 835.
Edinburgh 215 – Inverness 59.

🏨 **Dundonnell,** IV23 2QR, ℰ (01854) 633204, Fax (01854) 633366, ≤ Dundonnell Valley - ⟲ 🔲 ☎ 🅿 – ⚒ 60. 🆀 🅴 𝘝𝘐𝘚𝘈 𝘑𝘊𝘉
closed January – **Meals** (booking essential in winter) (bar lunch)/dinner 24.00 t. ♬ 6.25 – **28 rm** ⟷ 67.50/110.00 t. – SB.

---

**DUNFERMLINE** Fife 🗺️⬛ J 15 Scotland G. – pop. 29 436.
See : Town★ – Abbey★ (Abbey Church★★) AC.
Env. : Forth Bridges★★, S : 5 m. by A 823 and B 980.
Exc. : Culross★★ (Village★★★, Palace★★ AC, Study★ AC), W : 7 m. by A 994 and B 9037.
🏌️ Canmore, Venturefair ℰ (01383) 724969 – 🏌️ Pitreavie, Queensferry Rd ℰ (01383⬛ 722591 – 🏌️ Saline, Kinneddar Hill ℰ (01383) 852591.
🅱 13-15 Maygate, KY12 7NE ℰ (01383) 720999.
Edinburgh 16 – Dundee 48 – Motherwell 39.

🏨 **King Malcolm,** Queensferry Rd, KY11 5DS, South : 1 m. on A 823 ℰ (01383) 722611, Fax (01383) 730865 – ⟲ rm, ☰ rest, 🔲 ☎ 🅿 – ⚒ 150. 🆀 🅴 ① 𝘝𝘐𝘚𝘈 𝘑𝘊𝘉
**Meals** (closed lunch Saturday and Sunday) 9.95/18.50 st. ♬ 5.20 – ⟷ 10.25 – **48 rm** 80.00/120.00 st. – SB.

**Crossford** Southwest : 1 ¾ m. on A 994 – ⊠ Dunfermline.

🏛 **Keavil House** ⑤, Main St., KY12 8QW, ℘ (01383) 736258, Fax (01383) 621600, ₤₅, ≘ₛ, ⬛, ☞ – � ⊡ 🅿 & 🅿 – 🔬 300. ◑◐ 匥 ◑ 𝘝𝘐𝘚𝘈. ※
Meals (buffet lunch) 9.00/19.95 **st.** and a la carte ⅜ 6.95 – ⊇ 10.95 – **47 rm** 60.00/115.00 **st.** – SB.

ⓐ ATS 14 Dickson St., Elgin St. Est. ℘ (01383) 722802

---

**UNKELD** Perthshire and Kinross 𝟰𝟬𝟭 J 14 Scotland G. – pop. 4 069.
See : Village★ – Cathedral Street★.
🏌 Dunkeld & Birnam, Fungarth ℘ (01350) 727524.
🖪 The Cross, PH8 0AN ℘ (01350) 727688.
Edinburgh 58 – Aberdeen 88 – Inverness 98 – Perth 14.

🏰 **Kinnaird** ⑤, Dalguise, PH8 0LB, Northwest : 6 ¾ m. by A 9 on B 898 ℘ (01796) 482440, Fax (01796) 482289, ≼ Tay valley and hills, « Sporting estate, antique furnishings », ⬚, ☞, park, ※ – ⬛, ✜ rest, ⊡ ☎ ℃ 🅿. ◑◐ 𝘝𝘐𝘚𝘈. ※
closed Monday to Wednesday January-February – Meals 25.00/40.00 **t.** ⅜ 10.00 – **8 rm** ⊇ 245.00/350.00 **t.**, 1 suite.

🏰 **Stakis Dunkeld** ⑤, PH8 0HX, ℘ (01350) 727771, Fax (01350) 728924, ≼, « Tayside setting », ₤₅, ≘ₛ, ⬛, ☞, park, ※ – ⧫, ✜ rm, ⊡ ☎ & 🅿 – 🔬 80. ◑◐ 匥 ◑ 𝘝𝘐𝘚𝘈. ※
Meals (bar lunch)/dinner 15.00/30.00 **st.** – ⊇ 9.75 – **83 rm** 115.00/150.00 **t.**, 3 suites – SB.

⌂ **Bheinne Mhor,** Perth Rd, Birnam, PH8 0DH, Southeast : ¾ m. by A 923 ℘ (01350) 727779, ☞ – ✜ 🅿 ◑◐ 𝘝𝘐𝘚𝘈. ※
closed January and December – Meals (by arrangement) 16.00 **st.** – **3 rm** ⊇ 22.00/44.00 **st.** – SB.

*La **Grande-Bretagne** et l'**Irlande** sont maintenant couvertes*
*par un **atlas** disponible en trois versions :*
*broché, relié et à spirale.*

---

**DUNOON** Argyll and Bute 𝟰𝟬𝟭 F 16 Scotland G. – pop. 13 781 (inc. Kilmun).
Env. : The Clyde Estuary★.
🏌 Innellan, Knockamillie Rd ℘ (01369) 830242.
🚢 from Dunoon Pier to Gourock Railway Pier (Caledonian MacBrayne Ltd) frequent services daily (20 mn) – from Hunters Quay to McInroy's Point, Gourock (Western Ferries (Clyde) Ltd) frequent services daily (20 mn).
🖪 7 Alexandra Par., PA23 8AB ℘ (01369) 703785 (closed weekends in winter).
Edinburgh 73 – Glasgow 27 – Oban 77.

🏛 **Enmore,** Marine Par., Kirn, PA23 8HH, North : 1 ¼ m. on A 815 ℘ (01369) 702230, Fax (01369) 702148, ≼ Firth of Clyde, ☞, squash – ✜ rest, ⊡ ☎ ◑◐ 匥 𝘝𝘐𝘚𝘈
restricted opening in winter – Meals 12.00/23.00 **st.** and a la carte ⅜ 8.00 – **10 rm** ⊇ 59.00/150.00 **st.** – SB.

🏠 **Anchorage,** Shore Rd, Ardanadam, PA23 8QG, North : 3 m. on A 815 ℘ (01369) 705108, Fax (01369) 705108, ≼, ☞ – ✜ ⊡ & 🅿. ◑◐ 𝘝𝘐𝘚𝘈. ※
Meals a la carte 17.50/21.50 **t.** ⅜ 5.75 – **5 rm** ⊇ 45.00/70.00 **t.**

ⓐ ATS 247 Argyll St. ℘ (01369) 702853

---

**DUNVEGAN** Highland 𝟰𝟬𝟭 A 11 – see Skye (Isle of).

---

**DYCE** Aberdeenshire 𝟰𝟬𝟭 N 12 – see Aberdeen.

---

**EARLSTON** Borders 𝟰𝟬𝟭 𝟰𝟬𝟮 L 17 – pop. 1 968.
Edinburgh 34 – Hawick 22 – Newcastle upon Tyne 71.

⌂ **Birkhill** ⑤, TD4 6AR, North : 3 ¼ m. by A 68 and Birkenside rd on Lauder rd ℘ (01896) 849307, Fax (01896) 848206, ≼, « Georgian country house », ⬚, ☞, park – ✜ 🅿 ◑◐ 𝘝𝘐𝘚𝘈. ※
closed Christmas and New Year – Meals (by arrangement) (communal dining) 22.00 **st.** – **3 rm** ⊇ 43.00/66.00 **st.**

---

**EASDALE** Argyll and Bute 𝟰𝟬𝟭 D 15 – see Seil (Isle of).

**EAST KILBRIDE** South Lanarkshire 401 402 H 16 – pop. 73 378.

🖫 Torrance House, Strathaven Rd ☎ (01355) 248638.

Edinburgh 46 – Ayr 35 – Glasgow 10.

🏫 **Stakis East Kilbride,** Stewartfield Way, G74 5LA, Northwest : 2 ¼ m. on A 7... ☎ (01355) 236300, Fax (01355) 233552, 🛵, 🖙, 🔲 – 🛊 ﹦, 🍴 rest, 📺 ☎ ᴊ 🅿 – 🛦 40... **Point Grill :** Meals (closed Saturday lunch) 20.35 st. and a la carte – **Simpsons :** Mea... (closed Sunday and Monday) (dinner only) 27.50 t. – ☲ 11.50 – **99 rm** 117.00/162.00 s... 2 suites.

🏬 **Bruce,** 35 Cornwall St., G74 1AF, ☎ (01355) 229771, Fax (01355) 242216 – 🛊, ﹦ rm, 📺 ... 🅿 – 🛦 70. 🝿 🆎 ⓪ 𝘝𝘐𝘚𝘈 𝖩𝖢𝖡. 🞿 Meals (bar lunch)/dinner 14.95 st. and a la carte ⛟ 7.95 – **65 rm** ☲ 75.00/95.00 st. – SB.

🏠 **Travel Inn,** Brunel Way, The Murray, G75 0JY, ☎ (01355) 222809, Fax (01355) 230517 ﹦ rm, 📺 ᴊ 🅿. 🝿 🆎 ⓪ 𝘝𝘐𝘚𝘈. 🞿 Meals (grill rest.) – **40 rm** 38.00 t.

🏠 **Peel Park - Lodge Inn,** Eaglesham Rd, G75 8LW, Northwest : 1 ½ m. off A 72 ☎ (01355) 222747, Fax (01355) 234346 – ﹦ rm, 📺 ᴊ 🅿. 🝿 🆎 ⓪ 𝘝𝘐𝘚𝘈. 🞿 Meals (grill rest.) a la carte 9.10/15.75 st. – ☲ 5.50 – **40 rm** 39.00 st. – SB.

# EDINBURGH

**401** K 16 *Scotland G. – pop. 418 914.*

*Glasgow 46 – Newcastle upon Tyne 105.*

## TOURIST INFORMATION

🛈 *Edinburgh & Scotland Information Centre, 3 Princes St., EH2 2QP* ℘ *(0131) 557 1700.*
🛈 *Edinburgh Airport, Tourist Information Desk* ℘ *(0131) 333 2167.*

## PRACTICAL INFORMATION

▣, ▣ *Braid Hills, Braid Hills Rd* ℘ *(0131) 447 6666,* BX.
▣ *Craigmillar Park, 1 Observatory Rd* ℘ *(0131) 667 2837,* BX.
▣ *Carrick Knowe, Glendevon Park* ℘ *(0131) 337 1096,* AX.
▣ *Duddingston, Duddingston Road West* ℘ *(0131) 661 1005,* BV.
▣ *Silverknowes, Parkway* ℘ *(0131) 336 3843,* AV.
▣ *Liberton, 297 Gilmerton Rd* ℘ *(0131) 664 3009,* BX.
▣, ▣ *Dalmahoy Hotel C.C., Kirknewton* ℘ *(0131) 333 4105/1845,* AX.
▣ *Portobello, Stanley St.* ℘ *(0131) 669 4361,* BV.
✈ *Edinburgh Airport :* ℘ *(0131) 333 1000, W : 6 m. by A 8* AV – **Terminal :** *Waverley Bridge.*

## SIGHTS

**See :** *City*★★★ – *Edinburgh International Festival*★★★ *(August)* – *National Gallery of Scotland*★★ DY **M4** – *Royal Botanic Garden*★★★ AV – *The Castle*★★ *AC* DYZ : *Site*★★★ – *Palace Block (Honours of Scotland*★★★ *)* – *St. Margaret's Chapel (*❊★★★*)* – *Great Hall (Hammerbeam Roof*★★*)* – ≼★★ *from Argyle and Mill's Mount* DZ – *Abbey and Palace of Holyroodhouse*★★ *AC (Plasterwork Ceilings*★★★, ❊★★ *from Arthur's Seat)* BV – *Royal Mile*★★ : *St. Giles' Cathedral*★★ *(Crown Spire*★★★*)* EYZ – *Gladstone's Land*★ *AC* EY A – *Canongate Tolbooth*★ EY B – *New Town*★★ *(Charlotte Square*★★★ CY **14** – *Royal Museum of Scotland*★★ EZ **M2** – *The Georgian House*★ *AC* CY D – *Scottish National Portrait Gallery*★ EY **M3** – *Dundas House*★ EY E *)* – *Scottish National Gallery of Modern Art*★ AV **M1** – *Victoria Street*★ EZ **84** – *Scott Monument*★ *(*≼★*) AC* EY F – *Craigmillar Castle*★ *AC* BX – *Calton Hill (*❊★★★ *AC from Nelson's Monument)* EY.

**Env. :** *Edinburgh Zoo*★★ *AC* AV – *Hill End Ski Centre (*❊★★*) AC, S :* 5½ *m. by A 702* BX – *The Royal Observatory (West Tower* ≼★*) AC* BX – *Ingleston, Scottish Agricultural Museum*★, *W :* 6½ *m. by A 8* AV.

**Exc. :** *Rosslyn Chapel*★★ *AC (Apprentice Pillar*★★★ *) S :* 7½ *m. by A 701* – BX – *and B 7006* – *Forth Bridges*★★, *NW :* 9½ *m. by A 90* AV – *Hopetoun House*★★ *AC, NW :* 11½ *m. by A 90* – AV – *and A 904* – *Dalmeny*★ – *Dalmeny House*★ *AC, St. Cuthbert's Church*★ *(Norman South Doorway*★ *) NW : 7 m. by A 90* AV – *Crichton Castle (Italianate courtyard range*★*) AC, SE : 10 m. by A 7* – X – *and B 6372.*

# EDINBURGH
## CENTRE

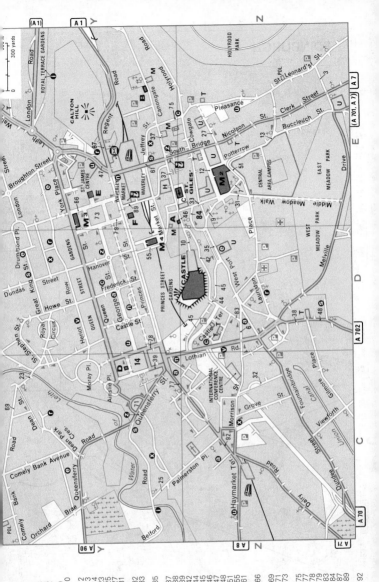

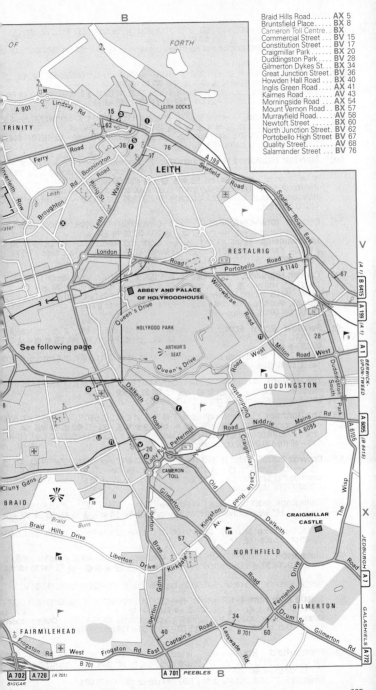

B

OF

FORTH

A 901    Lindsay Rd

TRINITY

LEITH DOCKS

15  a

62

36  S

17

76

LEITH

A 199  Seafield  Road

Ferry

Bonnington  Rd

Road

Leith  Row

Inverleith Row

Broughton

Leith  Walk

Ring St.

water

Seafield  Road  East

V

London

RESTALRIG

B 6415  (A 1)

Road

11 9

A 199  (A 1)

Portobello  Road  A 1140

67

Willowbrae

ABBEY AND PALACE
OF HOLYROODHOUSE

Queen's  Drive

HOLYROOD PARK

Road  West

Milton  Road  West

14

28

9

A 1  BERWICK-UPON-TWEED

See following page

ARTHUR'S
SEAT

Queen's  Drive

9

Road

Duddingston  Park

DUDDINGSTON

S

Dalkeith

Road

Peffermill

Road

Niddrie

Mains  Rd

A 6095

A 6095  (B 6415)

A 6106

8

Craigmillar  Castle  Road

14 9

U

20

V

Lady Rd

CAMERON
TOLL

Old  Dalkeith  Road

The  Wisp

JEDBURGH  A 7

BRAID

Cluny Gdns

18

U

Gilmerton

Liberton

Brae

CRAIGMILLAR
CASTLE

X

Braid  Burn

Braid  Hills  Drive

57

Kingston  Av.

18

NORTHFIELD

GALASHIELS  A 772

18

Liberton  Drive

Kirkgate

Liberton  Gdns

Fernehill  Drive

GILMERTON

Drum  St.

Gilmerton  Rd

A 7

FAIRMILEHEAD

Frogston  Rd

West  Frogston  Rd  East

B 701

40

Captain's  Road

Liberton  Brae

34  B 701

60

Lasswade  Rd

A 702  A 720  (A 701)

BIGGAR

A 701  PEEBLES  B

**Balmoral**, Princes St., EH2 2EQ, ℘ (0131) 556 2414, *Fax (0131) 557 3747*, 🏋, ≘s, 🏊 – 🛗 🚭 ❄ [TV] ☎ ♿ 🚗 – 👥 350. MO AE ① VISA JCB EY
Meals – (see ***Number One*** and ***Hadrian's*** below) – ☕ 15.00 – **168 rm** 180.00/215.00 st
21 suites.

**Caledonian**, Princes St., EH1 2AB, ℘ (0131) 459 9988, *Fax (0131) 225 6632*, 🏋, ≘s, 🏊
🛗, 🚭 rm, ❄ rest, [TV] ☎ 📞 ♿ [P] – 👥 300. MO AE ① VISA. 🐕 CY
***Carriages :*** Meals (bar lunch Sunday) a la carte 28.75/41.00 **st.** 🍷 6.95 – (see also ***La Pom-padour*** below) – ☕ 15.95 – **233 rm** 147.00/315.00 **t.**, 13 suites.

**Sheraton Grand**, 1 Festival Sq., EH3 9SR, ℘ (0131) 229 9131, *Fax (0131) 229 6254*, 🏋
≘s, 🏊 – 🛗, 🚭 rm, ❄ [TV] ☎ 📞 ♿ [P] – 👥 485. MO AE ① VISA JCB. 🐕 CDZ
***Terrace :*** Meals 20.50 **t.** and a la carte – (see also ***Grill Room*** below) – ☕ 15.00 – **244 rm**
190.00/270.00 **t.**, 17 suites – SB.

**Marriott Dalmahoy H. & Country Club** 🔇, Kirknewton, EH27 8EB, Southwest : 7 m
on A 71 ℘ (0131) 333 1845, *Fax (0131) 333 1433*, 🏞, « Part Georgian mansion », 🏋, ≘s, 🏊
⛳18, 🌳, park, 🎾 – 🛗 🚭, ❄ rest, [TV] ☎ ♿ [P] – 👥 400. MO AE ① VISA. 🐕
***Pentland :*** Meals *(closed Sunday lunch)* 15.00/25.00 **st.** and dinner a la carte 🍷 6.00 – ***Long***
***Weekend :*** Meals (grill rest.) a la carte 10.75/19.25 **st.** 🍷 6.00 – **150 rm** ☕ 130.00
145.00 **st.**, 1 suite – SB.

**George Inter-Continental**, 19-21 George St., EH2 2PB, ℘ (0131) 225 1251
*Fax (0131) 226 5644* – 🛗, 🚭 rm, [TV] ☎ – 👥 200. MO AE ① VISA. 🐕 DY
***Le Chambertin :*** Meals *(closed Saturday lunch and Sunday)* a la carte 26.00/37.50 **st**
🍷 12.50 – ***Carvers*** *(℘ (0131) 459 2305)* **: Meals** 16.50/19.50 **st.** and a la carte 🍷 8.50 – ☕
13.85 – **192 rm** 165.00/215.00 **st.**, 3 suites – SB.

**Carlton Highland**, North Bridge St., EH1 1SD, ℘ (0131) 472 3000, *Fax (0131) 556 2691*
🏋, ≘s, 🏊, squash – 🛗, 🚭 rm, ❄ rest, [TV] ☎ ♿ [P] – 👥 350. MO AE ① VISA JCB EY
***Quills :*** Meals *(closed Sunday and Monday)* (dinner only) 25.00 **t.** and a la carte 🍷 8.95 –
***Eureka :*** Meals (carving rest.) 10.95/18.95 **t.** and a la carte 🍷 6.50 – ☕ 12.50 – **193 rm**
119.00/184.00 **st.**, 4 suites – SB.

**Swallow Royal Scot**, 111 Glasgow Rd, EH12 8NF, West : 4 ½ m. on A 8
℘ (0131) 334 9191, *Fax (0131) 316 4507*, 🏋, ≘s, 🏊 – 🛗, 🚭 rm, ❄ rest, [TV] ☎ [P] – 👥 300
MO AE ① VISA
Meals 22.50 **st.** (dinner) and a la carte 22.50/33.00 **st.** 🍷 11.00 – **255 rm** ☕ 110.00/
145.00 **st.**, 4 suites – SB.

**The Howard**, 34 Great King St., EH3 6QH, ℘ (0131) 557 3500, *Fax (0131) 557 6515*, « Georgian town houses » – 🛗 [TV] ☎ [P] – 👥 40. MO AE ① VISA JCB. 🐕 DY s
Meals – (see ***36*** below) – **15 rm** ☕ 130.00/280.00 **st.** – SB.

**The Bonham**, 35 Drumsheugh Gdns., EH3 7RN, ℘ (0131) 226 6050, *Fax (0131) 226 6080*
« Contemporary interior design » – 🛗, 🚭 rm, [TV] ☎ 📞 ♿ – 👥 50. MO AE ① VISA. 🐕
*closed 24 to 28 December* – **Meals** (light lunch)/dinner a la carte 16.00/22.00 **t.** 🍷 8.00 – ☕
4.75 – **46 rm** 120.00/190.00, 2 suites – SB. CY z

**Crowne Plaza**, 80 High St., EH1 1TH, ℘ (0131) 557 9797, *Fax (0131) 557 9789*, 🏋, ≘s, 🏊
– 🛗, 🚭 rm, [TV] ☎ 📞 ♿ [P] – 👥 200. MO AE ① VISA JCB. 🐕 EY z
Meals (buffet Saturday lunch and Sunday) a la carte 16.45/27.70 **st.** – ☕ 13.50 – **229 rm**
170.00/195.00 **st.**, 9 suites.

**Channings**, 12-16 South Learmonth Gdns., EH4 1EZ, ℘ (0131) 315 2226,
*Fax (0131) 332 9631*, « Edwardian town houses » – 🛗 🚭 [TV] ☎ – 👥 35. MO AE ① VISA JCB.
🐕 CY e
Meals (bar lunch Saturday) 14.00/21.00 **t.** and a la carte 🍷 5.50 – **47 rm** ☕ 105.00/
155.00 **st.**, 1 suite – SB.

**Malmaison**, 1 Tower Pl., Leith, EH6 7DB, Northeast : 2 m. by A 900 ℘ (0131) 468 5000,
*Fax (0131) 468 5002*, « Contemporary interior », 🏋 – 🛗 [TV] ☎ ♿ [P] – 👥 55. MO AE ① VISA.
🐕 BV i
Meals - Brasserie - a la carte 20.45/25.25 **t.** 🍷 9.95 – ☕ 10.50 – **60 rm** 95.00/130.00 **st.**

**Thistle King James**, 107 Leith St., EH1 3SW, ℘ (0131) 556 0111, *Fax (0131) 557 5333* –
🛗, 🚭 rm, [TV] ☎ ♿ [P] – 👥 250. MO AE ① VISA JCB. 🐕 EY u
Meals (bar lunch Saturday and Sunday) a la carte approx. 10.95 🍷 5.50 – ***Craig's :*** Meals
9.75/19.50 **st.** and dinner a la carte 🍷 5.50 – ☕ 11.50 – **138 rm** 120.00/170.00 **st.**, 5 suites –
SB.

**Prestonfield House** 🔇, Priestfield Rd, EH16 5UT, ℘ (0131) 668 3346,
*Fax (0131) 668 3976*, 🏞, « Part 17C country house », ⛳18, 🌳, park – 🛗, 🚭 rm, [TV] ☎ 📞 [P] –
👥 650. MO AE ① VISA JCB BX r
Meals 20.00/27.00 **t.** and a la carte 🍷 7.00 – **31 rm** ☕ 185.00/375.00 **t.**

🏛🏛 **Royal Terrace**, 18 Royal Terr., EH7 5AQ, ℰ (0131) 557 3222, *Fax (0131) 557 5334*, « Georgian town houses », ₤₅, ☎, 🏊, 🌳 – 🛗 ↳ 🗹 ☎ – 🔬 80. 🝆 🝍 ① 𝘝𝘐𝘚𝘈. ℀    EY **i**
Meals (light lunch)/dinner 19.50 st. – ☲ 12.50 – **104 rm** 125.00/185.00 st., 3 suites.

🏛🏛 **Forte Posthouse Edinburgh**, Corstorphine Rd, EH12 6UA, West : 3 m. on A 8 ℰ (0131) 334 0390, *Fax (0131) 334 9237* – 🛗 ↳, 🍽 rest, 🗹 ☎ 🄿 – 🔬 120. 🝆 🝍 ①   AV **o**
𝘝𝘐𝘚𝘈 𝙅𝘾𝘽. ℀
Meals a la carte 20.00/30.00 t. – ☲ 10.95 – **295 rm** 99.00 st. – SB.

🏛🏛 **Point**, 34 Bread St., EH3 9AF, ℰ (0131) 221 9919, *Fax (0131) 221 9929* – 🛗, ↳ rm, 🗹 ☎.   DZ **a**
🝆 🝍 ① 𝘝𝘐𝘚𝘈
closed 25 and 26 December – Meals *(closed Sunday)* 7.90/10.90 st. – ☲ 8.00 – **94 rm** 80.00/130.00 st., 1 suite – SB.

🏛 **Edinburgh Residence** without rest., 7 Rothesay Terr., EH3 7RY, ℰ (0131) 226 3380, *Fax (0131) 226 3381*, ≤, « Georgian town houses » – 🗹 ☎ & 🄿. 🝆 🝍 ① 𝘝𝘐𝘚𝘈. ℀
**21 rm** ☲ 175.00/275.00 st., 8 suites.   CY **x**

🏛🏛 **Stakis Edinburgh Grosvenor**, Grosvenor St., EH12 5EF, ℰ (0131) 226 6001, *Fax (0131) 220 2387* – 🛗 🗹 ☎ – 🔬 500. 🝆 🝍 ① 𝘝𝘐𝘚𝘈 𝙅𝘾𝘽. ℀   CZ **a**
Meals (bar lunch Sunday) 13.75 t. and dinner a la carte – ☲ 9.50 – **187 rm** 130.00/170.00 st., 2 suites – SB.

🏛🏛 **Hilton National**, 69 Belford Rd, EH4 3DG, ℰ (0131) 332 2545, *Fax (0131) 332 3805* – 🛗, ↳ rm, 🗹 ☎ & 🄿 – 🔬 130. 🝆 🝍 ① 𝘝𝘐𝘚𝘈   CY **i**
Meals (bar lunch)/dinner 18.50 st. and a la carte ↥ 6.50 – **144 rm** 125.00/190.00 st.

🏛🏛 **Edinburgh Capital Moat House**, Clermiston Rd, EH12 6UG, ℰ (0131) 535 9988, *Fax (0131) 334 9712*, ₤₅, ☎, 🏊 – 🛗 ↳ 🗹 ☎ & 🄿 – 🔬 300. 🝆 🝍 ① 𝘝𝘐𝘚𝘈   AV **n**
Meals (bar lunch)/dinner 12.95 t. and a la carte ↥ 5.75 – ☲ 10.50 – **111 rm** 95.00/125.00 t. – SB.

🏛🏛 **Jarvis Ellersly House**, 4 Ellersly Rd, EH12 6HZ, ℰ (0131) 337 6888, *Fax (0131) 313 2543*, 🌳 – 🛗 ↳ 🗹 ☎ 🄿 – 🔬 70. 🝆 🝍 ① 𝘝𝘐𝘚𝘈   AV **v**
Meals *(closed Saturday lunch)* 10.95/14.95 t. and a la carte ↥ 7.00 – ☲ 8.50 – **57 rm** 115.00/135.00 t. – SB.

🏛 **Simpsons** without rest., 79 Lauriston Pl., EH3 9HZ, ℰ (0131) 622 7979, *Fax (0131) 622 7900* – 🛗 ↳ 🗹 ☎ &. 🝆 🝍 ① 𝘝𝘐𝘚𝘈 𝙅𝘾𝘽. ℀   DZ **r**
**57 rm** 80.00/100.00 st., 1 suite.

🏛 **Holiday Inn Garden Court**, 107 Queensferry Rd, EH4 3HL, ℰ (0131) 332 2442, *Fax (0131) 332 3408*, ≤, ₤₅ – 🛗 ↳, 🍽 rest, 🗹 ☎ & 🄿 – 🔬 60. 🝆 🝍 ① 𝘝𝘐𝘚𝘈 𝙅𝘾𝘽
Meals (carving lunch)/dinner 15.50 st. and a la carte – ☲ 10.50 – **118 rm** 95.00/126.00 st., 1 suite.   AV **x**

🏛 **Apex International**, 31-35 Grassmarket, EH1 2HS, ℰ (0131) 300 3456, *Fax (0131) 220 5345* – 🛗, ↳ rm, 🍽 rest, 🗹 ☎ 📞 🄿 – 🔬 225. 🝆 🝍 ① 𝘝𝘐𝘚𝘈. ℀   DZ **e**
Meals (bar lunch)/dinner 11.00 st. – ☲ 6.95 – **175 rm** 89.95 st.

🏛 **Frederick House** without rest., 42 Frederick St., EH2 1EX, ℰ (0131) 226 1999, *Fax (0131) 624 7064* – 🛗 🗹 ☎ 📞. 🝆 🝍 ① 𝘝𝘐𝘚𝘈 𝙅𝘾𝘽. ℀   DY **a**
**45 rm** ☲ 40.00/130.00 st.

🏛 **Apex European**, 90 Haymarket Terr., EH12 5LQ, ℰ (0131) 474 3456, *Fax (0131) 474 3400* – 🛗, ↳ rm, 🗹 ☎ 📞 & – 🔬 70. 🝆 🝍 ① 𝘝𝘐𝘚𝘈. ℀   CZ **u**
Meals 9.90/11.00 st. and lunch a la carte – ☲ 7.95 – **66 rm** 79.95 st.

🏛 **Parliament House** without rest., 15 Calton Hill, EH1 3BJ, ℰ (0131) 478 4000, *Fax (0131) 478 4001* – 🛗 🗹 ☎ 📞. 🝆 🝍 ① 𝘝𝘐𝘚𝘈. ℀   EY **r**
☲ 11.50 **53 rm** 95.00/160.00 st.

🏛 **Maitland** without rest., 23-33 Shandwick Pl., EH2 4RG, ℰ (0131) 229 1467, *Fax (0131) 229 7549* – 🛗 ↳ 🗹 ☎. 🝆 🝍 ① 𝘝𝘐𝘚𝘈 𝙅𝘾𝘽. ℀   CY **a**
**65 rm** ☲ 75.00/135.00 st.

🏛 **Jurys Edinburgh Inn**, 43 Jeffrey St., EH1 1DG, ℰ (0131) 200 3300, *Fax (0131) 200 0400* – 🛗, ↳ rm, 🗹 ☎ 📞 & – 🔬 50. 🝆 🝍 ① 𝘝𝘐𝘚𝘈. ℀   EY **x**
closed 4 days ChristmasMeals (bar lunch)/dinner 15.00 and a la carte ↥ 4.75 – ☲ 7.00 – **186 rm** 80.00/90.00 t.

🏠 **Albany**, 39 Albany St., EH1 3QY, ℰ (0131) 556 0397, *Fax (0131) 557 6633*, « Georgian town houses », 🌳 – 🗹 ☎ 𝘝𝘐𝘚𝘈   EY **e**
closed 25 December – Meals – (see ***Haldanes*** below) – ☲ 11.50 – **21 rm** 85.00/180.00 st.

🏠 **Kildonan Lodge**, 27 Craigmillar Park, EH16 5PE, ℰ (0131) 667 2793, *Fax (0131) 667 9777* – ↳ 🗹 🄿. 🝆 🝍 ① 𝘝𝘐𝘚𝘈 𝙅𝘾𝘽. ℀   BX **a**
closed 25 December – Meals (dinner only) a la carte 11.50/18.75 st. ↥ 4.50 – **12 rm** ☲ 45.00/90.00 st. – SB.

🏠 **Greenside**, 9 Royal Terr., EH7 5AB, ℰ (0131) 557 0022, *Fax (0131) 557 0022*, « Georgia town house », ℛ – 🔟 🕿 🐾 🐠 🖭 ⓪ *VISA* ﹒ʝᴄʙ﹒
EY
**Meals** (bar lunch)/dinner 13.00 st. ᵛ 7.00 – **14 rm** ⌑ 25.00/60.00 st.

🏠 **Ailsa Craig**, 24 Royal Terr., EH7 5AH, ℰ (0131) 556 6055, *Fax (0131) 556 6055*, « Georgia town house », ℛ – 🔟 🕿 🐾 🐠 🖭 ⓪ *VISA* ﹒ᛪ
EY
**Meals** (bar lunch)/dinner 13.50 st. – **17 rm** ⌑ 50.00/90.00 st. – SB.

🏠 **Lodge**, 6 Hampton Terr., West Coates, EH12 5JD, ℰ (0131) 337 3682, *Fax (0131) 313 17(* – 🔟 🕿 🅿 🐠 *VISA* ﹒ᛪ
AV
*closed 11 to 26 December* – **Meals** *(closed Sunday)* (booking essential) (residents on (dinner only) 14.50 t. ᵛ 4.95 – **9 rm** ⌑ 40.00/80.00 t.

🏠 **Travel Inn**, 1 Morrison Link, EH3 8DN, ℰ (0131) 228 9819, *Fax (0131) 228 9836* – ┇ ᛪ ☰ rest, 🔟 🕭 🅿 🐠 *VISA* ﹒ᛪ
CZ
**Meals** (grill rest.) – **128 rm** 38.00 t.

🏠 **Travel Inn**, 228 Willowbrae Rd, EH8 7NG, ℰ (0131) 661 3396, *Fax (0131) 652 2789* ᛪ rm, 🔟 🕭 🅿 🐠 *VISA* ﹒ᛪ
BV
**Meals** (grill rest.) – **39 rm** 38.00 t.

🏠 **Travelodge**, 48 Dreghorn Link, City Bypass, EH13 9QR, ℰ (0131) 441 429( *Fax (0131) 441 4296*, Reservations (Freephone) 0800 850950 – ᛪ rm, 🔟 🕭 🅿 🐠 🖭 *VISA* ʝᴄʙ﹒ᛪ
AX
**Meals** (grill rest.) – **40 rm** 39.95/59.95 t.

↑ **Sibbet House** without rest., 26 Northumberland St., EH3 6LS, ℰ (0131) 556 1078 *Fax (0131) 557 9445*, « Georgian town house » – ᛪ 🔟 🕿 🐾 🐠 *VISA* ﹒ᛪ
DY
**4 rm** ⌑ 65.00/100.00, 1 suite.

↑ **27 Heriot Row** without rest., 27 Heriot Row, EH3 6EN, ℰ (0131) 225 947( *Fax (0131) 220 1699*, « Georgian town house », ℛ – ᛪ 🔟 🕿 🐾 🐠 *VISA* ﹒ᛪ
DY
**3 rm** ⌑ 50.00/100.00 st.

↑ **Drummond House** without rest., 17 Drummond Pl., EH3 6PL, ℰ (0131) 557 918( *Fax (0131) 557 9189*, « Georgian town house » – ᛪ 🐠 *VISA* ﹒ᛪ
DY
*closed Christmas and restricted opening in winter* – **4 rm** ⌑ 75.00/110.00 t.

↑ **17 Abercromby Place** without rest., 17 Abercromby Pl., EH3 6LB, ℰ (0131) 557 803( *Fax (0131) 558 3453*, « Georgian town house » – ᛪ 🔟 🕿 🅿 🐠 *VISA* ﹒ᛪ
DY
**7 rm** ⌑ 60.00/100.00 t.

↑ **Number Two Saxe Coburg Place** without rest., 2 Saxe Coburg Pl., EH3 5BR ℰ (0131) 315 4752, *Fax (0131) 332 4934*, « Georgian town house », ℛ – ᛪ 🔟 🕿 🐾 🐠 *VISA* ﹒ᛪ
BV
**3 rm** ⌑ 50.00/90.00 st.

↑ **Saxe Coburg House** without rest., 24 Saxe Coburg Pl., EH3 5BP, ℰ (0131) 332 271( *Fax (0131) 315 3375*, « Georgian town house » – ᛪ 🔟 🕿 🐠 🖭 *VISA* ﹒ᛪ
BV
*closed 25 and 26 December* – **5 rm** ⌑ 45.00/90.00 st.

↑ **The Stuarts** without rest., 17 Glengyle Terr., EH3 9LN, ℰ (0131) 229 9559 *Fax (0131) 229 2226* – ᛪ 🔟 🕿 🐾 🐠 🖭 *VISA* ﹒ᛪ
DZ
*closed 1 week Christmas* – **3 rm** ⌑ 60.00/90.00 t.

↑ **16 Lynedoch Place** without rest., EH3 7PY, ℰ (0131) 225 5507, *Fax (0131) 226 4185* « Georgian town house », ℛ – ᛪ 🔟 🐾 🐠 *VISA*
CY
**3 rm** ⌑ 35.00/80.00 st.

↑ **Seven Danube Street** without rest., EH4 1NN, ℰ (0131) 332 2755, *Fax (0131) 343 3648*, « Georgian town house », ℛ – ᛪ 🔟 🕿 🐾 🐠 *VISA* ʝᴄʙ *closed Christmas* – **3 rm** ⌑ 50.00/90.00 s.
CY

↑ **Kew House** without rest., 1 Kew Terr., Murrayfield, EH12 5JE, ℰ (0131) 313 0700, *Fax (0131) 313 0747* – ᛪ 🔟 🕿 🅿 🐠 🖭 *VISA* ʝᴄʙ
AV
**6 rm** ⌑ 42.00/82.00 st.

↑ **22 Murrayfield Gardens** without rest., EH12 6DF, ℰ (0131) 337 3569, *Fax (0131) 337 3803*, « Victorian house », ℛ – ᛪ 🅿 🐠 *VISA*
AV
*closed 1 week Christmas* – **3 rm** ⌑ 45.00/80.00 st.

↑ **Teviotdale** without rest., 53 Grange Loan, EH9 2ER, ℰ (0131) 667 4376, *Fax (0131) 667 4376* – ᛪ 🔟 🕿 🐾 🐠 🖭 *VISA* ʝᴄʙ﹒ᛪ
BX
*closed 22 to 26 December* – **7 rm** ⌑ 45.00/70.00 st.

↑ **Stuart House** without rest., 12 East Claremont St., EH7 4JP, ℰ (0131) 557 9030, *Fax (0131) 557 0563* – ᛪ 🔟 🕿 🐠 🖭 *VISA* ʝᴄʙ﹒ᛪ
BV
**7 rm** ⌑ 40.00/90.00 st.

↑ **Ben-Craig House** without rest., 3 Craigmillar Park, EH16 5PG, ℰ (0131) 667 2593, ℛ – 🔟 ﹒ᛪ
BX
**5 rm** ⌑ 35.00/72.00 s.

↑ **Dorstan**, 7 Priestfield Rd, EH16 5HJ, ℰ (0131) 667 6721, *Fax (0131) 668 4644* – 🔟 🕿 🅿 🐠 🖭 *VISA* ﹒ᛪ
BX
**Meals** (by arrangement) 16.00 t. – **14 rm** ⌑ 39.00/80.00 t.

⛫ **Classic** without rest., 50 Mayfield Rd, EH9 2NH, ☎ (0131) 667 5847, *Fax (0131) 662 1016 –*
✦ 🗺 ⛌ 🆎 ⑩ 🆚 ⚓
BX **n**
7 rm ⇆ 28.00/60.00 st.

XXXX **Number One** (at Balmoral H.), 1 Princes St., EH2 2EQ, ☎ (0131) 556 6727,
*Fax (0131) 557 3747 –* ⛌ 🆎 ⑩ 🆚 J꜀ʙ
EY **n**
*closed lunch Saturday and Sunday –* **Meals** 18.00/32.00 t. and a la carte ⌀ 11.00.

XXXX **La Pompadour** (at Caledonian H.), Princes St., EH1 2AB, ☎ (0131) 459 9988,
*Fax (0131) 225 6632 –* ⓟ. ⛌ 🆎 ⑩ 🆚 J꜀ʙ
CY **n**
*closed Sunday and Monday –* **Meals** (dinner only) a la carte 29.50/43.50 t. ⌀ 9.25.

XXX **Grill Room** (at Sheraton Grand H.), 1 Festival Sq., EH3 9SR, ☎ (0131) 221 6423,
*Fax (0131) 229 6254 –* 🗖 ⓟ. ⛌ 🆎 ⑩ 🆚 J꜀ʙ
CDZ **v**
*closed Saturday lunch and Sunday –* **Meals** 27.50/35.50 st. and a la carte ⌀ 10.00.

XX **Bonars,** 56 St. Mary's St., EH1 1SX, ☎ (0131) 556 5888, *Fax (0131) 556 2588 –* ✦ 🗖. ⛌ 🆎
⑩ 🆚
EYZ **c**
**Meals** 14.95/24.95 t. and a la carte ⌀ 5.80.

XX **Martins,** 70 Rose St., North Lane, EH2 3DX, ☎ (0131) 225 3106 – ⛌. ⛌ 🆎 ⑩ 🆚
J꜀ʙ
DY **n**
*closed Saturday lunch, Sunday, Monday, 1 week in spring, 1 week in autumn, and 24
December-20 January –* **Meals** (booking essential) a la carte 18.55/33.00 t. ⌀ 6.00.

XX **Hadrian's** (at Balmoral H.), 2 North Bridge, EH1 1TR, ☎ (0131) 557 5000,
*Fax (0131) 557 3747 –* 🗖. ⛌ 🆎 ⑩ 🆚 J꜀ʙ
EY **n**
**Meals** a la carte 14.50/18.50 t.

XX **36** (at The Howard H.), 36 Great King St., EH3 6QH, ☎ (0131) 556 3636, *Fax (0131) 556 3663,*
« Contemporary decor » – ✦ 🗖 ⓟ. ⛌ 🆎 ⑩ 🆚 J꜀ʙ
DY **s**
*closed Saturday lunch –* **Meals** 14.00 t. (lunch) and dinner a la carte 20.50/27.50 t. ⌀ 6.00.

XX **(fitz)Henry,** 19 Shore Pl., Leith, EH6 6SW, ☎ (0131) 555 6625, *Fax (0131) 554 6216,* « Part
17C warehouse » – ⛌ 🆎 🆚
BV **s**
*closed Sunday, 25, 26 and 31 December and 1 January –* **Meals** 15.00/22.00-27.00 t. ⌀ 8.50.

XX **Haldanes** (at Albany H.), 39A Albany St., EH1 3QY, ☎ (0131) 556 8407, 🌣 – ✦. ⛌ 🆎 ⑩
🆚 J꜀ʙ
EY **e**
*closed Saturday and Sunday lunch –* **Meals** 12.50/25.25 t. ⌀ 7.00.

XX **The Rock,** 78 Commercial St., Leith, EH6 6LX, ☎ (0131) 555 2225, *Fax (0131) 555 1116 –*
ⓟ. ⛌ 🆚
BV **a**
*closed 25 December and 1-2 January –* **Meals** 12.75 t. (lunch) and dinner a la carte 17.50/
28.50 t. ⌀ 4.90.

XX **Vintners Room,** The Vaults, 87 Giles St., Leith, EH6 6BZ, ☎ (0131) 554 6767,
*Fax (0131) 467 7130 –* ✦. ⛌ 🆎 🆚
BV **r**
*closed Sunday and 2 weeks Christmas-New Year –* **Meals** 14.50 t. (lunch) and dinner a la carte 23.25/30.75 t. ⌀ 5.00.

XX **The Marque,** 19-21 Causewayside, EH9 1QF, ☎ (0131) 466 6660, *Fax (0131) 466 6661 –*
⛌ 🆚
BX **s**
*closed Monday, 25-26 December and 1 to 7 January –* **Meals** 14.50 t. (lunch) and dinner a la carte 19.25/25.75 t. ⌀ 6.00.

XX **Kelly's,** 46 West Richmond St., EH8 9DZ, ☎ (0131) 668 3847, *Fax (0131) 668 3847 –* ✦. ⛌
🆚
EZ **u**
*closed Sunday to Tuesday, 25-26 December and 1 January –* **Meals** 15.00/25.00 t. ⌀ 7.50.

XX **Yumi,** 2 West Coates, EH12 5JQ, ☎ (0131) 337 2173, *Fax (0131) 337 2818 –* ✦ ⓟ. ⛌ ⑩
🆚 J꜀ʙ
AV **e**
*closed Sunday and Christmas-New Year –* **Meals** - Japanese - (dinner only) 23.00 t.
and a la carte ⌀ 5.00.

X **Atrium,** 10 Cambridge St., EH1 2ED, ☎ (0131) 228 8882, *Fax (0131) 228 8808 –* 🗖. ⛌ 🆎
⑩ 🆚
DZ **c**
*closed Sunday and 1 week Christmas –* **Meals** a la carte 16.50/30.00 t. ⌀ 10.50.

X **Est, Est, Est,** 135 George St., EH2 4JS, ☎ (0131) 225 2555, *Fax (0131) 226 6103,* 🌣 – 🗖.
⛌ 🆎 ⑩ 🆚
DY **u**
*closed 25 December –* **Meals** - Italian - a la carte 13.50/18.00 t. ⌀ 5.50.

X **Café Saint-Honoré,** 34 North West Thistle Street Lane, EH2 1EA, ☎ (0131) 226 2211 –
✦. ⛌ 🆎 ⑩ 🆚 J꜀ʙ
DY **c**
*closed Saturday lunch, Sunday, 4 days Christmas, 4 days New Year, 2 weeks Easter and 1
week October –* **Meals** (booking essential) a la carte 17.55/28.90 t. ⌀ 9.00.

X **Daniels Bistro,** 88 Commercial St., Leith, EH6 6LX, ☎ (0131) 553 5933,
*Fax (0131) 553 3966 –* ⓟ. ⛌ 🆚
BV **a**
*closed 25 December and 1 January –* **Meals** 6.45 t. (lunch) and a la carte 10.95/17.80 t.
⌀ 5.45.

X **Blue,** 10 Cambridge St., EH1 2ED, ☎ (0131) 221 1222, *Fax (0131) 228 8808 –* 🗖. ⛌ 🆎 ⑩
🆚 J꜀ʙ
DZ **c**
**Meals** a la carte 16.00/20.00 t.

**at Bonnyrigg** *(Midlothian) Southeast : 8 m. by A 7 on A 6094 – BX – ⊠ Edinburgh.*

  🏬 **Dalhousie Castle** ⊗, EH19 3JB, Southeast : 1 ¼ m. on B 704 *℘ (01875) 820153,*
*Fax (01875) 821936,* ≤, « Part 13C and 15C castle with Victorian additions », *☞ – ↭ 🆃🆅 ☎*
**℗ – 🔬** 120. **🗭🗭 🗚🗉 ⓪ 𝘝𝘐𝘚𝘈 𝙹𝙲𝘉.** ⅏
*closed mid-late January –* **Dungeon :** Meals (booking essential to non-residents) 25.50 s*
(dinner) and a la carte 15.00/21.50 ▯ 7.50 – **34 rm** ⊇ 125.00/200.00 st., 1 suite – SB.

**at Edinburgh International Airport** *West : 7½ m. by A 8 – AV – ⊠ Edinburgh.*

  🏬 **Stakis Edinburgh Airport,** EH28 8LL, *℘ (0131) 519 4400, Fax (0131) 519 4422 – ▮*
↭ rm, ▤ rest, 🆃🆅 ☎ & ℗ – 🔬 220. **🗭🗭 🗚🗉 ⓪ 𝘝𝘐𝘚𝘈**
**Meals** (grill rest.) 5.95/14.00 **st.** and a la carte – ⊇ 9.75 – **134 rm** 130.00/170.00 **st.** – SB.

**at Ingliston** *West : 7¾ m. on A 8 – AV – ⊠ Edinburgh.*

  🏬 **Norton House** ⊗, EH28 8LX, on A 8 *℘ (0131) 333 1275, Fax (0131) 333 5305,* ≤, *☞*
↭ rm, 🆃🆅 ☎ ℗ – 🔬 300. **🗭🗭 🗚🗉 ⓪ 𝘝𝘐𝘚𝘈.** ⅏
**Meals** *(closed Saturday lunch)* 26.00 **t.** (dinner) and a la carte approx. 28.00 **t.** ▯ 7.50
**46 rm** ⊇ 120.00/165.00 **t.,** 1 suite – SB.

    🛢 ATS 167 Bonnington Rd, Leith *℘ (0131) 554 6617*     ATS 6 Gylemuir Rd, Corstorphine
                                               *℘ (0131) 334 6174*

---

**EDINBURGH INTERNATIONAL AIRPORT** *Edinburgh City* 🗺🗺🗺 *J 16 – see Edinburgh.*

---

**EDZELL** *Angus* 🗺🗺🗺 *M 13 Scotland G. – pop. 830.*
    Env. : *Castle★ AC (The Pleasance★★★) W : 2 m.*
    Exc. : *Glen Esk★, NW : 7 m.*
    *Edinburgh 94 – Aberdeen 36 – Dundee 31.*

  🏛 **Glenesk,** High St., DD9 7TF, *℘ (01356) 648319, Fax (01356) 647333,* ▮♣, ⊛, ◨, *☞ – ▯*
☎ ℗ – 🔬 150. **🗭🗭 🗚🗉 ⓪ 𝘝𝘐𝘚𝘈 𝙹𝙲𝘉**
**Meals** 16.00/12.50 **st.** and a la carte ▯ 4.50 – **23 rm** ⊇ 50.00/82.00 **st.** – SB.

---

**ELGIN** *Moray* 🗺🗺🗺 *K 11 Scotland G. – pop. 11 855.*
    See : *Town★ – Cathedral★ (Chapter house★★)AC.*
    Exc. : *Glenfiddich Distillery★, SE : 10 m. by A 941.*
    ▮◨, ▮◨ *Moray, Stotfield Rd, Lossiemouth ℘ (01343) 812018 –* ▮◨ *Hardhillock, Birnie R*
    *℘ (01343) 542338 –* ▮◨ *Hopeman, Moray ℘ (01343) 830578.*
    🅱 *17 High St., IV30 1EG ℘ (01343) 542666.*
    *Edinburgh 198 – Aberdeen 68 – Fraserburgh 61 – Inverness 39.*

  🏬 **Mansion House,** The Haugh, IV30 1AW, via Haugh Rd and Murdocks Wyn
    *℘ (01343) 548811, Fax (01343) 547916,* ▮♣, ⊛, ◨, *☞ – ↭* rest, 🆃🆅 ☎ ℗ – 🔬 200. **🗭🗭 ▮**
    **⓪ 𝘝𝘐𝘚𝘈 𝙹𝙲𝘉.** ⅏
    **Meals** 12.95/25.00 **t.** and a la carte – **23 rm** ⊇ 80.00/150.00 **st.** – SB.

  🏛 **Mansefield House,** 2 Mayne Rd, IV30 1NY, *℘ (01343) 540883, Fax (01343) 552491 –*
    ↭ 🆃🆅 ☎ ℗. **🗭🗭 𝘝𝘐𝘚𝘈.** ⅏
    **Meals** a la carte 18.50/25.00 **t.** ▯ 6.20 – **21 rm** ⊇ 55.00/80.00 **t.** – SB.

  🏠 **Travel Inn,** Linkwood Industrial Estate, East Rd, IV30 1XB, *℘ (01343) 55074*
    *Fax (01343) 540635 –* ↭ rm, 🆃🆅 & ℗. **🗭🗭 🗚🗉 ⓪ 𝘝𝘐𝘚𝘈**
    **Meals** (grill rest.) – **40 rm** 38.00 **t.**

  ⌂ **Lodge,** 20 Duff Av., IV30 1QS, *℘ (01343) 549981,* *☞ –* ↭ 🆃🆅 ℗. **🗭🗭 𝘝𝘐𝘚𝘈.** ⅏
    **Meals** (by arrangement) 20.00 **s.** – **8 rm** ⊇ 25.00/45.00 **s.**

    🛢 ATS Moycroft *℘ (01343) 546333*

---

**ELIE** *Fife* 🗺🗺🗺 *L 15 Scotland G. – pop. 903.*
    Env. : *The East Neuk★★.*
    Exc. : *Kellie Castle★, NE : 9 m. by A 917, B 942, B 9171 and minor roads.*
    *Edinburgh 41 – Dundee 29 – Dunfermline 29.*

  XX **Bouquet Garni,** 51 High St., KY9 1BZ, *℘ (01333) 330374, Fax (01333) 330374 –* **🗭🗭 𝘝𝘐𝘚𝘈**
    *closed Monday lunch, Sunday, 25-26 December, 1-2 January, last 2 weeks January and thi*
    *week November –* **Meals** a la carte 15.70/28.70 **t.** ▯ 4.90.

---

**ERBUSAIG** *Highland* 🗺🗺🗺 *C 12 Scotland G. – ⊠ Kyle of Lochalsh.*
    Env. : *Wester Ross★★★.*
    *Skye Bridge (toll).*
    *Edinburgh 206 – Dundee 184 – Inverness 84 – Oban 127.*

XX **Old Schoolhouse** ॐ with rm, IV40 8BB, ℰ (01599) 534369, Fax (01599) 534369, ☞ –
✤ rest, ⊤⊻ ℗. ⬤❸ Æ VISA JCB. ✸
*April-October* – **Meals** (booking essential) (dinner only) a la carte 18.60/25.60 t. ₰ 4.75 –
**3 rm** ⊇ 35.00/52.00 **t.**

---

**ERISKA (Isle of)** *Argyll and Bute* 401 D 14 – ⊠ Oban.

血血 **Isle of Eriska** ॐ, Ledaig, PA37 1SD, ℰ (01631) 720371, Fax (01631) 720531, ≤ Lismore
and mountains, « 19C Scots Baronial mansion, private island setting », ₭, 🖒, ☒, 🖑, ⚲,
☞, park, ※ – ✤ rest, ⊤⊻ ☎ 𝒞 ᐔ ℗. ⬤❸ VISA
*closed January* – **Meals** (booking essential) (bar lunch residents only)/dinner 37.50 **st.** ₰ 4.50
– **17 rm** ⊇ 165.00/250.00 **st.**

---

**FAIRLIE** *North Ayrshire* 401 402 F 16.
*Edinburgh 75 – Ayr 50 – Glasgow 36.*

X **Fins,** Fencebay Fisheries, Fencefoot Farm, KA29 0EG, South : 1 ½ m. on A 78
ℰ (01475) 568989, Fax (01475) 568921 – ℗. ⬤❸ Æ ⓞ VISA JCB
*closed Sunday dinner and Monday* – **Meals** - Seafood - (booking essential) a la carte 13.85/
24.85 **t.** ₰ 7.50.

---

**FALKIRK** 401 I 16 – *pop. 42 353.*

🏌 Grangemouth, Polmonthill ℰ (01324) 711500 – 🏌 Polmont, Manuel Rigg, Maddiston
ℰ (01324) 711277.
🛈 2-4 Glebe St., SK1 1HU ℰ (01324) 620244.
*Edinburgh 26 – Dunfermline 18 – Glasgow 25 – Motherwell 27 – Perth 43.*

🏨 **Park,** Camelon Rd, FK1 5RY, West : ¼ m. on A 803 ℰ (01324) 628331, Fax (01324) 611593 –
🛏, ✤ rm, ⊤⊻ ☎ ℗ – 🔏 300. ⬤❸ Æ ⓞ VISA
**Meals** 8.50/18.50 **st.** and a la carte ₰ 5.25 – ⊇ 9.50 – **55 rm** 75.00/115.00 **st.** – SB.

**at Polmont** *Southeast : 3 m. on A 803.*

血血 **Inchyra Grange,** Grange Rd, FK2 0YB, via Kirk Entry Boness Rd ℰ (01324) 711911,
Fax (01324) 716134, ₭, 🖒, ☒, ☞, park, ※ – 🛏 ✤, ⊟ rest, ⊤⊻ ☎ ᐔ ℗ – 🔏 500. ⬤❸ Æ
ⓞ VISA. ✸
*Priory :* **Meals** *(closed Saturday lunch)* 16.50/32.50 **st.** and dinner a la carte ₰ 6.25 – ⊇
10.50 – **108 rm** 98.00/120.00 **t.**, 1 suite – SB.

 @ ATS Burnbank Rd ℰ (01324) 622958

---

**FASNACLOICH** *Argyll and Bute* – ⊠ Appin.
*Edinburgh 133 – Fort William 34 – Oban 19.*

↑ **Lochside Cottage** ॐ, PA38 4BJ, ℰ (01631) 730216, Fax (01631) 730216, ≤ Loch Baile
Mhic Chailen and mountains, « Lochside setting », ☞ – ✤ ⊤⊻ ℗. ✸
**Meals** (by arrangement) (communal dining) 17.00 **t.** – **3 rm** ⊇ 21.00/56.00 **s.**

---

**FIONNPHORT** *Argyll and Bute* 401 A 15 – *Shipping Services : see Mull (Isle of).*

---

**FLODIGARRY** *Highland* 401 B 11 – *see Skye (Isle of).*

---

**FORFAR** *Angus* 401 L 14 *Scotland G.* – *pop. 14 159.*
Env. : Aberlemno Stones★, NE : 5 m. by B 9134.
Exc. : Brechin (Round Tower★), NE : 9½ m. by B 9134.
🏌 Cunninghill, Arbroath Rd ℰ (01307) 462120.
🛈 40 East High St., ℰ (01307) 467876 (summer only).
*Edinburgh 75 – Aberdeen 55 – Dundee 12 – Perth 31.*

🏛 **Chapelbank House,** 69 East High St., DD8 2EP, ℰ (01307) 463151, Fax (01307) 461922 –
✤ ⊤⊻ ☎ ℗. ⬤❸ Æ VISA. ✸
**Meals** *(closed Sunday dinner and Monday)* 19.95 **t.** ₰ 6.00 – **4 rm** ⊇ 55.00/82.00 **t.**

↑ **Finavon Farmhouse,** Finavon, DD8 3PX, Northeast : 5 ½ m. by B 9128 off A 90
ℰ (01307) 850269, Fax (01307) 850269, ☞ – ⊤⊻ ℗
*March-October* – **Meals** (by arrangement) (communal dining) 9.50 **t.** – **3 rm** ⊇ 26.00/
42.00.

 @ ATS Queenswell Rd ℰ (01307) 464501

701

**FORRES** *Moray* **401** *J 11 Scotland G.* – *pop. 5 559.*

Env. : *Sueno's Stone*★★, *N : ½ m. by A 940 on A 96* – *Brodie Castle*★ *AC, W : 3 m. by A 96.*
Exc. : – *Elgin*★ *(Cathedral*★, *chapter house*★★ *AC), E : 10¼m. by A 96.*
☒ *Muiryshade* ℘ *(01309) 672949.*
☐ *116 High St., IV6 0NP* ℘ *(01309) 672938 (summer only).*
*Edinburgh 165 – Aberdeen 80 – Inverness 27.*

🏠 **Knockomie** ⤵, *Grantown Rd, IV36 0SG, South : 1 ½ m. on A 940* ℘ *(01309) 673146*
*Fax (01309) 673290, ☞, park –* ⁕⊷ *rest,* 📺 ☎ ♿ ♗ – 🔏 *50.* 🏧 ℳ ℡ *VISA* 𝙅𝙲𝘽
*closed 24 to 26 December and 30 December-2 January –* **Meals** *28.00* t. *(din ner) and a la carte 11.50/29.35* t. ↑ *9.50 –* **14 rm** �).☐ *74.00/150.00* t., *1 suite – SB.*

🏠 **Ramnee**, *Victoria Rd, IV36 0BN,* ℘ *(01309) 672410, Fax (01309) 673392, ☞ –* 📺 ☎ ♿ –
🔏 *100.* ℳ ℡ ① *VISA* 𝙅𝙲𝘽
*closed 1 to 3 January –* **Meals** *12.50/25.00* t. *and dinner a la carte* ↑ *5.00 –* **20 rm** ☐ *60.00*
*120.00* t. – *SB.*

---

**FORT WILLIAM** *Highland* **401** *E 13 Scotland G.* – *pop. 10 391.*

See : *Town*★.
Exc. : *The Road to the Isles*★★ *(Neptune's Staircase (≤★★), Glenfinnan*★ *≤★, Arisaig*★, *Silve Sands of Morar*★, *Mallaig*★*), NW : 46 m. by A 830* – *Ardnamurchan Peninsula*★★ – *Arc namurchan Point (≤★★), NW : 65 m. by A 830, A 861 and B 8007* – *SE : Ben Nevis*★★ *(≤★★) Glen Nevis*★.
☒ *North Rd* ℘ *(01397) 704464.*
☐ *Cameron Centre, Cameron Sq., PH33 6AJ* ℘ *(01397) 703781.*
*Edinburgh 133 – Glasgow 104 – Inverness 68 – Oban 50.*

🏛 **Inverlochy Castle** ⤵, *Torlundy, PH33 6SN, Northeast : 3 m. on A 82* ℘ *(01397) 702177*
❀ *Fax (01397) 702953,* ≤ *loch and mountains,* « *Victorian castle in extensive park* », ⤚, ☞
⁕⊷ *rest,* 📺 ☎ ♿ ♗ ℳ ℡ *VISA* ⁕⊷
*closed 4 January-12 February –* **Meals** *(dinner booking essential to non-residents) 28.00*
*50.00* t. ↑ *15.50 –* **16 rm** ☐ *215.00/340.00* t., *1 suite – SB*
**Spec.** *Crab with horseradish potatoes and crushed avocado. Roast breast of duck with caramelised apple and cinnamon scented jus. Roasted white peach with caramel and nu sauce.*

🏠 **Travel Inn,** *An Aird, PH33 6AN, Northwest : ½ m. by A 82* ℘ *(01397) 703707*
*Fax (01397) 703618 –* ▯, ⁕⊷ *rm,* ▤ *rest,* 📺 ♿ ♗. ℳ ℡ ① *VISA*
**Meals** *(grill rest.) –* **40 rm** *38.00* t.

🏠 **Distillery House** *without rest., Nevis Bridge, North Rd, PH33 6LR,* ℘ *(01397) 700103*
*Fax (01397) 702980 –* 📺 ☎ ♗. ℳ ℡ *VISA*
*closed 25 December –* *16.00* st. – **7 rm** ☐ *35.00/70.00* st.

⌂ **The Grange** ⤵ *without rest., Grange Rd, PH33 6JF, South : ¾ m. by A 82 and Ashburr Lane* ℘ *(01397) 705516, Fax (01397) 701595,* ≤, ☞ – ⁕⊷ 📺 ♗. ⁕⊷
*Easter-November –* **4 rm** ☐ *80.00/90.00.*

⌂ **Crolinnhe** *without rest., Grange Rd, PH33 6JF, by Ashburn Lane* ℘ *(01397) 702709,* ≤
☞ – ⁕⊷ 📺 ♗. ⁕⊷ – *Easter-October –* **3 rm** ☐ *70.00/120.00.*

⌂ **Ashburn House** *without rest., 18 Achintore Rd, PH33 6RM, South : ½ m. on A 8*
℘ *(01397) 706000, Fax (01397) 706000, ☞ –* ⁕⊷ 📺 ♗. ℳ ℡ *VISA* 𝙅𝙲𝘽. ⁕⊷
*closed December and January –* **7 rm** ☐ *35.00/70.00.*

⌂ **Cabana House** *without rest., Union Rd, PH33 6RB,* ℘ *(01397) 705991*
*Fax (01397) 705991, ☞ –* ⁕⊷ 📺 ♗. ⁕⊷
*closed Christmas-New Year and restricted opening in winter –* **3 rm** ☐ *40.00/53.00* s.

**at Banavie** *North : 3 m. by A 82 and A 830 on B 8004 –* ☒ *Fort William.*

🏠 **Moorings,** *PH33 7LY,* ℘ *(01397) 772797, Fax (01397) 772441,* ≤, ☞ – ⁕⊷ *rest,* 📺 ☎ ♗
ℳ ℡ ① *VISA* 𝙅𝙲𝘽. ⁕⊷
*closed Christmas –* ***Jacobean* :** **Meals** *(lunch by arrangement)/dinner 23.00* st. ↑ *6.50*
**21 rm** ☐ *60.00/92.00* st. – *SB.*

---

**FOYERS** *Highland* **401** *G 12 Scotland G.* – ☒ *Loch Ness.*

Env. : *Loch Ness*★★ – *The Great Glen*★.
*Edinburgh 175 – Inverness 19 – Kyle of Lochalsh 63 – Oban 96.*

🏠 **Craigdarroch** ⤵, *IV1 2XU, North : ¼ m. on B 852* ℘ *(01456) 486400*
*Fax (01456) 486444,* ≤ *Loch Ness and mountains,* ☞, *park –* ⁕⊷ 📺 ☎ ♗. ℳ ℡ *VISA* 𝙅𝙲𝘽
*closed 3 January-12 February –* **Meals** *14.50/24.50* t. *and dinner a la carte* ↑ *7.50 –* **15 rm**
☐ *87.50/130.00* st. – *SB.*

🏠 **Foyers Bay House,** *Lower Foyers, IV1 2YB, West : 1 ¼ m. by B 852 on Lower Foyers r*
℘ *(01456) 486624, Fax (01456) 486337,* ≤, ☞ – ⁕⊷ *rm,* 📺 ☎ ♗. ℳ ℡ *VISA* 𝙅𝙲𝘽. ⁕⊷
**Meals** *(unlicensed) (bar lunch)/dinner 15.50* t. *and a la carte –* **4 rm** ☐ *34.00/54.00* st. – *SB*

**GAIRLOCH** Highland **401** C 10 Scotland G. – pop. 2 194.

Env. : Wester Ross★★★ – Loch Maree★★★, E : 5½ m. by A 832.

Exc. : Inverewe Gardens★★★ AC, NE : 8 m. by A 832 – Victoria Falls★, SE : 8 m. by A 832.

🄻 Gairloch ℰ (01445) 712407.

🄱 Auchtercairn ℰ (01445) 712130.

Edinburgh 228 – Inverness 72 – Kyle of Lochalsh 68.

🏦 **Creag Mor**, Charleston, IV21 2AH, ℰ (01445) 712068, Fax (01445) 712044, ≤, ☞ – 📺 ☎ 🄿. 🐃 🚾

April-October – Meals (bar lunch)/dinner a la carte 12.00/21.00 st. 🛭 6.00 – **18 rm** ⊋ 45.00/90.00 st., 1 suite – SB.

⌂ **Little Lodge** ♨, North Erradale, IV21 2DS, Northwest : 6 m. on B 8021 ℰ (01445) 771237, ≤ Torridon Mountains and Skye, ☞ – ⅙⅞ 🄿. 🛠

April-October (minimum stay 2 nights) – Meals – **3 rm** ⊋ (dinner included) 70.00/100.00 s.

⌂ **Birchwood**, Charleston, IV21 2AH, ℰ (01445) 712011, Fax (01445) 712011, ≤, ☞ – ⅙⅞ 🄿

March-November – Meals (by arrangement) 20.00 st. – **5 rm** ⊋ 48.00/76.00 st. – SB.

**GALSON** Western Isles (Outer Hebrides) **401** A 8 – see Lewis and Harris (Isle of).

**GATEHEAD** East Ayrshire **401** **402** G 17 – ⊠ Kilmarnock.

Edinburgh 72 – Ayr 10 – Glasgow 25 – Kilmarnock 5.

🄽 **Cochrane Inn**, 45 Main Rd, KA2 0AP, ℰ (01563) 570122 – ⅙⅞ 🄿

Meals a la carte 12.00/14.00 t. 🛭 6.50.

**GATEHOUSE OF FLEET** Dumfries and Galloway **401** **402** H 19 – pop. 919.

🄻 Gatehouse of Fleet ℰ (01557) 814766.

🄱 Car Park, DG7 2AE ℰ (01557) 814212 (summer only).

Edinburgh 113 – Dumfries 33 – Stranraer 42.

🏦 **Cally Palace** ♨, DG7 2DL, East : ½ m. on B 727 ℰ (01557) 814341, Fax (01557) 814522, ≤, « Part 18C country mansion », ☎s, 🄻, 🄻, 🅂, ☞, park, 🛠 – 🛊, ⅙⅞ rest, 📺 ☎ 🄿 – 🄰 80. 🐃 🚾

closed 4 January-mid February – Meals 23.00 t. (dinner) and a la carte 17.20/28.00 t. 🛭 6.00 – **50 rm** ⊋ (dinner included) 76.00/81.00 t., 5 suites – SB.

**GIFFNOCK** East Renfrewshire **401** ④ – see Glasgow.

**GIGHA (Isle of)** Argyll and Bute **401** C 16.

Edinburgh 168.

🄵 **Gigha** ♨, PA41 7AA, ℰ (01583) 505254, Fax (01583) 505244, ≤ Sound of Gigha and Kintyre Peninsula, ☞ – ⅙⅞ rest, 📺 ☎ 🄿 🐃 ① 🚾

mid March-October – Meals (bar lunch)/dinner 25.00 t. (dinner) and lunch a la carte 8.25/17.50 t. 🛭 6.00 – **13 rm** ⊋ 71.00/140.00 t.

**GIRVAN** South Ayrshire **401** **402** F 18 – pop. 7 719.

🄻 Brunston Castle, Dailly ℰ (01465) 811471 – 🄻 Golf Course Rd ℰ (01465) 714272/714346.

Edinburgh 100 – Ayr 20 – Glasgow 56 – Stranraer 31.

⌂ **Glendrissaig** ♨, Newton Stewart Rd., KA26 0HJ, South : 1 ¾ m. by A 77 on A 714 ℰ (01465) 714631, ≤, ☞ – ⅙⅞ 🄿. 🛠

March-October – Meals (by arrangement) 15.00 s. – **3 rm** ⊋ 32.00/54.00 – SB.

🅇🅇 **Wildings**, 56 Montgomerie St., KA26 9HE, ℰ (01465) 713481 – ⅙⅞

closed January and October – Meals (booking essential) 8.95/17.50 t..

**GLAMIS** Angus **401** K 14 Scotland G. – pop. 648 – ⊠ Forfar.

See : Village★ - Castle★★ AC – Angus Folk Museum★ AC.

Exc. : Meigle Museum★★ (early Christian Monuments★★) AC, SW : 7 m. by A 94.

Edinburgh 60 – Dundee 11 – Perth 25.

🅇🅇 **Castleton House** with rm, DD8 1SJ, West : 3 ¾ m. on A 94 ℰ (01307) 840340, Fax (01307) 840506, ☞ – ⅙⅞ rest, 📺 ☎ 🄿. 🐃 🚾. 🛠

Meals 7.95 t. (lunch) and a la carte 11.55/24.00 t. 🛭 6.95 – **6 rm** ⊋ 70.00/100.00 t. – SB.

703

# GLASGOW

401 402 H 16 *Scotland G. – pop. 662 853.*

*Edinburgh 46 – Manchester 221.*

## TOURIST INFORMATION

🛈 *11 George Square, G2 1DY ℘ (0141) 204 4400.*
🛈 *Glasgow Airport, Tourist Information Desk, Paisley ℘ (0141) 848 4440.*

## PRACTICAL INFORMATION

🛚 *Littlehill, Auchinairn Rd ℘ (0141) 772 1916.*
🛚 *Deaconsbank, Rouken Glen Park, Stewarton Rd, Eastwood ℘ (0141) 638 7044* AX.
🛚 *Linn Park, Simshill Rd ℘ (0141) 637 5871,* BX.
🛚 *Lethamhill, Cumbernauld Rd ℘ (0141) 770 6220,* BV.
🛚 *Alexandra Park, Dennistown ℘ (0141) 556 3991* BV.
🛚 *King's Park, 150a Croftpark Av., Croftfoot ℘ (0141) 630 1597,* BX.
🛚 *Knightswood, Lincoln Av. ℘ (0141) 959 6358* AV.
🛚 *Ruchill, Brassey St. ℘ (0141) 946 7676.*
*Access to Oban by helicopter.*
*Erskine Bridge (toll)* AV.
✈ *Glasgow Airport : ℘ (0141) 887 1111, W : 8 m. by M 8* AV – **Terminal :** *Coach service from Glasgow Central and Queen Street main line Railway Stations and from Anderston Cross and Buchanan Bus Stations.*
✈ *see also Prestwick.*

## SIGHTS

**See :** *City*★★★ – *Cathedral*★★★ *(≤★)* DZ – *The Burrell Collection*★★★ AX **M1** – *Hunterian Art Gallery*★★ *(Whistler Collection*★★★ – *Mackintosh Wing*★★★*) AC* CY **M4** – *Museum of Transport*★★ *(Scottish Built Cars*★★★*, The Clyde Room of Ship Models*★★★*)* AV **M3** – *Art Gallery and Museum Kelvingrove*★★ CY – *Pollok House*★ *(The Paintings*★★*)* AX D – *Tolbooth Steeple*★ DZ A – *Hunterian Museum (Coin and Medal Collection*★*)* CY **M1** – *City Chambers*★ DZ C – *Glasgow School of Art*★ *AC,* CY B – *Necropolis (≤★ of Cathedral)* DYZ.
**Env. :** *Paisley Museum and Art Gallery (Paisley Shawl Section*★*), W : 4 m. by M 8* AV.
**Exc. :** *The Trossachs*★★★*, N : 31 m. by A 879* – BV – *A 81 and A 821* – *Loch Lomond*★★*, NW : 19 m. by A 82* AV.

# GLASGOW
## BUILT UP AREA

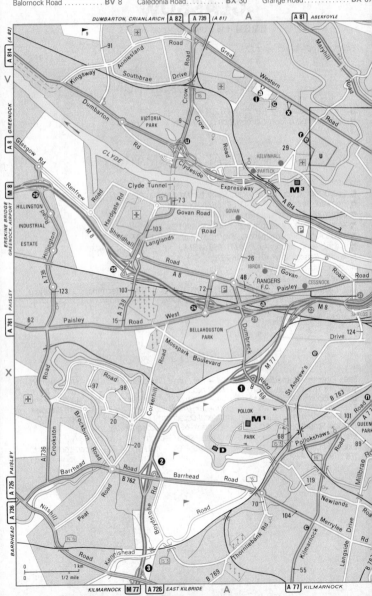

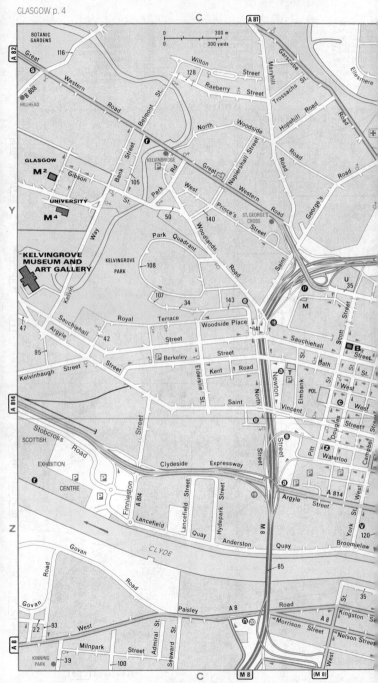

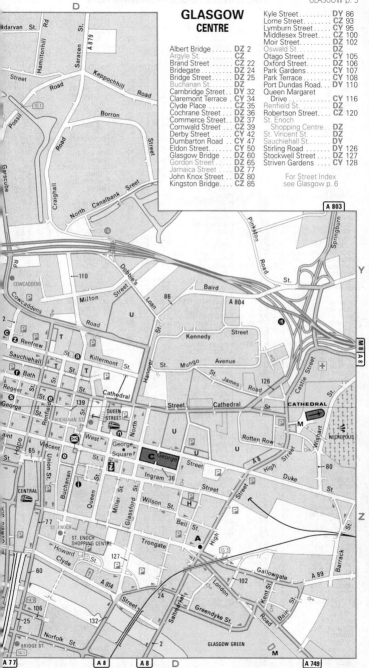

# GLASGOW
## CENTRE

For Street Index
see Glasgow p. 6

# STREET INDEX TO GLASGOW TOWN PLAN

**Glasgow Hilton,** 1 William St., G3 8HT, ℰ (0141) 204 5555, *Fax (0141) 204 5004*, ≤, *f₆*, ⩩, ⬛ – |ᵇ|, ⁑ rm, 🔲 🅰 ☎ 🖧 🅿 – ⩜ 1000. 🔘 🖭 ⓪ 𝘝𝘐𝘚𝘈 𝙹𝙲𝙱. ⅍
CZ s
*Minsky's :* Meals 21.50 **st.** and a la carte ⅋ 11.50 – (see also *Camerons* below) – ⚌ 14.50 –
**315 rm** 181.00 **st.**, 4 suites – SB.

**One Devonshire Gardens,** 1 Devonshire Gdns., G12 0UX, ℰ (0141) 339 2001,
*Fax (0141) 337 1663*, « Victorian town houses, opulent interior design » – ⁑ rest, 🔲 ☎ –
⩜ 50. 🔘 🖭 ⓪ 𝘝𝘐𝘚𝘈
AV a
Meals *(closed Saturday lunch)* 25.00/40.00 **st.** ⅋ 15.00 – ⚌ 14.50 – **25 rm** 140.00/190.00 **st.**,
2 suites
**Spec.** Home smoked lobster with lime and herb butter. Fillet of venison, macaroni and
truffle gratin, roasted celeriac. Iced vanilla parfait with roasted strawberries.

**Glasgow Moat House,** Congress Rd, G3 8QT, ℰ (0141) 306 9988, *Fax (0141) 221 2022*,
≤, *f₆*, ⩩, ⬛ – |ᵇ|, ⁑ rm, 🔲 ☎ 🖧 🅿 – ⩜ 800. 🔘 🖭 ⓪ 𝘝𝘐𝘚𝘈
CZ r
*Mariners :* Meals 16.50 **t.** (lunch) and a la carte 24.50/31.00 **t.** ⅋ 6.50 – *Pointhouse :* Meals
18.95/22.95 **st.** and a la carte ⅋ 5.75 – ⚌ 10.95 – **268 rm** 135.00/165.00 **st.**, 15 suites.

**Glasgow Marriott,** 500 Argyle St., Anderston, G3 8RR, ℰ (0141) 226 5577,
*Fax (0141) 221 7676*, ≤, *f₆*, ⩩, ⬛, squash – |ᵇ|, ⁑ rm, 🔲 🅰 ☎ 🖧 🖧 🅿 – ⩜ 720. 🔘 🖭
⓪ 𝘝𝘐𝘚𝘈 𝙹𝙲𝙱. ⅍
CZ a
*Terrace :* Meals (dinner only) 18.95 **t.** and a la carte ⅋ 7.45 – ⚌ 11.95 – **300 rm** 94.00/
145.00 **st.** – SB.

**Thistle Glasgow,** 36 Cambridge St., G2 3HN, ℰ (0141) 332 3311, *Fax (0141) 332 4050* –
|ᵇ|, ⁑ rm, ⬛ rest, 🔲 ☎ 🖧 🅿 – ⩜ 1500. 🔘 🖭 ⓪ 𝘝𝘐𝘚𝘈
DY z
*Garden Cafe :* Meals a la carte 13.00/23.00 **st.** ⅋ 7.00 – *Prince of Wales :* Meals *(closed
Sunday and Bank Holidays except 25 December)* 18.00/22.00 **st.** and a la carte ⅋ 7.00 – ⚌
13.95 – **300 rm** 117.00/164.00 **st.** – SB.

**Malmaison,** 278 West George St., G2 4LL, ℰ (0141) 572 1000, *Fax (0141) 572 1002*, « Con-
temporary interior », *f₆* – |ᵇ|, ⁑ rm, 🔲 ☎ 🖧 🖧 🅿 – ⩜ 30. 🔘 🖭 ⓪ 𝘝𝘐𝘚𝘈. ⅍
CY c
*Cafe Mal :* Meals a la carte 10.00/17.70 **st.** ⅋ 9.95 – *The Brasserie :* Meals a la carte 17.00/
21.50 **st.** ⅋ 9.95 – ⚌ 10.50 – **68 rm** 95.00 **st.**, 4 suites.

**Devonshire,** 5 Devonshire Gdns., G12 0UX, ℰ (0141) 339 7878, *Fax (0141) 339 3980*,
« Victorian town house » – 🔲 ☎ 🖧 – ⩜ 50. 🔘 🖭 ⓪ 𝘝𝘐𝘚𝘈
AV a
Meals *(closed lunch Saturday and Sunday)* a la carte 24.50/35.00 **t.** ⅋ 7.25 – ⚌ 10.75 –
**14 rm** 115.00/185.00 **st.** – SB.

**Copthorne Glasgow,** George Sq., G2 1DS, ℰ (0141) 332 6711, *Fax (0141) 332 4264*, *f₆*
– |ᵇ|, ⁑ rm, 🔲 ☎ 🅿 – ⩜ 90. 🔘 🖭 ⓪ 𝘝𝘐𝘚𝘈 𝙹𝙲𝙱. ⅍
DZ n
*closed 24 to 27 December* – Meals (bar lunch Saturday and Sunday) 9.95/11.95 **st.**
and a la carte ⅋ 5.95 – ⚌ 11.95 – **136 rm** 125.00/135.00 **t.**, 5 suites – SB.

**Forte Posthouse Glasgow City,** Bothwell St., G2 7EN, ℰ (0141) 248 2656,
*Fax (0141) 221 8986*, ≤ – |ᵇ|, ⁑ rm, ⬛ 🔲 ☎ 🅿 – ⩜ 1000. 🔘 🖭 ⓪ 𝘝𝘐𝘚𝘈 𝙹𝙲𝙱. ⅍
*closed 24 to 27 December* – *The Carvery :* Meals (dinner only and Sunday lunch)/dinner
15.75 **st.** ⅋ 7.00 – *Jules :* Meals *(closed Saturday lunch)* a la carte 18.00/28.00 **st.** ⅋ 7.00 – ⚌
10.95 – **246 rm** 89.00 **st.**, 1 suite – SB.
CZ z

**Stakis Glasgow Grosvenor,** Grosvenor Terr., Great Western Rd, G12 0TA,
ℰ (0141) 339 8811, *Fax (0141) 334 0710*, « Victorian terraced town houses » – |ᵇ|, ⁑ rm,
🔲 ☎ 🅿 – ⩜ 450. 🔘 🖭 ⓪ 𝘝𝘐𝘚𝘈 𝙹𝙲𝙱. ⅍
CY s
Meals (carving lunch Sunday) 15.00 **t.** (dinner) and a la carte 12.75/24.40 **t.** – ⚌ 9.95 –
**94 rm** 116.00/151.00 **st.**, 2 suites – SB.

**Holiday Inn,** Theatreland, 161 West Nile St., G1 2RL, ℰ (0141) 352 8305,
*Fax (0141) 332 7447*, *f₆* – ⁑ rm, 🔲 ☎ 🖧 🖧 – ⩜ 80. 🔘 🖭 ⓪ 𝘝𝘐𝘚𝘈 𝙹𝙲𝙱. ⅍
DY a
*La Bonne Auberge Brasserie :* Meals 7.95/9.95 **t.** and a la carte ⅋ 4.95 – ⚌ 9.95 – **110 rm**
89.95 **t.**, 3 suites – SB.

**Thistle Tinto Firs,** 470 Kilmarnock Rd, G43 2BB, ℰ (0141) 637 2353, *Fax (0141) 633 1340*
– ⁑ rm, 🔲 ☎ 🅿 – ⩜ 200. 🔘 🖭 ⓪ 𝘝𝘐𝘚𝘈
AX c
Meals (bar lunch)/dinner 17.95 **t.** ⅋ 5.85 – ⚌ 9.95 – **25 rm** 85.00/105.00 **t.**, 2 suites.

**Swallow Glasgow,** 517 Paisley Road West, G51 1RW, ℰ (0141) 427 3146,
*Fax (0141) 427 4059*, *f₆*, ⩩, ⬛ – |ᵇ| ⁑ rm, ⬛ rest, 🔲 ☎ 🅿 – ⩜ 350. 🔘 🖭 ⓪ 𝘝𝘐𝘚𝘈
*closed 23 December-1 January* – Meals (carving lunch) (bar lunch Saturday) 11.20/18.50 **st.**
and dinner a la carte ⅋ 8.00 – ⚌ 99.00/115.00 **st.** – SB.
AX a

**Ewington,** Balmoral Terr., 132 Queen's Drive, G42 8QW, ℰ (0141) 423 1152,
*Fax (0141) 422 2030* – |ᵇ|, ⁑ rm, 🔲 ☎ – ⩜ 40. 🔘 🖭 ⓪ 𝘝𝘐𝘚𝘈 𝙹𝙲𝙱
BX a
Meals 8.50/17.95 **t.** and a la carte ⅋ 6.50 – ⚌ 9.50 – **43 rm** 80.00/98.00 **st.**, 1 suite – SB.

🏨 **Charing Cross Tower,** Elmbank Gdns., G2 4PP, ℘ (0141) 221 1000, Fax (0141) 248 1000
← – 🛗 ✳️ 📺 ☎ – 🔬 60. 🌐 🆎 ⓪ 💳. ✀                                                   CY
*closed 24 to 26 December* – **Meals** (bar lunch)/dinner 7.50 **st.** and a la carte ⓵ 6.00 – ☲ 6.95
– **278 rm** 44.50/59.50 **st.**

🏨 **Terrace House,** 14 Belhaven Terr., G12 0TG, (off Great Western Rd) ℘ (0141) 337 3377,
Fax (0141) 400 3378 – ✳️ rest, 📺 ☎. 🌐 🆎 ⓪ 💳                                          AV
**Meals** (booking essential Saturday and Sunday) (dinner only) a la carte 8.65/14.70 **st.** ⓵ 3.95
– **11 rm** ☲ 62.00/78.00 **st.**

🏨 **Belhaven,** 15 Belhaven Terr., G12 0TG, (off Great Western Rd) ℘ (0141) 339 3222,
Fax (0141) 339 2212 – 📺 ☎. 🌐 🆎 ⓪ 💳                                                   AV
**Meals** (dinner only) a la carte 11.95/16.65 **st.** ⓵ 4.95 – **17 rm** ☲ 49.50/69.50 **st.**

🏨 **62 St. Andrews** without rest., 62 St. Andrew's Drive, Pollockshields, G41 5EZ,
℘ (0141) 427 1106, Fax (0141) 419 0756, ☞ – 📺 ☎ ☏ 🅿. 🌐 🆎 ⓪ 💳 💳 JCB. ✀         AX
**6 rm** ☲ 45.00/60.00 **st.** – SB.

🏨 **Manor Park,** 28 Balshagray Drive, G11 7DD, ℘ (0141) 339 2143, Fax (0141) 339 5842 – ✳️
📺 ☎. 🌐 💳. ✀                                                                           AV
**Meals** (dinner only) 16.50 **st.** ⓵ 6.00 – **9 rm** ☲ 45.00/75.00 – SB.

🏨 **Travelodge,** Hill St., G3 6PR, ℘ (0141) 333 1515, Fax (0141) 333 1221, Reservations (Free
phone) 0800 850950 – 🛗, ✳️ rm, 📺 ☎ &. – 🔬 35. 🌐 🆎 ⓪ 💳. ✀                         DY
**Meals** (cafe bar) – **93 rm** 39.95/59.95 **t.**

🏨 **Travelodge,** 251 Paisley Rd, G5 8RA, ℘ (0141) 420 3882, Fax (0141) 420 3884, Reservations (Freephone) 0800 850950 – ✳️ rm, ▤ rest, 📺 ☎ & 🅿. 🌐 🆎 ⓪ 💳 JCB. ✀          CZ
**Meals** (grill rest.) – **75 rm** 39.95/59.95 **t.**

↑ **Kirklee** without rest., 11 Kensington Gate, G12 9LG, ℘ (0141) 334 5555,
Fax (0141) 339 3828 – 📺 ☎. 🌐 🆎 ⓪ 💳. ✀                                               AV
*closed 25 and 26 December* – **9 rm** ☲ 48.00/64.00 **t.**

↑ **Town House** without rest., 4 Hughenden Terr., G12 9XR, ℘ (0141) 357 0862,
Fax (0141) 339 9605 – 📺 ☎. 🌐 💳. ✀                                                     AV
*booking essential December and January* – **10 rm** ☲ 60.00/70.00 **st.**

XXXX **Camerons** (at Glasgow Hilton H.), 1 William St., G3 8HT, ℘ (0141) 204 5511,
Fax (0141) 204 5004 – ▤ 🅿. 🌐 🆎 ⓪ 💳 JCB                                               CZ
**Meals** *(closed Saturday lunch and Sunday)* 24.50 **t.** (lunch) and a la carte 33.50/44.00
⓵ 11.50.

XXX **Buttery,** 652 Argyle St., G3 8UF, ℘ (0141) 221 8188, Fax (0141) 204 4639 – 🅿. 🌐 🆎 ⓪
💳 JCB                                                                                    CZ
*closed Saturday lunch, Sunday, 25-26 December, 1-2 January and Easter Monday* – **Meals**
16.85 **t.** (lunch) and dinner a la carte 28.00/35.75 **t.** ⓵ 9.80.

XXX **Yes,** 22 West Nile St., G1 2PW, ℘ (0141) 221 8044, Fax (0141) 248 9159 – ▤. 🌐 🆎 ⓪ 💳
*closed Sunday and Bank Holidays* – **Meals** 15.95/22.95 **st.**.                       DZ

XXX **Rogano,** 11 Exchange Pl., G1 3AN, ℘ (0141) 248 4055, Fax (0141) 248 2608, « Art Deco
» – ▤. 🌐 🆎 ⓪ 💳 JCB                                                                     DZ
*closed 25 December and 1 January* – **Meals** - Seafood - 16.50 **t.** (lunch) and a la carte
27.15/39.15 **t.** ⓵ 7.00.

XX **Nairns** with rm, 13 Woodside Cres., G3 7UP, ℘ (0141) 353 0707, Fax (0141) 331 1684 – 📺
☎. 🌐 🆎 ⓪ 💳. ✀                                                                         CY
*closed 25-26 December and 1-2 January* – Meals *(closed Monday)* 17.00/23.50 **t.** ⓵ 9.50 – ☲
7.50 – **4 rm** 90.00/125.00 **t.**

XX **Puppet Theatre,** 11 Ruthven Lane, G12 9BG, off Byres Rd ℘ (0141) 339 8444,
Fax (0141) 339 7666 – 🌐 🆎 ⓪ 💳 JCB                                                      AV
*closed Saturday lunch, Monday, 26 December and 1-2 January* – **Meals** 14.50/27.95
⓵ 9.95.

XX **Papingo,** 104 Bath St., G2 2EN, ℘ (0141) 332 6678, Fax (0141) 332 6549 – 🌐 🆎 ⓪
💳                                                                                        DY
*closed lunch Sunday and Bank Holidays and 1 January* – **Meals** 12.90/19.95 **t.** ⓵ 6.95.

XX **Ho Wong,** 82 York St., G2 8LE, ℘ (0141) 221 3550, Fax (0141) 248 5330 – ▤. 🌐 🆎 ⓪ 💳
*closed Sunday lunch and 3 days Chinese New Year* – **Meals** - Chinese (Peking) - 8.50/25.00
and a la carte ⓵ 6.95.                                                                    CZ

XX **Amber Regent,** 50 West Regent St., G2 2QZ, ℘ (0141) 331 1655, Fax (0141) 353 3398 –
▤. 🌐 🆎 ⓪ 💳. ✀                                                                          DY
*closed Sunday, 1 January and 3 days Chinese New Year* – **Meals** - Chinese - a la carte
18.65/26.75 **t.** ⓵ 5.95.

X **Ubiquitous Chip,** 12 Ashton Lane, G12 8SJ, off Byres Rd ℘ (0141) 334 5007,
Fax (0141) 337 1302 – 🌐 🆎 ⓪ 💳. ✀                                                      AV
*closed 25 and 31 December and 1 January* – **Meals** 23.60/31.60 **t.** ⓵ 5.45.

✗ **Bouzy Rouge,** 111 West Regent St., G2 2RU, ✆ (0141) 221 8804, Fax (0141) 221 6941 –
🍽, 🆎 AE ⑩ VISA
DY s
closed 1 January – **Meals** 12.95/19.95 t. and a la carte ▯ 6.95.

✗ **La Parmigiana,** 447 Great Western Rd, Kelvinbridge, G12 8HH, ✆ (0141) 334 0686,
Fax (0141) 332 3533 – 🍽, 🆎 AE VISA JCB
CY r
closed Sunday, 25-26 December, 1-2 January and Bank Holidays – **Meals** - Italian - 8.10 st.
(lunch) and a la carte 16.60/28.50 st. ▯ 7.80.

✗ **Shimla Pinks,** 777 Pollokshaws Rd, G41 2AX, ✆ (0141) 423 4488 – 🍽, 🆎 AE ⑩ VISA
closed lunch Saturday and Sunday and 1 January – **Meals** - Indian - 6.95
(lunch) and a la carte 10.85/20.85 ▯ 5.95.
AX n

**at Stepps** (North Lanarkshire) Northeast : 5½ m. by M 8 on A 80 – BV – ⊠ Glasgow.

🏨 **Garfield House,** Cumbernauld Rd, G33 6HW, ✆ (0141) 779 2111, Fax (0141) 779 9799 –
≒ rm, 📺 ☎ 🅿 – 🔬 150. 🆎 AE ⑩ VISA
closed 1 January – **Meals** (closed Saturday lunch and Sunday) 12.50/18.45 t. and a la carte
▯ 6.40 – **46 rm** � 75.00/102.00 t. – SB.

**at Giffnock** (East Renfrewshire) South : 5¼ m. by A 77 – AX – ⊠ Glasgow.

✗ **Turban Tandoori,** 2 Station Rd, G46 6JF, ✆ (0141) 638 0069 – 🆎 AE VISA
closed 1 January – **Meals** - Indian - (dinner only) a la carte 8.95/15.50 st.

**at Busby** (East Renfrewshire) South : 7¼ m. by A 77 – AX – on A 726 – ⊠ Glasgow.

🏨 **Busby,** 1 Field Rd, Clarkston, G76 8RX, ✆ (0141) 644 2661, Fax (0141) 644 4417 – ▯,
≒ rm, 📺 ☎ 🅿 – 🔬 200. 🆎 AE ⑩ VISA JCB
**Meals** 9.95/16.45 t. and a la carte ▯ 6.00 – **32 rm** � 66.00/94.00 t. – SB.

**at Glasgow Airport** (Renfrewshire) West : 8 m. by M 8 – AV – ⊠ Paisley.

🏨 **Forte Posthouse Glasgow Airport,** Abbotsinch, PA3 3TR, ✆ (0141) 887 1212,
Fax (0141) 887 3738 – ▯, ≒ rm, 🍽 📺 ☎ 🅿 – 🔬 250. 🆎 AE ⑩ VISA JCB
**The Junction :** Meals (closed Saturday lunch and Bank Holiday Monday) a la carte 10.25/
28.60 ▯ 7.50 – � 10.95 – **295 rm** 95.00 st., 2 suites – SB.

🏨 **Travel Inn,** Whitecart Rd, PA3 2TH, M 8 junction 28 ✆ (0141) 842 1563,
Fax (0141) 842 1570 – ▯ ≒ 📺 🅿 – 🔬 30. 🆎 AE ⑩ VISA. 🍽
**Meals** (grill rest.) (dinner only) – **104 rm** 38.00 t.

ⓐ ATS 192 Finnieston St. ✆ (0141) 248 6761       ATS 1 Sawmillfield St., off Garscube Rd
ATS Rutherglen Ind. Est., Glasgow Rd, Rutherglen   ✆ (0141) 332 1945
✆ (0141) 647 9341

**GLASGOW AIRPORT** Renfrewshire 401 402 G 16 – see Glasgow.

**GLENBORRODALE** Highland 401 C 13 – ⊠ Acharacle.
Edinburgh 190 – Inverness 116 – Oban 106.

🏠 **Feorag House** 🍽, PH36 4JP, ✆ (01972) 500248, Fax (01972) 500285, ≼ Loch Sunart,
« Lochside setting », 🌳, park – ≒ 🅿. 🆎 VISA. 🍽
**Meals** 22.50 st. – **3 rm** � (dinner included) 77.50/130.00 st. – SB.

**GLENCARSE** Perthshire and Kinross 401 K 14 – see Perth.

**GLENELG** Highland 401 D 12.
Edinburgh 229 – Inverness 75 – Kyle of Lochalsh 25.

🏨 **Glenelg Inn** 🍽, IV40 8JR, ✆ (01599) 522273, Fax (01599) 522283, ≼ Glenelg Bay, 🌳, 🍴
– 🅿. 🆎 VISA
March-October – **Meals** 24.00 (dinner) and lunch a la carte ▯ 5.00 – **6 rm** � (dinner in-
cluded) 84.00/168.00 st. – SB.

**GLENFINNAN** Highland 401 D 13 – ⊠ Fort William.
Edinburgh 150 – Inverness 85 – Oban 66.

🏨 **Prince's House,** PH37 4LT, West : ¾ m. on A 830 ✆ (01397) 722246, Fax (01397) 722307,
≼ – ≒ 📺 ☎ 📞 🅿 🆎 AE VISA
March-November – **Meals** (bar lunch Monday to Saturday)/dinner 27.00 st. ▯ 6.50 – **9 rm**
� (dinner included) 60.00/120.00 t. – SB.

*The Guide is updated annually so renew your Guide every year.*

**GLENLIVET** Moray 401 J 11 – pop. 3 559 – ⊠ Ballindalloch.
*Edinburgh 180 – Aberdeen 59 – Elgin 27 – Inverness 49.*

🛏 **Minmore House** ⏥, AB37 9DB, South : ¾ m. on Glenlivet Distillery r
*ℰ (01807) 590378, Fax (01807) 590472*, ≤, 🐎, 🛬, ✖ – ✸✖ rest, ☎ 🅿. 🕮 🚾
*April-September* – **Meals** (booking essential to non-residents) (dinner only) 26.50 **st.** ⌀ 5.8
– **10 rm** ⊆ (dinner included) 75.00/150.00 **st.** – SB.

---

**GLENROTHES** Fife 401 K 15 *Scotland G. – pop. 38 650.*
Env. : *Falkland★ (Village★, Palace of Falkland★ AC, Gardens★ AC) N : 5 ½ m. by A 92 an
A 912.*
🛅 Thornton, Station Rd ℰ (01592) 771173 – 🛅 Golf Course Rd ℰ (01592) 754561/758686
🛅 Balbirnie Park, Markinch ℰ (01592) 612095 – 🛅 Auchterderran, Woodend Rd, Cardende
ℰ (01592) 721579 – 🛅 Leslie, Balsillie Laws ℰ (01592) 620040.
🗗 Rothes Halls, Rothes Sq., Kingdom Centre, ℰ (01592) 610784/754954.
*Edinburgh 33 – Dundee 25 – Stirling 36.*

🏨 **Balbirnie House** ⏥, Markinch, KY6 6NE, Northeast : 1 ¾ m. by A 911 and A 92 on B 913
ℰ (01592) 610066, Fax (01592) 610529, « Part 18C mansion », 🛅, 🛬, park – ✸✖ rest, 🖵 🅿
🅿 – 🔬 150. 🕮 🖭 ⓪ 🚾
**Meals** 12.75/29.50 **t.** ⌀ 7.50 – **28 rm** ⊆ 115.00/210.00 **t.**, 2 suites – SB.

🛏 **Holiday Inn Express** without rest., Leslie Roundabout, Leslie Rd, KY6 6XX, West : 2 n
on A 911 ℰ (01592) 745509, Fax (01592) 743377 – ✸✖ 🖵 ☎ ✆ 🅱 🅿 – 🔬 25. 🕮 🖭 🚾 . ✑
**49 rm** 45.00.

🛏 **Travel Inn,** Beaufort Drive, Bankhead Roundabout, KY7 4UJ, Southeast : 1 ¾ m. by A 91
and A 92 at junction with B 921 ℰ (01592) 773473, Fax (01592) 773453 – ✸✖ rm, 🖵 🅱 🅿
🕮 🖭 ⓪ 🚾 . ✑
**Meals** (grill rest.) – **41 rm** 38.00 **t.**

**at Leslie** West : 3 m. by A 911.

🛏 **Rescobie,** 6 Valley Drive, KY6 3BQ, ℰ (01592) 742143, Fax (01592) 620231, 🛬 – 🖵 ☎ 🅿
🕮 🖭 🚾 . ✑
**Meals** 18.50 **t.** (dinner) and a la carte 8.00/20.55 **t.** – **10 rm** ⊆ 54.00/80.00 **t.** – SB.

---

**GOUROCK** Inverclyde 401 F 16 – pop. 4 778 – ⊠ Greenock.
🛅 Gowal View ℰ (01475) 631001.
*Edinburgh 73 – Glasgow 27 – Greenock 3.*

🏨 **Stakis Gourock,** Cloch Rd, PA19 1AR, Southwest : 2 m. on A 770 ℰ (01475) 63467'
Fax (01475) 632490, ≤, 🎣, ⛱, 🖵, ✖ – 🛗 ✸✖, 🍴 rest, 🖵 ☎ 🅿 – 🔬 200. 🕮 🖭 ⓪ 🚾
🎴 . ✑
**Meals** (dancing Friday and Saturday) 9.95/15.00 **t.** – ⊆ 9.50 – **98 rm** 98.00/128.00 **st**
1 suite.

---

**GRANTOWN-ON-SPEY** Highland 401 J 12 – pop. 2 391.
🛅 Abernethy, Nethy Bridge ℰ (01479) 821305.
🗗 High St., PH26 3EH ℰ (01479) 872773 (summer only).
*Edinburgh 143 – Inverness 34 – Perth 99.*

🛏 **Ravenscourt House,** Seafield Av., PH26 3JG, ℰ (01479) 872286, Fax (01479) 873260
✸✖ rest, 🖵 🅿. ✑
**Meals** (residents only) (light lunch)/dinner 17.50 **st.** ⌀ 4.00 – **6 rm** ⊆ 35.00/80.00 **st.** – SB.

🛏 **Culdearn House,** Woodlands Terr., PH26 3JU, ℰ (01479) 872106, Fax (01479) 87364
🛬 – ✸✖ 🖵 🅿. 🕮 🖭 ⓪ 🚾 🎴 . ✑
*March-October* – **Meals** (residents only) (dinner only) 25.00 ⌀ 7.00 – **9 rm** ⊆ (dinne
included) 65.00/130.00 **st.**

🏠 **Ardlarig,** Woodlands Terr., PH26 3JU, ℰ (01479) 873245, Fax (01479) 873245, 🛬 – ✸✖ 🖵
🅿. 🕮 🚾 🎴 . ✑
*closed 20 November-12 December and 22 to 27 December* – **Meals** (by arrangement
18.50 **t.** – **7 rm** ⊆ 19.50/57.00 **t.** – SB.

---

**GREENOCK** Inverclyde 401 F 16 – pop. 35 272.
🛅, 🛅 Forsyth St., ℰ (01475) 720793.
*Edinburgh 70 – Ayr 48 – Glasgow 24.*

🛏 **Travel Inn,** James Watt Way, PA15 2AD, East : 1 m. off A 8 ℰ (01475) 73091'
Fax (01475) 730890 – 🛗, ✸✖ rm, 🍴 rest, 🖵 🅱 🅿. 🕮 🖭 ⓪ 🚾 . ✑
**Meals** (grill rest.) – **40 rm** 38.00 **t.**

**GRETNA** *Dumfries and Galloway* 401 402 K 19 – *pop. 2 678.*
**8** *The Old Blacksmith's Shop* ℘ *(01461) 337834 (summer only).*
*Edinburgh 91 – Carlisle 10 – Dumfries 24.*

🏨 **Garden House,** Sarkfoot Rd, DG16 5EP, Southeast : ½ m. on B 7076 ℘ (01461) 337621,
*Fax (01461) 337692,* 🚗, ⬜ – ▤ rest, 📺 ☎ 🕻 🖕 🅿 – 🕍 150. 🐟 🝙 🕦 *VISA* JCB. 🌣
**Meals** 16.95 st. and a la carte ░ 5.20 – **21 rm** �)) 52.50/96.00 st. – SB.

🏨 **Gretna Chase,** DG16 5JB, Southeast : ¾ m. on B 7076 ℘ (01461) 337517,
*Fax (01461) 337766,* « *Gardens* » – 📺 ☎ 🅿. 🐟 🝙 🕦 *VISA*. 🌣
**Meals** *(closed Sunday)* a la carte 17.40/22.95 st. ░ 4.95 – **9 rm** �)) 45.00/120.00 st.

**GRETNA GREEN SERVICE AREA** *Dumfries and Galloway* 401 402 K 18 – ⊠ *Gretna.*
**8** *Welcome Break Service Area, M 74, Gretna Green DG16 5HQ* ℘ *(01461) 338500.*

🏨 **Welcome Lodge,** DG16 5HQ, on A 74 (M) (northbound carriageway) ℘ (01461) 337566,
*Fax (01461) 337823,* *Reservations (Freephone)* 0800 7314466 – 🖕 rm, 📺 🖕 🅿. 🐟 🝙 🕦
*VISA*
**Meals** (grill rest.) – �)) 7.50 – **64 rm** 50.00 t.

**GRIMSAY** *Western Isles (Outer Hebrides)* 401 Y 11 – *see Uist (Isles of).*

**GUILDTOWN** *Perthshire and Kinross* 401 J 14 – *see Perth.*

*Le Guide change, changez de* **guide Michelin** *tous les ans.*

**GULLANE** *East Lothian* 401 L 15 *Scotland G.* – *pop. 2 229.*
**Env. :** *Dirleton*★ *(Castle*★*) NE : 2 m. by A 198.*
🏌, 🏌, 🏌 *Gullane* ℘ *(01620) 843115.*
*Edinburgh 19 – North Berwick 5.*

🏨 **Greywalls** 🍃, Duncur Rd, Muirfield, EH31 2EG, ℘ (01620) 842144, *Fax (01620) 842241,* ≼
gardens and golf course, « *Lutyens house, gardens by Gertrude Jekyll* », 🌫 – 🖕 rest, 📺
☎ 🅿 – 🕍 30. 🐟 🝙 🕦 *VISA*
*April-October –* **Meals** 17.50/35.00 t. and lunch a la carte 13.50/24.65 t. ░ 6.50 – **23 rm**
�)) 95.00/195.00 t. – SB.

❌ **La Potinière** (Hilary Brown), Main St., EH31 2AA, ℘ (01620) 843214, *Fax (01620) 843214*
🕸 🖕 🅿
*closed 1 January, 1 week June, October and 25 December –* **Meals** *(lunch Sunday, Monday
and Thursday, dinner Friday and Saturday) (set menu only) (booking essential)* 21.00/32.00 t.
░ 6.75
**Spec.** Fried fillet of sea trout, braised fennel, lobster and vanilla sauce. Fillet of roe-deer,
roasted root vegetables, honey and thyme sauce. Panna cotta.

**HADDINGTON** *East Lothian* 401 L 16 *Scotland G.* – *pop. 7 342.*
**See :** *Town*★ *- High Street*★.
**Env. :** *Lennoxlove*★ *AC, S : 1 m – Gifford*★, *SE : 5 m. by B 6369.*
**Exc. :** *Tantallon Castle*★★ *(clifftop site*★★★*) AC, NE : 12 m. by A 1 and A 198 – Northern
foothills of the Lammermuir Hills*★★, *S : 14 m. by A 6137 and B 6368 – Stenton*★, *E : 7 m.*
🏌 *Amisfield Park* ℘ *(01620) 823627.*
*Edinburgh 17 – Hawick 53 – Newcastle upon Tyne 101.*

🏨 **Maitlandfield House,** 24 Sidegate, EH41 4BZ, ℘ (01620) 826513, *Fax (01620) 826713,*
🌫 – 🖕 rm, 📺 ☎ 🅿 – 🕍 240. 🐟 🝙 *VISA*
**Meals** a la carte 8.85/19.00 st. ░ 4.45 – **22 rm** �)) 58.00/80.00 st. – SB.

❌❌ **Brown's** with rm, 1 West Rd, EH41 3RD, ℘ (01620) 822254, *Fax (01620) 822254* – 🖕 rest,
📺 ☎ 🅿. 🐟 🝙 🕦 *VISA*. 🌣
**Meals** *(booking essential) (dinner only and Sunday lunch)/dinner* 28.50 t. ░ 5.00 – **5 rm**
�)) 65.00/90.00 t.

**HALKIRK** *Highland* 401 J 8 – *pop. 1 913.*
*Edinburgh 285 – Thurso 8 – Wick 17.*

↑ **Bannochmore Farm** 🍃, Harpsdale, KW12 6UN, South : 3 ¼ m. ℘ (01847) 841216,
« *Working farm* », *park* – 🖕 🅿. 🌣
*closed January and December –* **Meals** 10.00 – **3 rm** �)) 19.00/36.00.

**HAMILTON SERVICE AREA** South Lanarkshire 401 H 16.

ᴛ₉ Larkhall, Burnhead Rd ℘ (01698) 881113 – ᴛ₉ Strathclyde Park, Mote Hill ℘ (01698 429350.

🖪 Road Chef Services, M 74 northbound, ML3 6JW ℘ (01698) 285590.
Edinburgh 38 – Glasgow 12.

🏛 **RoadChef Lodge** without rest., ML3 6JW, M 74 between junctions 6 and 5 (northbound carriageway) ℘ (01698) 891904, Fax (01698) 891682, Reservations (Freephone) 0800 834719 – ⁴⁄₄ 📺 ☎ & 🅿 – 🛦 25. 🚳 🆎 🅪 💳. ✖
closed Christmas and New Year – **36 rm** 45.95 t.

---

**HARRIS (Isle of)** Western Isles (Outer Hebrides) 401 Z 10 – see Lewis and Harris (Isle of).

---

**HEITON** Borders 401 402 M 17 – see Kelso.

---

**HELENSBURGH** Argyll and Bute 401 F 15 Scotland G. – pop. 12 972.

See : Hill House★ AC.
Env. : Loch Lomond★★, NE : 4½ m. by B 832.
Exc. : The Clyde Estuary★.
⇌ to Gourock and via Kilcreggan (Caledonian MacBrayne Ltd and Clyde Marine Motoring Co. Ltd) (except Sunday).
🖪 The Clock Tower, J84 7NY ℘ (01436) 672642 (summer only).
Edinburgh 68 – Glasgow 22.

🏛 **Commodore Toby,** 112-117 West Clyde St., G84 8ES, ℘ (01436) 676924 Fax (01436) 677112, ≤ – ₪ ⁴⁄₄, 🍴 rest, 📺 ☎ 🅿 – 🛦 200. 🚳 🆎 💳 🏧. ✖
Meals (carving rest.) a la carte 9.35/15.35 t. ᵢ 4.45 – **44 rm** ☲ 63.00/78.00 t., 1 suite – SB.

---

**HELMSDALE** Highland 401 J 9.

🖪 Coupar Park ℘ (01431) 821640 (April-Sept).
Edinburgh 227 – Inverness 71 – Thurso 45 – Wick 37.

🏚 **Navidale House** ৯, KW8 6JS, North : ½ m. on A 9 ℘ (01431) 821258 Fax (01431) 821531, ≤, 🐖 – ⁴⁄₄ 📺 🅿. 🚳 💳
mid January-October – **Meals** (bar lunch Monday to Saturday)/dinner 23.00 t. ᵢ 5.75 – **9 rm** ☲ (dinner included) 53.00/134.00 t. – SB.

---

**INGLISTON** Edinburgh City 401 K 16 – see Edinburgh.

---

**INNERLEITHEN** Borders 401 402 K 17 Scotland G..

Env. : Traquair House★★, S : 1 m. on B 709 – Tweed Valley★★.
Edinburgh 30 – Galashiels 12 – Peebles 6.

↷ **The Ley** ৯, EH44 6NL, North : 2 m. on B 709 ℘ (01896) 830240, Fax (01896) 830240
« Part Victorian country house », 🐖, park – ⁴⁄₄ 🅿. ✖
closed November-mid February and April – **Meals** (by arrangement) 23.00 ᵢ 6.00 – **3 rm** ☲ 54.00/88.00.

---

**INVERCRERAN** Argyll and Bute 401 E 14 – ⊠ Appin.

Edinburgh 142 – Fort William 29 – Oban 19.

🏛 **Invercreran Country House** ৯, Glen Creran, PA38 4BJ, ℘ (01631) 730414 Fax (01631) 730532, ≤ Glen Creran and mountains, 🐖, park – ⁴⁄₄ rest, 📺 ☎ 🅿. 🚳 💳. ✖
15 March-14 November – **Meals** (closed Saturday and Sunday lunch) 30.00 t. (dinner) and lunch a la carte 20.00/28.00 t. ᵢ 9.00 – **9 rm** ☲ 70.00/150.00 t. – SB.

---

**INVERGARRY** Highland 401 F 12 Scotland G. – ⊠ Inverness.

Env. : The Great Glen★.
Edinburgh 159 – Fort William 25 – Inverness 43 – Kyle of Lochalsh 50.

🏛 **Glengarry Castle** ৯, PH35 4HW, on A 82 ℘ (01809) 501254, Fax (01809) 501207, ≤, ⟋
🐖, park, ✗ – ⁴⁄₄ 📺 ☎ ☏ 🅿. 🚳 💳
late March-mid November – **Meals** (light lunch Monday to Saturday)/dinner 23.00 – **26 rm** ☲ 52.00/130.00 st. – SB.

🏚 **Ardochy Lodge** ৯, Glengarry, PH35 4HR, West : 7 ½ m. by A 87 on Tomdoun rd
℘ (01809) 511232, Fax (01809) 511233, ≤, ⟋, 🐖, park – ⁴⁄₄ 🅿. 🚳 💳
**Meals** (residents only) (dinner only) ᵢ 4.00 – **8 rm** ☲ (dinner included) 52.50/90.00 t. – SB.

🏠 **Invergarry**, PH35 4HJ, ℰ (01809) 501206, Fax (01809) 501400, ⤴, 🐎 – ⑂ rest, 📺 ☎ 🅿. ⓒ🅑 🄰🄴 𝓥𝓘𝓢𝓐
*closed 1 week Christmas and 4-17 January* – **Meals** (bar lunch)/dinner 16.00 st. ⓘ 5.30 – 10 rm ⛭ 42.00/72.00 st. – SB.

---

**NVERKEILOR** Angus **401** M 14 – *pop. 902* – ✉ Arbroath.
*Edinburgh 85 – Aberdeen 32 – Dundee 22.*

✕✕ **Gordon's** with rm, Homewood House, Main St., DD11 5RN, ℰ (01241) 830364 – ⑂ 📺 🅿. ⓒ🅑 𝓥𝓘𝓢𝓐 𝓙𝓒𝓑
*closed Monday to non residents and last 2 weeks January* – **Meals** (lunch booking essential) a la carte 19.70/24.95 ⓘ 4.80 – **2 rm** ⛭ 25.00/50.00 t.

---

**NVERNESS** Highland **401** H 11 *Scotland G.* – *pop. 62 186.*

See : *Town★ – Museum and Art Gallery★* Y **M.**
Exc. : *Loch Ness★★, SW : by A 82* Z *– Clava Cairns★, E : 9 m. by Culcabock Rd, B 9006 and B 851* Z *– Cawdor Castle★ AC, NE : 14 m. by A 96 and B 9090* Y.
🏌 *Culcabock Rd* ℰ (01463) 239882 Z – 🏌 *Torvean, Glenurquhart Rd* ℰ (01463) 711434.
✈ *Inverness Airport, Dalcross :* ℰ (01463) 232471, *NE : 8 m. by A 96* Y.
🛈 *Castle Wynd, IV2 3BJ* ℰ (01463) 234353 Y.
*Edinburgh 156 – Aberdeen 107 – Dundee 134.*

*Plan on next page*

🏛 **Kingsmills**, Culcabock Rd, IV2 3LP, ℰ (01463) 237166, Fax (01463) 225208, 🎿, 🏊, ⬜, 🐎 – 🛗 ⑂ 📺 ☎ & 🅿 – 🔏 60. ⓒ🅑 𝓥𝓘𝓢𝓐
**Meals** 14.00/24.00 st. and dinner a la carte ⓘ 8.50 – **76 rm** ⛭ 110.00/185.00 st., 1 suite – SB.                                                                                                                Z  s

🏛 **Thistle Inverness**, Millburn Rd, IV2 3TR, East : 1 m. on B 865 ℰ (01463) 239666, Fax (01463) 711145 – 🛗, ⑂ rm, 📺 ☎ 🅿 – 🔏 230. ⓒ🅑 🄰🄴 ① 𝓥𝓘𝓢𝓐 𝓙𝓒𝓑
**Meals** 10.80/18.95 t. and dinner a la carte ⓘ 5.00 – ⛭ 10.75 – **117 rm** 95.00/115.00 st., 1 suite – SB.

🏛 **Caledonian**, 33 Church St., IV1 1DX, ℰ (01463) 235181, Fax (01463) 711206, 🎿, 🏊, ⬜ – 🛗, ⑂ rm, 📺 ☎ & 🅿 – 🔏 300. ⓒ🅑 🄰🄴 ① 𝓥𝓘𝓢𝓐
**Meals** (bar lunch Monday to Saturday)/dinner 16.95 st. and a la carte ⓘ 6.75 – ⛭ 8.50 – **103 rm** 85.00/105.00 st., 3 suites – SB.                                                                Y  u

🏠 **Craigmonie**, 9 Annfield Rd, IV2 3HX, ℰ (01463) 231649, Fax (01463) 233720, 🎿, 🏊, ⬜ – 🛗 ⑂ 📺 ☎ ✆ 🅿 – 🔏 140. ⓒ🅑 🄰🄴 ① 𝓥𝓘𝓢𝓐. ✻
*closed 24 to 27 and 31 December-3 January* – **Bistro :** Meals a la carte 11.45/22.45 t. ⓘ 6.00 – **Chardonnay :** Meals (dinner only and Sunday lunch)/dinner 10.50/25.00 t. ⓘ 6.75 – **32 rm** ⛭ 78.50/108.00 t., 3 suites – SB.                                                         Z  e

🏠 **The Glenmoriston Town House**, 20 Ness Bank, IV2 4SF, ℰ (01463) 223777, Fax (01463) 712378 – 📺 ☎ 🅿 – 🔏 30. ⓒ🅑 🄰🄴 𝓥𝓘𝓢𝓐. ✻
**Meals** – (see **La Riviera** below) – **15 rm** ⛭ 75.00/135.00 st. – SB.                          Z  x

🏠 **Glen Mhor**, 9-12 Ness Bank, IV2 4SG, ℰ (01463) 234308, Fax (01463) 713170 – 📺 ☎ 🅿. ⓒ🅑 𝓥𝓘𝓢𝓐. ✻
*closed 31 December-2 January* – **Meals** 21.00 t. (dinner) and a la carte 9.75/25.00 t. ⓘ 6.50 – **27 rm** ⛭ 58.00/120.00 t. – SB.                                                                              Z  r

🏠 **Culduthel Lodge**, 14 Culduthel Rd, IV2 4AG, ℰ (01463) 240089, Fax (01463) 240089 – ⑂ 📺 ☎ 🅿. ⓒ🅑 𝓥𝓘𝓢𝓐
**Meals** (by arrangement) (dinner only) 18.00 t. ⓘ 6.00 – **11 rm** ⛭ 45.00/95.00 t., 1 suite.                                                                                                                       Z  u

🏠 **Glendruidh House** ⤴, Old Edinburgh Rd South, IV1 2AA, Southeast : 2 m. ℰ (01463) 226499, Fax (01463) 710745, 🐎 – ⑂ 📺 ☎ 🅿. ⓒ🅑 🄰🄴 ① 𝓥𝓘𝓢𝓐 𝓙𝓒𝓑. ✻
**Meals** (residents only) (bar lunch)/dinner 24.50 st. ⓘ 8.50 – **6 rm** ⛭ 55.00/90.00 st. – SB.

🏠 **Loch Ness House**, Glenurquhart Rd, IV3 6JL, Southwest : 1 ½ m. on A 82 ℰ (01463) 231248, Fax (01463) 239327, 🐎 – 📺 ☎ 🅿 – 🔏 100. ⓒ🅑 🄰🄴 ① 𝓥𝓘𝓢𝓐 𝓙𝓒𝓑
**Meals** (bar lunch)/dinner 16.50 t. and a la carte ⓘ 5.75 – **22 rm** ⛭ 60.00/120.00 t.

🏠 **Travel Inn**, Milburn Rd, IV2 3QX, ℰ (01463) 712010 – ⑂ rm, 📺 & 🅿. ⓒ🅑 🄰🄴 ① 𝓥𝓘𝓢𝓐. ✻
**Meals** (grill rest.) – **39 rm** 38.00 t.                                                                                 Y  i

🏠 **Travel Inn**, Beechwood Retail Park, IV2 3BW, East : 2 m. on A 9 ℰ (01463) 232729, Fax (01463) 251553 – ⑂ rm, 📺 & 🅿. ⓒ🅑 🄰🄴 ① 𝓥𝓘𝓢𝓐
**Meals** (grill rest.) – **40 rm** 38.00 t.

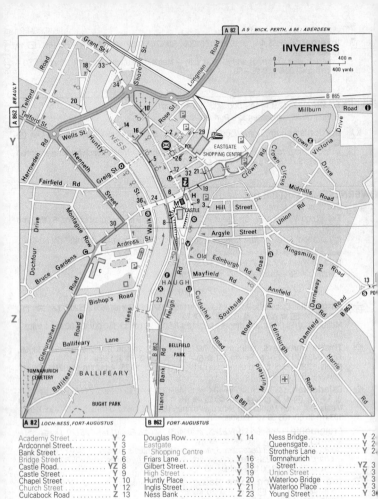

**INVERNESS**

A 82 | A 9 : WICK, PERTH, A 96 : ABERDEEN

A 82 | LOCH-NESS, FORT-AUGUSTUS

B 862 | FORT-AUGUSTUS

↑ **Braemore** without rest., 1 Victoria Drive, IV2 3QB, ℰ (01463) 243318, 🚗 – ⇆ 🅿. ⋘
*closed 1 week Christmas* – 3 rm ⫩ 45.00/55.00 st. Y

↑ **Moyness House**, 6 Bruce Gdns., IV3 5EN, ℰ (01463) 233836, Fax (01463) 233836, 🚗
⇆ rest, 📺 🅿. ⬤⬤ 𝘝𝘐𝘚𝘈 Z
*closed 20 December-4 January* – Meals 18.50 st. ⫝ 5.00 – 7 rm ⫩ 34.00/68.00 st.

↑ **Ballifeary House** without rest., 10 Ballifeary Rd, IV3 5PJ, ℰ (01463) 235572
Fax (01463) 717583, 🚗 – ⇆ 📺 🅿. ⬤⬤ 𝘝𝘐𝘚𝘈 𝘑𝘊𝘉. ⋘ Z
*Easter-October* – 5 rm ⫩ 60.00/72.00 s.

↑ **Old Rectory** without rest., 9 Southside Rd, IV2 3BG, ℰ (01463) 220969, 🚗 – ⇆ 📺 🅿
⬤⬤ 𝘝𝘐𝘚𝘈 𝘑𝘊𝘉. ⋘
*closed Christmas and New Year* – 4 rm ⫩ 22.00/44.00.

↑ **Craigside Lodge** without rest., 4 Gordon Terr., IV2 3HD, ℰ (01463) 23157◖
Fax (01463) 713409, ⇐ – ⇆ 📺 🅿. ⬤⬤ 𝘝𝘐𝘚𝘈. ⋘ Z
6 rm ⫩ 22.00/40.00 t.

✕✕ **La Riviera** (at Glenmoriston Town House), 20 Ness Bank, IV2 4SF, ℰ (01463) 22377◗
Fax (01463) 712378 – ⬤⬤ 𝘈𝘌 𝘝𝘐𝘚𝘈 Z
Meals - Italian - (lunch by arrangement) 22.95 st. (dinner) and a la carte 17.95/28.15 s
⫝ 5.95.

718

✗ **Riverhouse,** 1 Greig St., IV5 3PT, ℰ (01463) 222033, Fax (01463) 220890 – ✤, ◍ ꘎ 𝗩𝗜𝗦𝗔
closed Sunday, Monday except dinner June-September, 25 December and first 2 weeks
January – **Meals** (booking essential) 22.95 **t.** (dinner) and lunch a la carte approx. 17.70
≬ 6.00.                                                                                    Y o

✗ **Riva,** 4-6 Ness Walk, IV3 5NE, ℰ (01463) 237377 – ◍ 𝗩𝗜𝗦𝗔                            Y a
closed Sunday lunch, 25 December and 1 January – **Meals** 5.95 **t.** (lunch) and a la carte
11.85/23.15 **t.** ≬ 5.95.

✗ **Cafe 1,** Castle St., IV2 3EA, ℰ (01463) 226200, Fax (01463) 716363 – ◍ ꘎ 𝗩𝗜𝗦𝗔 𝗝𝗖𝗕
closed Sunday November-May, 25-26 December and 1-2 January – **Meals** a la carte 14.95/
23.85 **st.** ≬ 9.50.                                                                      Y e

**at Dalcross** Northeast : 9 m. by A 96 - Y - , B 9039 and Ardersier rd – ✉ Inverness.

⌂ **Easter Dalziel Farm** ⌂, IV1 2JL, on B 9039 ℰ (01667) 462213, Fax (01667) 462213,
« Working farm », ℛ – ꘎. ◍ 𝗩𝗜𝗦𝗔 𝗝𝗖𝗕
closed 20 December-8 January and booking essential in winter – **Meals** (by arrangement)
(communal dining) 12.00 **s** – **3 rm** ⛱ 28.00/40.00.

**at Culloden** East : 3 m. by A 96 – Y – ✉ Inverness.

🏛 **Culloden House** ⌂, IV1 2NZ, ℰ (01463) 790461, Fax (01463) 792181, ≼, « Georgian
mansion », ≋, ℛ, park, ✗ – ✤ ◳ ☎ ☏ ꘎. ◍ ꘎ ◍ 𝗩𝗜𝗦𝗔 𝗝𝗖𝗕
**Meals** 35.00 **st.** (dinner) and lunch a la carte 17.30/28.60 **st.** ≬ 6.50 – **22 rm** ⛱ 145.00/
190.00 **st.**, 6 suites – SB.

**at Dunain Park** Southwest : 2½ m. on A 82 – Z – ✉ Inverness.

🏛 **Dunain Park** ⌂, IV3 6JN, ℰ (01463) 230512, Fax (01463) 224532, ≼, « Country house,
gardens », ≋, ℛ, park – ✤ rest, ◳ ☎ ☏ ꘎. ◍ ꘎ 𝗩𝗜𝗦𝗔 𝗝𝗖𝗕. ✗
**Meals** (lunch by arrangement)/dinner a la carte 27.85/32.85 **t.** ≬ 7.00 – **6 rm** ⛱ 158.00 **t.**,
6 suites 138.00/178.00 **t.** – SB.

**at Bunchrew** West : 3 m. on A 862 – Y – ✉ Inverness.

🏛 **Bunchrew House,** IV3 6TA, ℰ (01463) 234917, Fax (01463) 710620, ≼, « 17C Scottish
mansion », ℛ, park – ✤ rest, ◳ ☎ ꘎. ◍ ꘎ 𝗩𝗜𝗦𝗔 𝗝𝗖𝗕
**Meals** a la carte 16.50/26.50 **st.** ≬ 6.50 – **11 rm** ⛱ 90.00/140.00 **st.** – SB.

◉ ATS Carsegate Rd North, The Carse ℰ (01463) 236167

---

**INVERURIE** Aberdeenshire ꘎ M 12 Scotland G. – pop. 8 647.

Exc. : Castle Fraser★ (exterior★★) AC, SW : 6 m. by B 993 – Pitmedden Gardens★★, NE : 10
m. by B 9170 and A 920 – Haddo House★, N : 14 m. by B 9170 and B 9005 – Fyvie Castle★,
N : 13 m. by B 9170 and A 947.

🛆 Blackhall Rd ℰ (01467) 620207 – 🛆 Kintore ℰ (01467) 632631 – 🛆 Kemnay, Monymusk
Rd ℰ (01467) 642225.

🅱 Town Hall, Market Pl., AB51 9SN ℰ (01467) 620600 (summer only).

Edinburgh 147 – Aberdeen 17 – Inverness 90.

🏛 **Thainstone House H. & Country Club** ⌂, AB51 5NT, South : 2 m. by B 993 on A 96
ℰ (01467) 621643, Fax (01467) 625084, ℉₄, ⬜, park – ⧒, ✤ rest, ◳ ☎ ☏ – 🔬 300. ◍ ꘎
◍ 𝗩𝗜𝗦𝗔 𝗝𝗖𝗕
**Simpson's : Meals** 17.00/31.00 **t.** and a la carte – ⛱ 12.50 – **47 rm** 120.00/140.00 **t.**,
1 suite – SB.

🏛 **Strathburn,** Burghmuir Drive, AB51 4GY, Northwest : 1¼ m. by A 96 ℰ (01467) 624422,
Fax (01467) 625133, ℛ – ✤, ▤ rest, ◳ ☎ ☏ ꘎ – 🔬 30. ◍ ꘎ 𝗩𝗜𝗦𝗔. ✗
closed 25-26 December and 1-2 January – **Meals** 21.75 **t.** (dinner) and a la carte 10.70/
22.75 **t.** ≬ 5.50 – **25 rm** ⛱ 70.00/95.00 **st.**

---

**ISLAY (Isle of)** Argyll and Bute ꘎ B 16 – pop. 3 840.

🛆 Machrie Hotel, Port Ellen ℰ (01496) 302310.

✈ Port Ellen Airport : ℰ (01496) 302022.

⛴ from Port Askaig to Isle of Jura (Feolin) (Western Ferries (Argyll) Ltd) frequent services
daily (5 mn) – from Port Ellen or Port Askaig to Kintyre Peninsula (Kennacraig) (Caledonian
MacBrayne Ltd) 1-3 daily – from Port Askaig to Oban via Isle of Colonsay (Scalasaig) (Caledonian MacBrayne Ltd) weekly (3 h 45 mn) – from Port Askaig to Isle of Colonsay (Scalasaig)
and Kintyre Peninsula (Kennacraig) (Caledonian MacBrayne Ltd) weekly.

🅱 at Bowmore, The Square ℰ (01496) 810254.

## Ballygrant.

⌂ **Kilmeny Farmhouse** ⬙, PA45 7QW, Southwest : ½ m. on A 846 ℘ (01496) 840668, Fax (01496) 840668, ≤, « Working farm », ⭆, park – ⇥ ❷
*March-October* – **Meals** (by arrangement) (communal dining) 23.00 **st.** – **3 rm** ⌑ 40.00/70.00 **s.** – SB.

🏠 **Ballygrant Inn** with rm, PA45 7QR, ℘ (01496) 840277, Fax (01496) 840277, ⭆ – ⇥ ❷
🐾 🗚 𝗩𝗜𝗦𝗔
**Meals** *(closed Sunday lunch)* 17.50 **st.** (dinner) and lunch a la carte 11.00/17.25 **st.** ⑆ 5.25 – **3 rm** ⌑ 27.50/55.00 **st.** – SB.

## Bridgend – ⊠ Bowmore.

🏨 **Bridgend**, PA44 7PQ, ℘ (01496) 810212, Fax (01496) 810960, ⭆ – ⭤ ☎ ❷. 🐾 𝗩𝗜𝗦𝗔 𝗝𝗖𝗕
**Meals** (bar lunch)/dinner 20.00 **t.** ⑆ 9.95 – **10 rm** ⌑ 42.00/84.00 **t.** – SB.

## Port Charlotte.

🏨 **Port Charlotte**, Main St., PA48 7TU, ℘ (01496) 850360, Fax (01496) 850361, ≤ – ⇥ 📺
☎ 🍴 ❷. 🐾 𝗩𝗜𝗦𝗔 𝗝𝗖𝗕
**Meals** (light lunch) a la carte 9.65/20.80 **t.** ⑆ 7.95 – **10 rm** ⌑ 55.00/85.00 **t.**

## Port Ellen.

⌂ **Glenmachrie Farmhouse**, PA42 7AW, Northwest : 4½ m. on A 846 ℘ (01496) 302560
Fax (01496) 302560, « Working farm », ⬙, ⭆, park – ⇥ 📺 ❷
**Meals** (by arrangement) 20.00 **st.** – **5 rm** ⌑ 38.00/56.00.

---

**ISLEORNSAY** Highland 𝟜𝟘𝟙 C 12 – *see Skye (Isle of)*.

---

**JEDBURGH** Borders 𝟜𝟘𝟙 𝟜𝟘𝟚 M 17 *Scotland G.* – pop. 4 768.
See : Town★ - Abbey★★ **AC** – Mary Queen of Scots House Visitor Centre★ **AC** – The Canongate Bridge★.
Env. : Waterloo Monument (⚹★★) N : 4 m. by A 68 and B 6400.
🏌 Jedburgh, Dunion Rd ℘ (01835) 863587.
🚩 Murray's Green, TD8 6BE ℘ (01835) 863435/863688.
Edinburgh 48 – Carlisle 54 – Newcastle upon Tyne 57.

🏛 **Glenfriars Country House**, The Friars, TD8 6BN, ℘ (01835) 862000
Fax (01835) 862000, ⭆ – 📺 ❷. 🐾 🗚 𝗩𝗜𝗦𝗔
*closed Christmas* – **Meals** (booking essential) (dinner only) 17.50 **t.** ⑆ 4.65 – **6 rm** ⌑ 37.00/80.00 **t.**

⌂ **Hundalee House** ⬙ without rest., TD8 6PA, South : 1½ m. by A 68 ℘ (01835) 863011
Fax (01835) 863011, ≤, ⬙, ⭆, park – ⇥ 📺 ❷. ⅗
*April-October* – **5 rm** ⌑ 35.00/40.00 **t.**

⌂ **The Spinney** without rest., Langlee, TD8 6PB, South : 2 m. on A 68 ℘ (01835) 863525
Fax (01835) 864883, ⭆ – ⇥ 📺 ❷. 🐾 𝗩𝗜𝗦𝗔. ⅗
*March-mid November* – **3 rm** ⌑ 42.00 **st.**

---

**JOHN O'GROATS** Highland 𝟜𝟘𝟙 K 8 – *Shipping Services : see Orkney Islands*.

---

**JOHNSTONE** Renfrewshire 𝟜𝟘𝟙 G 16 – pop. 18 635.
🏌 Cochrane Castle, Scott Ave., Craigstone ℘ (01505) 320146.
Edinburgh 58 – Ayr 35 – Glasgow 13 – Greenock 18.

✗ **Shimla Pinks**, 4 William St., PA5 8DS, ℘ (01505) 322588 – 🐾 🗚 ⓞ 𝗩𝗜𝗦𝗔
*closed 1 January* – **Meals** - Indian - (dinner only) a la carte 10.15/20.15.

---

**JURA (Isle of)** Argyll and Bute 𝟜𝟘𝟙 C 15 – pop. 196.
⛴ from Feolin to Isle of Islay (Port Askaig) (Western Ferries (Argyll) Ltd) frequent service daily (5 mn).

## Craighouse – ⊠ Jura.

🏛 **Jura**, PA60 7XU, ℘ (01496) 820243, Fax (01496) 820249, ≤ Small Isles Bay, ⭆ – ❷. 🐾 🗚
ⓞ 𝗩𝗜𝗦𝗔
*closed 2 weeks Christmas and New Year* – **Meals** (bar lunch)/dinner 16.95 **st.** and a la carte ⑆ 5.95 – **17 rm** ⌑ 32.00/90.00 **st.**

**KELSO** Borders 🗺️ M 17 *Scotland G. – pop. 6 167*.

See : *Town★ – The Square★★ – ≤★ from Kelso Bridge*.

Env. : *Tweed Valley★★ – Floors Castle★ AC, NW : 1½ m. by A 6089*.

Exc. : *Mellerstain★★ (Ceilings★★★, Library★★★) AC, NW : 6 m. by A 6089 – Waterloo Monument (※★★), SW : 7 m. by A 698 and B 6400 – Jedburgh Abbey★★ AC, SW : 8½ m. by A 698 – Dryburgh Abbey★★ AC (setting★★★), SW : 10½ m. by A 6089, B 6397 and B 6404 – Scott's View★★, W : 11 m. by A 6089, B 6397, B 6404 and B 6356 – Smailholm Tower★ (※★★), NW : 6 m. by A 6089 and B 6397 – Lady Kirk (Kirk o'Steil★), NE : 16 m. by A 698, A 697, A 6112 and B 6437*.

🏌️ *Berrymoss Racecourse Rd ℘ (01573) 23009.*

🛈 *Town House, The Square, PD5 7HC ℘ (01573) 223464 (summer only).*

*Edinburgh 44 – Hawick 21 – Newcastle upon Tyne 68.*

🏨 **Ednam House,** Bridge St., TD5 7HT, ℘ (01573) 224168, *Fax (01573) 226319*, ≤, « Part 18C », ☞ – ↩ rm, 📺 ☎ ❷ – 🔬 200. 🅾️ 🆅🆂🅰️
*closed Christmas and New Year –* **Meals** 13.00/21.00 **st.** and lunch a la carte 🍷 5.00 – **32 rm** ☷ 55.00/78.00 **st.** – SB.

**at Heiton** *Southwest : 3 m. by A 698 –* ⊠ *Kelso*.

🏨 **Sunlaws House** ❧, TD5 8JZ, ℘ (01573) 450331, *Fax (01573) 450611*, ≤, « Victorian country house », 🐟, ⚘, ☞, park, 🎾 – ↩ rest, 📺 ☎ ❷. 🅾️ 🅰️🅴 ⓪ 🆅🆂🅰️ 🅹🅲🅱️
*closed 23 to 29 December –* **Meals** 14.50/28.50 **t.** and a la carte 🍷 10.00 – **21 rm** ☷ 105.00/160.00 **t.**, 1 suite – SB.

🔧 *ATS The Butts ℘ (01573) 224997/8*

---

**KENMORE** *Perthshire and Kinross* 🗺️ I 14 *Scotland G. – pop. 596*.

See : *Village★*.

Env. : *Loch Tay★★*.

Exc. : *Ben Lawers★★, SW : 8 m. by A 827*.

🏌️ *Taymouth Castle, Aberfeldy ℘ (01887) 830228 –* 🏌️, 🏌️ *Mains of Taymouth ℘ (01887) 830226*.

*Edinburgh 82 – Dundee 60 – Oban 71 – Perth 38.*

🏨 **Kenmore,** PH15 2NU, ℘ (01887) 830205, *Fax (01887) 830262*, 🏊, 🎣, 🏌️, ⚘, ☞, 🎾 – 🛗, ↩ rest, 📺 ☎ ❷ – 🔬 35. 🅾️ 🅰️🅴 🆅🆂🅰️ 🅹🅲🅱️
**Meals** 15.00/30.00 **t.** and lunch a la carte 🍷 6.50 – **40 rm** ☷ 70.00/140.00 **t.** – SB.

---

**KENTALLEN** *Highland* 🗺️ E 14 – ⊠ *Appin (Argyll and Bute)*.

*Edinburgh 123 – Fort William 17 – Oban 33.*

🏨 **Ardsheal House** ❧, PA38 4BX, Southwest : ¾ m. by A 828 ℘ (01631) 740227, *Fax (01631) 740342*, ≤, « Part 18C country house », ☞, park – ↩ rest, ☎ ❷. 🅾️ 🆅🆂🅰️
*restricted opening in December, closed 25 and 31 December –* **Meals** (residents only) (dinner only) 24.00 **st.** 🍷 7.50 – **6 rm** ☷ 39.00/78.00 **st.**

---

**KEOSE (CEOS)** *Western Isles (Outer Hebrides)* 🗺️ A 9 – *see Lewis and Harris (Isle of)*.

---

**KILBERRY** *Argyll and Bute* 🗺️ D 16 – *see Kintyre (Peninsula)*.

---

**KILCHOAN** *Highland* 🗺️ B 13 – ⊠ *Acharacle*.

*Edinburgh 163 – Inverness 120 – Oban 84.*

⌂ **Far View Cottage** ❧, Mingary Pier Rd, PH36 4LH, ℘ (01972) 510357, ≤ *Sound of Mull*, ☞ – ↩ 📺 ❷. 🎾
*April-October –* **Meals – 3 rm** ☷ (dinner included) 74.00/82.00 – SB.

---

**KILCHRENAN** *Argyll and Bute* 🗺️ E 14 *Scotland G. –* ⊠ *Taynuilt*.

Env. : *Loch Awe★★, E : 1¼m.*

*Edinburgh 117 – Glasgow 87 – Oban 18.*

🏨 **Ardanaiseig** ❧, PA35 1HE, Northeast : 4 m. ℘ (01866) 833333, *Fax (01866) 833222*, ≤ gardens and Loch Awe, « Country house in extensive informal gardens beside Loch Awe », 🎣, park, 🎾 – ↩ rest, 📺 ☎ ❷. 🅾️ 🅰️🅴 ⓪ 🆅🆂🅰️
*closed 2 January-12 February –* **Meals** (dinner only and Sunday lunch)/dinner 35.00 **t.** and a la carte 🍷 10.00 – **16 rm** ☷ 98.00/238.00 **t.** – SB.

721

KILCHRENAN

🏛 **Taychreggan** ॐ, PA35 1HQ, Southeast : 1 ¼ m. ℰ (01866) 833211, Fax (01866) 833244, ≤ Loch Awe and mountains, « Lochside setting », ॐ, ॠ, park – ⅛⅞ rest, ☎ 🗘 🅿. 🕮🕮 Æ VISA 🕮
*closed New Year* – **Meals** 19.50/30.00 **t.** ⚗ 11.00 – **19 rm** ☲ (dinner included) 97.50/ 160.00 **t.** – SB.

**KILDRUMMY** Aberdeenshire 401 L 12 *Scotland G.* – ⊠ *Alford.*
See : *Castle⋆ AC.*
EXC. : *Huntly Castle (Heraldic carvings⋆⋆⋆) N : 15 m. by A 97 – Craigievar Castle⋆, SE : 13 m by A 97, A 944 and A 980.*
*Edinburgh 137 – Aberdeen 35.*

🏛 **Kildrummy Castle** ॐ, AB33 8RA, South : 1 ¼ m. on A 97 ℰ (019755) 71288, Fax (019755) 71345, ≤ gardens and Kildrummy Castle, « 19C mansion in extensive park », ॐ – ⅛⅞ rest, 🔟 ☎ 🅿. 🕮🕮 Æ VISA JCB
*closed 3 January-4 February* – **Meals** 15.50/29.00 **st.** and a la carte ⚗ 6.00 – **16 rm** ☲ 80.00/ 155.00 **st.** – SB.

**KILFINAN** Argyll and Bute 401 E 16 – *pop. 906* – ⊠ *Tighnabruaich.*
*Edinburgh 124 – Glasgow 78 – Oban 78.*

🏛 **Kilfinan** ॐ, PA21 2EP, ℰ (01700) 821201, Fax (01700) 821205, ॠ – 🔟 ☎ 🅿. 🕮🕮 Æ VISA JCB 🕮
*closed February* – **Meals** – (see ***The Restaurant*** below) – **11 rm** ☲ 48.00/98.00 **st.**

✗✗ **The Restaurant** (at Kilfinan H.), PA21 2EP, ℰ (01700) 821201, Fax (01700) 821205, ॠ – ⅛⅞ 🅿. 🕮🕮 Æ VISA JCB
*closed February* – **Meals** (bar lunch)/dinner 28.00 **st.** ⚗ 5.80.

*La guida cambia, cambiate la guida ogni anno.*

**KILLEARN** Stirling 401 G 15 – ⊠ *Glasgow.*
*Edinburgh 60 – Glasgow 19 – Perth 55 – Stirling 22.*

🏛 **Black Bull,** 2 The Square, G63 9NG, ℰ (01360) 550215, Fax (01360) 550143, ॠ – ⅛⅞ rm 🔟 ☎ 🅿 – ⚖ 65. 🕮🕮 Æ VISA
***Brasserie :*** Meals a la carte 15.90/20.65 **st.** ⚗ 6.75 – (see also ***Conservatory*** below) – **11 rm** ☲ 55.00/80.00 **st.** – SB.

✗ **Conservatory** (at Black Bull H.), 2 The Square, G63 9NG, ℰ (01360) 550215 Fax (01360) 550143, ॠ – 🅿. 🕮🕮 Æ VISA
*closed Sunday and Monday dinner* – **Meals** a la carte 19.40/27.40 **st.** ⚗ 6.75.

**KILLIECHRONAN** Argyll and Bute 401 C 14 – *see Mull (Isle of).*

**KILLIECRANKIE** Perthshire and Kinross 401 I 13 – *see Pitlochry.*

**KILLIN** Stirling 401 H 14 *Scotland G.* – *pop. 1 108.*
EXC. : *Loch Tay⋆⋆, Ben Lawers⋆⋆, NE : 8 m. by A 827 – Loch Earn⋆⋆, SE : 7 m. by A 827 an A 85.*
🏌 *Killin ℰ (01567) 820312.*
🛈 *Breadalbane Folklore Centre, Falls of Dochart, FK21 8XE ℰ (01567) 820254 (March. December).*
*Edinburgh 72 – Dundee 65 – Perth 43 – Oban 54.*

🏛 **Dall Lodge Country House,** Main St., FK21 8TN, ℰ (01567) 820217 Fax (01567) 820726, ॠ – ⅛⅞ rest, 🔟 ☎ ㄅ 🅿. 🕮🕮 VISA JCB
*March-October* – **Meals** (dinner only) 23.50 **st.** ⚗ 5.75 – **10 rm** ☲ 42.50/72.00 **st.** – SB.

⌂ **Breadalbane House,** Main St., FK21 8UT, ℰ (01567) 820386, Fax (01567) 820386 – ⅛⅞ 🔟 🅿. 🕮🕮 VISA
*March-October* – 13.00 – **5 rm** ☲ 40.00/44.00.

**at Ardeonaig** (Perthshire and Kinross) Northeast : 6 ¾ m. – ⊠ *Killin (Stirling).*

🏛 **Ardeonaig** ॐ, South Lochtayside, FK21 8SU, ℰ (01567) 820400, Fax (01567) 820282, ≤ ॐ, ॠ, park – ⅛⅞ rest, 🅿. 🕮🕮 VISA JCB
*restricted opening November to March* – **Meals** 29.75 **t.** (dinner) and lunch a la carte 14.75 29.75 **t.** ⚗ 6.50 – **12 rm** ☲ (dinner included) 68.00/136.00 **t.** – SB.

**KILMARNOCK** *East Ayrshire* 401 402 G 17 *Scotland G.*.
See : *Dean Castle (arms and armour★, musical instruments★ ).*
🖪 *62 Bank St., KA1 1ER* ℰ *(01563) 539090.*
*Edinburgh 64 – Ayr 13 – Glasgow 25.*

🏠 **Travel Inn,** Moorfield, KA1 2RS, Southwest : 2 m. by A 759 at junction with A 71
ℰ (01563) 570534, *Fax (01563) 570536* – ⁜ rm, ▤ rest, 🔟 Ꮡ 🅿. �@ AE ① VISA. ⁒
**Meals** (grill rest.) – **40 rm** 38.00 t.

🏠 **Travelodge,** Kilmarnock bypass, Bellfield Interchange, KA1 5LQ, Southeast : 1 ½ m. by A
735 at junction of A 71 with A 76 and A 77 ℰ (01563) 573810, *Fax (01563) 573810,* Reservations (Freephone) 0800 850950 – ⁜ rm, 🔟 Ꮡ 🅿. �@ AE ① VISA JCB. ⁒
**Meals** (grill rest.) – **40 rm** 39.95/59.95 t.

🔧 ATS Riccarton Rd, Hulford ℰ (01563) 520111

---

**KILMORE** *Argyll and Bute* 401 D 14 – *see Oban.*

---

**KILNINVER** *Argyll and Bute* 401 D 14 – *see Oban.*

---

**KINCLAVEN** *Perthshire and Kinross* 401 J 14 – pop. 394 – ⊠ *Stanley.*
*Edinburgh 56 – Perth 12.*

🏰 **Ballathie House** ⌂, PH1 4QN, ℰ (01250) 883268, *Fax (01250) 883396,* ≼, « Country
house in extensive grounds on banks of River Tay », ⌇, 🐎 – ⁜ rest, 🔟 ☎ Ꮡ 🅿. �@ AE
① VISA JCB
**Meals** 29.00 st. (dinner) and lunch a la carte approx. 14.00 st. ᐃ 5.50 – **26 rm** ⊆ 80.00/
160.00 t., 1 suite – SB.

---

| **Les prix** | Pour toutes précisions sur les prix indiqués dans ce guide, reportez-vous aux pages de l'introduction. |
|---|---|

---

**KINCRAIG** *Highland* 401 I 12 *Scotland G.* – ⊠ *Kingussie.*
See : *Highland Wildlife Park★ AC.*
Exc. : *The Cairngorms★★ (≼★★★) – ☀★★★ from Cairn Gorm, E : 14 m. by A 9 and B 970.*
*Edinburgh 119 – Inverness 37 – Perth 75.*

🏠 **Ossian,** The Brae, PH21 1QD, ℰ (01540) 651242, *Fax (01540) 651633,* ≼, ⌇, 🐎 – ⁜ rest,
🔟 ☎ Ꮧ 🅿. �@ VISA JCB
*closed 3 weeks January and 2 weeks November* – **Meals** (bar lunch)/dinner a la carte
19.95/26.40 st. ᐃ 5.25 – **9 rm** ⊆ 30.00/60.00 st.

---

**KINGUSSIE** *Highland* 401 H 12 *Scotland G.* – pop. 1 298.
Env. : *Highland Wildlife Park★ AC, NE : 4 m. by A 9.*
Exc. : *Aviemore★, NE : 11 m. by A 9 – The Cairngorms★★ (≼★★★) – ☀★★★ from Cairn Gorm,
NE : 18 m. by B 970.*
🖪 *Gynack Rd* ℰ *(01540) 661374.*
🖪 *King St., PH21 1HP* ℰ *(01540) 661297 (summer only).*
*Edinburgh 117 – Inverness 41 – Perth 73.*

🏰 **Scot House,** Newtonmore Rd, PH21 1HE, ℰ (01540) 661351, *Fax (01540) 661111* –
⁜ rest, 🔟 ☎ Ꮡ 🅿. �@ VISA JCB
*closed 25 December and 5 January-8 February* – **Meals** (bar lunch)/dinner 19.00 t.
and a la carte ᐃ 6.00 – **9 rm** ⊆ (dinner included) 57.50/105.00 t. – SB.

🏠 **Columba House,** Manse Rd, PH21 1JF, ℰ (01540) 661402, *Fax (01540) 661652,* 🐎 – 🔟
☎ Ꮡ 🅿. �@ AE ① VISA JCB
**Meals** 18.00 st. and lunch a la carte ᐃ 7.20 – **7 rm** ⊆ 47.00/70.00 t. – SB.

↑ **Avondale,** Newtonmore Rd, PH21 1HF, ℰ (01540) 661731, *Fax (01540) 661731,* 🐎 – ⁜
🔟 🅿
**Meals** (by arrangement) 9.00 st. – **6 rm** ⊆ 30.00/42.00 – SB.

↑ **St. Helens** without rest., Ardbroilach Rd, PH21 1JX, ℰ (01540) 661430 – ⁜ 🅿. ⁒
**3 rm** ⊆ 40.00 s.

XXX **The Cross** ⌂ with rm, Tweed Mill Brae, Ardbroilach Rd, PH21 1TC, ℰ (01540) 661166,
*Fax (01540) 661080,* « Converted tweed mill » – ⁜ 🔟 ☎ Ꮡ 🅿. ⁒
*closed 10 January-25 February and 1 to 26 December* – **Meals** *(closed Tuesday)* (booking
essential) (dinner only) 35.00 st. ᐃ 6.50 – **9 rm** ⊆ (dinner included) 80.00/120.00 st.

**KINLOCHMOIDART** Highland **401** C 13 – ⊠ Lochailort.
*Edinburgh 153 – Inverness 110 – Oban 74.*

X **Kinacarra**, PH38 4ND, ℰ (01967) 431238, ≤ – ⁵⊁⇐ **℗**
*Easter-October* – **Meals** *(closed Monday) (booking essential) (light lunch)* a la carte 8.70/
21.20.

**KINROSS** Perthshire and Kinross **401** J 15 – *pop. 5 047.*
ㅤ🏌, 🏌 Green Hotel, 2 The Muirs ℰ (01577) 863407 – 🏌 Milnathort, South St. ℰ (01577)
864064 – 🏌 Bishopshire, Kinnesswood ℰ (01592) 780203.
ㅤ🛈 Turfhills (junction 6, M 90) KY13 7NQ ℰ (01577) 863680.
*Edinburgh 28 – Dunfermline 13 – Perth 18 – Stirling 25.*

🏨 **Green**, 2 The Muirs, KY13 7AS, ℰ (01577) 863467, Fax (01577) 863180, ⇔, ◪, 🏌, ⌦, 🚗,
ㅤ⚗, squash – 📺 ☎ ✆ **℗** – 🕍 140. **◍0** 🆎 ⓪ **VISA** JCB
ㅤ**Meals** *(bar lunch)/dinner* 25.00 t. ₰ 5.25 – **47 rm** ⌦ 75.00/145.00 t. – SB.

🏨 **Windlestrae**, KY13 7AS, ℰ (01577) 863217, Fax (01577) 864733, ℟, ⇔, ◪, 🚗 – ⁵⊁⇐ 📺
ㅤ☎ & **℗** – 🕍 300. **◍0** 🆎 ⓪ **VISA**
ㅤ**Meals** 13.95/21.50 t. ₰ 5.50 – ⌦ 9.25 – **43 rm** 80.00/100.00 t., 2 suites – SB.

X **Croftbank House**, 30 Station Rd, KY13 7TG, ℰ (01577) 863819, Fax (01577) 863819 – ⁵⊁⇐
ㅤ**℗**. **◍0** **VISA** JCB
ㅤ*closed Monday, 1 week February and 2 weeks September* – **Meals** a la carte 13.15/23.15 t.
ㅤ₰ 5.25.

**at Cleish** *Southwest : 4½ m. by B 996 off B 9097* – ⊠ *Kinross.*

🏠 **Nivingston House** ⌖, KY13 7LS, ℰ (01577) 850216, Fax (01577) 850238, ≤, 🚗, park –
ㅤ⁵⊁⇐ rest, 📺 ☎ **℗** – 🕍 60. **◍0** 🆎 **VISA**
ㅤ*closed 2 weeks January* – **Meals** 15.50/25.00 t. ₰ 12.30 – **17 rm** ⌦ 82.00/137.00 t.

**at Kinross Service Area** *West : 1 m. by A 922 on A 977* – ⊠ *Kinross.*

🏩 **Travelodge**, Kincardine Rd, KY13 7NQ, ℰ (01577) 863123, Fax (01577) 864108, Reserva-
ㅤtions (Freephone) 0800 850950 – ⁵⊁⇐ 📺 ☎ & **℗**. **◍0** 🆎 ⓪ **VISA** JCB. ⚗
ㅤ**Meals** *(grill rest.)* – **35 rm** 39.95/59.95 t.

**KINROSS SERVICE AREA** Perthshire and Kinross **401** J 15 – *see Kinross.*

**KINTORE** Aberdeenshire **401** M 12.
*Edinburgh 136 – Aberdeen 14 – Inverness 91.*

🏩 **Torryburn**, School Rd, AB51 0XP, ℰ (01467) 632269, Fax (01467) 632271, 🚗, ⚗ – 📺 ☎
ㅤ**℗** – 🕍 100. **◍0** ⓪ **VISA**. ⚗
ㅤ*closed 26 December* – **Meals** *(bar lunch Monday to Friday)* a la carte 16.05/22.45 t. ₰ 4.75 –
ㅤ**9 rm** ⌦ 39.50/55.00 t.

**KINTYRE (Peninsula)** Argyll and Bute **401** D 16 Scotland G..
ㅤSee : *Carradale★ – Saddell (Collection of grave slabs★ ).*
ㅤ🏌, 🏌 Machrihanish, Campbeltown ℰ (01586) 810213.
ㅤ✈ Campbeltown Airport : ℰ (01586) 553797.
ㅤ⛴ from Claonaig to Isle of Arran (Lochranza) (Caledonian MacBrayne Ltd) frequent
ㅤservices daily (30 mn) – from Kennacraig to Isle of Islay (Port Ellen or Port Askaig) (Caledo-
ㅤnian MacBrayne Ltd) 1-3 daily – from Kennacraig to Oban via Isle of Colonsay (Scalasaig) and
ㅤIsle of Islay (Port Askaig) weekly – from Campbeltown to Ballycastle (Argyll and Antrim
ㅤSteam Packet Co.) 2 daily (2 h 45 mn).

**Campbeltown.**
ㅤ🛈 MacKinnon House, The Pier, PA28 6EF ℰ (01586) 552056.
ㅤ*Edinburgh 176.*

🏩 **Seafield**, Kilkerran Rd, PA28 6JL, ℰ (01586) 554385, Fax (01586) 552741 – 📺 ☎ **℗**. **◍0** 🆎
ㅤ**VISA**
ㅤ**Meals** a la carte 11.85/26.20 t. ₰ 4.95 – **9 rm** ⌦ 48.00/70.00 t.

🏠 **Balegreggan Country House** ⌖, Balegreggan Rd, PA28 6NN, Northeast : 1 m. by
ㅤA 83 ℰ (01586) 552062, Fax (01586) 552062, ≤, 🚗 – ⁵⊁⇐ 📺 **℗**. **◍0** **VISA**
ㅤ**Meals** 20.00 s. – **3 rm** ⌦ 40.00/70.00 s. – SB.

🏠 **Rosemount** without rest., Low Askomil, PA28 6EN, ℰ (01586) 553552, ≤, 🚗 – 📺 **℗**
ㅤ**5 rm** ⌦ 25.00/40.00 s.

**Kilberry.**
Edinburgh 165 – Glasgow 121 – Oban 75.

🍴 **Kilberry Inn** ⌂ with rm, PA29 6YD, ℘ (01880) 770223, Fax (01880) 770223 – ⇔ 📺 **🅿**. **🆗 VISA**
Easter-mid October – **Meals** (closed Sunday) a la carte 14.45/24.40 **t.** ⓵ 5.50 – **3 rm** ⊇ 38.50/67.00 **t.**

**Machrihanish** – pop. 5 722 – ⊠ Campbeltown.
Edinburgh 182 – Oban 95.

⚵ **Ardell House** without rest., PA28 6PT, ℘ (01586) 810235, Fax (01586) 810235, ≤, ⚐ – 📺 **🅿**. **🆗 VISA**
March-October – **10 rm** ⊇ 32.00/62.00.

**Tarbert.**
🔹 Kilberry Rd, Tarbert ℘ (01880) 820565.
🛈 Harbour St. ℘ (01880) 820429 (summer only).

🏨 **Columba**, East Pier Rd, PA29 6UF, East : ¾ m. ℘ (01880) 820808, Fax (01880) 820808, ≤, ⇔ – ⇔ rest, 📺 **🅿**. **🆗 VISA**
closed 25 and 26 December – **Meals** (bar lunch Monday to Saturday)/dinner 19.50 **t.** ⓵ 5.95 – **9 rm** ⊇ 33.95/68.00 **st.**, 1 suite – SB.

✗ **Anchorage**, Harbour St., PA29 6UD, ℘ (01880) 820881, Fax (01880) 820881 – **🆗 VISA JCB**
closed Sunday and Monday November-April – **Meals** (dinner only) a la carte 18.20/23.65 **t.** ⓵ 8.95.

🔘 ATS Burnside St., Campbeltown ℘ (01586) 554404

*Si vous cherchez un hôtel tranquille,*
*consultez d'abord les cartes de l'introduction*
*ou repérez dans le texte les établissements indiqués avec le signe ⌂ ou ⌂.*

---

**KIRKBEAN** Dumfries and Galloway **401 402** J 19 – ⊠ Dumfries.
Edinburgh 89 – Carlisle 41 – Dumfries 12.

⚵ **Cavens Country House** ⌂, DG2 8AA, ℘ (01387) 880234, Fax (01387) 880234, ⚐ – ⇔ rest, 📺 **🅿**. **🆗 VISA**. ⚘
closed late autumnMeals (by arrangement) 16.50 – **6 rm** ⊇ 32.00/60.00 **s.** – SB.

---

**KIRKCALDY** Fife **401** K 15 – pop. 147 053.
🛈 19 Whytescauseway ℘ (01592) 267775.
Edinburgh 30 – Dundee 30 – Glasgow 55 – Perth 29.

🍴 **Feuars Arms**, 28 Bogies Wynd, KY1 2NZ, East : 1 m. by A 921 and Flesh Wynd Rd ℘ (01592) 205025 – **🆗 VISA**
closed dinner Sunday to Thursday – **Meals** a la carte 10.15/15.45 **st.** ⓵ 3.95.

---

**KIRKCOLM** Dumfries and Galloway **401 402** E 19 – see Stranraer.

---

**KIRKCUDBRIGHT** Dumfries and Galloway **401 402** H 19 Scotland G. – pop. 4 188.
See : Town★.
Env. : Dundrennan Abbey★ AC, SE : 5 m. by A 711.
🔹 Stirling Cres. ℘ (01557) 330314.
🛈 Harbour Sq., DG6 4HY ℘ (01557) 330494 (summer only).
Edinburgh 108 – Dumfries 28 – Stranraer 50.

🏨 **Selkirk Arms**, Old High St., DG6 4JG, ℘ (01557) 330402, Fax (01557) 331639, ⚐ – ⇔ 📺 ☎ **🅿**. **🆗 🆔 ① VISA JCB**
**Meals** (bar lunch)/dinner 22.50 **st.** ⓵ 4.65 – **16 rm** ⊇ 60.00/85.00 **st.** – SB.

⚵ **Gladstone House** without rest., 48 High St., DG6 4JX, ℘ (01557) 331734, Fax (01557) 331734, ⚐ – ⇔ 📺. **🆗 VISA**. ⚘
**3 rm** ⊇ 35.00/58.00 **s.**

⚵ **Baytree House**, 110 High St., DG6 4JQ, ℘ (01557) 330824, Fax (01557) 330824, ⚐ – ⇔ 📺 **🅿**
**Meals** (by arrangement) (communal dining) 17.50 – **4 rm** ⊇ 60.00 **s.** – SB.

**KIRKTON OF GLENISLA** *Angus* **401** K 13.
*Edinburgh 73 – Aberdeen 60 – Arbroath 32 – Pitlochry 28.*

🏠 **Glenisla** ॐ, PH11 8PH, on B 951 ℘ (01575) 582223, Fax (01575) 582203 – ❧ rm, ℗. **OC** **VISA**
Meals a la carte 10.50/17.70 t. ⓖ 4.40 – **6 rm** ⊆ 35.00/65.00 t. – SB.

---

**KIRKWALL** *Orkney Islands* **401** L 7 – *see Orkney Islands (Mainland).*

---

**KIRRIEMUIR** *Angus* **401** K 13 – *pop. 6 347.*
*Edinburgh 65 – Aberdeen 50 – Dundee 16 – Perth 30.*

↑ **Purgavie Farm** ॐ, Lintrathen, DD8 5HZ, West : 6 ¾ m. on B 951 ℘ (01575) 560213, Fax (01575) 560213, ≤ – ❧ ▥ ℗
Meals (communal dining) 12.00 **s.** – **3 rm** ⊆ 25.00/40.00 **st.**

---

**KYLESKU** *Highland* **401** E 9 *Scotland G..*
**Env. :** *Loch Assynt★★, S : 6 m. by A 894.*
*Edinburgh 256 – Inverness 100 – Ullapool 34.*

🏠 **Kylesku** ॐ, IV27 4HW, ℘ (01971) 502231, Fax (01971) 502313, ≤ Loch Glencoul and mountains, ↘ – ❧ rest, ▥. **OC** **VISA**
*March-October* – Meals 12.00/15.00 **st.** and a la carte ⓖ 4.50 – **8 rm** ⊆ 35.00/65.00 t. – SB.

🏠 **Newton Lodge** ॐ, IV27 4HW, South : 2 m. on A 894 ℘ (01971) 502070, Fax (01971) 502070, ≤ Loch Glencoul and mountains – ❧ ▥ ℗. **OC** **VISA**
*mid March-mid October* – Meals (residents only) (dinner only) 15.00 **t.** ⓖ 5.50 – **7 rm** ⊆ 60.00 **t.**

*When looking for a quiet hotel*
*use the maps found in the introduction*
*or look for establishments with the sign* ॐ *or* ॐ.

---

**LADYBANK** *Fife* **401** K 15 *Scotland G.* – *pop. 1 373.*
**Env. :** *Falkland★ – Palace of Falkland★ – Gardens★ – Village★, S : ½ m. by A 914 on A 912.*
*Edinburgh 38 – Dundee 20 – Stirling 40.*

↑ **Redlands Country Lodge** ॐ, KY15 7SH, East : ¾ m. by Kingskettle rd taking first left after railway bridge on unmarked road ℘ (01337) 831091, Fax (01337) 831091, ❀ – ❧ ▥ ℗
*March-November* – Meals (by arrangement) 10.00 **s.** – **4 rm** ⊆ 36.00/48.00 **s.** – SB.

---

**LAID** *Highland* **401** F 8 – ⊠ *Lairg.*
🛆 *Balnakeil, Durness* ℘ (01971) 511364.
*Edinburgh 242 – Thurso 59 – Ullapool 95.*

↑ **Port-na-Con House** ॐ, Loch Eribol, IV27 4UN, ℘ (01971) 511367, Fax (01971) 511367, ≤ Loch Eribol – ❧. **OC** **VISA**
*March-October* – Meals (dinner only) 12.00 **st.** – **3 rm** ⊆ 26.00/40.00 **st.**

---

**LAIRG** *Highland* **401** G 9 – *pop. 857.*
*Edinburgh 218 – Inverness 61 – Wick 72.*

↑ **Park House**, IV27 4AU, ℘ (01549) 402208, Fax (01549) 402208, ≤, ❀ – ▥ ℗. **OC** **VISA**
*closed 20 December-6 January* – 16.00 ⓖ 8.50 **3 rm** ⊆ (dinner included) 50.00/80.00 – SB.

---

**LAMLASH** *North Ayrshire* **401** E 17 – *see Arran (Isle of).*

---

**LANGBANK** *Renfrewshire* **401** G 16 *Scotland G..*
**Env. :** *Greenock (≤★★), W : 6 m. by A 8.*
*Edinburgh 63 – Glasgow 17 – Greenock 7.*

🏛 **Gleddoch House** ॐ, PA14 6YE, Southeast : 1 m. by B 789 ℘ (01475) 540711, Fax (01475) 540201, ≤ Clyde and countryside, 🛆, ❀, park, squash – ▥ ☎ ℗ – ⚒ 80. **OC** **AE** **①** **VISA**
Meals 19.50/33.95 **st.** and a la carte – **38 rm** ⊆ 95.00/150.00 **st.** – SB.

**LARGS** *North Ayrshire* 401 402 F 16 *Scotland G. – pop. 11 297.*

See : *Largs Old Kirk★ AC.*

☞ *Irvine Rd ℰ (01475) 674681.*

⏴⏴ *to Great Cumbrae Island (Cumbrae Slip) (Caledonian MacBrayne Ltd) frequent services daily (10 mn) – to Isle of Bute (Rothesay) and Isle of Arran (Brodick) (Caledonian MacBrayne Ltd) 3 weekly.*

🛈 *Promenade, KA30 8BG ℰ (01475) 673765.*

*Edinburgh 76 – Ayr 32 – Glasgow 30.*

🏠 **Brisbane House,** 14 Greenock Rd, Esplanade, KA30 8NF, ℰ (01475) 687200, *Fax (01475) 676295,* ≼ – 🆅 ☎ 🅿 – 🔏 50. 🆗 🆎 🆇 𝒱𝐼𝑆𝐴. ✼
**Meals** (bar lunch)/dinner 19.75 **t.** and a la carte ▯ 8.50 – **23 rm** ⊆ 65.00/140.00 **t.** – SB.

🏠 **Priory House,** Broomfield, KA30 8DR, Southwest : ½ m. by A 78 and Charles St. ℰ (01475) 686460, *Fax (01475) 689070,* ≼, ☞ – 🆅 ☎ 🅿 – 🔏 120. 🆗 🆎 🆇 𝒱𝐼𝑆𝐴
**Meals** (bar lunch)/dinner 21.95 **t.** (dinner) and a la carte 11.40/27.00 **t.** ▯ 5.90 – **21 rm** ⊆ 75.00/125.00 **t.** – SB.

---

**LAUDER** *Berwickshire* 401 L 16 – *pop. 2 199.*

☞ *Galashiels Rd ℰ (01578) 722526.*

*Edinburgh 27 – Berwick-upon-Tweed 34 – Carlisle 74 – Newcastle-upon-Tyne 77.*

🏠 **The Lodge,** Carfraemill, TD2 6RA, Northwest : 4 m. by A 68 on A 697 ℰ (01578) 750750, *Fax (01578) 750751,* ㄹ – ✼ 🆅 ☎ 🅿 – 🔏 200. 🆗 🆎 𝒱𝐼𝑆𝐴 𝐽𝐶𝐵. ✼
**Meals** (grill rest.) a la carte 12.00/20.90 **t.** ▯ 4.95 – **10 rm** ⊆ 48.00/70.00 **t.** – SB.

---

**LERWICK** *Shetland Islands* 401 Q 3 – *see Shetland Islands (Mainland).*

---

**LESLIE** *Fife* 401 K 15 – *see Glenrothes.*

---

**LEVEN** *Fife* 401 K 15.

*Edinburgh 33 – Dundee 33 – Stirling 42.*

🏠 **Old Manor,** Leven Rd, Lundin Links, KY8 6AJ, East : 2 m. on A 915 ℰ (01333) 320368, *Fax (01333) 320911,* ≼, ☞ – ✼ rest, 🆅 ☎ 🅿 – 🔏 160. 🆗 🆎 𝒱𝐼𝑆𝐴 𝐽𝐶𝐵
**Meals** (grill dinner Sunday in winter) 13.50/26.00 **st.** ▯ 5.50 – **23 rm** ⊆ 80.00/170.00 **st.**, 1 suite – SB.

---

**LEVERBURGH** *Western Isles (Outer Hebrides)* 401 Y 10 – *see Lewis and Harris (Isle of).*

---

**LEWIS and HARRIS (Isle of)** *Western Isles (Outer Hebrides)* 401 A 9 *Scotland G..*

See : *Callanish Standing Stones★★ – Carloway Broch★ – St. Clement's Church, Rodel (tomb★ ).*

⏴⏴ *from Stornoway to Ullapool (Mainland) (Caledonian MacBrayne Ltd) (2 h 45 mn) – from Kyles Scalpay to the Isle of Scalpay (Caledonian MacBrayne Ltd) (10 mn) – from Tarbert to Isle of Skye (Uig) (Caledonian MacBrayne Ltd) 1-3 daily (1 h 45 mn) – from Tarbert to Portavadie (Caledonian MacBrayne Ltd) (summer only) frequent services daily (20 mn) – from Leverburgh to North Uist (Otternish) (Caledonian MacBrayne Ltd) (1 h 20 mn).*

### LEWIS.

**Breasclete.**

🏠 **Eshcol** ⏵, 21 Breasclete, HS2 9ED, ℰ (01851) 621357, *Fax (01851) 621357,* ≼, ☞ – ✼ 🆅 🅿
*mid March-mid October* – **Meals** (by arrangement) 19.00 **st.** – **3 rm** ⊆ 38.00/58.00 **st.**

**Galson.**

🏠 **Galson Farm** ⏵, South Galson, HS2 0SH, ℰ (01851) 850492, *Fax (01851) 850492,* ≼, « Working farm », ☞, park – ✼ 🅿. 🆗 𝒱𝐼𝑆𝐴
**Meals** (by arrangement) (communal dining) 16.00 **s.** ▯ 4.25 – **3 rm** ⊆ (dinner included) 51.00/90.00 **s.**

**Keose (Ceos).**

🏠 **Handa** ⏵, 18 Keose Glebe, HS2 9JX, ℰ (01851) 830334, ≼, ➘, ☞ – ✼ 🅿. ✼
*May-October* – (by arrangement) 16.00 – **3 rm** ⊆ 20.00/46.00.

LEWIS and HARRIS (Isle of)

## Stornoway.

🏌️ *Lady Lever Park* ℰ *(01851) 702240.*
🛈 *26 Cromwell St., HS1 2DD* ℰ *(01851) 703088.*

🏨 **Cabarfeidh,** Manor Park, HS1 2EU, North : ½ m. on A 859 ℰ (01851) 702604,
*Fax (01851) 705572 –* 🛗, ✳️ rest, 🍽 rest, 📺 ☎ 📞 🅿 – 🛆 300. 🆎 🆎 ① 𝘝𝘐𝘚𝘈
**Meals** 20.50 **st.** (dinner) and a la carte 26.50/32.50 **st.** 🍴 8.50 – **46 rm** ⇌ 72.00/98.00 **st.** –
SB.

↑ **Ravenswood** without rest., 12 Matheson Rd, HS1 2LR, ℰ (01851) 702673,
*Fax (01851) 702673,* 🚗 – ✳️ 📺 🅿. ✘
*closed 2 weeks October and 2 weeks Christmas-New Year –* **3 rm** ⇌ 20.00/40.00.

## HARRIS.

## Ardvourlie.

🏨 **Ardvourlie Castle** ⌖, HS3 3AB, ℰ (01859) 502307, Fax (01859) 502348, ≤ Loch Seaforth and mountains, « Restored Victorian hunting lodge on shore of Loch Seaforth », 🚗,
park – ✳️ rest, 🅿
*April-September –* **Meals** (residents only) (dinner only) 25.00 🍴 7.00 – **4 rm** ⇌ (dinner
included) 90.00/160.00 **s.**

## Leverburgh.

↑ **Carminish** ⌖, 1a Strond, HS5 3UD, South : 1 m. on Srandda rd ℰ (01859) 520400, ≤
Carminish Islands and Sound of Harris, 🚗 – ✳️ 🅿. ✘
*April-October –* **Meals** (by arrangement) (communal dining) 15.00 **st.** – **3 rm** ⇌ 38.00/
56.00 **st.**

## Scarista.

🏌️ ℰ *(01859) 520236.*

🏨 **Scarista House** ⌖, HS3 3HX, ℰ (01859) 550238, Fax (01859) 550277, ≤ Scarista Bay,
« Part 18C former manse », 🚗 – ✳️ 🅿. 🆎 𝘝𝘐𝘚𝘈. ✘
*May-early October –* **Meals** (booking essential to non-residents) (dinner only) 32.00 **st.**
🍴 5.00 – **5 rm** ⇌ 72.50/115.00 **st.**

## Tarbert – *pop. 795 –* ✉ *Harris.*

↑ **Leachin House** ⌖, HS3 3AH, Northwest : 1 ¼ m. on A 859 ℰ (01859) 502157,
*Fax (01859) 502157,* ≤ Loch Tarbert, 🚗 – ✳️ 📺 🅿. 🆎 𝘝𝘐𝘚𝘈. ✘
*closed 18 December-18 January –* **Meals** (communal dining) 25.00 **st.** – **3 rm** ⇌ 40.00/
80.00 **st.**

↑ **Allan Cottage,** HS3 3DJ, ℰ (01859) 502146 – ✳️ 📺
*5 April-25 September –* **Meals** (communal dining) 22.00 **s.** – **3 rm** ⇌ 32.00/62.00 **s.**

↑ **Hillcrest** ⌖, PA85 3BG, Northwest : 1 ¾ m. on A 859 ℰ (01859) 502119, 🚗 – ✳️ 🅿. ✘
*Easter-October –* **Meals** (by arrangement) (communal dining) 12.00 **s.** – **3 rm** ⇌ 30.00/
34.00 **s.**

## LEWISTON *Highland* 𝟜𝟘𝟙 G 12 *Scotland G.*
Env. : *Loch Ness★★ – The Great Glen★.*
Edinburgh 173 – Inverness 17.

↑ **Woodlands,** East Lewiston, IV3 6UL, ℰ (01456) 450356, 🚗 – ✳️ 📺 🅿. 🆎 𝘝𝘐𝘚𝘈. ✘
*closed 25 and 26 December –* **Meals** (by arrangement) 10.00 **st.** – **3 rm** ⇌ 25.00/40.00 **st.**

↑ **Glen Rowan** without rest., West Lewiston, IV3 6UW, ℰ (01456) 450235,
*Fax (01456) 450817,* 🚗 – ✳️ 📺 🅿. 🆎 🆎 𝘝𝘐𝘚𝘈. ✘
*closed 23 December-2 January –* **3 rm** ⇌ 40.00/45.00 **st.**

## LINICLATE *Western Isles (Outer Hebrides)* 𝟜𝟘𝟙 X/Y 11 – *see Uist (Isles of).*

---

Particularly pleasant hotels and restaurants
are shown in the Guide by a red symbol.

Please send us the names
of anywhere you have enjoyed your stay.

Your **Michelin Guide** will be even better.

🏨🏨🏨 ... 🏨, ↑

✗✗✗✗✗ ... ✗, 🛏

**INLITHGOW** *West Lothian* [401] J 16 *Scotland G. – pop. 13 689.*

**See :** *Town★★ – Palace★★* **AC** *: Courtyard (fountain★★), Great Hall (Hooded Fireplace★★), Gateway★ – Old Town★ – St. Michaels★.*

**Env. :** *Cairnpapple Hill★* **AC**, *SW : 5 m. by A 706 – House of the Binns (plasterwork ceilings★)* **AC**, *NE : 4½ m. by A 803 and A 904.*

**Exc. :** *Hopetoun House★★* **AC**, *E : 7 m. by A 706 and A 904 – Abercorn Parish Church (Hopetoun Loft★★) NE : 7 m. by A 803 and A 904.*

⛳18 *Braehead ☎ (01506) 842585 –* ⛳18 *West Lothian, Airngath Hill ☎ (01506) 826030.*

[i] *Burgh Halls, The Cross, EH49 7EJ ☎ (01506) 844600.*

*Edinburgh 19 – Falkirk 9 – Glasgow 35.*

🏨 **Champany Inn,** Champany, EH49 7LU, Northeast : 2 m. on A 803 at junction with A 904 ☎ (01506) 834532, *Fax (01506) 834302*, 🌳 – [TV] ☎ [P]. [MC] [AE] [D] VISA JCB. 🚫🐕
*closed 25 December* – **Meals** a la carte 29.00/44.40 **t.** 🍷 6.50 – (see also ***The Restaurant*** below) – **16 rm** ☕ 95.00/120.00 **st.**

🍴🍴🍴 **The Restaurant** (at Champany Inn H.), Champany, EH49 7LU, Northeast : 2 m. on A 803 at junction with A 904 ☎ (01506) 834532, *Fax (01506) 834302*, « Converted horse mill », 🌳 – [P]. [MC] [AE] [D] VISA JCB
*closed Saturday lunch and 25 December* – **Meals** (Beef Specialities) 19.50 **st.** (lunch) and a la carte 29.00/44.40 **t.** 🍷 6.50.

🍴🍴 **Livingston's,** 52 High St., EH49 7AE, ☎ (01506) 846565, 🌳 – [MC] VISA. 🚫🐕
*closed Sunday, Monday, 2 weeks January and 1 week June* – **Meals** 13.00 **t.** (lunch) and a la carte 23.95/27.25 **t.** 🍷 6.00.

**IVINGSTON** *West Lothian* [401] J 16 – *pop. 22 357.*

⛳18 *Bathgate, Edinburgh Rd ☎ (01506) 652232 –* ⛳18 *Deer Park C.C., Knightsridge ☎ (01506) 438843.*

*Edinburgh 16 – Falkirk 23 – Glasgow 32.*

🏨 **Hilton National,** Almondview, Almondvale, EH54 6QB, ☎ (01506) 431222, *Fax (01506) 434666*, 🏋, 🏊, 🏊 – 🚭 rm, [TV] ☎ ♿ [P] – 👥 120. [MC] [AE] [D] VISA
**Meals** *(closed Sunday lunch)* 15.95/17.95 **st.** and a la carte 🍷 5.95 – **120 rm** ☕ 155.00/172.00 **st.** – SB.

🏨 **Travel Inn,** Deer Park Av., Deer Park, Knightsridge, EH54 8AD, Northwest : 2 ¾ m. by A 899 at junction 3 of M 8 ☎ (01506) 439202, *Fax (01506) 438912* – 🚭 rm, ▤ rest, [TV] ♿ [P]. [MC] [AE] [D] VISA. 🚫🐕
**Meals** (grill rest.) – **52 rm** 38.00 **t.**

**OANS** *South Ayrshire* [401] [402] G 17 – *see Troon.*

**OCHBOISDALE** *Western Isles (Outer Hebrides)* [401] Y 12 – *see Uist (Isles of).*

**OCHCARRON** *Highland* [401] D 11 *Scotland G. – pop. 870.*

**Env. :** *Wester Ross★★★ – Loch Earn★★.*

[i] *Main St. ☎ (01520) 722357 (summer only).*

*Edinburgh 221 – Inverness 65 – Kyle of Lochalsh 23.*

🏨 **Rockvilla,** Main St., IV54 8YB, ☎ (01520) 722379, *Fax (01520) 722379*, ⋖ Loch Carron – 🚭 rest, [TV]. [MC] [AE] VISA JCB. 🚫🐕
*closed 25 December and 1 January* – **Meals** (bar lunch)/dinner a la carte 12.45/22.25 **t.** 🍷 3.75 – **4 rm** ☕ 36.00/52.00 **t.**

**OCHEARNHEAD** *Stirling* [401] H 14 *Scotland G..*

**Env. :** *Loch Earn★★.*

*Edinburgh 65 – Glasgow 56 – Oban 57 – Perth 36.*

🏨 **Mansewood Country House,** FK19 8NS, South : ½ m. on A 84 ☎ (01567) 830213, 🌳 – 🚭 rest, [TV] [P]. [MC] VISA. 🚫🐕
**Meals** (residents only) (dinner only) 20.00 **t.** 🍷 6.50 – **6 rm** ☕ 34.00/48.00 **t.**

Bitte beachten Sie die Geschwindigkeitsbeschränkungen in Großbritannien
- 60 mph (= 96 km/h) außerhalb geschlossener Ortschaften
- 70 mph (= 112 km/h) auf Straßen mit getrennten Fahrbahnen und Autobahnen.

**LOCHGILPHEAD** Argyll and Bute **401** D 15 Scotland G. – pop. 2 421.
Env. : Loch Fyne★★ , E : 3½ m. by A 83.
🏌 Blarbuie Rd ℘ (01546) 602340.
�🇭 Lochnell St., PA31 8JN ℘ (01546) 602344 (summer only).
Edinburgh 130 – Glasgow 84 – Oban 38.

🏠 **Empire Travel Lodge** without rest., Union St., PA31 8JS, ℘ (01546) 602381 – 📺 ⅄ 🅿
🚾 🚾 ⅏
closed 24 December-1 January – **9 rm** ⊆ 23.00/46.00 st.

**at Cairnbaan** Northwest : 2¼ m. by A 816 on B 841 – ⊠ Lochgilphead.

🏠🏠 **Cairnbaan**, PA31 8SQ, ℘ (01546) 603668, Fax (01546) 606045 – ⅄ 📺 ☎ 🅿 – 🔬 120. 🚾
🇦🇪 🚾 🇯🇨🇧 ⅏
**Meals** (bar lunch)/dinner a la carte 15.65/23.25 st. ⅃ 5.95 – **11 rm** ⊆ 55.00/110.00 st.

---

**LOCH HARRAY** Orkney Islands **401** K 6 – see Orkney Islands (Mainland).

---

**LOCHINVER** Highland **401** E 9 Scotland G. – ⊠ Lairg.
See : Village★.
Env. : Loch Assynt★★ , E : 6 m. by A 837.
🇭 Main St., ID27 4LF ℘ (01571) 844330 (summer only).
Edinburgh 251 – Inverness 95 – Wick 105.

🏠🏠🏠 **Inver Lodge**, IV27 4LU, ℘ (01571) 844496, Fax (01571) 844395, ⩽ Loch Inver Bay, Suilven
and Canisp mountains, ⅌, ⅏, ⅊, park – ⅄ rest, 📺 ☎ 🅿, 🚾 🇦🇪 🇴🇩 🚾 🇯🇨🇧
May-October – **Meals** (bar lunch)/dinner 28.50 st. and a la carte ⅃ 4.50 – **20 rm** ⊆ 80.00/
200.00 st. – SB.

🏠 **The Albannach** ⅏, Baddidarroch, IV27 4LP, West : 1 m. by Baddidarroch r•
⅏ ℘ (01571) 844407, Fax (01571) 844285, ⩽ Loch Inver Bay and Suilven, ⅊ – ⅄ ☎ 🅿. 🚾
🚾 ⅏
booking essential, March-28 December – **Meals** (set menu only) (booking essential) (dinner
only) 25.00 t. ⅃ 6.00 – **5 rm** ⊆ (dinner included) 95.00/140.00 t.

↑ **Davar** without rest., Baddidarroch Rd, IV27 4LJ, West : ½ m. on Baddidarroch r•
℘ (01571) 844501, ⩽ Loch Inver Bay and Suilven – 📺 🅿
April-October – **3 rm** ⊆ 30.00/40.00.

---

**LOCHMADDY** Western Isles (Outer Hebrides) **401** Y 11 – see Uist (Isles of).

---

**LOCHRANZA** North Ayrshire **401 402** E 16 – see Arran (Isle of).

---

**LOCKERBIE** Dumfries and Galloway **401 402** J 18 – pop. 2 301.
🏌 Corrie Rd ℘ (01576) 203363 – 🏌 Lochmaben, Castlehill Gate ℘ (01387) 810552.
Edinburgh 74 – Carlisle 27 – Dumfries 13 – Glasgow 73.

🏠🏠 **Dryfesdale**, DG11 2SF, Northwest : 1 m. on B 7068 ℘ (01576) 202427
Fax (01576) 204187, ⩽, ⅊ – ⅄ 📺 ☎ ⅄ 🅿. 🚾 🚾 🇦🇪 🚾
**Meals** 10.95/18.95 st. and a la carte ⅃ 5.95 – **15 rm** ⊆ 60.00/87.00 st. – SB.

---

**LOSSIEMOUTH** Moray **401** K 10.
🇭 Station Park, Pitgaveny St., IV31 6NT ℘ (01343) 814804 (May-September).
Edinburgh 181 – Aberdeen 70 – Fraserburgh 66 – Inverness 44.

🏠🏠 **Stotfield**, Stotfield Rd, IV31 6QS, ℘ (01343) 812011, Fax (01343) 814820, ⩽, 🇮𝟨, 🇮𝘀 – ⅄•
📺 ☎ ⅄ 🅿 – 🔬 150. 🚾 🇦🇪 🇴🇩 🚾 ⅏
**Meals** (bar lunch Monday to Saturday)/dinner 21.50 t. and a la carte ⅃ 6.50 – **45 rm**
⊆ 42.00/78.00 st.

---

**LUSS** Argyll and Bute **401** G 15 Scotland G. – pop. 402.
See : Village★.
Env. : E : Loch Lomond★★ .
Edinburgh 89 – Glasgow 26 – Oban 65.

🏠🏠 **Lodge on Loch Lomond**, G83 8PA, ℘ (01436) 860201, Fax (01436) 860203, ⩽ Loch•
Lomond, « Lochside setting », 🇮𝘀 – ⅄ rest, 📺 ☎ ⅄ 🅿 – 🔬 40. 🚾 🇦🇪 🚾
**Meals** a la carte 14.05/19.25 t. ⅃ 6.95 – ⊆ 8.00 – **28 rm** 84.00/115.00 t., 1 suite – SB.

🏠 **Inverbeg Inn**, Loch Lomond, G83 8PD, North : 3 m. on A 82 ℘ (01436) 860678
Fax (01436) 860686, ⩽, ⅌, ⅊ – ⅄ 📺 ☎ 🅿. 🚾 🇦🇪 🇴🇩 🚾
**Meals** (bar lunch)/dinner a la carte 14.00/20.00 st. ⅃ 7.50 – **20 rm** ⊆ 65.00/90.00 st. – SB.

**LYBSTER** Highland **401** K 9 Scotland G..

Env. : The Hill o'Many Stanes★, NE : 3½ m. by A 9 – Grey Cairns of Camster★, N : 6 m. by A 9 and minor rd.

Edinburgh 251 – Inverness 94 – Thurso 28 – Wick 14.

🏠 **Portland Arms,** KW3 6BS, on A 9 ℰ (01593) 721208, Fax (01593) 721446 – 📺 ☎ 🅿 – 🔥 200. 🐝 🗚 ⓪ 𝘝𝘐𝘚𝘈

Meals (bar lunch Monday to Saturday)/dinner 22.95 t. and a la carte ₰ 3.75 – **19 rm**
⟺ 45.00/68.00 – SB.

---

**MACHRIHANISH** Argyll and Bute **401** C 17 – see Kintyre (Peninsula).

---

**MARNOCH** Aberdeenshire **401** L 11 Scotland G. – pop. 1 706 – ✉ Huntly.

Exc. : Huntly Castle (elaborate Heraldic Carvings★★★) AC, SW : 10½ m. by B 9117, B 9118 and B 9022.

Edinburgh 170 – Aberdeen 40 – Fraserburgh 39 – Inverness 77.

🏠 **Old Manse of Marnoch** 🌲, AB54 7RS, on B 9117 ℰ (01466) 780873, Fax (01466) 780873, 🌺 – ✦ rest, 📺 🅿 🐝 𝘝𝘐𝘚𝘈 𝘑𝘊𝘉
closed January and February – Meals 27.00 t. ₰ 8.50 – **4 rm** ⟺ 55.00/94.00 t.

---

**MAYBOLE** South Ayrshire **401 402** F 17 Scotland G. – pop. 8 749.

Env. : Culzean Castle★ AC (setting★★★), Oval Staircase★★) W : 5 m. by B 7023 and A 719.

🏠 **Ladyburn** 🌲, KA19 7SG, South : 5½ m. by B 7023 off B 741 (Girvan rd) ℰ (01655) 740585, Fax (01655) 740580, ≼, 🌺, park – ✦ 📺 ☎ ✆ 🅿. 𝘝𝘐𝘚𝘈. ✼
restricted opening in winter – Meals (booking essential to non-residents) 15.00/30.00
₰ 7.50 – **5 rm** ⟺ 115.00/175.00 t. – SB.

---

**MELROSE** Borders **401 402** L 17 Scotland G. – pop. 2 414.

See : Town★ - Abbey★★ (decorative sculpture★★★) AC.

Env. : Eildon Hills (※★★★) – Scott's View★★ – Abbotsford★★ AC, W : 4½ m. by A 6091 and B 6360 – Dryburgh Abbey★★ AC (setting★★★), SE : 4 m. by A 6091 – Tweed Valley★★.

Exc. : Bowhill★★ AC, SW : 11½ m. by A 6091, A 7 and A 708 – Thirlestane Castle (plasterwork ceilings★★) AC, NE : 21 m. by A 6091 and A 68 – 🌰 Melrose, Dingleton ℰ (01896) 822855.

🛈 Abbey House, Abbey St. ℰ (01896) 822555 (summer only).

Edinburgh 38 – Hawick 19 – Newcastle upon Tyne 70.

🏨 **Burts,** Market Sq., TD6 9PN, ℰ (01896) 822285, Fax (01896) 822870, 🌺 – ✦ 📺 ☎ 🅿 – 🔥 30. 🐝 🗚 ⓪ 𝘝𝘐𝘚𝘈 𝘑𝘊𝘉
Meals – (see **The Restaurant** below) – **20 rm** ⟺ 50.00/84.00 t. – SB.

🏨 **Bon Accord,** Market Sq., TD6 9PQ, ℰ (01896) 822645, Fax (01896) 823474 – 📺 ☎. 🐝
𝘝𝘐𝘚𝘈
closed 25 December – Meals a la carte 10.20/19.75 t. ₰ 5.50 – **9 rm** ⟺ 43.00/72.00 t. – SB.

🏠 **Dunfermline House** without rest., Buccleuch St., TD6 9LB, ℰ (01896) 822148, Fax (01896) 822148 – ✦ 📺. ✼
**5 rm** ⟺ 24.00/48.00.

🍴🍴 **The Restaurant** (at Burts H.), Market Sq., TD6 9PN, ℰ (01896) 822285, Fax (01896) 822870, 🌺 – ✦ 🅿. 🐝 🗚 ⓪ 𝘝𝘐𝘚𝘈 𝘑𝘊𝘉
Meals 17.50/25.00 t. ₰ 7.20.

---

**MELVICH** Highland **401** I 8 Scotland G. – ✉ Thurso.

Env. : Strathy Point★ (≼★★★, Ben Loyal★★) NW : 5 m. by A 836 and minor rd.

Edinburgh 267 – Inverness 110 – Thurso 18 – Wick 40.

🏠 **The Sheiling** without rest., KW14 7YJ, on A 836 ℰ (01641) 531256, Fax (01641) 531256, ≼, 🌺 – ✦ 🅿. ✼
March-mid November – **3 rm** ⟺ 30.00/48.00 st.

---

**MEY** Highland **401** K 8.

Edinburgh 302 – Inverness 144 – Thurso 13 – Wick 21.

🏠 **Castle Arms,** KW14 8XH, ℰ (01847) 851244, Fax (01847) 851244 – 📺 ☎ ♿ 🅿. 🐝 🗚 𝘝𝘐𝘚𝘈
𝘑𝘊𝘉
Meals (bar lunch Monday to Saturday)/dinner 17.95 st. and a la carte ₰ 4.85 – **8 rm**
⟺ 39.00/58.00 st.

**MILNGAVIE** *East Dunbarton* **401** H 16 – *pop. 12 592* – ⊠ *Glasgow (Glasgow City)*.
*Edinburgh 53 – Glasgow 7.*

🏠 **Black Bull Thistle**, 1-5 Main St., G62 6BH, ℘ *(0141) 956 2291, Fax (0141) 956 1896* –
⇔ rm, 📺 ☎ 🅿 – 🔬 100. 🌐 🆎 ① 𝘝𝘐𝘚𝘈 𝐉𝐂𝐁
**Meals** 15.95 t. (dinner) and a la carte 18.95/27.85 t. ⒜ 5.25 – ☲ 9.75 – **27 rm** 77.00/93.00 t.
– SB.

**MOFFAT** *Dumfries and Galloway* **401 402** J 17 *Scotland G. – pop. 2 647*.
Exc. : *Grey Mare's Tail*★★, *NE : 9 m. by A 708.*
🏌 *Coatshill* ℘ *(01683) 220020.*
🄳 *Churchgate, DG10 9EG* ℘ *(01683) 220620 (summer only).*
*Edinburgh 61 – Dumfries 22 – Carlisle 43 – Glasgow 60.*

🏠 **Moffat House**, High St., DG10 9HL, ℘ *(01683) 220039, Fax (01683) 221288, � – ⇔ 📺
☎ 🅿. 🌐 𝘝𝘐𝘚𝘈*
**Meals** (bar lunch)/dinner 21.00 t. and a la carte ⒜ 5.75 – **20 rm** ☲ 57.00/98.00 t. – SB.

🏠 **Buccleuch Arms**, High St., DG10 9ET, ℘ *(01683) 220003, Fax (01683) 221291, � –
⇔ rest, 📺 ☎ 📞. 🌐 🆎 𝘝𝘐𝘚𝘈*
**Meals** a la carte 13.00/19.25 ⒜ 6.00 – **15 rm** ☲ 39.00/55.00 st. – SB.

🏠 **Beechwood Country House** ⌖, Harthope Pl., DG10 9RS, North : ½ m. by A 701
℘ *(01683) 220210, Fax (01683) 220889, ≤, � – ⇔ rest, 📺 ☎ 🅿. 🌐 🆎 𝘝𝘐𝘚𝘈 𝐉𝐂𝐁*
*closed 2 January-20 February –* **Meals** *(closed lunch Monday to Thursday)* (dinner booking
essential) 15.00/23.50 t. ⒜ 6.00 – **7 rm** ☲ 52.00/74.00 t. – SB.

🏠 **Fernhill** without rest., Grange Rd, DG10 9HT, North : ¼ m. by A 701 ℘ *(01683) 220077, 🌫
– 📺. ✻*
*April-September –* **3 rm** ☲ 26.00/40.00.

🏠 **Alba House** without rest., 20 Beechgrove, DG10 9RS, Northwest : ½ m. by A 701
℘ *(01683) 220418, Fax (01683) 220418, 🌫 – ⇔ 📺. ✻*
*restricted opening in winter –* **3 rm** ☲ 30.00/45.00 s.

🏠 **Hartfell House**, Hartfell Cres., DG10 9AL, Northeast : ½ m. by Well St. and Old Well Rd
℘ *(01683) 220153, 🌫 – ⇔ rest, 📺 🅿*
*April-October –* **Meals** (by arrangement) 12.50 st. ⒜ 4.50 – **8 rm** ☲ 26.00/48.00 t.

✕✕ **Well View** ⌖ with rm, Ballplay Rd, DG10 9JU, East : ¾ m. by Selkirk rd (A 708)
℘ *(01683) 220184, Fax (01683) 220088, ≤, 🌫 – ⇔ 📺 🅿. 🌐 🆎 𝘝𝘐𝘚𝘈*
*closed 2 weeks January –* **Meals** *(closed Saturday lunch)* (booking essential) 14.00/28.00 st.
⒜ 8.20 – **5 rm** ☲ 57.00/90.00 st., 1 suite – SB.

**at Beattock** *Southwest : 2¼ m. by A 701 – ⊠ Moffat.*

🏠 **Auchen Castle** ⌖, DG10 9SH, North : 2 m. by A 74 ℘ *(01683) 300407,
Fax (01683) 300667, ≤, 🎣, 🌫, park – 📺 ☎ 🅿 – 🔬 60. 🌐 🆎 ① 𝘝𝘐𝘚𝘈 𝐉𝐂𝐁*
*closed 22 December-12 January –* **Meals** (bar lunch Monday to Saturday)/dinner 22.00 t.
⒜ 7.00 – **25 rm** ☲ 55.00/110.00 t. – SB.

**MONTROSE** *Angus* **401** M 13 *Scotland G. – pop. 8 473*.
Exc. : *Edzell Castle★ (The Pleasance★★★) AC, NW : 17 m. by A 935 and B 966 – Cairn
O'Mount Road★ (≤★★) N : 17 m. by B 966 and B 974 – Brechin (Round Tower★) W : 7 m. by
A 935 – Aberlemno (Aberlemno Stones★, Pictish sculptured stones★) W : 13 m. by A 935
and B 9134.*
🏌, 🏌 *Traill Drive* ℘ *(01674) 672932.*
🄳 *Bridge St.,* ℘ *(01674) 672000 (summer only).*
*Edinburgh 92 – Aberdeen 39 – Dundee 29.*

🏠 **Oaklands** without rest., 10 Rossie Island Rd, DD10 9NN, on A 92 ℘ *(01674) 672018,
Fax (01674) 672018 –* 📺 🅿. 🌐 𝘝𝘐𝘚𝘈
**7 rm** ☲ 22.00/35.00 s.

**MOTHERWELL** *North Lanarkshire* **401** I 16.
🄳 *Library, Hamilton Rd, ML1 3DZ* ℘ *(01698) 267676.*
*Edinburgh 38 – Glasgow 12.*

🏠 **Holiday Inn Express** without rest., Strathclyde Country Park, Hamilton Rd, ML1 3RB,
Northwest : 4 ¼ m. by A 721 and B 7070 off A 725 ℘ *(01698) 858585, Fax (01698) 852375 –*
🤳, ⇔ rm, ≣ rest, 📺 ☎ & 🅿 – 🔬 30. 🌐 🆎 ① 𝘝𝘐𝘚𝘈 𝐉𝐂𝐁
**120 rm** 54.50 st.

🏠 **Travel Inn,** Edinburgh Rd, Newhouse, ML1 5SY, Northeast : 4 ¼ m. by A 723 on A 775 *ℰ* (01698) 860277, *Fax (01698) 861353* – ✸ rm, 📺 & 🄿 – 🛋 100. 🌐 🇦🇪 🅾 *VISA*. ⚘
**Meals** (grill rest.) – **40 rm** 38.00 **t.**

🏠 **Travel Inn,** Bellziehill Farm, Bellshill, ML4 3HH, Northwest : 3 ½ m. on A 721 at junction with A 725 *ℰ* (01698) 740180, *Fax (01698) 845969* – 🛗, ✸ rm, 📺 ☎ 🄿. 🌐 🇦🇪 🅾 *VISA*. ⚘
**Meals** (grill rest.) – **40 rm** 38.00 **t.**

---

**MUIR OF ORD** *Highland* **401** G 11 – *pop. 2 033.*
🏌 *Great North Rd ℰ (01463) 870825.*
*Edinburgh 173 – Inverness 10 – Wick 121.*

🏠 **Dower House** ⌂, Highfield, IV6 7XN, North : 1 m. on A 862 *ℰ* (01463) 870090, *Fax (01463) 870090, « Part 17C »*, ⚘ – ✸ 📺 🄿. 🌐 *VISA*
**Meals** (set menu only) (booking essential to non-residents) (lunch by arrangement)/dinner 25.00 **st.** – **5 rm** ⊆ 55.00/120.00 **st.**, 1 suite – SB.

---

**MULL (Isle of)** *Argyll and Bute* **401** BC 14/15 *Scotland G.* – *pop. 2 838.*
**See :** *Island★ - Calgary Bay★★ – Torosay Castle AC (Gardens★ ≤★ ).*
**Env. :** *Isle of Iona★ (Maclean's Cross★, St. Oran's Chapel★, St. Martin's High Cross★, Infirmary Museum★ AC (Cross of St. John★ )).*
🏌 *Craignure, Scallastle ℰ (01680) 812487/812416.*
🚢 *from Craignure to Oban (Caledonian MacBrayne Ltd) (40 mn) – from Fishnish to Lochaline (Mainland) (Caledonian MacBrayne Ltd) frequent services daily (15 mn) – from Tobermory to Isle of Tiree (Scarinish) via Isle of Coll (Arinagour) (Caledonian MacBrayne Ltd) 3 weekly (2 h 30 mn) – from Tobermory to Kilchoan (Caledonian MacBrayne Ltd) 4-6 daily (summer only) (35 mn) – from Tobermory to Oban (Caledonian MacBrayne Ltd) 3 weekly (1 h 30 mn).*
🚢 *from Fionnphort to Isle of Iona (Caledonian MacBrayne Ltd) frequent services daily (5 mn).*
🛈 *Main St., Tobermory ℰ 01688 (Tobermory) 302182.*

**Bunessan** – ✉ *Fionnphort.*

🏠 **Ardfenaig House** ⌂, PA67 6DX, West : 3 m. by A 849 *ℰ* (01681) 700210, *Fax (01681) 700210,* ≤ *Loch Scridain*, ⚘, park – ✸ 📺 🄿 *VISA*. ⚘
*April-October* – **Meals** (booking essential to non-residents) (dinner only) 28.50 **st.** ♦ 6.95 – **5 rm** ⊆ (dinner included) 82.00/164.00 **st.** – SB.

🏠 **Assapol House** ⌂, PA67 6DW, Southeast : 1 ½ m. by A 849 *ℰ* (01681) 700258, *Fax (01681) 700445,* ≤, « *Lochside setting* », ⚘ – ✸ 📺 ☎ 🄿. 🌐 *VISA*. ⚘
*Easter-mid October* – **Meals** (residents only) (dinner only) 25.00 **st.** ♦ 4.50 – **5 rm** ⊆ (dinner included) 52.00/132.00 **st.** – SB.

**Dervaig** – ✉ *Tobermory.*

🏠 **Druimard Country House** ⌂, PA75 6QW, on Salen rd *ℰ* (01688) 400345, *Fax (01688) 400345,* ≤, ⚘ – ✸ rest, 📺 ☎ 🄿. 🌐 *VISA*
*April-October* – **Meals** *(closed Sunday to non-residents)* (dinner only) 26.50 **t.** – **5 rm** ⊆ (dinner included) 72.00/143.00 **t.**, 1 suite.

🏠 **Balmacara,** PA75 6QN, East : ¼ m. on B 8073 *ℰ* (01688) 400363, *Fax (01688) 400363,* ≤, ⚘ – ✸ rm, 📺 🄿. ⚘
**Meals** (by arrangement) 13.50 **st.** – **3 rm** ⊆ 35.00/58.00 **st.** – SB.

**Killiechronan.**

🏠 **Killiechronan House** ⌂, PA72 6JU, on B 8073 *ℰ* (01680) 300403, *Fax (01680) 300463,* ≤, ⚘, ⚘, park – ✸ ☎ 🄿. 🌐 🇦🇪 *VISA*
*March-October* – **Meals** (booking essential to non-residents) (dinner only and Sunday lunch)/dinner 25.00 **t.** ♦ 5.95 – **6 rm** ⊆ (dinner included) 60.00/120.00 **t.** – SB.

**Tobermory** – *pop. 2 708.*
🏌 *Tobermory ℰ (01688) 2020.*

🏠 **Western Isles,** PA75 6PR, *ℰ* (01688) 302012, *Fax (01688) 302297,* ≤ *Tobermory harbour and Calve Island* – ✸ rest, 📺 ☎ 🄿. 🌐 🇦🇪 *VISA*
*closed 18 to 28 December* – **Meals** (bar lunch)/dinner 26.00 **t.** ♦ 8.00 – **Spices :** Meals - Asian - *(closed Monday, Tuesday and November-April)* (dinner only) a la carte 14.50/23.75 **t.** ♦ 8.00 – **24 rm** ⊆ 47.00/114.00 **t.**, 1 suite – SB.

**Tobermory,** 53 Main St., PA75 6NT, ℰ (01688) 302091, Fax (01688) 302254, ← – ⅍ rest 🖾 🐽 VISA. ⅍
*closed 1 week Christmas* – **Waters Edge :** Meals *(closed lunch in winter)* (booking essentia to non-residents) 23.50 **st.** (dinner) and lunch a la carte 11.00/19.00 **st.** 🕯 5.95 – **16 rm** ⊊ 39.00/90.00 **st.** – SB.

**Fairways Lodge** ⍊ without rest., Golf Course, PA75 6PS, Northeast : ½ m. by B 882 ℰ (01688) 302238, Fax (01688) 302238, ← Calve Island and Sound of Mull, ⟨ᵦ – ⅍ 🖾 🅿 **5 rm** ⊊ 36.00/72.00 **st.**

**Ulva House,** Strongarbh, PA75 6PR, ℰ (01688) 302044, ← Tobermory harbour and Calve Island, ⇗ – ⅍ 🅿
*March-October* – **Meals** 19.50 **st.** 🕯 6.50 – **6 rm** ⊊ (dinner included) 58.50/105.00 **st.**

---

**MUSSELBURGH** *East Lothian* 401 K 16 – *pop. 18 425.*

⟨ᵦ Monktonhall ℰ (0131) 665 2005 – ⟨ᵦ Royal Musselburgh, Prestongrange House, Prestonpans ℰ (01875) 810276 – ⟨ᵦ Musselburgh Old Course, Silver Ring Clubhouse, Millhill ℰ (0131) 665 6981.
🅱 Brunton Hall, EH21 6AF ℰ (0131) 665 6597 *(summer only).*
*Edinburgh 6 – Berwick 54 – Glasgow 53.*

**Travel Inn,** Carberry Rd, Inveresk, EH21 8PT, Southeast : 1 ½ m. on A 6124 ℰ (0131) 665 3005, Fax (0131) 653 2270 – ⅍ rm, 🖾 ⅍ 🅿. 🐽 ℀ ① VISA
**Meals** (grill rest.) – **40 rm** 38.00 **t.**

**Travelodge,** Old Craighall, EH21 8RE, South : 1 ½ m. by B 6415 at junction with A 1 ℰ (0131) 653 6070, Fax (0131) 653 6106, Reservations (Freephone) 0800 850950 – ⅍ rm, 🖾 🕿 🕹 🅿. 🐽 ℀ ① VISA JCB. ⅍
**Meals** (grill rest.) – **45 rm** 39.95/59.95 **t.**

---

**NAIRN** *Highland* 401 I 11 *Scotland G.* – *pop. 10 623.*

**Env. :** Forres (Sueno's Stone★★) E : 11 m. by A 96 and B 9011 – Cawdor Castle★ AC, S : 5½ m. by B 9090 – Brodie Castle★ AC, E : 6 m. by A 96.
**Exc. :** Fort George★, W : 8 m. by A 96, B 9092 and B 9006.
⟨ᵦ, ⟨ᵦ Seabank Rd ℰ (01667) 452103 – ⟨ᵦ Nairn Dunbar, Lochloy Rd ℰ (01667) 452741.
🅱 62 King St. ℰ (01667) 452753 *(summer only).*
*Edinburgh 172 – Aberdeen 91 – Inverness 16.*

**Golf View,** 63 Seabank Rd, IV12 4HD, ℰ (01667) 452301, Fax (01667) 455267, ←, 🕯𝔰, 🕿, 🔲, ⇗, ℀ – 📱, ⅍ rest, 🖾 🕿 🅿 – 🔬 120. 🐽 ℀ ① VISA JCB
**Meals** 24.95 **t.** (dinner) and a la carte 10.25/18.50 **t.** 🕯 6.75 – **46 rm** ⊊ 93.00/149.00 **t.**, 1 suite – SB.

**Newton** ⍊, IV12 4RX, ℰ (01667) 453144, Fax (01667) 454026, ⇗ – 📱, ⅍ rest, 🖾 🕿 🅿 – 🔬 60. 🐽 ℀ ① VISA JCB
**Meals** 21.50 **t.** (dinner) and a la carte 11.15/14.65 **t.** 🕯 6.75 – **29 rm** ⊊ 87.00/195.00 **t.** – SB.

**Claymore House,** 45 Seabank Rd, IV12 4EY, ℰ (01667) 453731, Fax (01667) 455290, ⇗ – ⅍ rest, 🖾 🕿 🕹 🕹 🅿. 🐽 ℀ VISA
**Meals** 7.50/9.95 **st.** and a la carte 🕯 4.50 – **15 rm** ⊊ 42.50/85.00 **st.**, 1 suite – SB.

**Clifton House** ⍊, Viewfield St., IV12 4HW, ℰ (01667) 453119, Fax (01667) 452836, ←, « Antiques », ⇗ – 🕹 🅿. 🐽 ℀ ① VISA
*closed mid December-mid January* – **Meals** (booking essential) a la carte 20.00/27.50 **st.** – **12 rm** ⊊ 60.00/107.00 **st.**

**Links,** 1 Seafield St., IV12 4HN, ℰ (01667) 453321, Fax (01667) 456092, ←, ⇗ – ⅍ rest, 🖾 🕿 🅿. 🐽 ℀ VISA
**Meals** (dinner only) 15.00 **st.** and a la carte 🕯 6.00 – **10 rm** ⊊ 35.00/75.00 **st.** – SB.

**Inveran Lodge** without rest., Seabank Rd, IV12 4HG, ℰ (01667) 455666, Fax (01667) 455666, ⇗ – ⅍ 🖾 🅿. 🐽 ℀ VISA
**3 rm** ⊊ 50.00/100.00 **st.**

**at Auldearn** *East : 2 m. on A 96* – ⊠ *Nairn.*

**Boath House,** IV12 5TE, ℰ (01667) 454896, Fax (01667) 454896, « Georgian mansion », 🕯𝔰, ⍊, ⇗ – ⅍ 🖾 🕿 🕹 🅿. 🐽 ℀ ① VISA
**Meals** a la carte 21.50/37.50 **t.** 🕯 6.40 – **7 rm** ⊊ 65.00/120.00 **st.**

---

**NETHERLEY** *Aberdeenshire* 401 N 12 *Scotland G.* – ⊠ *Stonehaven.*

**Env. :** Muchalls Castle (plasterwork ceilings★★) AC, SE : 5 m. by B 979 – Deeside★★, N : 2 m. by B 979 – Aberdeen★★, NE : 3 m. by B 979 and B 9077.
**Exc. :** Aberdeen★★, NE : 12 m. by – Dunnottar Castle★★ (site★★★) AC, S : 7 m. by B 979 – Crathes Castle★★ (Gardens★★★) AC, NW : 13 m. by B 979, B 9077 and A 93.
*Edinburgh 117 – Aberdeen 12 – Dundee 54.*

XX **Lairhillock**, AB39 3QS, Northeast : 1 ½ m. by B 979 on Portlethan rd *&* (01569) 730001,
Fax (01569) 731175 – 🅿. 🕮 🄰🄴 🄾 𝘝𝘐𝘚𝘈 JCB. ⌘
closed 25-26 December and 1-2 January – **Meals** (bar lunch Monday to Saturday)/dinner
27.95 t. and a la carte 🛔 6.10.

---

**NEWBURGH** Aberdeenshire 🈞 N 12 Scotland G..
Exc. : Pitmedden Gardens★★ AC, W : 6½ m. by B 9000 – Haddo House★ AC, NW : 14 m. by
B 900, A 92 and B 9005.
🖥 McDonald, Ellon *&* (01358) 720576 – 🖥 Newburgh-on-Ythan, Ellon *&* (01358) 789058.
Edinburgh 144 – Aberdeen 14 – Fraserburgh 33.

🏛 **Udny Arms**, Main St., AB41 6BL, *&* (01358) 789444, Fax (01358) 789012, ⌘ – 🅃🅅 ☎ 🅿 –
🛓 45. 🕮 🄰🄴 🄾 𝘝𝘐𝘚𝘈 JCB
**Meals** – (see **The Restaurant** below) – **24 rm** ⫸ 65.00/90.00 t. – SB.

XX **The Restaurant** (at Udny Arms H.), Main St., AB41 6BL, *&* (01358) 789444,
Fax (01358) 789012 – 🅿. 🕮 🄰🄴 🄾 𝘝𝘐𝘚𝘈.
**Meals** 18.95 t. (dinner) and a la carte 16.85/32.65 t. 🛔 9.75.

---

**NEW LANARK** Lanarkshire 🈞 I 17.
Edinburgh 44 – Dumfries 55 – Glasgow 31.

🏛 **New Lanark Mill**, Mill One, New Lanark Mills, MK11 9DB, *&* (01555) 667200,
Fax (01555) 667222, « Converted riverside cotton mill » – 🛗 ⌘, 🍴 rest, 🅃🅅 ☎ ✆ & 🅿 –
🛓 200. 🕮 🄰🄴 🄾 𝘝𝘐𝘚𝘈
**Meals** 16.50 t. (dinner) and lunch a la carte 10.00/14.00 t. – **38 rm** ⫸ 60.00/80.00 t. – SB.

---

**NEW SCONE** Perthshire and Kinross 🈞 J 14 – see Perth.

---

**NEWTONMORE** Highland 🈞 H 12 – pop. 1 044.
🖥 Newtonmore *&* (01540) 673328.
Edinburgh 113 – Inverness 43 – Perth 69.

⌂ **The Pines** ⌘, Station Rd, PH20 1AR, *&* (01540) 673271, ≤, ⌘ – ⌘ 🅃🅅 🅿. ⌘
mid April-mid October – **Meals** 10.00 st. 🛔 5.90 – **5 rm** ⫸ 24.50/49.00 st. – SB.

---

**NEWTON STEWART** Dumfries and Galloway 🈞 🈟 G 19 Scotland G. – pop. 2 543.
Env. : Galloway Forest Park★, Queen's Way★ (Newton Stewart to New Galloway) N : 19 m. by
A 712.
🖥, Kirroughtree Av., Minnigaff *&* (01671) 402172.
🄱 Dashwood Sq., DG8 6DQ *&* (01671) 402431 (summer only).
Edinburgh 131 – Dumfries 51 – Glasgow 87 – Stranraer 24.

🏛 **Kirroughtree House** ⌘, DG8 6AN, Northeast : 1 ½ m. by A 75 on A 712
*&* (01671) 402141, Fax (01671) 402425, ≤ woodland and Wigtown Bay, « 18C mansion in
landscaped gardens », ⌘ – ⌘ rest, 🅃🅅 ☎ 🅿. 🕮 🄰🄴 𝘝𝘐𝘚𝘈. ⌘
closed 3 January-mid February – **Meals** 30.00 st. (dinner) and lunch a la carte 17.25/
22.00 st. 🛔 8.00 – **15 rm** ⫸ 75.00/150.00, 2 suites – SB.

🏛 **Creebridge House** ⌘, Minnigaff, DG8 6NP, *&* (01671) 402121, Fax (01671) 403258, ⌘
– ⌘ rest, 🅃🅅 ☎ 🅿. 🕮 🄰🄴 𝘝𝘐𝘚𝘈 JCB
**Meals** 18.00 t. (dinner) and a la carte 10.55/20.20 t. 🛔 5.00 – **19 rm** ⫸ 55.00/120.00 t. – SB.

🏠 **Crown**, 101 Queen St., DG8 6JW, *&* (01671) 402727, Fax (01671) 402727 – 🅃🅅 ☎ 🅿. 🕮
𝘝𝘐𝘚𝘈
**Meals** (bar lunch)/dinner 13.50 t. and a la carte 🛔 5.50 – **10 rm** ⫸ 29.50/50.00 t. – SB.

---

**NORTH BERWICK** East Lothian 🈞 L 15 Scotland G. – pop. 5 871.
Env. : North Berwick Law (✳★★★) S : 1 m. - Tantallon Castle★★ (clifftop site★★★) AC,
E : 3½ m. by A 198 – Dirleton★ (Castle★ AC) SW : 2½ m. by A 198.
Exc. : Museum of Flight★, S : 6 m. by B 1347 – Preston Mill★, S : 8 ½ m. by A 198 and
B 1047 – Tyninghame★, S : 7 m. by A 198 – Coastal road from North Berwick to Portseton★,
SW : 13 m. by A 198 and B 1348.
🖥 North Berwick, West Links, Beach Rd *&* (01620) 892135 – 🖥 Glen, East Links *&* (01620)
892221.
🄱 Quality St., EH39 4HJ *&* (01620) 892197.
Edinburgh 24 – Newcastle upon Tyne 102.

**Marine,** 18 Cromwell Rd, EH39 4LZ, ☎ (01620) 892406, *Fax (01620) 894480*, ≤ golf course and Firth of Forth, ☎, ⌧, ☞, ⌧ – ⃚ ⌧ ⌧ ⊘ – ⃚ 250. ⃗ ⌧ ⌧
**Meals** (bar lunch Monday to Saturday)/dinner a la carte approx. 20.35 **s.** ⃚ 7.50 – ⌧ 10.25 – **78 rm** 100.00/140.00 **st.**, 5 suites – SB.

**Glebe House** ⌧ without rest., Law Rd, EH39 4PL, ☎ (01620) 892608, « Georgian manse », ☞ – ⌧ ⌧ ⊘. ⌧
*closed Christmas and New Year* – **3 rm** ⌧ 35.00/60.00 **st.**

**Craigview** without rest., 5 Beach Rd, EH39 4AB, ☎ (01620) 892257 – ⌧ ⌧. ⌧
**3 rm** ⌧ 45.00 **st.**

---

**NORTH QUEENSFERRY** Fife ⃗ J 15 *Scotland G.* – ⊠ *Inverkeithing.*
Env. : Forth Bridges★★ (toll).
*Edinburgh 13 – Dunfermline 7 – Glasgow 42 – Kirkcaldy 16 – Perth 33.*

**Queensferry Lodge,** St. Margarets Head, KY11 1HP, North : ½ m. on B 981 ☎ (01383) 410000, *Fax (01383) 419708*, ≤ – ⃚ ⌧ ⌧ ⌧ ⊘ – ⃚ 130. ⃗ ⌧ ⌧
**Meals** a la carte 11.85/19.95 **st.** ⃚ 5.25 – ⌧ 9.75 – **77 rm** 80.00/100.00 **st.** – SB.

---

**NORTH UIST** Western Isles (Outer Hebrides) ⃗ XY 10/11 – *see Uist (Isles of).*

---

**OBAN** Argyll and Bute ⃗ D 14 *Scotland G.* – pop. 8 203.
Exc. : Loch Awe★★, SE : 17 m. by A 85 – Bonawe Furnace★, E : 12 m. by A 85 – Cruachan Power Station★ *AC*, E : 16 m. by A 85 – Sea Life Centre★ *AC*, N : 14 m. by A 828.
⃗ Glencruitten, Glencruitten Rd ☎ (01631) 562868.
*Access to Glasgow by helicopter.*
⤶ to Isle of Mull (Craignure) (Caledonian MacBrayne Ltd) (40 mn) – to South Uist (Lochboisdale) via Isle of Barra (Castlebay) (Caledonian MacBrayne Ltd) (summer only) – to Isle or Tiree (Scarinish) via Isle of Mull (Tobermory) and Isle of Coll (Arinagour) (Caledonian MacBrayne Ltd) – to Isle of Islay (Port Askaig) and Kintyre Peninsula (Kennacraig) via Isle of Colonsay (Scalasaig) (Caledonian MacBrayne Ltd) (summer only) – to Isle of Lismore (Achnacroish) (Caledonian MacBrayne Ltd) 2-5 daily (except Sunday) (50 mn) – to Isle of Colonsay (Scalasaig) (Caledonian MacBrayne Ltd) 3 weekly (2 h 30 mn) – to Isle of Mull (Tobermory) (Caledonian MacBrayne Ltd) 3 weekly (1 h 30 mn).
⃗ Boswell House, Argyll Sq., PA34 4AR ☎ (01631) 563122.
*Edinburgh 123 – Dundee 116 – Glasgow 93 – Inverness 118.*

**Manor House,** Gallanach Rd, PA34 4LS, ☎ (01631) 562087, *Fax (01631) 563053*, ≤, ☞ – ⌧ ⌧ ⌧ ⊘. ⃗ ⌧ ⌧
*closed Monday and Tuesday mid November-March* – **Meals** (lunch by arrangement)/dinner 24.95 **t.** and a la carte ⃚ 7.10 – **11 rm** ⌧ (dinner included) 110.00/160.00 **t.** – SB.

**Dungallan House,** Gallanach Rd, PA34 4PD, ☎ (01631) 563799, *Fax (01631) 566711*, ≤, ☞ – ⌧ rest, ⌧ ⊘. ⃗ ⌧
*closed February and November* – **Meals** (lunch booking essential) 25.00 **t.** (dinner) and lunch a la carte 9.75/20.25 **t.** ⃚ 4.50 – **13 rm** ⌧ 46.50/93.00 **t.**

**Barriemore** without rest., Corran Esplanade, PA34 5AQ, ☎ (01631) 566356, *Fax (01631) 566356*, ≤ – ⌧ ⌧ ⌧ ⊘. ⃗ ⌧
*March-November* – **13 rm** ⌧ 30.00/58.00 **t.**

**Glenburnie** without rest., Corran Esplanade, PA34 5AQ, ☎ (01631) 562089, *Fax (01631) 562089*, ≤ – ⌧ ⌧ ⌧ ⊘. ⌧
*March-October* – **15 rm** ⌧ 30.00/70.00 **st.**

**Kilchrenan House** without rest., Corran Esplanade, PA34 5AQ, ☎ (01631) 562663, *Fax (01631) 562663*, ≤ – ⌧ ⌧ ⊘. ⌧
*Easter-October* – **10 rm** ⌧ 28.00/62.00 **t.**

**Sealladh Briagha** without rest., Gallanach Rd, PA34 4PD, ☎ (01631) 565067, *Fax (01631) 565067*, ≤ – ⌧ ⌧ ⊘. ⌧
*March-November* – **3 rm** ⌧ 35.00/45.00.

**at Kilmore** South : 4 m. on A 816 – ⊠ *Oban.*

**Invercairn** ⌧ without rest., Musdale Rd, PA34 4XX, ☎ (01631) 770301, ≤, ☞ – ⊘. ⌧
*May-September* – **3 rm** ⌧ 20.00/48.00.

**at Kilninver** Southwest : 8 m. by A 816 on B 844 – ⊠ *Oban.*

**Knipoch,** PA34 4QT, Northeast : 1½ m. on A 816 ☎ (01852) 316251, *Fax (01852) 316249*, ≤, ☞ – ⌧ ⌧ ⌧. ⃗ ⌧ ⌧ ⌧. ⌧
*March-early December* – **Meals** (lunch by arrangement)/dinner 29.50 **t.** ⃚ 8.00 – **16 rm** ⌧ 97.00/200.00 **t.**

**OLDMELDRUM** Aberdeenshire **401** N 11 Scotland G..

EXC. : Haddo House★, NE : 9 m. by B 9170 on B 9005.

Edinburgh 140 – Aberdeen 17 – Inverness 87.

🏛 **Meldrum House** ⬧, AB51 0AE, North : 1 ½ m. on A 947 ℘ (01651) 872294, Fax (01651) 872464, ≼, « Part 13C baronial house », 🐎, park – ✻ rest, 🆃 ☎ ❷ – 🛃 50. **◯◯** **VISA**
Meals 25.50 st. (dinner) and a la carte 23.00/26.95 st. ▯ 7.50 – **9 rm** ⌸ (dinner included) 75.00/130.00 st. – SB.

⌂ **Cromlet Hill** without rest., South Rd, A51 0AB, ℘ (01651) 872315, Fax (01651) 872164 – ✻ 🆃 ☎ ❷. ✻
**2 rm** ⌸ 35.00/65.00 s., 1 suite.

**ONICH** Highland **401** E 13 – ✉ Fort William.

Edinburgh 123 – Glasgow 93 – Inverness 79 – Oban 39.

🏛 **The Lodge on the Loch**, Creag Dhu, PH33 6RY, on A 82 ℘ (01855) 821237, Fax (01855) 821238, ≼ Loch Linnhe and mountains, ▯ – ✻ rest, 🆃 ☎ ⅄ ❷. **◯◯** **VISA**
closed 5 January-March – Meals 9.95/25.50 st. ▯ 7.00 – **18 rm** ⌸ (dinner included) 83.00/166.00 st., 1 suite – SB.

🏛 **Allt-Nan-Ros**, PH33 6RY, on A 82 ℘ (01855) 821210, Fax (01855) 821462, ≼ Loch Linnhe and mountains, 🐎 – ✻ rest, 🆃 ☎ ❷. **◯◯** **VISA**
Meals (bar lunch)/dinner 28.00 ▯ 6.50 – **20 rm** ⌸ (dinner included) 79.50/174.00 t. – SB.

🏛 **Onich**, PH33 6RY, on A 82 ℘ (01855) 821214, Fax (01855) 821484, ≼ Loch Linnhe and mountains, « Lochside setting », 🐎 – ✻ rest, 🆃 ☎ ❷ **◯◯** **AE** **◑** **VISA**
closed 1 week Christmas and 10 days January – Meals (bar lunch)/dinner 21.00 t. ▯ 5.25 – **25 rm** ⌸ 55.00/100.00 t. – SB.

| Les prix | Pour toutes précisions sur les prix indiqués dans ce guide, reportez-vous aux pages de l'introduction. |
|---|---|

**OPINAN** Highland **401** C 10 – ✉ Laide.

Edinburgh 233 – Inverness 77 – Kyle of Lochalsh 73.

⌂ **Obinan Croft** ⬧, IV22 2NU, ℘ (01445) 731548, Fax (01445) 731635, ≼ Mountains, estuary and bay, 🐎 – ✻ ❷. **◯◯** **VISA** **JCB**. ✻
March-October – Meals (communal dining) 20.00 st. ▯ 6.75 – **4 rm** ⌸ (dinner included) 65.00/110.00 st.

**ORD** Highland **401** C 12 – see Skye (Isle of).

**ORKNEY ISLANDS** Orkney Islands **401** KL 6/7 Scotland G. – pop. 19 612.

See : Old Man of Hoy★★★ – Islands★★ – Maes Howe★★ AC – Skara Brae★★ AC – Corrigal Farm Museum★ AC – Brough of Birsay★ AC – Birsay (≼★) – Ring of Brodgar★ – Unstan Cairn★.

⛵ see Kirkwall.

⛴ service between Isle of Hoy (Longhope), Isle of Hoy (Lyness), Isle of Flotta and Houton (Orkney Ferries Ltd) – from Stromness to Scrabster (P & O Scottish Ferries) (1 h 45 mn) – from Stromness to Shetland Islands (Lerwick) and Aberdeen (P & O Scottish Ferries) – from Kirkwall to Westray, Stronsay via Eday and Sanday (Orkney Ferries Ltd) – from Tingwall to Wyre via Eglisay and Rousay (Orkney Ferries Ltd) – from Kirkwall to Shapinsay (Orkney Ferries Ltd) (25 mn) – from Stromness to Isle of Hoy (Moness) (Orkney Ferries Ltd) – from Kirkwall to North Ronaldsay (Orkney Ferries Ltd) – from Houton to Isle of Hoy (Lyness) (Orkney Ferries Ltd) – from Stromness to Graemsay via Isle of Hoy (Orkney Ferries Ltd).

⛴ from Burwick (South Ronaldsay) to John O'Groats (John O'Groats Ferries) 1-4 daily (45 mn).

**Burray.**

⌂ **Ankersted**, KW17 2SS, East : ½ m. on A 961 ℘ (01856) 731217, Fax (01856) 731298, ≼, 🐎 – ✻ rm, 🆃 ❷. ✻
Meals (by arrangement) 14.00 st. – **4 rm** ⌸ 16.00/30.00 s.

**Dounby.**

🏛 **Smithfield**, KW17 2HT, ℘ (01856) 771215, Fax (01856) 771494 – ✻ rest, 🆃 ❷. **◯◯** **VISA**
April-October – Meals a la carte 10.00/17.80 t. – **6 rm** ⌸ 25.00/50.00 t.

**Kirkwall** *Scotland G.* – pop. 5 952.

> See : *Kirkwall★★ – St. Magnus Cathedral★★ – Western Mainland★★, Eastern Mainland (Italia Chapel★) – Earl's Palace★ AC – Tankerness House Museum★ AC – Orkney Farm and For Museum★.*

> 🏌 *Grainbank ℰ (01856) 872457.*

> ✈ *Kirkwall Airport : ℰ (01856) 872421, S : 3½ m.*

> 🛈 *6 Broad St., Kirkwall, KW15 1DH ℰ (01856) 872856.*

🏨 **Ayre,** Ayre Rd, KW15 1QX, ℰ (01856) 873001, Fax (01856) 876289 – 📺 ☎ 🅿 – 🔬 200. 🆀 AE VISA
Meals 6.95/19.00 t. and a la carte ↥ 4.30 – **33 rm** ⌂ 54.00/98.00 t. – SB.

🏨 **Albert,** Mounthoolie Lane, KW15 1JZ, pedestrian area off Junction Rd ℰ (01856) 87600C
Fax (01856) 875397 – 📺 ☎. 🆀 AE ① VISA
closed 25 and 26 December – Meals 8.50/21.50 t. and a la carte ↥ 6.25 – **19 rm** ⌂ 55.50 85.50 t. – SB.

🏨 **Foveran** ⤳, St. Ola, KW15 1SF, Southwest : 3 m. on A 964 ℰ (01856) 872389
Fax (01856) 876430, « Overlooking Scapa Flow », 🐎, park – ⇔ rest, 📺 ☎ 🅿. 🆀 VISA JCB
closed 25 December and January-mid February – Meals (closed Sunday to non-residents (dinner only) a la carte approx. 16.45 t. – **8 rm** ⌂ 45.00/70.00 t.

🏨 **Queens,** Shore St., KW15 1LG, ℰ (01856) 872200, Fax (01856) 873871 – ⇔ rest, 📺 ☎. 🆀 AE VISA. ⦇
closed 25 December and 1 January – Meals (in bar) a la carte 8.60/23.00 t. – **9 rm** ⌂ 33.00 46.00 t.

🏨 **St. Ola** without rest., Harbour St., KW15 1LE, ℰ (01856) 875090, Fax (01856) 875090 – 📺
☎. 🆀 AE VISA. ⦇
closed Christmas – **6 rm** ⌂ 30.00/42.00 t.

🏨 **West End,** Main St., KW15 1BU, ℰ (01856) 872368, Fax (01856) 876181 – 📺 ☎ 🅿. 🆀 A VISA JCB. ⦇
closed 2 weeks Christmas – Meals (closed Sunday lunch) (in bar) a la carte 7.90/15.70 st ↥ 3.50 – **16 rm** ⌂ 36.00/54.00 st. – SB.

⌂ **Royal Oak,** Holm Rd, KW15 1PY, South : 1 m. by A 960 on A 961 ℰ (01856) 877177
Fax (01856) 877177 – ⇔ rest, 📺 🅿. 🆀 VISA JCB. ⦇
Meals (by arrangement) 10.00 st. – **8 rm** ⌂ 26.00/44.00 st.

⌂ **Polrudden,** Peerie Sea Loan, KW15 1UH, West : ¾ m. by Pickaquoy Rd ℰ (01856) 874761
Fax (01856) 870950 – ⇔ rest, 📺 🅿. ⦇
closed Christmas and New Year – Meals (by arrangement) 12.50 st. – **7 rm** ⌂ 27.00 42.00 t.

⌂ **Brekk-Ness** without rest., Muddisdale Rd, KW15 1RS, West : 1 m. by Pickaquoy Rd ℰ (01856) 874317, Fax (01856) 874317 – 📺 🅿
**11 rm** ⌂ 29.00/48.00 t.

🅰 ATS Junction Rd, Kirkwall ℰ (01856) 872361

**Loch Harray.**

🏨 **Merkister** ⤳, KW17 2LF, off A 986 ℰ (01856) 771366, Fax (01856) 771515, ⩽ Loch Harray, ⤳, 🐎 – ⇔ rest, 📺 ☎ 🅿. 🆀 AE VISA JCB
closed Christmas-New Year – Meals (bar lunch Monday to Saturday)/dinner 17.00 t and a la carte ↥ 5.50 – **14 rm** ⌂ (dinner included) 57.50/130.00 t. – SB.

**St. Margaret's Hope.**

❌❌ **Creel** with rm, Front Rd, KW17 2SL, ℰ (01856) 831311, ⩽ – ⇔ 📺 🅿. 🆀 VISA. ⦇
closed Monday to Friday October-March, January and February – Meals (dinner only a la carte 25.00/34.50 t. – **3 rm** ⌂ 35.00/60.00.

**Stenness.**

🏨 **Standing Stones,** KW16 3JX, on A 965 ℰ (01856) 850449, Fax (01856) 851262, ⤳, 🐎 – ⇔ rm, 📺 ☎ 🅿. 🆀 AE VISA JCB
closed 25 December-3 January – Meals (booking essential) (bar lunch)/dinner 16.50 t and a la carte ↥ 4.50 – **17 rm** ⌂ 40.00/74.00 t.

**Stromness** *Scotland G..*

> See : *Town★ - Pier Gallery (collection of abstract art★).*

⌂ **Stenigar** without rest., Ness Rd, KW16 3DW, South : ½ m. by Main St. ℰ (01856) 850438
⩽, 🐎 – 📺 🅿. ⦇
April-October – **3 rm** ⌂ 30.00/50.00 st.

↑ **Thira** ⌂, Innertown, KW16 3JP, Northwest : 1 ½ m. by Back Rd, turning right at mini roundabout, taking first right onto unmarked road and then left at two junctions *ℰ* (01856) 851181, *Fax* (01856) 851182, *≤* Hoy Island and Sound, *☞ – ⚒ 📺 🄿. ⚓*
**Meals** (by arrangement) 10.00 **st. – 4 rm** �);= 23.00/46.00.

---

**PAISLEY** Renfrewshire **401** G 16 – pop. 43 602.
⛳ Braehead *ℰ* (0141) 884 2292.
Edinburgh 56 – Ayr 36 – Glasgow 11 – Greenock 16 – Kilmarnock 22.

🏠 **Travel Inn,** Phoenix Retail Park, Linwood, PA1 2BH, West : 2 ¼ m. by A 721 *ℰ* (0141) 887 4865, *Fax* (0141) 887 2799 – 📳, ⚒ rm, ▤ rest, 📺 ₰ 🄿. 🐵 🅰🄴 ① ▨▨▨. ⚓
**Meals** (grill rest.) **– 40 rm** 38.00 **t.**

↑ **Myfarrclan,** 146 Corsebar Rd, PA2 9NA, Southwest : 1 ¾ m. on B 775 *ℰ* (0141) 884 8285, *Fax* (0141) 884 8285, *☞ – ⚒ 📺. 🐵 ▨▨▨. ⚓*
**Meals** (by arrangement) (communal dining) 18.00 **st. – 3 rm** ☒= 60.00/70.00 **st. –** SB.

---

**PEAT INN** Fife **401** L 15 Scotland G. – ✉ Cupar.
Exc. : Kellie Castle★, SE : 7½ m. by B 940 and minor roads.
Edinburgh 45 – Dundee 21 – Perth 28.

XXX **The Peat Inn** ⌂ with rm, KY15 5LH, *ℰ* (01334) 840206, *Fax* (01334) 840530, *☞ –*
⚒ rest, 📺 ₰ ₰ 🄿. 🐵 🅰🄴 ① ▨▨▨ ᴊᴄʙ
closed Sunday, Monday, 25 December and 1 January – **Meals** (booking essential) 19.50/
29.00 **st.** and dinner a la carte 29.00/34.50 **st.** ₰ 7.00 **– 1 rm** 135.00 **st., 7 suites** 145.00 **st. –**
SB.

*Se cercate un albergo tranquillo,*
*oltre a consultare le carte dell'introduzione,*
*rintracciate nell'elenco degli esercizi quelli con il simbolo ⌂ o ⌂.*

---

**PEEBLES** Borders **401** **402** K 17 Scotland G. – pop. 7 065.
Env. : Tweed Valley★★.
Exc. : Traquair House★★ AC, SE : 7 m. by B 7062 – Rosslyn Chapel★★ AC, N : 16½ m. by A 703, A 6094, B 7026 and B 7003.
⛳ Kirkland St. *ℰ* (01721) 720197.
🅿 High St., EH45 8AG *ℰ* (01721) 720138.
Edinburgh 24 – Hawick 31 – Glasgow 53.

🏨 **Peebles Hydro,** Innerleithen Rd, EH45 8LX, *ℰ* (01721) 720602, *Fax* (01721) 722999, *≤,*
*₰, ≦s, 🏊, ☞, park, ⚒, squash – 📳 📺 ☎ ₰ 🄿 – 🕍 450. 🐵 🅰🄴 ① ▨▨▨. ⚓*
**Meals** 16.00/23.00 **st.** ₰ 7.50 **– 135 rm** ☒= (dinner included) 74.00/141.00 **st.,** 2 suites – SB.

🏨 **Park,** Innerleithen Rd, EH45 8BA, *ℰ* (01721) 720451, *Fax* (01721) 723510, *☞ – ⚒ 📺 ☎*
₰. 🐵 🅰🄴 ① ▨▨▨
**Meals** (bar lunch)/dinner 20.00 **t.** ₰ 7.95 **– 24 rm** ☒= (dinner included) 72.00/150.00 **t. –** SB.

🏨 **Cringletie House** ⌂, EH45 8PL, North : 3 m. on A 703 *ℰ* (01721) 730233, *Fax* (01721) 730244, *≤, « Victorian country house in extensive grounds », ☞, ⚒ – 📳,*
⚒ rest, 📺 ☎ ₰. 🐵 🅰🄴 ▨▨▨
**Meals** 14.95/29.50 ₰ 6.95 **– 13 rm** ☒= (dinner included) 94.50/130.00 **t. –** SB.

---

**PERTH** Perthshire and Kinross **401** J 14 Scotland G. – pop. 14 432.
See : City★ – Black Watch Regimental Museum★ Y **M1** – Georgian Terraces★ Y – Museum and Art Gallery★ Y **M2**.
Env. : Scone Palace★★ AC, N : 2 m. by A 93 Y – Branklyn Garden★ AC, SE : 1 m. by A 85 Z – Kinnoull Hill (≤★) SE : 1¼m. by A 85 Z – Huntingtower Castle★ AC, NW : 3 m. by A 85 Y – Elcho Castle★ AC, SE : 4 m. by A 912 – Z – and Rhynd rd.
Exc. : Abernethy (11C Round Tower★), SE : 8 m. by A 912 – Z – and A 913.
⛳ Craigie Hill, Cherrybank *ℰ* (01738) 624377 Z – ⛳ King James VI, Moncreiffe Island *ℰ* (01738) 625170/632460 Z – ⛳ Murrayshall, New Scone *ℰ* (01738) 551171 Y – ⛳ North Inch, c/o Perth & Kinross Council, 5 High St. *ℰ* (01738) 636481 Y.
🅿 45 High St., PH1 5TJ *ℰ* (01738) 638353 – Inveralmond, A 9 Western City bypass *ℰ* (01738) 638481.
Edinburgh 44 – Aberdeen 86 – Dundee 22 – Dunfermline 29 – Glasgow 64 – Inverness 112 – Oban 94.

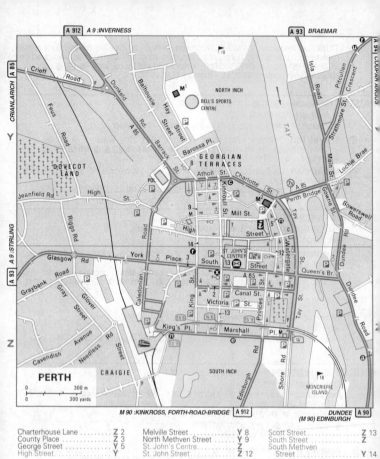

🏯 **Kinfauns Castle**, PH2 7JZ, East : 3 m. on A 90 ℰ (01738) 620777, Fax (01738) 620778
« Carefully restored 19C castle, oriental furnishings », ◜, ☞, park – ♨ rest, ⊡ ☎ ℗ –
🔬 60. ⑩ 🅰🅴 ⱽⁱˢᵃ 🄹🄲🄱
Meals (closed Monday to non-residents February-April) 18.50/32.50 t. and a la carte 🍷 7.50
– 14 rm ⇌ 120.00/220.00 t., 2 suites.

🏛 **Hunting Tower** ⌁, Crieff Rd, PH1 3JT, West : 3 ½ m. by A 85 ℰ (01738) 583771
Fax (01738) 582077, ☞ – ⊡ ☎ ℗ – 🔬 180. ⑩ 🅰🅴 ⱽⁱˢᵃ
Meals 11.95/18.95 **st.** and a la carte 🍷 6.75 – **24 rm** ⇌ 85.00/99.50 t., **19 suites** 95.50/
129.50 t – SB.

🏛 **Parklands**, St. Leonard's Bank, PH2 8EB, ℰ (01738) 622451, Fax (01738) 622046, ☞ –
♨ rest, ⊡ ☎ ℗ – 🔬 25. ⑩ 🅰🅴 ⱽⁱˢᵃ
Z r
closed 24 December-8 January – **Meals** a la carte 12.95/24.80 **st.** 🍷 6.20 – ⇌ 10.50 – **14 rm**
89.00/135.00 st. – SB.

🏛 **Dupplin Castle** ⌁, PH2 0PY, Southwest : 6 ¼ m. on A 9 ℰ (01738) 623224
Fax (01738) 444140, ≤, « Scottish mansion house, gardens », park – ♨ rm, ☎ ℃ ℗. ⑩
ⱽⁱˢᵃ 🄹🄲🄱, ⌘
Meals (booking essential) (residents only) (communal dining) (dinner only) 28.00 t. 🍷 8.00 –
6 rm ⇌ 55.00/110.00 t.

🏛 **Sunbank House**, 50 Dundee Rd, PH2 7BA, ℰ (01738) 624882, Fax (01738) 442515, ☞ –
♨ ⊡ ☎ ℃ ℗. ⑩ ⱽⁱˢᵃ. ⌘
Z a
Meals (dinner only) 22.50 t. and a la carte 🍷 6.75 – **9 rm** ⇌ 59.00/72.00 t.

🏠 **Park Lane** without rest., 17 Marshall Pl., PH2 8AG, ☎ (01738) 637218, *Fax (01738) 643519* – 🚭 [TV] [P]. [MC] [AE] VISA JCB. 🐕 Z e
*closed December-21 January* – **6 rm** ☕ 24.00/48.00 **s.**

🏠 **Aberdeen** without rest., Pitcullen Cres., PH2 7HT, ☎ (01738) 633183 – 🚭 [TV] [P]
**3 rm** ☕ 20.00/40.00. Y u

🏠 **Pitcullen** without rest., 17 Pitcullen Cres., PH2 7HT, ☎ (01738) 626506, *Fax (01738) 628265* – 🚭 [TV] [P]. [MC] VISA. 🐕 Y r
**6 rm** ☕ 25.00/60.00.

🍴🍴 **Let's Eat,** 77-79 Kinnoull St., PH1 5EZ, ☎ (01738) 643377, *Fax (01738) 621464* – [MC] [AE] VISA Y c
*closed Sunday, Monday, 2 weeks January and 2 weeks July* – **Meals** a la carte 15.90/24.45 **t.**

🍴 **Kerachers,** 168 South St., PH2 8NY, ☎ (01738) 449777 – 🚭. [MC] VISA JCB Z x
*closed Sunday* – **Meals** - Seafood - a la carte 9.90/23.30 **t.**

🍴 **Number Thirty Three,** 33 George St., PH1 5LA, ☎ (01738) 633771 – [MC] [AE] VISA JCB
*closed Sunday, Monday, 25-26 December, 1-2 and last week January and first 2 weeks February* – **Meals** - Seafood - a la carte 11.80/24.00 **t.** 🍷 7.50. Y n

🍴 **Exceed,** 65 South Methven St., PH1 5NX, ☎ (01738) 621189, *Fax (01738) 445758* – 🚭. [MC] VISA Z r
**Meals** a la carte 12.75/20.05 **t.** 🍷 7.75.

**at Guildtown** *North : 4½ m. on A 93 – Y – ✉ Perth.*

🏨 **Newmiln** 🐦, PH2 6AE, ☎ (01738) 552364, *Fax (01738) 553505*, ←, « Victorian mansion, sporting estate », 🎣, 🌳, 🎾 – [TV] ☎ 📞 [P]. [MC] [AE] [DC] VISA. 🐕
*Easter-October* **Meals** (dinner only and Sunday lunch)/dinner 32.50 **st.** 🍷 8.50 – **7 rm** ☕ 90.00/140.00 **t.**

**at New Scone** *Northeast : 2½ m. on A 94 – Y – ✉ Perth.*

🏨 **Murrayshall Country House** 🐦, PH2 7PH, East : 1 ¼ m. by Murraysall Rd ☎ (01738) 551171, *Fax (01738) 552595*, ←, 🏋, 🧖, ⛳18, 🌳, park, 🎾 – [TV] ☎ [P] – 🎤 180. [MC] [AE] [DC] VISA
**Meals** (bar lunch Monday to Saturday)/dinner 21.00 **st.** and a la carte 🍷 5.00 – **23 rm** ☕ 80.00/130.00 **st.**, 3 suites – SB.

**at Glencarse** *East : 6 ¼ m. on A 85 - Y - off A 90 – ✉ Perth.*

🏨 **Newton House,** PH2 7LX, ☎ (01738) 860250, *Fax (01738) 860717*, 🌳 – 🚭 rest, [TV] ☎ [P]. [MC] [AE] [DC] VISA JCB
**Meals** a la carte 15.70/22.50 **st.** – **10 rm** ☕ 50.00/75.00 **st.**

[M] ATS Inveralmond Ind. Est., Ruthvenfield Rd ☎ (01738) 629481

---

**PETERHEAD** *Aberdeenshire* [401] O 11 – *pop. 20 789.*

⛳18, ⛳9 *Cruden Bay* ☎ *(01779) 812285* – ⛳18, ⛳9 *Craigewan Links* ☎ *(01779) 472149.*

[i] *54 Broad St., AB42* ☎ *(01779) 471904 (summer only).*

*Edinburgh 165 – Aberdeen 35 – Fraserburgh 18.*

🏨 **Waterside Inn,** Fraserburgh Rd, AB42 3BN, Northwest : 2 m. on A 90 ☎ (01779) 471121, *Fax (01779) 470670*, 🏋, 🧖, 🏊 – 🚭 [TV] ☎ [P] – 🎤 100. [MC] [AE] [DC] VISA
**Meals** 10.00/20.00 **st.** and a la carte 🍷 7.00 – **109 rm** ☕ 87.00/108.50 **st.** – SB.

---

**PITCAPLE** *Aberdeenshire* [401] M 12.

*Edinburgh 51 – Aberdeen 21.*

🏨 **Pittodrie House** 🐦, AB51 5HS, Southwest : 1 ¾ m. by Chapel of Garioch rd ☎ (01467) 681444, *Fax (01467) 681648*, ←, « Country house atmosphere », 🌳, park, squash – 🚭 rest, [TV] ☎ 🚗 [P] – 🎤 120. [MC] [AE] [DC] VISA JCB
**Meals** 17.50/28.50 **st.** 🍷 7.50 – **27 rm** ☕ 123.00/163.00 **st.** – SB.

---

**PITLOCHRY** *Perthshire and Kinross* [401] I 13 *Scotland G.* – *pop. 3 126.*

See : *Town*★.

Exc. : *Blair Castle*★★ *AC, NW : 7 m. by A 9 A – Queen's View*★★*, W : 7 m. by B 8019 A – Falls of Bruar*★*, NW : 11 m. by A 9 A.*

⛳18 *Golf Course Rd* ☎ *(01796) 472792.*

[i] *22 Atholl Rd, PH16 5BX* ☎ *(01796) 472215/472751.*

*Edinburgh 71 – Inverness 85 – Perth 27.*

# PITLOCHRY

| | | | |
|---|---|---|---|
| Church Road ............ **AB** 2 | Clunie Bridge Rd ............ **A** 3 | Station Road ............ **A** 9 |
| | Higher Oakfield ............ **B** 4 | Strathview Terrace ............ **A** 10 |
| | Larchwood Rd ............ **A** 6 | Tom Na Moan Rd ............ **B** 12 |
| | Port Na Craig Rd ............ **A** 7 | Tummel Crescent ............ **A** 14 |

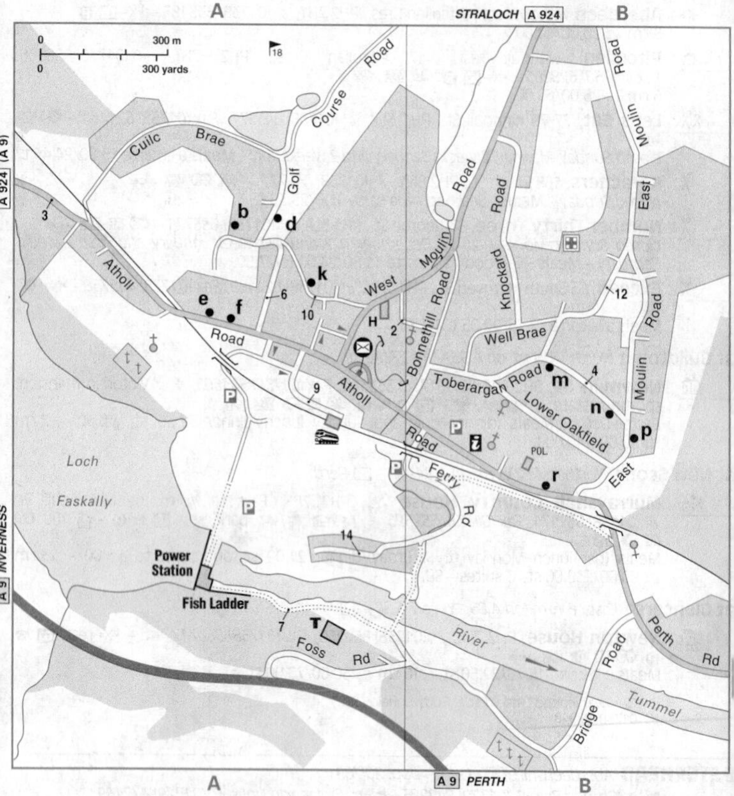


🏠 **Pine Trees** 🐦, Strathview Terr., PH16 5QR, ☎ (01796) 472121, *Fax (01796) 472460*, ≤, 🌳, park – [TV] ☎ [P]. [MC] [AE] [D] [VISA] **A b**
**Meals** 17.00/26.00 **st.** and lunch a la carte 🍷 8.75 – **20 rm** 🛏 56.00/88.00 **st.** – SB.

🏠 **Green Park,** Clunie Bridge Rd, PH16 5JY, ☎ (01796) 473248, *Fax (01796) 473520*, ≤, « Lochside setting », 🌳 – 🚭 [TV] ☎ [P]. [MC] [VISA]
**Meals** (residents only) (dinner only) 23.00 **t.** 🍷 3.95 – **39 rm** 🛏 (dinner included) 64.00/128.00 **t.** – SB.

🏠 **Dunfallandy House** 🐦, Logierait Rd, Dunfallandy, PH16 5NA, South : 1 ¼ m. by Bridge Rd ☎ (01796) 472648, *Fax (01796) 472017*, ≤, « Georgian mansion house », 🌳 – 🚭 [TV] [P] [MC] [AE] [VISA] [JCB]. 🐕
**Meals** (dinner only) 16.95 **st.** 🍷 4.95 – **8 rm** 🛏 34.00/68.00 **st.** – SB.

🏠 **Knockendarroch House,** 2 Higher Oakfield, PH16 5HT, ☎ (01796) 473473, *Fax (01796) 474068*, ≤, 🌳 – 🚭 [TV] ☎ [P]. [MC] [AE] [VISA]. 🐕 **B m**
*mid February-mid November* – **Meals** (residents only) (dinner only) 21.00 **t.** 🍷 4.25 – **12 rm** 🛏 (dinner included) 69.00/104.00 **t.**

🏠 **Westlands of Pitlochry,** 160 Atholl Rd, PH16 5AR, ☎ (01796) 472266, *Fax (01796) 473994*, 🌳 – 🚭 rest, [TV] ☎ [P] – 🎤 50. [MC] [VISA] **A f**
*closed 25 and 26 December* – **Meals** (bar lunch)/dinner 18.50 **t.** and a la carte 🍷 5.95 – **15 rm** 🛏 40.00/90.00 **t.**

🏠 **Claymore,** 162 Atholl Rd, PH16 5AR, ☎ (01796) 472888, *Fax (01796) 474037,* ☞ – ⅍ 🔲 ☎
🅿. ⓪⓪ 𝘝𝘐𝘚𝘈 A e
*March-November* – **Meals** (bar lunch)/dinner 18.95 **t.** and a la carte ♨ 4.35 – **11 rm**
⌑ 36.00/76.00 **t.** – SB.

🏠 **Acarsaid,** 8 Atholl Rd, PH16 5BX, ☎ (01796) 472389, *Fax (01796) 473952* – ⅍ rest, 🔲 ☎
🅿. ⓪⓪ 𝘝𝘐𝘚𝘈. ⅍ B r
*closed January and February* – **Meals** (light lunch)/dinner 17.95 **t.** ♨ 5.50 – **19 rm** ⌑ 36.00/
72.00 **t.** – SB.

🏠 **Queens View** ⌇, Strathtummel, PH16 5NR, West : 3 ¼ m. on B 8019 ☎ (01796) 473291,
*Fax (01796) 473515,* ≼ Loch Tummel and Hills, ⚲, ☞ – ☎ 🅿. ⓪⓪ 𝘝𝘐𝘚𝘈. ⅍
*closed mid January and February* – **Meals** 24.00 **t.** (dinner) and lunch a la carte 13.00/
21.00 **t.** ♨ 6.80 – **12 rm** ⌑ (dinner included) 70.00/140.00 **t.** – SB.

🏠 **Balrobin,** Higher Oakfield, PH16 5HT, ☎ (01796) 472901, *Fax (01796) 474200,* ≼, ☞ –
⅍ rest, 🔲 🅿. ⓪⓪ 𝘝𝘐𝘚𝘈 B n
*March-October* – **Meals** (residents only) (dinner only) 15.50 **t.** – **15 rm** ⌑ 29.00/75.00 **t.** –
SB.

🏠 **Birchwood,** 2 East Moulin Rd, PH16 5DW, ☎ (01796) 472477, *Fax (01796) 473951,* ☞ –
⅍ rest, 🔲 ☎ 🅿. ⓪⓪ 𝘝𝘐𝘚𝘈. ⅍ B p
*closed January-March 15* – **Meals** (dinner only) 21.00 **t.** ♨ 4.50 – **12 rm** ⌑ 39.00/78.00 **t.** –
SB.

🏠 **East Haugh House,** East Haugh, PH16 5JS, Southeast : 2 m. by A 924 ☎ (01796) 473121,
*Fax (01796) 472473,* ☞ – ⅍ rest, 🔲 ☎ 🅿. ⓪⓪ 𝘝𝘐𝘚𝘈. ⅍
*closed 22 to 26 December* – **Meals** (bar lunch)/dinner 27.95 **t.** and a la carte ♨ 6.50 – **13 rm**
⌑ 49.00/120.00 **t.** – SB.

↑ **Torrdarach** without rest., Golf Course Rd, PH16 5AU, ☎ (01796) 472136, « Gardens » –
⅍ 🔲 🅿. ⅍ A d
*Easter-mid October* – **7 rm** ⌑ 20.00/52.00 **st.**

↑ **Dundarave,** Strathview Terr., PH16 5AT, ☎ (01796) 473109, *Fax (01796) 473109,* ≼, ☞ –
⅍ rest, 🔲 🅿 A k
*March-November* – **Meals** (by arrangement) 16.95 **st.** – **7 rm** ⌑ 30.00/60.00 **st.** – SB.

**at Killiecrankie** *Northwest : 4 m. by A 924 -* A - *and B 8019 on B 8079 –* ✉ *Pitlochry.*

🏠 **Killiecrankie** ⌇, PH16 5LG, ☎ (01796) 473220, *Fax (01796) 472451,* ≼, ☞ – ⅍ 🔲 ☎
🅿. ⓪⓪ 𝘝𝘐𝘚𝘈
*closed 1 week December, January and March* – **Meals** (bar lunch)/dinner 29.50 ♨ 8.25 –
**9 rm** ⌑ (dinner included) 84.00/168.00 **t.**, 1 suite.

---

**PLOCKTON** *Highland* 401 *D 11 Scotland G..*
See : *Village★.*
Env. : *Wester Ross★★★.*
*Edinburgh 210 – Inverness 88.*

🏠 **The Haven,** 3 Innes St., IV52 8TW, ☎ (01599) 544223, *Fax (01599) 544467,* ☞ – ⅍ rest,
🔲 ☎ 🅿. ⓪⓪ 𝘝𝘐𝘚𝘈
*closed 20 December-1 February* – **Meals** (lunch by arrangement)/dinner a la carte approx.
20.50 **t.** ♨ 4.00 – **13 rm** ⌑ 36.00/76.00 **t.**, 2 suites.

📠 **Plockton** with rm, Harbour St., IV52 8TN, ☎ (01599) 544274, *Fax (01599) 544475,* ≼ Loch
Carron and mountains, ☞ – ⅍ rest, 🔲. ⓪⓪ 𝘝𝘐𝘚𝘈
**Meals** (bar lunch)/dinner a la carte 10.70/22.25 **t.** ♨ 4.75 – **8 rm** ⌑ 32.50/60.00 **t.**

📠 **Plockton Inn** with rm, Innes St., IV52 8TW, ☎ (01599) 544222, *Fax (01599) 544487,* ☞ –
⅍ rest, 🔲 ☎ 🅿. ⓪⓪ 𝘝𝘐𝘚𝘈 𝙅𝘊𝘉
**Meals** a la carte 11.45/19.40 **st.** – **6 rm** ⌑ 32.00/57.00 **st.** – SB.

---

**POLLACHAR** *Western Isles (Outer Hebrides)* 401 *X 12 – see Uist (Isles of).*

---

**POLMONT** *Falkirk* 401 402 *I 16 – see Falkirk.*

---

**POOLEWE** *Highland* 401 *D 10 Scotland G..*
Env. : *Wester Ross★★★ – Inverewe Gardens★★★, N : 1 m. on B 8057 – Loch Maree★★★.*
*Edinburgh 234 – Inverness 78 – Kyle of Lochalsh 74.*

🏠 **Pool House,** IV22 2LE, ☎ (01445) 781272, *Fax (01445) 781403,* ≼ Loch Ewe – ⅍ rm, 🔲
☎ 🅿. ⓪⓪ 𝘈𝘌 𝘝𝘐𝘚𝘈 𝙅𝘊𝘉. ⅍
*closed 5 January-28 February* – **Meals** (bar lunch)/dinner 28.00 **t.** and a la carte ♨ 8.00 –
**13 rm** ⌑ 45.00/108.00 **t.** – SB.

**PORT APPIN** *Argyll and Bute* 401 D 14 – ⊠ *Appin.*
*Edinburgh 136 – Ballachulish 20 – Oban 24.*

命命 **Airds** (Allen) ⊗, PA38 4DF, ℘ (01631) 730236, *Fax (01631) 730535*, ≤ Loch Linnhe and
❀ mountains of Kingairloch, « Former ferry inn », ⊸, 🐜, ⇔ rest, 📺 ☎ 🅿. 🐠 🝙 🚾. ❀
*closed 6 January-5 February and 20 to 27 December –* **Meals** (booking essential) (light
lunch)/dinner 40.00 **st.** ⓘ 16.00 **– 12 rm** ⊂ 98.00/198.00 **t.** – SB
**Spec.** Poached lobster, asparagus salad, gazpacho vinaigrette. Roast loin of rabbit, ballottine of foie gras, chanterelles and tagliatelle. Fillet of turbot with lobster, cockles, deep fried
oyster, shellfish sauce.

---

**PORT CHARLOTTE** *Argyll and Bute* 401 A 16 – see Islay (Isle of).

---

**PORT ELLEN** *Argyll and Bute* 401 B 17 – see Islay (Isle of).

---

**PORTLETHEN** *Aberdeenshire* 401 N 12 – see Aberdeen.

---

**PORTPATRICK** *Dumfries and Galloway* 401 402 E 19 – pop. 842 – ⊠ *Stranraer.*
📷₈, 📷₉ *Golf Course Rd* ℘ (01776) 810273.
*Edinburgh 141 – Ayr 60 – Dumfries 80 – Stranraer 9.*

命命 **Knockinaam Lodge** ⊗, DG9 9AD, Southeast : 5 m. by A 77 off B 7042
❀ ℘ (01776) 810471, *Fax (01776) 810435*, ≤, « Country house in picturesque coastal setting », ⊸, 🐜, park – ⇔ rest, 📺 ☎ 🅿. 🐠 🝙 🅾 🚾
**Meals** (set menu only) (booking essential) 27.00/38.00 **t.** ⓘ 9.00 **– 10 rm** ⊂ (dinner included) 130.00/300.00 **t.** – SB
**Spec.** Lobster filled courgette flower with cardamon. Best end of lamb, couscous, bell
pepper reduction. Christmas pudding soufflé, honey and Cognac ice cream.

命命 **Fernhill**, Heugh Rd, DG9 8TD, ℘ (01776) 810220, *Fax (01776) 810596*, ≤, 🐜 – ⇔ rest, 📺
☎ ⓖ 🅿. 🐠 🝙 🅾 🚾 🝐
*closed 25 and 26 December –* **Meals** 22.50 **t.** (dinner) and a la carte 18.70/30.40 **t.** ⓘ 5.50 **–
19 rm** ⊂ 58.00/110.00 **t.** – SB.

🍴 **Crown** with rm, North Cres., DG9 8SX, ℘ (01776) 810261, *Fax (01776) 810551*, ≤ –
⇔ rest, 📺 ☎. 🐠 🝙 🚾
*closed 25 December –* **Meals** a la carte 16.50/32.30 **t.** ⓘ 6.00 **– 12 rm** ⊂ 48.00/72.00 **t.**

⚲ **Blinkbonnie** without rest., School Brae, DG9 8LG, ℘ (01776) 810282, ≤, 🐜 – ⇔ 📺 🅿.
🝐
*closed December –* **5 rm** ⊂ 22.00/38.00 **st.**

---

**PORTREE** *Highland* 401 B 11 – see Skye (Isle of).

---

**PRESTWICK** *South Ayrshire* 401 402 G 17 – pop. 13 705.
✈ *Prestwick International Airport : ℘ (01292) 479822 – BY –* **Terminal :** *Buchanan Bus
Station.*
✈ *see also Glasgow.*
*Edinburgh 78 – Ayr 2 – Glasgow 32.*

Plan of Built up Area : see Ayr

命命 **Carlton Toby,** 187 Ayr Rd, KA9 1TP, ℘ (01292) 476811, *Fax (01292) 673712* – ⇔ 📺 ☎ 📞
🅿 – 🔏 25. 🐠 🝙 🚾                                                                                       BY  v
**Meals** (carving rest.) 8.50 **t.** and a la carte ⓘ 4.95 **– 34 rm** ⊂ 49.50/65.00 **st.** – SB.

🏠 **Travel Inn,** Kilmarnock Rd, Monkton, KA9 2RJ, Northeast : 3 m. by A 79 and A 78 at
junction with A 77 ℘ (01292) 678262, *Fax (01292) 678248* – ⇔ rm, 🍽 rest, 📺 ⅙ 🅿 –
🔏 70. 🐠 🝙 🅾 🚾. 🝐
**Meals** (grill rest.) **– 40 rm** 38.00 **t.**

---

**QUOTHQUAN** *South Lanarkshire* 401 J 27 Scotland G. – ⊠ *Biggar.*
Env. : *Biggar★ (Gladstone Court Museum★ AC – Greenhill Covenanting Museum★ AC,
SE : 4½ m. by B 7016.*
*Edinburgh 32 – Dumfries 50 – Glasgow 36.*

命命 **Shieldhill** ⊗, ML12 6NA, Northeast : ¾ m. ℘ (01899) 220035, *Fax (01899) 221092*, ≤,
« Victorian country house, 12C origins », 🐜 – ⇔ 📺 ☎ 🅿 – 🔏 25. 🐠 🚾
**Meals** 18.50/32.00 **t.** ⓘ 7.25 **– 12 rm** ⊂ 85.00/212.00 **t.**

**RHICONICH** Highland **401** F 8 *Scotland G.* – ✉ *Lairg.*

Exc. : *Cape Wrath*★★★ (≤★★) *AC, N : 21 m. (including ferry crossing) by A 838 and minor rd.*
*Edinburgh 249 – Thurso 87 – Ullapool 57.*

🏠 **Rhiconich**, IV27 4RN, 𝒫 (01971) 521224, *Fax* (01971) 521732, ≤ Loch Inchard, ⤢ –
⤢ rest, 📺 ☎ 🅿. ◗◗ VISA
**Meals** (bar lunch)/dinner 16.00 **st.** ⅙ 4.00 – **11 rm** ⨌ 32.00/68.00 **t.**

---

**ROGART** Highland **401** H 9 – *pop. 419.*
*Edinburgh 229 – Inverness 73 – Wick 63.*

🏠 **Sciberscross Lodge** ⟨⟩, Strath Brora, IV28 3YQ, North : 7 m. by Balnacoil rd
𝒫 (01408) 641246, *Fax* (01408) 641465, ≤ Brora valley and hills, ⤢, ⤢ – 🅿. ◗◗ VISA. ⤢
*February-October –* **Meals** (booking essential) (communal dining) (dinner only) 35.00 **st.** –
**4 rm** ⨌ 40.00/80.00 **st.**

---

**ROTHES** Moray **401** K 11 *Scotland G.* – *pop. 1 520.*

Exc. : *Glenfiddich Distillery*★, *SE : 7 m. by A 941.*
📘 *Dufftown* 𝒫 (01340) 820325.
*Edinburgh 192 – Aberdeen 62 – Fraserburgh 58 – Inverness 49.*

🏛 **Rothes Glen** ⟨⟩, AB38 7AQ, North : 3 m. on A 941 𝒫 (01340) 831254,
*Fax* (01340) 831566, ≤, « Country house atmosphere », ⤢, park – ⤢ rest, 📺 ☎ 🅿. ◗◗
AE VISA JCB. ⤢
**Meals** 32.50 **t.** (dinner) and lunch a la carte 14.00/21.00 **t.** ⅙ 7.50 – **13 rm** ⨌ 80.00/
110.00 **t.**, 2 suites – SB.

---

| Les prix | Pour toutes précisions sur les prix indiqués dans ce guide, reportez-vous aux pages de l'introduction. |
|---|---|

---

**ROTHESAY** Argyll and Bute **401** **402** E 16 – see Bute (Isle of).

---

**ROYBRIDGE** Highland **401** F 13 – see Spean Bridge.

---

**ST. ANDREWS** Fife **401** L 14 *Scotland G.* – *pop. 11 136.*

See : *City*★★ – *Cathedral*★ (⁂★★) *AC* B – *West Port*★ A.
Env. : *Leuchars (parish church*★*), NW : 6 m. by A 91 and A 919.*
Exc. : *The East Neuk*★★, *SE : 9 m. by A 917 and B 9131* B – *Crail*★★ (*Old Centre*★★, *Upper Crail*★) *SE : 9 m. by A 917* B – *Kellie Castle*★ *AC, S : 9 m. by B 9131 and B 9171* B – *Ceres*★, *SW : 9 m. by B 939 - E - Inland Fife*★ A.
📘 (x5), 📘 *Eden, Jubilee, New, Old, Strathtyrum and Balgove Courses* 𝒫 (01334) 466666 – 📘 *Duke's, Craigtoun Park* 𝒫 (01334) 479947.
🛈 *70 Market St., KY16 9NU* 𝒫 (01334) 472021.
*Edinburgh 51 – Dundee 14 – Stirling 51.*

Plan on next page

🏨🏨🏨 **The Old Course H. Golf Resort and Spa,** Old Station Rd, KY16 9SP,
𝒫 (01334) 474371, *Fax* (01334) 477668, ≤ golf courses and sea, 𝟙𝟞, ≘s, 🏊, 📘 – 🛗, ■ rest,
📺 ☎ 🕭 🅿 – 🛎 300. ◗◗ AE ◑ VISA JCB.
*closed Christmas –* **Conservatory :** Meals (May-October) 13.50/22.50 **t.** and a la carte
⅙ 12.00 – **Road Hole Grill :** Meals (closed lunch May-October) 15.50/38.50 **t.** and a la carte –
**108 rm** ⨌ 245.00/315.00 **t.**, 17 suites – SB.

🏨🏨 **Rusacks,** Pilmour Links, KY16 9JQ, 𝒫 (01334) 474321, *Fax* (01334) 477896, ≤, ≘s – 🛗,
⤢ rest, 📺 ☎ 🅿 – 🛎 80. ◗◗ AE ◑ VISA JCB                                                                  A a
**Meals** (light lunch Monday to Saturday)/dinner 26.50 **st.** and dinner a la carte ⅙ 9.50 – ⨌
13.50 – **44 rm** 110.00/250.00 **t.**, 4 suites – SB.

🏛 **Rufflets Country House,** Strathkinness Low Rd, KY16 9TX, West : 1 ½ m. on B 939
𝒫 (01334) 472594, *Fax* (01334) 478703, ≤, « Country house, gardens » – ⤢ 📺 ☎ 🅿 –
🛎 30. ◗◗ AE ◑ VISA. ⤢
*closed 3 to 10 January* **Meals** (bar lunch Monday to Friday)/dinner 30.00 **st.** ⅙ 11.85 – **25 rm**
⨌ 95.00/180.00 **st.** – SB.

# ST ANDREWS

🏨 **St. Andrews Golf,** 40 The Scores, KY16 9AS, ℘ (01334) 472611, Fax (01334) 472188, ≤ – 🛗, ❊ rest, 🆃🆅 ☎ 🅿 – 🔏 200. 🆆🅾 🄰🄴 🅾 𝘝𝘐𝘚𝘈 JCB         A e
Meals a la carte 20.00/27.50 – **22 rm** ☲ 89.00/170.00 **t.**

🏨 **The Scores,** 76 The Scores, KY16 9BB, ℘ (01334) 472451, Fax (01334) 473947, ≤, 🐾 – 🛗, ❊ rest, 🆃🆅 ☎ 🅿 – 🔏 160. 🆆🅾 🄰🄴 🅾 𝘝𝘐𝘚𝘈 JCB. ❊         A n
Meals (bar lunch)/dinner a la carte 12.50/27.00 **t.** – **29 rm** ☲ 85.00/142.00 **t.**, 1 suite – SB.

⌂ **Aslar House** without rest., 120 North St., KY16 9AF, ℘ (01334) 473460, Fax (01334) 477540, 🐾 – ❊ 🆃🆅. 🆆🅾 𝘝𝘐𝘚𝘈. ❊         A r
closed 1 week in spring and 1 week Christmas/New Year – **5 rm** ☲ 28.00/58.00 **s.**

**at Strathkinness** West : 3 ¾ m. on B 939 – A – ⊠ St. Andrews.

⌂ **Fossil House and Cottage** without rest., 12-14 Main St., KY16 9RU, ℘ (01334) 850639, Fax (01334) 850639 – ❊ 🆃🆅 🅿. 🆆🅾 𝘝𝘐𝘚𝘈. ❊ – **4 rm** ☲ 25.00/50.00 **st.**

---

**ST. BOSWELLS** Borders 🄰🄾🄸 🄰🄾🄸 L 17 Scotland G. – pop. 2 092.
Env. : Dryburgh Abbey★★ AC (setting★★★), NW : 4 m. by B 6404 and B 6356 – Tweed Valley★★.
Exc. : Bowhill★★ AC, SW : 11½ m. by A 699 and A 708.
🏌 St. Boswells ℘ (01835) 823527.
Edinburgh 39 – Glasgow 79 – Hawick 17 – Newcastle upon Tyne 66.

🏨 **Dryburgh Abbey** 🐾, Dryburgh, TD6 0RQ, North : 3 ½ m. by B 6404 on B 6356 ℘ (01835) 822261, Fax (01835) 823945, ≤, 🔲, 🐾, 🐾 – 🛗, ❊ rest, 🆃🆅 ☎ 🅿 – 🔏 120. 🆆🅾 🄰🄴 𝘝𝘐𝘚𝘈 JCB
Meals (dinner only and Sunday lunch) 24.00 **t.** ▯ 5.50 – **35 rm** ☲ 49.00/98.00 **t.**, 2 suites – SB.

---

**ST. CATHERINES** Argyll and Bute 🄰🄾🄸 E 15 Scotland G. – ⊠ Cairndow.
Env. : Loch Fyne★★.
Exc. : Inveraray★★ : Castle★★ (interior★★★) AC, NW : 12 m. by A 815 and A 83 – Auchindrain★, NW : 18 m. by A 815 and A 83.
Edinburgh 99 – Glasgow 53 – Oban 53.

⌂ **Arnish Cottage** 🐾 without rest., Poll Bay, PA25 8BA, Southwest : 2 m. on A 815 ℘ (01499) 302405, Fax (01499) 302405, ≤ Loch Fyne, « Lochside setting », 🐾 – ❊ 🅿. ❊ closed Christmas and New Year – **3 rm** ☲ 25.00/50.00.

⌂ **Thistle House** without rest., PA25 8AZ, on A 815 ℘ (01499) 302209, Fax (01499) 302531, ≤, 🐾 – 🆃🆅 🅿. 🆆🅾 𝘝𝘐𝘚𝘈. ❊ – April-October – **4 rm** ☲ 30.00/50.00.

**T. FILLANS** *Perthshire and Kinross* 401 H 14 *Scotland G..*
Env. : *Loch Earn**.*
*Edinburgh 67 – Glasgow 57 – Oban 64 – Perth 30.*

🏠 **Achray House**, PH6 2NF, 𝒫 (01764) 685231, *Fax* (01764) 685320, ≤ Loch Earn and mountains, 🌲 – 🙅 rest, 🖵 ☎ 🅿. 🕮 🖭 *VISA*. 🛠
**Meals** (bar lunch Monday to Saturday)/dinner 17.50 st. and a la carte ♨ 4.95 – **9 rm** ⛁ 46.50/69.00 st.

**T. MARGARET'S HOPE** *Orkney Islands* 401 K 6 – *see Orkney Islands.*

**ANDYHILLS** *Dumfries and Galloway* 401 402 I 19 – ⊠ *Dalbeattie.*
*Edinburgh 99 – Ayr 62 – Dumfries 19 – Stranraer 68.*

🏠 **Cairngill House** 🦢, DG5 4NZ, 𝒫 (01387) 780681, ≤, 🌲 – 🙅 rest, 🖵 🅿
**Meals** (bar lunch)/dinner 14.00 t. ♨ 3.50 – **6 rm** ⛁ 32.00/54.00 t.

**ANQUHAR** *Dumfries and Galloway* 401 402 I 17 *Scotland G.* – pop. 2 680.
Exc. : *Drumlanrig Castle** (cabinets*)*, SE : 8 m. by A 76.
🏌 *Blackaddie Rd* 𝒫 (01659) 50577.
🛈 *Tolbooth, High St.* 𝒫 (01659) 50185 (summer only).
*Edinburgh 58 – Dumfries 27 – Glasgow 24.*

🏠 **Blackaddie House** 🦢, Blackaddie Rd, DG4 6JJ, North : ¼ m. by A 76 𝒫 (01659) 50270, *Fax* (01659) 50270, « Riverside setting », 🏊, 🌲 – 🖵 ☎ 🅿. 🖭 *VISA*. 🛠
*closed 25 to 27 December* – **Meals** (lunch by arrangement)/dinner a la carte 11.95/24.00 t. – **10 rm** ⛁ 38.00/64.00 t. – SB.

*Le Grand Londres (GREATER LONDON) est composé de la City*
*et de 32 arrondissements administratifs (Borough)*
*eux-mêmes divisés en quartiers ou en villages*
*ayant conservé leur caractère propre (Area).*

**CALASAIG** *Argyll and Bute* 401 B 15 – *see Colonsay (Isle of).*

**CALLOWAY** *Shetland Islands* 401 Q 3 – *see Shetland Islands (Mainland).*

**CARISTA** *Western Isles (Outer Hebrides)* 401 Y 10 – *see Lewis and Harris (Isle of).*

**COURIE** *Highland* 401 E 8 *Scotland G.* – ⊠ *Lairg.*
Exc. : *Cape Wrath*** (≤**) AC, N : 31 m. (including ferry crossing) by A 894 and A 838 – Loch Assynt**, S : 17 m. by A 894.*
*Edinburgh 263 – Inverness 107.*

🏠 **Eddrachilles** 🦢, Badcall Bay, IV27 4TH, South : 2 ½ m. on A 894 𝒫 (01971) 502080, *Fax* (01971) 502477, ≤ Badcall Bay and islands, 🏊, 🌲, park – 🖵 ☎ 🅿. 🖭 *VISA* *JCB*. 🛠
*10 March-28 October* – **Meals** (bar lunch)/dinner 12.00 st. and a la carte ♨ 3.20 – **11 rm** ⛁ 52.00/82.00 st. – SB.

**SEIL (Isle of)** *Argyll and Bute* 401 D 15 – ⊠ *Oban.*

**Clachan Seil** – ⊠ *Oban.*

🏠 **Willowburn** 🦢, PA34 4TJ, 𝒫 (01852) 300276, *Fax* (01852) 300597, ≤, 🌲 – 🙅 rest, 🖵 🕮 *VISA*
*closed 2 January-15 March* – **Meals** (bar lunch)/dinner 22.00 t. ♨ 6.50 – **7 rm** ⛁ (dinner included) 55.00/110.00 t.

**Easdale** – ⊠ *Oban.*

🏠 **Inshaig Park** 🦢, PA34 4RF, 𝒫 (01852) 300256, *Fax* (01852) 300256, ≤ Inner Hebridean Islands, 🌲 – 🙅 rest, 🖵 🅿
*March-November* – **Meals** (bar lunch)/dinner 16.50 st. and a la carte – **6 rm** ⛁ (dinner included) 48.00/92.00.

**SELKIRK** Borders **401 402** L 17 Scotland G. – pop. 6 469.

Env. : Bowhill★★ AC, W : 3½ m. by A 708 – Abbotsford★★ AC, NE : 5½ m. by A 7 and B 63⁹ – Tweed Valley★★.

Exc. : Melrose Abbey★★ (decorative sculpture★★★) AC, NE : 8½ m. by A 7 and A 609 Eildon Hills (≼★★★) NE : 7½ m. by A 699 and B 6359.

ᵣₛ The Hill ℰ (01750) 20621.

🄱 Halliwell's House, TD7 4BL ℰ (01750) 20054 (summer only).

Edinburgh 48 – Hawick 11 – Newcastle upon Tyne 77.

🏠 **Philipburn Country House**, TD7 5LS, West : 1 m. at junction of A 707 with A 7⁰ ℰ (01750) 20747, Fax (01750) 21690, 🔼, 🦟 – 📺 ☎ 🅿 – 🔏 30. 🐠 🆎 ① 𝘝𝘐𝘚𝘈. ≉ closed 3 to 17 January – **Restaurant 1745 :** Meals (dinner only and lunch Saturday a Sunday) 15.50/25.00 t. ⭑ 9.50 – **Charlies Bar and Bistro :** Meals a la carte approx. 17.5⁰ – 15 rm ⊆ 79.00/99.50 t.

---

**SHETLAND ISLANDS** Shetland Islands **401** PQ 3 Scotland G. – pop. 22 522.

See : Islands★ - Up Helly Aa★★ (last Tuesday in January) – Mousa Broch★★★ AC (Mou Island) – Jarlshof★★ - Lerwick to Jarlshof★ (≼★) – Shetland Croft House Museum★ AC.

✈ Tingwall Airport : ℰ (01595) 840306, NW : 6½ m. of Lerwick by A 971.

🚢 from Lerwick (Mainland) to Aberdeen and via Orkney Islands (Stromness) (P & Scottish Ferries) – from Lerwick (Mainland) to Skerries (Shetland Islands Council) bookiⁿ essential 2 weekly (2 h 30 mn) – from Lerwick (Mainland) to Norway (Bergen) weekly (13 h mn) – from Lerwick (Mainland) to Bressay (Shetland Islands Council) frequent services da (5 mn) – from Laxo (Mainland) to Isle of Whalsay (Symbister) (Shetland Islands Coun◀ frequent services daily (30 mn) – from Toft (Mainland) to Isle of Yell (Ulsta) (Shetland Islanᵈ Council) frequent services daily (20 mn) – from Isle of Yell (Gutcher) to Isle of Fetlar (Odds◀ and via Isle of Unst (Belmont) (Shetland Islands Council) – from Fair Isle to Sumbur◀ (Mainland) (Shetland Islands Council) weekly (2 h 40 mn).

### MAINLAND.

**Brae.**

🏠 **Busta House** ⟫, ZE2 9QN, Southwest : 1½ m. ℰ (01806) 522506, Fax (01806) 52258 ≼, « Part 16C and 18C country house », 🦟 – 🔽, ≼≽ rest, 📺 ☎ 🅿. 🐠 🆎 ① 𝘝𝘐𝘚𝘈 closed 22 December-3 January – Meals (bar lunch)/dinner 21.00 t. and a la carte ⭑ 5.35 20 rm ⊆ 70.00/115.00 t.

**Lerwick** Scotland G. – pop. 7 590.

See : Clickhimin Broch★.

Env. : Gulber Wick (≼★), S : 2 m. by A 970.

ᵣₛ Lerwick ℰ (01595) 840369.

🄱 The Market Cross, Lerwick, ZE1 0LU ℰ (01595) 693434.

🏠 **Kveldsro House**, Greenfield Pl., ZE1 0AQ, ℰ (01595) 692195, Fax (01595) 696595 – 📺 ◀ 🅿 🐠 🆎 ① 𝘝𝘐𝘚𝘈. ≉ closed 24 December-4 January – Meals (bar lunch)/dinner 23.50 t. (dinner) and a la cartᵉ 15.00/26.00 t. ⭑ 9.95 – 16 rm ⊆ 70.00/90.00 t.

🏠 **Shetland**, Holmsgarth Rd, ZE1 0PW, ℰ (01595) 695515, Fax (01595) 695828, ≼ – 🛗 ≼≽ ◀ ☎ & 🅿 – 🔏 250. 🐠 🆎 ① 𝘝𝘐𝘚𝘈. ≉ Meals (bar lunch)/dinner 23.50 st. ⭑ 4.95 – 63 rm ⊆ 76.00/90.00 st., 1 suite.

🏠 **Lerwick**, 15 South Rd, ZE1 0RB, ℰ (01595) 692166, Fax (01595) 694419, ≼, 🦟 – 📺 ☎ – 🔏 60. 🐠 🆎 𝘝𝘐𝘚𝘈. ≉ Meals (dinner only) 21.50 st. and a la carte ⭑ 4.95 – 34 rm ⊆ 72.00/87.50 st., 1 suite – SB.

🏠 **Glen Orchy House**, 20 Knab Rd, ZE1 0AX, ℰ (01595) 692031, Fax (01595) 692031 ≼≽ rest, 📺 & 🅿 Meals (residents only) (dinner only) 14.00 t. ⭑ 5.75 – 14 rm ⊆ 37.50/64.00 t.

◍ ATS 3 Gremista Ind. Est., Lerwick ℰ (01595) 693857

**Scalloway.**

🏠 **Scalloway**, Main St., ZE1 0TR, ℰ (01595) 880444, Fax (01595) 880445, ≼ – ≼≽ 📺 ☎ ✆ 🄿 🐠 🆎 ① 𝘝𝘐𝘚𝘈 𝙅𝘾𝘽. ≉ Meals 14.95 t. (dinner) and a la carte 15.70/42.25 t. ⭑ 4.90 – 24 rm ⊆ 50.00/70.00 t. – SB.

🏠 **Hildasay** without rest., Upper Scalloway, ZE1 0UP, Northeast : ½ m. by A 970 takiⁿ unmarked road on left after school ℰ (01595) 880822 – 📺 & 🅿. ≉ 4 rm ⊆ 22.00/40.00.

**Walls.**

🏠 **Burrastow House** ♨, ZE2 9PD, Southwest: 2 ½ m. ℰ (01595) 809307, *Fax (01595) 809213*, « Part 18C house overlooking Vaila Sound », ⚓, park – ⅍ ⅍ ♿ **P**. **CB** **AE** **VISA** **JCB**. ⅍
*closed 14 to 29 October, 25 December, January and February* – **Meals** *(closed dinner Sunday and Monday to non-residents)* a la carte 15.25/27.25 **t.** ⅍ 6.70 – **5 rm** ⚏ (dinner included) 80.00/160.00 **t.** – SB.

## ISLAND OF UNST.

**Baltasound.**

🏠 **Buness House** ♨, ZE2 9DS, East : ½ m. by A 968 ℰ (01957) 711315, *Fax (01957) 711815*, ≼ Balta Sound, ☞ – ⅍ ⅍ **P**. **VISA**. ⅍
*closed January* – **Meals** *(by arrangement) (communal dining)* 22.00 **st.** ⅍ 6.50 – **4 rm** ⚏ 27.00/54.00 **st.**

**SHIELDAIG** Highland **401** D 11 *Scotland G.* – ✉ Strathcarron.
Env. : *Wester Ross***★★★**.
*Edinburgh 226 – Inverness 70 – Kyle of Lochalsh 36.*

🏠 **Tigh An Eilean**, IV54 8XN, ℰ (01520) 755251, *Fax (01520) 755321*, ≼ Shieldaig Islands and Loch, « Attractively furnished inn » – ⅍ rest. **CB** **VISA** **JCB**
*mid April-mid October* – **Meals** *(booking essential to non-residents) (bar lunch)/dinner* 24.50 **st.** ⅍ 6.00 – **11 rm** ⚏ 47.25/105.00 **t.**

*Pour visiter une ville ou une région : utilisez les Guides Verts Michelin.*

**SKYE (Isle of)** Highland **401** B 11 /12 *Scotland G.* – pop. 8 868.
See : *Island***★★** – The Cuillins**★★★** – Skye Museum of Island Life★ AC.
Env. : N : *Trotternish Peninsula***★★** – W : *Duirinish Peninsula*★ – *Portree*★.
*Skye Bridge (toll).*
⛴ – from Mallaig to Armadale (Caledonian MacBrayne Ltd) 3-7 daily (30 mn) – from Uig to North Uist (Lochmaddy) or Isle of Harris (Tarbert) (Caledonian MacBrayne Ltd) 1-3 daily – from Sconser to Isle of Raasay (Caledonian MacBrayne Ltd) 9-10 daily (except Sunday) (15 mn).
⛴ from Mallaig to Isles of Eigg, Muck, Rhum and Canna (Caledonian MacBrayne Ltd) 3 daily – from Mallaig to Kyle of Lochalsh (Caledonian MacBrayne Ltd) (summer only) weekly (2 h).
🛈 Meall House, Portree ℰ (01478) 612137.

**Ardvasar.**

🏠 **Ardvasar**, IV45 8RS, ℰ (01471) 844223, *Fax (01471) 844495*, ≼, ☞ – **TV** ☎ **P**. **CB** **VISA** **JCB**. ⅍
*closed 25-26 December, January and February* – **Meals** *(bar lunch)/dinner* a la carte 10.00/27.00 **t.** ⅍ 6.50 – **9 rm** ⚏ 50.00/85.00 **t.**

**Breakish.**

🍴 **The Seagull**, IV42 8PY, ℰ (01471) 822001, *Fax (01471) 822001* – **P**. **CB** **AE** **VISA**
*mid April-mid October* – **Meals** *(booking essential) (dinner only)* a la carte 14.00/24.00 **st.**

**Broadford.**

🏠 **Corry Lodge** ♨, Liveras, IV49 9AA, North : 1 m. by An Acarsaid rd ℰ (01471) 822235, *Fax (01471) 822318*, ≼, « Part 18C house », ☞, park – ⅍ ⅍ **TV** **P**. **CB** **VISA**
*March-October* – **Meals** *(by arrangement) (communal dining)* 17.50 **st.** – **4 rm** ⚏ 50.00/60.00 **st.**

🏠 **Ptarmigan** without rest., Harrapool, IV49 9AQ, East : ¾ m. on A 87 ℰ (01471) 822744, *Fax (01471) 822745*, ≼ Broadford Bay and islands, « Waterside setting », ☞ – ⅍ ⅍ **TV** ☎ **P**. **CB** **AE** **VISA**
*closed 2 weeks in winter* – **3 rm** ⚏ 35.00/55.00 **s.**

🏠 **Earsary** without rest., 7-8 Harrapool, IV49 9AQ, East : ¾ m. on A 87 ℰ (01471) 822697, *Fax (01471) 822781*, ≼, ☞, park – ⅍ ⅍ **TV** **P**. ⅍
**3 rm** ⚏ 30.00/44.00 **st.**

🏠 **Westside** without rest., Elgol Rd, IV49 9AB, on B 8083 ℰ (01471) 822320, *Fax (01471) 822320*, ☞ – **TV** **P**. ⅍
*March-November* – **3 rm** ⚏ 20.00/44.00.

## Carbost.

⌂ **Talisker House** ⛱, Talisker Bay, IV47 8SF, West : 4 ¼ m. on Talisker rd ☎ (01478) 64024 *Fax (01478) 640214*, ≤, « Part 18C country house », 🌳, 🪑, park – 🚭 ♿ [P]. [MC] [VISA] JCB 🚫
*15 February-October* – **Meals** (by arrangement) 23.00 **st.** – **4 rm** ☕ 55.00/80.00 **st.**

## Culnaknock – ✉ *Portree*

🏨 **Glenview Inn,** IV51 9JH, ☎ (01470) 562248, *Fax (01470) 562211*, ≤ – 🚭 [P]. [MC] [VISA]
*March-October* – **Meals** a la carte 14.15/22.85 **t.** 🍷 4.95 – **5 rm** ☕ 50.00/70.00 **t.**

## Dunvegan.

🏨 **Harlosh House** ⛱, IV55 8ZG, Southeast : 6 m. by A 863 ☎ (01470) 52136 *Fax (01470) 521367*, ≤ Loch Bracadale and Islands – 🚭 [P]. [MC] [VISA]. 🚫
*Easter-mid October* – **Meals** - Seafood - (set menu only) (booking essential) (lunch b arrangement and dinner Wednesday residents only) 25.00 **st.** 🍷 8.90 – **6 rm** ☕ 72.5 105.00 **st.**

🏨 **Dunorin House** ⛱, Herebost, IV55 8GZ, Southeast : 2 ½ m. by A 863 on Roag ☎ (01470) 521488, *Fax (01470) 521488*, ≤, 🪑 – 🚭 [TV] [P]. [MC] [VISA]. 🚫
*April-October* – **Meals** (booking essential) (dinner only) 21.50 **st.** 🍷 4.50 – **10 rm** ☕ 42.0 80.00 **st.** – SB.

⌂ **Kinlochfollart** ⛱, IV55 8WG, South : ¾ m. on Glendale rd ☎ (01470) 52147 *Fax (01470) 521470*, ≤, 🪑 – 🚭 [P]. [MC] [AE] [D] [VISA]. 🚫
*closed Christmas and New Year* – **Meals** (by arrangement) 18.50 – **3 rm** ☕ 42.00/72.00 **s.**

⌂ **Roskhill,** Roskhill, IV55 8ZD, Southeast : 2 ½ m. by A 863 ☎ (01470) 52131 *Fax (01470) 521761* – 🚭 [P]. [MC] [AE] [VISA]. 🚫
**Meals** 14.50 **st.** 🍷 5.50 – **5 rm** ☕ 40.00/64.00 **st.** – SB.

🍴 **Three Chimneys,** Colbost, IV55 8ZT, Northwest : 5 ¾ m. by A 863 on B 88 ☎ (01470) 511258, *Fax (01470) 511358* – 🚭 [P]. [MC] [VISA]
*closed Sunday except Easter and late May Bank Holiday and November-March* – **Meals** Seafood - (booking essential) 24.95 **t.** (dinner) and a la carte 13.40/32.95 **t.** 🍷 6.45.

## Flodigarry – ✉ *Staffin.*

🏨 **Flodigarry Country House** ⛱, IV51 9HZ, ☎ (01470) 552203, *Fax (01470) 552301*, Staffin Island and coastline, 🪑 – 🚭 ☎ [P]. [MC] [VISA]
**Meals** (bar lunch Monday to Saturday)/dinner 28.50 **t.** 🍷 7.50 – **19 rm** ☕ 48.00/150.00 – SB

## Isleornsay – ✉ *Sleat*

🏨 **Kinloch Lodge** ⛱, IV43 8QY, North : 3 ½ m. by A 851 ☎ (01471) 833214 *Fax (01471) 833277*, ≤ Loch Na Dal, « 17C former shooting lodge », 🌳, 🪑, park – 🚭 ☎ [P]. [MC] [AE] [VISA]. 🚫
*closed Christmas-15 January* – **Meals** (booking essential to non-residents) (dinner only 25.00 **t.** 🍷 5.50 – **15 rm** ☕ 45.00/200.00 **t.**

🏨 **Eilean Iarmain** ⛱, IV43 8QR, ☎ (01471) 833332, *Fax (01471) 833275*, ≤, « 19C inn » 🌳, 🪑, park – 🚭 ☎ [P]. [MC] [AE] [VISA]
**Meals** (lunch by arrangement)/dinner 30.50 **t.** 🍷 6.25 – **12 rm** ☕ 80.00/125.00 **t.** – SB.

## Ord – ✉ *Sleat.*

⌂ **Fiordhem** ⛱, IV44 8RN, ☎ (01471) 855226, ≤ Loch Eishort and The Cuillins, « Idylli setting on shores of Loch Eishort », 🪑 – 🚭 [TV] [P]. 🚫
*Easter-October* – **Meals** (by arrangment) (communal dining) – **3 rm** ☕ (dinner included 50.00/84.00.

## Portree – *pop. 2 126.*

ℹ *Bayfield House, Bayfield Rd, IV51 9BZ ☎ (01478) 612137.*

🏨 **Cuillin Hills** ⛱, IV51 9LU, Northeast : ¾ m. by A 855 ☎ (01478) 612003 *Fax (01478) 613092*, ≤, 🪑, park – 🚭 rest, [TV] ☎ [P] – 🧑‍🏫 140. [MC] [AE] [VISA]. 🚫
**Meals** (bar lunch Monday to Saturday) (buffet lunch Sunday)/dinner 26.00 **t.** 🍷 6.50 – **21 rm** ☕ 55.00/140.00 **t.** – SB.

🏨 **Bosville,** Bosville Terr., IV51 9DG, ☎ (01478) 612846, *Fax (01478) 613434*, ≤ – 🚭 [TV] ☎ 📞 [MC] [AE] [VISA] JCB
***Chandlery :*** **Meals** (dinner only) 22.50 **t.** and a la carte 🍷 6.50 – **15 rm** ☕ 60.00/76.00 **t.**

🏨 **Rosedale,** Beaumont Cres., IV51 9DF, ☎ (01478) 613131, *Fax (01478) 612531*, ≤ harbour 🪑 – 🚭 rest, [TV] ☎ [P]. [MC] [VISA]
*May-September* – **Meals** (dinner only) 22.00 **t.** 🍷 7.30 – **23 rm** ☕ 48.00/96.00 **t.** – SB.

⌂ **Almondbank** without rest., Viewfield Rd, IV51 9EU, Southwest : 3/4 m. on A 87 ✆ (01478) 612696, *Fax (01478) 613114*, ≤ Portree Bay, 🌳 – TV ☎ P. MC VISA JCB
**4 rm** ☐ 56.00 **st.**

⌂ **Burnside** without rest., 5 Budmhor, IV51 9DJ, Northeast : 1/2 m. off A 855 via Budmhor Pl. ✆ (01478) 612669, 🌳 – ⇔ TV P
*restricted opening in winter* – **3 rm** ☐ 19.00/38.00 **st.**

⌂ **Kings Haven** without rest., 11 Bosville Terr., IV51 9DG, ✆ (01478) 612290, 🌳 – TV. MC VISA. ✗
*closed Christmas and restricted opening December-February* – **6 rm** ☐ 68.00 **t.**

**reaslane** – ✉ *Skeabost Bridge.*

⌂ **Auchendinny** ⛐, IV51 9NX, South : 1 m. on A 850 ✆ (01470) 532470, *Fax (01470) 532470*, ≤ Loch Snizort Beag, 🌳 – ⇔ ♿ P. MC AE VISA. ✗
*Easter-mid October* – **Meals** (by arrangement) 13.00 **st.** – **7 rm** ☐ 33.00/54.00 **st.**

**SOUTH QUEENSFERRY** *W. Lothian* 401 J 16 – ✉ *Edinburgh.*
*Edinburgh 10 – Glasgow 42 – Perth 35.*

**Travel Inn,** Queen's Crossing, Builyeon Rd, EH30 3YJ, ✆ (0131) 331 5056, *Fax (0131) 331 4746* – |≑|, ⇔ rm, ▤ rest, TV ♿ P. MC AE ⊕ VISA. ✗
**Meals** (grill rest.) – **46 rm** 38.00 **t.**

**SOUTH UIST** *Western Isles (Outer Hebrides)* 401 XY 11/12 – *see Uist (Isles of).*

**SPEAN BRIDGE** *Highland* 401 F 13.
*Edinburgh 143 – Fort William 10 – Glasgow 94 – Inverness 58 – Oban 60.*

**Corriegour Lodge,** Loch Lochy, PH34 4EB, North : 8 3/4 m. on A 82 ✆ (01397) 712685, *Fax (01397) 712696*, ≤, 🌳 – ⇔ rest, TV P. MC AE ⊕ VISA JCB. ✗
*20 March-November and weekends only February and March* – **Meals** (dinner only) 25.50 **t.** 🍷 6.50 – **9 rm** ☐ 40.00/90.00 **t.** – SB.

⌂ **Coinachan,** Gairlochy Rd, PH34 4EG, Northwest : 1 1/4 m. by A 82 on B 8004 ✆ (01397) 712417, *Fax (01397) 712417*, ≤, 🌳 – ⇔ P. ✗
*closed 25 December* – **Meals** 12.50 **st.** – **3 rm** ☐ 40.00/70.00 **st.** – SB.

XX **Old Station,** Station Rd, PH34 4EP, ✆ (01397) 712535, « Former Victorian railway station » – ⇔ P. MC VISA JCB
*closed Monday and November-March* – **Meals** (booking essential) (dinner only) a la carte 17.20/23.50 **t.** 🍷 6.95.

X **Old Pines** ⛐ with rm, PH34 4EG, Northwest : 1 1/2 m. by A 82 on B 8004 ✆ (01397) 712324, *Fax (01397) 712433*, ≤, park – ⇔ ♿ P. MC VISA JCB. ✗
*closed 2 weeks late November-early December* – **Meals** 23.50 **st.** (dinner) and lunch a la carte 14.50 **st.** – **8 rm** ☐ (dinner included) 60.00/120.00 **st.** – SB.

**at Roybridge** *East : 3 m. on A 86.*

**Glenspean Lodge** ⛐, PH31 4AW, East : 2 m. on A 86 ✆ (01397) 712223, *Fax (01397) 712660*, ≤, 🌳 – ⇔ rest, TV ☎ P. MC AE ⊕ VISA
**Meals** 17.50 **t.** (dinner) and a la carte 11.85/25.70 **t.** 🍷 6.55 – **17 rm** ☐ 53.00/130.00 **t.** – SB.

**SPITTAL OF GLENSHEE** *Perthshire and Kinross* 401 J 13 *Scotland G.* – ✉ *Blairgowrie.*
Env. : *Glenshee (✻★★) (chairlift AC).*
*Edinburgh 69 – Aberdeen 74 – Dundee 35.*

**Dalmunzie House** ⛐, PH10 7QG, ✆ (01250) 885224, *Fax (01250) 885225*, ≤, ⛳9, ⛐, 🌳, park, ✂ – |≑|, ⇔ rest, TV ☎ P. MC VISA
*closed 1 to 27 December* – **Meals** (bar lunch)/dinner 22.00 **t.** 🍷 5.00 – **16 rm** ☐ 50.00/94.00 **t.**

**STENNESS** *Orkney Islands* 401 K 7 – *see Orkney Islands.*

**STEPPS** *North Lanarkshire* 401 H 16 – *see Glasgow.*

**STEWARTON** *East Ayrshire* 401 402 G 16 *Scotland G. – pop. 7 091.*
Env. : *Kilmarnock (Dean Castle, arms and armour★, musical instruments★ AC) S : 5 1/2 m. by A 735 and B 7038.*
*Edinburgh 68 – Ayr 21 – Glasgow 22.*

XXX **Chapeltoun House** with rm, Irvine Rd, KA3 3ED, Southwest : 2 ½ m. by A 735 off
769 ☏ (01560) 482696, *Fax (01560) 485100*, « Country house in extensive grounds »,
– rest, TV ☎ P – 50. MC AE VISA
**Meals** 13.95/24.80 **t.** 6.95 – **8 rm** 79.00/145.00 **t.** – SB.

---

**STIRLING** 401 I 15 *Scotland G.* – *pop. 30 515.*

See : *Town*★★ – *Castle*★★ AC *(Site*★★★*, external elevations*★★★*, Stirling Heads*★★*, Argyll a Sutherland Highlanders Regimental Museum*★*)* B – *Argyll's Lodging*★ *(Renaissance dec ration*★*)* B A – *Church of the Holy Rude*★ B B.

Env. : *Wallace Monument (※*★★*) NE : 2½ m. by A 9* – A – *and B 998.*

Exc. : *Dunblane*★ *(Cathedral*★★*, West Front*★★*), N : 6½ m. by A 9* A.

*41 Dumbarton Rd, FK8 2QQ ☏ (01786) 475019 – Royal Burgh Stirling Visitor Centre, T Esplanade ☏ (01786) 479901 – Motorway Service Area, M 9/M 80, junction 9 ☏ (0178 814111 (summer only).*

*Edinburgh 37 – Dunfermline 23 – Falkirk 14 – Glasgow 28 – Greenock 52 – Motherwell 30 Oban 87 – Perth 35.*

## STIRLING

Barnton Street . . . . . . . . . B 2
Borestone Crescent . . . . . . . A 3
Causewayhead Road . . . . . . B 4
Corn Exchange Road . . . . . . B 5
Cornton Road . . . . . . . . . . A 7
Coxithill Road . . . . . . . . . . A 8
Drummond Place . . . . . . . . B 9
Dumbarton Road . . . . . . . . B 10
Goosecroft Road . . . . . . . . B 12
King Street . . . . . . . . . . . B 13
Leisure Centre . . . . . . . . . B
Murray Place . . . . . . . . . . B 15
Newhouse . . . . . . . . . . . . A 16
Park Place . . . . . . . . . . . A 18
Port Street . . . . . . . . . . . B
Queen Street . . . . . . . . . . B 20
Randolph Terrace . . . . . . . A
St. John Street . . . . . . . . . B
St. Mary's Wynd . . . . . . . . B
Seaforth Place . . . . . . . . . B
Shirra's Brae Road . . . . . . A
Spittal Street . . . . . . . . . . B
Thistle Centre . . . . . . . . . B
Union Street . . . . . . . . . . B
Upper Craigs . . . . . . . . . . B
Weaver Row . . . . . . . . . . A

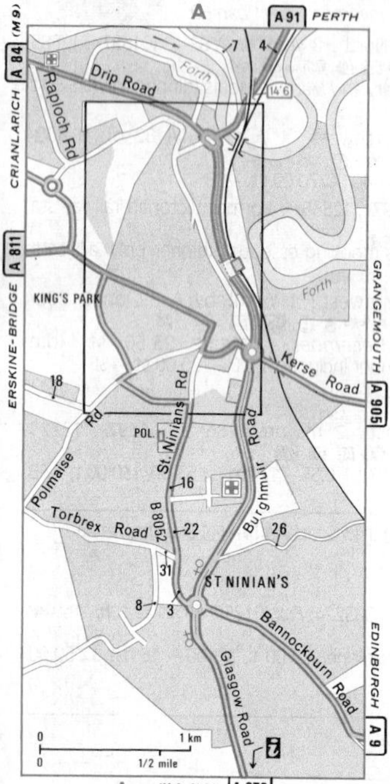


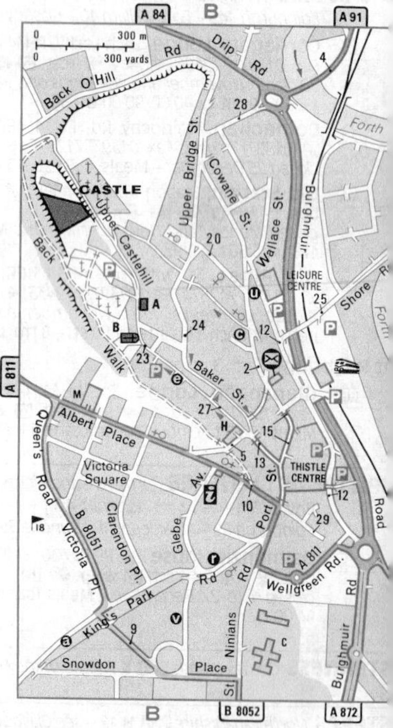


**Stirling Highland,** Spittal St., FK8 1DU, ☏ (01786) 475444, *Fax (01786) 462929*, , squash – TV ☎ P – 150. MC AE VISA JCB B
***Scholars :*** **Meals** *(closed Saturday lunch)* 11.95/19.95 **t.** and a la carte 9.50 – ***Rizzios*** **Meals** - Italian - 7.50 **t.** and a la carte 5.45 – 12.50 – **76 rm** 99.00/130.00 **t.**, 2 suites - SB.

🏨 **Park Lodge,** 32 Park Terr., FK8 2JS, ℘ (01786) 474862, *Fax (01786) 449748*, « Part Georgian, part Victorian house, antiques », 🐴 – ⇔ 🔟 ☎ ℅ 🅟 – 🖊 60. 🐠 *VISA*      B a
*closed Christmas and New Year* – Meals 8.50 st. (lunch) and a la carte 11.55/25.95 st. ⓘ 7.25
– 10 rm 🖭 60.00/85.00 st.

🏨 **Holiday Inn Express,** Springkerse Business Park, FK7 7XH, Northeast : 2 m. by A 905 off A 91 ℘ (01786) 449922, *Fax (01786) 449932* – 🗲, ⇔ rm, 🔟 ☎ ℅ & 🅟 – 🖊 30. 🐠 🖭 ⓞ
*VISA* 🄹🄲🄱
Meals (dinner only) a la carte approx. 14.00 st. ⓘ 4.75 – **80 rm** 52.00 st. – SB.

🏨 **Travel Inn,** Whins of Milton, Glasgow Rd, FK7 8EX, South : 3 m. by A 9 on A 872 ℘ (01786) 811256, *Fax (01786) 816415* – 🗲, ⇔ rm, 🗏 rest, 🔟 & 🅟. 🐠 🖭 ⓞ *VISA*. 🛇
Meals (grill rest.) – **40 rm** 38.00 t.

↥ **Ashgrove House** without rest., 2 Park Av., FK8 2LX, ℘ (01786) 472640, *Fax (01786) 472640*, 🐴 – ⇔ 🔟 🅟. 🛇      B r
*closed Christmas and New Year* – **3 rm** 🖭 30.00/55.00.

↥ **Number 10** without rest., Gladstone Pl., FK8 2NN, ℘ (01786) 472681, *Fax (01786) 472681*, 🐴 – ⇔ 🔟. 🛇      B v
**3 rm** 🖭 30.00/40.00 t.

↥ **West Plean House** 🛇 without rest., FK7 8HA, South : 3 ½ m. on A 872 (Denny rd) ℘ (01786) 812208, *Fax (01786) 480550*, « Working farm », 🐴, park – ⇔ 🔟 🅟. 🛇
*closed January and February* – **3 rm** 🖭 30.00/48.00 st.

↥ **Fairfield** without rest., 14 Princes St., FK8 1HQ, ℘ (01786) 472685 – ⇔ 🔟. 🛇      B c
– **6 rm** 🖭 25.00/42.00.

💥💥 **East India Company,** 7 Viewfield Pl., FK8 1NQ, ℘ (01786) 471330 – 🐠 🖭 *VISA*
*closed 25 December and 1 January* – Meals - Indian - (dinner only) 9.95 t. and a la carte      B u
ⓘ 6.95.

**at Blairlogie** *Northeast : 4½ m. by A 905 on A 91* – A – ✉ *Stirling.*

🏨 **Blairlogie House,** FK9 5QE, ℘ (01259) 761441, *Fax (01259) 761441*, 🐴, park – 🔟 ☎ 🅟. 🐠 *VISA*
*closed 1 week Christmas and New Year* – Meals *(closed Sunday)* (bar lunch)/dinner 18.50 st.
ⓘ 5.90 – **7 rm** 🖭 52.50/72.00 st. – SB.

🔘 ATS 45 Drip Rd ℘ (01786) 450770

---

**STIRLING SERVICE AREA** *Stirling* 🄰🄾🄸 I 15 – ✉ *Stirling.*

🏨 **Travelodge,** Pirnhall roundabout, Snabhead, FK7 8EU, at junction 9 of M 9 ℘ (01786) 813614, *Fax (01786) 815900*, Reservations (Freephone) 0800 850950 – ⇔ 🔟 ☎ & 🅟. 🐠 🖭 ⓞ *VISA* 🄹🄲🄱. 🛇
Meals (grill rest.) – **37 rm** 39.95/59.95 t.

---

**STONEHAVEN** *Aberdeenshire* 🄰🄾🄸 N 13 *Scotland G..*
Env. : Dunnottar Castle★★ *(site★★★)*, SE : 1 m.
Exc. : Crathes Castle★★ *(Gardens★★★)*, NW : 14½ m. by A 957 and A 93.
*Edinburgh 114 – Aberdeen 16 – Dundee 51.*

💥 **The Tolbooth,** Old Pier Rd, AB39 2JU, ℘ (01569) 762287, *Fax (01569) 762287* – 🐠 *VISA*
*closed Monday, 25 to 28 December and first 2 weeks January* – Meals - Seafood - (dinner only) a la carte 18.85/31.40 t. ⓘ 6.75.

🔘 ATS 64-72 Barclay St. ℘ (01569) 762077

---

**STORNOWAY** *Western Isles (Outer Hebrides)* 🄰🄾🄸 A 9 – *see Lewis and Harris (Isle of).*

---

**STRANRAER** *Dumfries and Galloway* 🄰🄾🄸 🄰🄾🄲 E 19 *Scotland G.* – pop. 11 348.
Exc. : Logan Botanic Garden★ *AC*, S : 11 m. by A 77, A 716 and B 7065.
🄸🄸 Creachmore, Leswalt ℘ (01776) 870245.
⛴ to Northern Ireland (Belfast) (Stena Line) (3 h 15 mn) – to Northern Ireland (Belfast) (Sea Containers Ferries Scotland Ltd) 4-5 daily (1 h 30 mn).
🄱 Burns House, 28 Harbour St., DG9 7RA ℘ (01776) 702595.
*Edinburgh 132 – Ayr 51 – Dumfries 75.*

🏨🏨 **North West Castle,** Port Rodie, DG9 8EH, ℘ (01776) 704413, *Fax (01776) 702646*, 🛋, 🖾 – 🗲, ⇔ rest, 🔟 ☎ ℅ 🅟 – 🖊 100. 🐠 🖭 *VISA*. 🛇
Meals 21.00 t. (dinner) and a la carte 16.00/23.00 t. ⓘ 6.50 – **71 rm** 🖭 52.00/104.00 t. – SB.

↥ **Kildrochet House** 🛇, DG9 9BB, South : 3 ¼ m. by A 77 on A 716 at junction with B 7077 (Newton Stewart rd) ℘ (01776) 820216, *Fax (01776) 820216*, « 18C former dower house », 🐴 – ⇔ 🅟. 🐠 *VISA* 🄹🄲🄱. 🛇
Meals (by arrangement) 16.00 – **3 rm** 🖭 30.00/50.00.

↑ **Windyridge Villa** without rest., 5 Royal Cresent, DG9 8HB, off Port Rodie (A77 Ayr r
  ℰ (01776) 889900, Fax (01776) 889900 – ⇶ 📺 ⇌
  *closed 25 December, 1 January and 2 weeks November* – **3 rm** ⊇ 25.00/40.00.

**at Kirkcolm** *Northwest : 6 m. by A 718* – ⊠ *Stranraer.*

🏛 **Corsewall Lighthouse** ♤, Corsewall Point, DG9 0QG, Northwest : 4 ¼ m. by B 7³
  ℰ (01776) 853220, Fax (01776) 854231, ≤, park – ⇶ 📺 🖪 🕭 👬 👤. ⏀⑨ 🅰🅴 ⓪ 𝗩𝗜𝗦𝗔 𝗝𝗖𝗕. ⚘
  **Meals** (dinner only) 27.95 and a la carte ᵠ 7.95 – **6 rm** ⊇ (dinner included) 125.00/300.00

  Ⓐ ATS Commerce Rd Ind. Est. ℰ (01776) 702131

---

**STRATHBLANE** *Stirling* 𝟒𝟎𝟏 H 16 – *pop. 2 355* – ⊠ *Glasgow.*
  *Edinburgh 52 – Glasgow 11 – Stirling 26.*

🏨 **Kirkhouse Inn,** Glasgow Rd, G63 9AA, ℰ (01360) 770621, Fax (01360) 770896 – 📺 ☎ ●
  – 🔏 30. ⏀⑨ 🅰🅴 ⓪ 𝗩𝗜𝗦𝗔 𝗝𝗖𝗕
  **Meals** a la carte 11.05/20.85 t. ᵠ 4.95 – **14 rm** ⊇ 48.00/65.00 t., 1 suite – SB.

🏨 **Country Club** ♤, Milngavie Rd, G63 9EH, South : ½ m. on A 81 ℰ (01360) 77049
  Fax (01360) 770345, ☞, park – ⇶ rest, 📺 ☎ 👤. ⏀⑨ 🅰🅴 ⓪ 𝗩𝗜𝗦𝗔. ⚘
  **Ardinning Room : Meals** 27.95 t. (dinner) and lunch a la carte approx. 23.90 t. ᵠ 8.25
  **Brasserie : Meals** a la carte 22.75/28.95 t. ᵠ 8.25 – ⊇ 7.50 – **10 rm** 75.00/150.00 t. – SB.

---

**STRATHCONON** *Highland* 𝟒𝟎𝟏 F 11 *Scotland G.* – ⊠ *Muir of Ord.*
  Exc. : *Wester Ross★★★.*
  *Edinburgh 184 – Inverness 28.*

🏛 **East Lodge** ♤, IV6 7QQ, West : 11 m. from Marybank off A 832 ℰ (01997) 477222
  Fax (01997) 477243, ≤, ☜, ☞, park – ⇶ rest, 📺 ☎ 🕻 👤. ⏀⑨ 𝗩𝗜𝗦𝗔. ⚘
  *closed 24 to 26 December and restricted opening January and December* – **Meals** (ba
  lunch)/dinner 25.00 **st.** ᵠ 5.95 – **9 rm** ⊇ 50.00/100.00 **st.** – SB.

---

**STRATHKINNESS** *Fife* 𝟒𝟎𝟏 L 14 – *see St. Andrews.*

---

**STRATHPEFFER** *Highland* 𝟒𝟎𝟏 G 11 – *pop. 966.*
  🏌 *Strathpeffer Spa* ℰ (01997) 421219/421011.
  🖪 *The Square, IV14 9DW* ℰ (01997) 421415 *(April-November).*
  *Edinburgh 174 – Inverness 18.*

↑ **Craigvar** without rest., The Square, IV14 9DL, ℰ (01997) 421622, Fax (01997) 421796, ☞
  – ⇶ 📺 👤. 𝗩𝗜𝗦𝗔. ⚘
  *closed Christmas and New Year* – **3 rm** ⊇ 29.00/54.00 **st.**

---

**STRATHYRE** *Stirling* 𝟒𝟎𝟏 H 15 *Scotland G.* – ⊠ *Callander.*
  Exc. : *The Trossachs★★★ (Loch Katherine★★) SW : 14 m. by A 84 and A 821 – Hilltop*
  *viewpoint★★★ (⚘★★★ ) SW : 16½ m. by A 84 and A 821.*
  *Edinburgh 62 – Glasgow 53 – Perth 42.*

↑ **Ardoch Lodge** ♤, FK18 8NF, West : ¼ m. ℰ (01877) 384666, Fax (01877) 384666, ≤
  ☞, park – ⇶ rest, 👤. ⏀⑨ 𝗩𝗜𝗦𝗔 𝗝𝗖𝗕
  *restricted opening in winter* – **Meals** (by arrangement) 21.00 **st.** – **3 rm** ⊇ 33.50/62.00 **st.**

✗ **Creagan House** with rm, FK18 8ND, on A 84 ℰ (01877) 384638, Fax (01877) 384319, ≤ –
  👤. ⏀⑨ 🅰🅴 𝗩𝗜𝗦𝗔
  *closed February and 1 week October* – **Meals** (booking essential) (dinner only) 23.00 t
  ᵠ 7.75 – **5 rm** ⊇ 47.50/70.00 **t.** – SB.

---

**STROMNESS** *Orkney Islands* 𝟒𝟎𝟏 K 7 – *see Orkney Islands.*

---

**STRONTIAN** *Highland* 𝟒𝟎𝟏 D 13.
  🖪 *Village Square, PH36* ℰ (01967) 402131 *(summer only).*
  *Edinburgh 139 – Fort William 23 – Oban 66.*

🏨 **Kilcamb Lodge** ♤, PH36 4HY, ℰ (01967) 402257, Fax (01967) 402041, ≤, « Lochside
  *setting* », ☜, ☞, park – ⇶ 📺 👤. ⏀⑨ 𝗩𝗜𝗦𝗔 𝗝𝗖𝗕. ⚘
  *March-November and New Year* – **Meals** (light lunch) (dinner booking essential to non-
  residents) 29.50 t. ᵠ 7.00 – **11 rm** ⊇ (dinner included) 80.00/220.00 **t.**

**TAIN** Highland **401** H 10 – pop. 4 540.

  🏌 Tain ℰ (01862) 892314.
  Edinburgh 191 – Inverness 35 – Wick 91.

🏨 **Morangie House,** Morangie Rd, IV19 1PY, ℰ (01862) 892281, Fax (01862) 892872, ☞ –
  ⇄ rm, 📺 ☎ 🅿. 🆆🅾 🆀🅴 🅾 🆅🅸🆂🅰
  Meals 10.50/19.70 t. and a la carte ⅄ 5.20 – **26 rm** ☷ 55.00/85.00 t. – SB.

🏨 **Mansfield House,** Scotsburn Rd, IV19 1PR, ℰ (01862) 892052, Fax (01862) 892260, ☞ –
  ⇄ rm, 📺 ☎ ☏ 🅿 – 🔬 35. 🆆🅾 🆀🅴 🆅🅸🆂🅰
  Meals (bar lunch)/dinner 25.00 t. and a la carte ⅄ 5.00 – **18 rm** ☷ 50.00/120.00 t. – SB.

⌂ **Aldie House** 🅂 without rest., IV19 1LZ, Southeast : 1 ½ m. by B 9174 off A 9
  ℰ (01862) 893787, Fax (01862) 893787, ≤, ☞, park – ⇄ 📺 🅿. 🆆🅾 🆅🅸🆂🅰. 🛇
  **3 rm** ☷ 30.00/44.00 s.

⌂ **Golf View House** without rest., 13 Knockbreck Rd, IV19 1BN, ℰ (01862) 892856,
  Fax (01862) 892856, ≤, ☞ – ⇄ 📺 🅿. 🆆🅾 🆅🅸🆂🅰. 🛇
  closed 15 December-15 January – **5 rm** ☷ 25.00/45.00.

---

**TALLADALE** Highland **401** D 10 Scotland G. – ✉ Achnasheen.

  Env. : Wester Ross★★★ – Loch Maree★★★ – Victoria Falls★, N : 2 m. by A 832.
  Edinburgh 218 – Inverness 62 – Kyle of Lochalsh 58.

⌂ **Old Mill Highland Lodge** 🅂, IV22 2HL, ℰ (01445) 760271, ☞ – ⇄ 🅿
  closed 1 week in spring and 19 October-16 December – Meals 25.00 st. ⅄ 8.00 – **6 rm** ☷
  (dinner included) 59.50/119.00 st. – SB.

---

**TARBERT** Argyll and Bute **401** D 16 – see Kintyre (Peninsula).

---

**TARBERT** Western Isles (Outer Hebrides) **401** Z 10 – see Lewis and Harris (Isle of).

---

**THORNHILL** Dumfries and Galloway **401** **402** I 18 Scotland G. – pop. 1 633.

  Env. : Drumlanrig Castle★★ (cabinets★) AC, NW : 4 m. by A 76.
  Edinburgh 64 – Ayr 44 – Dumfries 15 – Glasgow 63.

🏛 **Trigony House,** Closeburn, DG3 5EZ, South : 1 ½ m. on A 76 ℰ (01848) 331211,
  Fax (01848) 331303, ☞ – ⇄ rest, 📺 ☎ 🅿. 🆆🅾 🆅🅸🆂🅰 🅹🅲🅱. 🛇
  closed 25-26 December and 1 January – Meals (bar lunch Monday to Saturday)/dinner
  19.50 t. ⅄ 5.95 – **8 rm** ☷ 45.00/90.00 t. – SB.

---

**THORNHILL** Stirling **401** H 15 – pop. 550 – ✉ Stirling.

  Edinburgh 46 – Glasgow 36.

⌂ **Corshill Cottage** 🅂, FK8 3QD, East : 1 m. on A 873 ℰ (01786) 850270, ☞ – ⇄ 🅿. 🛇
  Meals (by arrangement) 15.00 – **3 rm** ☷ 30.00/48.00.

---

**THURSO** Highland **401** J 8 Scotland G. – pop. 9 110.

  Exc. : Strathy Point★ (≤★★★) W : 22 m. by A 836.
  🏌 Newlands of Geise ℰ (01847) 893807.
  ⛴ from Scrabster to Stromness (Orkney Islands) (P & O Scottish Ferries) (1 h 45 mn).
  🛈 Riverside, KW14 8BU ℰ (01847) 892371 (summer only).
  Edinburgh 289 – Inverness 133 – Wick 21.

🏨 **Forss House** 🅂, Bridge of Forss, KW14 7XY, West : 5 ½ m. on A 836 ℰ (01847) 861201,
  Fax (01847) 861301, ⌕, ☞, park – ⇄ rest, 📺 ☎ 🐾 🅿. 🆆🅾 🆀🅴 🆅🅸🆂🅰. 🛇
  closed 23 December-4 January – Meals (bar lunch)/dinner 22.50 t. ⅄ 6.30 – **10 rm** ☷ 54.50/
  110.00 t. – SB.

⌂ **Murray House** without rest., 1 Campbell St., KW14 7HD, ℰ (01847) 895759 – ⇄ 📺 🅿.
  🛇
  closed 24 December-3 January – **4 rm** ☷ 18.00/40.00 st.

---

**TILLICOULTRY** Clackmannanshire **401** I 15 – pop. 4 586.

  🏌 Alva Rd ℰ (01259) 50124.
  Edinburgh 35 – Dundee 43 – Glasgow 38.

🏛 **Harviestoun Country Inn,** Dollar Rd, FK13 6PQ, East : ¼ m. off A 91
  ℰ (01259) 752522, Fax (01259) 752523 – ⇄ 📺 ☎ 🅿 – 🔬 70. 🆆🅾 🆀🅴 🆅🅸🆂🅰
  Meals a la carte 11.75/25.85 st. ⅄ 4.90 – **10 rm** ☷ 55.00/68.50 st. – SB.

**TOBERMORY** *Argyll and Bute* **401** *B 14 – see Mull (Isle of).*

---

**TONGUE** *Highland* **401** *G 8 Scotland G. – pop. 552 –* ⊠ *Lairg.*
Exc. : *Cape Wrath*★★★ *(*≤★★*) W : 44 m. (including ferry crossing) by A 838 – Ben Loyal*★★
*S : 8 m. by A 836 – Ben Hope*★ *(*≤★★★*) SW : 15 m. by A 838 – Strathy Point*★ *(*≤★★★
*E : 22 m. by A 836 – Torrisdale Bay*★ *(*≤★★*) NE : 8 m. by A 836.*
*Edinburgh 257 – Inverness 101 – Thurso 43.*

🏠 **Ben Loyal,** Main St., IV27 4XE, ℰ *(01847) 611216, Fax (01847) 611212,* ≤ Ben Loyal and
Kyle of Tongue – ⊁ rest, 📺 ℗. 🎴 *VISA*
*closed Christmas and New Year –* **Meals** (bar lunch)/dinner 24.50 t. ₰ 6.95 – **12 rm** ⊑ 40.00.
117.00 t. – SB.

---

**TORRIDON** *Highland* **401** *D 11 Scotland G. –* ⊠ *Achnasheen.*
Env. : *Wester Ross*★★★.
*Edinburgh 234 – Inverness 62 – Kyle of Lochalsh 44.*

🏨 **Loch Torridon** ❦, IV22 2EY, South : 1 ½ m. on A 896 ℰ *(01445) 791242,*
*Fax (01445) 791296,* ≤ Upper Loch Torridon and mountains, « 19C former shooting
lodge », ☜, ☞, park – 🛗 ⊁ 📺 ☎ & ℗ – 🔬 25. 🎴 🎴 🎴 *VISA* *JCB.* ✀
**Meals** (bar lunch)/dinner 37.50 st. and a la carte ₰ 10.60 – **19 rm** ⊑ 85.00/250.00 st.
2 suites – SB.

---

**TREASLANE** *Highland – see Skye (Isle of).*

---

**TROON** *South Ayrshire* **401 402** *G 17 – pop. 15 116.*
🏌, 🏌, 🏌 *Troon Municipal, Harling Drive* ℰ *(01292) 312464.*
🚹 *Municipal Buildings, South Beach* ℰ *(01292) 317696 (summer only).*
*Edinburgh 77 – Ayr 7 – Glasgow 31.*

🏨 **Marine Highland,** 8 Crosbie Rd, KA10 6HE, ℰ *(01292) 314444, Fax (01292) 316922,* ≤,
🏋, ☎, 🏊, squash – 🛗, ⊁ rm, ▤ rest, 📺 ☎ & ℗ – 🔬 220. 🎴 🎴 🎴 *VISA*
*Rizzio's :* **Meals** 9.95 st. (dinner) and a la carte 11.70/20.05 st. ₰ 5.45 – *Fairways :* Meals
(restricted opening in winter) 22.00 st. (dinner) and a la carte 20.00/27.25 st. ₰ 5.95 – ⊑
12.50 – **69 rm** ⊑ 99.00/160.00 t., 5 suites – SB.

🏨 **Lochgreen House** ❦, Monktonhill Rd, Southwood, KA10 7EN, Southeast : 2 m. on
B 749 ℰ *(01292) 313343, Fax (01292) 318661,* « Edwardian house, antiques », ☞, park, ✀
– ⊁ rest, 📺 ☎ & ℗ – 🔬 30. 🎴 🎴 *VISA*
**Meals** 17.95/29.95 t. and lunch a la carte ₰ 8.95 – **14 rm** ⊑ 99.00/140.00 t., 1 suite – SB.

🏨 **Piersland House,** 15 Craigend Rd, KA10 6HD, ℰ *(01292) 314747, Fax (01292) 315613,*
☞ – 📺 ☎ & ℗ – 🔬 100. 🎴 🎴 🎴 *VISA*
**Meals** 12.95/22.50 t. ₰ 5.95 – **17 rm** ⊑ 82.50/140.00 t., 11 suites.

🏠 **Glenside** without rest., 2 Darley Pl., KA10 6JQ, ℰ *(01292) 313677, Fax (01292) 313677,* ☞
– 📺 ℗
**5 rm** ⊑ 30.00/50.00.

**at Loans** *East : 2 m. on A 759 –* ⊠ *Troon.*

🏨 **Highgrove House,** Old Loans Rd, KA10 7HL, East : ¼ m. on Dundonald rd
ℰ *(01292) 312511, Fax (01292) 318228,* ≤, ☞ – 📺 ☎ ☍ ℗. 🎴 🎴 *VISA.* ✀
**Meals** 16.95/22.50 t. and a la carte ₰ 7.00 – **9 rm** ⊑ 74.00/95.00 t.

---

**TURNBERRY** *South Ayrshire* **401 402** *F 18 Scotland G. –* ⊠ *Girvan.*
Env. : *Culzean Castle*★ *AC (setting*★★★*, Oval Staircase*★★*) NE : 5 m. by A 719.*
*Edinburgh 97 – Ayr 15 – Glasgow 51 – Stranraer 36.*

🏨 **Turnberry** ❦, KA26 9LT, on A 719 ℰ *(01655) 331000, Fax (01655) 331706,* « Part
Edwardian, ≤ golf courses, bay, Ailsa Craig and Mull of Kintyre », 🏋, ☎, 🏊, 🏌, ☞, ✀,
squash – 🛗 📺 ☎ & ℗ – 🔬 150. 🎴 🎴 🎴 *VISA* *JCB.* ✀
*Turnberry :* **Meals** (dinner only and Sunday lunch)/dinner 47.50 t. and a la carte – *Bay at*
*Turnberry :* **Meals** a la carte 25.00/45.00 t. – *The Clubhouse :* **Meals** (lunch only) (summer
only) a la carte 13.25/21.00 t. – **122 rm** ⊑ 175.00/318.00 t., 10 suites – SB.

---

**TWYNHOLM** *Dumfries and Galloway* **402** *H 19 – pop. 1 068.*
*Edinburgh 107 – Ayr 54 – Dumfries 27 – Stranraer 48.*

🏠 **Fresh Fields** ❦, Arden Rd, DG6 4PB, Southwest : ¾ m. by Burn Brae ℰ *(01557) 860221,*
*Fax (01557) 860221,* ☞ – ⊁ ℗. ✀
*March-October –* **Meals** (by arrangement) 15.00 st. ₰ 4.25 – **5 rm** ⊑ 28.00/56.00 st. – SB.

**DDINGSTON** *South Lanarkshire* 401 402 H 16 – *pop. 5 367* – ⊠ *Glasgow*.
  ⌐₁₈ *Coatbridge, Townhead Rd* ℘ *(01236) 28975*.
  *Edinburgh 41 – Glasgow 10*.

  🏠 **Redstones,** 8-10 Glasgow Rd, G71 7AS, ℘ (01698) 813774, *Fax (01698) 815319* – 📺 ☎ 🅿.
  🆗 🄰🄴 ① VISA. ✦
  **Meals** (bar lunch Monday to Friday)/dinner 16.95 **st.** and a la carte ≬ 6.50 – **15 rm** ⊊ 60.00/
  80.00 **st.**

  🏠 **Travel Inn,** 601 Hamilton Rd, G71 7SA, Northwest : 2. m. by B 7071 and A 721
  ℘ (0141) 773 1133, *Fax (0141) 771 8354*, 🚗 – |≋|, ✦ rm, ▤ rest, 📺 ঙ 🅿. 🆗 🄰🄴 ① VISA.
  ✦
  **Meals** (grill rest.) – **64 rm** 38.00 **t.**

**IST (Isles of)** *Western Isles (Outer Hebrides)* 401 XY 10 /11/12 – *pop. 3 510*.
  ⚓ *see Liniclate.*
  🚢 *from Lochboisdale to Oban via Isle of Barra (Castlebay) and Malaig (Mainland) (Caledonian MacBrayne Ltd) (summer only) – from Lochmaddy to Isle of Skye (Uig) (Caledonian
  MacBrayne Ltd) 1-3 daily (1 h 50 mn) – from Otternish to Berneray (Caledonian MacBrayne
  Ltd) frequent services daily (5 mn) – from Otternish to Isle of Lewis and Harris (Leverburgh)
  (Caledonian MacBrayne Ltd) (1 h 10 mn).*

### NORTH UIST.

**Grimsay.**

  ⌂ **Glendale** ⌂, 7 Kallin, HS6 5HY, ℘ (01870) 602029, ≤ – ✦ 🅿. ✦
  *closed Christmas and New Year* – **Meals** (by arrangement) (communal dining) 12.00 **st.** –
  **3 rm** ⊊ 20.00/38.00 **st.**

**ochmaddy.**

  🏠 **Lochmaddy,** HS6 5AA, ℘ (01876) 500331, *Fax (01876) 500210*, 🍷 – ✦ rest, 📺 ☎ 🅿.
  🆗 🄰🄴 VISA JCB
  **Meals** (bar lunch)/dinner 15.00 **t.** and a la carte ≬ 5.00 – **15 rm** ⊊ 40.00/75.00 **t.**

### BENBECULA.

**Liniclate.**

  ⚓ *Benbecula Airport :* ℘ (01870) 602051.

  🏨 **Dark Island,** HS7 5PJ, ℘ (01870) 603030, *Fax (01870) 602347* – 📺 ☎ 🅿 – 🕍 100. 🆗 VISA
  *closed 26 December and 1 January* – **Meals** *closed 2 January* 12.00/19.75 **st.** and dinner a la carte ≬ 4.50 – **42 rm** ⊊ 62.00/88.00 **st.** – SB.

  ⌂ **Borve** without rest., 5 Torlum, HS7 5PP, Northwest : ¾ m. on B 892 ℘ (01870) 602685,
  *Fax (01870) 603235*, 🚗 – ✦ 📺 🅿. ✦
  **4 rm** ⊊ 20.00/40.00.

### SOUTH UIST.

**_ochboisdale.**

  ⌂ **Brae Lea** ⌂, Lasgair, HS8 5TH, Northwest : 1 m. by A 865 ℘ (01878) 700497,
  *Fax (01878) 700497*, ☎ – ✦ rm, 🅿
  **Meals** (by arrangement) 15.00 **st.** – **6 rm** ⊊ 25.00/60.00 – SB.

**Pollachar.**

  🏠 **Polochar Inn** ⌂, HS8 5TT, ℘ (01878) 700215, *Fax (01878) 700768*, ≤ Sound of Barra –
  🛏, ✦ rm, 📺 ☎ 🅿. 🆗 VISA. ✦
  **Meals** a la carte 8.25/26.20 **st.** – **10 rm** ⊊ 35.00/55.00 **st.**

**ULLAPOOL** *Highland* 401 E 10 *Scotland G.* – *pop. 1 231*.
  **See :** *Town★*.
  **Env. :** *Wester Ross★★★ – Loch Broom★★*.
  **Exc. :** *Falls of Measach★★, S : 11 m. by A 835 and A 832 - Corrieshalloch Gorge★, SE : 10 m.
  by A 835 – Northwards to Lochinver★★, Morefield (≤★★ of Ullapool), ≤★ Loch Broom.*
  🚢 *to Isle of Lewis (Stornoway) (Caledonian MacBrayne Ltd) (2 h 45 mn).*
  🛈 *Argyle St., IV26 2UR* ℘ (01854) 612135 *(April-November).*
  *Edinburgh 215 – Inverness 59.*

**Altnaharrie Inn** (Gunn Eriksen) ॐ, IV26 2SS, Southwest : ½ m. by private ferr
🕸🕸 𝒫 (01854) 633230, « Former drovers' inn on banks of Loch Broom », ☞ – 🕸
🕸 **VISA** . 🕸
*mid April-late October* – **Meals** (set menu only) (booking essential) (residents only) (dinne
only) 75.00 **st.** 🍴 6.60 – **8 rm** ⌂ (dinner included) 180.00/410.00 **st.**
**Spec.** Young turbot and summer truffles with caramelised baby fennel and carrots. Sou
and mousseline of asparagus with taste of foie gras and langoustine. Ravioli of lobster wit
three sauces.

🏠 **Ardvreck** ॐ without rest., Morefield Brae, IV26 2TH, Northwest : 2 m. by A 83
𝒫 (01854) 612028, Fax (01854) 613000, ≤ Loch Broom and mountains, ☞ – 🕸 📺 🅿 . ◐
**VISA** . 🕸
*March-October* – **10 rm** ⌂ 27.00/54.00 **t.**

🏠 **The Sheiling** without rest., Garve Rd, IV26 2SX, 𝒫 (01854) 612947, Fax (01854) 612947,
Loch Broom, ⇆, ☜, ☞ – 🕸 🅿 . 🕸
*closed Christmas and New Year* – **7 rm** ⌂ 21.00/50.00 **st.**

🏠 **Dromnan** without rest., Garve Rd, IV26 2SX, 𝒫 (01854) 612333, Fax (01854) 613364, ◄
☞ – 🕸 📺 🅿 . ◐ **VISA** . 🕸
**7 rm** ⌂ 20.00/48.00 **t.**

🏠 **Point Cottage** without rest., West Shore St., IV26 2UR, 𝒫 (01854) 612494, ≤ Loc
Broom, ☞ – 🕸 📺 🅿 . 🕸
*February-October* – **3 rm** ⌂ 40.00/50.00 **st.**

---

**UNST (Island of)** *Shetland Islands* **401** R 1 – *see Shetland Islands.*

---

**UPHALL** *West Lothian* **401** J 16 – *pop. 14 600.*
🏌 *Uphall, Houston Mains 𝒫 (01506) 856404.*
*Edinburgh 13 – Glasgow 32.*

🏨 **Houstoun House,** EH52 6JS, 𝒫 (01506) 853831, Fax (01506) 854220, « Gardens », 🗲
⇆, 🔲, park, 🕸 – 🕸 📺 🅿 ᵭ 🅿 – 🔏 400. ◐ 🆎 ◑ **VISA** . 🕸
**Meals** 16.50/32.50 **st.** and a la carte 🍴 6.50 – ⌂ 11.50 – **72 rm** 115.00/135.00 **st.**, 1 suite
SB.

---

**WALKERBURN** *Borders* **401** **402** K 17 *Scotland G.* – *pop. 1 038 (inc. Traquair).*
**Env.** : *The Tweed Valley★★ – Traquair House★★ , W : 4 m. by A 72 and B 709.*
**Exc.** : *Abbotsbury★★ AC, W : 10½ m. by A 72, A 6091 and B 6360.*
🏌 *Innerleithen, Leithen Water, Leithen Rd 𝒫 (01896) 830951.*
*Edinburgh 32 – Galashiels 10 – Peebles 8.*

🏨 **Tweed Valley** ॐ, Galashiels Rd, EH43 6AA, 𝒫 (01896) 870636, Fax (01896) 870639, 🗲
⇆, ☜, ☞ – 🕸 rest, 📺 ☎ 🅿 . ◐ 🆎 **VISA**
**Meals** (bar lunch)/dinner 19.00 **st.** and a la carte 🍴 6.75 – ⌂ 7.50 – **19 rm** 35.00/100.00 **st.**

---

**WALLS** *Shetland Islands* **401** PQ 3 – *see Shetland Islands (Mainland).*

---

**WHITEBRIDGE** *Highland* **401** G 12 *Scotland G..*
**Env.** : *Loch Ness★★ – The Great Glen★.*
*Edinburgh 171 – Inverness 23 – Kyle of Lochalsh 67 – Oban 92.*

🏨 **Knockie Lodge** ॐ, IV1 2UP, Southwest : 3 ½ m. by B 862 𝒫 (01456) 486276
Fax (01456) 486389, ≤ Loch Nan Lann and mountains, « 18C former shooting lodge », ☜
park – 🕸 ☎ 🅿 . ◐ 🆎 **VISA**
*May-October* – **Meals** (booking essential) (light lunch residents only) 35.00 **st.** 🍴 6.00 –
**10 rm** ⌂ 60.00/160.00 **st.** – SB.

---

**WHITING BAY** *North Ayrshire* **401** **402** E 17 – *see Arran (Isle of).*

---

**WICK** *Highland* **401** K 8 *Scotland G.* – *pop. 9 713.*
**Exc.** : *Duncansby Head★ (Stacks of Duncansby★★) N : 14 m. by A 9 – Grey Cairns o
Camster★ (Long Cairn★★) S : 17 m. by A 9 – The Hill O'Many Stanes★, S : 10 m. by A 9.*
🏌 *Reiss 𝒫 (01955) 602726.*
✈ *Wick Airport : 𝒫 (01955) 602215, N : 1 m.*
🚩 *Whitechapel Rd, KW1 4EA 𝒫 (01955) 602596.*
*Edinburgh 282 – Inverness 126.*

↑ **Clachan** without rest., South Rd, KW1 5NH, South : ¾ m. on A 9 ℰ (01955) 605384, 🚗 –
 ✿ 📺. ✿
 **3 rm** � 25.00/40.00.

↑ **Meadowbank House** without rest., Thurso Rd, KW1 5LE, West : 1 m. on A 882
 ℰ (01955) 603760 – ✿ 📺 🅿
 **3 rm** ⊂ 20.00/40.00.

---

**ᴡIGTOWN** Dumfries and Galloway **401** G 19 Scotland G. – pop. 1 344 – ⊠ Newton Stewart.
 Exc. : Whithorn Museum (early Christian crosses★★ ) S : 10 m. by A 746.
 🖪 Wigtown & Bladnoch, Lightlands Terr. ℰ (01988) 403354.
 Edinburgh 137 – Ayr 61 – Dumfries 61 – Stranraer 26.

🏠 **Corsemalzie House** ⬙, DG8 9RL, Southwest : 6 ½ m. by A 714 on B 7005
 ℰ (01988) 860254, Fax (01988) 860213, ✎, 🚗, park – ✿ rest, 📺 ☎ 🅿. 🆗 🕮 𝗩𝗜𝗦𝗔
 closed mid January-early March and 25-26 December – **Meals** 10.95/19.90 **t.** and a la carte
 🛦 4.90 – **14 rm** ⊂ (dinner included) 76.00/126.00 **st.** – SB.

---

**ᴡORMIT** Fife **401** L 14 – ⊠ Newport-on-Tay.
 🖪 Scotscraig, Golf Rd, Tayport ℰ (01382) 552515.
 Edinburgh 53 – Dundee 6 – St. Andrews 12.

🏠 **Sandford Country House** ⬙, DD6 8RG, South : 2 m. at junction of A 914 with B 946
 ℰ (01382) 541802, Fax (01382) 542136, ≼, 🚗 – ✿ rest, 📺 ☎ 🅿 – 🔬 60. 🆗 🕮 ① 𝗩𝗜𝗦𝗔
 closed 31 December – **Meals** 22.00/25.00 **t.** 🛦 6.20 – **16 rm** ⊂ 80.00/95.00 **t.** – SB.

# *Wales*

## Place with at least

a hotel or restaurant       ● Adare
a pleasant hotel or restaurant      🏰, ↑, ⋊
a quiet, secluded hotel
a restaurant with    ⁂, ⁂⁂, ⁂⁂⁂,   Meals
See this town for establishments      **DUBLIN**
   located in its vicinity

## Localité offrant au moins

une ressource hôtelière       ● Adare
un hôtel ou restaurant agréable     🏰, ↑, ⋊
un hôtel très tranquille, isolé
une bonne table à   ⁂, ⁂⁂, ⁂⁂⁂,   Meals
Localité groupant dans le texte      **DUBLIN**
les ressources de ses environs

## La località possiede come minimo

una risorsa alberghiera       ● Adare
Albergo o ristorante ameno      🏰, ↑, ⋊
un albergo molto tranquillo, isolato
un'ottima tavola con   ⁂, ⁂⁂, ⁂⁂⁂,   Meals
La località raggruppa nel suo testo    **DUBLIN**
le risorse dei dintorni

## Ort mit mindestens

einem Hotel oder Restaurant      ● Adare
ein angenehmes Hotel oder Restaurant   🏰, ↑, ⋊
einem sehr ruhigen und abgelegenen Hotel
einem Restaurant mit   ⁂, ⁂⁂, ⁂⁂⁂,   Meals
Ort mit Angaben über Hotels und Restaurants   **DUBLIN**
in der Umgebung

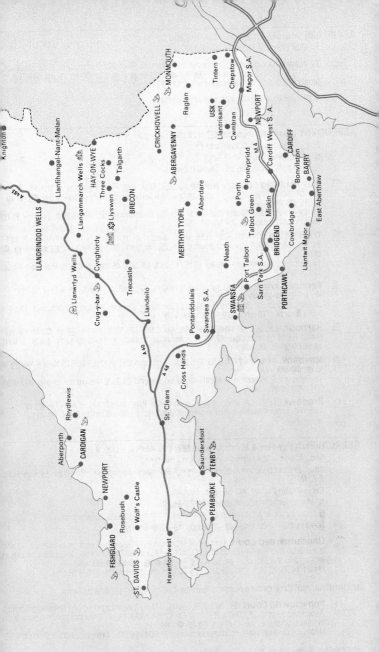

## ABERDARE (Aberdâr) *Rhondda Cynon Taff* **403** J 28 – *pop. 29 040.*

*London 178 – Cardiff 23 – Swansea 27.*

**Ty Newydd Country,** Penderyn Rd, Hirwaun, CF44 9SX, Northwest : 5 m. on A 405
℘ (01685) 813433, Fax (01685) 813139, ☞ – 🆃🆅 ☎ 🄿 – 🕭 300. 🆀🆂 🄰🄴 🄾 🆅🅸🆂🅰 🄹🄲🄱. ⋘
**Meals** 10.90/14.90 t. and a la carte 🍴 4.10 – **27 rm** ⌕ 53.00/67.00 – SB.

🅾 ATS Canal Rd, Cwmbach ℘ (01685) 873914/875491

---

## ABERDOVEY (Aberdyfi) *Gwynedd* **403** H 26 *Wales G.* – *pop. 869.*

Env. : *Snowdonia National Park★★★.*

🏌 Aberdovey ℘ (01654) 767210.

*London 230 – Dolgellau 25 – Shrewsbury 66.*

**Plas Penhelig Country House** 🌫, LL35 0NA, East : 1 m. by A 493 ℘ (01654) 767676
*Fax (01654) 767783,* ≤, « Victorian house with terraced gardens », park – 🍽 🆃🆅 ☎ 🄿 ·
🕭 35. 🆀🆂 🆅🅸🆂🅰 🄹🄲🄱
*March-November* – **Meals** (bar lunch Monday to Saturday)/dinner 19.50 t. 🍴 6.95 – **11 rm**
⌕ (dinner included) 63.00/128.00 – SB.

**Trefeddian,** Tywyn Rd, LL35 0SB, West : 1 m. on A 493 ℘ (01654) 767213
*Fax (01654) 767777,* ≤ golf course and sea, 🔲, ☞, park, ※ – 📶 🍽 rest, 🆃🆅 ☎ 🚗 🄿 🆀🆂
🆅🅸🆂🅰
*15 March-20 November* – **Meals** 10.95/17.25 t. 🍴 6.30 – **46 rm** ⌕ (dinner included) 64.00/
128.00 t. – SB.

**Penhelig Arms,** LL35 0LT, ℘ (01654) 767215, *Fax (01654) 767690,* ≤, « Part 18C inn » –
🍽 rm, 🆃🆅 ☎ 🄿. 🆀🆂 🆅🅸🆂🅰
*closed 25 and 26 December* – **Meals** (bar lunch Monday to Saturday)/dinner 19.50 t.
and a la carte – **10 rm** ⌕ 39.50/79.00 t. – SB.

**Harbour,** LL35 0EB, ℘ (01654) 767250, *Fax (01654) 767792,* ≤ – 🍽 🆃🆅 ☎. 🆀🆂 🄰🄴 🄾 🆅🅸🆂🅰
**Meals** (booking essential) 17.50 st. (dinner) and a la carte 11.40/15.40 st. 🍴 8.30 – **9 rm**
⌕ 50.00/99.00 st. – SB.

**Maybank,** 4 Penhelig Rd, LL35 0PT, East : 1 m. on A 493 ℘ (01654) 767500, ≤ – 🍽 🆃🆅 🄾
📱 🄿. 🆀🆂 🆅🅸🆂🅰 🄹🄲🄱
*16 February-8 November* – **Meals** (by arrangement) 21.95 t. – **6 rm** ⌕ (dinner included)
60.00/98.00 st. – SB.

**Brodawel,** LL35 0SA, West : 1 ¼ m. on A 493 ℘ (01654) 767347, ≤, ☞ – 🍽 🆃🆅 🄿
*March-October* – **Meals** (by arrangement) 14.00 st. 🍴 3.50 – **5 rm** ⌕ 28.00/50.00 t.

---

## ABERGAVENNY (Y-Fenni) *Monmouthshire* **403** L 28 *Wales G.* – *pop. 9 593.*

See : *Town★ – St. Mary's Church★ (Monuments★★).*

Env. : *Brecon Beacons National Park★★ – Blaenavon Ironworks★, SW : 5 m. by A 465 and
B 4246.*

Exc. : *Raglan Castle★ AC, SE : 9 m. by A 40.*

🏌 Monmouthshire, Llanfoist ℘ (01873) 852606.

🛈 Swan Meadow, Monmouth Rd, NP7 5HH ℘ (01873) 857588 (summer only).

*London 163 – Gloucester 43 – Newport 19 – Swansea 49.*

**Llansantffraed Court,** Llanvihangel Gobion, NP7 9BA, Southeast : 6 ½ m. by A 40 and
B 4598 off old Raglan rd ℘ (01873) 840678, *Fax (01873) 840674,* ≤, « Country house in
William and Mary style », ☞, park – 📶 🍽 🆃🆅 ☎ 🄿. 🆀🆂 🄰🄴 🄾 🆅🅸🆂🅰 🄹🄲🄱
**Meals** 14.50/19.50 t. and a la carte 🍴 5.00 – **21 rm** ⌕ 68.00/95.00 t. – SB.

**at Llanfihangel Crucorney** *North : 6½ m. by A 40 on A 465* – ⊠ *Abergavenny.*

**Penyclawdd Court** 🌫, NP7 7LB, South : 1 ¼ m. by Pantygelli rd and following signs to
Penyclawdd Farm ℘ (01873) 890719, *Fax (01873) 890848,* ≤, « Tudor manor house with
medieval origins », ☞ – 🍽 rm, 🆃🆅 🄿. 🆀🆂 🆅🅸🆂🅰. ⋘
**Meals** (by arrangement) (communal dining) 23.00 t. 🍴 6.00 – **4 rm** ⌕ 50.00/100.00 st. – SB.

**at Govilon** *West : 5¼ m. by A 465 on B 4246* – ⊠ *Abergavenny.*

**Llanwenarth House** 🌫, NP7 9SF, North : 1 m. on B 4246 ℘ (01873) 830289,
*Fax (01873) 832199,* ≤, « 16C manor house », ☞ – 🍽 🆃🆅 🄿. ⋘
*closed mid January-February* – **Meals** (by arrangement) (residents only) (communal dining)
(dinner only) 23.50 s. 🍴 7.20 – **4 rm** ⌕ 58.00/78.00 st. – SB.

at **Llanwenarth** *Northwest : 3 m. on A 40* – ✉ *Abergavenny.*

🏠 **Llanwenarth Arms,** Brecon Rd, NP8 1EP, ✆ (01873) 810550, *Fax (01873) 811880,* <, 🎣 – [TV] ☎ 📞 [P]. [MO] [AE] [D] [VISA]. 🐕
**Meals** a la carte 18.00/25.00 **st.** 🍷 5.00 – **18 rm** ☕ 59.00/69.00 **st.** – SB.

ⓐ ATS 11 Monmouth Rd ✆ (01873) 854348/855829

---

## ABERPORTH *Ceredigion* [403] G 27 – *pop. 1 431* – ✉ *Cardigan.*
*London 249 – Carmarthen 29 – Fishguard 26.*

🏠 **Glandwr Manor** 🔇, Tresaith, SA43 2JH, Northeast : 1 ¾ m. ✆ (01239) 810197, 🌳 – 🚭 [P]. 🐕
*Easter-October* – **Meals** *(closed Sunday)* (dinner only) a la carte 12.80/17.90 **t.** 🍷 3.95 – **7 rm** ☕ 28.00/56.00 **t.** – SB.

---

## ABERSOCH *Gwynedd* [402] [403] G 25 *Wales G.* – *pop. 805* – ✉ *Pwllheli.*
**Env.** : *Lleyn Peninsula★★ – Plas-yn-Rhiw★ AC, W : 6 m. by minor roads.*
**Exc.** : *Bardsey Island★, SW : 15 m. by A 499 and B 4413 – Mynydd Mawr★, SW : 17 m. by A 499, B 4413 and minor roads.*
⛳18 *Golf Rd* ✆ *(01758) 712622.*
*London 265 – Caernarfon 28 – Shrewsbury 101.*

🏠 **White House,** LL53 7AG, ✆ (01758) 713427, *Fax (01758) 713512,* <, 🌳 – 🚭 [TV] ☎ [P]. [MO] [VISA]. 🐕
*closed 1 week February* – **Meals** (dinner only and Sunday lunch)/dinner 20.50 **st.** and a la carte 🍷 6.00 – **11 rm** ☕ 37.50/80.00 **st.** – SB.

🏠 **Riverside,** LL53 7HW, ✆ (01758) 712419, *Fax (01758) 712671,* 🏊, 🌳 – [TV] ☎ [P]. [MO] [AE] [VISA]. 🐕
*March-October* – **Meals** (bar lunch)/dinner 24.00 **st.** 🍷 6.75 – **12 rm** ☕ 48.00/88.00 **st.** – SB.

🏠 **Neigwl,** Lon Sarn Bach, LL53 7DY, ✆ (01758) 712363, *Fax (01758) 712363,* < Cardigan Bay – [TV] [P]. [MO] [D] [VISA] [JCB]. 🐕
**Meals** (dinner only) 19.50 **st.** 🍷 5.00 – **9 rm** ☕ 48.00/80.00 **st.** – SB.

at **Bwlchtocyn** *South : 2 m.* – ✉ *Pwllheli.*

🏠 **Porth Tocyn** 🔇, LL53 7BU, ✆ (01758) 713303, *Fax (01758) 713538,* < Cardigan Bay and mountains, 🏊, 🌳, 🎾 – [TV] ☎ [P]. [MO] [VISA]. 🐕
*Easter-mid November* – **Meals** (bar lunch Monday to Saturday)/dinner 21.00 **st.** 🍷 5.75 – ☕ 5.00 – **17 rm** 63.00/116.00 **st.** – SB.

🏠 **Crowrach Isaf** 🔇, LL53 7BY, ✆ (01758) 712860, <, 🌳, park – 🚭 [TV] [P]. 🐕
*March-mid October* – **Meals** (by arrangement) 12.95 **st.** – **3 rm** ☕ 24.00/48.00 **st.**

---

## ABERYSTWYTH *Ceredigion* [403] H 26 *Wales G.* – *pop. 8 359.*
**See** : *Town★★ – The Seafront★ – National Library of Wales★ (Permanent Exhibition★).*
**Env.** : *Vale of Rheidol★ (Railway★★ AC) – St. Padarn's Church★, SE : 1 m. by A 44.*
**Exc.** : *Devil's Bridge (Pontarfynach)★, E : 12 m. by A 4120 – Strata Florida Abbey★ AC (West Door★), SE : 15 m. by B 4340 and minor rd.*
⛳18 *Bryn-y-Mor* ✆ *(01970) 615104.*
🛈 *Terrace Rd, SY23 2AG* ✆ *(01970) 612125.*
*London 238 – Chester 98 – Fishguard 58 – Shrewsbury 74.*

🏠 **Belle Vue Royal,** Marine Terrace, SY23 2BA, ✆ (01970) 617558, *Fax (01970) 612190,* < – 🚭 rm, [TV] ☎ 🚗 – 👥 40. [MO] [AE] [D] [VISA]. 🐕
*closed 25 and 26 December* – **Meals** 12.50/22.50 **t.** and a la carte 🍷 5.50 – **34 rm** ☕ 54.00/90.00 **st.** – SB.

🏠 **Four Seasons,** 50-54 Portland St., SY23 2DX, ✆ (01970) 612120, *Fax (01970) 627458* – 🚭 [TV] ☎ [P]. [MO] [VISA]. 🐕
*closed 24 December-2 January* – **Meals** (bar lunch Monday to Saturday)/dinner 17.50 **t.** 🍷 6.50 – **14 rm** ☕ 55.00/82.50 **t.** – SB.

🏠 **Sinclair** without rest., 43 Portland St., SY23 2DX, ✆ (01970) 615158, *Fax (01970) 615158* – 🚭 [TV] [P]. 🐕
*closed 2 weeks Christmas-New Year* – **3 rm** ☕ 30.00/45.00 **s.**

🏠 **Nanteos Mansion** 🔇, Rhydyfelin, SY23 4LU, Southeast : 2 m. by A 487 and B 4340 (Tregaron Rd) ✆ (01970) 624363, *Fax (01970) 626332,* <, « Georgian mansion in extensive parklands », 🌳, park – 🚭 [TV] [P]. [MO] [VISA]. 🐕
*closed January* – **Meals** (by arrangement) 19.50 **t.** 🍷 5.50 – **3 rm** ☕ 55.00/80.00 **t.** – SB.

**at Chancery (Rhydgaled)** South : 4 m. on A 487 – ⊠ Aberystwyth.

🏨 **Conrah Country House** ⌂, SY23 4DF, ℰ (01970) 617941, Fax (01970) 624546, « Part 18C mansion house », ⌂⌂, ◻, ☞, park – ⊟, ✗ rest, ⊡ ☎ ℗ – 🔏 50. 🐵 🕮 ⓒ
*VISA* *JCB*, ⌀
*closed 1 week Christmas* – **Meals** 18.00/28.00 t. ⌀ 7.50 – **20 rm** ⊇ 77.00/125.00 t. – SB.

🔧 ATS Glanyrafon Ind. Est., Llanbadarn ℰ (01970) 611166

---

**ARTHOG** Gwynedd 402 403 I 25 – see Dolgellau.

---

**BALA** Gwynedd 402 403 J 25 Wales G. – pop. 1 922.
Env. : *Snowdonia National Park*★★★ – *Bala Lake*★.
Exc. : *Bwlch y Groes*★★, SE : 11 m. by A 494, B 4403 and minor rd.
🔧 Bala Lake Hotel ℰ (01678) 520344/520111.
🛈 Penllyn, Pensarn Rd, LL23 7SR ℰ (01678) 521021 (Friday to Sunday only in winter).
London 216 – Chester 46 – Dolgellau 18 – Shrewsbury 52.

↑ **Fron Feuno Hall** ⌂, LL23 7YF, Southwest : 1 m. on A 494 ℰ (01678) 521111,
Fax (01678) 521151, ≤ Bala Lake, ⌂, ☞, park, ✗ – ⊟, ✗ rest, ℗
*April-October* – **Meals** (by arrangement) (communal dining) 16.20 st. – **3 rm** ⊇ 36.00/
72.00 st.

↑ **Melin Meloch,** LL23 7DP, East : 1 ¾ m. by A 494 on B 4401 ℰ (01678) 520101, « Part 13
converted water mill, gardens » – ✗ ⊡ ℗
*March-October* – **Meals** (by arrangement) (communal dining) 12.50 st. – **4 rm** ⊇ 25.00/
46.00 st.

*Groß-London (GREATER LONDON) besteht aus der City und 32
Verwaltungsbezirken (Borough). Diese sind wiederum in kleinere
Bezirke (Area) unterteilt, deren Mittelpunkt ehemalige Dörfer
oder Stadtviertel sind, die oft ihren eigenen Charakter bewahrt haben.*

---

**BANGOR** Gwynedd 402 403 H 24 Wales G. – pop. 11 173.
Env. : *Snowdonia National Park*★★★ – *Penrhyn Castle*★★ AC, E : 3 m. by A 5122 – Menai
Bridge★, SW : 1½ m. by A 5122.
Exc. : *Anglesey*★★ – *Plas Newydd*★★ AC, SW : 7½ m. by A 5122 and A 4080 – Anglesey Sea
Zoo★ AC, SW : 10 m. by A 5122, A 4080 and B 4419 – Llangefni (Oriel Ynys Mon★ AC), NW :
7 m. by A 5122 and B 5420.
🔧 St. Deiniol, Penybryn ℰ (01248) 353098.
London 247 – Birkenhead 68 – Holyhead 23 – Shrewsbury 83.

🏨 **Menai Court,** Craig-y-Don Rd, LL57 2BG, ℰ (01248) 354200, Fax (01248) 354200, ≤, ☞ -
✗ rest, ⊡ ☎ ℗ – 🔏 60. 🐵 *VISA* *JCB*
*closed Christmas-New Year* – **Meals** (closed Sunday dinner) 11.95/21.95 t. and a la carte
⌀ 5.50 – **13 rm** ⊇ 51.00/90.00 t. – SB.

🏨 **Travelodge,** One Stop Services, Llandegai, LL57 4BG, Southeast : 2 ½ m. by A 5122, at
junction of A 5 with A 55 ℰ (01248) 370345, Fax (01248) 370345, Reservations (Freephone)
0800 850950 – ✗ rm, ⊡ ⅙ ℗. 🐵 🕮 ⓒ *VISA* *JCB*, ⌀
**Meals** (grill rest.) – **61 rm** 39.95/59.95 t.

↑ **Country Bumpkin** without rest., Cefn-y-Coed, Llandegai, LL57 4BG, South : 3 m. on
A 5122 ℰ (01248) 370477, Fax (01248) 354166, ≤ – ⊡ ℗. 🐵 *VISA*
*closed December and January* – **3 rm** ⊇ 30.00/40.00.

---

**BARMOUTH** (Abermaw) Gwynedd 402 403 H 25 Wales G. – pop. 2 306.
See : *Town*★ – *Bridge*★ AC.
Env. : *Snowdonia National Park*★★★.
🛈 The Old Library, Station Rd, LL42 1LU ℰ (01341) 280787 (summer only).
London 231 – Chester 74 – Dolgellau 10 – Shrewsbury 67.

↑ **Llwyndû Farmhouse** ⌂, LL42 1RR, Northwest : 2 ¼ m. on A 496 ℰ (01341) 280144,
Fax (01341) 281236, « Part 17C farmhouse and 18C barn conversion », ☞ – ✗ ⊡ ℗. 🐵
*VISA*
*restricted opening in winter* – **Meals** (by arrangement) 16.95 st. ⌀ 5.45 – **7 rm** ⊇ 58.00/
64.00 t. – SB.

**BARRY** (Barri) *Vale of Glamorgan* 403 K 29 – *pop. 46 368.*

🏌 Brynhill, Port Rd ℘ (01446) 735061 – 🏌 RAF St. Athan ℘ (01446) 751043.

🖪 The Triangle, Paget Rd, Barry Island, CF62 5TQ ℘ (01446) 747171 (summer only).

*London 167 – Cardiff 10 – Swansea 39.*

🏛 **Egerton Grey Country House** ⌖, CF62 3BZ, Southwest : 4 ½ m. by B 4226 and A 4226 and Porthkerry rd via Cardiff Airport ℘ (01446) 711666, *Fax (01446) 711690*, ≼, « Part Victorian rectory », ☞ – ⌖ rest, 📺 ☎ 🄿. 🏧 🆎 ⑩ *VISA* 🃏. ⌖

**Meals** 17.50 **st.** and a la carte ↥ 7.50 – **10 rm** ⇌ 65.00/120.00 **st.** – SB.

🏠 **Mount Sorrel**, Porthkerry Rd, CF62 7XY, ℘ (01446) 740069, *Fax (01446) 746600*, ↧, ≋, 🔲 – 📺 ☎ 🄿 – 🔬 150. 🏧 🆎 ⑩ *VISA*

**Meals** (bar lunch)/dinner a la carte 11.50/18.00 **t.** ↥ 5.95 – **43 rm** ⇌ 40.00/84.00 **t.** – SB.

🏡 **Aberthaw House**, 28 Porthkerry Rd, CF62 7AX, ℘ (01446) 737314, *Fax (01446) 732376* – ⌖ rest, 📺 ☎. 🏧 🆎 *VISA*. ⌖

*closed 24 December-7 January* – **Meals** (residents only Sunday) (dinner only) a la carte 11.15/21.70 **t.** ↥ 4.75 – ⇌ 6.50 – **9 rm** 37.50/57.50 **st.**

🏡 **Cwm Ciddy Toby**, Airport Rd, CF62 3BA, Northwest : 1 ½ m. by B 4266 on A 4226 ℘ (01446) 700075, *Fax (01446) 700075* – 📺 ☎ 🄿. 🏧 🆎 *VISA*. ⌖

**Meals** (grill rest.) a la carte 8.50/13.50 **t.** ↥ 3.95 – **14 rm** ⇌ 49.00/59.00 **t.** – SB.

**at Penmark** Northwest : 4 ¼ m. by B 4266 off A 4226 – ⊠ *Barry.*

🏚 **Six Bells Inn**, CF62 3BP, ℘ (01446) 710229, *Fax (01446) 710671* – 🍴 🄿 – 🔬 70. 🏧 🆎 *VISA* 🃏. ⌖

*closed Sunday dinner* – **Meals** 13.50 **t.** (dinner) and a la carte 12.00/23.75 **t.**

**BEAUMARIS** *Anglesey* 402 403 H 24 *Wales G.* – *pop. 2 050.*

See : Town★ – Castle★★ AC.

Env. : *Anglesey★★ – Penmon Priory★, NE : 4 m. by B 5109 and minor roads.*

Exc. : *Plas Newydd★ AC, SW : 7 m. by A 545 and A 4080.*

*London 253 – Birkenhead 74 – Holyhead 25.*

🏡 **Ye Olde Bull's Head Inn**, Castle St., LL58 8AP, ℘ (01248) 810329, *Fax (01248) 811294* – ⌖ 📺 ☎ 🄿. 🏧 🆎 *VISA* 🃏. ⌖

*closed 25-26 December and 1 January* – **Meals** – (see below) – **15 rm** ⇌ 51.00/94.00 **st.** – SB.

🏡 **Bishopsgate House**, 54 Castle St., LL58 8BB, ℘ (01248) 810302, *Fax (01248) 810816* – ⌖ 📺 ☎ 🄿. 🏧 🆎 *VISA*

*closed January* – **Meals** (dinner only and Sunday lunch)/dinner a la carte 15.65/22.40 **t.** ↥ 5.95 – **9 rm** ⇌ 40.00/69.00 **t.** – SB.

🏠 **Plas Cichle** ⌖ without rest., LL58 8PS, Northwest : 2 ¾ m. by B 5109 and Llanfaes Rd ℘ (01248) 810488, ≼, « Working farm », ☞, park – ⌖ 📺 🄿. 🏧 *VISA*. ⌖

*February-October* – **3 rm** ⇌ 30.00/48.00 **s.**

🍴🍴 **The Restaurant** (at Ye Olde Bull's Head Inn H.), Castle St., LL58 8AP, ℘ (01248) 810329, *Fax (01248) 811294* – 🄿. 🏧 🆎 *VISA* 🃏

*closed 25-26 December and 1 January* – **Meals** (dinner only) 21.95 **st.** and a la carte ↥ 7.00.

**BEDDGELERT** *Gwynedd* 402 403 H 24 *Wales G.* – *pop. 535.*

Env. : *Snowdonia National Park★★★ – Aberglaslyn Pass★, S : 1½ m. on A 498.*

*London 249 – Caernarfon 13 – Chester 73.*

🏛 **Royal Goat**, LL55 4YE, ℘ (01766) 890224, *Fax (01766) 890422*, ≋ – 🍴 ⌖ 📺 ☎ 🄿. 🏧 🆎 ⑩ *VISA* 🃏. ⌖

**Meals** 11.00/19.00 **st.** and a la carte ↥ 7.00 – **29 rm** ⇌ 44.00/80.00 **st.**, 1 suite – SB.

🏠 **Sygun Fawr Country House** ⌖, LL55 4NE, Northeast : ¾ m. by A 498 ℘ (01766) 890258, ≼ mountains and valley, « Part 16C stone built house », ≋, ☞, park – 🄿. 🏧 *VISA* 🃏

**Meals** (by arrangement) 15.00 **st** ↥ 5.50 – **10 rm** ⇌ 32.00/57.00 **st.** – SB.

**BERRIEW** (Aberriw) *Powys* 402 403 K 26 – *pop. 1 305* – ⊠ *Welshpool.*

*London 190 – Chester 49 – Shrewsbury 26.*

🏚 **Lion** with rm, SY21 8PQ, ℘ (01686) 640452, *Fax (01686) 640604*, « Part 17C inn » – 📺 ☎ 🄿. 🏧 🆎 *VISA* 🃏. ⌖

*closed 25 and 26 December* – **Meals** (booking essential) (bar lunch Monday to Saturday)/ dinner 18.95 **t.** ↥ 5.00 – **7 rm** ⇌ 55.00/90.00 **t.** – SB.

# BETWS-Y-COED Conwy 402 403 I 24 *Wales G.* – pop. 848.

See : *Town*★.

Env. : *Snowdonia National Park*★★★.

Exc. : *Blaenau Ffestiniog*★ *(Llechwedd Slate Caverns*★ *AC)*, SW : 10 ½ m. by A 470 – *Th Glyders and Nant Ffrancon (Cwm Idwal*★ *)*, W : 14 m. by A 5.

🅵 *Clubhouse* ✆ *(01690) 710556.*

🅳 *Royal Oak Stables, LL24 0AH* ✆ *(01690) 710426.*

*London 226 – Holyhead 44 – Shrewsbury 62.*

**Tan-y-Foel Country House** 🦢, LL26 0RE, East : 4 m. by A 5 and A 470 on Nebo r✆ *(01690) 710507, Fax (01690) 710681, ≤* Vale of Conwy and Snowdonia, « *Part 16C coun try house* », 🐴 – ✝✗ 📺 📞. 🐵 AE ① VISA JCB. ✼
*closed Christmas* – **Meals** (booking essential) (dinner only) 25.00 st. ⬩ 6.00 – **7 rm** ⚌ 70.00 150.00 st. – SB.

**Henllys**, Old Church Rd, LL24 0AL, ✆ *(01690) 710534, Fax (01690) 710534*, « *Former Vic torian magistrates court* », 🐴 – ✝✗ 📺 📞. 🐵 VISA JCB. ✼
*February-October* – **Meals** *(closed Sunday)* (dinner only) 16.95 t. – **10 rm** ⚌ 35.00/70.00 st – SB.

**Park Hill**, Llanrwst Rd, LL24 0HD, Northeast : 1 m. by A 5 on A 470 ✆ *(01690) 710540 Fax (01690) 710540, ≤* Vale of Conwy, 🕿, 🔲, 🐴 – ✝✗ rest, 📺 📞. 🐵 VISA. ✼
**Meals** (residents only) (dinner only) 14.50 t. ⬩ 4.15 – **11 rm** ⚌ 19.50/62.00 t. – SB.

**Bryn Bella** without rest., Llanrwst Rd, LL24 0HD, Northeast : 1 m. by A 5 on A 470 ✆ *(01690) 710627, ≤* Vale of Conwy – 📺 📞. ✼
**5 rm** ⚌ 19.00/46.00 st.

## at Penmachno *Southwest : 4 ¾ m. by A 5 on B 4406 – ⊠ Betws-y-Coed.*

**Penmachno Hall** 🦢, LL24 0PU, ✆ *(01690) 760207, Fax (01690) 760207, ≤,* 🐴 – ✝✗ rm 📞. 🐵 VISA. ✼
*closed 23 December-15 January* – **Meals** (by arrangement) (communal dining) 16.00 st. - **4 rm** ⚌ 33.00/56.00 st.

---

# BLAENAU FFESTINIOG Gwynedd 402 403 I 25.

🅳 *Isallt, High St., LL41 3HD* ✆ *(01766) 830360 (summer only).*

*London 237 – Bangor 32 – Caernarfon 32 – Dolgellau 23 – Chester 70.*

**Queens**, 1 High St., LL41 3ES, ✆ *(01766) 830055, Fax (01766) 830046* – ✝✗ 📺 ☎ 📞 - 🍴 100. 🐵 VISA. ✼
*closed 25 December* – **Meals** (bar lunch Monday to Saturday)/dinner a la carte 9.65 15.95 st. ⬩ 4.30 – **12 rm** ⚌ 35.00/70.00 st. – SB.

---

# BONTDDU Gwynedd 402 403 I 25 – see Dolgellau.

---

# BONVILSTON (Tresimwn) Vale of Glamorgan 403 J 29.

*London 164 – Cardiff 9 – Swansea 25.*

**Great Barn** 🦢 without rest., Lillypot, CF5 6TR, Northwest : 1 m. by A 48 off Tre-Dodridge rd ✆ *(01446) 781010, Fax (01446) 781185, ≤,* « *Converted corn barn* », 🐴 – ✝✗ 📺 📞. ✼
**5 rm** ⚌ 34.00/48.00.

---

# BRECON (Aberhonddu) Powys 403 J 28 *Wales G.* – pop. 7 523.

See : *Town*★ – *Cathedral*★ *AC* – *Penyclawdd Court*★.

Env. : *Brecon Beacons National Park*★★.

Exc. : *Llanthony Priory*★★, S : 8 m. of Hay-on-Wye by B 4423 – *Dan-yr-Ogof Showcaves*★ *AC*, SW : 20 m. by A 40 and A 4067 – *Pen-y-Fan*★★, SW : by A 470.

🅵 *Cradoc, Penoyre Park* ✆ *(01874) 623658 –* 🅵 *Newton Park, Llanfaes* ✆ *(01874) 622004.*

🅳 *Cattle Market Car Park, LD3 9DA* ✆ *(01874) 622485/625692.*

*London 171 – Cardiff 40 – Carmarthen 31 – Gloucester 65.*

**Peterstone Court**, Llanhamlach, LD3 7YB, Southeast : 3 ¼ m. on A 40 ✆ *(01874) 665387, Fax (01874) 665376, ≤,* « *Georgian manor house* », 🛌, 🕿, 🔲, 🐴 - ✝✗ rm, 📺 ☎ 📞. 🐵 AE ① VISA. ✼
**Meals** 22.50 t. (dinner) and a la carte 15.85/21.85 ⬩ 6.50 – **12 rm** ⚌ (dinner included 85.00/115.00 – SB.

**Cantre Selyf**, 5 Lion St., LD3 7AU, ✆ *(01874) 622904, Fax (01874) 622315*, « *17C town house* », 🐴 – ✝✗ 📞. ✼
*closed December and January* – **Meals** (by arrangement) 15.00 t. ⬩ 6.00 – **3 rm** ⚌ 30.00/ 50.00 t. – SB.

t Pwllgloyw *Northwest : 4 m. on B 4520 (Upper Chapel rd)* – ⊠ *Brecon.*

XX **Seland Newydd,** LD3 9PY, 𝒫 (01874) 690282 – **🅿**. 🐵 𝒱𝒾𝒮𝒜 ᴊᴄʙ
*closed lunch Tuesday and Wednesday October-June and 27-29 December* – **Meals** a la carte
18.65/25.85 **st.**

🔘 ATS The Watton 𝒫 (01874) 624496/624163

---

**RIDGEND** (Pen-y-Bont) 🔲 J 29 – *pop. 35 841.*
*London 177 – Cardiff 20 – Swansea 23.*

🏨 **Heronston,** Ewenny Rd, CF35 5AW, *South : 2 m. on B 4265* 𝒫 (01656) 668811,
*Fax (01656) 767391,* 🕿, 🏊, 🔲 – 🕴, ✳ rm, 🔲 🕿 🅿 – 🔬 200. 🐵 🅰🅴 ⓞ 𝒱𝒾𝒮𝒜
*closed 26 to 31 December* – **Meals** (bar lunch Monday to Saturday)/dinner 15.95 **st.**
and a la carte – **75 rm** ⊇ 75.00/90.00 **st.**

X **Martin's Bistro,** 9 Dunraven Pl., CF31 1JF, 𝒫 (01656) 767095 – 🐵 𝒱𝒾𝒮𝒜
*closed Monday dinner, Sunday, 25-26 December and Bank Holidays* – **Meals** 15.00 **t.**
(dinner) and a la carte 17.00/28.40 **t.**

t Pencoed *Northeast : 4½ m. by A 473.*

🏨 **Travel Inn,** Pantruthyn Farm, CF35 5HY, *East : 1 m. by A 473 at junction 35 on M 4*
𝒫 (01656) 860133, *Fax (01656) 864792* – ✳ rm, 🗐 rest, 🔲 🕿 🅿. 🐵 🅰🅴 ⓞ 𝒱𝒾𝒮𝒜. ✻
**Meals** (grill rest.) – **40 rm** 38.00 **t.**

🏨 **Travelodge,** CF3 5HU, *East : 1 ¼ m. by Felindre rd* 𝒫 (01656) 864404,
*Fax (01656) 864404,* Reservations (Freephone) 0800 850950 – ✳ rm, 🔲 🕭 🅿. 🐵 🅰🅴 ⓞ
𝒱𝒾𝒮𝒜 ᴊᴄʙ. ✻
**Meals** (grill rest.) – **40 rm** 39.95/59.95 **t.**

t Coychurch (Llangrallo) *East : 2¼ m. by A 473* – ⊠ *Bridgend.*

🏨 **Coed-y-Mwstwr** ⑳, CF35 6AF, *North : 1 m.* 𝒫 (01656) 860621, *Fax (01656) 863122,* ≼,
🏊, 🎾, park, ✾ – 🕴, ✳ rm, 🔲 🕿 🅿 – 🔬 150. 🐵 🅰🅴 ⓞ 𝒱𝒾𝒮𝒜 ᴊᴄʙ. ✻
**Meals** 14.50/24.00 **st.** and a la carte ⅄ 8.30 – **21 rm** ⊇ 90.00/135.00, 2 suites – SB.

t Southerndown *Southwest : 5½ m. by A 4265* – ⊠ *Bridgend.*

XX **Frolics,** Beach Rd, CF32 0RP, 𝒫 (01656) 880127 – 🐵 ⓞ 𝒱𝒾𝒮𝒜
*closed Sunday dinner, Monday and 25 to 31 December* – **Meals** (dinner only and Sunday
lunch)/dinner 17.50 **t.** and a la carte ⅄ 6.00.

t Laleston *West : 2 m. on A 473* – ⊠ *Bridgend.*

🏨 **Great House,** High St., CF32 0HP, *on A 473* 𝒫 (01656) 657644, *Fax (01656) 668892,* 🖪,
🕿, 🎏 – ✳ 🔲 🕿 🕭 🅿. 🐵 🅰🅴 ⓞ 𝒱𝒾𝒮𝒜 ᴊᴄʙ. ✻
*closed Saturday lunch, Sunday dinner and 1 week Christmas* – **Meals** – (see *The Restaurant* below) – **16 rm** ⊇ 80.00/130.00 **t.** – SB.

XX **The Restaurant** (at Great House H.), High St., CF32 0HP, *on A 473* 𝒫 (01656) 657644,
*Fax (01656) 668892,* 🎏 – ✳ 🅿. 🐵 🐵 ⓞ 𝒱𝒾𝒮𝒜. ✻
*closed 25-26 December and 1 January* – **Meals** (residents only Sunday dinner) 21.00 **t.**
(dinner) and a la carte 11.40/31.40 **t.** ⅄ 6.50.

🔘 ATS 122 Coity Rd 𝒫 (01656) 658775/6

---

ᴃWLCHTOCYN *Gwynedd* 🔲 🔲 G 25 – *see Abersoch.*

---

ᴄAERNARFON *Gwynedd* 🔲 🔲 H 24 *Wales G.* – *pop. 9 695.*
*See : Town*★★★ – *Castle*★★★ *AC* – *Town Walls*★.
*Env. : Snowdonia National Park*★★★.
🖪 Aberforeshore, Llanfaglan 𝒫 (01286) 673783/678359.
🛈 Oriel Pendeitsh, Castle St., LL55 2NA 𝒫 (01286) 672232.
*London 249 – Birkenhead 76 – Chester 68 – Holyhead 30 – Shrewsbury 85.*

🏨 **Celtic Royal,** Bangor St., LL55 1AY, 𝒫 (01286) 674477, *Fax (01286) 674139,* 🖪, 🕿, 🔲 –
🕴 ✳ 🔲 🕿 🕭 🅿 – 🔬 500. 🐵 🅰🅴 ⓞ 𝒱𝒾𝒮𝒜. ✻
**Meals** (bar lunch)/dinner 15.95 **st.** and a la carte ⅄ 8.50 – **110 rm** ⊇ 60.00/90.00 **st.** – SB.

🏨 **Seiont Manor** ⑳, Llanrug, LL55 2AQ, *East : 3 m. on A 4086* 𝒫 (01286) 673366,
*Fax (01286) 672840,* 🖪, 🕿, 🔲, 🎏, park – ✳ 🔲 🕿 🅿 – 🔬 80. 🐵 🅰🅴 ⓞ 𝒱𝒾𝒮𝒜. ✻
**Meals** 15.50/23.50 **st.** and a la carte ⅄ 6.25 – **28 rm** ⊇ 95.00/170.00 **st.** – SB.

🏠 **Pengwern** 🪑, Saron, LL54 5UH, Southwest : 3 ½ m. by A 487 on Llanfaglan
☎ (01286) 831500, *Fax (01286) 831500*, « Working farm », 🌳, park – 🚭 [TV] Ⓟ. 🚫🐕
*closed December and January* – **Meals** (by arrangement) 15.00 – **3 rm** ☕ 35.00/50.00 s
SB.

🏠 **Isfryn,** 11 Church St., LL55 1SW, ☎ (01286) 675628, *Fax (01286) 675628* – 🚭 rest, [TV].
*16 March-29 October* – **Meals** (by arrangement) 17.50 **st.** – **6 rm** ☕ 19.00/42.00 **s.**

**at Seion** *Northeast : 5½ m. by A 406 and B 4366 on Seion rd* – ✉ *Caernarfon.*

🏨 **Ty'n Rhos Country H.** 🪑, Llanddeiniolen, LL55 3AE, Southwest : ¼
☎ (01248) 670489, *Fax (01248) 670079*, <, 🌳, park – 🚭 [TV] ☎ ♿ Ⓟ. [MC] [AE] [VISA] [JCB]. 🚫🐕
*closed 1 week January, 1 week August and 23 to 30 December* – **Meals** (by arrangeme
(residents only Sunday) (dinner only and Sunday lunch)/dinner 19.50 **t.** and a la carte 🍷 6.
– **14 rm** ☕ 49.00/96.00 **t.** – SB.

Ⓜ ATS Bangor Rd ☎ (01286) 673110

## CAERSWS *Powys* [402] [403] J 26.

*London 194 – Aberystwyth 39 – Chester 63 – Shrewsbury 42.*

🏨 **Maesmawr Hall** 🪑, SY17 5SF, East : 1 m. on A 489 ☎ (01686) 68825
*Fax (01686) 688410*, « Part 16C hunting lodge », 🌳 – [TV] ☎ Ⓟ – 👥 120. [MC] [AE] [VISA]. 🚫🐕
*closed 23 December-1 January* – **Meals** (bar lunch)/dinner 24.00 **t.** 🍷 5.95 – **17 rm** ☕ 58.5
78.50 **t.**

🏠 **Lower Ffrydd,** SY17 5QS, West : 2 m. by B 4569 ☎ (01686) 688269, *Fax (01686) 68826*
« 16C farmhouse », 🌳, park – 🚭 Ⓟ
*April-November* – **Meals** (by arrangement) (communal dining) 12.50 **st.** – **3 rm** ☕ 25.0
44.00 **st.** – SB.

*The Guide is updated annually so renew your Guide every year.*

## CARDIFF (Caerdydd) [403] K 29 *Wales G.* – *pop. 279 055.*

See : *City*★★★ – *National Museum and Gallery*★★★ *AC (Evolution of Wales*★★, *Pictu
galleries*★★ *(Galleries 12 and 13*★★*), Pottery and Porcelain*★*)* **BY** – *Castle*★★ *AC* **BZ** – *Ci
Centre*★ **BY** – *Llandaff Cathedral*★ **AV B** – *Cardiff Bay*★ *(Techniquest*★ *AC)* **AX**.

Env. : *Museum of Welsh Life*★★★ *AC, St. Fagan's, W : 5 m. by A 4161* **AV** – *Castell Coch*★
*AC, NW : 5 m. by A 470* **AV**.

Exc. : *Caerphilly Castle*★★ *AC, N : 7 m. by A 469* **AV** – *Dyffryn Gardens*★ *AC, W : 8 m.
A 48* **AX**.

⛳18 *Dinas Powis, Old Highwalls* ☎ *(01222) 512727,* **AX**.

✈ *Cardiff (Wales) Airport :* ☎ *(01446) 711111, SW : 8 m. by A 48* **AX** – **Terminal** : *Centr
Bus Station.*

ℹ *Central Station, CF1 1QY* ☎ *(01222) 227281.*

*London 155 – Birmingham 110 – Bristol 46 – Coventry 124.*

Plans on following pages

🏨 **Copthorne,** Copthorne Way, Culverhouse Cross, CF5 6XJ, West : 4 ¾ m. by A 4161 ar
A 48 at junction with A 4232 ☎ (01222) 599100, *Fax (01222) 599080*, 🏋, [s], 🏊, 🌳 – 🛗
🚭 rm, ❄ rest, [TV] ☎ ♿ Ⓟ – 👥 300. [MC] [AE] [D] [VISA]. 🚫🐕
***Raglan's :*** Meals (dinner only) 18.95 **t.** and a la carte 🍷 5.95 – ***Beauchamps :*** Meals 9.50
(lunch) and a la carte approx. 27.50 **t.** 🍷 5.95 – ☕ 11.50 – **134 rm** 115.00/135.00 **st.**, 1 sui
– SB.

🏨 **Cardiff Marriott,** Mill Lane, CF1 1EZ, ☎ (01222) 399944, *Fax (01222) 395578*, <, 🏋, [s]
🏊 – 🛗, 🚭 rm, ❄ [TV] ☎ ☎ ♿ Ⓟ – 👥 300. [MC] [AE] [D] [VISA] [JCB]. 🚫🐕 BZ
***Mediterrano :*** Meals a la carte 15.45/24.90 **st.** 🍷 7.45 – ☕ 11.95 – **178 rm** 105.0
125.00 **st.**, 4 suites – SB.

🏨 **Thistle Park,** Park Pl., CF1 3UD, ☎ (01222) 383471, *Fax (01222) 399309* – 🛗, 🚭 rn
❄ rest, [TV] ☎ ♿ Ⓟ – 👥 300. [MC] [AE] [D] [VISA] [JCB] BZ
***Oval Brasserie :*** Meals 14.95/17.25 **t.** and a la carte 🍷 5.50 – ☕ 12.00 – **132 rm** 102.0
115.00 **t.**, 4 suites – SB.

🏨 **Cardiff Bay,** Schooner Way, Atlantic Wharf, CF1 5RT, ☎ (01222) 46588
*Fax (01222) 481491*, « Part Victorian warehouse », 🏋, [s], 🏊 – 🛗, 🚭 rm, ❄ rest, [TV] ☎
♿ Ⓟ – 👥 250. [MC] [AE] [D] [VISA] BZ
***Haylards :*** Meals *(closed Saturday lunch)* 9.95/19.50 **st.** and dinner a la carte 🍷 9.50 –
9.50 – **152 rm** 110.00/120.00 **t.**, 4 suites.

🏨 **Angel,** Castle St., CF1 2QZ, ☎ (01222) 232633, *Fax (01222) 396212*, 🏋, [s] – 🛗 🚭 [TV] ☎
Ⓟ – 👥 300. [MC] [AE] [VISA]. 🚫🐕 BZ
Meals a la carte 19.25/19.95 **t.** – ☕ 10.95 – **101 rm** 95.00/110.00 **st.**, 2 suites – SB.

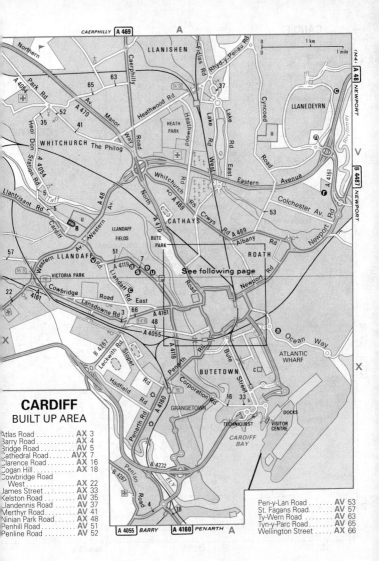

## CARDIFF
### BUILT UP AREA

**Jurys Cardiff**, Mary Ann St., CF1 2EQ, ℘ (01222) 341441, *Fax (01222) 223742* – 📶,
✵ rm, ▤ rest, 📺 ☎ ♿ ❶ – 🔬 40. 🅭🅰 🆎 ① 𝗩𝗜𝗦𝗔, ✂         BZ u
**Meals** (bar lunch Monday to Saturday)/dinner a la carte 12.25/26.45 **st.** – ☑ 10.50 – **141 rm**
130.00/140.00 **st.**, 3 suites – SB.

**Forte Posthouse Cardiff**, Pentwyn Rd, CF2 7XA, Northeast : 4 m. by A 48
℘ (01222) 731212, *Fax (01222) 549147*, ₁₆, ⇌s, 🏊, – 📶 ✵, ▤ rest, 📺 ☎ ♿ – 🔬 120. 🅭🅰
🆎 ① 𝗩𝗜𝗦𝗔 🅹🅲🅱
**Meals** a la carte 16.35/24.85 – ☑ 8.95 – **142 rm** 75.00 **t.** – SB.

**Quality**, Merthyr Rd, CF4 7LD, Northwest : 5 m. by A 470 on A 4054 at junction with M 4
℘ (01222) 529988, *Fax (01222) 529977*, ₁₆, ⇌s, 🏊, – 📶, ✵ rm, ▤ rest, 📺 ☎ ♿ ♿ –
🔬 180. 🅭🅰 🆎 ① 𝗩𝗜𝗦𝗔 🅹🅲🅱, ✂
**Meals** (carving rest.) 14.50 **st.** and a la carte ₤ 4.00 – ☑ 8.00 – **95 rm** 74.25/107.00 **st.**

# CARDIFF

CENTRE
0   200 m
0   200 yards

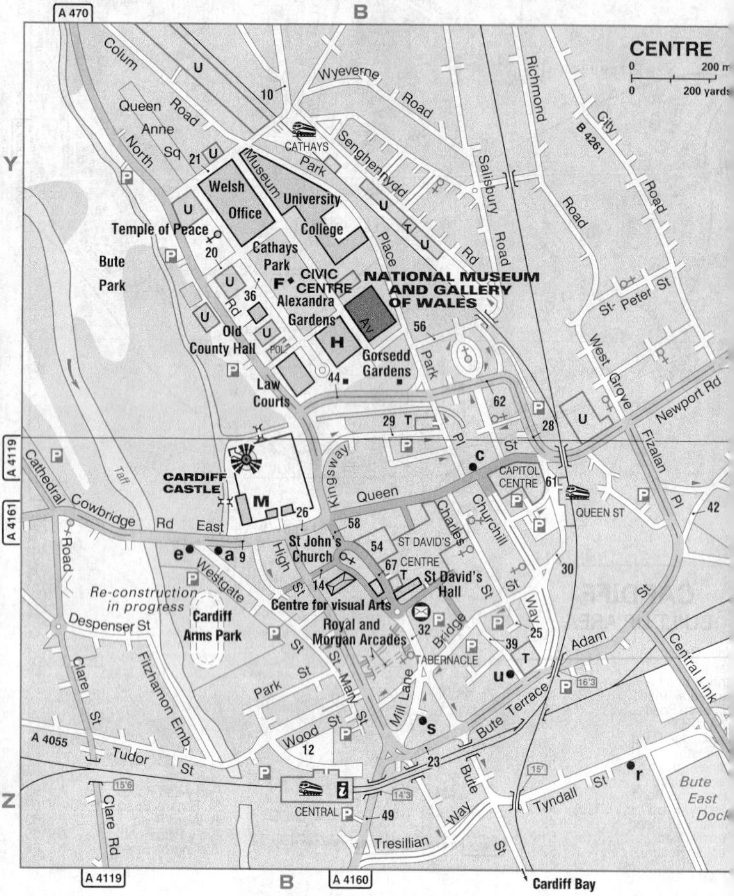

🏥 **Forte Posthouse Cardiff City**, Castle St., CF1 2XB, ℘ (01222) 388681
*Fax (01222) 371495* – 🛗, ✳️ rm, 📺 ☎ 🅿 – 🔬 150. 🐼 🅰🅴 ⓪ 𝘝𝘐𝘚𝘈 𝗝𝗖𝗕    BZ
**Meals** a la carte 15.85/27.85 **st.** 🍷 7.95 – 🖃 9.95 – **155 rm** 95.00 **st.** – SB.

🏥 **Cardiff Moat House**, Circle Way East, Llanedeyrn, CF3 7XF, Northeast : 3 m. by A 48
℘ (01222) 589988, *Fax (01222) 549092*, 🏋️, ≘s, 🔲 – 🛗, ✳️ rm, 🍴 rest, 📺 ☎ & 🅿 –
🔬 300. 🐼 🅰🅴 ⓪ 𝘝𝘐𝘚𝘈. ⚒    AV
**Meals** (bar lunch Monday to Saturday)/dinner 16.95 – 🖃 9.50 – **130 rm** 85.00/100.00 **st.**
2 suites – SB.

🏠 **Churchills**, Cardiff Rd, CF5 2AD, ℘ (01222) 562372, *Fax (01222) 568347* – 🍴 rest, 📺 ☎ &
🅿 – 🔬 110. 🐼 🅰🅴 ⓪ 𝘝𝘐𝘚𝘈. ⚒    AV
**Meals** (bar lunch Saturday) 9.50/16.50 **t.** and a la carte 🍷 4.25 – **28 rm** 🖃 80.00/100.00 **t.**
7 suites – SB.

🏠 **Lincoln House** without rest., 118 Cathedral Rd, CF1 9LQ, ℘ (01222) 395558, *Fax (01222) 230537* – 🔟 ☎ 📵. 📵 🖭 𝚅𝙸𝚂𝙰 𝙹𝙲𝙱. ⌘
AV **e**
**18 rm** ⚌ 48.00/68.00 **st.**

🏠 **Holiday Inn Express** without rest., Malthouse Av., Cardiff Gate Business Park, Pont-prennau, CF2 7RA, Northeast : 5 ¾ m. by A 48 and A 4232 at junction 30 of M 4 ℘ (01222) 733222, *Fax (01222) 734222* – 🛗 ⇆ 🔟 ☎ & 📵 – 🔬 30. 📵 🖭 𝚅𝙸𝚂𝙰. ⌘
**78 rm** ⚌ 49.50.

🏠 **Travel Inn** without rest., The David Lloyd Leisure Club, Ipswich Rd, Roath, CF3 7AQ, Northeast : 2 ½ m. by A 4161 ℘ (01222) 462481, *Fax (01222) 462482* – 🛗 ⇆ 🔟 & 📵. 📵 🖭 ⓪ 𝚅𝙸𝚂𝙰. ⌘
AV **r**
**70 rm** 38.00 **t.**

🏠 **Travel Inn**, Keen Rd, CF1 5JR, ℘ (01222) 489675, *Fax (01222) 489757* – ⇆ rm, 🍽 rest, 🔟 & 📵 – 🔬 30. 📵 🖭 ⓪ 𝚅𝙸𝚂𝙰. ⌘
AX **a**
**Meals** (grill rest.) – **73 rm** 38.00 **t.**

🏠 **Travel Inn**, Port Rd, Nant Isaf, Wenvoe, CF5 6DD, Southwest : 5 ¾ m. by A 4161 and A 48 on A 4050 ℘ (01222) 593896, *Fax (01222) 591436* – ⇆ rm, 🍽 rest, 🔟 & 📵. 📵 🖭 ⓪ 𝚅𝙸𝚂𝙰. ⌘
**Meals** (grill rest.) – **39 rm** 38.00 **t.**

🏠 **Travelodge** without rest., Circle Way East, Llanedeyrn, CF3 7ND, Northeast : 3 ½ m. by A 48 on Coed-y-Gores rd ℘ (01222) 549564, *Fax (01222) 549564*, Reservations (Freephone) 0800 850950 – ⇆ 🔟 & 📵. 📵 🖭 ⓪ 𝚅𝙸𝚂𝙰 𝙹𝙲𝙱. ⌘
AV **c**
**32 rm** 39.95/59.95 **t.**

🏠 **Townhouse** without rest., 70 Cathedral Rd, CF1 9LL, ℘ (01222) 239399, *Fax (01222) 223214* – 🔟 ☎ 📵. 📵 𝚅𝙸𝚂𝙰
AV **u**
**6 rm** ⚌ 49.50/69.50 **st.**

🏠 **Georgian** without rest., 179 Cathedral Rd, CF1 9PL, ℘ (01222) 232594, *Fax (01222) 232594* – 🔟. ⌘
AV **a**
*closed 25 and 26 December* – **8 rm** ⚌ 29.00/49.00 **st.**

🏠 **Annedd Lon** without rest., 157-159 Cathedral Rd, CF1 9PL, ℘ (01222) 223349, *Fax (01222) 640885* – ⇆ 🔟 📵. 📵 𝚅𝙸𝚂𝙰. ⌘
AV **s**
*closed 24 to 27 December* – **6 rm** ⚌ 25.00/45.00 **s.**

🍴🍴 **Gilby's**, Old Port Rd, Culverhouse Cross, CF5 6DN, West : 5 m. by A 4161 and A 48 off A 4050 ℘ (01222) 670800, *Fax (01222) 594437*, 🎆 – 📵. 📵 🖭 𝚅𝙸𝚂𝙰
*closed Sunday dinner, Monday, 25-26 December and Bank Holidays* – **Meals** 9.95 **t.** (dinner) and a la carte 17.95/26.60 **t.**

🍴 **Le Cassoulet**, 5 Romilly Cres., Canton, CF1 9NP, ℘ (01222) 221905, *Fax (01222) 221905* – 📵 🖭 ⓪ 𝚅𝙸𝚂𝙰 𝙹𝙲𝙱.
AX **c**
*closed Sunday, Monday, 3 weeks August and 10 days Christmas* – **Meals** - French - 14.95 **t.** (lunch) and a la carte 23.00/30.00 **t.** 🍷 7.50.

**at Thornhill** *North : 5 ¼ m. by A 470 on A 469* – AV – ✉ *Cardiff.*

🏨 **New House Country**, Thornhill Rd, CF4 5UA, on A 469 ℘ (01222) 520280, *Fax (01222) 520324*, ≤, 🎆, park – ⇆ 🔟 ☎ & 📵 – 🔬 200. 📵 🖭 ⓪ 𝚅𝙸𝚂𝙰 𝙹𝙲𝙱. ⌘
**Meals** 14.95/18.50 **t.** and a la carte 🍷 4.55 – ⚌ 8.50 – **32 rm** 82.50/102.80 **t.** – SB.

🏨 **Manor Parc**, Thornhill Rd, CF4 5UA, on A 469 ℘ (01222) 693723, *Fax (01222) 614624*, 🎆, 🍽 – 📵 – 🔬 120. 📵 🖭 𝚅𝙸𝚂𝙰. ⌘
*closed 24 to 31 December* – **Meals** (closed Sunday dinner) a la carte 25.95/29.95 **t.** 🍷 8.50 – **12 rm** ⚌ 62.00/110.00 **t.**

**at Castleton (Cas-Bach)** *(Newport) Northeast : 7 m. on A 48* – AV – ✉ *Cardiff.*

🏨 **St. Mellons**, CF3 8XR, on A 48 ℘ (01633) 680355, *Fax (01633) 680399*, 🛏, ⌚, 🔲, 🎆, 🍽, squash – 🔟 ☎ 📵 – 🔬 300. 📵 🖭 𝚅𝙸𝚂𝙰
**Meals** (dinner only and Sunday lunch)/dinner 18.00 **t.** and a la carte 🍷 6.00 – **41 rm** ⚌ 90.00/120.00 **t.**

🏠 **Travel Inn**, Newport Rd, CF3 8UQ, ℘ (01633) 680070, *Fax (01633) 681143* – ⇆ rm, 🔟 & 📵. 📵 🖭 ⓪ 𝚅𝙸𝚂𝙰. ⌘
**Meals** (grill rest.) – **49 rm** 38.00 **t.**

**at Pentyrch** *Northwest : 7 m. by A 4119* – AV – ✉ *Cardiff.*

🍴🍴🍴🍴 **De Courcey's**, Tyla Morris Av., CF4 8QN, South : 1 m. ℘ (01222) 892232, *Fax (01222) 891949*, 🎆 – 📵 – 🔬 100. 📵 🖭 ⓪ 𝚅𝙸𝚂𝙰
*closed Monday, 24 to 30 December and Bank Holidays* – **Meals** (dinner only and Sunday lunch)/dinner 24.75 **st.** and a la carte 🍷 6.75.

🔧 ATS Hadfield Rd ℘ (01222) 228251/226336

*Le Guide change, changez de* **guide Michelin** *tous les ans.*

**CARDIFF WEST SERVICE AREA** Cardiff 403 K 29 – ⊠ Pontycwn (Rhondda Cynon Taff).

🏠 **Travelodge**, CF72 8SA, M 4 junction 33 ℰ (01222) 891141, Fax (01222) 892497, Reservations (Freephone) 0800 850950 – ✺⊱ 🆃🆅 ☎ ৬ 🅿 – 🔬 30. 🆀🅾 🅰🅴 ① 💳 🅹🅲🅱. ⅍
Meals (grill rest.) – **50 rm** 39.95/59.95 **t.**

---

**CARDIGAN** (Aberteifi) Ceredigion 403 G 27 Wales G. – pop. 3 758.
Env. : Pembrokeshire Coast National Park★★.
🏌 Gwbert-on-Sea ℰ (01239) 612035/621775.
🅱 Theatr Mwldan, Bath House Rd, SA43 2JY ℰ (01239) 613230.
London 250 – Carmarthen 30 – Fishguard 19.

🏠 **Penbontbren Farm** 🐾, Glynarthen, SA44 6PE, Northeast : 9 ½ m. by A 48 ℰ (01239) 810248, Fax (01239) 811129, park – ✺⊱ 🆃🆅 ☎ ৬ 🅿 – 🔬 50. 🆀🅾 🅰🅴 ① 💳 🅹🅲🅱 ⅍
closed 23 to 29 December – **Meals** (dinner only) a la carte 17.20/19.10 **t.** ⅃ 4.60 – **10 rm** ⌫ 46.00/80.00 **st.** – SB.

**at St. Dogmaels** West : 1½ m. by A 487 on B 4546 – ⊠ Cardigan.

⋔ **Berwyn** 🐾 without rest., Cardigan Rd, SA43 3HS, ℰ (01239) 613555, ≤, 🌢 – ✺⊱ 🆃🆅 🅿 ⅍
closed Christmas-New Year – **3 rm** ⌫ 20.00/40.00.

**at Gwbert on Sea** Northwest : 3 m. on B 4548 – ⊠ Cardigan.

🏠 **Gwbert**, SA43 1PP, on B 4548 ℰ (01239) 612638, Fax (01239) 621474, ≤ Cardigan Bay – 🛗 ✺⊱ rest, 🆃🆅 ☎ 🅿. 🆀🅾 🅰🅴 💳. ⅍
Meals (bar lunch Monday to Saturday)/dinner 14.95 **t.** and a la carte ⅃ 6.70 – **15 rm** ⌫ 46.50/117.00 **t.** – SB.

🔧 ATS 4 Bath House Rd ℰ (01239) 612917

---

**Les prix** Pour toutes précisions sur les prix indiqués dans ce guide, reportez-vous aux pages de l'introduction.

---

**CASTLETON** (Cas-Bach) Newport 403 K 29 – see Cardiff.

---

**CEMAES** Anglesey 402 403 G 23 Wales G..
Env. : Anglesey★★.
London 272 – Bangor 25 – Caernarfon 32 – Holyhead 16.

⋔ **Hafod Country House**, LL67 0DS, South : ½ m. on Llanfechell rd ℰ (01407) 710500, ≤, 🌢 – ✺⊱ 🆃🆅 🅿. ⅍
March-October – **Meals** (by arrangement) 13.50 – **3 rm** ⌫ 40.50/45.00.

---

**CHANCERY** (Rhydgaled) Ceredigion 403 H 26 – see Aberystwyth.

---

**CHEPSTOW** Monmouthshire 403 404 M 29 Wales G. – pop. 9 461.
See : Town★ – Castle★★ AC (Great Tower★★).
Env. : Wynd Cliff★, N : 2½ m. by A 466 – Caerwent★ (Roman Walls★), SW : 4 m. by A 48.
🏌, 🏌 St. Pierre, St. Pierre Park ℰ (01291) 625261.
🅱 Castle Car Park, Bridge St., NP6 5EY ℰ (01291) 623772.
London 131 – Bristol 17 – Cardiff 28 – Gloucester 34.

🏨 **Marriott St. Pierre H. & Country Club**, St. Pierre Park, NP6 6YA, Southwest : 3 ½ m. on A 48 ℰ (01291) 625261, Fax (01291) 629975, ⅃₅, ≘s, 🔲, 🏌, park, ⅍ – ✺⊱ 🆃🆅 ☎ 🅿 – 🔬 300. 🆀🅾 🅰🅴 ① 💳 🅹🅲🅱. ⅍
*Orangery :* Meals (dinner only and Sunday lunch)/dinner 15.25 **st.** and a la carte – *Long Weekend :* Meals a la carte 12.20/20.85 **t.** – ⌫ 10.50 – **132 rm** 81.00/88.00 **t.**, 16 suites.

🏨 **George**, Moor St., NP6 5DB, ℰ (01291) 625363, Fax (01291) 627418 – ✺⊱ 🆃🆅 ☎ 🅿 – 🔬 30. 🆀🅾 🅰🅴 ① 💳. ⅍
Meals (bar lunch Monday to Saturday)/dinner a la carte 11.35/23.00 **t.** ⅃ 6.00 – ⌫ 8.95 – **14 rm** 70.00/110.00 **t.** – SB.

🏠 **Castle View**, 16 Bridge St., NP6 5EZ, ℰ (01291) 620349, Fax (01291) 627397, 🌢 – ✺⊱ rest, 🆃🆅 ☎. 🆀🅾 🅰🅴 ① 💳
Meals (bar lunch Monday to Saturday) (Sunday dinner residents only)/dinner a la carte 16.45/19.40 **st.** ⅃ 7.50 – ⌫ 5.95 – **13 rm** 44.95/65.95 **st.** – SB.

## COLWYN BAY (Bae Colwyn) Conwy 402 403 I 24 Wales G. – pop. 29 883.

See : Welsh Mountain Zoo★ AC (≤★).

Env. : Bodnant Garden★★ AC, SW : 6 m. by A 55 and A 470.

🔼 Abergele and Pensarn, Tan-y-Goppa Rd, Abergele ℘ (01745) 824034 – 🔼 Old Colwyn, Woodland Av. ℘ (01492) 515581.

🖪 40 Station Rd, LL29 8BU ℘ (01492) 530478 – The Promenade, Rhos-on-Sea, LL28 4EP ℘ (01492) 548778 (summer only).

London 237 – Birkenhead 50 – Chester 42 – Holyhead 41.

🏨 **Norfolk House**, 39 Princes Drive, LL29 8PF, ℘ (01492) 531757, Fax (01492) 533781, 🐾 – 🛗 📺 🐕 ℗ – 🕍 35. 🐵 🖭 ⓪ 𝘝𝘐𝘚𝘈

closed 23 December-10 January – **Meals** (dinner only) 16.50 t. and a la carte 🍴 5.95 – **21 rm** ⊇ 45.00/65.00 t. – SB.

🏨 **Hopeside**, 63-67 Princes Drive, West End, LL29 8PW, ℘ (01492) 533244, Fax (01492) 532850 – 🦶 rm, 📺 🕿 🐕 ℗ – 🕍 50. 🐵 🖭 𝘝𝘐𝘚𝘈

**Meals** 16.50 t. (dinner) and a la carte 10.95/19.70 t. 🍴 3.95 – **18 rm** ⊇ 49.00/85.00 t. – SB.

XX **Café Niçoise**, 124 Abergele Rd, LL29 7PS, ℘ (01492) 531555 – 🐵 🖭 𝘝𝘐𝘚𝘈 𝘑𝘊𝘉

closed lunch Monday and Tuesday, Sunday, 25-26 December, 1 week January and 1 week June – **Meals** 13.95 t. and a la carte 🍴 4.75.

**at Rhos-on-Sea (Llandrillo-yn-Rhos)** Northwest : 1 m. – ⊠ Colwyn Bay.

🏨 **Ashmount**, College Av., LL28 4NT, ℘ (01492) 544582, Fax (01492) 545479 – 🦶 rest, 📺 🕿 ℗ 🐵 🖭 ⓪ 𝘝𝘐𝘚𝘈 𝘑𝘊𝘉

**Meals** (bar lunch)/dinner 13.50 st. and a la carte 🍴 4.25 – **17 rm** ⊇ 35.00/70.00 st. – SB.

## CONWY 402 403 I 24 Wales G. – pop. 3 627.

See : Town★★★ – Castle★★★ AC – Town Walls★★ – Plas Mawr★★.

Env. : Snowdonia National Park★★★ – Bodnant Garden★★ AC, S : 8 m. by A 55 and A 470 – Conwy Crossing (suspension bridge★).

🔼 Morfa ℘ (01492) 593400 – 🔼 Penmaenmawr, Conway Old Rd ℘ (01492) 623330.

🖪 Conwy Castle Visitor Centre, Castle St., LL32 8LD ℘ (01492) 592248.

London 241 – Caernarfon 22 – Chester 46 – Holyhead 37.

🏨 **Berthlwyd Hall** ⤢, Llechwedd, LL32 8DQ, Southwest : 2 ¼ m. by B 5106 and Sychnant rd, off Hendre Rd ℘ (01492) 592409, Fax (01492) 572290, ≤, « Victorian manor house », 🍴, 🐾 – 🦶 rm, 📺 🕿 ℗ 🐵 🖭 ⓪ 𝘝𝘐𝘚𝘈 𝘑𝘊𝘉

**Meals** 14.95/18.95 st. and dinner a la carte 🍴 9.50 – ⊇ 4.95 – **7 rm** 58.00/85.00 st. – SB.

**at Roewen** Southwest : 5 m. by B 5106 – ⊠ Conwy.

⌂ **Tir-y-Coed Country House** ⤢, LL32 8TP, ℘ (01492) 650219, Fax (01492) 650219, ≤, « Gardens » – 🦶 rest, 📺 ℗. 🖭

March-early November – **Meals** 12.75 st. 🍴 4.00 – **7 rm** ⊇ 30.25/56.50 st. – SB.

**at Tyn-y-Groes (Gwynedd)** South : 3 ¾ m. on B 5106 – ⊠ Conwy.

🏨 **Groes Inn**, LL32 8TN, South : 1 ½ m. on B 5106 ℘ (01492) 650545, Fax (01492) 650855, ≤, « Part 16C », 🐾 – 🦶 rm, 📺 🕿 ℗. 🐵 🖭 ⓪ 𝘝𝘐𝘚𝘈. 🛠

closed 25 December – **Meals** 12.50/19.50 st. and a la carte 🍴 6.50 – **14 rm** ⊇ 63.25/113.00 t. – SB.

**at Tal-y-Bont** South : 5 ¾ m. on B 5106 – ⊠ Conwy.

🏨 **Lodge**, LL32 8YX, ℘ (01492) 660766, Fax (01492) 660534, 🐾 – 🦶 rest, 📺 🕿 ℗ – 🕍 30. 🐵 🖭 𝘝𝘐𝘚𝘈 𝘑𝘊𝘉

restricted opening in winter – **Meals** (closed Monday lunch) 6.25/15.95 st. and a la carte 🍴 6.95 – **10 rm** ⊇ 40.00/70.00 st. – SB.

## CORWEN Denbighshire 402 403 J 25.

London 205 – Chester 34 – Dolgellau 30 – Llandudno 40 – Shrewsbury 40.

⌂ **Powys House Estate**, Bonwm, LL21 9EG, East : 1 ½ m. on A 5 ℘ (01490) 412367, 🐾, 🛠 – 📺 ℗. 🛠

closed 24 to 27 December – **Meals** (by arrangement) 15.00 s. – **3 rm** ⊇ 25.00/40.00 s. – SB.

## COWBRIDGE Vale of Glamorgan 403 J 29 – pop. 6 167.

London 167 – Cardiff 12 – Swansea 30.

🏨 **Bear**, 63 High St., CF71 7AF, ℘ (01446) 774814, Fax (01446) 775425, « 18C coaching inn, 12C origins » – 📺 🕿 ℗ – 🕍 100. 🐵 🖭 𝘝𝘐𝘚𝘈

**Meals** (closed Sunday dinner) (bar lunch Monday to Saturday)/dinner 15.00 t. 🍴 3.95 – **34 rm** ⊇ 65.00/75.00 t. – SB.

**COYCHURCH** (Llangrallo) *Bridgend* 403 J 29 – *see Bridgend.*

---

**CRICCIETH** *Gwynedd* 402 403 H 25 *Wales G. – pop. 1 720.*
Env. : *Lleyn Peninsula*★★ – *Ffestiniog Railway*★★.
📷 *Ednyfed Hill* ✆ *(01766) 522154.*
*London 249 – Caernarfon 17 – Shrewsbury 85.*

🏨 **Mynydd Ednyfed Country House** ⍋, Caernarfon Rd, LL52 0PH, Northwest : ¾ m.
on B 4411 ✆ (01766) 523269, ≤, ₤₅, ☞, ⁂ – 🆃🆅 ☎ 🅿. 🕦🅾 🅰🅴 🆅🆂🅰
*closed 23 December-4 January* – **Meals** (dinner only) a la carte 14.25/21.25 rm 4.95 – **9 rm**
⭤ 30.00/65.00 t. – SB.

---

**CRICKHOWELL** *Powys* 403 K 28 *Wales G. – pop. 2 166.*
Env. : *Brecon Beacons National Park*★★.
Exc. : *Llanthony Priory*★★, *NE : 10 m. by minor roads.*
*London 169 – Abergavenny 6 – Brecon 14 – Newport 25.*

🏨 **Bear,** High St., NP8 1BW, ✆ (01873) 810408, *Fax* (01873) 811696, « Part 15C former coaching inn », ☞ – 🆃🆅 ☎ 🅿 – 🔬 50. 🕦🅾 🅰🅴 🆅🆂🅰 �🅹🅲🅱
**Meals** (lunch booking essential) (bar meal Sunday dinner) a la carte 16.70/28.40 t. 4.25 –
**27 rm** ⭤ 45.00/110.00 t., 1 suite.

🏨 **Gliffaes Country House** ⍋, NP8 1RH, West : 3 ¾ m. by A 40 ✆ (01874) 730371
*Fax* (01874) 730463, ≤, « Victorian country house and gardens on the banks of the River
Usk », ⍌, park, ⁂ – ⁂ rest, 🆃🆅 ☎ 🅿. 🕦🅾 🅰🅴 🅾 🆅🆂🅰. ⁂
**Meals** (bar lunch Monday to Saturday)/dinner 23.50 st. – **22 rm** ⭤ 40.50/119.50 st. – SB.

🏨 **Ty Croeso** ⍋, The Dardy, NP8 1PU, West : 1 ½ m. by A 4077 off Llangynidr rd
✆ (01873) 810573, *Fax* (01873) 810573, ≤, ☞ – 🆃🆅 ☎ 🅿. 🕦🅾 🅰🅴 🆅🆂🅰
*closed 24 and 25 December* – **Meals** (dinner only and Sunday lunch)/dinner 15.95 t.
and a la carte 5.25 – **8 rm** ⭤ 30.00/75.00 t. – SB.

🍴 **Nantyffin Cider Mill Inn,** NP8 1SG, West : 1 ½ m. on A 40 ✆ (01873) 810775
*Fax* (01873) 810775, « Converted 16C cider mill », ☞ – 🅿. 🕦🅾 🅰🅴 🆅🆂🅰 🅹🅲🅱
*closed Monday except Bank Holidays, 2 weeks January, 1 week November and 25 December*
– **Meals** a la carte 12.20/26.20 t. 4.95.

**at Llangenny** *East : 3 m. by A 40 via Glangrwyney* – ⊠ *Crickhowell.*

🏠 **Gellirhydd Farm** ⍋ without rest., NP8 1HF, North : 1 ½ m. taking unmarked road
before bridge and turning left at crossroads (no through rd) ✆ (01873) 810466, ≤, « 17C
farmhouse », ⍌, ☞, park – ⁂ 🅿. 🕦🅾 🆅🆂🅰. ⁂
*closed 21 December-3 January* – **3 rm** ⭤ 20.00/50.00 – SB.

---

**CROSSGATES** *Powys* 403 J 27 – *see Llandrindod Wells.*

---

**CROSS HANDS** *Carmarthenshire* 403 H 28 – *pop. 9 520.*
*London 208 – Fishguard 63 – Swansea 19.*

🏨 **Travelodge,** SA14 6NW, on A 48 ✆ (01269) 845700, Reservations (Freephone) 0800
850950 – ⁂ rm, 🆃🆅 &. 🅿. 🕦🅾 🅰🅴 🅾 🆅🆂🅰 🅹🅲🅱. ⁂
**Meals** (grill rest.) – **32 rm** 39.95/59.95 t.

---

**CRUGYBAR** *Carmarthenshire* 403 I 27 – ⊠ *Llanwrda.*
*London 213 – Carmarthen 26 – Swansea 36.*

🏨 **Glanrannell Park** ⍋, SA19 8SA, Southwest : ½ m. by B 4302 ✆ (01558) 685230
*Fax* (01558) 685784, ≤, ⍌, ☞, park – ⁂ rest. 🆃🆅 🅿. 🕦🅾 🆅🆂🅰 🅹🅲🅱
*April-October* – **Meals** (booking essential to non-residents) (bar lunch)/dinner 17.00 t.
4.00 – **8 rm** ⭤ 41.00/72.00 t. – SB.

---

**CWMBRAN** *Torfaen* 403 K 29 – *pop. 46 021.*
*London 149 – Bristol 35 – Cardiff 17 – Newport 5.*

🏨 **Parkway,** Cwmbran Drive, NP44 3UW, South : 1 m. by A 4051 ✆ (01633) 871199
*Fax* (01633) 869160, ₤₅, ≘s, 🆂 – ⁂ rm, 🆃🆅 ☎ &. 🅿 – 🔬 500. 🕦🅾 🅰🅴 🆅🆂🅰. ⁂
*closed 23 December-1 January* – **Meals** (light lunch Monday to Saturday)/dinner 14.95 st.
and a la carte – ⭤ 9.40 – **69 rm** 89.25/125.00 t., 1 suite – SB.

🅰 ATS Station Rd ✆ (01633) 484964

---

**GWM GWAUN** *Pembrokeshire* 403 F 28 – *see Fishguard.*

**CWM TAF** *Merthyr Tydfil* **403** *J 28 – see Merthyr Tydfil.*

---

**CYNGHORDY** *Carmarthenshire* **403** *I 27 –* ⊠ *Llandovery.*
London 210 – Carmarthen 31 – Swansea 41.

↑ **Llanerchindda Farm** ♨, SA20 0NB, North : 2 ½ m. by Station rd, turning right at T-junction and under viaduct ✆ (01550) 750274, *Fax (01550) 750300*, ≤ Black Mountains, « Working farm », ⚞ – ✼ 📺 ☎ & ℗
*closed 1 week Christmas-New Year* – **Meals** (by arrangement) (communal dining) 10.00 **st.**
§ 3.00 – **9 rm** ☲ 22.00/44.00 **st.** – SB.

---

**DEGANWY** *Conwy* **402 403** *I 24 – see Llandudno.*

---

**DENBIGH** (Dinbych) *Denbighshire* **402 403** *J 24 – pop. 8 529.*
🖪 *Henllan Rd* ✆ (01745) 814159.
London 217 – Chester 30 – Colwyn Bay 21 – Shrewsbury 53.

↑ **Berllan Bach** ♨, Fford Las, LL16 4LR, Southeast : 5 ¾ m. by Ruthin Rd and Llandyrnog rd on Llangynhafal rd ✆ (01824) 790732, *Fax (01824) 790732*, ⚞ – 📺 ☎ ℗
**Meals** 12.50 **st.** – **3 rm** ☲ 32.50/45.00 **st.** – SB.

    ℗ ATS Rhyl Rd ✆ (01745) 812217

---

**DOLGELLAU** *Gwynedd* **402 403** *I 25 Wales G. – pop. 2 396.*
See : *Town★.*
Env. : *Snowdonia National Park★★★ – Cadair Idris★★★ – Precipice Walk★, NE : 3 m. on minor roads.*
🖪 *Pencefn Rd* ✆ (01341) 422603.
🛈 *Ty Meirion, Eldon Sq., LL40 1PU* ✆ (01341) 422888.
London 221 – Birkenhead 72 – Chester 64 – Shrewsbury 57.

🏨 **Penmaenuchaf Hall** ♨, Penmaenpool, LL40 1YB, West : 1 ¾ m. on A 493 (Tywyn Rd) ✆ (01341) 422129, *Fax (01341) 422787*, ≤, « Victorian mansion in extensive gardens », ♧, park – ✼ 📺 ☎ ℗ – ᴁ 50. 🅒🅞 🅐🅔 ① 𝘝𝘐𝘚𝘈 🅹🅲🅱
*closed 5 to 12 January* – **Meals** 14.95/25.00 **t.** and a la carte § 7.85 – **14 rm** ☲ 65.00/155.00 **t.** – SB.

🏨 **Dolserau Hall** ♨, LL40 2AG, Northeast : 2 ¾ m. by A 494 ✆ (01341) 422522, *Fax (01341) 422400*, ≤, ⚞ – 📶, ✼ rest, 📺 ☎ ℗. 🅒🅞 𝘝𝘐𝘚𝘈
*closed 7 November-22 December and 1 January-11 February* – **Meals** (residents only) (dinner only) 19.95 **t.** – **15 rm** ☲ 50.00/100.00 **st.**

🏠 **George III**, Penmaenpool, LL40 1YD, West : 2 m. by A 493 ✆ (01341) 422525, *Fax (01341) 423565*, ≤ Mawddach estuary and mountains, ♧ – ✼ rest, 📺 ☎ ℗. 🅒🅞 𝘝𝘐𝘚𝘈 🅹🅲🅱 ✁
**Meals** (bar lunch Monday to Saturday)/dinner a la carte 16.75/26.95 **t.** § 7.50 – **11 rm** ☲ 50.00/94.00 **t.** – SB.

↑ **Abergwynant Hall** ♨, Penmaenpool, LL40 1YF, West : 3 ½ m. on A 493 ✆ (01341) 422160, *Fax (01341) 422160*, ≤, « Victorian mansion in extensive parklands », ⚞ – ✼ 📺 ℗. 🅒🅞 𝘝𝘐𝘚𝘈. ✁
*closed 2 January- mid February* – **Meals** (by arrangement) 19.75 **st.** § 5.50 – **5 rm** ☲ (dinner included) 89.50/150.00 **st.** – SB.

**at Ganllwyd** *North : 5½ m. on A 470 –* ⊠ *Dolgellau.*

🏨 **Plas Dolmelynllyn** ♨, LL40 2HP, ✆ (01341) 440273, *Fax (01341) 440273*, ≤, « Part 17C manor house », ♧, ⚞, park – ✼ 📺 ☎ ℗. 🅒🅞 🅐🅔 𝘝𝘐𝘚𝘈. ✁
*March-November* – **Meals** (bar lunch)/dinner 24.50 **st.** § 6.00 – **9 rm** ☲ 52.50/115.00 **st.**, 1 suite – SB.

**at Llanfachreth** *Northeast : 3 ¾ m. –* ⊠ *Dolgellau.*

↑ **Ty Isaf Farmhouse**, LL40 2EA, ✆ (01341) 423261, ≤, « 17C longhouse », ⚞ – ✼ ℗. ✁
**Meals** (by arrangement) (communal dining) 13.50 – **3 rm** ☲ 36.00/52.00 **s.**

**at Arthog** *Southwest : 7 m. on A 493 –* ⊠ *Dolgellau.*

↑ **Cyfannedd Uchaf** ♨, LL39 1LX, South : 4 ½ m. by A 493 Cregennan Lakes rd, taking right turn at T. junction at end of road (gated roads) ✆ (01341) 250526, ≤ Barmouth, Mawddach estuary and mountains, park – ✼ ℗. ✁
*mid May-September* – **Meals** (communal dining) 7.00 – **3 rm** ☲ 38.00 **st.**

**at Bontddu** West : 5 m. on A 496 (Barmouth Rd) – ⊠ Dolgellau.

🏛 **Bontddu Hall Country House,** LL40 2UF, ℰ (01341) 430661, Fax (01341) 430284, ≤ Mawddach estuary and mountains, « Victorian mansion in extensive gardens » – ⇐↝ rest 📺 ☎ 🅿 🐠 🕮 ⓪ *VISA* 🃏
*closed January and February* – *Garden* : Meals 12.95/23.50 **t.** and a la carte ⅙ 6.95 – *Brasserie* : Meals 12.95/23.50 **t.** and a la carte ⅙ 6.95 – **17 rm** ⊇ 62.50/130.00 **t.**, 3 suites – SB.

↑ **Borthwnog Hall,** LL40 2TT, East : 1 m. on A 496 ℰ (01341) 430271, Fax (01341) 430682 ≤ Mawddach estuary and mountains, « Part Regency house, art gallery », �, park – ⇐↝ rest, 📺 ☎ 🅿, 🐠 🕮 *VISA*, ℅
*closed 1 to 18 November and 24 to 26 December* – **Meals** (by arrangement) a la carte 25.00 **t.** ⅙ 5.50 – **3 rm** ⊇ (dinner included) 138.00 **t.** – SB.

---

**DRENEWYDD YN NOTAIS** (Nottage) Bridgend **403** I 29 – see Porthcawl.

---

**DYFFRYN ARDUDWY** Gwynedd **402 403** H 25 Wales G. – pop. 1 452 (inc. Tal-y-Bont).
Env. : Snowdonia National Park★★★.
London 237 – Dolgellau 16 – Caernarfon 44.

↑ **Ystumgwern Hall Farm** ℅ without rest., LL44 2DD, Northwest : 1 m. by A 496 ℰ (01341) 247249, Fax (01341) 247171, « Working farm », �, park – 📺 🅿
**5 suites** ⊇ 25.00/44.00 **st.**.

---

**EAST ABERTHAW** (Aberddawan) Vale of Glamorgan **403** J 29 – ⊠ Barry.
London 180 – Cardiff 20 – Swansea 33.

🍴 **Blue Anchor Inn,** CF62 3DD, ℰ (01446) 750329, Fax (01446) 750077, « Characterful part 14C thatched inn » – 🅿. 🐠 *VISA*
*closed Sunday dinner* – **Meals** (in bar Monday to Saturday lunch)/dinner 15.75 **t.** and a la carte ⅙ 4.75.

---

**EWLOE** Flintshire **402 403** K 24 – pop. 3 263.
🛏 Autolodge Site, Gateway Services, A 55 Expressway westbound, Northophall, CH7 6HE ℰ (01244) 541597 (summer only).
London 200 – Chester 8.5 – Shrewsbury 48.

🏨 **St David's Park,** St. David's Park, CH5 3YB, on B 5125 at junction with A 494 ℰ (01244) 520800, Fax (01244) 520930, ↧, ☎, 🔲, 🛏, �, ℅ – ▯ ⇐↝, 🍽 rest, 📺 ☎ & 🅿 – 🔬 270. 🐠 🕮 ⓪ *VISA*
*Fountains* : Meals 18.50 **st.** and a la carte – ⊇ 9.95 – **145 rm** 109.00 **st.** – SB.

🔧 ATS Holywell Rd (Nr. Queensferry) ℰ (01244) 520380

---

**FISHGUARD** (Abergwaun) Pembrokeshire **403** F 28 Wales G. – pop. 3 128.
Env. : Pembrokeshire Coast National Park★★.
⛴ to Republic of Ireland (Rosslare) (Stena Line) 2 daily (3 h 30 mn).
⛴ to Republic of Ireland (Rosslare) (Stena Line) 3-4 daily (1 h 40 mn).
🛏 The Square ℰ (01348) 873484 – Passenger Concourse, The Harbour, Goodwick, SA64 0BU ℰ (01348) 872037.
London 265 – Cardiff 114 – Gloucester 176 – Holyhead 169 – Shrewsbury 136 – Swansea 76.

🏠 **Plas Glyn-Y-Mel** ℅ without rest., Lower Town, SA65 9LY, ℰ (01348) 872296, Fax (01348) 874521, ≤, « Georgian country house », 🔲, 🌲, park – 📺 🅿
**5 rm** ⊇ 45.00/80.00 **t.**

🏠 **Manor House,** 11 Main St., SA65 9HG, ℰ (01348) 873260, Fax (01348) 873260, 🌲 – ⇐↝ rest, 📺. 🐠 *VISA*
*closed Christmas and 2 weeks November and restricted opening February* – **Meals** (dinner only) 18.00 **st.** ⅙ 4.50 – **6 rm** ⊇ 27.00/52.00 **st.**

✕✕ **Three Main Street** with rm., 3 Main St., SA65 9HG, ℰ (01348) 874275 – ⇐↝ 📺, ℅
*closed February* – **Meals** (closed Tuesday in winter, Sunday and Monday) (lunch booking essential) 25.00 **t.** ⅙ 6.25 – **3 rm** ⊇ 35.00/60.00 **t.** – SB.

**at Cwm Gwaun** Southeast : 5½ m. by B 4313 – ⊠ Fishguard.

🏠 **Tregynon Country Farmhouse** ℅, SA65 9TU, East : 6 ¼ m. ℰ (01239) 820531, Fax (01239) 820808, 🌲, park – ⇐↝ 📺 ☎ 🅿. 🐠 *VISA* 🃏. ℅
*closed 2 weeks in winter* – **Meals** (booking essential) (dinner only) 21.95 **st.** – **6 rm** ⊇ 58.00/75.00 **t.** – SB.

**Letterston** *South : 5 m. on A 40.*

⌂ **Heathfield Mansion** ⌖, SA62 5EG, Northwest : 1 ½ m. by B 4331 ℰ (01348) 840263, *Fax* (01348) 840263, ≼ – ✳ �📺 🅿. ⚘
*March-October* – **Meals** (by arrangement) (communal dining) 10.00 **st.** ⚬ 5.00 – **3 rm** ⚌ 30.00/44.00 **st.** – SB.

**Welsh Hook** *Southwest : 7½ m. by A 40 –* ✉ *Haverfordwest.*

XX **Stone Hall** ⌖ with rm, SA62 5NS, ℰ (01348) 840212, *Fax* (01348) 840815, « Part 14C manor house with 17C extension », 🍴 – �📺 🅿. ⚫ 🆎 ⓞ 𝘝𝘐𝘚𝘈. ⚘
**Meals** (dinner only) 18.50 **t.** a la carte ⚬ 5.50 – **5 rm** ⚌ 48.00/70.00 **t.** – SB.

⬤ ATS Scleddau ℰ (01348) 873522

---

**ANLLWYD** *Gwynedd* 402 403 I 25 – *see Dolgellau.*

---

**ARTHMYL** *Powys* 402 403 K 26.
*London 192 – Birmingham 78 – Chester 50 – Shrewsbury 29.*

⌂ **Garthmyl Hall** ⌖, SY15 6RS, ℰ (01686) 640550, *Fax* (01686) 640550, ≼, « 18C manor house », 🍴 – ✳ ☎ 🅿. ⚫ 𝘝𝘐𝘚𝘈 ᴊᴄʙ. ⚘
**Meals** 17.50 **st.** ⚬ 5.00 – **9 rm** ⚌ 37.50/90.00 **st.**

---

**OVILON** *Monmouthshire – see Abergavenny.*

---

**RESFORD** (Groes-ffordd) *Wrexham* 402 403 L 24 – *pop. 2 667.*
*London 187 – Chester 11 – Shrewsbury 32.*

🍴 **Pant-yr-Ochain,** Old Wrexham Rd, LL12 8TY, South : 1 m. ℰ (01978) 853525, *Fax* (01978) 853505, 🍴, « Part 16C inn », 🍴 – ✳ 🅿. ⚫ 🆎 𝘝𝘐𝘚𝘈
*closed 25 and 26 December* – **Meals** a la carte 13.55/22.15 **t.** ⚬ 4.50.

---

**UILSFIELD** *Powys* 402 403 K 26 – *see Welshpool.*

---

**WBERT ON SEA** *Ceredigion* 403 F 27 – *see Cardigan.*

---

**ANMER** *Wrexham* 402 403 L 25 – *pop. 565 –* ✉ *Whitchurch (Shrops.).*
*London 237 – Chester 26 – Shrewsbury 27 – Stoke-on-Trent 28.*

🏠 **Hanmer Arms,** SY13 3DE, ℰ (01948) 830532, *Fax* (01948) 830740, 🍴 – ✳ rest, 📺 ☎ 🅿 – ⚒ 80. ⚫ 🆎 ⓞ 𝘝𝘐𝘚𝘈
**Meals** a la carte 10.60/25.10 **t.** ⚬ 4.80 – **20 rm** ⚌ 38.00/48.00 **t.**, 6 suites.

---

**ARLECH** *Gwynedd* 402 403 H 25 *Wales G. – pop. 1 233.*
See : *Castle★★ AC.*
Env. : *Snowdonia National Park★★★.*
🏌 *Royal St. David's* ℰ (01766) 780203.
🛈 *Gwyddfor House, High St., LL46 2YA* ℰ (01766) 780658 (summer only).
*London 241 – Chester 72 – Dolgellau 21.*

⌂ **Gwrach Ynys,** LL47 6TS, North : 2 ¼ m. on A 496 ℰ (01766) 780742, *Fax* (01766) 781199, 🍴 – ✳ 📺 🅿. ⚘
*March-October* – **Meals** (by arrangement) 12.50 – **7 rm** ⚌ 23.00/46.00 – SB.

XX **Castle Cottage** with rm, Pen Llech, LL46 2YL, off B 4573 ℰ (01766) 780479, *Fax* (01766) 780479 – ✳. ⚫ 𝘝𝘐𝘚𝘈. ⚘
*closed 3 weeks February* – **Meals** (booking essential) (dinner only and Sunday lunch)/dinner 22.50 **t.** ⚬ 6.00 – **6 rm** ⚌ 27.00/58.00 **t.** – SB.

---

**HAVERFORDWEST** (Hwlffordd) *Pembrokeshire* 403 F 28 *Wales G. – pop. 11 099.*
See : *Scolton Museum and Country Park★.*
Env. : *Pembrokeshire Coast National Park★★.*
Exc. : *Skomer Island and Skokholm Island★, SW : 14 m. by B 4327 and minor roads.*
🏌 *Arnolds Down* ℰ (01437) 763565.
🛈 *19 Old Bridge, SA61 2EZ* ℰ (01437) 763110.
*London 250 – Fishguard 15 – Swansea 57.*

🏠 **Wilton House,** 6 Quay St., SA61 1BG, ℰ (01437) 760033, Fax (01437) 760297, 🛋, 🌲 – 🗖
🕿 📞 🅿. 🐠 🖭 VISA. ⨯
**Meals** (closed Sunday) a la carte 8.70/18.20 **st.** ≬ 3.25 – **9 rm** ⊊ 35.00/52.50 **st.**

🔘 ATS Back Lane, Prendergast ℰ (01437) 763756

---

**HAY-ON-WYE** Powys 🔢 K 27 Wales G. – pop. 1 407.
See : Town★.
Env. : Brecon Beacons National Park★★.
Exc. : Llanthony Priory★★, SE : 12 m. by minor roads.
🏌 Rhosgoch, Builth Wells ℰ (01497) 851251.
London 154 – Brecon 16 – Hereford 21 – Newport 62.

🏨 **Swan,** Church St., HR3 5DQ, ℰ (01497) 821188, Fax (01497) 821424, 🕸, 🌲 – ⨯ rest, 🗖
🕿 🅿 – 🕍 160. 🐠 🖭 ① VISA JCB
**Meals** (lunch booking essential) a la carte 13.00/20.50 **st.** ≬ 5.75 – **19 rm** ⊊ 50.00/90.00 s▮
– SB.

↑ **York House,** Hardwick Rd, Cusop, HR3 5QX, East : ½ m. on B 4348 ℰ (01497) 820705, 🌲
– ⨯ 🗖 🅿. 🐠 🖭 VISA
closed 2 weeks January – **Meals** (by arrangement) 14.00 **st.** – **4 rm** ⊊ 25.00/50.00 **st.** – SB

🔘 **Old Black Lion** with rm, Lion St., HR3 5AD, ℰ (01497) 820841, « Part 13C and 17C inn »
⨯ rest, 🖭 🕿 🅿. 🐠 🖭 VISA
**Meals** a la carte 16.95/24.45 **st.** ≬ 5.50 – **10 rm** ⊊ 27.00/57.50 **st.** – SB.

**at Llanigon** Southwest : 2½ m. by B 4350 – ⊠ Hay-on-Wye.

↑ **Old Post Office** without rest., HR3 5QA, ℰ (01497) 820008, « 17C house » – ⨯ 🅿
**3 rm** ⊊ 20.00/50.00.

---

**HOLYHEAD** (Caergybi) Anglesey 🔢 🔢 G 24 Wales G. – pop. 11 796.
Env. : South Stack Cliffs★, W : 3 m. by minor roads.
🚢 to Republic of Ireland (Dun Laoghaire) (Stena Line) 4-5 daily (1 h 40 mn) – to Republi▮
of Ireland (Dublin) (Irish Ferries) 2 daily (3 h 15 mn) – to Republic of Ireland (Dublin) (Sten▮
Line) daily (4 h).
London 269 – Birkenhead 94 – Cardiff 215 – Chester 88 – Shrewsbury 105 – Swansea 190.

↑ **Yr Hendre,** Porth-y-Felin Rd, LL65 1AH, Northwest : ¾ m. by Prince of Wales Rd of
Walthew Av. ℰ (01407) 762929, Fax (01407) 762929 – ⨯ 🖭 🅿. ⨯
closed 25 and 26 December – **Meals** (by arrangement) 10.00 – **3 rm** ⊊ 25.00/40.00 **st.**

🔘 ATS Derwyn Garage, Stanley Embankment, Valley ℰ (01407) 742000

---

**HOLYWELL** (Treffynnon) Flintshire 🔢 🔢 K 24 Wales G. – pop. 8 770.
See : Town★.
🏌 Holywell, Brynford ℰ (01352) 710040/713937.
London 217 – Chester 19 – Liverpool 34.

🏨 **Kinsale Hall** 🕭, Llanerchymor, CH8 9DX, North : 3 ½ m. by B 5121 off A 548▮
ℰ (01745) 560001, Fax (01745) 561298, 🏌, 🌲, park – |🕴|, ⨯ rest, 🗏 rest, 🖭 🕿 📞 🅿 –
🕍 350. 🐠 🖭 VISA. ⨯
closed 26 and 27 December – **Meals** 18.00 **t.** and a la carte ≬ 7.15 – **34 rm** ⊊ 69.00▮
105.00 **t.**, 1 suite – SB.

🏠 **Travelodge,** Halkyn, CH8 8RF, Southeast : 3 ½ m. on A 55 (westbound carriageway▮
ℰ (01352) 780952, Reservations (Freephone) 0800 850950 – ⨯ rm, 🖭 ⅓ 🅿. 🐠 🖭 ① VIS▮
JCB. ⨯
**Meals** (grill rest.) – **31 rm** 39.95/59.95 **t.**

---

**HOWEY** Powys – see Llandrindod Wells.

---

**In this guide**

a symbol or a character, printed in red or **black**, in **bold** or light
type, does not have the same meaning.
Pay particular attention to the explanatory pages.

**NIGHTON** (Trefyclawdd) *Powys* 403 K 26 *Wales G. – pop. 2 851.*

See : *Town★*.

Exc. : *Offa's Dyke★, NW : 9½ m.*

ਿ *Little Ffrydd Wood* ℘ *(01547) 528646.*

🛈 *The Offas Dyke Centre, West St., LD7 1EW* ℘ *(01547) 528753.*

*London 162 – Birmingham 59 – Hereford 31 – Shrewsbury 35.*

🏦 **Milebrook House**, Ludlow Rd, Milebrook, LD7 1LT, East : 2 m. on A 4113 ℘ (01547) 528632, Fax (01547) 520509, 🍴, 🐎 – ⥂ 📺 ☎ 🅿, 🕻 🖭 *VISA* JCB, 🛇
**Meals** *(closed Monday lunch)* 11.25/18.95 **t.** and a la carte ≬ 6.50 – **10 rm** 🖃 50.00/82.00 **t.** – SB.

---

**AKE VYRNWY** *Powys* 402 403 J 25 *Wales G. – ⊠ Llanwddyn.*

See : *Lake★*.

🛈 *Unit 2, Vyrnwy Craft Workshops, SY10 OLY* ℘ *(01691) 870346 (summer only).*

*London 204 – Chester 52 – Llanfyllin 10 – Shrewsbury 40.*

🏨 **Lake Vyrnwy** ⤫, SY10 OLY, ℘ (01691) 870692, Fax (01691) 870259, ≤ Lake Vyrnwy, « Victorian sporting estate », 🍴, 🐎, park, 🛇 – ⥂ rest, 📺 ☎ 🅿 – 🔬 120. 🕻 🖭 ① *VISA*
**Meals** *(lunch booking essential)* 16.95/27.50 **t.** ≬ 6.25 – **34 rm** 🖃 75.00/170.00 **t.**, 1 suite – SB.

---

**ALESTON** *Bridgend* 403 J 29 – *see Bridgend.*

---

**AMPHEY** *Pembrokeshire* 403 F 28 – *see Pembroke.*

---

**ANGSTONE** *Newport* 403 L 29 – *see Newport.*

---

**ETTERSTON** *Pembrokeshire* 403 F 28 – *see Fishguard.*

---

**LANARMON DYFFRYN CEIRIOG** *Wrexham* 402 403 K 25 – ⊠ *Llangollen (Denbighshire).*

*London 196 – Chester 33 – Shrewsbury 32.*

🏦 **West Arms**, LL20 7LD, ℘ (01691) 600665, Fax (01691) 600622, « Part 16C », 🍴, 🐎 – 📺 ☎ 🅿 – 🔬 30. 🕻 *VISA* JCB
**Meals** *(bar lunch Monday to Saturday)/dinner* 17.50 **st.** ≬ 5.25 – **11 rm** 🖃 40.00/70.00 **st.**, 1 suite – SB.

---

**LANBEDR** *Gwynedd* 402 403 H 25 *Wales G. – pop. 1 101.*

Env. : *Snowdonia National Park★★★.*

*London 262 – Holyhead 54 – Shrewsbury 100.*

🏠 **Pensarn Hall** ⤫, LL45 2HS, North : ¾ m. on A 496 ℘ (01341) 241236, ≤, 🐎 – ⥂ 📺 🅿. 🕻 *VISA*. 🛇
*15 March-October* – **Meals** *(residents only) (dinner only)* 13.50 – **7 rm** 🖃 30.00/52.00 **s.** – SB.

---

**LLANBERIS** *Gwynedd* 403 H 24 *Wales G. – pop. 1 986.*

See : *Town★ – Welsh Slate Museum★ AC – Power of Wales★.*

Env. : *Snowdonia National Park★★★ (Snowdon★★★, Snowdon Mountain Railway★★ AC – panorama★★★).*

🛈 *41a High St., LL55 4EO* ℘ *(01286) 870765.*

*London 243 – Caernarfon 7 – Chester 65 – Shrewsbury 78.*

🍴🍴 **Y Bistro**, 43-45 High St., LL55 4EU, ℘ (01286) 871278, Fax (01286) 871278 – ⥂. 🕻 🖭 *VISA* JCB
*restricted opening in winter* – **Meals** *(booking essential) (dinner only)* 23.50 **t.** ≬ 4.50.

---

**LLANDEGLA** *Denbighshire* 402 403 K 24 – ⊠ *Wrexham.*

*London 201 – Birkenhead 31 – Caernarfon 66 – Chester 22 – Llandudno 43 – Shrewsbury 40.*

🏦 **Bodidris Hall** ⤫, LL11 3AL, Northeast : 1 ½ m. on A 5104 ℘ (01978) 790434, Fax (01978) 790335, « 15C manor of 12C origins », 🍴, 🐎, park – ⥂ rest, 📺 ☎ 🅿 – 🔬 50. 🕻 🖭 ① *VISA* JCB
**Meals** 16.00/30.00 **t.** ≬ 8.50 – **9 rm** 🖃 80.00/140.00 **t.** – SB.

---

**LLANDEGLEY** *Powys* 403 K 27 – *see Llandrindod Wells.*

**LLANDEILO** *Carmarthenshire* [403] I 28 *Wales G. – pop. 850.*

See : *Town★ – Dinefwr Park★ AC.*

Env. : *Brecon Beacons National Park★★ – Black Mountain★, SE : by minor roads – Carre Cennen Castle★ AC, SE : 4 m. by A 483 and minor roads.*

⛳18 *Glynhir, Glynhir Rd, Llandybie, Ammanford ☎ (01269) 850472.*

*London 218 – Brecon 34 – Carmarthen 15 – Swansea 25.*

🏨 **Plough Inn,** Rhosmaen, SA19 6NP, North : 1 m. on A 40 ☎ (01558) 823431 *Fax (01558) 823969,* ←, 🏋, 🏊 – 🚭 rm, 📺 ☎ ♿ 🅿 – 🎤 45. [MC] [AE] [VISA] [JCB]. ✗ *closed 25 December* – **Meals** (bar meals Sunday dinner) a la carte 16.95/28.25 **t.** 🍷 6.00 – ☕ 5.50 – **12 rm** 47.50/70.00 **t.**

🔧 ATS Towy Terr., Ffairfach ☎ (01558) 822567

**LLANDRILLO** *Denbighshire* [402] [403] J 25 – *pop. 1 048* – ✉ *Corwen.*

*London 210 – Chester 40 – Dolgellau 26 – Shrewsbury 46.*

🏨 **Tyddyn Llan Country House** 🌿, LL21 0ST, ☎ (01490) 440264, *Fax (01490) 440414* « Part Georgian country house, gardens », 🎣 – 🚭 rest, 📺 ☎ 🅿. [MC] [AE] [D] [VISA] [JCB] **Meals** *(closed Monday lunch)* 15.00/25.00 **t.** 🍷 9.00 – **10 rm** ☕ (dinner included) 105.00/190.00 **t.** – SB.

**LLANDRINDOD WELLS** *Powys* [403] J 27 *Wales G. – pop. 4 943.*

Exc. : *Elan Valley★★ (Dol-y-Mynach and Claerwen Dam and Reservoir★★, Caban Coch Dam and Reservoir★, Garreg-ddu Viaduct★, Pen-y-Garreg Reservoir and Dam★, Craig Goch Dam and Reservoir★), NW : 12 m. by A 4081, A 470 and B 4518.*

⛳18 *Llandrindod Wells ☎ (01597) 822010/823873.*

ℹ *Old Town Hall, Memorial Gardens, LD1 5DL ☎ (01597) 822600.*

*London 204 – Brecon 29 – Carmarthen 60 – Shrewsbury 58.*

🏨 **Metropole,** Temple St., LD1 5DY, ☎ (01597) 823700, *Fax (01597) 824828,* 🏊, 🏊, 🌳 – 🛗 🚭 rest, 📺 ☎ 📞 🅿 – 🎤 300. [MC] [AE] [VISA] **Meals** 9.95/17.95 **st.** 🍷 4.95 – **120 rm** ☕ 67.00/88.00 **st.**, 2 suites – SB.

🏠 **Charis** without rest., Pentrosfa, LD1 5AL, South : ¾ m. by A 483 ☎ (01597) 824732 *Fax (01597) 824732,* 🌳 – 🚭 📺 🅿 *closed 24 December-2 January* – **3 rm** ☕ 17.50/32.00 **t.**

**at Crossgates** *Northeast : 3½ m. on A 483 –* ✉ *Llandrindod Wells.*

🏠 **Guidfa House,** LD1 6RF, ☎ (01597) 851241, *Fax (01597) 851875,* 🌳 – 🚭 📺 🅿. [MC] [VISA] ✗ **Meals** (by arrangement) 16.50 **st.** 🍷 4.95 – **7 rm** ☕ 25.00/50.00 **st.** – SB.

**at Llandegley** *East : 7 m. by A 483 on A 44 –* ✉ *Llandrindod Wells.*

🏠 **Ffaldau Country House,** LD1 5UD, ☎ (01597) 851421, *Fax (01597) 851421,* « 16C origins », 🌳 – 🚭 🅿. [MC] [VISA]. ✗ **Meals** (by arrangement) 15.00 🍷 5.50 – **4 rm** ☕ 32.00/48.00.

**at Howey** *South : 1½ m. by A 483 –* ✉ *Llandrindod Wells.*

🏠 **Holly Farm** 🌿, Holly Lane, LD1 5PP, off A 483 ☎ (01597) 822402, « Working farm », 🌳 park – 🚭 rest, 📺 🅿. [VISA]. ✗ *April-November* – **Meals** (by arrangement) 10.00 **st.** – **5 rm** ☕ 22.00/38.00 **st.** – SB.

🏠 **Brynhir Farm** 🌿, Chapel Rd, LD1 5PB, Northeast : 1 m. ☎ (01597) 822425 *Fax (01597) 822425,* ←, « Working farm », 🎣, 🌳, park – 📺 🅿. [MC] [VISA]. ✗ **Meals** (by arrangement) 9.00 🍷 4.00 – **6 rm** ☕ 20.00/40.00 – SB.

🔧 ATS Waterloo Road Ind Est., Waterloo Rd ☎ (01597) 874874

**LLANDUDNO** *Conwy* [402] [403] I 24 *Wales G. – pop. 18 647.*

See : *Town★ – Seafront★ (Pier★)* B – *The Great Orme★ (panorama★★, Tramway★, Ancient Copper Mines★ AC)* AB.

Exc. : *Bodnant Garden★★ AC, S : 7 m. by A 470* B.

⛳18 *Rhos-on-Sea, Penrhyn Bay ☎ (01492) 549641,* A – ⛳18 *72 Bryniau Rd, West Shore ☎ (01492) 875325* A – ⛳18 *Hospital Rd ☎ (01492) 876450* B.

ℹ *1-2 Chapel St., LL30 2YU ☎ (01492) 876413.*

*London 243 – Birkenhead 55 – Chester 47 – Holyhead 43.*

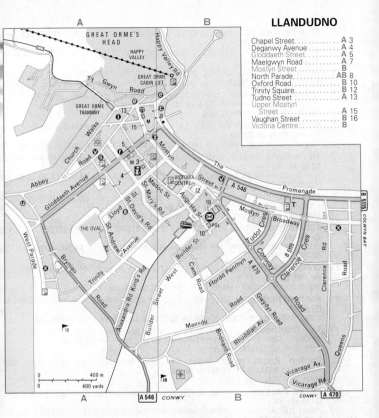

## LLANDUDNO

| | |
|---|---|
| Chapel Street | A 3 |
| Deganwy Avenue | A 4 |
| Gloddaeth Street | A 5 |
| Maelgwyn Road | A 7 |
| Mostyn Street | B |
| North Parade | AB 8 |
| Oxford Road | B 10 |
| Trinity Square | B 12 |
| Tudno Street | A 13 |
| Upper Mostyn Street | A 15 |
| Vaughan Street | B 16 |
| Victoria Centre | B |

**Bodysgallen Hall** ⊗, LL30 1RS, Southeast : 2 m. on A 470 ℰ (01492) 584466, *Fax (01492) 582519*, ≼ gardens and mountains, « Part 17C and 18C hall with terraced gardens », ℔, ≋, ▨, park, ℀ – ⋈ rest, 🆃🆅 ☎ ☏ ☉ – 🔬 50. 🆀🆂 🆅🅸🆂🅰 🅹🅲🅱. ℀
**Meals** (booking essential) 15.50/29.50 **st.** ⅃ 10.75 – ☲ 11.50 – **19 rm** 100.00/210.00 **st.**, 16 suites 165.00/210.00 **st.** – SB.

**Imperial,** The Promenade, LL30 1AP, ℰ (01492) 877466, *Fax (01492) 878043*, ℔, ≋, ▨ – ▯ 🆃🆅 ☎ ☉ – 🔬 150. 🆀🆂 🅰🅴 🆅🅸🆂🅰                                                    B  v
**Meals** 12.00/20.00 **st.** ⅃ 7.00 – **96 rm** ☲ 65.00/115.00 **t.**, 4 suites – SB.

**Empire,** 73 Church Walks, LL30 2HE, ℰ (01492) 860555, *Fax (01492) 860791*, « Collection of Russell Flint prints », ≋, ▨, ▨ – ▯, ⊟ rest, 🆃🆅 ☎ ☏ ☉ – 🔬 40. 🆀🆂 🅰🅴 🅾 🆅🅸🆂🅰 🅹🅲🅱.
℀                                                                                                        A  e
*closed 19 to 29 December –* **Watkins and Co. : Meals** (dinner only and Saturday and Sunday lunch)/dinner 25.50 **st.** ⅃ 8.50 – (see also *Empire (No. 72)* below) – **43 rm** ☲ 55.00/110.00 **st.** – SB.

**Empire (No. 72)** (at Empire H.), 72 Church Walks, LL30 2HE, ℰ (01492) 860555, *Fax (01492) 860791*, « Victoriana » – ⊟ 🆃🆅 ☎ ☉. 🆀🆂 🅰🅴 🅾 🆅🅸🆂🅰 🅹🅲🅱. ℀      A  e
*closed 19 to 29 December –* **8 rm** ☲ 55.00/120.00 **st.** – SB.

**St. Tudno,** North Par., LL30 2LP, ℰ (01492) 874411, *Fax (01492) 860407*, ≼, ▨ – ▯ 🆃🆅 ☎.
🆀🆂 🅰🅴 🅾 🆅🅸🆂🅰 🅹🅲🅱. ℀                                                                             A  c
**Meals** – (see *Garden Room* below) – **19 rm** ☲ 75.00/198.00 **st.**, 1 suite – SB.

**Dunoon,** Gloddaeth St., LL30 2DW, ℰ (01492) 860787, *Fax (01492) 860031*, ☞ – ▯ 🆃🆅 ☎
☉. 🆀🆂 🅰🅴 🆅🅸🆂🅰                                                                                      A  r
*mid March-mid November –* **Meals** 9.50/15.00 **st.** and dinner a la carte ⅃ 6.00 – **55 rm** ☲ 42.00/84.00 – SB.

**Bedford,** Promenade, Craig-y-Don, LL30 1BN, East : 1 m. on B 5115 ℰ (01492) 876647, *Fax (01492) 860185* – ▯ 🆃🆅 ☉. 🆀🆂 🅰🅴 🅾 🆅🅸🆂🅰
**Gigolos : Meals** – Italian – 12.00 **st.** and a la carte ⅃ 5.00 – **27 rm** ☲ 28.00/50.00 **st.** – SB.

783

🏠 **Bryn Derwen,** 34 Abbey Rd, LL30 2EE, &#x260E; (01492) 876804, *Fax (01492) 876804*, ☎, ≉
✦ TV P. ⑩ VISA. ✆
A
*March-October* – **Meals** *(closed Sunday)* (dinner only) 18.00 **st.** ₳ 4.95 – **9 rm** ⚏ 40.00
70.00.

🏠 **Wilton,** 14 South Par., LL30 2LN, &#x260E; (01492) 876086, *Fax (01492) 876086* – TV ☎
*March-November* – **Meals** (dinner only) 10.00 **t.** ₳ 3.50 – **14 rm** ⚏ 24.00/48.00. AB

🏠 **Travel Inn,** Glan Conwy Corner, LL28 5LB, Southeast : 4 m. by A 470 &#x260E; (01582) 414341
*Fax (01582) 400024* – ✦ rm, TV &#x267F; P. ⑩ AE ① VISA. ✆
**Meals** (grill rest.) – **40 rm** 38.00.

🏠 **Belle Vue,** 26 North Par., LL30 2LP, &#x260E; (01492) 879547, *Fax (01492) 870001,* ≼ – ▮
✦ rest, TV ☎ P. ⑩ VISA
B
*February-November* – **Meals** (dinner only) 12.00 **st.** ₳ 7.50 – **15 rm** ⚏ 25.50/55.00 **st.** – SB

🏠 **Sunnymede,** West Par., West Shore, LL30 2BD, &#x260E; (01492) 877130, *Fax (01492) 871824 -*
TV P. ⑩ VISA JCB
A
*April-October* – **Meals** (bar lunch)/dinner 14.95 **st.** and a la carte ₳ 3.50 – **16 rm** ⚏ (dinne
included) 38.00/80.00. **st.** – SB.

🏠 **Tan Lan,** 14 Great Orme's Rd, West Shore, LL30 2AR, &#x260E; (01492) 860221
*Fax (01492) 870219* – ✦ rest, TV P. ⑩ VISA JCB
A
**Meals** (bar lunch)/dinner 15.00 **t.** – **17 rm** ⚏ 40.00/82.00 **t.** – SB.

⌂ **Epperstone,** 15 Abbey Rd, LL30 2EE, &#x260E; (01492) 878746, *Fax (01492) 871223* – ✦ TV ☎
P. ⑩ VISA
A
*closed January-mid February* – **Meals** (by arrangement) 16.00 **st.** ₳ 4.50 – **8 rm** ⚏ 30.00
60.00. **st.** – SB.

⌂ **Craiglands,** 7 Carmen Sylva Rd, LL30 1LZ, East : 1 m. by B 5115 &#x260E; (01492) 875090 -
✦ rest, TV. ✆
*March-mid November* – **Meals** 10.50 – **6 rm** ⚏ 20.00/46.00 – SB.

⌂ **Banham House,** 2 St. David's Rd, LL30 2UL, &#x260E; (01492) 875680, *Fax (01492) 875680* – ✦
TV P. ✆
A
*closed 31 December-4 January* – **Meals** 10.50 **st.** ₳ 5.50 – **6 rm** ⚏ 30.00/50.00 **st.**

⌂ **The Lighthouse** ⌂ without rest., Marine Drive, Great Orme's Head, LL30 2XD
&#x260E; (01492) 876819, ≼, « Converted Victorian lighthouse » – ✦ TV P. ✆
**2 rm** ⚏ 89.00/95.00 **st.**, 1 suite.

XX **Garden Room** (at St. Tudno H.), North Par., LL30 2LP, &#x260E; (01492) 874411
*Fax (01492) 860407* – ✦ ▤. ⑩ AE ① VISA JCB
A
**Meals** 16.95/25.00 **st.** ₳ 7.00.

XX **Martin's** with rm, 11 Mostyn Av., LL30 1YS, &#x260E; (01492) 870070, *Fax (01492) 866671,* ░ –
⑩ AE VISA. ✆
B
*closed 2 weeks January* – **Meals** (booking essential) 12.50/15.95 **t.** and a la carte ₳ 6.90 –
**4 rm** ⚏ 35.00/50.00 **t.** – SB.

X **Richard's Bistro,** 7 Church Walks, LL30 2HD, &#x260E; (01492) 877924 – ⑩ AE ① VISA A
**Meals** (dinner only) a la carte 16.90/25.85 **st.** ₳ 4.95.

X **Number 1's Bistro,** 1 Old Rd, LL30 2HA, &#x260E; (01492) 875424, *Fax (01492) 875424* – ⑩ AE
VISA JCB
A
*closed Monday lunch and Sunday* – **Meals** 16.95 **st.** (dinner) and a la carte 14.00/23.85 **st.**
₳ 6.95.

▯ **Queens Head,** Glanwydden, LL31 9JP, Southeast : 2 ½ m. by A 470 and Goddaeth ro
(Penrhyn Bay rd) &#x260E; (01492) 546570 – P. ⑩ VISA
*closed 25 December* – **Meals** a la carte 12.40/21.95 **t.** ₳ 5.50.

**at Deganwy** South : 2 ¾ m. on A 546 – A – ✉ Llandudno.

X **Paysanne,** Station Rd, LL31 9EJ, &#x260E; (01492) 582079, *Fax (01492) 583848* – ⑩ VISA
*closed Sunday, Monday and 25 December* – **Meals** (booking essential) (dinner only) 15.00 **t.**
₳ 5.80.

---

**LLANERCHYMEDD** *Anglesey* 402 403 G 24 *Wales G..*

Env. : *Anglesey★★.*
*London 262 – Bangor 18 – Caernarfon 23 – Holyhead 15.*

⌂ **Llwydiarth Fawr** ⌂, LL71 8DF, North : 1 m. on B 5111 &#x260E; (01248) 470321, ≼, « Georgian farmhouse », ⌔, *park* – ✦ TV P. ⑩ VISA. ✆
*closed 25 December* – **Meals** (by arrangement) 12.50 **st.** – **4 rm** ⚏ 25.00/50.00 **st.**, 1 suite
– SB.

⌂ **Drws-Y-Coed** ⌂, LL71 8AD, East : 1 ½ m. by B 5111 on Benllech rd &#x260E; (01248) 470473,
*Fax (01247) 470473,* ≼, ⌔, *park* – ✦ TV P. ⑩ VISA. ✆
*closed Christmas* – **Meals** (by arrangement) 12.50 **s.** – **3 rm** ⚏ 26.00/47.00.

**LLANFACHRETH** *Gwynedd* 402 403 I 25 – see Dolgellau.

---

**LLANFIHANGEL** *Powys* 402 403 J 25 – see Llanfyllin.

---

**LLANFIHANGEL CRUCORNEY** *Monmouthshire* 403 L 28 – see Abergavenny.

---

**LLANFIHANGEL-NANT-MELAN** *Powys Wales G.*.
    **Env.** : Old Radnor (St. Stephen's Church★), E : 6 m. by A 44 and minor rd.
    London 180 – Brecon 20 – Carmarthen 40 – Shrewsbury 74.

    **Red Lion** with rm, LD8 2TN, on A 44 $\mathscr{P}$ (01544) 350220, Fax (01544) 350220 – ⇔ ❄ **P**. **①③**
    **VISA JCB**
    closed 26 December, Tuesday and 1 week November – **Meals** (dinner only and Sunday lunch)/dinner a la carte 13.15/17.15 **t.** – 3 rm ⊇ 20.00/40.00 **st.**

---

**LLANFYLLIN** *Powys* 402 403 K 25 *Wales G.* – pop. 1 267.
    **Exc.** : Pistyll Rhaeadr★, NW : 8 m. by A 490, B 4391, B 4580 and minor roads.
    London 188 – Chester 42 – Shrewsbury 24 – Welshpool 11.

    ✕ **Seeds,** 5 Penybryn Cottages, High St., SY22 5AP, $\mathscr{P}$ (01691) 648604, « 16C cottages », 🚗
        – ❄ **①③** **VISA**
        closed Sunday dinner and Monday in winter, 2 weeks January-February and 1 week November – **Meals** 18.95 **t.** (dinner) and lunch a la carte 13.00/16.20 **t.** ⅆ 6.25.

**at Llanfihangel** Southwest : 5 m. by A 490 and B 4393 on B 4382 – ✉ Llanfyllin.

    ☖ **Cyfie Farm** ⌖, SY22 5JE, South : 1 ½ m. by B 4382 $\mathscr{P}$ (01691) 648451,
        Fax (01691) 648451, ≤ Meifod valley, « Restored 17C longhouse, working farm », 🚗, park
        – ❄ rm, **TV** **P**. ✀
        closed Christmas – **Meals** (by arrangement) (communal dining) 13.50 **st.** – 1 rm ⊇ 23.50/
        55.00 **st.**, 3 suites 53.00/55.00 **st.** – SB.

---

**LLANGAMMARCH WELLS** *Powys* 403 J 27.
    London 200 – Brecon 17 – Builth Wells 8.

    ▲▲▲ **Lake Country House** ⌖, LD4 4BS, East : ¾ m. $\mathscr{P}$ (01591) 620202, Fax (01591) 620457,
        ≤, « Victorian country house in extensive grounds », ⅄, ☍, 🚗, ✕, – ❄ **TV** ☎ 🕿 **P** –
        🔼 30. **①③** **AE** **①** **VISA JCB**
        **Meals** 17.50/30.00 **st.** ⅆ 5.45 – 9 rm ⊇ 85.00/135.00 **st.**, 10 suites 165.00 **st.** – SB.

---

**LLANGENNY** *Powys* 403 K 28 – see Crickhowell.

---

**LLANGOLLEN** *Denbighshire* 402 403 K 25 *Wales G.* – pop. 3 267.
    **See** : Town★ – Railway★ *AC* – Plas Newydd★ *AC*.
    **Env.** : Pontcysyllte Aqueduct★★, E : 4 m. by A 539 – Castell Dinas Bran★, N : by footpath –
    Valle Crucis Abbey★ *AC*, N : 2 m. by A 542.
    **Exc.** : Chirk Castle★★ *AC* (wrought iron gates★), SE : 7 ½ m. by A 5 – Rug Chapel★ *AC*,
    W : 11 m. by A 5 and A 494.
    ⛳ Vale of Llangollen, Holyhead Rd $\mathscr{P}$ (01978) 860613.
    🛈 Town Hall, Castle St., LL20 5PD $\mathscr{P}$ (01978) 860828.
    London 194 – Chester 23 – Holyhead 76 – Shrewsbury 30.

    ▲▲ **Bryn Howel,** LL20 7UW, East : 2 ¾ m. on A 539 $\mathscr{P}$ (01978) 860331, Fax (01978) 860119, ≤,
        ⇔s, ☍, 🚗 – ⅋ **TV** ☎ **P** – 🔼 300. **①③** **AE** **VISA JCB**
        **Cedar Tree :** Meals a la carte 22.45/28.00 **t.** ⅆ 8.00 – ⊇ 9.00 – 35 rm 71.50/90.00 **t.**, 1 suite
        – SB.

    ▲▲ **Royal,** Bridge St., LL20 8PG, $\mathscr{P}$ (01978) 860202, Fax (01978) 861824, ≤, ☍ – ❄ **TV** ☎ **P** –
        🔼 60. **①③** **AE** **①** **VISA**
        **Meals** (bar lunch Monday to Saturday)/dinner 15.95 **st.** ⅆ 8.95 – ⊇ 9.25 – 33 rm 55.00/
        75.00 **t.** – SB.

    ☖ **Gales Wine Bar,** 18 Bridge St., LL20 8PF, $\mathscr{P}$ (01978) 860089, Fax (01978) 861313 –
        ❄ rm, **TV** ☎ **P**. **①③** **AE** **①** **VISA JCB**. ✀
        closed 25 December-2 January – **Meals** (closed Sunday) (in bar) a la carte 9.60/15.90 **t.**
        ⅆ 4.00 – 13 rm ⊇ 38.00/50.00 **t.**, 2 suites.

↑ **Hillcrest**, Hill St., LL20 8EU, ℘ (01978) 860208, Fax (01978) 860208 – ✻ 🔟 🅿. ℅
closed 25 December – **Meals** 12.00 st. – **7 rm** ⇌ 35.00/45.00 st.

↑ **Oakmere** without rest., Regent St., LL20 8HS, on A 5 ℘ (01978) 861126, 🐾, ℅ – ✻ 🔟
🅿. ℅
**6 rm** ⇌ 35.00/45.00 st.

---

**LLANGYBI** Monmouthshire 403 L 28/29 – see Usk.

---

**LLANIGON** Powys 403 K 27 – see Hay-on-Wye.

---

**LLANNEFYDD** Conwy 402 403 J 24 – pop. 567 – ⊠ Denbigh (Denbighshire).
London 225 – Chester 37 – Shrewsbury 63.

🏠 **Hawk and Buckle Inn**, LL16 5ED, ℘ (01745) 540249, Fax (01745) 540316, ≼, « Part 18C
coaching inn » – ✻ 🔟 ☎ 🅿. 🆎 VISA JCB. ℅
**Meals** (closed Sunday and Monday) (bar lunch)/dinner a la carte 13.55/18.85 st. ₰ 5.25 –
**10 rm** ⇌ 40.00/55.00 st. – SB.

---

**LLANRHIDIAN** Swansea 403 H 29 – see Swansea.

---

*Per spostarvi più rapidamente utilizzate le* **carte Michelin "Grandi Strade"**
*n°* **970** *Europa, n°* **976** *Rep. Ceca/Slovacchia, n°* **980** *Grecia,*
*n°* **984** *Germania, n°* **985** *Scandinavia-Finlandia,*
*n°* **986** *Gran Bretagna-Irlanda, n°* **987** *Germania-Austria-Benelux,*
*n°* **988** *Italia, n°* **989** *Francia, n°* **990** *Spagna-Portogallo.*

---

**LLANRWST** Conwy 402 403 I 24 Wales G. – pop. 3 012.
Env. : Snowdonia National Park★★★.
London 230 – Holyhead 50 – Shrewsbury 66.

🏠 **Hafod Country H.**, Trefriw, LL27 0RQ, Northwest : 2 m. on B 5106 ℘ (01492) 640029,
Fax (01492) 641351, 🐾 – ✻ 🔟 ☎ 🅿. 🆎 VISA. ℅
closed 10 January-11 February – **Meals** (closed Tuesday lunch) 9.00/17.75 t. ₰ 4.75 – **7 rm**
⇌ (dinner included) ⇌ 47.25/99.50 t. – SB.

---

**LLANSANFFRAID GLAN CONWY** Conwy 402 403 I24 Wales G. – pop. 2 194 – ⊠ Aberconwy
Env. : Snowdonia National Park★★★ – Bodnant Garden★★ AC, S : 2½ m. by A 470.
London 241 – Colwyn Bay 4 – Holyhead 42.

🏠 **Old Rectory** ⌖, Llanrwst Rd, LL28 5LF, on A 470 ℘ (01492) 580611, Fax (01492) 584555,
≼ Conwy estuary, « Georgian country house with antique furnishings », 🐾 – ✻ 🔟 ☎ 🅿
🆎 VISA JCB. ℅
February-November – **Meals** (set menu only) (booking essential) (dinner only) 25.00 st.
₰ 7.90 – **6 rm** ⇌ 129.00/149.00 st. – SB.

---

**LLANTRISANT** Monmouthshire 403 L 28 – pop. 9 136 (inc. Pontyclun) – ⊠ Usk.
London 148 – Bristol 34 – Gloucester 43 – Newport 8.

🏠 **Greyhound Inn**, NP5 1LE, Northeast : ½ m. on Usk rd ℘ (01291) 672505,
Fax (01291) 673255, 🐾 – ✻ 🔟 ☎ ✆ ₺ 🅿. 🆎 VISA. ℅
closed 24 and 25 December – **Meals** (closed Sunday dinner) a la carte 11.30/18.20 t. ₰ 5.00
– **10 rm** ⇌ 48.00/62.00 t.

---

**LLANTWIT MAJOR** Vale of Glamorgan 403 J 29 – pop. 12 909.
London 175 – Cardiff 18 – Swansea 33.

🏠 **West House Country**, West St., CF61 1SP, ℘ (01446) 792406, Fax (01446) 796147, 🐾 –
✻ rest, 🔟 ☎ 🅿. 🆎 AE VISA
closed 26 December – **Meals** (lunch booking essential) 15.50 t. (dinner) and a la carte
17.45/21.70 st. ₰ 4.25 – **21 rm** ⇌ 49.50/69.50 t. – SB.

---

**LLANWENARTH** Monmouthshire – see Abergavenny.

**LLANWRTYD WELLS** *Powys* 403 J 27 *Wales G. – pop. 649.*

**Exc.** : *Abergwesyn-Tregaron Mountain Road*★, *NW : 19 m. on minor roads.*

*London 214 – Brecon 32 – Carmarthen 39.*

**Lasswade Country House**, Station Rd, LD5 4RW, ☎ (01591) 610515, *Fax (01591) 610611*, ≤, ≘s, ☜, ☞ – ⇔ TV ☎ P. MC VISA JCB

**Meals** (dinner only) 16.95 **t.** and a la carte 4.95 – **8 rm** ☐ 32.50/59.00 **t.** – SB.

**Carlton House** with rm, Dolycoed Rd, LD5 4RA, ☎ (01591) 610248, *Fax (01591) 610242* – ⇔ rest, TV. MC VISA JCB

*closed 20 to 30 December* – **Meals** *(closed Monday lunch)* (booking essential to non-residents) 12.50/19.95 **t.** and a la carte 23.50/32.70 **t.** 5.00 – **6 rm** ☐ 30.00/75.00 **t.** – SB.

**LLWYNGWRIL** *Gwynedd* 402 403 H 25 *Wales G.* – ✉ *Dolgellau.*

**Env.** : *Snowdonia National Park*★★★.

*London 226 – Aberystwyth 44 – Birkenhead 80 – Chester 72 – Shrewsbury 67.*

**Pentre Bach** ⛰, LL37 2JU, ☎ (01341) 250294, *Fax (01341) 250885*, ≤, ☞ – ⇔ TV P. MC VISA JCB. ⛌

*closed November and 17 December-2 January* – **Meals** (by arrangement) 14.95 – **3 rm** ☐ 28.00/54.00.

**LLYSWEN** *Powys* 403 K 27 *Wales G.* – ✉ *Brecon.*

**Env.** : *Brecon Beacons National Park*★★.

*London 188 – Brecon 8 – Cardiff 48 – Worcester 53.*

**Llangoed Hall** ⛰, LD3 0YP, Northwest : 1 ¼ m. on A 470 ☎ (01874) 754525, *Fax (01874) 754545*, ≤, « Edwardian mansion by Sir Clough Williams-Ellis of 17C origins », ☜, ☞, park, ⚔ – ⇔ rest, TV ☎ P – 🔺 50. MC AE ⓓ VISA JCB. ⛌

**Meals** (booking essential to non-residents) 18.00/35.00 **t.** and a la carte 36.50/43.00 **t.** 11.00 – **20 rm** ☐ 270.00/300.00 **t.**, 3 suites – SB

**Spec.** Rabbit stuffed with wild mushrooms, cep risotto and tarragon sauce. Salmon with shrimp mousse, braised leeks and herb linguine. Milk chocolate parfait, dark chocolate ice cream.

**Griffin Inn** with rm, LD3 0UR, on A 470 ☎ (01874) 754241, *Fax (01874) 754592*, « Part 15C », ☜, ☞ – ⇔ rest, TV ☎ P. MC AE ⓓ VISA JCB

*closed 25 and 26 December* – **Meals** (Sunday dinner residents only) (bar lunch Monday to Saturday)/dinner 15.00 **t.** and a la carte 6.75 – **7 rm** ☐ 40.00/80.00 **t.** – SB.

**MACHYNLLETH** *Powys* 402 403 I 26 *Wales G. – pop. 2 033.*

**See** : *Town*★ – *Celtica*★ *AC.*

**Env.** : *Snowdonia National Park*★★★ – *Centre for Alternative Technology*★★ *AC, N : 3 m. by A 487.*

⛳9 *Ffordd Drenewydd* ☎ *(01654) 702000.*

ℹ *Canolfan Owain Glyndwr, SY20 8EE* ☎ *(01654) 702401.*

*London 220 – Shrewsbury 56 – Welshpool 37.*

**Ynyshir Hall** ⛰, Eglwysfach, SY20 8TA, Southwest : 6 m. on A 487 ☎ (01654) 781209, *Fax (01654) 781366*, ≤, « Part Georgian country house, gardens », park – ⇔ TV ☎ P. MC AE ⓓ VISA JCB. ⛌

*closed 5 to 20 January* – **Meals** (booking essential) 21.00/33.00 **st.** 8.00 – **6 rm** ☐ 95.00/175.00 **st.**, 2 suites – SB.

**MAGOR SERVICE AREA** *Newport* 403 L 29 – ✉ *Newport (Newport).*

ℹ *First Services & Lodge, Junction 23a, M 4, NP6 3YL* ☎ *(01633) 881122.*

**Comfort Inn** without rest., NP6 3YL, M 4 junction 23A ☎ (01633) 881887, *Fax (01633) 881896* – ⇔ TV ☎ ♿ P. MC AE ⓓ VISA. ⛌

☐ 6.95 – **43 rm** 44.95 **st.**

**MERTHYR TYDFIL** 403 J 28 *Wales G. – pop. 59 317.*

**Env.** : *Brecon Beacons National Park*★★.

**Exc.** : *Ystradfellte*★, *NW : 13 m. by A 4102, A 465, A 4059 and minor roads.*

⛳18 *Morlais Castle, Pant, Dowlais* ☎ *(01685) 722822* – ⛳9 *Cilsanws Mountain, Cefn Coed* ☎ *(01685) 723308.*

ℹ *14a Glebeland St., CF47 8AU* ☎ *(01685) 379884.*

*London 179 – Cardiff 25 – Gloucester 59 – Swansea 33.*

🏠 **Tregenna,** Park Terr., CF47 8RF, ℰ (01685) 723627, Fax (01685) 721951 – 📺 🕾 **P.** 🕮 *L* ⓪ *VISA* JCB
Meals 9.65 **t.** and a la carte ⍮ 4.80 – **24 rm** ⌑ 45.00/57.00 **t.** – SB.

🏠 **Travel Inn,** Pentrebach, CF48 4BD, South : 2 ½ m. by A 470 ℰ (01443) 69361●
Fax (01443) 690188 – 쓱 rm, 🗏 rest, 🕾 ₲ **P.** 🕮 ⒶⒺ ⓪ *VISA*. ⌇
Meals (grill rest.) – **40 rm** 38.00 **t.**

**at Cwm Taf** *Northwest : 6 m. on A 470 –* ⊠ *Merthyr Tydfil.*

🏠🏠 **Nant Ddu Lodge,** CF48 2HY, on A 470 ℰ (01685) 379111, Fax (01685) 377088, 🐎 – [🖫
🕾 ℂ **P.** 🕮 ⒶⒺ *VISA*
closed 1 week Christmas – **Meals** (in bar Monday to Saturday lunch) a la carte 13.15/22.85 ●
⍮ 4.95 – **22 rm** ⌑ 50.00/77.50 **t.**

ⓜ ATS Dowlais Ind Est. ℰ (01685) 385872

---

**MISKIN** *Rhondda Cynon Taff* **403** *J 29 –* ⊠ *Cardiff.*
*London 169 – Cardiff 22 – Swansea 31.*

🏠🏠🏠 **Miskin Manor,** CF72 8ND, East : 1 ¾ m. by A 4119 (Groesfaen rd) ℰ (01443) 224204
Fax (01443) 237606, ≼, « Part 17C manor house », Ⅰ₅, ☎s, 🖳, 🐎, park, squash – 쓱 rest
📺 🕾 ₲ **P.** – 🔬 170. 🕮 ⒶⒺ ⓪ *VISA*. ⌇
Meals (closed Saturday lunch) 22.95 **t.** and a la carte ⍮ 6.95 – **42 rm** ⌑ 95.00/130.00 **t**
1 suite – SB.

*La guida cambia, cambiate la guida ogni anno.*

---

**MOLD** (Yr Wyddgrug) *Flintshire* **402 403** *K 24 Wales G. – pop. 9 168.*
**See :** *St. Mary's Church★.*

ⓖ Pantmwyn ℰ (01352) 740318/741513 – ⓖ, ⓖ Old Padeswood, Station Rd ℰ (01244)
547401 – ⓖ Padeswood & Buckley, The Caia, Station Lane, Padeswood ℰ (01244) 550537 –
ⓖ Caerwys ℰ (01352) 720692.
🖪 *Library, Museum and Art Gallery, Earl Rd, CH7 1AP ℰ (01352) 759331 (summer only).*
*London 211 – Chester 12 – Liverpool 29 – Shrewsbury 45.*

🏠🏠🏠 **Soughton Hall** ⤸, CH7 6AB, North : 2 ½ m. by A 5119 and Alltami rd ℰ (01352) 840811
Fax (01352) 840382, ≼, « Early 18C italianate mansion », 🐎, ⌇ – 쓱 rest, 📺 🕾 ₲ **P.** 🕮 Ⓐ
*VISA*. ⌇
Meals (dinner only) 32.50 **st.** and a la carte ⍮ 6.95 – (see also **The Stables** below) – **14 rm**
⌑ 80.00/150.00 **st.** – SB.

🏠 **Tower** ⤸ without rest., Nercwys, CH7 4ED, South : 1 m. by B 5444 and Nercwys rd
ℰ (01352) 700220, « 15C fortified house », 🐎, park – 📺 ₲ **P.** 🕮 ⒶⒺ *VISA*. ⌇
closed 16 December-7 January – **3 rm** ⌑ 40.00/60.00.

❌ **The Stables** (at Soughton Hall H.), CH7 6AB, North : 2 ½ m. by A 5119 and Alltami Rd
ℰ (01352) 840577, Fax (01352) 840382, « Converted 17C stables » – **P.** 🕮 ⒶⒺ *VISA*
Meals a la carte 14.45/27.95 **st.** ⍮ 6.95.

ⓜ ATS Wrexham Rd ℰ (01352) 753682

---

**MONMOUTH** (Trefynwy) *Monmouthshire* **403** *L 28 Wales G. – pop. 8 204.*
**See :** *Town★.*
**Exc. :** *Raglan Castle★ AC, SW : 7 m. by A 40.*
ⓖ The Rolls of Monmouth, The Hendre ℰ (01600) 715353 – ⓖ Leasebrook Lane ℰ (01600
712212.
🖪 *Shire Hall, Agincourt Sq., NP5 3DY ℰ (01600) 713899 (summer only).*
*London 147 – Gloucester 26 – Newport 24 – Swansea 64.*

🏠 **Riverside,** Cinderhill St., NP5 3EY, ℰ (01600) 715577, Fax (01600) 712668 – 쓱 rest, 📺 🕾
**P.** – 🔬 120. 🕮 *VISA*
Meals (bar lunch)/dinner 12.95 **t.** – **16 rm** ⌑ 48.00/68.00 **t.** – SB.

**at Whitebrook** *Southeast : 8½ m. by A 466 –* ⊠ *Monmouth.*

❌❌ **Crown at Whitebrook** ⤸ with rm, NP5 4TX, ℰ (01600) 860254, Fax (01600) 860607
🐎 – 쓱 rest, 📺 🕾 ₲ **P.** 🕮 ⒶⒺ ⓪ *VISA* JCB
closed 2 weeks January, 2 weeks August and 25-26 December – **Meals** (closed Monday
lunch and Sunday dinner to non-residents) 16.95/28.95 **t.** and a la carte ⍮ 6.75 – **10 rm**
⌑ 50.00/80.00 **t.** – SB.

ⓜ ATS Wonastow Rd, Wonastow Ind. Est. ℰ (01600) 716832

**MONTGOMERY** (Trefaldwyn) Powys 403 K 26 Wales G. – pop. 1 059.
>   See : Town★.
>   London 194 – Birmingham 71 – Chester 53 – Shrewsbury 30.

🏠 **Dragon**, Town Square, SY15 6PA, ℘ (01686) 668359, Fax (01686) 668359, 🔍 – ¾ rm, 📺
>   ☎ 🅿. 🕮🕲 🗚 VISA JCB
>   Meals 10.75/17.25 **t.** and a la carte 🍴 4.50 – **20 rm** ☲ 44.00/74.00 **t.** – SB.

⌂ **Little Brompton Farm** ⟋ without rest., SY15 6HY, Southeast : 2 m. on B 4385
>   ℘ (01686) 668371, Fax (01686) 668371, « Working farm », park – ¾ 📺 🅿. ⁒
>   **3 rm** ☲ 22.00/44.00.

---

**MOYLGROVE** Pembrokeshire 403 F 27 – see Newport.

---

**MUMBLES (The)** Swansea 403 I 29 – see Swansea.

---

**NANNERCH** Flintshire 402 403 K 24 – pop. 513 – ⊠ Mold.
>   London 218 – Chester 19 – Liverpool 36 – Shrewsbury 52.

🏠 **Old Mill**, Melin-y-Wern, Denbigh Rd, CH7 5RH, Northwest : ¾ m. on A 541
>   ℘ (01352) 741542, Fax (01352) 740254, « Converted 19C corn mill and stables », 🚗 – ¾
>   📺 ☎ 🅿. 🕮🕲 🗚 ① VISA JCB
>   closed 1 week Christmas and restricted opening during winter – **Meals** (closed Monday to
>   Thursday) (residents only) (dinner only) 15.50 **st.** – **6 rm** ☲ 42.00/62.00 **st.** – SB.

>   *Great Britain and Ireland is now covered*
>   *by an Atlas at a scale of 1 inch to 4.75 miles.*
>   *Three easy to use versions: Paperback, Spiralbound and Hardback.*

---

**NEATH** (Castell-Ned) Neath Port Talbot 403 I 29 Wales G. – pop. 45 965.
>   Env. : Aberdulais Falls★ AC, NE : 2½ m. by B 4434 and A 4109.
>   🟦 Swansea Bay, Jersey Marine ℘ (01792) 812198.
>   London 188 – Cardiff 40 – Swansea 8.

⌂ **Cwmbach Cottages** ⟋ without rest., Cwmbach Rd, Cadoxton, SA10 8AH, Northwest :
>   1 ¾ m. by A 474 ℘ (01639) 639825, ≤, 🚗 – ¾ 📺 ⅙ 🅿. ⁒
>   **5 rm** ☲ 28.00/46.00 **st.**

---

**NEFYN** Gwynedd 402 403 G 25 Wales G. – pop. 1 987.
>   Env. : Lleyn Peninsula★★ – Tre'r Ceiri★, NE : 5½ m. by B 4417 – Porth Dinllaen★, W : 1½ m.
>   by B 4417.
>   🟦, 🟦 Nefyn & District, Morfa Nefyn ℘ (01758) 720218.
>   London 265 – Caernarfon 20.

🏠 **Caeau Capel** ⟋, Rhodfar Mor, LL53 6EB, ℘ (01758) 720240, 🚗 – ¾ rest, 📺 🅿. 🕮🕲 VISA
>   Easter-October – **Meals** (bar lunch)/dinner 13.50 **t.** 🍴 4.95 – **18 rm** ☲ 26.00/53.00 **t.** – SB.

---

**NEWPORT** Pembrokeshire 403 F 27 Wales G. – pop. 1 162.
>   Env. : Pembrokeshire Coast National Park★★.
>   🟦 Newport ℘ (01239) 820244.
>   London 258 – Fishguard 7.

🏠 **Cnapan**, East St., SA42 0SY, on A 487 ℘ (01239) 820575, Fax (01239) 820878, 🚗 –
>   ¾ rest, 📺 🅿. 🕮🕲 VISA. ⁒
>   closed January, February and 25-26 December – **Meals** (closed Tuesday) (booking essential)
>   a la carte 10.00/21.50 **t.** 🍴 6.00 – **5 rm** ☲ 35.00/54.00 **t.**

**at Moylgrove** Northeast : 6 m. – ⊠ Cardigan (Cardiganshire).

⌂ **Old Vicarage Country** ⟋, SA43 3BN, South : ¼ m. on Glanrhyd rd ℘ (01239) 881231,
>   Fax (01239) 881341, ≤, 🚗 – ¾. ⁒
>   March-November – **Meals** (dinner only) 14.00 – **3 rm** ☲ 35.00/50.00 – SB.

## NEWPORT (Casnewydd-Ar-Wysg) 403 L 29 Wales G. – pop. 115 522.

See : Museum and Art Gallery★ AX – Transporter Bridge★ AC AY – Civic Centre (murals★) AX

Env. : Caerleon Roman Fortress★★ AC (Fortress Baths★ – Legionary Museum★ – Amphitheatre★), NE : 2 ½ m. by B 4596 AX – Tredegar House★★ (Grounds★ – Stables★), SW 2½ m. by A 48 AY – Exc. : Penhow Castle★, E : 8 m. by A 48 AX.

🏌 Tredegar Park, Bassaleg Rd ℰ (01633) 895219 – 🏌 Caerleon, Broadway ℰ (01633) 42034. – 🏌 Parc, Church Lane, Coedkernew ℰ (01633) 680933.

🛈 Museum and Art Gallery, John Frost Sq., NP9 1HZ ℰ (01633) 842962.

London 145 – Bristol 31 – Cardiff 12 – Gloucester 48.

### NEWPORT

| | | | | | | | |
|---|---|---|---|---|---|---|---|
| Allt-yr-yn Avenue | **AY** 2 | Clyffard Crescent | **AX** 13 | Kensington Place | **AX** 30 |
| Bellevue Lane | **BX** 5 | Clytha Park Road | **AX** 14 | Keynsham Avenue | **AY** 32 |
| Blewitt Street | **AY** 7 | Commercial Street | **AXY** 15 | Kingsway Centre | **AX** |
| Caerau Crescent | **AXY** 9 | Dewsland Park Road | **AY** 17 | Lower Dock Street | **AXY** 35 |
| Cambrian Centre | **AX** | Dock Street | **AX** 19 | Malpas Road | **AX** 37 |
| Capel Street | **AY** 10 | Godfrey Road | **AX** 21 | Newport Bridge | **AX** 39 |
| Clarence Place | **AX** 12 | Hereford Street | **AX** 24 | Oakfield Road | **AX** 42 |
| | | High Street | **AX** 26 | Queensway | **AX** 44 |
| | | John Frost Square | **AX** 27 | Summerhill Avenue | **AX** 47 |
| | | | | Waterloo Road | **AY** 50 |

🏛️ **Celtic Manor H. & Country Club,** Coldra Woods, NP6 2YA, East : 3 m. on A 48
℘ (01633) 413000, Fax (01633) 412910, ₤₅, ≘, ⊠, ♣, park – ☲, ⇔ rm, ▤ 🆃🆅 ☎ 🅿 –
🔏 500. 🆎 🆇 🅞 *VISA*. ⚘
**Meals** a la carte 16.85/29.40 **t.** ₰ 7.00 – (see also *Hedley's* below) – ⊒ 9.95 – **64 rm**
105.00/130.00 **st.** – SB.

🏛️ **Holiday Inn,** The Coldra, NP6 2YG, East : 3 m. on A 48  ℘ (01633) 412777,
Fax (01633) 413087, ₤₅, ≘, ⊠ – ⇔ rm, 🆃🆅 ☎ 🅿 – 🔏 350. 🆎 🆇 🅞 *VISA* 🄹🄲🄱. ⚘
**Meals** 11.50/15.50 **st.** and dinner a la carte ₰ 7.50 – ⊒ 11.50 – **119 rm** 105.00 **st.** – SB.

🏠 **Newport Lodge,** 147 Bryn Bevan, Brynglas Rd, NP9 5QN, North : ¾ m. by A 4042 off
A 4051  ℘ (01633) 821818, Fax (01633) 856360 – ⇔ rm, 🆃🆅 ☎ 🅿 . 🆎 🆇 🅞 *VISA* 🄹🄲🄱. ⚘
**Meals** (bar lunch)/dinner a la carte 16.00/20.75 **st.** ₰ 4.75 – **27 rm** ⊒ 70.00/95.00 **st.**

🏠 **Kepe Lodge,** 46a Caerau Rd, NP9 4HH,  ℘ (01633) 262351, Fax (01633) 262351, ☞ – ⇔
🆃🆅 🅿 . ⚘  AY s
**Meals** (by arrangement) 8.00 **st.** – **8 rm** ⊒ 23.00/46.00.

🍴 **Hedley's** (at Celtic Manor H. & Country Club), Coldra Woods, NP6 2YA, East : 3 m. on A 48
℘ (01633) 413000, Fax (01633) 412910 – 🅿 . 🆎 🆇 🅞 *VISA*
**Meals** (closed Saturday lunch, Sunday, Monday and Bank Holidays) 16.00/23.00 **t.**
and a la carte ₰ 7.00.

**at Langstone** East : 4½ m. on A 48 – AX – ✉ Newport.

🏛️ **Stakis Newport,** Chepstow Rd, NP6 2LX,  ℘ (01633) 413737, Fax (01633) 413713, ₤₅,
≘, ⊠ – ⇔ rm, ▤ rest, 🆃🆅 ☎ ₺ 🅿 – 🔏 90. 🆎 🆇 🅞 *VISA*. ⚘
**Meals** (bar lunch Monday to Saturday)/dinner 17.25 **st.** (dinner) and a la carte – ⊒ 9.95 –
**147 rm** 109.00/139.00 **st.**, 2 suites.

**at Redwick** Southeast : 9½ m. by M 4 - AY - off B 4245 – ✉ Magor.

🏠 **Brick House** ≫, NP6 3DX,  ℘ (01633) 880230, Fax (01633) 882441, ☞ – ⇔ 🆃🆅 🅿 . ⚘
**Meals** (by arrangement) 12.50 **st.** – **7 rm** ⊒ 26.00/45.00 **st.**

🔘 ATS  Maesglas  Ind.  Est.  Port  Rd  ATS Parish Rd, Town Wharf ℘ (01633) 214213/
℘ (01633) 216115/216117  214216

---

**NEWTOWN** (Y Drenewydd) *Powys* **402 403** K 26.
London 188 – Aberystwyth 43 – Chester 57 – Shrewsbury 35.

🏠 **Cilthriew** ≫ without rest., Kerry, SY16 4PF, Southeast : 5 m. by A 489 on B 4368
℘ (01686) 670667, Fax (01686) 670667, ≤, « 17C farmhouse », ⚘, ☞, park – ⇔ ₺ 🅿
**3 rm** ⊒ 25.00/42.00 – SB.

🔘 ATS Dulas Garage, Llanidloes Rd ℘ (01686) 626069

---

**NORTHOP HALL** *Flintshire* **402 403** K 24 – pop. 4 155 (Northop).
London 220 – Chester 9 – Shrewsbury 52.

🏛️ **Holiday Inn Garden Court,** Gateway Services, A 55 (westbound carriageway), CH7 6HB,
℘ (01244) 550011, Fax (01244) 550763 – ⇔ rm, 🆃🆅 ☎ ₺ 🅿 – 🔏 200. 🆎 🆇 🅞 *VISA* 🄹🄲🄱.
⚘
*closed 24 to 26 December* – **Meals** (dinner only) a la carte 11.20/24.00 **t.** ₰ 6.05 – ⊒ 7.50 –
**55 rm** 69.00/80.00 **st.**

🏠 **Travelodge,** CH7 6HB, A 55 (eastbound carriageway) ℘ (01244) 816473, Reservations
(Freephone) 0800 850950 – ⇔ 🆃🆅 ₺ 🅿 . 🆎 🆇 🅞 *VISA* 🄹🄲🄱. ⚘
**Meals** (grill rest.) – **40 rm** 39.95/59.95 **t.**

---

**NOTTAGE** (Drenewydd Yn Notais) *Bridgend* **403** I 29 – see Porthcawl.

---

**LES GUIDES VERTS MICHELIN**

Paysages, monuments

Routes touristiques

Géographie

Histoire, Art

Itinéraires de visite

Plans de villes et de monuments

**PEMBROKE** (Penfro) Pembrokeshire **408** F 28 Wales G. – pop. 7 230.

See : Town★★ – Castle★★ AC.

Env. : Pembrokeshire Coast National Park★★ – Carew★ (Castle★ AC), NE : 4 m. by A 4075.

Exc. : Bosherston (St. Govan's Chapel★ ), S : 7 m. by B 4319 and minor roads – Stack Rocks★
SW : 9 m. by B 4319 and minor roads.

🏌 Military Rd, Pembroke Dock ℘ (01646) 621453.
Cleddau Bridge (toll).

⛴ to Republic of Ireland (Rosslare) (Irish Ferries) 2 daily (3 h 45 mn) – to Republic of
Ireland (Cork) (Swansea Cork Ferries) 3 weekly (10 h).

🛈 Pembroke Visitor Centre, Commons Rd, SA71 4EA ℘ (01646) 622388.
London 252 – Carmarthen 32 – Fishguard 26.

🏠 **Coach House,** 116 Main St., SA71 4HN, ℘ (01646) 684602, Fax (01646) 687456 – 📺 ☎ 🄿
🕅 🄰🄴 𝘃𝘐𝘚𝘈. ⁂
Meals (bar lunch)/dinner 13.95 st. and a la carte – **13 rm** � 45.00/80.00 st. – SB.

✕✕ **Left Bank,** 63 Main St., SA71 4DA, ℘ (01646) 622333 – ⇖. 🕅 𝘃𝘐𝘚𝘈
closed Sunday and Monday except in summer, 25-26 December, 1 to 5 to 19 January
Meals (light lunch) a la carte 19.95/26.45 t. ₷ 5.50.

**at Lamphey** East : 1¾ m. on A 4139 – ⊠ Pembroke.

🏨 **Court** ⚿, SA71 5NT, ℘ (01646) 672273, Fax (01646) 672480, ₤₅, ≘s, ⬛, 🌧, park, ⁂
⇖ rest, 📺 ☎ 🄿 – 🔬 80. 🕅 🄰🄴 ① 𝘃𝘐𝘚𝘈. ⁂
Meals 20.00 (dinner) and a la carte 18.20/25.40 st. ₷ 6.25 – **37 rm** ⊒ 69.00/135.00 st. – SB

🏠 **Bethwaite's Lamphey Hall,** SA71 5NR, ℘ (01646) 672394, Fax (01646) 672369, 🌧
🌧 – 📺 ☎ 🄿. 🕅 🄰🄴 𝘃𝘐𝘚𝘈 🄹🄲🄱. ⁂
closed 23 December-3 January – Meals (closed Sunday dinner) 8.95/17.50 t. and dinner a la carte ₷ 5.50 – **10 rm** ⊒ 35.00/50.00 t. – SB.

**at Stackpole** South : 5 m. by B 4319 – ⊠ Pembroke.

🍴 **Armstrong Arms,** SA71 5DF, ℘ (01646) 672324, 🌧 – 🄿
Meals a la carte 11.70/17.15 t. ₷ 4.30.

⑩ ATS Well Hill Garage, Well Hill ℘ (01646) 683217/683836

---

**PENALLY** (Penalun) Pembrokeshire **408** F 29 – see Tenby.

---

**PENCOED** Bridgend **408** J 29 – see Bridgend.

---

**PENMACHNO** Conwy **402 408** I 24 – see Betws-y-Coed.

---

**PENMARK** Vale of Glamorgan **408** J 29 – see Barry.

---

**PENTYRCH** Cardiff **408** K 29 – see Cardiff.

---

**PONTARDDULAIS** Swansea **408** H 28 – pop. 1 634 – ⊠ Swansea.
London 203 – Fishguard 69 – Swansea 15.

🏠 **The Fountain Inn,** 11 Bolgoed Rd, SA4 1JP, ℘ (01792) 882501, Fax (01792) 881281 – 📺
🄿. 🕅 🄰🄴 𝘃𝘐𝘚𝘈 🄹🄲🄱. ⁂
closed 25 December – Meals a la carte 9.45/20.40 t. – **4 rm** ⊒ 37.50/42.50 st.

---

**PONTYPRIDD** Rhondda Cynon Taff **408** K 29 Wales G. – pop. 28 487.

Exc. : Caerphilly Castle★★ AC, SE : 7 m. by A 470 and A 468 – Llancaiach Fawr Manor★ AC
NE : 6½ m. by A 4054, A 472, B 4255 and B 4254.
London 164 – Cardiff 9 – Swansea 40.

🏨 **Llechwen Hall** ⚿, Llanfabon, CF37 4HP, Northeast : 4¼ m. by A 4223 off A 4054
℘ (01443) 742050, Fax (01443) 742189, 🌧 – ⇖ rm, 📺 ☎ 🄿 – 🔬 80. 🕅 🄰🄴 ① 𝘃𝘐𝘚𝘈
Meals 10.95/18.95 t. and a la carte ₷ 4.95 – **20 rm** ⊒ 48.50/68.50 t. – SB.

⑩ ATS Nile St., off Broadway ℘ (01443) 403796

---

*To visit a town or region: use the* **Michelin Green Guides.**

**PORTH** Rhondda Cynon Taff **403** J 29 Wales G. – pop. 6 225 – ⊠ Pontypridd.
Env. : Trehafod (Rhondda Heritage Park★), E : 1½ m. by A 4058.
London 168 – Cardiff 13 – Swansea 45.

🏨 **Heritage Park,** Coed Cae Rd, Trehafod, CF37 2NP, on a 4058 ℰ (01443) 687057,
Fax (01443) 687060, ₤ᴐ, ≘s, ⬛ – ⥱, ▤ rest, �📺 ☎ ₺ ₽ – 🛣 200. **◑◑** 🖭 **VISA** **JCB**
Meals 16.95 t. and a la carte – **44 rm** ⊇ 50.00/75.00 t. – SB.

---

**PORTHCAWL** Bridgend **403** I 29 Wales G. – pop. 16 099.
Env. : Glamorgan Heritage Coast★.
🛈 The Old Police Station, John St., CF36 3DT ℰ (01656) 786639/782211 (summer only).
London 183 – Cardiff 28 – Swansea 18.

🏨 **Atlantic,** West Drive, CF36 3LT, ℰ (01656) 785011, Fax (01656) 771877, ≼ – 🛗 📺 ☎ ₽.
**◑◑** 🖭 **◑** **VISA** **JCB**. ⅏
Meals (bar dinner Sunday) 13.50 t. and a la carte ⅄ 4.95 – **18 rm** ⊇ 59.00/92.00 t. – SB.

**at Nottage** North : 1 m. by A 4229 – ⊠ Porthcawl.

🏨 **Rose and Crown,** Heol-y-Capel, CF36 3ST, ℰ (01656) 784850, Fax (01656) 772345 –
⥱ rest, 📺 ☎ ₽. **◑◑** 🖭 **◑** **VISA**. ⅏
Meals (carving rest.) 11.00 st. – **8 rm** ⊇ 41.95/47.90 st.

---

**PORTHGAIN** Pembrokeshire **403** E 28 – see St. Davids.

---

*En saison, surtout dans les stations fréquentées,*
*il est prudent de retenir à l'avance.*
*Cependant, si vous ne pouvez pas occuper la chambre*
*que vous avez retenue, prévenez immédiatement l'hôtelier.*

*Si vous écrivez à un hôtel à l'étranger, joignez à votre lettre*
*un coupon-réponse international (disponible dans les bureaux de poste).*

---

**PORTMEIRION** Gwynedd **402** **403** H 25 Wales G..
See : Village★★★ AC.
Env. : Snowdonia National Park★★★ – Lleyn Peninsula★★ – Ffestiniog Railway★★ AC.
London 245 – Caernarfon 23 – Colwyn Bay 40 – Dolgellau 24.

🏨 **Portmeirion** ⊗, LL48 6ET, ℰ (01766) 770000, Fax (01766) 771331, ≼ village and estuary,
« Private Italianate village, antiques », ⬛, ☞, park, ⅏ – ⥱ rest, 📺 ☎ ℰ ₽ – 🛣 120. **◑◑**
🖭 **◑** **VISA** **JCB**. ⅏
Meals (closed Monday lunch) 9.50/30.00 t. ⅄ 7.00 – ⊇ 9.50 – **27 rm** 80.00/140.00 t.,
12 suites – SB.

---

**PORT TALBOT** Neath Port Talbot **403** I 29 Wales G. – pop. 37 647.
Env. : Margam Park★ AC (Orangery★), SE : 4 m. by A 48.
London 193 – Cardiff 35 – Swansea 11.

🏨 **Travel Inn,** Baglan Rd, SA12 8ES, M 4 junction 41 (westbound) or junction 42 (eastbound)
ℰ (01639) 813017, Fax (01639) 823096 – ⥱ rm, ▤ rest, 📺 ₺ ₽. **◑◑** 🖭 **◑** **VISA**. ⅏
Meals (grill rest.) – **42 rm** 38.00 t.

@ ATS Afan Way ℰ (01639) 883895/885747

---

**PRESTATYN** Denbighshire **402** **403** J 23 – pop. 15 020.
London 230 – Bangor 35 – Birkenhead 43 – Chester 35 – Holyhead 56.

🏨 **Traeth Ganol,** 41 Beach Rd West, LL19 7LL, ℰ (01745) 853594, Fax (01745) 886687 – ⥱
📺 ₺ ₽. **◑◑** 🖭 **◑** **VISA** **JCB**. ⅏
Meals (booking essential) (dinner only and Sunday lunch)/dinner 12.50 t. and a la carte
⅄ 4.60 – **9 rm** ⊇ 40.00/60.00 t. – SB.

---

**PWLLGLOYW** Powys **403** J 28 – see Brecon.

**PWLLHELI** Gwynedd 402 403 G 25 Wales G. – pop. 3 974.
　　Env. : Lleyn Peninsula★★.
　　🏌 Golf Rd ℘ (01758) 701644.
　　🛈 Min-y-Don, Station Sq., LL53 5HG ℘ (01758) 613000.
　　London 261 – Aberystwyth 73 – Caernarfon 21.

XXX　**Plas Bodegroes** ⬡ with rm, LL53 5TH, Northwest : 1 ¾ m. on A 497 ℘ (01758) 612363
　　Fax (01758) 701247, « Georgian country house », 🌲, park – ❦ ☎ 📷. ⬛ VISA JCB. �︎
　　March-November – **Meals** (closed Monday dinner except Bank Holidays) (booking essential
　　(dinner only and Sunday lunch)/dinner 24.50 **t.** and a la carte 🍷 7.00 – **11 rm** ⌷ (dinner
　　included) 70.00/200.00 **t.** – SB.

---

**RAGLAN** Monmouthshire 403 L 28 Wales G. – pop. 1 857 – ✉ Abergavenny.
　　See : Castle★ AC.
　　London 154 – Gloucester 34 – Newport 18 – Swansea 58.

🏠　**Travelodge** without rest., NP5 4BG, Northeast : 2 m. on A 40 (eastbound carriageway
　　℘ (01600) 740455, Fax (01600) 740329, Reservations (Freephone) 0800 850950 – ❦ TV 📷
　　🕭 📷. ⬛ AE ① VISA JCB. 🌫
　　42 rm 39.95/59.95 **t.**

🏠　**Clytha Arms** with rm, NP7 9BW, West : 3 m. on Clytha rd (old Abergavenny Rd
　　℘ (01873) 840206, Fax (01873) 840206 – ❦ rest, TV 📷. ⬛ VISA
　　**Meals** (closed Sunday dinner and Monday) a la carte 17.80/24.50 **t.** 🍷 6.75 – **3 rm** ⌷ 45.00/
　　70.00 **t.**

*Groß-London (GREATER LONDON) besteht aus der City und 32
Verwaltungsbezirken (Borough). Diese sind wiederum in kleinere
Bezirke (Area) unterteilt, deren Mittelpunkt ehemalige Dörfer
oder Stadtviertel sind, die oft ihren eigenen Charakter bewahrt haben.*

---

**REDWICK** Newport 403 L 29 – see Newport (Newport).

---

**RHOSCOLYN** Anglesey 402 403 G 24 Wales G. – pop. 539 – ✉ Holyhead.
　　Env. : Anglesey★★.
　　Exc. : Barclodiad y Gawres Burial Chamber★, SE : 10 m. by B 4545, A 5 and A 4080.
　　London 269 – Bangor 25 – Caernarfon 30 – Holyhead 5.5.

🏠　**Old Rectory** ⬡ without rest., LL65 2SQ, ℘ (01407) 860214, ≤, 🌲 – ❦ TV 📷. ⬛ VISA
　　closed 21 December-3 January and restricted opening in winter – – **5 rm** ⌷ 35.00/56.00 s.

---

**RHOS-ON-SEA** (Llandrillo-Yn-Rhos) Conwy 402 403 I 24 – see Colwyn Bay.

---

**RHYDLEWIS** Ceredigion 403 G 27 Wales G. – ✉ Llandysul.
　　Exc. : Aberaeron★, NE : 11½ m. by B 4334 and A 487.
　　London 235 – Carmarthen 26 – Fishguard 38.

🏠　**Broniwan** ⬡, SA44 5PF, Northeast : ¼ m. by Pentregat rd, taking first turn right onto
　　unmarked road ℘ (01239) 851261, Fax (01239) 851261, « Working farm », 🌲, park – ❦
　　📷
　　restricted opening January and February – **Meals** (by arrangement) 11.00 **st.** – **3 rm**
　　⌷ 20.00/40.00 **st.**

---

**ROEWEN** Conwy – see Conwy.

---

**ROSEBUSH** Pembrokeshire 403 F 28 – ✉ Clynderwen (Carmarthenshire).
　　London 252 – Fishguard 9 – Haverfordwest 12.

🏠　**Tafarn Newydd**, SA66 7RA, West : 1 m. at junction of B 4313 and B 4329
　　℘ (01437) 532542, Fax (01437) 532926, « 17C former coaching inn » – ❦ 📷. ⬛ VISA JCB
　　closed 25 December and second week January – **Meals** (closed Sunday dinner in winter
　　a la carte 17.00/24.50 **t.**

**ROSSETT** (Yr Orsedd) Wrexham 402 403 L 24 – *pop. 1 986.*
*London 203 – Chester 8 – Shrewsbury 39.*

🏛 **Llyndir Hall** ⏳, Llyndir Lane, LL12 0AY, North : ¾ m. by B 5445 ℘ (01244) 571648,
Fax (01244) 571258, « Part Strawberry Gothic country house », 🌭, 🏊, 🐎 – ✦ 📺 ☎ & 🅿
– 🔬 120. 🆎 🎗 🅾 🆅🆂🅰. ✦
**Meals** *(closed Saturday lunch)* a la carte 14.95/25.80 **t.** 🍷 6.45 – **37 rm** ⌂ 79.00/118.00 **st.**,
1 suite – SB.

🏛 **Rossett Hall**, Chester Rd, LL12 0DE, ℘ (01244) 571000, Fax (01244) 571505, 🐎 – ✦ 📺
☎ 🅿 – 🔬 120. 🆎 🎗 🅾 🆅🆂🅰 🅹🅲🅱. ✦
**Meals** 12.95/18.50 **t.** and a la carte 🍷 5.95 – ⌂ 7.95 – **29 rm** 70.00/90.00 **st.**, 1 suite – SB.

---

**RUTHIN** (Rhuthun) Denbighshire 402 403 K 24 *Wales G. – pop. 5 029.*
**Env. :** *Llandyrnog (St. Dyfnog's Church★), Llanrhaeder-yng-Nghinmeirch (Jesse Window★★), N : 5½ m. by A 494 and B 5429.*
**Exc. :** *Denbigh★ (Castle★), NW : 7 m. on A 525.*
🏌 *Ruthin-Pwllglas* ℘ (01824) 702296.
🛈 *Ruthin Craft Centre, Park Rd, LL15 1BB* ℘ (01824) 703992.
*London 210 – Birkenhead 31 – Chester 23 – Shrewsbury 46.*

🏠 **Ye Olde Anchor Inn**, Rhos St., LL15 1DX, ℘ (01824) 702813, Fax (01824) 703050 –
✦ rest, 📺 ☎ 🅿. 🆎 🎗 🆅🆂🅰 🅹🅲🅱.
**Meals** 12.95/18.95 **st.** and a la carte 🍷 5.95 – **17 rm** ⌂ 35.00/65.00 **st.** – SB.

↑ **Eyarth Station** ⏳, Llanfair Dyffryn Clwyd, LL15 2EE, South : 1 ¾ m. by A 525
℘ (01824) 703643, Fax (01824) 707464, ≤, 🏊, 🐎 – ✦ rm, 🅿. 🆎 🎗 🆅🆂🅰
**Meals** 14.50 **st.** 🍷 4.00 – **6 rm** ⌂ 30.00/48.00 **s.** – SB.

---

*When visiting the West Country,*
*use the **Michelin Green Guide** "**The West Country of England**".*

*– Detailed descriptions of places of interest*
*– Touring programmes by county*
*– Maps and street plans*
*– The history of the region*
*– Photographs and drawings of monuments,*
*beauty spots, houses...*

---

**ST. ASAPH** (Llanelwy) Denbighshire 402 403 J 24 *Wales G. – pop. 3 399.*
**See :** *Cathedral★.*
**Env. :** *Rhuddlan Castle★★ AC, N : 2½ m. by A 525 and A 547 – Bodelwyddan★★ AC, W :
2½ m. by A 55 – Denbigh★ (Castle★), S : 6 m. by A 525 and A 543.*
*London 225 – Chester 29 – Shrewsbury 59.*

🏛 **Plas Elwy**, The Roe, LL17 0LT, North : ½ m. at junction of A 525 with A 55
℘ (01745) 582263, Fax (01745) 583864 – ✦ rest, 📺 ☎ 🅿. 🆎 🎗 🅾 🆅🆂🅰 🅹🅲🅱. ✦
*closed 26 to 30 December* – **Meals** *(closed Sunday dinner to non-residents)* (lunch by
arrangement Monday to Saturday)/dinner a la carte 17.25/25.00 **t.** 🍷 4.95 – **13 rm** ⌂ 40.00/
68.00 **t.** – SB.

---

**ST. CLEARS** (Sancler) Carmarthenshire 403 G 28 *Wales G. – pop. 3 014.*
**Env. :** *Laugharne★ (Castle★, The Boat House★), S : 4 m. on A 4066.*
*London 229 – Carmarthen 9 – Fishguard 37.*

🏛 **Forge Lodge**, SA33 4NA, East : 1 m. on A 40 ℘ (01994) 230300, Fax (01994) 231577, 🌭,
≘s, 🏊, 🐎 – 📺 ☎ 🅿 – 🔬 100. 🆎 🎗 🆅🆂🅰
*closed 25 and 26 December* – **Meals** (grill rest.) a la carte 9.25/16.45 **t.** 🍷 3.25 – **18 rm**
⌂ 42.50/60.00 **st.**

---

**ST. DAVIDS** (Tyddewi) Pembrokeshire 403 E 28 *Wales G. – pop. 1 959. – ⌧ Haverfordwest.*
**See :** *Town★★ – Cathedral★★ – Bishop's Palace★ AC.*
**Env. :** *Pembrokeshire Coast National Park★★.*
🏌 *St. Davids City, Whitesands Bay* ℘ (01437) 721751.
🛈 *City Hall, SA62 6SD* ℘ (01437) 720392 (moving to High St. in March 1999).
*London 266 – Carmarthen 46 – Fishguard 16.*

🏛 **Warpool Court** ⚶, SA62 6BN, Southwest : ½ m. by Porth Clais rd ℘ (01437) 720300
Fax (01437) 720676, ≤, ⌀, 🔲, 🚗, ⚒ – ⚭ rest, 🔲 ☎ 🅿. 🝔 🆚 🅾 VISA
closed January – **Meals** 19.95/34.00 st. ₰ 5.50 – **25 rm** ⌂ 89.00/164.00 st. – SB.

🏛 **St. Nons**, Catherine St., SA62 6RJ, Southwest : ¼ m. on Porth Clais rd ℘ (01437) 720239
Fax (01437) 721839 – ⚭ rest, 🔲 ☎ 🅿. VISA
closed November and December – **Meals** (bar lunch)/dinner 19.50 ₰ 5.50 – **21 rm** ⌂ 53.00/
82.00 st. – SB.

🏛 **Old Cross**, Cross Sq., SA62 6SP, ℘ (01437) 720387, Fax (01437) 720394, 🚗 – ⚭ rm, 🔲
☎ 🅿. 🝔 VISA JCB
March-24 December – **Meals** (bar lunch)/dinner 17.25 t. and a la carte ₰ 4.50 – **16 rm**
⌂ 45.00/79.00 t. – SB.

⌂ **Ramsey House**, Lower Moor, SA62 6RP, Southwest : ½ m. on Porth Clais rd
℘ (01437) 720321, Fax (01437) 720025, 🚗 – ⚭ 🔲 🅿. 🝔 VISA JCB
**Meals** (by arrangement) 15.00 st. ₰ 5.75 – **7 rm** ⌂ (dinner included) 82.00/92.00 st. – SB.

⌂ **Y-Gorlan**, 77 Nun St., SA62 6NU, ℘ (01437) 720837, Fax (01437) 720837 – ⚭ 🔲. 🝔 VISA
⚸
**Meals** (by arrangement) 13.50 st. ₰ 4.20 – **5 rm** ⌂ 26.00/50.00 st.

✗ **Morgan's Brasserie**, 20 Nun St., SA62 6NT, ℘ (01437) 720508, Fax (01437) 720508 – 🝔
🆎 VISA
closed Sunday except Bank Holidays, January, February and restricted opening in winter –
**Meals** (dinner only) a la carte a la carte 15.75/23.75 st.

**at Porthgain** Northeast : 7 ¾ m. by A 487 and Llanrian rd – ✉ Haverfordwest.

✗ **Harbour Lights**, SA62 5BW, ℘ (01348) 831549, Fax (01348) 831549 – 🝔 VISA JCB
closed Sunday to Wednesday, 2 weeks Christmas, Bank Holidays and restricted opening in
winter – **Meals** - Seafood - (booking essential) (dinner only) 23.00 t. ₰ 10.50.

---

**ST.DOGMAELS** Ceredigion 403 G 27 – see Cardigan.

---

**SARN PARK SERVICE AREA** Bridgend 403 J 29 – ✉ Bridgend.
🛈 M 4, Junction 36, CF32 9SY ℘ (01656) 654906.
London 174 – Cardiff 17 – Swansea 20.

🏛 **Welcome Lodge**, CF32 9RW, M 4 junction 36 ℘ (01656) 655332, Fax (01656) 645004
Reservations (Freephone) 0800 7314466 – ⚭ rm, 🔲 ⅋ 🅿. 🝔 🆎 🅾 VISA
**Meals** (grill rest.) (bar lunch)/dinner 20.00 t. and a la carte ₰ 5.50 – ⌂ 7.50 – **40 rm** 45.00 t.

---

**SAUNDERSFOOT** Pembrokeshire 403 F 28 Wales G. – pop. 3 221.
Env. : Pembrokeshire Coast National Park★★.
London 245 – Carmarthen 25 – Fishguard 34 – Tenby 3.

⌂ **Vine Farm**, The Ridgeway, SA69 9LA, ℘ (01834) 813543, 🚗 – 🔲 🅿
March-October – **Meals** (by arrangement) 12.00 – **5 rm** ⌂ 23.00/50.00 st. – SB.

---

**SEION** Gwynedd 402 403 H 24 – see Caernarfon.

---

**SOUTHERNDOWN** Bridgend 403 J 29 – see Bridgend.

---

**STACKPOLE** Pembrokeshire 403 F 29 – see Pembroke.

---

**SWANSEA** (Abertawe) 403 I 29 Wales G. – pop. 181 906.
See : Town★ – Maritime Quarter★ B – Maritime and Industrial Museum★ B M – Glynn Vivian
Art Gallery★ – Guildhall (British Empire Panels★ ).
Env. : Gower Peninsula★★ (Rhossili★★), W : by A 4067 A.
Exc. : The Wildfowl and Wetlands Trust★, Llanelli, NW : 6 ½ m. by A 483 and A 484 A –
Kidwelly Castle★, NW : 19 m. by A 483 and A 484 A.
🛈8 Morriston, 160 Clasemont Rd ℘ (01792) 771079, A – 🛈8 Clyne, 120 Owls Lodge Lane,
Mayals ℘ (01792) 401989, A – 🛈8 Langland Bay ℘ (01792) 366023, A – 🛈8 Fairwood Park,
Blackhills Lane, Upper Killay ℘ (01792) 203648, A – 🛈9 Inco, Clydach ℘ (01792) 844216, A.
⚓ to Republic of Ireland (Cork) (Swansea Cork Ferries) (10 h).
🛈 P.O. Box 59, Singleton St., SA1 3QG ℘ (01792) 468321.
London 191 – Birmingham 136 – Bristol 82 – Cardiff 40 – Liverpool 187 – Stoke-on-Trent
175.

## SWANSEA
### BUILT UP AREA



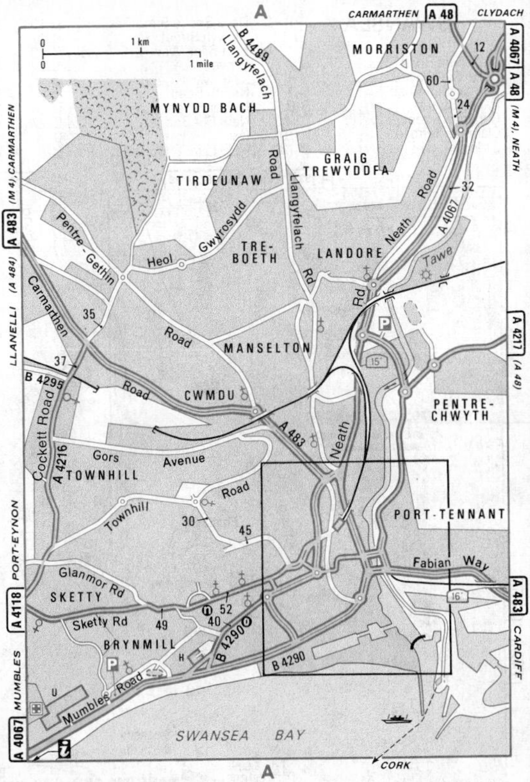


*This Guide is not a comprehensive list of all hotels and restaurants, nor even of all good hotels and restaurants in Great Britain and Ireland.*

*Since our aim is to be of service to all motorists, we must show establishments in all categories and so we have made a selection of some in each.*

**Swansea Marriott,** Maritime Quarter, SA1 3SS, ☎ (01792) 642020, *Fax (01792) 650345,* <, Fб, ≘s, ⊠ – |‡|, ⇔ rm, ▤ TV ☎ & Ⓟ – 🏛 300. MC AE ⊙ VISA. ✂ — B e
**Meals** *(closed Saturday lunch)* 17.95/18.95 **st.** and a la carte 7.75 – ☐ 11.95 – **117 rm** 88.00 **st.**

**Forte Posthouse Swansea,** 39 The Kingsway, SA1 5LS, ☎ (01792) 651074, *Fax (01792) 456044,* Fб, ≘s, ⊠ – |‡|, ⇔ rm, TV ☎ Ⓟ – 🏛 350. MC AE ⊙ VISA JCB. ✂
**Meals** (bar lunch Monday to Saturday)/dinner a la carte 21.00/25.00 – ☐ 9.95 – **93 rm** 85.00 **st.**, 6 suites – SB. — B a

**Beaumont,** 72-73 Walter Rd, SA1 4QA, ☎ (01792) 643956, *Fax (01792) 643044* – TV ☎ Ⓟ. MC AE ⊙ VISA — A n
*closed 20 December-4 January* – **Meals** (bar lunch) (bar meals Sunday dinner)/dinner 24.50 **st.** 8.25 – **16 rm** ☐ 49.50/80.00 **st.**

**Windsor Lodge,** Mount Pleasant, SA1 6EG, ☎ (01792) 642158, *Fax (01792) 648996* – TV ☎ Ⓟ. MC AE ⊙ VISA JCB — B r
*closed 25 and 26 December* – **Meals** (lunch by arrangement) (bar meals Sunday) 15.00/18.00 **st.** 5.75 – **18 rm** ☐ 49.50/70.50 **st.** – SB.

**Annie's,** 56 St. Helen's Rd, SA1 4BE, ☎ (01792) 655603 – MC VISA — A o
*closed Sunday, Monday, 25-26 December and Bank Holidays* – **Meals** (booking essential) (dinner only) 19.50 **t.** 4.45.

**at Swansea Enterprise Park** *Northeast : 4 m. by A 4067* - **A** - *off A 48* – ✉ *Swansea.*

**Hilton National,** Phoenix Way, SA7 9EG, ☎ (01792) 310330, *Fax (01792) 797535,* Fб, ≘s, ⊠ – ⇔ rm, ▤ rest, TV ☎ & Ⓟ – 🏛 180. MC AE ⊙ VISA JCB
**Meals** 11.95/15.95 **st.** and dinner a la carte 5.95 – ☐ 10.50 – **120 rm** 85.00 **st.** – SB.

**at The Mumbles** *Southwest : 7¾ m. by A 4067* – **A** – ✉ *Swansea.*

**Norton House,** 17 Norton Rd, SA3 5TQ, ☎ (01792) 404891, *Fax (01792) 403210,* 🌳 – ⇔ rest, TV ☎ Ⓟ – 🏛 25. MC AE ⊙ VISA. ✂
*closed 1 week Christmas* – **Meals** (dinner only) 25.50 **t.** 4.75 – **15 rm** ☐ 57.50/82.50 **t.**

## SWANSEA

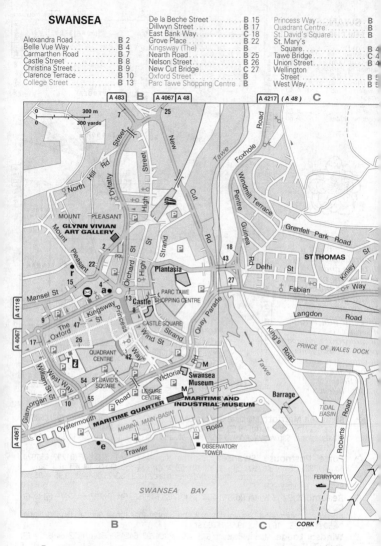

---

🏠 **Hillcrest House**, 1 Higher Lane, SA3 4NS, West : ¾ m. on Langland rd ℰ (01792) 363700,
  Fax (01792) 363768 – ⇔ 📺 ☎ 🅿. 🆎 🎫 *VISA*. ⚘
  *closed 23 December-3 January* – **Meals** *(closed Sunday and Monday)* (dinner only) 18.00 **t**. –
  **7 rm** ⊇ 48.00/80.00 **t**.

%% **L'Amuse**, 93 Newton Rd, SA3 4BN, ℰ (01792) 366006 – 🆎 *VISA*
  *closed Sunday dinner, Monday and 3 weeks January* – **Meals** - Bistro - 12.95/20.50 **t**. ₰ 6.80.

**at Llanrhidian** *West : 10½ m. by A 4118 - A - and B 4271 on B 4295* – ⊠ *Reynoldston.*

🏠 **Fairyhill** ⚘, Reynoldston, SA3 1BS, West : 2 ½ m. by B 4295 (Llangennith rd)
  ℰ (01792) 390139, Fax (01792) 391358, ⇔, ⇗, park – ⇔ rest, 📺 ☎ 🅿 – 🔬 35. 🆎 🎫
  *VISA* JCB
  *closed dinner 25 December to 6 January* – **Meals** 17.50/32.00 **t**. ₰ 8.50 – **8 rm** ⊇ 95.00/
  160.00 **t**. – SB.

  @ ATS 139 Neath Rd, Hafod ℰ (01792) 456379

**WANSEA SERVICE AREA** Swansea 403 I 28.

🏛 **Travelodge,** Penllergaer, SA4 1GT, M 4 junction 47 ℰ (01792) 896222, Fax (01792) 898806, Reservations (Freephone) 0800 850950 – 🛏 rm, 📺 Ꮽ 🅿 – 🔬 25. 🕩🕗 AE ⓞ VISA JCB. 🕸
Meals (grill rest.) – **50 rm** 39.95/59.95 **t.**

---

**ALBOT GREEN** Rhondda Cynon Taff – pop. 2 405.
London 163 – Cardiff 9 – Swansea 34.

🍽 **Woods Bistro,** 79 Talbot Rd, CF72 8AE, ℰ (01443) 222458, Fax (01443) 222458 – 🕩🕗 AE
🍴 VISA JCB
closed Monday and Saturday lunch, Sunday, 25-26 December, 1 week in spring, 1 week in autumn and Bank Holidays – Meals 9.95 (lunch) and dinner a la carte 16.85/25.85 **t.** 🍷 5.50.

---

**ALGARTH** Powys 403 K 28 Wales G. – pop. 1 818.
Env. : Brecon Beacons National Park★★.
London 182 – Brecon 10 – Hereford 29 – Swansea 53.

🛏 **Upper Trewalkin** 🐾, Pengenffordd, LD3 0HA, South : 2 m. by A 479 (turn right onto unmarked road after 1 m.) ℰ (01874) 711349, Fax (01874) 711349, ≤, « Part Georgian farmhouse, working farm », 🌳, park – 🛏 🅿. 🕸
mid April-mid November – Meals (by arrangement) 12.50 **st.** – **3 rm** 🍽 22.00/44.00 – SB.

*Great Britain* and *Ireland* are covered entirely
at a scale of 16 miles to 1 inch by our «*Main roads*» map 986.

---

**ALSARNAU** Gwynedd 402 403 H 25 Wales G. – pop. 647 – ⊠ Harlech.
Env. : Snowdonia National Park★★★.
London 236 – Caernafon 33 – Chester 67 – Dolgellau 25.

🏛🏛 **Maes-y-Neuadd** 🐾, LL47 6YA, South : 1 ½ m. by A 496 off B 4573 ℰ (01766) 780200, Fax (01766) 780211, ≤, « Part 14C country house », 🌳, park – 🛏 rest, 📺 ☎ 🅿 – 🔬 25. 🕩🕗 AE ⓞ VISA JCB
Meals 13.25/25.00 **t.** 🍷 9.20 – **15 rm** 🍽 (dinner included) 82.00/220.00 **t.**, 1 suite – SB.

---

**TAL-Y-BONT** Conwy 402 403 I 24 – see Conwy.

---

**TAL-Y-LLYN** Gwynedd 402 403 I 25 Wales G. – ⊠ Tywyn.
Env. : Snowdonia National Park★★★ – Cadair Idris★★★.
London 224 – Dolgellau 9 – Shrewsbury 60.

🏛🏛 **Tynycornel,** LL36 9AJ, on B 4405 ℰ (01654) 782282, Fax (01654) 782679, ≤ Tal-y-Llyn Lake and mountains, 😴, 🏊, 🌳 – 🛏 rest, 📺 ☎ 🅿. 🕩🕗 AE ⓞ VISA JCB
Meals (lunch by arrangement Monday to Saturday)/dinner 21.50 **t.** 🍷 5.95 – **15 rm** 🍽 (dinner included) 70.00/140.00 **t.**, 2 suites.

🏛 **Minfford,** LL36 9AJ, Northeast : 2 ¼ m. by B 4405 on A 487 ℰ (01654) 761665, Fax (01654) 761517, ≤, 🌳 – 🛏 rest, ☎ 🅿. 🕩🕗 VISA
March-October and weekends only in November – Meals (booking essential) (dinner only) 19.95 **st.** 🍷 6.95 – **6 rm** 🍽 (dinner included) 66.00/114.00 **st.** – SB.

---

**TENBY** (Dinbych-Y-Pysgod) Pembrokeshire 403 F 28 Wales G. – pop. 4 809.
See : Town★★ – Harbour and seafront★★.
Env. : Pembrokeshire Coast National Park★★ – Caldey Island★, S : by boat.
🏌 The Burrows ℰ (01834) 842787/842978.
🅱 The Croft, SA70 8AP ℰ (01834) 842402.
London 247 – Carmarthen 27 – Fishguard 36.

🏛🏛 **Waterwynch House** 🐾, Narberth Rd, Waterwynch Bay, SA70 8TJ, North : 1 ¾ m. by A 478 ℰ (01834) 842464, Fax (01834) 845076, ≤, 🌳, park – 🛏 rest, 📺 ☎ 📞 🅿. 🕩🕗 VISA. 🕸
March-October – Meals (closed Sunday dinner) (dinner only and Sunday lunch)/dinner a la carte 10.00/17.50 **t.** 🍷 6.00 – **14 rm** 🍽 (dinner included) 60.00/120.00 **t.**, 2 suites.

🏛🏛 **Atlantic,** Esplanade, SA70 7DU, ℰ (01834) 842881, Fax (01834) 842881 (ext. 256), 🏊, 🌳 – 🛗, 🛏 rest, 📺 Ꮽ 🅿. 🕩🕗 AE VISA. 🕸
closed 19 December-22 January – **Carrington's :** Meals a la carte 15.95/23.40 **t.** 🍷 4.95 – **40 rm** 🍽 63.00/126.00 **t.**

🏛 **Broadmead,** Heywood Lane, SA70 8DA, Northwest : ¾ m. ℰ (01834) 84264'
Fax (01834) 845757, 🌶 – 📺 ☎ 🅿, 🐾 VISA JCB. ⅍
closed January and February – **Meals** (bar lunch Sunday in winter)/dinner 14.00 st. ▯ 4.50
**20 rm** �???? 29.00/58.00 st. – SB.

🏛 **Fourcroft,** North Beach, SA70 8AP, ℰ (01834) 842886, Fax (01834) 842888, ≤, ⇌, ⌁
⏐ ⅍ 📺 ☎ – 🔏 80. 🐾 🆎 VISA
**Meals** (bar lunch)/dinner 18.00 st. and a la carte ▯ 4.50 – **46 rm** ⊆ 30.00/84.00 st. – SB.

⌂ **Myrtle House,** St. Marys St., SA70 7HW, ℰ (01834) 842508, Fax (01834) 842508 – ⅙⅞ 🖻
⇌, 🐾 VISA. ⅍
March-September – **Meals** 10.00 s. – **8 rm** ⊆ 26.00/52.00 s.

**at Penally (Penalun)** Southwest : 2 m. by A 4139 – ⊠ Tenby.

🏛 **Penally Abbey** ♨, SA70 7PY, ℰ (01834) 843033, Fax (01834) 844714, ≤, 🐾 – ⅙⅞ rest
📺 ☎ 🅿, 🐾 🆎 VISA JCB. ⅍
**Meals** (lunch by arrangement) 18.00/25.00 st. and a la carte ▯ 10.95 – **11 rm** ⊆ (dinne
included) 116.00/168.00 st., 1 suite – SB.

---

**THORNHILL** Cardiff **403** K 29 – see Cardiff.

---

*Le Grand Londres (GREATER LONDON) est composé de la City
et de 32 arrondissements administratifs (Borough)
eux-mêmes divisés en quartiers ou en villages
ayant conservé leur caractère propre (Area).*

---

**THREE COCKS** (Aberllynfi) Powys **403** K 27 Wales G. – ⊠ Brecon.
Env. : Brecon Beacons National Park★★.
London 184 – Brecon 11 – Hereford 25 – Swansea 55.

✕✕ **Three Cocks** with rm, LD3 0SL, on A 438 ℰ (01497) 847215, Fax (01497) 847339, « Par
15C inn », 🐾 – 🅿, 🐾 VISA. ⅍
mid February-November – **Meals** (closed Sunday lunch and Tuesday) (lunch by arrange
ment) 27.00 st. and a la carte ▯ 9.75 – **7 rm** ⊆ 45.00/67.00 st. – SB.

---

**TINTERN** (Tyndyrn) Monmouthshire **403 404** L 28 Wales G. – pop. 749 – ⊠ Chepstow.
See : Abbey★★ AC.
London 137 – Bristol 23 – Gloucester 40 – Newport 22.

🏛 **Beaufort,** NP6 6SF, on A 466 ℰ (01291) 689777, Fax (01291) 689727, 🐾 – ⅙⅞ rest, 📺 ☎
🅿 – 🔏 50. 🐾 🆎 VISA
**Meals** (bar lunch Monday to Saturday)/dinner 15.95 st. ▯ 5.95 – **24 rm** ⊆ 55.00/75.00 st. –
SB.

🏠 **Royal George,** NP6 6SF, on A 466 ℰ (01291) 689205, Fax (01291) 689448, 🐾 – ⅙⅞ 📺 ☎
🅿, 🐾 🆎 ① VISA JCB. ⅍
**Meals** 12.50/22.00 t. and dinner a la carte ▯ 4.25 – **19 rm** ⊆ 60.00/95.00 t. – SB.

✕✕ **Parva Farmhouse** with rm, NP6 6SQ, on A 466 ℰ (01291) 689411, Fax (01291) 689557 –
⅙⅞ rest, 📺 ☎ 🅿, 🐾 🆎 VISA JCB
**Meals** (bar lunch)/dinner 19.50 st. ▯ 6.50 – **9 rm** ⊆ 48.00/74.00 st. – SB.

---

**TREARDDUR BAY** Anglesey **402 403** G 24 Wales G. – ⊠ Holyhead.
Env. : Anglesey★★.
Exc. : Barclodiad y Gawres Burial Chamber★, SE : 10 m. by B 4545, A 5 and A 4080.
London 269 – Bangor 25 – Caernarfon 29 – Holyhead 3.

🏛 **Trearddur Bay,** LL65 2UN, ℰ (01407) 860301, Fax (01407) 861181, 🔟, 🐾 – 📺 ☎ 🅿 –
🔏 65. 🐾 🆎 ① VISA JCB. ⅍
**Meals** (bar lunch)/dinner 18.50 t. and a la carte ▯ 5.95 – **43 rm** ⊆ 73.00/130.00 t. – SB.

---

**TRECASTLE** Powys **403** J 28.
London 192 – Aberystwyth 60 – Cardiff 47 – Carmarthen 37 – Gloucester 81.

🏠 **Castle Coaching Inn,** LD3 8UH, ℰ (01874) 636354, Fax (01874) 636457 – ⅙⅞ 📺 ☎ 🅿
🐾 VISA JCB
**Meals** (bar lunch)/dinner 18.00 st. and a la carte ▯ 5.00 – **9 rm** ⊆ 40.00/50.00 st., 1 suite –
SB.

**REMEIRCHION** *Denbighshire* [402] [403] J 24 – ✉ *St. Asaph.*
*London 225 – Chester 29 – Shrewsbury 59.*

⌂ **Bach-Y-Graig** 🌿 without rest., LL17 0UH, Southwest : 2 m. by B 5429 off Denbigh rd ☎ (01745) 730627, *Fax (01745) 730627*, « 16C brick built house, working farm », 🌳, park – 🚭 [TV] Ⓟ. 🐕
*closed Christmas and New Year* – **3 rm** ☕ 28.00/42.00 **s.**

**YN-Y-GROES** *Gwynedd – see Conwy (Aberconwy and Colwyn).*

**USK** (Brynbuga) *Monmouthshire* [403] L 28 *Wales G. – pop. 2 187.*
Exc. : *Raglan Castle★ AC, NE : 7 m. by A 472, A 449 and A 40.*
⛳18, ⛳18 *Alice Springs, Bettws Newydd ☎ (01873) 880772/880708.*
*London 144 – Bristol 30 – Gloucester 39 – Newport 10.*

🏨 **Glen-yr-Afon House,** Pontypool Rd, NP5 1SY, ☎ (01291) 672302, *Fax (01291) 672597*, 🌳 – 🛗 🚭 [TV] ☎ ♿ Ⓟ – 🏛 200. [MC] [AE] ⓓ [VISA]
**Meals** 18.25 **t.** and a la carte 🍷 7.60 – **26 rm** ☕ 65.80/79.90 **t.** – SB.

🏨 **Three Salmons,** Bridge St., NP5 1BQ, ☎ (01291) 672133, *Fax (01291) 673979* – [TV] ☎ Ⓟ – 🏛 100. [MC] [AE] ⓓ [VISA]. 🐕
**Meals** *(closed Sunday dinner)* 20.00 (dinner) and a la carte 16.00/28.00 **st.** 🍷 7.50 – **24 rm** ☕ 66.00/90.00 **st.** – SB.

**at Llangybi** *South : 2½ m. on Llangybi rd* – ✉ *Usk.*

🏨 **Cwrt Bleddyn,** NP5 1PG, South : 1 m. ☎ (01633) 450521, *Fax (01633) 450220*, 🏋, 🏊, 🏊, 🌳, park, 🎾, squash – 🚭 rm, [TV] ☎ Ⓟ – 🏛 200. [MC] [AE] ⓓ [VISA]. 🐕
***Nicholls :*** **Meals** a la carte 16.25/32.50 **st.** 🍷 6.25 – **31 rm** ☕ 95.00/145.00 **st.**, 2 suites – SB.

***In alta stagione,*** *e soprattutto nelle stazioni turistiche, è prudente prenotare con un certo anticipo.*
*Avvertite immediatamente l'albergatore se non potete più occupare la camera prenotata.*

*Se scrivete ad un albergo all'estero, allegate alla vostra lettera un tagliando-risposta internazionale (disponibile presso gli uffici postali).*

**WELSH HOOK** *Pembrokeshire* [403] F 28 – *see Fishguard.*

**WELSHPOOL** (Trallwng) *Powys* [402] [403] K 26 *Wales G. – pop. 5 900.*
See : *Town★.*
Env. : *Powis Castle★★★ AC, SW : 1½ m. by A 483.*
⛳18 *Golfa Hill ☎ (01938) 83249.*
ℹ *Vicarage Gdn, Church St., SY21 7DD ☎ (01938) 552043.*
*London 182 – Birmingham 64 – Chester 45 – Shrewsbury 19.*

🏨 **Royal Oak,** The Cross, SY21 7DG, ☎ (01938) 552217, *Fax (01938) 556652* – [TV] ☎ 📞 Ⓟ – 🏛 150. [MC] [VISA]
**Meals** a la carte 12.35/16.85 **t.** – **24 rm** ☕ 50.00/80.00 **st.** – SB.

⌂ **Moat Farm** 🌿, SY21 8SE, South : 2 ¼ m. on A 483 ☎ (01938) 553179, « Working farm », 🌳, park – 🚭 [TV] Ⓟ. 🐕
*March-October* – **Meals** (by arrangement) (communal dining) 11.00 **st.** 🍷 3.00 – **3 rm** ☕ 25.00/40.00 **st.** – SB.

**at Guilsfield** *North : 3 m. by A 490 on B 4392* – ✉ *Welshpool.*

⌂ **Lower Trelydan** 🌿, SY21 9PH, South : ¾ m. by B 4392 on unmarked road ☎ (01938) 553105, *Fax (01938) 553105*, « 16C farmhouse, working farm », 🌳, park – 🚭 [TV] Ⓟ. 🐕
*closed Christmas and New Year* – **Meals** (by arrangement) (communal dining) 13.00 **st.** 🍷 4.00 – **3 rm** ☕ 27.00/48.00 **st.**

**WHITEBROOK** *Monmouthshire – see Monmouth.*

**WOLF'S CASTLE** (Cas-Blaidd) *Pembrokeshire* **403** F 28 *Wales G. – pop. 616 –* ⊠ *Haverfordwes*
   Env. : *Pembrokeshire Coast National Park★★*.
   *London 258 – Fishguard 7 – Haverfordwest 8.*

🏠 **Wolfscastle Country H.,** SA62 5LZ, ℰ (01437) 741225, Fax (01437) 741383, ℛ, squas
   – ✺ rest, 🖸 ☎ 🅿, 🐠 🖭 *VISA* JCB
   *closed 24 to 26 December –* **Meals** (lunch by arrangement)/dinner a la carte 15.65/22.40
   ▯ 4.95 – **20 rm** ⊇ 40.00/75.00 **t.** – SB.

---

**WREXHAM** (Wrecsam) **402 403** L 24 *Wales G. – pop. 40 614.*
   See : *St. Giles Church★*.
   Env. : *Erddig★★ AC (Gardens★★), SW : 2 m – Gresford (All Saints Church★), N : 4 m.*
   *A 5152 and B 5445.*
   🏌 *Holt Rd* ℰ (01978) 261033 – 🏌, 🏌 *Chirk* ℰ (01691) 774407.
   🛈 *Lambpit St., LL11 1WN* ℰ (01978) 292015.
   *London 192 – Chester 12 – Shrewsbury 28.*

🏠 **Llwyn Onn Hall** ⤫, Cefn Rd, LL13 0NY, Northeast : 2 ½ m. by A 534 off Cefn R
   ℰ (01978) 261225, Fax (01978) 363233, ≤, 🏠, ℛ – ✺ 🖸 ☎ 🅿, 🐠 🖭 ① *VISA* JCB. ✹
   **Meals** 10.95/16.00 **st.** and a la carte ▯ 4.75 – **13 rm** ⊇ 62.00/85.00 **t.** – SB.

🏠 **Cross Lanes,** Marchwiel, LL13 0TF, Southeast : 3 ½ m. on A 525 ℰ (01978) 780555
   Fax (01978) 780568, ☎s, 🔲, ℛ, park – 🖸 ☎ 🅿 – 🔏 100. 🐠 🖭 ① *VISA* JCB. ✹
   *closed 25 and 26 December –* **Meals** a la carte 15.45/22.95 **st.** – ⊇ 8.00 – **16 rm** 60.00
   85.00 **st.** – SB.

🏠 **Travel Inn,** Chester Rd, LL12 8PW, Northeast : 2 ½ m. by A 483 on B 544
   ℰ (01978) 853214 – |鄭|, ✺ rm, 🖸 & 🅿 – 🔏 30. 🐠 🖭 ① *VISA*. ✹
   **Meals** (grill rest.) – **36 rm** 38.00 **t.**

🏠 **Travelodge,** Croes-Foel roundabout, Rhostyllen, LL14 4EJ, Southwest : 2 ½ m. off A 48
   (Wrexham bypass) ℰ (01978) 365705, Reservations (Freephone) 0800 850950 – ✺ 🖸 &
   🅿. 🐠 🖭 ① *VISA* JCB. ✹
   **Meals** (grill rest.) – **32 rm** 39.95/59.95 **t.**

   ⓐ ATS Dolydd Rd, Croesnewydd ℰ (01978) 352301/352928

# *Ireland*

# Northern Ireland

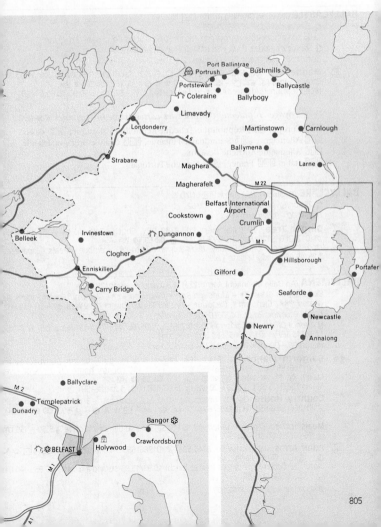

**ANNALONG** (Áth na Long) *Down* 923 O 5 *Ireland G.* – pop. 1 937.

Exc. : *W* : *Mourne Mountains*★★ :– *Bryansford, Tollymore Forest Park*★ *AC* – *Silent Valle Reservoir*★ *(*≤★*)* – *Spelga Pass and Dam*★ – *Drumena Cashel and Souterrain*★ – *Kilbrone Forest Park (viewpoint*★*).*
Belfast 37 – Dundalk 36.

🏠🏠 **Glassdrumman Lodge** ⤗, 85 Mill Rd, BT34 4RH, ℰ (013967) 6845 *Fax (013967) 67041*, ≤ Irish Sea and Mourne mountains, 🛋, park – 🍴 rest, 📺 ☎ 🅿. 🕮 *VISA*. ⩔
**Meals** (booking essential) (dinner only) 32.50 **t.** ⬧ 6.00 – **8 rm** ⊇ 85.00/135.00 **t.**, 2 suites SB.

**BALLYBOGY** (Baile an Bhogaigh) *Antrim* 923 M 2 – ⊠ *Ballymoney.*
Belfast 50 – Ballymena 22 – Londonderry 35 – Omagh 70.

⌂ **Heagles Lodge** without rest., 3 Heagles Rd, BT53 6NZ, ℰ (012657) 4112 *Fax (012657) 41001*, 🛋 – 🍴 📺 🅿. 🕮 *VISA*. ⩔
**3 rm** ⊇ 27.00/40.00 **s.**

**BALLYCASTLE** (Baile an Chaistil) *Antrim* 923 N 2.
🔸 Cushendall Rd ℰ (012657) 62536.
⤙ to Campbeltown (Argyll and Antrim Steam Packet Co.) 2 daily (2 h 45 mn).
🅱 Sheskburn House, 7 Mary St. BT54 6QH ℰ (012657) 62024.
Belfast 55 – Ballymena 27 – Coleraine 22.

🏠🏠 **Marine**, North St., BT64 6BN, ℰ (012657) 62222, *Fax (012657) 69507*, ≤ Fair Head an Rathlin Island, 🛁, 🚗, 🔲 – 🛄, 🍴 rm, 📺 ☎ 🕻 🅿 – 🔬 150. 🕮 🖭 ⓘ *VISA*. ⩔
**Meals** (bar lunch)/dinner 14.00 **t.** and a la carte ⬧ 4.95 – **32 rm** ⊇ 50.00/70.00 **t.** – SB.

*Pour voyager rapidement, utilisez les* **cartes Michelin "Grandes Routes"** :

970 Europe, 976 République Tchèque-République Slovaque, 980 Grèce, 984 Allemagne, 985 Scandinavie-Finlande, 986 Grande-Bretagne-Irlande, 987 Allemagne-Autriche-Benelux, 988 Italie, 989 France, 990 Espagne-Portugal.

**BALLYCLARE** (Bealach Cláir) *Antrim* 923 N/O 3.
🔸 25 Springvale Rd ℰ (01960) 342352.
Belfast 10 – Ballymena 14 – Larne 10.

XX **Ginger Tree**, 29 Ballyrobert Rd, BT39 9RY, South : 3 ¼ m. by A 57 on B 5 ℰ (01232) 848176, *Fax (01232) 844077* – 🅿. 🕮 🖭 ⓘ *VISA* JCB
*closed Saturday lunch, Sunday, 12-13 July and 24 to 26 December* – **Meals** - Japanese 7.25/15.95 **t.** and a la carte ⬧ 5.95.

**BALLYMENA** (An Baile Meánach) *Antrim* 923 N 3 *Ireland G.* – pop. 28 717.
Exc. : *Antrim Glens*★★★ – *Murlough Bay*★★ *(Fair Head* ≤★★*), Glengariff Forest Park*★★ *A (Waterfall*★★*), Glengariff*★*, Glendun*★ – *Antrim (Round Tower*★*) S* : 9½ m. by A 26.
🔸 128 Raceview Rd ℰ (01266) 861207/861487.
🅱 Council Offices, 80 Galgorm Rd, BT42 1AB ℰ (01266) 44111 – Morrows Shop, 17 Bridge St., BT43 5EJ ℰ (01266) 653663 (summer only).
Belfast 28 – Dundalk 78 – Larne 21 – Londonderry 51 – Omagh 53.

🏠🏠🏠 **Galgorm Manor** ⤗, BT42 1EA, West : 3 ¾ m. by A 42 on Cullybackey rd ℰ (01266) 881001, *Fax (01266) 880080*, ≤, « Part 19C country house on banks of River Main », 🔸, ⬱, 🚗, park – 📺 ☎ 🅿 – 🔬 500. 🕮 🖭 ⓘ *VISA*. ⩔
**Meals** 15.50/25.50 **t.** ⬧ 8.00 – **20 rm** ⊇ 95.00/130.00 **t.**, 3 suites – SB.

🏠🏠 **Country House** ⤗, 20 Doagh Rd, BT42 3LZ, Southeast : 6 m. by A 36 on B 59 ℰ (01266) 891663, *Fax (01266) 891477*, 🛁, ⬱, 🚗 – 📺 ☎ & 🅿 – 🔬 300. 🕮 🖭 ⓘ *VISA* ⩔
**Meals** *(closed Saturday lunch)* 12.95/18.50 **st.** and dinner a la carte ⬧ 5.50 – **39 rm** ⊇ 70.00/120.00 **st.** – SB.

🏠🏠 **Adair Arms**, Ballymoney Rd, BT43 5BS, ℰ (01266) 653674, *Fax (01266) 40436* – 📺 ☎ 🕻 🅿 – 🔬 250. 🕮 🖭 ⓘ *VISA*. ⩔
*closed 25 December* – **Meals** (buffet lunch) 10.95/15.95 **st.** and a la carte ⬧ 5.95 – **40 rm** ⊇ 59.50/85.00 **st.** – SB.

🔟 ATS Antrim Rd ℰ (01266) 652888

**BANGOR** (Beannchar) *Down* 923 O/P 4 *Ireland G.*.

See : *North Down Heritage Centre★*.

Exc. : *Priory (Cross Slabs★) – Mount Stewart★★★ AC, SE : 10 m. by A 2, A 21 and A 20 – Scrabo Tower (<★★) S : 6½ m. by A 21 – Ballycopeland Windmill★, SE : 10 m. by B 21 and A 2, turning right at Millisle – Strangford Lough★ (Castle Espie Centre★ AC - Nendrum Monastery★) – Grey Abbey★ AC, SE : 20 m. by A 2, A 21 and A 20.*

🛈 *34 Quay St. BT20 5ED* ℰ *(01247) 270069.*

*Belfast 14 – Newtownards 5.*

🏨🏨 **Marine Court,** 18-20 Quay St., BT20 5ED, ℰ (01247) 451100, *Fax* (01247) 451200, ➶, 🏊
– 🛗, ↹ rm, 📺 ☎ ㏐ 🅿 – 🔬 350. ◍◎ 🆑 ◉ 𝑽𝑰𝑺𝑨. ⚶
**Meals** a la carte 15.50/23.50 **t.** ⱥ 5.50 – **52 rm** ⌂ 88.00/125.00 **t.** – SB.

🏨 **Clandeboye Lodge,** Estate Rd, Clandeboye, BT19 1UR, Southwest : 3 m. by A 2 and
B 170 following signs for Blackwood Golf Centre ℰ (01247) 852500, *Fax* (01247) 852772,
🏋, ☞ – 🛗, ↹ rm, 📺 ☎ ㏐ & 🅿 – 🔬 350. ◍◎ 🆑 ◉ 𝑽𝑰𝑺𝑨
*closed 24 to 26 December –* **Meals** (bar lunch Monday to Saturday)/dinner 18.50 **st.** – **43 rm**
⌂ 85.00/95.00 **st.** – SB.

🏨 **Royal,** 26 Quay St., BT20 5ED, ℰ (01247) 271866, *Fax* (01247) 467810, ≤ – 🛗, ▤ rest, 📺 ☎
– 🔬 60. ◍◎ 🆑 ◉ 𝑽𝑰𝑺𝑨. ⚶
*closed 25 December –* **Meals** 17.50 **t.** (dinner) and a la carte 16.65/25.70 **t.** ⱥ 4.50 – **50 rm**
⌂ 75.00/90.00 **t.** – SB.

🏠 **Cairn Bay Lodge,** 278 Seacliffe Rd, BT20 5HS, East : 1¼ m. by Quay St.
ℰ (01247) 467636, *Fax* (01247) 457728, ≤, ☞ – ↹ 📺 ☎ 🅿 ◍◎ 𝑽𝑰𝑺𝑨. ⚶
*closed 1 week Christmas –* **Meals** (by arrangement) (communal dining) 15.00 **st.** – **3 rm**
⌂ 35.00/70.00 **st.**

🏠 **Shelleven,** 61 Princetown Rd, BT20 3TA, ℰ (01247) 271777, *Fax* (01247) 271777 – ↹ 📺
☎ 🅿 ◍◎ 𝑽𝑰𝑺𝑨. ⚶
**Meals** (by arrangement) 12.50 **st.** ⱥ 3.75 – **12 rm** ⌂ 25.00/50.00 **st.**

✕✕ **Shanks** (Millar), The Blackwood, Crawfordsburn Rd, Clandeboye, BT19 1GB, Southwest : 3
✿ ¼ m. by A 2 and B 170 following signs for Blackwood Golf Centre ℰ (01247) 853313,
*Fax* (01247) 852493, 🏋 – 🅿. ◍◎ 🆑 𝑽𝑰𝑺𝑨
*closed Saturday lunch, Sunday, Monday, Easter Tuesday, 25-26 December and 1 January –*
**Meals** 17.95/29.50 **t.** ⱥ 7.00
**Spec.** Fricasee of lobster and ceps, potato and truffle gnocchi, lobster sauce. Loin of lamb,
parsley purée, roast garlic, red wine and tapenade. Millefeuille of pistachio meringue,
poached pear and chocolate mousse.

◍ ATS 161 Clandeboye Rd ℰ (01247) 271736

---

*When travelling for business or pleasure*
*in England, Wales, Scotland and Ireland:*

- use the series of five maps
  (nos 401, 402, 403, 404 and 923) at a scale of 1:400 000

- they are the perfect complement to this Guide

# BELFAST - (Béal Feirste)

*Antrim* 923 O 4 *Ireland G. – pop. 279 237.*

*Dublin 103 – Londonderry 70.*

## TOURIST INFORMATION

- *St. Anne's Court, 59 North St., BT1 1NB &ℯ (01232) 246609.*
- *Belfast International Airport, BT29 4AB &ℯ (01849) 422888.*
- *Belfast City Airport, Sydenham Bypass, BT3 9JH &ℯ (01232) 457745.*

## PRACTICAL INFORMATION

- *Balmoral, 518 Lisburn Rd &ℯ (01232) 381514, AZ.*
- *Belvoir Park, Church Rd, Newtonbreda &ℯ (01232) 491693 AZ.*
- *Fortwilliam, Downview Av. &ℯ (01232) 370770, AY.*
- *The Knock Club, Summerfield, Dundonald &ℯ (01232) 482249.*
- *Shandon Park, 73 Shandon Park &ℯ (01232) 793730.*
- *Cliftonville, Westland Rd &ℯ (01232) 744158/746595, AY.*
- *Ormeau, 50 Park Rd &ℯ (01232) 641069, AZ.*

*Belfast International Airport, Aldergrove : &ℯ (01849) 422888, W : 15½ m. by A 52 AY –*
*Belfast City Airport : &ℯ (01232) 457745 – **Terminal** : Coach service (Ulsterbus Ltd.) from*
*Great Victoria Street Station (40 mn).*

*to Isle of Man (Douglas) (Isle of Man Steam Packet Co. Ltd) (summer only) (4 h 30 mn) –*
*to Stranraer (Stena Line) (3 h 15 mn), (Sea Containers Ferries Scotland Ltd and Stena Line)*
*4-5 daily (1 h 30 mn) – to Liverpool (Norse Irish Ferries Ltd) weekly (11 h).*

## TOURIST INFORMATION

**See :** *City★ - Ulster Museum★★ (Spanish Armada Treasure★★, Shrine of St. Patrick's Hand★)*
*AZ **M1** – City Hall★ BZ – Donegall Square★ BZ **20** – Botanic Gardens (Palm House★) AZ –*
*St Anne's Cathedral★ BY – Crown Liquor Saloon★ BZ – Sinclair Seaman's Church★ BY –*
*St Malachy's Church★ BZ.*

**Env. :** *Belfast Zoological Gardens★★ AC, N : 5 m. by A 6 AY.*

**Exc. :** *Carrickfergus (Castle★★ AC, St. Nicholas' Church★) NE : 9 ½ m. by A 2 – Talnotry*
*Cottage Bird Garden, Crumlin★ AC, W : 13½ m. by A 52.*

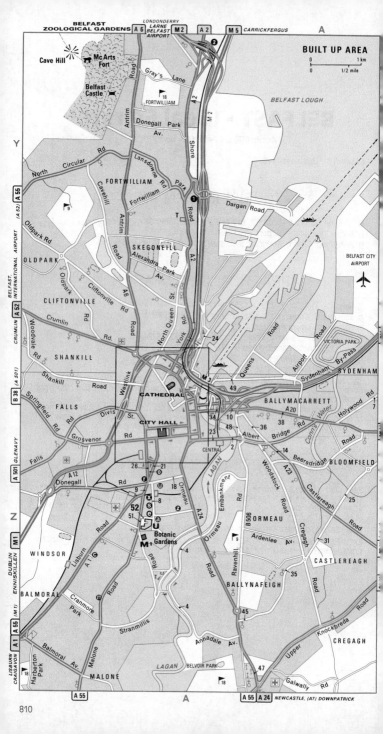

# BELFAST

n Northern Ireland traffic and parking are controlled in the town centres. No vehicle may be left unattended in a Control Zone.

*Your recommendation is self-evident if you always walk into a hotel Guide in hand.*

**Hilton Belfast**, 4 Lanyon Pl., BT1 3LP, ℘ (01232) 277000, Fax (01232) 277277, 16, ≋, 
– |⋕|, ⁂ rm, ▤ ▥ ☎ ℃ & ℗ – 益 400. ⬤ ℡ ⑩ VISA JCB                    BZ
Meals a la carte 18.00/21.00 ⅟ 7.00 – ⋥ 14.50 – **189 rm** 160.00/208.00 s., 6 suites.

**Europa**, Great Victoria St., BT2 7AP, ℘ (01232) 327000, Fax (01232) 327800 – |⋕|, ⁂ rm
▤ rest, ▥ ☎ & – 益 750. ⬤ ℡ ⑩ VISA. ⁂                    BZ
closed 24 and 25 December – **Gallery** : Meals (closed Saturday lunch and Sunday) 15.75
24.50 t. and dinner a la carte ⅟ 10.00 – **Brasserie** : Meals a la carte 11.70/21.40 t. ⅟ 3.00 –
⋥ 10.00 – **179 rm** 105.00/150.00 st., 5 suites.

**Stormont**, Upper Newtownards Rd, BT4 3LP, East : 4 ½ m. by A 2 on A 20
℘ (01232) 658621, Fax (01232) 480240 – |⋕|, ⁂ rm, ▥ ☎ ℃ & ℗ – 益 400. ⬤ ℡ ⑩ VISA
⁂
closed 25 December – **McMaster's** : Meals (closed Saturday lunch and Sunday) a la carte
21.00/26.00 st. – **La Scala** : Meals a la carte 14.50/20.00 st. – ⋥ 10.00 – **109 rm** 102.00
185.00 st. – SB.

**The Crescent Townhouse**, 13 Lower Cres., BT7 1NR, ℘ (01232) 323349
Fax (01232) 320646, « Regency house » – ▥ ☎. ⬤ ℡ VISA. ⁂                    AZ
**Metro Brasserie** : Meals (closed Sunday and Bank Holidays) a la carte 13.50/24.50 t. –
**11 rm** ⋥ 70.00/110.00 t. – SB.

**Jurys Inn**, Fisherwick Pl., Great Victoria St., BT2 7AP, ℘ (01232) 533500
Fax (01232) 533511 – |⋕|, ⁂ rm, ▥ ☎ ℃ & – 益 35. ⬤ ℡ ⑩ VISA. ⁂                    BZ
closed 24 to 26 December – **Meals** (grill rest.) (bar lunch Monday to Friday)/dinner 16.50 t.
and a la carte ⅟ 5.50 – ⋥ 7.00 – **190 rm** 70.00 st.

**Madison's**, 59-63 Botanic Av., BT7 1JL, ℘ (01232) 330040, Fax (01232) 328007 – |⋕|
▤ rest, ▥ ☎ &. ⬤ ℡ VISA. ⁂                    AZ
Meals a la carte 9.95/20.85 st. – **35 rm** ⋥ 65.00/82.00 st.

**Dukes**, 65 University St., BT7 1HL, ℘ (01232) 236666, Fax (01232) 237177, ≋ – |⋕|, ⁂ rm
▤ rest, ▥ ☎ – 益 130. ⬤ ℡ ⑩ VISA. ⁂                    AZ
Meals (bar lunch Saturday to Tuesday) 10.50/15.00 st. and a la carte ⅟ 5.95 – **21 rm**
⋥ 95.00/110.00 st. – SB.

**Travelodge**, 15 Brunswick St., BT2 7GE, ℘ (01232) 333555, Fax (01232) 232999, Reserva
tions (Freephone) 0800 850950 – |⋕|, ⁂ rm, ▤ rest, ▥ ☎ & – 益 70. ⬤ ℡ ⑩ VISA
⁂                    BZ
Meals (grill rest.) – **76 rm** 39.95/59.95 t. – SB.

**Holiday Inn Express**, 106A University St., BT7 1HP, ℘ (01232) 311909
Fax (01232) 311910 – |⋕|, ⁂ rm, ▥ ☎ & ℗ – 益 200. ⬤ ℡ ⑩ VISA JCB. ⁂                    AZ
closed 25 December – Meals 7.95 st. (lunch) and a la carte 9.70/15.75 st. – ⋥ 5.95 –
**114 rm** 59.95 st.

**Ash Rowan**, 12 Windsor Av., BT9 6EE, ℘ (01232) 661758, Fax (01232) 663227, ⇆ – ⁂
▥ ☎ ℗. ⬤ ℡ VISA. ⁂                    AZ
closed 2 weeks Christmas – Meals (by arrangement) 28.00 st. – **5 rm** ⋥ 46.00/79.00 st.

**Malone** without rest., 79 Malone Rd, BT9 6SH, ℘ (01232) 669565 – ▥ ℗. ⁂                    AZ
**8 rm** ⋥ 35.00/50.00 t.

**Deanes**, 38-40 Howard St., BT1 6PD, ℘ (01232) 331134, Fax (01232) 560001 – ▤. ⬤ ℡
VISA                    BZ
closed Sunday, Monday, 1 week July and 25-26 December – Meals (dinner only) 33.50 t. –
(see also **Downstairs at Deanes** below)
Spec. Clear soup of scallops and lobster, wonton, chilli and coriander. Lamb with couscous
ratatouille and goat's cheese. Assiette of apple, caramel and toffee.

**Roscoff**, 7 Lesley House, Shaftesbury Sq., BT2 7DB, ℘ (01232) 331532, Fax (01232) 31209.
– ▤. ⬤ ℡ ⑩ VISA                    AZ
closed Saturday lunch, Sunday, 1 January, Easter Monday, 12-13 July and 25 December –
Meals 17.50/29.95 t. ⅟ 12.00.

**Downstairs at Deanes**, 38-40 Howard St., BT1 6PD, ℘ (01232) 560000
Fax (01232) 560001 – ▤. ⬤ ℡ VISA                    BZ
closed Sunday, 1 week July and 25-26 December – Meals a la carte 17.50/22.45 t.

**Mizuna**, 99 Botanic Av., BT7 1JN, ℘ (01232) 230063, Fax (01232) 244808 – ⬤ VISA
closed Easter Monday, 12-13 July and 25-26 December – Meals (dinner only) 18.95 t.
and a la carte ⅟ 6.50.                    AZ

**Nick's Warehouse**, 37-39 Hill St. (1st Floor), BT1 2LB, ℘ (01232) 439690
Fax (01232) 230514 – ▤. ⬤ ℡ ⑩ VISA                    BY
closed Saturday lunch, Monday dinner, Sunday, 2 days Easter, 12 July and 25 to 28 Decem
ber – Meals a la carte 13.15/24.50 t. ⅟ 6.85.

✗ **La Belle Epoque,** 61-63 Dublin Rd, BT2 7HE, ℰ (01232) 323244, Fax (01232) 323244 – ◍◍
    ◭ ◍ ᴠɪsᴀ                                                                                        AZ o
    closed Saturday lunch, Sunday, 12-13 July, 25-26 December and 1 January – **Meals** 15.00 st.
    (dinner) and a la carte 14.70/20.40 **st.**

✗ **Manor House,** 43-47 Donegall Pass, BT7 1DQ, ℰ (01232) 238755, Fax (01232) 238755 –
    ▤. ◍◍ ᴠɪsᴀ                                                                                     AZ u
    closed 11 to 13 July and 25-26 December – **Meals** - Chinese (Canton) - 5.50/15.50 **t.**
    and a la carte ᵇ 4.50.

⊫ **Morning Star,** 17-19 Pottinger's Entry, BT1 4DT, ℰ (01232) 235986, Fax (01232) 438696
    – ◍◍ ◭ ᴠɪsᴀ
    closed Sunday, 11-12 July and 25 December – **Meals** a la carte 9.35/23.15 **st.**

**at Dundonald** East : 5½ m. on A 20 – AZ – ⊠ Belfast.

⌂ **Cottage** without rest., 377 Comber Rd, BT16 0XB, Southeast : 1 ¾ m. on Comber Rd
    (A 22) ℰ (01247) 878189, ☞ – ⊁ ℗. ⅍
    **3 rm** ⊊ 22.00/40.00.

**at Carryduff** South : 6 m. by A 24 – AZ – ⊠ Belfast.

▥ **Ivanhoe,** 556 Saintfield Rd, BT8 8EU, North : 1 m. on A 24 ℰ (01232) 812240,
    Fax (01232) 815516 – ⌖ ◍ ☎ ₺ ℗ – ⚶ 150. ◍◍ ᴠɪsᴀ
    closed 25 December – **Meals** 12.95/18.50 **t.** – **21 rm** ⊊ 70.00/90.00 **st.**

**at Dunmurry** Southwest : 5½ m. on A 1 – AZ – ⊠ Belfast.

▦ **Forte Posthouse Belfast,** 300 Kingsway, BT17 9ES, on A 1 ℰ (01232) 612101,
    Fax (01232) 626546, ☞, park – ⌖, ⊁ rm, ▤ rest, ◍ ☎ ℗ – ⚶ 400. ◍◍ ◭ ◍ ᴠɪsᴀ
    **Meals** (bar lunch Monday to Saturday) (carving lunch Sunday)/dinner 16.00 **st.**
    and a la carte ᵇ 6.95 – ⊊ 9.95 – **82 rm** 85.00 **st.** – SB.

▥ **Beechlawn House,** 4 Dunmurry Lane, BT17 9RR, ℰ (01232) 612974, Fax (01232) 623601
    – ◍ ☎ ◖ ℗ – ⚶ 300. ◍◍ ◭ ◍ ᴠɪsᴀ. ⅍
    **Meals** 11.95/14.95 **t.** and a la carte – **34 rm** ⊊ 66.00/76.00 **t.** – SB.

    ◉ ATS 4 Duncrue St. ℰ (01232) 749531                   ATS 26 Castlereagh Rd ℰ (01232) 798000
    ATS 37 Boucher Rd ℰ (01232) 663623

*The Guide is updated annually so renew your Guide every year.*

**BELFAST INTERNATIONAL AIRPORT** (Aerphort Béal Feirste) Antrim ◫◫◫ N 4 – ⊠ Aldergrove.
    ⤴ Belfast International Airport, Aldergrove : ℰ (01849) 422888.
    Belfast 15 – Ballymena 20 – Larne 23.

▥ **Aldergrove,** Aldergrove, BT29 4ZY, ℰ (01849) 422033, Fax (01849) 423500, ₧, ⊜s, ☞ –
    ⌖, ⊁ rm, ▤ ◍ ☎ ₺ ℗ – ⚶ 230. ◍◍ ◭ ◍ ᴠɪsᴀ. ⅍
    **Meals** 9.95/14.95 **st.** and dinner a la carte ᵇ 4.50 – ⊊ 7.50 – **108 rm** 75.00 **st.**

**BELLEEK** (Béal Leice) Fermanagh ◫◫◫ H 4 – pop. 550.
    Belfast 117 – Londonderry 56.

▥ **Carlton,** Main St., BT93 3FX, ℰ (013656) 58282, Fax (013656) 59005 – ⊁ rm, ◍ ☎ –
    ⚶ 200. ◍◍ ᴠɪsᴀ. ⅍
    closed 25 December – **Meals** (bar lunch)/dinner 16.95 **t.** and a la carte ᵇ 5.25 – **19 rm**
    ⊊ 52.00/75.00 **t.** – SB.

**BUSHMILLS** (Muileann na Buaise) Antrim ◫◫◫ M 2 Ireland G. – pop. 1 348 – ⊠ Bushmills.
    Exc. : Causeway Coast★★ : Giant's Causeway★★★ (Hamilton's Seat ≤★★), Carrick-a-rede
    Rope Bridge★★, Dunluce Castle★★ AC, Gortmore Viewpoint★ – Dunseverick Castle (≤★★),
    Magilligan Strand★, Downhill★ (Mussenden Temple★ ).
    ₆ Bushfoot, Bushfoot Rd, Portballintrae ℰ (012657) 31317.
    Belfast 57 – Ballycastle 12 – Coleraine 10.

▥ **Bushmills Inn,** 25 Main St., BT57 8QA, ℰ (012657) 32339, Fax (012657) 32048, « Part
    18C » – ◍ ☎ ◖ ℗ – ⚶ 50. ◍◍ ᴠɪsᴀ
    **Meals** (carving lunch Sunday) 14.25/22.00 **t.** and a la carte ᵇ 6.00 – **31 rm** ⊊ 58.00/
    118.00 **st.**, 1 suite – SB.

⌂ **Craig Park** ⏆ without rest., 24 Carnbore Rd, BT57 8YF, Southeast : 2 ½ m. by B 66 and
    Ballycastle rd (B 17), off How Rd ℰ (012657) 32496, Fax (012657) 32479, ≤, ☞ – ⊁ ◍ ℗.
    ◍◍ ᴠɪsᴀ. ⅍
    closed 20 December-3 January – **3 rm** ⊊ 30.00/50.00 **st.**

**CARNLOUGH** (Carnlach) *Antrim* 923 O 3 – *pop. 1 493.*
Belfast 35 – Ballymena 16 – Larne 14.

🏨 **Londonderry Arms,** 20 Harbour Rd, BT44 0EU, ℰ (01574) 885255, *Fax (01574) 885263–*
⌾ 📺 ☎ & ℗ – 🔬 120. 🆚 🗚 ⓪ 𝘝𝘐𝘚𝘈. ⅌
Meals 13.95/18.95 **t.** ◊ 6.25 – **35 rm** ☑ 48.00/80.00 **t.** – SB.

---

**CARRY BRIDGE** *Fermanagh* 923 J 5 – ✉ *Lisbellaw.*
Belfast 80 – Dundalk 62 – Londonderry 60.

⌂ **Aghnacarra House,** BT94 5HX, ℰ (01365) 387077, ⌇, 🐾 – ℗. ⅌
April-October – **Meals** (by arrangement) 8.50 – **7 rm** ☑ 25.00/38.00 – SB.

---

**CARRYDUFF** (Ceathrî Aodha Dhuibh) *Antrim* – see Belfast.

---

**CLOGHER** (Clochar) *Tyrone* 923 K 4.
Belfast 73 – Londonderry 55.

🏨 **Corick House** ⌇, 20 Corick Rd, BT76 0BZ, Northeast : 2 ½ m. by A 4 on unclassified r⌷
ℰ (016625) 48216, *Fax (016625) 49531,* ≤, ⌇, 🐾, park – 📺 ☎ & ℗. 🆚 🗚 ⓪ 𝘝𝘐𝘚𝘈. ⅌
Meals 7.95/21.95 **t.** and a la carte ◊ 4.95 – **10 rm** ☑ 30.00/70.00 **st.** – SB.

---

**COLERAINE** (Cîil Raithin) *Londonderry* 923 L 2 *Ireland G.* – *pop. 20 721.*
Exc. : Antrim Glens★★★ – Murlough Bay★★ (Fair Head ≤★★), Glenariff Forest Park★★ A⌷
(Waterfall★★), Glenariff★, Glendun★ – Causeway Coast★★ : Giant's Causeway★★★ (Hamil⌷
ton's Seat ≤★★) – Carrick-a-rede Rope Bridge★★ – Dunluce Castle★★ AC – Dunseveric
Castle (≤★★) – Gortmore Viewpoint★ – Magilligan Strand★ – Downhill★ (Mussender⌷
Temple★ ).
🏌, 🏌 Castlerock, Circular Rd ℰ (01265) 848314 – 🏌 Brown Trout, 209 Agivey Rd ℰ (01265⌷
868209 – 🛈 Railway Rd, BT52 1PE ℰ (01265) 44723.
Belfast 53 – Ballymena 25 – Londonderry 31 – Omagh 65.

🏨 **Bushtown House,** 283 Drumcroone Rd, BT51 3QT, South : 2 ½ m. on A 2⌷
ℰ (01265) 58367, *Fax (01265) 320909,* ℐ⌷, ⌇, ☒, 🐾 – 📺 ☎ & ℗ – 🔬 300. 🆚 🗚 𝘝𝘐𝘚𝘈
closed 25 and 26 December – **Meals** 17.50 **st.** (dinner) and a la carte 11.35/20.25 **st.** ◊ 4.5⌷
– **39 rm** ☑ 52.00/100.00 **st.** – SB.

🏨 **Brown Trout Golf and Country Inn,** 209 Agivey Rd, Aghadowey, BT51 4AD, South⌷
east : 9 m. on A 54 ℰ (01265) 868209, *Fax (01265) 868878,* �─, ℐ⌷, 🏌, ⌇, park – ⅍ rest⌷
📺 ☎ & ℗ – 🔬 40. 🆚 🗚 ⓪ 𝘝𝘐𝘚𝘈
Meals (bar lunch Monday to Saturday)/dinner a la carte 13.50/20.00 **st.** – **17 rm** ☑ 60.00⌷
85.00 **t.** – SB.

⌂ **Greenhill House** ⌇, 24 Greenhill Rd, Aghadowey, BT51 4EU, South : 9 m. by A 29 o⌷
B 66 ℰ (01265) 868241, *Fax (01265) 868365,* 🐾, park – ⅍ rest, 📺 ☎ ℗. 🆚 𝘝𝘐𝘚𝘈. ⅌
March-October – **Meals** (by arrangement) 16.00 – **6 rm** ☑ 30.00/49.00.

🅐 ATS Loguestown Ind. Est., Bushmills Rd ℰ (01265) 42329

---

**COOKSTOWN** (An Chorr Chráochach) *Tyrone* 923 L 4 *Ireland G..*
Env. : Ardboe Cross★, E : 4 m. by B 73.
🏌 Killymoon, 200 Killymoon Rd ℰ (016487) 63762/62254.
🛈 48 Molesworth St. BT80 8TA ℰ (016487) 66727.
Belfast 45 – Ballymena 27 – Londonderry 49.

🏨 **Tullylagan Country House** ⌇, 40B Tullylagan Rd, Sandholes, BT80 8UP, South : 4 m⌷
by A 29 ℰ (016487) 65100, *Fax (016487) 61715,* ⌇, 🐾, park – ⅍ rm, 📺 ☎ & ℗ – 🔬 180⌷
🆚 🗚 𝘝𝘐𝘚𝘈. ⅌
closed 24 to 26 December – **Meals** (bar lunch Saturday and Sunday dinner) a la cart⌷
18.65/21.85 **st.** ◊ 5.95 – ☑ 5.95 – **15 rm** 39.50/90.00 **st.** – SB.

---

**CRAWFORDSBURN** (Sruth Chráfard) *Down* 923 O 4 *Ireland G.* – *pop. 572.*
Env. : North Down Heritage Centre, Bangor★, E : 3 m. by B 20.
Exc. : – Priory (Cross Slabs★) – Mount Stewart★★★ AC, SE : 12 m. by A 2, A 21 and A 20 –
Scrabo Tower (≤★★), SW : 8 m. – Ballycopeland Windmill★ AC, E : 13 m. by A 2, A 21 an⌷
B 172 – Strangford Lough★ (Castle Espie Centre★ AC - Nendrum Monastery★ ) – Gre⌷
Abbey★ AC, SE : 14 m. by A 2, A 21 and A 20.
Belfast 10 – Bangor 3.

🏨 **Old Inn,** 15 Main St., BT19 1JH, ℰ (01247) 853255, *Fax (01247) 852775,* 🐾 – 📺 ☎ ℗ –
🔬 100. 🆚 🗚 ⓪ 𝘝𝘐𝘚𝘈. ⅌
Meals 21.00/22.50 **t.** and dinner a la carte ◊ 5.75 – **33 rm** ☑ 70.00/150.00 **t.** – SB.

**CRUMLIN** (Cromghlinn) Antrim 923 N 4 – pop. 2 697.
*Belfast 14 – Ballymena 20.*

⌂ **Caldhame Country Guest Lodge,** 102 Moira Rd, Nutts Corner, BT29 4HG, Southeast :
1 ¼ m. on A 26 &#x2118; (01849) 423099, Fax (01849) 422378, ⇆ – ⇆ 🖵 ☎ & 🅿. **ⓒⓞ** ⒜⒠ **VISA**. ✻
**Meals** (by arrangement) 15.00 **s. – 6 rm** �𝍌 25.00/45.00 **s.** – SB.

---

**DUNADRY** (Dîn Eadradh) Antrim 923 N 3 *Ireland G..*
Env. : *Antrim (Round tower★ ) NW : 4 m. by A 6.*
Exc. : *Crumlin : Talnotry Cottage Bird Garden★ AC, SW : 10½ m. by A 5, A 26 and A 52.*
*Belfast 15 – Larne 18 – Londonderry 56.*

🏨 **Dunadry,** 2 Islandreagh Drive, BT41 2HA, &#x2118; (01849) 432474, Fax (01849) 433389, ᛫᠍, ⃝,
⃝, ⇆, park – ⇆ rm, 🖵 ☎ 🅿 – ⃝ 300. **ⓒⓞ** ⒜⒠ ⓞ **VISA**. ✻
*closed 26 December* – **Meals** (buffet lunch Saturday) 9.50/17.95 **st.** and dinner a la carte ⃒ 5.00 – �𝍌 8.00 – **66 rm** 95.00/130.00 **st.**, 1 suite – SB.

---

**DUNDONALD** (Dîn DÉnaill) Antrim 923 O 4 – *see Belfast.*

*Groß-London (GREATER LONDON) besteht aus der City und 32
Verwaltungsbezirken (Borough). Diese sind wiederum in kleinere
Bezirke (Area) unterteilt, deren Mittelpunkt ehemalige Dörfer
oder Stadtviertel sind, die oft ihren eigenen Charakter bewahrt haben.*

---

**DUNGANNON** (Dîn Geanainn) Tyrone 923 L 4 *Ireland G.*
Env. : *The Argory★, S : 5 m. by A 29 and east by minor rd.*
Exc. : *Armagh★★ (St. Patrick's Cathedral★ (Anglican), St. Patrick's Cathedral★ (Roman Cath-
olic), The Mall★, Armagh County Museum★, – Regimental Museum of the Royal Irish
Fusiliers★ ), Navan Fort★ ), S : 12 m. by A 29.*
*Belfast 42 – Ballymena 37 – Dundalk 47 – Londonderry 60.*

🏨 **Inn on the Park,** Parkmount, Moy Rd, BT71 6BS, South : ¾ m. on A 29
&#x2118; (01868) 725151, Fax (01868) 724953, ⇆ – 🖵 ☎ 🅿 – ⃝ 120. **ⓒⓞ** ⒜⒠ ⓞ **VISA**
*closed 25 December* – **Meals** (bar meals Saturday lunch and Sunday dinner) 10.95/16.95 **st.**
and dinner a la carte ⃒ 4.25 – **13 rm** ⊑ 45.00/90.00 **st.** – SB.

🏠 **Cohannon Inn & Auto Lodge,** 212 Ballynakelly Rd, BT71 6HJ, East : 6 ¼ m. by A 29 and
M 1 on A 45 &#x2118; (01868) 724488, Fax (01868) 752217 – 🖵 & 🅿 – ⃝ 150. **ⓒⓞ** ⒜⒠ ⓞ **VISA**. ✻
*closed 25 December* – **Meals** (carving lunch)/dinner a la carte 10.35/18.65 **st.** ⃒ 3.95 – ⊑
4.95 – **50 rm** 34.95 **st.**

⌂ **Grange Lodge** ⃝, Grange Rd, BT71 7EJ, Southeast : 3 ½ m. by A 29 &#x2118; (01868) 784212,
Fax (01868) 723891, ⇆ – ⇆ 🖵 🅿. **ⓒⓞ** **VISA**. ✻
*closed 20 December-1 February* – **Meals** (by arrangement) 22.00 **t.** ⃒ 6.00 – **5 rm** ⊑ 49.00/
69.00 **t.**

🅐 ATS 51 Oaks Rd &#x2118; (01868) 723772

---

**DUNMURRY** (Dún Muirígh) Antrim 923 N 4 – *see Belfast.*

---

**ENNISKILLEN** (Inis Ceithleann) Fermanagh 923 J 4 *Ireland G. – pop. 11 436.*
Env. : *Castle Coole★★★ AC, SE : 1 m.*
Exc. : *NW : Lough Erne★★ : Cliffs of Magho Viewpoint★★★ AC – Devenish Island★ AC –
White Island★ – Janus Figure★ – Tully Castle★ AC – Florence Court★★ AC, SW : 8 m. by A 4
and A 32 – Marble Arch Caves and Forest Nature Reserve★ AC, SW : 10 m. by A 4 and A 32.*
᛫ᛃ *Castlecoole* &#x2118; (01365) 325250.
🅱 *Fermanagh Tourist Information Centre, Wellington Rd, BT74 7EF* &#x2118; (01365) 323110.
*Belfast 87 – Londonderry 59.*

🏨 **Killyhevlin,** Killyhevlin, BT74 6RW, Southeast : 1 ¾ m. on A 4 &#x2118; (01365) 323481,
Fax (01365) 324726, ≼, ⇆ – 🖵 ☎ & 🅿 – ⃝ 500. **ⓒⓞ** ⒜⒠ ⓞ **VISA**
*closed 25 December* – **Meals** 13.50/19.50 **st.** and a la carte ⃒ 6.25 – **42 rm** ⊑ 62.50/
95.00 **st.**, 1 suite – SB.

🏨 **Manor House Country** ⃝, Killadeas, BT94 1NY, North : 7 ½ m. by A 32 on B 82
&#x2118; (01365 6) 21561, Fax (01365 6) 21545, ≼, ᛫᠍, ⃝, ⃝, ⇆ – ⃧ 🖵 ☎ & 🅿 – ⃝ 300. **ⓒⓞ** ⒜⒠
**VISA**. ✻
**Meals** 11.75/21.50 **st.** – **46 rm** ⊑ 65.00/120.00 **st.** – SB.

**GILFORD** (Áth Mhic Giolla) Down 🔲🔲🔲 M 4 – pop. 1 639.
Belfast 30 – Dundalk 32.

XX **Yellow Door,** Whinney Hill, BT63 6EP, ℰ (01762) 831543 – ⛄. ⓪❾ ㏄ ₥₥
closed Sunday dinner and Monday – Meals 22.50/27.50 **t.** and dinner a la carte ⓦ 12.50.

---

**HILLSBOROUGH** (Cromghlinn) Down 🔲🔲🔲 N 4 Ireland G..
See : Town★ – Fort★.
Exc. : – The Argory★, W : 25 m. by A 1 and M 1.
Belfast 13.

🏨 **White Gables,** 14 Dromore Rd, BT26 6HS, Southwest : ½ m. ℰ (01846) 682755
Fax (01846) 689532 – ⛄ rm, ▤ rest, ☎ ☎ ℗ – 🔏 120. ⓪❾ ㏄ ⓪ ₥₥. ⅀
closed 24 and 25 December – Meals (closed Sunday) 15.50/22.50 **t.** and dinner a la carte –
ⓦ 9.50 – **31 rm** 85.00/110.00 **t.**

⌂ **Fortwilliam** without rest., 210 Ballynahinch Rd, BT26 6BH, Southeast : 3 ½ m. on B 177
ℰ (01846) 682255, Fax (01846) 689608, « Working farm », ⌨, park – ⛄ ☎ ℗. ⓪❾ ₥₥. ⅀
**3 rm** ⇌ 30.00/50.00.

X **Hillside,** 21 Main St., BT26 6AE, ℰ (01846) 682765, Fax (01846) 689888 – ⓪❾ ㏄ ⓪ ₥₥
closed Sunday and Monday – Meals (dinner only) a la carte 22.00/24.00 **t.** ⓦ 6.95.

---

**HOLYWOOD** (Ard Mhic Nasca) Down 🔲🔲🔲 O 4 Ireland G. – pop. 9 252.
Env. : Cultra : Ulster Folk and Transport Museum★★ AC, NE : 1 m. by A 2.
Belfast 5 – Bangor 6.

🏨 **Culloden,** 142 Bangor Rd, BT18 0EX, East : 1 ½ m. on A 2 ℰ (01232) 425223
≤, « Part Victorian Gothic manor », ₤₅, 🔲, ⌨, park, ⅍, squash – 🔾
⛄ rm, ☎ ☎ ℗ – 🔏 500. ⓪❾ ㏄ ⓪ ₥₥. ⅀
closed 24 and 25 December – **Mitre :** Meals (closed Saturday lunch) 22.50/25.00 **t**
and a la carte ⓦ 8.00 – **Cultra Inn :** Meals (closed Good Friday and 24 to 26 December) (gri
rest.) a la carte 12.45/22.45 **t.** – ⇌ 13.00 – **79 rm** 135.00/160.00 **t.**, 1 suite – SB.

🏨 **Rayanne House,** 60 Demesne Rd, BT18 9EX, by High St. and Downshire Rc
ℰ (01232) 425859, Fax (01232) 423364, ≤, ⌨ – ⛄ ☎ ℗. ⓪❾ ㏄ ₥₥. ⅀
closed 24 December-3 January – Meals (closed Sunday) (booking essential) (dinner only
a la carte 23.00/27.90 **t.** ⓦ 6.50 – **9 rm** ⇌ 75.00/90.00 **st.** – SB.

⌂ **Beech Hill** ⅏ without rest., 23 Ballymoney Rd, Craigantlet, BT23 4TG, Southeast : 4 ½ m
by A 2 on Craigantlet rd ℰ (01232) 425892, Fax (01232) 425892, ⌨, park – ⛄ ☎ ℗. ⓪❾
₥₥. ⅀
**3 rm** ⇌ 35.00/60.00 **st.**

X **Sullivans,** Unit 5, Sullivan Pl., BT18 9JF, ℰ (01232) 421000, Fax (01232) 426664 – ⓪❾ ㏄
₥₥
closed 1 week January, 11-12 July, 25 December and 1 January – Meals (restricted lunch
a la carte 12.00/18.50 **t.** ⓦ 5.00.

---

**IRVINESTOWN** (Baile an Irbhinigh) Fermanagh 🔲🔲🔲 J 4 Ireland G. – pop. 1 906.
Exc. : NW : Lough Erne★★ : Cliffs of Magho Viewpoint★★★ AC – Devenish Island★ AC –
White Island★ – Janus Figure★ – Tully Castle★ AC.
Belfast 78 – Dublin 132 – Donegal 27.

🏨 **Mahon's,** 2-10 Mill St., BT94 1GS, ℰ (013656) 21656, Fax (013656) 28344 – ☎ ☎ ℗. ⓪❾ ㏄
₥₥. ⅀
closed 25 December – Meals 10.50/14.50 **t.** and dinner a la carte ⓦ 5.50 – **18 rm** ⇌ 37.50
60.00 **t.** – SB.

---

**LARNE** (Latharna) Antrim 🔲🔲🔲 O 3 Ireland G. – pop. 17 575.
Env. : – SE : Island Magee (Ballylumford Dolmen★ ).
Exc. : NW : Antrim Glens★★★ – Murlough Bay★★ (Fair Head ≤★★ ), Glenariff Forest Park★★
AC (Waterfall★★ ), Glenariff★, Glendun★ – Carrickfergus (Castle★★ – St. Nicholas' Church★.
SW : 15 m. by A 2.
⛳ Cairndhu, 192 Coast Rd, Ballygally ℰ (01574) 583248.
⚓ – to Cairnryan (P & O European Ferries Ltd) 5-6 daily (1 h).
🏢 Narrow Gauge Rd, BT40 1XB ℰ (01574) 260088.
Belfast 23 – Ballymena 20.

⌂ **Derrin House** without rest., 2 Prince's Gdns., BT40 1RQ, off Glenarm Rd (A 2
ℰ (01574) 273269, Fax (01574) 273269 – ☎ ℗. ⓪❾ ㏄ ₥₥
closed 25 and 26 December – **6 rm** ⇌ 25.00/36.00.

**LIMAVADY** (Léim an Mhadaidh) *Londonderry* [923] L 2.
*Belfast 62 – Ballymena 39 – Coleraine 13 – Londonderry 17 – Omagh 50.*

🏨 **Radisson Roe Park H. & Golf Resort** 🪑, Roe Park, BT49 9LB, West : ½ m. on A 2 ✆ (015047) 22222, *Fax (015047) 22313*, 🏋, ♨, [🏊], ⛳18, 🎣, park – ⇅ [TV] ☎ ♿ [P] – 👥 440. [MC] [AE] [VISA]. 🚫🐕
Meals (bar lunch)/dinner a la carte 13.20/18.50 **t.** – ***The Courtyard* : Meals** *(closed Sunday and Monday)* (dinner only) 18.50 **t.** and a la carte 🍷 6.95 – **63 rm** ☕ 90.00/130.00 **st.**, 1 suite – SB.

**LONDONDERRY** (Doire) *Londonderry* [923] K 2/3 *Ireland G. – pop. 72 334.*
See : *Town★ – City Walls and Gates★★ – Long Tower Church★ – Tower Museum★.*
Env. : *Grianan of Aileach★★ (👁★★) (Republic of Ireland) NW : 5 m. by A 2 and N 13.*
Exc. : *SE : by A 6 – Sperrin Mountains★ : Ulster-American Folk Park★★ – Glenshane Pass★ (✳★★) – Sawel Mountain Drive★ (👁★★) – Roe Valley Country Park★ – Beaghmore Stone Circles★ – Ulster History Park★ – Oak Lough Scenic Road★.*
⛳18, ⛳9 *City of Derry, 49 Victoria Rd* ✆ *(01504) 311610/46369.*
✈ *Eglinton Airport :* ✆ *(01504) 810784, E : 6 m. by A 2.*
[i] *8 Bishop St., BT48 6PW* ✆ *(01504) 267284.*
*Belfast 70 – Dublin 146.*

🏨 **Everglades,** Prehen Rd, BT47 2PA, South : 1 ½ m. on A 5 ✆ (01504) 346722, *Fax (01504) 349200* – ⇅, 🚭 rest, [TV] ☎ [P] – 👥 400. [MC] [AE] [Diners] [VISA]. 🚫🐕
*closed 25 December* – ***The Satchmo* : Meals** (bar lunch)/dinner a la carte 16.70/21.95 **t.** 🍷 10.50 – **63 rm** ☕ 82.00/98.00 **st.**, 1 suite – SB.

🏨 **Waterfoot H. & Country Club,** 14 Clooney Rd, Caw Roundabout, BT47 6TB, Northeast : 3 ¾ m. at junction of A 39 with A 5 and A 2 ✆ (01504) 345500, *Fax (01504) 311006*, 🏋, ♨, [🏊] – [TV] ☎ ♿ [P] – 👥 100. [MC] [AE] [Diners] [VISA]. 🚫🐕
*closed 25 and 26 December* – **Meals** (bar lunch Saturday) a la carte 12.50/17.95 **t.** 🍷 4.95 – ☕ 7.00 – **48 rm** 65.00/75.00 **t.** – SB.

🏨 **Trinity,** 22-24 Strand Rd, BT48 7AB, ✆ (01504) 271271, *Fax (01504) 271277* – ⇅, 🚭 rest, [TV] ☎ 📞 ♿ [P] – 👥 55. [MC] [AE] [Diners] [VISA]. 🚫🐕
Meals (bar lunch)/dinner 14.95 **t.** and a la carte – **37 rm** ☕ 70.00/85.00 **t.**, 3 suites – SB.

🏨 **Beech Hill House** 🪑, 32 Ardmore Rd, BT47 3QP, Southeast : 3 ½ m. by A 6 ✆ (01504) 349279, *Fax (01504) 345366*, « 18C merchant's house », 🎣, 🌳, park, 🎾 – 🚭 rest, [TV] ☎ [P] – 👥 100. [MC] [AE] [VISA]. 🚫🐕
*closed 24 and 25 December* – **Meals** 15.95 **t.** (lunch) and dinner a la carte 22.85/29.85 **t.** 🍷 6.95 – **17 rm** ☕ 67.50/90.00 **t.** – SB.

🏨 **White Horse,** 68 Clooney Rd, BT47 3PA, Northeast : 6 ½ m. on A 2 (Coleraine rd) ✆ (01504) 860606, *Fax (01504) 860371* – [TV] ☎ [P] – 👥 500. [MC] [AE] [Diners] [VISA]. 🚫🐕
**Meals** (grill rest.) a la carte 10.95/20.50 **st.** – **43 rm** ☕ 50.00/60.00 **st.** – SB.

**MAGHERA** (Machaire Rátha) *Londonderry* [923] L 3.
*Belfast 40 – Ballymena 19 – Coleraine 21 – Londonderry 32.*

🏨 **Ardtara Country House** 🪑, 8 Gorteade Rd, Upperlands, BT46 5SA, North : 3 ¼ m. by A 29 off B 75 ✆ (01648) 44490, *Fax (01648) 45080*, 👁, « 19C », 🌳, 🎾 – 🚭 rest, [TV] ☎ [P]. [MC] [AE] [VISA]. 🚫🐕
*closed 25 and 26 December* – **Meals** *(closed Saturday lunch and Sunday dinner)* (booking essential) 14.50/25.00 **t.** and dinner a la carte 🍷 5.00 – **8 rm** ☕ 80.00/120.00 **t.** – SB.

**MAGHERAFELT** (Machaire Fáolta) *Londonderry* [923] M 3 – *pop. 7 143.*
*Belfast 35 – Ballymena 17 – Coleraine 29 – Londonderry 40.*

🍴🍴 **Trompets,** 25 Church St., BT45 6AP, ✆ (01648) 32257, *Fax (01648) 34441* – 🚭. [MC] [AE] [VISA]
*closed Sunday dinner, Monday, 4 to 11 January, 12 to 20 July and 25 December* – **Meals** 23.95 **t.** (dinner) and lunch a la carte 12.50/18.00 **t.**

**MARTINSTOWN** (Baile Uí Mháirtán) *Antrim* [923] N 3 – ✉ *Ballymena.*
*Belfast 36 – Dundalk 86 – Larne 28 – Londonderry 58 – Omagh 61.*

🏠 **Caireal Manor** without rest., 90 Glenravel Rd, Glen's of Antrim, BT43 6QQ, ✆ (012667) 58465, *Fax (012667) 58465* – [TV] ♿ [P]. [MC] [VISA]. 🚫🐕
**5 rm** ☕ 25.00/50.00 **st.**

Les prix — Pour toutes précisions sur les prix indiqués dans ce guide, reportez-vous aux pages de l'introduction.

**NEWCASTLE** (An Caisleán Nua) *Down* 923 O 5 *Ireland G. – pop. 7 214.*

Env. : *Castlewellan Forest Park*★★ *AC, NW : 4 m. by A 50 – Dundrum Castle*★ *AC, NE : 4 m* by A 2 – Downpatrick (Down Cathedral★ – Down County Museum★), NE : by A 2.

Exc. : *SW : Mourne Mountains*★★ *: Bryansford, Tollymore Forest Park*★ *AC – Silent Valle* Reservoir★ (≤★) – *Spelga Pass and Dam*★ – Kilbroney Forest Park (viewpoint★) – Stru Wells★, *NE : 12 m. by A 2 – Ardglass*★, *NE : 18 m. by A 2.*

🖪 *The Newcastle Centre, 10-14 Central Promenade, BT33 0AA* ℰ *(013967) 22222.*
*Belfast 30 – Londonderry 101.*

🏨 **Burrendale H. & Country Club,** 51 Castlewellan Rd, BT33 0JY, North : 1 m. on A 5 ℰ (013967) 22599, *Fax (013967) 22328,* ℐ₅, ⌺, ◩, ℱ – ⱡ, 🔲 rest, 🔟 ☎ ♿ ℗ – ♨ 15 ⓒⓢ ⒶⒺ ⓞ VISA. ⚘
**Meals** (dinner only and Sunday lunch)/dinner 19.50 **t.** and a la carte ⓙ 6.95 – **67 r** ⌇ 60.00/110.00 **t.,** 1 suite – SB.

🏨 **Briers** ≫, 39 Middle Tollymore Rd, BT33 0JJ, North : 1 ½ m. by Bryansford Rd (B 180) an Tollymore Rd ℰ (013967) 24347, *Fax (013967) 24347,* ≤, ℱ – ⌲ rm, 🔟 ☎ ♿ ℗. ⓒⓢ Ⓛ VISA. ⚘
**Meals** a la carte 12.00/16.00 **st.** ⓙ 5.00 – **9 rm** ⌇ 35.00/50.00 **st.** – SB.

---

**NEWRY** (An tIÍr) *Down* 923 M 5 *Ireland G. – pop. 21 633.*

See : *Bernish Rock Viewpoint*★★.
*Belfast 37 – Dundalk 16.*

🏨 **Mourne Country,** 52 Belfast Rd, BT34 1TR, North : 1 ¼ m. ℰ (01693) 6792 *Fax (01693) 60896* – 🔟 ☎ ℗ – ♨ 400. ⓒⓢ ⒶⒺ ⓞ VISA. ⚘
*closed 25 December –* **Meals** (bar lunch Monday to Saturday)/dinner 14.95 **t.** and a la cart ⓙ 5.95 – **41 rm** ⌇ 49.50/65.00 **st.,** 2 suites – SB.

🔧 ATS Downshire Rd ℰ (01693) 63077

---

**PORTAFERRY** (Port an Pheire) *Down* 923 P 4 *Ireland G. – pop. 2 324.*

See : *Aquarium*★.
Env. : *Castle Ward*★★ *AC, SW : 4 m. by boat and A 25.*
Exc. : *SE : Lecale Peninsula*★★ *– Struell Wells*★, *Quoile Pondage*★, *Ardglass*★, *Strangford*★ Audley's Castle★.
🖪 *Shore St., Nr Strangford Ferry Departure Point (summer only).*
*Belfast 29 – Bangor 24.*

🏨 **Portaferry,** 10 The Strand, BT22 1PE, ℰ (012477) 28231, *Fax (012477) 28999,* ≤, « Pa 18C, loughside setting » – 🔟 ☎ ℗. ⓒⓢ ⒶⒺ ⓞ VISA. ⚘
*closed 24 and 25 December –* **Meals** (bar lunch Monday to Saturday)/dinner 21.50 **t.** ⓙ 6.8 – **13 rm** ⌇ 55.00/90.00 **t.** – SB.

---

**PORT BALLINTRAE** (Port Bhaile an Trá) *Antrim* 923 M 2 *Ireland G. – pop. 756 –* ⊠ *Bushmills.*

Exc. : *Causeway Coast*★★ *: Giant's Causeway*★★★ *(Hamilton's Seat* ≤★★*) – Carrick-a-rea* Rope Bridge★★ *– Dunluce Castle*★★ *AC – Dunseverick Castle* (≤★★*) – Gortmore Viewpoint* – *Magilligan Strand*★ *– Downhill*★ *(Mussenden Temple*★ *).*
*Belfast 68 – Coleraine 15.*

🏨 **Bayview,** 2 Bayhead Rd, BT57 8RZ, ℰ (012657) 31453, *Fax (012657) 32360,* ≤, ⌺, ◩ 🔟 ☎ ℃ ℗ – ♨ 200. ⓒⓢ VISA.
*closed 25 December –* **Meals** *(closed Sunday dinner)* (bar lunch)/dinner 12.95 **t.** ⓙ 6.75 **15 rm** ⌇ 40.00/70.00 **t.** – SB.

---

**PORTRUSH** (Port Rois) *Antrim* 923 L 2 *Ireland G. – pop. 5 703.*

Exc. : *Causeway Coast*★★ *: Giant's Causeway*★★★ *(Hamilton's Seat* ≤★★*) – Carrick-a-rea* Rope Bridge★★ *– Dunluce Castle*★★ *AC – Dunseverick Castle* (≤★★*) – Gortmore Viewpoint* – *Magilligan Strand*★ *– Downhill*★ *(Mussenden Temple*★ *).*
⌐₈, ⌐₈, ⌐₉ *Royal Portrush, Dunluce Rd* ℰ *(01265) 822311.*
🖪 *Dunluce Centre, Sandhill St., BT56 8BT* ℰ *(01265) 823333 (summer only).*
*Belfast 58 – Coleraine 4 – Londonderry 35.*

🏨 **Magherabuoy House,** 41 Magheraboy Rd, BT56 8NX, Southwest : 1 m. by A 2 ℰ (01265) 823507, *Fax (01265) 824687,* ≤, ⌺, ℱ – ⌲ rest, 🔟 ☎ ℗ – ♨ 400. ⓒⓢ ⒶⒺ ⓒ VISA. ⚘
*closed 25 December –* **Meals** (bar lunch)/dinner a la carte 10.15/14.40 **st.** – **38 rm** ⌇ 60.00 100.00 **st.** – SB.

🏛 **Causeway Coast,** 36 Ballyreagh Rd, BT56 8LR, Northwest : 1 ¼ m. on A 2 (Portstewart rd) *℘ (01265) 822435, Fax (01265) 824495,* ≤ – 🆃🆅 ☎ 🅿 – 🔬 500. 🆖 🆎 ⓪ 𝘝𝘐𝘚𝘈. ⋘
*closed 25 December –* **Meals** *(bar lunch)/dinner a la carte 15.00/20.00* **st.** – **21 rm** � 45.00/
75.00 **st.** – SB.

✕✕ **Ramore,** The Harbour, BT56 8BN, *℘ (01265) 824313, Fax (01265) 823194,* ≤ – ▤ 🅿. 🆖
🍴 𝘝𝘐𝘚𝘈
*closed Sunday, Monday, 24 to 26 December and 1 January –* **Meals** *(booking essential)*
*(dinner only) a la carte 16.25/29.95* **t.** ⌀ 5.25.

---

**PORTSTEWART** (Port Stíobhaird) *Londonderry* 🄌🄌🄌 L 2 *Ireland G. – pop. 6 459.*

Exc. : *Causeway Coast*★★ *(Giant's Causeway*★★★ *(Hamilton's Seat* ≤★★*) – Carrick-a-rede
Rope Bridge*★★ *– Dunluce Castle*★★ *AC – Dunseverick Castle (*≤★★*) – Gortmore Viewpoint*★
*– Magilligan Strand*★ *– Downhill*★ *(Mussenden Temple*★*).*

🄱 *Town Hall, The Crescent, BT55 7AB ℘ (01265) 832286 (summer only).*

*Belfast 67 – Coleraine 6.*

🏛 **Edgewater,** 88 Strand Rd, BT55 7LZ, *℘ (01265) 833314, Fax (01265) 832224,* ≤, 🛁, 🚇 –
🆃🆅 ☎ 🅿 – 🔬 150. 🆖 🆎 ⓪ 𝘝𝘐𝘚𝘈. ⋘
**Meals** *10.00/16.50* **t.** *and dinner a la carte* ⌀ 5.50 – **31 rm** � 40.00/90.00 **t.** – SB.

---

**SEAFORDE** (Baile Forda) *Down* 🄌🄌🄌 O 5 – *pop. 186 –* ✉ *Downpatrick.*

*Belfast 25 – Dundalk 45 – Dungannon 53.*

⋔ **Drumgooland House** ⌂ *without rest.,* 29 Dunnanew Rd, BT30 8PJ, North : 2 m. by
A 24 *℘ (01396) 811956, Fax (01396) 811265,* ≤, ⟍, 🌧, *park –* 🆃🆅 🅿. 🆖 🆎 𝘝𝘐𝘚𝘈. ⋘
**3 rm** � 26.50/43.00 **st.** – SB.

---

**STRABANE** (An Srath Bán) *Tyrone* 🄌🄌🄌 J 3 *Ireland G. – pop. 11 981.*

Exc. : *Sperrin Mountains*★ : *Ulster-American Folk Park*★★ *– Glenshane Pass*★ *(*⋇★★*) – Sawel
Mountain Drive*★ *(*≤★★*) – Roe Valley Country Park*★ *– E : Beaghmore Stone Circles*★ *– Ulster
History Park*★ *– Oak Lough Scenic Road*★.

🄶 *Ballycolman ℘ (01504) 382271/382007.*

🄱 *Abercorn Square, BT82 8DY ℘ (01504) 883735 (summer only).*

*Belfast 87 – Donegal 34 – Dundalk 98 – Londonderry 14.*

🏛 **Fir Trees,** Melmount Rd, BT82 9JT, South : 1 ¼ m. on A 5 *℘ (01504) 382382,
Fax (01504) 383116 –* 🆃🆅 ☎ 🅿. 🆖 🆎 ⓪ 𝘝𝘐𝘚𝘈. ⋘
**Meals** *(bar lunch Monday to Saturday)/dinner 10.00* **st.** *and a la carte* ⌀ 4.95 – **25 rm**
⊹ 35.00/55.00 **st.** – SB.

---

**TEMPLEPATRICK** (Teampall Phádraig) *Antrim* 🄌🄌🄌 N 3 – *pop. 1 414 –* ✉ *Ballyclare.*

*Belfast 12 – Ballymena 16 – Dundalk 65 – Larne 16.*

🏛 **Templeton,** 882 Antrim Rd, BT39 0AH, *℘ (01849) 432984, Fax (01849) 433406,* 🌧 – 🆃🆅
☎ 🅿 – 🔬 300. 🆖 🆎 ⓪ 𝘝𝘐𝘚𝘈. ⋘
*closed 25 and 26 December –* **Templeton :** **Meals** *(closed Saturday lunch) 10.50/19.95* **t.**
*and dinner a la carte* ⌀ 6.25 – **Upton Grill :** **Meals** *(grill rest.) a la carte 7.50/18.05* **st.** –
**24 rm** ⊹ 90.00/130.00 **st.**

---

# *Republic of Ireland*

# Dear Reader

This 26th edition of the Michelin Guide Great Britain & Ireland offers the latest selection of hotels and restaurants. Independently compiled by our inspectors, the Guide offers travellers a wide choice of establishments at all levels of comfort and price.

In 1999, prices in EURO will become more widely used, although to a large extent they remain optional, so that a customer may settle their bill in EURO (either by cheque or credit card) or in the local currency. Only the Republic of Ireland is affected by this decision.

The implementation of the EURO is still under development, and we have therefore decided to continue to include prices in this Guide in local currency.

On your travels look out for the many restaurants awarded the **"Bib Gourmand"** symbol, which indicates moderately priced menus and good value for money.

Thank you for your comments which are always appreciated.

Bon voyage ! _____


# Ami lecteur

Cette 26e édition du Guide Michelin Great Britain & Ireland propose une sélection actualisée d'hôtels et de restaurants. Réalisée en toute indépendance, par nos inspecteurs, elle offre au voyageur de passage un large choix d'adresses à tous les niveaux de confort et de prix.

En 1999, l'application des tarifs commerciaux exprimés en EUROS tend à se répandre, mais reste néanmoins facultative, chaque client pouvant régler indifféremment sa note en EUROS (par chèque ou carte banquaire) ou en devise nationale. Cette mesure ne concerne que la République d'Irlande. Toutefois, cette mise en œuvre étant progressive, nous avons choisi d'indiquer dans notre ouvrage les prix dans la monnaie nationale.

Sur votre route, pour trouver de bonnes adresses à petits prix, suivez donc les nombreux restaurants que vous signale le **"Bib Gourmand"**.

Merci de vos commentaires toujours appréciés.
Michelin vous souhaite «Bon voyage !» _____

# Amico lettore

*Questa 26esima edizione della Guida Michelin Great Britain & Ireland propone una selezione aggiornata di alberghi e ristoranti. Realizzata dai nostri ispettori in piena autonomia, offre al viaggiatore di passaggio un'ampia scelta a tutti i livelli di confort e prezzo.*

*NEl 1999 l'applicazione delle tariffe commerciali in EURO tende a diffondersi, ma resta ancora facoltativa, potendo il cliente scegliere di pagare il conto in EURO (con assegno o carta di credito) od in valuta nazionale. Questa indicazione riguarda solo la Repubblica d'Irlanda.*
*Essendo questa trasformazione ancora in atto, abbiamo preferito indicare nella nostra pubblicazione i prezzi in moneta nazionale.*

*Lungo la vostra strada, per trovare dei buoni indirizzi a prezzi interessanti, cercate i tanti ristoranti contrassegnati dal*

**"Bib Gourmand"**

*Grazie delle vostre segnalazioni sempre gradite.*

*Buon viaggio con Michelin.* ⸻

# Lieber Leser

*Die vorliegende 26. Ausgabe des Roten Michelin-Führers Great Britain & Ireland bringt eine aktuelle Auswahl an Hotels und Restaurants. Sie wurde von unseren Inspektoren in völliger Unabhängigkeit erstellt und bietet dem Reisenden eine breit gefächerte Auswahl von Adressen in allen Komfort- und Preisklassen.*

*1999 gehen immer mehr Geschäfte dazu über, ihre Preise in EURO anzugeben, wenn dies auch noch nicht verbindlich vorgeschrieben ist und es dem Kunden freigestellt bleibt, ob er seine Rechnung in EURO (bei bargeldloser Zahlung) oder in der Landeswährung begleichen will. Diese Massnahme betrifft nur die Republik Irland.*
*Da sich diese Umstellung aber nach und nach vollzieht, haben wir uns entschieden, in der vorliegenden Ausgabe die Preise noch in der Landeswährung anzugeben.*

*Wenn Sie unterwegs gut und preiswert essen möchten, folgen Sie dem* **"Bib Gourmand"***, der Ihnen den Weg zu zahlreichen Restaurants mit besonder, günstigem Preis-/Leistungsverhältnis weist.*

*Vielen Dank für Ihre Anregungen und Hinweise, die uns stets willkommen sind.*

*Gute Reise mit Michelin* ⸻

- *Prices quoted in this section of the guide are in Irish pounds (punt)*
- *Dans cette partie du guide, les prix sont indiqués en monnaie irlandaise «Punt»*
- *In questa parte della guida, i prezzi sono indicati in livres irlandesi «Punt»*
- *In diesem Teil des Führers sind die Preise in irländischer Währung «Punt» angegeben*

## ABBEYLEIX (Mainistir Laoise) Laois 923 J 9 – pop. 1 299.
Dublin 60 – Kilkenny 22 – Limerick 67.

**Hibernian**, Pembroke Terr., ℰ (0502) 31252, Fax (0502) 31888 – TV ☎. ◐◐ ◐ VISA. ⋇
closed Good Friday and 25 December – **Meals** 8.00 st. (lunch) and dinner a la carte 7.80/16.15 st. ⬧ 6.50 – **10 rm** ⊆ 30.00/60.00 st. – SB.

**Preston House**, Main St., ℰ (0502) 31432, Fax (0502) 31662, 🌲 – ⋇ TV ☎ ℗. ◐◐ VISA
closed 23 to 31 December and January**Meals** – (see **Preston House Cafe** below) – **4 rm** ⊆ 30.00/52.00 t.

**Preston House Cafe** (at Preston House H.), Main St., ℰ (0502) 31432, Fax (0502) 31662, 🌲 – ℗. ◐◐ VISA
closed Sunday dinner, Monday, 23 to 31 December and January – **Meals** 13.00/20.00 t. and a la carte ⬧ 5.50.

## ACHILL ISLAND (Acaill) Mayo 923 B 5/6 Ireland G..
See : Island★.
🖪 Achill Sound ℰ (098) 45384 (1 July-31 August).

**Doogort** (Dumha Goirt) – ⊠ Achill Island.
🖫 Keel ℰ (098) 43456.

**Gray's** ⤸, ℰ (098) 43244, 🌲 – ⋇ rest, TV ℗
closed 25 December – **Meals** (by arrangement) 17.50 st. ⬧ 5.00 – **15 rm** ⊆ 25.00/50.00 st.

## ADARE (Áth Dara) Limerick 923 F 10 Ireland G. – pop. 1 042.
See : Town★ – Adare Friary★ – Adare Parish Church★.
Exc. : Rathkeale (Castle Matrix★ AC – Irish Palatine Heritage Centre★) W : 7½ m. by N 21 – Newcastle West★, W : 16 m. by N 21 – Glin Castle★ AC, W : 29 m. by N 21, R 518 and N 69.
🖪 ℰ (061) 396255 (1 June-30 October).
Dublin 131 – Killarney 59 – Limerick 10.

**Adare Manor** ⤸, ℰ (061) 396566, Fax (061) 396124, ≤, « 19C Gothic mansion in extensive parkland », ℩₅, ⓕ, ◻, ⓟ, ◜, 🌲 – ⬧ TV ☎ ℗ – 🔬 180. ◐◐ AE ◐ VISA. ⋇
Meals 21.50/34.50 t. and a la carte – ⊆ 12.50 – **63 rm** 215.00/355.00 st.

**Dunraven Arms**, Main St., ℰ (061) 396633, Fax (061) 396541, ℩₅, ◻, 🌲 – ⬧ TV ☎ ℃ ℗ – 🔬 400. ◐◐ AE ◐ VISA. ⋇
closed 25 December – **Meals** – (see **Maigue** below) – ⊆ 9.95 – **76 rm** 90.00/160.00 t. – SB.

**Woodlands House** ⤸, Knockanes, Southeast : 2 m. by N 21 on Croom rd ℰ (061) 396118, Fax (061) 396073, 🌲 – TV ☎ ℗ – 🔬 350. ◐◐ AE ◐ VISA
closed 24 and 25 December – **Meals** a la carte 10.75/14.00 st. ⬧ 6.50 – **57 rm** ⊆ 50.00/100.00 st. – SB.

**Adare Lodge** without rest., Kildimo Rd, ℰ (061) 396629, Fax (061) 395060 – ⋇ TV ℗. ◐◐ VISA. ⋇
**6 rm** ⊆ 35.00/45.00 st.

**Carrabawn Guesthouse** without rest., Killarney Rd, Southwest : ½ m. on N 21 ℰ (061) 396067, Fax (061) 396925, 🌲 – ⋇ TV ☎ ℗. ◐◐ VISA
**8 rm** ⊆ 40.00/60.00 st.

**Sandfield House** without rest., Castleroberts, Southeast : 3 ¼ m. by N 21 on Croom rd ℰ (061) 396119, Fax (061) 396119, 🌲 – ℗. ◐◐ VISA. ⋇
March-October – **4 rm** ⊆ 27.00/46.00 st.

**Abbey Villa** without rest., Kildimo Rd, ℰ (061) 396113, Fax (061) 396969 – TV ℗. ◐◐ VISA. ⋇
closed December – **6 rm** ⊆ 25.00/50.00.

**Maigue** (at Dunraven Arms H.), Main St., ℰ (061) 396633, Fax (061) 396541, 🌲 – ℗. ◐◐ AE ◐ VISA
closed 25 December – **Meals** (dinner only and Sunday lunch)/dinner 23.95 t. and a la carte ⬧ 5.95.

XX **The Wild Geese,** Main St., ℰ (061) 396451, Fax (061) 396451 – **🅼🅲 🅰🅴 🅾 VISA**
closed Sunday, Monday, 1 week November and 2 weeks January – **Meals** (light lunch May-September) a la carte 15.40/28.95 **t.**

---

**AGLISH** (An Eaglais) Tipperary **🄦🄦🄦** H 8 – ✉ Borrisokane.
Dublin 114 – Galway 53 – Limerick 43.

↑ **Ballycormac House** ⬙, ℰ (067) 21129, Fax (067) 21200, ╲, ⌗, park – ⇇ **🅿**. **🅼🅲 VISA**. ⬤
**Meals** (by arrangement) (communal dining) 24.00 **t.** ↑ 10.00 – **4 rm** ⚌ 35.00/70.00 **t.**, 1 suite.

---

**AHAKISTA** (Áth an Chiste) Cork **🄦🄦🄦** D 13 – ✉ Bantry.
Dublin 217 – Cork 63 – Killarney 59.

XX **Shiro** (Kei Pilz), ℰ (027) 67030, Fax (027) 67206, ⬱ Dunmanus Bay, ⌗ – **🅿**. **🅼🅲 🅰🅴 🅾 VISA**
☸ closed 25 December, January and February **Meals** - Japanese - (booking essential) (dinner only) 42.00 **t.**
**Spec.** Sashimi. Tempura. Sushi.

---

**AHERLOW** (Eatharlach) Tipperary **🄦🄦🄦** H 10 – see Glen of Aherlow.

---

**ARAN ISLANDS** (Oileáin Árann) Galway **🄦🄦🄦** CD 8 Ireland G..
See : Islands★ – Inishmore (Dun Aenghus★★★).
Access by boat or aeroplane from Galway city or by boat from Kilkieran, Rossaveel or Fisherstreet (Clare) and by aeroplane from Inverin.
🖪 ℰ (099) 61263 (30 May-15 September).

**Inishmore** – ✉ Aran Islands.

↑ **Ard Einne** ⬙, Killeany, ℰ (099) 61126, Fax (099) 61388, ⬱ Killeany Bay – **🅿**. **🅼🅲 🅾 VISA**
⬤ closed 10 November-2 February – **Meals** (by arrangement) 13.00 **t.** ↑ 6.00 – **12 rm** ⚌ 35.00/40.00 **t.** – SB.

↑ **Kilmurvy House** ⬙, Kilmurvy, ℰ (099) 61218, Fax (099) 61397, ⬱, park – **☎**. **🅼🅲 VISA**. ⬤
closed January and February – **Meals** (by arrangement) 14.00 **st.** ↑ 7.00 – **12 rm** ⚌ 27.00/40.00 **st.**

---

**ARDEE** (Baile Átha Fhirdhia) Louth **🄦🄦🄦** M 6 Ireland G – pop. 3 440.
Exc. : Dún a' Rá Forest Park★, SW : by N 52 and northwest by R 165.
Dublin 44 – Drogheda 15 – Dundalk 13.

↑ **Red House** ⬙,, Northeast : ¾ m. on N 52 ℰ (041) 6853523, Fax (041) 6853523, « Georgian house », ☎, ⬦, ⬒, ⌗, park – ⇇ **🅿**. **🅼🅲 🅰🅴 VISA**. ⬤
closed 20 December-7 January – **Meals** (by arrangement) (communal dining) 22.50 **st.** ↑ 6.00 – **3 rm** ⚌ 45.00/90.00 **st.**

---

**ARDMORE** (Aird MhÉr) Waterford **🄦🄦🄦** I 12 Ireland G. – pop. 436.
See : Town★ – Round Tower★ – Church★ (arcade★).
Env. : Whiting Bay★, W : 2 m. by the coast road.
🖪 Ardmore Tourist Office ℰ (024) 94444 (mid May-mid September).
Dublin 133 – Cork 57 – Waterford 45.

🏠 **Cliff House,** ℰ (024) 94106, Fax (024) 94496, ⬱, ⌗ – **☎ 🅿**. **🅼🅲 🅾 VISA**. ⬤
March-October – **Meals** 10.95/19.95 **t.** and a la carte ↑ 6.50 – **13 rm** ⚌ 32.50/65.00 **t.** – SB.

---

**ASHTOWN** Co. Dublin **🄦🄦🄦** ㊳ – see Dublin.

---

*Benutzen Sie für weite Fahrten in Europa die* **Michelin-Länderkarten :**

**🄦🄦🄦** Europa, **🄦🄦🄦** Tschechische Republik-Slowakische Republik,
**🄦🄦🄦** Griechenland, **🄦🄦🄦** Deutschland, **🄦🄦🄦** Skandinavien-Finnland,
**🄦🄦🄦** Großbritannien-Irland, **🄦🄦🄦** Deutschland-Österreich-Benelux, **🄦🄦🄦** Italien,
**🄦🄦🄦** Frankreich, **🄦🄦🄦** Spanien-Portugal.

## ATHLONE (Baile Átha Luain) Westmeath 🎠 I 7 Ireland G. – pop. 7 691.

EXC. : Clonmacnois★★★ (Grave Slabs★, Cross of the Scriptures★) S : 13 m. by N 6 and N 62 – N : Lough Ree (Ballykeeran Viewpoint★, Glassan★).

🏌 Hodson Bay ℘ (0902) 92073/92235.

🖪 Tourist Office, The Castle ℘ (0902) 94630/92856 (April-October).

Dublin 75 – Galway 57 – Limerick 75 – Roscommon 20 – Tullamore 24.

🏨 **Hodson Bay,,** Northwest : 4 ¾ m. by N 61 ℘ (0902) 92444, Fax (0902) 92688, ≤, Ið, ≊s 🔄, 🏌, ⬜, ℀ – 🕴 🗂 🗂 🕿 🕭 🕭 – 🏌 750. ◍◍ ◍ 👁 ᴠɪsᴀ. ℀
🍴 6.00 **L'Escale :** Meals 12.00/22.00 st. and dinner a la carte – **95 rm** ⬜ 107.00/142.00 st. 2 suites – SB.

↖ **Riverview House** without rest., Summerhill, Galway Rd, West : 3 m. by N 61, R 362, or N 6 ℘ (0902) 94532 – 🗂 🕭. ◍◍ ᴠɪsᴀ. ℀
closed 18 December-1 February – **5 rm** ⬜ 25.00/40.00.

↖ **Shelmalier House** without rest., Retreat Rd, Cartrontroy, East : ½ m. by Dublin rd (N 6) ℘ (0902) 72245, Fax (0902) 73190, 🌿 – 🗂 🕿 🕭. ◍◍ ᴠɪsᴀ. ℀
closed 2 weeks Christmas – **7 rm** ⬜ 25.00/36.00 st.

↖ **The Mill,** Tuam Rd, Northwest : 3 ½ m. by Roscommon rd on R 362 ℘ (0902) 92927 – 🗂 🕭. ◍◍. ℀
closed 22 December-7 January – **Meals** (by arrangement) 13.50 st. 🍴 6.00 – **6 rm** ⬜ 23.00/ 34.00 – SB.

XX **Wineport,,** Northeast : 4 ¼ m. by N 55 ℘ (0902) 85466, Fax (0902) 85471, « Loughside setting ≤ Lough Ree » – 🔽 🕭. ◍◍ ◍ AE ᴠɪsᴀ
closed Good Friday, 25-26 December, 1 January and Monday-Tuesday November-Easter – **Meals** (dinner only and Sunday lunch)/dinner a la carte 17.50/28.70 t. 🍴 10.95.

X **Left Bank Bistro,** Bastion St., ℘ (0902) 94446, Fax (0902) 94446, 🌫 – ◍◍ ᴠɪsᴀ
closed lunch Monday to Wednesday in winter, Sunday, 25 December-6 January and Bank Holidays – **Meals** (light lunch)/dinner a la carte 8.25/23.10 t. 🍴 5.00.

**at Glassan** Northeast : 5 m. on N 55 – ✉ Athlone.

XX **Glasson Village,** ℘ (0902) 85001 – ✾ 🕭. ◍◍ ◍ AE ◍ ᴠɪsᴀ
closed Sunday dinner except Bank Holiday weekends, Monday, 24 to 27 December and 3 weeks October – **Meals** (dinner only and Sunday lunch)/dinner 21.00 t. and a la carte 🍴 6.75.

## ATHY (Baile Átha Á) Kildare 🎠 L 9 Ireland G. – pop. 5 306.

EXC. : Emo Court★★, N : 20 m. by R 417 (L 18), west by N 7 (T 5) and north by R 422 – Stradbally★, NW : 9 m. by R 428 (L 109) – Castledermot High Crosses★, SE : 9½ m. by R 418 – Moone High Cross★, S : 12 m. by Ballitore minor rd and south by N 9 – Rock of Dunamase★ (≤★), NW : 12 m. by R 428 (L 109) and N 80 (T 16) – Timahoe Round Tower★, W : 10 m. by R 428 (L 109) and N 80 (T 16).

Dublin 40 – Kilkenny 29 – Wexford 59.

🏨 **Tonlegee House** ♨,, Southwest : 2 ¼ m. by N 78 ℘ (0507) 31473, Fax (0507) 31473, 🌿 – 🗂 🕿 🕭. ◍◍ AE ᴠɪsᴀ
closed 1 week March, 2 weeks November and 20 December-2 January – **Meals** – (see **The Restaurant** below) – **9 rm** ⬜ 55.00/75.00 st. – SB.

XX **The Restaurant** (at Tonlegee House H.),, Southwest : 2 ¼ m. by N 78 ℘ (0507) 31473, Fax (0507) 31473, 🌿 – 🕭. ◍◍ AE ᴠɪsᴀ
closed Sunday and Monday to non-residents, 1 week March,2 weeks November and 20 December-2 January – **Meals** (dinner only) 24.50 st. 🍴 6.00.

## AUGHRIM (Eachroim) Wicklow 🎠 N 9 – pop. 745.

🖪 ℘ (0905) 73939 (April-early October).

Dublin 46 – Waterford 77 – Wexford 60.

🏠 **Lawless's,** ℘ (0402) 36146, Fax (0402) 36384, 🦢 – 🗂 🕿 🕭. ◍◍ AE ᴠɪsᴀ. ℀
closed 24 to 26 December – **Meals** (bar lunch Monday to Saturday)/dinner a la carte 9.20/25.40 st. – **14 rm** ⬜ 65.50/94.00 st. – SB.

## AVOCA (AbhÉca) Wicklow 🎠 N 9 – pop. 490.

EXC. : Meeting of the Waters★, N : by R 752 – Avondale★, N : by R 752.

Dublin 47 – Waterford 72 – Wexford 55.

↖ **Keppel's Farmhouse** ♨ without rest., Ballanagh, South : 2 m. by unmarked road ℘ (0402) 35168, ≤, « Working farm », 🌿, park – ✾ ◍◍ ᴠɪsᴀ. ℀
closed 15 October-1 April – **Meals** – **5 rm** ⬜ 30.00/40.00 st.

**BAGENALSTOWN** (Muine Bheag) *Carlow* [923] L 9 – *pop. 2 553.*
*Dublin 63 – Carlow 10 – Kilkenny 13 – Wexford 37.*

**Kilgraney Country House** ⓢ,, South : 4 m. by R 705 (Borris Rd) ☎ (0503) 75283, *Fax (0503) 75595*, ≤, « Late Georgian house with collection of Far Eastern furnishings and artefacts », 🌳 – ⊭ rm, 🅿. [MO] [AE] [VISA]. ✈
*March-October* – **Meals** *(closed Sunday to Thursday, except July-August)* (booking essential) (residents only) (communal dining) (dinner only) 25.00 **st.** 🍷 7.50 – **5 rm** ☕ 37.50/90.00 **st.**

**BALLINA** (Béal an Átha) *Mayo* [923] E 5 *Ireland G. – pop. 6 852.*
**Env.** : *Mayo* ★ *– Rosserk Abbey* ★*, N : 4 m. by R 314.*
**Exc.** : *Moyne Abbey* ★*, N : 7 m. by R 314 – Pontoon Bridge View (≤ ★), S : 12 m. by N 26 and R 310 – Downpatrick Head* ★*, N : 20 m. by R 314.*
⛳18 *Mossgrove, Shanaghy* ☎ *(096) 21050.*
ℹ ☎ *(096) 70848 (April-30 September).*
*Dublin 150 – Galway 73 – Roscommon 64 – Sligo 37.*

**Mount Falcon Castle** ⓢ, Foxford Rd, South : 4 m. on N 26 ☎ (096) 70811, *Fax (096) 71517*, ≤, 🎣, park, 🎾 – ☎ 🅿. [MO] [AE] [D] [VISA]
*closed February, March and 1 week Christmas* – **Meals** (by arrangement) (communal dining) (dinner only) 17.50 **st.** 🍷 6.00 – **9 rm** ☕ 60.00/120.00 **st.** – SB.

**Brigown** without rest., Quay Rd, Northeast : 1 ¾ m. by N 59 on Enniscrone rd (R 297) ☎ (096) 22609, *Fax (096) 71247*, 🌳 – [TV] 🅿
**4 rm** ☕ 18.00/34.00 **t.**

**BALLINA** (Béal an Átha) *Tipperary* [923] G 9 *Ireland G – pop. 598.*
**Exc.** : *W : Killaloe* ★ *(St. Flannan's Cathedral* ★ *) – Graves of the Leinstermen (≤ ★), NE : 4 m. by R 494 and minor rd – Holy Island* ★ *AC, N : 16 m. by R 463 and boat from Tuamgraney.*
*Dublin 107 – Galway 62 – Limerick 16 – Tullamore 58.*

**Waterman's Lodge,** ☎ (061) 376333, *Fax (061) 376333*, 🌳 – ⊭ rm, ☎ 🅿. [MO] [D] [VISA]. ✈
*closed 20 December-15 March* – **Meals** *(closed Sunday and Monday)* (booking essential to non-residents) (dinner only) 27.00 **st.** – **10 rm** ☕ 65.00/120.00 **st.** – SB.

**BALLINADEE** (Baile na Daibhche) *Cork* [923] G 12 – ✉ *Bandon.*
*Dublin 174 – Cork 20.*

**Glebe Country House** ⓢ, ☎ (021) 778294, *Fax (021) 778456*, « Georgian rectory », 🌳 – ☎ 🅿. [MO] [VISA]
*closed 20 December-1 January* **Meals** (by arrangement) (communal dining) 16.50 **st.** – **4 rm** ☕ 45.00/60.00 **st.** – SB.

**BALLINASLOE** (Béal Átha na Sluaighe) *Galway* [923] H 8 *Ireland G. – pop. 5 634.*
**Env.** : *Clonfert Cathedral* ★ *(west doorway* ★★ *), SW : by R 355 and minor roads.*
**Exc.** : *Turoe Stone, Bullaun* ★*, SW : 18 m. by R 348 and R 350 – Loughrea (St. Brendan's Cathedral* ★ *), SW : 18 m. by N 6.*
⛳18 *Rossgloss* ☎ *(0905) 42126 –* ⛳9 *Mountbellew* ☎ *(0905) 79259.*
ℹ *Main St.* ☎ *(0905) 42131 (1 July-31 August).*
*Dublin 91 – Galway 41 – Limerick 66 – Roscommon 36 – Tullamore 34.*

**Haydens,** Dunlo St., ☎ (0905) 42347, *Fax (0905) 42895*, 🌳 – [lift], ▤ rest, [TV] ☎ 🅿 – 🎤 250. [MO] [AE] [D] [VISA]. ✈
*closed 24 to 27 December* – **Meals** (bar lunch in winter) 11.50/15.00 **t.** and dinner a la carte 🍷 5.50 – ☕ 6.50 – **48 rm** 35.00/72.00 **t.** – SB.

**BALLINCLASHET** *Cork* [923] G 12 – *see Kinsale.*

**BALLINGARRY** (Baile an GharraÁ) *Limerick* [923] F 10 *Ireland G – pop. 389.*
**Exc.** : *Kilmallock* ★ *(Kilmallock Abbey* ★*, Collegiate Church* ★ *), SE : 15 m. by R 518 – Monasteranenagh Abbey* ★*, NE : 15 m. – Lough Gur Interpretive Centre* ★*, NE : 24 m..*
*Dublin 141 – Killarney 56 – Limerick 18.*

**Mustard Seed at Echo Lodge** ⓢ, ☎ (069) 68508, *Fax (069) 68511*, 🌳 – ⊭ rest, [TV] ☎ ♿ 🅿 – 🎤 25. [MO] [AE] [VISA]. ✈
*closed mid January-early March* – **Meals** (residents only Sunday and Monday) (dinner only) 30.00 🍷 10.00 – **11 rm** ☕ 90.00/150.00 **t.**, 1 suite – SB.

**BALLSBRIDGE** (Droichead na Dothra) Co. Dublin 923 40 – see Dublin.

**BALLYBOFEY** (Bealach Féich) Donegal 923 I 3 – pop. 3 047 (inc. Stranorlar).
  🏌 Ballybofey & Stranorlar ℰ (074) 31093.
  Dublin 148 – Londonderry 30 – Sligo 58.

🏨 **Kee's**, Main St., Stranorlar, Northeast : ½ m. on N 15 ℰ (074) 31018, Fax (074) 31917, ₤₅
  ⇌s, ◻ – 📺 ☎ 🅿. 🏧 🆎 ① 𝘝𝘐𝘚𝘈. ⋘
  **Meals** (bar lunch Monday to Saturday)/dinner 23.50 t. and a la carte ⅙ 7.75 – **53 rm**
  ⇌ 54.00/94.00 t. – SB.

🏨 **Jackson's**, ℰ (074) 31021, Fax (074) 31096, ₤₅, ⇌s, ◻, ⩜ – ▮, ⋙ rm, ☰ rest, 📺 ☎ ♿
  🅿. 🏧 🆎 ① 𝘝𝘐𝘚𝘈. ⋘
  **Meals** (carvery lunch)/dinner 19.95 st. and a la carte ⅙ 5.50 – **88 rm** ⇌ 45.00/90.00 st. – SB

**BALLYBUNNION** (Baile an Bhuinneánaigh) Kerry 923 D 10 Ireland G. – pop. 1 470.
  Exc. : Carrigafoyle Castle★, NE : 13 m. by R 551 – Glin Castle★ AC, E : 19 m. by R 551 and
  N 69.
  🏌, 🏌 Ballybunnion, Sandhill Rd ℰ (068) 27146.
  Dublin 176 – Limerick 56 – Tralee 26.

🏨 **Marine Links**, Sandhill Rd, ℰ (068) 27139, Fax (068) 27666, ⩤ – 📺 ☎ 🅿. 🏧 🆎 ① 𝘝𝘐𝘚𝘈. ⋘
  13 March-October – **Meals** (bar lunch Monday to Saturday)/dinner 19.00 t. and a la carte
  ⅙ 6.50 – **11 rm** ⇌ 50.00/80.00 – SB.

🏠 **Teach de Broc** without rest., Link Rd, South : 1 ½ m. by Golf Club rd ℰ (068) 27581,
  Fax (068) 27919, ⩤ – ⋙ 📺 ☎ ♿ 🅿. 🏧 𝘝𝘐𝘚𝘈. ⋘
  **6 rm** ⇌ 35.00/60.00 st.

*The Guide is updated annually so renew your Guide every year.*

**BALLYCONNEELY** (Baile Conaola) Galway 923 B 7 Ireland G. – ✉ Clifden.
  Exc. : Connemara★★★ – Sky Road★★ (⩤★★), N : by R 341.
  Dublin 189 – Galway 54.

🏨 **Erriseask House** ⮣, ℰ (095) 23553, Fax (095) 23639, ⩤ Mannin Bay and Twelve Bens,
  park – ☎ 🅿. 🏧 ① 𝘝𝘐𝘚𝘈. ⋘
  May-October and restricted opening April – **Meals** – (see **The Restaurant** below) – **12 rm**
  ⇌ 59.50/96.00 t. – SB.

🍴🍴 **The Restaurant** (at Erriseask House H.), ℰ (095) 23553, Fax (095) 23639 – ⋙ 🅿. 🏧 🆎
  ⏯ ① 𝘝𝘐𝘚𝘈
  May-October and restricted opening in April – Meals (closed Wednesday dinner to non-
  residents April-June and September-October) (lunch by arrangement)/dinner 25.00 t.
  and a la carte 21.50/30.90 t. ⅙ 7.00.

**BALLYCONNELL** (Béal Atha Conaill) Cavan 923 J 5 – pop. 433.
  Dublin 89 – Drogheda 76 – Enniskillen 23.

🏨 **Slieve Russell H. Golf and Country Club**,, Southeast : 1 ¾ m. on R 200
  ℰ (049) 26444, Fax (049) 26474, ⩤, ₤₅, ⇌s, ◻, 🏌, ⩜, park, ⋘, squash – ▮, ☰ rest, 📺 ☎
  ♿ 🅿 – 🔬 800. 🏧 🆎 ① 𝘝𝘐𝘚𝘈. ⋘
  **Conall Cearnach** : Meals (dinner only and Sunday lunch)/dinner 26.00 t. and a la carte
  ⅙ 6.00 – **Brackley** : Meals (closd Sunday) (carving lunch) 11.75 t. and dinner a la carte
  26.95/32.70 t. ⅙ 6.00 – **151 rm** ⇌ 95.00/180.00 t. – SB.

**BALLYCOTTON** (Baile Choitán) Cork 923 H 12 Ireland G. – pop. 477.
  Exc. : Cloyne Cathedral★, NW : by R 629.
  Dublin 165 – Cork 27 – Waterford 66.

🏨 **Bayview**, ℰ (021) 646746, Fax (021) 646075, ⩤ Ballycotton Bay, harbour and island, ⩜ –
  ▮ 📺 ☎ 🅿 – 🔬 40. 🏧 🆎 ① 𝘝𝘐𝘚𝘈. ⋘
  2 April-27 October – **Meals** (bar lunch Monday to Saturday)/dinner 28.00 st. ⅙ 8.50 – **33 rm**
  ⇌ 90.00/130.00 st., 2 suites.

🍴🍴 **Spanish Point** with rm, ℰ (021) 646177, Fax (021) 646179, ⩤ Ballycotton Bay – 📺 ☎ 🅿.
  🏧 ① 𝘝𝘐𝘚𝘈
  closed 2 January-14 February, Monday to Saturday February-April and mid October-Decem-
  ber and 1 week Christmas – **Meals** (closed lunch Monday to Saturday October-April) 22.00 t.
  (dinner) and lunch a la carte 11.95/21.95 t. ⅙ 6.00 – **5 rm** ⇌ 30.00/40.00 st.

**BALLYHACK** (Baile Hac) *Wexford* [923] L 11 – *pop. 212* – ✉ *New Ross.*
*Dublin 105 – Waterford 8.5.*

🍴 **Neptune,** Ballyhack Harbour, ☎ (051) 389284, *Fax (051) 389284* – ⊁. [MC] [AE] [D] [VISA]
*March-mid November* – **Meals** (dinner only) 17.50 **st.** and a la carte 🍷 7.50.

**BALLYHEIGE** (Baile Uí Thaidhg) *Kerry* [923] C 10 – *pop. 679.*
*Dublin 186 – Limerick 73 – Tralee 11.*

🏨 **White Sands,** ☎ (066) 33102, *Fax (066) 33357* – [TV] ☎ [P]. [MC] [AE] [VISA]
*mid April-mid October* – **Meals** (bar lunch Monday to Saturday)/dinner 17.00 **st.** and a la carte 🍷 6.75 – **81 rm** ☕ 45.00/81.50 **st.** – SB.

**BALLYLICKEY** (Béal Átha Leice) *Cork* [923] D 12 *Ireland G.* – ✉ *Bantry.*
Env. : *Bantry Bay★ – Bantry House★ AC, S : 3 m. by R 584.*
Exc. : *Glengarriff★ (Garinish Island★★, access by boat) NW : 8 m. by N 71 – Healy Pass★★ (≤★★) W : 23 m. by N 71, R 572 and R 574 – Slieve Miskish Mountains (≤★★) W : 29 m. by N 71 and R 572 – Lauragh (Derreen Gardens★ AC) NW : 27 ½ m. by N 71, R 572 and R 574 – Allihies (copper mines★) W : 41 ½ m. by N 71, R 572 and R 575 – Garnish Island (≤★) W : 44 m. by N 71 and R 572.*
⛳9 *Bantry Park, Donemark* ☎ *(027) 50579.*
*Dublin 216 – Cork 55 – Killarney 45.*

🏨 **Ballylickey Manor House** ⛰, ☎ (027) 50071, *Fax (027) 50124,* ≤, « Extensive gardens », 🏊, 🎣, park – [TV] ☎ [P]. [MC] [AE] [VISA]. ⊁
*third week March-mid November* – ***Le Rendez-vous :*** **Meals** (light lunch)/dinner 28.00 **t.** and a la carte 🍷 12.00 – **5 rm** ☕ 120.00/130.00 **t.**, **7 suites** 150.00/200.00 **t.** – SB.

🏨 **Sea View House** ⛰, ☎ (027) 50462, *Fax (027) 51555,* ≤, 🌳 – [TV] ☎ 📞 ♿ [P]. [MC] [AE] [D] [VISA]
*mid March-mid November* – **Meals** (bar lunch Monday to Saturday)/dinner 24.50 **t.** 🍷 8.50 – **16 rm** ☕ 60.00/123.00 **st.** – SB.

🏠 **Reendesert,** ☎ (027) 50153, *Fax (027) 50597* – [TV] ☎ [P] – 🎤 100. [MC] [AE] [D] [VISA]. ⊁
*April-October* – **Meals** (bar lunch Monday to Saturday)/dinner 13.50 **st.** and a la carte 🍷 5.00 – **19 rm** ☕ 40.50/71.00 **st.** – SB.

🍴🍴 **Larchwood House** ⛰ with rm, Pearsons Bridge, Northeast : 1 ¾ m. by R 584 ☎ (027) 66181, ≤, 🌳 – [P]. [MC] [AE] [D] [VISA]. ⊁
*closed 1 week Christmas and restricted opening in winter* – **Meals** *(closed Sunday)* (dinner only) 25.00 **t.** 🍷 6.50 – **4 rm** ☕ 25.00/50.00 **t.**

**BALLYMACARBRY** (Baile Mhac Cairbre) *Waterford* [923] I 11 *Ireland G.* – *pop. 381* – ✉ *Clonmel.*
Exc. : *W : Nier Valley Scenic Route★★.*
*Dublin 118 – Cork 49 – Waterford 39.*

🏡 **Glasha Farmhouse** ⛰,, Northwest : 2 ½ m. by T 27 ☎ (052) 36108, « Working farm », 🌳 – [TV] [P]. [VISA]. ⊁
*closed 15 to 27 December* – **Meals** 20.00 **s.** – **6 rm** ☕ 25.00/50.00 **st.**

🏡 **Hanora's Cottage** ⛰, Nire Valley, East : 4 m. by Nire Drive rd and Nire Valley Lakes rd ☎ (052) 36134, *Fax (052) 36540,* 🌳 – ⊁ [TV] ☎ [P]. [MC] [VISA]. ⊁
*closed 1 week Christmas* – **Meals** (by arrangement) 23.00 **t.** – **6 rm** ☕ 50.00/80.00 **t.**

**BALLYMOTE** (Baile an MhÉta) *Sligo* [923] G 5 – *pop. 994* – ✉ *Sligo.*
*Dublin 124 – Longford 48 – Sligo 15.*

🏡 **Mill House** without rest., Keenaghan, ☎ (071) 83449, 🌳, 🎾 – ⊁ [TV] [P]. ⊁
*closed 21 December-7 January* – **5 rm** ☕ 18.00/36.00 **st.**

**BALLYNABOLA** *Wexford* [923] L 10 – *see New Ross.*

**BALLYNAHINCH** (Baile na hInse) *Galway* [923] C 7 – ✉ *Recess.*
Exc. : *Connemara★★★ – Roundstone★, S : by R 341 – Cashel★, SE : by R 341 and R 340.*
*Dublin 140 – Galway 41 – Westport 49.*

🏨 **Ballynahinch Castle** ⛰, ☎ (095) 31006, *Fax (095) 31085,* ≤ Owenmore River and woods, 🎣, 🌳, park, 🎾 – [TV] ☎ [P]. [MC] [AE] [D] [VISA]. ⊁
*closed February* – **Meals** (bar lunch)/dinner 25.00 **t.** and a la carte 🍷 6.50 – **28 rm** ☕ 85.00/150.00 **t.** – SB.

REPUBLIC OF IRELAND

**BALLYVAUGHAN** (Baile Uí Bheacháin) *Clare* 923 E 8 *Ireland G. – pop. 257.*
Env. : *The Burren★★ (Cliffs of Moher★★★ , Scenic Routes★★ , Poulnabrone Dolmen★ , Aillwee Cave★ AC (Waterfall★★ ), Corcomroe Abbey★ , Kilfenora Crosses★ ).*
*Dublin 149 – Ennis 34 – Galway 29.*

**Gregans Castle** ⟂,, Southwest : 3 ¾ m. on N 67 ℘ (065) 707 7005, Fax (065) 707 7111
≤ countryside and Galway Bay, ➾, park – ☎ ℗. ⓪⓪ VISA. ⋇
*closed mid October-mid December* – **Meals** (bar lunch)/dinner 28.00 st. and a la carte
⌀ 7.50 – **18 rm** ⌒ 100.00/190.00 st., 4 suites

**Hyland's,** ℘ (065) 77037, Fax (065) 77131 – ⋇ rm, ⊡ ☎ ℗. ⓪⓪ ⒶⒺ ⓪ VISA. ⋇
*closed 6 January-12 February and 18 to 27 December* – **Meals** (bar lunch)/dinner
a la carte approx. 18.50 st. ⌀ 5.50 – **30 rm** ⌒ 53.75/94.00 st. – SB.

**Rusheen Lodge** without rest.,, Southwest : ¾ m. on N 67 ℘ (065) 77092,
Fax (065) 77152, ➾ – ⋇ ⊡ ☎ ℗. ⓪⓪ ⒶⒺ VISA. ⋇
*closed January and December* – **8 rm** ⌒ 40.00/60.00 st.

**Cappabhaile House** without rest.,, Southwest : 1 m. on N 67 ℘ (065) 77260,
Fax (065) 77300, ≤, ➾ – ⊡ ☎ ℗. ⓪⓪ VISA. ⋇
*11 March-4 November* – **8 rm** ⌒ 45.00/56.00 st.

**BALTIMORE** (Dín na Séad) *Cork* 923 D 13 *Ireland G – pop. 232.*
Exc. : *Sherkin Island★ (by ferry).*
*Dublin 214 – Cork 59 – Killarney 77.*

**Baltimore Harbour,** ℘ (028) 20361, Fax (028) 20466, ℐ♨, ≘s, ⊠, ➾ – ⊡ ☎ ℗ –
⚄ 130. ⓪⓪ ⒶⒺ ⓪ VISA. ⋇
*closed 3 January-12 February* – **Meals** (bar lunch)/dinner 18.00 st. – **64 rm** ⌒ 63.00/
115.00 st. – SB.

**Casey's of Baltimore,** ℘ (028) 20197, Fax (028) 20509, ≤ – ▤ rest, ⊡ ☎ ℅ ℗. ⓪⓪ ⒶⒺ
⓪ VISA
*closed 19 to 25 February, 1 to 14 November and 21 to 27 December* – **Meals** 22.50 t.
(dinner) and a la carte 18.90/34.50 t. ⌀ 10.00 – **14 rm** ⌒ 59.50/81.00 t. – SB.

**Rathmore House,,** North : 1 ½ m. on R 595 (Skibbereen Rd) ℘ (028) 20362,
Fax (028) 20362, ≤, ➾ – ℗. ⓪⓪ ⒶⒺ ⓪ VISA
**Meals** (by arrangement) 12.50 st. – **6 rm** ⌒ 23.00/36.00 t. – SB.

**BANDON** (Droichead na Bandan) *Cork* 923 F 12 – pop. 1 697.
*Dublin 174 – Cork 19.*

**Munster Arms,** Oliver Plunkett St., ℘ (023) 41562, Fax (023) 41562 – ⊡ ☎ – ⚄ 200. ⓪⓪
ⒶⒺ ⓪ VISA. ⋇
*closed 25 and 26 December* – **Meals** 20.00 st. (dinner) and lunch a la carte 10.85/20.00 st.
⌀ 10.00 – **34 rm** ⌒ 45.00/65.00 st. – SB.

**St. Anne's** without rest., Clonakilty Rd, ℘ (023) 44239, Fax (023) 44239, ➾ – ⋇ ℗. ⓪⓪
VISA. ⋇
*closed 24 and 25 December* – **5 rm** ⌒ 23.00/36.00 t.

**BANSHA** (An Bháinseach) *Co. Tipperary* 923 H 10 – pop. 288.
*Dublin 103 – Cork 55 – Limerick 30 – Waterford 48.*

**Bansha House** ⟂, ℘ (062) 54194, Fax (062) 54215, ➾, park – ⋇ ℗. ⓪⓪ VISA. ⋇
*closed 20 December-1 January* – **Meals** 18.00 t. – **8 rm** ⌒ 30.00/50.00 t.

**BANTEER** (Bántár) *Cork* 923 F 11 – pop. 257.
*Dublin 158 – Cork 30 – Killarney 29 – Limerick 48.*

**Clonmeen Lodge** ⟂,, East : 2 m. on Mallow rd ℘ (029) 56238, Fax (029) 56294, ↖, ➾,
park – ℗. ⓪⓪ ⓪ VISA
*closed 23 to 30 December* – **Meals** (booking essential) (residents only) (dinner only) 18.00 t.
⌀ 7.50 – **6 rm** ⌒ 40.00/70.00 st.

**BANTRY** (Beanntraá) *Cork* 923 D 12 *Ireland G.* – pop. 2 936.

See : *Bantry House★ AC (Bantry Bay★ ).*

Exc. : *Gougane Barra Forest Park★, NE : 15 m. by R 584.*

🛈 *Wolfe Tone Sq.* ℰ *(027) 50229 (June-September).*

*Dublin 210 – Cork 56 – Killarney 53.*

🏠 **Bantry House** ⌛,, ℰ *(027) 50047, Fax (027) 50795*, ≤, 🛋, « Georgian country house, formal gardens, extensive parklands », 🔌, ✵ – ✵ ☎ 🅿. ⬚⑨ Æ **VISA**. ✵
*March-October* – **Meals** *(closed dinner Saturday and Sunday)* (light lunch)/dinner 25.00 **st.**
🛆 7.00 – **9 rm** ⌂ 85.00/150.00 **st.**

---

**BAREFIELD** (Gort Lomán) *Clare* 923 F 9 – see Ennis.

---

**BARRELLS CROSS** *Cork* – see Kinsale.

---

**BELTURBET** (Béal Tairbirt) *Cavan* 923 J 5 – pop. 1 248.
*Dublin 89 – Drogheda 76 – Enniskillen 23.*

🏠 **International Fishing Centre** ⌛,, North : 1 ½ m. ℰ *(049) 9522616,*
*Fax (049) 9522616,* « Riverside setting », 🔌, 🐎, ✵ – 🛄 🅿. ⬚⑨ **VISA**. ✵
*March-November* – **Meals** (dinner only) 14.00 **st.** 🛆 4.40 – **16 rm** ⌂ (dinner included)
38.00/76.00 **st.**

---

**BETTYSTOWN** (Baile an Bhiataigh) *Meath* 923 N 6.
*Dublin 43 – Drogheda 6 – Dundalk 28.*

✗✗ **Bacchus at the Coastguard,** Bayview, ℰ *(041) 28251, Fax (041) 28236,* ≤ Bettystown
Bay – 🅿. ⬚⑨ Æ **VISA**
*closed Sunday dinner, Monday, 25 to 26 December, 2 weeks February and last 2 weeks*
*October* – **Meals** (dinner only and Sunday lunch)/dinner 21.00 **t.** and a la carte.

---

**BIRR** (Biorra) *Offaly* 923 I 8 *Ireland G.* – pop. 3 355.

See : *Town★ – Birr Castle Demesne★★ AC (Telescope★★ ).*

Exc. : *Roscrea★ (Damer House★ AC) S : 12 m. by N 62 – Slieve Bloom Mountains★, E : 13 m.*
*by R 440 – Clonfert Cathedral★ (West doorway★★), NW : 15 m. by R 439, R 356 and minor*
*roads.*

🛈 *The Glenns* ℰ *(0509) 20082.*

🛈 ℰ *(0509) 20110 (mid May-mid September).*

*Athlone 28 – Dublin 87 – Kilkenny 49 – Limerick 49.*

🏠 **County Arms,** Railway Rd, South : ½ m. on N 62 ℰ *(0509) 20791, Fax (0509) 21234,* 🐎,
squash – 📺 ☎ ✆ ♿ 🅿 – 🔬 300. ⬚⑨ Æ ⑩ **VISA**.
*closed 25 December* – **Meals** 12.00/20.00 **t.** and a la carte 🛆 6.00 – **24 rm** ⌂ 40.00/84.00 **t.**
– SB.

🏠 **Dooly's,** Emmet Sq., ℰ *(0509) 20032, Fax (0509) 21332* – 📺 ☎ – 🔬 300. ⬚⑨ Æ ⑩ **VISA**.
✵
**Meals** (bar lunch Monday to Saturday)/dinner a la carte 10.50/18.50 **t.** 🛆 5.50 – **18 rm**
⌂ 35.00/65.00 **t.** – SB.

🏠 **The Maltings,** Castle St., ℰ *(0509) 21345, Fax (0509) 22073,* 🛋, 🖰 – 📺 ☎ 🅿. ⬚⑨ **VISA**.
✵
**Meals** a la carte 7.95/13.70 **st.** 🛆 5.50 – **20 rm** ⌂ 26.50/45.00 **st.** – SB.

⌂ **Emmet Guest House** without rest., Emmet Sq., ℰ *(0509) 20395* – 📺
*closed 28 November-31 January* – **6 rm** ⌂ 16.50/40.00 **t.**

⌂ **Spinners Town House,** Castle St., ℰ *(0509) 21673, Fax (0509) 21673* – ☎. ⬚⑨ Æ **VISA**.
✵
*closed November-17 March* – **Meals** – (see *Spinners Bistro* below) – **8 rm** ⌂ 25.00/
40.00 **st.**

✗ **Spinners Bistro** (at Spinners House), Castle St., ℰ *(0509) 21673, Fax (0509) 21673* – ⬚⑨
Æ **VISA**
*closed 14 January-17 February* – **Meals** *(closed Sunday and Monday October-June)* (dinner
only and lunch June-August)/dinner a la carte approx. 16.50 **st.** 🛆 6.95.

**at Kinnitty** *East : 8 ¼ m. on R 440* – ⊠ *Birr.*

🏰 **Kinnitty Castle** ⌛,, East : 1 m. on R 440 ℰ *(0509) 37318, Fax (0509) 37284,* « 12C
origins », 🛋, 🖰, 🔌, 🐎, park, ✵ – ☎ ♿ – 🔬 200. ⬚⑨ Æ ⑩ **VISA**. ✵
**Meals** (bar lunch Monday to Saturday)/dinner 25.00 **st.** and a la carte 🛆 9.00 – **37 rm**
⌂ 95.00/210.00 **st.** – SB.

**BLACKLION** (An Blaic) *Cavan* 923 I 5 – *pop. 153.*
*Dublin 121 – Drogheda 106 – Enniskillen 12.*

XX **Mac Nean House & Bistro** with rm, ℰ (072) 53022, Fax (072) 53404 – ⇆ rest, 🆟 ☎ ✆ ⬤🌐 VISA ⌘
*closed 24 to 27 December* – **Meals** *(closed Monday)* (dinner only and Sunday lunch)/dinner 25.00 **t.** and a la carte ₤ 10.80 – **5 rm** ☑ 26.00/46.00 **t.**

**BLACKROCK** *Co. Dublin* 923 N 8 – *see Dublin.*

**BLARNEY** (An Bhlarna) *Cork* 923 G 12 *Ireland G.* – *pop. 1 963* – ✉ *Cork.*
See : *Blarney Castle*★★ *AC* – *Blarney House*★ *AC.*
*Dublin 167 – Cork 6.*

🏩 **Blarney Park**, ℰ (021) 385281, Fax (021) 381506, ₤₅, ≦s, 🔲, 🗙, 🎾 – 🆟 ☎ ⅙ ❷ –
🔬 300. ⬤🌐 VISA ⌘
**Meals** 11.50/17.50 **st.** ₤ 8.00 – **91 rm** ☑ 64.00/118.00 **st.** – SB.

⌂ **Killarney House** without rest., Station Rd, Northeast : 1 m. ℰ (021) 381841
Fax (021) 381841, 🗙 – ⇆ 🆟 ❷.
*closed 25 December* – **5 rm** ☑ 25.00/36.00 **st.**

**at Tower** *West : 2 m. on R 617* – ✉ *Cork.*

⌂ **Ashlee Lodge**, ℰ (021) 385346, Fax (021) 385726, 🗙 – ⇆ ❷. ⬤🌐 VISA ⌘
*closed 22 December-5 January* – **Meals** (by arrangement) 16.00 – **6 rm** ☑ 26.00/40.00 **st.**

**BLESSINGTON** (Baile Coimán) *Wicklow* 923 M 8 *Ireland G.* – *pop. 1 860.*
Env. : *Russborough House*★★★, *SW : 2½ m. by N 81.*
*Dublin 19 – Kilkenny 56 – Wexford 70.*

🏩 **Tulfarris House** ⌘,, *South : 6 m. by N 81* ℰ (045) 867555, Fax (045) 867561, ≤, ₤₅, ≦s
🔲, ᴦ₅, ⬱, 🗙, park, 🎾 – ⇆ 🆟 ☎ ✆ ⅙ ❷ – 🔬 150. ⬤🌐 AE ⓪ VISA ⌘
*closed 23 to 27 December* – **Meals** (bar lunch Monday to Saturday)/dinner 25.00 **st.** ₤ 6.00 –
**20 rm** ☑ 90.00/156.00 **st.** – SB.

**BRAY** (Bré) *Wicklow* 923 N 8 *Ireland G.* – *pop. 25 252.*
Env. : *Powerscourt*★★ *(Waterfall*★ *AC)* W : 4 m. – *Killruddery House and Gardens*★ *AC,*
*S : 2 m. by R 761.*
Exc. : *Wicklow Mountains*★★.
ᴦ₈ *Woodbrook, Dublin Rd* ℰ (01) 282 4799 – ᴦ₈ *Old Conna, Ferndale Rd* ℰ (01) 282 6055.
*Dublin 13 – Wicklow 20.*

XX **Tree of Idleness**, Seafront, ℰ (01) 286 3498, Fax (01) 282 8183 – ⬤🌐 AE VISA
*closed Monday, 2 weeks late August and 1 week Christmas* – **Meals** - Greek-Cypriot - (dinner only) 20.00 **t.** and a la carte ₤ 7.00.

**BUNBEG** (An Bun Beag) *Donegal* 923 H 2 *Ireland G.* – *pop. 1 400* (inc. Derrybeg).
Exc. : *The Rosses*★, *S : by R 257.*
*Dublin 195 – Donegal 66 – Londonderry 55.*

🏩 **Ostan Gweedore** ⌘, ℰ (075) 31177, Fax (075) 31726, ≤, ₤₅, ≦s, 🔲, park – 🆟 ☎ ❷ –
🔬 50. ⬤🌐 AE VISA ⌘
*closed January and February* – **Meals** (bar lunch)/dinner 24.50 **st.** ₤ 9.60 – **36 rm** ☑ 55.00/
93.50 **st.**, 3 suites – SB.

**BUNCRANA** (Bun Cranncha) *Donegal* 923 J 2 *Ireland G.* – *pop. 3 312.*
Exc. : – *Malin Head*★★ *(≤*★★*)*, *NE : 31½ m. by R 238 and R 242 – Inishowen Peninsula*★★ –
*Dunree Fort*★, *NW : 6 m. by coast rd – Carndonagh High Cross*★, *NE : 18½ m. by R 238 –*
*Gap of Mamore*★, *NW : 8 m. – Lag Sand Dunes*★, *NE : 24½ m. by R 238, R 244 and R 242 –*
*Inishowen Head*★, *E : 30 m. by R 238, R 244 and R 242.*
*Dublin 160 – Londonderry 15 – Sligo 99.*

🏩 **Inishowen Gateway**, Railway Rd, ℰ (077) 61144, Fax (077) 62278, ≤, ₤₅, ≦s, 🔲, ᴦ₅ –
🄸, ⇆ rm, ▤ rest, 🆟 ☎ ⅙ ❷ – 🔬 150. ⬤🌐 AE VISA ⌘
**Meals** (bar lunch Monday to Saturday)/dinner 18.95 **st.** and a la carte ₤ 7.00 – **63 rm**
☑ 55.00/90.00 **st.** – SB.

🏩 **Lake of Shadows**, Grianan Park, ℰ (077) 61005, Fax (077) 62131 – 🆟 ☎ ❷. ⬤🌐 AE VISA
⌘
*closed 24 and 25 December* – **Meals** (dinner only and Sunday lunch)/dinner 14.50 **st.**
and a la carte ₤ 7.00 – **23 rm** ☑ 24.50/58.00 **st.** – SB.

**BUNDORAN** (Bun Dobhráin) Donegal 923 H 4 – pop. 1 707.
  🖪 Main St. ℰ (072) 41350 (June-September).
  Dublin 161 – Donegal 17 – Sligo 23.

🏨 **Great Northern** ⬩,, North : ¼ m. ℰ (072) 41204, Fax (072) 41114, ≤, Fⓢ, ≘ₛ, 🗔, fⱼ₈, ஈ, ஜ – ⓗ ⓣⱽ ☎ ⓒ 㐂 ⓟ. ⓒⓞ ⒶⒺ ⱽⁱˢᵃ. ℅
  Meals 10.00/16.00 t. and a la carte ⓘ 7.00 – 110 rm 🖙 70.00/180.00 t. – SB.

🏨 **Holyrood**, Main St., ℰ (072) 41232, Fax (072) 41100 – ⓗ ⓣⱽ ☎ 㐂 ⓟ. ⓒⓞ ⱽⁱˢᵃ. ℅
  closed Christmas – Meals (bar lunch Monday to Saturday)/dinner 17.00 and a la carte –
  100 rm 🖙 57.00/86.00 t. – SB.

🏨 **Allingham Arms**, ℰ (072) 41075, Fax (072) 41171 – ⓗ, ⁴⁰ rm, ⓣⱽ ☎ 㐂 ⓟ. ⓒⓞ ⒶⒺ ⓞ ⱽⁱˢᵃ. ℅
  closed 4 days Christmas – Meals 9.50/18.00 st. and dinner a la carte ⓘ 5.00 – 118 rm
  🖙 40.00/80.00 st. – SB.

🏨 **Bay View** without rest., Main St., ℰ (072) 41296, Fax (072) 41147, ≤, ≘ₛ – ⓣⱽ ☎ ⓟ. ⓒⓞ ⱽⁱˢᵃ. ℅
  18 rm 🖙 26.00/36.00 st.

🏠 **Leitrim House** without rest., Kinlough Rd, ℰ (072) 41904, Fax (072) 41452, ஈ – ⓣⱽ ☎ ⓟ. ⓒⓞ ⱽⁱˢᵃ. ℅
  March-October – 8 rm 🖙 22.50/35.00.

🏠🏠 **Le Chateaubrianne**, Sligo Rd, West : 1 m. on N 5 ℰ (072) 42160, Fax (072) 42160 – ⓟ. ⓒⓞ ⒶⒺ ⱽⁱˢᵃ. ℅
  closed Monday, 24 to 26 December and January – Meals (dinner only and Sunday lunch)/
  dinner 23.50 t. ⓘ 7.50.

*Le Guide change, changez de guide Michelin tous les ans.*

---

**BUNRATTY** (Bun Raite) Clare 923 F 9 Ireland G..
  See : Town★★ – Bunratty Castle★★.
  Dublin 129 – Ennis 15 – Limerick 8.

🏨 **Fitzpatrick Bunratty**, ℰ (061) 361177, Fax (061) 364863, Fⓢ, ≘ₛ, 🗔, ஈ – ⁴⁰ rm, ⓣⱽ ☎ ⓟ – 🔏 1200. ⓒⓞ ⒶⒺ ⓞ ⱽⁱˢᵃ. ℅
  closed 24 to 26 December – Meals (closed Saturday lunch) 14.00/22.00 st. and a la carte
  ⓘ 7.50 – 🖙 8.95 – 115 rm 90.00/120.00 st.

🏠 **Bunratty Lodge** without rest.,, North : 1½ m. ℰ (061) 369402, Fax (061) 369363, ஈ – ⁴⁰ rm ⓣⱽ ⓟ. ⓒⓞ ⱽⁱˢᵃ. ℅
  March-October – 6 rm 🖙 34.00/38.00 st.

🏠 **Shannon View** without rest.,, Northwest : 1 m. on N 18 (south-eastbound carriageway) completing U-turn at junction with R 471 ℰ (061) 364056, Fax (061) 364056, ஈ – ⓟ. ⓒⓞ ⱽⁱˢᵃ. ℅
  17 March-November – 4 rm 🖙 25.00/36.00 s.

---

**BUTLERSTOWN** (Baile an Bhuitléaraigh) Cork 923 F 13 Ireland G. – ✉ Bandon.
  Env. : Courtmacsherry★, N : 3 m.
  Exc. : Carbery Coast★.
  Dublin 193 – Cork 32.

🏠 **Atlantic Sunset** ⬩ without rest., ℰ (023) 40115, ≤ – ⁴⁰ ⓟ
  closed 20 December-1 January – 4 rm 🖙 16.00/36.00.

🏠 **Dunworley Cottage**, Dunworley, South : 2 m. ℰ (023) 40314, Fax (023) 40314 – ⓟ. ⓒⓞ ⒶⒺ ⓞ ⱽⁱˢᵃ
  closed Monday, Tuesday and November-mid March except Christmas – Meals (lunch by arrangement)/dinner 21.75 st..

---

**BUTLERSTOWN** (Baile an Bhuitléaraigh) Waterford – see Waterford.

---

**CAHERDANIEL** (Cathair DÉnall) Kerry 923 B 12 Ireland G – ✉ Killarney.
  Exc. : Iveragh Peninsula★★ (Ring of Kerry★★) – Derrynane National Historic Park★★ – Staigue Fort★, E : 5 m. by N 70 and minor rd – Sneem★, E : 12 m. by N 70.
  Dublin 238 – Killarney 48.

🏠 **Derrynane Bay House**,, West : ½ m. on N 70 ℰ (066) 9475404, Fax (066) 9475436, ≤ – ⁴⁰ rm, ⓣⱽ ☎ ⓟ. ⓒⓞ ⱽⁱˢᵃ. ℅
  closed February – Meals 16.00 s. – 6 rm 🖙 25.00/40.00 s.

**CAHIR/CAHER** (An Chathair) *Tipperary* 923 I 10 *Ireland G.* – pop. 2 236.

See : *Caher Castle*★★ *AC*.

Env. : *Swiss Cottage*★ *AC, S : 1 m. by R 670.*

Exc. : *Clonmel*★ *(County Museum*★*, St. Mary's Church*★*) E : 10 m. by N 24.*

🏌 *Cahir Park, Kilcommon* ℰ *(052) 41474.*

🛈 *Castle Street* ℰ *(052) 41453 (1 May-1 October).*

*Dublin 114 – Limerick 39 – Cork 47 – Waterford 39.*

🏠 **Cahir House,** The Square, ℰ *(052) 42727, Fax (052) 42727,* 🌲 – 📺 ☎ 🅿 – 🔬 500. 🆎 🅰
🕦 🚾. 🛠
*closed 25 December* – **Meals** (bar lunch Monday to Saturday)/dinner 19.00 **t.** 🛈 6.00 – **31 rm**
⇌ 50.00/80.00 **st.** – SB.

---

**CAMP** (An Com) *Kerry* 923 C 11 – ⊠ *Tralee.*

*Dublin 195 – Killarney 44 – Limerick 76 – Tralee 10.*

↑ **Barnagh Bridge** without rest., Cappaclough, West : 2 m. on R 560 ℰ *(066) 7130145,*
*Fax (066) 7130299,* ≤, 🌲 – 🖂 📺 ☎ 🅿. 🆎 🚾. 🛠
*March-October* – **5 rm** ⇌ 32.00/50.00 **st.**

---

**CAPPOQUIN** (Ceapach Choinn) *Waterford* 923 I 11 *Ireland G.* – pop. 780.

Env. : *Lismore*★ *(Lismore Castle Gardens*★ *AC, St. Carthage's Cathedral*★*), W : 4 m. by N 72 –*
*Mount Melleray Abbey*★*, N : 4 m. by R 669.*

Exc. : *The Gap*★ *(≤*★*) NW : 9 m. by R 669.*

*Dublin 136 – Cork 31 – Waterford 40.*

XX **Richmond House** ⤵ with rm,, Southeast : ½ m. on N 72 ℰ *(058) 54278,*
*Fax (058) 54988,* « *Georgian house* », 🌲 – 📺 ☎ 🅿. 🆎 🅰 🕦 🚾. 🛠
*closed 23 December-1 March* – **Meals** *(closed Sunday and Monday to non-residents)*
*(dinner only)* 28.00 **t.** 🛈 8.00 – **9 rm** ⇌ 50.00/120.00 **t.** – SB.

---

**CARAGH LAKE** (Loch Cárthai) *Kerry* 923 C 11 *Ireland G.*.

See : *Lough Caragh*★.

Exc. : *Iveragh Peninsula*★★ *(Ring of Kerry*★★*).*

🏌 *Dooks, Glenbeigh* ℰ *(066) 68205/68200.*

*Dublin 212 – Killarney 22 – Tralee 25.*

🏠 **Caragh Lodge** ⤵, ℰ *(066) 69115, Fax (066) 69316,* ≤, « *Lakeside setting* », ⬚, ⬚, 🌲,
🛠 – 🖂 ☎ 🅿. 🆎 🕦 🚾. 🛠
*23 April-16 October* – **Meals** (residents only) (dinner only) 30.00 **st.** 🛈 7.00 – **14 rm** ⇌ 66.00/
132.00 **st.**, 1 suite.

🏠 **Ard-Na-Sidhe** ⤵, ℰ *(066) 69105, Fax (066) 69282,* ≤, « *Lakeside setting* », ⬚, 🌲, park
– 🖂 ☎ 🅿. 🆎 🕦 🚾. 🛠
*May-September* – **Meals** (dinner only) 28.00 **st.** – **20 rm** ⇌ 76.00/158.00 **st.**

↑ **Carrig House** ⤵, ℰ *(066) 69100, Fax (066) 69166,* « *Lakeside setting* », ⬚, 🌲 – 🖂 ☎
🛠 🅿. 🆎 🕦 🚾. 🛠
*closed February and 24 to 26 December* – **Meals** (by arrangement) a la carte 18.45/27.75 **t.**
🛈 6.50 – **6 rm** ⇌ 86.00/126.00 **t.** – SB.

---

**CARLINGFORD** (Cairlinn) *Louth* 923 N 5 *Ireland G.* – pop. 647.

See : *Town*★.

Exc. : *Windy Gap*★*, NW : 8 m. by R 173 – Proleek Dolmen*★*, SW : 9 m. by R 173.*

*Dublin 66 – Dundalk 13.*

🏠 **McKevitt's Village,** Market Sq., ℰ *(042) 73116, Fax (042) 73144,* 🌲 – 📺 ☎ 📞. 🆎 🚾.
🛠
**Meals** 8.50/18.50 **t.** and a la carte 🛈 5.75 – **13 rm** ⇌ 35.00/70.00 **st.** – SB.

XX **Jordan's** with rm, Newry St., ℰ *(042) 73223, Fax (042) 73827,* ≤ – 📺 ☎ 🅿. 🆎 🅰 🚾. 🛠
*closed Sunday dinner and Monday in winter and 3 weeks January* – **Meals** (dinner only and
Sunday lunch)/dinner 25.00 **st.** and a la carte 🛈 7.00 – **5 rm** ⇌ 47.50/80.00 **st.** – SB.

---

**CARLOW** (Ceatharlach) *Carlow* 923 L 9 – pop. 11 721.

*Dublin 50 – Kilkenny 23 – Wexford 47.*

🏠 **Dolmen,** Kilkenny Rd, Southwest : 1 ¾ m. on N 9 ℰ *(0503) 42002, Fax (0503) 42375,* 🌲 –
▤ rest, 📺 ☎ & 🅿 – 🔬 800. 🆎 🅰 🕦 🚾. 🛠
*closed 25 December* – **Meals** (carving lunch Monday to Saturday)/dinner 15.95 **t.**
and a la carte 🛈 – **37 rm** ⇌ 60.00/95.00 **t.** – SB.

🏨 **Seven Oaks**, Athy Rd, ℰ (0503) 31308, *Fax* (0503) 32155, ⇆ – 🛗 📺 ☎ 🅿 – 🔬 300. ◍◐
◼️ ⓪ *VISA*. ⌘
*closed 25 December and Good Friday* – **Meals** (carving lunch Saturday) 10.50/16.00 **st.**
and a la carte – **32 rm** ⇌ 40.00/80.00 **st.** – SB.

🏛 **Barrowville Town House** without rest., Kilkenny Rd, ℰ (0503) 43324,
*Fax* (0503) 41953, ⇆ – ⇥ 📺 ☎ 🅿. ◍◐ ◼️ *VISA*. ⌘
**7 rm** ⇌ 25.00/50.00 **st.**

✗ **Danette's Feast**, Urglin Glebe, East : 3 m. by R 726 (Hacketstown rd) turning left after
petrol station onto Burton Hall rd ℰ (0503) 40817, *Fax* (0503) 40817 – ⇥ 🅿. ◍◐ *VISA*
*closed Sunday dinner to Wednesday, 1 week Christmas and restricted opening in winter* –
**Meals** (booking essential) (dinner only and Sunday lunch)/dinner 26.50 **t.**.

---

**CARNA** Galway 🎤🎤🎤 C 8 *Ireland G.*
Exc. : *Connemara***★★★*** – *Cashel*★, N : *by R 340.*
*Dublin 186 – Cork 169 – Galway 48 – Limerick 112.*

🏛 **Carna Bay** ⌁,, ℰ (095) 32255, *Fax* (095) 32530, ⩽, ⌁, ⇆ – 📺 ☎ 🅿. ◍◐ ◼️ *VISA*
**Meals** (bar lunch Monday to Saturday)/dinner 18.00 **st.** ⑄ 6.00 – **26 rm** ⇌ 40.00/80.00 **t.** –
SB.

---

**CARNE** Wexford 🎤🎤🎤 M 11.
*Dublin 105 – Waterford 51 – Wexford 13.*

🍴 **The Lobster Pot**, ℰ (053) 31110, *Fax* (053) 31401 – ⇥ 🅿. ◍◐ ◼️ *VISA*
*closed 25 December, Good Friday, January and Monday October-May* – **Meals** - Seafood -
(bar lunch)/dinner a la carte 12.20/27.15 **t.** ⑄ 5.00.

---

*Le Grand Londres (GREATER LONDON) est composé de la City*
*et de 32 arrondissements administratifs (Borough)*
*eux-mêmes divisés en quartiers ou en villages*
*ayant conservé leur caractère propre (Area).*

---

**CARRICKCARNON** Louth – *see Dundalk.*

---

**CARRICKMACROSS** (Carraig Mhachaire Rois) Monaghan 🎤🎤🎤 L 6 *Ireland G.* – *pop. 1 926.*
Env. : *Dún a' Rá Forest Park*★, SW : 5 m. by R 179.
🏌 Nuremore ℰ (042) 9661438.
*Dublin 57 – Dundalk 14.*

🏰 **Nuremore** ⌁,, South : 1 m. on N 2 ℰ (042) 9661438, *Fax* (042) 9661853, ⩽, ⌨️, ⌁, 🔲,
🏌, ⌁, ⇆, park, squash – 🛗, ⬛ rest, 📺 ☎ ఉ 🅿 – 🔬 600. ◍◐ ◼️ ⓪ *VISA*. ⌘
**Meals** (closed Saturday lunch) 15.50/30.00 **st.** ⑄ 8.00 – **69 rm** ⇌ 85.00/150.00 **st.** – SB.

---

**CARRICK-ON-SHANNON** (Cora Droma Rúisc) Leitrim 🎤🎤🎤 H 6 *Ireland G.* – *pop. 1 868.*
See : *Town*★.
Exc. : *Lough Rynn Demesne*★.
*Dublin 97 – Ballina 50 – Galway 74 – Roscommon 26 – Sligo 34.*

⌂ **Hollywell** ⌁ without rest., Liberty Hill, ℰ (078) 21124, *Fax* (078) 21124, ⩽, « Part 18C
country house », ⇆ – 🅿. ◍◐ *VISA*. ⌘
*closed 1 week Christmas* – **4 rm** ⇌ 47.50/75.00 **t.**

---

**CARRICK-ON-SUIR** (Carraig na Siúire) Tipperary 🎤🎤🎤 J 10 *Ireland G* – *pop. 5 172.*
Env. : *Ormond Castle*★ – *Ahenny High Crosses*★, N : by R 697.
🏌 Garravone ℰ (051) 640047.
*Dublin 95 – Cork 68 – Limerick 62 – Waterford 16.*

🏨 **Carraig**, Main St., ℰ (051) 641455, *Fax* (051) 641604 – ⬛ rest, 📺 ☎ 🅿. ◍◐ ◼️ ⓪ *VISA*. ⌘
*closed Good Friday and 25 December* – **Meals** 8.15/17.95 **st.** and dinner a la carte – **14 rm**
⇌ 40.00/70.00 **st.** – SB.

🏛 **Bell and Salmon Arms**, 95-97 Main St., ℰ (051) 645555, *Fax* (051) 641293 – 📺 ☎ 🅿.
◍◐ ◼️ ⓪ *VISA*. ⌘
*closed 25 December* – **Meals** (dinner only and Sunday lunch)/dinner 15.00 **st.** ⑄ 6.00 –
**13 rm** ⇌ 33.00/55.00 **st.** – SB.

**CARRIGALINE** (Carraig Uí Leighin) Cork 923 G 12 – pop. 7 827.
*Dublin 163 – Cork 9.*

⌂ **Glenwood House** without rest., Ballinrea Rd, North : ¾ m. by R 611 (Cork rd)
𝒫 (021) 373878, Fax (021) 373878, � – 📺 ☎ 🕭 🅿. 🐵 🐵 VISA. ✵
*closed 25 December-2 January* – **8 rm** ⚏ 35.00/60.00 **st.**

⌂ **Raffeen Lodge** without rest., Ringaskiddy Rd, Monkstown, Northeast : 2 ½ m. by R 61
and N 28 off R 610 𝒫 (021) 371632, Fax (021) 371632 – 📺 🅿. 🐵 🐵 VISA
*March-October* – **6 rm** ⚏ 28.00/40.00 **st.**

---

**CASHEL** (An Caiseal) Galway 923 C 7 *Ireland G..*
See : *Town★.*
Exc. : *Connemara★★★.*
*Dublin 173 – Galway 41.*

🏛 **Cashel House** ৯, 𝒫 (095) 31001, Fax (095) 31077, ≤, « Country house and gardens »,
🔦, park, ※ – 📺 ☎ 🅿. 🐵 🐵 AE ⓘ VISA. ✵
*closed 3 January-3 February* – **Meals** (booking essential to non-residents) (bar lunch)
dinner 32.00 **t.** ▯ 8.50 – **32 rm** ⚏ 80.00/160.00 **t.** – SB.

🏛 **Zetland Country House** ৯, 𝒫 (095) 31111, Fax (095) 31117, ≤ Cashel Bay, « Gardens », ※ – 📺 ☎ 🅿. 🐵 🐵 VISA
*10 April-October* – **Meals** – (see *The Restaurant* below) – **19 rm** ⚏ 81.00/158.00 **t.** – SB.

🏚 **Glynsk House** ৯,, Southwest : 5 ¾ m. on R 340 𝒫 (095) 32279, Fax (095) 32342, ≤ – 📺
☎ 🅿. 🐵 🐵 VISA
*June-September* – **Meals** (dinner only) 20.00 **st.** and a la carte ▯ 6.50 – **12 rm** ⚏ 35.00/
60.00 **t.** – SB.

✕✕ **The Restaurant** (at Zetland Country House H.), 𝒫 (095) 31111, Fax (095) 31117, ≤ Cashel Bay, 🌼 – ✵ 🅿. 🐵 🐵 ⓘ VISA
*closed 10 April-October* – **Meals** (booking essential) (dinner only) 29.50 **t.** ▯ 7.00.

---

**CASHEL** (Caiseal) Tipperary 923 I 10 *Ireland G.* – pop. 2 346.
See : *Town★★★ – Rock of Cashel★★★ AC – Cormac's Chapel★★ – Round Tower★ – Museum★ – Cashel Palace Gardens★ – GPA Bolton Library★ AC.*
Env. : *Holy Cross Abbey★★ , N : 9 m. by R 660 – Athassel Abbey★, W : 5 m. by N 74.*
🛈 *Bolton Library 𝒫 (062) 61333 (1 April-1 October).*
*Dublin 101 – Cork 60 – Kilkenny 34 – Limerick 36 – Waterford 44.*

⌂ **Ros Guill House** without rest.,, Northeast : ¾ m. on R 691 𝒫 (062) 62699,
Fax (062) 61507, 🌼 – ✵ 🅿. 🐵 VISA. ✵
*May-20 October* – **5 rm** ⚏ 28.00/42.00 **st.**

✕✕✕ **Chez Hans**, Rockside, 𝒫 (062) 61177, « Converted synod hall » – 🅿. 🐵 VISA
*closed Sunday, Monday, 24 to 26 December, Good Friday and 3 weeks January* – **Meals** (dinner only) a la carte 25.50/35.00 **t.** ▯ 8.00.

✕ **The Spearman**, 97 Main St., 𝒫 (062) 61143 – 🐵 AE ⓘ VISA
*closed Sunday dinner and Monday October-May, November and 25-26 December* – **Meals** (restricted lunch Monday to Saturday)/dinner a la carte 11.95/20.95 **t.** ▯ 4.95.

---

**CASTLEBALDWIN** (Béal Átha na gCarraigíní) Sligo 923 G 5 *Ireland G.* – ✉ Boyle (Roscommon).
Env. : *Carrowkeel Megalithic Cemetery (≤★★), S : 3 m.*
Exc. : *Arigna Scenic Drive★, N : 2 m. by N 4 – Lough Key Forest Park★ AC, SE : 10 m. by N 4 – View of Lough Allen★, N : 9 m. on N 4 on R 280 – Mountain Drive★, N : 6 m. on N 4 – Boyle Abbey★ AC, SE : 8 m. by N 4 – King House★, SE : 8 m. by N 4.*
*Dublin 118 – Longford 42 – Sligo 15.*

🏛 **Cromleach Lodge** ৯, Ballindoon, Southeast : 3 ½ m. 𝒫 (071) 65155, Fax (071) 65455,
🏞 ≤ Lough Arrow and Carrowkeel Cairns, 🔦, 🌼, park – ✵ 📺 ☎ 🅿. 🐵 🐵 AE ⓘ VISA
*February-October* – **Meals** (dinner only) 25.00 **t.** and a la carte 25.00/32.50 **t.** ▯ 6.50 – **10 rm**
⚏ 99.50/179.00 **t.** – SB.

---

**CASTLEBAR** (Caisleán an Bharraigh) Mayo 923 E 6 *Ireland G.* – pop. 6 585.
Env. : *Ballintubber Abbey★★ , S : 8 m. by N 84.*
Exc. : *Errew Abbey★, N : 22 m. by R 310, R 315 and minor rd.*
*Dublin 161 – Galway 49 – Sligo 47.*

🏛 **Breaffy House** ৯,, Southeast : 3 m. on N 60 𝒫 (094) 22033, Fax (094) 22276, ▯₆, 🌼,
park – ▮ 📺 ☎ 🕭 🅿 – ⛊ 300. 🐵 AE ⓘ VISA
*closed 24 to 27 December* – **Meals** 11.50/21.00 **st.** ▯ 6.00 – ⚏ 7.50 – **62 rm** 64.00/
140.00 **st.** – SB.

**CASTLEBELLINGHAM** (Baile an Ghearlánaigh) *Louth* [923] M 6 – *pop. 792 (inc. Kilsaran).*
*Dublin 43 – Dundalk 8 – Drogheda 14.*

🏨 **Bellingham Castle** 🌙, ✆ (042) 72176, *Fax (042) 72766*, 🎣, park – [TV] ☎ [P]. [MC] [AE] [DC] VISA JCB
*closed 24 and 26 December* – **Meals** 8.00/12.50 **t.** and a la carte 🍷 5.00 – **21 rm** ☕ 40.00/90.00 **st.** – SB.

**CASTLECONNELL** (Caisleán Uí Chonaill) *Limerick* [923] G 9 *Ireland G. – pop. 1 414* – ✉ *Limerick.*
See : *Town*★.
Env. : *Clare Glens*★, *SE : 5 m. by N 7 and R 503.*
*Dublin 111 – Limerick 9.*

🏨 **Castle Oaks House** 🌙, ✆ (061) 377666, *Fax (061) 377717*, <, 🏋, ♨, 🏊, 🎣, 🌳, park, 🍴 – [TV] ☎ [P] – 👥 200. [MC] [AE] [DC] VISA. ⛔
*closed 24 to 26 December* – **Meals** (bar lunch Monday to Saturday)/dinner 22.00 **st.** and a la carte 🍷 5.25 – **20 rm** ☕ 50.00/130.00 **t.** – SB.

**CASTLEDERMOT** (Díseart Diarmada) *Kildare* [923] L 9 *Ireland G. – pop. 733.*
Env. : *Castledermot High Crosses*★ – *Moone High Cross*★, *N : by N 9.*
Exc. : *Carlow Cathedral (Marble Monument*★*) NE : 7 m. by N 9.*
*Dublin 44 – Kilkenny 30 – Wexford 54.*

🏨 **Kilkea Castle** 🌙, Kilkea, Northwest : 3 m. by R 418 ✆ (0503) 45156, *Fax (0503) 45187*, <, « Part 12C », 🏋, ♨, 🏊, ⛳, 🎣, 🌳, park, 🍴 – ⇅ [TV] ☎ [P] – 👥 200. [MC] [AE] [DC] VISA. ⛔
*closed 23 to 27 December* – **Meals** 17.50/30.00 **t.** 🍷 6.50 – ☕ 12.00 – **29 rm** ☕ 115.00/170.00 **t.**, 7 suites – SB.

**CASTLEGREGORY** (Caisleán Ghriaire) *Kerry* [923] B 11 *Ireland G – pop. 163.*
Exc. : *Dingle Peninsula*★★★ – *Connor Pass*★★.
*Dublin 203 – Killarney 36 – Limerick 85 – Tralee 16.*

🏠 **The Shores Country House,** ✆ (066) 7139196, *Fax (066) 7139196*, <, 🌳 – 🚭 [TV] [P]. [MC] VISA. ⛔
*18 March-29 November* – **Meals** (communal dining) 15.50 **st.** – **3 rm** ☕ 23.00/40.00.

**CASTLEISLAND** (Oileán Ciarraá) *Kerry* [923] D 11 – *pop. 2 233.*
*Dublin 170 – Cork 59 – Killarney 16 – Limerick 52 – Tralee 12.*

🏨 **River Island,** Lower Main St., ✆ (066) 42555, *Fax (066) 42544* – ⇅ [TV] ☎ – 👥 200. [MC] [AE] [DC] VISA. ⛔
**Meals** *(closed Good Friday and 25 December)* 8.50/15.50 **t.** and a la carte 🍷 8.25 – **52 rm** ☕ 30.00/60.00 **t.**

**CASTLEKNOCK** *Co. Dublin* [923] ㊱ – *see Dublin.*

**CASTLELYONS** (Caisleán Ó Liatháin) *Cork* [923] H 11 – *pop. 164.*
*Dublin 136 – Cork 19 – Killarney 65 – Limerick 40.*

🏠 **Ballyvolane House** 🌙,, Southeast : 3 ½ m. by Midleton rd on Britway rd ✆ (025) 36349, *Fax (025) 36781*, <, « 18C Italianate mansion, extensive parklands », 🎣 – 🚭 [TV] [P]. [MC] [AE] [DC] VISA. ⛔
*closed 24 to 28 December* – **Meals** (by arrangement) 23.00 **t.** 🍷 6.00 – **6 rm** ☕ 45.00/90.00 **t.**

**CASTLEREA** (An Caisleán Riabhach) *Roscommon* [923] G 6 *Ireland G. – pop. 1 790.*
Env. : *Clonalis House*★, *W : ½ m. by N 60.*
*Dublin 108 – Galway 62 – Limerick 105.*

🏠 **Clonalis House** 🌙,, West : ½ m. on N 60 ✆ (0907) 20014, <, « Victorian Italianate mansion in extensive grounds », 🎣, 🌳, 🍴 – 🚭 [P]. [MC] [AE] VISA. ⛔
*April-September (booking essential)* – **Meals** (by arrangement) (communal dining) 22.50 🍷 8.50 – **4 rm** ☕ 55.50/99.00.

*Halten Sie beim Betreten des Hotels oder des Restaurants den Führer in der Hand.*
*Sie zeigen damit, daß Sie aufgrund dieser Empfehlung gekommen sind.*

**CASTLETOWNBERE** Cork 923 C 13 Ireland G. – pop. 926.

Env. : Beara Peninsula★, W : by R 572 (Allihies, mines★ - Garnish Bay ≤★) – Slieve Miskish Mountains (≤★).

Dublin 224 – Cork 81 – Killarney 58.

↑ **Rodeen** ⤳,, Northeast : 1 ¾ m. by R 572 ℰ (027) 70158, Fax (027) 70158, ≤, ଛ – ℗. ⚫ℂ ᴬᴱ ⓪ 𝚅𝙸𝚂𝙰 ᴶᶜᴮ. ⅏

booking essential in winter – **Meals** (by arrangement) 18.00 – **7 rm** ⊇ 25.00/37.00 – SB.

---

**CAVAN** (An Cabhán) Cavan 923 J 6 Ireland G. – pop. 3 509.

Env. : Killykeen Forest Park★, W : 6 m. by R 198.

🛈 Farnham St. ℰ (049) 4331942.

Dublin 71 – Drogheda 58 – Enniskillen 40.

🏨 **Kilmore**, Dublin Rd, East : 2 m. on N 3 ℰ (049) 4332288, Fax (049) 4332458 – 𝚃𝚅 ☎ ♿ ℗ – 🔏 550. ⚫ℂ ᴬᴱ ⓪ 𝚅𝙸𝚂𝙰

**Meals** 9.95/18.50 st. and dinner a la carte ⌗ 5.25 – **39 rm** ⊇ 46.00/74.00 st.

---

**CHEEKPOINT** (Pointe na Ságe) Waterford 923 K/L 11 – see Waterford.

---

**CLADDAGHDUFF** (An Cladach Dubh) Galway 923 B 7 Ireland G. – ✉ Clifden.

Exc. : Connemara★★★ – Sky Road★★ (≤★★), S : by minor roads.

Dublin 189 – Ballina 85 – Galway 58.

↑ **Acton's** ⤳, Leegaun, Southeast : 1 ¾ m. ℰ (095) 44339, Fax (095) 44309, ≤, ଛ – ⅍⤸ rm, 𝚃𝚅 ☎ ℗. ⚫ℂ ᴬᴱ ⓪ 𝚅𝙸𝚂𝙰. ⅏

April-September – **Meals** (by arrangement) 20.00 t. ⌗ 6.50 – **6 rm** ⊇ 35.00/60.00 st. – SB.

---

**CLARINBRIDGE** (Droichead an Chláirán) Galway 923 F 8.

Dublin 145 – Galway 11.

🏨 **Oyster Manor**, ℰ (091) 796777, Fax (091) 796770 – 𝚃𝚅 ☎ ℗ – 🔏 80. ⚫ℂ ᴬᴱ ⓪ 𝚅𝙸𝚂𝙰. ⅏

**Meals** (bar lunch Monday to Saturday)/dinner 19.50 st. – **14 rm** ⊇ 90.00/120.00 – SB.

---

**CLIFDEN** (An Clochán) Galway 923 B 7 Ireland G. – pop. 920.

Exc. : Connemara★★★, NE : by N 59 – Sky Road★★ (≤★★), NE : by N 59 – Connemara National Park★, NE : 1 m by N 59.

🛈 Market St. ℰ (095) 21163 (March-early October).

Dublin 181 – Ballina 77 – Galway 49.

🏨🏨 **Station House**, ℰ (095) 21699, Fax (095) 21667, ⅃ᴴ, ⤴s, ⛰ – ⌹ ⅍⤸, ▤ rest, 𝚃𝚅 ☎ ♿ ♿ ℗ – 🔏 200. ⚫ℂ ᴬᴱ ⓪ 𝚅𝙸𝚂𝙰. ⅏

**Meals** (dinner only) 18.00 t. and a la carte ⌗ 6.00 – **Signal :** **Meals** (dinner only) 19.00 t. and a la carte ⌗ 6.50 – **78 rm** ⊇ 105.00/155.00 st. – SB.

🏨 **Rock Glen Country House** ⤳,, South : 1 ¼ m. by R 341 ℰ (095) 21035, Fax (095) 21737, ଛ, ⅏ – ⅍⤸ rest, 𝚃𝚅 ☎ ℗. ⚫ℂ ᴬᴱ ⓪ 𝚅𝙸𝚂𝙰. ⅏

closed 3 January-14 February and restricted opening November-early December – **Meals** (bar lunch)/dinner 25.00 t. ⌗ 7.00 – **29 rm** ⊇ 78.00/130.00 st. – SB.

🏨 **Ardagh** ⤳, Ballyconneely rd, South : 1 ¾ m. on R 341 ℰ (095) 21384, Fax (095) 21314, ≤ Ardbear Bay – 𝚃𝚅 ☎ ♿ ℗. ⚫ℂ ᴬᴱ ⓪ 𝚅𝙸𝚂𝙰. ⅏

April-October – **Meals** (bar lunch)/dinner a la carte 23.00/29.50 st. ⌗ 7.50 – **21 rm** ⊇ 67.50/121.00 st. – SB.

🏠 **Quay House** without rest., Beach Rd, ℰ (095) 21369, Fax (095) 21608, ≤ – 𝚃𝚅 ☎. ⚫ℂ ᴬᴱ 𝚅𝙸𝚂𝙰. ⅏

**14 rm** ⊇ 55.00/90.00 t.

↑ **Mal Dua** without rest., Galway Rd, East : ½ m. on N 59 ℰ (095) 21171, Fax (095) 21739, ଛ – ⅍⤸ 𝚃𝚅 ☎ ♿ ℗. ⚫ℂ ᴬᴱ 𝚅𝙸𝚂𝙰. ⅏

March-October – **14 rm** ⊇ 30.00/70.00 t.

↑ **Sunnybank House** ⤳ without rest., Church Hill, ℰ (095) 21437, Fax (095) 21976, ⤴s, ⅃, ଛ, ⅏ – 𝚃𝚅 ☎ ♿ ℗. ⚫ℂ 𝚅𝙸𝚂𝙰. ⅏

March-October – **9 rm** ⊇ 40.00/80.00 st.

✗ **O'Grady's**, Market St., ℰ (095) 21450, Fax (095) 21976 – ⚫ℂ ᴬᴱ 𝚅𝙸𝚂𝙰

April-November – **Meals** - Seafood - (closed Sunday) (light lunch)/dinner a la carte 20.00/27.45 t. ⌗ 7.00.

✗ **High Moors,** Dooneen, Southeast : ¾ m. off Ballyconneely rd ℰ (095) 21342, ≼ – **☉**. **⬢⑨**
**㏂ 𝖵𝖨𝖲𝖠**
*closed Monday, Tuesday and November-April* – **Meals** (dinner only) a la carte 14.75/21.05 **t.**
⅙ 5.25.

✗ **Destry's,** Main St., ℰ (095) 21722 – **⬢⑨ ㏂ 𝖵𝖨𝖲𝖠**
*closed Monday October-March* – **Meals** (light lunch)/dinner a la carte approx. 20.50 **t.**
⅙ 5.00.

---

**CLONAKILTY** (Cloich na Coillte) Cork **❾❷❸** F 13 *Ireland G.* – pop. 2 724.
　　See : *West Cork Regional Museum★ AC* – *West Cork Model Railway Village★*.
　　Env. : *Timoleague★ (Franciscan Friary★, gardens★) E : 5 m. by R 600.*
　　Exc. : *Carbery Coast★*.
　　*Dublin 193* – *Cork 32.*

⌂ **Árd na Gréine Farm House** ⟲, Ballinascarthy, Northwest : 5 ¾ m. by N 71
　　ℰ (023) 39104, Fax (023) 39397, « Working farm », 𝒜 – **㏄ ☉**
　　**Meals** 18.00 **st.** – **6 rm** ⊃ 20.00/40.00.

---

**CLONMEL** (Cluain Meala) Tipperary **❾❷❸** I 10 – pop. 15 215.
　　See : *Town★ – County Museum★, St. Mary's Church★*.
　　Env. : *Fethard★, N : 8 m. by R 689.*
　　Exc. : *Nier Valley Scenic Route★★ – Ahenny High Crosses★, E : 19 m. by N 24 and R 697 –
　　Ormond Castle★, E : 21 m. by N 24.*
　　㏒₁₈ Lyreanearla, Mountain Rd ℰ (052) 21138/24050.
　　🅱 Community Office, Town Centre ℰ (052) 22960.
　　*Dublin 108* – *Cork 59* – *Kilkenny 31* – *Limerick 48* – *Waterford 29.*

🏰 **Minella** ⟲, Coleville Rd, ℰ (052) 22388, Fax (052) 24381, ⟍, 𝒜, park – **㏄ ☎ ☉** –
　　⚱ 550. **⬢⑨ ㏂ ⓪ 𝖵𝖨𝖲𝖠**. ⍩
　　*closed 24 to 27 December* – **Meals** 14.00/23.00 **st.** and a la carte ⅙ 6.50 – **67 rm** ⊃ 70.00/
　　150.00 **st.**, 3 suites – SB.

🏦 **Clonmel Arms,** Sarsfield St., ℰ (052) 21233, Fax (052) 21526 – ⫯ **㏄ ☎** – ⚱ 450. **⬢⑨ ㏂**
　　**⓪ 𝖵𝖨𝖲𝖠 𝖩𝖢𝖡**. ⍩
　　*closed 25 December* – **Meals** a la carte 8.00/16.25 **st.** ⅙ 5.95 – **31 rm** ⊃ 38.00/70.00 **st.** –
　　SB.

---

**CLONTARF** (Cluain Tarbh) Co. Dublin **❾❷❸** N 7 – see Dublin.

---

**COBH** (An CÉbh) Cork **❾❷❸** H 12 *Ireland G.* – pop. 6 468.
　　See : *Town★ – St Colman's Cathedral★ – Lusitania Memorial★*.
　　Exc. : *Fota Island★ (Fota Wildlife Park★), N : 4 m. by R 624 – Cloyne Cathedral★, SE : 15 m. by
　　R 624/5, N 25, R 630 and R 629.*
　　*Dublin 173* – *Cork 13* – *Waterford 71.*

⌂ **Tearmann** ⟲, Ballynoe, North : 1 ½ m. by R 624 ℰ (021) 813182, Fax (021) 814011, 𝒜 –
　　**☉**. ⍩
　　*March-October* – **Meals** (by arrangement) 12.00 **s.** – **3 rm** ⊃ 24.50/36.00 **s.**

---

**CONG** (Conga) Mayo **❾❷❸** E 7 *Ireland G.* – pop. 197.
　　See : *Town★*.
　　Env. : *Lough Corrib★★*.
　　Exc. : *Ross Abbey★ (Tower ≼★) – Joyce Country★★ (Lough Nafooey★) W : by R 345.*
　　*Dublin 160* – *Ballina 49* – *Galway 28.*

🏰🏰 **Ashford Castle** ⟲, ℰ (092) 46003, Fax (092) 46260, ≼, « Part 13C and 18C castle, in
　　extensive formal gardens on shores of Lough Corrib », ㏆, ⇌, ㏒, ⟍, park, ⅌ – ⫯,
　　↤⇥ rest, **㏄ ☎ 🆚 ☉** – ⚱ 110. **⬢⑨ ㏂ ⓪ 𝖵𝖨𝖲𝖠**. ⍩
　　*George V Room :* **Meals** (closed 24 December-2 January to non-residents) 24.00/38.00 **t.**
　　and a la carte ⅙ 10.00 – *Connaught Room :* **Meals** (booking essential) (residents only)
　　(dinner only May-September) a la carte 50.00/65.00 **t.** ⅙ 10.00 – ⊃ 14.00 – **77 rm** 242.00/
　　440.00 **st.**, 6 suites – SB.

**CORK** (Corcaigh) Cork 𝟵𝟮𝟴 G 12 *Ireland G.* – pop. 127 187.

See : *City*★★ – *Shandon Bells*★★ EY, *St. Fin Bar's Cathedral*★★ AC Z, *Cork Public Museum*★ X M – *Grand Parade*★ Z , *South Mall*★ Z , *St. Patrick Street*★ Z , *Crawford Art Gallery*★ Y – *Christ the King Church*★ X D , *Elizabethan Fort*★ Z .

Env. : *Dunkathel House*★ AC, E : 5¾m. by N 8 and N 25 X.

Exc. : *Fota Island*★ (*Fota Wildlife Park*★), E : 8 m. by N 8 and N 25 X – *Cobh*★ (*St. Colman* *Cathedral*★, *Lusitania Memorial*★) SE : 15 m. by N 8, N 25 and R 624 X.

🏌 Douglas ℘ (021) 891086, X – 🏌 Mahon, Cloverhill, Blackrock ℘ (021) 362480 X – 🏌 Monkstown, Parkgarriffe ℘ (021) 841376, X – 🏌 Harbour Point, Clash, Little Island ℘ (021) 353094, X.

✈ Cork Airport : ℘ (021) 313131, S : 4 m. by L 42 X – **Terminal** : Bus Station, Parnell Pl.

⛴ to France (Le Havre) (Irish Ferries) (summer only) weekly (22 h), (Roscoff) (Brittany Ferries and Irish Ferries) weekly (14 h), (St. Malo) (Brittany Ferries) weekly (17 h 30 mn) – to Pembroke (Swansea Cork Ferries) 4 weekly (8 h 30 mn) – to Swansea (Swansea Cork Ferries) (10 h).

🛈 Cork City, Grand Parade ℘ (021) 273251.
Dublin 154.

### CORK
### BUILT UP AREA

| | | | | |
|---|---|---|---|---|
| Baker's Road | X 4 | Curragh Road | X 14 | Lower Mayfield Road . . . . . . . . X 3? |
| Commons Road | X 12 | Dublin Street | X 16 | Thomas Davis Street . . . . . . . X 4? |
| | | Gardiner's Hill | X 20 | Victoria Cross Rd. . . . . . . . . . . X 5? |
| | | Great William | | Watercourse Road . . . . . . . . . X 52 |
| | | O'Brien Street | X 22 | Western Road . . . . . . . . . . . . . X 53 |
| | | Horgan Quay | X 23 | Wilton Road . . . . . . . . . . . . . . X 55 |

🏯 **Rochestown Park**, Rochestown Rd, Douglas, Southeast : 3 m. by R 609 ℘ (021) 892233, Fax (021) 892178, 𝐼𝛿, ⇌, 🏊, 🌲 – 🛗, ⇌ rm, 📺 ☎ 🕻 🅿 – 🕍 900. 🆎 🆎 ① 𝘝𝘐𝘚𝘈 . ⋘
🍴 6.50 *Windsor :* Meals 10.00/20.00 t. and dinner a la carte – **114 rm** ⊒ 60.00/120.00 t., 1 suite.

🏯 **Fitzpatrick Cork**, Tivoli, East : 2 ½ m. on N 8 ℘ (021) 507533, Fax (021) 507641, 𝐼𝛿, ⇌, 🏊, 🏌, 🌲, park, ⋘, squash – 🛗, ⇌ rm, ▤ rest, 📺 ☎ 🅿 – 🕍 800. 🆎 🆎 ① 𝘝𝘐𝘚𝘈 X c
Meals 14.00 st. (lunch) and dinner a la carte 16.50/24.00 st. 🍴 7.00 – ⊒ 7.50 – **106 rm** 90.00/130.00 st., 3 suites – SB.

🏯 **The Kingsley**, Victoria Cross, ℘ (021) 346800, Fax (021) 346789, ≤, 𝐼𝛿, ⇌, 🏊 – 🛗, ⇌ rm, 📺 ☎ 🅿 – 🕍 120. 🆎 🆎 ① 𝘝𝘐𝘚𝘈 . ⋘ X o
Meals 11.95 st. (lunch) and dinner a la carte 19.85/25.00 st. 🍴 11.95 – **55 rm** ⊒ 95.00/140.00 st., 2 suites – SB.

🏯 **Ambassador**, Military Hill, ℘ (021) 551996, Fax (021) 551997 – 🛗, ⇌ rm, 📺 ☎ 🅿 – 🕍 80. 🆎 🆎 ① 𝘝𝘐𝘚𝘈 X a
closed 25 December – Meals 24.00 st. (dinner) and a la carte 12.75/27.50 st. – **59 rm** ⊒ 75.00/95.00 st., 1 suite – SB.

**Shandon Court,** Shandon, ℘ (021) 551793, *Fax (021) 551665* – |≩|, ⇔̲ rest, ☰ ☎ ❷ – ⚠ 150. ◑ ◪ ◌ *VISA*. ⋘
Y e
*closed 25 and 26 December* – *The Belfry :* Meals (bar lunch Monday to Saturday)/dinner a la carte 19.95/26.00 **t.** ⧍ 5.95 – **6 rm** ☲ 80.00/140.00 **t.**, **18 suites** 110.00/140.00 – SB.

**Jurys,** Western Rd, by Washington St., ℘ (021) 276622, *Fax (021) 274477*, ⌊ₔ, ⇔ₛ, ⤓, ⌁, squash – |≩|, ⇔̲ rm, ☰ rest, ☰ ☎ ₫ ❷ – ⚠ 500. ◑ ◪ ◌ *VISA*. ⋘
Z v
*closed 24 to 26 December* – *Glandore :* Meals a la carte 16.95/20.00 **t.** ⧍ 6.00 – *Fastnet :* Meals *(closed Sunday and Monday)* (dinner only) 26.00 **t.** and a la carte ⧍ 6.00 – ☲ 9.50 – **184 rm** 125.00/150.00 **t.**, 1 suite – SB.

**Hayfield Manor,** Perrott Av., College Rd, ℘ (021) 315600, *Fax (021) 316839*, ⌊ₔ, ⬛, ⌁ – |≩| ☰ ☰ ☎ ₫ ❷ – ⚠ 120. ◑ ◪ ◌ *VISA*. ⋘
X z
Meals (bar lunch Saturday) 17.50/29.50 **st.** and a la carte ⧍ 9.00 – **51 rm** ☲ 140.00/220.00 **st.**, 2 suites – SB.

**Morrisons Island,** Morrisons Quay, ℰ (021) 275858, Fax (021) 275833 – ▯, ▤ rest, ▯ ☎
▯. 𝗠𝗢 𝗔𝗘 ⓪ 𝘝𝘐𝘚𝘈
*Riverbank :* Meals 14.00/16.50 st. and dinner a la carte ▯ 6.95 – **18 rm** 80.00/110.00 st
**24 suites** 110.00 st..

**Arbutus Lodge,** Middle Glanmire Rd, Montenotte, ℰ (021) 501237, Fax (021) 50289.
☞, ℅ – ▯ ☎ ▯ – 🕭 100. 𝗠𝗢 𝗔𝗘 ⓪ 𝘝𝘐𝘚𝘈. ℅
*closed 23 to 28 December* – **Meals** – (see *The Restaurant* below) – **16 rm** ☲ 55.00
125.00 st., **4 suites** – SB.

**Imperial,** South Mall, ℰ (021) 274040, Fax (021) 275375 – ▯ ▯ ☎ ▯ – 🕭 500. 𝗠𝗢 𝗔𝗘
𝘝𝘐𝘚𝘈 𝗝𝗖𝗕
*closed 24 December-2 January* – **Meals** a la carte 12.00/23.75 t. ▯ 5.50 – ☲ 7.50 – **98 rm**
65.00/85.00 t. – SB.

**Country Club,** Middle Glanmire Rd, Montenotte, ℰ (021) 502922, Fax (021) 502082, ☞
▯ ☎ ▯ – 🕭 300. 𝗠𝗢 𝗔𝗘 ⓪ 𝘝𝘐𝘚𝘈. ℅
*closed 23 to 27 December* – **Meals** (bar lunch Monday to Saturday)/dinner 15.50 st
and a la carte ▯ 10.50 – **60 rm** ☲ 45.00/85.00 st. – SB.

**Jurys Cork Inn,** Anderson's Quay, ℰ (021) 276444, Fax (021) 276144 – ▯, ⋇ rm, ▯ ☎
▯ & ▯ – 🕭 40. 𝗠𝗢 𝗔𝗘 ⓪ 𝘝𝘐𝘚𝘈
*closed 24 to 26 December* – **Meals** (carving lunch)/dinner 15.00 st. and a la carte ▯ 6.00 –
☲ 6.00 – **133 rm** 57.00 st.

**The Commons Inn,** Commons Rd, North : 1 ½ m. on N 20 ℰ (021) 210300
Fax (021) 210333 – ▯ ☎ & ▯ – 🕭 45. 𝗠𝗢 𝗔𝗘 ⓪ 𝘝𝘐𝘚𝘈. ℅
**Meals** (by arrangement Bank Holidays) (grill rest.) 4.50 (lunch) and dinner a la carte 8.85
17.45 st. ▯ 5.50 – ☲ 4.50 – **40 rm** 39.50 st.

**Victoria Lodge** without rest., Victoria Cross, ℰ (021) 542233, Fax (021) 542572, ☞ – ▯
⋇ ▯ ☎ & ▯. 𝗠𝗢 𝗔𝗘 𝘝𝘐𝘚𝘈
**30 rm** ☲ 35.00/50.00 st.

**Ibis Cork,** Dunkettle Roundabout, East : 4 ¾ m. by N 8 and N 25 on R 639 ℰ (021) 354354
Fax (021) 354202 – ▯, ⋇ rm, ▯ & ▯ – 🕭 65. 𝗠𝗢 𝗔𝗘 ⓪ 𝘝𝘐𝘚𝘈
**Meals** (dinner only) a la carte approx. 12.50 st. ▯ 5.25 – ☲ 5.25 – **100 rm** 49.50 st.

**Travelodge,** Blackash, South : 2 ¼ m. by R 600 ℰ (021) 310722, Reservations (Free
phone) 0800 850950 – ⋇ rm, ▯ & ▯. 𝗠𝗢 𝗔𝗘 ⓪ 𝘝𝘐𝘚𝘈 𝗝𝗖𝗕. ℅
**Meals** (grill rest.) – **40 rm** 39.95/59.95 t.

**Garnish House** without rest., Western Rd, ℰ (021) 275111, Fax (021) 273872 – ⋇ ▯ ☎
▯. 𝗠𝗢 𝗔𝗘 ⓪ 𝘝𝘐𝘚𝘈. ℅
**14 rm** ☲ 40.00/66.00.

**Seven North Mall** without rest., 7 North Mall, ℰ (021) 397191, Fax (021) 300811 – ▯ ☎
& ▯. 𝗠𝗢 𝘝𝘐𝘚𝘈. ℅
*closed 17 December-8 January* – **5 rm** ☲ 40.00/70.00 st.

**Killarney House** without rest., Western Rd, ℰ (021) 270290, Fax (021) 271010 – ⋇ ▯
☎ ▯. 𝗠𝗢 𝗔𝗘 ⓪ 𝘝𝘐𝘚𝘈. ℅
*closed 25 and 26 December* – **19 rm** ☲ 25.00/70.00 st.

**Acorn House** without rest., 14 St. Patrick's Hill, ℰ (021) 502474 – ▯. 𝗠𝗢 𝘝𝘐𝘚𝘈. ℅
*closed 23 December-10 January* – **9 rm** ☲ 30.00/50.00 st.

XXX **Flemings** with rm, Silver Grange House, Tivoli, East : 2 ¾ m. on N 8 ℰ (021) 821621
Fax (021) 821800, ☞ – ▯ ☎ ▯. 𝗠𝗢 𝗔𝗘 ⓪ 𝘝𝘐𝘚𝘈. ℅
*closed 24 to 26 December* – **Meals** 16.00 t. (lunch) and a la carte – **4 rm** ☲ 45.00/65.00 t.

XXX **The Restaurant** (at Arbutus Lodge H.), Middle Glanmire Rd, Montenotte
ℰ (021) 501237, Fax (021) 502893, ☞ – ▤ ▯. 𝗠𝗢 𝗔𝗘 ⓪ 𝘝𝘐𝘚𝘈
*closed Sunday and 23 to 28 December* – **Meals** 15.00/24.50 st. and a la carte ▯ 7.95.

XX **Lovetts** (Restaurant), Churchyard Lane, off Well Rd, Douglas, ℰ (021) 294909
Fax (021) 294024 – ▯. 𝗠𝗢 𝗔𝗘 ⓪ 𝘝𝘐𝘚𝘈
*closed Saturday lunch, Sunday, Monday, 1 week August and 1 week Christmas* – **Meals**
15.50/24.00 t. and dinner a la carte ▯ 6.95.

XX **Wylam,** Victoria Cross, ℰ (021) 341063, Fax (021) 272146 – ▤ ▯. 𝗠𝗢 𝗔𝗘 ⓪ 𝘝𝘐𝘚𝘈 𝗝𝗖𝗕
**Meals** - Chinese - (dinner only) 16.00 t. and a la carte ▯ 6.50.

X **Jacques,** 9 Phoenix St., ℰ (021) 277387, Fax (021) 270634 – ▤. 𝗠𝗢 𝗔𝗘 𝘝𝘐𝘚𝘈
*closed Saturday lunch, Sunday, 24 December-2 January and Bank Holidays* – **Meals** 10.90/
19.90 t. and a la carte ▯ 6.90.

**CRATLOE** (An Chreatalach) *Clare* 923 *F 9 – pop. 557 –* ⊠ *Bunratty.*
*Dublin 127 – Ennis 17 – Limerick 7.*

⌂ **Bunratty View** without rest., ℰ *(061) 357352, Fax (061) 357491,* ≤, ✍ – ⇥ 🔟 ☎ 🅿. ◑◐ 凪 *VISA*. ⋇
6 rm ☲ 25.00/40.00 st.

⌂ **Cratloe Lodge** without rest., Setrights Cross, ℰ *(061) 357168 –* 🔟 🅿. ◑◐ *VISA*
7 rm ☲ 20.00/36.00 – SB.

---

**CROOKEDWOOD** (Tigh Munna) *Westmeath* 923 *K 7 – see Mullingar.*

---

**CROSSMOLINA** (Crois Mhaoilíona) *Mayo* 923 *E 5 Ireland G. – pop. 1 103.*
Env. : *Errew Abbey★, SE : 6 m. by R 315.*
Exc. : *Broad Haven★, NW : 27 m. by N 59 and R 313.*
*Dublin 157 – Ballina 6.5.*

🏠 **Enniscoe House** ≫, Castlehill, South : 2 m. on R 315 ℰ *(096) 31112, Fax (096) 31773,*
≤, « *Georgian country house, antiques* », ⤪, park – ⇥ 🅿. ◑◐ 凪 *VISA*. ⋇
*April-14 October* – **Meals** (dinner only) 25.00 st. ⓘ 9.00 – 6 rm ☲ 62.00/116.00 st. – SB.

*When visiting Scotland,*
*use the **Michelin Green Guide** "Scotland".*

- *Detailed descriptions of places of interest*
- *Touring programmes*
- *Maps and street plans*
- *The history of the country*
- *Photographs and drawings of monuments,*
  *beauty spots, houses...*

---

**DELGANY** (Deilgne) *Wicklow* 923 *N 8 – pop. 6 682 (inc. Greystones) –* ⊠ *Bray.*
🛆 *Delganny ℰ (01) 287 4536.*
*Dublin 19.*

🏨 **Glenview**, Glen of the Downs, Northwest : 2 m. by L 164 on N 11 ℰ *(01) 287 3399,*
*Fax (01) 287 7511,* ≤, ℹ6, ⌺, ⧈, ✍, park – 🛗 🔟 ☎ ✆ ♿ 🅿 – 🔬 250. ◑◐ 凪 ⓪ *VISA*. ⋇
**Woodlands** : **Meals** 16.00/27.00 t. and dinner a la carte ⓘ 6.50 – **74 rm** ☲ 99.00/148.00 t.
– SB.

---

**DINGLE** (An Daingean) *Kerry* 923 *B 11 Ireland G. – pop. 1 536.*
See : *Town★ – St. Mary's Church★ (Presentation Convent Chapel★ ).*
Env. : *Gallarus Oratory★★, NW : 5 m. by R 559 – NE : Connor Pass★★ – Kilmalkedar★, NW :*
*5½ m. by R 559.*
Exc. : *Dingle Peninsula★★★ – Stradbally Strand★★, NE : 10½ m. via Connor Pass – Mount*
*Eagle (Beehive Huts★), W : 9 m. by R 559 – Corca Dhuibhne Regional Museum★ AC, NW :*
*8 m. by R 559 – Blasket Islands★, W : 13 m. by R 559 and ferry from Dunquin.*
🛈 *Main St. ℰ (066) 9151188 (April-late October).*
*Dublin 216 – Killarney 51 – Limerick 95.*

🏨 **Dingle Skellig,**, Southeast : ½ m. by T 68 ℰ *(066) 9151144, Fax (066) 9151501,* ≤, ℹ6, ⌺,
✍ – 🛗 🔟 ☎ 🅿 – 🔬 250. ◑◐ 凪 ⓪ *VISA*. ⋇
*closed 4 January-12 February and 23 to 27 December* – **Meals** (bar lunch)/dinner 25.00 t.
and a la carte ⓘ 8.50 – **109 rm** ☲ 83.00/136.00 st., 1 suite – SB.

🏠 **Milltown House** ≫ without rest.,, West : ¾ m. by Slea Head Drive ℰ *(066) 9151372,*
*Fax (066) 9151095,* ≤, ✍ – 🔟 ☎ ♿ 🅿. ◑◐ 凪 *VISA*. ⋇
*closed 23 to 27 December* – **10 rm** ☲ 60.00/70.00 st.

🏠 **Greenmount House** without rest., Gortonora, by John St. ℰ *(066) 9151414,*
*Fax (066) 9151974,* ≤ – ⇥ 🔟 ☎ 🅿. ◑◐ *VISA*. ⋇
*closed 21 to 26 December* – **12 rm** ☲ 35.00/70.00 t.

🏠 **Doyle's Townhouse,** 5 John St., ℰ *(066) 9151174, Fax (066) 9151816 –* 🔟 ☎. ◑◐ ⓪
*VISA*. ⋇
*mid March-November* – **Meals** – (see **Doyle's Seafood Bar** below) – 8 rm ☲ 65.00/
80.00 st.

845

**Captains House** without rest., The Mall, ℘ (066) 9151531, *Fax (066) 9151079*, – TV ☎. MC AE Ⓓ VISA. ✻
*April-October* – **7 rm** ⊐ 30.00/46.00 **st.**

**Cleevaun** without rest., Lady's Cross, Milltown, West : 1 ¼ m. on R 559 following signs fo Slea Head Drive ℘ (066) 9151108, *Fax (066) 9152228*, ←, – ✻ TV ☎ P. MC VISA. ✻
*mid March-mid November* – **9 rm** ⊐ 42.00/50.00 **t.**

**Bambury's** without rest., Mail Rd, East : on T 68 ℘ (066) 9151244, *Fax (066) 9151786*, ← – TV ☎ P. MC VISA. ✻
**12 rm** ⊐ 40.00/50.00 **st.**

**Alpine House** without rest., Mail Rd, East : on T 68 ℘ (066) 9151250, *Fax (066) 915196*
– TV ☎ P. MC VISA. ✻
**10 rm** ⊐ 35.00/45.00 **t.**

XX **Beginish,** Green St., ℘ (066) 9151588, *Fax (066) 9151591*, – MC AE Ⓓ VISA
*mid March-mid November* – **Meals** - Seafood - *(closed Sunday and Tuesday dinner an Monday)* (light lunch)/dinner a la carte 20.20/27.45 **t.** 6.00.

X **Doyle's Seafood Bar,** 4 John St., ℘ (066) 9151174, *Fax (066) 9151816* – ▤. MC Ⓓ VISA
*mid March-November* – **Meals** a la carte 18.50/30.40 7.00.

*Halten Sie beim Betreten des Hotels oder des Restaurants*
*den Führer in der Hand.*
*Sie zeigen damit, daß Sie aufgrund dieser Empfehlung gekommen sind.*

## DONEGAL (Dîn na nGall) *Donegal* 923 H 4 *Ireland G. – pop. 2 296.*

See : *Donegal Castle★ AC.*
Exc. : *Donegal Coast★★ – Cliffs of Bunglass★★, W : 30 m. by N 56 and R 263 – Glencolmcill Folk Village★★ AC, W : 33 m. by N 56 and R 263 – Rossnowlagh Strand★★, S : 22 m. by N 1 and R 231 – Trabane Strand★, W : 36 m. by N 56 and R 263.*
✈ *Donegal Airport ℘ (075) 48232.*
*The Quay ℘ (073) 21148.*
*Dublin 164 – Londonderry 48 – Sligo 40.*

**St. Ernan's House** , St. Ernan's Island, Southwest : 2 ¼ m. by N 15 ℘ (073) 21065 *Fax (073) 22098*, « Wooded island setting ← Donegal Bay », park – ✻ rest, TV ☎ P. MC VISA. ✻
*April-28 October* – **Meals** (dinner only) 29.00 **st.** 12.00 – **12 rm** ⊐ 172.00 **t.**

**Harvey's Point Country H.** , Lough Eske, Northeast : 4 ½ m. by T 27 (Killibegs rd ℘ (073) 22208, *Fax (073) 22352*, ←, « Loughside setting », , , park, ✻ – TV ☎ P – 50. MC AE Ⓓ VISA
*April-October and restricted opening November-March* – **Meals** – (see ***The Restauran*** below) – **20 rm** ⊐ 70.00/150.00 **st.** – SB.

**Island View House** without rest., Ballyshannon rd, Southwest : ¾ m. on N 15 ℘ (073) 22411, ←, – TV P. ✻
**4 rm** ⊐ 30.00/40.00.

XX **The Restaurant** (at Harvey's Point Country H.), Lough Eske, Northeast : 4 ½ m. by N 56 (Killibegs rd) ℘ (073) 22208, *Fax (073) 22352*, ←, « Loughside setting », – P. MC AE Ⓓ VISA
*April-October and restricted opening November-March* – **Meals** 13.75/30.00 **st.** 10.00.

## DONNYBROOK (Domhnach Broc) *Co. Dublin* 923 ⑩ – *see Dublin.*

## DOOGORT (Dumha Goirt) *Mayo* 923 B 5/6 – *see Achill Island.*

## DOOLIN (Dîlainm) *Clare* 923 D 8 *Ireland G..*

Env. : *The Burren★★ (Cliffs of Moher★★★, Scenic Routes★★, Aillwee Cave★ AC (Water fall★★), Corcomrow Abbey★, Kilfenora Crosses★).*
*Dublin 171 – Galway 43 – Limerick 50.*

**Aran View House** ,, Northeast : ½ m. ℘ (065) 74061, *Fax (065) 74540*, ←, « Working farm », , park – ✻ TV ☎ P. MC AE Ⓓ VISA
*April-30 October* – **Meals** *(closed Sunday dinner and Bank Holidays)* (dinner only and Sunda lunch)/dinner 20.00 **t.** and a la carte 4.95 – **19 rm** ⊐ 45.00/90.00 – SB.

**Doonmacfelim House** without rest., ℘ (065) 74503, *Fax (065) 74129*, ✻ – ☎ P. MC VISA. ✻
*closed 22 to 28 December* – **6 rm** ⊐ 28.00/40.00 **t.**

**DROGHEDA** (Droichead Átha) *Louth* 923 M 6 *Ireland G.* – *pop. 24 460.*

See : *Town* – *Drogheda Museum* – *St. Laurence Gate*.
Env. : *Monasterboice*, *N : 6 ½ m. by N 1* – *Boyne Valley*, *on N 51* – *Termonfeckin*, *NE : 5 m. by R 166.*
Exc. : – *Newgrange*, *W : 3 m. by N 51 on N 2* – *Old Mellifont* – *Knowth*.
*Dublin 29* – *Dundalk 22.*

🏨 **Boyne Valley H. and Country Club**,. Southeast : 1 ¼ m. on N 1 ℘ (041) 9837737, *Fax (041) 9839188*, ♣, ⌚s, ⬛, 🌳, park, ⚗ – ⛌ rm, 📺 ☎ ✆ Ⓟ – ⚖ 350. 🔾🔾 Æ 𝘝𝘐𝘚𝘈
**Meals** 12.25/23.00 st. ▮ 6.00 – **37 rm** ⌱ 52.00/140.00 st. – SB.

🏨 **Westcourt**, West St., ℘ (041) 9830965, *Fax (041) 9830970* – ⛌ rm, 📺 ☎ ⬠ – ⚖ 350. 🔾🔾 Æ ⓪ 𝘝𝘐𝘚𝘈
*closed 25 December* – **Meals** (carving lunch) 7.50/11.95 t. and dinner a la carte ▮ 4.95 – **26 rm** ⌱ 42.00/100.00 t. – SB.

⌂ **Tullyesker House** without rest., Tullyesker, Monasterboice, North : 3 ½ m. by N 1 ℘ (041) 9830430, *Fax (041) 9832624*, ≤, 🌳 – ⛌ 📺 Ⓟ. ⚯
*closed December and January* – **5 rm** ⌱ 33.00/38.00 st.

⌂ **Boynehaven House** without rest., Dublin Rd, Southeast : 2 ½ m. on N 1 ℘ (041) 9836700, 🌳 – ⛌ 📺 Ⓟ. 🔾🔾 𝘝𝘐𝘚𝘈. ⚯
**4 rm** ⌱ 35.00/50.00 s.

✗✗ **Abbotts Bistro**, 32 Shop St., ℘ (041) 9830288, *Fax (041) 9830288* – 🔾🔾 Æ ⓪ 𝘝𝘐𝘚𝘈
*closed Sunday dinner, Monday, 25 to 28 December and Bank Holidays* – **Meals** 11.95 t. (lunch) and dinner a la carte 20.35/25.40 t. ▮ 6.90.

**DRUMCONDRA** (Droim Conrach) *Co. Dublin* 923 ⑱ – *see Dublin.*

---

**LES GUIDES VERTS MICHELIN**

Paysages, monuments
Routes touristiques
Géographie
Histoire, Art
Itinéraires de visite
Plans de villes et de monuments

# DUBLIN - (Baile Átha Cliath)

*Dublin* 923 *N 7 Ireland G. – pop. 859 976.*

*Belfast 103 – Cork 154 – Londonderry 146.*

## TOURIST INFORMATION

🛈 *Baggot Street Bridge, D2 – Arrivals Hall, Dublin Airport – Tallaght, D24.*

## PRACTICAL INFORMATION

🏌 *Elm Park G. & S.C., Nutley House, Donnybrook ✆ (01) 269 3438/269 3014, GV.*
🏌 *Milltown, Lower Churchtown Rd ✆ (01) 467 6090.*
🏌 *Royal Dublin, North Bull Island, Dollymount ✆ (01) 833 6346.*
🏌 *Forrest Little, Cloghran ✆ (01) 840 1183/840 1763.*
🏌 *Lucan, Celbridge Rd, Lucan ✆ (01) 628 0246.*
🏌 *Edmondstown, Rathfarnham ✆ (01) 493 2461.*
🏌 *Coldwinters, Newtown House, St. Margaret's ✆ (01) 864 0324.*
✈ *Dublin Airport : ✆ (01) 844 4900, N : 5 ½ m. by N 1 BS –* **Terminal :** *Busaras (Central Bus Station) Store St.*
⛴ *to Holyhead (Irish Ferries) 2 daily (3 h 15 mn) – to Holyhead (Stena Line) daily (4 h) – to the Isle of Man (Douglas) (Isle of Man Steam Packet Co. Ltd) (4 h 30 mn).*

## SIGHTS

**See :** *City*★★★ *– Trinity College*★★★ *(Library*★★★ *AC) JY – Chester Beatty Library*★★★ *FV – Phoenix Park*★★★ *AS – Dublin Castle*★★ *HY – Christ Church Cathedral*★ *HY – St. Patrick's Cathedral*★★ *HZ – Marsh's Library*★★ *HZ – National Museum*★★ *(Treasury*★★*), KZ – National Gallery*★★ *KZ – Merrion Square*★★ *KZ – Rotunda Hospital Chapel*★★ *JX – Kilmainham Hospital*★★ *AT – Kilmainham Gaol Museum*★★ *AT M6 – National Botanic Gardens*★★ *BS – No 29*★ *KZ D – Liffey Bridge*★ *JY – Tailors' Hall*★ *HY – City Hall*★ *HY – St. Audoen's Gate*★ *HY B – St. Stephen's Green*★ *JZ – Grafton Street*★ *JYZ – Powerscourt Centre*★ *JY – Civic Museum*★ *JY M1 – Bank of Ireland*★ *JY – O'Connell Street*★ *(Anna Livia Fountain*★*) JX – St. Michan's Church*★ *HY E – Hush Lane Municipal Gallery of Modern Art*★ *JX M4 – Pro-Cathedral*★ *JX – Garden of Remembrance*★ *JX – Custom House*★ *KX – Bluecoat School*★ *BS F – Guinness Museum*★ *BT M7 – Marino Casino*★ *CS – Zoological Gardens*★ *AS – Newman House*★ *AC JZ.*

**Exc.** *Powerscourt*★★ *(Waterfall*★★★ *AC), S : 14 m. by N 11 and R 117 EV – Russborough House*★★★*, SW : 22 m. by N 81 BT – Rathfarnham Castle*★*, S : 3 m. by N 81 and R 115 BT.*

**The Merrion,** Upper Merrion St., D2, ℘ (01) 603 0600, *Fax (01) 603 0700,* « Carefully restored Georgian town houses, collection of contemporary Irish art », *Ⅰ₅,* ▨, *≈* – ▮, �⊱ rm, ▤ ▥ ☎ ⇐⊷ – ⚒ 45. ⅏ 丞 ⓞ *VISA* JCB. ⪼
KZ e
*Mornington :* Meals *(closed Saturday lunch)* 16.00/23.00 st. and dinner a la carte 22.20/35.50 st. ♪ 7.50 – ▭ 13.00 – **135 rm** 190.00/255.00 st., 10 suites.

**Conrad International,** Earlsfort Terr., D2, ℘ (01) 676 5555, *Fax (01) 676 5424, Ⅰ₅* – ▮, ⁺⊱ rm, ▤ ▥ ☎ ⓒ ❾ – ⚒ 370. ⅏ 丞 ⓞ *VISA* JCB. ⪼
JZ w
*Alexandra :* Meals *(closed Saturday lunch, Sunday and Bank Holidays)* 18.50 t. (lunch) and a la carte 27.00/34.75 t. ♪ 6.75 – *Plurabelle Brasserie :* Meals 15.50/18.50 t. and a la carte ♪ 6.75 – ▭ 12.50 – **182 rm** 195.00/220.00 t., 9 suites.

**The Shelbourne Meridien,** 27 St. Stephen's Green, D2, ℘ (01) 676 6471, *Fax (01) 661 6006, Ⅰ₅,* ≘, ▨ – ▮, ⁺⊱ rm, ▥ ☎ ⇐⊷ – ⚒ 400. ⅏ 丞 ⓞ *VISA*
JZ s
*No. 27 The Green :* Meals *(closed Saturday lunch)* 18.50/28.50 t. and a la carte ♪ 8.50 – *The Side Door :* Meals a la carte 14.95/25.00 t. ♪ 7.00 – ▭ 13.50 – **181 rm** 180.00/240.00 t., 9 suites.

**The Westbury,** Grafton St., D2, ℘ (01) 679 1122, *Fax (01) 679 7078* – ▮, ⁺⊱ rm, ▤ rest, ▥ ☎ ⇐⊷ – ⚒ 150. ⅏ 丞 ⓞ *VISA*. ⪼
JY b
*Russell Room :* Meals 15.00/27.50 t. and a la carte ♪ 5.90 – *The Sandbank :* Meals a la carte 12.20/23.25 t. – ▭ 10.95 – **195 rm** 195.00/240.00 t., 8 suites.

**The Burlington,** Upper Leeson St., D4, ℘ (01) 660 5222, *Fax (01) 660 8496* – ▮, ⁺⊱ rm, ▤ rest, ▥ ☎ ❾ – ⚒ 1200. ⅏ 丞 ⓞ *VISA*. ⪼
EU e
Meals 12.00/19.50 t. and a la carte ♪ 7.00 – ▭ 11.00 – **506 rm** 108.00/133.00 t. – SB.

**The Clarence,** 6-8 Wellington Quay, D2, ℘ (01) 670 9000, *Fax (01) 670 7800,* « Contemporary interior design » – ▮, ⁺⊱ rm, ▥ ☎ ❞ ❾ – ⚒ 60. ⅏ 丞 ⓞ *VISA* JCB. ⪼
HY a
Meals – (see *The Tea Room* below) – ▭ 14.00 – **45 rm** 180.00/195.00 t., 4 suites.

**Fitzwilliam,** 12 St. Stephens Green, D2, ℘ (01) 478 7000, *Fax (01) 478 7878,* « Contemporary interior » – ⁺⊱ rm, ▥ ☎ ❞ ❾ – ⚒ 80. ⅏ 丞 ⓞ *VISA*. ⪼
JZ d
*Christopher's :* Meals 18.95/22.50 t. and a la carte ♪ 11.00 – (see also *Peacock Alley* below) – ▭ 13.50 – **128 rm** 190.00/210.00 t., 2 suites.

**Brooks,** Drury St., D2, ℘ (01) 670 4000, *Fax (01) 670 4455* – ▮, ⁺⊱ rm, ▤ ▥ ☎ ❞ & ❾ – ⚒ 70. ⅏ 丞 *VISA*. ⪼
JY
*Francesca's :* Meals *(dinner only)* 21.95 t. and a la carte – ▭ 10.95 – **75 rm** 135.00/210.00 t.

**The Gresham,** O'Connell St., D1, ℘ (01) 874 6881, *Fax (01) 878 7175, Ⅰ₅* – ▮, ▤ rest, ▥ ☎ ❞ ❾ – ⚒ 250. ⅏ 丞 ⓞ *VISA*. ⪼
JX
Meals a la carte 19.00/35.00 t. – ▭ 15.00 – **282 rm** 200.00 t., 6 suites – SB.

**Academy,** Findlater Pl., D1, ℘ (01) 878 0666, *Fax (01) 878 0600* – ▮ ▤ ▥ ☎ ❞ ❾. ⅏ 丞 ⓞ *VISA* JCB
JX
Meals 9.95/14.95 st. and a la carte – **100 rm** ▭ *(dinner included)* 109.00/129.00 st. – SB.

# DUBLIN
## BUILT UP AREA

Adelaide Road . . . . . . . . . . . . . . BT
Bath Avenue . . . . . . . . . . . . . . . CT
Benburb Street . . . . . . . . . . . . . BS
Berkeley Road . . . . . . . . . . . . . BS
Botanic Road . . . . . . . . . . . . . . BS
Bow Street . . . . . . . . . . . . . . . BS

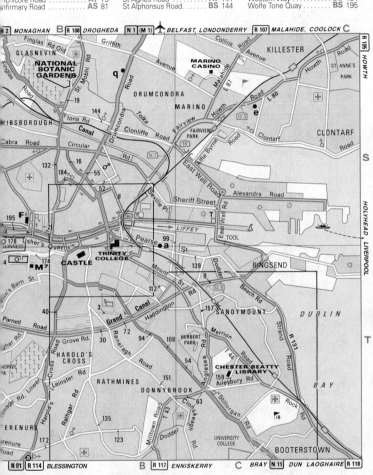

🏨 **Stakis**, Charlemont Pl., D2, ℰ (01) 402 9988, Fax (01) 402 9966 – |‡|, ❀ rm, ▤ rest, 📺 ☎ ✆ ૯ ⇔ – ⚠ 300. ◑◐ ⚞ ⓪ 𝘝𝘐𝘚𝘈 𝘫𝘊𝘉. ✘
DU b
*Waterfront:* Meals 15.50/21.50 and a la carte ∦ 5.50 – ⚌ 11.50 – **189 rm** 145.00/185.00 st.

🏨 **The Morgan**, 10 Fleet St., D2, ℰ (01) 679 3939, Fax (01) 679 3946, « Contemporary interior design » – |‡|, ▤ rest, 📺 ☎ ✆ – ⚠ 30. ◑◐ ⚞ ⓪ 𝘝𝘐𝘚𝘈. ✘
JY p
*closed 24 to 26 December* – **All Sports Cafe :** Meals *(closed Good Friday)* (grill rest.) 7.95/10.00 t. and a la carte ∦ 7.95 – **59 rm** 99.00/155.00 st., 2 suites.

🏨 **Camden Court**, Camden St., D2, ℰ (01) 475 9666, Fax (01) 475 9677 – |‡| ▤ 📺 ☎ ⇔ – ⚠ 100. ◑◐ ⚞ ⓪ 𝘝𝘐𝘚𝘈. ✘
DU d
*closed 24 to 26 December* – Meals 9.50/12.00 t. and dinner a la carte ∦ 5.50 – **246 rm** ⚌ 150.00/180.00 st.

851

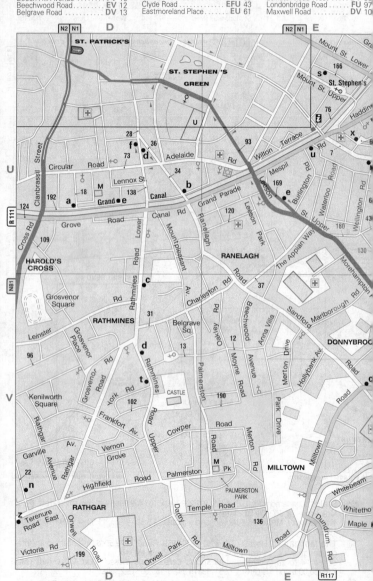

*Your recommendation is self-evident if you always walk into a hotel Guide in hand.*

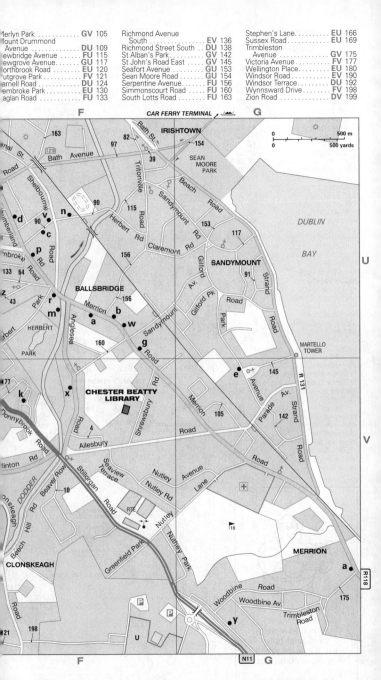

*Entrate nell'albergo con la Guida alla mano, dimostrando in tal
modo la fiducia in chi vi ha indirizzato.*

853

# DUBLIN
## CENTRE

When looking
for a quiet hotel
use the maps found
in the introduction
or look
for establishments
with the sign ⌂ or ⌂.

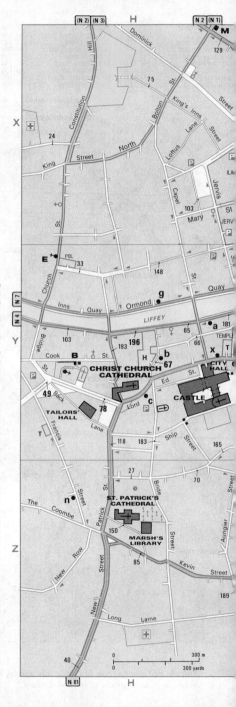

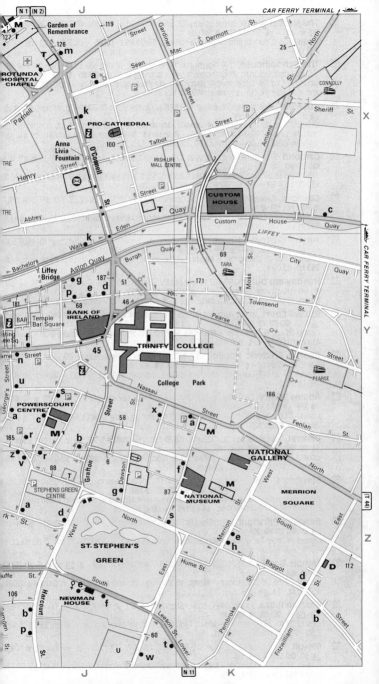

**The Mercer,** Mercer Street Lower, D2, ℰ (01) 478 2179, *Fax (01) 478 0328* – |↕|, ✝ rm, 🗔 🗔 ☎ ⇔ – 🔬 50. ⬤⬤ 🖭 ⓪ 𝘝𝘐𝘚𝘈. ⚘
JZ
Meals 9.95 t. (lunch) and dinner a la carte 10.85/19.85 t. ⅋ 5.95 – ☑ 7.00 – **21 rm** 100.00/ 132.00 – SB.

**The Schoolhouse,** 2-8 Northumberland Rd, D4, ℰ (01) 667 5014, *Fax (01) 667 5015,* « Converted Victorian schoolhouse », ☂ – |↕| 🗐 🗔 ☎ ⓟ. ⬤⬤ 🖭 ⓪ 𝘝𝘐𝘚𝘈. ⚘
EU
*closed 24 to 26 December* – **Satchels :** Meals *(closed Saturday lunch)* 15.00/26.00 s¹ and a la carte ⅋ 6.00 – **31 rm** ☑ 150.00/180.00 st.

**Buswells,** Molesworth St., D2, ℰ (01) 676 4013, *Fax (01) 676 2090* – |↕|, 🗐 rest, 🗔 ☎ ⓟ 🔬 80. ⬤⬤ 🖭 ⓪ 𝘝𝘐𝘚𝘈. ⚘
KZ
*closed 24 to 26 December* – **Trumans :** Meals *(closed Sunday)* 12.95 st. (lunch) and dinner a la carte 18.20/34.40 st. ⅋ 6.00 – **Brasserie :** Meals (carving lunch)/dinner a la carte 9.40/24.50 st. ⅋ 6.00 – **67 rm** ☑ 99.00/160.00 st., 2 suites – SB.

**Ormond,** 7-11 Upper Ormond Quay, D7, ℰ (01) 872 1811, *Fax (01) 872 1362* – |↕| 🗔 ☎ ✆ ⬤⬤ 🖭 𝘝𝘐𝘚𝘈. ⚘
HY
*closed 23 to 27 December* – Meals 12.50/16.50 t. and a la carte ⅋ 6.95 – **60 rm** ☑ 70.00/ 150.00 st. – SB.

**Cassidys,** Cavendish Row, Upper O'Connell St., D1, ℰ (01) 878 0555, *Fax (01) 878 0687* – |↕|, ✝ rm, 🗔 ☎ ✆ – 🔬 80. ⬤⬤ 🖭 ⓪ 𝘝𝘐𝘚𝘈. ⚘
JX n
*closed 24 to 27 December* – Meals 13.95 st. (dinner) and a la carte 10.75/22.40 st. ⅋ 4.95 – **73 rm** ☑ 75.00/105.00 st., 1 suite.

**Jurys Custom House Inn,** Custom House Quay, D1, ℰ (01) 607 5000, *Fax (01) 829 0400,* 𝘍𝘴 – |↕|, ✝ rm, 🗔 ☎ ✆ ⅋ – 🔬 100. ⬤⬤ 🖭 ⓪ 𝘝𝘐𝘚𝘈. ⚘
KX
*closed 24 to 26 December* – Meals (bar lunch)/dinner 14.50 st. and a la carte – ☑ 6.00 – **239 rm** 62.00 t.

**Holiday Inn Dublin,** 99-107 Pearse St., D2, ℰ (01) 670 3666, *Fax (01) 670 3636,* 𝘍ъ, 🚐 |↕|, ✝ rm, 🗐 rest, 🗔 ☎ ✆ ⇔ – 🔬 40. ⬤⬤ 🖭 ⓪ 𝘝𝘐𝘚𝘈. ⚘
BST
Meals 10.50/15.95 t. and a la carte – ☑ 8.95 – **90 rm** 119.00/139.00 st. – SB.

**Russell Court,** 21-25 Harcourt St., D2, ℰ (01) 478 4066, *Fax (01) 478 1576* – |↕| 🗔 ☎ ⓟ 🔬 150. ⬤⬤ 🖭 ⓪ 𝘝𝘐𝘚𝘈. ⚘
JZ
*closed 23 to 26 December* – Meals 11.95/19.00 st. and dinner a la carte ⅋ 6.00 – ☑ 6.95 – **41 rm** 70.00/95.00 t., 6 suites – SB.

**George Frederic Handel,** 16-18 Fishamble St., Christchurch, D2, ℰ (01) 670 9400, *Fax (01) 670 9410* – |↕|, 🗐 rest, 🗔 ☎ ⬤⬤ 🖭 ⓪ 𝘝𝘐𝘚𝘈. ⚘
HY
*closed 24 to 27 December*Meals a la carte approx. 16.95 st. ⅋ 7.00 – **40 rm** ☑ 90.00/ 130.00 st.

**Adams Trinity,** 28 Dame St., D2, ℰ (01) 670 7100, *Fax (01) 670 7101* – |↕| 🗔 ☎ ✆. ⬤⬤ 🖭 ⓪ 𝘝𝘐𝘚𝘈. ⚘
JY
*closed 24 to 26 December* – Meals 10.95 t. (dinner) and a la carte 14.50/15.50 t. ⅋ 5.50 – **28 rm** ☑ 75.00/120.00 st. – SB.

**Central,** 1-5 Exchequer St., D2, ℰ (01) 679 7302, *Fax (01) 679 7303* – |↕|, 🗐 rest, 🗔 ☎ ✆ – 🔬 80. ⬤⬤ 🖭 ⓪ 𝘝𝘐𝘚𝘈 𝘑𝘊𝘉. ⚘
JY
*closed 23 to 26 December* – Meals (bar lunch)/dinner a la carte 14.50/23.00 t. ⅋ 4.95 – **68 rm** ☑ 99.00/142.00 st., 2 suites – SB.

**Stephen's Hall,** Earlsfort Centre, 14-17 Lower Leeson St., D2, ℰ (01) 638 1111, *Fax (01) 638 1122* – |↕| ✝ 🗔 ☎ ✆ ⇔. ⬤⬤ 🖭 ⓪ 𝘝𝘐𝘚𝘈. ⚘
JZ
*restricted service 24 to 30 December* – Meals – (see **Morels at Stephen's Hall** below) – ☑ 8.00 – **3 rm** 130.00/160.00 st., **34 suites** 160.00 st.

**Bewley's Principal,** 19-20 Fleet St., D2, ℰ (01) 670 8122, *Fax (01) 670 8103* – |↕|, ✝ rm 🗔 ☎ ⬤⬤ 🖭 ⓪ 𝘝𝘐𝘚𝘈. ⚘
JY c
*closed 24 to 26 December* – Meals (dinner only) 15.00 st. – ☑ 6.00 – **70 rm** 78.00/98.00 st – SB.

**Temple Bar,** Fleet St., D2, ℰ (01) 677 3333, *Fax (01) 677 3088* – |↕| 🗔 ☎ ⓟ – 🔬 75. ⬤⬤ 🖭 ⓪ 𝘝𝘐𝘚𝘈. ⚘
JY e
*closed 24 to 26 December* – Meals 10.50/17.00 st. and a la carte – **126 rm** ☑ 100.00/ 130.00 st., 1 suite – SB.

**Grafton Plaza,** Johnsons Pl., Lower Stephens St., D2, ℰ (01) 475 0888, *Fax (01) 475 0908* – |↕| 🗔 ☎. ⬤⬤ 🖭 ⓪ 𝘝𝘐𝘚𝘈. ⚘
JZ v
*closed 23 to 26 December* – Meals (grill rest.) (dinner only) a la carte 14.25/23.00 st. – ☑ 8.50 – **75 rm** 105.00/120.00 st.

**Mespil,** 50-60 Mespil Rd, D4, ℰ (01) 667 1222, *Fax (01) 667 1244* – |↕|, ✝ rm, 🗔 ☎ ✆ ⓟ – 🔬 50. ⬤⬤ 🖭 ⓪ 𝘝𝘐𝘚𝘈. ⚘
EU u
*closed 24 to 26 December* – Meals (bar lunch)/dinner a la carte 16.85/24.45 st. ⅋ 7.50 – ☑ 8.50 – **153 rm** 85.00 st. – SB.

🏨 **Drury Court**, 28-30 Lower Stephens St., D2, ℰ (01) 475 1988, *Fax (01) 478 5730* – 📶,
⇔ rm, 🔟 🕿. 🐠 AE ➀ *VISA*. �‰                                                                     JYZ   z
*closed 24 to 26 December* – **Meals** (bar lunch)/dinner a la carte 15.20/21.35 **t.** 🛈 5.00 –
**32 rm** ⊇ 90.00/150.00 **t.** – SB.

🏨 **Jurys Christchurch Inn**, Christchurch Pl., D8, ℰ (01) 454 0000, *Fax (01) 454 0012* – 📶,
⇔ rm, 🔟 🕿 &. ➀. 🐠 *VISA*. ⋘                                                                       HY   c
*closed 24 to 26 December* – **Meals** (bar lunch)/dinner 15.50 **st.** and a la carte – ⊇ 6.50 –
**182 rm** 62.00 **st.**

🏨 **Arlington**, 23-25 Bachelors Walk, D1, ℰ (01) 804 9100, *Fax (01) 804 9112* – 📶 🔟 🕿 –
🔬 35. 🐠 AE *VISA*                                                                                  JY   k
**Meals** (bar lunch)/dinner a la carte 12.95/21.40 **t.** – **115 rm** ⊇ 90.00/120.00 **st.**

🏨 **Trinity Arch**, 46-49 Dame St., D2, ℰ (01) 679 4455, *Fax (01) 679 4511* – 📶 🔟 🕿. 🐠 *VISA*
⋘                                                                                                  JY   f
**Meals** (bar lunch)/dinner a la carte 12.85/20.65 **t.** 🛈 6.00 – **29 rm** ⊇ 75.00/110.00 **st.**

🏨 **Longfield's**, 10 Lower Fitzwilliam St., D2, ℰ (01) 676 1367, *Fax (01) 676 1542* – 📶 🔟 🕿.
🐠 AE ➀ *VISA*. ⋘                                                                                    KZ   d
*closed 23 December-3 January* – **Meals** 11.95/27.50 **st.** and a la carte 🛈 7.00 – **26 rm**
⊇ 90.00/130.00 **st.** – SB.

🏨 **Trinity Lodge** without rest., 12 South Frederick St., D2, ℰ (01) 679 5044,
*Fax (01) 679 5223* – 📶 🔟 🕿. 🐠 AE ➀ *VISA*. ⋘                                                     JY   x
*closed 25 and 26 December* – **10 rm** ⊇ 60.00/320.00 **st.**, 3 suites.

🏨 **Camden Hall**, 1 Upper Camden St., D2, ℰ (01) 475 7906, *Fax (01) 475 7905* – 📶 🔟 🕿 ➀.
🐠 AE ➀ *VISA*. ⋘                                                                                    DU   f
*closed 24 to 26 December* – ***One Pico*** : Meals *(closed lunch Saturday,Sunday and Bank
Holidays)* (booking essential) 10.95 **t.** (lunch) and a la carte 21.85/29.85 **t.** 🛈 9.50 – **28 rm**
⊇ 90.00/180.00 **st.** – SB.

🏨 **Aston** without rest., 7-9 Aston Quay, D2, ℰ (01) 677 9300, *Fax (01) 677 9007* – 📶 🔟 🕿 &.
🐠 AE *VISA*. ⋘                                                                                      JY   g
*closed 24 to 28 December* – **27 rm** ⊇ 55.00/150.00 **st.**

🏨 **Stauntons on the Green** without rest., 83 St. Stephen's Green South, D2,
ℰ (01) 478 2300, *Fax (01) 478 2263*, 🌫 – 🔟 🕿 ⇌. 🐠 AE ➀ *VISA*. ⋘                                  JZ   f
*closed 24 to 26 December* – **39 rm** ⊇ 75.00/120.00 **st.**

🏠 **Grafton House** without rest., 26-27 South Great Georges St., D2, ℰ (01) 679 2041,
*Fax (01) 677 9715* – 🔟 🕿. 🐠 *VISA*. ⋘                                                             JY   a
*closed 23 to 29 December* – **16 rm** ⊇ 45.00/90.00 **st.**

XXXX **Patrick Guilbaud**, 21 Upper Merrion St., D2, ℰ (01) 676 4192, *Fax (01) 661 0052*, 🌫,
❀❀ « Contemporary Irish Art collection » – 🗏. 🐠 AE ➀ *VISA*                                         KZ   e
*closed Sunday, Monday, 17 March, Good Friday and 1 week January* – **Meals** 20.00 **st.**
(lunch) and a la carte 42.00/64.00 **st.** 🛈 15.00
**Spec.** Poached Connemara lobster with apple and lemon jus. Roast new season Wicklow
lamb with oriental spices. Croustillant of spiced pineapple with a ginger sorbet.

XXX **The Commons**, Newman House, 85-86 St. Stephen's Green, D2, ℰ (01) 478 0530,
*Fax (01) 478 0551*, « Contemporary collection of James Joyce inspired Irish Art » – 🐠 AE
➀ *VISA*                                                                                            JZ   e
*closed Saturday lunch, Sunday, 1 week Christmas and Bank Holidays* – **Meals** 20.00/35.00 **st.**
and a la carte 🛈 9.00.

XXX **Thornton's**, 1 Portobello Rd, D8, ℰ (01) 454 9067, *Fax (01) 453 2947* – 🗏. 🐠 AE ➀ *VISA*
❀ *closed Sunday, Monday and 2 weeks Christmas-New Year* – **Meals** (booking essential)
(dinner only and lunch Thursday-Friday) 22.00 **t.** (lunch) and a la carte 37.45/45.45 **t.** 🛈 10.00
**Spec.** Sautéed foie gras with scallops, celeriac and cep jus. Suckling pig with trotter, Maxim
potatoes and poitin jus. Nougat pyramid with glazed fruit and orange sauce.         DU   e

XXX **Peacock Alley** (Gallagher) (at Fitzwilliam H.), St. Stephen's Green, D2, ℰ (01) 478 7015,
❀ *Fax (01) 478 7025* – 🗏 ➀. 🐠 AE ➀ *VISA*                                                          JZ   d
*closed Sunday, 25 December and Bank Holidays* – **Meals** 18.95 **t.** (lunch) and a la carte
29.85/42.40 **t.** 🛈 12.00
**Spec.** Roast scallops, grilled aubergine and coconut cream. Terrine of foie gras with pain
d'épices, salad of truffles and apricots. Loin of lamb wrapped in leeks, ratatouille, polenta
and thyme jus.

XX **The Tea Room** (at The Clarence H.), 6-8 Wellington Quay, D2, ℰ (01) 670 7766,
*Fax (01) 670 7800* – 🐠 AE ➀ *VISA* JCB                                                              HY   a
*closed lunch Saturday, Sunday and Bank Holidays* – **Meals** (booking essential) 18.50 **st.**
(lunch) and a la carte 24.50/42.00 **st.** 🛈 12.50.

REPUBLIC OF IRELAND

XX ⊛ **Chapter One,** The Dublin Writers Museum, 18-19 Parnell Sq., D1, ℘ (01) 873 2266
*Fax (01) 873 2330* – 🗏 **℗. ⓂⓈ 🄰🄴 ① 𝘝𝘐𝘚𝘈** JX
*closed Saturday lunch, Monday dinner, Sunday, 24 December-7 January and Bank Holidays* –
Meals 14.50 **t.** (lunch) and dinner a la carte 23.00/25.50 **t.**

XX **Saagar,** 16 Harcourt St., D2, ℘ (01) 475 5060, *Fax (01) 475 5741* – **ⓂⓈ 🄰🄴 ① 𝘝𝘐𝘚𝘈** JZ
*closed Saturday and Sunday lunch, 25 December and 1 January* – Meals - Indian - 7.70/
19.00 **t.** and a la carte ₰ 9.25.

XX ⊛ **L'Ecrivain,** 109 Lower Baggot St., D2, ℘ (01) 661 1919, *Fax (01) 661 0617*, 🏤 – 🗏 **ⓂⓈ 🄰
① 𝘝𝘐𝘚𝘈** KZ
*closed Saturday lunch, Sunday, 10 days Christmas and Bank Holidays* – Meals (booking
essential) 15.50/25.00 **t.** and dinner a la carte approx. 34.50 **t.** ₰ 7.00.

XX **Les Frères Jacques,** 74 Dame St., D2, ℘ (01) 679 4555, *Fax (01) 679 4725* – **ⓂⓈ 🄰🄴 ①
𝘝𝘐𝘚𝘈** HY
*closed Saturday lunch, Sunday, 24 December-2 January and Bank Holidays* – **Meals** - French
- 13.50/21.00 **t.** and dinner a la carte ₰ 5.50.

XX ⊛ **Morels at Stephen's Hall,** 14-17 Lower Leeson St., D2, ℘ (01) 662 2480,
*Fax (01) 662 8595* – 🗏. **ⓂⓈ 🄰🄴 ① 𝘝𝘐𝘚𝘈** JZ
*closed Saturday lunch, Sunday and 6 days Christmas* – Meals (booking essential) 13.95/
25.00 **t.** and dinner a la carte 18.40/28.65 **t.** ₰ 9.50.

XX **Locks,** 1 Windsor Terr., Portobello, D8, ℘ (01) 4543391, *Fax (01) 4538352* – **ⓂⓈ 🄰🄴 ①
𝘝𝘐𝘚𝘈** DU
*closed Saturday lunch, Sunday, last week July-first week August, 25 December-5 January
and Bank Holidays* – Meals 15.95/26.50 **t.** and a la carte ₰ 10.95.

XX **Old Dublin,** 90-91 Francis St., D8, ℘ (01) 4542028, *Fax (01) 4541406* – **ⓂⓈ 🄰🄴 ① 𝘝𝘐𝘚𝘈**
*closed Saturday lunch, Sunday and Bank Holidays* – Meals - Russian-Scandinavian - 12.00/
21.50 **t.** and dinner a la carte ₰ 7.80. HZ

XX **La Stampa,** 35 Dawson St., D2, ℘ (01) 677 8611, *Fax (01) 677 3336*, « 19C former ball
room » – 🗏. **ⓂⓈ 🄰🄴 ① 𝘝𝘐𝘚𝘈** JZ
*closed lunch Saturday and Sunday, Good Friday and 25-26 December* – Meals a la carte
11.10/30.95 **t.** ₰ 8.00.

XX **Eden,** Meeting House Sq., Templebar, D2, ℘ (01) 670 5372, *Fax (01) 670 3330*, 🏤 – 🗏. **ⓂⓈ
🄰🄴** HY
*closed 25 December and Bank Holidays* – Meals 15.00 **t.** (lunch) and dinner a la carte 17.00/
26.00 **t.** ₰ 6.00.

X ⊛ **Jacobs Ladder,** 4-5 Nassau St., D2, ℘ (01) 670 3865, *Fax (01) 670 3868* – **ⓂⓈ 🄰🄴 ① 𝘝𝘐𝘚𝘈**
*closed Sunday, Monday, 17 March and 25 December-15 January* – Meals a la carte 20.75/
28.95 **st.** ₰ 9.50. KY

X **Cooke's Café,** 14 South William St., D2, ℘ (01) 679 0536, *Fax (01) 679 0546*, 🏤 – 🗏. **ⓂⓈ
🄰🄴 ① 𝘝𝘐𝘚𝘈** JY
Meals 18.00 **st.** (lunch) and a la carte 35.00/50.00 **st.** ₰ 7.00.

X **Muscat,** 64 South William St., D2, ℘ (01) 679 7699 – **ⓂⓈ 🄰🄴 𝘝𝘐𝘚𝘈** JY
*closed Sunday, Monday, 10 days Christmas and New Year and 2 weeks in summer* – Meals
a la carte 19.15/28.70 **t.** ₰ 6.50.

X ⊛ **Lloyds Brasserie,** 20 Upper Merrion St., D2, ℘ (01) 662 7240, *Fax (01) 662 7243* – 🗏. **ⓂⓈ
🄰🄴 ① 𝘝𝘐𝘚𝘈** KZ
*closed 25 December and 1 January* – Meals 13.50 **t.** (lunch) and a la carte 18.85/30.85 **t.**
₰ 9.50.

X ⊛ **Mermaid Cafe,** 69-70 Dame St., D2, ℘ (01) 670 8236, *Fax (01) 670 8205* – 🗏. **ⓂⓈ
𝘝𝘐𝘚𝘈** HY
*closed Sunday dinner and Christmas-New Year* – Meals a la carte 18.95/28.20 ₰ 8.50.

X **Rhino Room,** 14a South William St., D2, ℘ (01) 670 5260, *Fax (01) 679 0546* – **ⓂⓈ 🄰🄴
① 𝘝𝘐𝘚𝘈 𝗝𝗖𝗕** JY
Meals a la carte 20.00/30.00 **st.**

X **Mao,** 2-3 Chatham Row, D2, ℘ (01) 670 4899, *Fax (01) 670 4893*, 🏤 – 🗏. **ⓂⓈ 𝘝𝘐𝘚𝘈**
*closed Good Friday and 25-26 December* – **Meals** - South East Asian - (bookings not
accepted) a la carte 10.85/15.95 **t.** ₰ 6.50. JZ

X **Dobbin's,** 15 Stephen's Lane, off Lower Mount St., D2, ℘ (01) 676 4679,
*Fax (01) 661 3331*, 🏤 – 🗏 **℗. ⓂⓈ 🄰🄴 ① 𝘝𝘐𝘚𝘈** EU
*closed Saturday lunch, Monday dinner, Sunday and Bank Holidays* – **Meals** - Bistro -
(booking essential) 15.50/30.00 **t.** and a la carte ₰ 6.75.

## Ballsbridge.
*Dublin 4.*

🏨🏨 **Berkeley Court,** Lansdowne Rd, D4, ℘ (01) 660 1711, *Fax (01) 661 7238*, 🗜 – 🔃, 🔀 rm,
🗏 rest, 📺 ☎ 📞 ⇔ ℗ – 🕍 450. **ⓂⓈ 🄰🄴 ① 𝘝𝘐𝘚𝘈**. 🛇 FU
**Berkeley Room :** Meals 17.95/29.95 **t.** and a la carte ₰ 6.75 – **Conservatory Grill :** Meals
a la carte 12.95/24.65 **t.** ₰ 6.90 – ☲ 10.75 – **183 rm** 165.00/185.00 **t.**, 5 suites – SB.

**The Towers,** Lansdowne Rd, D4, ℰ (01) 667 0033, *Fax (01) 660 5540*, **Ⅰ₆**, **⇌**, **⊒** – **⊦⊒⊦**, **⇷** rm, ⊟ ⊡ ☎ & **❷**. **Ⓜ◎** **Æ** **◎** **VISA**. **⪼**
FU p
**Meals** – (see *Jurys H.* below) – ⊒ 13.40 – **100 rm** 190.00/220.00 **t.**, 4 suites – SB.

**Jurys** (at The Towers H.), Pembroke Rd, D4, ℰ (01) 660 5000, *Fax (01) 660 5540*, **Ⅰ₆**, **⇌**, **⊒** – **⊦⊒⊦**, **⇷** rm, ⊟ rest, ⊡ ☎ & **❷** – **⊿** 850. **Ⓜ◎** **Æ** **◎** **VISA**. **⪼**
FU p
**Raglans :** Meals 18.00/25.00 **t.** and a la carte ⓝ 6.00 – ⊒ 10.75 – **290 rm** 155.00/195.00 **t.**, 3 suites – SB.

**Herbert Park,** D4, ℰ (01) 667 2200, *Fax (01) 667 2595*, **⇪**, **Ⅰ₆** – **⊦⊒⊦**, **⇷** rm, ⊟ ⊡ ☎ ❤ **❷** – **⊿** 180. **Ⓜ◎** **Æ** **◎** **VISA**. **⪼**
FU m
**The Pavilion :** Meals 17.50/27.50 **st.** and dinner a la carte ⓝ 8.50 – ⊒ 11.50 – **150 rm** 150.00/185.00 **t.**, 3 suites.

**The Hibernian,** Eastmoreland Pl., D4, ℰ (01) 668 7666, *Fax (01) 660 2655* – **⊦⊒⊦**, **⇷** rm, ⊡ ☎ ❤ **❷**. **Ⓜ◎** **Æ** **◎** **VISA** **JCB**. **⪼**
EU x
*closed 25 and 26 December* – *Patrick Kavanagh Room :* Meals *(closed Saturday lunch and Sunday dinner to non-residents)* 14.95/29.50 **t.** ⓝ 8.50 – **40 rm** ⊒ 120.00/185.00 **st.** – SB.

**Ariel House** without rest., 52 Lansdowne Rd, D4, ℰ (01) 668 5512, *Fax (01) 668 5845*, **⇪** – **⇷** ⊡ ☎ **❷**. **Ⓜ◎** **VISA**. **⪼**
FU n
*closed 24 December-12 January* – ⊒ 8.50 – **28 rm** 70.00/170.00 **t.**

**Butlers Town House,** 44 Lansdowne Rd, D4, ℰ (01) 667 4022, *Fax (01) 667 3960* – ⊟ ⊡ ☎ ❤ **❷**. **Ⓜ◎** **Æ** **◎** **VISA**. **⪼**
FU v
*closed 24 to 27 December* – **Meals** *(room service only)* – **19 rm** ⊒ 96.00/143.00 **st.**

**Aberdeen Lodge,** 53-55 Park Av., D4, ℰ (01) 283 8155, *Fax (01) 283 7877*, **⇪** – **⇷** ⊡ ☎ **❷**. **Ⓜ◎** **Æ** **◎** **VISA**. **⪼**
GV e
**Meals** *(residents only)* *(dinner only)* 24.00 **t.** ⓝ 8.50 – **17 rm** ⊒ 65.00/95.00 **t.** – SB.

**Merrion Hall** without rest., 54-56 Merrion Rd, D4, ℰ (01) 668 1426, *Fax (01) 668 4280*, **⇪** – ⊡ ☎ **❷**. **Ⓜ◎** **VISA**. **⪼**
FU b
*closed 22 December-2 January* – **23 rm** ⊒ 60.00/120.00 **st.**

**Glenogra House** without rest., 64 Merrion Rd, D4, ℰ (01) 668 3661, *Fax (01) 668 3698* – **⇷** ⊡ ☎ **❷**. **Ⓜ◎** **Æ** **◎** **VISA**. **⪼**
FU w
*closed January-March* – **10 rm** ⊒ 50.00/80.00 **st.**

**Number Eighty Eight** without rest., 88 Pembroke Rd, D4, ℰ (01) 660 0277, *Fax (01) 660 0291* – **⊦⊒⊦** ⊡ ☎ ❤ **❷**. **Ⓜ◎** **Æ** **◎** **VISA**. **⪼**
FU f
*closed Christmas* – **40 rm** ⊒ 80.00/120.00 **st.**

**Cedar Lodge Guesthouse** without rest., 98 Merrion Rd, D4, ℰ (01) 668 4410, *Fax (01) 668 4533*, **⇪** – **⇷** ⊡ ☎ ❤ **❷**. **Ⓜ◎** **Æ** **VISA**. **⪼**
FU g
*closed 23 to 27 December* – **15 rm** ⊒ 60.00/85.00 **st.**

**Glenveagh Town House** without rest., 31 Northumberland Rd, D4, ℰ (01) 668 4612, *Fax (01) 668 4559* – ⊡ ☎ **❷**. **Ⓜ◎** **Æ** **VISA**. **⪼**
FU u
*closed 22 to 29 December* – **10 rm** ⊒ 70.00/90.00 **st.**

**Raglan Lodge** without rest., 10 Raglan Rd, off Pembroke Rd, D4, ℰ (01) 660 6697, *Fax (01) 660 6781*, **⇪** – ⊡ ☎ **❷**. **Ⓜ◎** **VISA**. **⪼**
FU z
*closed 22 December-7 January* – **7 rm** ⊒ 50.00/110.00.

**Anglesea Town House** without rest., 63 Anglesea Rd, D4, ℰ (01) 668 3877, *Fax (01) 668 3461* – ⊡ ☎. **Ⓜ◎** **Æ** **VISA**. **⪼**
FV x
**7 rm** ⊒ 45.00/90.00 **t.**

**Northumberland Lodge** without rest., 68 Northumberland Rd, D4, ℰ (01) 660 5270, *Fax (01) 668 8679*, **⇪** – ⊡ ☎ **❷**. **Ⓜ◎** **VISA**. **⪼**
FU d
*closed 23 to 27 December* – **7 rm** ⊒ 65.00/130.00 **st.**

**XXX Le Coq Hardi,** 35 Pembroke Rd, D4, ℰ (01) 668 9070, *Fax (01) 668 9887* – **❷**. **Ⓜ◎** **Æ** **◎** **VISA** **JCB**
EU m
*closed Saturday lunch, Sunday, 2 weeks August and 2 weeks Christmas* – **Meals** 21.00/35.00 **t.** and a la carte ⓝ 8.00.

**XX Fitzers,** RDS, Merrion Rd, D4, ℰ (01) 667 1301, *Fax (01) 667 1303*, « Located in east wing of Royal Dublin Society » – **❷**. **Ⓜ◎** **Æ** **◎** **VISA**
FU a
*closed Sunday dinner, 25-26 December and Bank Holidays* – **Meals** *(booking essential)* a la carte 27.50/34.50 **t.** ⓝ 8.95.

**X Roly's Bistro,** 7 Ballsbridge Terr., D4, ℰ (01) 668 2611, *Fax (01) 660 8535* – ⊟. **Ⓜ◎** **Æ** **◎** **VISA**
FU r
*closed Good Friday and 25 to 27 December* – **Meals** *(booking essential)* 12.50 **t.** (lunch) and dinner a la carte 19.80/25.65 **t.** ⓝ 5.25.

## Donnybrook.

*Dublin 4.*

🏠 **Morehampton Lodge** without rest., 113 Morehampton Rd, D4, ℰ (01) 283 749
*Fax (01) 283 7595* – 📺 ☎ 📵. 🐼 ᴀᴇ 𝘝𝘐𝘚𝘈. ⋇ EV
*closed 24 and 25 December* – **15 rm** ⚏ 60.00/85.00 **st.**

🏠 **Eglinton Manor** without rest., 83 Eglinton Rd, D4, ℰ (01) 269 3273, *Fax (01) 269 752*
⇗ – 📺 ☎ ℂ 📵. 🐼 ᴀᴇ 𝘝𝘐𝘚𝘈. ⋇ EV
**8 rm** ⚏ 50.00/80.00 **t.**

XX **Ernie's,** Mulberry Gdns., off Morehampton Rd, D4, ℰ (01) 269 3300, *Fax (01) 269 326*
🍴 « Contemporary Irish Art collection » – ▤. 🐼 ᴀᴇ 𝘝𝘐𝘚𝘈 FV
*closed Sunday, Monday and 1 week Christmas* – Meals 14.25/25.00 **t.** and a la carte 28.20
38.10 **t.** ⚭ 8.00.

## Drumcondra.

*Dublin 5.*

🏨 **Doyle Skylon,** Upper Drumcondra Rd, D9, North : 2 ½ m. on N 1 ℰ (01) 837 912
*Fax (01) 837 2778* – ⫾⫿|, ⇤ rm, ▤ rest, 📺 ☎ & 📵. 🐼 ᴀᴇ ⓪ 𝘝𝘐𝘚𝘈. ⋇ BS
**Meals** 12.00/16.00 **t.** and a la carte ⚭ 5.60 – ⚏ 7.35 – **88 rm** 95.00/115.00 **t.** – SB.

## Merrion.

*Dublin 6.*

🏨 **Doyle Tara,** Merrion Rd, D4, Southeast : 4 m. on R 118 ℰ (01) 269 4666, *Fax (01) 269 102*
– ⫾⫿|, ▤ rest, 📺 ☎ & 📵 – ⚐ 300. 🐼 ᴀᴇ ⓪ 𝘝𝘐𝘚𝘈 GV
**Meals** 17.00 **t.** (dinner) and a la carte 15.45/20.00 ⚭ 6.00 – ⚏ 7.35 – **114 rm** 95.00/115.00
– SB.

## Rathgar.

*Dublin 6.*

🏠 **Roslyn House** without rest., 63 Terenure Rd East, D6, ℰ (01) 492 5807, *Fax (01) 492 937*
– 📺 ☎ 📵. 🐼 𝘝𝘐𝘚𝘈. ⋇ DV
**7 rm** ⚏ 37.00/70.00 **st.**

🏠 **St. Aiden's** without rest., 32 Brighton Rd, D6, ℰ (01) 490 2011, *Fax (01) 492 0234* – 📺 ☎
📵. 🐼 𝘝𝘐𝘚𝘈. ⋇ DV
*closed 20 December-6 January* – **8 rm** ⚏ 45.00/80.00 **st.**

## Rathmines.

*Dublin 6.*

🏨 **Rathmines Plaza,** Lower Rathmines Rd, D6, ℰ (01) 496 6966, *Fax (01) 491 0603* – ⫾⫿ 📺
☎ & 📵. 🐼 ᴀᴇ ⓪ 𝘝𝘐𝘚𝘈 DV
*closed 24 to 26 December* – **Meals** (carving lunch) 8.50/14.50 **st.** and dinner a la carte
**54 rm** ⚏ 70.00/90.00 **st.** – SB.

🏠 **Uppercross House,** 26-30 Upper Rathmines Rd, D6, ℰ (01) 4975486, *Fax (01) 497536*
– 📺 ☎ 📵. 🐼 ᴀᴇ ⓪ 𝘝𝘐𝘚𝘈 DV
**Meals** *(closed lunch Monday to Friday)* a la carte 10.95/20.50 **st.** – **25 rm** ⚏ 45.00/79.00 **s**

XX **Zen,** 89 Upper Rathmines Rd, D6, ℰ (01) 4979428 – ▤. 🐼 ᴀᴇ ⓪ 𝘝𝘐𝘚𝘈 DV
*closed lunch Monday to Wednesday, Saturday and 25 to 27 December* – **Meals** - Chines
(Szechuan) - a la carte 12.00/21.00 **t.** ⚭ 6.00.

## Terenure.

*Dublin 4.*

XX **Popjoys,** 4 Rathfarnham Rd, D6, South : 3 m. on N 81 ℰ (01) 492 9346, *Fax (01) 492 929*
– ▤. 🐼 ᴀᴇ ⓪ 𝘝𝘐𝘚𝘈 BT
*closed Saturday lunch, Sunday dinner, Monday, Good Friday and 25-26 December* – **Mea**
12.95 **t.** (lunch) and a la carte 16.50/29.50 **t.** ⚭ 6.75.

## at Clontarf *Northeast : 3½ m. by R 105* – ✉ *Dublin.*

🏨 **Clontarf Castle,** Castle Av., D3, ℰ (01) 853 2321, *Fax (01) 833 0418,* « Part 18C » – ⫾⫿
☎ & 📵 – ⚐ 550. 🐼 ᴀᴇ ⓪ 𝘝𝘐𝘚𝘈. ⋇ CS
*closed 25 December* – **Templars Bistro :** Meals (bar lunch Saturday) 14.50/23.50 **s**
and dinner a la carte ⚭ 6.50 – ⚏ 9.95 – **111 rm** 119.00/145.00 **st.** – SB.

🏠 **Hedigan's** without rest., Tullyallan House, 14 Hollybrook Park, D3, ℰ (01) 853 1663
*Fax (01) 833 3337,* ⇗ – ⇤ 📺 ☎ 📵. 🐼 𝘝𝘐𝘚𝘈. ⋇ CS
*closed 20 December-12 January* – **9 rm** ⚏ 35.00/70.00 **st.**

**t Blackrock** *Southeast : 5½ m. by R 118 – CT – ⊠ Dublin.*

✗ **Ayumi-Ya,** Newpark Centre, Newtownpark Av., Southeast : 1 ¼ m. on R 113 ℰ (01) 283 1767, Fax (01) 288 0478 – ▦, ⬛◉ 鮏 ◉ ▥
*closed 1 January, Good Friday and 24-25 December* – **Meals** - Japanese - (dinner only) 12.95 **t.** and a la carte ⸂ 6.45.

**t Monkstown** *Southeast : 6½ m. by R 118 - CT - on R 119 – ⊠ Dublin.*

✗✗ **Siam,** 8a The Crescent, ℰ (01) 284 3309 – ⬛◉ 鮏 ◉ ▥
*closed Good Friday and Christmas* – **Meals** - Thai - (dinner only) 18.95 **s.** and a la carte ⸂ 6.95.

**t Foxrock** *Southeast : 7½ m. by N 11 – CT – ⊠ Dublin.*

✗ **Bistro One,** 3 Brighton Rd., D18, ℰ (01) 289 7711 – ⬛◉ ▥
*closed Sunday, Monday, 25-26 December and Bank Holidays* – **Meals** (booking essential) (dinner only) a la carte 18.70/23.70 **t.**

**t Tallaght** *Southwest : 7½ m. by N 81 – BT – ⊠ Dublin.*

🏨 **Abberley Court,** Belgard Rd, D24, on R 113 ℰ (01) 459 6000, Fax (01) 462 1000 – ▯, ✳⃝ rm, ▥ ☎ & ⬅⃝ – 🔏 200. ⬛◉ 鮏 ◉ ▥. ❀
*closed 25 and 26 December* – **Meals** (closed lunch Saturday and Sunday and Bank Holidays) 12.95/16.95 **st.** ⸂ 6.95 – **40 rm** ⊐ 79.00/98.00. **st.** – SB.

**t Saggart** *Southwest : 9¼ m. off N 7 – AT – ⊠ Dublin.*

🏨 **Citywest,** ℰ (01) 458 8566, Fax (01) 458 8565, ℉₆, ☎ₛ, ∏₆, ⌖, ☞, park – ▯, ▤ rest, ▥ ☎ ✆ & ⬤ – 🔏 600. ⬛◉ 鮏 ◉ ▥. ❀
**Meals** 13.95/24.95 **t.** ⸂ 6.50 – **200 rm** ⊐ 99.00/180.00 **st.** – SB.

**t Ashtown** *Northwest : 4¾ m. by N 3 – AS – ⊠ Dublin.*

🏠 **Ashbrook House** without rest., River Rd, D15, ℰ (01) 838 5660, Fax (01) 838 5660, « Georgian country house », ☞, ✗ – ✳⃝ ▥ ☎ ⬤ ⬛◉ ▥. ❀
*closed 20 December-2 January* – **4 rm** ⊐ 40.00/60.00.

**t Castleknock** *Northwest : 5½ m. by N 3 – AS – ⊠ Dublin.*

🏨 **Travelodge,** Auburn Av. roundabout, D15, on N 3 ℰ (01) 820 2626, Fax (01) 820 2151, Reservations (Freephone) 0800 850950 – ✳⃝ rm, ▤ rest, ▥ ☎ & ⬤. ⬛◉ 鮏 ◉ ▥ ᴶᴄᴮ. ❀
**Meals** (grill rest.) – **60 rm** 39.95/59.95 **t.**

*to the Southeast.*

🏨 **Radisson SAS St. Helen's,** Stillorgan Rd, Southeast : 4 ½ m. on N 11 ℰ (01) 218 6000, Fax (01) 260 2295, « Part 18C », ℉₆, ☞ – ▤ ▥ ☎ ✆ & ⬤ – 🔏 350. ⬛◉ 鮏 ◉ ▥ ᴶᴄᴮ
**Meals** a la carte 24.85/33.50 **t.** – ⊐ 11.50 – **151 rm** 175.00/195.00 **st.**

🏨 **Stillorgan Park,** Stillorgan Rd, Southeast : 5 m. on N 11 ℰ (01) 288 1621, Fax (01) 283 1610 – ✳⃝ rm, ▤ ▥ ☎ & ⬤ – 🔏 180. ⬛◉ 鮏 ◉ ▥. ❀
**Meals** 11.95 **t.** (lunch) and dinner a la carte 16.85/24.45 **t.** ⸂ 8.00 – **99 rm** ⊐ 95.00/125.00 **st.** – SB.

🏨 **Doyle Montrose,** Stillorgan Rd, D4, Southeast : 4 m. by N 11 ℰ (01) 269 3311, Fax (01) 269 1164 – ▯, ✳⃝ rm, ▥ ☎ ✆ ⬤ – 🔏 70. ⬛◉ 鮏 ◉ ▥. ❀      **GV y**
**Meals** a la carte 15.00/21.50 **t.** ⸂ 6.50 – ⊐ 7.50 – **179 rm** 89.00/119.00 **t.**

*to the Southwest.*

🏨 **Red Cow Moran's,** Naas Rd, D22, Southwest : 5 m. on N 7 ℰ (01) 459 3650, Fax (01) 459 1588 – ▯, ✳⃝ rm, ▤ ▥ ☎ ✆ & ⬤ – 🔏 700. ⬛◉ 鮏 ◉ ▥. ❀
**Meals** 14.50/22.50 **t.** and dinner a la carte ⸂ 8.50 – **120 rm** ⊐ 90.00/170.00 **t.**, 3 suites – SB.

🏨 **Doyle Green Isle,** Naas Rd, D22, Southwest : 7 ¾ m. off N7 (eastbound carriageway) ℰ (01) 459 3406, Fax (01) 464 1532 – ▯, ✳⃝ rm, ▥ ☎ & ⬤ – 🔏 250. ⬛◉ 鮏 ◉ ▥. ❀
**Meals** 14.00/21.00 **st.** and a la carte ⸂ 6.50 – ⊐ 7.50 – **90 rm** 95.00 **t.**

🏨 **Bewley's H. at Newlands Cross,** Newlands Cross, D22, Southwest : 7 m. by N 7 on R 113 ℰ (01) 464 0140, Fax (01) 464 0900 – ▯, ✳⃝ rm, ▤ rest, ▥ ☎ & ⬤ – 🔏 30. ⬛◉ 鮏 ◉ ▥. ❀
*closed 24 to 26 December* – **Meals** (carving lunch) a la carte 13.50/24.50 **st.** ⸂ 7.50 – ⊐ 5.50 – **200 rm** 49.00 **st.**

🏨 **Sheldon Park,** Kylemore Rd, D12, Southwest : 4 ¾ m. by N 7 on R 112 ℰ (01) 460 1055, Fax (01) 460 1880, ℉₆, ☎ₛ – ▯ ▥ ☎ ✆ & ⬤ – 🔏 550. ⬛◉ 鮏 ◉ ▥. ❀
*closed 25 December* – **Meals** (carving lunch)/dinner 12.95 **t.** and a la carte ⸂ 4.50 – **72 rm** ⊐ 60.00/85.00 **st.** – SB.

🏨 **Ibis Dublin,** Monastery Rd, Clondalkin, D22, Southwest : 5 ¼ m. off N 7 ℰ (01) 464 1480, Fax (01) 464 1484 – ▯, ✳⃝ rm, ▥ ☎ ✆ & ⬤ – 🔏 30. ⬛◉ 鮏 ◉ ▥. ❀
**Meals** a la carte 12.00/14.75 **st.** ⸂ 5.25 – ⊐ 5.25 – **150 rm** 49.50 **t.**

**DUBLIN AIRPORT** Dublin 🕮🕮🕮 N 7 – ✉ Dublin.

🏛 **Forte Posthouse Dublin Airport**, ℰ (01) 808 0500, Fax (01) 844 6002 – ⥱ rm
▦ rest, 📺 ☎ & ₽ – ⚐ 130. 🕮🕮 Æ ① 𝘝𝘐𝘚𝘈. ❀
closed 24 and 25 December – **Bistro :** Meals (closed Saturday lunch) 11.50/18.50 t
and a la carte ⓙ 6.50 – **Sampan's :** Meals - South East Asian - (closed Bank Holidays) (dinner
only) a la carte 14.25/26.95 t. ⓙ 6.75 – ☞ 12.00 – **249 rm** 108.00 t. – SB.

🏛 **Great Southern**, ℰ (01) 844 6000, Fax (01) 844 6001 – 🛗, ⥱ rm, 📺 ☎ ✆ ₽ – ⚐ 350.
🕮🕮 Æ ① 𝘝𝘐𝘚𝘈. ❀
closed 24 and 25 December – **Potters Bistro :** Meals (bar lunch Monday to Saturday)
dinner 18.00 st. and a la carte ⓙ 7.00 – ☞ 10.00 – **147 rm** 110.00 st.

**DUNDALK** (Dun Dealgan) Louth 🕮🕮🕮 M 5/6 Ireland G – pop. 25 762.
Exc. : Dún a' Rá Forest Park★, W : 21 m. by R 178 and R 179.
Dublin 51 – Drogheda 22.

🏛 **Ballymascanlon,**, North : 3 ½ m. by N 1 on R 173 ℰ (042) 9371124, Fax (042) 9371598,
Ⅰ₅, ≦s, 🏊, 🏊₈, 🌳, park, ※ – 🛗 📺 ☎ & ₽. 🕮🕮 Æ ① 𝘝𝘐𝘚𝘈
closed 24 to 26 December – Meals 14.00/24.00 t. and dinner a la carte ⓙ 8.00 – **54 rm**
☞ 60.00/100.00 st. – SB.

🏨 **Fairways,**, South : 3 m. on N 1 ℰ (042) 9321500, Fax (042) 9321511, ≦s, 🏊, 🌳, ※,
squash – 📺 ☎ ₽ – ⚐ 400. 🕮🕮 Æ ① 𝘝𝘐𝘚𝘈
closed 25 December – Meals 11.50/17.50 st. and dinner a la carte ⓙ 6.50 – **48 rm** ☞ 55.00/
95.00 st. – SB.

**at Carrickcarnon** North : 8 m. on N 1 – ✉ Dundalk.

🏨 **Carrickdale**, ℰ (042) 9371397, Fax (042) 9371740, Ⅰ₅, ≦s, 🏊, 🌳 – 📺 ☎ ₽ – ⚐ 40. 🕮🕮
Æ ① 𝘝𝘐𝘚𝘈. ❀
closed 25 December – Meals (carving lunch) 10.95/21.00 t. and dinner a la carte ⓙ 7.50 –
**48 rm** ☞ 50.00/80.00 st. – SB.

**DUNDRUM** (Dún Droma) Tipperary 🕮🕮🕮 H 10 – pop. 219 – ✉ Cashel.
Dublin 104 – Cork 66 – Limerick 33.

🏨 **Dundrum House** ⤳,, Southeast : ¾ m. on R 505 ℰ (062) 71116, Fax (062) 71366, ▛,
🌳, park, ※ – 🛗 📺 ☎ ₽ – ⚐ 150. 🕮🕮 Æ ① 𝘝𝘐𝘚𝘈
Meals (bar lunch Monday to Saturday) 20.00 t. and a la carte ⓙ 8.00 – **61 rm** ☞ 70.00/
105.00 t. – SB.

**DUNFANAGHY** (Dún Fionnachaidh) Donegal 🕮🕮🕮 I 2 Ireland G. – pop. 290 – ✉ Letterkenny.
Env. : Horn Head Scenic Route★, N : 2½ m.
Exc. : Doe Castle★, SE : 7 m. by N 56 – The Rosses★, SW : 25 m. by N 56 and R 259.
Dublin 172 – Donegal 54 – Londonderry 43.

🏨 **Arnold's**, Main St., ℰ (074) 36208, Fax (074) 36352, ≤, 🌳, ※ – 📺 ☎ ₽. 🕮🕮 Æ ① 𝘝𝘐𝘚𝘈.
❀
closed 3 January-16 March, 25 December and Sunday to Friday November-December –
**Tramore rest. :** Meals (dinner only) 30.00 t. ⓙ 5.75 – **Garden bistro :** Meals a la carte
11.50/22.50 t. ⓙ 5.75 – **30 rm** ☞ 47.00/94.00.

🏠 **Carrig Rua**, Main St., ℰ (074) 36133, Fax (074) 36277, ≤ – 📺 ☎ ₽. 🕮🕮 Æ ① 𝘝𝘐𝘚𝘈. ❀
mid March-October – **Sheephaven Room :** Meals (dinner only) 25.00 t. ⓙ 6.50 – **Copper
grill :** Meals a la carte 12.50/23.50 t. ⓙ 6.50 – **22 rm** ☞ 41.00/82.00 t. – SB.

When visiting London use the Green Guide **"London"**

- Detailed descriptions of places of interest
- Useful local information
- A section on the historic square-mile of the
  City of London with a detailed fold-out plan
- The lesser known London boroughs
  - their people, places and sights
- Plans of selected areas and important buildings.

**DUNGARVAN** (Dún Garbháin) *Waterford* 923 J 11 *Ireland G – pop. 7 175.*

See : *East Bank (Augustinian priory, ≤★).*

Exc. : *Ringville (≤★), S : 8 m. by N 25 and R 674 – Helvick Head★ (≤★), SE : 8 m. by N 25 and R 674.*

🔩 *Knocknagrannagh ℰ (058) 41605/43310 –* 🔩 *Gold Coast, Ballinacourty ℰ (058) 42249/ 44055.*

*Dublin 118 – Cork 44 – Waterford 30.*

🏠 **Lawlors**, Meagher St., ℰ (058) 41122, Fax (058) 41000 – 🛗, 🍴 rest, 📺 ☎ – 🎴 150. ◖◗ 🎴 ⓪ 💳
*closed 25 December –* **Meals** 8.95/14.95 **st.** and dinner a la carte 🛈 7.25 – **89 rm** ☲ 38.00/ 75.00 **t.** – SB.

✕✕ **The Tannery**, 10 Quay St., via Parnell St. ℰ (058) 45420, Fax (058) 44025, « 19C former
🔶 tannery » – ◖◗ 🎴 ⓪ 💳
*closed Sunday, Monday, late January-early February and 25-26 December –* Meals a la carte
13.25/24.40 **t.** 🛈 6.50.

---

**DUNGLOW** (An Clochán Liath) *Donegal* 923 G 3 *Ireland G – pop. 1 042.*

Env. : *The Rosses★.*

Exc. : *Gweebarra Estuary★, S : by N 56.*

*Dublin 173 – Londonderry 51 – Sligo 76.*

🏠 **Ostan na Rosann**, Mill Rd, ℰ (075) 22444, Fax (075) 22400, ≤, ☎, 🔲 – 📺 📞 ⓟ. ◖◗ 🎴
💳
*closed 4 January-12 March and weekends only November-December –* **Meals** (bar lunch
Monday to Saturday)/dinner 17.50 **st.** and a la carte 🛈 6.50 – **48 rm** ☲ 55.00/70.00 **st.** – SB.

---

*Per spostarvi più rapidamente utilizzate le* **carte Michelin "Grandi Strade"** *:*

*n° 970 Europa, n° 976 Rep. Ceca/Slovacchia, n° 980 Grecia,*

*n° 984 Germania, n° 985 Scandinavia-Finlandia,*

*n° 986 Gran Bretagna-Irlanda, n° 987 Germania-Austria-Benelux,*

*n° 988 Italia, n° 989 Francia, n° 990 Spagna-Portogallo.*

---

**DUNKINEELY** (Dún Cionnaola) *Donegal* 923 G 4 *Ireland G – pop. 395.*

Exc. : *Donegal Coast★★ – Cliffs of Bunglass★★ – Glengesh Pass★★ – Glencolmcille Folk
Village★★.*

*Dublin 157 – Londonderry 56 – Sligo 50.*

✕✕ **Castle Murray House** with rm, St. Johns Point, Southwest : 1 ¼ m. by N 56 and
St. Johns Point rd turning left at T junction ℰ (073) 37022, Fax (073) 37330, ≤ McSweeney
Bay – 📺 ☎ ⓟ. ◖◗ 💳
*closed 3 weeks January and February –* **Meals** - French - (dinner only and Sunday lunch)/
dinner a la carte 14.50/25.00 **st.** 🛈 7.00 – **10 rm** ☲ 38.00/64.00 **st.**

---

**DUN LAOGHAIRE** (Dún Laoghaire) *Dublin* 923 N 8 *Ireland G. – pop. 55 540.*

Env. : *– ≤★★ of Killiney Bay from coast road south of Sorrento Point.*

🚢 *to Holyhead (Stena Line) 4-5 daily (1 h 40 mn).*

*Dublin 9.*

Plan on next page

🏨 **Royal Marine**, Marine Rd, ℰ (01) 280 1911, Fax (01) 280 1089, ≤, 🌳 – 🛗, 🍴 rest, 📺 ☎
ⓟ – 🎴 500. ◖◗ 🎴 ⓪ 💳. ✎     n
**Meals** a la carte 20.00/35.00 **t.** 🛈 10.00 – ☲ 15.00 – **103 rm** 180.00.

🏠 **Chestnut Lodge** without rest., 2 Vesey Pl., Monkstown, ℰ (01) 280 7860,
Fax (01) 280 1466, « Regency house, antiques », 🌳 – 📺 ☎. ◖◗ 💳. ✎     u
*closed 23 December-2 January –* **4 rm** ☲ 45.00/70.00 **st.**

✕✕ **Morels Bistro**, 1st floor (above Eagle House pub), 18 Glasthule Rd, ℰ (01) 230 0210,
🔶 Fax (01) 230 0466 – ◖◗ 🎴 ⓪ 💳     c
*closed lunch Monday to Wednesday and Saturday, 24 to 27 December and 1 January –*
Meals (dinner only and Sunday lunch)/dinner a la carte 19.40/24.95 **t.** 🛈 5.50.

✕✕ **Brasserie Na Mara**, 1 Harbour Rd, ℰ (01) 280 6767, Fax (01) 284 4649 – ◖◗ 🎴 ⓪ 💳
*closed Saturday lunch, Sunday, Good Friday, 25 to 27 December and Bank Holidays –* Meals
11.95/19.95 **t.** and dinner a la carte 🛈 6.00.     i

✕ **Cavistons**, 59 Glasthule Rd, ℰ (01) 280 9120, Fax (01) 284 4054 – ✎. ◖◗ 💳 🎴     a
*closed Sunday, Monday and 19 December-5 January –* **Meals** - Seafood - (booking essential)
(lunch only) a la carte 13.00/22.00 **t.** 🛈 4.50.

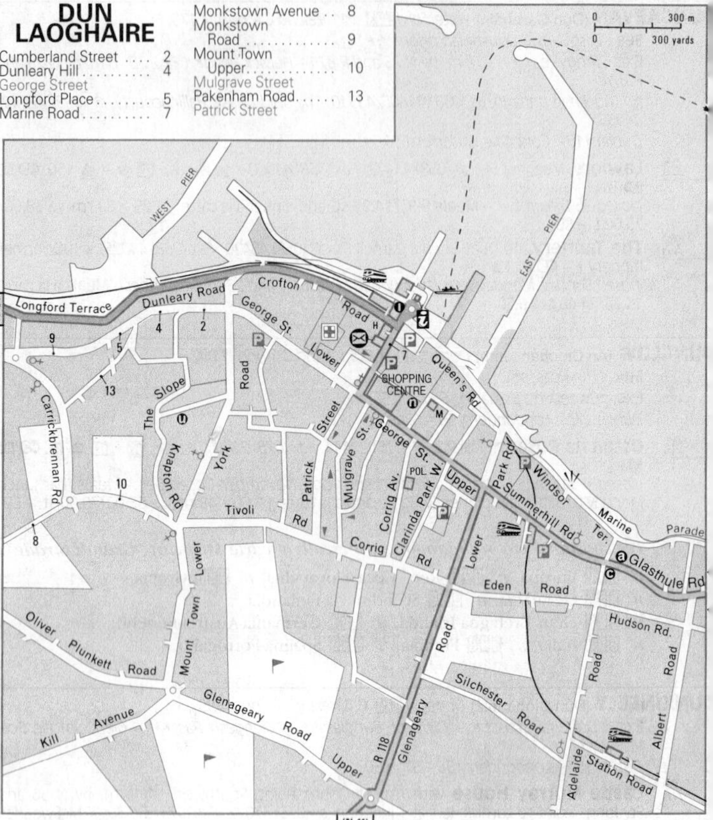


**DUNLAVIN** (Dún Luáin) *Wicklow* [923] L 8 – *pop. 693.*

*Dublin 31 – Kilkenny 44 – Wexford 61.*

🏠 **Rathsallagh House** 🐚,, Southwest : 2 m. on Grangecon Rd ☎ (045) 403112 *Fax (045) 403343*, ≤, « 18C converted stables, walled garden », [s], [pool], 🏌, park, 🎾 – [TV] ☎ [P] – 🎤 50. [MC] [AE] [D] [VISA]. ✂
*closed 23 to 27 December* – **Meals** (dinner only) 30.00 **t.** 🍷 6.00 – **16 rm** ☕ 95.00/190.00 t 1 suite – SB.

**DUNMANWAY** (Dún Mánmhaí) *Cork* [923] E 12 – *pop. 1 427.*

*Dublin 191 – Cork 37 – Killarney 49.*

🏠 **Dún Mhuire House,** Kilbarry Rd, West : ½ m. by R 586 taking first right at fork junctio ☎ (023) 45162, *Fax (023) 45162*, 🌳 – [TV] ☎ [P]. [MC] [D] [VISA]. ✂
*closed 1 week Christmas* – **Meals** *(closed Sunday to Tuesday October-June)* (bookin essential) (dinner only) a la carte 15.00/19.00 **t.** 🍷 7.00 – **6 rm** ☕ 35.00/50.00 **t.** – SB.

**DUNMORE EAST** (Dún MÉr) *Waterford* [923] L 11 *Ireland G.* – *pop. 1 430* – ✉ *Waterford.*

See : *Village*★ – *Dublin 108 – Waterford 12.*

🏠 **Lakefield House** 🐚, Dunmore East Rd, Rosduff, Northwest : 5 m. on R 68 ☎ (051) 382582, *Fax (051) 382582*, ≤, 🐕, 🌳, park – ✂ rest, [TV] [P]. [MC] [VISA]
*18 March-October* – **Meals** (by arrangement) 16.00 – **5 rm** ☕ 30.00/40.00 **st.** – SB.

🍴 **The Ship,** Dock Rd, ☎ (051) 383141 – [MC] [AE] [VISA]
*closed 24 to 26 December* **Meals** - Seafood - *(closed Sunday and Monday November-March)* (dinner only and lunch Monday to Saturday June-August) a la carte 12.95/20.95 **t.** 🍷 6.75.

**DUNSHAUGHLIN** (Dún Seachlainn) *Meath* 923 M 7 – *pop. 2 139.*
*Dublin 17 – Drogheda 19.*

↑ **Old Workhouse**, Ballinlough, South : 1 ½ m. on N 3 ℰ (01) 8259251, *Fax (01) 825 9251,*
⌗ – ⅍ rm, 📺 🅿. ✺
*closed 20 December-7 January* – **Meals** (by arrangement) (communal dining) 25.00 **s.** –
**4 rm** ⌇ 70.00.

↑ **Gaulstown House** ⌂,, Northeast : 1 ½ m. by Ratoath rd ℰ (01) 825 9147,
*Fax (01) 825 9147,* « Working farm », ⌗, park – ⅍ 📺 🅿. ✺ 💳 VISA. ✺
*April-September* – **Meals** (by arrangement) 14.00 **st.** – **3 rm** ⌇ 25.00/40.00 **s.**

**DURRUS** (Dúras) *Cork* 923 D 13 – *pop. 204.*
*Dublin 210 – Cork 56 – Killarney 53.*

XX **Blairs Cove**,, Southwest : 1 m. on L 56 ℰ (027) 61127, *Fax (027) 61487,* « Converted
barn », ⌗ – 🅿. 💳 VISA
*closed Sunday, Monday except July and August and November-March* – **Meals** (booking
essential) (dinner only) 29.00 **st..**

**ENNIS** (Inis) *Clare* 923 F 9 *Ireland G.* – *pop. 15 333.*
See : *Ennis Friary★ AC.*
Exc. : *Dysert O'Dea★, N : 6 m. by N 85 and R 476, turning left after 4 m. and right after 1m.*
*– Quin Franciscan Friary★, SE : 6½ m. by R 469 – Knappogue Castle★ AC, SE : 8 m. by R 469*
*– Corrofin (Clare Heritage Centre★ AC), N : 8½ m. by N 85 and R 476 – Craggaunowen*
*Centre★ AC, SE : 11 m. by R 469 – Kilmacduagh Churches and Round Tower★, NE : 11 m. by*
*N 18 – Kilrush★ (Scattery Island★ by boat) SW : 27 m. by N 68 – Bridge of Ross, Kilkee★, SW :*
*35½ m. by N 68 and N 67.*
🏌 *Drumbiggle Rd* ℰ (065) 6824074.
🗓 *Clare Rd* ℰ (065) 6828366.
*Dublin 142 – Galway 42 – Limerick 22 – Roscommon 92 – Tullamore 93.*

🏨 **West County**, Clare Rd, Southeast : ¾ m. on N 18 ℰ (065) 6828421, *Fax (065) 6823759,*
Central reservations (065) 6823000, ⌖, ⇌, ⧄ – ⧉, ▤ rest, 📺 ☎ & 🅿 – 🕭 1000. 💳 AE
① VISA. ✺
**Meals** 9.00/15.00 **st.** and a la carte ⌗ 5.50 – **152 rm** ⌇ 65.00/100.00 **st.** – SB.

🏨 **Old Ground**, ℰ (065) 6828127, *Fax (065) 6828112,* ⌗ – ⧄, ⅍ rm, 📺 ☎ & 🅿 – 🕭 70.
💳 AE ① VISA. ✺
*closed 24 and 25 December* – **Meals** 11.45/18.45 **t.** and dinner a la carte ⌗ 12.50 – **83 rm**
⌇ 76.00/130.00 **st.** – SB.

🏨 **Auburn Lodge**, Galway Rd, North : 1 ½ m. on N 18 ℰ (065) 6821247, *Fax (065) 6821202,*
⌗ – 📺 ☎ 🅿. 💳 ① VISA. ✺
**Meals** (carving lunch) 10.00/19.50 **st.** and dinner a la carte ⌗ 7.00 – **99 rm** ⌇ 55.00/
90.00 **st.** – SB.

🏨 **Temple Gate**, The Square, ℰ (065) 6823300, *Fax (065) 6823322* – ⧄ 📺 ☎ 🅿. 💳 AE ①
VISA. ✺
*closed 25 December* – **Meals** (bar lunch Monday to Saturday)/dinner 18.50 **t.** and a la carte
⌗ 5.95 – **74 rm** ⌇ 62.50/110.00 **st.** – SB.

↑ **Cill Eoin House** without rest., Killadysert Cross, Clare Rd, Southeast : 1 ½ m. at junction
of N 18 with R 473 ℰ (065) 6841668, *Fax (065) 6841669,* ⌗, ✺ – ⅍ 📺 ☎ 🅿. 💳 AE VISA
**14 rm** ⌇ 25.00/42.00 **st.** – SB.

XX **Garvello's**, Clare Abbey, Limerick Rd, Southeast : 1 ½ m. on N 18 ℰ (065) 6840011,
*Fax (065) 6840022* – ▤ 🅿. 💳 ① VISA
*closed Sunday, Monday and 25 December* – **Meals** (dinner only) 22.00 **t.** and a la carte
⌗ 8.70.

**at Barefield** *Northeast : 3½ m. on N 18* – ✉ *Ennis.*

↑ **Carraig Mhuire**,, Northeast : 1 ¾ m. on N 18 ℰ (065) 6827106, *Fax (065) 6827375,* ⌗ –
🅿. 💳 VISA. ✺
**Meals** 12.00 **s.** – **5 rm** ⌇ 20.00/36.00 **st.** – SB.

**at Inch** *Southwest : 4 m. on R 474 (Kilmaley rd)* – ✉ *Ennis.*

🏨 **Magowna House** ⌂,, West : 1 m. by R 474 ℰ (065) 6839009, *Fax (065) 6839258,* ≤, ⌕,
⌗ – 📺 ☎ 🅿. 💳 AE ① VISA
*closed 24 to 26 December* – **Meals** 9.95/16.00 **st.** and a la carte ⌗ 5.00 – **10 rm** ⌇ 39.00/
60.00 **st.** – SB.

**ENNISCORTHY** (Inis CÉrthaidh) *Wexford* 🅑🅩🅑 M 10 *Ireland G –* pop. 3 788.
See : *Enniscorthy Castle★ (County Museum★).*
Exc. : *Ferns★, NE : 8 m. by N 11 – Mount Leinster★, N : 17 m. by N 11.*
🆘 *Knockmarshal* ℘ (054) 33191.
*Dublin 76 – Kilkenny 46 – Waterford 34 – Wexford 15.*

🏨🏨🏨 **Riverside Park,** The Promenade, ℘ (054) 37800, Fax (054) 37900 – 🛗 📺 ☎ 🚗 🅿
🍸 800. 🐼 🆎 ⓪ 𝘝𝘐𝘚𝘈. 🎇
Meals 13.00/22.50 st. and dinner a la carte – **60 rm** ⊇ 48.00/140.00 st. – SB.

🏨🏨 **Treacy's,** ℘ (054) 37798, Fax (054) 37733 – 🛗 📺 ☎ 🍸 – 🍸 350. 🐼 🆎 ⓪ 𝘝𝘐𝘚𝘈. 🎇
closed 25 December – **Meals** (bar lunch Monday to Saturday)/dinner 16.95 st. and a la cart
§ 6.95 – **48 rm** ⊇ 45.00/90.00 st. – SB.

↑ **Ballinkeele House** 🌀, Ballymurn, Southeast : 6 ½ m. by unmarked road on Curraclo
rd ℘ (053) 38105, Fax (053) 38468, ≼, « 19C country house », 🌲, park – ≒⇥ rm, 🅿. 🐼 🎡
𝘝𝘐𝘚𝘈 𝙅𝘾𝘽. 🎇
March-12 November – **Meals** (by arrangment) (communal dining) 22.00 st. – **5 r**
⊇ 55.00/90.00 st.

---

**ENNISKERRY** (Áth an Sceire) *Wicklow* 🅑🅩🅑 N 8 – pop. 1 275.
*Dublin 16 – Wicklow 20.*

🏨🏨 **Summerhill House,** Cookstown Rd, South : ½ m. ℘ (01) 286 7928, Fax (01) 286 7929
🛗 ≒⇥ 📺 ☎ 🅿 – 🍸 220. 🐼 🆎 𝘝𝘐𝘚𝘈. 🎇
Meals (bar lunch Monday to Saturday)/dinner 16.50 st. and a la carte § 5.75 – **57 r**
⊇ 60.00/100.00 st. – SB.

🏠 **Enniscree Lodge** 🌀, Glencree Valley, West : 4 m. on Glencree Rd ℘ (01) 286 354
Fax (01) 286 6037, ≼ Djouce, Tanduff and Kippure mountains – 📺 ☎. 🐼 🆎 ⓪ 𝘝𝘐𝘚𝘈. 🎇
Meals 14.50/26.00 st. § 8.00 – **10 rm** ⊇ 50.00/100.00 t. – SB.

---

**ENNISTIMON** (Inis Dáomáin) *Clare* 🅑🅩🅑 E 9 – pop. 920.
*Dublin 158 – Galway 52 – Limerick 39.*

↑ **Grovemount House** without rest., Lahinch Rd, West : ½ m. on N 67 ℘ (065) 707143
Fax (065) 7071823, 🌲 – 📺 ☎ 🅿. 🐼 𝘝𝘐𝘚𝘈. 🎇
April-October – **8 rm** ⊇ 30.00/40.00 st.

---

**FAHAN** (Fathain) *Donegal* 🅑🅩🅑 J 2 *Ireland G.* – pop. 284 – ⊠ *Inishowen.*
Exc. : *Inishowen Peninsula★★ – Grianán of Aileach★★ (≼★★), SE : 7 m. by R 238 and west*
*N 13 – Dunree Fort★ AC, N : 11 m. by R 238 and coast rd – Gap of Mamore★, N : by R 2.*
*and coast rd.*
🆘 *North West, Lisfannon* ℘ (077) 61027.
*Dublin 156 – Londonderry 11 – Sligo 50.*

✕✕ **St. John's Country House** with rm, ℘ (077) 60289, Fax (077) 60612, ≼, « Loughsid
setting », 🌲 – ≒⇥ rest, ▤ rest, 📺 ☎ 🅿. 🐼 𝘝𝘐𝘚𝘈. 🎇
closed 4 weeks February-March and 25-26 December – **Meals** (closed Monday in winte
(dinner only and Sunday lunch)/dinner 22.00 t. and a la carte § 6.95 – **5 rm** ⊇ 45.0
150.00 t. – SB.

---

**FERNS** (Fearna) *Wexford* 🅑🅩🅑 M 10 *Ireland G.* – pop. 915 – ⊠ *Enniscorthy.*
See : *Town★.*
Exc. : – *Mount Leinster★, NW : 17 m – Enniscorthy Castle★ (County Museum★ AC), S : 8 r*
*by N 11.*
*Dublin 69 – Kilkenny 53 – Waterford 41 – Wexford 22.*

↑ **Clone House** 🌀,, South : 2 m. by Boolavogue rd off Monageer rd ℘ (054) 6611
Fax (054) 66225, « Working farm », ⇥, 🌲, park – ≒⇥ 📺 🅿. 🎇
April-30 October – **Meals** (by arrangement) (communal dining) 14.00 st. – **4 rm** ⊇ 26.5
50.00 st.

---

**FOXROCK** (Carraig an tSionnaigh) *Dublin* 🅑🅩🅑 N 7 – see Dublin.

---

**FURBOGH/FURBO** (Na Forbacha) *Galway* 🅑🅩🅑 E 8.
*Dublin 42 – Galway 7.*

🏨🏨🏨 **Connemara Coast,** ℘ (091) 592108, Fax (091) 592065, ≼, 🛁, ⇔, 🔲, 🌲, 🎾 – 📺 ☎
– 🍸 500. 🐼 🆎 ⓪ 𝘝𝘐𝘚𝘈. 🎇
closed 25 December – **Meals** (bar lunch)/dinner 22.50 st. and a la carte § 6.25 – **111 r**
⊇ 105.00/160.00 st., 1 suite – SB.

**GALWAY** (Gaillimh) *Galway* **923** E 8 *Ireland G.* – *pop. 57 241.*

See : *City*★★ – *Lynch's Castle*★ BY – *St. Nicholas' Church*★ BY – *Roman Catholic Cathedral*★ AY – *Eyre Square : Bank of Ireland Building (sword and mace*★*)* BY D.

Env. : NW : *Lough Corrib*★★.

Exc. : W : *by boat, Aran Islands (Inishmore – Dun Aenghus*★★★*)* BZ – *Thoor Ballylee*★, SE : 21 m. by N 6 and N 18 BY – *Athenry*★, E : 14 m. by N 6 and R 348 BY – *Dunguaire Castle, Kinvara*★ AC, S : 16 m. by N 6, N 18 and N 67 BY – *Aughnanure Castle*★, NW : 16 m. by N 59 – *Oughterard*★ (≤★★), NW : 18 m. by N 59 – *Knockmoy Abbey*★, NE : 19 m. by N 17 and N 63 BY – *Coole Park (Autograph Tree*★*)*, SE : 21 m. by N 6 and N 18 BY – **St. Mary's Cathedral, Tuam**★, NE : 21 m. by N 17 BY – *Loughrea (St. Brendan's Cathedral*★*)*, SE : 22 m. by N 6 BY – *Turoe Stone*★, SE : 22 m. by N 6 and north by R 350.

ᴙ *Galway, Blackrock, Salthill 𝒫 (091) 522033.*

✈ *Carnmore Airport : 𝒫 (091) 752874, NE : 4 m.*

🛈 *Victoria Pl., Eyre Sq. 𝒫 (091) 563081.*

*Dublin 135 – Limerick 64 – Sligo 90.*

Plan on next page

🏰🏰 **Glenlo Abbey,** Bushypark, Northwest: 3 ¼ m. on N 59 𝒫 (091) 526666, *Fax (091) 527800,* ≤, « Restored part 18C house and church », ᴙ, ◜, park – |ṡ|, ▤ rest, 📺 ☎ ᴕ ᴖ – 🔏 90. **⬤◉** 🆎 ⬤ *VISA*. 
*River Room :* **Meals** (dinner only and Sunday lunch)/dinner 30.00 t. – *Pullman :* **Meals** *(closed Saturday lunch, Sunday and Monday)* 12.50 t. (lunch) and dinner a la carte 16.25/26.00 t. ⑃ 8.00 – ⇌ 7.50 – **43 rm** 115.00/180.00 t., 3 suites – SB.

🏰🏰 **Great Southern,** Eyre Sq., 𝒫 (091) 564041, *Fax (091) 566704,* ⌨, ◫ – |ṡ|, ↝ rm, 📺 ☎ ◜ – 🔏 450. **⬤◉** 🆎 ⬤ *VISA*.   BY a
*closed 25 and 26 December* – **Meals** (carving lunch Monday to Saturday)/dinner 20.00 t. and a la carte ⑃ 7.00 – **115 rm** ⇌ 99.50/155.00 t., 1 suite – SB.

🏰🏰 **Corrib Great Southern,** Merlin Park, East: 1 ¾ m. on N 6 𝒫 (091) 755281, *Fax (091) 751390,* ◫ – |ṡ|, ↝ rm, ▤rest, 📺 ☎ ◜ ᴕ ᴖ – 🔏 750. **⬤◉** 🆎 ⬤ *VISA*. 
*closed 25 and 26 December* – **Meals** (carving lunch Monday to Saturday)/dinner 20.00 t. and a la carte ⑃ 7.00 – **176 rm** ⇌ 92.00/144.00 t., 4 suites – SB.

🏰🏰 **Ardilaun House,** Taylor's Hill, West : 1 ½ m. on R 336 𝒫 (091) 521433, *Fax (091) 521546,* ᴷ◜, ⌨, ↝ – |ṡ|, ↝ rm, 📺 ☎ ᴕ ᴖ – 🔏 450. **⬤◉** 🆎 ⬤ *VISA*
*closed 22 to 28 December* – **Meals** (bar lunch Saturday) 13.50/23.50 t. and dinner a la carte ⑃ 7.50 – **88 rm** ⇌ 70.00/125.00 t., 1 suite – SB.

🏰 **Jurys Galway Inn,** Quay St., 𝒫 (091) 566444, *Fax (091) 568415,* ↝ – |ṡ|, ↝ rm, ▤ rest, 📺 ᴕ ᴕ – 🔏 40. **⬤◉** 🆎 ⬤ *VISA*   BZ c
*closed 24 to 26 December* – **Meals** (carving lunch) (bar lunch Saturday and Sunday)/dinner 15.50 st. and a la carte ⑃ 5.50 – ⇌ 6.50 – **128 rm** 66.00 st.

🏰 **Park House,** Forster St., Eyre Sq., 𝒫 (091) 564924, *Fax (091) 569219* – |ṡ|, ▤ rest, 📺 ☎ ◜ ᴕ ᴖ – 🔏 35. **⬤◉** 🆎 ⬤ *VISA*. 
*closed 24 to 26 December* – **Meals** (carving lunch)/dinner a la carte 12.75/24.40 t. ⑃ 6.75 – **57 rm** ⇌ 75.00/125.00 t. – SB.   BY c

🏰 **Brennan's Yard,** Lower Merchants Rd, 𝒫 (091) 568166, *Fax (091) 568262* – |ṡ| 📺 ☎. **⬤◉** 🆎 ⬤ *VISA*.   BZ e
*closed 24 to 26 December* – **Meals** (booking essential) (bar lunch)/dinner 14.95 t. and a la carte ⑃ 7.00 – **24 rm** ⇌ 60.00/95.00 st.

🏰 **Galway Ryan,** Dublin Rd, East : 1 ¼ m. on N 6 𝒫 (091) 753181, *Fax (091) 753187,* ᴷ◜, ⌨, ◫, ↝, ⬤ – |ṡ|, ↝ rm, ▤ rest, 📺 ☎ ᴖ – 🔏 30. **⬤◉** 🆎 ⬤ *VISA*. 
**Meals** (bar lunch)/dinner a la carte 15.00/30.00 st. ⑃ 10.00 – ⇌ 10.00 – **96 rm** 90.00/130.00 st. – SB.

🏰 **Menlo Park,** Terryland, Northeast : 1 ¼ m. by N 84 (Castlebar rd) 𝒫 (091) 761122, *Fax (091) 761222* – |ṡ| ▤ 📺 ☎ ᴕ ᴖ – 🔏 160. **⬤◉** 🆎 ⬤ *VISA*
*closed 24 and 25 December* – **Meals** (bar lunch Monday to Saturday)/dinner 16.00 st. and a la carte ⑃ 6.50 – **44 rm** ⇌ 75.00/85.00 st. – SB.

🏠 **Spanish Arch,** Quay St., 𝒫 (091) 569600, *Fax (091) 569191,* « Part 18C Carmelite convent » – |ṡ| 📺 ☎. **⬤◉** 🆎 ⬤ *VISA*.   BZ u
*closed 25 December* – **Meals** (bar lunch)/dinner 17.00 st. ⑃ 6.00 – ⇌ 7.50 – **20 rm** 75.00/99.00 st.

🏠 **Ibis,** Headford Rd, Northeast : 1 ¼ m. by N 84 (Castlebar rd) 𝒫 (091) 771166, *Fax (091) 771646* – |ṡ|, ↝ rm, 📺 ☎ ◜ ᴕ. **⬤◉** 🆎 ⬤ *VISA*
**Meals** (bar lunch Saturday and Sunday) a la carte approx. 8.40 st. ⑃ 5.25 – ⇌ 5.25 – **100 rm** 49.50 st. – SB.

🏠 **Adare House** without rest., 9 Father Griffin Pl., 𝒫 (091) 582638, *Fax (091) 583963* – ↝ 📺 ☎ ᴖ. **⬤◉** *VISA*.   AZ n
*closed 15 to 29 December* – **12 rm** ⇌ 35.00/70.00 st.

XX **de Burgos,** 15-17 Augustine St., 𝒫 (091) 562188, *Fax (091) 520364,* « Cellars of 16C house » – **⬤◉** 🆎 ⬤ *VISA*.   BY e
*closed Sunday and 25-26 December* – **Meals** (dinner only) a la carte 18.40/27.40 t. ⑃ 6.95.

Claddagh Bridge . . . . . . . . . **AZ** 2
Corrib Shopping Centre . . . **BY**
Dominick Street . . . . . . . . . **AZ** 3
Father Griffin
  Avenue . . . . . . . . . . . . . . **AZ** 5

Forster Street . . . . . . . . . . . **BY** 6
High Street . . . . . . . . . . . . **BY** 7
Main Guard St. . . . . . . . . . **BY** 8
Market Street . . . . . . . . . . **BY** 9
Mary Street . . . . . . . . . . . **BY** 10
New Dock Street . . . . . . . **BZ** 13
Newton Smith . . . . . . . . . **BY** 14
O'Brien Bridge . . . . . . . . . **AY** 15

Presentation Street . . . . . . **AY** 1
Quay Street . . . . . . . . . . . . **BZ** 1
St. Francis Street . . . . . . . **BY** 2
St. Vincent's
  Avenue . . . . . . . . . . . . . **BY** 2
Shantalia Road . . . . . . . . . **AY** 2
Shop Street . . . . . . . . . . . **BY** 2
William Street . . . . . . . . . . **BY** 2

at Salthill *Southwest : 2 m.* – AZ.

ⓐⓐⓐ **Galway Bay,** The Promenade, ℘ (091) 520520, *Fax (091) 520530*, ≤ Galway Bay, Ⅰ₅, ≋ₛ
 🔲, 🐎 – 📳, ⸝⸝ rm, ▤ rest, 📺 ☎ ℃ & ⒫ – 🔬 500. 🆎 🔘 🆎 🔘 *VISA*. ⸝⸝
 ***Lobster Pot :*** Meals 12.50/21.00 **st.** ⅊ 9.50 – **149 rm** ⇄ 105.00/150.00, 4 suites – SB.

 ⓑⓑ **Jameson's,** Upper Salthill, ℘ (091) 528666, *Fax (091) 528626* – ⎮📳 📺 ☎ & ⒫ – 🔬 60. 🆎🔘
 🆎 🔘 *VISA*. ⸝⸝
 *closed 24 to 26 December* – Meals (carving lunch)/dinner 18.95 **st.** and a la carte ⅊ 5.30
 **20 rm** ⇄ 65.00/100.00 **st.** – SB.

 ⌂ **Devondell** without rest., 47 Devon Park, Lower Salthill, off Lower Salthill Ro
 ℘ (091) 528306 – ⸝⸝. ⸝⸝
 *March-October* – **4 rm** ⇄ 20.00/40.00.

**GARRYVOE** (Garraí Uí Bhuaigh) *Cork* 923 H 12 – ✉ *Castlemartyr.*
*Dublin 161 – Cork 23 – Waterford 62.*

🏨 **Garryvoe,** ℰ (021) 646718, Fax (021) 646824, ≤, ☞, ✗ – 📺 ☎ 🅿 – 🔬 300. 🆖 🆎 ①
**VISA**. ✗
*closed 25 December* – **Meals** 12.00/20.00 st. and dinner a la carte ᕃ 7.00 – **19 rm** ☲ 40.00/
120.00 **st.** – SB.

---

**GLASSAN** (Glasán) *Westmeath* 923 I 7 – *see Athlone.*

---

**GLENBEIGH** (Gleann Beithe) *Kerry* 923 C 11 *Ireland G* – *pop. 251.*
EXC. : *Iveragh Peninsula★★ – Ring of Kerry★★ – Lough Caragh★.*
*Dublin 197 – Killarney 21 – Tralee 24.*

🏠 **Foxtrot** without rest., Mountain Stage, Southwest : 3 m. on N 70 ℰ (066) 68417,
Fax (066) 68552, ≤ Coomasaharn lake and mountains – ↳✗ 🅿. ✗
*April-October* – **4 rm** ☲ 24.50/36.00 st.

---

**GLENDALOUGH** (Gleann dá Loch) *Wicklow* 923 M 8 *Ireland G.*
See : *Monastic ruins★★★ – Lower Lake★★ – Cathedral★★ – Upper Lake★★ – Round Tower★
– St. Kevin's Church★ – St. Saviour's Priory★.*
EXC. : *Wicklow Mountains★★ – Wicklow Gap★★.*
*Dublin 28 – Kilkenny 68 – Wexford 63.*

🏨 **Glendalough,** ℰ (0404) 45135, Fax (0404) 45142, ☞ – ᕃ 📺 ☎ ᕃ 🅿 – 🔬 200. 🆖 🆎 ①
**VISA**
*closed 5 December-4 February* – **Meals** 10.00 t. (lunch) and a la carte 9.90/24.40 t. ᕃ 6.75 –
**40 rm** ☲ 40.00/80.00 st. – SB.

---

**GLENGARRIFF** (An Gleann Garbh) *Cork* 923 D 12 *Ireland G..*
See : *Town★ – Garinish Island★★.*
ENV. : *Healy Pass★★ (≤★★), W : by R 572 – Derreen Gardens★, W : by R 572 and north by
R 574 (Healy Pass).*
🅱 ℰ (027) 63084 (July-August).
*Dublin 213 – Cork 60 – Killarney 37.*

🏠 **Cois Coille** ﹀ without rest., ℰ (027) 63202, ≤, ☞ – ↳✗ 🅿. ✗
*April-October* – **6 rm** ☲ 25.00/36.00 st.

---

**GLEN OF AHERLOW** (Gleann Eatharlaí) *Tipperary* 923 H 10 *Ireland G.* – ✉ *Tipperary.*
See : *Glen of Aherlow★.*
EXC. : *Caher Castle★★ AC – Swiss Cottage★ AC, SE : 7 m. by N 24 and R 670 – Clonmel★
(County Museum★, St. Mary's Church★), NE : 16 m. by N 24 – Kilmallock★ (Abbey★,
Collegiate Church★), W : 27½ m. by R 664 and R 515.*
*Dublin 118 – Cahir 6 – Tipperary 9.*

🏨 **Aherlow House** ﹀, ℰ (062) 56153, Fax (062) 56212, ≤ Galty Mountains, park – 📺 ☎ 🅿
– 🔬 150. 🆖 🆎 ① **VISA**. ✗
*restricted opening January-March* – **Meals** 10.95/18.50 st. – **30 rm** ☲ 47.00/74.00 st. – SB.

---

**GLIN** (An Gleann) *Limerick* 923 E 10 – *pop. 554.*
*Dublin 152 – Limerick 32 – Tralee 32.*

🏨 **Glin Castle** ﹀, ℰ (068) 34112, Fax (068) 34364, ≤, « Georgian castle in extensive parklands », ☞ – ↳✗ rest., ☎ 🅿. 🆖 🆎 ① **VISA**. ✗
*closed January and February* – **Meals** (booking essential) (lunch by arrangement)/dinner
27.50 t. ᕃ 6.00 – **15 rm** ☲ 95.00/270.00 t.

---

**GOREY** (Guaire) *Wexford* 923 N 9 *Ireland G.* – *pop. 2 150.*
EXC. : *Ferns★, SW : 11 m. by N 11.*
🏌 *Courtown, Kiltennel* ℰ (055) 25166/25432.
🅱 *Town Centre* ℰ (055) 21248 (July and August).
*Dublin 58 – Waterford 55 – Wexford 38.*

GOREY

🏛 **Marfield House** ⊗, Courtown Rd, Southeast : 1 . m. on R 742 ℰ (055) 21124, Fax (055) 21572, ≤, « Regency mansion, extensive gardens and woodland », ⇐, ℅ – ℅
📺 ☎ 🅿, 🆀 ℀ 🅐🅔 ⑩ 𝘝𝘐𝘚𝘈
closed 3 weeks December – **Meals** (light lunch Monday to Saturday)/dinner 35.00 **t.** ⓵ 9.00 – **18 rm** ⊇ 95.00/166.00, 1 suite – SB.

---

**GREYSTONES** (Na Clocha Liatha) Wicklow 🄳🄳🄳 N 8 – pop. 9 995.
Dublin 22.

✕ **Hungry Monk,** Southview Church Rd, ℰ (01) 287 5759, Fax (01) 287 7183 – 🆀 ℀ 🅐🅔 𝘝𝘐𝘚𝘈
closed Monday, Tuesday and 24 to 26 December – **Meals** (dinner only and Sunday lunch)/dinner a la carte a la carte 20.40/27.45 **t.** ⓵ 6.95.

---

**HOWTH** (Binn Èadair) Dublin 🄳🄳🄳 N 7 Ireland G. – ⊠ Dublin.
See : Town★ – The Summit★ (≤★).
🄸🄸, 🄸🄸, 🄸 Deer Park Hotel, Howth Castle ℰ (01) 822 2624.
Dublin 10.

🏛 **Marine,** Sutton Cross, D13, West : 1 ½ m. ℰ (01) 839 0000, Fax (01) 839 0442, ≤, ⇐, 🔲, 🏊 – 📺 ☎ 🅿 – 🔏 175. 🆀 ℀ 🅐🅔 ⑩ 𝘝𝘐𝘚𝘈. ℀
closed 25 and 26 December – **The Meridian :** **Meals** 14.50 **st.** (lunch) and a la carte 11.00/21.00 **st.** ⓵ 5.25 – **26 rm** ⊇ 100.00/160.00 **st.** – SB.

🏨 **Howth Lodge,,** West : ½ m. ℰ (01) 832 1010, Fax (01) 832 2268, ≤, 🄵🄶, ⇐, 🔲 – 🛗 📺 ☎ 🅿 – 🔏 200. 🆀 ℀ 🅐🅔 ⑩ 𝘝𝘐𝘚𝘈. ℀
closed 23 to 29 December – **Meals** (closed Sunday dinner) (bar lunch Monday to Saturday)/dinner 22.50 **t.** ⓵ 5.00 – **46 rm** ⊇ 80.00/140.00 **st.** – SB.

🏨 **Deer Park,,** West : ¾ m. ℰ (01) 832 2624, Fax (01) 839 2405, ≤, ⇐, 🔲, 🄸🄸, 🄸🄸, park – 🍴 rest, 📺 ☎ & 🅿 – 🔏 100. 🆀 ℀ 🅐🅔 ⑩ 𝘝𝘐𝘚𝘈 𝙅𝘾𝘽. ℀
closed 23 to 27 December – **Meals** 12.00/22.00 **st.** and dinner a la carte ⓵ 5.50 – **77 rm** ⊇ 65.00/105.00 **st.** – SB.

✕✕ **King Sitric,** Harbour Rd, East Pier, ℰ (01) 832 5235, Fax (01) 839 2442 – 🆀 ℀ 🅐🅔 ⑩ 𝘝𝘐𝘚𝘈
closed Sunday, 2 weeks January and Bank Holidays – **Meals** - Seafood - (light lunch Monday to Saturday in summmer)/dinner 28.00 **t.** and a la carte ⓵ 6.50.

---

**INCH** (An Inis) Clare – see Ennis.

---

**INISHANNON** (Inis Eonáin) Cork 🄳🄳🄳 G 12 – pop. 498.
Dublin 169 – Cork 15.

🏨 **Innishannon House** ⊗,, South : ¾ m. on R 605 ℰ (021) 775121, Fax (021) 775609, ≤, « Riverside setting, gardens », ⌇, park – 🍴 📺 ☎ 📞 🅿 – 🔏 150. 🆀 ℀ 🅐🅔 ⑩ 𝘝𝘐𝘚𝘈
closed 15 January-15 March – **Meals** 12.50/25.00 **t.** and a la carte ⓵ 7.50 – **13 rm** ⊇ 80.00/250.00 **st.** – SB.

---

**INISHCRONE** (Inis Crabhann) Sligo 🄳🄳🄳 E 5 – pop. 692.
Dublin 160 – Ballina 8 – Galway 79 – Sligo 34.

🛖 **Ceol na Mara,** Main St., ℰ (096) 36351, Fax (096) 36642, ≤ – 📺 ☎ 🅿. 🆀 ℀ 𝘝𝘐𝘚𝘈. ℀
restricted opening in winter – **Meals** (by arrangement) 14.00 **st.** – **9 rm** ⊇ 25.00/38.00 – SB.

---

**INISHMORE** (Inis MÉr) Galway 🄳🄳🄳 CD 8 – see Aran Islands.

---

**INISTIOGE** (Inis Tíog) Kilkenny 🄳🄳🄳 K 10.
Dublin 82 – Kilkenny 16 – Waterford 19 – Wexford 33.

🛖 **Berryhill** ⊗,, Southeast : ¾ m. by R 700 ℰ (056) 58434, Fax (056) 58434, ≤, « Working farm », ⌇, ⌸, park – ℅ rm, 🅿. 🆀 ℀ 𝘝𝘐𝘚𝘈. ℀
mid April-early November – **Meals** (by arrangement) (communal dining) 18.00 **s.** ⓵ 7.00 – **3 rm** ⊇ 50.00/80.00.

🛖 **Rathsnagadan House** ⊗,, Southeast : 4 ½ m. by R 700 ℰ (051) 423641, ≤, ⌸, park – ℅ 🅿. 🆀 ℀ 🅐🅔 ⑩ 𝘝𝘐𝘚𝘈. ℀
closed December and January – **Meals** (by arrangement) 21.00 **st.** ⓵ 7.00 – **3 rm** ⊇ 30.00/50.00 **st.**

✕✕ **The Motte,** Plass Newid, Northwest : ¼ m. on R 700 ℰ (056) 58655 – 🅿. 🆀 ℀ 𝘝𝘐𝘚𝘈
closed Sunday, Monday, 1 week in spring, 1 week in autumn and 1 week Christmas – **Meals** (dinner only) 23.00 **st.** ⓵ 6.00.

**INVERIN** (Indreabhán) *Galway* **923** D8.
*Dublin 149 – Galway 17.*

⌂ **Tigh Chualain** without rest., Kilroe East, on R 336 ℰ (091) 553609 – ⇖ 📺 ☎ 🅿. ⋘
*April-October* – **9 rm** � 25.00/40.00.

**KANTURK** (Ceann Toirc) *Cork* **923** F 11 *Ireland G.* – pop. 1 666.
See : *Town★ - Castle★.*
🏌 *Fairy Hill* ℰ (029) 50534.
*Dublin 161 – Cork 33 – Killarney 31 – Limerick 44.*

🏠 **Assolas Country House** ⌂,, East : 3 ¼ m. by R 576 and R 580 on Cecilstown rd
ℰ (029) 50015, *Fax (029) 50795*, ≤, « Part 17C and 18C country house, gardens, riverside
setting », ⚓, park, ⅍ – ☎ 🅿. 💵 🆎 ① 𝘝𝘐𝘚𝘈. ⋘
*26 March-October* – **Meals** (booking essential) (dinner only) 32.00 **st.** ≬ 8.00 – **9 rm**
� 78.00/168.00 **st.** – SB.

⌂ **Glenlohane** ⌂,, East : 2 ½ m. by R 576 and R 580 on Cecilstown rd ℰ (029) 50014,
*Fax (029) 51100*, ≤, « Georgian country house, extensive parkland, working farm », ⚓ –
⇖ 🅿. 💵 🆎 𝘝𝘐𝘚𝘈. ⋘
**Meals** (by arrangement) (communal dining) 25.00 – **5 rm** � 60.00/100.00 **st.**

🍴 **The Vintage,** O'Brien St., ℰ (029) 50549, *Fax (029) 51209* – 💵 𝘝𝘐𝘚𝘈
*closed 25 December* – **Meals** 8.95 **t.** (lunch) and a la carte 9.00/19.00 **t.** ≬ 5.95.

*The Guide is updated annually so renew your Guide every year.*

**KENMARE** (Neidín) *Kerry* **923** D 12 *Ireland G.* – pop. 1 420.
Exc. : *Iveragh Peninsula★★ (Ring of Kerry★★)* – *Healy Pass★★ (≤★★)*, SW : 19 m. by R 571 and
R 574 AY – *Mountain Road to Glengarriff (≤★★) S* : by N 71 AY – *Slieve Miskish Mountains
(≤★★)*, SW : 30 m. by R 571 AY – *Gougane Barra Forest Park★★*, SE : 10 m. AY – *Lauragh
(Derreen Gardens★ AC)*, SW : 14½ m. by R 571 AY – *Allihies (Copper Mines★)*, SW : 35½ m.
by R 571 and R 575 AY – *Garnish Island (≤★)*, SW : 42½ m. by R 571, R 575 and R 572 AY.
🏌 *Kenmare* ℰ (064) 41291.
🛈 *Heritage Centre, The Square* ℰ (064) 41233 *(April-October)* BY.
*Dublin 210 – Cork 58 – Killarney 20.*

### KENMARE

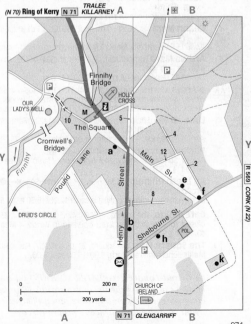

🏨🏨🏨 **Park** ⊗, 🖉 (064) 41200, *Fax (064) 41402*, ← Kenmare Bay and hills, « Antiques, paintings », ⌂, 🕭, 🔌, 🌲, park, 🏃 – 🛐 🔟 🕿 🕭 🅿 – 🔬 35. 🕮 🕮 🕦 ㎺. ⋘     BY k
*17 April-1 November and 24 December-1 January* – **Meals** (dinner only) 37.50 t.
and a la carte 39.85/61.45 t. ≬ 9.50 – **47 rm** ⊇ 154.00/332.00 st., 2 suites – SB
**Spec.** Lasagne of mushrooms on baby spinach, tarragon and tomato essence. Roasted
Aylesbury duck in pepper, Kirsch sabayon, lavender jus. Deep-fried strawberries, pistachio
ice cream.

🏨🏨🏨 **Sheen Falls Lodge** ⊗,, Southeast : 1 ¼ m. by N 71 🖉 (064) 41600, *Fax (064) 41386*, 🌲,
« Wooded setting on banks of Sheen River and Kenmare Bay ← Sheen Falls », ⌂, 🕾, ☒,
🔌, 🌲, park, 🏃 – 🛐, ⋛ rm, 🔟 🕿 🕭 🅿 – 🔬 120. 🕮 🕮 🕦 ㎺ ᴊᴄʙ. ⋘
*closed 4 January-5 February and 28 November-23 December* – **La Cascade :** Meals (dinner
only) a la carte 37.50 t. ≬ 11.00 – ⊇ 13.00 – **52 rm** 258.00, 8 suites – SB.

🏨🏨 **Dromquinna Manor** ⊗, Blackwater Bridge P.O., West : 3 m. on N 70 🖉 (064) 41657,
*Fax (064) 41791*, ←, « Situated on the banks of Kenmare River », 🔌, 🌲, park, 🏃 – 🖳 🔟 🕿
🅿 – 🔬 30. 🕮 🕮 🕦 ㎺. ⋘
**Meals** (bar lunch Monday to Saturday)/dinner 18.50 t. and a la carte ≬ 6.00 – **Boathouse
Bistro :** Meals *(May-September)* a la carte 6.50/20.00 t. ≬ 6.50 – **46 rm** ⊇ 42.00/130.00 t. –
SB.

🏨 **Shelburne Lodge**,, East : ½ m. on R 569 (Cork Rd) 🖉 (064) 41013, *Fax (064) 42135*,
« Stylishly decorated 18C house », 🌲, 🏃 – 🔟 🕿 🅿. 🕮 ㎺. ⋘
*April-October* – **Meals** – (see **Packies** below) – **6 rm** ⊇ 50.00/80.00.

🏨 **Dunkerron** ⊗, Sneem Rd, West : 2 ½ m. on N 70 🖉 (064) 41102, *Fax (064) 41102*, « 12C
fortified castle in grounds », 🌲, park – 🕿 🅿. 🕮 ㎺. ⋘
*April-October* – **Meals** (booking essential) (dinner only) 22.00 t. – **10 rm** ⊇ 50.00/80.00 t.

🏨 **The Rosegarden**,, West : ¾ m. by N 71 on Sneem rd 🖉 (064) 42288, *Fax (064) 42305*, 🌲
– 🔟 🕿 🅿. 🕮 🕮 🕦 ㎺. ⋘
*April-October* – **Meals** (dinner only) 13.95 t. and a la carte ≬ 7.00 – **8 rm** ⊇ 37.50/55.00 t. –
SB.

⌂ **Sallyport House** without rest.,, South : ¼ m. on N 71 🖉 (064) 42066, *Fax (064) 42067*,
←, « Antique furnishings », 🌲 – ⋛⋗ 🔟 🕿 🅿. ⋘
*Easter-October* – **5 rm** ⊇ 70.00/90.00 s.

⌂ **Mylestone House** without rest., Killowen Rd, East : ¼ m. 🖉 (064) 41753, 🌲 – 🅿. 🕮
㎺. ⋘
*March-10 November* – **5 rm** ⊇ 28.00/38.00 st.

⌂ **Rosewood House** without rest.,, East : ½ m. on R 569 (Cork Rd) 🖉 (064) 41699, 🌲 –
⋛⋗ 🅿. 🕮 ㎺
*22 May-4 September* – **4 rm** ⊇ 30.00/35.00.

⌂ **Ceann Mara** ⊗,, East : 1 m. on R 569 (Cork Rd) 🖉 (064) 41220, ← Kenmare Bay and hills,
🌲 – 🅿. ⋘
*April-15 September* – **Meals** (by arrangement) 15.00 – **4 rm** ⊇ 26.00/36.00 – SB.

⌂ **Ard Na Mara** without rest., Pier Rd, 🖉 (064) 41399, *Fax (064) 41399*, ← Kenmare Bay and
hills, 🌲 – 🅿. ⋘
*closed 25 December* – **4 rm** ⊇ 22.00/34.00 st.

✗✗ **d'Arcys** with rm, Main St., 🖉 (064) 41589, *Fax (064) 41589* – 🕮 ㎺     BY f
*closed Monday to Wednesday January-Easter, 2 weeks January and 25-26 December* –
**Meals** (dinner only) a la carte 18.45/26.45 ≬ 8.00 – **5 rm** ⊇ 20.00/40.00 – SB.

✗ **Lime Tree**, Shelburne Lane, 🖉 (064) 41225, *Fax (064) 41402*, « Characterful former
schoolhouse » – 🅿. 🕮 ㎺     BY h
*April-6 November* – Meals (dinner only) a la carte 18.75/25.00 t. ≬ 6.95.

✗ **Packies**, Henry St., 🖉 (064) 41508 – 🕮 ㎺     AY b
*closed Sunday, Monday and November-March* – **Meals** (dinner only) a la carte 19.00/
26.00 t. ≬ 6.50.

✗ **An Leath Phingin,** 35 Main St., 🖉 (064) 41559 – ⋛⋗. 🕮 ㎺     BY e
*closed November.*
Meals - Italian - (dinner only) a la carte 12.90/19.50 t. ≬ 5.50.

✗ **Café Indigo**, The Square, 🖉 (064) 42356, *Fax (064) 42358* – 🍴. 🕮 🕮 🕦 ㎺     AY a
*closed Tuesday and restricted opening in winter* – **Meals** (dinner only) a la carte 19.00/
30.00 st. ≬ 9.00.

🍴 **The Square Pint**, The Square, 🖉 (064) 42357, *Fax (064) 42358* – 🍴. 🕮 🕮 🕦 ㎺     AY a
**Meals** (lunch only) a la carte 8.90/15.00 st. ≬ 6.00.

*Le Grand Londres (GREATER LONDON) est composé de la City
et de 32 arrondissements administratifs (Borough)
eux-mêmes divisés en quartiers ou en villages
ayant conservé leur caractère propre (Area).*

**KILCOLGAN** (Cill Cholgáin) Galway **923** F 8 – ⊠ Oranmore.
Dublin 137 – Galway 11.

🏠 **Moran's Oyster Cottage,** The Weir, Northwest : 1 ¼ m. by N 18 ℰ (091) 796113,
Fax (091) 796503, 🌇 , « Part 18C thatched cottage » – 🌐 🏧 VISA
closed 25 December and Good Friday – **Meals** a la carte 20.00/25.00 t.

**KILCUMMIN** (Cill Chuimán) Kerry **923** B 11 Ireland G.
Exc. : Dingle Peninsula★★★ – Connor Pass★★ – Dingle★, SW : by Connor Pass.
Dublin 203 – Killarney 34 – Limerick 85 – Tralee 21.

🏠 **Strand View House** without rest., Conor Pass Rd, ℰ (066) 38131, Fax (066) 39434, ≤ –
📺 🄿 . 🌐 VISA . ⅍
February-October – **4 rm** ⌁ 26.00/40.00.

**KILDARE** (Cill Dara) Kildare **923** L 8 Ireland G – pop. 4 278.
See : Town★ – Cathedral★★.
Env. : Irish National Stud★★ (Japanese Gardens★★), SE : 1 m..
Dublin 32 – Kilkenny 50 – Galway 112.

🏨 **Curragh Lodge,** Dublin Rd, ℰ (045) 522144, Fax (045) 522098 – 📺 ☎ . 🌐 🄰🄴 ① VISA
**Meals** 7.50/12.95 st. and a la carte 🖌 5.50 – **21 rm** ⌁ 35.00/70.00 st. – SB.

**KILKEE** (Cill Chaoi) Clare **923** D 9 Ireland G – pop. 1 331.
Exc. : Kilrush★ (Scattery Island★ by boat), SE : 10 m. by N 67 – SW : Loop Head Peninsula
(Bridge of Ross★ ).
Dublin 177 – Galway 77 – Limerick 58.

🏨 **Halpin's,** Erin St., ℰ (065) 56032, Fax (065) 56317 – ⅍≠ rest, 📺 ☎ 🄿 . 🌐 🄰🄴 ① VISA . ⅍
10 March-9 November – **Meals** (bar lunch Monday to Saturday)/dinner 11.50/22.00 t.
and dinner a la carte 🖌 8.50 – **12 rm** ⌁ 40.00/80.00 t. – SB.

**KILKENNY** (Cill Chainnigh) Kilkenny **923** K 10 Ireland G. – pop. 8 507.
See : Town★★ – St. Canice's Cathedral★★ – Kilkenny Castle and Grounds★★ AC – Cityscope★
AC – Black Abbey★ – Rothe House★ .
Exc. : Jerpoint Abbey★★ AC, S : 12 m. by R 700 and N 9 – Dunmore Cave★ AC, N : 7 m. by
N 77 and N 78 – Kells Priory★ , S : 8 m. by R 697.
🏌 Glendine ℰ (056) 65400 – 🏌 Callan, Geraldine ℰ (056) 25136 – 🏌 Castlecomer, Drum-
goole ℰ (056) 41139.
🛈 Rose Inn St. ℰ (056) 51500.
Dublin 71 – Cork 86 – Killarney 115 – Limerick 69 – Tullamore 52 – Waterford 29.

🏨 **Kilkenny,** College Rd, Southwest : ¾ m. at junction with N 76 ℰ (056) 62000,
Fax (056) 65984, 🖌, ☎s, 🅂, 🐾, ⅍ – 📺 ☎ 🄿 – 🕍 400. 🌐 🄰🄴 ① VISA . ⅍
**Meals** (bar lunch)/dinner a la carte 16.25/26.50 t. 🖌 7.00 – **80 rm** ⌁ 50.00/120.00 st. – SB.

🏨 **Springhill Court,** Waterford Rd, South : 1 ¼ m. on N 10 ℰ (056) 21122, Fax (056) 61600
– 📺 ☎ ⅍ 🄿 – 🕍 400. 🌐 🄰🄴 ① VISA . ⅍
**Meals** a la carte 7.95/21.80 st. 🖌 5.75 – **44 rm** ⌁ 45.00/90.00 st. – SB.

🏨 **Newpark,** Castlecomer Rd, North : 1 m. on N 77 ℰ (056) 22122, Fax (056) 61111, 🖌, ☎s,
🅂, 🐾, park – 📼 rest, 📺 🐾 🄾 🄿 – 🕍 600. 🌐 🄰🄴 ① VISA . ⅍
**Meals** 13.50/21.00 t. and a la carte 🖌 8.00 – ⌁ 8.50 – **84 rm** 55.00/90.00 t. – SB.

🏨 **Langton's House,** 69 John St., ℰ (056) 65133, Fax (056) 63693 – 📼 📺 ☎ 🄿 . 🌐 🄰🄴 ①
VISA . ⅍
closed 25 December and Good Friday – **Meals** 9.00/18.50 st. and a la carte 🖌 6.00 – **10 rm**
⌁ 65.00/150.00 st. – SB.

🏠 **Butler House** without rest., 15-16 Patrick St., ℰ (056) 65707, Fax (056) 65626, 🐾 – 📺
☎ 🄿 – 🕍 100. 🌐 🄰🄴 ① VISA . ⅍
closed 24 to 29 December – **12 rm** ⌁ 69.00/129.00 st., 1 suite.

🏠 **Berkeley House** without rest., 5 Patrick St., ℰ (056) 64848, Fax (056) 64829 – 📺 ☎ 🄿 .
🌐 ① VISA . ⅍
closed 20 to 30 December – **10 rm** ⌁ 35.00/60.00 st.

🏠 **Blanchville House** ⌂, Dunbell, Maddoxtown, Southeast : 7 ½ m. by N 10 turning right
½ m. after the Pike Inn ℰ (056) 27197, Fax (056) 27636, ≤, « Georgian country house »,
🐾, park – ⅍≠ rest, 🄿 . 🌐 🄰🄴 VISA . ⅍
March-October – **Meals** (by arrangement) (communal dining) 22.00 st. – **6 rm** ⌁ 35.00/
70.00 st. – SB.

⌂ **Shillogher House** without rest., Callan Rd, Southwest : 1 m. on N 76 ℘ (056) 63249
Fax (056) 64865, 🚗 – ❄ 📺 ☎ 🅿. 🆎 VISA. ⊗
5 rm 🖙 32.00/39.00 st.

XX **Lacken House** with rm, Dublin Rd, East : ¾ m. on N 10 ℘ (056) 61085, Fax (056) 62435
🚗 – ▤ rest, 📺 ☎ 🅿. 🆎 VISA. ⊗
closed 1 week Christmas – **Meals** (closed Sunday and Monday) (dinner only) 23.00 st
and a la carte 🍴 7.00 – **8 rm** 🖙 36.00/60.00 st. – SB.

XX **Ristorante Rinuccini**, 1 The Parade, ℘ (056) 61575, Fax (056) 51288 – ▤. 🆎 AE ① VISA
**Meals** - Italian - a la carte 16.85/25.80 t. 🍴 5.95.

---

**KILL** (An Chill) Kildare ⬛⬛⬛ M 8 – pop. 1 711.
Dublin 15 – Carlow 36.

🏨 **Ambassador,**, on N 7 ℘ (045) 877064, Fax (045) 877515 – 📺 ☎ 📞 🅿 – ⚖ 280. 🆎 AE
① VISA. ⊗
**Meals** (dinner only and Sunday lunch)/dinner 20.50 st. and a la carte 🍴 5.50 – **36 rm**
🖙 58.00/95.00 st. – SB.

---

**KILLALOE** (Cill Dalua) Clare ⬛⬛⬛ G 9 Ireland G. – pop. 972.
See : Town★ – St. Flannan's Cathedral★.
Env. : Graves of the Leinstermen (≤★), N : 4½ m. by R 494.
Exc. : Nenagh★ (Heritage Centre★ AC, Castle★), NE : 12 m. by R 496 and N 7 – Holy Island★
AC, N : 16 m. by R 463 and boat from Tuamgraney.
🔼 Lock House ℘ (061) 376866 (May-September).
Dublin 109 – Ennis 32 – Limerick 13 – Tullamore 58.

🏨 **Kincora Hall,**, North : ¾ m. on R 463 ℘ (061) 376000, Fax (061) 376665, 🚗 – ▤ rest, 📺
☎ 📞 🅿. 🆎 AE ① VISA. ⊗
**Meals** (bar lunch Monday to Saturday)/dinner 21.95 st. and a la carte 🍴 6.50 – **25 rm**
🖙 65.00/95.00 st. – SB.

**at Ogonnelloe** North : 6¼ m. on R 463.

⌂ **Lantern House** ⊗, ℘ (061) 923034, Fax (061) 923139, ≤, 🚗 – ❄ rm, 📺 ☎ 🅿. 🆎 AE
① VISA. ⊗
15 February-October – **Meals** (by arrangement) 17.50 t. 🍴 5.00 – **6 rm** 🖙 26.00/44.00 t.

---

**KILLARNEY** (Cill Airne) Kerry ⬛⬛⬛ D 11 Ireland G. – pop. 8 809.
See : Town★★ – St. Mary's Cathedral★ CX.
Env. : Killarney National Park★★★ (Muckross Abbey★, Muckross House and Farms★) AZ –
Gap of Dunloe★★, SW : 6 m. by R 62 AZ – Ross Castle★ AC, S : 1 m. by N 71 and minor rd –
Torc Waterfall★, S : 5 m. by N 71 BZ.
Exc. : Iveragh Peninsula★★ (Ring of Kerry★★) – Ladies View★★, SW : 12 m. by N 71 BZ –
Moll's Gap★, SW : 15½ m. by N 71 BZ.
🏌, 🏌 Mahoney's Point ℘ (064) 31034, AZ.
✈ Kerry (Farranfore) Airport : ℘ (066) 64644, N : 9½ m. by N 22.
🔼 Town Hall ℘ (064) 31633.
Dublin 189 – Cork 54 – Limerick 69 – Waterford 112.

Plans on following pages

🏰 **Europe** ⊗, Fossa, West : 3 ½ m. on R 562 ℘ (064) 31900, Fax (064) 32118, ≤ Lough
Leane and mountains, 🎣, ≋, 🏊, 🐎, 🚗, park, ※ – 🛗 ⬇ 📺 ☎ 🅿 – ⚖ 500. 🆎 AE ① VISA.
⊗
mid March-October – **Meals** (light lunch)/dinner 28.00 st. and a la carte – **202 rm** 🖙 94.00/
158.00 st., 3 suites.

🏨 **Killarney Park**, Kenmare Pl., ℘ (064) 35555, Fax (064) 35266, 🎣, ≋, 🏊 – 🛗, ▤ rest, 📺
☎ 📞 🅿 – ⚖ 70. 🆎 AE ① VISA. ⊗                                                  DX k
closed 24 to 26 December – **Park :** **Meals** (dinner only and Sunday lunch)/dinner 28.00 t.
and a la carte 🍴 9.00 – **75 rm** 🖙 135.00/190.00 st., 1 suite – SB.

🏨 **Aghadoe Heights** ⊗,, Northwest : 3 ½ m. by N 22 ℘ (064) 31766, Fax (064) 31345, ≤
Lough Leane, Macgillycuddy's Reeks and countryside, ≋, 🏊, 🚗, ※ – 📺 ☎ 📞 🅿 –
⚖ 100. 🆎 AE ① VISA. ⊗
**Meals** – (see **Fredrick's at the Heights** below) – **57 rm** 🖙 99.00/205.00 t., 3 suites – SB.

🏨 **Great Southern**, East Avenue Rd, ℘ (064) 31262, Fax (064) 31642, 🎣, ≋, 🏊, 🚗, park,
※ – 🛗 📺 ☎ 🅠 🅿 – ⚖ 900. 🆎 AE ① VISA. ⊗                                         DX j
**Dining Room :** **Meals** (dinner only) 20.00 t. 🍴 6.50 – 🖙 8.50 – **177 rm** 91.00/138.00 t.,
3 suites – SB.

874

**Dunloe Castle** 🪑, Beaufort, West : 6 m. by R 562 ☎ (064) 44111, *Fax (064) 44583*, ‹ Gap of Dunloe, countryside and mountains, ≘s, 🏊, 🏇, 🌳, park, 🎾 – ⇕ [TV] ☎ [P] – 🎤 250. [MC] [AE] [D] [VISA]. 🚫🐕
*mid April-mid October* – **Meals** 27.00 **st.** (dinner) and a la carte 23.00/29.50 **st.** 🍷 9.00 – **102 rm** ☕ 88.00/142.00 **st.**, 1 suite – SB.

**Muckross Park,**, South : 2 ¾ m. on N 71 ☎ (064) 31938, *Fax (064) 31965*, 🌳 – [TV] ☎ [P] – 🎤 200. [MC] [AE] [D] [VISA]. 🚫🐕
*March-November* – **Meals** (bar lunch)/dinner 23.00 **t.** and a la carte 🍷 6.50 – **25 rm** ☕ 85.00/130.00, 2 suites – SB.

**Randles Court,** Muckross Rd, ☎ (064) 35333, *Fax (064) 35206* – ⇕ [TV] ☎ [P]. [MC] [AE] [D] [VISA] DY p
*closed 24 and 25 December* – **Meals** (bar lunch)/dinner 25.00 **st.** and a la carte 🍷 6.00 – **49 rm** ☕ 100.00/180.00 **st.** – SB.

**The Killarney Heights,** Cork Rd, ☎ (064) 31158, *Fax (064) 35198* – ⇕ [TV] ☎ 📞 ♿ [P] – 🎤 400. [MC] [D] [VISA]. 🚫🐕
**Meals** 18.00 **t.** (dinner) and a la carte 14.50/21.00 **t.** – **38 rm** ☕ 55.00/90.00 **t.** – SB.

**Killeen House,** Aghadoe, West : 4 m. by R 562 ☎ (064) 31711, *Fax (064) 31811*, 🌳 – [TV] ☎ [P]. [MC] [AE] [D] [VISA]
*April-October* – **Meals** (dinner only) 26.95 **st.** 🍷 7.50 – **19 rm** ☕ 60.00/125.00 **t.**

**Foley's Townhouse,** 23 High St., ☎ (064) 31217, *Fax (064) 34683* – ❄ rest, [TV] ☎ [P]. [MC] [AE] [VISA]. 🚫🐕 DX e
*accommodation closed November-March* – **Meals** *(closed 23 to 26 December)* 12.50/20.00 **st.** and a la carte 🍷 8.50 – **28 rm** ☕ 49.50/82.50 **st.**

**Cahernane** 🪑, Muckross Rd, South : 1 m. on N 71 ☎ (064) 31895, *Fax (064) 34340*, ‹, 🌳, 🎾 – ☎ [P]. [MC] [AE] [D] [VISA] JCB. 🚫🐕 AZ w
*closed 3 November-22 December* – **Meals** (bar lunch)/dinner 28.50 **st.** and a la carte 🍷 8.00 – **44 rm** ☕ 90.00/130.00 **st.** – SB.

**Killarney Royal,** College St., ☎ (064) 31853, *Fax (064) 34001* – ⇕ [TV] ☎. [MC] [AE] [D] [VISA]
*closed 22 to 28 December* – **Meals** (bar lunch Monday to Saturday)/dinner a la carte 18.50/22.95 **st.** 🍷 8.95 – **30 rm** ☕ 11.00/150.00 **st.** – SB. DX g

**Torc Great Southern,** Park Rd, ☎ (064) 31611, *Fax (064) 31824*, ≘s, 🏊, 🌳, 🎾 – [TV] ☎ ♿ [P]. [MC] [AE] [D] [VISA]. 🚫🐕 BZ v
*April-mid October* – **Meals** (bar lunch)/dinner 16.00 **t.** 🍷 8.00 – **94 rm** ☕ 64.00/96.00 **st.** – SB.

**Castle Oaks House** without rest., Muckross Rd, South : 2 ½ m. on N 71 ☎ (064) 34154, *Fax (064) 36980* – [TV] ☎ ♿ [P]. [MC] [D] [VISA]. 🚫🐕
*closed 14 to 29 December* – **16 rm** ☕ 35.00/50.00 **st.**

**Gleann Fia Country House** 🪑, Deerpark, North : 1 ½ m. by N 22 bypass ☎ (064) 35035, *Fax (064) 35000*, « Riverside setting, extensive woodlands », 🌳 – 🚭 [TV] ☎ [P]. [MC] [AE] [VISA]. 🚫🐕
*March-November* – **Meals** 12.50 **st. 14 rm** ☕ 35.00/60.00 **st.**

**Earls Court House** without rest., Woodlawn Junction, Muckross Rd, South : ¾ m. by N 71 ☎ (064) 34009, *Fax (064) 34366* – 🚭 [TV] ☎ [P]. [MC] [VISA]. 🚫🐕 DY t
*closed 6 November-December* – **11 rm** ☕ 38.50/85.00 **st.**

**Fuchsia House** without rest., Muckross Rd, South : ¾ m. on N 71 ☎ (064) 33743, *Fax (064) 36588*, 🌳 – 🚭 [TV] ☎ [P]. [MC] [D] [VISA]. 🚫🐕 DY u
*March-mid December* – **10 rm** ☕ 58.00/76.00 **st.**

**Old Weir Lodge** without rest., Muckross Rd, South : ¾ m. on N 71 ☎ (064) 35593, *Fax (064) 35583* – 🚭 [TV] ☎ 📞 [P]. [MC] [VISA]. 🚫🐕
*closed 25 December* – **15 rm** ☕ 35.00/56.00 **st.**

**Killarney Lodge** without rest., Countess Rd, ☎ (064) 36499, *Fax (064) 31070* – ❄ [TV] ☎ ♿ [P]. [MC] [AE] [D] [VISA]. 🚫🐕
*closed 15 to 28 December* – **12 rm** ☕ 70.00/80.00 **st.**

**Kathleens Country House** without rest., Tralee Rd, North : 2 m. on N 22 ☎ (064) 32810, *Fax (064) 32340*, ‹, 🌳 – 🚭 [TV] ☎ [P]. [MC] [AE] [VISA]. 🚫🐕
*7 March-13 November* – **16 rm** ☕ 70.00/80.00.

**Victoria House,** Muckross Rd, South : 1 ¼ m. on N 71 ☎ (064) 35430, *Fax (064) 35439* – 🚭 [TV] ☎ 📞 [P]. [MC] [AE] [VISA]. 🚫🐕 AZ y
**Meals** *(booking essential)* 9.50/13.50 **st.** 🍷 6.00 – **15 rm** ☕ 32.00/48.00 **st.**

**Beaufield House** without rest., Park Rd, East : 1 m. ☎ (064) 34440, *Fax (064) 34663*, 🌳 – [TV] ☎ 📞 [P]. [MC] [AE] [D] [VISA]. 🚫🐕 BZ x
*closed 20 to 28 December* – **14 rm** ☕ 30.00/44.00.

N 22  TRALEE , LIMERICK

A          B

North

Ring

North

Allman's Terrace

R 877

R 562

Z

Deenagh

KILLARNEY

NATIONAL

PARK

ROSS CASTLE

Ross Road

Road

Flesk

B

● w

● y

A      MUCKKUSS  N 71  KENMARE , BLENGARRIFF     B

Park   Rd

R 876

● v

● X

Ballycasheen

Woodlawn   Rd

Flesk

Road

Flesk Bridge

Mill

Loreto

Road

● z

0        1 km
0     1/2 mile

---

**Lime Court** without rest., Muckross Rd, South : ¾ m. on N 71 *ℰ* (064) 34547, Fax (064) 34121 – 🆀 ☎ ❤ 🅿. 🆎 🆎 ᴠɪꜱᴀ. ❀    DY r
closed 25 December – **12 rm** ⇄ 26.00/52.00 st.

**Beaufort House** 🅂, Beaufort, West : 6 ½ m. by R 562 and N 72 *ℰ* (064) 44764, Fax (064) 44764, ≤, « Former 18C shooting lodge », ⬚, 🍴, park – ⇇ 🅿. 🆎 ᴠɪꜱᴀ. ❀ Easter-September – **Meals** (by arrangement) (communal dining) 27.50 st. ≬ 8.50 – **4 rm** ⇄ 65.00/110.00 st.

**Naughton's Villa** without rest., Muckross Rd, *ℰ* (064) 36025 – 🆀 ☎ 🅿. 🆎 ᴠɪꜱᴀ. ❀ March-October – **5 rm** ⇄ 25.00/44.00 st.    DY m

**Lohans Lodge** without rest., North : 3½ m. on N 22 *ℰ* (064) 33871, Fax (064) 33871, 🍴 – ⇇ 🆀 🅿. 🆎 ᴠɪꜱᴀ. ❀ closed 4 December-24 November – **5 rm** ⇄ 30.00/37.00 st.

**Sika Lodge** without rest., Ballydowney, West : 1 m. on R 562 *ℰ* (064) 36304, Fax (064) 36746 – 🆀 ☎ 🅿. 🆎 ᴠɪꜱᴀ. ❀ closed 4 days Christmas – **6 rm** ⇄ 30.00/40.00 st.

**Avondale House** without rest., Tralee Rd, North : 3 m. on N 22 *ℰ* (064) 35579, Fax (064) 35579, ≤, 🍴 – 🆀 🅿. ❀ closed Christmas – **5 rm** ⇄ 28.00/37.00 t.

**Lake Lodge** without rest., Muckross Rd, South : ¾ m. on N 71 *ℰ* (064) 33333, Fax (064) 35109 – 🆀 ☎ 🅿. 🆎 🅾 ᴠɪꜱᴀ    DY s
**11 rm** ⇄ 25.00/45.00 st.

**McCarthy's Town House**, 19 High St., *ℰ* (064) 35655, Fax (064) 35745 – 🆀 ☎ 🅿. 🆎 🆎 ᴠɪꜱᴀ. ❀    DX b
closed 25 December – **Meals** (closed December and January) 13.50 st. ≬ 6.95 – **8 rm** ⇄ 25.00/50.00 st.

**Fredrick's at the Heights** (at Aghadoe Heights H.),, Northwest : 3 ½ m. by N 22 *ℰ* (064) 31766, Fax (064) 31345, ≤ Lough Leane, Macgillycuddy's Reeks and countryside – ▤ 🅿. 🆎 🆎 🅾 ᴠɪꜱᴀ ᴊᴄʙ
**Meals** (booking essential) (buffet lunch Sunday) 23.50/35.50 t. and a la carte ≬ 11.50.

XX **Gaby's**, 27 High St., ℰ (064) 32519, *Fax (064) 32747* – **M⊙** ⛁ ⊙ **VISA**  DX **b**
*closed Sunday, 20 December-5 January and 14 February-14 March* – **Meals** - Seafood -
(dinner only) a la carte 21.10/32.90 **t.** ⌂ 8.00.

XX **Strawberry Tree**, 24 Plunkett St., ℰ (064) 32688, *Fax (064) 32689* – **M⊙** ⛁ ⊙
**VISA**  DX **f**
*closed Sunday, January and February* – **Meals** (dinner only) a la carte 25.70/30.45 **st.**
⌂ 7.75.

**KILLEAGH** (Cill Ia) Cork 📒📒📒 H 12 – *pop. 362.*
*Dublin 151 – Cork 23 – Waterford 53.*

⌂ **Ballymakeigh House** ⟅,, North : 1 m. ℰ (024) 95184, *Fax (024) 95370*, « Working
farm », ☂, park, ⨯ – ⓟ. **M⊙**. ⨯
*March-October* – **Meals** (by arrangement) 18.00 **st.** ⌂ 8.00 – **5 rm** ⌑ 35.00/60.00 **st.** –
SB.

**KILLINEY** (Cill Iníon Léinín) *Dublin* 923 N 8.

᠍ᕱ *Killiney, Ballinclea Rd* ℘ *(01) 285 1983.*

*Dublin 8 – Bray 4.*

🏯 **Fitzpatrick Castle**, ℘ *(01) 284 0700, Fax (01) 285 0207,* ⅃₅, ⇖s, ◪, 屛 – ⫯, ✸ rm, 🍽 rest, 📺 ☎ 🅿 – 🔬 500. Ⓙ ⒶⒺ 𝘝𝘐𝘚𝘈. ⨯
**Meals** 12.50 t. (lunch) and dinner a la carte 19.00/24.75 t. ⅃ 7.00 – �);  8.95 – **106 rm** 85.00/130.00 st., 6 suites – SB.

🏯 **Court**, Killiney Bay, ℘ *(01) 285 1622, Fax (01) 285 2085,* ⩽, 屛 – ⫯, ✸ rm, 📺 ☎ ✆ 🅿 – 🔬 250. Ⓙ ⒶⒺ ⓞ 𝘝𝘐𝘚𝘈. ⨯
**Meals** 13.00/23.50 t. and a la carte ⅃ 5.95 – ☲ 10.00 – **86 rm** 80.00/95.00 t. – SB.

---

**KILLORGLIN** (Cill Orglan) *Kerry* 923 C 11 – *pop. 1 278.*

*Dublin 207 – Killarney 12 – Tralee 16.*

🏠 **Grove Lodge** without rest., Killarney Rd, East : ½ m. on R 562 ℘ *(066) 9761157,* *Fax (066) 9762330,* « Riverside setting », ⑨, 屛 – ⬇ 📺 ☎ 🅿. Ⓙ ⓞ 𝘝𝘐𝘚𝘈. ⨯
*closed 23 December to 1 January* – **10 rm** ☲ 35.00/60.00 t.

🏠 **Bianconi**, Annadale Rd, ℘ *(066) 9761146, Fax (066) 9761950,* ⑨ – 📺 ☎ ✆. Ⓙ ⒶⒺ ⓞ 𝘝𝘐𝘚𝘈
*closed 23 to 28 December* – **Meals** *(closed Sunday)* (bar lunch)/dinner a la carte 14.30/22.50 t. ⅃ 5.95 – **15 rm** ☲ 38.00/58.00 t.

⌂ **Westfield House**, Glenbeigh Rd, West : ¾ m. by N 70 ℘ *(066) 9761909,* *Fax (066) 9761996,* ⇖s, 屛 – ✸ rm, 📺 ☎ 🅿. Ⓙ ⒶⒺ ⓞ 𝘝𝘐𝘚𝘈
**Meals** (by arrangement) 14.00 st. – **10 rm** ☲ 30.00/42.00 st. – SB.

---

**KILLYBEGS** (Na Cealla Beaga) *Donegal* 923 G 4 *Ireland G.* – *pop. 1 408.*

Exc. : – *Glengesh Pass**, SW : 15 m. by N 56 and R 263 – Glencolmcille Folk Village**, W : by R 263 – Gweebarra Estuary*, NE : 19 m. by R 262 and R 252 – Trabane Strand*.*

*Dublin 181 – Donegal 17 – Londonderry 64 – Sligo 57.*

🏨 **Bay View**, Main St., ℘ *(073) 31950, Fax (073) 31856,* ⩽, ⅃₅, ⇖s, ◪, ◪ – ⫯, 🍽 rest, 📺 ☎ ᓀ – 🔬 200. Ⓙ ⒶⒺ 𝘝𝘐𝘚𝘈. ⨯
*closed 24 and 25 December* **Meals** (bar lunch Monday to Saturday)/dinner 17.00 st. and a la carte – **40 rm** ☲ 87.00/114.00 st. – SB.

---

**KILMUCKRIDGE** (Cill Mhucraise) *Wexford* 923 N 10.

*Dublin 70 – Waterford 47 – Wexford 21.*

✕✕ **The Rafters**, ℘ *(053) 30591, Fax (053) 30181,* « Converted 19C corn store » – Ⓙ ⒶⒺ 𝘝𝘐𝘚𝘈
**Meals** (dinner only and Sunday lunch)/dinner 20.00 st. and a la carte.

---

**KILTIMAGH** (Coillte Mach) *Mayo* 923 EF 6 – *pop. 917.*

*Dublin 138 – Galway 52 – Westport 26.*

🏨 **Cill Aodain**, ℘ *(094) 81761, Fax (094) 81838* – 📺 ☎. Ⓙ ⓞ 𝘝𝘐𝘚𝘈
*closed 25 and 26 December* – **Meals** 10.50/19.50 st. and dinner a la carte ⅃ 4.95 – **15 rm** ☲ 37.50/64.00 st. – SB.

---

**KINNITTY** (Cionn Eitigh) *Offaly* 923 I 8 – *see Birr.*

---

**KINSALE** (Cionn Eitigh) *Cork* 923 G 12 *Ireland G.* – *pop. 2 007.*

See : *Town** – St. Multose Church* – Kinsale Regional Museum* AC.*

Env. : *Kinsale Harbour* (⩽* from St. Catherine's Anglican Church, Charles Fort*).*

Exc. : *Carbery Coast*, W : 38 m. by R 600.*

🖪 *Pier Rd* ℘ *(021) 772234 (March-November).*

*Dublin 178 – Cork 17.*

🏯 **Actons**, Pier Rd, ℘ *(021) 772135, Fax (021) 772231,* ⩽, ⅃₅, ⇖s, ◪, 屛 – ⫯ 📺 ☎ 🅿 – 🔬 300. Ⓙ ⒶⒺ ⓞ 𝘝𝘐𝘚𝘈. ⨯
**Meals** (bar lunch Monday to Saturday)/dinner 24.00 st. and a la carte ⅃ 6.25 – **76 rm** ☲ 90.00/130.00 st. – SB.

🏨 **Blue Haven**, 3 Pearse St., ℘ *(021) 772209, Fax (021) 774268* – 📺 ☎. Ⓙ ⒶⒺ ⓞ 𝘝𝘐𝘚𝘈 ᴊᴄʙ. ⨯
*closed 24-25 December and 6 to 29 January* – **Meals** - Seafood - (bar lunch)/dinner 28.50 st. and a la carte ⅃ 8.50 – **17 rm** ☲ 75.00/150.00 st. – SB.

🏠 **Old Bank House** without rest., 11 Pearse St., ℘ *(021) 774075, Fax (021) 774296* – 📺 ☎. Ⓙ ⒶⒺ 𝘝𝘐𝘚𝘈. ⨯
*closed 22 to 26 December* – **9 rm** ☲ 45.00/90.00 st.

**Moorings** without rest., Scilly, ✆ (021) 772376, *Fax (021) 772675*, ≤ Kinsale harbour – TV ☎ ✆ P. MC D VISA. ✱
8 rm ☕ 90.00/110.00 **st.**

**Scilly House Inn** without rest., Scilly, ✆ (021) 772413, *Fax (021) 774629*, ≤, 🌲 – ☎ P. MC AE VISA. ✱
*April-14 October* – **6 rm** ☕ 80.00/135.00 **st.**, 1 suite.

**Sovereign House,** Newmans Mall, ✆ (021) 772850, *Fax (021) 774723*, « Queen Anne town house », 🌲 – ✱ TV ☎. MC AE VISA. ✱
*closed December* – **Meals** (by arrangement) 20.00 **st.** 🍷 5.00 – **3 rm** ☕ 70.00/130.00 **st.**, 1 suite.

**Quayside House** without rest., Pier Rd, ✆ (021) 772188, *Fax (021) 772664* – TV ☎. MC AE VISA
6 rm ☕ 30.00/60.00.

**Kilcaw Guesthouse** without rest.,, East : 1 m. on R 600 ✆ (021) 774155, *Fax (021) 774755*, 🌲 – ✱ TV ☎ P. MC AE VISA. ✱
*mid February-mid November* – **7 rm** ☕ 40.00/50.00 **st.**

**Murphys Farm House** without rest.,, Northeast : 1 ¼ m. by R 600 ✆ (021) 772229, *Fax (021) 774176*, 🌲 – P. ✱
*April-October* – **4 rm** ☕ 20.00/36.00 **t.**

XX **Vintage,** Main St., ✆ (021) 772502, *Fax (021) 774828* – ▤. MC AE D VISA JCB
*closed Sunday and Monday in low season and January-1 March* – **Meals** (dinner only) 28.00 **t.** and a la carte 26.50/37.50 **t.** 🍷 9.00.

XX **Annelie's,** 18-19 Lower O'Connell St., ✆ (021) 773074, *Fax (021) 773075* – ▤. MC AE D VISA
*closed Sunday and Monday in winter, 4 days Christmas, February and November* – **Meals** (dinner only) a la carte 14.50/24.40 **t.** 🍷 6.95.

X **Max's,** Main St., ✆ (021) 772443 – MC VISA
*March-October* – **Meals** 12.00 **t.** and a la carte 🍷 7.50.

**at Barrells Cross** *Southwest : 3 m. on R 600 – ✉ Kinsale.*

**Rivermount House** without rest., ✆ (021) 778033, *Fax (021) 778225*, 🌲 – ✱ TV ☎ P. MC VISA. ✱
*February-October* – **6 rm** ☕ 30.00/50.00.

---

**KINSALEY** *Dublin* 923 N 7 – *see Malahide.*

---

**KINVARRA (Cinn Mhara)** *Galway* 923 F 8 – *pop. 432.*
*Dublin 142 – Galway 17 – Limerick 37.*

**Merriman Inn,** Main St., ✆ (091) 638222, *Fax (091) 637686* – |‡|, ✱ rm, TV ☎ ♿ P. MC AE D VISA. ✱
*closed January and February* – **Meals** (bar lunch Monday to Saturday)/dinner 19.00 **t.** and a la carte 🍷 5.25 – **32 rm** ☕ 55.00/70.00 **t.** – SB.

---

**KNOCK (An Cnoc)** *Mayo* 923 F 6 *Ireland G. – pop. 575.*
**See** : *Basilica of our Lady, Queen of Ireland*★.
✈ *Knock (Connaught) Airport : ✆ (094) 67222, NE : 9 m. by N 17.*
ℹ *Knock Airport ✆ (094) 67247 (June-September) – Knock ✆ (094) 88193 (May-September).*
*Dublin 132 – Galway 46 – Westport 32.*

*Hotel see :* **Cong** *SW : 36 m. by N 17, R 331, R 334 and R 345.*

*When visiting Great Britain,*
*use the Michelin Green Guide* **"Great Britain".**
- *Detailed descriptions of places of interest*
- *Touring programmes*
- *Maps and street plans*
- *The history of the country*
- *Photographs and drawings of monuments, beauty spots, houses...*

**LAHINCH** (An Leacht) *Clare* 923 D 9 *Ireland G. – pop. 580.*
  Env. : Cliffs of Moher★★★.
  🏌, 🏌 Lahinch ℰ (065) 81003 – 🏌 Spanish Point, Miltown Malbay ℰ (065) 84198.
  *Dublin 162 – Galway 49 – Limerick 41.*

🏨 **Aberdeen Arms,** ℰ (065) 81100, Fax (065) 81228, 🕭s – 🛏 rest, 📺 ☎ 🅿 – 🛁 200. 🟠🟥
  🅰🅴 ⓞ 𝘝𝘐𝘚𝘈. 🛇
  **Meals** (bar lunch Monday to Saturday)/dinner 10.95 **st.** and a la carte – **55 rm** 🖙 60.00/
  90.00 **st.** – SB.

🏠 **Atlantic,** Main St., ℰ (065) 81049, Fax (065) 81029 – 🕭 rm, 📺 ☎ 🅿. 🟠🟥 ⓞ 𝘝𝘐𝘚𝘈
  *closed 25 December, November and February* – **Meals** (bar lunch Monday to Saturday)/
  dinner 20.00 **t.** and a la carte 👖 6.00 – **14 rm** 🖙 45.00/80.00 **st.** – SB.

---

**LARAGH** (Láithreach) *Wicklow* 923 N 8 *Ireland G – pop. 267 –* ✉ *Wicklow.*
  Env. : Glendalough★★★, NW : by R 756.
  Exc. : Wicklow Mountains★★ (Wicklow Gap★★ – Sally Gap★★ – Glenmacnass Waterfall★ –
  Glenmalur★ – Loughs Tay and Dan★ ).
  *Dublin 26 – Kilkenny 70 – Wexford 61.*

🏠 **Laragh Trekking Centre** 🍃, Glendalough East, Northwest : 1 ½ m. on Sallygap rd
  ℰ (0404) 45282, Fax (0404) 45204, ≤, 🌳, park – 🕭 📺 ☎ 🅿. 🟠🟥 𝘝𝘐𝘚𝘈. 🛇
  *closed Christmas* – **Meals** (by arrangement) 15.00 **st.** – **6 rm** 🖙 35.00/45.00 **st.**

✗ **Mitchell's** with rm, The Old Schoolhouse, ℰ (0404) 45302, Fax (0404) 45302 – 🅿. 🟠🟥 🅰🅴
  𝘝𝘐𝘚𝘈. 🛇
  *closed Monday and Tuesday October-February, Good Friday, 24 to 26 December and
  3 weeks January* – **Meals** 18.50 **st.** (dinner) and lunch a la carte 10.00/18.50 **st.** – **5 rm**
  🖙 37.00 **st.** – SB.

---

**LEENANE** (An Líonán) *Galway* 923 C 7 *Ireland G. –* ✉ *Clifden.*
  See : Killary Harbour★.
  Env. : Joyce Country★★ – Lough Nafooey★, SE : 6 ½ m. by R 336 – Aasleagh Falls★, NE :
  2½ m.
  Exc. : Connemara★★★ – Lough Corrib★★, SE : 10 m. by R 336 and R 345 – Doo Lough Pass★,
  NW : 9 m. by N 59 and R 335.
  *Dublin 173 – Ballina 56 – Galway 41.*

🏠 **Delphi Lodge** 🍃,, Northwest : 8 ¼ m. by N 59 on Louisburgh rd ℰ (095) 42211,
  Fax (095) 42296, ≤, « Georgian sporting lodge, loughside setting », 🎣, park – ☎ 🅿 –
  🛁 30. 🟠🟥 🅰🅴 𝘝𝘐𝘚𝘈. 🛇
  *closed mid December-mid January* – **Meals** (residents only) (communal dining) (dinner
  only) 30.00 **t.** 👖 7.50 – **12 rm** 🖙 50.00/120.00 **st.**

🏠 **Portfinn Lodge,** ℰ (095) 42265, Fax (095) 42315, ≤ – ☎ 🅿. 🟠🟥 ⓞ 𝘝𝘐𝘚𝘈. 🛇
  *April-September* – **Meals** (by arrangement) 14.50 **t.** – **8 rm** 🖙 39.00/49.00 **t.**

---

**LEIXLIP** (Léim an Bhradáin) *Kildare* 923 M 7 – pop. 13 451.
  *Dublin 14 – Drogheda 39 – Galway 125 – Kilkenny 73.*

🏨 **Leixlip House,** Captain's Hill, ℰ (01) 624 2268, Fax (01) 624 4177, « Georgian house » –
  📺 ☎ 🅿 – 🛁 100. 🟠🟥 🅰🅴 ⓞ 𝘝𝘐𝘚𝘈. 🛇
  *closed 25 December* – **Meals** – (see *The Bradaun* below) – **15 rm** 🖙 90.00/140.00 **st.** – SB.

✗✗ **The Bradaun** (at Leixlip House H.), Captain's Hill, ℰ (01) 624 2268, Fax (01) 624 4177 – 🅿.
  🟠🟥 🅰🅴 ⓞ 𝘝𝘐𝘚𝘈
  *closed 25 December* – **Meals** 13.95/27.50 **st.** and dinner a la carte 👖 7.95.

---

**LETTERFRACK** (Leitir Fraic) *Galway* 923 C 7 *Ireland G..*
  Env. : Connemara★★★ – Sky Road★★ (≤★★) – Connemara National Park★ – Kylemore
  Abbey★, E : 3 m. by N 59.
  *Dublin 189 – Ballina 69 – Galway 57.*

🏨 **Rosleague Manor** 🍃,, West : 1 ½ m. on N 59 ℰ (095) 41101, Fax (095) 41168, ≤
  Ballynakill harbour and Tully mountain, 🕭s, 🌳, park, ✗ – 🕭 rest, ☎ 🅿. 🟠🟥 🅰🅴 𝘝𝘐𝘚𝘈
  *April-October* – **Meals** a la carte 14.00/26.50 **t.** 👖 7.50 – **20 rm** 🖙 65.00/150.00 **t.** – SB.

---

**LETTERKENNY** (Leitir Ceanainn) *Donegal* 923 I 3 *Ireland G. – pop. 7 606.*
  Exc. : Glenveagh National Park★★ (Gardens★★), NW : 12 m. by R 250, R 251 and R 254 –
  Grianan of Aileach★★ (≤★★) NE : 17½ m. by N 13 – Church Hill (Glebe House and Gallery★
  AC) NW : 10 m. by R 250.
  🏌 Barnhill ℰ (074) 21150 – 🏌 Dunfanaghy ℰ (074) 36335.
  *Dublin 150 – Londonderry 21 – Sligo 72.*

🏠 **Castlegrove House** ॐ, Ramelton Rd, Northeast : 4 ½ m. by N 13 off R 245
🖉 (074) 51118, Fax (074) 51384, ≼, « Late 17C country house », ☜, 🚗, park – ✻ ☎ 🅿.
🐵 🕮 ⓪ 𝖵𝖨𝖲𝖠. ℀
*closed 23 to 30 December* – **Meals** *(closed Sunday January-May)* (dinner only) 18.50 **t**. ⓼ 6.50
– **15 rm** ⚏ 35.00/180.00 **t**. – SB.

🏠 **Gleneany House,** Port Rd, 🖉 (074) 26088, Fax (074) 26090 – 🛏 rest, 🆃🆅 ☎ 🅿. 🐵 𝖵𝖨𝖲𝖠.
℀
**Meals** a la carte 13.00/16.50 **st**. ⓼ 5.00 – **22 rm** ⚏ 35.00/65.00 **st**.

---

**LIMERICK** (Luimneach) *Limerick* 𝟵𝟮𝟯 G 9 *Ireland G.* – pop. 52 039.

**See :** *City*★★ - St Mary's Cathedral★★ Y – Limerick Museum★ Z – King John's Castle★ AC Y –
*John Square*★ Z **20** – St. John's Cathedral★ Z.
**Env. :** Hunt Museum★★ AC, E : 2 m. by N 7 Y – Cratloe Wood (≼★) NW : 5 m. by N 18 Z.
**Exc. :** Castleconnell★, E : 7 m. by N 7 – Lough Gur Interpretive Centre★ AC, S : 11 m.
by R 512 and R 514 Z – Clare Glens★, E : 13 m. by N 7 and R 503 Y – Monasteranenagh
Abbey★, S : 13 m. by N 20 Z.
🛫 Shannon Airport : 🖉 (061) 471444, W : 16 m. by N 18 Z – **Terminal :** Limerick Railway
Station.
🄑 Arthur's Quay 🖉 (061) 317522 Y.
*Dublin 120 – Cork 58.*

Plan on next page

🏨🏨 **Castletroy Park,** Dublin Rd, East : 2 ¼ m. by N 7 🖉 (061) 335566, Fax (061) 331117, ₤ₔ,
⬛, 🖵, 🚗 – ⫯, ✻ rm, 🆃🆅 ☎ ✔ 🅿 – 🔏 450. 🐵 🕮 ⓪ 𝖵𝖨𝖲𝖠. ℀
*McLaughlin's :* **Meals** *(closed Sunday dinner and Monday)* (dinner only and Sunday lunch)/
dinner 26.00 **st**. and a la carte ⓼ 7.95 – **105 rm** ⚏ 140.00/185.00 **st**., 2 suites – SB.

🏨🏨 **South Court,** Raheen Roundabout, Southwest : 2 ¾ m. on N 20 🖉 (061) 487487,
Fax (061) 487499, ₤ₔ, ⬛ – ⫯, ✻ rm, 🛏 rest, 🆃🆅 ☎ ✔ 🅿 – 🔏 200. 🐵 🕮 ⓪ 𝖵𝖨𝖲𝖠. ℀
*Seasons :* **Meals** *(closed Sunday dinner)* (dinner only and Sunday lunch)/dinner a la carte
20.00/40.00 **st**. – *Boru's :* **Meals** (carvery lunch)/dinner a la carte 7.00/15.00 **st**. – ⚏ 8.50 –
**64 rm** 65.00/90.00 **st**. – SB.

🏨🏨 **Limerick Inn,** Ennis Rd, Northwest : 4 m. on N 18 🖉 (061) 326666, Fax (061) 326281, ₤ₔ,
⬛, 🖵, 🚗, ℀ – ⫯, 🛏 rest, 🆃🆅 ☎ 🅿 – 🔏 600. 🐵 🕮 ⓪ 𝖵𝖨𝖲𝖠. ℀
*closed 24 and 25 December* – **Meals** 12.95/24.50 **st**. and dinner a la carte ⓼ 6.25 – ⚏ 8.00 –
**150 rm** 103.00/120.00 **st**., 3 suites.

🏨🏨 **Jurys,** Ennis Rd, 🖉 (061) 327777, Fax (061) 326400, ₤ₔ, ⬛, 🖵, 🚗, ℀ – ✻ rm, 🛏 rest,
🆃🆅 ☎ 🅿 – 🔏 200. 🐵 🕮 ⓪ 𝖵𝖨𝖲𝖠. ℀                                                             Y z
*closed 25 to 28 December* – *Copper Room :* **Meals** (dinner only) 24.00 **t**. and a la carte
⓼ 8.50 – ⚏ 8.50 – **94 rm** 105.00/130.00 **t**., 1 suite – SB.

🏨🏨 **Limerick Ryan,** Ennis Rd, Northwest : 1 ¼ m. on R 587 🖉 (061) 453922,
Fax (061) 326333, 🚗 – ⫯, ✻ rm, 🛏 rest, 🆃🆅 ☎ 🅿 – 🔏 120. 🐵 🕮 ⓪ 𝖵𝖨𝖲𝖠. ℀
**Meals** 10.50/20.00 **t**. and dinner a la carte ⓼ 6.95 – ⚏ 10.00 – **179 rm** 95.00/125.00 **t**.,
2 suites – SB.

🏨 **Greenhills,** Ennis Rd, Northwest : 2 ¼ m. on R 587 🖉 (061) 453033, Fax (061) 453307, ₤ₔ,
⬛, 🖵, 🚗, ℀ – ✻ rm, 🆃🆅 ☎ ✔ & 🅿 – 🔏 600. 🐵 🕮 ⓪ 𝖵𝖨𝖲𝖠. ℀
**Meals** (carvery lunch) 10.50 **t**. (lunch) and dinner a la carte 13.20/22.20 **st**. ⓼ 5.75 – ⚏ 8.80
– **60 rm** 50.00/70.00 **st**. – SB.

🏨 **Jurys Inn Limerick,** Lower Mallow St., 🖉 (061) 207000, Fax (061) 400966, ≼ – ⫯, ✻ rm,
🛏 rest, 🆃🆅 ☎ ✔ & ⇦ – 🔏 40. 🐵 🕮 ⓪ 𝖵𝖨𝖲𝖠. ℀                                              Z a
*closed 24 to 26 December* – **Meals** (dinner only) 15.00 **st**. and a la carte ⓼ 5.50 – ⚏ 6.00 –
**151 rm** 51.00 **st**.

🏨 **Kilmurry Lodge,** Castletroy, East : 3 ¼ m. by N 7 🖉 (061) 331133, Fax (061) 330011 – 🆃🆅
☎ & 🅿 – 🔏 300. 🐵 🕮 ⓪ 𝖵𝖨𝖲𝖠. ℀
*closed 25 December* – **Meals** 10.50 **st**. (lunch) and dinner a la carte 15.45/20.75 **st**. ⓼ 6.00 –
**43 rm** ⚏ 45.00/58.00 **st**. – SB.

🏠 **Clifton House** without rest., Ennis Rd, Northwest : 1 ¼ m. on R 587 🖉 (061) 451166,
Fax (061) 451224, 🚗 – 🆃🆅 ☎ 🅿. 🐵 ⓪ 𝖵𝖨𝖲𝖠. ℀
*closed 20 December-5 January* – **16 rm** ⚏ 20.00/45.00 **t**.

🏠 **Clonmacken House** without rest., Clonmacken Rd, off Ennis Rd, Northwest : 2 m. by
N 18 🖉 (061) 327007, Fax (061) 327785, 🚗 – ✻ rm, 🆃🆅 ☎ 🅿. 🐵 𝖵𝖨𝖲𝖠.
*closed 1 week Christmas* – **10 rm** ⚏ 28.00/45.00 **st**.

✗✗ **Quenelle's on the Waterfront,** Unit 4 Steamboat Quay, Dock Rd, 🖉 (061) 411111,
Fax (061) 400111, ≼ – 🛏. 🐵 🕮 ⓪ 𝖵𝖨𝖲𝖠.                                                           Z r
*closed Sunday, Good Friday and 24 to 26 December* – **Meals** (dinner only) 24.95 **t**. ⓼ 5.75.

# LIMERICK

Les hôtels ou restaurants agréables
sont indiqués dans le guide par un signe rouge.

Aidez-nous en nous signalant les maisons où,
par expérience, vous savez qu'il fait bon vivre.

Votre **guide Michelin** sera encore meilleur.

**LISDOONVARNA** (Lios Dúin Bhearna) *Clare* 923 E 8 *Ireland G. – pop. 890.*

Env. : *The Burren★★ (Cliffs of Moher★★★, Scenic Routes★★, Aillwee Cave★ AC (Waterfall★★), Corcomroe Abbey★, Kilfenora Crosses★ ).*
Dublin 167 – Galway 39 – Limerick 47.

🏫 **Ballinalacken Castle** ⑤,, Northwest : 3 m. by N 67 (Doolin rd) on R 477 ℰ (065) 74025, *Fax* (065) 74025, ≼, park – ⁕ rest, 🖵 ☎ 🅿, ⑩ ⑧ VISA. ⅍
2 April-4 October – **Meals** (bar lunch)/dinner 16.00 t. and a la carte 🍷 5.75 – **12 rm** ⊇ 70.00/78.00 t.

🏫 **Carrigann,** ℰ (065) 74036, *Fax* (065) 74567 – ⁕ rest, 🖵 ☎ 🅿 – 🔬 70. ⑩ VISA. ⅍
12 March-October – **Meals** (bar lunch)/dinner 18.00 t. and a la carte 🍷 5.00 – **20 rm** ⊇ 35.00/69.00 t. – SB.

🏠 **Sheedy's Spa View,** Sulphir Hill, ℰ (065) 74026, *Fax* (065) 74555, ☞, ⅍ – ☎ 🅿. ⑩ ⑧ ⅍E VISA. ⅍
April-September – **Meals** – (see *Orchid* below) – **11 rm** ⊇ 40.00/65.00 st.

⌂ **Woodhaven** without rest., Doolin Coast Rd, West : 1 m. by N 67 (Doolin rd) off R 477 ℰ (065) 74017, ☞ – 🅿. ⑩ VISA. ⅍
closed 1 week Christmas – **4 rm** ⊇ 23.00/36.00 s.

XX **Orchid** (at Sheedy's Spa View H.), Sulphir Hill, ℰ (065) 74026, *Fax* (065) 74555 – 🅿. ⑩ ⑧ ⅍E VISA
April-September – **Meals** (dinner only) a la carte 17.00/23.25 t. 🍷 8.00.

---

**LISTOWEL** (Lios Tuathail) *Kerry* 923 D 10 – *pop. 3 393.*
Dublin 168 – Killarney 34 – Limerick 47 – Tralee 17.

🍴 **Allo's,** 41 Church St., ℰ (068) 22880 – ⑩ ⑧ ⅍E VISA
closed Sunday, Good Friday, 25 December and Bank Holiday Mondays – **Meals** (booking essential) a la carte 10.20/24.50 t. 🍷 5.00.

---

**MACROOM** (Maigh Chromtha) *Cork* 923 F 12 – *pop. 2 457.*
🏌 Lackaduve ℰ (026) 41072.
Dublin 186 – Cork 25 – Killarney 30.

🏫 **Castle,** Main St., ℰ (026) 41074, *Fax* (026) 41505, **f₆**, 🖂, – 🖵 ☎ 📞 – 🔬 60. ⑩ ⑧ ⅍E ⑩ VISA. ⅍
closed 25 to 27 December – **Meals** 11.50/18.50 t. and a la carte 🍷 9.50 – **42 rm** ⊇ 50.00/85.00 st. – SB.

---

**MALAHIDE** (Mullach Íde) *Dublin* 923 N 7 *Ireland G. – pop. 13 539.*
See : *Castle★★.*
Env. : *Fingal★.*
🏌, 🏌 Beechwood, The Grange ℰ (01) 846 1611.
Dublin 9 – Drogheda 24.

🏨 **Grand,** ℰ (01) 845 0000, *Fax* (01) 845 0987, **f₆**, ≘s, 🖂 – 🛗, ⁕ rm, 🖵 ☎ 📞 🅿 – 🔬 500. ⑩ ⑧ ⅍E ⑩ VISA. ⅍
closed 25 and 26 December – **Meals** 13.00/27.00 t. and dinner a la carte – **100 rm** ⊇ 120.00/180.00 t. – SB.

XX **Siam Thai,** Gas Yard Lane, off Strand St. ℰ (01) 845 4698, *Fax* (01) 478 4798 – 🗐. ⑩ ⑧ ⑩ VISA
closed Good Friday and 25-26 December – **Meals** - Thai - (dinner only) 18.50 t. and a la carte 🍷 8.95.

**at Kinsaley** *Southwest : 2½ m. on Dublin rd (L 87) – ✉ Malahide.*

🏠 **Belcamp Hutchinson** without rest., Carrs Lane, Balgriffin, D17, South : 1 m. by L 87 ℰ (01) 846 0843, *Fax* (01) 848 5703, « Georgian house », ☞, park – 🖵 ☎ 🅿. ⑩ ⑧ VISA
closed 22 to 30 December – **8 rm** ⊇ 44.00/88.00 st.

⌂ **Liscara** without rest., Malahide Rd, D17, South : ½ m. ℰ (01) 848 3751, *Fax* (01) 848 3751, ☞ – ⁕ 🅿. ⅍ – March-November – **6 rm** 30.00/40.00.

---

**MALLOW** (Mala) *Cork* 923 F 11 *Ireland G. – pop. 6 434.*
See : *Town★ – St. James' Church★.*
Exc. : *Doneraile Wildlife Park★ AC, NE : 6 m. by N 20 and R 581 – Buttevant Friary★, N : 7 m. by N 20 – Annes Grove Gardens★, E : 11 m. by N 72 and minor rd.*
🏌 Ballyellis ℰ (022) 21145.
Dublin 149 – Cork 21 – Killarney 40 – Limerick 41.

🏨 **Longueville House** ⑤,, West : 3½ m. by N 72 ℰ (022) 47156, *Fax* (022) 47459, ≼, « Part Georgian mansion in extensive grounds, working farm », ⌁, ☞ – ⁕ 🖵 ☎ 🅿. ⑩ ⑧ ⅍E ⑩ VISA. ⅍
closed January-12 February and 20 to 31 December – **Presidents** : Meals (booking essential) (bar lunch)/dinner 31.00 t. 🍷 8.00 – **20 rm** ⊇ 60.00/166.00 t. – SB.

**Springfort Hall** ⚘,, North : 4 ¾ m. by N 20 on R 581 ☎ (022) 21278, *Fax (022) 21557*, 🌳, park – [TV] ☎ [P] – 🎤 300. [MC] [AE] [DI] [VISA]. 🐕
*closed 24 December-2 January* – **Meals** *(closed Sunday lunch)* 15.00/22.50 **st.** and dinner a la carte 🍷 6.00 – **50 rm** 🛏 42.50/77.50 **st.** – SB.

**Central,** Main St., ☎ (022) 21527, *Fax (022) 21527* – [TV] ☎ [P] – 🎤 350. [MC] [AE] [VISA]. 🐕
*closed 25 December* – **Meals** 10.95/16.95 **st.** and a la carte 🍷 5.95 – **20 rm** 🛏 30.00/60.00 **st.** – SB.

## MAYNOOTH (Maigh Nuad) *Kildare* [923] M 7 *Ireland G. – pop. 8 528.*

Env. : *Castletown House*★★ *AC, SE : 4 m. by R 405.*
*Dublin 15.*

**Moyglare Manor** ⚘, Moyglare, North : 2 m. ☎ (01) 628 6351, *Fax (01) 628 5405*, ≤, « Georgian country house, extensively furnished with antiques », 🌳, park – [TV] ☎ [P] – 🎤 35. [MC] [AE] [DI] [VISA] [JCB]. 🐕
*closed 24 to 26 December* – **Meals** *(closed Saturday lunch)* 26.95 **t.** (dinner) and a la carte 18.95/38.50 **t.** 🍷 7.95 – **16 rm** 🛏 95.00/150.00 **t.**, 1 suite.

**Glenroyal,** Straffan Rd, ☎ (01) 629 0909, *Fax (01) 629 0919*, 🏋, ♨, 🏊 – 🛗, ▤ rest, [TV] ☎ [P] – 🎤 450. [MC] [AE] [DI] [VISA]. 🐕
*closed 25 December* – **Meals** (carving lunch) 12.00/20.00 **st.** and dinner a la carte 🍷 6.50 – **52 rm** 🛏 60.00/95.00 **st.**, **18 suites** 95.00/105.00 **st.** – SB.

## MERRION (Muirfin) *Co. Dublin – see Dublin.*

## MIDLETON (Mainistir na Corann) *Cork* [923] H 12 *– pop. 3 266.*

⛳18 *East Cork, Gortacrue ☎ (021) 631687.*
[i] *Jameson Heritage Centre ☎ (021) 613702 (April-September).*
*Dublin 161 – Cork 12 – Waterford 61.*

**Midleton Park,** Old Cork Rd, ☎ (021) 631767, *Fax (021) 631605*, 🌳 – ▤ rest, [TV] ☎ ♿ [P] – 🎤 400. [MC] [AE] [DI] [VISA]. 🐕
*closed 25 December* – **Meals** 11.75 **st.** (lunch) and dinner a la carte 14.00/21.90 **st.** 🍷 6.00 – **39 rm** 🛏 60.00/100.00 **st.**, 1 suite.

## MONAGHAN (Muineachán) *Monaghan* [923] L 5 *– pop. 5 628.*

*Dublin 83 – Belfast 43 – Drogheda 54 – Dundalk 22 – Londonderry 75.*

**Hillgrove,** Old Armagh Rd, Southeast : ¾ m. by N 2 ☎ (047) 81288, *Fax (047) 84951* – 🛗, ▤ rest, [TV] ☎ ♿ [P] – 🎤 800. [MC] [AE] [DI] [VISA]. 🐕
***Cavendish :*** **Meals** 11.50/18.50 **st.** and dinner a la carte 🍷 6.50 – ***Bracken :*** **Meals** 11.50/16.00 **st.** and a la carte 🍷 6.50 – **44 rm** 🛏 46.00/104.00 **st.** – SB.

**Four Seasons,** Coolshannagh, North : 1 m. on N 2 ☎ (047) 81888, *Fax (047) 83131*, 🏋, 🏊, 🌳 – [TV] ☎ [P]. [MC] [AE] [DI] [VISA]. 🐕
*closed 25 December* – **Meals** (carving lunch) 12.50/20.00 **st.** and a la carte 🍷 6.00 – **44 rm** 🛏 57.50/95.00 **st.** – SB.

## MONKSTOWN (Baile na Mhanaigh) *Co. Dublin* [923] (40) *– see Dublin.*

## MOYARD (Maigh Ard) *Galway* [923] B/C 7.

*Dublin 190 – Galway 53 – Sligo 97.*

**Garraunbaun House** ⚘,, West : 1 m. off N 59 ☎ (095) 41649, *Fax (095) 41649*, ≤, « 19C manor house », 🎣, 🌳, park – [P]. [MC]. 🐕
**Meals** (by arrangement) 20.00 **st.** 🍷 4.50 – **3 rm** 🛏 30.00/60.00.

## MOYCULLEN (Maigh Cuilinn) *Galway* [923] E 7 *– pop. 601.*

*Dublin 139 – Galway 7.*

**Knockferry Lodge** ⚘, Knockferry (on Lough Corrib), Northeast : 6 ½ m. by Knockferry rd ☎ (091) 550122, *Fax (091) 550328*, ≤, 🎣, 🌳 – 🚭 rest, [P]. [MC] [AE] [DI] [VISA]. 🐕
**Meals** (booking essential mid May-mid September) (bar lunch)/dinner 17.50 **t.** 🍷 5.00 – **10 rm** 🛏 29.00/44.00 **t.**

**Moycullen House** ⚘,, Southwest : 1 m. by Spiddle rd ☎ (091) 555566, *Fax (091) 555566*, 🌳 – 🚭 [P]. [MC] [AE] [VISA]. 🐕
*closed mid January-February and 25 December* – **Meals** (communal dining) (by arrangement) 25.00 **st.** 🍷 6.50 – **3 rm** 🛏 60.00/80.00 **st.**

XX **Drimcong House**,, Northwest : 1 m. on N 59 $\mathscr{E}$ (091) 555115, *Fax (091) 555836*, « 17C estate house », $\not\approx$ – $\bigcirc$. $\mathbf{\mathscr{00}}$ $\underline{AE}$ $\underline{\mathbf{0}}$ $\overline{VISA}$
*closed Sunday, Monday and Christmas-March* – **Meals** (booking essential) (dinner only) 19.50 **st.** and a la carte $\mathring{\textrm{a}}$ 6.00.

---

**MULLINAVAT** (Muileann an Bhata) *Kilkenny* 923 K 10 – *pop. 275.*
*Dublin 88 – Kilkenny 21 – Waterford 8.*

🏠 **Rising Sun**, Main St., $\mathscr{E}$ (051) 898173, *Fax (051) 898435* – $\overline{TV}$ $\mathbf{\mathscr{E}}$ $\bigcirc$. $\mathbf{\mathscr{00}}$ $\overline{VISA}$. $\mathscr{K}$
*closed 25 December and Good Friday* – **Meals** (bar lunch)/dinner a la carte approx. 13.10 **st.** $\mathring{\textrm{a}}$ 4.50 – **10 rm** $\rightleftarrows$ 35.00/52.00. **st.** – SB.

---

**MULLINGAR** (An Muileann gCearr) *Westmeath* 923 JK 7 *Ireland G.* – *pop. 8 040.*
Env. : *Belvedere House and Gardens* $\star$ *AC*, *S : 3½ m. by N 52.*
Exc. : *Multyfarnhan Franciscan Friary* $\star$, *N : 8 m. by N 4 – Tullynally Castle* $\star$ *AC*, *N : 13 m. by N 4 and R 394 – Fore Abbey* $\star$, *NE : 17 m. by R 394.*
🏌 Belvedere $\mathscr{E}$ (044) 48366/48629.
🛈 *Dublin Road* $\mathscr{E}$ (044) 48650.
*Dublin 49 – Drogheda 36.*

🏨 **Greville Arms**, Pearse St., $\mathscr{E}$ (044) 48563, *Fax (044) 48052* – 🍽 rest, $\overline{TV}$ $\mathbf{\mathscr{E}}$ $\bigcirc$ – $\underline{\mathring{\textrm{a}}}$ 100. $\mathbf{\mathscr{00}}$ $\underline{AE}$ $\underline{\mathbf{0}}$ $\overline{VISA}$. $\mathscr{K}$
*closed 25 and 26 December* – **Meals** 11.00 **t.** (lunch) and dinner a la carte 9.00/25.00 **t.** $\mathring{\textrm{a}}$ 7.00 – **39 rm** $\rightleftarrows$ 45.00/100.00. **st.**, 1 suite – SB.

🏠 **Marlinstown Court** without rest., Dublin Rd, East : 1 ½ m. on Dublin Rd (N 4) $\mathscr{E}$ (044) 40053, *Fax (044) 41358*, $\not\approx$ – $\overline{TV}$ $\bigcirc$. $\mathbf{\mathscr{00}}$ $\overline{VISA}$. $\mathscr{K}$
*closed 15 December-1 January* – **5 rm** $\rightleftarrows$ 25.00/38.00. **st.**

🏠 **Hilltop Country House** without rest., Rathconnell, Northeast : 2 ½ m. by N 52 $\mathscr{E}$ (044) 48958, *Fax (044) 48013*, $\not\approx$ – $\overleftarrow{\times}$ $\overline{TV}$ $\bigcirc$. $\mathscr{K}$
*closed 21 December-7 January* – **5 rm** $\rightleftarrows$ 25.00/40.00. **st.**

**at Crookedwood** North : 6½ m. on R 394 – $\boxtimes$ Mullingar.

🏨 **Crookedwood House** $\gtrsim$,, East : 1 ½ m. on Delvin rd, turning right at The Wood pub $\mathscr{E}$ (044) 72165, *Fax (044) 72166*, $\leqslant$, $\not\approx$, $\mathscr{K}$ – $\overleftarrow{\times}$ $\overline{TV}$ $\mathbf{\mathscr{E}}$ $\bigcirc$. $\mathbf{\mathscr{00}}$ $\underline{AE}$ $\underline{\mathbf{0}}$ $\overline{VISA}$. $\mathscr{K}$
*closed 4 days Christmas and 2 weeks January* – **Meals** – (see **The Restaurant** below) – **8 rm** $\rightleftarrows$ 60.00/100.00 **st.** – SB.

XX **The Restaurant** (at Crookedwood House H.),, East : 1½ m. on Delvin rd, turning right at The Wood pub $\mathscr{E}$ (044) 72165, *Fax (044) 72166*, « Cellars of 18C rectory », $\not\approx$ – $\bigcirc$. $\mathbf{\mathscr{00}}$ $\underline{AE}$ $\underline{\mathbf{0}}$ $\overline{VISA}$
*closed Sunday dinner, Monday, 4 days Christmas and 2 weeks January* – **Meals** (dinner only and Sunday lunch)/dinner 25.00 **st.** and a la carte $\mathring{\textrm{a}}$ 5.95.

**at Rathconrath** West : 7¾ m. on R 392 – $\boxtimes$ Mullingar.

🏠 **Meares Court** $\gtrsim$,, Northwest : 3 ¾ m. on Moyvore rd $\mathscr{E}$ (044) 55112, *Fax (044) 55112*, $\leqslant$, « Georgian mansion in parkland », $\not\approx$ – $\bigcirc$. $\mathbf{\mathscr{00}}$ $\overline{VISA}$. $\mathscr{K}$
*closed 21 to 30 December* – **Meals** (by arrangement) 18.50 $\mathring{\textrm{a}}$ 7.00 – **4 rm** $\rightleftarrows$ 35.00/50.00.

---

**NAAS** (An Nás) *Kildare* 923 L/M 8 – *pop. 14 074.*
*Dublin 19 – Kilkenny 52 – Tullamore 53.*

X **Jo Olive's**, 10 South Main St., $\mathscr{E}$ (045) 894788 – $\mathbf{\mathscr{00}}$ $\overline{VISA}$
*closed Sunday, Monday, 25 December and Bank Holidays* – **Meals** (dinner only) a la carte 17.75/28.00 **t.** $\mathring{\textrm{a}}$ 5.50.

---

**NAVAN** (An Uaimh) *Meath* 923 L 7 *Ireland G* – *pop. 3 447.*
Env. : *Bective Abbey* $\star$, *S : 4 m. by R 161.*
Exc. : *Trim* $\star$ *(castle* $\star\star$*), SW : 8 m. by R 161 – Kells* $\star$ *(Round Tower and High Crosses* $\star\star$*, St. Columba's House* $\star$*), NW : by N 3 – Tara* $\star$, *S : 6 m. by N 3.*
*Dublin 30 – Drogheda 16 – Dundalk 32.*

🏠 **Killyon**, Dublin Rd, South : 1 m. on N 3 $\mathscr{E}$ (046) 71224, *Fax (046) 72766* – $\overline{TV}$ $\mathbf{\mathscr{E}}$ $\bigcirc$. $\mathbf{\mathscr{00}}$ $\overline{VISA}$
*closed 24 and 25 December* – **Meals** (by arrangement) – **4 rm** $\rightleftarrows$ 25.00/50.00 – SB.

X **Hudson's Bistro**, 30 Railway St., $\mathscr{E}$ (046) 29231, *Fax (046) 73382* – $\mathbf{\mathscr{00}}$ $\underline{AE}$ $\overline{VISA}$
*closed Monday, Good Friday, 24-26 December and 1 January* – **Meals** (dinner only) a la carte 14.95/21.95 **t.** $\mathring{\textrm{a}}$ 5.00.

**NENAGH** (An tAonach) *Tipperary* 923 H 9 *Ireland G.*– pop. 5 645.

See : *Town★ – Heritage Centre★ – Castle★.*
*Dublin 96 – Galway 63 – Limerick 26.*

🏠 **St. David's Country House** ⌂, Puckane, Northwest : 7 ½ m. by N 52 and R 493
turning left after church in Puckane ℘ (067) 24145, *Fax* (067) 24388, ≤, « Loughside setting », ⌅, ☞, park – ⇜ rm, ☎ ℗. ⓪ ⒶⒺ 𝘝𝘐𝘚𝘈. ⌘
*closed January-Easter* – **Meals** (booking essential) (dinner only) 32.00 st. ⚱ 10.00 – **10 rm**
⚌ 80.00/180.00 st.

---

**NEWBRIDGE** (An Droichead Nua) *Kildare* 923 L 8 *Ireland G.* – pop. 12 970.

Env. : *Irish National Stud★★ AC (Japanese Gardens★★ AC) SW : 6 m. by N 7 – Kildare★*
*(Cathedral★★) SW : 5½ m. by N 7.*
🛆 *Curragh* ℘ (045) 441238/441714.
🅱 *Main St.* ℘ (045) 33835 (July-August).
*Dublin 28 – Kilkenny 57 – Tullamore 36.*

🏠🏠 **Keadeen,** Ballymany, Southwest : 1 m. ℘ (045) 431666, *Fax* (045) 434402, ⌱ₐ, ⇋s, ⬚, ☞
– ⒯⒱ ☎ & ℗ – ⚿ 800. ⓪ ⒶⒺ ⓪ 𝘝𝘐𝘚𝘈. ⌘
*closed 24 to 30 December* – **The Derby Room :** **Meals** (bar lunch Monday to Saturday)/
dinner 23.50 t. – **54 rm** ⚌ 90.00/135.00 t., 1 suite – SB.

---

**NEWMARKET-ON-FERGUS** (Cora Chaitlán) *Clare* 923 F 7 – pop. 1 542.

*Dublin 136 – Ennis 8 – Limerick 15.*

🏯 **Dromoland Castle** ⌂,, Northwest : 1 ½ m. on N 18 ℘ (061) 368144, *Fax* (061) 363355,
≤, ⌖, « Converted castle », ⌱ₐ, ⇋s, ⬚, ⌅, ☞, park, ⛳ – ⇜ rest, ⒯⒱ ☎ ℗ – ⚿ 450. ⓪
ⒶⒺ ⓪ 𝘝𝘐𝘚𝘈. ⌘
**Earl of Thormond :** **Meals** 17.50/38.00 t. and a la carte ⚱ 9.00 – ⚌ 13.50 – **67 rm**
242.00 st., 6 suites – SB.

🏠🏠 **Clare Inn,,** Northwest : 2 m. on N 18 ℘ (065) 23000, *Fax* (065) 23759, ⌱ₐ, ⇋s, ⬚, ⬚, ⛳ –
⒯⒱ ☎ ℅ ℗ – ⚿ 400. ⓪ ⒶⒺ ⓪ 𝘝𝘐𝘚𝘈. ⌘
**Meals** (bar lunch Monday to Saturday)/dinner 15.00 st. and a la carte ⚱ 5.50 – **161 rm**
⚌ 62.50/85.00 st. – SB.

🏠 **Carrygerry Country House** ⌂,, Southwest : 8 m. by N 18 ℘ (061) 363739,
*Fax* (061) 363823, ☞, park – ⇜ rm, ⒯⒱ ☎ ℗. ⓪ ⒶⒺ ⓪ 𝘝𝘐𝘚𝘈. ⌘
*closed 5 January-5 March* – **Meals** *(closed Sunday)* (dinner only) a la carte 21.00/27.00 t. –
**12 rm** ⚌ 54.50/89.00 t. – SB.

---

**NEWPORT** (Baile Uí Fhiacháin) *Mayo* 923 D 6 *Ireland G.* – pop. 567.

Env. : *Burrishoole Abbey★, NW : 2 m. by N 59 – Furnace Lough★, NW : 3 m. by N 59.*
*Dublin 164 – Ballina 37 – Galway 60.*

🏠 **Newport House** ⌂, ℘ (098) 41222, *Fax* (098) 41613, « Antique furnished country
house », ⌅, ☞, park – ⇜ rest, ☎ ℅ ℗. ⓪ ⒶⒺ ⓪ 𝘝𝘐𝘚𝘈. ⌘
*20 March-4 October* – **Meals** (dinner only) 32.00 st. ⚱ 6.00 – **18 rm** ⚌ 78.00/156.00 st.

---

**NEW ROSS** (Ros Mhic Thriúin) *Wexford* 923 L 10 *Ireland G.* – pop. 5 012 – ✉ Newbawn.

See : *St. Mary's Church★.*
Exc. : *Kennedy Arboretum, Campile★ AC, S : 7½ m. by R 733 – Dunbrody Abbey★, S : 8 m.*
*by R 733 – Inistioge★, NW : 10 m. by N 25 and R 700 – Graiguenamanagh★ (Duiske Abbey★★*
*AC), N : 11 m. by N 25 and R705.*
🛆 *Tinneranny* ℘ (051) 421433.
🅱 *The Quay* ℘ (051) 21857 (mid June-August).
*Dublin 88 – Kilkenny 27 – Waterford 15 – Wexford 23.*

🏠 **Brandon House,,** South : ¾ m. on N 25 ℘ (051) 421703, *Fax* (051) 421567, ☞, park –
▤ rest, ⒯⒱ ☎ ℗ – ⚿ 200. ⓪ ⒶⒺ ⓪ 𝘝𝘐𝘚𝘈
**Meals** (carving lunch) 11.00/20.00 st. ⚱ 5.00 – **36 rm** ⚌ 45.00/70.00 st. – SB.

🏠 **Riversdale House** without rest., Lower William St., ℘ (051) 422515, *Fax* (051) 422800,
☞ – ⇜ ⒯⒱ ℗. ⌘
**4 rm** ⚌ 36.00 s.

**at Ballynabola** *Southeast : 6 m. on N 25* – ✉ New Ross.

🏠 **Cedar Lodge,** Carrigbyrne, East : 3 m. on N 25 ℘ (051) 428386, *Fax* (051) 428222, ☞ –
⒯⒱ ☎ ℗ ⓪ 𝘝𝘐𝘚𝘈. ⌘
*closed December and January* – **Meals** (bar lunch)/dinner 25.00 st. ⚱ 9.75 – **28 rm**
⚌ 60.00/100.00 st. – SB.

**OGONNELLOE** (Tuath Ó gConaále) *Clare* 923 G 9 – *see Killaloe.*

---

**OMEATH** (Ó Méith) *Louth* 923 N 5 – *pop. 249.*
*Dublin 63 – Dundalk 10.*

🏠 **Omeath Park** ⬙,, Northwest : ½ m. on B 79 ℘ (042) 75116, *Fax (042) 75116,* ⬳, 🐎, park – ⬲ rm, 📺 ☎ 🄿, 🆖 VISA. ⬙
Meals 10.50/14.50 t. and dinner a la carte – **13 rm** ⬄ 35.00/60.00 t. – SB.

🏠 **Granvue House,** ℘ (042) 75109, *Fax (042) 75415,* ⬳ – 📺 ☎ 🄿, 🆖 AE VISA. ⬙
closed Monday to Wednesday dinner and 20 December-1 January – **Meals** (bar lunch Monday to Saturday)/dinner 15.00 t. – **8 rm** ⬄ 30.00/48.00 t. – SB.

---

**ORANMORE** (Órán Mór) *Galway* 923 F 8 *Ireland G* – *pop. 1 410.*
Env. : *Galway*★★ (*St. Nicholas Church*★, *Lynch's Castle*★, *Roman Catholic Church*★, *Eyre Square, Bank of Ireland Building, sword and mace*★), *NW : 5 m. by N 6.*
Exc. : *Athenry*★, *NE : 7 m. by N 6 and R 348 – Dunguaire Castle*★, *SW : 12 m. by N 18 and N 67 – Thoor Ballylee*★, *S : 15 m. by N 18 and minor rd – Coole Park*★, *S : 15 m. by N 18 and N 66 – Loughrea (St. Brendan's Cathedral*★), *SE : 17 m. by N 6 – Knockmoy Abbey*★, *NE : 17 m. by N 18, N 17 and N 63 – Tuam (St. Mary's Cathedral*★), *N : 18 m. by N 18 and N 17 – Turoe Stone*★, *SE : 20 m. by N 6 and north by R 348.*
🏌 Athenry, Palmerstown ℘ (091) 794466/790795.
*Dublin 131 – Galway 7.*

🏠 **Quality,,** North : ¾ m. on N 6 ℘ (091) 792244, *Fax (091) 792246,* 🄵, ⬳, 🔲 – 🛗, ⬲ rm, 📺 ☎ ♿ 🄿 – 🔬 60. 🆖 AE ① VISA. ⬙
closed 25 and 26 December – **Meals** (carvery lunch) 10.00/15.90 st. and a la carte ⅙ 6.00 – ⬄ 4.95 – **93 rm** 75.00/95.00 st. – SB.

🏠 **Mooring's,** Main St.,  ℘ (091) 790462, *Fax (091) 790462* – 📺 ☎ 🄿 – 🔬 30. 🆖 AE VISA. ⬙
closed 24 to 27 December – **Meals** (dinner only) a la carte 15.85/22.95 t. ⅙ 6.60 – **6 rm** ⬄ 30.00/50.00 st.

*La guida cambia, cambiate la guida ogni anno.*

---

**OUGHTERARD** (Uachtar Ard) *Galway* 923 E 7 *Ireland G* – *pop. 751.*
See : *Town*★.
Env. : *Lough Corrib*★★ (*Shore road – NW – ⬳★★*) *– Aughnanure Castle*★ *AC, SE : 2 m. by N 59.*
🏌 Gortreevagh ℘ (091) 552131.
🄱 Main St. ℘ (091) 82808.
*Dublin 149 – Galway 17.*

🏠 **Connemara Gateway,,** Southeast : ¾ m. on N 59 ℘ (091) 552328, *Fax (091) 552332,* ⬱, 🔲, 🐎, ⬙ – 📺 ☎ 🄿 🆖 VISA. ⬙
closed 5 January-5 February and 1 to 27 December – **Meals** (bar lunch)/dinner 22.00 st. and a la carte ⅙ 7.50 – **61 rm** ⬄ 87.50/120.00 st., 1 suite – SB.

🏠 **Currarevagh House** ⬙,, Northwest : 4 m. ℘ (091) 552312, *Fax (091) 552731,* ⬳, « Country house atmosphere », ⬱, 🐎, park, ⬙ – ⬲ rest, 🄿
April-21 October – **Meals** (booking essential) (dinner only) 21.00 t. ⅙ 5.20 – **15 rm** ⬄ 52.00/104.00 t. – SB.

🏠 **Ross Lake House** ⬙, Rosscahill, Southeast : 4 ½ m. by N 59 ℘ (091) 550109, *Fax (091) 550184,* 🐎, ⬙ – 📺 ☎ 🄿. 🆖 AE ① VISA
mid March-October – **Meals** (dinner only) 24.00 t. ⅙ 7.00 – **13 rm** ⬄ 60.00/120.00 t. – SB.

🏠 **Boat Inn,** ℘ (091) 552196, *Fax (091) 552694* – 📺 ☎. 🆖 AE ① VISA. ⬙
closed 25 December – **Meals** 10.95/15.50 st. and a la carte ⅙ 7.95 – **11 rm** ⬄ 30.00/50.00 st. – SB.

---

**PARKNASILLA** (Páirc na Saileach) *Kerry* 923 C 12 *Ireland G.*.
Env. : *Sneem*★, *NW : 2½ m. by N 70.*
Exc. : *Iveragh Peninsula*★★ (*Ring of Kerry*★★) *– Derrynane National Historic Park*★★, *W : 16 m. by N 70 – Staigue Fort*★, *W : 13 m. by N 70.*
*Dublin 224 – Cork 72 – Killarney 34.*

🏨 **Great Southern** ⬙, ℘ (064) 45122, *Fax (064) 45323,* ⬳ Kenmare River, bay and mountains, ⬱, 🔲, 🏌, ⬱, 🐎, park, ⬙ – 🛗 💆 📺 ☎ ✆ ♿ 🄿 – 🔬 80. 🆖 AE VISA. ⬙
Meals (bar lunch)/dinner a la carte 26.50/33.00 st. ⅙ 7.50 – **84 rm** ⬄ 130.00/210.00 st., 1 suite – SB.

**PORTLAOISE** (Port Laoise) *Laois* 923 K 8 *Ireland G.* – pop. 3 531.
Env. : *Rock of Dunamase★* (≤★), *E : 4 m. by N 80 – Emo Court★★ AC, NE : 7 m. by N 7.*
Exc. : *Stradbally★, E : 6½ m. by N 80 – Timahoe Round Tower★, SE : 8 m. by R 426.*
☗ *The Heath* ℘ (0502) 46533.
🛈 *James Fintan Lawlor Av.* ℘ (0502) 21178 (May-December).
*Dublin 54 – Kilkenny 31 – Limerick 67.*

🏨 **Killeshin,** Dublin Rd, East : 1 ¼ m. on N 7 ℘ (0502) 21663, *Fax (0502) 21976* – ⇔ rm, 📺
☎ 🅿 – 🔬 350. 🟢🟥 ⑩ *VISA*. ⫶
**Meals** (carving lunch Saturday) a la carte 8.50/13.00 **st.** ⬧ 5.50 – **80 rm** ⚏ 40.00/60.00 **t.** –
SB.

⌂ **Chez Nous** without rest., Kilminchy, Northeast : 2 ¼ m. by N 7 ℘ (0502) 21251, ⚏ – ⇔
🅿. ⫶
*closed 20 December-3 January* – **5 rm** ⚏ 25.00/44.00 **t.**

---

**PORTMAGEE** (An Caladh) *Kerry* 923 A 12 *Ireland G.*
Exc. : *Iveragh Peninsula★★ (Ring of Kerry★★).*
*Dublin 227 – Killarney 45 – Tralee 51.*

🏨 **Moorings,** ℘ (066) 77108, *Fax (066) 77220,* ≤ – 📺 ☎ 🅿. 🟢🟥 *VISA*. ⫶
*March-October* – **Meals** *(closed Monday dinner)* (bar lunch)/dinner 19.00 **t.** and a la carte
⬧ 5.60 – **14 rm** ⚏ 25.00/50.00 **t.** – SB.

*To visit a town or region: use the **Michelin** Green Guides.*

---

**PORTMARNOCK** (Port Mearnóg) *Dublin* 923 N 7 *Ireland G.* – pop. 9 145.
Env. : *Fingal★.*
*Dublin 5 – Drogheda 28.*

🏨🏨 **Portmarnock H. and Golf Links,** ℘ (01) 846 0611, *Fax (01) 846 2442,* ≤, ☗, ⚏ – ▮,
⇔ rm, 🗐 rest, 📺 ☎ ✆ ₺ 🅿 – 🔬 250. 🟢🟥 ﹖ ⑩ *VISA*. ⫶
**The Links :** Meals a la carte 13.60/22.40 **t.** ⬧ 6.00 – **The Osborne :** Meals (dinner only and
Sunday lunch)/dinner a la carte 25.70/36.85 **st.** ⬧ 6.00 – **101 rm** ⚏ 135.00/195.00 **st.,**
2 suites – SB.

---

**PORTUMNA** (Port Omna) *Galway* 923 H 8 *Ireland G.* – pop. 984.
See : *Town★ – Castle★.*
Exc. : *Clonfert Cathedral★ (west doorway★★), N : 15 m. by R 355 and minor roads.*
*Dublin 114 – Galway 42 – Limerick 45.*

🏨 **Shannon Oaks H. and Country Club,** ℘ (0509) 41777, *Fax (0509) 41357,* ₺₆, ≋, ▨,
⚏ – ▮, ⇔ rm, 🗐 📺 ☎ ✆ ₺ 🅿 – 🔬 600. 🟢🟥 ﹖ ⑩ *VISA*. ⫶
*closed 25 December* – **Meals** (dinner only and Sunday lunch)/dinner 19.95 **st.** and a la carte
⬧ 8.50 – **61 rm** ⚏ 85.00/105.00 **st.,** 2 suites – SB.

---

**RATHCONRATH** (Ráth Conarta) *Westmeath* 923 J 7 – *see Mullingar.*

---

**RATHGAR** (Ráth Garbh) *Co. Dublin* – *see Dublin.*

---

**RATHKEALE** (Ráth Caola) *Limerick* 923 F 10 – pop. 1 546.
*Dublin 138 – Killarney 31 – Limerick 18.*

🏨 **Rathkeale House,** ℘ (069) 63333, *Fax (069) 63300,* ⚏ – ▮ 📺 ☎ ✆ 🅿 – 🔬 400. 🟢🟥 ﹖
⑩ *VISA*
*closed 25 December* – **Meals** (bar lunch Monday to Saturday)/dinner 17.95 **st.** ⬧ 5.95 –
**26 rm** ⚏ 45.00/80.00 **st.** – SB.

---

**RATHMELTON** (Ráth Mealtain) *Donegal* 923 J 2 *Ireland G.*
See : *Town★.*
*Dublin 154 – Donegal 37 – Londonerry 27 – Sligo 76.*

⌂ **Ardeen** ⌖ without rest., ℘ (074) 51243, *Fax (074) 51243,* ⚏, ⫶ – 🅿. 🟢🟥 *VISA*. ⫶
*Easter-October* – **4 rm** ⚏ 20.00/40.00 **s.**

---

**RATHMINES** (Ráth Maonais) *Co. Dublin* 923 ④ – *see Dublin.*

**RATHMULLAN** (Ráth Maoláin) *Donegal* 923 J 2 *Ireland G.* – pop. 491 – ⊠ *Letterkenny*.
   Exc. : *Knockalla Viewpoint★, N : 8 m. by R 247 – Rathmelton★, SW : 7 m. by R 247.*
   📷 *Otway, Saltpans* ℘ *(074) 58319.*
   *Dublin 165 – Londonderry 36 – Sligo 87.*

🏨 **Rathmullan House** ⟩,, North : ½ m. on R 247 ℘ (074) 58188, Fax (074) 58200, ≤,
   « Part 19C country house, gardens », 🔲, park, ℀ – 📺 ☎ 🅿. ⑩ 🆀 ⑩ VISA. ℀
   *closed 25 December and 3 January-13 February* – **Meals** 15.00/27.00 **t.** and a la carte
   🍴 11.50 – **24 rm** ⊇ 50.00/145.00 **t.** – SB.

🏨 **Fort Royal** ⟩,, North : 1 m. by R 247 ℘ (074) 58100, Fax (074) 58103, ≤, 🐴, park, ℀,
   squash – ✻ rest, 📺 ☎ 🅿. ⑩ 🆀 ⑩ VISA
   *April-October* – **Meals** (bar lunch Monday to Saturday)/dinner 22.00 **t.** 🍴 8.00 – **15 rm**
   ⊇ 70.00/120.00 **st.** – SB.

**RATHNEW** (Ráth Naoi) *Wicklow* 923 N 8 – *see Wicklow.*

**RECESS** (Sraith Salach) *Galway* 923 C 7 *Ireland G..*
   Exc. : *Connemara★★★ – Cashel★, SW : by N 59 and R 340.*
   *Dublin 173 – Ballina 72 – Galway 36.*

🏨 **Lough Inagh Lodge** ⟩,, Northwest : 4 ¾ m. by N 59 on R 344 ℘ (095) 34706,
   Fax (095) 34708, ≤ Lough Inagh and The Twelve Bens, 🐟, 🐴 – 📺 ☎ 🅿. ⑩ 🆀 ⑩ VISA
   *mid March-November* – **Meals** (bar lunch)/dinner 27.50 **st.** and a la carte 🍴 9.00 – **12 rm**
   ⊇ 82.00/144.00 – SB.

**RINVYLE/RENVYLE** (Rinn Mhaoile) *Galway* 923 C 7 *Ireland G..*
   Exc. : *Connemara★★★.*
   *Dublin 193 – Ballina 73 – Galway 61.*

🏨 **Renvyle House** ⟩, ℘ (095) 43511, Fax (095) 43515, ≤ Atlantic Ocean, 🌊, 📷, 🐟, 🐴,
   park, ℀ – ✻ rm, 📺 ☎ 🅿 – 🔆 120. 🆀 ⑩ VISA JCB
   *closed 3 January-26 February and 28 November-23 December* – **Meals** (dinner only) 25.00 **t.**
   and a la carte 🍴 8.50 – **64 rm** ⊇ 100.00/200.00 **st.**, 1 suite – SB.

**RIVERSTOWN** (Baile idir Dhá Abhainn) *Sligo* 923 G 5 – pop. 266.
   *Dublin 123 – Sligo 13.*

🏠 **Coopershill** ⟩, ℘ (071) 65108, Fax (071) 65466, ≤, « Georgian country house », 🐟,
   🐴, park, ℀ – ✻ rm, ☎ 🅿. 🆀 🆀 ⑩ VISA JCB. ℀
   *April-October* – **Meals** (residents only) (dinner only) 26.00 **st.** 🍴 5.50 – **8 rm** ⊇ 67.00/
   114.00 **st.** – SB.

**ROSAPENNA** (Rosapenna) *Donegal* 923 I 2 *Ireland G..*
   Env. : *Rosguill Peninsula Atlantic Drive★ – Doe Castle, S : by R 248 and R 245.*
   📷 *Downings* ℘ (074) 55301.
   *Dublin 216 – Donegal 52 – Londonderry 47.*

🏨 **Rosapenna** ⟩, Downings, ℘ (074) 55301, Fax (074) 55128, ≤, 📷, ℀ – 📺 ☎ 🅿. 🆀 🆀
   ⑩ VISA
   *27 March-October* – **Meals** (dinner only) 25.00 **t.** 🍴 6.50 – **46 rm** ⊇ 62.50/120.00 **st.** – SB.

**ROSCOMMON** (Ros Comáin) *Roscommon* 923 H 7 *Ireland G.* – pop. 1 432.
   See : *Castle★.*
   Exc. : *Castlestrange Stone★, SW : 7 m. by N 63 and R 362 – Strokestown★ (Famine Museum★ AC, Strokestown Park House★ AC), N : 12 m. by N 61 and R 368 – Castlerea : Clonalis House★ AC, NW : 19 m. by N 60.*
   📷 *Moate Park* ℘ (0903) 26382.
   🎫 ℘ (0903) 26342 (20 June-4 September).
   *Dublin 94 – Galway 57 – Limerick 94.*

🏨 **Abbey** ⟩,, on N 63 (Galway rd) ℘ (0903) 26240, Fax (0903) 26021, 🐴 – 📺 ☎ 🅿 –
   🔆 200. 🆀 🆀 ⑩ VISA. ℀
   *closed 25 and 26 December* – **Meals** 12.50/22.50 **st.** and dinner a la carte 🍴 8.50 – **25 rm**
   ⊇ 65.00/120.00 – SB.

*Pour visiter une ville ou une région : utilisez les Guides Verts Michelin.*

REPUBLIC OF IRELAND

**ROSCREA** (Ros Cré) *Tipperary* 923 I 9 *Ireland G.* – *pop. 4 170.*
See : *Town★* – *Damer House★.*
*Dublin 76 – Kilkenny 37 – Limerick 95.*

🏦 **Grant's**, Castle St., ℰ (0505) 23300, Fax (0505) 23209 – 📺 ☎ ✆ 🅿 – 🔬 550. ⓦ 🆎 ⓞ 𝘝𝘐𝘚𝘈
Meals 10.50/18.50 t. and dinner a la carte ⬧ 5.50 – **25 rm** ⇆ 35.00/85.00 st. – SB.

🏠 **The Tower**, Church St., ℰ (0505) 21774, Fax (0505) 22425 – 📺 ☎ 🅿. ⓦ 🆎 ⓞ 𝘝𝘐𝘚𝘈. ⌗
*closed December –* **Meals** a la carte 11.55/16.95 t. – **10 rm** ⇆ 28.00/50.00 st. – SB.

⌂ **Monaincha House** ⌁ without rest., Monaincha, East : 1 ½ m. on N 7 ℰ (0505) 23181,
« Georgian house, working farm », ⌲, park, ⌗ – 🅿. ⌗
*April-October –* **3 rm** ⇆ 28.50/45.00 st.

---

**ROSSCARBERY** (Ros Ó gCairbre) *Cork* 923 E 13 *Ireland G* – *pop. 406.*
Env. : *Drombeg Stone Circle★*, SW : 2m. by R 597 – *Glandore★*, SW : 4 m. by R 597.
Exc. : *Carbery Coast★.*
*Dublin 194 – Cork 39 – Killarney 75.*

🏰 **Celtic Ross**, ℰ (023) 48722, Fax (023) 48723, ≤ Rosscarbery Bay, 𝑓ₛ, ≘s, ⬜ – 🛗 📺 ☎ ⅙
🅿 – 🔬 250. ⓦ 🆎 ⓞ 𝘝𝘐𝘚𝘈. ⌗
**Meals** (bar lunch Monday to Saturday)/dinner 20.00 t. and a la carte ⬧ 6.50 – **66 rm**
⇆ 75.00/120.00 t., 1 suite – SB.

---

**ROSSES POINT** (An Ros) *Sligo* 923 G 5 – *pop. 799.*
*Dublin 139 – Belfast 132 – Sligo 6.*

🏦 **Yeats Country H.**, ℰ (071) 77211, Fax (071) 77203, ≤, 𝑓ₛ, ≘s, ⬜, ⌗ – 🛗, ⅙⌖ rm, 📺 ☎
🅿. ⓦ 🆎 ⓞ 𝘝𝘐𝘚𝘈. ⌗
**Meals** (bar lunch)/dinner 20.00 st. – **99 rm** ⇆ 80.00/130.00 – SB.

---

**ROSSLARE** (Ros Láir) *Wexford* 923 M 11 – *pop. 929.*
𝑓₁₈, 𝑓₉ *Rosslare Strand* ℰ (053) 32203.
🚆 *Rosslare Terminal* ℰ (053) 33622.
*Dublin 104 – Waterford 50 – Wexford 12.*

🏰 **Kelly's Resort**, ℰ (053) 32114, Fax (053) 32222, ≤, 𝑓ₛ, ≘s, ⬜, ⌲, ⌗indoor/outdoor,
squash – 🛗, 🍽 rest, 📺 ☎ ⅙ 🅿. ⓦ 🆎 𝘝𝘐𝘚𝘈. ⌗
*March-November –* **Kelly's :** **Meals** (dancing nightly) 12.00/23.00 t. ⬧ 6.00 – **La Marine :**
**Meals** (light lunch) a la carte 14.05/20.20 ⬧ 6.00 – **103 rm** ⇆ 47.00/100.00 t. – SB.

---

**ROSSLARE HARBOUR** (Calafort Ros Láir) *Wexford* 923 N 11 – *pop. 1 023.*
🚢 to France (Cherbourg, Le Havre and Roscoff) (Irish Ferries) – to Fishguard (Stena Line)
2 daily (1 h 40 mn) – to Pembroke (Irish Ferries) 2 daily (3 h 45 mn).
🚆 Kilrane ℰ (053) 33232 (May-mid September).
*Dublin 105 – Waterford 51 – Wexford 13.*

🏦 **Great Southern**, ℰ (053) 33233, Fax (053) 33543, ⬜, ⌗ – 🛗 📺 ☎ 🅿 – 🔬 230. ⓦ 🆎
ⓞ 𝘝𝘐𝘚𝘈. ⌗
*closed late January-early March –* **Meals** (bar lunch)/dinner 15.00 t. and a la carte ⬧ 6.50 –
⇆ 7.00 – **100 rm** 58.00/84.00 t. – SB.

🏦 **Tuskar House**, St. Martins Rd, ℰ (053) 33363, Fax (053) 33363, ≤, ⌲ – ⅙⌖ rest, 🍽 rest,
📺 ☎ ✆ 🅿. ⓦ 🆎 ⓞ 𝘝𝘐𝘚𝘈. ⌗
*closed 25 December –* **Meals** 16.95 t. (dinner) and a la carte 8.90/18.50 t. ⬧ 5.50 – **30 rm**
⇆ 45.00/74.00 t. – SB.

🏦 **Rosslare**, ℰ (053) 33110, Fax (053) 33386, ≤, « Nautical memorabilia », ≘s, 𝑓₁₈, squash –
📺 ☎ 🅿. ⓦ 🆎 ⓞ 𝘝𝘐𝘚𝘈. ⌗
*closed 25 December –* **Meals** 10.95/20.00 st. and a la carte ⬧ 3.95 – **25 rm** ⇆ 24.00/
90.00 st. – SB.

🏠 **Devereux**, Wexford Rd, ℰ (053) 33216, Fax (053) 33301 – 📺 ☎ 🅿. ⓦ 🆎 𝘝𝘐𝘚𝘈. ⌗
*closed 24 and 25 December –* **Meals** (closed Monday and Tuesday) a la carte 14.50/24.45 st.
– **24 rm** ⇆ 46.00/70.00 st. – SB.

🏠 **Ferryport House** without rest.,, on N 25 ℰ (053) 33933, Fax (053) 33363 – 📺 ☎ 🅿. ⓦ
𝘝𝘐𝘚𝘈. ⌗
– **17 rm** ⇆ 36.00/58.00 st.

**at Tagoat** *West : 2½ m. on N 25 –* ✉ *Rosslare.*

🏠 **Churchtown House** ⌁,, North : ½ m. on Rosslare rd ℰ (053) 32555, Fax (053) 32555,
⌲ – ⅙⌖ 📺 ☎ 🅿. ⓦ 𝘝𝘐𝘚𝘈. ⌗
*March-October –* **Meals** (closed Sunday) (booking essential) (residents only) (dinner only)
19.50 st. ⬧ 7.50 – **14 rm** ⇆ 45.00/90.00 st.

**ROSSNOWLAGH** (Ros Neamhlach) *Donegal* [923] H 4 *Scotland G.*.
See : *Rossnowlagh Strand*★★.
*Dublin 153 – Donegal 14 – Sligo 31.*

**Sand House** 🌿, ☎ (072) 51777, *Fax (072) 52100*, ≤ bay, beach and mountains, 🌿, 🎾 – ⊭ rm, ☎ 📞 [P]. [MO] [AE] [D] [VISA]. ✂
*Easter-late October* – **Meals** (lunch booking essential Monday to Saturday) 13.50/24.00 **t.** and dinner a la carte 🍷 8.50 – **45 rm** ☕ 70.00/200.00 **t.**

**ROUNDSTONE** (Cloch na Rón) *Galway* [923] C 7 *Ireland G. – pop. 241.*
See : *Town*★.
Exc. : *Connemara*★★★.
*Dublin 193 – Galway 47.*

**Eldon's,** ☎ (095) 35933, *Fax (095) 35722*, ≤, 🌿 – |♦| [TV] ☎. [MO] [AE] [D] [VISA]. ✂
*16 March-October* – **Meals** (bar lunch)/dinner a la carte 19.95/24.40 **s.** 🍷 6.00 – **19 rm** ☕ 30.00/80.00 – SB.

**SAGGART** (Teach Sagard) *Dublin* [923] M 8 – *see Dublin.*

**SALTHILL** (Bóthar na Trá) *Galway* [923] E 8 – *see Galway.*

*Per visitare una città o una regione : utilizzate le **guide verdi Michelin.***

**SHANAGARRY** (An Seangharraí) *Cork* [923] H 12 *Ireland G. – pop. 230 –* ✉ *Midleton.*
Env. : – *Cloyne Cathedral*★, *NW : 4 m. by R 629.*
*Dublin 163 – Cork 25 – Waterford 64.*

**Ballymaloe House** 🌿,, Northwest : 1 ¾ m. on L 35 ☎ (021) 652531, *Fax (021) 652021*, ≤, « Part 16C, part Georgian country house », 🏊, 🌿, park, 🎾 – ⊭ rest, ☎ 📞 [P]. [MO] [AE] [D] [VISA]. ✂
*closed 23 to 26 December* – **Meals** (buffet dinner Sunday) 18.00/34.00 🍷 7.00 – **32 rm** ☕ 90.00/155.00 **t.** – SB.

**SHANNON** (Sionainn) *Clare* [923] F 9 – *pop. 7 811.*
⛳18 *Shannon Airport* ☎ *(061) 471020.*
✈ *Shannon Airport :* ☎ *(061) 471444.*
[i] *Shannon Airport* ☎ *(061) 471644.*
*Dublin 136 – Ennis 16 – Limerick 15.*

**Oak Wood Arms,**, on N 19 ☎ (061) 361500, *Fax (061) 361414*, 🏋 – ⊭ rm, ▤ [TV] ☎ [P] – 🏛 400. [MO] [AE] [D] [VISA]. ✂
*closed 24 and 25 December* – **Meals** (carving lunch Monday to Saturday) 12.50 **t.** (lunch) and dinner a la carte 14.40/30.00 **t.** 🍷 5.50 – **73 rm** ☕ 70.00/96.00 **st.**, 2 suites.

**at Shannon Airport** *Southwest : 2½ m. on N 19 –* ✉ *Shannon.*

**Great Southern,** ☎ (061) 471122, *Fax (061) 471982* – |♦|, ⊭ rm, ▤ rest, [TV] ☎ [P] – 🏛 200. [MO] [AE] [D] [VISA]. ✂
*closed 25 and 26 December* – **Meals** (bar lunch Saturday and Sunday) (carving lunch)/dinner 19.00 **t.** and a la carte 🍷 8.50 – ☕ 7.50 – **112 rm** 75.00/100.00 **t.**, 2 suites – SB.

**SHANNON AIRPORT** *Clare* [923] F 9 – *see Shannon.*

**SKERRIES** (Na Sceirí) *Dublin* [923] N 7 – *pop. 7 339.*
Env. : – *Fingal*★.
⛳18 *Skerries* ☎ *(01) 849 1204.*
[i] *Community Office* ☎ *(01) 849 0888.*
*Dublin 19 – Drogheda 15.*

**Redbank Lodge** without rest., 12 Convent Lane, ☎ (01) 849 0439, *Fax (01) 849 1598*, 🌿 – [TV] ☎. [MO] [AE] [D] [VISA]. ✂
*closed 24 to 26 December* – **5 rm** ☕ 40.00/50.00 **st.**

🍴🍴 **Redbank** with rm, 7 Church St., ☎ (01) 849 1005, *Fax (01) 849 1598* – [TV] ☎. [MO] [AE] [D] [VISA]
*closed Sunday dinner and 24 to 26 December* – **Meals** - Seafood - (dinner only and Sunday lunch)/dinner 25.00 **t.** and a la carte 🍷 6.00 – **7 rm** ☕ 40.00/70.00 **st.** – SB.

**SKIBBEREEN** (An Sciobairán) *Cork* 923 E 13 *Ireland G* – pop. 1 926.
  Env. : *Creagh Gardens★, W : 3½ m. by R 595 – Castletownshend★, SE : 5½ m. by R 596.*
  *Dublin 205 – Cork 51 – Killarney 64.*

🏨 **Liss Ard Lake Lodge** ⌖,, Southeast : 2 ¾ m. by R 596 *&* (028) 40000, *Fax (028) 40001,*
  ≤, « Minimalistic interior, themed feature gardens », ⌖, park, ✻ – ⌖ rm, 📺 ☎ ✆ 🅟 –
  🛗 30. 🆖 🆎 ⓪ 𝘝𝘐𝘚𝘈. ✵
  *closed 10 January-10 February* – **Meals** *(closed Tuesday)* (booking essential) (dinner only)
  28.00 **t.** ₰ 14.00 – **16 rm** ⌑ 140.00/250.00 **t.**

**SKULL/SCHULL** (An Scoil) *Cork* 923 D 13 *Ireland G* – pop. 595.
  See : *Town★.*
  Exc. : *Sherkin Island★ (by ferry) – Mizen Peninsula (≤★★ from pass).*
  *Dublin 226 – Cork 65 – Killarney 64.*

⌂ **Corthna Lodge Country House** ⌖ without rest.,, West : ¾ m. by R 592
  *&* (028) 28517, *Fax (028) 28032,* ≤, ✿ – ☎ 🅟. ✵
  *April-October* – **6 rm** ⌑ 25.00/50.00 **t.**

✕✕ **Restaurant in Blue**,, West : 2½ m. on R 592 *&* (028) 28305 – 🅟. 🆖 🆎 ⓪ 𝘝𝘐𝘚𝘈
  *closed Monday, Tuesday and restricted opening in winter* – **Meals** (booking essential)
  (dinner only) 25.00 **st.** ₰ 5.95.

**SLIEVEROE** (Sliabh Rua) *Waterford* – see Waterford.

**SLIGO** (Sligeach) *Sligo* 923 G 5 *Ireland G.* – pop. 17 786.
  See : *Town★★ – Abbey★.*
  Env. : *SE : Lough Gill★★ – Carrowmore Megalithic Cemetery★, SW : 3 m. – Knocknarea★*
  *(≤★★) SW : 6 m. by R 292.*
  Exc. : *Drumcliff★, N : by N 15 – Parke's Castle★ AC, E : 9 m. by R 286 – Glencar Waterfall★,*
  *NE : 9 m. by N 16 – Creevykeel Court Cairn★, N : 16 m. by N 15.*
  ⛳ *Rosses Point &* (071) 77134/77186.
  ✈ *Sligo Airport, Strandhill : &* (071) 68280.
  🅱 *Temple St. &* (071) 61201.
  *Dublin 133 – Belfast 126 – Dundalk 106 – Londonderry 86.*

🏨 **Tower**, Quay St., *&* (071) 44000, *Fax (071) 46888* – 📶 ⌖ 📺 ☎ ✆ & 🅟 – 🛗 150. 🆖 🆎
  ⓪ 𝘝𝘐𝘚𝘈. ✵
  *closed 24 to 27 December* – **Meals** (bar lunch Monday to Saturday)/dinner 21.00 **st.**
  and a la carte ₰ 7.00 – **58 rm** ⌑ 65.00/130.00 **st.** – SB.

⌂ **Tree Tops** without rest., Cleveragh Rd, South : ¼ m. by Dublin rd *&* (071) 60160,
  *Fax (071) 62301,* ✿ – ⌖ 📺 ☎ 🅟. 🆖 🆎 𝘝𝘐𝘚𝘈. ✵
  **5 rm** ⌑ 25.00/36.00 **st.**

⌂ **Benwiskin Lodge** without rest., Shannon Eighter, North : 2 m. by N 15 *&* (071) 41088,
  *Fax (071) 41088,* ✿ – ⌖ 📺 🅟. 🆖 𝘝𝘐𝘚𝘈. ✵
  **5 rm** ⌑ 22.00/38.00 **t.**

⌂ **Lisadorn** without rest., Donegal Rd, North : 2 m. by N 15 *&* (071) 43417, *Fax (071) 46418,*
  ✿ – 📺 ☎ 🅟. 🆖 𝘝𝘐𝘚𝘈
  **Meals** – **7 rm** ⌑ 25.00/39.00 **st.**

**SPANISH POINT** (Rinn na Spáinneach) *Clare* 923 D 9 – ✉ *Milltown Malbay.*
  *Dublin 171 – Galway 65 – Limerick 52.*

🏨 **Armada**, *&* (065) 84110, *Fax (065) 84632* – 📶 📺 ☎ 🅟 – 🛗 300. 🆖 𝘝𝘐𝘚𝘈. ✵
  **Meals** (bar lunch Monday to Saturday)/dinner a la carte 20.00 **st.** and a la carte ₰ 5.50 –
  **24 rm** ⌑ 50.00/80.00 **st.** – SB.

**SPIDDAL/SPIDDLE** (An Spidéal) *Galway* 923 E 8.
  *Dublin 143 – Galway 11.*

🏨 **Bridge House**, Main St., *&* (091) 553118, *Fax (091) 553435,* ✿ – 📺 ☎ 🅟. 🆖 🆎 ⓪ 𝘝𝘐𝘚𝘈
  𝘑𝘊𝘉. ✵
  *closed 20 December-1 March* – **Meals** 10.95 **t.** and a la carte – **12 rm** ⌑ 40.00/100.00 **t.** –
  SB.

⌂ **Ardmor Country House** without rest.,,, West : ½ m. on R 336 *&* (091) 553145,
  *Fax (091) 553596,* ≤, ✿ – ⌖ 🅟. 🆖 𝘝𝘐𝘚𝘈. ✵
  *closed January and February* – **7 rm** ⌑ 25.00/40.00.

**STRAFFAN** (Teach Srafáin) *Kildare* 923 M 8 – *pop. 341.*

⌐₁₈ *Naas, Kerdiffstown* ℘ *(045) 874644.*
*Dublin 15 – Mullingar 47.*

🏯🏯🏯 **Kildare H. & Country Club** ⑤, ℘ *(01) 601 7200, Fax (01) 601 7299,* 斎 , « Part early 19C country house overlooking River Liffey, riverside gardens and arboretum », ⅓, ⅗, 🗌, ⌐₁₈, ⑤, park, %indoor/outdoor, squash – 🛗 📺 ☎ ℗ – 益 130. 🕼 🖭 ① 💟 . 🛇
**Byerley Turk :** Meals (dinner only and Sunday lunch)/dinner 45.00 **t.** and a la carte 45.00/62.00 – **Legends** (in K Club) **:** Meals a la carte approx. 25.00 **t.** ▮ 8.75 – ☷ 15.00 – **38 rm** 280.00/350.00 **st.**, 17 suites – SB.

🏯🏯 **Barberstown Castle,,** North : ½ m. ℘ *(01) 628 8157, Fax (01) 627 7027,* « Part Elizabethan, part Victorian house with 13C castle keep », 寿 – ⸯⸯ rest, 📺 ☎ ✆ 丆 ℗ – 益 30. 🕼 🖭 ① 💟 . 🛇
*closed 24 to 27 December and first week January –* Meals (booking essential) (dinner only) 29.50 **t.** ▮ 8.50 – **25 rm** ☷ 82.50/154.00 **st.**, 1 suite – SB.

---

**SWORDS** (Sord) *Dublin* 923 N 7 – *pop. 22 314.*

Env. : *Fingal★ – Newbridge House★, N : by N 1 and east by R 126.*
Exc. : *Malahide Castle★★, SE : by N 1 and R 106.*
⌐₁₈ *Balcarrick, Corballis, Donabate* ℘ *(01) 843 6228.*
*Dublin 8 – Drogheda 22.*

🏛 **Travelodge,** Miltons Field, South : ½ m. on N 1 ℘ *(01) 840 9233, Fax (01) 840 9235,* Reservations (Freephone) 0800 850950 – ⸯⸯ rm, 📺 丆 ℗. 🕼 🖭 ① 💟 🞘 . 🛇
Meals (grill rest.) – **40 rm** 39.95/59.95 **t.**

🍴 **Old Schoolhouse,** Well Rd, off Main St. ℘ *(01) 840 4160, Fax (01) 840 5060 –* 🖳 ℗. 🕼 🖭 ① 💟 . 🛇
*closed Saturday lunch, Sunday, Bank Holiday Mondays, Easter, Christmas and New Year –* Meals 13.95/23.95 **t.** and a la carte.

*When looking for a quiet hotel*
*use the maps found in the introduction*
*or look for establishments with the sign* ⑤ *or* ⑤.

---

**TAGOAT** (Teach Gót) *Wexford* 923 M 11 – *see Rosslare Harbour.*

---

**TAHILLA** (Tathuile) *Kerry* 923 C 12 *Ireland G..*

Exc. : *Iveragh Peninsula★★ (Ring of Kerry★★) – Sneem★, NW : 4 m. by N 70.*
*Dublin 222 – Cork 70 – Killarney 32.*

🏛 **Tahilla Cove** ⑤, ℘ *(064) 45204, Fax (064) 45104,* ≤ Tahilla Cove and mountains, « Waterside setting », ⑤, 寿, park – 🛓 📺 ☎ ℗. 🕼 🖭 ① 💟
*Easter-mid October –* Meals (bar meals lunch and dinner Tuesday)/dinner 18.00 – **9 rm** ☷ 60.00/80.00 **st.** – SB.

---

**TALLAGHT** (Tamhlacht) *Dublin* 923 N 8 – *see Dublin.*

---

**TEMPLEGLANTINE** (Teampall an Ghleanntáin) *Limerick* 923 E 10 *Ireland G..*

Exc. : *Newcastle West★, NE : 4½ m. by N 21.*
⌐₁₈ *Newcastle West, Ardagh* ℘ *(069) 76500.*
*Dublin 154 – Killarney 36 – Limerick 33.*

🏯🏯 **Devon Inn,,** on N 21 ℘ *(069) 84122, Fax (069) 84255 –* 📺 ☎ ℗ – 益 500. 🕼 🖭 ① 💟
*closed 24 and 25 December –* Meals 9.50/13.00 **st.** and dinner a la carte ▮ 6.00 – **60 rm** ☷ 38.00/120.00 **st.** – SB.

---

**TERENURE** (Tír an Iúir) *Co. Dublin* 923 ⑩ – *see Dublin.*

---

**TERMONBARRY** *Longford* 923 I 6 *Ireland G.*

Exc. : *Strokestown★ (Famine Museum★ AC, Strokestown Park House★ AC), NW : by N 5.*
*Dublin 81 – Galway 85 – Roscommon 22 – Sligo 62.*

⌂ **Shannonside House,** ℘ *(043) 26052 –* 📺 ☎ ℗. 🕼 🖭 ① 💟
Meals (by arrangement) 17.50 **t.** ▮ 5.00 – **9 rm** ☷ 16.00/35.00 **t.**

**TERRYGLASS** (Tír Dhá Ghlas) *Tipperary* 923 H 8 *Scotland G.* – ⊠ *Nenagh.*
Exc. : *Portumna★ (castle★), N : 9 m. by R 493 and N 65.*
*Dublin 114 – Galway 51 – Limerick 43.*

⌂ **Riverrun House** ⊗ without rest., ℘ (067) 22125, *Fax (067) 22187*, 🐎, ℅ – 🕿 🅿. 📷
  AE VISA
  *closed 25 December* – **6 rm** ⊊ 30.00/50.00 **st.**

⌂ **Tír na Fiúise** ⊗ without rest., Southeast : 1 ½ m. ℘ (067) 22041, *Fax (067) 22041,*
  « Working farm », 🐎, park – ⅙ 🅿. 📷 VISA. ℅
  *May-September* – **4 rm** ⊊ 30.00/50.00 **st.**

---

**THOMASTOWN** (Baile Mhic Andáin) *Kilkenny* 923 K 10 *Ireland G.* – pop. 1 581 – ⊠ *Kilkenny.*
Env. : *Jerpoint Abbey★★, SW : 1½ m. by N9.*
ᵗ₈ Mount Juliet ℘ (056) 24455.
*Dublin 77 – Kilkenny 11 – Waterford 30 – Wexford 38.*

🏯 **Mount Juliet** ⊗,, West : 2 ½ m. by N 9 on Stonyford rd ℘ (056) 73000, *Fax (056) 73019*
  « 18C manor and sporting estate, ≤ River Nore and park », Ⅰ♣, ≊, ▣, ᵗ₈, ⸙, 🐎, ℅ –
  ⅙ rest, 🕥 🕿 🅿 – 🏄 40. 📷 AE ① VISA. ℅
  **Lady Helen McCalmont :** Meals (dinner only) 33.00 **st.** and a la carte ⓖ 8.00 – (see also
  **Hunters Yard at Mount Juliet** below) – ⊊ 12.50 – **30 rm** 160.00/260.00 **st.**, 2 suites – SB.

🏠 **Hunters Yard at Mount Juliet**,, West : 2 ½ m. by N 9 on Stonyford rd ℘ (056) 73000,
  *Fax (056) 73019*, « Converted 18C stables », Ⅰ♣, ≊, ▣, ᵗ₈, ⸙, 🐎, park, ℅ – 🕥 🕿 🅿 –
  🏄 40. 📷 AE ① VISA. ℅
  **The Loft :** Meals *(June-September)* (dinner only and Sunday lunch) a la carte 15.00/
  25.00 **st.** ⓖ 8.00 – ⊊ 12.50 – **13 rm** 150.00 **st.** – SB.

⌂ **Abbey House,** Jerpoint Abbey, Southwest : 1 ¼ m. on N 9 ℘ (056) 24166,
  *Fax (056) 24192*, 🐎 – 🕿 🅿. 📷 VISA
  *closed 24 December-1 January* – **Meals** (by arrangement) 17.00 **t.** – **7 rm** ⊊ 22.00/50.00 –
  SB.

*Pas de publicité payée dans ce guide.*

---

**TOORMORE** (An Tuar Mór) *Cork* 923 D 13 – ⊠ *Goleen.*
*Dublin 221 – Cork 68 – Killarney 65.*

⌂ **Fortview House** ⊗ without rest., Gurtyowen, Northeast : 1 ½ m. on Durrus rd (R 591)
  ℘ (028) 35324, *Fax (028) 35324* – ⅙ rest, 🅿. ℅
  *March-October* – **5 rm** ⊊ 20.00/50.00 **st.**

---

**TOWER** *Cork* 923 G 12 – see Blarney.

---

**TRALEE** (Trá Lí) *Kerry* 923 C 11 *Ireland G.* – pop. 19 056.
Env. : *Blennerville Windmill★ AC, SW : 2 m. by N 86 – Ardfert Cathedral★, NW : 5½ m. by*
*R 551.*
Exc. : *Banna Strand★, NW : 8 m. by R 551 – Crag Cave★ AC, W : 13 m. by N 21 – Rattoo*
*Round Tower★, N : 12 m. by R 556.*
🛈 Ashe Memorial Hall, Denny St. ℘ (066) 7121288.
*Dublin 185 – Killarney 20 – Limerick 64.*

🏯 **Ballyseede Castle** ⊗,, Southeast : 3 ¼ m. by N 22 ℘ (066) 7125799, *Fax (066) 7125287,*
  « 15C castle in extensive parklands », 🐎 – 🕥 🕿 🅿. 📷 ① VISA. ℅
  **Meals** (dinner only) 22.00 **t.** and a la carte ⓖ 6.95 – ⊊ 8.50 – **14 rm** 95.00/190.00 **t.**

🏠 **Grand,** Denny St., ℘ (066) 7121499, *Fax (066) 7122877* – ▤ rest, 🕥 🕿 ✆ – 🏄 250. 📷 AE
  VISA.
  *closed 24 to 26 December* – **Meals** 10.00/15.00 **st.** and a la carte ⓖ 6.00 – **44 rm** ⊊ 35.00/
  72.00 **st.** – SB.

🏢 **Brook Manor Lodge** without rest., Fenit Rd, Spa, Northwest : 2 ¼ m. by R 551 on R 558
  ℘ (066) 7120509, *Fax (066) 7127552*, 🐎 – ⅙ 🕥 🕿 🅿. 📷 AE VISA. ℅
  **6 rm** ⊊ 38.00/64.00 **t.**

⌂ **Barnakyle** without rest., Clogherbrien, Northwest : 1 ½ m. on R 551 ℘ (066) 7125048,
  *Fax (066) 7181259*, 🐎 – ⅙ 🕥 🕿 🅿. 📷 AE ① VISA JCB. ℅
  *April-October* – **4 rm** ⊊ 25.00/34.00 **st.**

⌂ **Kilteely House** ⊗, Ballyard, South : 1 m. via Princes St. ℘ (066) 7123376,
  *Fax (066) 7125766*, 🐎 – ⅙ rest, 🕿 🅿. 📷 AE VISA. ℅
  **Meals** (by arrangement) 20.00 **st.** – **11 rm** ⊊ 28.00/60.00 **st.**

↑ **Knockanish House** without rest., The Spa, Northwest : 3 m. by R 551 on R 558 ⌂ (066) 7136268, 🚗 – **Ⓟ**. ⅍
*April-October* – **6 rm** ⌷ 24.50/36.00 **s.**

XX **Aisling Gheal,** Ivy House, Ivy Terr., ⌂ (066) 7129292, Fax (066) 7123870 – **ⓒⓔ** ⒶⒺ **ⓞ** **VISA**
*closed Monday in winter and first week November* – **Meals** (dinner only and Sunday lunch)/dinner 18.95 **t.** and a la carte ⌘ 7.95.

---

**TRAMORE** (Trá Mhór) Waterford 🈸🈸 K 11 – pop. 6 536.
Dublin 106 – Waterford 6.

↑ **Glenorney** without rest., Newtown, Southwest : 1 m. by R 675 ⌂ (051) 381056, Fax (051) 381103, ≤, 🚗 – **⅍** 🆃🆅 ☎ **Ⓟ**. **VISA**. ⅍
*closed December and January* – **6 rm** ⌷ 23.00/42.00 **s.**

---

**TRIM** (Baile Átha Troim) Meath 🈸🈸 L 7 Ireland G. – pop. 1 740.
See : Trim Castle★★ – Town★.
Env. : Bective Abbey★, NE : 4 m. by R 161.
Dublin 27 – Drogheda 26 – Tullamore 43.

↑ **Crannmór** ⅋ without rest., Dunderry Rd, North : 1 ¼ m. ⌂ (046) 31635, Fax (046) 31635, 🚗 – **⅍** 🅖 **Ⓟ**. **ⓒⓔ** **VISA**. ⅍
*April-September* – **4 rm** ⌷ 24.50/36.00 **s.**

---

**TULLAMORE** (Tulach Mhór) Offaly 🈸🈸 J 8 – pop. 9 221.
Dublin 65 – Kilkenny 52 – Limerick 80.

🏨 **Tullamore Court,** O'Moore St., ⌂ (0506) 46666, Fax (0506) 46677, ₤₅, ≦s, 🔲 – ⎹ 🆃🆅 ☎ 🅖 **Ⓟ**. **ⓒⓔ** ⒶⒺ **ⓞ** **VISA**. ⅍
*closed 24 to 26 December* – **Meals** 12.00/25.00 **t.** and dinner a la carte ⌘ 8.75 – **72 rm** ⌷ 80.00/150.00 **st.** – SB.

↑ **Sea Dew House** without rest., Clonminch Rd, Southeast : ½ m. on N 80 ⌂ (0506) 52054, Fax (0506) 52054, 🚗 – **⅍** 🆃🆅 ☎ 🅖 **Ⓟ**. **ⓒⓔ** **VISA**. ⅍
*closed 23 December-4 January* – **10 rm** ⌷ 30.00/50.00 **st.**

↑ **Pine Lodge** ⅋, Screggan, Southwest : 4 ½ m. by N 52 on Mountbolus rd ⌂ (0506) 51927, Fax (0506) 51927, ≦s, 🔲, 🚗 – **⅍** rm, **Ⓟ**. ⅍
*15 March-15 December* – **Meals** (by arrangement) 22.00 **st.** – **4 rm** ⌷ 30.00/50.00 **st.** – SB.

---

**VIRGINIA** (Achadh an Iúir) Cavan 🈸🈸 K 6 Ireland G– pop. 811.
Exc. : Kells★ (Round Tower and High Crosses★★, St. Columba's House★ ), SE : 10 m. by N 3 – Loughcrew Passage Graves★, S : 10 m. by R 195, turning right into L 3.
Dublin 51 – Drogheda 39 – Enniskillen 60.

🏠 **Sharkey's,** Main St., ⌂ (049) 47561, Fax (049) 47761, 🚗 – 🆃🆅 ☎ 🅖. **ⓒⓔ** **VISA**. ⅍
*closed 25 December* – **Meals** (carving lunch) 11.50/18.50 **t.** and dinner a la carte ⌘ 5.95 – **13 rm** ⌷ 40.00/80.00 **st.** – SB.

---

**WATERFORD** (Port Láirge) Waterford 🈸🈸 K 11 Ireland G.– pop. 42 540.
See : Town★ – City Walls★.
Env. : Waterford Crystal★, SW : 1½ m. by N 25 Y.
Exc. : – Duncannon★, E : 12 m. by R 683, ferry from Passage East and R 374 (south) Z – Dunmore East★, SE : 12 m. by R 684 Z – Tintern Abbey★, E : 13 m. by R 683, ferry from Passage East, R 733 and R 734 (south) Z.
⛳ Newrath ⌂ (051) 74182.
✈ Waterford Airport, Killowen : ⌂ (051) 875589.
🅱 41 The Quay ⌂ (051) 75788 Y.
Dublin 96 – Cork 73 – Limerick 77.

Plan on next page

🏨 **Waterford Castle** ⅋, The Island, Ballinakill, East : 2 ½ m. by R 683, Ballinakill Rd and private ferry ⌂ (051) 878203, Fax (051) 879316, ≤, « Part 15C and 19C castle, river island setting », 🔲, ₈, ⚲, 🚗, park, ⅍ – ⎹, **⅍** rest, 🆃🆅 ☎ **ⓥ** 🅖. **ⓒⓔ** ⒶⒺ **ⓞ** **VISA**. ⅍
**Meals** (light lunch October-May)/dinner 34.50 **t.** – ⌷ 11.00 – **14 rm** 160.00/220.00 **t.**, 5 suites.

🏨 **Granville,** Meagher Quay, ⌂ (051) 305555, Fax (051) 305566 – ⎹, 🍴 rest, 🆃🆅 ☎ **ⓥ** – **⅍** 200. **ⓒⓔ** ⒶⒺ **ⓞ** **VISA**. ⅍        Y a
*closed 25 and 26 December* – **Meals** 10.95/18.50 **st.** and dinner a la carte ⌘ 5.25 – **74 rm** ⌷ 67.50/140.00 **st.**

## WATERFORD

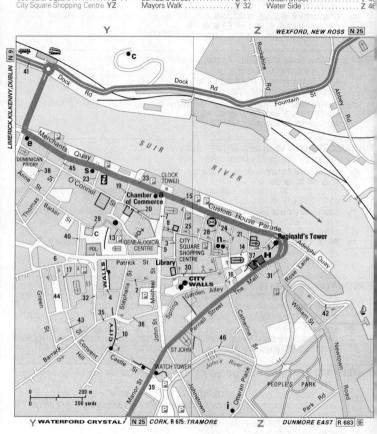

896

🏨 **Waterford Marina,** Canada St., The Quays, ℰ (051) 856600, *Fax (051) 856605,* « Riverside setting » – 📵 📶 🔞 ☎ 📞 ⅙ ⇌ 🅿. 🍾 🆎 ⓪ *VISA*. ⅜
Meals (bar lunch Monday to Saturday)/dinner 16.95 **t.** and a la carte – **81 rm** ⊇ 48.00/150.00 **t.** – SB.

🏨 **Jurys,** Ferrybank, ℰ (051) 832111, *Fax (051) 832863,* ≼ City, *₤₆,* ≋s, 🔲, 🛲, park, ⅞ – 📵
📺 ☎ 🅿 – 🛦 800. 🍾 🆎 ⓪ *VISA*. ⅜                                                                  Y c
*closed 24 to 28 December* – Meals 13.00/15.95 **st.** and a la carte ₤ 8.00 – ⊇ 8.95 – **97 rm**
80.00/110.00 **t.**, 1 suite – SB.

🏨 **Dooley's,** The Quay, ℰ (051) 873531, *Fax (051) 870262* – 📵, ⅌⅌ rm, 🍴 rest, 📺 ☎ 📞 –
🛦 30. 🍾 🆎 ⓪ *VISA* 🇯🇨🇧. ⅜                                                                        Y s
*closed 25 to 27 December* – Meals (carvery lunch Monday to Saturday)/dinner 17.00 **t.**
and a la carte ₤ 6.00 – **113 rm** ⊇ 50.00/100.00 **t.** – SB.

🏨 **Bridge,** The Quay, ℘ (051) 877222, Fax (051) 877229 – 🛗 📺 ☎ ✆ 👄 – ⚿ 250. 🐠 🖭 ⓪
🚾. ⅍                                                                                                               Y  e
*closed 25 December* – **Meals** (carvery lunch Monday to Saturday)/dinner 17.95 **t.**
and a la carte ⅄ 4.95 – **110 rm** ⊑ 65.00/120.00 **t.** – SB.

🏨 **Ivory's,** Tramore Rd, Southwest : 1 ¼ m. by N 25 on Tramore Rd ℘ (051) 358888,
Fax (051) 358899, ☞ – ⅀ rm, 📺 ☎ ✆ ఉ 🅿. 🐠 🖭 ⓪ 🚾. ⅍
**Meals** 11.95/14.95 **st.** and a la carte ⅄ 5.00 – ⊑ 6.75 – **40 rm** 52.50/69.00 **st.** – SB.

🏨 **Travelodge,** Cork Rd, Southwest : 1 ¼ m. on N 25 ℘ (051) 358885, Fax (051) 358890,
Reservations (Freephone) 0800 850950 – ⅀ rm, 🗏 rest, 📺 ☎ ఉ 🅿. 🐠 🖭 ⓪ 🚾 🇯🇨🇧. ⅍
**Meals** (grill rest.) – **32 rm** 39.95/59.95 **t.**

⌂ **Foxmount Farm** ⑊,, Southeast : 4 ½ m. by R 683, off Cheekpoint rd ℘ (051) 874308,
Fax (051) 854906, ⑊, « Working farm », park, ⅍ – ⅀ rest, 🅿. ⅍
*March-October* – **Meals** (by arrangement) 20.00 **st.** – **6 rm** ⊑ 30.00/50.00 **st.** – SB.

⌂ **Brown's Town House** without rest., 29 South Par., ℘ (051) 870594, Fax (051) 871923 –
📺 ☎. 🐠 🚾. ⅍                                                                                           Z  i
*closed 22 to 27 December* – **6 rm** ⊑ 35.00/60.00 **st.**

💥💥 **Dwyer's,** 8 Mary St., ℘ (051) 877478, Fax (051) 871183 – 🐠 🖭 ⓪ 🚾
*closed Sunday and 1 week Christmas* – **Meals** (dinner only) a la carte 17.25/25.25 ⅄ 6.10.

💥 **Wine Vault,** High St., ℘ (051) 853444, Fax (051) 853777, « Converted bonded warehouse » – 🗏. 🐠 🖭 🚾                                                                                   Z  n
*closed Sunday and 25-26 December* – **Meals** 22.50 **st.** (dinner) and a la carte 19.40/22.40 **st.**
⅄ 6.40.

💥 **McCluskeys,** 18 High St., ℘ (051) 857766, Fax (051) 857766 – 🐠 🚾                          Z  n
*closed Sunday, Monday and 1 week Christmas* – **Meals** 16.95 **t.** (dinner) and a la carte
16.50/23.50 **t.** ⅄ 5.50.

**at Slieveroe** *Northeast : 2 ¼ m. by N 25 – Z –* ⊠ *Waterford.*

⌂ **Diamond Hill** without rest., ℘ (051) 832855, Fax (051) 832254, ☞ – ⅀ rest, 📺 ☎ 🅿.
🐠 🚾
**10 rm** ⊑ 32.00/54.00 **st.**

**at Cheekpoint** *East : 7 m. by R 683 – Z –* ⊠ *Waterford.*

🏨 **Three Rivers** ⑊ without rest., ℘ (051) 382520, Fax (051) 382542, ⑊ – ⅀ ☎ ✆ 🅿. 🐠
🖭 ⓪ 🚾. ⅍
*closed December and January* – **14 rm** ⊑ 28.00/56.00 **st.**

**at Butlerstown** *Southwest : 5 ¼ m. by N 25 – Y –* ⊠ *Waterford.*

🏨 **Coach House** ⑊ without rest., Butlerstown Castle, Cork Rd, ℘ (051) 384656,
Fax (051) 384751, ⑊, « Butlerstown Castle in grounds », ⇔, ☞ – 📺 ☎ 🅿. 🐠 🖭 ⓪ 🚾.
⅍
**7 rm** ⊑ 42.00/64.00 **st.**

---

**WATERVILLE** (An Coireán) *Kerry* 🔢🔢🔢 B 12 *Ireland G.* – pop. 466.
Exc. : *Iveragh Peninsula★★ (Ring of Kerry★★) – Skellig Islands★★, W : 8 m. by N 70 , R 567
and ferry from Ballinskelligs – Derrynane National Historic Park★★ AC, S : 9 m. by N70 –
Leacanabuaile Fort (⇐★★), N : 13 m. by N 70.*
🏌 *Ring of Kerry* ℘ (066) 74102.
*Dublin 238 – Killarney 48.*

🏨 **Butler Arms,** ℘ (066) 9474144, Fax (066) 9474520, ⑊, ⑊, ☞, ⅍ – 📺 ☎ 🅿. 🐠 🖭 🚾.
⅍
*April-17 October* – **Meals** (bar lunch)/dinner 25.00 **t.** and a la carte ⅄ 7.25 – **30 rm** ⊑ 60.00/
160.00 **t.** – SB.

🏨 **Waterville House and Golf Links** without rest., ℘ (066) 74244, Fax (066) 74567, ⑊,
⇔, ⌇, 🏌, ⑊, ☞ – 📺 ☎ 🅿. 🐠 🖭 🚾. ⅍
*16 April-October* – **6 rm** ⊑ 60.00/120.00 **st.**, 4 suites.

⌂ **Golf Links View** without rest., Murreigh, North : 1 m. on N 70 ℘ (066) 74623,
Fax (066) 74623 – 📺 🅿. 🐠 🚾. ⅍
*March-October* – **6 rm** ⊑ 23.00/36.00.

⌂ **Klondyke House** without rest., New Line Rd, North : ½ m. on N 70 ℘ (066) 74119,
Fax (066) 74666, ⑊ – 🅿. 🐠 🚾
**6 rm** ⊑ 21.00/34.00 **st.**

*Si vous cherchez un hôtel tranquille,*
*consultez d'abord les cartes de l'introduction*
*ou repérez dans le texte les établissements indiqués avec le signe* ⑊ *ou* ⑊.

**WESTPORT** (Cathair na Mart) Mayo 📖 D 6 *Ireland G.* – pop. 4 253.

See : *Town★★* (*Centre★*) – *Westport House★★ AC.*

Exc.: SW : *Murrisk Peninsula★★ – Ballintubber Abbey★*, SE : 13 m. by R 330 – *Croagh Patrick★*, W : 6 m. by R 335 – *Bunlahinch Clapper Bridge★*, W : 16 m. by R 335 – *Doo Lough Pass★*, W : 24 m. by R 335 – *Aasleagh Falls★*, S : 22 m. by N 59.

🛅 Carowholly ℘ (098) 28262/27070.

🅱 The Mall ℘ (098) 25711.

Dublin 163 – Galway 50 – Sligo 65.

🏨🏨 **Knockranny House**, Knockranny, East : ½ m. off N 5 ℘ (098) 28600, Fax (098) 28611, ≤, – 🔃, 🍴 rest, 📺 ☎ & 🅿 – 🔬 700. 🆎 🎴 *VISA*. 🛇
closed 25 and 26 December – **La Fougère :** Meals (bar lunch Monday to Saturday)/dinner 25.00 **st.** and a la carte ₫ 7.00 – **50 rm** 😑 85.00/180.00 **st.** – SB.

🏨🏨 **Westport Woods**, Louisburgh Rd, West : ½ m. ℘ (098) 25811, Fax (098) 26212, 🌫, 🛇 – 📺 ☎ 🅿 – 🔬 300. 🆎 🎴 ① *VISA*
Meals (bar lunch Monday to Saturday)/dinner 18.00 **st.** and a la carte ₫ 7.50 – **111 rm** 😑 69.00/150.00 **st.** – SB.

↑ **Wilmaur** 🛏 without rest., Rosbeg, West : 2 m. by R 335 ℘ (098) 25784, Fax (098) 26224, ≤, 🌫 – 🅿
Easter-September – **5 rm** 😑 27.50/38.00 **st.**

*For maximum information from town plans:*
*consult the conventional signs key.*

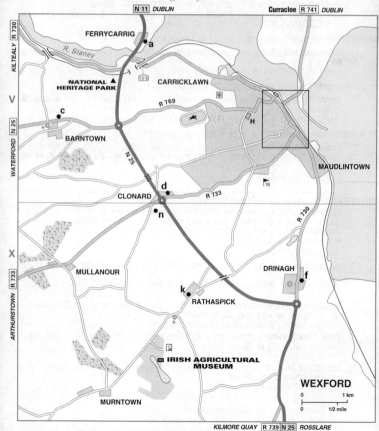

**WEXFORD** (Loch Garman) *Wexford* 923 *M 10 Ireland G.* – pop. 9 533.

See : *Town★ – Main Street★ YZ – Franciscan Friary★ Z – St. Iberius' Church★ Y D – Twin Churches★ Z – Env. : Irish Agricultural Museum, Johnstown Castle★★ AC, SW : 4½ m. X – Irish National Heritage Park, Ferrycarrig★ AC, NW : 2½ m. by N 11 V – Curracloe★, NE : 5 m. by R 741 and R 743 V.*

Exc. : *– Kilmore Quay★, SW : 15 m. by N 25 and R 739 (Saltee Islands★ - access by boat) X – Enniscorthy Castle★ (County Museum★ AC) N : 15 m. by N 11 V.*

🏌 *Mulgannon* 𝒫 (053) 42238 – 🛈 *Crescent Quay* 𝒫 (053) 23111 (1 March-4 November).

*Dublin 88 – Kilkenny 49 – Waterford 38.*

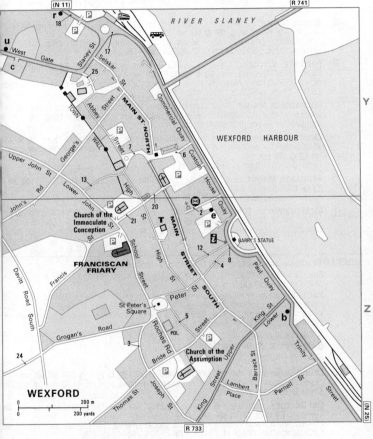

WEXFORD

| | | | | | |
|---|---|---|---|---|---|
| Anne Street | Z 2 | Crescent Quay | Z 8 | Redmond Road | Y 18 |
| Carrigeen Street | Z 3 | Henrietta Street | Z 12 | Rowe Street | |
| Cinema Lane | Z 4 | John's Gate Street | Y 13 | Lower | YZ 20 |
| Clifford Street | Z 5 | Main St. North | Y | Rowe Street | |
| Common | | Main St. South | Z | Upper | Z 21 |
| Quay Street | Y 6 | Peter Street | Z 16 | Summerthil Road | Z 24 |
| Cornmarket | Y 7 | Redmond Place | Y 17 | Temperance Row | Y 25 |

🏰🏰 **Ferrycarrig,** Ferrycarrig Bridge, Northwest : 2 ¾ m. on N 11 𝒫 (053) 20999, *Fax* (053) 20982, ≤, ℐ₆, ≤s, ☒, ≋ – ᶴ, ⅙↦ rm, ▤ rest, ☒ ☎ ❷ – 🚗 400. 🅾🅾 🆎 ① 𝗩𝗜𝗦𝗔. ⸜⸝
V a

*Tides :* Meals *(closed Sunday)* (dinner only) a la carte 24.00/28.50 **st.** ⬩ 6.00 – *Boathouse Bistro :* Meals 11.50 **st.** (lunch) and a la carte 15.00/25.00 **st.** ⬩ 6.00 – **86 rm** ⸌ 72.00/170.00 **st.**, 4 suites – SB.

🏨 **Talbot,** Trinity St., ℰ (053) 22566, Fax (053) 23377, ₤₅, ☎, ◰, – ▯, ▤ rest, ▥ ☎ ♿ ♣ ♿ –
🔏 400. ◍◎ 🆎 ⓪ 𝘝𝘐𝘚𝘈. ⅏
Z b
**Meals** (carving lunch)/dinner a la carte 9.40/18.50 t. ⅊ 7.50 – **99 rm** ⊃ 62.50/99.00 t. – SB.

🏨 **Whitford House,** New Line Rd, West : 2 ¼ m. on R 733 ℰ (053) 43444, Fax (053) 46399
◰, ⅏, ⅌ – ▥ ☎ ♿ 𝘝𝘐𝘚𝘈. ⅏
V d
closed 23 December-13 January – **Meals** (bar lunch)/dinner a la carte 15.50/22.50 **st.** ⅊ 5.85
– **23 rm** ⊃ 34.00/68.00 **st.** – SB.

🏨 **White's,** George St., ℰ (053) 22311, Fax (053) 45000, ₤₅, ☎, – ▯ ▥ ☎ ♿ – 🔏 400. ◍◎ 🆎
⓪ 𝘝𝘐𝘚𝘈. ⅏
Z e
**Meals** 10.50 **st.** (lunch) and a la carte 15.40/24.40 **st.** ⅊ 9.00 – **81 rm** ⊃ 62.50/87.00 **st.**,
1 suite – SB.

🏠 **Slaney Manor** ⅏, Ferrycarrig, West : 3 m. on N 25 ℰ (053) 20051, Fax (053) 20510, ⩽
⅌, park – ▯ ⅌ ▥ ☎ ♿. ◍◎ 𝘝𝘐𝘚𝘈. ⅏
V c
closed December and January – **Meals** (booking essential) (residents only) (bar lunch)/
dinner 12.00 **st.** ⅊ 5.00 – **28 rm** ⊃ 35.00/70.00 **st.** – SB.

🏠 **Farmers Kitchen,** Drinagh, South : 2 ½ m. on Rosslare Rd ℰ (053) 43295
Fax (053) 45827, ⅌, squash – ▥ ☎ ♿. ◍◎ 𝘝𝘐𝘚𝘈. ⅏
X l
closed 25 December – **Meals** (bar lunch Monday to Saturday)/dinner 16.00 **st.** and a la carte
⅊ 5.00 – **11 rm** ⊃ 30.00/52.00 **st.** – SB.

🏡 **Rathaspeck Manor** ⅏ without rest., Rathaspeck, Southwest : 4 m. by Rosslare Rd off
Bridgetown rd ℰ (053) 42661, « Georgian country house », ₤₅, ⅌, ⅌ – ▥ ♿. ⅏
X k
May-October – **6 rm** ⊃ 25.00/44.00 **st.**

🏡 **Clonard House** ⅏ without rest., Clonard Great, Southwest : 2 ½ m. by R 733
ℰ (053) 43141, Fax (053) 43141, ⩽, « Georgian country house, working farm », ⅌, park –
⅌ ▥ ♿. ◍◎ 𝘝𝘐𝘚𝘈. ⅏
X n
Easter-October – **9 rm** ⊃ 25.00/40.00 **st.**

🏡 **Ardruadh Manor** ⅏ without rest., Spawell Rd, ℰ (053) 23194, Fax (053) 23194, ⅌ –
▥ ♿. ◍◎ 𝘝𝘐𝘚𝘈. ⅏
Y u
closed 24 to 31 December – **6 rm** ⊃ 24.00/50.00 **t.**

🏡 **McMenamin's Townhouse** without rest., 3 Auburn Terr., Redmond Rd,
ℰ (053) 46442, Fax (053) 46442 – ▥ ♿. ◍◎ 𝘝𝘐𝘚𝘈. ⅏
Y r
closed 20 to 29 December – **4 rm** ⊃ 30.00/48.00 **st.**

---

**WICKLOW** (Cill Mhantáin) Wicklow 𝟵𝟮𝟴 N 9 Ireland G. – pop. 6 416.

Env. : Mount Usher Gardens, Ashford★ AC, NW : 4 m. by R 750 and N 11 – Devil's Glen★,
NW : 8 m. by R 750 and N 11.

Exc. : Glendalough★★★ (Lower Lake★★★, Upper Lake★★, Cathedral★★, Round Tower★, St.
Kevin's Church★, St. Saviour's Priory★), – W : 14 m. by R 750, N 11, R 763, R 755 and R 756 –
Wicklow Mountains★★ (Wicklow Gap★★, Sally Gap★★, Avondale★, Meeting of the Waters★,
Glenmacnass Waterfall★, Glenmalur★, – Loughs Tay and Dan★ ).

🛆 Blainroe ℰ (0404) 68168.

🛈 Fitzwilliam St. ℰ (0404) 69117.

Dublin 33 – Waterford 84 – Wexford 67.

🏨 **Grand,** Abbey St., ℰ (0404) 67337, Fax (0404) 69607 – ▥ ☎ ♿ – 🔏 300. ◍◎ 𝘝𝘐𝘚𝘈. ⅏
closed 25 December – **Meals** 12.00 **st.** (lunch) and dinner a la carte 14.70/19.70 **t.** ⅊ 5.50 –
**32 rm** ⊃ 50.00/80.00 **st.** – SB.

🏠 **Old Rectory,,** Northwest : ¼ m. on R 750 ℰ (0404) 67048, Fax (0404) 69181, ₤₅, ☎, ⅌
– ⅌ rest, ▥ ☎ ♿. ◍◎ 𝘝𝘐𝘚𝘈. ⅏
closed January and February – **Meals** (booking essential) (dinner only) 30.50 **st.**
and a la carte 29.00/33.50 **st.** ⅊ 9.00 – **7 rm** ⊃ 78.00/104.00 **st.** – SB.

XX **The Bakery,** Church St., ℰ (0404) 66770, Fax (0404) 66717 – ◍◎ 𝘝𝘐𝘚𝘈
closed Good Friday and 25 December – **Meals** (dinner only and Sunday lunch)/dinner
a la carte 12.50/28.00 **t.** ⅊ 6.00.

**at Rathnew** Northwest : 2 m. on R 750 – ✉ Wicklow.

🏨 **Tinakilly House** ⅏,, on R 750 ℰ (0404) 69274, Fax (0404) 67806, ⩽, « Part Victorian
country house », ⅌, ⅌ – ⅌ rest, ▤ rest, ▥ ♿ ♣ ♿ – 🔏 80. ◍◎ 🆎 𝘝𝘐𝘚𝘈 𝘑𝘊𝘉. ⅏
**The Brunel Room :** Meals (booking essential) 19.00/33.00 **st.** and a la carte ⅊ 7.50 – **38 rm**
⊃ 117.00/144.00 **st.**, 2 suites – SB.

🏨 **Hunter's,** Newrath Bridge, North : ¾ m. by N 11 on R 761 ℰ (0404) 40106,
Fax (0404) 40338, « Converted 18C inn, gardens » – ⅌ ▥ ☎ ♿ ⓪ 𝘝𝘐𝘚𝘈. ⅏
closed 24 to 26 December – **Meals** 15.00/22.50 **t.** – **16 rm** ⊃ 52.50/120.00 **st.** – SB.

**WOODENBRIDGE** Wicklow 🗺️🗺️🗺️ N 9.

*Dublin 46 – Waterford 68 – Wexford 41.*

🏨 **Woodenbridge,** Vale of Avoca, ℘ (0402) 35146, Fax (0402) 35573, ☞ – 📺 ☎ 🍴 🅿 – 🛏️ 250. 🆎 🆎 *VISA*. 🍽️
Meals 12.95/19.50 **st.** and a la carte 🍷 6.50 – **23 rm** ⬜ 55.00/90.00 **st.** – SB.

---

**YOUGHAL** (Eochaill) Cork 🗺️🗺️🗺️ I 12 *Ireland G.* – pop. 5 630.

See : *Town★ – St. Mary's Collegiate Church★★ – Town Walls★ – Clock Gate★ .*
Exc. : *Helvick Head★ (≤★), NE : 22 m. by N 25 and R 674 – Ringville (≤★), NE : 20 m. by N 25 and R 674 – Ardmore★ – Round Tower★ – Church★ (arcade★ ), N : 10 m. by N 25 and R 673 – Whiting Bay★ , SE : 12 m. by N 25, R 673 and the coast road.*
🏌️ *Knockaverry* ℘ (024) 92787.
🇮 *Heritage Centre* ℘ (024) 92390 (June-mid September).
*Dublin 146 – Cork 30 – Waterford 47.*

🏨 **Aherne's,** 163 North Main St., ℘ (024) 92424, Fax (024) 93633 – 📺 ☎ 🔥 🅿 🆎 🆎 ⓪
*VISA*. 🍽️
closed 23 December-3 January – Meals – (see **Aherne's Seafood Bar** below) – **12 rm**
⬜ 80.00/120.00 **st.** – SB.

🏨 **Devonshire Arms,** Pearse Sq., ℘ (024) 92827, Fax (024) 92900 – 📺 ☎ 🅿 🆎 🆎 ⓪ *VISA*.
🍽️
Meals 9.00/17.00 **t.** and a la carte – **10 rm** ⬜ 45.00/77.00 **st.** – SB.

🍴🍴 **Aherne's Seafood Bar** (at Aherne's H.), 163 North Main St., ℘ (024) 92424,
Fax (024) 93633 – 🅿 🆎 🆎 ⓪ *VISA*
closed 23 December-3 January – Meals 15.00/26.00 **t.** and a la carte.

# Major hotel groups
*Central reservation telephone numbers*

# Principales chaînes hôtelières
*Centraux téléphoniques de réservation*

# Principali catene alberghiere
*Centrali telefoniche di prenotazione*

# Die wichtigsten Hotelketten
*Zentrale für telefonische Reservierung*

| | |
|---|---|
| DE VERE HOTELS PLC | *01925 639499* |
| FORTE HOTELS | *0345 404040 or 0800 404040 (Freephone)* |
| FRIENDLY HOTELS | *0500 616263 (Freephone)* |
| HILTON HOTELS | *0990 445866* |
| HOLIDAY INN WORLDWIDE | *0800 897121 (Freephone)* |
| HYATT HOTELS | *0345 581666* |
| INTERCONTINENTAL HOTELS LTD | *0181 847 2277 or calls from outside London 0345 581444* |
| JARVIS HOTELS | *0345 581811* |
| MARRIOTT HOTELS | *0800 221222 (Freephone)* |
| MILLENNIUM COPTHORNE HOTELS | *0645 455445* |
| MOUNT CHARLOTTE/THISTLE HOTELS | *0800 181716 (Freephone)* |
| NOVOTEL | *0181 283 4500* |
| PREMIER LODGES & INNS | *0800 118833 (Freephone)* |
| QUEENS MOAT HOUSES PLC | *0500 213214 (Freephone) or 01708 766677* |
| RADISSON EDWARDIAN HOTELS | *0800 374411 (Freephone)* |
| RAMADA INTERNATIONAL | *0800 181737 (Freephone)* |
| REGAL HOTEL GROUP | *0345 334400* |
| SHERATON HOTELS | *0800 353535 (Freephone)* |
| STAKIS HOTELS | *0990 383838* |
| SWALLOW HOTELS LTD | *0191 419 4666* |
| TRAVEL INNS | *01582 414341* |
| TRAVELODGES | *0800 850950 (Freephone)* |
| VIRGIN HOTELS | *0800 716919 (Freephone)* |

# Distances

All distances in this edition are quoted in miles. The distance is given from each town to other nearby towns and to the capital of each region as grouped in the guide.
To avoid excessive repetition some distances have only been quoted once – you may therefore have to look under both town headings.
The distances in miles quoted are not necessarily the shortest but have been based on the roads which afford the best driving conditions and are therefore the most practical.

# Distances en miles

Pour chaque région traitée, vous trouverez au texte de chacune des localités sa distance par rapport à la capitale et aux villes environnantes.
La distance d'une localité à une autre n'est pas toujours répétée aux deux villes intéressées : voyez au texte de l'une ou de l'autre.
Ces distances ne sont pas nécessairement comptées par la route la plus courte mais par la plus pratique, c'est-à-dire celle offrant les meilleures conditions de roulage.

| Belfast | Cork | Dublin | Dundalk | Galway | Killarney | Limerick | Londonderry | Omagh | Sligo | Tullamore | Waterford |
|---|---|---|---|---|---|---|---|---|---|---|---|
| 262 | | | | | | | | | | | |
| 105 | 158 | | | | | | | | | | |
| 53 | 209 | 53 | | | | | | | | | |
| 195 | 121 | 136 | 154 | | | | | | | | |
| 288 | 55 | 184 | 235 | 134 | | | | | | | |
| 228 | 57 | 124 | 175 | 65 | 70 | | | | | | |
| 72 | 297 | 143 | 102 | 173 | 299 | 229 | | | | | |
| 68 | 264 | 109 | 69 | 157 | 290 | 186 | 34 | | | | |
| 124 | 202 | 134 | 106 | 89 | 214 | 145 | 85 | 68 | | | |
| 141 | 126 | 65 | 83 | 82 | 141 | 72 | 158 | 127 | 95 | | |
| 206 | 72 | 102 | 153 | 142 | 115 | 78 | 241 | 208 | 179 | 84 | |

137 Miles

Dublin - Sligo

# Distanze in miglia

Per ciascuna delle regioni trattate, troverete nel testo di ogni località la sua distanza dalla capitale e dalle dittà circostanti.
Le distanza da una località all'altra non è sempre ripetuta nelle due città interessate : vedere nel testo dell'una o dell'altra.
Le distanze non sono necessariamente calcolate seguendo il percorso più breve, ma vengono stabilite secondo l'itinerario più pratico, che offre cioè le migliori condizioni di viaggio.

# Entfernungsangaben in meilen

Die Entfernungen der einzelnen Orte zur Landeshauptstadt und zu den nächstgrößeren Städten in der Umgebung sind im allgemeinen Orstext angegeben.
Die Entfernung zweier Städte voneinander können Sie aus den Angaben im Ortstext der einen oder der anderen Stadt ersehen.
Die Entfernungsangaben gelten nicht immer für der kürzesten, sondern für den günstigsten Weg.

# Distances between major towns
## Distances entre principales villes
## Distanze tra le principali città
### Entfernungen zwischen den größeren Städten

Edinburgh – Southampton  **431 Miles**

Aberdeen · Ayr · Blackpool · Birmingham · Brighton · Bristol · Cambridge · Cardiff · Carlisle · Coventry · Dover · Dumfries · Edinburgh · Dundee · Glasgow · Inverness · Ipswich · Kingston-upon-Hull · Leeds · Leicester · Liverpool · London · Manchester · Middlesbrough · Newcastle · Norwich · Oban · Nottingham · Oxford · Plymouth · Portsmouth · Sheffield · Southampton · Stoke-on-Trent · Swansea · Wick

The page contains a triangular mileage chart giving the road distances between the major towns listed above. Each column below a town name gives the distances from that town to the towns listed after it.

| From | Distances to the following towns (in list order) |
|------|----------------------------------------------------|
| Aberdeen | 184, 430, 323, 599, 513, 463, 533, 229, 447, 584, 208, 67, 123, 148, 518, 359, 323, 413, 356, 546, 352, 272, 228, 489, 393, 178, 500, 630, 582, 359, 564, 386, 527, 216 |
| Ayr | 291, 184, 460, 374, 351, 490, 90, 308, 490, 82, 113, 82, 35, 210, 246, 210, 217, 407, 213, 183, 145, 376, 280, 125, 361, 491, 443, 246, 425, 247, 388, 318 |
| Blackpool | 133, 167, 303, 216, 226, 193, 96, 204, 332, 57, 82, 297, 43, 153, 128, 145, 122, 103, 121, 55, 181, 210, 165, 153, 389, 206, 150, 86, 267, 48, 89, 145, 651, 568 |
| Birmingham | 161, 121, 152, 89, 99, 203, 96, 235, 363, 190, 192, 299, 82, 153, 145, 122, 103, 145, 59, 153, 128, 210, 125, 206, 267, 48, 89, 145, 461, 318 |
| Brighton | 161, 216, 226, 193, 204, 372, 156, 403, 532, 446, 383, 468, 210, 460, 263, 214, 266, 459, 271, 168, 186, 558, 473, 449, 492, 188, 406, 588, 315, 505, 660, 609 |
| Bristol | 45, 79, 156, 34, 162, 96, 98, 98, 402, 339, 339, 359, 35, 352, 145, 122, 70, 152, 120, 57, 196, 108, 74, 82, 273, 146, 305, 492, 128, 142, 154, 671 |

*(Numeric data transcribed from the triangular mileage chart; remaining rows continue in the same manner for the towns Cambridge, Cardiff, Carlisle, Coventry, Dover, Dumfries, Edinburgh, Dundee, Glasgow, Inverness, Ipswich, Kingston-upon-Hull, Leeds, Leicester, Liverpool, London, Manchester, Middlesbrough, Newcastle, Norwich, Oban, Nottingham, Oxford, Plymouth, Portsmouth, Sheffield, Southampton, Stoke-on-Trent, Swansea and Wick.)*

| Birmingham | Cardiff | Dublin | Glasgow | London | |
|---|---|---|---|---|---|
| 423 | 450 | 592 | 717 | 296 | *Amsterdam* |
| 1026 | 1053 | 1194 | 1320 | 899 | **Barcelona** |
| 617 | 644 | 785 | 911 | 490 | *Basel* |
| 779 | 806 | 947 | 1073 | 652 | *Berlin* |
| 673 | 701 | 842 | 967 | 547 | *Bern* |
| 533 | 518 | 494 | 834 | 613 | *Bordeaux* |
| 1064 | 1091 | 1232 | 1358 | 937 | *Bratislava* |
| 1449 | 1476 | 1617 | 1743 | 1322 | *Brindisi* |
| 322 | 350 | 491 | 617 | 196 | *Bruxelles-Brussel* |
| 135 | 120 | 310 | 436 | 81 | *Cherbourg* |
| 642 | 669 | 810 | 936 | 515 | *Clermont-Ferrand* |
| 447 | 474 | 615 | 741 | 320 | *Düsseldorf* |
| 566 | 593 | 734 | 860 | 439 | *Frankfurt am Main* |
| 663 | 690 | 831 | 957 | 536 | *Genève* |
| 673 | 700 | 841 | 967 | 546 | *Hamburg* |
| 867 | 895 | 1036 | 361 | 741 | *København* |
| 266 | 293 | 435 | 560 | 139 | *Lille* |
| 1279 | 1264 | 1240 | 1579 | 1359 | *Lisboa* |
| 457 | 484 | 625 | 751 | 330 | *Luxembourg* |

| Birmingham | Cardiff | Dublin | Glasgow | London | |
|---|---|---|---|---|---|
| 665 | 692 | 833 | 959 | 538 | *Lyon* |
| 963 | 948 | 924 | 1264 | 1043 | *Madrid* |
| 1291 | 1276 | 1252 | 1592 | 1371 | *Málaga* |
| 858 | 885 | 1027 | 1152 | 731 | *Marseille* |
| 831 | 858 | 999 | 1125 | 704 | *Milano* |
| 795 | 823 | 964 | 1089 | 669 | *München* |
| 331 | 316 | 292 | 632 | 278 | *Nantes* |
| 1311 | 1338 | 1479 | 1605 | 1184 | *Palermo* |
| 377 | 404 | 545 | 671 | 250 | *Paris* |
| 1150 | 1135 | 1111 | 1451 | 1230 | *Porto* |
| 878 | 906 | 1047 | 1173 | 752 | *Praha* |
| 1183 | 1210 | 1351 | 1477 | 1056 | *Roma* |
| 683 | 668 | 644 | 984 | 763 | *San Sebastián* |
| 582 | 609 | 750 | 876 | 455 | *Strasbourg* |
| 813 | 669 | 645 | 1107 | 686 | *Toulouse* |
| 1241 | 1009 | 986 | 1535 | 1114 | *Valencia* |
| 1124 | 1151 | 1292 | 1418 | 997 | *Warszawa* |
| 1013 | 1040 | 1182 | 1307 | 886 | *Wien* |
| 1149 | 1176 | 1317 | 1443 | 1022 | *Zagreb* |

*or distances refer to the colour key in the table
*es distances sont indiquées dans la couleur du point de passage
*e distanze sono indicate con il colore del punto di passaggio
*ie Entfernungen sind angegeben in der Farbe des betroffenen
*assagepunktes*

● FOLKESTONE
(CHANNEL TUNNEL)
● SOUTHAMPTON
● TYNEMOUTH

**Glasgow - Barcelona** | 1320 Miles |

| | |
|---|---|
| **Major roads and principal shipping routes** | **Principales routes et liaisons maritimes** |
| Motorway | Autoroute |
| Road number ...... A 4. T 35. N 2 | N° de route ........ A 4. T 35. N 2 |
| Mileage .............. ▼ 20 ▲ | Distance en miles ..... ▼ 20 ▲ |

| | |
|---|---|
| **Principali strade e itinerari marittimi** | **Hauptverkehrsstrassen und Schiffsverbindungen** |
| Autostrada | Autbahn |
| Numero di strada... A 4. T 35. N 2 | Straßennummer .... A 4. T 35. N 2 |
| Distanza in miglia .... ▼ 20 ▲ | Entfernung in Meilen .. ▼ 20 ▲ |

NORTH SEA

CHANNEL

Hartlepool
Middlesbrough
Scarborough
York
KINGSTON UPON HULL
Immingham
Scunthorpe
Great Grimsby
Doncaster
Rotherham
Wakefield
SHEFFIELD
Lincoln
Skegness
Boston
NOTTINGHAM
LEICESTER
Stamford
Wisbech
King's Lynn
NORWICH
Cromer
Great Yarmouth
Lowestoft
Peterborough
Ely
Bury St.Edmunds
CAMBRIDGE
Ipswich
Northampton
Bedford
Stevenage
Colchester
Felixstowe
Harwich
Luton
Aylesbury
Harlow
Chelmsford
OXFORD
LONDON
Reading
Newbury
Windsor
Basingstoke
Guildford
Crawley
Maidstone
Royal-Tunbridge Wells
Sheerness
Canterbury
Margate
Ramsgate
Deal
Dover
Folkestone
Channel Tunnel
Southend-on-Sea
Tilbury
Winchester
SOUTHAMPTON
Chichester
BRIGHTON
Worthing
Eastbourne
Newhaven
Hastings
PORTSMOUTH
Newport
Isle of Wight
Rugby
Coventry
Rotterdam Zeebrugge
Esbjerg
Göteborg
Hoek van Holland
Hamburg
Kingston upon Hull
Zeebrugge
OOSTENDE
BRUGGE
Dunkerque
BELGIË
BELGIQUE
St-Omer
LILLE
Boulogne
Arras
Cambrai
Abbeville
Somme
AMIENS
St-Quentin
Dieppe
Beauvais
Compiègne
St-Malo
Rosslare
LE HAVRE
ROUEN
Senlis
CAEN
SEINE
FRANCE

*Illustrations Cécile Imbert/MICHELIN : pages 4 à 48 – Narratif Systèmes/Geneclo :*
*pages 50 à 55, 60, 62 – Rodolphe Corbel pages 118, 342, 391, 446, 692, 704, 803, 808.*

*Manufacture française des pneumatiques Michelin*
*Société en commandite par actions au capital de 2 000 000 000 de F.*
*Place des Carmes-Déchaux – 63 Clermont-Ferrand (France)*
*R.C.S. Clermont-Fd B 855 200 507*

**Michelin et Cie, Propriétaires-Éditeurs 1999**
*Dépôt légal Janvier 99 – ISBN 2-06-006579-8*

# International Dialling Codes

Note: when making an international call, do not dial the first «0» of the city code (except for calls to Italy).

# Indicatifs Téléphoniques Internationaux

Important : pour les communications internationales, le zéro (0) initial de l'indicatif interurbain n'est pas à composer (excepté pour les appels vers l'Italie).

| from \ to | A | B | CH | CZ | D | DK | E | FIN | F | GB | GR |
|---|---|---|---|---|---|---|---|---|---|---|---|
| **A Austria** | | 0032 | 0041 | 00420 | 0049 | 0045 | 0034 | 00358 | 0033 | 0044 | 0030 |
| **B Belgium** | 0043 | | 0041 | 00420 | 0049 | 0045 | 0034 | 00358 | 0033 | 0044 | 0030 |
| **CH Switzerland** | 0043 | 0032 | | 00420 | 0049 | 0045 | 0034 | 00358 | 0033 | 0044 | 0030 |
| **CZ Czech Republic** | 0043 | 0032 | 0041 | | 0049 | 0045 | 0034 | 00358 | 0033 | 0044 | 0030 |
| **D Germany** | 0043 | 0032 | 0041 | 00420 | | 0045 | 0034 | 00358 | 0033 | 0044 | 0030 |
| **DK Denmark** | 0043 | 0032 | 0041 | 00420 | 0049 | | 0034 | 00358 | 0033 | 0044 | 0030 |
| **E Spain** | 0043 | 0032 | 0041 | 00420 | 0049 | 0045 | | 00358 | 0033 | 0044 | 0030 |
| **FIN Finland** | 0043 | 0032 | 0041 | 00420 | 0049 | 0045 | 0034 | | 0033 | 0044 | 0030 |
| **F France** | 0043 | 0032 | 0041 | 00420 | 0049 | 0045 | 0034 | 00358 | | 0044 | 0030 |
| **GB United Kingdom** | 0043 | 0032 | 0041 | 00420 | 0049 | 0045 | 0034 | 00358 | 0033 | | 0030 |
| **GR Greece** | 0043 | 0032 | 0041 | 00420 | 0049 | 0045 | 0034 | 00358 | 0033 | 0044 | |
| **H Hungary** | 0043 | 0032 | 0041 | 00420 | 0049 | 0045 | 0034 | 00358 | 0033 | 0044 | 0030 |
| **I Italy** | 0043 | 0032 | 0041 | 00420 | 0049 | 0045 | 0034 | 00358 | 0033 | 0044 | 0030 |
| **IRL Ireland** | 0043 | 0032 | 0041 | 00420 | 0049 | 0045 | 0034 | 00358 | 0033 | 0044 | 0030 |
| **J Japan** | 00143 | 00132 | 00141 | 001420 | 00149 | 00145 | 00134 | 001358 | 00133 | 00144 | 00130 |
| **L Luxembourg** | 0043 | 0032 | 0041 | 00420 | 0049 | 0045 | 0034 | 00358 | 0033 | 0044 | 0030 |
| **N Norway** | 0043 | 0032 | 0041 | 00420 | 0049 | 0045 | 0034 | 00358 | 0033 | 0044 | 0030 |
| **NL Netherlands** | 0043 | 0032 | 0041 | 00420 | 0049 | 0045 | 0034 | 00358 | 0033 | 0044 | 0030 |
| **PL Poland** | 0043 | 0032 | 0041 | 00420 | 0049 | 0045 | 0034 | 00358 | 0033 | 0044 | 0030 |
| **P Portugal** | 0043 | 0032 | 0041 | 00420 | 0049 | 0045 | 0034 | 00358 | 0033 | 0044 | 0030 |
| **RUS Russia** | 81043 | 81032 | 810420 | 6420 | 81049 | 81045 | * | 810358 | 81033 | 81044 | * |
| **S Sweden** | 00943 | 00932 | 00941 | 009420 | 00949 | 00945 | 00934 | 009358 | 00933 | 00944 | 00930 |
| **USA** | 01143 | 01132 | 01141 | 001420 | 01149 | 01145 | 01134 | 01358 | 01133 | 01144 | 01130 |

*Direct dialling not possible                    *Pas de sélection automatique

*Importante: per le comunicazioni internazionali, non bisogna comporre lo zero (0)
iniziale dell'indicativo interurbano (escluse le chiamate per l'Italia)*

## Telefon-Vorwahlnummern international

*Wichtig: bei Auslandgesprächen darf die Null (0) der Ortsnetzkennzahl nicht
gewählt werden (ausser bei Gesprächen nach Italien).*

| H | I | IRL | J | L | N | NL | PL | P | RUS | S | USA | |
|---|---|---|---|---|---|---|---|---|---|---|---|---|
| 0036 | 0039 | 00353 | 0081 | 00352 | 0047 | 0031 | 0048 | 00351 | 007 | 0046 | 001 | **A Austria** |
| 0036 | 0039 | 00353 | 0081 | 00352 | 0047 | 0031 | 0048 | 00351 | 007 | 0046 | 001 | **B Belgium** |
| 0036 | 0039 | 00353 | 0081 | 00352 | 0047 | 0031 | 0048 | 00351 | 007 | 0046 | 001 | **CH Switzerland** |
| 0036 | 0039 | 00353 | 0081 | 00352 | 0047 | 0031 | 0048 | 00351 | 007 | 0046 | 001 | **CZ Czech Republic** |
| 0036 | 0039 | 00353 | 0081 | 00352 | 0047 | 0031 | 0048 | 00351 | 007 | 0046 | 001 | **D Germany** |
| 0036 | 0039 | 00353 | 0081 | 00352 | 0047 | 0031 | 0048 | 00351 | 007 | 0046 | 001 | **DK Denmark** |
| 0036 | 0039 | 00353 | 0081 | 00352 | 0047 | 0031 | 0048 | 00351 | 007 | 0046 | 001 | **E Spain** |
| 0036 | 0039 | 00353 | 0081 | 00352 | 0047 | 0031 | 0048 | 00351 | 007 | 0046 | 001 | **FIN Finland** |
| 0036 | 0039 | 00353 | 0081 | 00352 | 0047 | 0031 | 0048 | 00351 | 007 | 0046 | 001 | **F France** |
| 0036 | 0039 | 00353 | 0081 | 00352 | 0047 | 0031 | 0048 | 00351 | 007 | 0046 | 001 | **GB United Kingdom** |
| 0036 | 0039 | 00353 | 0081 | 00352 | 0047 | 0031 | 0048 | 00351 | 007 | 0046 | 001 | **GR Greece** |
| | 0039 | 00353 | 0081 | 00352 | 0047 | 0031 | 0048 | 00351 | 007 | 0046 | 001 | **H Hungary** |
| 0036 | | 00353 | 0081 | 00352 | 0047 | 0031 | 0048 | 00351 | * | 0046 | 001 | **I Italy** |
| 0036 | 0039 | | 0081 | 00352 | 0047 | 0031 | 0048 | 00351 | * | 0046 | 001 | **IRL Ireland** |
| 00136 | 00139 | 001353 | | 001352 | 00147 | 00131 | 00148 | 001351 | * | 00146 | 0011 | **J Japan** |
| 0036 | 0039 | 00353 | 0081 | | 0047 | 0031 | 0048 | 00351 | 007 | 0046 | 001 | **L Luxembourg** |
| 0036 | 0039 | 00353 | 0081 | 00352 | | 0031 | 0048 | 00351 | 007 | 0046 | 001 | **N Norway** |
| 0036 | 0039 | 00353 | 0081 | 00352 | 0047 | | 0048 | 00351 | 007 | 0046 | 001 | **NL Netherlands** |
| 0036 | 0039 | 00353 | 0081 | 00352 | 0047 | 0031 | | 00351 | 007 | 0046 | 001 | **PL Poland** |
| 0036 | 0039 | 00353 | 0081 | 00352 | 0047 | 0031 | 0048 | | 007 | 0046 | 001 | **P Portugal** |
| 81036 | * | * | * | * | * | 81031 | 81048 | * | | * | * | **RUS Russia** |
| 00936 | 00939 | 009353 | 00981 | 009352 | 00947 | 00931 | 00948 | 009351 | 0097 | | 0091 | **S Sweden** |
| 01136 | 01139 | 011353 | 01181 | 011352 | 01147 | 01131 | 01148 | 011351 | * | 011146 | | **USA** |

\* *Selezione automatica impossibile*      \* *Automatische Vorwahl nicht möglich*